BIOLOGY

SECOND CANADIAN EDITION

ROBERT J. BROOKER
University of Minnesota—Minneapolis

ERIC P. WIDMAIER
Boston University

LINDA E. GRAHAM
University of Wisconsin—Madison

PETER D. STILING
University of South Florida

CLARE HASENKAMPF
University of Toronto—Scarborough

FIONA F. HUNTER
Brock University

MICHAEL J. BIDOCHKA
Brock University

C. DANIEL RIGGS
University of Toronto—Scarborough

McGraw-Hill Ryerson

Connect. Learn. Succeed.

McGraw-Hill Ryerson
Connect. Learn. Succeed.

Biology
Second Canadian Edition

Copyright © 2013, 2010 by McGraw-Hill Ryerson Limited, a Subsidiary of The McGraw-Hill Companies.
Copyright © 2013, 2011, 2008 by The McGraw-Hill Companies, Inc. All rights reserved. No part of this publication may be reproduced or transmitted in any form or by any means, or stored in a data base or retrieval system, without the prior written permission of McGraw-Hill Ryerson Limited, or in the case of photocopying or other reprographic copying, a license from The Canadian Copyright Licensing Agency (Access Copyright). For an Access Copyright licence, visit www.accesscopyright.ca or call toll free to 1-800-893-5777.

ISBN-13: 978-0-07-105189-7
ISBN-10: 0-07-105189-9

1 2 3 4 5 6 7 8 9 0 TCP 1 9 8 7 6 5 4 3

Printed and bound in Canada.

Care has been taken to trace ownership of copyright material contained in this text; however, the publisher will welcome any information that enables it to rectify any reference or credit for subsequent editions.

Director of Product Management: *Rhondda McNabb*
Group Product Manager: *Leanna MacLean*
Marketing Manager: *Jeremy Guimond*
Developmental Editor: *Suzanne Simpson Millar*
Product Team Associate: *Stephanie Giles*
Photo/Permissions Research: *Tracy Leonard*
Supervising Editor: *Joanne Limebeer*
Copy Editors: *Dawn Hunter, Karen Rolfe*
Proofreaders: *Ann Firth, Karen Rolfe*
Production Coordinator: *Tammy Mavroudi*
Cover Design: *Dave Murphy/Valid Design & Layout*
Cover Image: *Image Courtesy of San Diego Zoo Global*
Interior Design: *Laserwords Private Limited*
Page Layout: *Laserwords Private Limited*
Printer: *Transcontinental Printing Group*

Library and Archives Canada Cataloguing in Publication

Biology/Robert J. Brooker . . . [et al.].—2nd Canadian ed.

Includes index.
ISBN 978-0-07-105189-7

1. Biology–Textbooks. I. Brooker, Robert J

QH308.2.B568 2013   570   C2012-905301-5

About the Authors

Robert J. Brooker

Rob Brooker (Ph.D., Yale University) received his B.A. in biology at Wittenberg University, Springfield, Ohio, in 1978. At Harvard, he studied lactose permease, the product of the *lacY* gene of the *lac* operon. He continues working on transporters at the University of Minnesota, where he is a Professor in the Department of Genetics, Cell Biology and Development, and has an active research laboratory. Dr. Brooker teaches undergraduate courses in biology, genetics, and cell biology. In addition to many other publications, he has written two undergraduate genetics texts published by McGraw-Hill: *Genetics: Analysis & Principles,* 4th edition, copyright 2012, and *Concepts of Genetics,* copyright 2012.

Eric P. Widmaier

Eric Widmaier received his Ph.D. in 1984 in endocrinology from the University of California at San Francisco. His research focuses on the control of body mass and metabolism in mammals, the hormonal correlates of obesity, and the effects of high-fat diets on intestinal cell function. Dr. Widmaier is currently Professor of Biology at Boston University, where he teaches undergraduate human physiology and recently received the university's highest honour for excellence in teaching. Among other publications, he is a coauthor of *Vander's Human Physiology: The Mechanisms of Body Function,* 13th edition, published by McGraw-Hill, copyright 2014.

Linda E. Graham

Linda Graham received her Ph.D. in botany from the University of Michigan, Ann Arbor. Her research explores the evolutionary origin of land-adapted plants, focusing on their cell and molecular biology as well as ecological interactions. Dr. Graham is now Professor of Botany at the University of Wisconsin-Madison. She teaches undergraduate courses in biology and plant biology. She is the coauthor of, among other publications, *Algae,* 2nd edition, copyright 2008, a major's textbook on algal biology, and *Plant Biology,* 2nd edition, copyright 2006, both published by Prentice Hall/Pearson.

Peter D. Stiling

Peter Stiling obtained his Ph.D. from University College, Cardiff, Wales, in 1979. Subsequently, he became a postdoctoral fellow at Florida State University and later spent two years as a lecturer at the University of the West Indies, Trinidad. During this time, he began photographing and writing about butterflies and other insects, which led to publication of several books on local insects. Dr. Stiling is currently a Professor of Biology at the University of South Florida at Tampa. His research interests include plant–insect relationships, parasite–host relationships, biological control, restoration ecology, and the effects of elevated carbon dioxide levels on plant–herbivore interactions. He teaches graduate and undergraduate courses in ecology and environmental science as well as introductory biology. He has published many scientific papers and is the author of *Ecology: Global Insights and Investigations,* published by McGraw-Hill, copyright 2012.

The authors are grateful for the help, support, and patience of their families, friends, and students,

Deb, Dan, Nate, and Sarah Brooker,

Maria, Rick, and Carrie Widmaier,

Jim, Michael, and Melissa Graham, and

Jacqui, Zoe, Leah, and Jenna Stiling.

American author team, left to right: Eric Widmaier, Linda Graham, Peter Stiling, and Rob Brooker

About the Authors

Clare Hasenkampf

Clare Hasenkampf received her Ph.D. in genetics from Florida State University. After immigrating to Canada in 1989, she won a Natural Science and Engineering Research Council of Canada Women's Faculty Award. Dr. Hasenkampf is an Associate Professor in the Department of Biological Sciences at the University of Toronto where she teaches courses in cell and molecular biology, genetics, and microscopy, and works with the Science Engagement program to explore ways for students to enrich their science education. Her current research examines the structure and function of chromosomes. Dr. Hasenkampf is a 3M National Teaching Fellow and serves as the Associate Dean for Teaching and Learning.

Fiona F. Hunter

Fiona F. Hunter received her Ph.D. in biology from Queen's University and is a Professor at Brock University in the Department of Biological Sciences. She teaches a variety of courses, including introductory biology and medical and veterinary entomology. Her current research, which includes the study of mosquito-borne viruses, will be enhanced by the addition of Brock's Containment Level 3 lab. Dr. Hunter was the lead investigator for several large-scale biodiversity projects, including the identification and cataloguing of mosquitoes responsible for West Nile virus transmission in Canada. She also served as the director of the Wildlife Research Station in Algonquin Park, the president of the Entomological Society of Ontario, and an associate editor of *The Canadian Entomologist*.

Michael J. Bidochka

Michael J. Bidochka received his Ph.D. in applied microbiology from the University of Saskatchewan in 1989 and continued with postdoctoral training at the Boyce Thompson Institute for Plant Protection at Cornell University in New York. Dr. Bidochka is now a Professor at Brock University in the Department of Biological Sciences. His interests include behavioural ecology, microbiology, population genetics, and molecular biology, and his current research involves molecular biology of virulence factors, population genetics of insect pathogenic fungi, and the evolution of pathogenesis using insects as model systems. Dr. Bidochka has published more than 100 peer-reviewed papers and book chapters, and he is an associate editor of the Federation of European Microbiological Societies' *Microbiology Letters*.

C. Daniel Riggs

C. Daniel Riggs received his Ph.D. in Genetics and Cell Biology from The Florida State University in 1986 and was a National Institutes of Health postdoctoral fellow at the University of California at San Diego. He joined the faculty at the University of Toronto in 1989 and is an Associate Professor in the Department of Cell and Systems Biology. Dr. Riggs teaches a second-year Molecular Biology course and a fourth-year course in Genomics. His current research focuses on various aspects of plant development and chromosome structure/function. He serves on the editoral board of the National Research Council journal *Botany*.

The authors thank their families for their love and support:

Tess and Aaron
    — C.H. and D.R.
Maia and Emily
    — F.H. and M.B.

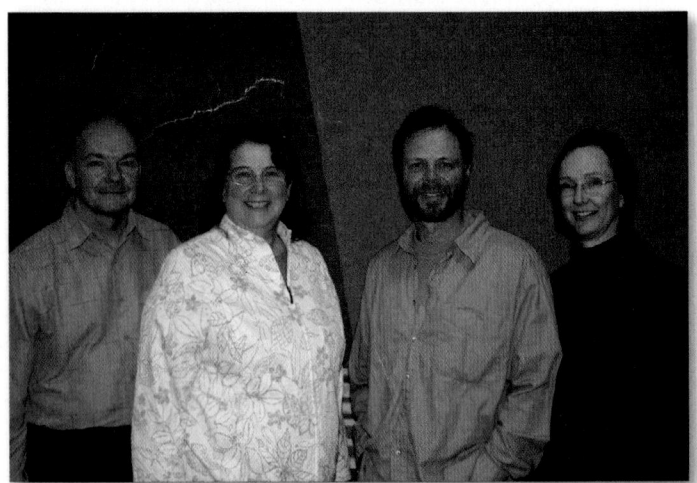

Canadian author team, left to right: Daniel Riggs, Clare Hasenkampf, Michael Bidochka, and Fiona Hunter

Brief Contents

v

Contents

UNIT IV   EVOLUTION

UNIT V   DIVERSITY

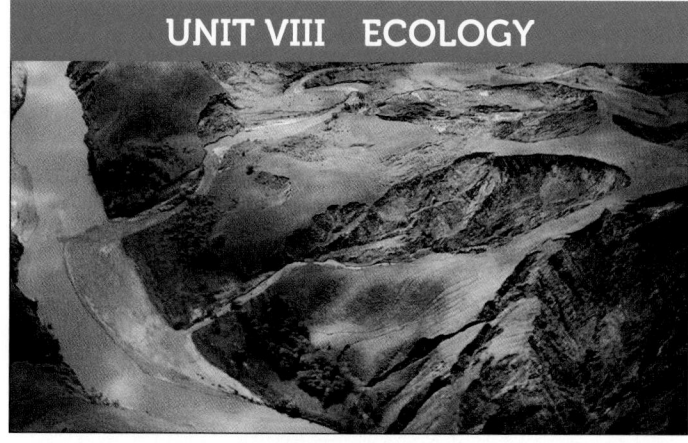

UNIT VIII   ECOLOGY

Chapter 56

Ecosystem Ecology 1299

Chapter 57

Conservation Biology and Biodiversity 1320

IMPROVING BIOLOGY EDUCATION: WE LISTENED TO YOU

A New Vision for Learning

A New Vision for Learning describes what we set out to accomplish with this Second Canadian edition of *Biology*. As authors and educators, we know your goal is to ensure your students are prepared for the future—their future coursework, lab experiences, and careers in the sciences. Building a strong foundation in biology for your students required a new vision for how they learn.

Through our classroom experiences and research work, we became inspired by the prospect that the first editions of *Biology* could move biology education forward. We are confident that this new edition of *Biology* is another step in the right direction because we listened to you. Based on our own experience and our discussions with educators and students, we continue to concentrate our efforts on these crucial areas:

- Experimentation and the process of science
- Modern content
- Evolutionary perspective
- Emphasis on visuals
- Accuracy and consistency
- Critical thinking
- Media—active teaching and learning with technology

Continued feedback from instructors using this textbook and other educators in the field of biology has been extremely valuable in refining the presentation of the material. Likewise, we have used the textbook in our own classrooms. This hands-on experience has provided much insight for areas for improvement. Our textbook continues to be comprehensive and cutting edge, featuring an evolutionary focus and an emphasis on scientific inquiry.

The First Canadian edition of *Biology* was truly innovative in its visual program, and this edition continues to emphasize this highly instructional visual program. In watching students study as well as in extensive interviews, it is clear that students rely heavily on the artwork as a primary study tool. As you will see when you scan this textbook, the illustrations have been crafted with the student's perspective in mind. They are very easy to follow, particularly those that have multiple steps, and have complete explanations of key concepts. We have taken the approach that students should be able to look at the figures and understand the key concepts, without having to glance back and forth between the text and art. Many figures contain text boxes that explain what the illustration is showing. In those figures with multiple steps, the boxes are numbered to guide students through the biological processes.

A New Vision Serving Teachers and Learners

To accurately and thoroughly cover a course as wide-ranging as biology, we felt it was essential that our team reflect the diversity of the field. We saw an opportunity to reach students at an early stage in their education and provide their biology training with a solid and up-to-date foundation. We have worked to balance coverage of classic research with recent discoveries that extend biological concepts in surprising new directions or that forge new concepts. Some new discoveries were selected because they highlight scientific controversies, showing students that we don't have all the answers yet. There is still a lot of work for new generations of biologists. With this in mind, we've also spotlighted discoveries made by diverse people doing research in different countries to illustrate the global nature of modern biological science.

As active teachers and writers, one of the great joys of this process for us is that we have been able to meet many more educators and students during the creation of this textbook. It is humbling to see the level of dedication our peers bring to their teaching. Likewise, it is encouraging to see the energy and enthusiasm so many students bring to their studies. We hope this book and its media package will serve to aid both faculty and students in meeting the challenges of this dynamic and exciting course. For us, this remains a work in progress, and we encourage you to let us know what you think of our efforts and what we can do to serve you better.

Rob Brooker, Eric Widmaier, Linda Graham, Peter Stiling, Clare Hasenkampf, Fiona Hunter, Michael Bidochka, Dan Riggs.

CHANGES TO THIS EDITION

The author team is dedicated to producing the most engaging and current text available for undergraduate students majoring in biology. We have listened to educators and reviewed documents, such as *Vision and Change: A Call to Action,* which includes a summary of recommendations made at a national conference organized by the American Association for the Advancement of Science (see www.visionandchange.org). We want our textbook to reflect core competencies and provide a more learner-centred approach. To achieve these goals, we have made the following innovations to *Biology,* Second Canadian edition.

- **Biological Principles of Life:** Based on educational literature and feedback from biology educators, we have listed nine Biological Principles of Life in Chapter 1.

- The biological principles are are threaded throughout the entire textbook. This is achieved in two ways. First, the principles are explicitly stated in selected figure legends in every chapter. Such legends are given a **"Principles"** icon ◯. Second, the principles covered in any particular unit are listed and explained in new Unit opening pages.

- **Unit openers:** We have added Unit openers to the second Canadian edition. These openers serve two purposes. They allow the student to see the "big picture" of the unit, and draw attention to the principles of biology that will be emphasized in that unit.

- **BioConnections:** We have also added a new feature called BioConnections, which are found in selected figure legends in each chapter. The BioConnections inform students of how a topic in one chapter is connected to a topic in another.

- **Learning Outcomes:** Educational materials should have well-defined learning goals. In this second edition of *Biology,* we begin each section of every chapter with a set of Learning Outcomes. These outcomes inform students of the major concepts to be mastered in each section and, along with Feature Investigations and end-of-chapter materials, model and test student acquisition of these key concepts and their ability to use the concepts in real-life situations. The assessments in Connect were developed using these Learning Outcomes as a guide in formulating online questions, thereby linking the learning goals of the text with the assessment in Connect.

With regard to the scientific content in the textbook, the author teams have worked with hundreds of faculty reviewers to refine this new edition and to update the content so that our students are exposed to the most current material. Some of the key changes are summarized below.

Chemistry Unit

Chapter 1
- New content about Canadian Fishery scientist Dr. Kristi Miller-Saunders
- New section on learning biology and the introduction of concept maps

Chapter 2
- Reworking and split of section 2.2 into sections 2.2 and 2.3 with the reviewers' suggestion to include van der Waal forces (and a more accurate characterization of hydrogen bonding)
- New Table 2.4: A Comparison of the Energy Associated with Different Types of Bonds and Molecular Interactions
- Concept map assignment

Chapter 3
- Clarification of details on several figures
- Inclusion of amylose and amylopectin as per reviewers' suggestions
- New Genome and Proteome section
- Concept map assignment

Cell Unit

Chapter 4
- Improved and more concise coverage of microscopy
- More accurate coverage of Archae
- Integration of the evolution of membrane lipid composition in Archae and their ecology
- Concept map assignment

Chapter 5
- Sections rewritten to be more clear and concise
- Introduction of the concept of leaflets of membrane bilayers as per reviewers' requests, in section 5.3
- Reduction to one Feature Investigation
- Concept map assignment

Chapter 6
- New lead photo highlights the work of Nobel Laureate Roderick MacKinnon
- Removal of table on historical development of fluid-mosaic model of membrane structure
- Inclusion of floppases and scramblase in text and Figure 6.2: Semifluidity of the lipid bilayer
- New Figure 6.11: Gradients across cell membranes, to help students visualize concentration and ion gradients
- Improved labelling of lipid anchor and added text for lipid rafts
- Figure to help students visualize differences between iso-, hypo-, and hypertonic environments

- Clarified text for section on osmosis
- Concept map assignment

Chapter 7

- Revised description of thermodynamics and enzyme action, making coupled reactions, and their importance, easier to grasp
- Modified figures make it easier to partition the energy investment, cleavage, and energy liberation phases of glycolysis
- New Figure 7.2: Entropy
- New Figure 7.4: The ATP cycle and coupled reactions
- Additional Canadian content in section 7.5: Secondary Metabolism

Chapter 8

- Numerous figures have been modified for clarity and to enable linkages to the "big picture"
- New Figure 8.16: Photostasis and excitation pressure, features the research of Canadian scientist Norm Hüner, included to link the oxidation state of the plastoquinone pool to cellular/organismal responses

Chapter 9

- Signalling processes discussed in Chapter 9 have been simplified by subtle, yet important, changes to colours (e.g., of ligands/receptors) and shapes to inform actions of ligand binding and receptor/enzyme structure change

Genetics Unit

Chapter 10

- Simplified and improved explanation of Meselson and Stahl experiment
- 'Thought experiment' for replication initiation and better explanation of the concepts of antiparallel, bidirectional, and '5 to 3' directionality
- Inclusion of exonuclease functions of polymerases, proofreading
- Improvement of many figures and development of a consistent colour scheme for DNA and the components of deoxyribonucleotides
- Concept map assignment

Chapter 11

- Better background is provided to help students understand the rationale of the Beadle and Tatum experiments (as per reviewers' requests)
- Modernization of RNA processing coverage
- Enhanced explantion of '5 to 3' directionality, to assist students in getting past a key learning obstacle

- Two new photos, and again consistent colour scheme, helping students distinguishing DNA from RNA
- New student interview
- Two new applied problems to help students assess their learning, and concept map question

Chapter 12

- Several new figures have been added to Chapter 12 to facilitate a discussion of eukaryotic gene regulation mediated by chromatin remodelling and to highlight the importance of histone modifications and DNA methylation in gene regulation
- Many of the Canadian first edition figures have been slightly modified for clarity

Chapter 13

- Several figures have been removed and several others modified to focus the reader on the topics and remove extraneous information. This should result in a better flow of the text. One of the figures nicely makes a link between exposure to sun (at the organismal level) and damage to DNA at the molecular level

Chapter 14

- More logical ordering of topics
- Rewrite and reorganization of chromosome packaging, putting it in the content of the cell cycle
- New figure on chromosome packaging and cell cycle: Figure 14.5: Structure of chromosomal DNA throughout the cell cycle
- Change in colour scheme of figures with chromosomes such that homologous chromosomes are consistently depicted as two shades of the same primary colour, and nonhomologous chromosomes are different colours
- Reduction from two to one Feature Investigation and Genome and Proteome
- New concept map question

Chapter 15

- Extra paragraph and figure for gene interaction
- Reduction from two to one Feature Investigation and Genome and Proteome
- New concept map question

Chapter 16

- Numerous changes (colour/shape changes, addition of labels) have been made to the figures to enable students to better follow DNA strands and molecular events
- New Figure 16.6: Antigenic shift and antigenic drift in influenza viruses
- Human focus on the processes of antigenic drift and antigenic shift that are believed to be involved in generating the new H5N1 bird flu virus

Chapter 17

- Several figures have been eliminated from this edition and the text streamlined to allow for better flow
- Several figures have been modified to simplify them and to better illustrate developmental patterning

Chapter 18

- Streamlined to feature recombinant DNA technology and its utility in biotechnology
- Proteomics techniques have been removed to permit better coverage of genomics and biotechnology
- Figures have been improved by colour/labelling changes

Chapter 19

- Reorganized to distinguish prokaryotic from eukaryotic genomes in separate sections
- Several paragraphs on metagenomics and synthetic genomics added; they offer significant tools for ecosystem monitoring, cataloguing biodiversity, and creating new organisms with specialized functions
- New information on the creation of Genome Canada, an organization that funds research and education initiatives in genomics
- Changes to the end-of-chapter test questions, including one that brings in one of the biological principles

Evolution Unit

Chapter 20

- Added new chapter-opening image of a Ginkgo fossil (found in B.C.) compared with a present-day Ginkgo
- Expanded discussion on biological communities near deep-sea vents, including University of Victoria research findings of more than 75 new species
- New Figure 20.8 shows timeline for the five mass extinctions, major volcanic eruptions, and meteorite impacts during the past 500 million years

Chapter 21

- New chapter-opening image added, to show results of selective breeding in corn over thousands of years
- Clarified the difference between 'selected for' and 'fail to be selected against' in terms of survival of individuals in a population
- New Figure 21.14 that shows structural differences between *E. coli* and *C. acetylbutylicum* for ease of understanding

Chapter 22

- New chapter-opening image added, to show polymorphism in the white-throated sparrow, a commonly encountered bird in the forests of northern Canada

- New Figure 22.10 shows genetic drive and population size over 50 generations, for numerous populations rather than just three
- New Figure 22.11 shows the bottleneck effect using a hypothetical frog population that shrinks in size due to drought (instead of the more commonly used example of beans being poured from a bottle)

Chapter 23

- New chapter-opening image shows different species of mosquito
- Expanded section on species concepts now includes evolutionary lineage concept (Gaylord), ecological species concept (Van Valen), and general lineage concept (de Queiroz)
- New example uses Lodgepole pine and jack pine, from northern Alberta and N.W.T., to help illustrate hybrid zones; new accompanying Figure 23.12 on their distribution in Canada

Chapter 24

- Updated description and figure discusses the seven supergroups contained within the domain Eukarya
- Redesigned Figure 24.9: Schematic relationship between a phylogenetic tree and taxonomy, to be more realistic
- Simplified and clarified sections on molecular clocks, concept of derived characters

Diversity Unit

Chapter 25

- New chapter-opening image shows an archaea, *Staphylothermus marinus,* found in deep hydrothermal vents
- Updated discussion and explanation of life on Earth to include classification into three domains: Eukarya, Archaea, and Bacteria; all related content updated throughout chapter, as well as related figures
- Examples of Cyanobacterial blooms updated to include ones in Lake Winnipeg and Lake Erie
- Simplified and clarified section on horizontal gene transfer
- Added discussion of distinguishing Gram-positive from Gram-negative bacteria as a tool in choosing antibiotics (due to synthesis of peptidoglycan)
- More detail added to methods of counting bacteria, to address majority of microoorganisms that cannot be cultured
- New Feature Investigation: Dantas and Colleagues Found that Many Bacteria Can Break Down and Consume Antibiotics as Sole Carbon Source

Chapter 26

- New chapter-opening image shows a diatom cell wall with ornamentation of the silicate structure
- Numerous updates throughout chapter reflect current taxonomy of protist supergroups
- New Feature Investigation added: Burkholder and Colleagues Demonstrated That Strains of the Dinoflagellate Genus *Pfiesteria* Are Toxic to Mammalian Cells
- New subsection and figure illustrates ancestry of *Plasmodium falciparum* being related to gorilla *Plasmodium*

Chapter 27

- Numerous updates throughout chapter reflect current taxonomy of Kingdom Fungi
- Representative photos of the five major groups of fungi added to Figure 27.1

Chapter 28

- Introduction of key term streptophytes, and related updates to text and figures throughout the chapter, including streptophyte algae
- Revised discussion includes critical innovations
- Revised discussion of simple land plants, including alternation of generations
- New Genomes and Proteomes: Comparison of Plant Genomes Reveals Genetic Changes that Occurred During Plant Evolution
- Expanded figure on early angiosperms and gymnosperms

Chapter 29

- Expanded information on the evolution of Angiosperms
- Discussion on double fertilization added to section on flower parts and their reproductive roles
- New Figure 29.20 to show the diversity of plants and their co-evolved pollinators
- Clarification of secondary plant metabolites

Chapter 30

- Moved subsection on Body Cavity divisions to new section for better flow
- Removed further methods of classification discussion, and moved "Segmentation" into its own subsection to streamline content
- Removed figure on traditional animal phylogeny based on body plans

Chapter 31

- New opening photo of a coral reef
- New Figure 31.18 to show fossil ammonite
- Numerous additional figure updates and revisions

Chapter 32

- New chapter-opening photo shows migrating salmon in British Columbia
- Discussion of Caecilians moved to section on modern amphibians

Plants Unit

Chapter 33

- Significant changes; coverage is the same, but editing has improved the flow and some extraneous information has been removed
- Kept the text explaining the ground-breaking work performed on canola breeding to make this one of the healthiest alternatives for cooking oil

Chapter 34

- Like Chapter 33, this chapter has been extensively edited to improve readability
- Several figures have been improved with changes to labels, colours, and contrasts

Chapter 35

- Links to Chapter 8 (Photosynthesis) and Chapter 56 (Ecosystems Ecology)
- Figures improved by changes to labelling
- End-of-chapter testing materials have been improved

Chapter 36

- Reduced in length
- Several figures have been modified, primarily by labelling changes

Chapter 37

- Feature Investigation replaced with one that centres on the mucilage modified mutants that were identified and characterized by Haughn and Western at UBC
- Labelling changes to figures
- Revision of the treatment of apomixis

Animals Unit

Chapter 38

- Various updates to figures and photos for increased clarity
- New Figure 38.11 showing relationship between surface area and value of cells, to determine how waste products cross cell membranes

Chapter 39

- Various updates to figures and photos for increased clarity

Chapter 40

- Chapter trimmed to reduce level of depth and detail, including removal of some figures reviewers felt were unnecessary

Chapter 41

- New Figure 42.2 to compare different vertebrate brains
- Chapter now has more non-human examples, as requested by reviewers

Chapter 42

- This chapter is an amalgamation of the previous edition's Neuroscience II and Neuroscience III chapters, and now flows as follows:
  - Evolution of the Brain and Nervous Systems
  - Central and Peripheral Nervous Systems
  - Cellular Basis of Learning and Memory
  - Sensory Reception
  - Mechanoreception
  - Thermoreception, Nociception, and Electromagnetic Sensing
  - Photoreception
  - Chemoreception
  - Human Health Connection
- Additional content moved online for students and instructors who want extra study, Appendix 42A: Human Brain and Nervous System, including more detail on the following topics:
  - Structure and Function of the Human Brain
  - Central and Peripheral Nervous System (Somatic Nervous System, Autonomic Nervous System, Hindbrain, Midbrain, Forebrain, and Assessing Human Brain Function)

Chapter 43

- Significant revisions to figures in this chapter improve the flow and clarity

Chapter 44

- New Genomes and Proteomes: The Four-Chambered Heart Evolved from Simple Contractile Tubes
- New Figure 44.5 compares gene expression in embryonic vertebrate hearts
- Chapter trimmed to reduce detail reviewers felt was unnecessary, including some figures that are now available online as a supplement

Chapter 45

- Updated figures throughout the chapter help students understand the relationships among respiratory structures

Chapter 46

- Revised section on ADH concentrations in the blood and the mechanism of aquaporins

- Significant revisions to figures in this chapter improve the flow and clarity

Chapter 47

- Updated labels in figures throughout the chapter help students understand the endocrine system

Chapter 48

- Chapter trimmed, with content that reviewers reported as unnecessary (such as Contraception) removed
- Additional comparative information included, as requested by reviewers, to avoid coverage being biased toward humans
- New image on external fertilization added to help students

Chapter 49

- Previous Genomes and Proteomes removed, and replaced with discussion on groups of embryonic cells producing specific body structures, pulled from main chapter content
- Significant revisions to figures in this chapter improve the flow and clarity

Chapter 50

- Numerous revisions to the text and figures in this chapter help clarify and streamline material for students

Ecology Unit

Chapter 51

- Considerable rewrites in this section to increase clarity, currency, and applicability to students, including global climate change, effects of humans in tropical rain forests, and aquatic biomes

Chapter 52

- Discussion of Peter Berthold's work on blackcap *Sylvia atricapilla* added

Chapter 53

- Expanded discussion of the effects of increasing K, the carry capacity, on populations
- Added section on K-selected versus r-selected species, as requested by reviewers

Chapter 54

- Paragraph describing negative frequency-dependent selection added

Chapter 55

- Discussion on measuring diversity of a community expanded to include three levels of species diversity (alpha, beta, gamma), as well as further examples of indices used (Simpson's index, rarefaction curves, for example)
- New subsection on conservation and the theory of island biogeography added

Chapter 56

- New Figure 56.4 illustrates a detritivore food web
- New Figure 56.15 illustrates energy flow in a salt marsh

Chapter 57

- New chapter-opening photo of the white-headed woodpecker, a species ranked as Endangered by COSEWIC
- New Feature Investigation about Ecotron simulations
- New discussion about destruction of habitat by oil spills

A NEW VISION FOR LEARNING: PREPARING STUDENTS FOR THE FUTURE

MAKING CONNECTIONS

Cuticular wax

Trichome

Closed stomatal pores with guard cells

├─ 27 μm ─┤

Figure 33.14 Leaf surface features. These features, viewed by SEM, include cuticular wax, stomatal pores with guard cells, and trichomes

BioConnections: *Look ahead to Figure 36.17 to learn how the control of stomatal pore aperature regulates water and gas exchange.*

BioConnections New in the second Canadian edition, BioConnections are questions found in selected figure legends that help students make connections between biological concepts. BioConnections help students understand that their study of biology involves linking concepts and building on previously learned information.

Algae (diatoms)

Protozoan (ciliate)

21 μm

Figure 26.2 A heterotrophic protozoan feeding on photosynthetic algae. The large heterotrophic ciliate protozoan shown here has consumed several oil-rich, golden-pigmented, glass-walled algal cells known as diatoms. The algal cells were ingested by the process of phagocytosis and will be digested as food. Diatom cells that have avoided capture glide nearby.

Principle: *Living organisms use energy. The diatoms were ingested by the process of phagocytosis, and their organic components will be digested as food.*

Biological Principles of Life are introduced in Chapter 1 and are then threaded throughout the textbook. This is achieved in two ways. First, the principles are explicitly stated in the figure legends for figures in which the specific principle is illustrated. The legends that relate to a principle are highlighted with an icon ◯.

In addition, a Conceptual Question at the end of each chapter is directly aimed at exploring a particular principle related to the content of the chapter.

UNIT IV
Evolution

Evolution is a heritable change in one or more characteristics of a population from one generation to the next. This process not only alters the characteristics of populations but also leads to the formation of new species.

We will begin Unit IV with a discussion of the hypotheses that have been proposed to explain the origin of life on Earth, and then we'll examine a timeline for the evolution of species from 4 billion years ago to the present. In Chapter 21 you will be introduced to the fundamental concepts of evolution, with an emphasis on natural selection. We will examine observations of evolutionary change, which include the fossil record, a comparison of the characteristics of modern species, and an analysis of molecular data. Chapter 22 continues our discussion of evolution at the molecular level and focuses on how changes in allele and genotype frequencies from one generation to the next are driven by a variety of factors. Chapter 23 shifts the emphasis of evolution to the level of species. We will examine how species are identified and discuss the evolutionary mechanisms by which new species arise. Finally, in Chapter 24 we will examine how biologists determine the evolutionary relationships among different species and produce phylogenic trees that describe those relationships.

20

21

22

23

24

◯ Several biological principles will be emphasized in this unit:

- *Populations of organisms evolve from one generation to the next.* This concept is important to the discussion in all chapters.

- *Living organisms interact with their environment.* As we discuss in Chapters 21 and 22, natural selection results in certain individuals having greater reproductive success than others in a given environment.

- *Structure determines function.* Chapters 21 and 22 also consider how structural features change during the evolution of new species. Such changes are related to changes in function.

- *All life is related by an evolutionary history.* Chapter 24 is devoted to examining how biologists determine evolutionary relationships among organisms.

Collaborate to Assess and Extend Your Learning

1. Discuss and compare several different types of cell-to-cell communication. What are some advantages and disadvantages of each type?
2. How does differential gene regulation enable various cell types to respond differently to the same signalling molecule? Why is this useful to multicellular organisms?
3. Certain mutations can alter the structure of the Ras protein so it will not hydrolyze GTP. Such mutations cause cancer. Explain why.
4. ◯ A principle of biology is that living organisms interact with their environment. Discuss how cell signalling helps organisms to interact with their environment.

Unit openers have been added in the second Canadian edition and serve two purposes. They allow the student to see the "big picture" of the unit, and draw attention to the biological principles of life that will be emphasized in that unit.

A GUIDED LEARNING SYSTEM AND CRITICAL THINKING

sequence, and the right column describes the percentages of amino acids within the entire sequence that are identical to the entire human sequence. Amino acids in the other species that are identical to humans are highlighted in orange. The sequences from the two monkeys are closest to humans, followed by the other two mammalian species (rabbit and dog). The three fish sequences are the least similar to the human sequence, but you may notice that the fish sequences are similar to each other. Taken together, the data shown in Figure 21.13 illustrate two critical points regarding gene evolution. First, certain genes are found in a diverse array of species, such as mammals, birds, and fish. Second, the sequences of closely related species tend to be more similar to each other than they are to distantly related species. The mechanism for this second observation is described in the next section.

21.3 THE MOLECULAR PROCESSES THAT UNDERLIE EVOLUTION

Learning Outcomes:
1. Explain how paralogs and orthologs are produced.
2. Describe how new types of genes arise via exon shuffling.
3. Distinguish between vertical evolution and horizontal gene transfer.

Historically, the study of evolution was based on comparing the anatomies of extinct and modern species to identify similarities between related species. However, the advent of molecular approaches for analyzing DNA sequences has revolutionized the field of evolutionary biology. Now we can analyze how changes in the genetic material are associated with changes in phenotype and how those changes have led to the formation of new species. In this section we will examine some of the molecular changes in the genetic material that are associated with evolution.

Figure 21.14 The evolution of orthologs: homologous genes from different species. After two species diverged the genes accumulated random mutations that created similar but not identical gene sequences called orthologs. These orthologs in *E. coli* and *C. acetylbutylicum* encode metal transporters. Only one of the two DNA strands is shown from each gene. Bases that are identical between the two genes are shown in orange.

Concept check: Why do these orthologs have similar gene sequences? Why are they not identical?

At the beginning of each section, *Learning Outcomes* have been added in the second Canadian edition that inform students of the major concepts to be mastered in each section and, along with Feature Investigations and end-of-chapter materials, model and test student acquisition of these key concepts and their ability to use the concepts in real-life situations. The assessments in Connect use these Learning Outcomes as a guide to developing online questions.

Critical Thinking—in the text:

- *Concept Checks* ask students to apply or interpret information presented in the illustrations.
- Questions with the Feature Investigations continually ask students to check their understanding and push a bit further.

And . . . continued online:

- *NEW! Quantitative Question Bank in Connect®* Developing quantitative reasoning skills is important to the success of today's students. In addition to the Question Bank and Test Bank in Connect®, a separate bank of quantitative questions is readily available for seamless use in homework/practice assignments, quizzes, and exams. These algorithmic-style questions provide an opportunity for students to more deeply explore quantitative concepts and to experience repeated practice that enables quantitative skill building over time.

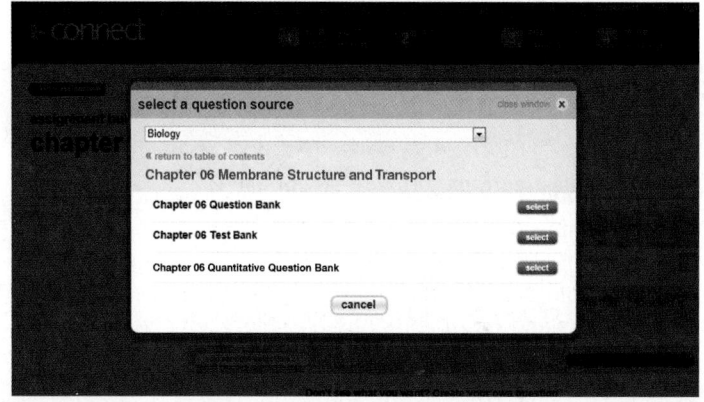

EVOLUTIONARY PERSPECTIVE

Modern techniques have enabled researchers to study many genes simultaneously, allowing them to explore genomes (all the genes an organism has) and proteomes (all the proteins encoded by those genes). This allows us to understand biology in a broader way. Beginning in Chapter 3, each chapter contains a box called *Genomes and Proteomes* that provides an understanding of how genomes and proteomes underlie the inner workings of cells and explains how evolution works at the molecular level. The topics that are covered in *Genomes and Proteomes* are very useful in preparing students for future careers in biology. The study of genomes and proteomes has revolutionized many careers in biology, including those in medicine, research, and biotechnology, to name a few.

A VISUAL OUTLINE

Because students rely on the art as a primary study tool, the authors worked with a team of editors, scientific illustrators, educators, and students to create an accurate, up-to-date, realistic, and visually appealing illustration program that is instructive and also easy to follow. The artwork and photos serve as a visual outline and guide students through complex processes.

Figure 7.6 **The steps of an enzyme-catalyzed reaction.** The example shown here involves the enzyme hexokinase, which binds glucose and ATP. The products are glucose-phosphate and ADP, which are released from the enzyme.

EXPERIMENTAL APPROACH

Feature Investigations provide a complete description of experiments, including data analysis, so students can understand how experimentation leads to an understanding of biological concepts. There are two types of *Feature Investigations*. Most describe experiments according to the scientific method. They begin with observations and then progress through the hypothesis, experiment, data, and interpretation of the data (conclusion). Some *Feature Investigations* involve discovery-based science, which does not rely on a preconceived hypothesis. The illustrations of the *Feature Investigations* are particularly innovative by having parallel drawings at the experimental and conceptual levels. By comparing the two levels, students will be able to understand how the researchers were able to interpret the data and arrive at their conclusions.

WHAT'S NEW?

An interview with Dr. Steve Marshall from University of Guelph by Adam Jewiss-Gaines, a postgraduate student at Brock University.

Students across Canada interviewed researchers in various fields of biology to learn about their current experiments. One interview is presented in each unit, giving students a close-up view of what professional biologists are currently working on. Most of these are new to the second Canadian edition.

Dr. Marshall is a professor and collection director, School of Environmental Sciences, at University of Guelph.

As an entomologist, what kind of research do you do and what are some of your current goals?

I want to know the identities of the species of insect I find, what they do, how they are related to one another, and how they came to their current distributions and biologies. And once I have worked this out, often including the discovery and naming of new taxa, I put a priority on making the information widely accessible.

Are there any specific families or genera of insects that you think are especially important for current study?

Every taxon offers its own set of challenges and rewards. Even well-known pest taxa will still yield secrets to the patient specialist, and poorly studied taxa (like most of the fly groups I work on) offer a steady flow of new discoveries.

How do you define the words *taxonomy* and *systematics,* and how do they relate to one another?

I think of systematics as the study of taxa and any and all relationships between them, and I think of taxonomy as more focused on classification and description than on phylogeny or zoogeography. The terms *taxonomy* and *systematics* have become confounded in recent decades, and are now used interchangeably to refer to the study of biodiversity including classification, identification, phylogeny, and biogeography. I see no problem in following Ross's influential text (*Biological Systematics*) by treating *taxonomy* and *systematics* as synonyms but I still think that that they imply slightly different emphases.

Why do you think the study of taxonomy is an important field of practice for biologists?

It is obviously fundamental to our understanding of the world around us. If you don't know the parts, your understanding of the whole is flawed.

With the onset of technology and methods such as DNA barcoding, do you believe that the study of taxonomy and systematics will continue to remain of importance?

The "onset of technology" was long before I was born, and throughout my lifetime technological advances have influenced every discipline, including systematics. Better optics, computers, critical-point driers, ever-improving cameras, and, most importantly, digital photography and the Web have steadily increased the scope, quality, and quantity of any good taxonomist's work. The downside of "new" technologies is the perception that they are more than just tools to be adopted as practical and useful. This perception can be to the detriment of the discipline as a whole.

Your example of DNA barcoding is a case in point, since it is an application of a technology already widely adopted by the taxonomic community, before it was cleverly branded and vigorously promoted as something totally new and superior to "traditional taxonomy." This led to a huge amount of publicity, and a widespread public perception that "barcoding" is the new taxonomy and that it is on the cusp of providing a system of instantly, cheaply, and reliably naming all life, or at least providing access to the names that taxonomists have assigned to described species of living things. Barcoding is not taxonomy, but instead it is one approach to harvesting and delivering the products of taxonomy. It is thus entirely dependent on good taxonomy. Increasing accessibility of sequence data should have the same effect as other newly available technologies—to increase the scope, quality, and quantity of the taxonomist's work, not to undermine or devalue it.

Do you have any projects that you plan on releasing or starting in the near future?

Of course, there are always ongoing revisions, reviews, and books. My latest book, reviewing the order Diptera on a world basis, will be published this September. [Note from Editor: This interview took place prior to September 2012, when Dr. Marshall's book was published.]

A NEW VISION IN PREPARING YOUR COURSE

MCGRAW-HILL HIGHER EDUCATION AND BLACKBOARD HAVE TEAMED UP

Blackboard®, the Web-based course management system, has partnered with McGraw-Hill to better allow students and faculty to use online materials and activities to complement face-to-face teaching. Blackboard features exciting social learning and teaching tools that foster more logical, visually impactful, and active learning opportunities for students. You'll transform your closed-door classrooms into communities where students remain connected to their educational experience 24 hours a day.

This partnership allows you and your students access to McGraw-Hill's Connect® and McGraw-Hill Create™ right from within your Blackboard course—all with one single sign-on. Not only do you get single sign-on with Connect and Create, you also get deep integration of McGraw-Hill content and content engines right in Blackboard. Whether you're choosing a book for your course or building Connect assignments, all the tools you need are right where you want them—inside of Blackboard.

Gradebooks are now seamless. When a student completes an integrated Connect assignment, the grade for that assignment automatically (and instantly) feeds your Blackboard grade centre.

McGraw-Hill and Blackboard can now offer you easy access to industry leading technology and content, whether your campus hosts it or we do.

MCGRAW-HILL CONNECT®

McGraw-Hill Connect® provides online presentation, assignment, and assessment solutions. It connects your students with the tools and resources they'll need to achieve success. With Connect you can deliver assignments, quizzes, and tests online. A robust set of questions and activities are presented and aligned with the textbook's learning outcomes. As an instructor, you can edit existing questions and author entirely new problems. Track individual student performance—by question, assignment, or in relation to the class overall—with detailed grade reports. Integrate grade reports easily with Learning Management Systems (LMS), such as WebCT and Blackboard—and much more. Connect also provides students with 24/7 online access to the eBook. This media-rich version of the book is available through the McGraw-Hill Connect platform and allows seamless integration of text, media, and assessments.

To learn more, visit www.connect.mcgraw-hill.com

MY LECTURES—TEGRITY®

McGraw-Hill Tegrity® records and distributes your class lectures with just a click of a button. Students can view them anytime/anywhere via computer, iPod, or mobile device. It indexes as it records your PowerPoint® presentations and anything shown on your computer so students can use keywords to find exactly what they want to study. Tegrity is available as an integrated feature of McGraw-Hill Connect® Biology and as a standalone.

PERSONALIZED AND ADAPTIVE LEARNING

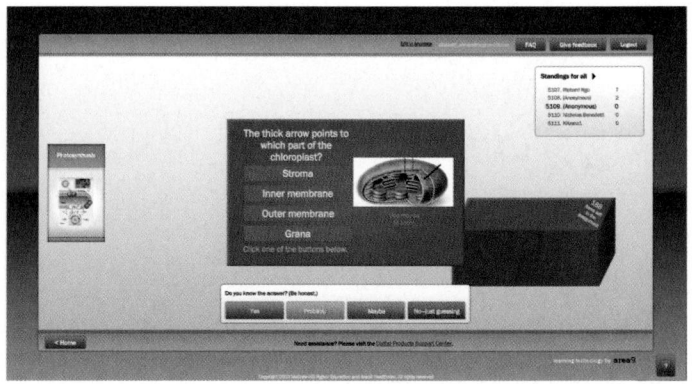

McGraw-Hill LearnSmart™ is available as an integrated feature of McGraw-Hill Connect® Biology. It is an adaptive learning system designed to help students learn faster, study more efficiently, and retain more knowledge for greater success. LearnSmart assesses a student's knowledge of course content through a series of adaptive questions. It pinpoints concepts the student does not understand and maps out a personalized study plan for success. This innovative study tool also has features that allow instructors to see exactly what students have accomplished and a built-in assessment tool for grading assignments. Visit www.mhrlearnsmart.ca for a demonstration.

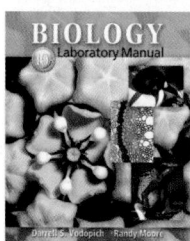

Biology Laboratory Manual, Tenth Edition
Vodopich/Moore
ISBN: 0-07-353225-8

This laboratory manual is designed for an introductory majors-level biology course with a broad survey of basic laboratory techniques. The experiments and procedures are simple, safe, easy to perform, and especially appropriate for large classes. Few experiments require a second class meeting to complete the procedure. Each exercise includes many photographs, traditional topics, and experiments that help students learn about life. Procedures within each exercise are numerous and discrete so that an exercise can be tailored to the needs of the students, the style of the instructor, and the facilities available.

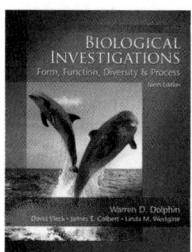

Biological Investigations Lab Manual,
Ninth Edition
Dolphin
ISBN: 0-07-338305-8

This independent lab manual can be used for a one- or two-semester majors-level general biology lab and can be used with any majors-level general biology textbook. The labs are investigative and ask students to use more critical thinking and hands-on learning. The author emphasizes investigative, quantitative, and comparative approaches to studying the life sciences.

LabSmart Based on the same world-class super-adaptive technology as LearnSmart™, McGraw-Hill LabSmart™ is a must-see, outcomes-based lab simulation. It assesses a student's knowledge and adaptively corrects deficiencies, allowing the student to learn faster and retain more knowledge with greater success. Whether your need is to overcome the logistical challenges of a traditional lab, provide better lab prep, improve student performance, or create an online experience that rivals the real world, LabSmart accomplishes it all.

Instructor's Manual

This manual contains instructional strategies and activities, student misconceptions, etymology of key terms, "Beyond the Book" interesting facts, and sources for additional Web resources.

Computerized Test Bank

All questions have been written to fully align with the content of the textbook, and are tagged to both chapter sections and Learning Outcomes. Provided in McGraw-Hill Ryerson's flexible electronic testing program, EZ Test Online, instructors can create paper and online tests or quizzes in this easy-to-use program. A new tagging scheme allows you to sort questions by difficulty level, topic, and section. Imagine being able to create and access your test or quiz anywhere, at any time, without installing the testing software.

Powerful Presentation Tools

Everything you need for outstanding presentation in one place!

- FlexArt Image PowerPoints—including every piece of art that has been sized and cropped specifically for superior presentations as well as labels that you can edit, flexible art that can be picked up and moved, tables, and photographs.
- Animation PowerPoints—Numerous full-colour animations illustrating important processes. Harness the visual impact of concepts in motion by importing these slides into classroom presentations or online course materials.
- Lecture PowerPoints with animations fully embedded.
- Labelled and unlabelled JPEG images—Full-colour digital files of all illustrations that can be readily incorporated into presentations, exams, or custom-made classroom materials.

Additional Technology and Learning Solutions

To see the latest technology and Learning Solutions offered by McGraw-Hill Ryerson and its partners, www.mcgrawhill.ca/digital-solutions.

Acknowledgements

We would like to thank the many reviewers for providing feedback:

Eric Alcorn, *Acadia University*
Edward Awad, *Vanier College*
Greg Beaulieu, *University of Victoria*
David Beresford, *Trent University*
Peter Boag, *Queen's University*
Tom Booth, *University of Manitoba*
David Creasey, *University of Victoria*
Keith Egger, *University of Northern British Columbia*
Kerri Finlay, *University of Regina*
Diana Fletcher, *Mount Royal University*
Anna Hicks, *Memorial University*
William Huddleston, *University of Calgary*
Mark Johnston, *Dalhousie University*
Pamela Kalas, *University of British Columbia*
Wendy Keenleyside, *University of Guelph*
Tamara Kelly, *York University*
Andrea Kirkwood, *University of Ontario Institute of Technology*
Herbert Kronzucker, *University of Toronto*
Paul McMillan, *Capilano University*
Terrance Michael Stock, *Grant MacEwan University*
Cindy Paszkowski, *University of Alberta*
Fiona Rawle, *University of Toronto*
Ross Shaw, *Grant MacEwan University*
Nigel Waltho, *Carleton University*
Brian Watts, *John Abbott College*

In putting together this second Canadian edition, the authors have all relied heavily on the editorial team assigned to this textbook by McGraw-Hill Ryerson.

For months on end, the authors were in almost daily contact with Suzanne Simpson Millar (developmental editor), Joanne Limebeer (supervising editor), and Tracy Leonard (photo researcher). Then, after the book was completed, there was a strange void when the daily emails stopped. We thank Suzanne, Joanne, and Tracy for keeping us motivated and on track. For the fine-tuning of the text, we thank the copy editors, Dawn Hunter and Karen Rolfe, as well as the proofreaders, Karen Rolfe and Ann Firth. The continued support of Leanna MacLean, the group product manager, was greatly appreciated, as were the ongoing efforts of all other staff at McGraw-Hill Ryerson.

The authors would like to thank their families for their unfailing support and daily reminders of the joys of life—both within and beyond science. The authors are also indebted to the many instructors across Canada who provided detailed feedback on the first edition. We are particularly grateful to our students, who have helped us see the challenges of understanding biology through their many probing questions, and who have given us the privilege of seeing the world afresh each year as we teach and learn with them.

Clare Hasenkampf
Fiona F. Hunter
Michael J. Bidochka
C. Daniel Riggs

Living organisms can be thought of as collections of cells (or sometimes just one cell) within which exist a wide array of chemical reactions. These reactions occur between atoms and molecules and may require, or in some cases release, energy. Chemical reactions and interactions between molecules play a role in virtually all aspects of a cell's activities. To understand how living organisms function, grow, develop, behave, and interact with their environments, we therefore first need to understand some basic principles of atomic and molecular structure, and the forces that allow them to interact with each other.

We begin this unit with an overarching view of how scientists approach the study of biology—what mental frameworks, assumptions, concepts, and experimental approaches we use (Chapter 1). Chapter 2 is an overview of inorganic chemistry— that is, the nature of atoms and molecules, with the exception of those that contain rings or chains of carbon. Such carbon-containing molecules form the basis of organic chemistry and are covered in Chapter 3.

Several biological principles will be emphasized in this unit:

- *Living organisms use energy.* We will see how the chemical energy stored in certain bonds of such molecules as sugars and fats can be released and used by living organisms to perform functions that support life, including growth, digestion, locomotion, and many others.

- *Genetic material provides a dynamic blueprint for sustaining life, and all species (past and present) are related by an evolutionary history.* Nucleic acids, the basis of inherited genetic material, are first introduced in Chapter 3.

- *Organisms follow the laws of chemistry and physics and structure determines function.* Cells follow the rules of chemistry and physics in all aspects of their function. The most important physico-chemical principles are reviewed in this unit.

An Introduction to Biology

Chapter Outline

Sockeye salmon at their spawning grounds.

Biology is the study of life. The diverse forms of life found on Earth provide biologists with an amazing array of organisms to study, and the investigation of living things has led to unexpected discoveries. For example, researchers have determined that the venom from certain poisonous snakes contains a chemical that lowers blood pressure in humans (**Figure 1.1a**). The bark of the white willow tree contains the compound salicylic acid and was used from ancient times to fight fever. Modern chemists developed a related compound, acetyl-salicylic acid, better known as Aspirin (**Figure 1.1b**). Naturalists have long admired the functionality and beauty of spider webs (**Figure 1.1c**), but scientists have learned that silk fibres are stronger, by weight, than steel. Work is underway to develop silk body armour and even silk artificial limbs. Researchers have learned that even microorganisms must defend themselves against attack from viruses (**Figure 1.1d**). As scientists came to understand how bacteria accomplish this, they discovered restriction enzymes that can recognize and cut up foreign DNA, leading to a recombinant-DNA technological revolution. Jellyfish naturally produce a greenish glow (**Figure 1.1e**) because of a molecule they make called green fluorescent protein (GFP). Scientists have been able to transfer GFP to other organisms and use it as a research tool to study the functions of cells. Finally, locust plagues have wreaked havoc on agriculture for millennia (**Figure 1.1f**). In 2009, Canadian scientist Michael Anstey was part of a team that discovered that the neurotransmitter serotonin is the chemical mediator that dramatically transforms solitary desert locusts into swarming masses of ravenous, destructive feeders. The study of life has not only revealed the amazing diversity and fascinating characteristics of living species but has also led to the development of drugs and research tools that have benefitted mankind and that, when used wisely, can help us solve many of the urgent problems facing the planet and its peoples.

To make new discoveries, biologists view life from many different perspectives. What is life made of? How is it organized? How do organisms reproduce? Sometimes, the questions posed by biologists are fundamental and even philosophical in nature. Where did we come from? What is the physical basis for memory? Can we save endangered species? Biologists are scientific explorers looking for answers to some of the world's most enduring mysteries. Unravelling these mysteries presents an exciting challenge. Our society has been substantially affected by discoveries in biology, and biologists will continue to make important advances. The rewards of a career in biology include the excitement of working in uncharted territory, the thrill of making discoveries that change the health and lives of people, and the satisfaction of seeing the impact biology makes on the preservation of the environment and endangered species. For these and many other compelling reasons, students looking for challenging and rewarding careers may want to choose biology as their field.

In this chapter, we will begin our survey of biology by examining the basic features that are common to all living organisms. In the second section, we will consider how evolution has led to the development of modern genomes—the entire genetic compositions of organisms that can explain the unity and diversity that we observe among modern species. In the third section of the chapter, we will explore the general approaches that scientists follow when making new discoveries. Last, we will look at the training of the next generation of scientists and how you can ready yourself for that role.

(a) A chemical in the venom of the Brazilian arrowhead viper lowers blood pressure. Derivatives of this chemical, called angiotensin-converting enzyme (ACE) inhibitors, are now commonly used to treat high blood pressure in people.

(b) Modern Aspirin, acetylsalicylic acid, was developed after analyzing a chemical found in the bark of the white willow tree.

(c) Spiders make beautiful silk webs, and scientists have discovered that, by weight, silk is five times as strong as steel. Spiders dehydrate a liquid mix of silk proteins and then coax it to flow out from their spinners as a dry, flexible thread (shown in the inset).

(d) A bacterial cell (the large rod-shaped structure) is being attacked by lambda viruses (the small particles). While investigating how bacteria defend themselves, scientists discovered restriction enzymes. Our understanding of how these enzymes can cut DNA at very specific sites (shown in the inset) led to recombinant DNA technology.

(e) Jellyfish naturally produce a green glow caused by green fluorescent protein (GFP). GFP can be transferred to other organisms, such as mice, and used as a research tool to study the functions of cells.

(f) Under specific conditions, desert locusts can undergo an amazing behavioural and physical transformation, moving from a solitary existence to a swarming mass of voracious eaters that can devastate crops. Canadian scientist Michael Anstey was part of a team that identified the neurotransmitter serotonin (shown in the inset) as the chemical mediator of this transformation.

Figure 1.1 Amazing discoveries in biology.

1.1 THE PRINCIPLES OF LIFE AND LEVELS OF BIOLOGICAL ORGANIZATION

Learning Outcomes:

1. Describe the principles of biology.
2. Explain how life can be viewed at different levels of biological complexity.

A fitting way to begin a biology textbook is to distinguish living organisms from nonliving objects. At first, the distinction might seem intuitively obvious. A person is alive, but a rock is not. However, the distinction between living and nonliving may seem less obvious when we consider microscopic entities. Is a bacterium alive? Is a virus alive? Is a chloroplast alive? Biologists have wrestled with such questions and have determined that all living organisms display certain characteristics that set them apart from nonliving things. These traits are illustrated in **Figure 1.2**.

The Unifying Principles That Guide Our Understanding of Life

Biologists have studied many different species and biological phenomena, and they have observed a set of common principles. The first seven principles are often used as criteria to define the basic features of life. Principle 8 relates to how life on Earth evolved, and principle 9 relates the physico-chemical constraints of biological systems. You will see these principles often as you progress through this textbook. In particular, we will draw your attention to them at the beginning of each unit, and we will refer to them within particular figures.

Principle 1: Cells Are the Simplest Units of Life. The term organism can be applied to all living things. Organisms maintain an internal order that is separated from the environment (**Figure 1.2a**). The simplest unit of such organization is the cell, which we will examine in Unit II. One of the foundations of biology is the cell theory, which states that (1) all organisms are composed of cells, (2) cells are the smallest units of life, and (3) new cells come from pre-existing cells via cell division. Unicellular organisms are composed of one cell, whereas multicellular organisms, such as plants and animals, contain many cells.

Principle 2: Living Organisms Use Energy. The maintenance of organization requires energy. Therefore, all living organisms acquire energy from the environment and use that energy to maintain their internal order. Cells carry out a variety of chemical reactions that are responsible for the breakdown of nutrients. Such reactions often release energy in a process called respiration. The energy can be used to synthesize the components that make up individual cells and living organisms. Chemical reactions involved with the breakdown and synthesis of cellular molecules are collectively known as metabolism. Plants, algae, and certain bacteria can directly harness light energy to produce their own nutrients in the process of photosynthesis (**Figure 1.2b**). They are the primary producers of food

(a) Cells and organization: Organisms maintain an internal organization. The simplest unit of organization is the cell. Diatoms are shown here. The variety of shapes also reflects the differences in the way each diatom species functions.

(b) Energy use and metabolism: To maintain their internal order, organisms need energy. Energy is utilized in chemical reactions collectively known as metabolism.

(c) Response to environmental changes: Organisms react to environmental changes to promote their survival.

(d) Regulation and homeostasis: Organisms regulate their cells and bodies to maintain relatively stable internal conditions, a process called homeostasis.

(e) Growth and development: Growth produces more or larger cells, while development produces organisms with a defined set of characteristics.

(f) Reproduction and transmission of the genetic material: To sustain life over many generations, organisms must reproduce. Through the transmission of the genetic material, offspring tend to have traits like their parents'.

(g) Biological evolution: Populations of organisms change over many generations. Evolution results in traits that promote survival and reproductive success.

Figure 1.2 Seven characteristics are common to all life.

on Earth. In contrast, animals and fungi are consumers—they must use other organisms as food to obtain energy. Further, some other bacteria can use inorganic compounds, such as sulphur, iron, or ammonium, as sources of energy.

Principle 3: Living Organisms Interact with Their Environment. To survive, living organisms must be able to interact with their environment, which includes other organisms they may encounter. All organisms must respond to environmental changes. For example, bacterial cells have mechanisms to detect that certain nutrients in the environment are in short supply, while others are readily available. In the winter, many species of mammals develop a thicker coat of fur that protects them from the cold temperatures. Plants respond to changes in the angle of the sun. If you place a plant in a window, it will grow toward the light (**Figure 1.2c**).

Principle 4: Living Organisms Have Mechanisms That Maintain Homeostasis. Although life is a dynamic process, living organisms regulate their cells and bodies to maintain relatively stable internal conditions, a process called homeostasis (from the Greek, meaning "to stay the same"). The degree to which homeostasis is achieved varies among different organisms. For example, most mammals and birds maintain a relatively stable body temperature in spite of changing environmental temperatures (**Figure 1.2d**), whereas reptiles and amphibians tolerate a wider fluctuation in body temperature. But all organisms continually regulate their cellular metabolism so that nutrient molecules are used at an appropriate rate and new cellular components are synthesized when they are needed.

Principle 5: Living Organisms Grow, Develop, and Reproduce. All living organisms have an ability to grow, develop, and reproduce. Growth produces more or larger cells. Multicellular organisms may begin as a single-celled, fertilized egg, and then undergo multiple cell divisions to develop into a complete organism with many cells. Development is a series of changes in the state of a cell, tissue, organ, or organism, eventually resulting in organisms with a defined set of characteristics (**Figure 1.2e**). Unicellular organisms have a simpler development; new cells are relatively small, and they increase in volume by the synthesis of additional cellular components. But all living organisms have a finite lifespan. To sustain life, organisms must reproduce to generate offspring (**Figure 1.2f**).

Principle 6: The Genetic Material, DNA, Provides a Dynamic Plan for Sustaining Life. A key feature of reproduction is that offspring tend to have characteristics that greatly resemble those of their parent(s) (Figure 1.2f). How is this possible? All living organisms contain genetic material composed of DNA (deoxyribonucleic acid), which provides a dynamic plan for their organization, development, and function. During reproduction, a copy of the DNA is transmitted from parent to offspring. This DNA is used dynamically to fit the needs of the organism.

Principle 7: Populations of Organisms Evolve from One Generation to the Next. The first six characteristics of life, which we have just considered, apply to individual organisms over the short run. Over the long run, another universal

characteristic of life is biological evolution, which refers to a heritable change in the DNA for a population of organisms from generation to generation. Sometimes the heritable changes in DNA are neutral and do not result in any organismal changes; but in other cases the DNA changes result in detectable differences in populations that become better adapted to the environment in which they live. For example, the long snout of an anteater is an adaptation that enhances its ability to obtain food, namely ants, from hard-to-reach places (**Figure 1.2g**). The fossil record suggests that over many generations, the long snout anteaters arose from short snout ancestors via evolution.

Principle 8: All Life Is Related by an Evolutionary History. Principle 8 considers evolution as an ongoing process that happens from one generation to the next. Evidence from a variety of sources, including the fossil record and DNA sequences, all indicate that all organisms on Earth share a common ancestry.

Principle 9: Organisms Follow the Laws of Chemistry and Physics, and Structure Determines Function. In addition to the preceding characteristics that are unique to living organisms, another important principle is that living organisms follow the rules of chemistry and physics, and the interaction of the two in living systems can be seen in the additional principle that "structure determines function." This principle works across the levels of biological organization, from the critical role that shape plays in the function of biological molecules within cells, to the size and shape of a species' body parts.

Living Organisms Can Be Viewed and Studied at Different Levels of Organization

As you have just learned, life exhibits a set of characteristics, beginning with the concept of organization. The organization of living organisms can be analyzed in a hierarchical manner. **Figure 1.3** depicts a scientist's view of biological organization at different levels.

1. *Atoms:* An **atom** is the smallest component of an element that has the chemical properties of that element. All matter is composed of atoms.
2. *Molecules and macromolecules:* Atoms bond with each other to form **molecules**. When many similarly structured molecules bond together to form a polymer, a **macromolecule** results. Carbohydrates, proteins, and the nucleic acids DNA and RNA are important macromolecules found in living organisms.
3. *Cells:* Molecules and macromolecules associate with one another to form organized larger structures (organelles) that are enclosed in a cell membrane.
4. *Tissues:* In the case of multicellular organisms, many cells of the same type associate with each other to form **tissues**. An example is muscle tissue.
5. *Organs:* An **organ** comprises two or more types of tissue. For example, the heart of a wolf comprises several types of tissues, including muscle, nervous, and connective tissue.
6. *Organ systems:* Several organs can work together as an **organ system** to accomplish a larger function for the

organism. For example, the human cardiovascular system consists of the heart, blood vessels, and blood.

7. *Organism:* As distinct units of life, organisms vary in complexity. Some organisms exist as single-celled entities, and some organisms consist of billions of cells organized into organ systems.

8. *Species:* Biologists classify organisms as belonging to a particular **species**, which is a related group of organisms that share a distinctive form and set of attributes in nature. The members of the same species are closely related genetically.

9. *Population:* A group of organisms of the same species that occupy a continuous space is called a **population**.

10. *Community:* A biological community is an assemblage of populations of different species. The types of species that are found in a **community** are determined by the environment and by the interactions of the species.

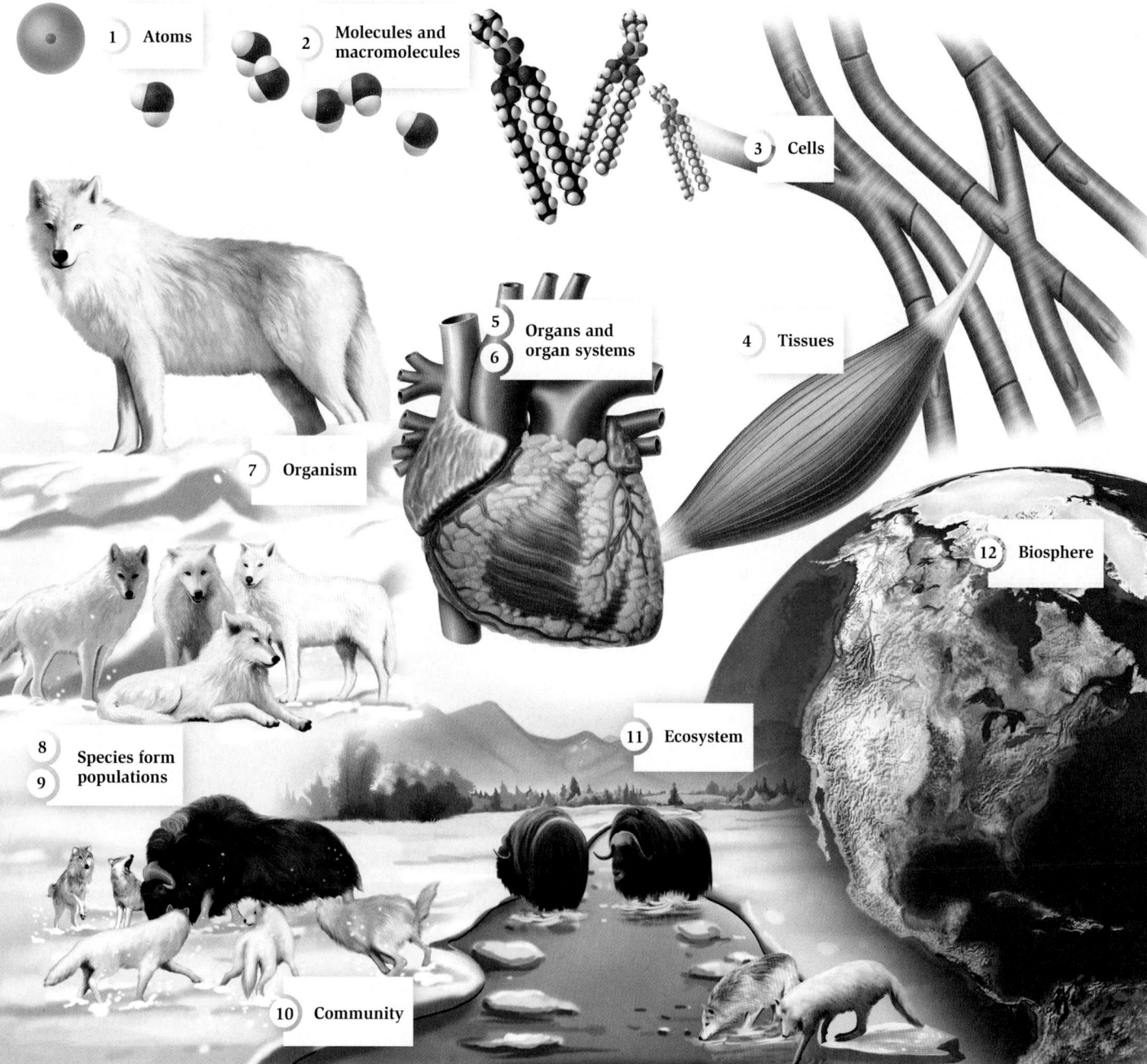

Figure 1.3 **The levels of biological organization.** Atoms (1) combine into small and large molecules (2). Macromolecules carry information, create compartments, and sometimes form organelles within cells (3). Multicellular organisms organize cells into tissues with specialized functions (4). Different tissues can be combined to form organs (5) and organ systems (6) in complex multicellular organisms (7). A group of interbreeding organisms of the same species (8) form populations (9) that interact with other species within their local community (10). This community of diverse organisms and their relationship to their physical environment define the local ecosystem (11).The ecosystem is strongly influenced by its global position with the consequent radiant energy and atmospheric condition for that region (12). In turn, activity within ecosystems can influence the atmosphere and have potentially biosphere-changing consequences, such as global warming.

11. *Ecosystem:* Living organisms interact with their environment. **Ecosystems** are formed by the interactions of a community of organisms with their physical environment.
12. *Biosphere:* The **biosphere** includes all the places on Earth where living organisms exist, encompassing the air, water, and land.

1.2   UNITY AND DIVERSITY OF LIFE

Learning Outcomes:

1. Explain the two basic mechanisms by which evolutionary change occurs: vertical descent with mutation and horizontal gene transfer.
2. Outline how organisms are classified (taxonomy).
3. Describe how changes in genomes and proteomes underlie evolutionary changes.

The words *unity* and *diversity* are often are used to describe the living world. Unity can be viewed from both modern and prehistorical perspectives. In this section, we examine how all existing forms of life display a common set of characteristics that distinguish them from nonliving objects. This commonality is rooted in a shared evolutionary history. Life on Earth is united by an evolutionary past in which modern organisms have evolved from pre-existing organisms. Sharing this evolutionary unity does not mean that organisms are exactly alike. In fact, one of life's most impressive attributes is its diversity. Diverse forms of life have evolved to prosper in Earth's many different environments. In this section, we also will begin to examine the diversity that exists within the biological world.

Modern Forms of Life Are Connected by an Evolutionary History

Life began with primitive single-celled organisms about 3.5 billion to 4 billion years ago. Over time, those primitive organisms underwent evolutionary changes that ultimately gave rise to today's species. Biologist Theodosius Dobzhansky made the famous statement "nothing in biology makes sense except in the light of evolution." Indeed, understanding an organism's evolutionary history places its biomolecules, cellular activities, structures, and behaviour in a context that allows us to more fully understand their function as part of the organism's life history. As a metaphor to help you appreciate this idea, **Figure 1.4** shows a photograph of a bird using a milk carton as a nest. If we did not know the milk carton's history—that its original purpose was to contain milk—we might wonder why the bird had made such an odd-looking nest. We do not puzzle over this because we immediately grasp that the milk carton has been modified during its history to serve a new purpose as a nesting site for a bird.

Likewise, evolutionary change involves modifications of characteristics in earlier populations. Over long periods, populations may change such that structures with a particular function

Figure 1.4   **An example of modification of a structure for a new function.**   The milk carton had its original purpose modified during its history. The structure that was designed to efficiently carry milk has been modified to accommodate a bird's nest. Over evolutionary history, pre-existing structures have been modified for new functions.

may become modified and serve a new function. For example, a bat uses its wings for flying, while a dolphin uses its flippers for swimming (**Figure 1.5**). Both structures represent adaptations of a limb design that was originally used for walking by an ancestor.

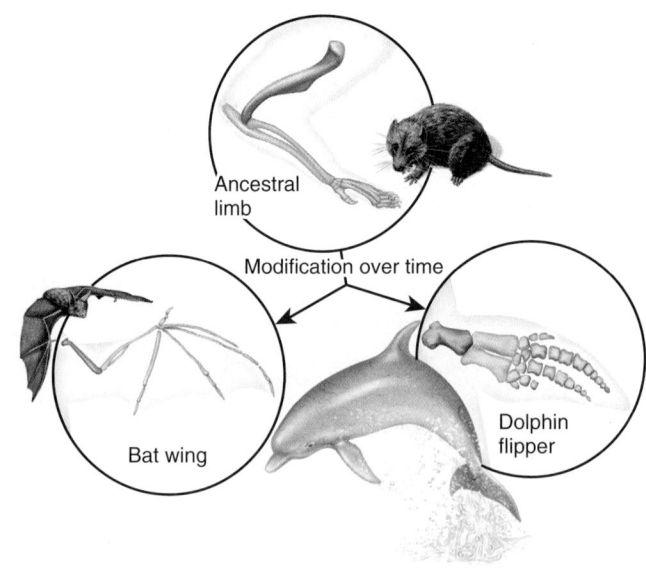

Figure 1.5   **An example showing a modification that has occurred as a result of biological evolution.**   The bat's wing and the dolphin's flipper were modified from a limb used for walking in an ancestor.

Concept check: *Give two examples among mammals of how the tail has been modified for different purposes.*

Evolutionary change occurs through two mechanisms: vertical descent with mutation and horizontal gene transfer. Let's take a brief look at these mechanisms.

Vertical Descent with Mutation   The traditional way to view evolution involves a progression of changes in a series of ancestors. Such a series is called a **lineage**. **Figure 1.6** shows a portion of the lineage that gave rise to modern horses. This type of evolution is called **vertical evolution** because biologists have traditionally depicted such evolutionary change in a vertical diagram, like the one shown in Figure 1.6. In this mechanism of evolution, new species evolve from pre-existing species by the accumulation of mutations. A **mutation** is an inheritable change in the genetic material of organisms. Why do some mutations accumulate in a population and eventually change the characteristics of an entire species? One reason is that a mutation may alter the traits of organisms in a way that increases their chances of survival or reproduction. When a mutation causes such a beneficial change, the mutation is more likely to increase in a population over many generations, a process called **natural selection**, which is discussed in Units IV and V.

Evolution also involves the accumulation of neutral changes that do not benefit a species and some rare changes that may be harmful. Reflecting upon the hemoglobin molecule illustrates this point. Hemoglobin is the major protein of red blood cells and is critical for carrying oxygen throughout the human body. Some mutations in hemoglobin create minor changes that are neutral; oxygen is still carried efficiently, and the red blood cells function well. However, one particular mutation creates a change in hemoglobin's structure, and the red blood cells become sickle shaped. The sickle-shaped red blood cells are more prone to clumping (look ahead to

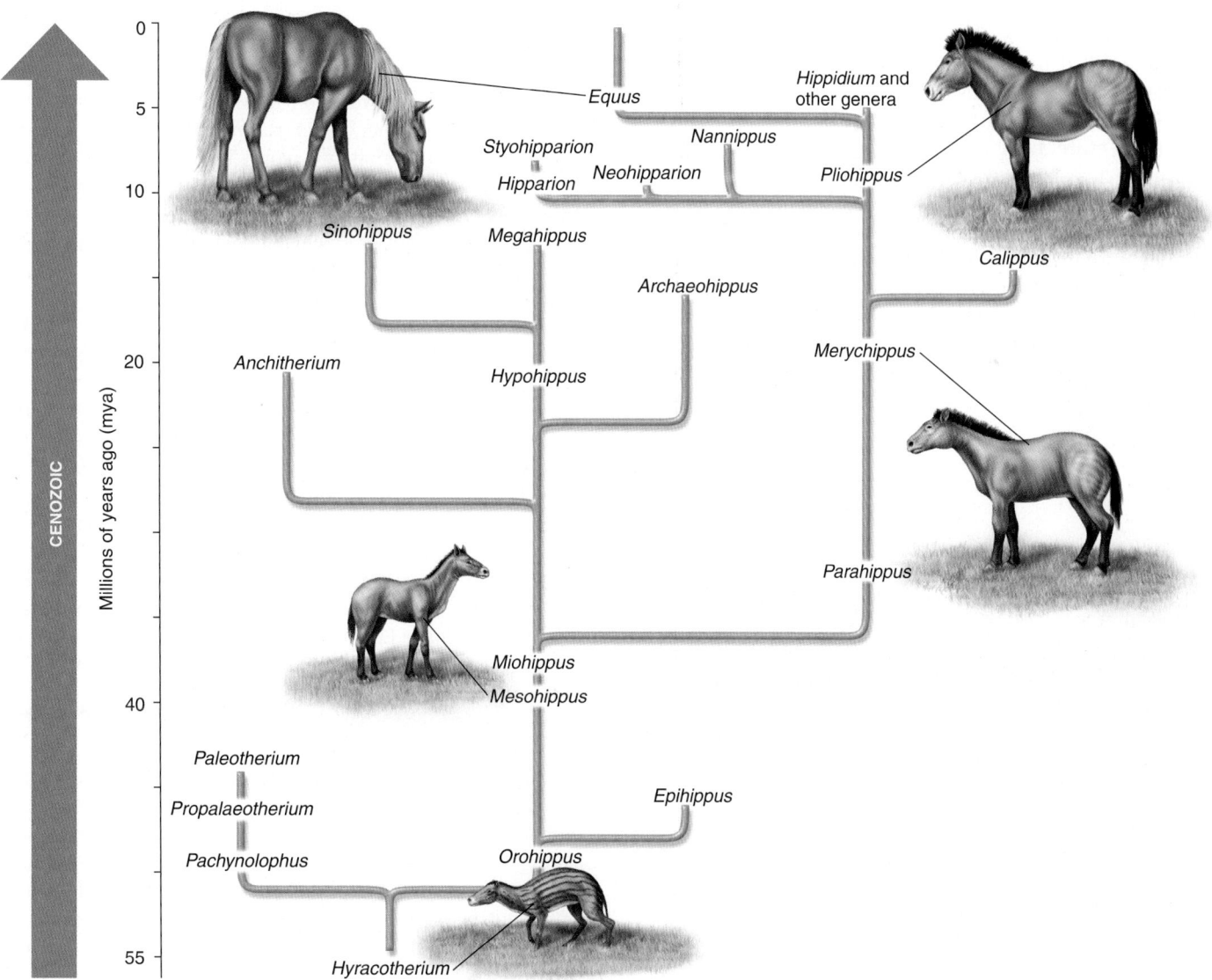

Figure 1.6   An example of vertical evolution: the horse.   The modern horse evolved from ancestors that were much smaller. The vertical evolution shown here occurred through the accumulation of mutations that altered the traits of the species.

Figure 13.1). This sickle-cell mutation occurs fairly frequently in human populations that originated in parts of the world where malaria is common, because the sickle-shaped cells are more resistant to infection by the microorganism that causes malaria.

Horizontal Gene Transfer In addition to vertical evolution, which produces a lineage, species also evolve by another process that involves genetic exchanges between different species. Sexually reproducing species usually mate with members of their own species. Asexual species, such as bacteria, can occasionally transfer genetic material between cells, but, again, that tends to occur most readily between members of the same bacterial species. However, on relatively rare occasions, genetic exchanges occur between different species. For example, you may have heard that resistance to antibiotics among bacteria is a growing medical problem. Genes that confer antibiotic resistance are sometimes transferred between different bacterial species (**Figure 1.7**).

When genes are transferred from one species to another, this event is called **horizontal gene transfer**. In a lineage in which the timescale is depicted on a vertical axis, horizontal gene transfer is shown as a horizontal line between two different species (**Figure 1.8**). Genes that are transferred horizontally may be acted on by natural selection to eventually promote changes in an entire species. This has been an important mechanism of evolutionary change, particularly among bacterial species. In addition, during the early stages of life on Earth, horizontal gene transfer was an important part of the process that gave rise to all modern species.

Traditionally, biologists have described evolution by using diagrams that depict the vertical evolution of species on a long timescale. This is the type of evolutionary tree that was shown in Figure 1.6. For many decades, the simplistic view held that all living organisms evolved from a common ancestor, resulting in a "tree of life," which could describe the vertical evolution that gave rise to modern species. Now that we understand the great importance of horizontal gene transfer in the evolution of life, biologists have re-evaluated the concept of evolution as it occurs over time. Rather than a tree of life, a more appropriate way to view the unity of living organisms is to describe it as a "web of life," which accounts for both vertical evolution and horizontal gene transfer. Figure 1.8 illustrates such a diagram.

The Classification of Living Organisms Allows Biologists to Appreciate and Understand the Unity and Diversity of Life

As biologists discover new species, they try to understand the new species' relationships to known species. **Taxonomy** is a subdiscipline of biology in which scientists attempt to determine the extent of the relatedness of species and then group related species together. This is an arduous task because researchers estimate that the world has between 10 million and 100 million different species! The rationale for categorization is usually based on vertical descent. Species with a recent common ancestor are grouped together, while species whose common ancestor is in the very distant past are placed into different groups.

Let's first consider taxonomy on a broad scale. You may have noticed that Figure 1.8 showed three main groups of organisms. All forms of life can be placed into three large categories or domains called **Bacteria**, **Archaea**, and **Eukarya** (**Figure 1.9**). Bacteria and Archaea are microorganisms that are also termed prokaryotic because their cell structure is relatively simple. At the cellular level, bacterial and archaeal cells show significant differences in their lipid composition (lipids are another category of macromolecules), packaging of hereditary material, metabolic pathways, and regulation of the production of mRNA and protein. By comparison, organisms in the domain Eukarya are **eukaryotic** and have larger cells with membrane-bound internal compartments that serve various functions. A defining distinction between prokaryotic and eukaryotic cells is that eukaryotic cells have a cell nucleus in which the genetic material is surrounded by a membrane. The organisms in the domain Eukarya are subdivided into eight **supergroups**. The well-known kingdoms of Animalia (animals), Plantae (plants), and Fungi each reside within one of these supergroups. The term **protist** is used to collectively describe the remaining extremely diverse collection of eukaryotic organisms. The methods and challenges of organizing species into accurate and useful taxonomic groupings are considered in Chapter 24.

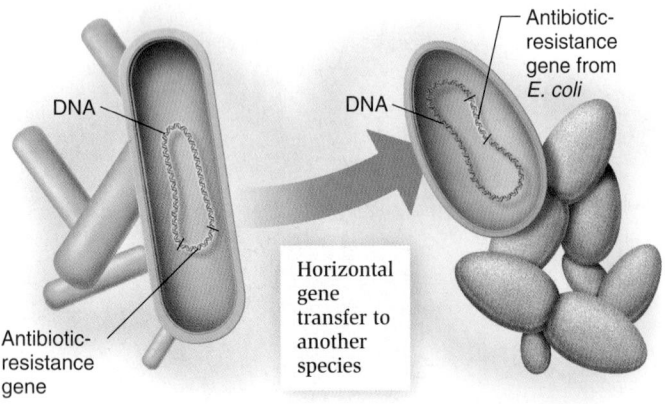

Figure 1.7 An example of horizontal gene transfer: antibiotic resistance. One bacterial species may transfer a gene, such as a gene that confers resistance to an antibiotic, to a different bacterial species.

Figure 1.8   The web of life.   This diagram of evolution includes both vertical evolution and horizontal gene transfer as important mechanisms in the evolution of life on Earth. Note: Archaea are unicellular species that are similar in structure to bacteria.

Concept check: *How does the concept of a tree of life differ from a web of life?*

Taxonomy involves multiple levels in which particular species are placed into progressively smaller and smaller groups of organisms that are more closely related to one another evolutionarily (**Figure 1.10**). Such an approach emphasizes the unity and diversity of different species. As an example, let's consider the jaguars. The broadest grouping for the jaguar is the domain Eukarya, followed by progressively smaller divisions, from kingdom (Animalia) to species. In the animal kingdom, jaguars are part of the phylum Chordata, which is subdivided into classes. Jaguars are in a class called Mammalia, which includes all mammals. The common ancestor that gave rise to mammals arose more than 200 million years ago. Mammalia is subdivided into several smaller orders. The jaguar is in the order Carnivora. The order is divided into families; the jaguar and all other cats belong to the family Felidae. The genus *Panthera* is the smallest group

of different species that contains the jaguar. As you can see in Figure 1.10, the genus contains only four species: the lions, leopards, tigers, and jaguars. The genus has species that are very similar to one another in form and that have evolved from a common (extinct) ancestor that lived relatively recently on an evolutionary timescale, approximately 5 million years ago.

Biologists use a two-part naming system called **binomial nomenclature**, to provide each species with a unique scientific name. The scientific name of the jaguar is *Panthera onca*. The first part is the genus and the second part is the specific epithet or species descriptor. By convention, the genus name is capitalized, while the specific epithet is not. Both names are italicized. By tradition, all scientific names are put into a form consistent with the scholarly language of Latin.

(a) Domain Bacteria: Unicellular prokaryotes that inhabit many diverse environments.

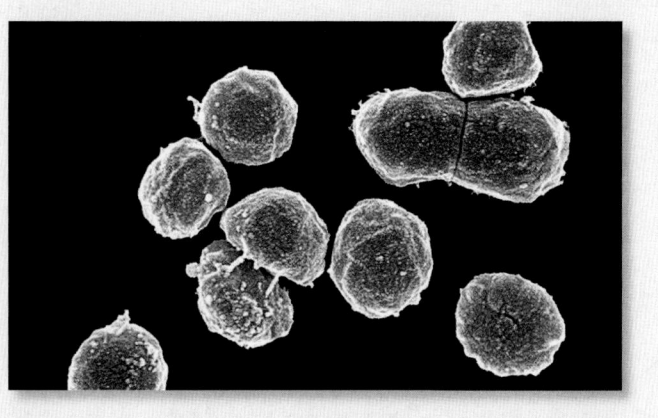

(b) Domain Archaea: Unicellular prokaryotes that are less common than bacteria. Some live in extreme environments, such as hot springs.

Protists: Protists are a very diverse group of single-celled or simply organized multicellular eukaryotes. Shown here is a spheroid of Volvox cells.

Kingdom Fungi: Unicellular and multicellular organisms that have a cell wall but cannot carry out photosynthesis. Fungi usually survive on decaying organic material.

Kingdom Plantae: Multicellular organisms that can carry out photosynthesis.

Kingdom Animalia: Multicellular organisms that usually have a nervous system and are capable of locomotion. They must eat other organisms to live.

(c) Domain Eukarya

Figure 1.9   **The three domains of life.**   Two of these domains, **(a)** Bacteria and **(b)** Archaea, are prokaryotes, while the third domain, **(c)** Eukarya, comprises species that are eukaryotes.

BioConnections: *Look ahead to Figure 26.1. Are fungi more closely related to plants or animals?*

Taxonomic group	Jaguar is found in	Approximate time when the common ancestor for this group arose	Approximate number of modern species in this group	
Domain	Eukarya	2,000 mya	> 5,000,000	
Kingdom	Animalia	600 mya	> 1,000,000	
Phylum	Chordata	525 mya	50,000	
Class	Mammalia	200 mya	5,000	
Order	Carnivora	60 mya	270	
Family	Felidae	40 mya	38	
Genus	*Panthera*	5 mya	4	
Species	*onca*	1.5 mya	1	

Figure 1.10   Taxonomic and evolutionary groupings leading to the jaguar.

GENOMES AND PROTEOMES

The Study of Genomes and Proteomes Provides an Evolutionary Foundation for Our Understanding of Biology

The term **genome** refers to the complete genetic makeup of an organism: its complete collection of DNA. The genome is critical to life because it performs these functions:

- It acts as a stable informational unit and encodes the information for organismal function. The genome of an organism stores the encoded information needed to

make, locate, and modify all the organism's proteins. The **proteome** is the collection of all proteins being made in a cell under a particular set of conditions. The proteome determines cellular and organismal function; the genome encodes the proteome.

- It provides continuity from generation to generation. The genome is copied and transmitted to each generation.

- It serves as the substrate of evolutionary change. The genome may undergo mutations that change the encoded information. In addition, a genome may acquire new genes by horizontal gene transfer. These changes to the genome can alter an organism's ability to survive and reproduce; over evolutionary time they may lead to the emergence of new characteristics within a species and even to new species.

The Mechanism for Reading the DNA Blueprint Is Common to All Forms of Life

How does the genome function? We can think about this in a focused way by asking, how is the DNA used? An organism's metabolism, its ability to respond to environmental changes, to maintain homeostasis, to grow, to develop, and reproduce, are all delimited by its dynamic DNA blueprint. The way the DNA is read is unlike the way a building blueprint is read. The reading of the DNA blueprint is influenced by the organism's environment. DNA occurs in functional units called genes. The DNA of specific genes is used at appropriate times as a template to create specific messenger molecules called mRNA. Thus, the genome is not read "all or none" like a real blueprint would be read. The diverse mRNAs are made in response to the current needs of the organism; in turn, these RNAs are used to control the production of proteins. Proteins collectively catalyze most metabolic reactions, are major structural components of cells, and often serve to control cell-to-cell and cell-to-environment interactions. The functioning of proteins is largely responsible for the traits of living organisms. The multistep process by which DNA gives rise to RNA, which in turn gives rise to proteins, is one of the most highly conserved and unifying properties of life forms.

The Power of Genomic and Proteomic Approaches Integrated with Organismal Data

The evolutionary history and relatedness of all living organisms can be illuminated by genome analysis. The genome of every organism carries the results and the evidence of millions of years of evolution. The genomes of prokaryotes usually contain a few thousand genes, while those of eukaryotes may contain tens of thousands. An exciting advance in biology in the past few decades has been the ability to analyze the information content of the DNA sequence for entire genomes, a technology called genomics. For example the spotted and black jaguars shown in **Figure 1.11** look strikingly different and live in different habitats. But analysis of their genomes show that the only major difference is in one gene, a gene that determines the underlying coat colour.

An extension of genome analysis is proteomics, a technical approach that involves the analysis of the proteome of a single species and the comparison of the proteomes of different species, or comparisons of different members of the same species living under different conditions. Proteomics can help us to understand how the various levels of biology, from the molecular level—at the level of protein molecules—to the higher levels,

Figure 1.11   How the study of genomes and proteomes can provide us with connections to different biological levels. Spotted jaguars differ from panthers because they make an enzyme that produces a tan pigment, while a mutation in the same gene in panthers results in black pigment. With regard to hunting success, the spotted jaguars perform better in grasslands, and the panthers do better in the forest.

Concept check: *Biologists sometimes say that the genome is a storage unit, and the proteome is largely the functional unit of life. Explain this statement.*

are related to one another, such as the way the functioning of proteins produces the characteristics of cells and organisms, and the ability of populations of organisms to survive in their natural environments.

Genomic and proteomic approaches often are used first with **model organisms**. Selection of model organisms is usually based on a combination of practical considerations (e.g., the relative ease of growth in a lab setting and the wealth of knowledge of its life history and inheritance patterns) and their representation of a major group of organisms. Knowledge obtained from these model organisms is then used to understand the biology of the wealth of other diverse life forms. For example, the mustard weed (*Arabidopsis thaliana*) is one of the two model organisms initially selected from the plant kingdom for genomic analysis. Findings derived from studies of this model plant are extended to investigate related phenomenon in other plant species, including plants that produce the food we rely on.

Evolution in biology is a recurring theme in this textbook. As a concrete way to understand this unifying theme, we've included in almost all chapters a feature like this one, called Genomes and Proteomes, that will allow you to appreciate how evolution has produced the characteristics of modern species. These topics explore (1) how the genomes of different species are similar to one another and how they are different, and (2) how genome changes can alter the proteome and thereby change the traits of species.

Genome and proteome analysis can also be used to understand how a cell or an organism's local environment and developmental history determine the way the genome is used to produce the appropriate subset of its proteome, and how the production of these proteins can be modified to meet the cell's role in the organism's life cycle.

The photograph at the beginning of this chapter shows two sockeye salmon that have entered a river to spawn. In the salt water of the Pacific Ocean, the salmon do not show the brilliant red colouring seen in that photograph. The red develops as the salmon enter the fresh water of the river. The west coast salmon fishery is in some danger, and the number of salmon returning to spawn has decreased in recent years. Dr. Kristi Miller-Saunders is a research scientist with Fisheries and Oceans Canada. Using a functional genomics approach, her team caught salmon in both the ocean and the river and electronically tagged the fish to track them. Before the fish were released, a small amount of tissue was taken from them for genomic analysis. In January 2011, her team reported in *Science* that fish that died before spawning preferentially expressed a set of genes, which suggested they might have been weakened by a viral infection. Tagged salmon that successfully spawned had a lower occurrence of expression of these same genes. Such studies as this one that integrate genomic, physiological, and ecological data are very powerful. To make sense of genomic and proteomic data, biologists need information from other types of studies that consider life histories, physiology, ecology, and behaviour.

1.3 BIOLOGY AS A SCIENTIFIC DISCIPLINE

Learning Outcomes:

1. Explain how researchers study biology at different levels, ranging from molecules to ecosystems.
2. Compare and contrast discovery-based science and hypothesis testing, and describe the scientific method.

Science is conducted in different ways and at different levels. Some biologists study the molecules that compose life, and others try to understand how organisms survive in their natural environments. In some cases, experiments are designed to test the validity of ideas that are suggested by researchers. In this section, we will examine how biologists follow a standard approach, called the **scientific method**, to test their ideas. Scientists make predictions that can be experimentally or observationally tested. But not all discoveries are the result of experimentation; some discoveries are made by collection and comparison of new information. This **discovery-based science** is initiated without a preconceived notion of what will be found.

Biologists Investigate Life at Different Levels of Organization

In Figure 1.3, we examined the various levels of biological organization. The study of these different levels depends not only on the scientific interests of biologists but also on the tools that are available to them. Before the development of high-quality microscopes, biologists primarily focused their attention on characteristics they could observe with their unaided eyes (**Figure 1.12a–b**). As microscope technology improved, many researchers shifted their attention to the study of cells (**Figure 1.12c**). In the 1970s, genetic tools to study single genes and the proteins they encode became available. This genetic technology enabled researchers to study individual macromolecules in living cells. Genetic technology spawned the field of molecular biology. Together with chemists and biochemists, molecular biologists focus their efforts on the structure and function of the molecules of life (**Figure 1.12d**), striving to understand how biological systems work at the molecular and even at the atomic levels. Overall, the twentieth century saw a progressive increase in the number of biologists using a reductionist approach. **Reductionism** involves reducing a complex system to its components as a way to understand how the parts of the system work.

Ecologists study species in their native environments.

(a) Ecology—species/ population/community/ ecosystem levels

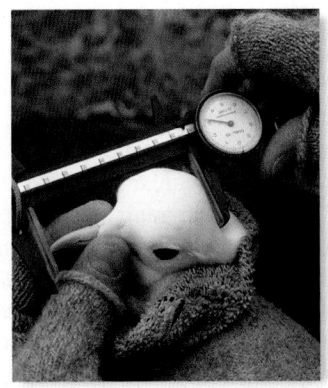

Anatomists and physiologists study how the structure of organisms are related to their functions.

(b) Anatomy and physiology— tissue/organ/organ systems/ organism levels

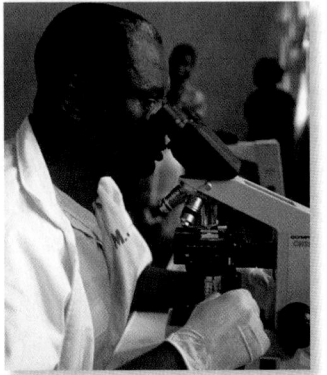

Cell biologists often use the microscope to learn how cells function.

(c) Cell biology—cellular levels

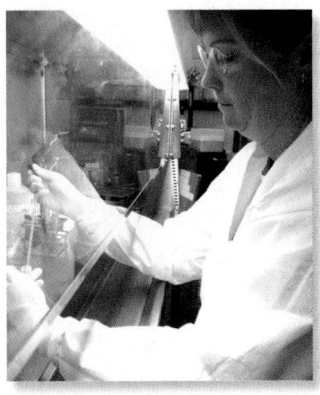

Molecular biologists and biochemists study the molecules and macromolecules that make up cells.

(d) Molecular biology— molecular/atomic levels

Systems biologists may study groups of molecules. The microarray shown in the inset indicates the amount of mRNA produced (red = highest, black = lowest) for many genes simultaneously.

(e) Systems biology—all levels, shown here at the molecular level

Figure 1.12   Biological investigation at different levels.

In the 1980s, the pendulum began to swing in the other direction. Scientists had invented new tools that allowed for the study of groups of genes (genomic techniques) and groups of proteins (proteomic techniques). Biologists now use the term **systems biology** to describe research that is aimed at understanding how the properties of life arise from complex interactions. This term is often applied to the study of cells; here, systems biology may involve the investigation of a collection of proteins, each with a specific role in a complex process that requires the coordinated functioning of this set of proteins and, hence, the coordinated production of the RNAs that control the synthesis of this group of proteins (**Figure 1.12e**). For example, a systems biologist may conduct experiments that try to characterize an entire cellular process, which is driven by dozens of different proteins. Systems biology is not new; animal and plant physiologists have been studying the functions of complex organ systems for centuries. Likewise, ecologists have been characterizing ecosystems for a very long time. The novelty and excitement of systems biology in recent years has been the result of new experimental tools that allow for the study of complex interactions at the molecular level. Investigation of genomes and proteomes has expanded our ability to do systems biology.

A Hypothesis Is a Proposed Explanation, and a Theory Is an Explanation Backed by Extensive Evidence

In biology, a **hypothesis** is a proposed explanation for a natural phenomenon. It is a proposition based on previous observations or experimental studies. For example, with knowledge of seasonal changes, you might hypothesize that maple trees drop their leaves in the autumn because of the shortened amount of daylight. An alternative hypothesis might be that the trees drop their leaves because of colder temperatures. In biology, a hypothesis requires work by researchers to either accept or reject it.

A useful hypothesis makes predictions that can be shown to be correct or incorrect. The validity of a prediction usually is determined by making comparative observations or doing experiments. If the observations or experiments show that the predictions are incorrect, the hypothesis is rejected. Alternatively, if the data of the experiment or observations agree with the predictions, the hypothesis is supported. Even so, a hypothesis is never really proven; it remains provisional. Researchers accept the possibility that they may have not yet conceived of the experiment that will reveal the hypothesis's flaws. If many different experiments support a hypothesis and none disprove it, biologists may say they accept the hypothesis, but they don't usually say that the hypothesis is proven.

By comparison, the term **theory**, as used in biology, is a broad explanation of some aspect of the natural world that is substantiated by a large body of evidence. Biological theories incorporate observations, hypothesis testing, and the laws of other disciplines, such as chemistry and physics. The power of theories is that they allow us to make many predictions regarding the properties of living organisms. As an example, let's consider the theory that DNA is the genetic material and that it is organized into units called genes. An overwhelming body of evidence has substantiated this theory. Thousands of living species have been analyzed, and all have been found to use DNA as their genetic material and to express genes that produce the proteins that lead to their characteristics. This theory makes many valid predictions. For example, certain types of mutations in genes are expected to affect the traits of organisms. This prediction has been confirmed observationally for many individuals with inherited diseases and experimentally in model organisms. Similarly, genetic material is copied and transmitted from parents to offspring. By comparing the DNA of parents and offspring, this prediction has also been confirmed. Furthermore, the theory explains the observation that offspring resemble their parents. Two other important biological theories that we have touched on in this chapter are the cell theory and the theory of evolution by natural selection.

The meaning of the term *theory* is sometimes muddled because it is used in different situations. In everyday language, a theory is often viewed as little more than a guess or speculation. However, in biology, a theory is much more than a guess. Overall, two key attributes of a scientific theory are consistency with a vast amount of data and the ability to make many correct predictions that can be tested. Like a hypothesis, a theory can never be proven to be true absolutely. Even so, biologists would say that theories are extremely likely to be true, based on all known information. In this regard, theories are viewed as knowledge, which is the awareness and understanding of information.

Discovery-Based Science and Hypothesis Testing Are Scientific Approaches That Help Us Understand Biology

The path that leads to an important discovery is rarely a straight line. Rather, scientists ask questions, make observations, ask modified questions, and may eventually conduct experiments to test their hypotheses. The first attempts at experimentation may fail, and new experimental approaches may be needed. To suggest that scientists follow a rigid scientific method is an oversimplification of the process of science. Scientific advances often occur as scientists dig deeper into a topic that interests them. Curiosity is the key phenomenon that sparks scientific inquiry. Researchers typically follow two general types of approaches: discovery-based science and hypothesis testing.

Discovery-Based Science The collection and analysis of data without the need for a preconceived hypothesis is called **discovery-based science** or simply discovery science. The information gained from discovery-based science may have practical applications. Drug companies, for example, may test hundreds or even thousands of drugs to determine if any of them are useful in the treatment of disease. Once a drug has

been discovered that is effective in disease treatment, researchers may dig deeper and try to understand how the drug exerts its effects. In this way, discovery-based science can help us learn about basic concepts in medicine and biology. Another example involves the study of genomes. Over the past few decades, researchers have systematically set out to identify all of the genes of humans and many other species representing all major taxa. The goal is to identify the genes and then understand their function, often with hypothesis testing. Discovery-based science often leads to hypothesis testing.

Hypothesis Testing In biological science, the scientific method, also known as hypothesis testing, is often followed to test the validity of a hypothesis. This strategy can be described as a five-stage process:

1. Observations are made regarding natural phenomena.
2. These observations lead to a hypothesis that tries to explain the phenomena. As mentioned, a useful hypothesis is one that is testable because it makes specific predictions.
3. Experimentation is conducted to determine whether the predictions are correct.
4. The data from the experiment are analyzed.
5. The hypothesis is accepted or rejected.

The scientific method is intended to be an objective way to gather knowledge. As an example, let's return to our scenario of maple trees dropping their leaves in autumn. By observing the length of daylight throughout the year and comparing that data with the time of the year when leaves fall, one hypothesis might be that shorter daylight causes the leaves to fall (**Figure 1.13**). This hypothesis makes a prediction: Exposure of maple trees to less daylight will cause their leaves to fall. To test this prediction, researchers would design and conduct an experiment.

Although hypothesis testing may follow many paths, certain features are common to this approach. First, data are often collected in two parallel ways. One set of experiments is done on the **control sample**, while another set is conducted on the **experimental sample**. In an ideal experiment, the control and experimental samples differ by only one factor (often called a variable). For example, an experiment could be conducted in which two groups of trees are observed and the only difference between their environments would be the hours of light each day. To conduct such an experiment, researchers would ensure that the size and composition of their sample adequately represented the natural populations of the type of tree being studied. They would then grow trees in a greenhouse, where they could keep such factors as temperature and water the same between the control and experimental samples, while providing them with different amounts of daylight. In the control group, the hours of light provided by light bulbs would be kept constant each day, while in the experimental group, the amount of light each day would become progressively shorter to mimic seasonal light changes. The researchers would then record the number of leaves dropped by each group of trees over a certain time.

1 **OBSERVATIONS** The leaves on maple trees fall in autumn, when the days get colder and shorter.

2 **HYPOTHESIS** The shorter amount of daylight causes the leaves to fall.

3 **EXPERIMENTATION**
Small maple trees are grown in two greenhouses where the only variable is the length of light.

Control group:
Amount of daily light remains constant for 200 days.

Experimental group:
Amount of daily light becomes progressively shorter for 200 days.

4 **THE DATA**

A statistical analysis can determine whether the control and the experimental data are significantly different. In this case, they are.

5 **CONCLUSION** The hypothesis cannot be rejected.

Figure 1.13 **The steps of the scientific method, also known as hypothesis testing.** In this example, the goal is to test the hypothesis that maple trees drop their leaves in the autumn because they receive less daylight.

Concept check: *The hypothesis has not been rejected, but has the hypothesis been proven?*

Another key feature of hypothesis testing is data analysis, from which a biologist tries to draw conclusions. Data often come in the form of numbers, such as the number of dropped leaves. When experimentation involves a control and experimental sample, a common form of analysis is to determine whether the data collected from the two samples are significantly different from each other. In this regard, the word *significant* means statistically significant. Biologists apply statistical analyses to their data to determine whether the control and experimental samples are likely to be different from each other because of the single variable that is different between the two samples. When they are statistically significant, this means that the differences between the control and experimental data are not likely to have occurred through random chance. In our tree example shown in Figure 1.13, the trees in the control sample dropped far fewer leaves than did those in the experimental sample. A statistical analysis could determine whether the data sets collected from the two greenhouses are significantly different from each other. If the two sets of data are found not to be significantly different, we would reject our hypothesis. Alternatively if the differences between the two data sets are significant, we would accept our hypothesis, though it has not been proven.

Discovery-based and hypothesis-testing methods often are used together to investigate a particular phenomenon. Let's look at how both approaches have led to successes in the study of the disease cystic fibrosis.

The Study of Cystic Fibrosis Provides Examples of Both Discovery-Based Science and Hypothesis Testing

Cystic fibrosis (CF), affects about 1 in every 3,600 children born in Canada. People with CF produce abnormally thick and sticky mucus that obstructs the lungs and causes life-threatening lung infections. The thick mucus also blocks the pancreas, which prevents the digestive enzymes that this organ produces from reaching the intestine. For this reason, CF patients tend to have excessive appetites but low body weights. People with this disease may also experience liver damage because the thick mucus can obstruct the liver. Currently, the average lifespan for people with CF is about 35 years. Fortunately, as more advances have been made in treatment, this number has steadily increased.

Because of its medical significance, many scientists are interested in this disorder and have conducted studies aimed at learning more about its underlying cause. As described next, discovery-based science and hypothesis testing have been critical to gaining a better understanding of this disorder.

The CF Gene and Discovery-Based Science In 1945, Dorothy Anderson determined that cystic fibrosis is a genetic disorder. People with CF have inherited two faulty CF genes, one from each parent. More than 40 years later, researchers used discovery-based science to identify the CF gene. Their search for the CF gene did not require any preconceived hypothesis regarding the function of the gene. Rather, they used genetic strategies that are similar to those described in Chapter 18. In 1989, research groups headed by Lap-Chi Tsui, Francis Collins, and John Riordan identified the CF gene. The discovery of the gene made it possible to devise diagnostic testing methods to determine whether a person carries a faulty CF gene. Identification of the CF gene is also leading to better treatments for people with this disorder.

The CF Gene and Hypothesis Testing Analysis of the CF gene suggested it encoded a protein involved in the transport of substances across membranes. Indeed, patients with the disorder have an abnormal regulation of salt balance across their plasma membranes. Researchers hypothesized that the normal CF gene encodes a protein that transports chloride ions (Cl$^-$), a component of common table salt (NaCl), across the membrane of cells (**Figure 1.14**). This hypothesis led to experimentation in which researchers tested normal cells and cells from CF patients for their ability to transport Cl$^-$. The CF cells were found to be defective in chloride transport. In 1990, scientists successfully transferred the normal gene to CF cells in the laboratory.

The introduction of the normal CF gene into the cells from CF patients corrected the defect in chloride transport. Overall, the results showed that the CF gene does encode a protein that transports Cl$^-$ across the plasma membrane. A mutation in this gene causes it to encode a defective transporter protein, leading to a salt imbalance that affects water levels outside the cell, explaining the thick and sticky mucus in CF patients. In this example, hypothesis testing has provided a way to accept or reject an idea regarding how a disease is caused by genetic change. As discussed in Chapter 18, gene replacement is a technology in which people with a faulty gene are given treatments that involve the introduction of the normal gene into their bodies. Clinical trials are underway to determine whether the CF gene from normal individuals can be used to overcome the symptoms of the faulty gene in CF patients.

Inquiry in Biological Sciences Can Be Collaborative and International, and Is Nested Within Society

Both discovery-based and experimental studies in biological sciences are increasingly dependent on sophisticated technologies and extensively trained individuals. This technology and training requires public funding. In Canada, public funding of

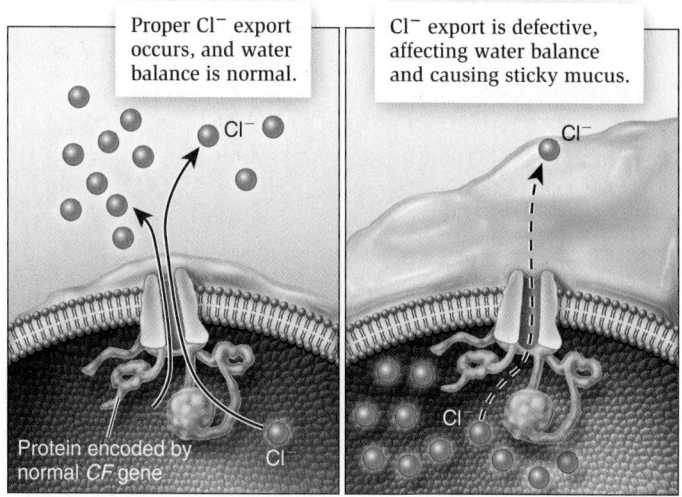

Figure 1.14 A hypothesis that suggests an explanation of the function of the gene that is defective in patients with cystic fibrosis. The normal CF gene, which does not carry a mutation, encodes a transporter protein that transports chloride ions (Cl$^-$) across the plasma membrane to the outside of the cell. In people with CF, this transporter is defective because of a mutation in the CF gene.

Concept check: *Explain how discovery-based science helped researchers to hypothesize that the CF gene encodes a transporter protein.*

biological research is done nationally by government (for example, by the Natural Sciences and Engineering Research Council of Canada [NSERC], the Canadian Institutes of Health Research [CIHR], and Agriculture and Agri-Food Canada [AAFC]) and by nonprofit organizations (such as the Canadian Cancer Society, March of Dimes Canada, and the Canadian Cystic Fibrosis Foundation [CCFF]), and provincially or territorially through funds that support universities and their employees.

The work on cystic fibrosis and the CF gene illustrates the collaborative and international nature of scientific investigation and its dependence on citizens. The discovery of the CF gene was reported in 1989 by three teams of scientists—two teams funded in Canada (led by Lap-Chi Tsui and John Riordan) and one U.S. team (led by Francis Collins)—but the work included contributions by many scientists from around the world. In 2007, three Canadian teams based in Montreal, Toronto, and Vancouver identified two modifier genes that affect the severity of cystic fibrosis. The investigation was made possible because thousands of Canadians with cystic fibrosis agreed to participate. Funding for the research came from Genome Canada and the CCFF. The CCFF derives it support from private donations, with a major source being Shinerama, a fundraiser involving postsecondary students across Canada (**Figure 1.15**). Through

Figure 1.15 **Biological research is nested within society.** Shinerama was started in 1961 by a student at Sir Wilfrid Laurier University. Since then, many other campuses and students have volunteered to raise money to help in the fight against cystic fibrosis.

the efforts of more than 35,000 student volunteers, Shinerama raised nearly $1 million dollars in 2007 for the treatment and understanding of cystic fibrosis.

Finally, it is worthwhile to point out that science is a social discipline. After performing observations and experiments, scientists report their conclusions to the scientific community (**Figure 1.16**). They comment on one another's ideas and work, eventually shaping together the information that builds scientific theories over many years. As you become skilled at scrutinizing experiments, it is satisfying to discuss your ideas with other people, including fellow students and faculty members.

Figure 1.16 **The social aspects of science.** At scientific meetings, researchers gather to discuss new data and discoveries. Research that is conducted by professors, students, lab technicians, and industrial participants is sometimes hotly debated.

1.4 MAKING SENSE OF BIOLOGY: LEARNING STRATEGIES

Learning Outcomes:

1. Describe the different levels of cognitive engagement.
2. Apply the principles of concept mapping to link and explore concepts and their interrelationships.

A dominant theory about learning is that we construct our own knowledge. As we make observations in life we create mental frameworks and, over time, add new ideas to these frameworks and delete old ones. How solid and valuable these constructs are depends on how deeply we engage the material and ideas that we are exposed to as we read a textbook or go to class. Thus even if we have read a textbook twice and have the instructor's own note set, they will be of little value unless we make the effort to add (or reject) them from our own knowledge database. If we give value to the new ideas, we also need to determine their impact on any of our dearly held conceptions. Educator Benjamin Bloom developed the idea of a taxonomy of learning; other educators have refined his taxonomy and have found the taxonomy a robust way to predict deep learning. Going from the lower to the higher order cognitive processes, the steps in learning are recall, understand, apply, analyze, synthesize, and evaluate. If we engage only at lower cognitive levels (memorizing and understanding) in shallow learning, we will be less likely to add any of this information to our own mental frameworks and hence will neither recall nor be able to use the information beyond a few days. To engage in deep learning—the kind that will allow us to function as scientists—we also need to be able to apply the ideas, analyze the implications of the ideas, take several ideas and synthesize them into a coherent body of information, and then evaluate their soundness and predictive value when compared with competing ideas.

By reading this textbook and attending your introductory biology course, you will be exposed to many new terms and concepts. Resist the temptation to just memorize them. Look at how the terms fit into the concepts and processes you are studying. Organize the major processes into stories: What are the major ideas and competing processes? Who are the key players? You need to talk and write about the ideas and how they fit together.

To help you engage in deep learning, this book has Feature Investigations within chapters and several types of end-of-chapter exercises. One frequently used exercise is concept mapping; a tutorial follows that explains how to do concept mapping.

Concept Mapping

Concept mapping is a graphic tool to help organize and interrelate concepts and processes. Many of the most impressive discoveries in biology have been made by scientists who integrated ideas from many different fields of study. Concept mapping is also a great way to integrate ideas across the subdisciplines of

FEATURE INVESTIGATION

Observation and Experimentation Form the Core of Biology

Biology is largely about the process of discovery. Therefore, another recurring theme in this textbook is discovery-based science and hypothesis testing. Although each chapter contains many examples of data collection and experiments, a consistent element is a Feature Investigation—an actual study by current or past researchers. Some of these involve discovery-based science in which biologists collect and analyze data in an attempt to make discoveries that are not hypothesis driven. Most Feature Investigations involve hypothesis testing in which a hypothesis is stated and the experiment and resulting data are presented.

The Feature Investigations typically will provide you the opportunity to see the relationship between doing science and scientific theories. We hope you will find this an interesting and rewarding way to learn about biology. As you read a Feature

Investigation, you may find yourself thinking about different approaches and alternative hypotheses. Different people can view the same data and arrive at very different conclusions. As you progress through the experiments in this textbook, you will enjoy biology far more if you try to develop your own skills at formulating hypotheses, designing experiments, and interpreting data.

Experimental Questions

1. Discuss the difference between discovery-based science and hypothesis testing.
2. What are the steps in the scientific method, also called hypothesis testing?
3. Explain how a control group and an experimental group differ when conducting an experiment.

biology. In concept mapping, key terms or concepts are put into boxes. Lines are drawn between concepts that are related. Words are placed just above or below the lines to define the relationship between any two terms. An example is given in

Figure 1.17. You might make a different map with the same purpose; the goal is to 'make meaning' for yourself.

As we close Chapter 1, its author (herself an instructor of a large first-year course) has two more tips for success for you.

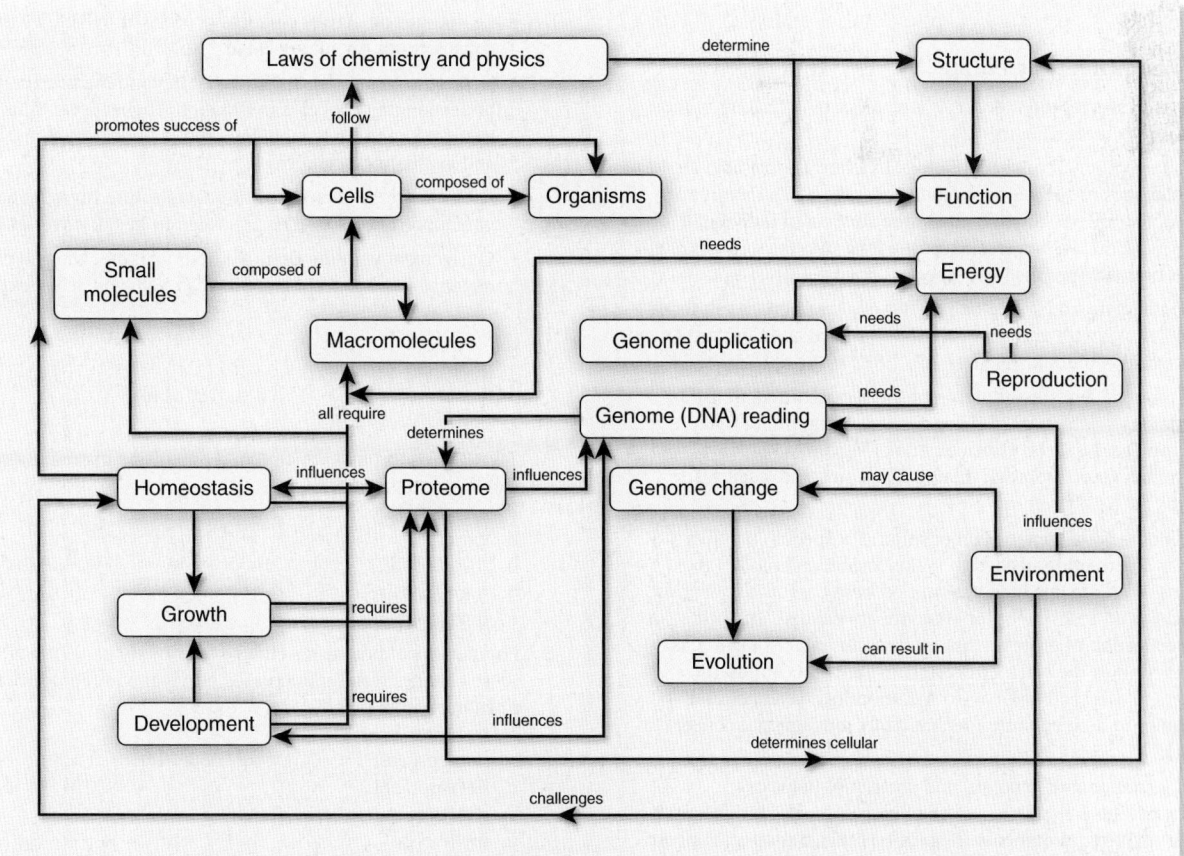

Figure 1.17   A concept map that attempts to integrate the unifying principles of biology with cells and organisms.

Each course instructor has his or her own way of communicating information to students. Be sure you understand and can use the communication network established for each of your courses, and realize they might be quite different for different courses. If you don't "plug in" correctly, you may create a large amount of needless and fruitless work for yourself. Finally, think of yourself as a scientist in training. Think critically, challenge ideas, find the place in your own mind for new ideas to create your own, ever more sophisticated, view of the world of biology.

Summary of Key Concepts

- Biology is the study of life. Discoveries in biology help us understand how life exists, and they have many practical applications, such as in the development of drugs to treat human diseases. (Figure 1.1)

1.1 The Principles of Life and Levels of Biological Organization

- Seven characteristics are common to all forms of life. All living things (1) are composed of cells, (2) use energy, (3) respond to environmental changes, (4) regulate their internal conditions (homeostasis), (5) grow and develop and reproduce, (6) have DNA as their hereditary material, and (7) evolve over the course of many generations. (Figure 1.2). There are two additional unifying principles: (8) all life is related by an evolutionary history, and (9) life follows the laws of chemistry and physics, and structure determines function.

- Living organisms can be viewed at different levels of complexity: atoms, molecules and macromolecules, cells, tissues, organs and organ systems, organisms, species and populations, communities, ecosystems, and the biosphere. (Figure 1.3)

1.2 Unity and Diversity of Life

- Changes in species often occur as a result of modification of pre-existing structures. (Figures 1.4, 1.5)

- Vertical evolution involves mutations in a lineage that alter the characteristics of species over many generations. During this process, natural selection results in the survival of individuals with greater reproductive success. Over the long run, this process alters species and may produce new species. (Figure 1.6)

- Horizontal gene transfer is the transfer of genes between different species. Along with vertical evolution, it is also an important force in biological evolution. (Figures 1.7, 1.8)

- Taxonomy involves the grouping of species according to their evolutionary relatedness to other species. Going from broad to narrow, each species is placed into a domain, a kingdom, a phylum, a class, an order, a family, a genus, and a species. (Figures 1.9, 1.10)

- The genome is the genetic composition of a species. It stores the encoded information needed to make, locate, and modify the proteins of an organism; is transmitted from parents to offspring; and acts as an instrument for evolutionary change. The proteome is the collection of proteins that a cell or an organism can make and determines the cell's or organism's function. Almost all chapters in this textbook have a feature called Genomes and Proteomes to help you to understand this fundamental concept in biology.

- An understanding of genomes and proteomes helps us to understand the characteristics of individuals and how they survive in their native environments. (Figure 1.11, chapter-opening photo)

1.3 Biology as a Scientific Discipline

- Biological science involves the observation, identification, experimental investigation, and theoretical explanation of natural phenomena.

- Biologists study life at different levels, ranging from ecosystems to molecular components in cells. (Figure 1.12)

- A hypothesis is a proposed explanation of a natural phenomenon. A biological theory is a broad explanation that makes many valid predictions. A theory is based on vast amounts of data.

- Discovery-based science is an approach in which researchers conduct experiments without a preconceived hypothesis. It is a fact-finding mission.

- The scientific method, also called hypothesis testing, is a series of steps to test the validity of a hypothesis. The experimentation often involves a comparison between control and experimental samples. (Figure 1.13)

- The study of cystic fibrosis is an interesting example in which both discovery-based science and hypothesis testing have provided key insights regarding the nature of the disease. (Figures 1.14, 1.15)

- Advances in science often occur when scientists gather and discuss their data. (Figure 1.16)

1.4 Making Sense of Biology: Learning Strategies

- Learning is an active, personal process for which we must construct our own knowledge.

- Deep learning requires that we go beyond memorizing terms and understanding concepts in isolation. Higher-level thinking goes past recall and understanding, and includes applying, analyzing, and evaluating new ideas.

- Each chapter in this textbook has a Feature Investigation to help you appreciate how science has led to key discoveries in biology.

- Engagement with the Featured Investigations, the end-of-chapter materials, and concept mapping can help you achieve deep learning.

Test to Assess Your Learning

1. The process through which living organisms maintain a relatively stable internal condition is
   a. adaptation.
   b. evolution.
   c. metabolism.
   d. homeostasis.
   e. development.

2. Populations of organisms change over many generations. Many of these changes result in increased survival and reproduction. This phenomenon is called
   a. evolution.
   b. homeostasis.
   c. development.
   d. genetics.
   e. metabolism.

3. All the places where living organisms are found is
   a. the ecosystem.
   b. a community.
   c. the biosphere.
   d. a viable land mass.
   e. a population.

4. Horizontal gene transfer is
   a. the accumulation of mutations over many generations.
   b. the transfer of genetic material between individuals of different species.
   c. the transfer of genetic material from parent to offspring.
   d. all of the above.
   e. (a) and (c) only.

5. The scientific name for humans is *Homo sapiens.* The name *Homo* is the _____ to which humans are classified.
   a. kingdom
   b. phylum
   c. order
   d. genus
   e. species

6. The complete genetic makeup of an organism is called
   a. the genus.
   b. the genome.
   c. the proteome.
   d. the genotype.
   e. the phenotype.

7. A proposed explanation for a natural phenomenon is
   a. a theory.
   b. a law.
   c. a prediction.
   d. a hypothesis.
   e. an assay.

8. In science, a theory should
   a. be equated with knowledge.
   b. be supported by a substantial body of evidence.
   c. provide the ability to make many correct predictions.
   d. all of the above.
   e. (b) and (c) only.

9. Conducting research without a preconceived hypothesis is called
   a. discovery-based science.
   b. the scientific method.
   c. hypothesis testing.
   d. a control experiment.
   e. none of the above.

10. What is the purpose of using a control in scientific experiments?
    a. A control allows the researcher to practise the experiment first before actually conducting it.
    b. A researcher can compare the results in the experimental group and control group to determine whether a single variable is causing a particular outcome in the experimental group.
    c. A control provides the framework for the entire experiment so the researcher can recall the procedures that should be conducted.
    d. A control allows the researcher to conduct other experimental changes without disturbing the original experiment.
    e. All of the above.

Articulate to Assess Your Learning

1. Give the levels of organism organization from the simplest to the most complex.

2. List the taxonomic groups from most inclusive to least inclusive.

3. Define the terms *genome* and *proteome,* and explain the relationship between the two.

Collaborate to Assess and Extend Your Learning

1. Debate the use of the following analogy: "DNA is the blueprint of organisms." What are the strengths and weaknesses of this analogy?

2. If most of an organism's cells have identical genomes, how is it that not all the cells will be expressing the same subset of the proteome? In other words, why won't all cells be making the same proteins?

3. What tools did taxonomists have during Darwin's lifetime? What additional tools do taxonomists have today? Identify some changes that have occurred in phylogenetic trees as a result of the use of these additional tools.

4. Would you classify a virus as a living organism? Justify your answer using (or refuting) information in this chapter.

5. Create a concept map by using the following terms: reductionism, the scientific method, hypotheses, theories, experimental sample, control samples, discovery-based science.

6. In your own words describe the nine principles of life listed in this chapter. Which of these principles apply only to living organisms?

Visit McGraw-Hill Ryerson Connect™ for additional study resources.

The Chemical Basis of Life I:
Atoms, Molecules, and Water

Chapter Outline

Snowflakes' classic symmetry occurs because individual water molecules can form hydrogen bonds with four neighbouring water molecules.

Biology—the study of life—is founded on the principles of chemistry and physics. All living organisms are a collection of atoms and molecules bound together and interacting with one another through the forces of nature. Knowledge of chemistry is important for studying biology at all levels, from molecular studies to the effect organisms can have on the biosphere. This chapter lays the groundwork for understanding these interactions. We begin with an overview of the nature of atoms and molecules, focusing on the structure of the atom, and how it was discovered. We next explore the various ways that atoms combine with other atoms to create molecules, and we look at intermolecular forces that relate to the stability and state of molecules. We end with an examination of the water molecule and the properties that make it a crucial component of living organisms and their environment.

2.1 ATOMS

Learning Outcomes:

1. Understand the general structure of atoms and their constituent particles.
2. Discuss the way electrons orbit the nucleus of an atom within discrete energy levels.
3. Relate atomic structure to the periodic table of the elements.
4. Quantify atomic mass by using units, such as daltons and moles.
5. Explain how a single element may exist in more than one form, called isotopes, and how certain isotopes have importance in human medicine.
6. Know which elements compose most of the mass of all living organisms.

All life is composed of atoms, which in turn are composed of smaller, subatomic particles. A major role of the physicist is to uncover the properties of subatomic particles. Chemists, by contrast, are interested in the properties of atoms and molecules. Chemistry and physics merge when attempts are made to understand the mechanisms by which atoms and molecules interact; in the context of a living organism, the science of biochemistry emerges. In this section, we explore the physical properties of atoms.

Atoms Are the Smallest Functional Units in Living Organisms

An **atom** is the smallest functional unit of matter that forms all chemical substances and that cannot be further broken down into other substances by ordinary chemical or physical means. Many types of atoms are known. The simplest atom, hydrogen, is approximately 1 angstrom (10^{-10} metres) in diameter, roughly one-millionth the diameter of a human hair. Each specific type of atom—hydrogen, nitrogen, oxygen, and so on—occurs as a **chemical element**.

Three subatomic particles—**protons**, **neutrons**, and **electrons**—are found within atoms. The protons and neutrons are confined to a very small volume at the centre of an atom, the **atomic nucleus**, whereas the electrons are found in regions at various distances from the nucleus. The numbers of protons and electrons in a given type of atom are identical, but the number of neutrons can vary. Each subatomic particle has a different electric charge. Protons have one unit of positive charge, electrons have one unit of negative charge, and neutrons are electrically neutral (**Table 2.1**). Because the protons are located in the atomic nucleus, the nucleus has a net positive charge equal to the number of protons it contains. The entire atom usually has no net electric charge because the positively charged protons tend to attract an equal number of negatively charged electrons. As shown in Table 2.1, the masses

Table 2.1	Characteristics of Major Subatomic Particles			
Particle		Location	Charge	Mass relative to electron
Electron	●−	Around the nucleus	−1	1
Proton	⊕	Nucleus	+1	1,836
Neutron	○	Nucleus	0	1,839

of protons and neutrons are similar to each other and much greater than the mass of electrons.

Electrons Occupy Orbitals Around an Atom's Nucleus

After Rutherford's experiments, scientists initially visualized an atom as a little solar system, with the nucleus being the sun and the electrons travelling around it in clearly defined orbits at terrific speeds. Some estimates suggest that the electron in a typical hydrogen atom could circle Earth in less than 20 seconds!

FEATURE INVESTIGATION

Rutherford Determined the Planetary Model of the Atom

Nobel Laureate Ernest Rutherford was born in 1871; he did his greatest work at McGill University in Montreal and later at the University of Manchester in England, around 1900. Scientists knew that atoms contained charged particles but had no idea how those particles were arranged. Neutrons had not yet been discovered, and many scientists believed that the positive charge and the mass of an atom were evenly dispersed throughout the atom. In what came to be called the "plum pudding" model of an atom, electrons were like plums dispersed in a positively charged pudding.

Rutherford aimed a fine beam of positively charged alpha particles (helium nuclei) at an extremely thin sheet of gold foil only 400 atoms thick (**Figure 2.1**). Surrounding the gold foil was a zinc sulphide screen that registered any alpha (α) particles passing through or bouncing off the foil. Rutherford hypothesized that if the positive charges of the gold atoms were uniformly distributed, most of the alpha particles would be slightly deflected as they passed through the foil, because one of the most important features of electric charge is that like charges repel each other. Rutherford did not expect electrons to have any impact on the ability of an alpha particle to move through the metal foil, because the electrons had a much smaller mass.

HYPOTHESIS Atoms in gold foil are composed of diffuse, evenly distributed positive charges that should usually cause alpha (α) particles to be slightly deflected as they pass through.

KEY MATERIALS Thin sheet of gold foil, α particle emitter, zinc sulphide detection screen.

Figure 2.1 Rutherford's gold foil experiment demonstrates that most of the volume of an atom is empty space.

Figure 2.1 *(Continued)*

3 Detect α particles on zinc sulphide screens after they pass through foil or bounce back. Record number of α particles detected on zinc sulphide screens and their locations.

α particle that bounced back
α particle that was undeflected
α particle that was slightly deflected
Detection of α particles

4 **THE DATA**

% of α particles detected on zinc sulphide screens	Location
98%	Undeflected
<2%	Slightly deflected
0.01%	Bounced back

5 **CONCLUSION** Most of the volume of an atom is empty space, with the positive charges concentrated in a small volume.

6 **SOURCE** Rutherford, E. 1911. The scattering of α and β particles by matter and the structure of the atom. *Philosophical Magazine* 21:669–688.

Although some alpha particles were indeed deflected as they passed through the foil, more than 98% of them passed right through, as if the foil were not there, and a few bounced nearly straight back. To explain the 98% that passed right through, Rutherford concluded that most of the volume of an atom is empty space. To explain the few alpha particles that bounced back, he postulated that most of the atom's positive charge is localized in a highly compact area. The existence of this small, dense region of highly concentrated positive charge—which we now call the atomic nucleus—explains how some alpha particles could be so strongly deflected by the gold foil. Alpha particles would bounce back if they directly collided with the atomic nucleus. Based on these results Rutherford rejected the plum pudding model of the atom and proposed the more nearly correct "planetary" model of an atom, with its small, positively charged nucleus surrounded at relatively great distances by negatively charged electrons. Today we know that more than 99.99% of an atom's volume is outside the nucleus. Indeed, the nucleus accounts for only about 1/10,000 of an atom's diameter—most of an atom is empty space!

Experimental Questions

1. Before Rutherford's experiment, how did most scientists envision the structure of an atom? If this plum pudding model of an atom had been correct, what might have been the expected results from Rutherford's experiment?
2. What was the hypothesis tested by Rutherford? What were the results of Rutherford's experiment? How did he interpret the results?

Figure 2.2 shows a diagram of the two simplest atoms, hydrogen and helium, which have the smallest numbers of protons. This model of the atom is now considered an oversimplification, because electrons do not orbit the nucleus in a defined path. However, this depiction of an atom remains a convenient way to diagram atoms in two dimensions.

It is impossible to precisely predict where a given electron will be located at a given moment. Electrons travel within regions that surround the nucleus. These areas, in which the probability is high of finding an electron, are called **orbitals**. Thus, another way of depicting atoms is a central nucleus surrounded by cloudlike orbitals. The cloud represents the region in which a given electron is most likely to be found. Some orbitals are spherical, called *s* orbitals, while others, called *p* orbitals, assume a shape similar to a propeller or dumbbell (**Figure 2.3**).

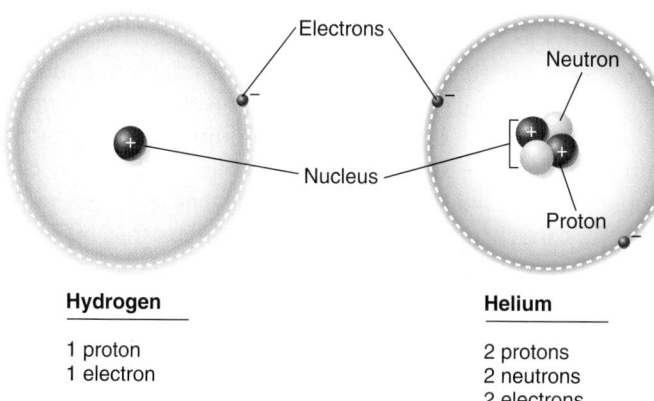

Figure 2.2   **The nuclei of two simple atoms and their electrons.**   This is a model of the two simplest atoms: hydrogen and helium. In all figures of atoms, the sizes and distances are not to scale, and the orbits of real atoms are not as regular.

An orbital can contain a maximum of two electrons; consequently, any atom with more than two electrons must contain more than one orbital. Orbitals occupy **energy shells** that are associated with specific energy levels. These energy shells are numbered so that energy shell number 1 is closest to the nucleus. Atoms with progressively more electrons have orbitals within energy shells that are at greater distances from the nucleus. The innermost energy shell of all atoms has room for only two electrons spinning in opposite directions within a spherical orbital (1s). The second energy shell is farther from the nucleus and can accommodate two orbitals, one spherical orbital (2s), and three dumbbell-shaped orbitals (2p). Thus, the second energy shell can hold up to eight electrons (Figure 2.3). Significantly, we will see that not all atoms have full outermost orbitals.

	Shell 1	Shell 2	
Orbital designation	**1s**	**2s**	**2p**
Orbital shape	Spherical	Spherical	Dumbbell
Maximum number of electrons per energy shell	2	8 [2s + (3 × 2p)]	

Figure 2.3   **Diagrams of individual electron orbitals.** Electrons are found outside the nucleus in orbitals that may resemble spherical or dumbbell-shaped clouds. The orbital cloud represents a region of high probability for locating a particular electron.

Electrons vary in the amount of energy they have. The energy shell closest to the nucleus fills up with the lowest-energy electrons first, and then each subsequent energy shell fills with progressively higher-energy electrons. Within an energy shell, the energy of electrons can vary among different orbitals. In the second energy shell, for example, the spherical orbital has lower energy and fills up first, while the three dumbbell-shaped orbitals have roughly equal energies, and all are higher than those of the spherical orbital.

Although electrons are actually found in orbitals of varying shapes, as shown in Figure 2.3, chemists often use more simplified diagrams when depicting the energy shells of electrons. **Figure 2.4a** illustrates an example involving nitrogen. An atom of this element has seven protons and seven electrons. Two electrons fill the first energy shell, and five electrons are

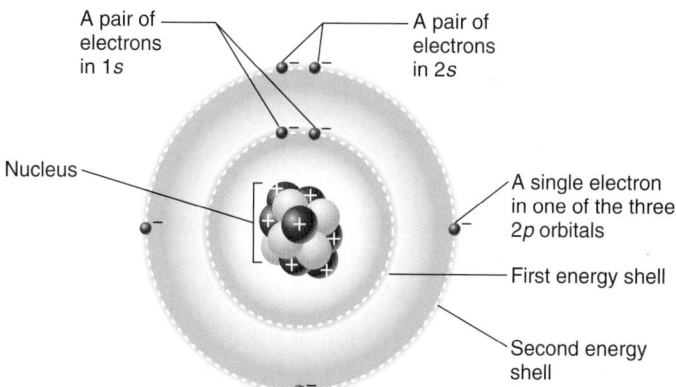

(a) Simplified depiction of a nitrogen atom (7 electrons; 2 electrons in first energy shell, 5 in second energy shell)

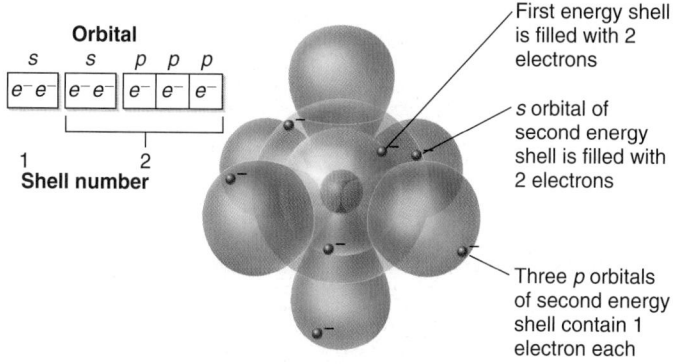

(b) Nitrogen atom showing electrons in orbitals

Figure 2.4   **Diagrams showing the multiple energy shells, orbitals and electrons of a nitrogen atom.**   The simplified view of nitrogen is shown in **(a)**. View **(b)** shows all of nitrogen's orbitals and energy shells. Atom's energy shells fill up one by one. Energy shells containing more than one orbital fill the orbital that has the lowest energy first. Subsequent orbitals gain one electron at a time. The electrons of nitrogen are shown schematically in boxes, where e represents an electron.

Concept check: *What is the difference between an energy shell and an orbital?*

found in the outer energy shell. Two are in the 2s orbital, and the other three are found singly in each of the three p orbitals. The diagram in Figure 2.4a makes it easy to see whether electrons are paired within the same orbital, and whether the outer energy shell is full. This information is essential for understanding the potential of elements to form chemical bonds. **Figure 2.4b** shows a more realistic depiction of a nitrogen atom, showing how the electrons actually occupy orbitals with different shapes.

The number of electrons an element has determines how many orbitals and energy shells are filled. Most atoms have outer energy shells that are not completely filled with electrons. Nitrogen, as you just saw, has a first energy shell filled with two electrons and a second energy shell with five electrons (Figure 2.4a). Because the second energy shell can hold eight electrons, the outer energy shell of a nitrogen atom is not full. As discussed later in this chapter, atoms that have unfilled energy shells tend to share, release, or obtain electrons to fill their outer energy shell. Those electrons in the outer energy shell that are available to combine with other atoms are called **valence electrons**. Such valence electrons allow atoms to form chemical bonds with one another.

Each Element Has a Unique Number of Protons

Each chemical element has a specific and unique number of protons that distinguishes one element from another. The number of protons in an atom is its **atomic number**. For example, hydrogen, the simplest atom, has an atomic number of 1, corresponding to its single proton. Magnesium has an atomic number of 12, corresponding to its 12 protons. Atoms are electrically neutral (have a net charge of zero). Therefore, the atomic number also indicates the number of electrons in the atom.

Atomic number and electron energy shells are useful criteria for organizing the chemical elements into the periodic table. **Figure 2.5** shows the first three rows of the periodic table of the elements. The elements (symbolized with one- or two- letter abbreviations) are listed in the order of their atomic numbers and consequent orbital and energy shell characteristics. Each row contains elements with the same number of energy shells. Hydrogen (H), in row 1, has one energy shell; lithium (Li), in row 2, has two energy shells; sodium (Na), in row 3, has three energy shells. The columns, from left to right, group elements based on the numbers of electrons in the outermost energy shell. H, Li, and Na are listed in column 1 because they all have

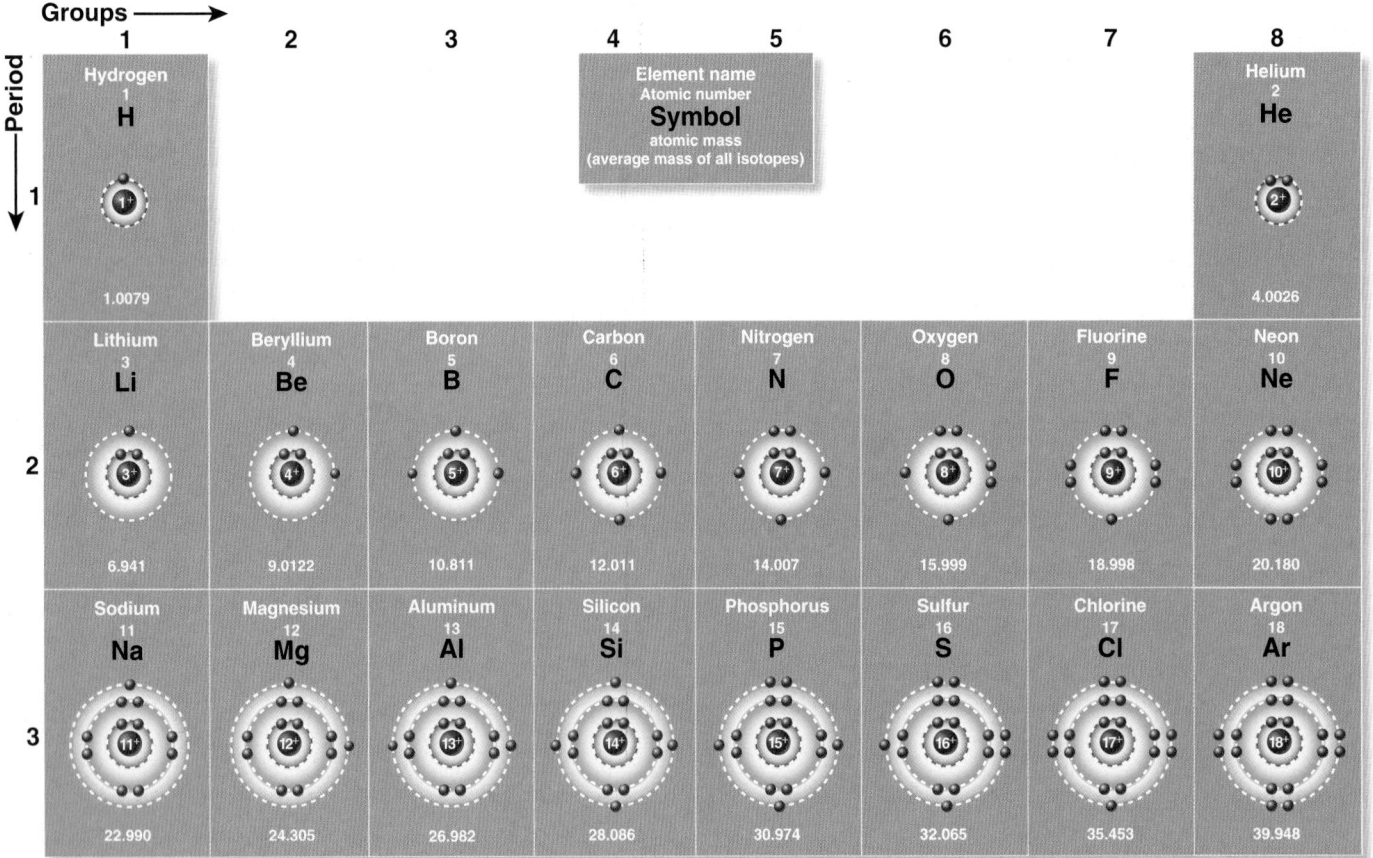

Figure 2.5 **A portion of the periodic table of the elements.** The atoms are shown in models that depict the energy shells in different colours. Whether an element's outermost energy shell of electrons is full affects its chemical properties. Elements that have the same tendency to contribute (or receive) electrons are displayed in the same column of the table.

one electron in their outermost energy shell. Similarly, all elements in column 2 have two electrons in their outermost energy shell. This organization of the periodic table tends to arrange elements based on similar chemical properties. For example, helium (He), neon (Ne), and argon (Ar) are inert gases and don't participate in chemical reactions because they have completely full outer energy shells. By comparison, beryllium (Be) and magnesium (Mg) are both reactive metals because they have only two electrons in their outer energy shell. The similarities of elements within a column occur because they have the same number of electrons in their outer energy shells; therefore, they have similar chemical bonding properties. These properties will be discussed later in this chapter.

Atoms Have a Small but Measurable Mass

Atoms are extremely tiny and therefore have very little mass. A single hydrogen atom, for example, has a mass of only 1.67×10^{-24} g (grams). Protons and neutrons are nearly equal in mass, and both are more than 1,800 times the mass of an electron. Despite the great difference in mass of protons and electrons, they possess equal but opposite amounts of electric charge (see Table 2.1).

Atomic mass is measured in units called **daltons (Da)**, named after the chemist John Dalton, who postulated that matter is composed of minute, indivisible units he called atoms. Because carbon is a key element for life, it is used as the reference for atomic mass units. The most common form of carbon atom, with six protons and six neutrons, is assigned an atomic mass of exactly 12 daltons. On this scale, a hydrogen atom has an atomic mass of 1 dalton, indicating that it has 1/12 the mass of a carbon atom. A magnesium atom, with an atomic mass of 24 daltons, has twice the mass of a carbon atom.

The term mass is sometimes confused with *weight*, but these terms refer to different features of matter. Weight is derived from the gravitational pull on a given mass and hence depends on location. However, mass is the same in all locations. On Earth we can assume that the gravitational tug on all matter is roughly equivalent and thus the terms become essentially interchangeable for most purposes.

Because some atoms, such as hydrogen, have a small mass, and some atoms, such as carbon, have a larger mass, 1g of hydrogen has more atoms than 1 g of carbon. For chemical reactions, knowing the number of atoms is often more important than knowing the mass; therefore, the term *mole* was developed. Carbon is again the reference element: a **mole** contains the same number of atoms as are present in exactly 12 g of carbon. Twelve grams of carbon equals 1 mole. One hydrogen atom has 1/12 the mass of carbon, and it takes only 1 g of hydrogen to contain 1 mole of hydrogen atoms. How many atoms are in 1 mole of every substance? As first described by Italian physicist Amedeo Avogadro, 1 mole of any element contains 6.022×10^{23} atoms. This number, known today as **Avogadro's constant**, is large enough to be somewhat mind-boggling. To visualize the enormity of this number, imagine that people could move through a turnstile at a rate of 1 million people per second. It would require almost 20 billion years for 6.022×10^{23} people to move through that turnstile!

Isotopes Vary in Their Number of Neutrons

Although the number of neutrons in an atom is often equal to the number of protons, many elements can exist in multiple forms, called **isotopes**, that differ in the number of neutrons they contain. For example, the most abundant form of the carbon atom, ^{12}C, contains six protons and six neutrons, and thus has an atomic number of 6 and an atomic mass of 12 daltons. The superscript placed to the left in ^{12}C is the sum of the protons and neutrons. The rare carbon isotope ^{14}C, however, contains six protons and eight neutrons, giving it an atomic number of 6 but an atomic mass of 14 daltons. Nearly 99% of the carbon in living organisms is ^{12}C. Thus, the average atomic mass of carbon is very close to, but slightly greater than, 12 daltons because of the existence of a small number of heavier isotopes. This explains why the average atomic masses given in the periodic table do not add up exactly to the predicted masses based on the atomic number and the number of neutrons (Figure 2.5).

Many isotopes found in nature are inherently unstable. Such isotopes are called **radioisotopes**, and they lose energy through radiation by emitting subatomic particles (radioactivity). At the very low amounts found in nature, radioisotopes usually pose no serious threat to life, but exposure of living organisms to high amounts of radioactivity can result in the disruption of cellular function and even death.

Modern medicine makes use of the high energy level of radioisotopes in many ways. For example, solutions containing radioisotopes of iodine can be given to a person with an overactive thyroid gland. The thyroid gland controls many important body functions. It is the only structure in the human body that uses iodine in large quantities, and so the isotope becomes concentrated there. This localizes the radiation of the isotope to the thyroid and preferentially kills the cells in the hyperactive regions of the gland without harming other parts of the body. Other applications make use of the fact that radiation emitted by radioisotopes as they lose protons is easily detectable with imaging techniques. These techniques, such as the positron emission tomography scan (PET scan), can detect the activities of cells following the injection of a compound that contains a radioisotope, such as ^{131}I.

Researchers also use isotopes to study many different types of biological processes. The carbon isotope ^{14}C was used to understand how carbon dioxide in our environment is incorporated into sugar molecules during the process of photosynthesis (Chapter 8); as we will see in Chapter 10, the heavy isotope of nitrogen, ^{15}N, was used in experiments that helped determine how hereditary material is duplicated. Chapter 20 considers how isotopes are used to estimate the period when fossilized organisms lived on Earth and to relate global biosphere events to mass extinctions. Thus, the applied chemistry of isotopes has an important role in our studies of biology at many levels of organization.

Four Elements Constitute the Vast Majority of Living Organisms

Just four elements—oxygen, carbon, hydrogen, and nitrogen—account for the vast majority of atoms in living organisms (**Table 2.2**). These elements typically make up about 95% of the mass of living organisms. Much of the hydrogen and oxygen occur in the form of water, which accounts for approximately 60% of the mass of most animals and up to 95% or more in some plants. Nitrogen and carbon, along with hydrogen and oxygen, are major building blocks of all living matter. Other vital elements in living organisms include the mineral elements, such as calcium and phosphorus, which are important constituents of the skeletons and shells of animals. Sodium and potassium are key regulators of water movement and electrical potentials that occur across membranes.

Table 2.2	Chemical Elements Essential for Life in Most Organisms	
Element	**Symbol**	**Percentage of human body mass**
Most abundant in living organisms* (approximately 95% of total mass)		**These values include water.**
Oxygen	O	65
Carbon	C	18
Hydrogen	H	9
Nitrogen	N	3
Mineral elements that are less than 1% of total mass		
Calcium	Ca	
Chlorine	Cl	
Magnesium	Mg	
Phosphorus	P	
Potassium	K	
Sodium	Na	
Sulphur	S	
Trace elements that are less than 0.01% of total mass		
Chromium	Cr	
Cobalt	Co	
Copper	Cu	
Fluorine	F	
Iodine	I	
Iron	Fe	
Manganese	Mn	
Molybdenum	Mo	
Selenium	Se	
Silicon	Si	
Tin	Sn	
Vanadium	V	
Zinc	Zn	

*Although these are the most common elements in living organisms, many other trace and mineral elements have reported functions. For example, aluminum is believed to be a cofactor for certain chemical reactions in animals, but it is generally toxic to plants.

In addition, all living organisms require trace elements. These atoms are present in extremely small quantities but still are essential for normal growth and function (Table 2.2). For example, iron plays an important role in how vertebrates store oxygen in their blood, and copper serves a similar role in some invertebrates.

2.2   CHEMICAL BONDS THAT CREATE AND STABILIZE MOLECULES

Learning Outcomes:

1. Compare and contrast the types of atomic interactions that lead to the formation of molecules.
2. Explain the concept of electronegativity and its contribution to the polarity of some covalent bonds.
3. Understand the concepts of a chemical reaction and chemical equilibrium.

The linkage of atoms with other atoms serves as the basis for life and gives life its great diversity. Two or more atoms bonded together make up a molecule. Atoms occur in a multitude of combinations. For example, two oxygen atoms can combine to form one oxygen molecule, represented as O_2. This representation is called a **molecular formula** and consists of the chemical symbols for all the atoms present (here, O for oxygen) and a subscript that shows how many of those atoms are present (in this case, 2). The term **compound** refers to a molecule made of two or more different elements. Examples include water (H_2O), with 2 hydrogen atoms and 1 oxygen atom, and glucose ($C_6H_{12}O_6$), which has 6 carbon atoms, 12 hydrogen atoms, and 6 oxygen atoms.

One of the most important features of compounds is the new properties that emerge, meaning that the properties of a compound can differ greatly from the elements that combined to form it. Consider sodium as an example. Elemental sodium (Na) is a soft, silvery-white metal that can be cut evenly with a knife; adding it to water can produce an explosive reaction. When sodium forms a compound with chlorine, table salt (NaCl) is made. NaCl is a white, relatively hard crystal that dissolves readily in water. Thus, the properties of sodium in a compound can be dramatically different from its properties as an element.

The atoms in **molecules** are held together by chemical bonds. The type of bonds that an atom tends to form and the likelihood of it forming the bonds are determined, in large measure, by the number of electrons in its outer energy shell. This principle is illustrated in the periodic table: elements in the same column have the same capacity to accept or donate electrons to the shared bond of a compound.

Covalent Bonds Join Atoms Through the Sharing of Electrons

Covalent bonds, in which atoms share a pair of electrons, can occur between atoms whose outer energy shells are not full. A fundamental principle of chemistry is that atoms tend to be

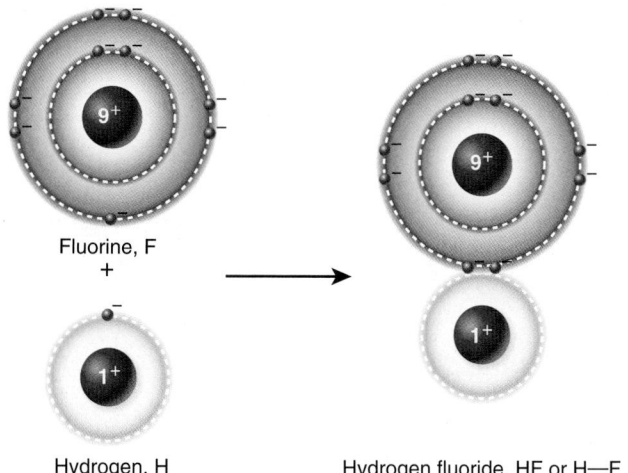

Fluorine, F
+

Hydrogen, H   Hydrogen fluoride, HF or H—F

Figure 2.6   The formation of covalent bonds.   In covalent bonds, electrons from the outer energy shell of two atoms are shared to complete the outer energy shells of both atoms. This simplified illustration shows hydrogen forming a covalent bond with fluorine.

most stable when their outer energy shells are full of electrons. **Figure 2.6** shows this principle as it applies to the formation of hydrogen fluoride. The outer energy shell of a hydrogen atom would be full if it contained two electrons, but a hydrogen atom has only one electron. The outer energy shell of a fluorine atom has seven electrons, and its outer energy shell would be full if it contained eight electrons. When the compound hydrogen fluoride (HF) is created, the two atoms share a pair of electrons. This allows both of their outer energy shells to be full. Covalent bonds are strong chemical bonds, because the shared electrons behave as if they belong to both atoms.

In diagrams of molecules, each covalent bond is represented by a solid line, which symbolizes a pair of shared electrons. For example, hydrogen fluoride is diagrammed as

$$H—F$$

A molecule of water can be diagrammed as

$$H—O—H$$

showing that the oxygen atom shares one electron with each of two hydrogen atoms (forming one covalent bound with each). This compound also can be indicated with the shorthand molecular formula: H_2O.

Each atom of the periodic table has the potential to form a characteristic number of covalent bonds based on the number of electrons needed to fill its outermost energy shell. The atoms of some elements important for life (oxygen, nitrogen, and carbon) can form more than one covalent bond (two, three, and four bonds, respectively) and therefore can become linked simultaneously to two or more other atoms. **Figure 2.7** shows the number of covalent bonds that can be formed by several atoms that are commonly found in the molecules of living cells.

In some molecules, a double bond occurs when atoms share two pairs of electrons rather than one pair. As shown in **Figure 2.8**, this is the case for an oxygen molecule (O_2), which can be diagrammed as

$$O{=}O$$

Another common example occurs when two carbon atoms form bonds in compounds. They may share one pair of electrons (single bond) or two pairs (double bond), depending on how many other covalent bonds each carbon forms with other atoms. In rare cases, carbon might even form triple bonds, in which three pairs of electrons are shared between two atoms.

Electrons Are Not Always Evenly Shared Between Atoms

Some atoms attract shared electrons more readily than do other atoms. The **electronegativity** of an atom is a measure of its ability to attract electrons in a bond from another atom. When two atoms with different electronegativity form a covalent bond, the shared electron's orbit is more likely to be closer to the atom of higher electronegativity than to the atom of lower electronegativity, creating a polarity in the distribution of the charge. Such bonds are called polar covalent bonds, because the skewed distribution of electrons toward one of the two atoms creates a polarity across the molecule. The molecule

Atom name	Hydrogen	Oxygen	Nitrogen	Carbon
	Nucleus Electron			
	1+	8+	7+	6+
Electron number needed to complete outer energy shell (typical number of covalent bonds)	1	2	3	4

Figure 2.7   The most abundant elements found in living organisms.   These elements can form different maximum numbers of covalent bonds because of the electron configurations in their outer energy shells.

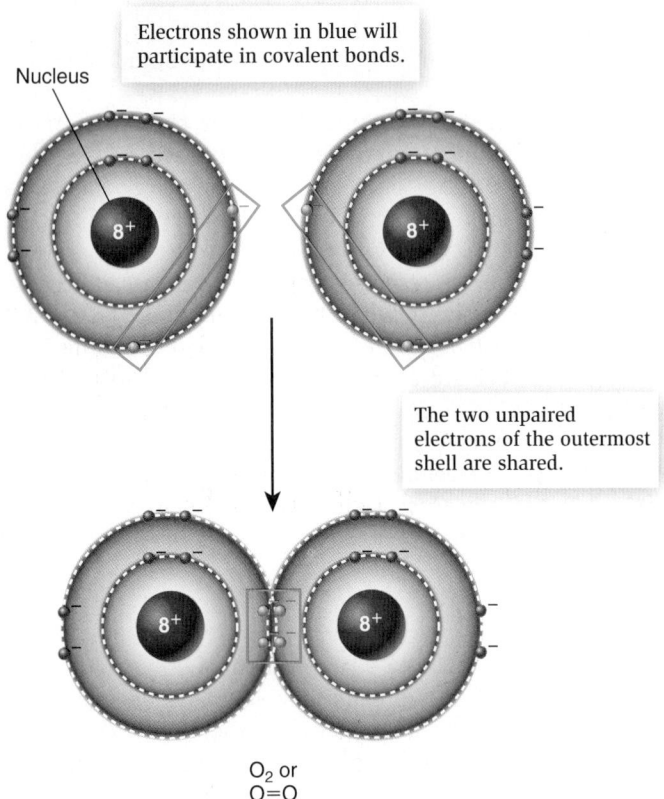

Electrons shown in blue will participate in covalent bonds.

Nucleus

The two unpaired electrons of the outermost shell are shared.

O_2 or
$O=O$

Figure 2.8   A double bond between two oxygen atoms.

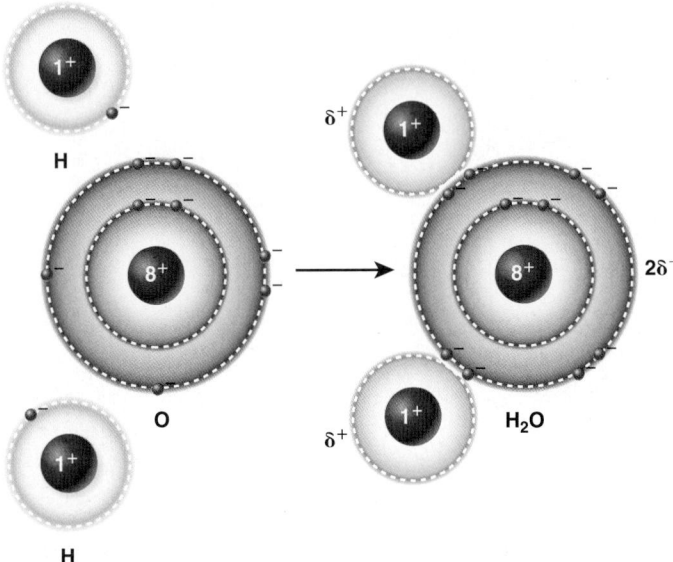

H

O

H

δ^+

$2\delta^-$

δ^+

H_2O

Figure 2.9   Polar covalent bonds in water molecules.   In a water molecule, two hydrogen atoms share electrons with an oxygen atom. Because oxygen has a higher electronegativity, the shared electrons spend more time closer to oxygen. This gives oxygen a partial negative charge, designated as $2\delta^-$, and each hydrogen a partial positive charge, designated as δ^+.

itself is called a polar molecule or occasionally a **dipole**. H_2O is the classic example of a molecule containing polar covalent bonds (**Figure 2.9**). The shared electrons at any moment tend to be closer to the oxygen atom than to either of the hydrogen atoms. This unequal sharing of electrons gives the water molecule a region of partial negative charge (δ^-) and two regions of partial positive charge (δ^+) and leads to many of its remarkable physical properties.

Atoms with high electronegativity, such as oxygen and nitrogen, have a relatively strong attraction for electrons; they form polar covalent bonds with hydrogen atoms, which have low electronegativity. Examples of polar bonds include O—H and N—H. In contrast, bonds between carbon atoms (C—C) and between carbon and hydrogen atoms (C—H) are electrically neutral or nonpolar because carbon and hydrogen both have low electronegativity. Molecules containing significant numbers of polar bonds are known as polar molecules, whereas molecules composed predominantly of nonpolar bonds are called nonpolar molecules. Larger molecules might have some regions with nonpolar bonds and other regions with polar bonds. For example, the detergent molecules found in soap have polar and nonpolar ends. The nonpolar ends dissolve in the oil of your skin, and the polar ends help the detergent rinse off in water. The physical characteristics of polar and nonpolar molecules, especially their solubility in water, are quite different.

Ionic Bonds Involve an Attraction Between Positive and Negative Ions

Atoms are electrically neutral because they contain equal numbers of negative electrons and positive protons. If an atom or a molecule gains or loses one or more electrons (with no change in number of protons), it acquires a net electric charge and becomes an **ion**. For example, when a sodium atom (Na), which has 11 electrons, loses one, it becomes a sodium ion (Na^+) with a net positive charge. A sodium ion still has 11 protons, but only 10 electrons. Ions, such as Na^+, are depicted with a superscript that indicates the net charge of the ion. Some atoms can gain or lose more than one electron. For instance, a calcium atom can lose two electrons to become a calcium ion, depicted as Ca^{2+}. Conversely, a chlorine atom (Cl), which has 17 electrons, can gain an electron and become a chloride ion (Cl^-) with a net negative charge—it has 18 electrons but only 17 protons. Hydrogen atoms and most mineral and trace element atoms readily form ions. Ions that have a net positive charge are called **cations**, while those that have a net negative charge are **anions**. Ionization, the process of ion formation, can occur in single atoms or in atoms that are covalently linked in molecules. **Table 2.3** lists the ionic forms of several elements that are relatively stable because the loss of electrons (in cations) or gain of electrons (in anions) yields elements with a full outermost electron energy shell. For example, a sodium atom has one electron in its third (outer) energy shell. If it loses this electron to become Na^+, it no longer has a third energy shell, and the second energy shell is full. Alternatively, a Cl atom has

Table 2.3	Ionic Forms of Some Common Elements			
Atom	**Chemical symbol**	**Ion**	**Ion symbol**	**Electrons gained or lost**
Calcium	Ca	Calcium ion	Ca^{2+}	2 lost
Chlorine	Cl	Chloride ion	Cl^-	1 gained
Hydrogen	H	Hydrogen ion	H^+	1 lost
Magnesium	Mg	Magnesium ion	Mg^{2+}	2 lost
Potassium	K	Potassium ion	K^+	1 lost
Sodium	Na	Sodium ion	Na^+	1 lost

seven electrons in its third (outer) energy shell. If it gains an electron to become a chloride ion (Cl^-), its outer energy shell becomes full with eight electrons.

An **ionic bond** forms when a cation binds to an anion. **Figure 2.10a** shows an ionic bond between Na^+ and Cl^- to form NaCl. The general name, salt, is given to compounds that are formed from an attraction between a positively charged ion (a cation) and negatively charged ion (an anion). Examples of salts include NaCl, KCl, and $CaCl_2$. Salts may create crystals in which the cations and anions form a regular array. **Figure 2.10b** shows a NaCl crystal in which the sodium and chloride ions are held together by ionic bonds.

Molecules Can Change Shape as Bond Angles Change

When atoms combine, they can form molecules with various three-dimensional shapes, depending on the arrangements and numbers of bonds between their atoms. Consider the covalent bonds in three simple molecules (**Figure 2.11**). As these molecules form, newly configured orbitals cause the atoms to have defined angles relative to each other.

Molecules containing covalent bonds are not rigid, inflexible structures. Think of a covalent bond, for example, as an axle around which the joined atoms can rotate. Within certain limits, the shape of a molecule can change without breaking covalent bonds. As illustrated in **Figure 2.12**, a molecule of six carbon atoms can assume a number of shapes as a result of rotations around various covalent bonds. Molecules will take on somewhat different shapes based on their environment and neighbouring molecules. The flexible shape of biological molecules contributes to their biological properties as it allows changes in shape to transmit information or accomplish specific chemical changes.

Free Radicals Are a Special Class of Highly Reactive Molecules

Recall that an atom or ion is most stable when each of its orbitals is occupied by its full complement of electrons. A molecule containing an atom with a single, unpaired electron in its outer energy shell is known as a **free radical**. Free radicals can react with other molecules to "steal" an electron from one of their atoms, thereby

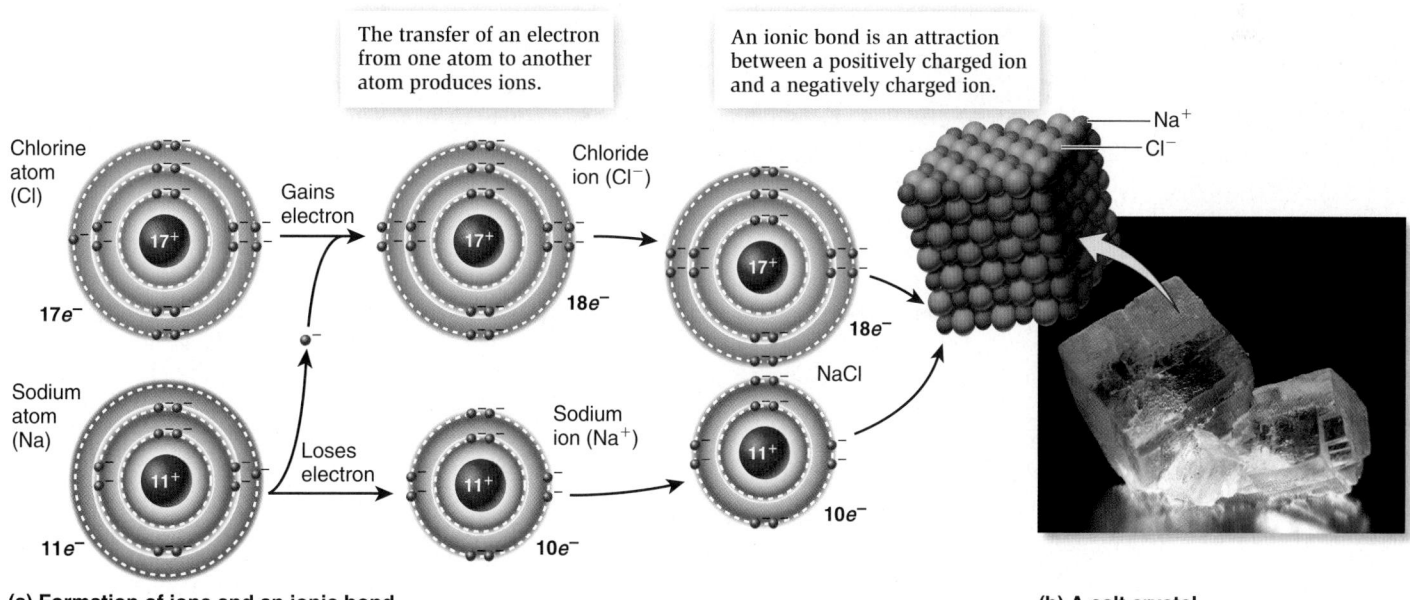

(a) Formation of ions and an ionic bond

(b) A salt crystal

Figure 2.10 Ionic bonding in table salt (NaCl). (a) When an electron is transferred from a sodium atom to a chlorine atom, the resulting ions are attracted to each other via an ionic bond. (b) In a salt crystal, a lattice is formed in which the positively charged sodium ions (Na^+) are attracted to negatively charged chloride ions (Cl^-).

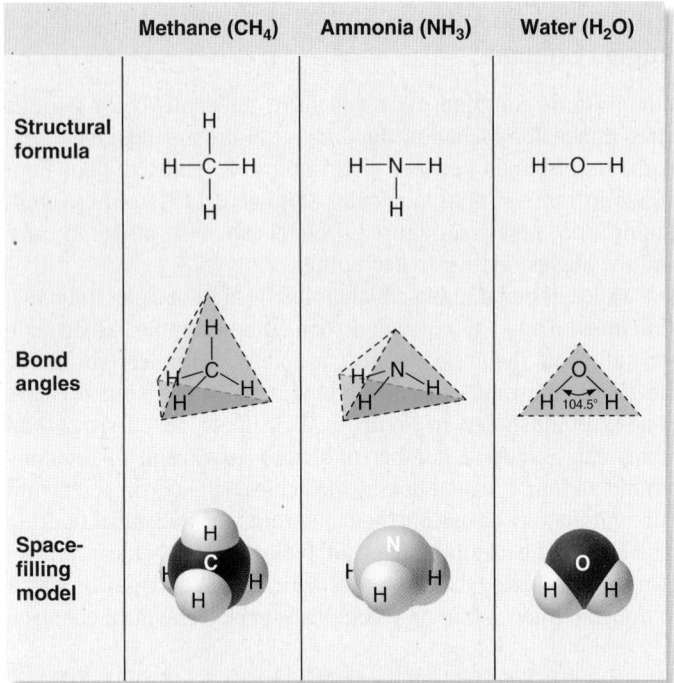

	Methane (CH₄)	Ammonia (NH₃)	Water (H₂O)
Structural formula			
Bond angles			
Space-filling model			

Figure 2.11 **Shapes of molecules.** Molecules can assume different shapes depending on the types of bonds between their atoms. The angles between groups of atoms are well defined. For example, in liquid water at room temperature, the angle formed for each hydrogen-to-oxygen bond is approximately 104.5°. This bond angle can vary slightly, depending on the temperature and degree of hydrogen bonding between adjacent water molecules.

Bond rotation in a small molecule

Figure 2.12 **Shape changes in molecules.** A single molecule can assume different three-dimensional shapes without breaking any of the covalent bonds between its atoms, as shown for a six-carbon molecule. Hydrogen atoms above the blue plane are shown in white; those below the blue plane are blue.

filling the orbital in the free radical. This "theft" may create a new free radical in the donor molecule, setting off a chain reaction.

Free radicals can be formed in several ways, including exposure of cells to radiation and toxins. Free radicals can do considerable harm to living cells, such as causing a cell's membrane to rupture or damaging the genetic material. Surprisingly, the lethal effect of free radicals is sometimes put to good use. Some cells in animals' bodies create free radicals and use them to kill invading cells, such as bacteria. Likewise, people use hydrogen peroxide, which can break down to create free radicals, to kill bacteria.

Despite the exceptional case of fighting off bacteria, though, most free radicals that arise in an organism need to be inactivated so that they do not kill healthy cells. Cells need molecules that can donate electrons to the free radicals without becoming highly reactive themselves to protect themselves. Examples of such protective compounds are certain vitamins found in fruits and vegetables, and the numerous plant compounds known as flavonoids. These compounds are one reason that a diet rich in fruits and vegetables is beneficial to health.

Chemical Reactions Change Elements or Compounds into Different Compounds

A **chemical reaction** occurs when one or more substances are changed into other substances. This can happen when elements or compounds combine to form a new compound, when one compound breaks down into two or more molecules, or when electrons are added to or taken away from an atom. Chemical reactions share many similar properties. First, they all require a source of energy for molecules to encounter each other. Such energy is provided partly by heat. In the complete absence of any heat (a temperature called absolute zero), atoms and molecules would be stationary and unable to interact. Heat energy causes atoms and molecules to vibrate and move, a phenomenon known as **Brownian motion**. Second, chemical reactions that occur in living organisms often require more than just Brownian motion to proceed at a reasonable rate. Such reactions need to be catalyzed. A **catalyst** is a substance that speeds up a chemical reaction without itself being affected. Often, cells use specific biomolecule-catalysts, some made of RNA and some made of protein. Third, chemical reactions tend to proceed in a particular direction but will eventually reach a state of equilibrium. As an example, consider a chemical reaction between methane, a component found in natural gas, and oxygen. These molecules react with each other to produce carbon dioxide and water:

$$CH_4 + 2\ O_2 \rightleftharpoons CO_2 + 2\ H_2O$$

(methane) (oxygen)   (carbon dioxide) (water)

As it is written here, methane and oxygen are the reactants, while carbon dioxide and water are the products. Whether a chemical reaction is likely to proceed in a forward or reverse direction depends on changes in free energy, as described in Chapter 7. If the reaction began with only methane and oxygen, the forward reaction would be very favourable. The reaction would produce a large amount of carbon dioxide and water, as well as heat. This is why natural gas is used as a fuel to heat homes. However, all chemical reactions will eventually reach **chemical equilibrium** when the rate of the forward reaction is balanced by the rate of the reverse reaction. In the case of the reaction described above, this equilibrium would occur when nearly all the reactants had been converted to products.

Different types of chemical bonds require different amounts of energy to form, and the bonds hold different amounts of energy. Bond strength not only determines how stable compounds and molecules are but also allows organisms to store energy in energy-rich covalent bonds and use this energy in a controlled fashion to do work at the cellular level. In Chapter 8 you will see how radiant energy from the sun is stored in the covalent bonds of sugars, and in Chapter 7 you will see how the energy stored in sugars is used to create even more energy-rich bonds to fuel the cellular activities and ultimately can be used by organisms to do work.

A final feature common to chemical reactions in living organisms is that they occur in water environments. Just as a crystal of sodium chloride will not dissolve in air but will dissolve in water, so too do the chemical reactions in organisms require water. We will examine the properties of water in the last section of this chapter.

2.3 CHEMICAL FORCES THAT PROMOTE AND STABILIZE MOLECULAR INTERACTIONS

Learning Outcomes:

1. Compare and contrast covalent and ionic bonds with ion–dipole and dipole–dipole interactions.
2. Understand the nature of hydrogen bonds and how they form in living systems.
3. Describe how a molecule's shape is important for its ability to interact with other molecules and how van der Waal forces contribute.

We have discussed covalent and ionic bonds, the relatively strong bonds that hold the atoms of a molecule together. Now we will look at the chemical forces that occur intermolecularly (between molecules) or between different regions of large molecules. These forces collectively are called **van der Waal forces**; van der Wall forces are due to electrostatic interactions between molecules of opposite charges. The strength of the interaction is determined by the degree of the charges and the distance between the two molecules. These forces are weaker than covalent and ionic bonds (**Table 2.4**) because the charges are smaller

Table 2.4	A Comparison of the Energy Associated with Different Types of Bonds and Molecular Interactions		
Type of Interaction	**Basis of Attraction**	**Energy (kJ/mol)**	**Example**
Ionic bonds	Cation–anion	400–4000	NaCl
Covalent bonds	Atomic nuclei share electron pair	150–1000	O_2
Van der Waal forces			
Ion–dipole	Ion charge with dipole charge	40–600	NaCl in water
Dipole–dipole	Dipole charges	5–40	I—Cl I—Cl
Hydrogen bonding	Polar H with polar N, O, or F	10–40	H_2Os of water

and the distances are greater. Even though van der Waal forces are weaker than covalent and ionic bonds, they are vital to life on Earth and determine many of the remarkable properties of water (as you will see in the last section).

Two types of van der Waal forces are stronger than the remainder and are particularly important to life: **ion–dipole force** interactions and **dipole–dipole force** interactions. Ion-dipole interactions occur between ions and polar molecules. The most important examples occur when ionic molecules are dissolved in water, a polar molecule. Dipole–dipole interactions can occur between many different polar molecules, but one very important type of dipole–dipole bond occurs between the hydrogen of one polar molecule and the oxygen, nitrogen, or fluorine of another nearby polar molecule. This category of bond is known as **hydrogen bonds**. In biological systems hydrogen bonds most often occur between the hydrogen and oxygen or the hydrogen and nitrogen of nearby molecules.

Hydrogen bonds are stronger than other dipole–dipole bonds because all three of the relevant atoms are small, and the hydrogen–oxygen and hydrogen–nitrogen covalent bonds are very polar. Thus the hydrogen atoms of each of these types of molecules are very positive (δ^+), and the relevant oxygen or nitrogen is very electronegative (δ^-). Hydrogen bonds occur as the electropositive hydrogen of one molecule is attracted to an electronegative oxygen or nitrogen of a neighbouring molecule. Hydrogen bonds, like those between water molecules, are represented in diagrams by dashed or dotted lines to distinguish them from covalent bonds (**Figure 2.13a**). A single hydrogen bond is weak. The strength of an individual hydrogen bond is only a few percent of the strength of the polar covalent bonds linking the hydrogen and oxygen within a water molecule. Nonetheless, hydrogen bonds have a profound affect on living things, both in determining the physical properties of water and in influencing the shape and behaviour of many large biomolecules, such as double-stranded DNA helices (**Figure 2.13b**). Because of the large number of hydrogen bonds found in DNA, considerable energy is needed to separate the two strands of DNA; hence, the double helix is a fairly stable structure. Hydrogen bonds also can occur within a single large molecule; indeed

(a) Hydrogen bonds between water molecules

The hydrogen bond (H bond) is a weak attraction between a partially positive hydrogen atom and a partially negative atom, such as oxygen.

(b) Hydrogen bonds in a DNA molecule

A DNA molecule consists of two twisted strands held together along their entire length by millions of hydrogen bonds.

H bonds

(c) van der Waal forces help geckos climb smooth surfaces

Figure 2.13 **Examples of van der Waal forces.**   Hydrogen bonds occur between molecules with three of life's four most abundant elements, affect water's properties, and influence the shape and stability of biomolecules. **(a)** This example depicts hydrogen bonds (shown as dashed lines) between nearby water molecules. The atoms are depicted as solid spheres, which represent the outer energy shell. This is called a space-filling model for an atom. **(b)** A DNA molecule is composed of two twisting strands connected to each other by hydrogen bonds (dashed lines). Although each individual bond is weak, the sum of all the hydrogen bonds in a large molecule like DNA imparts considerable stability to the molecule. **(c)** Other van der Waal forces are influenced by shape, provide attractive forces, and allow geckos to climb vertical surfaces.

Principle: *Structure determines function. The three-dimensional structure of DNA allows it to function as the hereditary material. The structure of the gecko's footpads maximizes van der Waal forces and its ability to climb smooth vertical surfaces.*

Concept check: *As discussed in Chapter 11, DNA strands must separate for DNA to be replicated. Do you think the process of strand separation requires energy, or do you think the strands can separate spontaneously?*

hydrogen bonding is often very important in determining the shape of proteins, as we discuss in Chapter 3.

There are yet other types of progressively weaker van der Waal forces that are nonetheless important. A common characteristic of all van der Waal forces (including hydrogen bonds) is that the closer the two molecules are to each other, the stronger is the van der Waal force, because there can be more effective electrostatic interactions. Two molecules that have complementary shapes can be in very close contact, as can two very flat surfaces; both types of contact can be stabilized by van der Waal forces. This is one important reason why shape (structure) is very important in biology. Another important factor is the extent of contact: the more extensive the contact, the stronger collectively are the van der Waal forces. The ability of the gecko (a small lizard) to make stunning vertical climbs (**Figure 2.13c**) is likely made possible through van der

Waal forces generated as it makes extensive contact with its climbing surface.

2.4   THE IMPORTANCE OF WATER AND ITS PHYSICAL AND CHEMICAL PROPERTIES

Learning Outcomes:

1. Describe how hydrogen bonding determines many properties of water.
2. List the properties of water that make it a valuable solvent, and distinguish between hydrophilic and hydrophobic substances.

3. Understand how the molarity of a solution—the number of moles of a solute per litre of solution—is used to measure the concentration of solutes in solution.
4. Discuss the properties of water that are critical for the survival of living organisms.
5. Explain how water has the ability to ionize into hydroxide ions (OH^-) and into hydrogen ions (H^+), and how the H^+ concentration is expressed as a solution's pH.
6. Give examples of how buffers maintain a stable environment in an animal's body fluids.

It would be difficult to imagine life without water. Earth is a watery planet with ~70% of its surface covered by water. The bodies of organisms are composed largely of water. Up to 95% of the weight of certain plants comes from water. In people, typically 60%–70% of body weight is from water. Most of the chemical reactions that occur in nature involve molecules that are dissolved in water, including those reactions that happen inside cells and in the intercellular spaces that surround the cells of living organisms. However, not all molecules dissolve in water. In this section we will examine the properties of chemicals that influence whether they dissolve in water and consider how biologists measure the amounts of dissolved substances. In addition, we examine some of the other special properties of water that make it a vital component of living organisms and their environments.

Water's Physical Properties and Their Effect on Life

Substances can exist in three states: solid (ice), liquid (water), and gas (water vapour). Changes in state involve an input or a release of energy. As a substance goes from the liquid to the gaseous state, it vaporizes; vaporization requires energy. The heat required to vaporize 1 mole of any substance at its boiling point under standard pressure is called the substance's **heat of vaporization**. Conversely, when a substance goes from the liquid to the solid state in a process called fusion, energy is released. The **heat of fusion** is the amount of energy that is released during that process. For H_2O, the absolute values of both the heat of vaporization and the heat of fusion are unusually high because of the large number of hydrogen bonds H_2O can form in both the liquid and solid state. Thus, although ice and water vapour are common on Earth, the majority of H_2O is found as water, where hydrogen bonds between water molecules are continually being formed, broken, and formed again.

If the temperature falls enough, hydrogen bonds are broken less frequently so that larger and larger clusters of H_2O molecules are formed until, at 0°C, water begins to solidify. Because of its unique structure and ability to form hydrogen bonds, H_2O forms a crystalline structure as it solidifies that is more open (occupying a greater amount of space) than a comparable number of liquid H_2O molecules. Thus, solid H_2O (ice) is less dense than its liquid counterpart (water), which is why ice floats on water (**Figure 2.14**). This openly configured floating

Figure 2.14 Structure of water and ice. In its liquid form, the hydrogen bonds between water molecules continually form, break, and re-form, resulting in an ever-changing arrangement of molecules. Water forms a crystalline matrix called ice at temperatures at or below its freezing point. In this solid form, hydrogen bonds are more stable. Ice has a hexagonally shaped crystal structure. The greater space between H_2O molecules in this crystal structure causes ice to have a lower density compared with water. For this reason, ice floats on water, as can be seen on this river in winter.

ice insulates the water below it and makes the lower regions less likely to freeze solid, which allows aquatic organisms to inhabit the deeper regions of lakes and oceans throughout the year. Snow is a special form of ice that takes shape as ice crystals form directly from water vapour. A blanket of snow with small pockets of air trapped between snowflakes provides thermal insulation to organisms living below it. Thus, the structure of ice and snow provide protection to organisms.

Another important feature of water is its high specific heat. The **specific heat** of a substance is the amount of heat required per unit of mass to raise the temperature of that mass by one degree Celsius. The high specific heat of water is due to the fact the much heat is needed to break the hydrogen bonds that occur between neighbouring water molecules. Because of water's unusually high heat capacity, it takes a lot of heat to raise water's temperature. Water and water vapour moderate the difference between day and night temperatures even though there is a large difference in solar energy. This characteristic also accounts, in part, for the relatively stable temperatures of large bodies of water compared with temperatures inland. Internal water also moderates temperature changes within organisms.

Polar Molecules and Ions Readily Dissolve in Water

Substances dissolved in a liquid are known as **solutes**, and the liquid in which they are dissolved is the **solvent**. Solutes dissolve in a solvent to form a **solution**. In all living organisms, the solvent for chemical reactions is water, which is the most abundant solvent in nature. Solutions made with water are called aqueous solutions. Water is an excellent solvent for many types of solutes. Because H_2O is a polar molecule, it can readily dissolve polar compounds and compounds held together by ionic bonds. For example, table salt (NaCl) is a solid crystalline substance with ionic bonds between positive sodium ions (Na^+) and negative chloride ions (Cl^-). When a crystal of sodium chloride is placed in water, the polar water molecules are attracted to the charged Na^+ and Cl^- (**Figure 2.15**). Water is also able to dissolve many nonpolar compounds, such as glucose ($C_6H_{12}O_6$), as it forms hydrogen bonds with them. Thus, many molecules can interact with water. These molecules are **hydrophilic**, which literally means "water-loving."

In contrast, molecules composed predominantly of carbon and hydrogen (without nitrogen and oxygen) are relatively insoluble in water, because carbon–carbon and carbon–hydrogen bonds are nonpolar. These molecules do not have partial positive and negative charges, and therefore are not attracted to water molecules. Such molecules are **hydrophobic**, or "water-fearing." Oils are a familiar example of hydrophobic molecules.

Although hydrophobic molecules dissolve poorly in water, they normally dissolve readily in nonpolar solvents. For example, cholesterol is a compound found in the blood and cells of animals. It is a hydrophobic molecule that is barely soluble in water but that easily dissolves in nonpolar solvents, such as ether, used in chemical laboratories. Biological membranes, like those that encase cells, contain about 50% nonpolar compounds. Because of this, cholesterol also inserts into biological membranes, where it helps to maintain the membrane structure.

Molecules that have polar or ionized regions at one or more sites and that have nonpolar regions at one or more other sites are called **amphipathic**—consisting of two parts. When mixed with water, long amphipathic molecules may form spheres called **micelles**, with their polar (hydrophilic) regions at the surface of the micelle, where they are attracted to the surrounding water molecules. The nonpolar (hydrophobic) ends are oriented toward the interior of the micelle (**Figure 2.16**).

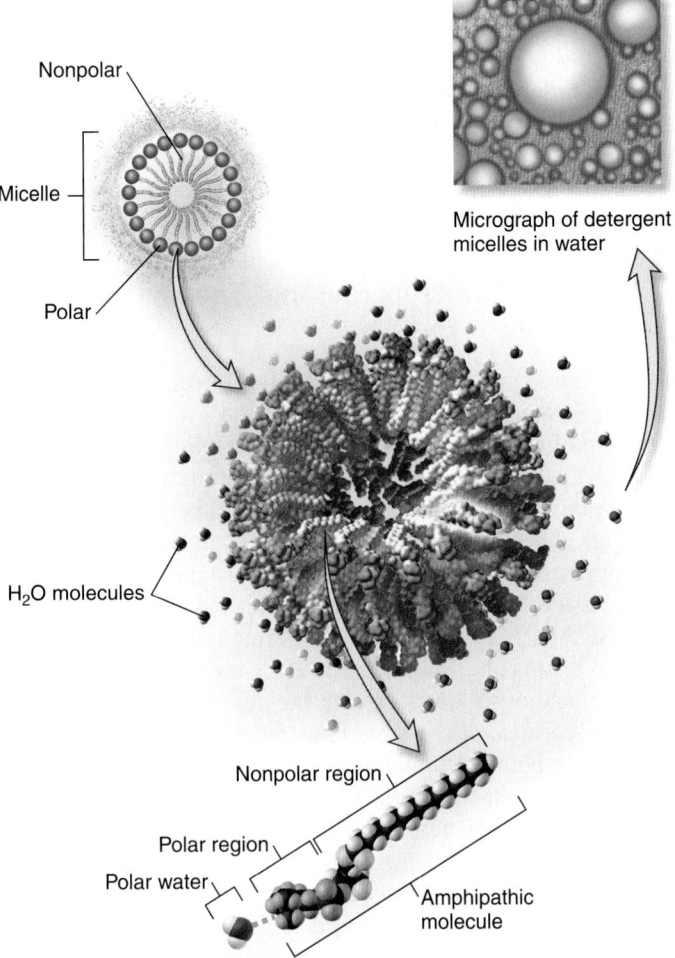

Figure 2.15 NaCl crystals dissolving in water. The ability of water to dissolve sodium chloride crystals depends on the electrical attraction between the polar water molecules and the charged sodium and chloride ions. Water molecules surround each ion as it becomes dissolved.

Principle: *Organisms follow the laws of chemistry and physics. Table salt, an ionic compound, dissolves readily in water because of water's ability to form ion–dipole interactions with it.*

Figure 2.16 The formation of micelles by amphipathic molecules. In water, amphipathic molecules tend to arrange themselves so their nonpolar regions are directed away from water molecules. The polar regions are directed toward the water and can form hydrogen bonds with it.

Such an arrangement minimizes the interaction between water molecules and the nonpolar ends of the amphipathic molecules. Instead of micelles, other amphipathic molecules form structures called bilayers. As you will learn in Chapter 5, lipid bilayers play a key role in membrane structure.

Water's properties drive structure as different biomolecules, with their hydrophilic or hydrophobic properties (or both), interact with H_2O within organisms.

Physical Properties of a Solvent Are Affected by Solute Concentration

Solute **concentration** is defined as the amount of a solute dissolved in a unit volume of solution. For example, if 1 g of NaCl is dissolved in enough water to make 1 litre (L) of solution, we say that its solute concentration is 1 g/L. A comparison of the concentrations of two different substances on the basis of the number of grams per litre of solution does not directly indicate how many molecules of each substance are present. For example, compare 10 g each of glucose ($C_6H_{12}O_6$) and sodium chloride (NaCl). Because the individual molecules of glucose have more mass than those of NaCl, 10 g of glucose will contain fewer molecules than 10 g of NaCl. Therefore, another way to describe solute concentration is according to the moles of dissolved solute per volume of solution. To make this calculation requires three things: the amount of dissolved solute, the molecular mass of the dissolved solute, and the volume of the solution.

The **mass** of a molecule is equal to the sum of the atomic mass of all the atoms in the molecule. For example, glucose ($C_6H_{12}O_6$) has a molecular mass of 180 ([6 × 12] + [12 × 1] + [6 × 16] = 180). As mentioned earlier, 1 mole (abbreviated mol) of a substance is the amount of the substance in grams equal to its atomic or molecular mass. The **molarity** of a solution is defined as the number of moles of a solute dissolved in 1 L of solution. A solution containing 180 g of glucose (1 mol) dissolved in enough water to make 1 L is a 1 molar solution of

glucose (1 mol/L). By convention, a 1 mol/L solution is usually written as 1 M, where the capital M stands for molar and is defined as mol/L. If 90 g of glucose (half its molecular mass) is dissolved in enough water to make 1 L, the solution has a concentration of 0.5 mol/L, or 0.5 M.

The concentrations of solutes dissolved in the fluids of living organisms are usually much less than 1 mol/L. Many have concentrations in the range of millimoles per litre (1 mM = 0.001 M = 10^{-3} M), while others are present in even smaller concentrations—micromoles per litre (1 M = 0.000001 M = 10^{-6} M) or nanomoles per litre (1 μM = 0.000000001 M = 10^{-9} M).

The temperature at which a solution freezes or vaporizes is influenced by the amounts of dissolved solutes. These are examples of **colligative properties**, which depend strictly on the concentration of dissolved solute particles, not on the specific type of particle. Pure water freezes at 0°C and vaporizes at 100°C. The addition of solutes to water lowers its freezing point below 0°C and raises its boiling point above 100°C. Adding a small amount of the compound ethylene glycol—antifreeze— to the water in your car's radiator, for instance, prevents the water from freezing in cold weather. Similarly, the presence of large amounts of solutes partly explains why the oceans do not freeze when the temperature falls below 0°C. Likewise, the colligative properties of water also account for the remarkable ability of certain animals that are unable to maintain warm body temperatures in cold environments, to nonetheless escape becoming frozen solid. Such cold-blooded animals produce antifreeze molecules that dissolve in their body fluids, thereby lowering the freezing point of the fluids and preventing their blood and cells from freezing in the extreme cold. The emerald rockcod (*Trematomus bernacchii*), found in the waters of Antarctica, for example, manages to live in ocean waters that are at or below 0°C (**Figure 2.17a**). Similarly, many insects, such as the larvae of the parasitic wasp (*Brachon cephi*), also make use of natural antifreeze to stay alive in extreme conditions (**Figure 2.17b**).

Figure 2.17 Antifreeze in living organisms. Many animals, such as **(a)** the emerald rockcod (*Trematomus bernacchii*) and **(b)** the larvae of the parasitic wasp (*Brachon cephi*), can withstand extremely cold temperatures.

(a) Emerald rockcod in the waters of Antarctica   **(b) Wasp larvae can withstand freezing temperatures**

Principle: *Living organisms interact with their environment. These organisms respond to the harsh conditions of their environment, buy adding natural antifreeze to their body fluids.*

Hydrogen Ion Concentrations Are Changed by Acids and Bases

Pure water has the ability to ionize to a very small extent into hydrogen ions (H^+) and hydroxide ions (OH^-). In pure water, the concentrations of H^+ and OH^- are each 10^{-7} mol/L, or 10^{-7} M. An inherent property of water is that the product of the concentrations of H^+ and OH^- is always 10^{-14} M at 25°C. Therefore, in pure water, $[H^+][OH^-] = [10^{-7}$ M$][10^{-7}$ M$] = 10^{-14}$ M. (The square brackets around the symbols for the hydrogen and hydroxide ions indicate concentration.)

When certain substances are dissolved in water, they may release or absorb H^+ or OH^-, thereby altering the relative concentrations of these ions. Molecules that release hydrogen ions in solution are called **acids**. Two examples are

$$HCl \quad \rightarrow \quad H^+ \; + \quad Cl^-$$
(hydrochloric acid)   (chloride)

$$H_2CO_3 \quad \rightleftharpoons \quad H^+ \; + \quad HCO_3^-$$
(carbonic acid)   (bicarbonate)

Hydrochloric acid is called a strong acid because it completely dissociates into H^+ and Cl^- when added to water. By comparison, carbonic acid is a weak acid because some of it will remain in the H_2CO_3 state when dissolved in water.

Compared with an acid, a **base** has the opposite effect when dissolved in water—it lowers the H^+ concentration. This can occur in different ways. Some bases, such as sodium hydroxide (NaOH), release OH^- when dissolved in water:

$$NaOH \rightarrow Na^+ + OH^-$$

Recall that the product of $[H^+]$ and $[OH^-]$ is always 10^{-14} M. When a base, such as NaOH, raises the OH^- concentration, some of the hydrogen ions bind to these hydroxide ions to form water. Therefore, increasing the OH^- concentration lowers the H^+ concentration. Alternatively, other bases, such as ammonia, react with water:

$$NH_3 \; + \; H_2O \quad \rightleftharpoons \quad NH_4^+ \; + \; OH^-$$
(ammonia)

Both NaOH and ammonia have the same effect: they lower the concentration of H^+. NaOH achieves this by directly increasing the OH^- concentration, while NH_3 reacts with water to produce OH^+. The addition of acids and bases to water can greatly change the H^+ and OH^- concentrations over a very broad range. Therefore, chemists and biologists use a log scale to describe the concentrations of these ions. The H^+ concentration is expressed as the solution's **pH**, which is defined as the negative logarithm to the base 10 of the H^+ concentration:

$$pH = -\log_{10}[H^+]$$

To understand what this equation means, consider a few examples. A solution with a H^+ concentration of 10^{-7} M has a pH of 7. A concentration of 10^{-7} M is the same as 0.1 μM. A solution in which $[H^+] = 10^{-6}$ M has a pH of 6. A

concentration of 10^{-6} M is the same as 1.0 μM. A solution at pH 6 is said to be more acidic, because the H^+ concentration is tenfold higher than a solution at pH 7. Note that as the acidity increases, the pH decreases. A solution in which the pH is 7 is said to be neutral because $[H^+]$ and $[OH^-]$ are equal. An acidic solution has a pH that is below 7, while an alkaline solution has a pH above 7. **Figure 2.18** considers the pH values of some familiar fluids.

Why is pH of importance to biologists? The answer lies in the observation that H^+ and OH^- can readily bind to many

Figure 2.18 The pH scale and the relative acidities of common substances. The pH scale (right) is a log scale based on the concentration of H^+ ions (left). As the H^+ concentration increases, the pH decreases, as can be visualized by the width of the middle region of the figure.

Concept check: *What is the OH^- concentration at pH 8?*

BioConnections: *Look ahead to Figure 4.5b. Only Archaea that can live at extreme pHs can survive in this river acidified from mining runoff.*

kinds of ions and molecules. For this reason, the pH of a solution can affect

- the shapes and functions of molecules
- the rates of many chemical reactions
- the ability of two molecules to bind to each other
- the ability of ions or molecules to dissolve in water

Because of the various effects of pH, many biological processes function best within very narrow ranges of pH, and even small shifts can have a negative effect. In living cells, the pH ranges from 6.5 to 7.8 and is carefully regulated to avoid major shifts in pH. The blood of the human body has a normal range of about pH 7.35 to 7.45 and is thus slightly alkaline. Certain diseases can reduce or increase blood pH by a few tenths of a unit. When this happens, the enzymes in the body needed for normal metabolism are rendered less functional, leading to illness and even death. As described next, living organisms have molecules called buffers to prevent such changes in pH.

Buffers Minimize Fluctuations in the pH of Fluids

What factors might alter the pH of an organism's fluids? External factors, such as acid rain and other forms of pollution, can reduce the pH of water entering the roots of plants. In animals, exercise generates lactic acid, and certain diseases can raise or lower the pH of blood.

Organisms have several ways to cope with changes in pH. Complex animals, such as mammals, for example, can use such structures as the kidney to secrete acidic or alkaline compounds into the bloodstream when the blood pH becomes imbalanced. Similarly, the kidneys can transfer hydrogen ions from the body into the urine and adjust the body's pH in that way. Another mechanism by which pH balance is regulated in diverse organisms involves the actions of acid–base buffers. An acid–base **buffer** is composed of a weak acid and its related base. One such buffer is the bicarbonate pathway:

$$CO_2 \; + \; H_2O \; \rightleftharpoons \; H_2CO_3 \; \rightleftharpoons \; H^+ \; + \; HCO_3^-$$
$$\text{(carbonic acid)} \qquad\qquad \text{(bicarbonate)}$$

This buffer system can work in both directions. If the pH of an animal's blood increased (that is, the H^+ concentration decreased), the bicarbonate pathway would proceed from left to right. CO_2 would combine with water to make carbonic acid, and then the carbonic acid would dissociate into H^+ and bicarbonate. This would raise the H^+ concentration and thereby lower the pH. Alternatively, when the pH of an animal's blood decreases, this pathway runs in reverse. Bicarbonate combines with H^+ to make carbonic acid, which then dissociates to carbon dioxide and water. This process removes H^+ from the blood, restoring it to its normal pH, and the CO_2 is exhaled from the lungs. Many buffers, including this example, exist in nature. Buffers found in living organisms are adapted to function most efficiently at the normal range of pH values seen in that organism.

Water Has Many Other Important Roles in Organisms

As discussed earlier, water is the primary solvent in the fluids of all living organisms, from unicellular bacteria to the largest Sequoia tree. Water permits atoms and molecules to interact in ways that would be impossible in their undissolved states. In Unit II we will consider myriad ions and molecules that are solutes in living cells. It is important to recognize that in addition to acting as a solvent, water serves many other remarkable functions that are critical for the survival of living organisms. For example, water molecules themselves take part in many chemical reactions of this general type:

$$R1\text{—}R2 + H\text{—}O\text{—}H \;\rightarrow\; R1\text{—}OH + H\text{—}R2$$

R is a general symbol to represent a group of atoms. In this equation, R1 and R2 are distinct groups of atoms. On the left side, R1—R2 is a compound in which the groups of atoms are connected by a covalent bond. To be converted to products, a covalent bond is broken in each reactant, R1—R2 and H—O—H, and OH and H (from water) form covalent bonds with R1 and R2, respectively. Reactions of this type are known as hydrolytic reactions (*hydro*, "water"; *lysis*, "break apart"), because water is used to break apart another molecule. This process is also called **hydrolysis** (**Figure 2.19a**). As discussed in later chapters, many large molecules are broken down into smaller units by hydrolysis. Alternatively, other chemical reactions in living organisms involve the removal of a water molecule so that a covalent bond can be formed between two separate molecules. For example, consider a chemical reaction that is the reverse of our previous hydrolytic reaction:

$$R1\text{—}OH + H\text{—}R2 \;\rightarrow\; R1\text{—}R2 + H\text{—}O\text{—}H$$

Such a reaction involves the removal of a water molecule and the formation of a covalent bond between two separate molecules. This is termed a **dehydration** or **condensation reaction**. As discussed in later chapters, this common reaction is used to build larger molecules in living organisms.

Another feature of water is that it is incompressible—its volume does not significantly decrease when subjected to high pressure. This has biological importance for many organisms that use water to provide force or support (**Figure 2.19b**). For example, water forms the so-called hydrostatic skeleton of worms and some other invertebrates, and it provides turgidity (stiffness) and support for plants.

Water is also the means by which unneeded and potentially toxic waste compounds are eliminated from an animal's body (**Figure 2.19c**). In mammals, for example, the kidneys filter out soluble waste products derived from the breakdown of proteins and other compounds. The filtered products remain in solution in the watery fluid, which eventually becomes urine and is excreted.

Water's high heat of vaporization has great biological significance. Although everyone is familiar with the fact that boiling water is converted to water vapour, water can vaporize into

(a) Water participates in chemical reactions.

Blood enters and is purified by kidney cells.

Waste products are carried away in the watery urine.

(c) Water is used to eliminate soluble wastes.

(b) Water provides support. The plant on the right is wilting due to lack of water.

(d) Evaporation helps animals dissipate body heat.

(e) The cohesive force of water molecules aids in the movement of fluid through vessels in plants.

(f) Water is an essential component of the lubricant that reduces friction between knee bones.

(g) The surface tension of water explains why this water strider doesn't sink.

Figure 2.19 Some amazing roles of water in biology. In addition to acting as a solvent, water serves many crucial functions in nature.

Principle: *Living organisms have mechanisms that maintain homeostasis. Healthy organisms have a normal supply of water that maintains such homeostatic functions as body temperature, salt balance, and waste levels.*

the gaseous state even at ordinary temperatures. This process is known as **evaporation**. The simplest way to understand evaporation is to imagine that in any volume of water at any temperature, some water molecules will have higher energy than others. Not every molecule is vibrating identically with the same energy. Those with highest energy escape into the gaseous state. The important point, however, is that even at ordinary temperatures, a large amount of energy must be absorbed by water to convert it to water vapour; this heat can come from organisms as water evaporates from its surfaces. Thus, evaporative cooling is an important mechanism by which organisms can cool themselves on hot days (**Figure 2.19d**).

The hydrogen-bonding properties of water affect its ability to form droplets and to adhere to surfaces. When the molecules within a substance tend to noncovalently attract each other, this phenomenon is called cohesion. Water exhibits strong cohesion because of hydrogen bonding. Cohesion aids in the movement of water through the vessels of plants (**Figure 2.19e**). A property that is similar to cohesion is adhesion, which refers to the ability of water to adhere to another surface. Water tends to cling to surfaces to which it can form hydrogen bonds. For this reason, water can coat the surfaces of the digestive tract of animals and act as a lubricant for the passage of food (**Figure 2.19f**). Surface tension is a measure of how difficult it is to break the interface between a liquid and air. In the case of water, the attractive force between hydrogen-bonded water molecules at the interface between water and air is what causes water to form droplets. The surface water molecules attract each other into a configuration (a sphere) that reduces the number of water molecules in contact with air. Likewise, surface tension allows certain insects, such as water striders, to walk on the surface of a pond without sinking (**Figure 2.19g**).

Summary of Key Concepts

2.1 Atoms

- Atoms are the smallest functional units of matter that form all chemical elements and that cannot be further broken down into other substances by ordinary chemical or physical means. Atoms are composed of protons (positive charge), electrons (negative charge), and neutrons (electrically neutral). Electrons are found in orbitals around the nucleus. (Table 2.1, Figures 2.1, 2.2, 2.3, 2.4)

- Each element contains a unique number of protons, its atomic number. The periodic table organizes all known elements by atomic number and energy shells. (Figure 2.5)

- Each atom has a small but measurable mass, measured in daltons. The atomic mass scale indicates an atom's mass relative to the mass of other atoms.

- Many atoms exist as isotopes, which differ in the number of neutrons they contain. Some isotopes are unstable radioisotopes and emit radiation.

- Four elements—oxygen, carbon, hydrogen, and nitrogen—account for the vast majority of atoms in living organisms. In addition, living organisms require mineral and trace elements that are essential for growth and function. (Table 2.2)

2.2 Chemical Bonds That Create and Stabilize Molecules

- A molecule consists of two or more atoms bonded together. The properties of a molecule are different from the properties of the atoms that combined to form it. A compound is composed of two or more different elements.

- Atoms tend to form bonds that fill their outer energy shell with electrons.

- Covalent bonds, in which atoms share electrons, are strong chemical bonds. Atoms form two covalent bonds—a double bond—when they share two pairs of electrons. (Figures 2.6, 2.7, 2.8)

- The electronegativity of an atom is a measure of its ability to attract bonded electrons. When two atoms with different electronegativities combine, the atoms form a polar covalent bond because the distribution of electrons around the atoms creates polarity, or a difference in electric charge, across the molecule. Polar molecules, such as water, are largely composed of polar bonds, while most nonpolar molecules are composed predominantly of nonpolar bonds. (Figure 2.9)

- If an atom or molecule gains or loses one or more electrons, it acquires a net electric charge and becomes an ion. The strong attraction between two oppositely charged ions forms an ionic bond. (Table 2.3, Figure 2.10)

- The three-dimensional, flexible shape of molecules allows them to interact and contributes to their biological properties. (Figures 2.11, 2.12)

- A free radical is an unstable molecule that interacts with other molecules by stealing electrons from their atoms.

2.3 Chemical Forces That Promote and Stabilize Molecular Interactions

- Van der Waal forces are a collection of forces that are weaker than covalent and ionic bonds. (Table 2.4)

- Van der Waal forces between neighbouring molecules are within different regions of the same molecule.

- One very important type of van der Waal force is hydrogen bonding, which can occur when the hydrogen of one polar molecule interacts with the oxygen, nitrogen, or fluorine of another polar molecule. (Figure 2.13)

- Van der Waal interactions are individually weak, but in large numbers they can be collectively strong and help biomolecules achieve their functional configurations. (Figure 2.13)

2.4 The Importance of Water and Its Physical and Chemical Properties

- Chemical reactions change compounds or elements into different compounds. All chemical reactions require energy. In living organisms, chemical reactions take place in a liquid environment, and many are readily reversible.

- H_2O on Earth exists as ice, water, and water vapour, but water's high heat of vaporization and high heat of fusion make it very stable in liquid form. Because of the unique crystalline structure of ice, it floats. Ice insulates bodies of water and snow insulates land. (Figure 2.14)

- Water (because of its polarity and ability to form hydrogen bonds with other molecules) is the solvent for chemical reactions in all organisms (Figure 2.15).

- Solutes dissolve in a solvent to form a solution. Solute concentration refers to the amount of a solute dissolved in a unit volume of solution. The molarity of a solution is defined as the number of moles of a solute dissolved in 1 L of solution.

- Polar molecules are hydrophilic, while nonpolar molecules are composed predominantly of carbon and hydrogen are hydrophobic. Amphipathic molecules, such as detergents, have polar and nonpolar regions. (Figure 2.16)

- The colligative properties of water allow it to function as antifreeze in certain organisms. (Figure 2.17)

- The pH of a solution refers to its hydrogen ion concentration. The pH of pure water is 7 (a neutral solution). Alkaline solutions have a pH higher than 7, and acidic solutions have a pH lower than 7. (Figure 2.18)

- Buffers are compounds that act to minimize pH fluctuations in the fluids of living organisms. Buffer systems can raise or lower pH as needed.

- Water molecules participate in many chemical reactions in living organisms. Hydrolysis breaks down large molecules into smaller units, and dehydration reactions combine two smaller molecules into one larger one. In living organisms, water provides support, is used to eliminate wastes, dissipates body heat, aids in the movement of liquid through vessels, and serves as a lubricant. Surface tension allows insects to walk on water. (Figure 2.19)

Test to Assess Your Learning

1. _____ make up the nucleus of an atom.
   a. Protons and electrons
   b. Protons and neutrons
   c. DNA and RNA
   d. Neutrons and electrons
   e. DNA only

2. Living organisms are composed mainly of
   a. calcium, hydrogen, nitrogen, and oxygen.
   b. carbon, hydrogen, nitrogen, and oxygen.
   c. hydrogen, nitrogen, oxygen, and helium.
   d. carbon, helium, nitrogen, and oxygen.
   e. carbon, calcium, hydrogen, and oxygen.

3. The ability of an atom to attract bonded electrons is
   a. polarity.
   b. electronegativity.
   c. solubility.
   d. valence.
   e. both (a) and (b).

4. Hydrogen bonds differ from covalent bonds in that
   a. covalent bonds can form between any type of atom, and hydrogen bonds only form between H and O.
   b. covalent bonds involve sharing of electrons and hydrogen bonds involve the complete transfer of electrons.
   c. covalent bonds result from equal sharing of electrons but hydrogen bonds involve unequal sharing of electrons.
   d. covalent bonds involve sharing of electrons between atoms, but hydrogen bonds are the result of weak attractions between a hydrogen atom of a polar molecule and an electronegative atom of another polar molecule.
   e. covalent bonds are weak bonds that break easily, but hydrogen bonds are strong links between atoms that are not easily broken.

5. A free radical
   a. is a positively charged ion.
   b. is an atom with one unpaired electron in its outer energy shell.

c. is a stable atom that is not bonded to another atom.
d. can cause considerable cellular damage.
e. both (b) and (d).

6. Chemical reactions in living organisms
   a. require energy to begin.
   b. usually require a catalyst to initiate the process.
   c. are usually reversible.
   d. occur in liquid environments, such as water.
   e. all of the above.

7. Solutes that easily dissolve in water are said to be
   a. hydrophobic.
   b. hydrophilic.
   c. polar molecules.
   d. all of the above.
   e. (b) and (c) only.

8. The sum of the atomic masses of all the atoms of a molecule is its
   a. atomic weight.
   b. molarity.
   c. molecular mass.
   d. concentration.
   e. polarity.

9. Reactions that involve water in the breaking apart of other molecules are known as _____ reactions.
   a. hydrophilic
   b. dehydration
   c. hydrophobic
   d. anabolic
   e. hydrolytic

10. A difference between a strong acid and a weak acid is
    a. strong acids have a higher molecular mass than weak acids.
    b. strong acids completely ionize in solution, but weak acids do not completely ionize in solution.
    c. strong acids give off two hydrogen ions per molecule, but weak acids only give off one hydrogen ion per molecule.
    d. strong acids are water-soluble, but weak acids are not.
    e. strong acids give off hydrogen ions and weak acids give off hydroxyl groups.

Articulate to Assess Your Learning

1. Describe the types of bonds that are commonly found in and between biological molecules. Describe them in order of their bond strength.

2. Distinguish among the terms *hydrophobic, hydrophilic,* and *amphiphatic.*

3. Distinguish between the bonds that connect hydrogen to oxygen *within one* H_2O molecule, to the type of bond that forms between the hydrogen and oxygen of neighbouring H_2O molecules in water.

4. In a cell, which reaction would require more energy: breaking one covalent bond or disrupting five hydrogen bonds? Defend your answer with a numerical analysis.

5. Describe how you think lemon juice or beer acts as a meat tenderizer.

6. Antacid tablets are often composed of calcium carbonate. How do you think they work?

Collaborate to Assess and Extend Your Learning

1. Create a concept map that includes all the special properties of water and relate it to the following terms: hydrogen bonding, heat of fusion, heat of vaporization, specific heat, cohesion, adhesion, solvent, ionic molecules, polar molecules, hydrophilic, hydrophobic, amphiphatic, and structure.

2. Use the colligative properties of water to explain why roads are salted during the winter. When would salting be ineffective?

3. A common saying is that "life on Earth is carbon-based." Consider the number of electrons in the outer energy shell of carbon, and discuss the properties that make it an excellent element for producing large, complex biological molecules. If Earth had only trace amounts of carbon, which element do you think might have served a similar purpose? Justify your answer.

4. Organisms follow the laws of chemistry and physics, and structure determines function. Explain the importance of buffers within organisms.

Visit McGraw-Hill Ryerson Connect™ for additional study resources.

The Chemical Basis of Life II:
Organic Molecules

3

Potatoes and parsley are both loaded with complex carbohydrates but have very different amounts of stored, accessible energy.

Chapter Outline

In Chapter 2, we learned that all life is composed of subatomic particles that form atoms, which in turn combine to form molecules. Molecules can be simple in composition, as in hydrogen gas (H_2) or water (H_2O), or can bind with other molecules to form larger molecules. Of the countless possible molecules that can be produced from the known elements in nature, life forms on Earth are rich in molecules with carbon. These carbon-containing molecules are collectively referred to as **organic molecules**, so named because they were first discovered in living organisms. Among these are the lipids and large, complex compound called **macromolecules**, which include carbohydrates, proteins, and nucleic acids. In this chapter we will survey the structures of these molecules and examine their chief functions. We begin by examining carbon, the element whose chemical properties are fundamental to the formation of biologically important molecules.

3.1 THE CARBON ATOM AND THE STUDY OF ORGANIC MOLECULES

Learning Outcomes:

1. Explain the properties of carbon that make it the chemical basis of all life.
2. Appreciate the chemical characteristics of common functional groups of organic compounds.
3. Understand the differences between isomeric compounds.

The science of studying carbon-containing molecules is known as organic chemistry. Before the eighteenth century, the study of organic molecules was considered a fruitless endeavour because of a concept called **vitalism** that persisted into the nineteenth century. Vitalism held that organic molecules were created by, and therefore imparted with, a vital life force contained within a plant or an animal's body. Supporters of vitalism argued there was no point in trying to synthesize an organic compound, because such molecules could arise only through the intervention of mysterious qualities associated with life. This all changed with the pioneering experiments of Friedrich Wöhler in 1828.

Wöhler's Synthesis of an Organic Compound Transformed Misconceptions About Life's Molecules

Friedrich Wöhler was a German physician and chemist interested in the properties of inorganic and organic compounds, including urea. Urea is found in urine; it is a natural organic product formed from the breakdown of proteins in an animal's body. In mammals, urea accumulates in the urine, which is formed by the kidneys, and then is excreted from the body. During his studies, Wöhler purified urea from mammalian urine. He noted the colour, size, shape, and other characteristics of the crystals that formed when urea was isolated (**Figure 3.1**). This experience would serve him well in later years when he quite accidentally helped put the concept of vitalism to rest.

In 1828 Wöhler attempted to synthesize an inorganic molecule, ammonium cyanate (NH_4OCN). Instead, Wöhler discovered, to his surprise, that ammonia and cyanic acid reacted to produce a third compound that, when heated, formed familiar-looking crystals (Figure 3.1). After careful analysis, he concluded that these crystals were, in fact, urea. He announced to the scientific community that he had synthesized urea, an organic compound, "without the use of kidneys, either man or dog." This study was a major breakthrough in the way in

Figure 3.1 Crystals of urea.

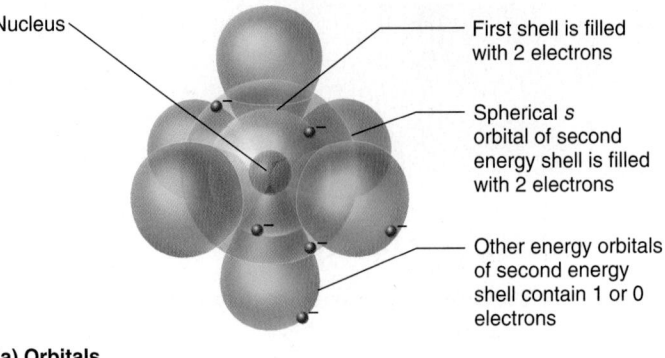

(a) Orbitals

which scientists viewed life and began the field of organic chemistry. From that time to the present, the fields of chemistry and biology have been viewed as intricately related. Urea and acetic acid, like all organic compounds, contain carbon atoms bound to other atoms. Let's now consider the chemical features that make carbon such an important element in living organisms.

Carbon Forms Four Covalent Bonds with Other Atoms

One of the properties of the carbon atom that makes life possible is its ability to form four covalent bonds with other atoms, including other carbon atoms. This occurs because carbon has four valence electrons in its outer energy shell, and it needs four additional electrons for its outer shell to be full (**Figure 3.2**). In living organisms, carbon atoms most commonly form covalent bonds with other carbons and with hydrogen, oxygen, nitrogen, and sulphur atoms. Bonds between two carbon atoms, between carbon and oxygen, or between carbon and nitrogen can be single or double bonds. The ability of carbon to bond with another carbon and up to three other atoms allows a vast number of organic compounds to be formed from only a few chemical elements. Carbon bonds can also occur in configurations that are linear, ringlike, or highly branched. Such a variety of molecular shapes produces molecules with a variety of functions.

Because carbon and hydrogen have similar electronegativities, carbon–carbon and carbon–hydrogen bonds are nonpolar. As a consequence, molecules with predominantly hydrogen–carbon bonds, called **hydrocarbons**, tend to be hydrophobic and not very soluble in water. In contrast, when carbon forms polar covalent bonds with oxygen or nitrogen, for example, the molecule is much more soluble in water because of the electrical attraction of polar water molecules. The ability of carbon to form both polar and nonpolar bonds contributes to its ability to serve as the backbone for an astonishing variety of molecules (**Figure 3.3**).

Another feature of carbon that is important to biology is that carbon bonds are stable at the different temperatures associated with life. This property arises in part because the carbon atom is very small compared with most other atoms, and

(b) Simplified depiction of carbon's electron shells

Figure 3.2 Models for the electron orbitals and energy shells of carbon.   Carbon atoms have only four electrons in their outer (second) energy shell, which allows carbon to form four covalent bonds. When carbon forms four covalent bonds, the result is four hybrid orbitals of equal energy called *sp*3 orbitals.

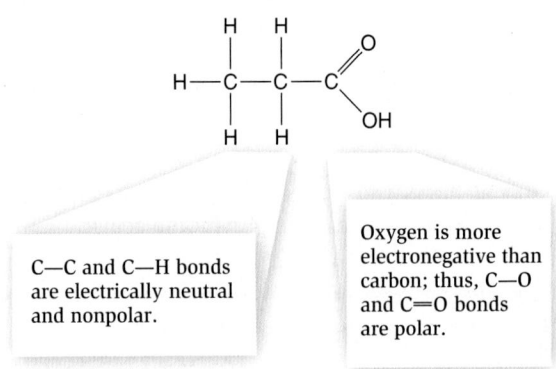

C—C and C—H bonds are electrically neutral and nonpolar.

Oxygen is more electronegative than carbon; thus, C—O and C=O bonds are polar.

Figure 3.3 Nonpolar and polar bonds in the organic molecule propionic acid.   Carbon can form both nonpolar and polar bonds, and single and double bonds.

Concept check: *Do you think propionic acid would dissolve in water?*

therefore the distance between carbon atoms forming a carbon–carbon bond is quite short. Shorter bonds tend to be stronger and more stable than longer bonds between two large atoms.

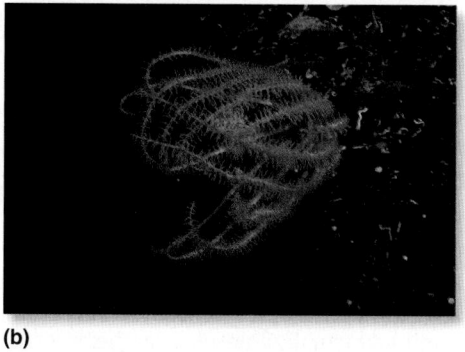

(a)

(b)

Figure 3.4 The stability of carbon bonds makes life possible even in extreme environments. (a) This isopod was found in the Weddell Sea of Antarctica. (b) Deep-sea vents can reach temperatures greater than 345°C. Such organisms as the brisingid sea stars in the Lau Basin of the South Pacific can live at these vent systems.

Table 3.1	Biologically Important Functional Groups That May Be Present in Organic Molecules	
Functional group	**Formula/ properties***	**Examples of where found†**
Amino	$\begin{array}{c} H \\ | \\ R-\overset{+}{N}-H \\ | \\ H \end{array}$	Amino acids (proteins)
Carbonyl‡	$\begin{array}{c} O \\ \| \\ R-C-R' \end{array}$	Steroids, eicosanoids, waxes, proteins
Ketone		Glucose, glyceraldehyde
Aldehyde	$\begin{array}{c} O \\ \| \\ R-C-H \end{array}$	
Carboxyl	$R-C\overset{O}{\underset{OH}{\diagdown}}$	Amino acids, fatty acids
Hydroxyl	$R-OH$	Steroids, alcohol, carbohydrates, some amino acids
Methyl	$\begin{array}{c} H \\ | \\ R-C-H \\ | \\ H \end{array}$	May be attached to DNA, proteins, carbohydrates
Phosphate	$\begin{array}{c} O \\ \| \\ R-O-P-O^- \\ | \\ O^- \end{array}$	Nucleic acids, ATP, attached to amino acids
Sulphate	$\begin{array}{c} O \\ \| \\ R-O-S-O^- \\ \| \\ O \end{array}$	May be attached to carbohydrates, proteins, lipids
Sulphhydryl	$R-SH$	Proteins that contain the amino acid cysteine

* The letters R and RN are used to represent the other atoms or molecules that are attached to the functional groups. The chemical structure of R and RN varies.
†This list contains many of the functional groups that are important in biology; however, many more functional groups have been identified by biochemists.
‡A carbonyl group is C=O. When the carbon is linked to a free hydrogen atom, this is an aldehyde. In a ketone, the carbon forms covalent bonds with two other carbon atoms.

Thus, carbon bonds are compatible with what we observe about life today: namely that living organisms can inhabit environments ranging from the Earth's icy poles to deep-sea vents (**Figure 3.4**).

Carbon Atoms Can Bond to Several Biologically Important Functional Groups

Most organic molecules and macromolecules contain **functional groups**—groups of atoms with special chemical features that contribute to the molecules' properties. Each type of functional group exhibits the same properties in all molecules in which it occurs. **Table 3.1** describes examples of functional groups that are found in many different types of organic molecules. We will discuss each of these groups throughout this textbook.

Carbon-Containing Molecules Can Exist in Multiple Forms Called Isomers

When Wöhler did his famous experiment, he was surprised to discover that urea, $(NH_2)_2CO$, and ammonium cyanate, NH_4OCN, apparently contained the same ratio of carbons, nitrogens, hydrogens, and oxygens, yet they were different molecules

with distinct chemical and biological properties. Two structures with an identical molecular formula but different structures and characteristics are called **isomers**.

Figure 3.5 depicts three ways in which isomers can occur. **Structural isomers** contain the same atoms but in different bonding relationships (**Figure 3.5a**) and hence have different properties. Wöhler's compounds fall into this category. **Stereoisomers** have identical bonding relationships, but the spatial positioning of the atoms differs in the two isomers. Two types of stereoisomers are geometric isomers and enantiomers. In **geometric isomers**, such as those shown in **Figure 3.5b**, the two hydrogen atoms linked to the two carbons of a C=C double bond may be on the same side of the carbons (Figure 3.5b, top left), in which case the C=C bond is called a *cis* double bond. If the hydrogens are on opposite sides (Figure 3.5b, top right), it is a *trans* double bond. *Cis* and *trans* stereoisomers can have very different chemical properties. For instance, the light-sensitive region of your eye contains a molecule called retinal, which can exist in either a *cis* or a *trans* form because of a pair of double-bonded carbons in its string of carbon atoms. In darkness, the *cis* form predominates. The energy of sunlight, however, causes retinal to isomerize to

(a) Structural isomers

(b) Two types of stereoisomers

Figure 3.5 **Types of isomers.** Isomers are compounds with the same molecular formula but different structures. The differences in structure, though small, are sufficient to result in very different biological properties.

the *trans* form. Only *trans*-retinal activates the light-capturing cells in the eye.

A second category of stereoisomers, **enantiomers**, exist as a pair of molecules that are mirror images. Four different atoms can bind to a single carbon atom in two possible ways, designated as a left-handed and a right-handed structure. If the resulting structures are not identical but instead are mirror images of each other, the molecules are enantiomers (Figure 3.5b, bottom). A pair of enantiomers share identical chemical properties, such as solubility and melting point; however, because of the different orientation of atoms in space, their ability to noncovalently bind to other molecules, such as proteins, can be strikingly different. For example, the right-handed form of glucose, called D-glucose, binds very well to certain enzymes in living cells, while the left-handed form, L-glucose, binds poorly. Most enzymes recognize only one member of an enantiomer pair, not both.

3.2 CLASSES OF ORGANIC MOLECULES AND MACROMOLECULES

Learning Outcomes:

1. Understand how small molecules can be assembled into larger molecules by dehydration reactions and how hydrolysis reactions can reverse this process.
2. List the four major classes of organic molecules and macromolecules found in living organisms.

As you have seen, organic molecules have various shapes because of the bonding properties of carbon. Many of these compounds are relatively small molecules, containing a few or a few dozen atoms. However, some organic molecules are extremely large macromolecules composed of thousands or even millions of atoms. Four major categories of macromolecules are found within organisms: lipids, carbohydrates, nucleic acids (DNA and RNA), and proteins. The last three are often found as polymers. **Polymers** are large molecules formed by the linkage of many smaller molecules (building blocks) called **monomers**. The structure and function of each type of macromolecule depends on the nature of its monomers, the number of monomers linked together, and the three-dimensional way in which the monomers are linked.

A **condensation reaction** is one in which two or more molecules combine into a larger one, with the loss of a small molecule. When the lost molecule is water, we call this specific type of condensation reaction a **dehydration reaction**. An idealized dehydration reaction is illustrated in **Figure 3.6a**. Notice that the length of a polymer can be extended repeatedly with additional dehydration reactions. Some polymers can reach great lengths by this mechanism. For example, human DNA occurs in polymers with millions of monomer units.

Cells often need to break a polymer into its monomer units. The process by which a polymer is broken down into monomers is called a **hydrolysis reaction**, because a molecule of water is

A polymer begins as two monomers combine in a dehydration reaction.

Elongation of the polymer continues with additional dehydration reactions.

The final length of a polymer may consist of thousands of monomers.

(a) Polymer formation by dehydration reactions

Polymers are broken down one monomer at a time by hydrolysis reactions.

(b) Breakdown of a polymer by hydrolysis reactions

Figure 3.6 Formation and breakdown of polymers. (a) Monomers combine to form polymers in living organisms by dehydration reactions, in which a molecule of water is removed each time a new monomer is added to the growing polymer. (b) Polymers can be broken down into their constituent monomers by hydrolysis reactions, in which a molecule of water is added each time a monomer is released.

added back each time a monomer is released (**Figure 3.6b**). Our digestion of food has many hydrolytic reactions as polymers of carbohydrates and proteins are broken into their monomer units. Dehydration and hydrolysis reactions within cells are both catalyzed by enzymes.

3.3 CARBOHYDRATES INCLUDE SIMPLE SUGARS AND POLYMERS COMPOSED OF SUGAR MONOMERS

Learning Outcomes:

1. Distinguish among different forms of carbohydrate molecules, including monosaccharides, disaccharides, and polysaccharides.
2. Relate the functions of plant and animal polysaccharides to their structure.

Carbohydrates are composed of carbon, hydrogen, and oxygen atoms in the proportions represented by the general formula $Cn(H_2O)n$, where n is a whole number. Most of the carbon atoms in a carbohydrate are linked to a hydrogen atom and a hydroxyl (OH) group; the prevalence of the OH groups with their polar covalent bonds makes carbohydrates soluble in water. Other functional groups, such as amino and carboxyl groups, are also found in certain carbohydrates.

Sugars

Sugars are small carbohydrates that may taste sweet. The simplest sugars are the **monosaccharides**, which consist of a single monomer unit. The most common types are those with five carbons, called pentoses, or six carbons, called hexoses. Important pentoses are ribose ($C_5H_{10}O_5$) and the closely related deoxyribose ($C_5H_{10}O_4$), which are part of RNA and DNA molecules, respectively. The most common hexose is glucose ($C_6H_{12}O_6$); it is an essential sugar present in cells. It is produced by photosynthetic organisms and used by them and by the organisms that eat them. Cells can use enzymes to break down glucose and some of the energy released in this process is used to make many molecules of ATP (adenosine triphosphate), which powers a variety of cellular processes. In this way, glucose is often used indirectly as a source of energy by living organisms.

Figure 3.7a illustrates two traditional ways of depicting the bonds between atoms in a monosaccharide. The ring structure is a better approximation of the true shape of the molecule in solution, with the carbon atoms numbered by convention as shown. The ring is made from the linear structure as the fifth carbon's oxygen atom forms a bond with the first carbon. Hydrogen atoms and the hydroxyl groups can lie above or below the plane of a particular carbon-ring structure.

Figure 3.7b compares different types of isomers of glucose. Glucose can exist as D-glucose and L-glucose, which are mirror-image enantiomers. Other types of isomers have the relative positions of the hydrogens and hydroxyl groups changed along the sugar ring. For example, glucose exists in two interconvertible

(a) Linear and ring structures of α-D-glucose

(b) Isomers of glucose

Figure 3.7   Monosaccharide structure.   (a) A comparison of the linear and ring structures of glucose. In solution, such as the fluids of organisms, nearly all glucose is in the ring form. (b) Isomers of glucose. Glucose exists as stereoisomers designated α- and β-glucose, which differ in the position of the OH group attached to carbon atom number 1. Glucose and galactose differ in the position of the OH group attached to carbon atom number 4. Enantiomers of glucose, called D-glucose and L-glucose, are mirror images of each other. D-glucose is the form that is used by living cells. Note: The letters *D* and *L* are derived from dextrorotatory (rotating to the right) and levorotatory (rotating to the left).

Concept check: *With regard to their binding to enzymes, why do enantiomers, such as D-glucose and L-glucose, have different biological properties?*

forms. For α-glucose the first carbon's hydroxyl group lies on the opposite side of the ring as the sixth carbon (Figure 3.7a); for β-glucose it lies on the same side (Figure 3.7b).

The side on which the hydroxyl group lies may seem a mere detail, but these types of small differences can have a large impact on the biological function of the molecule in the organism. These different isoforms of glucose have different biological properties and can be used to make complex polysaccharides with very different functions in organisms.

Monosaccharides can join together to form larger carbohydrates. **Disaccharides** are carbohydrates composed of two monosaccharides. The linking of most monosaccharides involves the removal of a hydroxyl group from one monosaccharide and a hydrogen atom from the other, and the bonding of the two sugars together through an oxygen atom. This occurs through a dehydration reaction. The bond formed between two sugar molecules is called a **glycosidic bond**. Glucose can form either α or β glycosidic linkages. This distinction is based on whether the glucose molecule that bonds its first carbon in the glycosidic linkage is α-glucose (forming an α-glycosidic linkage) or β-glucose (forming a β-glycosidic linkage). A familiar disaccharide

is sucrose (table sugar), which is composed of α-glucose and fructose linked by an α-glycosidic linkage between the first carbon of α-glucose and the fructose (**Figure 3.8**). Other disaccharides frequently found in nature are maltose and lactose. Maltose is formed in the intestinal tract of animals during the digestion of larger carbohydrates. In maltose α-D-glucose is linked at its first carbon to β-D-glucose at its fourth carbon to yield an α-1,4 glycosidic linkage. Lactose is present in the milk of mammals and consists of β-D-galactose linked to β-D-glucose. Hydrolysis can break the glycosidic bonds of disaccharides by adding water, thus uncoupling the two monosaccharides. By using enzymes or acids, cells can quickly break disaccharides, such as sucrose, maltose, and lactose, to generate glucose.

Polysaccharides

Many monosaccharides can be successively linked to form long polymers, called **polysaccharides**. Starch is the common name of the storage polysaccharide found in plants. Plant starch consists of two polysaccharides: amylose and amylopectin. Amylose can pack itself more tightly than amylopectin because it can form a helical structure or linear chains. Amylopectin readily forms branched structures. Plants typically have about 30% amylose and 70% amylopectin, but some plants, such as Russett potatoes or long-grain rice, have higher levels of amylose. Glycogen is found in animal cells. Glycogen and starch are examples of polysaccharides that are composed of thousands of α-D-glucose molecules connected by α-glycosidic linkages to form long branched chains, differing only in the extent of

Figure 3.8   Formation of a disaccharide. Two monosaccharides can bond to form a disaccharide. Shown here, the first carbon of α-glucose is bonded with fructose through a dehydration reaction to create sucrose.

branching along the chain (**Figure 3.9**). The α-glycosidic linkages facilitate branching. Both starch and glycogen can readily have individual glucose molecules removed by hydrolysis, providing an efficient source of glucose.

Other polysaccharides provide a structural role, rather than storing energy, and this is reflected in their different structure. The plant polysaccharide **cellulose** is a polymer of β-glucose held by β-glycosidic linkages. As a result of the β-glycosidic linkages, branching is not readily done; instead a linear arrangement of carbon–carbon bonds occurs (Figure 3.9).

The unbranched, linear fibres of adjacent cellulose molecules can be very closely packed and form hydrogen bonds between the multiple hydroxyl groups on the glucose molecules of one chain and the oxygen molecules on a neighbouring chain. The linear structure and large number of hydrogen bonds hold neighbouring cellulose fibres firmly together and form cellulose aggregates (microfibrils) that have high tensile strength. Because of the tight packing the microfibrils can form stabilizing van der Waal interactions, and most of the glucose molecules are not readily accessible for hydrolysis. Thus, cellulose

Figure 3.9 **Polysaccharides that are polymers of glucose.** These polysaccharides differ in their arrangement, extent of branching, and type of glucose isomer. Starch and glycogen use α-glucose and readily form branched structures. This allows easy access to glucose molecules to meet the organism's energy needs. For cellulose, β-glucose molecules are used. This allows the ready formation of extensive hydrogen bonds between neighbouring fibres to produce tough fibres that can support plants.

Principle: *Structure determines function, and living organisms use energy. Starch and glycogen, because of their structure, are readily used as energy sources. In contrast cellulose's structure is better suited for structural support.*

BioConnections: *Look ahead to Figure 5.20 to get a sense of the large amount of biomass associated with plant cell walls. Considering the amount of plant life on earth, what might you conclude about the abundance of cellulose on the planet?*

is ill suited for energy storage but is wonderfully suited for providing structural support. Cellulose is the major structural component of the primary cell wall of plants, algae, and some protists. Approximately 33% of plant biomass consists of cellulose. Some bacteria also secrete cellulose to encase themselves in a protective biofilm. Because cellulose is such a major structural component of plants and plants are so plentiful on Earth, cellulose is the most abundant organic molecule on our planet.

Starch and cellulose are good examples of the significance of isomers and bond types. A simple change in bond orientation of glucose molecules, namely α versus β, dramatically alters the biological properties of the resultant polymers. The photograph in the chapter opener evokes a strong sense of this. The potato is loaded with starch and is a good source of energy. The parsley garnish has almost no starch but is loaded with cellulose and is there only for flavour and vitamins.

Some bacteria within the gastrointestinal tracts of grass and wood eaters can digest cellulose into usable monosaccharides, because they contain an enzyme that can hydrolyze β-glucose bonds. We lack this enzyme and eliminate most of the cellulose ingested in our diet. Nonetheless, cellulose is quite important to humans, being a major source of insoluble dietary fibre and the major component of paper, cardboard, and cotton and linen fibres.

Polysaccharides play structural roles in some animals too. Chitin, a tough, structural polysaccharide, forms the external skeleton of many insects and the cell walls of fungi. The sugar monomers within chitin have nitrogen-containing groups attached to them. Glycosaminoglycans (GAGs), which have amino acids and sulphate groups attached to polysaccharides, are another category of polysaccharide with structural roles in animals. GAGs are a major component of connective tissues, such as cartilage and tendons.

3.4 LIPIDS ARE MOSTLY HYDROPHOBIC AND ARE HETEROGENEOUS IN STRUCTURE AND FUNCTION

Learning Outcomes:

1. List the different classes of lipid molecules that are important in living organisms.
2. Understand the structure of triglycerides and how the structure and melting point are affected by the presence of saturated and unsaturated fatty acids.
3. Discuss why fats function more efficiently than carbohydrates as energy-storage molecules.
4. Relate phospholipid's structure to its ability to form bilayers in aqueous environments.
5. Describe the chemical nature of steroids and give two examples of their biological function.

Lipids are molecules composed predominantly of hydrogen and carbon atoms held together by nonpolar covalent bonds. They do not interact with water (which has polar covalent bonds) and are therefore insoluble in water. This hydrophobicity is their unifying characteristic. Lipids account for about 40% of the organic matter in the average human body and include fats, phospholipids, and steroids.

Fats

Fats are a mixture of **triglycerides**, also known as **triacylglycerols**. Fats consist of glycerol bonded to three fatty acids (**Figure 3.10**). A fatty acid is a chain of carbon and hydrogen

Glycerol · Three fatty acids · Triglyceride (fat)

Figure 3.10   The formation of a fat.   The formation of a triglyceride requires three dehydration reactions in which fatty acids are bonded to glycerol and three H_2O molecules are released.

 Principle: *Living organisms use energy.*   *Fats are a major source of stored energy that organisms can use to do work.*

atoms with a carboxyl group at the end. Because the carboxyl group (COOH) releases an H^+ in water to become COO^+, these molecules are called fatty acids. Each of the three hydroxyl groups (OH) in glycerol is linked to the carboxyl group of a fatty acid by the removal of a molecule of water in a dehydration reaction. The resulting covalent bonds are each called an ester bond.

The fatty acids found in fats and other lipids can differ in length and in the presence of double bonds. Fatty acids are synthesized by the linking of two carbon fragments. Therefore, most fatty acids in nature have an even number of carbon atoms, with 16- and 18-carbon fatty acids being the most common in the cells of plants and animals. When all the carbons in a fatty acid are linked by single covalent bonds, the fatty acid is said to be a **saturated fatty acid**, because all the carbons are saturated with covalently bound hydrogen. A fatty acids containing one or more carbon–carbon double bonds is known as an **unsaturated fatty acid**. A fatty acid with one carbon–carbon double bond is a monounsaturated fatty acid, while two or more double bonds constitute a polyunsaturated fatty acid (**Figure 3.11**). Certain fatty acids are necessary for good health; organisms, including humans, who cannot make the required fatty acids must obtain them their diet. These fats are called **essential fatty acids**.

Most unsaturated fats have the hydrogen atoms in the *cis-*position, on the same side of carbon's double bond; **trans fats** are monounsaturated fat isomers or polyunsaturated fats that have the hydrogens in the *trans-* position, on opposite sides of the double bond. Trans fats are rare in nature but are a common by-product of the industrial hydrogenation of fats. The location of the hydrogen in trans fats is important; unsaturated fats, in general, are considered healthful fats, but trans fats are not. Both trans fats and saturated fats affect cholesterol metabolism in ways that are detrimental to health.

Fats that contain high amounts of saturated fatty acids or trans fats have high melting points, and therefore tend to be solid at room temperature. Conversely, fats high in unsaturated fatty acid usually have low melting points and thus are liquids at lower temperatures. Such fats are called oils. Animal fats generally contain a high proportion of saturated fatty acids, whereas vegetable oils contain more unsaturated fatty acids.

Like starch and glycogen, fats are important for storing energy. Cells have evolved metabolic pathways that can use the stored bond energy to do work. The hydrolysis of triglycerides releases the fatty acids from glycerol, and the fatty acids can be metabolized to provide energy. The energy of a C—H bond is larger than that of a C—OH bond, and triglycerides have a

Oleic acid

Oleic acid is a *cis* unsaturated fatty acid that composes 55–80% of olive oil.

Elaidic acid

Elaidic acid is a *trans* unsaturated fatty acid often found in partially hydrogenated vegetable oils.

Linoleic acid

Linoleic acid is a polyunsaturated fatty acid that composes 45–75% of sunflower oil.

Stearic acid

Stearic acid is a saturated fatty acid found in animal fats and is the intended product in hydrogenation.

Figure 3.11 **Examples of fatty acids.** The double bonds of unsaturated fats (e.g., oleic acid and linoleic acid) create bends in the structure. In contrast straight hydrocarbon tails are produced in trans fats (e.g., elaidic acid) and saturated fats (e.g., stearic acid).

Concept check: *Fats called shortenings are used in baking. They are solid at room temperature. Shortenings are often manufactured from vegetable oils by a process called hydrogenation. What do you think happens to the structure of an oil when it is hydrogenated?*

greater proportion of these than do carbohydrates. One gram of fat stores twice the energy of 1 g of glycogen or starch because it contains more energy-rich bonds. In animals, fats can also play a structural role by forming cushions that support organs, and fats provide insulation under the skin that helps protect terrestrial animals during cold weather and marine mammals in cold water.

Phospholipids

Another class of lipids, **phospholipids**, is similar in structure to triglycerides but with one important difference. The third hydroxyl group of glycerol is linked to a phosphate group instead of to a fatty acid. In most phospholipids, a small polar or charged nitrogen-containing molecule is attached to this phosphate (**Figure 3.12**). These groups constitute a polar hydrophilic (water-loving) region at one end of the phospholipid. At the opposite end is the nonpolar, hydrophobic (water-fearing) fatty acid chains. Phospholipids are thus **amphipathic.** In water the amphipathic nature of phospholipids allow them to organize into bilayers, with their polar ends facing out, interacting with water, and their nonpolar ends facing one other in the interior (Figure 3.12). This bilayer arrangement of phospholipids is critical for determining the structure of plasma membranes (Chapter 4).

Steroids

Steroids have a distinctly different chemical structure from that of the other types of lipid molecules. Four fused rings of carbon atoms form the skeleton of all steroids (**Figure 3.13a**). A few polar hydroxyl groups may be attached to this ring structure, but they are not numerous enough to make a steroid highly water soluble. Steroids with a hydroxyl group are known as sterols. Sterols are important components of cellular membranes: sitosterol, stigmasterol, and 24-methylcholesterol in plants and cholesterol in animals.

Cholesterol also is found in the blood of animals, where, if present in excess, it can contribute to the formation of clots that can block major blood vessels. Because cholesterol biosynthesis is linked to fat metabolism, a diet rich in unsaturated fats, and low in trans fats and saturated fats, produces more healthful levels of cholesterols. The development of the monosaturated oil known as canola oil is a Canadian success story. The natural oil of *Brassica napa* and *rapus* is monosaturated and contains essential fatty acids, but it is high in the undesirable compounds eurcic acid and glucosinalate. Through a plant-breeding program, Canadian plant breeders Keith Downey and Baldur Stefansson reduced these undesirable components to produce a pleasant-tasting and healthful vegetable oil that they named canola, which stands for <u>Can</u>adian <u>oi</u>l <u>l</u>ow <u>ac</u>id.

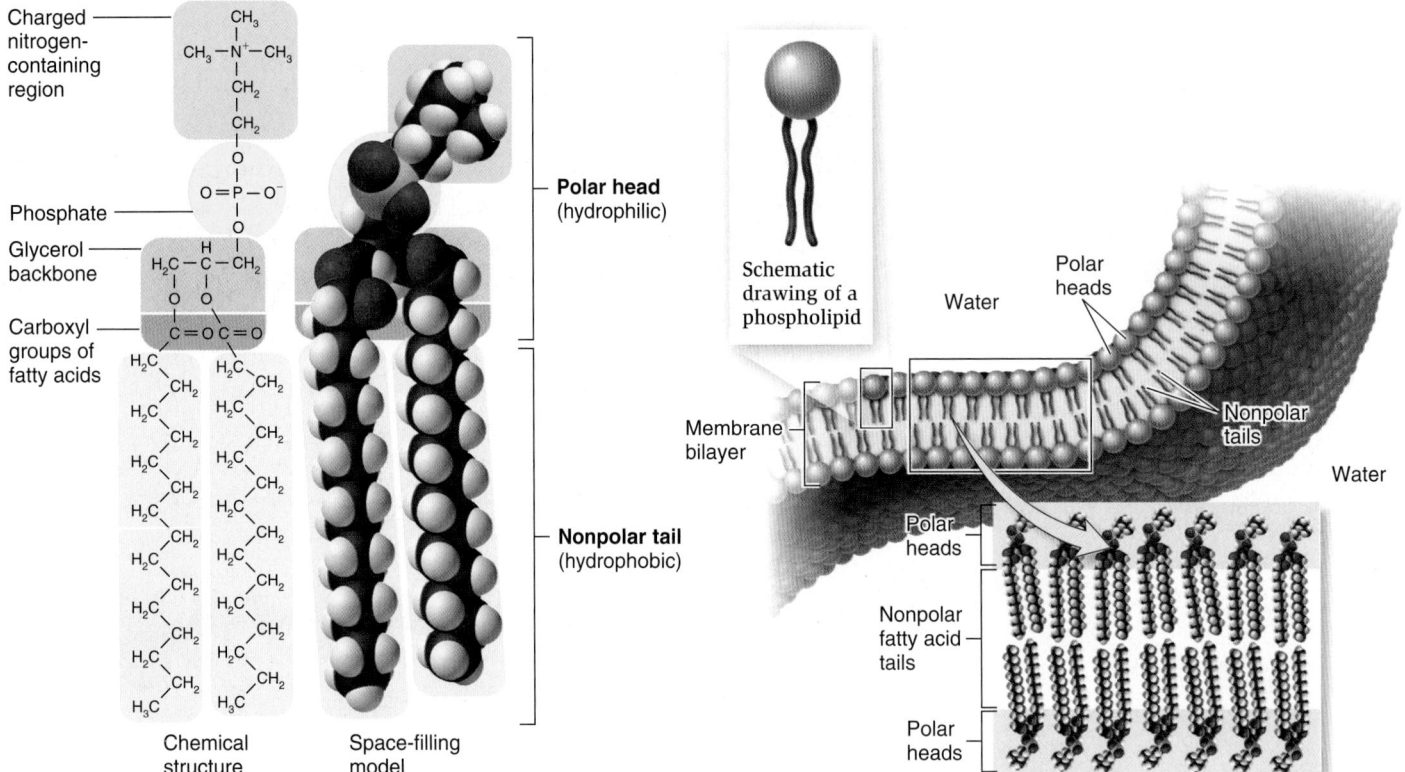

(a) Structure and model of a phospholipid

(b) Arrangement of phospholipids in a bilayer

Figure 3.12 **Structure of phospholipids.** Phospholipids contain both polar and nonpolar regions, making them amphipathic. The fatty acyl tails, formed from fatty acids, are the nonpolar region. The rest of the molecule is polar. In an aqueous environment, phospholipids can form a bilayer with the hydrophobic tails facing the interior of the bilayer, away from the water.

BioConnections: *For a more detailed view of the components of cellular membranes, including the phospholipid bilayer, look ahead to Figure 5.1.*

(a) The steroid ring structure

Side groups can be added to the rings.

Removal of hydrogens can create double bonds.

Cholesterol
Can be converted to other steroids by modifying side groups.

Estrogen ♀

Testosterone ♂

(b) Female cardinal   **(c) Male cardinal**

Figure 3.13 Structure of cholesterol and steroid hormones derived from cholesterol.   (a) The structure of a steroid has four rings. Steroids include cholesterol and molecules derived from cholesterol, such as steroid hormones. These include the reproductive hormones (b) estradiol, a type of estrogen and (c) testosterone.

 Principle: *Structure determines function.   The few seemingly minor chemical (structural) differences between estrogen and testosterone are sufficient to completely alter their biological functions. The striking difference in appearance between these two cardinals is just one example of sex-dependent differences in form and function in the animal world that are due to these two molecules.*

In steroids, tiny differences in chemical structure can lead to profoundly different biological properties. This is dramatically apparent for two steroids that function as **hormones**, molecules that are produced in one part of the body but can function elsewhere. The steroid hormones estrogen (**Figure 3.13b**) and testosterone (**Figure 3.13c**) are created from cholesterol, but have slightly different side groups. Estrogen is the dominant sex hormone of females and testosterone that of males. The small chemical differences between estrogen and testosterone are sufficient to produce very different sexual characteristics.

Waxes

Although any wax can contain hundreds of different compounds, all waxes contain one or more hydrocarbons and long structures that resemble a fatty acid attached by its carboxyl group to another long hydrocarbon chain. Most waxes are very nonpolar and thus repel water, providing a barrier to water loss. For this reason many plants and animals produce waxes that are typically secreted onto their surface, such as the leaves of plants and the cuticles of insects. They can also be used as structural elements in colonies like those of bees, where beeswax forms the honeycomb of the hive.

3.5 PROTEINS ARE POLYMERS COMPOSED OF AMINO ACIDS

Learning Outcomes:

1. Give examples of the general types of functions that are carried out in cells by different types of proteins.
2. Explain how amino acids are joined to form a polypeptide, and distinguish between a polypeptide and protein.
3. Describe the levels of protein structure, and understand the bonding forces and factors that are important in determining polypeptide and protein shape.
4. Explain what domains are and their importance in proteins.

Proteins account for about 50% of the organic material in a typical animal's body; in plants the percentage varies because of the differing amount of woody support structures. Nonetheless, proteins play equally vital and diverse roles in all the kingdoms of organisms (**Table 3.2**).

Table 3.2	Major Categories and Functions of Proteins	
Category	**Functions**	**Examples**
Proteins involved in gene replication, expression, and regulation	Control production of nucleic acids and polypeptides	RNA polymerases use DNA as a template to make RNA; transcription factor proteins regulate RNA polymerase access to genes.
Motor proteins	Initiate movement	Myosin is a motor protein that provides the contractile force of muscles; kinesin is a key protein that helps cells to sort their chromosomes.
Defence proteins	Protect organisms against disease	Antibodies ward off infection caused by bacteria or viruses.
Metabolic enzymes	Increase rates of chemical reactions	Hexokinase is an enzyme involved in sugar metabolism.
Cell signalling proteins	Enable cells to communicate with one another and with the environment	Taste receptors in the tongue allow animals to taste molecules in food.
Structural proteins	Support and strengthen structures	Actin provides shape to the cytoplasm of cells, such as plant and animal cells; collagen gives strength to tendons.
Transporters	Promote movement of solutes across plasma membranes	Ion channels allow movement of charged molecules across plasma membranes; glucose transporters move glucose from outside cells to inside cells, where it can be used for energy.

Proteins are polymers composed of carbon, hydrogen, oxygen, nitrogen, and small amounts of other elements, notably sulphur. The building blocks of proteins are monomer units known as **amino acids**. Amino acids have a common skeleton in which a carbon atom, called the α-carbon, is linked to an amino group (NH_2) and a carboxyl group (COOH). The α-carbon also is linked to a hydrogen atom and a side chain, which is given a general designation R.

When dissolved in water at neutral pH (the normal condition within cells), the amino group accepts a hydrogen ion and is positively charged, while the carboxyl group loses a hydrogen ion and is negatively charged. Thus an amino acid is an example of a **zwitterion**, an overall neutral molecule with a positive charge at one location (NH_3^+) and a negative charge (COO^-) at a different location.

The 20 amino acids found in proteins differ with regard to the structures of their side chains (**Figure 3.14**). Amino acids are categorized as those that are nonpolar, polar and uncharged, or polar and charged. The varying structures of the side chains are critical features of protein structure and function. The arrangement and chemical features of the side chains cause proteins to fold and adopt their three-dimensional shapes. In addition, certain amino acids may be individually critical to protein function, such as amino acid side chains found within the active sites of enzymes.

Amino acids are joined by linking the carboxyl group of one amino acid to the amino group of another in a dehydration reaction that releases a molecule of H_2O (**Figure 3.15a**). The covalent bond formed between a carboxyl and an amino group is called a **peptide bond**. When many amino acids are joined by peptide bonds, the resulting molecule is called a **polypeptide** (**Figure 3.15b**). When two or more amino acids are linked, one end of the resulting molecule has a free amino group; this is the amino terminus, or N-terminus. The other end of the polypeptide, called the carboxyl terminus, or C-terminus, has a free carboxyl group. As shown in **Figure 3.15c**, amino acids of a polypeptide are numbered starting at the amino terminus. Polypeptides contain their own characteristic number of amino acids. Ribonuclease is composed of a relatively small polypeptide with 124 amino acids. An average polypeptide is larger, containing about 300 amino acids. Large polypeptides can be several thousand amino acids long.

Proteins Have a Hierarchy of Structure

We use the term *polypeptide* to refer to an ordered, covalently linked collection of amino acids, without considering its shape. In contrast, a protein is a functional unit composed of one or more polypeptides that have been folded and twisted into their precise three-dimensional shapes to allow it to carry out its particular function. Scientists view protein structure at four progressive levels: primary, secondary, tertiary, and quaternary, shown schematically in **Figure 3.16**. These levels of structure are dependent on one another. If one level changes, the other levels may change as a consequence. For example,

Figure 3.14 **The 20 amino acids found in living organisms.**   The various amino acids have different chemical properties (e.g., polar versus nonpolar). These properties contribute to the differences in the three-dimensional shapes of proteins, which in turn influence their biological functions.

if the primary structure is changed, this can affect the secondary, tertiary, and quaternary structures. Let's now consider each level.

Primary Structure   The **primary structure** of a polypeptide is its amino acid sequence, from beginning to end (**Figure 3.16a**). For a particular polypeptide, the specific sequence of amino acids is specified by the gene that encodes it (Chapter 11). The primary structure of a polypeptide is stabilized by the covalent peptide bonds that link adjacent amino acids.

Secondary Structure   The amino acid sequence of a polypeptide, with the distinctive chemistry of their R groups, together with the laws of chemistry and physics, cause a polypeptide to fold into a three-dimensional structure. Amino acids can rotate around bonds within a polypeptide. Consequently, polypeptides

(a) Formation of a peptide bond between 2 amino acids, water is released

> The amino end of a polypeptide is called the N-terminus.

> The peptide bond is shown in red, the amino and carboxyl group involved in peptide bond formation are shown in yellow.

> The carboxyl end of a polypeptide is called the C-terminus.

(b) Polypeptide—a linear chain of amino acids

> This is an octapeptide (8 amino acids).

(c) Numbering system of amino acids in a polypeptide. The blue circle represents the R group of each amino acid

Figure 3.15   **The chemistry of polypeptide formation.**   Polypeptides are polymers of amino acids formed by linking amino acids via dehydration reactions to make peptide bonds. Every polypeptide has an amino end, or N-terminus, and a carboxyl end, or C-terminus.

Concept check: *How many water molecules would be produced by dehydration reactions in making a polypeptide that is 72 amino acids long?*

are flexible and can fold into a number of shapes, just as a string of beads can be twisted into many configurations. Which configuration they adapt depends on the nature of the R groups. **Secondary structure** usually refers to regular repeating patterns. The two types of secondary structures that amino acids can bend into are the α helix and β pleated sheet (**Figure 3.16b**). For both patterns, hydrogen bonding is the key driving force.

In an α helix, the polypeptide backbone forms a repeating helical structure that is stabilized by hydrogen bonds. As shown in Figure 3.16, the hydrogen linked to a nitrogen atom forms a hydrogen bond with an oxygen atom that is double-bonded to a carbon. These hydrogen bonds occur at regular intervals and cause the polypeptide backbone to form a helix. In a β sheet, regions of the polypeptide backbone come to lie parallel to each

other. When these parallel regions form hydrogen bonds, again between the hydrogen linked to a nitrogen atom and a double-bonded oxygen, the polypeptide backbone adopts a repeating zigzag shape called a β pleated sheet.

α helices and β sheets are two key determinants of a polypeptide's characteristics. For example, α helices in certain proteins are composed primarily of nonpolar amino acids. Proteins containing many such regions with an α helix structure tend to anchor themselves into a lipid-rich environment, such as a cell's plasma membrane. In this way, a protein whose function is needed in a specific location, such as a plasma membrane, can be retained there. Secondary structure also contributes to the great strength of certain proteins, including the keratins found in hair and hooves, the proteins that make up the silk

(a)

Primary structure: The linear sequence of amino acids is the primary structure.

(b)

Secondary structure: Certain sequences of amino acids form hydrogen bonds that cause the region to fold into a spiral (α helix) or sheet (β pleated sheet).

(c)

Tertiary structure: Secondary structures and random coiled regions fold into a three-dimensional shape.

Random coiled regions

NH₃⁺

Met
Pro
Tyr
Leu
His

α helix

H bond

β pleated sheet

H bond

Arg
Pro
Tyr
Leu
His

COO⁻

(d)

Quaternary structure: Two or more polypeptides can bind together to form a functional protein. Here the polypeptide of (c) bind with another polypeptide, shown in dark blue.

Figure 3.16   The hierarchy of forces governing polypeptide and protein structure.

webs of spiders, and collagen, the chief component of cartilage in mammals.

Some regions along a polypeptide chain do not assume an α helix or β sheet conformation. In other words, they do not have a regular secondary structure. These regions are sometimes called random coiled regions; however, this term is somewhat misleading because the shapes of these so-called random coiled regions are usually very specific and nonrandom, and are important to the function of a protein.

Tertiary Structure   As the secondary structure becomes established through the particular primary structure, a polypeptide folds and refolds on itself to assume a complex three-dimensional shape—its **tertiary structure** (**Figure 3.16c**). The tertiary structure is the three-dimensional shape of a single polypeptide, it is determined by the totality of the amino acid interactions with one another and the aqueous and nonaqueous environment surrounding them. Hydrophobic regions either

tuck into the interior of the polypeptide or anchor in a lipid bilayer. Hydrophilic portions of polypeptides face and interact with water. Some proteins, such as ribonuclease, are composed of a single polypeptide; the tertiary structure of the polypeptide is the final structure of a functional protein. (Ribonuclease is the focus of this chapter's Feature Investigation.) However, as described next, other proteins are composed of two or more polypeptides that interact in a precise way to form the protein's quaternary structure.

Quaternary Structure   Most functional proteins are composed of two or more polypeptides that each adopt a tertiary structure and then assemble together (**Figure 3.16d**). The individual polypeptides are called protein subunits of a **multimeric protein**. Subunits may be identical polypeptides or they may be different. The combined three-dimensional structure of multimeric proteins is its **quaternary structure**.

1 **Hydrogen bonds:** Bonds form between atoms in the polypeptide backbone and between atoms in different side chains.

2 **Ionic bond:** Bonds form between oppositely charged side chains.

3 **Hydrophobic effect:** Nonpolar amino acids in the centre of the protein avoid contact with water.

4 **van der Waals forces:** Attractive forces occur between atoms that are optimal distances apart.

5 **Disulphide bridge:** A covalent bond forms between two cysteine side chains.

Figure 3.17 The factors that influence protein folding and stability.

Factors That Influence Protein Structure Several factors determine the way that polypeptides adopt their secondary, tertiary, and quaternary structures. The amino acid sequences of polypeptides are the defining features that distinguish the structure of one protein from another. As shown in **Figure 3.17**, five factors are critical for protein folding and stability:

1. *Hydrogen bonds.* The large number of hydrogen bonds within a polypeptide and between polypeptides adds up to a strong force that promotes protein folding and stability. It is a critical determinant of protein secondary structure and is also important in tertiary and quaternary structure.

2. *Ionic bonds and other polar interactions.* Some amino acid side chains are positively charged while others are negatively charged. Positively charged side chains may bind to negatively charged side chains via ionic bonds. Similarly, uncharged polar side chains in a protein may interact with ionic amino acids. These ionic and polar interactions promote protein folding and stability.

3. *Hydrophobic effect.* Some amino acid side chains are nonpolar. These amino acids tend to avoid water. As a protein folds, the hydrophobic amino acids are likely to be found in the centre of the protein to avoid contact with water. As mentioned, some proteins have stretches of nonpolar amino acids that anchor them in the hydrophobic portion of membranes.

4. *The van der Waals forces.* Atoms within molecules have weak electrostatic attractions for each other if they are an optimal distance apart. This optimal distance is called the van der Waals radius, and the weak attraction is the van der Waals force. If two atoms are too close together, their electron clouds will repel each other. If they are too far apart, the van der Waals force will diminish. Thus the ability of two regions to be stabilized by a collection of weak van der Waal forces will be strongly influenced by how well their shapes allow them to be optimally aligned.

5. *Disulphide bridges.* The side chain of the amino acid cysteine (—CH$_2$—SH) contains a sulphhydryl group, which can react with a sulphhydryl group in another cysteine side chain to produce a **disulphide bridge** or bond, which links the two amino acid side chains (—CH$_2$—S—S—CH$_2$). Disulphide bonds are covalent bonds that can occur within a single polypeptide or between different polypeptides. Though other forces are usually more important in protein folding, the covalent nature of disulphide bonds can help to stabilize the structure of a protein.

The interactions described in Figure 3.17 are also important in the ability of different proteins to interact with each other. Many cellular processes involve steps in which two or more different proteins interact. Such **protein–protein interactions** are critically important to cellular processes occurring in a series of defined steps. In addition, protein–protein interactions are important in building large cellular structures that provide shape and organization to cells.

Determining Protein Structure   Understanding a protein's three-dimensional structure is important for understanding and manipulating its function. Once the primary structure of a polypeptide is determined, scientists use the five principles listed above to attempt to predict its tertiary structure, and refine or verify this structure through direct observations. The Structural Genomics Consortium (SGC) is a nonprofit organization dedicated to solving the structure of medically relevant proteins. The consortium is affiliated with the University of Oxford in the United Kingdom, the University of Toronto in Canada, and the Karolinska Institutet in Sweden, and is funded by 11 separate organizations. In 2011 the SGC celebrated the solving of its 1,000th protein structure; one such protein is shown in **Figure 3.18**.

> Note the extensive amount of a helix formation.

Figure 3.18   Scientists work in a directed fashion to determine the structure of important proteins.   The structure of the calcium-dependent protein kinase of the human parasite *Toxoplasma gondii* in its inactive form was published in *Nature Structural & Molecular Biology* in 2010 (Vol. 17, pp. 596–601). Note the extensive amount of a helix formation. When this protein binds calcium, it changes conformation and becomes an active kinase. Knowledge of this structure may lead to a treatment for toxoplasmosis.

GENOMES AND PROTEOMES

Proteins Contain Functional Domain Within Their Structures

Research into the functions of proteins has revealed that many proteins have a modular structure. This means that portions within proteins, called **domains**, have distinct structures and functions. These particular amino acid sequences have been duplicated during evolution so that the same kind of domain can be found in several different proteins. When the same domain is found in different proteins, the domain has the same characteristic three-dimensional shape, chemical properties, and function. For example, **Figure 3.19** shows the structure of a protein composed of a heterotetramer, meaning that the protein has four subunits, and not all subunits are the same. The protein is made of two subunits of GABPβ and two subunits of GABPα. The GABPα subunit has a domain called ETS, which is responsible for DNA binding. This domain is a common feature of a large family of proteins that all bind specifically to DNA regions under specific conditions. But the GABPα subunit's activity is regulated by its partnership with another polypeptide. To get efficient and specific binding to the region of DNA it regulates, there must be two subunits of GABPα bound with two subunits of GABPβ. The first domain of two molecules of GABPβ allow the two identical subunits to interact. When the GABPβ's activation domains (domain 2) receive the proper cellular signal they change conformation. Their change, in turn, creates a change in domain 3 of GABPβ subunits, which ultimately activate the ETS domains of the GABPα subunits such that they can efficiently bind DNA. As you can see in Figure 3.19 each domain has its own characteristic shape that facilitates its interaction with either the DNA (for the ETS domain) or with other subunits. For the GABPα/GABPβ protein to function, all these interactions must occur.

These domains allow two
β subunits to interact

GABPα

GABPβ

2 1 1 2

Activation
domains

ETS
domain

Figure 3.19 The domain structure of the subunits of GABPβ/GABPα. Each subunit has distinct domains with specific functions.

Principle: *Structure determines function.* The subunits fit together because of their shape and the ETS region can bind DNA (and influence the DNA's expression) because of its shape.

FEATURE INVESTIGATION

Anfinsen Showed That the Primary Structure of Ribonuclease Determines Its Three-Dimensional Structure

Before the 1960s, the mechanisms by which proteins assume their three-dimensional structures were not understood. Scientists believed that correct folding required unidentified cellular factors, or that ribosomes, the site at which polypeptides are synthesized, somehow shaped proteins as they were being made. Christian Anfinsen, however, postulated that proteins contain all the information to fold into their proper conformation without needing organelles or cellular factors. He hypothesized that proteins spontaneously assume their most stable conformation based on the laws of chemistry and physics (**Figure 3.20**).

To test this hypothesis, Anfinsen studied ribonuclease at the National Institute of Health in the United States. Ribonuclease is an abundant enzyme that degrades RNA. Biochemists had already determined that ribonuclease has four disulphide bonds between eight cysteine amino acids. Anfinsen began with purified ribonuclease—this approach is called an in vitro experiment, meaning "done in glass," as in a test tube. The key point is that other cellular components were not present, only the purified protein. He exposed ribonuclease to a chemical called urea that disrupted the hydrogen and ionic bonds, and to another chemical called β-mercaptoethanol that broke the S—S bonds. Following this treatment, he measured the ability of the treated enzyme to degrade RNA. The enzyme had lost nearly all of its ability to degrade RNA.

The key step in this experiment came when Anfinsen removed the urea and β-mercaptoethanol from the solution. Because these molecules are much smaller than ribonuclease,

removing them from the solution was accomplished with a technique called column chromatography. For column chromatography, the column is filled with beads of a special nature that allow selective passage of certain molecules. Anfinsen used column chromatography to separate ribonuclease from the urea and β-mercaptoethanol. Then he retested the ribonuclease. The result revolutionized our understanding of proteins. The activity of the ribonuclease was almost completely restored! This meant that even in the complete absence of any cellular factors or organelles, an unfolded protein can refold into its functional structure. This was later confirmed by chemical analyses that demonstrated that the disulphide bonds had re-formed at the proper locations.

Since Anfinsen's time, we have learned that his experiments with ribonuclease are not representative of all proteins. Some proteins do require certain enzymes and other proteins to assist them in their proper folding. Nonetheless, Anfinsen's experiments provided compelling evidence that the primary structure of a polypeptide is the key determinant of a protein's tertiary structure, a correct observation that earned him a Nobel Prize in 1972.

Experimental Questions

1. Before the experiments conducted by Anfinsen, what were the common beliefs among scientists about protein folding?
2. Explain the hypothesis tested by Anfinsen.
3. Why did Anfinsen use urea and β-mercaptoethanol in his experiments? Explain the result that was crucial to the discovery that the tertiary structure of a protein is dependent on the primary structure.

HYPOTHESIS Within their amino acid sequence, proteins contain all the information needed to fold into their correct, three-dimensional shapes.

KEY MATERIALS Purified ribonuclease, RNA, denaturing chemicals, size-exclusion columns.

Experimental level   Conceptual level

1 Incubate purified ribonuclease in test tube with RNA, and measure its ability to degrade RNA.

Purified ribonuclease

Numerous H bonds and ionic bonds (not shown) and 4 S—S bonds. Protein is properly folded.

2 Denature ribonuclease by adding β-mercaptoethanol (breaks S—S bonds) and urea (breaks H bonds and ionic bonds). Measure its ability to degrade RNA.

β-Mercaptoethanol + Urea

No more H bonds, ionic bonds, or S—S bonds. Protein is unfolded.

Denatured ribonuclease

3 Layer mixture from step 2 atop a chromatography column. Beads in the column allow ribonuclease to escape, while β-mercaptoethanol and urea are retained. Collect ribonuclease in a test tube and measure its ability to degrade RNA.

Mixture from step 2 containing denatured ribonuclease, β-mercaptoethanol, and urea

Column containing beads suspended in a watery solution

Collection port with filter to prevent beads from escaping

Solution of ribonuclease

β-Mercaptoethanol   Urea

Beads have microscopic pores that trap β-mercapto-ethanol and urea, but not ribonuclease.

Denatured ribonuclease

Renatured ribonuclease

4   THE DATA

Ribonuclease function (%)

Activity restored

| Purified ribonuclease (step 1) | Denatured ribonuclease (step 2) | Ribonuclease after column chromatography (step 3) |

5   CONCLUSION Certain proteins, like ribonuclease, can spontaneously fold into their final, functional shapes without assistance from other cellular structures or factors. (However, as described in the text, this is not true of many other proteins.)

6   SOURCE Haber, E., and Anfinsen, C.B. 1961. Regeneration of enzyme activity by air oxidation of reduced subtilisin-modified ribonuclease. *Journal of Biological Chemistry* 236:422–424.

Figure 3.20 Anfinsen's experiments with ribonuclease demonstrating that the primary structure of a polypeptide plays a key role in protein folding.

3.6 NUCLEIC ACIDS ARE POLYMERS AND ARE THE SOURCE OF GENETIC INFORMATION

Learning Outcomes:

1. Describe the three components of nucleotides, and be able to number the carbons of the monomer's sugar.
2. Understand what polarity means for a strand of DNA or RNA.
3. Distinguish between the structures of DNA and RNA.
4. Explain the term *antiparallel* and describe its importance for base pairing.
5. Describe how certain bases can pair with others to form a DNA double helix.

Nucleic acids account for only a small percentage of the mass of organisms yet these molecules are extremely important because they are responsible for the storage, expression, and transmission of genetic information. The pattern of expression of an organism's genetic information determines the time, duration, and location of the production of specific proteins, which in turn gives rise to the defining traits of an organism.

The two classes of nucleic acids are **deoxyribonucleic acid (DNA)** and **ribonucleic acid (RNA)**. Both types of nucleic acids are polymers and consist of linear sequences of repeating monomers. Each monomer, known as a **nucleotide**, has three components: a phosphate group, a five-carbon sugar (either ribose or deoxyribose), and a single or double ring of carbon and nitrogen atoms known as a **nitrogenous base** (**Figure 3.21**). The phosphate group of one nucleotide is linked to the sugar of the adjacent nucleotide by a phosphodiester bond to form a polynucleotide strand, with the bases protruding from the side of the phosphate–sugar backbone (**Figure 3.22**). Each polynucleotide has a polarity. The term **nucleic acid polarity** as used here does not refer to electrical charge; it refers to the orientation of the monomers: one pole (end) has a free phosphate group off the sugar, and the other pole end has a free OH group. This polarity is very important to the structure and function of DNA.

DNA

DNA molecules store genetic information coded in the sequence of their monomer building blocks. The nucleotides in DNA contain the five-carbon sugar **deoxyribose**. Four different nucleotides are present in DNA, corresponding to the four different bases that can be linked to deoxyribose. The **purine** bases, **adenine (A)** and **guanine (G)**, have double (fused) rings of nitrogen and carbon atoms, and the **pyrimidine** bases, **cytosine (C)** and **thymine (T)**, have only a single ring (see Figure 3.22).

DNA of cells consists of two polymers (each called a strand) of deoxyribonucleotides coiled around each other to form a

Example of a ribonucleotide

Example of a deoxyribonucleotide

Figure 3.21 **Examples of two nucleotides.** A nucleotide has a phosphate group, a five-carbon sugar, and a nitrogenous base.

double helix (**Figure 3.23**). The two strands are held together by hydrogen bonds between a purine base in one strand and a pyrimidine base in the opposite strand. The ring structure of each base lies in a flat plane perpendicular to the sugar–phosphate backbone, somewhat like steps on a spiral staircase. This base pairing maintains a constant distance between the sugar–phosphate backbones of the two strands as they coil around each other. The regular helical structure with maximized hydrogen bonding can occur only if the two strands are oriented **antiparallel**, meaning of opposite polarity, such that the free OH end of one strand faces the free phosphate end of the other strand. This is the only configuration that puts the oxygen and nitrogens of one strand in the appropriate location to hydrogen bond with the relevant hydrogen of the other strand (Figure 3.23).

As you will see in Chapter 10, only certain bases can pair with others because of the location of the hydrogen-bonding groups in the four bases (see Figure 3.23). Two hydrogen bonds can be formed between adenine and thymine (A–T pairing), while three hydrogen bonds are formed between guanine and cytosine (G–C pairing). In a DNA molecule, A is usually paired with T, and G is usually paired with C. This specificity provides the mechanism for duplicating and transferring genetic information.

RNA

RNA molecules differ in only a few respects from DNA, but these differences collectively make RNA less stable than DNA. RNA in nature usually consists of single rather than double strands. In

This nucleotide has a free phosphate group on the fifth carbon of its sugar.

Adjacent nucleotides are held together by a covalent ester bond between the third carbon of one nucleotide and the phosphate group of its neighbour. Because the second nucleotide has its fifth carbon attached to the same phosphate group by another covalent ester bond, the linkage is called a phosphodiester linkage.

This nucleotide has a free OH group on the third carbon of its sugar.

Figure 3.22 Structure of a DNA strand. Nucleotides are linked to form a strand of DNA. The four bases found in DNA are shown. A strand of RNA is similar, except the sugar is ribose and uracil is substituted for thymine.

The two strands are antiparallel (they have opposite polarity). Notice that the sugars of the left strand are upside down relative to the other strand.

Figure 3.23 The double-stranded structure of DNA. DNA consists of two strands coiled together into a double helix. The bases form hydrogen bonds in which A pairs with T, and G pairs with C.

RNA, the sugar in each nucleotide is **ribose** rather than deoxyribose. Also, the pyrimidine base thymine in DNA is replaced in RNA with the pyrimidine base **uracil (U)** (see Figure 3.21). The other three bases, adenine, guanine, and cytosine, are found in both DNA and RNA.

RNA molecules take the information from the DNA and the sequence of its monomers is used as code to create proteins. In Chapter 11 we will consider the mechanisms by which the information encoded by the order of the nitrogenous bases of the DNA is decoded and used by RNAs to create specific polypeptides.

Summary of Key Concepts

3.1 The Carbon Atom and the Study of Organic Molecules

- Organic chemistry is the science of studying carbon-containing molecules, which are found in living organisms. Wöhler's work with urea marked the birth of organic chemistry. (Figure 3.1)
- One property of the carbon atom that makes life possible is its ability to form four covalent bonds with other atoms. Carbon can form both polar and nonpolar bonds. The combination of different elements and different types of bonds allows a vast number of organic compounds to be formed from only a few chemical elements. (Figures 3.2, 3.3)
- Organic molecules occur in various shapes. Their structures determine their functions.
- Carbon bonds are stable at the different temperatures associated with life. (Figure 3.4)
- Organic compounds can contain functional groups. (Table 3.1)
- Carbon-containing molecules can exist as isomers, which have identical molecular composition but different structures and characteristics. Structural isomers contain the same atoms but

in different bonding relationships. Stereoisomers have identical bonding relationships but different spatial positioning of their atoms. Enantiomers exist as mirror images of each other. (Figure 3.5)

3.2 Classes of Organic Molecules and Macromolecules

- The four major classes of organic macromolecules are carbohydrates, lipids, proteins, and nucleic acids. Macromolecules are large organic molecules that are composed of many thousands of atoms.
- Carbohydrates, proteins, and nucleic acids all can create large macromolecules by combining monomer units via dehydration reactions. (Figure 3.6)

3.3 Carbohydrates Include Simple Sugars and Polymers Composed of Sugar Monomers

- Carbohydrates are composed of carbon, hydrogen, and oxygen atoms. Most cells can break down carbohydrates, releasing energy and storing it in newly created bonds in ATP.
- Carbohydrates include monosaccharides (the simplest sugars), disaccharides, and polysaccharides. The polysaccharides starch (in plant cells) and glycogen (in animal cells) provide an efficient means of storing energy. The plant polysaccharide cellulose serves a support or structural function. (Figures 3.7, 3.8, 3.9)

3.4 Lipids Are Mostly Hydrophobic and Are Heterogeneous in Structure and Function

- Lipids, composed predominantly of hydrogen and carbon atoms, are nonpolar and insoluble in water. Major classes of lipids include fats, phospholipids, steroids, and waxes.
- Fats, a mixture of triglycerides, are formed by bonding glycerol with three fatty acids. In a saturated fatty acid, all the carbons are linked by single covalent bonds. Unsaturated fatty acids contain one or more carbon–carbon double bonds. Animal fats generally contain a high proportion of saturated fatty acids, and vegetable fats contain more unsaturated fatty acids. (Figures 3.10, 3.11)
- Phospholipids are similar in structure to triglycerides, except they are amphipathic because one fatty acid is replaced with a charged polar group. (Figure 3.12)
- Steroids are constructed of four fused rings of carbon atoms. Small differences in steroid structure can lead to profoundly different biological properties, such as the differences between estrogen and testosterone. (Figure 3.13)
- Waxes, another class of lipids, are nonpolar and repel water, and they are often found as protective coatings on the leaves of plants and the outer surfaces of animals' bodies.

3.5 Proteins Are Polymers Composed of Amino Acids

- Proteins are composed of carbon, hydrogen, oxygen, nitrogen, and small amounts of other elements, such as sulphur. Proteins are macromolecules that play critical roles in almost all life processes. The proteins of living organisms are composed of the same set of 20 amino acids, corresponding to 20 different side chains. (Figure 3.14, Table 3.2)
- Amino acids are joined by linking the carboxyl group of one amino acid to the amino group of another, forming a peptide bond. A polypeptide is a structural unit composed of amino acids, while a

protein is a functional unit composed of one or more polypeptides that have been folded and twisted into precise three-dimensional shapes. (Figure 3.15)

- The four levels of protein structure are primary (its amino acid sequence), secondary (bending or twisting into α helices or β sheets), tertiary (folding and refolding to assume a three-dimensional shape), and quaternary (multimeric proteins that consist of more than one polypeptide chain). If the primary structure of a protein changes, the other levels would change as a consequence. The three-dimensional structure of a protein determines its function, for example, by creating binding sites for other molecules. (Figures 3.16, 3.17, 3.18, 3.19, 3.20)

3.6 Nucleic Acids Are Polymers and Are the Source of Genetic Information

- Nucleic acids are responsible for the storage, expression, and transmission of genetic information. The two types of nucleic acids are deoxyribonucleic acid (DNA) and ribonucleic acid (RNA). Nucleic acids are polymers made from nucleotide monomers. (Figure 3.21)
- Nucleotide monomer units are held together by phosphodiester bonds. (Figures 3.21, 3.22)
- DNA molecules store genetic information coded in the sequence of their monomers. DNA contains the sugar deoxyribose and the bases adenine, guanine, cytosine, and thymine. A DNA molecule usually consists of two strands of nucleotides, oriented antiparallel, forming a double helix. The two strands are held together by hydrogen bonds between a purine base on one strand and a pyrimidine base on the opposite strand: G with C and A with T. (Figures 3.21, 3.22, 3.23)
- RNA molecules are involved in decoding this information into instructions for linking a specific sequence of amino acids to form a specific polypeptide chain. RNA consists of a single strand of nucleotides. The sugar in each nucleotide is ribose rather than deoxyribose, and the base uracil replaces thymine.

Test to Assess Your Learning

1. Molecules that contain the element _____ are considered organic molecules.
   a. hydrogen
   b. carbon
   c. oxygen
   d. nitrogen
   e. calcium

2. _____ was the first scientist to synthesize an organic molecule. The organic molecule synthesized was _____.
   a. Kolbe, urea
   b. Wöhler, urea
   c. Wöhler, acetic acid
   d. Kolbe, acetic acid
   e. Wöhler, glucose

3. The versatility of carbon to serve as the backbone for a variety of different molecules is due to
   a. the ability of carbon atoms to form four covalent bonds.
   b. the fact that carbon usually forms ionic bonds with many different atoms.
   c. the abundance of carbon in the environment.

d. the ability of carbon to form covalent bonds with many different types of atoms.

e. both (a) and (d).

4. _____ are molecules that have the same molecular composition but differ in structure or bonding association.

a. Isotopes

b. Isomers

c. Free radicals

d. Analogues

e. Ions

5. _____ is a storage polysaccharide commonly found in the cells of animals.

a. Glucose

b. Sucrose

c. Glycogen

d. Starch

e. Cellulose

6. In contrast to other fatty acids, essential fatty acids

a. are always saturated fats.

b. cannot be synthesized by the organism and are necessary for survival.

c. can act as building blocks for large, more complex macromolecules.

d. are the simplest form of lipids found in plant cells.

e. are structural components of plasma membranes.

7. Phospholipids are said to be amphipathic, which means these molecules

a. are partially hydrolyzed during cellular metabolism.

b. are composed of a hydrophilic portion and hydrophobic portion.

c. may be poisonous to organisms if in combination with certain other molecules.

d. are molecules composed of lipids and proteins.

e. all of the above.

8. The monomers of proteins are _____ and these are linked by polar covalent bonds commonly referred to as _____ bonds.

a. nucleotides, peptide

b. amino acids, ester

c. hydroxyl groups, phosphodiester

d. amino acids, peptide

e. monosaccharides, glycosidic

9. The _____ of a nucleotide determines whether it is a component of DNA or a component of RNA.

a. phosphate group

b. five-carbon sugar

c. side chain

d. fatty acid

e. both (b) and (d)

10. A _____ is a portion of protein with a particular structure and function.

a. peptide bond

b. domain

c. phospholipid

d. wax

e. monosaccharide

Articulate to Assess Your Learning

1. Define the three types of isomers. Give one example of isomers that are functionally different in organisms.

2. List the four major classes of biologically important macromolecules and give a function of each.

3. Explain what the common features of all polymers are. Explain what is different about each major category of polymer.

4. List and explain the differences between saturated and unsaturated fatty acids.

5. Discuss several types of carbohydrates. Include a consideration of how their structure supports their function.

6. Discuss some of the roles that proteins play in organisms. Briefly discuss how one group of molecules can play so many different roles.

7. If you were backpacking and space was at a premium, would you pack high-fat or high-carbohydrate foods? Justify your answer.

Collaborate to Assess and Extend Your Learning

1. What is the generalized formula for a carbohydrate? You are told the specific chemical formulas for several carbohydrates:

$C_6H_{12}O_6$ $C_{10}H_{18}O_9$ $C_{18}H_{32}O_{16}$

Indicate whether they are monomers, dimers, polymers, and so on.

2. Define the primary structure of a polypeptide. How does the primary structure contribute to secondary structure?

3. Why are DNA and RNA called nucleic acids?

4. Create a concept map that interrelates the following terms: van der Waal forces, hydrogen bonding, hydrophobic, hydrophilic, amphipathic, secondary structure of polypeptides, tertiary and quaternary structure of proteins, base pairing, nucleic acid strand polarity, antiparallel, DNA helix, and water.

5. If you are told that a double-stranded DNA molecule is 23% cytosine, can you predict the percentages of adenine, guanine, and thymine? Why or why not?

6. A biological principle of life is that structure determines function. What does this mean for organic molecules such as carbohydrates, lipids, and proteins?

Visit McGraw-Hill Ryerson Connect™ for additional study resources.

WHAT'S NEW?

An interview with Dr. Kristi Miller-Saunders from Fisheries and Oceans Canada, by Shahneen Arif, a third-year student at the University of Toronto Scarborough.

Dr. Miller-Saunders is a research scientist at Fisheries and Oceans Canada.

❯ I know that your research interests lie in biotechnology and genetics. What sparked your interest in these fields?

I did my PhD at Stanford University when biotechnology was just starting to flourish. I gravitated toward it because I really liked the speed of the technological changes. I wanted to be a part of that, and I wanted to use technology to solve ecological questions.

❯ What is the focus of your current research?

My current research focuses on ecological genomics of wild species. We're using genomic technology to try to understand what kinds of stressors wild salmon are under, and we'll use this information to identify the areas we need to conduct further studies in. For instance, if you compare the response of salmon to different pathogens and you find that the salmon carry a strong molecular response to three, those might be the ones to follow up in future research. Currently we're using genomics to understand what pathogens salmon are exposed to, which hasn't been done on a broad scale before.

❯ It must have been very exciting to have your article published in *Science* in January 2011 but also very frustrating to not be allowed to speak to the media immediately following the article's publication. How would you describe that whole experience?

I've seen a new side of science: the politics around science. It was frustrating to not be able to speak directly with the media, because the media had to figure out on their own what the science meant. However, the media did work hard in getting some messages out from both the paper and the related Cohen inquiry. A simple Google search shows that 10 years ago, there were half a million hits for Pacific salmon. In 2011 alone, there were 15.5 million hits for Pacific salmon. That's mostly because of the Cohen commission, but I think our work also is discussed in a lot of that news. I'm really excited that genomics has been put on the table and people are talking about its potential applications in the world of wild species conservation research. After my issues with the media, people have emailed me from throughout the world to express their support, and it was an eye-opener to learn of the support that exists for the scientific community. When I testified, I was able to explain my perspective regarding the messaging behind the research we were doing. It was great to be able to do that.

❯ In your *Science* paper, you focused heavily on genomic signatures. What are they?

In the context of our research, that is, functional genomics, a genomic signature is a suite of genes that respond transcriptionally to a specific variable of interest. In some instances, genomic signatures may be used to predict the presence of such a variable. An example from the human medical world is the early work defining genomic signatures in cancer research, which showed that there are many more tumour types than recognized by histology; these tumour-specific genomic signatures are now used in personalized medicine to determine optimal treatment regimes for specific tumour types. In salmon, our research has identified genomic signatures associated with pathogen response, restricted feeding, osmoregulatory preparation, heat stress, hypoxia, maturation, and migratory behaviour, and fate.

❯ What techniques did you employ in the study of the wild Canadian sockeye salmon's mortality published in *Science*?

The technologies we used were radio-tagging and tracking, nondestructive biopsy sampling, genetic stock identification, and genomics. To employ radio-tracking, we caught wild salmon and put a radio-tag in their stomach (they were no longer feeding) and collected a small nondestructive sample of gill tissue. Then, we tracked their movement and speed of migration by using a series of receivers that were placed throughout the river. We coupled that with genetic stock identification. Salmon have a very high fidelity to the same natal region that they were born in, so there are very strong genetic differences between stocks. My lab has developed a stock identification program where we can now take an individual fish caught in the ocean and be able to tell you genetically which stock from which river that fish came from in the river, whether it was caught off the coast of British Columbia or in Alaska. By combining the radio-tracking and the individual stock ID, we were able to determine which fish were successful in reaching the spawning grounds and which were not. Using the gill tissue sample, we designed a microarray experiment in which we contrasted successful and unsuccessful migrants from specific stocks and asked, were the fish physiologically compromised well before they die in the river? We were looking for genomic signatures associated with fate.

> ### In your research, you have utilized microarray technology. Could you describe the concept behind it?

Microarrays are slides that have printed on their surface tens of thousands of genes from your organism of interest. To apply microarray technology, you extract RNA from a tissue sample, label it with a fluorescent tag, allow it to bind to complementary DNA sequences of genes on the slide, and then wash the non-bound RNA off the slide. If there are lots of copies of RNA from a particular gene on the array, the probe for that gene will light up really brightly. If there aren't very many copies, there will be a very dim signal. The observed signal is then run against a control to compare which genes are turned on (making RNA) or turned off (not making RNA) among various different treatment groups. In the case of the *Science* study, we were looking for genes associated with premature mortality. We have also used microarrays to understand how organisms respond to different pathogens and other stressors. We are using it for wild ecological genomics, which is very novel.

> ### What advice do you have for students interested in pursuing applied research at the graduate level?

Having a really well-rounded bachelor's education where an individual has taken a wide variety of courses really helps because you learn so much about different things, and you can then choose to specialize in the fields that interest you in graduate school. A multidisciplinary background is also an asset when working in a team. Coming out of high school, most people aren't aware of the range of possibilities that exist in science. You may learn of a field that you didn't even know existed and perhaps you love it even more than your original choice. In my case, I discovered that my favourite field is immunology.

Cell biology is the study of life at the cellular level. Although cells are the simplest units of life, biologists have come to realize that they are wonderfully complex and interesting, providing information about all living things. In this unit Chapter 4 begins with an overview of cell structure and function, and then explores the technique of microscopy. In Chapter 5 we look at the cell as a dynamic system that accomplishes its many functions. Chapter 6 examines the structure and synthesis of cell membranes and the regulation of substances in and out of the cell. Chapters 7 and 8 are largely devoted to metabolism, the sum of the chemical reactions in a cell or an organism. Specifically, Chapter 7 explores the topic of energy and considers how enzymes facilitate chemical reactions in a cell. It also looks at the pathways for carbohydrate breakdown and how those pathways are used to make an energy intermediate called ATP. In Chapter 8 we explore how carbohydrates are made via photosynthesis by capturing the energy of sunlight. In Chapter 9 we examine how cells respond to signals, both those that come directly from their environment and those made by other cells.

 Certain biology principles are emphasized in this unit, including the following:

- *Cells are the simplest units of life.* Throughout this unit, we will examine how life exists at the cellular level.
- *Living organisms use energy.* Chapters 7 and 8 examine how cells use and store energy contained within organic molecules, such as glucose.
- *Living organisms interact with their environment.* Chapters 4 and 9 largely focus on the plasma membrane of the cell and how it provides an interface between the cell and its environment.
- *The genetic material, DNA, provides a dynamic plan for sustaining life.* In Chapter 5 we look at how parts of the genome are selected to produce the proteome required by the cell at a given time.
- *Living organisms have mechanisms that maintain homeostasis.* In Chapters 5 and 6 we see how cells respond to changes in their environment in ways that allow them to maintain homeostasis.
- *Structure determines function.* Throughout this unit, we will see many examples in which the structure of proteins determines their cellular functions.

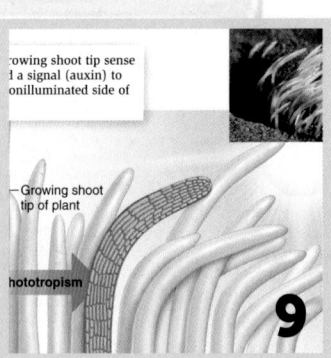

The Principles and Structures of Cellular Organization

Chapter Outline

HeLa cancer cells viewed with a fluorescent microscope with specific staining of different cell components.

Cell biology is the study of cells and their interactions with their environment and other cells. The study of cells began when German botanist Matthias Schleiden examined plant material under the microscope. He was struck by the presence of many similar-looking compartments, each of which contained a dark area. In 1838 Schleiden speculated that cells are living entities and plants are aggregates of cells arranged according to definite laws. Schleiden discussed his findings with his good friend Theodor Schwann, a physiologist, who remembered having seen similar structures in animal tissues. They extended the hypothesis to include animals. In 1855 German biologist Rudolf Virchow added to the theory by proposing *omnis cellula e cellula* ("every cell originates from another cell"). These men provided us with our first unifying principles of biology:

- All living things are composed of one or more cells.
- Cells are the fundamental working units of organisms.
- All new cells come from existing cells by cell division.

Most cells are so small that they cannot be seen with the unassisted eye. Nonetheless they have structural and functional complexity. In this chapter we will look at techniques that allow us to observe cellular and subcellular structures, and then take a big-picture view of cellular structure and function. In later chapters we will explore aspects of cell biology in greater detail.

4.1 MICROSCOPY AS A TOOL TO SEE CELLS

Learning Outcomes:

1. Explain the three important parameters in microscopy: resolution, contrast, and magnification.
2. Describe the major differences between light and electron microscopes.

The **microscope** is an instrument that allows us to move beyond the limits of the human eye and probe the structure and function of cells. The first compound microscope (one with more than one lens) was invented in 1595, but more than 400 years later, scientists continue to develop new types of microscopes that allow us to probe ever more deeply into the organization that occurs within cells.

Three important parameters in microscopy are magnification, resolution, and contrast. **Magnification** is the ratio between the size of an image of a specimen and the specimen's actual size. Every microscope has an optimal magnification beyond which the objects appear too blurry; optimal magnification is determined by a microscope's resolution. **Resolution** is the ability to observe (resolve) two nearby, adjacent objects as being distinct from each other. For example,

Figure 4.1   A comparison of the sizes of various chemical and biological structures, and the resolving power of the unaided eye, light microscopes, and electron microscopes.   The scale shown at the bottom is a logarithmic scale to accommodate the wide range of sizes shown in this drawing.

a microscope with good resolution enables a researcher to distinguish two adjacent chromosomes as separate objects. The third important parameter in microscopy is **contrast**, the ability of an object to stand out from its surroundings. The ability to visualize a particular structure will depend on how different (how contrasted) it is from adjacent structures. If the structure, such as a particular protein, can be specifically highlighted (stained), that makes viewing it much easier. **Stains** are molecules that bind to a structure and improve our ability to distinguish it from its surroundings, greatly improving contrast.

Microscopes are grouped into two broad categories based on the source of illumination. The resolving power of a microscope depends on several factors, including the quality of the lenses and the wavelength of the source of illumination. Light microscopes use light for illumination, while electron microscopes use an electron beam. Light microscopes can resolve structures that are as close as 0.2 μm (1 μm = 1 micrometer = 1×10^{-6} metre) apart. Resolution can be improved when the illumination source has a shorter wavelength. In 1931 Max Knoll and Ernst Ruska invented a prototype electron microscope. Scientists at the University of Toronto created the design for the first commercial transmission electron microscope in 1937. Electron microscopes can resolve some structures down to 0.2 nm (nanometres = 1×10^{-9} metres) but the practical limit for biological specimens is typically around 2 nm, which is about 100 times better resolution than with the light microscope. **Figure 4.1** shows the resolving powers of light and electron microscopes and relates them to the levels of organismal structure that can be examined for each.

(a) Chromosome viewed with an electron microscope   **(b) Chromosome viewed with a light microscope**

Figure 4.2   A comparison of electron and light microscope technologies.   (a) Human chromosomes that are stained with heavy metals and viewed with an electron microscope reveal structural details. (b) The same human chromosomes fluorescently stained and viewed with a light microscope lack detail because of the lower resolving power of light microscopes.

Figure 4.2 allows us to compare levels of detail seen for light and electron microscopy.

Because the wavelength of an electron beam is much shorter than that of visible light, the resolution of the electron microscope is far better than any light microscope. But biological specimens absorb a beam of electrons more readily than light. Therefore, the first electron microscopy technique, transmission electron microscopy (TEM), requires the scientist to create very thin slices before the specimen can be examined. Scanning electron microscopy (SEM) was developed to scan the surface of structures without the need to make thin slices (see **Figure 4.3**).

(a) Transmission electron micrograph

(b) Scanning electron micrograph

Figure 4.3 **A comparison of transmission and scanning electron microscopy.** **(a)** A developing human egg cell, observed by TEM, shortly before it was released from an ovary. **(b)** An egg cell, with a few attached sperm, was coated with heavy metal and observed via SEM. This SEM is colourized.

Concept check: *What is the primary advantage of SEM?*

Over the past several decades, enormous technological advances have increased the utility of microscopy in studying cells. Improvements in lens technology, sample preparation, sample illumination, and computerized image processing have enabled researchers to create different types of microscopes, each with its own advantages and disadvantages (**Figure 4.4**). Revolutionary types of stains and staining techniques have also been developed.

Stains for electron microscopy are most often metals that either deflect or absorb electrons. For light microscopy, stains either absorb light (making the structure darker than its surroundings) or emit light (making the structure brighter). The creation of a variety of light-emitting fluorescent dyes has greatly enhanced the contrast and power of light microscopy. Scientists also have learned to take naturally fluorescing molecules, like the green fluorescent protein considered in Figure 1.1e, and insert them into many different cellular components. Some of these staining techniques can be used with live cells and allow biologists to follow macromolecules as they move and function in cells. Improved resolving and contrasting power and highly specific staining techniques have improved our ability to study macromolecules in cells.

Although some imaging techniques, such as phase contrast, differential interference contrast, specialized fluorescence microscopy, and atomic force microscopy, allow us to look at live (intact) cells, many techniques still require that cells be killed in a controlled manner that fixes the structures into a biologically

Micrographs of nerve cells	Type of microscope	Micrographs of nerve cells	Type of microscope
(a) 30 μm	**Standard light microscope (bright field, unstained sample).** Light is passed directly through a sample and is focused by using glass lenses. Simple, inexpensive, and easy to use but offers little contrast.	**(b)** 46 μm	**Standard light microscope (bright field, stained sample).** This is the same type of microscope as in part (a) but the cell has been treated with a stain that selectively binds to certain regions of the cell. This provides better contrast.
(c) 30 μm	**Phase contrast microscope.** As an alternative to staining, this microscope controls the path of light and amplifies differences in the phase of light transmitted or reflected by a sample and can be used to view living, unstained cells. The dense structures appear darker than the background, thereby improving the contrast in different parts of the specimen.	**(d)** 30 μm	**Differential-interference-contrast (Nomarski) microscope.** This is similar to a phase contrast microscope in that it uses optical modifications to improve contrast in unstained specimens. It is usually used to view whole cells or larger cell structures, such as nuclei.
(e) 30 μm	**Fluorescent microscope.** Fluorescent molecules absorb light at a particular wavelength. Microscopes equipped with lamps and filter sets are used to illuminate the specimen with the light the fluorescent molecule absorbs. Fluorescent molecules can be used to tag macromolecules by binding them to an antibody or incorporating them into proteins. In this image actin filaments are visualized with a green-tagged fluorescent antibody.	**(f)** 23 μm	**Confocal microscope.** It uses lasers that illuminate various points in the sample. These points are processed by a computer to give a very clear three-dimensional image. This technique also can be used to view fluorescent molecules within a cell.

Figure 4.4 Micrographs of nerve cells taken with different types of light microscopes.

meaningful preserved state, a process called **fixation**. After it has been embedded with a supporting matrix, a sample often has to be cut into thin slices to achieve sufficient contrast. The fixation, embedding, sectioning, and staining processes can be quite elaborate and always alter the specimen. Thus, biologists must be mindful of the limitations of their imaging techniques and of the potential of the techniques to create **artifacts** (artificial structures that do not accurately mimic the natural condition). Biologists collaborate with chemists and physicists to continually develop new protocols and imaging techniques that expand our ability to probe the inner organization and workings of cells. Peter Moens, distinguished research professor emeritus at York University and member of the Royal Society of Canada, was one such pioneer. He explored the structure and behaviour of the reproductive cells of plants and animals by using light and electron microscopy in combination with a wide variety of gold- and fluorescent-tagged molecules. Armed with the tools developed by such scientists such as Dr. Moens, let's explore the marvellous world of cells.

4.2   PHYSICAL AND BIOLOGICAL PRINCIPLES THAT INFLUENCE CELL STRUCTURE

Learning Outcomes:

1. Explain how cells form boundaries.
2. Discuss how the proteome influences the composition and structure of cellular compartments and how this may differ in two cells of the same organism, or how it might differ in the same cell under different conditions.

All forms of life can be placed into two broad categories: prokaryotes and eukaryotes. As we look at their cell structures, consider several key organizing features: (1) The cell membrane is the border between a cell's exterior and its interior. (2) The interior of the cell is called cytoplasm. (3) Virtually all cells export macromolecules from their cytoplasm to outside the cell to form a protective matrix on the exterior side of the cell's membrane. (4) The cytoplasm is an aqueous environment further organized into specific compartments by internal membranes or complex protein assemblages known as cytoskeletal elements. Although both prokaryotes and eukaryotes have all four organizing features, eukaryotic cells have more elaborate cytoskeletons and have a much more complex system of internal membrane compartments.

Creating and maintaining cell structure requires matter, energy, organization, and information. In Chapters 2 and 3 we considered that matter that is found in living organisms; it is composed of atoms, molecules, and macromolecules. We will discuss the second factor, energy, throughout this unit, particularly in Chapters 7 and 8. Energy is needed to create molecules and macromolecules, and to carry out many cellular functions. Cells also need energy to create and maintain their organization. As discussed throughout this chapter and the rest of Unit II, a cell is not a haphazard bag of components. The molecules and macromolecules that constitute cells have specific sites or compartments in which they are found. While all compartments provide an aqueous environment, the solutes may vary to create compartments with different solute composition, concentration, and pH.

If we compare the structure of a nerve cell in two different people, or two nerve cells within the same individual, we would see striking similarities in their overall structures. Thus, a key attribute of all living cells is the ability to maintain their own characteristic type of internal structure and organization. Finally, a fourth critical issue is information. Cell organization requires instructions that are found in the dynamic blueprint of life, namely, the genetic material. How a cell copies its blueprint for the next generation, and how the dynamic blueprint is read and implemented, will be considered in detail in Unit III. But a brief overview here will help you appreciate cell structure and understand better some of the challenges to maintaining it.

GENOMES AND PROTEOMES

A Cell's Proteome Determines the Characteristics of a Cell

Some organisms consist of a single cell; their ability to survive requires that they change their structure in response to changes in their environment. Many organisms, such as plants and animals, are multicellular, meaning that their bodies are composed of many cells. However, the individual cells of a multicellular organism are not all identical. For example, your body contains nerve cells, muscle cells, skin cells, and so on. How does a single-celled organism change its structure? How do multicellular organisms produce different types of cells?

To answer these questions, we need to consider the distinction between genomes and proteomes. Recall that the **genome** consists of the hereditary material of the organism, all its genes.

Most genes encode information for the production of polypeptides, which assemble into functional proteins. The **proteome** is defined as all the types and relative amounts of proteins that are made in a particular cell at a particular time and under specific conditions. The number and type of genes in an organism's genome set the outer limit of the number and type of proteins that can possibly be made. But not all the protein-encoding genes that an organism has in its genome are used all the time or in all cells of its body. In a single-celled organism a subset of the genome is used to create the specific RNAs needed to make the specific proteins the cell needs to adapt to its environment. Similarly, different cell types are created in a multicellular organism as a different subset of the organism's genome is decoded to produce the characteristic proteins of that cell type. This complement of proteins, in turn, determines the structures a cell can assemble, and the functions it has. A typical eukaryotic cell produces thousands of different types of proteins.

As a complex organism develops, many cells take on a distinctive structure to perform a specific function. This results from the interplay between a cell's environment and its genome and will determine which genes are used to make specific RNAs and which of these RNAs are used to produce the required proteins. These proteins, in turn, strongly influence the cell's shape, internal structure, and ability to accomplish certain organismal tasks. As an example consider human muscle and nerve cells—two cell types that have dramatically different organization and structure. The genome of a muscle cell of a particular person is identical to the genome in his or her nerve cell. Nonetheless, the proteomes of the two different cells are quite different. An important principle in cell biology is that the proteome of a cell determines its structure and function. Several phenomena underlie the differences that are observed in the proteomes of different cell types. Comparing muscle and nerve cells illustrates these phenomena:

1. Certain proteins found in muscle cells are not found in nerve cells and vice versa. For a protein to be expressed in a particular cell, the gene that encodes that protein must be used as a template during **transcription** to make RNA. Because of gene regulation, which is described in Chapter 12, certain genes that are transcribed in muscle cells are not transcribed in nerve cells and vice versa.

2. The relative amounts of certain proteins are different in muscle and nerve cells. The amount of a given protein depends on many factors including how frequently the corresponding gene is transcribed, how efficiently the resulting RNA is used during **translation** to produce a polypeptide, and how long the resulting protein lasts within a cell. Some proteins are found in both nerve and muscle cells but in greatly different amounts. For example a protein called actin occurs abundantly in muscle cells,

where it plays a key role in muscle contraction, but is present to a much lesser extent in nerve cells.

3. The amino acid sequences of particular proteins can vary somewhat in different cell types. As discussed in Chapter 12, the transcribed RNA from one gene can be used to produce two or more polypeptides with slightly different amino acid sequences. For example, tropomyosin is a protein that regulates cell movement. In muscle cells tropomyosin has a slightly different amino acid sequence from the tropomyosin found in nerve cells, even though the same gene encodes both.

4. Nerve and muscle cells can alter their proteins in different ways. After a protein is made, its structure can be changed in a variety of ways. These include the covalent attachment of molecules, such as phosphate and carbohydrate, and the cleavage of a protein to a smaller size.

These phenomena enable nerve and muscle cells (and other cell types) to produce different proteomes and thus different structures and functions. Likewise, these phenomena allow both multicellular and unicellular organisms to change their proteome to survive in a changing environment.

During the last decade or so, researchers have also discovered an association between proteome changes and disease. For example, the proteomes of healthy cells are different from the proteomes of cancer cells. Furthermore, the proteomes of cancer cells change as the disease progresses. One reason for studying cancer cell proteomes is to improve the early detection of cancer by identifying proteins that are made in the early stages, when the disease is most treatable. In addition, information about the ways that the proteomes of cancer cells change may help researchers uncover new treatment options. A key challenge for biologists is to understand the synthesis and function of proteomes in different cell types and how proteome changes may lead to disease conditions.

4.3 PROKARYOTIC CELLS HAVE SMALL GENOMES, PROTEOMES, AND SIMPLE CELLULAR ORGANIZATION

Learning Outcomes:

1. Describe the two domains of prokaryotes and indicate the hallmark feature that distinguishes them from each other.
2. Give the name and function of each detectable structure of prokaryotes.
3. Explain the role of the plasma membrane.
4. Explain what limits the size of prokaryotic cells.

The **prokaryotes** have small genomes and proteomes and simple structural organization. The term *prokaryote* refers to the fact that this group of organisms evolved before the evolution

of the structure known as a nucleus. Prokaryotic cells lack a membrane-enclosed nucleus.

There are two domains of prokaryotes: **Bacteria** and **Archaea**. Both types are unicellular microorganisms of relatively small size. Both groups are abundant and well recognized throughout the world, being found in soil, water, and even our digestive tracts. Most bacterial species are not harmful to humans, but some species are pathogenic—capable of causing disease. Examples of pathogenic bacteria include *Vibrio cholerae*, the source of cholera, and *Bacillus anthracis*, which causes anthrax. To date, no pathogenic Archaea have been found. But some remarkable species of Archaea have been found in extreme environments, such as hot springs and artificially acidified rivers (**Figure 4.5a** and **4.5b**). These species can exist in these extreme environments because, unlike Bacteria and eukaryotes, species of Archaea have a more stable type of covalent bond in their membrane phospholipids (**Figure 4.5c** and **4.5d**) that allows their cell membranes to maintain their integrity even in temperature and pH extremes.

(a)

(b)

(c)

(d)

Figure 4.5 **Archaea are well adapted to extreme environments.** (a) Hot Springs, Yellowstone National Park, Wyoming. Along edges are orange mats of algae and Archaea. (b) The waters of the Rio Tinto in Spain run orange from Archaea that can survive in the mine-acidified waters. (c) The fatty acids of the membrane phospholipids of Archaea are connected to glycerol by ether bonds. (d) The fatty acids of the membrane phospholipids of Bacteria and eukaryotes are connected to glycerol by ester bonds.

Principle: *Structure determines function. The durable ether bonds of the Archaea make its cell membrane particularly strong and able to maintain its integrity in a range of harsh conditions*

In this chapter we discuss the structure of prokaryotic cells. We will examine the genetics of prokaryotes in Chapter 16 and the evolutionary origins of Bacteria and Archaea in Chapter 20. **Figure 4.6** shows a typical bacterial cell. The **plasma membrane** consists of a phospholipid bilayer with embedded proteins. Recall from Chapter 3 that the phospholipid bilayer has an interior region that consists of the hydrophobic hydrocarbon tails of the fatty acids. Water-soluble molecules in the cell's surroundings (and cell's interior) cannot readily pass through this hydrophobic region. Thus, the cell's membrane forms an important barrier between the cell and its external environment. Some of the embedded proteins can form channels that provide regulated pathways for water-soluble molecules to move in to and out of cells.

The chemical activity within a cell's volume requires that materials be exchanged with the environment, both for obtaining raw materials and for exporting undesirable by-products. Such exchanges typically occur on membrane surfaces. The upper limit on cell size is set by the ratio of the cell's membranous surface area to its cell volume. Because the plasma membrane is the only membrane system of the cell, the upper limit on prokaryotic size (volume) is set by how much surface area there is along its plasma membrane. This limitation results in microscopic-sized cells.

All prokaryotes have a plasma membrane; prokaryotic cells that carry out complex biochemical reactions requiring the sequestering of ions on opposite sides of membranes, such as photosynthetic prokaryotes, also have some infoldings of plasma membrane that extend into the interior of the cell.

The **cytoplasm** is the region of the cell that is contained within the interior, delimited by the plasma membrane. Within the fluid environment of the cytoplasm, only a limited number of structural features are visible via microscopy. These include the **nucleoid**, which is the region where the genetic material (DNA) is located, and **ribosomes**, which are complex assemblages of RNAs and proteins, that are required for polypeptide synthesis.

Some important bacterial structures are located outside the plasma membrane. Nearly all species of prokaryotes have a relatively rigid cell wall. The cell wall is porous, so it does not prevent nutrient and waste product exchange between the cell's environment and the plasma membrane, but the cell wall does provide support and protects the plasma membrane and cytoplasm. Many bacteria also secrete a **glycocalyx**, a viscous outer covering surrounding the bacterium. The glycocalyx traps water and helps protect bacteria from drying out. Certain strains of bacteria that infect animals produce a very thick, gelatinous glycocalyx called a **capsule** that may help them avoid being destroyed by the animal's immune (defence) system. Although prokaryotic organisms are all unicellular, some do associate in colonies and often these colonies are held together by **mucilage**, a complex mixture of carbohydrates and polypeptides.

Cell wall

Hydrophilic heads

Membrane bilayer

Cell interior

Nucleoid region: Site where the DNA is found.

Ribosomes: Synthesize polypeptides.

Plasma membrane: Phospholipid bilayer creates a barrier that encloses the cytoplasm.

Cytoplasm: Site of metabolism.

Cell wall: Provides support and protection.

Pili: Allow bacteria to attach to surfaces and to each other.

Glycocalyx: Outer gelatinous covering.

Flagella: Allow certain bacteria to swim.

0.5 μm

(a) A typical rod-shaped bacterium

(b) A colourized electron micrograph of *Escherichia col*

Figure 4.6   Structure of a typical prokaryotic cell.   Prokaryotic cells, which include Bacteria and Archaea cells, lack internal compartmentalization.

 Principle: *Cells are the simplest units of life. In prokaryotes, the organism consists of a single cell.*

The mucilage is shipped from the cell's interior (where it is made) to its external environment.

Finally, many prokaryotes have additional filamentous structures that extend from the cytoplasm outward to the exterior of the cell; these structures are known as pili and flagella. **Pili** are short and numerous and allow prokaryotes to attach to surfaces and to each other. **Flagella** are longer and less abundant; they beat in coordinated fashion and provide a way for prokaryotes to swim. More details on prokaryotic structure and colony-forming abilities are given in Chapter 25. Ribosomes, cell walls, pili, and flagella are examples of organelles. An **organelle** is a structurally well-defined aggregate of macromolecules or membrane-bound compartments with its own unique structure and function.

Because few organelles had been observed inside prokaryotic cells with conventional microscopy techniques, the cytoplasm of bacterial cells was thought to be a fluid-filled space with little internal organization. With the advent of new techniques to fluorescently label macromolecules, used in combination with powerful genetic and molecular approaches, these notions have been revisited. Researchers have discovered that bacteria cells are organized inside their cytoplasm. Furthermore, at least three of the proteins (Ftsz, MreB, and CreS) that contribute to this

prokaryotic organization are related evolutionarily to proteins with analogous functions in eukaryotic cells.

4.4   EUKARYOTIC CELLS HAVE COMPLEX GENOMES, PROTEOMES, AND INTERNAL ORGANIZATION

Learning Outcomes:

1. Compare and contrast the general structural features of prokaryotic and eukaryotic cells.
2. Give three examples of plasma membrane functions, and indicate if the function differs in prokaryotes and eukaryotes.
3. Describe the structure and organization of the cell nucleus.
4. Outline the structures and general functions of the components of the endomembrane system.
5. Distinguish between the rough endoplasmic reticulum and the smooth endoplasmic reticulum.
6. Identify the location of the cytosol in a eukaryotic cell and know its general functions.

7. Describe the three types of protein filaments that make up the cytoskeleton.
8. Explain how motor proteins interact with microtubules or actin filaments to promote cellular movement.

Eukaryotes (meaning "true nucleus") include the kingdoms of animals, fungi, and plants, as well as the diverse collection of eukaryotes known as protists. As their name suggests, eukaryotes have a **nucleus**, a membrane-bound structure containing most of their hereditary material. The nucleus is one of many organelles found in eukaryotes. In contrast to prokaryotes, eukaryotic cells are larger and have far more organelles and compartments, allowing eukaryotic cells to carry out specialized chemical reactions in different environments. The larger size of eukaryotic cells is related to their more extensive use of membranes; the elaborate membrane system of eukaryotes increases their functional surface area, improving their ability to exchange materials with the exterior. The increased surface area allows for an increase in volume and hence allows for larger cells. Eukaryotic cells have a more complex internal organization because they have larger, more complex genomes and have evolved ways to use these genomes in more complex ways that creates even larger proteomes.

Before we consider the complex structural features of eukaryotic cells, let's think briefly about the origins of this complexity. Molecular evidence suggests that eukaryotic cells originated from the union of two prokaryotic cells, one from the domain Bacteria and the other from the domain Archaea. The combined genomes of these two very different organisms, with a wealth of distinct but functionally overlapping units of heredity, were then able to evolve new functions that have produced an array of elaborate organelles. Later in Earth's life history, additional unions of prokaryotic cells with primitive eukaryotic cells likely gave rise to the complex organelles specialized for energy metabolism. You will learn more about the evidence supporting these theories of the origins of eukaryotes in Chapters 6 and 26.

Figure 4.7 and **Figure 4.8** describe the structural features of typical animal and plant cells, respectively. Most of the

Figure 4.7 General structure of an animal cell.   A schematic drawing of a typical animal cell.

Nuclear envelope:
Double membrane that encloses the nucleus.

Nucleus:
Area where genetic material is organized and expressed.

Nuclear pore:
Passageway for molecules into and out of the nucleus.

Ribosome:
Site of polypeptide synthesis.

Central vacuole:
Site that provides storage and regulation of cell volume.

Nucleolus:
Site for ribosome assembly.

Smooth ER:
Site of detoxification and lipid synthesis.

Chromatin:
A complex of protein and DNA.

Rough ER:
Site of protein synthesis, sorting, and secretion.

Cytosol:
Site of many metabolic pathways.

Plasma membrane:
Envelope that controls movement of substances into and out of the cell; site of cell signalling.

Mitochondrion:
Site of ATP synthesis.

Cell wall:
Structure that provides cell support.

Chloroplast:
Site of photosynthesis.

Peroxisome:
Site where hydrogen peroxide and other harmful molecules are broken down.

Cytoskeleton:
Protein filaments provide shape and aid in movement.

Golgi apparatus:
Site of modification, sorting, and secretion of lipids and proteins.

Figure 4.8 General structure of a plant cell. Plant cells lack lysosomes and centrioles. Unlike animal cells, plant cells have an outer cell wall; a large central vacuole that functions in storage, digestion, and cell volume; and chloroplasts, which carry out photosynthesis.

organelles and macromolecule assemblages described in this chapter are found in all eukaryotic cells. Even so, the relative numbers of different membrane-bound compartments and the shape, size, and organization of cells can vary considerably among different species and even among different cell types of the same species.

In the rest of this chapter we will survey the organelles of eukaryotic cells. All cells have a plasma membrane. As in prokaryotes, the term *cytoplasm* refers to the entire region inside the plasma membrane. Figures 4.7 and 4.8 highlight the major types of compartments seen within an animal cell and a plant cell. The compartments of a eukaryote include the interior of the nucleus (blue); the endomembrane system (purple/pink); the semiautonomous organelles (green), which include the chloroplasts (in photosynthetic eukaryotes) and mitochondria; and the cytosol (yellow). The cell wall (orange area) of the plant cell is not part of the cytoplasm, being exterior to the plasma

membrane. The important process of using genes to make RNA (transcription) occurs in the nucleus for the vast majority of genes and to a much more limited extent in the semiautonomous mitochondrial and chloroplast organelles. Translation of RNAs (using the RNAs to make polypeptides) derived from nuclear genes occurs in the cytosol or at the interface of the cytosol with specific portions of the endomembrane system. A limited amount of translation also occurs in the chloroplasts and mitochondria.

Although we discuss structure, which gives the impression of solidity in cells, it is important to remember that cells are a water world and structures form within, and in response to, this aqueous environment. It is remarkable that the aqueous environment of each membrane-bound compartment has its own precise chemical composition, concentration of small solutes and macromolecules, and pH specific to its the function. Nonetheless, mechanisms do allow for small and large molecules to move between the compartments in a regulated fashion that meets the needs of the cell and organism.

The Plasma Membrane Is the Interface Between a Cell and Its Environment

The cytoplasm of all cells is surrounded by a plasma membrane and provides a boundary between a cell and the extracellular environment. Proteins in the plasma membrane play many important roles that affect the activities inside the cell. First, many plasma membrane proteins are involved in **membrane transport** (**Figure 4.9**). Some of these proteins function to transport essential nutrients or ions into the cell, while others are involved in the export of substances. Because of the functioning of these transporters, the plasma membrane is selectively permeable; it allows only certain substances in and out. We will examine the structures and functions of a variety of transporters in Chapter 6.

A second vital function of the plasma membrane is cell signalling. To survive and adapt to changing conditions, cells must be able to sense changes in their environment and react accordingly. In addition, the cells of a multicellular organism need to communicate with one another to coordinate their activities. The plasma membranes of all cells contains receptors that recognize signalling molecules—either environmental agents or molecules secreted by other cells. Once signalling molecules bind to a receptor, this elicits a series of steps known as a signal cascade that causes the cell to respond (Figure 4.9). For example, when you eat a meal, the hormone insulin is secreted into your bloodstream. Insulin binds to receptors in the plasma membrane of cells, resulting in a cellular response that allows cells to take up the glucose from the blood into the cytosol. We will explore the details of signal cascades in Chapter 9.

A third important role of the plasma membrane in animal cells is cell adhesion. Proteins in the plasma membranes of adjacent cells bind to each other and promote cell-to-cell adhesion (Figure 4.9). This phenomenon is critical for animal cells to properly interact to form a multicellular organism.

Just external to the plasma membrane, plants, fungi, and many protists have a cell wall (Figure 4.8) that is composed largely of complex carbohydrates, such as cellulose. The detailed composition of cell walls will be considered later in this chapter, but it is important here to realize that cell walls provide a relatively rigid supporting structure. On its inner face the plasma membrane is connected via vesicles with the endomembrane system.

The Nucleus and the Endomembrane System

In cell biology, the term *nucleus* refers to the organelle found in eukaryotic cells that contains most of the cell's genetic material. The outer membrane that encloses the nucleus is part of a larger network of membranes called the **endomembrane system**. The endomembrane system includes not only the outer membrane of the nuclear envelope but also the endoplasmic reticulum, Golgi apparatus, lysosomes, peroxisomes, secretory vesicles, and vacuoles. The prefix *endo*—meaning "inside"—originally referred only to these organelles and internal membranes. However, we now know that the plasma membrane is also part of this integrated membrane system (**Figure 4.10**). Some of these membranes, such as the outer member of the nuclear envelope and the membrane of the endoplasmic reticulum, have direct connections to one another. Other organelles of the endomembrane system pass materials to one another via **vesicles**—small membrane-enclosed spheres. The movement of vesicles occurs in both directions. For example, vesicles that are formed from the endoplasmic reticulum can fuse with the Golgi apparatus and vesicles from the Golgi apparatus can fuse with the endoplasmic reticulum. Therefore, the endomembrane system forms a dynamic, integrated network of membranes. In this section, we will survey the structures and functions of the organelles of the endomembrane system.

The Eukaryotic Nucleus Contains Chromosomes

The nucleus is the internal compartment that is enclosed by a double-membrane structure termed the **nuclear envelope** (**Figure 4.11**). While the outer membrane of the nuclear envelope is part of the endomembrane system, the phospholipid bilayer of the inner membrane and the interior of the nucleus are not. **Nuclear pores** are formed where the inner and outer nuclear membranes make contact with each other. These pores provide a regulated passage for the movement of molecules and macromolecules into and out of the nucleus. The **nucleoplasm** refers to the fluid component of the nucleus within which nuclear structures and components exist.

In most cells, the nucleus is a relatively large organelle that typically occupies 10%–20% of the total cell volume. Inside the

Figure 4.9 Major functions of the plasma membrane. These include membrane transport, cell signalling, and cell adhesion.

Principle: *Living organisms have mechanisms that maintain homeostasis. Cells receive and send signals, as part of a response to changes in their environment.*

Animal cell

Nucleus

Nuclear envelope

Lysosome

Peroxisomes

Vacuole

Endoplasmic reticulum

Golgi apparatus

Plasma membrane

Plant cell

Figure 4.10   The nucleus and endomembrane system.   This figure highlights the internal compartment of the nucleus (blue), the membranes of the endomembrane system (purple), and the fluid-filled interiors of the endomembrane system (pink). The nuclear envelope is considered part of the endomembrane system but the interior of the nucleus is not.

Pore   Nucleus

Chromatin

Nucleolus

Two membranes of nuclear envelope

Nucleus

Nuclear pore complex

Nucleolus

Chromatin

Nuclear lamina

Nuclear envelope

Pore in nuclear envelope

5.4 μm

Pore complexes

0.4 μm

Chromatin in nucleus

Internal nuclear matrix

Inner membrane

Outer membrane

} Nuclear envelope

Nuclear lamin proteins

Cytosol

Figure 4.11   The nucleus and nuclear envelope.   The nuclear envelope is composed of an inner and an outer membrane that meet at the nuclear pore complex. The inner nuclear membrane is lined with lamin proteins to form the nuclear lamina. The interior of the nucleus contains chromatin, which is attached to the nuclear matrix, and a nucleolus, where ribosomes are assembled. The transmission electron micrograph (top right) is an electron micrograph of an embedded, sectioned nucleus. The image of the pore complexes (middle right) is a scanning electron micrograph. (Micrographs: (top right) © Dr. Don W. Fawcett/Visuals Unlimited; and (middle right) © Dr. Richard Kessel & Dr. Gene Shih/Visuals Unlimited.)

Principle: *The genetic material, DNA, provides a dynamic plan for sustaining life. The genetic material is kept safely in the nucleus, but its products can leave the nucleus via nuclear pores to affect change in the cytoplasm.*

Figure 4.12 Chromosome territories in the cell nucleus. Chromosomes from a chicken were labelled with chromosome-specific fluorescent probes. Each of the seven types of chicken chromosomes is coloured with a different dye. In this fluorescent light micrograph, each chromosome is shown to occupy its own distinct, nonoverlapping territory within the cell nucleus.

BioConnections: *Look ahead to Figure 14.8 What happens to chromosome territories during cell division?*

nucleus are the **chromosomes** and a filamentous network of proteins called the **nuclear matrix**. Each chromosome is composed of genetic material, namely DNA, and many types of proteins that help to compact the chromosome to fit inside the nucleus and organize it for function. The DNA, with its organizing proteins, is termed **chromatin**. The nuclear matrix consists of two parts: the nuclear lamina, which is composed of intermediate

filaments that line the inner nuclear membrane, and an internal nuclear matrix, which is connected to the lamina and fills the interior of the nucleus. The nuclear matrix serves to organize the chromosomes within the nucleus. Each chromosome is located in a distinct, nonoverlapping chromosome territory, which is visible when cells are exposed to dyes that label each type of chromosome (**Figure 4.12**).

The primary function of the nucleus involves the protection, organization, and expression of the genetic material. Because this hereditary material never leaves the nucleus, it is here that transcription of nuclear genes occurs to produce different types of RNA. The mRNAs that contain the information to make specific polypeptides and the tRNAs, which are needed to make all proteins, leave the nucleus through the nuclear pores. Another category of RNA, the rRNA, is synthesized in the nucleus and then interacts with specific proteins to create ribosomal subunits. These ribosomal subunits are assembled in prominent regions of the nucleus known as the **nucleoli** (singular: nucleolus). Once assembled, the ribosomal subunits then exit through the nuclear pores into the cytosol, where they will be assembled into functional ribosomes that work with mRNAs and tRNAs to produce polypeptides during the process of translation.

The Endoplasmic Reticulum Initiates Protein Sorting and Carries Out Certain Metabolic Functions

The **endoplasmic reticulum (ER)** is a convoluted network of membranes that form flattened, fluid-filled tubules or **cisternae** (**Figure 4.13**). The terms *endoplasmic* (which means "in the

Figure 4.13 Structure of the endoplasmic reticulum. The ER is composed of a network of flattened tubules called cisternae that enclose a continuous ER lumen. The rough ER is studded with ribosomes, while the smooth ER lacks ribosomes. The rough ER is continuous with the outer nuclear membrane. The image on the right is a colourized transmission electron micrograph of an embedded, sectioned portion of a cell.

cytoplasm") and *reticulum* ("little net") refer to the location and shape of this organelle. The term **lumen** describes the internal space of an organelle. The ER membrane encloses a single compartment called the **ER lumen**. In some cells, the ER membrane makes up more than half of the total membrane in the cell. The rough ER has its outer surface studded with ribosomes, giving it a bumpy appearance. Once bound to the ER membrane, the ribosomes actively synthesize polypeptides, pushing them through the ER membrane. The smooth ER lacks ribosomes.

Rough ER The **rough endoplasmic reticulum (rough ER)** plays a key role in the initial synthesis and sorting of proteins to their appropriate compartment within the endomembrane system—the ER, Golgi apparatus, lysosomes, vacuoles, plasma membrane—or to outside of the cell. To reach any of these locations, a nascent polypeptide must first be directed to the ER membrane. In conjunction with protein sorting, a second function of the rough ER is the insertion of certain newly made proteins into the membrane. A third important function of the rough ER is the attachment of carbohydrates to proteins and lipids. This process is called **glycosylation**. The topics of protein sorting, membrane protein insertion, and protein glycosylation will be discussed in more detail in Chapter 5, because they are important in the maintenance of cell organization.

Smooth ER The **smooth endoplasmic reticulum (smooth ER)** is continuous with the rough ER and functions in diverse metabolic processes. The extensive network of smooth ER membranes allows increased surface area for key enzymes that play important metabolic roles. In liver cells, enzymes in the smooth ER detoxify thousands of potentially harmful organic molecules; two examples are barbiturate drugs and ethanol. These enzymes convert hydrophobic toxic molecules into more hydrophilic molecules, which are easily excreted from the body.

The smooth ER of liver cells also plays a role in carbohydrate metabolism. The liver cells of animals store energy in the form of glycogen. Glycogen granules in the cytosol sit very close to the smooth ER membrane. When chemical energy is needed, enzymes are activated that break down the glycogen to glucose-6-phosphate. An enzyme in the smooth ER called glucose-6-phosphatase then removes the phosphate group, and glucose is released into the bloodstream.

Another important function of the smooth ER in all eukaryotes is the accumulation of calcium ions. The smooth ER contains calcium pumps that transport Ca^{2+} into the ER lumen. The regulated release of Ca^{2+} into the cytosol is involved in many vital cellular processes, including muscle contraction.

Finally, enzymes in the smooth ER are critical in the synthesis and modification of lipids. For example, steroid hormones, such as estrogen and testosterone, are derived from the lipid cholesterol. Enzymes in the smooth ER are necessary for certain modifications that are needed to produce these hormones. In addition, the smooth ER is the primary site for the synthesis of phospholipids, which are the main lipid component of eukaryotic cell membranes.

The Golgi Apparatus Directs the Secretion, Processing, and Sorting of Cellular Molecules

In 1898 Camillo Golgi, an Italian scientist, discovered the **Golgi apparatus** (also called the Golgi body, Golgi complex, or simply Golgi). It consists of a stack of flattened, membranes; each flattened membrane encloses a single compartment (**Figure 4.14**). The Golgi stacks are named according to their position; *cis* Golgi is close to the ER membrane, the *trans* Golgi is near the plasma membrane, and the *medial* Golgi is found in the middle. Materials are transported between the Golgi stacks via membrane vesicles that bud from one region of the Golgi (for example, the *cis* Golgi) and fuse with another region (for example, the medial Golgi).

The Golgi apparatus performs three overlapping functions: (1) processing, (2) protein sorting, and (3) secretion. For its processing function, enzymes in the Golgi apparatus chemically modify certain proteins and lipids. Carbohydrates can be attached to proteins and lipids in the endoplasmic reticulum. Additional glycosylation can occur in the Golgi. For this to occur, a protein or lipid is transported via vesicles from the ER to the *cis* Golgi. Most of the glycosylation occurs in the medial Golgi. A second type of processing event is proteolysis—enzymes called proteases cut proteins into smaller polypeptides. For example, the hormone insulin is made as a large precursor protein termed proinsulin. In the Golgi, proinsulin is packaged into vesicles containing proteases. Before secretion, the proteases cut out a portion of the proinsulin to create the smaller functional hormone of insulin.

The second function of the Golgi is protein sorting. After a protein enters the Golgi from the ER, it is directed to one of six locations. Either it will stay in the Golgi or it will be transported via vesicles to the ER, a lysosome (in animal cells), a vacuole (in plant cells), the plasma membrane, or the exterior of the cell. The details of this sorting process are covered in Chapter 5.

For the third function, secretion, the Golgi packages different types of materials into secretory vesicles that later fuse with the plasma membrane, thereby releasing their contents outside the cell (Figure 4.14). Proteins that are destined for secretion are synthesized into the ER, travel to the Golgi, and then move to the plasma membrane. This route is called the secretory pathway. Let's now look at exocytosis, the cellular process that accomplishes secretion.

Exocytosis **Exocytosis** is a process in which material inside the cell, which is packaged into vesicles, is excreted into the extracellular environment (**Figure 4.15**). These vesicles are usually derived from the Golgi apparatus. As the vesicles form, a specific cargo is loaded into their interior. For example, in animal cells, large polysaccharides are made within the lumen of the Golgi and packaged within vesicles that bud from the Golgi. The budding process involves the formation of a protein coat around the emerging vesicle. The assembly of coat proteins on the surface of the membrane causes the bud to form. Eventually, the bud separates from the membrane to form a vesicle. After the vesicle is released, the coat is shed. Finally, the vesicle fuses with the plasma membrane and releases its contents into the extracellular medium.

Figure 4.14 **The Golgi apparatus and secretory pathway.** The Golgi is composed of stacks of membranes that enclose separate compartments. Transport to and from the Golgi compartments occurs via membrane vesicles. Vesicles can bud from the ER and go to the Golgi, and vesicles from the Golgi can fuse with the plasma membrane to release cargo to the outside. The pathway from the ER to the Golgi to the plasma membrane is termed the secretory pathway.

Concept check: *Consider the Golgi apparatus as three compartments (cis, medial, and trans) and describe the compartments that a protein will travel through to be secreted.*

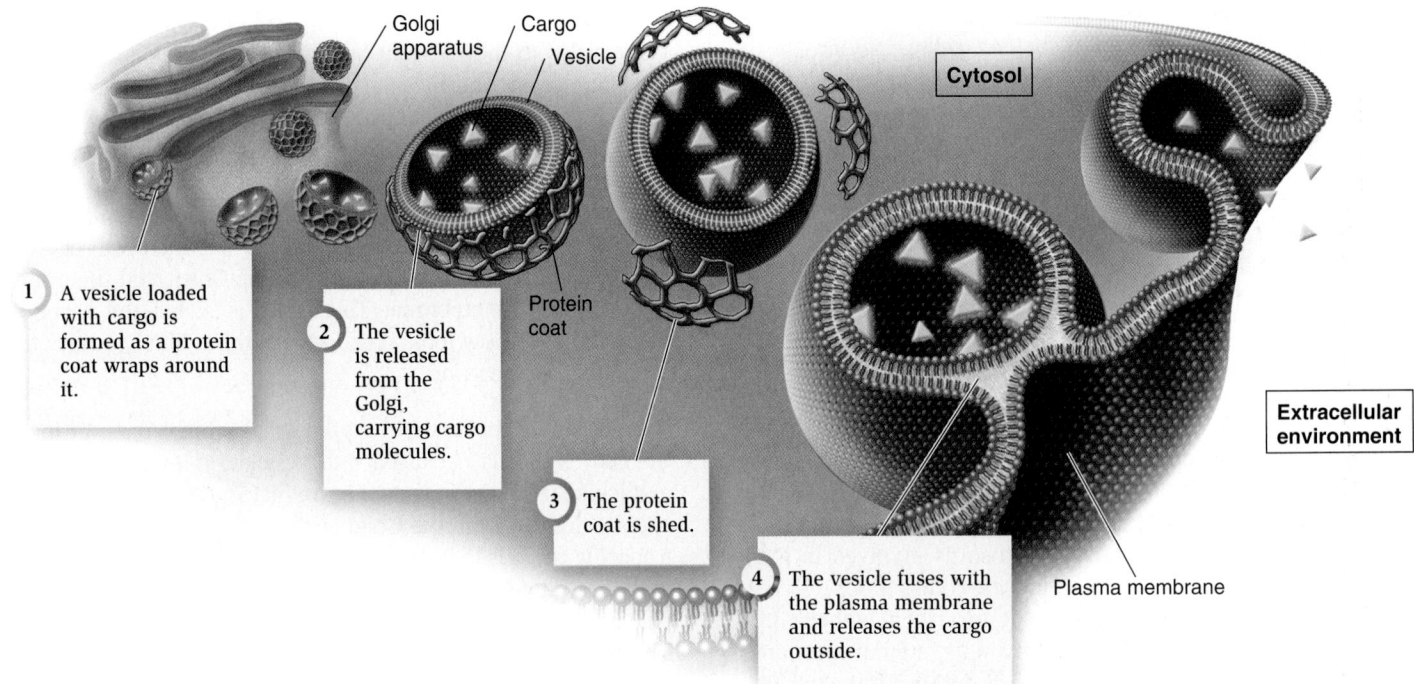

① A vesicle loaded with cargo is formed as a protein coat wraps around it.

② The vesicle is released from the Golgi, carrying cargo molecules.

③ The protein coat is shed.

④ The vesicle fuses with the plasma membrane and releases the cargo outside.

Figure 4.15 **Exocytosis.** Membrane vesicles bud from an organelle inside the cell, such as the Golgi apparatus, and are loaded with a specific cargo. The budding process involves the formation of a protein coat around the emerging vesicle. The protein coat interacts with receptors on the cell membrane and assists in the process by which the vesicle fuses with the membrane. When the vesicle fuses with the plasma membrane, it releases its cargo's contents into the extracellular environment.

Figure 4.16 Receptor-mediated endocytosis. Cargo binds to receptors, which stimulates the aggregation of many receptors and the formation of a vesicle with a protein coat. Once inside the cell, the vesicle sheds its coat. In most cases, the vesicle fuses with an organellar membrane and releases its cargo into the cytosol.

The process of exocytosis illustrates the dynamic and fluid nature of membranes. They readily bud and fuse with other membranes. The same is true for endocytosis, which is described next.

Endocytosis During **endocytosis**, the plasma membrane invaginates, or folds inward, to form a vesicle that brings substances into the cell (**Figure 4.16**). A common form of endocytosis is **receptor-mediated endocytosis**, in which a receptor is specific for a given cargo. When a receptor binds to that cargo, this stimulates the binding of coat proteins to the membrane, which initiates the formation of a vesicle. Many receptors aggregate as a protein coat forms around the vesicle. Once inside the cell, the vesicle sheds its coat. In most cases, the vesicle fuses with an internal membrane organelle, such as a lysosome, and the receptor releases its cargo. Depending on the cargo, the lysosome may release it directly into the cytosol or digest it into simpler building blocks before releasing it.

Other specialized forms of endocytosis occur in certain types of cells. **Pinocytosis** (meaning "cell drinking") involves the formation of membrane vesicles from the plasma membrane as a way for cells to internalize the extracellular fluid. This allows cells to sample the extracellular solutes. Pinocytosis is particularly important in cells that are actively involved in nutrient absorption, such as cells that line the intestine in animals.

Phagocytosis ("cell eating") is an extreme form of endocytosis. It involves the formation of an enormous membrane vesicle called a phagosome, or phagocytic vacuole, that engulfs a large particle, such as a bacterium. Only certain kinds of cells can carry out phagocytosis. For example, macrophages, which are cells of the immune system in mammals, kill bacteria via phagocytosis. Once inside the cell, the phagosome fuses with lysosomes and the digestive enzymes within the lysosomes destroy the bacterium.

Lysosomes Are Involved in Degrading Macromolecules

Lysosomes are small organelles found in animal cells that are able to lyse macromolecules, hence their name. Lysosomes contain many **acid hydrolases**, which are hydrolytic enzymes that use a molecule of water to break a covalent bond. This type of chemical reaction is called hydrolysis. The hydrolases found in a lysosome function optimally at an acidic pH. The fluid-filled interior of a lysosome has a pH of approximately 4.8. If a lysosomal membrane accidentally breaks, releasing acid hydrolases into the cytosol, the enzymes are not very active because the cytosolic pH is neutral (approximately pH 7.0). This prevents significant damage to the cell from accidental leakage.

Lysosomes contain many different types of acid hydrolases that can break down proteins, carbohydrates, nucleic acids, and lipids. One function of lysosomes involves the digestion of substances that are taken up from outside the cell by the process of endocytosis. In addition, lysosomes help digest intracellular materials. In a process known as **autophagy** (meaning "the eating of one's self"), cellular material, such as a worn-out organelle, becomes enclosed in a double membrane (**Figure 4.17**). This **autophagosome** then fuses with a lysosome, the material inside the autophagosome is digested, and the small molecules that are released are recycled back into the cytosol.

Organelle

Autophagosome

Outer membrane
Inner membrane
Lysosome

1 Membrane tubule begins to enclose an organelle.

2 Double membrane completely encloses an organelle to form an autophagosome.

3 Autophagosome fuses with a lysosome. Contents are degraded and recycled back to the cytosol.

Figure 4.17 **Autophagy.**   In the example shown here, a double membrane surrounds a mitochondrion to form an autophagosome, which fuses with a lysosome. The contents of the autophagosome are degraded and released back into the cytosol.

Concept check: *Why do you think autophagy is useful to a cell?*

Peroxisomes Catalyze an Array of Chemical Reactions That Generate Hydrogen Peroxide

Peroxisomes are relatively small organelles found in all eukaryotic cells. They were discovered in 1965 by Christian de Duve. Peroxisomes consist of a single membrane that encloses a fluid-filled lumen (**Figure 4.18**). A typical eukaryotic cell contains several hundred of them. Peroxisomes contain the enzymes to catalyze a diverse array of chemical reactions.

In general, peroxisomes catalyze chemical reactions that typically break down molecules by removing hydrogen or adding oxygen, and they generate hydrogen peroxide, H_2O_2, as a byproduct. One way that hydrogen peroxide can be broken down causes the formation of a hydroxide ion (OH^-) and a molecule

1 Vesicles bud from the ER and fuse with each other to form a premature peroxisome.

2 The import of additional proteins and lipids results in a mature peroxisome.

Premature peroxisome

Mature peroxisome

Division

3 Mature peroxisomes may divide to produce more peroxisomes.

ER

(a) Peroxisome formation

(b) Structure of a peroxisome

Figure 4.18 **Formation and structure of a peroxisome.**   (a) Peroxisome formation. (b) This image is a high-magnification transmission electron micrograph of an embedded, sectioned portion of a cell containing a peroxisome.

called a hydroxide free radical (OH•). The hydroxide free radical is highly reactive and can damage proteins, lipids, and DNA. Therefore, it is beneficial for cells to break down hydrogen peroxide in an alternative manner that does not form a hydroxide free radical. Peroxisomes contain an enzyme called **catalase** that breaks down hydrogen peroxide to make water and oxygen gas, avoiding the production of the dangerous hydroxide free radical.

Depending on the cell type, peroxisomes may contain enzymes that detoxify other molecules. These reactions can generate hydrogen peroxide, which is broken down via catalase. In mammals, for example, large numbers of peroxisomes can be found in the cells of the liver, where toxic molecules accumulate and are broken down.

In addition to detoxification, peroxisomes also contain enzymes involved in the metabolism of fats and amino acids. For instance, plant seeds contain specialized organelles called **glyoxysomes** that are similar to peroxisomes. Glyoxysomes contain enzymes that are needed to convert fats to sugars. These enzymes become active when a seed germinates and the seedling begins to grow.

A general model for peroxisome formation is shown in Figure 4.18, though the details may differ among animal, plant, and fungal cells. To initiate peroxisome formation, vesicles bud from the ER membrane and form a premature peroxisome. Following the import of additional proteins, the premature peroxisome becomes a mature peroxisome. Once the mature peroxisome has formed, it may then divide to further increase the number of peroxisomes in the cell.

Vacuoles Are Specialized Compartments That Function in Storage, Regulation of Cell Volume, and Degradation

The term **vacuole** (literally, "empty space") came from early microscopic observations of these compartments. We now know that vacuoles are not empty but instead contain fluid and sometimes even solid substances. Most vacuoles are made from the fusion of many smaller membrane vesicles. Vacuoles are prominent organelles in plant cells, fungal cells, and certain protists. In animal cells, vacuoles tend to be smaller and are more commonly used to temporarily store materials or transport substances. In animals, such vacuoles are sometimes called storage vesicles.

The functions of vacuoles are extremely varied, and they differ among cell types and even environmental conditions. The best way to appreciate vacuole function is to consider a few examples. Mature plant cells often have a large central vacuole that occupies 80% or more of the cell volume (**Figure 4.19a**). The membrane of this vacuole is called the tonoplast. The central vacuole serves two important purposes. First, it stores a large amount of water, enzymes, and inorganic ions, such as calcium; it also stores other materials, including proteins and pigments. Second, it performs a space-filling function. The fluid-filled vacuole exerts a pressure that meets resistance at the cell wall; this is called turgor pressure. If a plant becomes dehydrated and this pressure is lost, a plant will wilt. Turgor pressure is important in maintaining the structure of plant cells and the plant itself, and it helps to drive the expansion of the cell wall, which is necessary for growth.

Certain species of protists also use vacuoles to maintain cell volume. Freshwater organisms, such as the alga *Chlamydomonas reinhardtii*, have small, water-filled contractile vacuoles that expand as water enters the cell (**Figure 4.19b**). Once they reach a certain size, the vacuoles suddenly contract, expelling their contents to the exterior of the cell. This mechanism is necessary to remove the excess water that continually enters the cell by diffusing across the plasma membrane.

Another function of vacuoles is degradation. Some protists engulf their food into large phagocytic vacuoles or food vacuoles (**Figure 4.19c**). As in the lysosomes of animal cells, food vacuoles contain digestive enzymes to break down the macromolecules within the food. Macrophages, a type of cell found in animals' immune systems, engulf bacterial cells into phagocytic vacuoles, where the bacteria are destroyed.

The Cytosol and Its Organization

The **cytosol** (shown in yellow in Figures 4.8 and 4.9) is defined as all the cytoplasm that is not within a membrane-bounded organelle or organelle system. Though the amount varies

(a) Central vacuole in a plant cell

(b) Contractile vacuoles in an algal cell

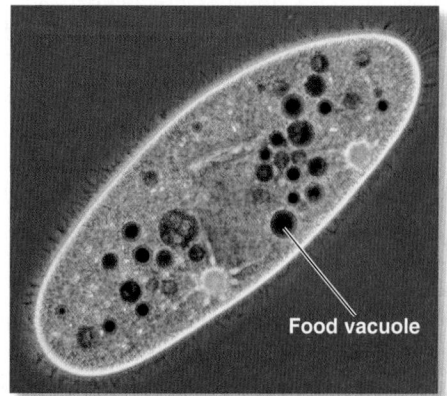

(c) Food vacuoles in a paramecium

Food vacuole

Figure 4.19   **Examples of vacuoles.**   Images **(a)** and **(b)** are transmission electron micrographs; **(c)** is a colourized light micrograph.

among different types of cells, the cytosol typically occupies about 50% of the total cell volume. In this section, we will consider the primary functions of the cytosol. First, it is the site of many chemical reactions that produce the materials and energy necessary for life, such as breaking down food molecules into smaller components. Such reactions release energy, and the components can be used as building blocks to create new cellular molecules and macromolecules. All the cell's proteins begin synthesis on ribosomes free in the cytosol; many are completed there. We will examine the structure and function of large protein filaments found in the cytosol, which provide organization to the cytosol, facilitate vesicular traffic in the endomembrane system, and allow cells to move.

Synthesis and Breakdown of Molecules in the Cytosol

Metabolism is defined as the sum of the chemical reactions by which cells produce the materials and energy that are necessary to sustain life. Although specific steps of metabolism also occur in cell organelles, the cytosol is a central coordinating region for many metabolic activities of eukaryotic cells. Metabolism often involves a series of steps called a **metabolic pathway**. A specific **enzyme** is responsible for speeding up each step in a metabolic pathway. In Chapter 7, we will examine the functional properties of enzymes and consider a few metabolic pathways that occur in the cytosol and cellular organelles.

Some pathways involve the breakdown of a molecule into smaller components, a process termed **catabolism**. Such pathways are needed to generate energy for use by the cell and to generate molecules that provide the building blocks to construct cellular macromolecules. Conversely, other metabolic pathways are involved in **anabolism**, the synthesis of cellular molecules and macromolecules. For example polysaccharides are made by linking sugar molecules together to make complex carbohydrates. To create proteins, amino acids are covalently connected to form a polypeptide.

The Cytoskeleton Provides Cell Organization, Shape, and Movement

Although the cytosol is not defined and structured by membranes, it is nonetheless highly organized by its cytoskeleton. The **cytoskeleton** is a network of three different types of protein filaments: **microtubules**, **intermediate filaments**, and **actin filaments** (**Table 4.1**). Let's first consider the structure of these protein filaments and their roles in the construction and organization of cells. Later, we will examine how they are involved in cell movement.

Microtubules   Microtubules are long, hollow, cylindrical structures about 25 nm in diameter composed of the protein tubulin. The assembly of tubulin to form a microtubule results in a polar structure with a plus end and a minus end (Table 4.1). The designations plus and minus have nothing to do with electrical charge but rather are used to indicate where

growth of microtubules occurs. Growth occurs at the plus end, while shortening of microtubules can occur at either the plus or the minus end. A single microtubule can oscillate between growing and shortening phases, a phenomenon termed **dynamic instability**. Dynamic instability is important in many cellular activities including the sorting of chromosomes during cell division.

Animal cells that are not preparing to divide contain a single structure near their nucleus called the **centrosome** (Table 4.1). Within the centrosome are the centrioles, a conspicuous pair of structures arranged perpendicular to each other, and a **microtubule-organizing centre (MTOC)**. In animal cells, microtubule growth starts at the centrosome such that the minus end is anchored there. In contrast, most plant cells and many protists lack centrosomes and centrioles; they nonetheless do have MTOCs that can organize formation of microtubules. Microtubules are important for cell shape and organization. Organelles, such as the Golgi apparatus, often are attached to microtubules, and vesicles travelling to and from the Golgi can move along microtubular railway tracks. In addition, microtubules are involved in the movement of chromosomes during mitosis and in the orientation of cells during cell division. We will examine these events in Chapter 14.

Actin Filaments   Actin filaments are long, thin fibres approximately 7 nm in diameter; they also are known as **microfilaments** because they are the thinnest cytoskeletal filament (Table 4.1). Each fibre is composed of two strands of actin monomers that spiral around each other. Despite their thinness, actin filaments play a key role in cell strength and shape. Although actin filaments can be dispersed throughout the cytosol, they tend to be highly concentrated near the plasma membrane where the minus ends are anchored. In many types of cells, actin filaments support the plasma membrane and provide strength and shape to the cell. Like microtubules, actin filaments have plus and minus ends, and they are very dynamic structures that grow at the plus end. Cell shape that is defined by actin filaments will also be dynamic. A classic example of this capacity for change is the amoeboid movement of some protists.

Intermediate Filaments   Intermediate filaments are another class of cytoskeletal filament found in cells. Intermediate filament proteins bind to each other in a staggered array to form a twisted, ropelike structure with a diameter of approximately 10 nm (Table 4.1). Intermediate filaments tend to be more stable than microtubules and actin filaments, because they do not polymerize and depolymerize rapidly. They function as tension-bearing fibres that help maintain cell shape and rigidity.

Several types of related proteins can assemble into intermediate filaments. Desmins form intermediate filaments in muscle cells and provide mechanical strength. Keratins form intermediate filaments in skin, intestinal, and kidney cells, where they are important for mechanical strength and cell shape. They are also a major constituent of hair and nails. In addition, nuclear lamins are a category of intermediate filaments that function inside the cell nucleus.

Table 4.1	Types of Cytoskeletal Filaments		
Characteristic	Microtubules	Intermediate filaments	Actin filaments
Diameter	25 nm	10 nm	7 nm
Structure	Hollow tubule	Twisted filament	Spiral filament

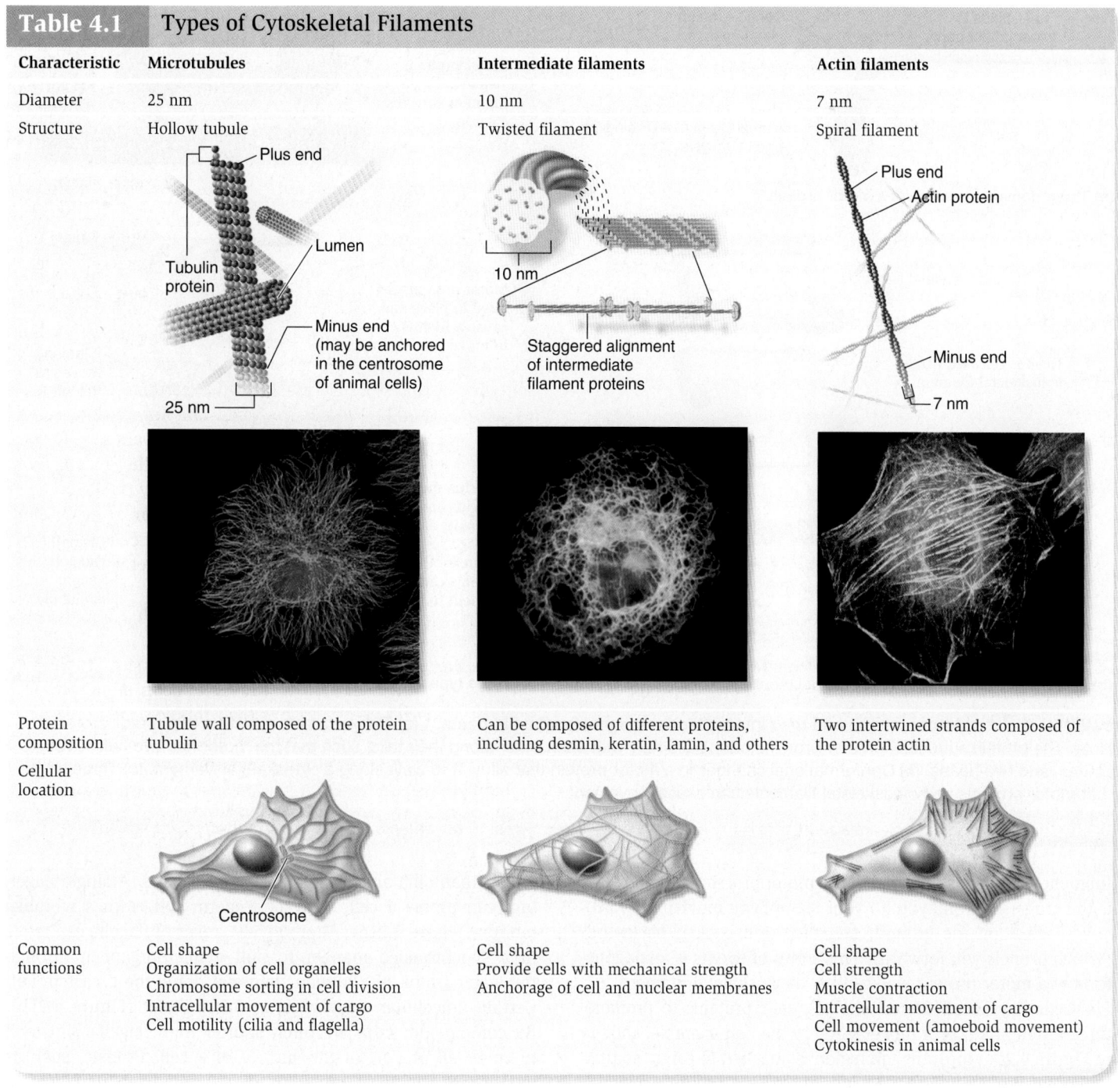

Protein composition	Tubule wall composed of the protein tubulin	Can be composed of different proteins, including desmin, keratin, lamin, and others	Two intertwined strands composed of the protein actin
Cellular location			
Common functions	Cell shape Organization of cell organelles Chromosome sorting in cell division Intracellular movement of cargo Cell motility (cilia and flagella)	Cell shape Provide cells with mechanical strength Anchorage of cell and nuclear membranes	Cell shape Cell strength Muscle contraction Intracellular movement of cargo Cell movement (amoeboid movement) Cytokinesis in animal cells

Motor Proteins Interact with Microtubules or Actin Filaments to Promote Cellular Movements

Motor proteins are a category of cellular proteins that use ATP as a source of energy to promote movement. As shown in **Figure 4.20a**, a motor protein consists of three domains called the head, hinge, and tail. The head is the site where ATP binds and is hydrolyzed to ADP and a molecule of inorganic phosphate (P_i). ATP binding and hydrolysis cause a bend in the hinge, which results in movement when the tail region is attached to other proteins or to other kinds of cellular molecules.

To promote cellular movement, the head region of a motor protein interacts with a cytoskeletal filament (**Figure 4.20b**). When ATP binds and is hydrolyzed, the motor protein attempts to "walk" along the filament. The head of the motor protein is initially attached to a filament. To move forward, the head detaches from the filament, cocks forward, binds to the filament, and cocks backward. To imagine how this works, consider the act of walking in which the ground is a cytoskeletal

(a) Three-domain structure of a motor protein

Tail—binds to other components

Hinge—region that bends

Head—binds to cytoskeletal filament; site of ATP binding and hydrolysis

Cytoskeletal filament

1 Head is released from cytoskeletal filament.

2 Head cocks forward and binds to filament.

3 Head cocks backward (this moves the tail from left to right).

(b) Movement of a motor protein along a cytoskeletal filament

Cargo

Motor proteins "walk" along a filament carrying a cargo.

Motor protein

Cytoskeletal filament

Motor proteins are fixed in place and cause a filament to move.

Motor proteins in a fixed position

Filament moves to the left

Linker protein

Both the motor proteins and filaments are fixed in place so the actions of the motor proteins cause the filament to bend.

Motor proteins pulling on adjacent microtubule

(c) Three types of movements

Figure 4.20 Motor proteins and their interactions with cytoskeletal filaments. (a) Three-domain structure of a motor protein. Note: The protein subunits of motor proteins often associate with each other along their tails, such that the motor has two tails, two hinges, and two heads. **(b)** Conformational changes in a motor protein that allow it to walk along a cytoskeletal filament. **(c)** Three ways that motor proteins and cytoskeletal filaments can cause movement.

BioConnections: *Look ahead to figure 44.7. Which of these three types of movements occurs during muscle contraction?*

filament, your leg is the head of the motor protein, and your hip is the hinge. To walk, you lift your leg up, you move it forward, you place it on the ground, and then you cock it backward (which propels you forward). This series of events is analogous to how a motor protein walks along a cytoskeletal filament.

Cells have used the actions of motor proteins to promote three different kinds of movements. In the first example, shown in **Figure 4.20c** (top), the tail region is attached to cargo, so that the motor protein moves the cargo from one location to another along the cytoskeletal filament. Alternatively, a motor protein can remain in place and cause the filament to move (Figure 4.20c, middle). As discussed in Chapter 44, this occurs during muscle contraction. A third possibility is that both the motor protein and filament are restricted in their movement. In this case, when the motor protein attempts to walk, it exerts a force that causes the filament to bend (Figure 4.20c, bottom). As described next, this occurs during the bending of cilia and flagella.

Let's now consider some specific examples in which motor proteins and cytoskeletal filaments interact and result in movement. In certain kinds of cells, microtubules and motor proteins facilitate movement involving cell appendages called cilia and flagella (singular: cilium and flagellum). Flagella are usually

longer than cilia and present singly or in pairs. A single flagellum can propel a cell, such as a sperm cell, with a whiplike motion (**Figure 4.21a**). Alternatively, a pair of flagella can move in a synchronized manner to pull a microorganism through the water (think of a human swimmer doing the breaststroke). Certain unicellular algae swim in this manner (**Figure 4.21b**). By comparison, **cilia** are often shorter than flagella and tend to cover all or part of the surface of a cell. Protists, such as paramecia, can have hundreds of adjacent cilia that beat in a coordinated fashion to propel the organism through water (**Figure 4.21c**).

Despite their differences in length, cilia and flagella share the same internal structure (**Figure 4.22b**). This arrangement, containing microtubules, the motor protein dynein, and linking proteins is called an **axoneme**. In the cilia and flagella of most eukaryotic organisms, the microtubules form an arrangement called a 9 + 2 array. Each of the two central microtubules consists of a single microtubule, while the outer nine are doublet microtubules, which are two merged microtubules. The microtubules in cilia and flagella emanate from basal bodies, which are anchored to the cytoplasmic side of the plasma membrane. Much like the centrosome of animal cells, the basal bodies

(a) Sperm with a long flagellum

(b) *Chlamydomonas* with 2 flagella

(c) Paramecium with many cilia

Figure 4.21   **Cellular movements caused by the actions of flagella and cilia.**   Both flagella and cilia cause movement by a bending motion. In flagella, movement occurs by a whiplike motion that is due to the propagation of a bend from the base to the tip. In addition, the nature of swimming depends on the length of the appendage and whether it involves coordination among multiple flagella or cilia. **(a)** Sperm swim by means of a single long flagellum that moves in a whiplike motion. **(b)** The swimming of *Chlamydomonas reinhardtii* also involves a whiplike motion at the base, but the motion is precisely coordinated between two flagella. This results in swimming behaviour that resembles a breaststroke. **(c)** Ciliated protozoa swim via many shorter cilia. The bending motion is coordinated among multiple adjacent cilia. All three images are light micrographs; (a) and (c) are colourized.

Concept check: *Describe the type of movements that are occurring in dynein and microtubules during the movement of a cilium or flagellum.*

(a) Human sperm cell

(b) Molecular structure of a flagellum

Figure 4.22   **Structure of a eukaryotic flagellum.**   **(a)** SEM of a human sperm cell. **(b)** Drawing of the axoneme. The core structure consists of a 9 + 2 arrangement of nine outer doublet microtubules and two central microtubules. This structure is anchored to the basal body, which has nine triplet microtubules, in which three microtubules are fused together. Note: The structure of the basal body is very similar to centrioles in animal cells.

provide a site for microtubules to grow. In addition to microtubules, the core structure of a cilium and flagellum also has motor proteins, namely dynein, and linking proteins, such as nexin, that hold the axoneme together.

The movement of both cilia and flagella involves the propagation of a bend, which begins at the base of the structure and proceeds toward the tip (see **Figure 4.22a**). The bending occurs because dynein is activated to walk toward the basal body of the microtubules. ATP hydrolysis is required for this process. However, the microtubules and dynein are not free to move relative to each other because of linking proteins. Therefore, instead of dyneins freely walking along the microtubules, they exert a force that bends the microtubules (see Figure 4.22b, bottom panel). The dyneins at the base of the structure are activated first, followed by dyneins that are progressively closer to the tip of the appendage. The resulting movement propels the organism.

As a second example, consider how motor proteins interact with actin. In protists, such as the amoeba, movement occurs via the dynamic rearrangement of the actin cytoskeleton (**Figure 4.23**). Actin filaments are formed near the leading edge to create a projection called a lamellipodium. The cell is pulled toward the leading edge by using motor proteins, such as myosin, which tug on actin filaments and promote cellular movement. As discussed in Chapter 44,

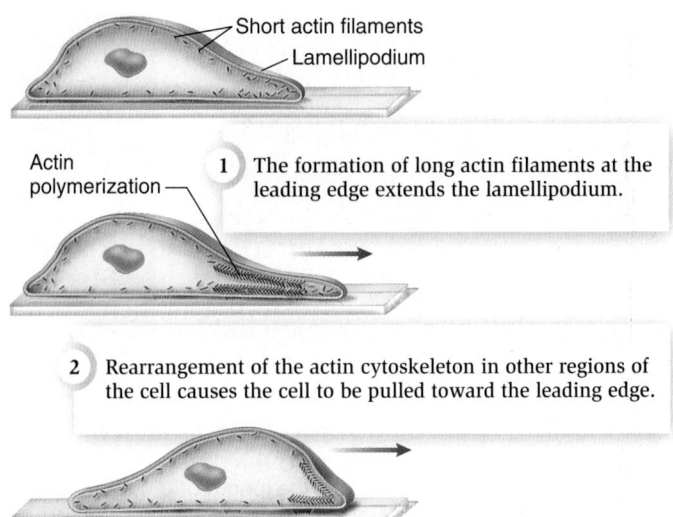

Figure 4.23 Amoeboid movement promoted by changes in the locations of actin filaments.

actin and myosin are responsible for the movement observed in muscle cells. Actin filaments and myosin motors are also involved in other types of movement, as we will see next in our Feature Investigation.

FEATURE INVESTIGATION

Sheetz and Spudich Showed That Myosin Walks Along Actin Filaments

Cell biologists often gain clues to protein function from studying living cells. In the early 1950s, Hugh Huxley, Andrew F. Huxley, and their colleagues studied muscle contraction via microscopy and other techniques. They proposed the sliding-filament model for muscle contraction, in which actin filaments slide past thicker filaments composed of myosin. This model was based on observations involving intact muscle cells. Research at that time and during subsequent decades indicated that actin and myosin were necessary for muscle movement.

Biologists want to understand how a process, such as muscle contraction, works at the molecular level in living cells. This is challenging because the proteome of every living cell is composed of thousands of different proteins, making it difficult to establish the function of any one protein, isolated from its cellular context. As an alternative to studying a process in living cells **in vivo** (meaning "in life") another approach is to isolate and purify cellular components and study their functions outside the cell. This is an **in vitro** approach (literally "in glass," such as in a glass test tube).

In 1983, approximately 30 years after the sliding-filament model was proposed, Michael Sheetz and James Spudich devised a clever approach to studying myosin function

in vitro. Before their work, researchers had learned how to purify myosin protein from muscle cells. A fragment of myosin could be attached to a fluorescently labelled bead, making it possible to follow myosin movement by using a fluorescence microscope. However, to study movement, Sheetz and Spudich also needed actin filaments. Although actin filaments can be purified from cells, they become a tangled mess during the purification process. Luckily the researchers were aware that the alga *Nitella axillaris* has arrays of actin filaments that lie inside the cell and parallel to the plasma membrane. These parallel arrays function in the phenomenon known as **cytoplasmic streaming**, in which the cytoplasm circulates throughout the cell to distribute resources efficiently in large cells. They also knew that Nitella has extraordinarily large cells (~1 mm × 4 cm).

Figure 4.24 illustrates the in vitro approach of Sheetz and Spudich. Their procedure involved cutting open the large *Nitella* cells and pinning down the plasma membrane to the substrate. They then carefully rinsed the cells. Except for chloroplasts, which are found between the plasma membrane and the actin filaments, the rest of the cellular contents were washed away, exposing the actin filaments. Next, a solution containing purified myosin attached to fluorescent beads was added and observed via fluorescence microscopy. Sheetz and Spudich conducted their experiments with and without ATP, because it

HYPOTHESIS Myosin is a motor protein that can walk along actin filaments.

KEY MATERIALS Myosin proteins had already been purified and attached to fluorescent beads. The researchers also obtained cells of *Nitella axillaris*, an alga with relatively large cells that have parallel actin filaments running under the plasma membrane.

Experimental level   **Conceptual level**

1   Cut apart *Nitella axillaris* cells and pin the plasma membrane down. Wash away the rest of the cellular components except for the actin filaments and the chloroplasts that lie between the actin filaments and the plasma membrane.

2   Add a solution containing purified myosin attached to fluorescent beads. This is done in the presence and absence of ATP and using myosin treated with and without NEM, a chemical that inhibits myosin.

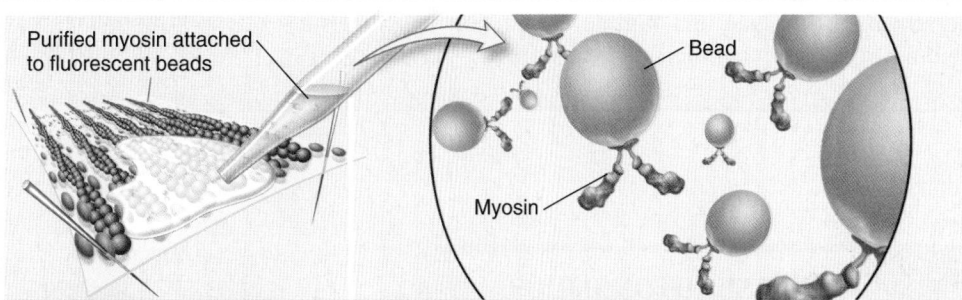

3   Observe by fluorescence microscopy whether the beads move.

Myosin walking along an actin filament

4   **THE DATA**

Results from step 3:

Conditions	Movement observed?
Plus ATP, plus NEM	No
No ATP, no NEM	No
Plus ATP, no NEM	Yes

This is a time-lapse micrograph in which photos were taken every few seconds. It shows a single bead (yellow) moving from left to right. The red objects are stained chloroplasts, which are below the actin filaments. The actin filaments are not visible in this micrograph because they are not fluorescently labeled.

5   **CONCLUSION**

Myosin is a protein that uses ATP to move along actin filaments.

6   Source: Sheetz MP, Spudich JA. Movement of myosin-coated fluorescent beads on actin cables in vitro. *Nature* 303(5912): 31–35.

Figure 4.24   Movement of myosin-coated beads along actin filaments.

was known that ATP was needed for muscle cell movement. In addition, the researchers tested the effects of N-ethylmaleimide (NEM), a chemical that was already known to bind to myosin and inhibit its function. The researchers looked for myosin movement under the various conditions. The results are summarized in Figure 4.24 part (4). Myosin was observed moving along actin filaments only when ATP was present and NEM was absent.

Taken together, these in vitro experiments confirmed that myosin is a motor protein that uses ATP to walk along actin filaments and that all that is needed for movement are actin, myosin, and ATP. In addition, the results are consistent with the idea that different types of movement, such as cytoplasmic streaming in algae and muscle contraction in animals, use the same underlying molecular mechanism—in this case,

an interaction between the motor protein myosin and actin filaments.

Experimental Questions

1. What hypothesis was tested in the experiment of Figure 4.24? What observations led to the proposal of this hypothesis?
2. What is the benefit of purifying cellular components and studying them in vitro instead of in intact cells? What was the benefit of using *Nitella axillaris* to determine the function of myosin? What was the purpose of using the fluorescent beads in the experiment? What was the purpose of NEM in the experiment?
3. Explain the results of the experiment of Figure 4.24.

4.5   THE SEMIAUTONOMOUS EUKARYOTIC ORGANELLES

Learning Outcomes:

1. Describe the structures and general functions of mitochondria and chloroplasts.

Now we will examine those eukaryotic organelles that are considered semiautonomous: mitochondria and chloroplasts (**Figure 4.25**). These organelles can grow and divide, and they contain DNA that encodes some essential polypeptides. But these organelles are not completely autonomous because they must import materials from other parts of the cell for their internal components. For example, most of the proteins that are found in mitochondria must be imported because they are encoded by the nuclear genome and synthesized in the cytosol. In this section we will survey the structures and functions of the semiautonomous organelles in eukaryotic cells. In Chapter 5 we will consider the evolutionary origins of these organelles, and in Chapters 7 and 8 we will explore the functions of mitochondria and chloroplasts in greater depth.

Mitochondria Supply Cells with Most of Their ATP

Mitochondrion (plural: mitochondria) literally means "thread granule." They are similar in size to bacteria. Depending on its function, a cell may contain a few hundred to a few thousand mitochondria; cells with particularly heavy energy demands, such as muscle cells, have more mitochondria than other cells. Indeed, research has shown that regular exercise increases the number and size of mitochondria in human muscle cells to meet the expanded demand for energy.

Figure 4.25   Semiautonomous organelles.   These are the mitochondria and chloroplasts.

Principle: *Living organisms use energy. Mitochondria and chloroplasts generate energy molecules.*

A mitochondrion has an outer membrane and an inner membrane separated by a region called the intermembrane space (**Figure 4.26**). The inner membrane is highly invaginated (folded) to form projections called cristae. These invaginations greatly increase the surface area of the inner membrane, which is the site at which ATP is made. The compartment inside the inner membrane is the mitochondrial matrix. These separate compartments are essential for mitochondrial function.

The primary role of mitochondria is to convert the chemical energy stored within the covalent bonds of the food animals eat

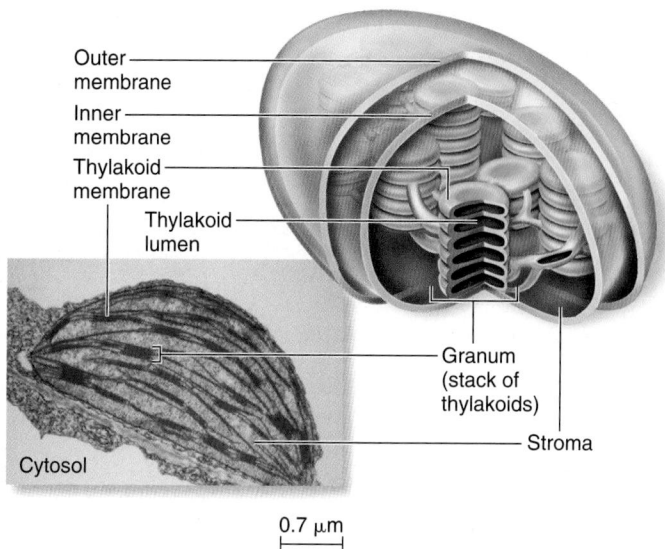

Figure 4.26 **Structure of a mitochondrion.** This organelle is enclosed in two membranes. Numerous cristae in the inner membrane increase the membrane's surface area. The mitochondrial matrix lies inside the inner membrane. The transmission electron micrograph is a colourized image of an embedded, sectioned mitochondrion.

Figure 4.27 **Structure of a chloroplast.** Like a mitochondrion, a chloroplast is enclosed in a double membrane. In addition, it has an internal thylakoid membrane system that forms flattened compartments. These compartments stack on each other to form grana. The stroma is located inside the inner membrane but outside the thylakoid membrane. The transmission electron micrograph is a colourized image of an embedded sectioned cell in a region with a chloroplast.

or the carbohydrates that plants make into a form that can be readily used by cells; this form is the molecule ATP. Covalent bonds in sugars, fats, and amino acids store a large amount of energy. The breakdown of these molecules into simpler molecules releases energy that is used to make ATP. Many proteins in living cells use ATP to carry out their functions, such as muscle contraction, uptake of nutrients, cell division, and many other cellular processes.

Mitochondria perform other functions as well. They are involved in the synthesis, modification, and breakdown of several types of cellular molecules. For example, the synthesis of certain hormones requires enzymes that are found in mitochondria. Therefore, if mitochondria do not function properly, this affects not only ATP synthesis but the synthesis of other products as well. Another interesting role of mitochondria is to generate heat in specialized fat cells known as brown fat cells. Groups of brown fat cells serve as "heating pads" that help to revive hibernating animals and protect sensitive areas of young animals from the cold.

Chloroplasts Carry Out Photosynthesis

Chloroplasts are organelles that can capture light energy and use some of that energy to synthesize organic molecules, such as glucose. This process, called **photosynthesis**, is described in Chapter 8. Chloroplasts are found in nearly all species of plants and algae. **Figure 4.27** shows the structure of a typical chloroplast. Like the mitochondrion, a chloroplast contains an outer

and an inner membrane. An intermembrane space lies between these two membranes. A third membrane, the **thylakoid membrane**, forms many flattened, fluid-filled tubules that enclose a single, convoluted compartment. These tubules tend to stack on top of each other to form a structure called a **granum** (plural: grana). The **stroma** is the compartment of the chloroplast that is inside the inner membrane but outside the thylakoid membrane. The thylakoid membrane encloses the **thylakoid lumen**. The chloroplast's elaborate membrane system is required for the amazing process of photosynthesis, in which the radiant energy of the sun is captured and ultimately stored in the covalent bonds of glucose.

Chloroplasts are a specialized version of plant organelles that are more generally known as **plastids**. All plastids are derived from unspecialized **proplastids**. The plastid types are distinguished by their synthetic abilities and by the types of pigments they contain. Chloroplasts, which carry out photosynthesis, contain the green pigment chlorophyll. The abundant number of chloroplasts in the leaves of plants gives them their green colour (**Figure 4.28a**). Chromoplasts, a second type of plastid, function in synthesizing and storing yellow, orange, and red pigments. Chromoplasts give many fruits and flowers their colours (**Figure 4.28b**). In autumn, the chromoplasts also give many leaves their yellow, orange, and red colours. A third type of plastid, leucoplasts, typically lacks pigment molecules. Different types of leucoplasts can store and produce different macromolecules. The amyloplast is the most common type of leucoplast; it synthesizes and stores starch. Amyloplasts are common in underground structures, such as roots and tubers (**Figure 4.28c**).

(a) Leaves, which contain chloroplasts   **(b) Fruit, which contain chromoplasts**   **(c) Roots, which contain amyloplasts**

Figure 4.28 Types of plastids. (a) Chloroplasts are involved in photosynthesis and give plants their green colour. **(b)** Chromoplasts store yellow, orange, and red pigments, typically found in fruit and flowers. **(c)** Amyloplasts are colourless plastids that store starch in roots.

4.6   BEYOND THE CELL MEMBRANE: THE EXTRACELLULAR MATRIX

Learning Outcomes:

1. Give an example of the extracellular matrix in plants, animals, and fungi, and name a feature common to them all.
2. Explain the relationship of exocytosis to the extracellular matrix.

All eukaryotic organisms export material, via exocytosis, to the exterior of the cells. In plants, fungi, and many protists a cell wall is created surrounding the cell. The cell wall is usually semirigid and provides support and protection, as well as the filtering of materials from the environment. The plant cell wall is made of carbohydrates with some embedded proteins; the dominant polysaccharide is cellulose. We will look at the plant cell wall in detail in the next chapter. The cell wall of fungi is made of chitin, which consists of repeating units of glucosamine (a sucrose that has an amino group added). The cell wall composition of protists is quite varied; some samples of their components include polysaccharides, glycoproteins, and silicon.

Animal cells do not have cell walls. They nonetheless also export material to their exterior to create an extracellular matrix. The **extracellular matrix (ECM)** consists of fibrous proteins in a gel-like substance made of proteoglycans (polypeptides with sugars attached). The physical properties (such as strength) of the ECM are variable based on the composition of its proteins and proteoglycans, but one common characteristic is that the ECM resists compression. The ECM is very important to the structure of multicellular organisms, as we will see in the next chapter, because in addition to support it can be a media through which communication can occur.

Summary of Key Concepts

4.1   Microscopy as a Tool To See Cells

- Three important parameters in microscopy are magnification, resolution, and contrast. A light microscope uses light for illumination, and an electron microscope uses an electron beam.
- Transmission electron microscopy (TEM) provides the highest-resolution microscopy, and scanning electron microscopy (SEM) produces an image of a three-dimensional surface. Light microscopy, especially with macromolecule-specific staining, allows for detailed analysis of cells. (Figures 4.1, 4.2, 4.3, 4.4)

4.2   Physical and Biological Principles that Influence Cell Structure

- Cell structure relies on four phenomena: matter, energy, organization, and information.
- Every living organism has a genome. The genes within the genome contain the information to create RNA molecules by the process of transcription. These RNA molecules are decoded during the process of translation to make polypeptides that fold into proteins.
- All the proteins that a cell makes are collectively called its proteome. The proteome determines a cell's particular structures and functions.

4.3   Prokaryotic Cells Have Small Genomes and Proteomes and Simple Cellular Organization

- We can classify all forms of life into two categories based on cell structure: prokaryotes and eukaryotes.
- The prokaryotes have a relatively simple structure and lack a membrane-enclosed nucleus. The two domains of prokaryotes are Bacteria and Archaea. Structures of prokaryotic cells include the plasma membrane and the cytoplasm; the nucleoid and ribosomes are within the cytoplasm. Many prokaryotes also have a cell wall and a glycocalyx, exterior to the plasma membrane, and pili or flagella that extend from the plasma membrane into the exterior. (Figure 4.5 and 4.6)
- Despite their relatively simple structure, prokaryotic cells are capable of organizing their cytoplasm.

4.4 Eukaryotic Cells Have Complex Genomes, Proteomes, and Internal Organization

- Eukaryotic cells are compartmentalized into organelles and contain a nucleus that houses most of their DNA. (Figures 4.7, 4.8)

- Proteins in the plasma membrane perform many important roles that affect activities inside the cell, including membrane transport, cell signalling, and cell adhesion. (Figure 4.9)

- The primary function of the nucleus involves the organization, duplication, and transcription of the cell's genetic material. A second important function is the assembly of ribosomes. (Figures 4.10, 4.11, 4.12)

- The endomembrane system includes the outer membrane of the nuclear envelope, endoplasmic reticulum, Golgi apparatus, lysosomes, vacuoles, and plasma membrane. The rough endoplasmic reticulum (rough ER) plays a key role in the initial sorting of proteins. The smooth endoplasmic reticulum (smooth ER) functions in metabolic processes, such as detoxification, carbohydrate metabolism, accumulation of calcium ions, and synthesis and modification of lipids. (Figure 4.13)

- The Golgi apparatus performs three overlapping functions: processing, protein sorting, and secretion. (Figure 4.14)

- Eukaryotic cells have two other mechanisms, exocytosis and endocytosis, to transport large molecules and particles. Exocytosis is a process in which material inside the cell is packaged into vesicles and excreted into the extracellular environment. During endocytosis, the plasma membrane folds inward to form a vesicle that brings substances into the cell. Forms of endocytosis include pinocytosis, phagocytosis, and receptor-mediated endocytosis. (Figures 4.15, 4.16)

- Lysosomes degrade macromolecules and help digest substances taken up from outside the cell (endocytosis) and inside the cell (autophagy). (Figure 4.17)

- Peroxisomes catalyze certain chemical reactions, typically those that break down molecules by removing hydrogen or adding oxygen. Peroxisomes usually contain enzymes involved in the metabolism of fats and amino acids. (Figure 4.18)

- Types and functions of vacuoles include central vacuoles, contractile vacuoles, and phagocytic or food vacuoles. (Figure 4.19)

- The cytosol is a central coordinating region for many metabolic activities of eukaryotic cells. A critical activity of all cells is translation, the synthesis of polypeptides.

- The cytoskeleton is a network of three different types of protein filaments: microtubules, intermediate filaments, and actin filaments. Microtubules are important for cell organization, shape, and movement. Intermediate filaments help maintain cell shape and rigidity. Actin filaments support the plasma membrane and play a key role in cell strength, shape, and movement. (Table 4.1, Figures 4.20, 4.21, 4.22, 4.23, 4.24)

4.5 The Semiautonomous Eukaryotic Organelles

- Mitochondria and chloroplasts are considered semiautonomous because they can grow and divide, and they contain DNA that encodes some essential polypeptides, but they still depend on other parts of the cell for their internal components. (Figure 4.25)

- Mitochondria produce most of a cell's ATP, which is used by many proteins to carry out their functions. Other mitochondrial functions include the synthesis, modification, and breakdown of cellular molecules and the generation of heat in specialized fat cells. (Figure 4.26)

- Chloroplasts, which are found in nearly all species of plants and algae, carry out photosynthesis. (Figure 4.27)

- Plastids, such as chloroplasts, chromoplasts, and amyloplasts, differ in their function and the pigments they store. (Figure 4.28)

4.6 Beyond the Cell Membrane: The Extracellular Matrix

- The extracellular matrix (ECM) is a network of material that is secreted from plant and animal cells and forms a complex meshwork outside of cells.

- In the ECM of animals, proteins and polysaccharides are the major constituents. These materials are involved in strength, structural support, organization, and cell signalling.

Test to Assess Your Learning

1. The cell doctrine states that
   a. any living organism is composed of one or more cells.
   b. new cells are derived from organic molecules from the environment.
   c. the smallest units of living organisms are atoms.
   d. the function of cells depends on the shape of the cell.
   e. all of the above.

2. When using microscopes, the resolution refers to
   a. the ratio between the size of the image produced by the microscope and the actual size of the object.
   b. the degree to which a particular structure looks different from other structures around it.
   c. how well a structure takes up certain dyes.
   d. the ability to see two closely associated objects as distinct.
   e. the degree to which the image is magnified.

3. A bacterial cell may possess a _____, which may protect it from the immune system of other multicellular organisms that it may infect.
   a. cell wall
   b. flagellum
   c. pili
   d. nucleoid
   e. capsule

4. Different cells of the same multicellular individual have different proteomes because of all the following except
   a. differences in the types of proteins made in different cell types.
   b. differences in the genomes of the different cell types.
   c. the abundance of certain proteins may not be the same in different cell types.
   d. the amino acid sequences of proteins may be different in different cell types.
   e. different cell types may alter the proteins in different ways.

5. The process of polypeptide synthesis is called
   a. metabolism.
   b. transcription.
   c. translation.
   d. hydrolysis.
   e. both (c) and (d).

6. Which of the following is not part of the endomembrane system?
   a. The outer membrane of the nuclear envelope.
   b. The endoplasmic reticulum.
   c. The Golgi apparatus.
   d. Lysosomes.
   e. Mitochondria.

7. Molecules move into and out of the nucleus by
   a. diffusing through the nuclear membrane.
   b. using transport proteins.
   c. moving through nuclear pores.
   d. attaching to the nucleolus.
   e. all of the above.

8. Functions of the smooth endoplasmic reticulum include
   a. detoxification of harmful organic molecules.
   b. metabolism of carbohydrates.
   c. protein sorting.
   d. all of the above.
   e. (a) and (b) only.

9. The central vacuole in many plant cells is important for
   a. storage.
   b. photosynthesis.
   c. structural support.
   d. all of the above.
   e. (a) and (c) only.

10. Peroxisomes
    a. are vesicles similar to lysosomes that break down different classes of macromolecules.
    b. play an important role in the synthesis of ATP.
    c. are vesicles that contain enzymes necessary for manufacturing complex sugars.
    d. are the organelles primarily involved in protein synthesis.
    e. contain the enzyme catalase, which breaks down hydrogen peroxide to water and oxygen.

11. The function of the extracellular matrix (ECM) in most multicellular organisms is
    a. to provide strength.
    b. to provide structural support.
    c. to organize cells and other body parts.
    d. cell signalling.
    e. all of the above.

Articulate to Assess Your Learning

1. What are the common characteristics of all organelles? What additional feature do some have?

2. Explain how actin filaments are involved in movement.

3. Explain the function of the Golgi apparatus.

4. Compare and contrast organization within prokaryotic and eukaryotic cells.

Collaborate to Assess and Extend Your Learning

1. Imagine you touch a doorknob just after someone has sneezed on it, and you have many cold virus particles on your hand. If you took a picture of your hand with a good digital camera, went to the poster shop, and enlarged it 25,000 times, would you be able to see the viral particles? Explain your answer in terms of the size of the virus and the terms *resolution* and *magnification*.

2. Think about a protein that functions as part of a ribosomal subunit. Describe the route it follows in the cell from the time it is made by the process of translation until the time it helps (as part of a ribosome) in the production of other proteins.

3. A new variety of apple tree produces delicious fruit that keeps well in storage but is very susceptible to a particular root disease. An enterprising horticulturist attempts to solve the plant's shortcomings by grafting the main stem of this apple tree onto a very hardy wild apple rootstock. The graft takes and the resulting tree is very resistant to the root disease and has delicious fruit. But the fruit no longer keeps well in storage. Provide a plausible answer for the three results (delicious fruit, short storage, and disease resistance) in terms of the genome and proteome of the shoot and root.

4. Create a concept map that includes the following terms: endomembrane system, rough endoplasmic reticulum, smooth endoplasmic reticulum, vesicles, endoplasmic reticulum lumen, glycosylation, Golgi apparatus, lysosomes, acid hydrolase, autophagy, endocytosis, exocytosis, pinocytosis, phagocytosis, extracellular matrix.

5. A biological principle of life is that structure determines function. Explain how the invaginations of the inner mitochondrial membrane are related to mitochondrial function.

Visit McGraw-Hill Ryerson Connect™ for additional study resources.

Systems Biology of Cell Organization

Chapter Outline

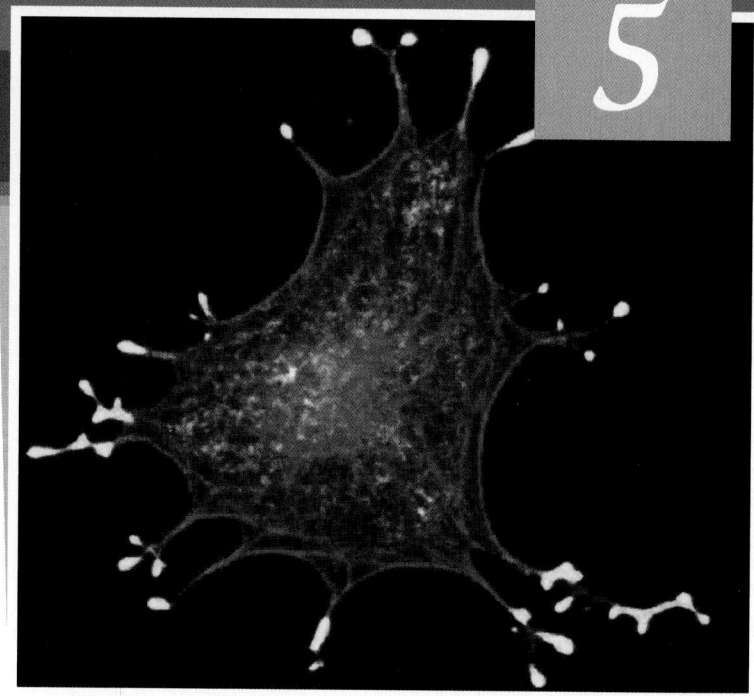

This **confocal micrograph** of an isolated melanin-producing cell (a melanocyte) shows the vesicles that hold the melanin granules in yellow, the actin in red, and the microtubules in blue. Melanocytes produce melanin and then export it to epidermal cells.

The first three chapters of this textbook laid the foundation for understanding cell structure and function. You learned that life depends on water, small molecules, and the organic molecules that form the building blocks for macromolecules such as lipids, proteins, nucleic acids, and carbohydrates. You also learned the principles of chemistry that determine an organic molecule's structure and function.

In Chapter 4 we surveyed the structures and functions of cells, with an emphasis on describing the various parts of cells. We have taken a reductionist approach, which involves reducing a complex system to simpler components to understand those components. In cell biology, reductionists study the parts of a cell as individual units. In this chapter, however, we will view the cell from a broader perspective. In systems biology, researchers study living organisms in terms of their underlying network structure: groups of structural and functional connections. Biological systems vary in their complexity; a system can be anything from a metabolic pathway to a cell, an organ, or even an entire organism. In this chapter, we focus on the cell as a system. The goal is to understand how the dynamic organization of a cell arises by complex interactions among its various components and compartments.

5.1 AN OVERVIEW OF THE DYNAMIC INTERACTIONS OF THE GENOME, PROTEOME, AND ENVIRONMENT

Learning Outcomes:

1. Describe the relationship of the macromolecules DNA, RNA, and protein to the terms genome and proteome.

One organizing principle of biology is that the hereditary material (DNA) provides a dynamic plan for sustaining life. DNA accomplishes its role indirectly:

$$DNA \rightarrow RNA \rightarrow Protein$$

We will look in detail at this important principle in Chapter 11; in this chapter we want to focus on how information is exchanged between the nucleus and the other compartments of the cell's system. An organism's genome is the complete collection of the organism's hereditary material (its DNA). Individual functional regions of the genome are known as **genes**. Genes can be used as templates to make RNA during the process of **transcription**. Structural genes are discrete segments of DNA that are a template for a specific mRNA, which in turn encodes the information to make a specific polypeptide. Other

Table 5.1	DNA Is Used Dynamically to Make Proteins

1. The genome contains all the hereditary material of the cell. The genome can create structure because it contains the information that encodes the proteome.

2. The proteome—the entire collection of proteins that a cell makes—is largely responsible for the distinctive structures and functions of living cells.

3. The use of encoded information within the genome and the production of proteins are regulated and responsive to changes occurring within the cell. In multicellular organisms, the regulation of genes causes the amounts of proteins to vary in different cell types. This allows a multicellular organism to have cells with specialized structures and functions. Nerve and muscle cells have different organizations because their proteomes are different. In addition, the regulation of genes and proteins allows a cell to respond in a dynamic way to changes in the environment. For example, when a yeast cell lacks a nitrogen source, it tries to undergo sexual reproduction.

4. Proteins can have sorting signals—short amino acid sequences in their structure—that direct them to their correct location. For example, one sorting signal directs certain proteins to the mitochondria, while a different sorting signal sends other proteins to the endoplasmic reticulum. We will explore the molecular mechanisms that facilitate protein sorting, a key event in maintaining cell organization.

5. Because their structures can bind to one another and interlock, proteins often undergo protein–protein interactions. These interactions are very specific and can build larger structures that provide organization to the cell. An example is the cytoskeleton that forms complex networks of filaments in the cell.

6. Because many molecules and macromolecules in cells are short lived or need to be broken down as a cell's needs change, cells must continually synthesize new components and break down unwanted components. Proteins typically exist for just minutes or a few hours. Cells have mechanisms to degrade proteins to individual amino acids so that the amino acids can be recycled.

genes serve as templates to make other vital types of RNAs, such as the collection of tRNAs and rRNAs that assist in the production of all polypeptides during the process known as **translation**. Functional proteins are formed as these polypeptides fold into their appropriate three-dimensional configurations.

Because proteins play so many pivotal roles in cells, cells must have mechanisms to control the production, localization, and even removal of proteins. Cells must be able to produce different proteins in response to different functional demands. **Table 5.1** is a summary of key features that allow cells to use their DNA dynamically to make proteins to serve the cells' needs.

5.2 ATTAINING STRUCTURE IN CELLS

Learning Outcomes:

1. Understand how the unifying biological principle that structure determines function is particularly important in creation of molecular machines.

A machine is an object that has moving parts and does useful work. If the size of the machine is measured in nanometres, it is called a **molecular machine**. Even a single protein

can be considered a molecular machine if it undergoes conformational changes as part of its function. Some proteins associate with one another and with nucleic acid molecules to form larger and more complex molecular machines. These machines provide structure and organization to cells and enable them to carry out complex processes. (Look back to Figure 3.20 for one example.)

Large molecular machines are assembled. In some cases, interactions between the protein components of a machine may occur spontaneously, without requiring external guidance or an input of energy. However, sometimes additional proteins are required to help the molecular machine to form, but these guiding proteins are not retained in the machine's final structure. Some machines require an input of energy, such as from ATP hydrolysis, to promote the assembly process.

Figure 5.1 illustrates the assembly of ATP synthase, a machine that makes ATP. Because all living organisms use ATP for energy, ATP synthase is found in both prokaryotes and eukaryotes. ATP synthase is composed of eight different protein subunits called a, b, c, alpha (α), beta (β), gamma (γ), delta (δ), and epsilon (ε). The a, b, and c subunits are transmembrane proteins, found either in the bacterial plasma membrane or in the mitochondrial and thylakoid membranes of eukaryotes. Nine to 12 of the c subunits assemble together to form a ring in the membrane, and one a subunit and two b subunits bind to this ring. The α, β, γ, δ, and ε subunits associate with one another to form a complex of three β subunits, three γ subunits,

Figure 5.1 Assembly of a molecular machine, the ATP synthase found in bacteria, mitochondria, and chloroplasts. Nine to 12 of the c subunits form a ring in the membrane, and one a subunit and two b subunits bind to the ring. The α, β, γ, δ, and ε subunits form a complex of three α subunits, three β subunits, and one subunit each of γ, δ, and ε. This complex binds to the membrane components.

 Principle: *Structure determines function. Many of the ATP synthase subunits self-assemble based on shape, but the entire structure must also be correctly oriented relative to the cell membrane to allow this molecular machine to function properly.*

Concept check: *Explain why the ATP synthase assembles the way it does.*

and one subunit each of γ, δ, and ε. This complex then binds to the membrane components to complete the assembly process. Once assembled this enzyme can create ATP, as discussed in Chapters 7 and 8.

Why does ATP synthase assemble in this manner? The reason is molecular recognition—surfaces on the various protein subunits recognize one another in a very specific way, causing them to bind and promote the assembly process. Said another way, the amino acid sequences of these proteins produce surfaces that fold in a way that causes the proteins to interlock. Thus, the amino acid sequences of proteins, which are stored in the genome, contain the information for protein–protein interactions.

Molecular machines carry out complex cellular functions. The ribosome (**Figure 5.2a**), a molecular machine composed of many types of proteins and several large RNA molecules, functions as a molecular arena for the synthesis of new polypeptides. The flagellum (**Figure 5.2b**) is a molecular machine composed of microtubules, motor proteins, and many other proteins that enables eukaryotic cells, such as sperm cells, to move.

(a) Ribosomes in the act of making polypeptides

(b) The flagella of sperm contain a molecular machine for locomotion

Figure 5.2   Other examples of molecular machines. **(a)** The ribosome, which plays a role in protein synthesis, is composed of many types of proteins and several large RNA molecules. In the electron micrograph shown here, many ribosomes are gliding along an mRNA molecule, synthesizing polypeptides as they go. **(b)** The flagellum of a sperm contains a molecular machine composed of microtubules and accessory proteins. The cross-section shows the 9 + 2 arrangement of microtubules in which nine double microtubules form a ring with two central microtubules that are single microtubules.

Molecular machines also are vital in promoting cell organization. We will consider one such machine, the cytoskeleton, as we discuss the organization of the cytosol. Although some molecular machines can assemble spontaneously from their components, the complex interacting machinery of the cell is so complex that it needs existing structure to guide assembly of the new components. Thus, we can see why one biological principle is that all cells originate from existing cells.

5.3 THE CELL IS A SYSTEM WITH FOUR MAJOR COMPARTMENTS

Learning Outcomes:

1. Describe how a eukaryotic cell can be viewed as four interacting systems: the nucleus, cytosol, endomembrane system, and semiautonomous organelles.
2. Create a labelled diagram describing the flow of information from the nucleus, to the cytoplasm, to the environment, to the cytoplasm, and back to the nucleus, and label key structures and molecules.
3. Name the particular RNA molecules that are intermediates for producing the proteome, and indicate which proteins are important decision makers in producing these RNA molecules.
4. Justify thinking of the outer leaflet of the cell membrane as an important part of the cell.
5. Discuss which compartment is most directly involved in interacting with the cell's immediate environment, and consider major mechanisms for this interaction.

We can view a eukaryotic cell as a system with four interacting compartments: the interior of the nucleus, the cytosol, the semiautonomous organelles (**Figure 5.3**), and the endomembrane system and its exterior face (the outer face of the cell membrane and the extracellular matrix).

The Nucleus Is the Major Site for Genome to Proteome Decision Making

In eukaryotes the nucleus houses the DNA that encodes the vast majority of an organism's proteins. Most of the genetically controlled reactions that occur in the nucleus are associated with protecting the DNA from damage, replicating and packaging it for cell division, using the DNA as a template to make RNA, and processing the RNA. Production of proteins is accomplished through two complex processes that are separated in both time and space. In the first process, called transcription, DNA is used to make RNA. In the second process, called translation, RNA is used to make protein. The DNA does not leave the nucleus; therefore, the first process must be done within the nucleus, the site of RNA production (**Figure 5.4a**). Translation, however, occurs in the cytoplasm.

Nucleus
- Location of the genome
- Gene regulation
- Organization and protection of chromosomes via the nuclear matrix

Endomembrane system
1. Nuclear envelope
   - Boundary that surrounds the nucleus
2. Endoplasmic reticulum
   - Protein secretion and sorting
   - Glycosylation
   - Lipid synthesis
   - Metabolic functions and accumulation of Ca^{2+}
3. Golgi apparatus
   - Protein secretion and sorting
   - Glycosylation
4. Lysosome/vacuoles
   - Degradation of organic molecules
   - Storage of organic molecules
   - Accumulation of water (plant vacuoles)
5. Peroxisomes
   - Breakdown of toxic molecules such as H_2O_2
   - Breakdown and synthesis of organic molecules
6. Plasma membrane
   - Uptake and excretion of ions and molecules
   - Cell signalling
   - Cell adhesion

Cytosol
- Coordination of responses to the environment
- Coordination of metabolism
- Synthesis of the proteome
- Organization and movement via a cytoskeleton and motor proteins

Semiautonomous organelles
1. Mitochondria
   - Synthesis of ATP
   - Synthesis and modification of other organic molecules
   - Production of heat
2. Chloroplasts (plants and algae)
   - Photosynthesis

Figure 5.3 The four interacting compartments within eukaryotic cells.   These include the nucleus, cytosol, semiautonomous organelles, and endomembrane system.

Principle: *Cells are the simplest units of life. Eukaryotic cells use their genetic code and raw materials to build and maintain their structure and function.*

Three categories of RNA are essential for the production of polypeptides: mRNA, tRNA, and rRNA. They all are created in the nucleus, exit the nucleus through the nuclear pores, and function in the cytoplasm for the process of translation. The rRNA leaves the nucleus only after it has partnered with the relevant proteins to form ribosomal subunits. These subunits exit the nucleus via nuclear pores and combine with mRNA to form the molecular machinery. Individual mRNAs encode the information to make a specific polypeptide. During translation, the information held in the mRNAs is decoded with the assistance of tRNAs, as the ribosomes provide the structure and enzymatic functions to join specific amino acids to create polypeptides (**Figure 5.4b**).

Once created, a polypeptide must fold into its proper shape and get to the correct part of the cell to become a functional protein. When proteins reach their destination, they create the foundation for cell structure, function, and organization by providing structural proteins, transport proteins, extracellular proteins, signalling proteins, and enzymes. The enzymes, in turn, control most of the cell's chemical reactions, including those that are essential for transcription and translation. We will look in detail at the processes of transcription and translation in Chapter 11.

Some of the proteins that are made in the cytoplasm actually function in the nucleus for such processes as DNA repair, DNA replication, and DNA packaging. The long linear double helices are packaged with proteins to form chromosomes, as you will see in Chapter 10. Other proteins that function in the nucleus are used for RNA transcription and RNA processing. All of these proteins must make their way back into the nucleus. One important category of proteins that function in the nucleus is **transcription factors**. Transcription factors are proteins that help determine which parts of the genome will be selected for transcription. The cycle for the dynamic production of RNAs

Activating transcription factor

mRNA

tRNA

rRNA

Gene

Gene

Gene

DNA

(a) The genome is used to produce RNA

Nucleolus

Cell organization: Proteins organize the components within cells.

Transport proteins: Proteins facilitate the uptake and export of substances.

Enzymes: Proteins function as enzymes to synthesize and break down cellular molecules and macromolecules.

Extracellular proteins: Proteins hold cells together in tissues.

Cell

Cell signalling: Proteins are needed for cell signalling with other cells and with the environment.

Polypeptide – a chain of amino acids

Cytoskeleton: Proteins are involved in cell shape and movement.

tRNAs carrying amino acids

Ribosome

tRNA

5'

A ribosome moves relative to an mRNA molecule, allowing tRNAs with specific amino acids to bind. This results in the synthesis of a polypeptide with a specific amino acid sequence.

Direction of ribosome

mRNA

3'

(b) The proteome is decoded from RNA in the cytosol; the RNA was produced in the nucleus

Figure 5.4   Information flows from the nucleus to the cytoplasm and back.

Principle: *The genetic material, DNA, provides a dynamic plan for sustaining life. The nucleus contains all nuclear-encoded genes, but which genes will be decoded to produce the cell's proteome depends on the cell's needs and its role in the organism.*

and proteins comes full circle as specific transcription factors are produced and activated. Once an activated transcription factor recognizes and binds to its target gene, that gene will be expressed (transcribed), and the mRNA will leave the nucleus and be translated to create the next protein required to meet the cell's changing needs. We will look closely at transcription factors in Chapter 12. For now we are focusing on the important concept that transcription factors help modulate which portion of the genome is used to produce the specific proteins that a cell needs at a given time.

The Cytosol

The cytosol is an important coordination centre for cell function and organization. Along with the plasma membrane, the cytosolic components coordinate responses to the environment. Factors in the environment may stimulate signalling pathways in the cytosol that affect the functions of cellular proteins and change the expression of genes in the nucleus. Equally important, the cytosol is a major site for translation, the production of proteins.

The cytosol also has a large impact on cell function because it is the compartment in which many small molecules are metabolized in the cell. The region receives molecules that are taken up from the environment. In addition, many pathways for the synthesis and breakdown of cellular molecules are found in the cytosol, and pathways in organelles are often regulated by events that occur in the cytosol.

As you saw in Chapter 4, the cytosol is organized by the cytoskeleton. Intermediate filaments provide mechanical strength. Actin microfilaments form a protein network on the inner face of the plasma membrane that can anchor specific membrane proteins (**Figure 5.5**). These membrane proteins have many important roles in the way a cell interacts with its environment. As well, protein–protein interactions occur between actin and other cellular proteins that can produce changes in cell shape (look back to Figure 4.23) or muscle contraction (look ahead to Figure 43.5).

The cytoskeleton also provides pathways for directed, intracellular movement. Membrane-bound vesicles, chromosomes, and even mitochondria and chloroplasts are transported within the cell by movement along microtubules to the locations where they are needed. **Figure 5.6** illustrates how a vesicle can move along microtubules in a large nerve cell. In this example, accessory proteins connect a motor protein to the vesicle. The motor protein uses the energy from ATP hydrolysis to "walk" along a microtubule, transporting the vesicle to its final destination.

Semiautonomous Organelles

The semiautonomous organelles—the mitochondria and chloroplasts—are found in the cytosol but operate semiautonomously.

Mitochondria and Chloroplasts Contain Their Own Genetic Material and Divide by Binary Fission   To appreciate the structure and organization of mitochondria and chloroplasts,

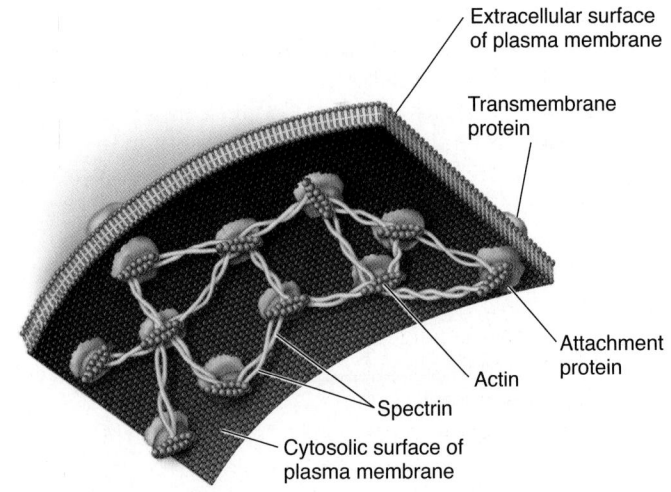

Cytoskeletal connections to the red blood cell membrane

Figure 5.5   Role of the cytoskeleton in promoting the cell's structural integrity.   The fluid phospholipid bilayer is supported and shaped by membrane spanning, transmembrane proteins, and an underlying network of cytoskeletal proteins, including actin and spectrin.

we need to briefly examine their genetic properties. In 1951 Yasutane Chiba discovered that chloroplasts contain their own DNA. Researchers in the 1970s and 1980s then isolated DNA

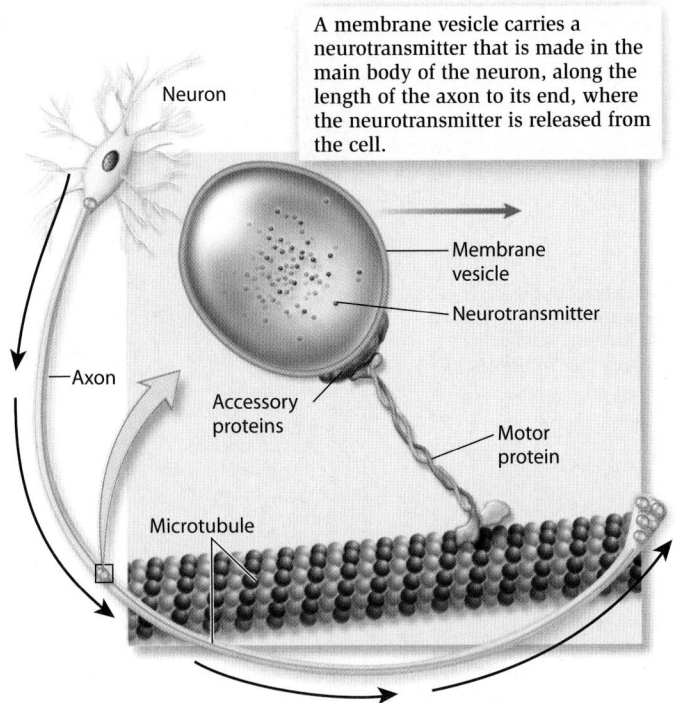

A membrane vesicle carries a neurotransmitter that is made in the main body of the neuron, along the length of the axon to its end, where the neurotransmitter is released from the cell.

Figure 5.6   Movement of a membrane vesicle along a microtubule.   In this example, a motor protein walks along a microtubule in the axon of a nerve cell. The vesicle carries a neurotransmitter, which is released at the end of the axon. Accessory proteins link the motor protein to the vesicle and also control the activity of the motor protein.

from both chloroplasts and mitochondria. In contrast to eukaryotes, but like bacteria, the DNA of these organelles is organized as closed, circular DNA helices.

The chromosomes found in mitochondria and chloroplasts constitute the **mitochondrial genome** and **chloroplast genome**, respectively, while the chromosomes found in the nucleus of the cell form the **nuclear genome**. Compared with the nuclear genome, these organelle genomes are very small, but each encodes some genes that are essential for organelle function.

Just as the genomes of mitochondria and chloroplast resemble bacterial genomes, the production of new mitochondria and chloroplasts bears a striking resemblance to the division of bacterial cells. Like bacteria, mitochondria and chloroplasts increase in number via **binary fission**. We will look more closely at binary fission in bacteria in Chapter 16; **Figure 5.7** illustrates the process for mitochondria. Mitochondrial and chloroplast division are needed to maintain a full complement of these organelles when cells grow and require additional energy.

The Semiautonomous Organelles Are Vital Energy-Generating Systems with Dual-Origin Proteomes As you saw in Chapter 4, mitochondria and chloroplasts are involved in energy conversions. The chloroplasts of photosynthetic eukaryotes take up CO_2, capture light energy, and synthesize more complex carbon-containing molecules that store energy and can be broken down when energy is needed. Mitochondria take up sugars from the cytosol and generate ATP, which is used throughout the cell to drive processes that are energetically unfavourable. This energy is crucial for cell organization. The functions of these organelles involve biochemical pathways that are described in greater detail in Chapter 7 (mitochondria) and Chapter 8 (chloroplasts). These biochemical pathways require many enzymes that must be very precisely oriented within a specific compartment of these organelles.

The mitochondria and chloroplast genomes each have some organelle-encoded polypeptides that are produced by translation that occurs within these organelles. But the majority of the proteins that function in their energy-production reactions are actually encoded by nuclear genes. The nucleus-encoded polypeptides are produced on ribosomes in the cytoplasm and then targeted to the mitochondria or chloroplast. Later in this chapter we will look at the targeting mechanism and consider the origins of these organelles' semiautonomy.

The Endomembrane System

The endomembrane system is a collection of membranes and cell compartments in eukaryotic cells that includes the outer membrane of the nuclear envelope, endoplasmic reticulum (ER), Golgi apparatus, lysosomes, peroxisomes, vacuoles, secretory vesicles, and plasma membrane (**Figure 5.8**). The system is impressively dynamic, and its structures change over time. Much of the activity of the endomembrane system is related to the transport of membrane vesicles among its various compartments. Transport of vesicles can occur in both directions, for different purposes. For example, membrane-bound vesicles bud from the ER and fuse with the Golgi, releasing their content into the lumen of the Golgi apparatus. Empty cargo vesicles can bud off the Golgi and return to the ER. Through vesicle-mediated exocytosis and endocytosis, the endomembrane system allows the cell to exchange materials with the cell's exterior.

The endomembrane system contributes to the structure and organization of eukaryotic cells in many ways. It is a major site of metabolic reactions. Most of a cell's lipids are made in the endoplasmic reticulum membrane and exported to other parts of the cell. The endoplasmic reticulum is also a major site of protein synthesis and modification. Another important function of the endomembrane system is the storage and recycling of organic molecules; vacuoles often play a role in the storage of organic molecules, such as proteins, carbohydrates, and fats. When needed, lysosomes in animal cells and vacuoles in the cells of other eukaryotes assist in breaking down these macromolecules. The building blocks are then recycled back to the cytosol and used to construct new macromolecules. Peroxisomes are the sites of some of the reactions for the metabolism of fats and amino acids, especially those that generate the

Mitochondrial chromosome in nucleoid

1 Mitochondrial genome replicates and the resulting two genomes separate.

2 Mitochondrion begins to divide by binary fission.

3 Binary fission is completed.

(a) Binary fission of mitochondria

(b) Electron micrographs of mitochondrial division

Figure 5.7 Division of mitochondria by binary fission.

(a)

(b)

Figure 5.8 **The dynamic nature of the endomembrane system.** (a) Vesicle transport occurs in both directions, allowing materials to be shared among the various membranes and compartments of the endomembrane system. (b) An electron micrograph of a rat intestinal epithelium cell. The fingerlike microvilli absorb a fatty meal from the intestines. During absorption, droplets of lipid accumulate in the lumen of the smooth endoplasmic reticulum (arrows).

potentially dangerous hydrogen peroxide. Finally, the endo-memberane system provides the routing system for transporting many cellular and extracellular proteins to their correct final destination. With this overview for perspective, let's look more closely at how the endomembrane system helps the cell work as an integrated set of systems.

Membranes Are Dynamic Structural Components of the Endomembrane System

As you saw in Chapter 4, the fluid part of biological membranes is composed of phospholipid bilayers; one layer is called the outer leaflet and the other layer is called the inner leaflet. The precise chemical composition of the phospholipids of the two leaflets of the bilayer can be different, reflecting the fact that they may have different functions and interact with different chemical environments. For example, the outer leaflet of the cell membrane faces the exterior of the cell, while the inner leaflet faces the cytosol. The cell has a system to manufacture a variety of phospholipids and membrane sterols (such as cholesterol) and to direct them to their proper cellular location.

The cytosol and endomembrane system work together to synthesize most lipids. This process occurs at the ER membrane's **cytosolic leaflet** (the portion of the bilayer that faces the cytosol). **Figure 5.9** shows a simplified pathway for the synthesis of phospholipids, the main components of cell and organelle membranes. Recall from Chapter 3 that phospholipids have two of glycerol's carbons bonded with two fatty acids; the third carbon is bonded to a phosphate-containing molecule (Figure 3.12).

Creation of membrane phospholipids is a multistep process. First, two fatty acids are activated by attachment to coenzyme A (CoA) (step 1 in Figure 5.9). Then the energy from

the activation is used to transfer the fatty acids to a glycerol-phosphate molecule that is inserted into the cytosolic leaflet of the ER membrane (step 2). Next, the phosphate is removed from glycerol (step 3) and replaced with phosphate-containing organic molecule, such as choline (step 4). All membrane phospholipids are initially made in the cytosolic leaflet of the ER, but enyzmes known as flippases transfer specific phospholipids to the other leaflet of the ER membrane, the one facing the lumen of the ER (step 5). We will look at flippase action in more detail in Chapter 6.

The lipids that are made in the ER membrane can be transferred to other membranes in the cell by a variety of mechanisms. Phospholipids in the outer leaflet of the ER can diffuse laterally to the nuclear envelope (**Figure 5.10a**). In addition, lipids can be transported through the cytosol via vesicles to the Golgi, lysosomes, vacuoles, and plasma membrane (**Figure 5.10b**). A third mode of lipid movement involves lipid exchange proteins, which extract a lipid from one membrane, diffuse through the cell, and insert the lipid into another membrane (**Figure 5.10c**). Such transfer can occur between any two membranes, even between the endomembrane system and semiautonomous organelles.

In addition to the fluid phospholipid bilayer, proteins are found in all types of membranes. These proteins play many important roles that affect the activities inside and at the surface of cells. Some proteins have hydrophobic domains that are embedded in the bilayer interior, and other domains extend out of the membrane to its outer leaflet, inner leaflet, or both. We will look at the systems that cells have in place to get these proteins to their proper membrane location in Section 5.4, after we look at our Feature Investigation.

| 1 | In the cytosol, fatty acids are activated by the attachment of a CoA molecule. | 2 | The activated fatty acids bond to glycerol-phosphate and are inserted into the cytosolic leaflet of the ER membrane via the enzyme acyl transferase. | 3 | The phosphate is removed by a phosphatase enzyme. | 4 | A molecule of choline already linked to phosphate is attached via choline phosphotransferase. | 5 | Flippases transfer some of the phospholipids to the other leaflet. |

Figure 5.9   A simplified diagram for the pathway for synthesis of membrane phospholipids at the ER membrane.

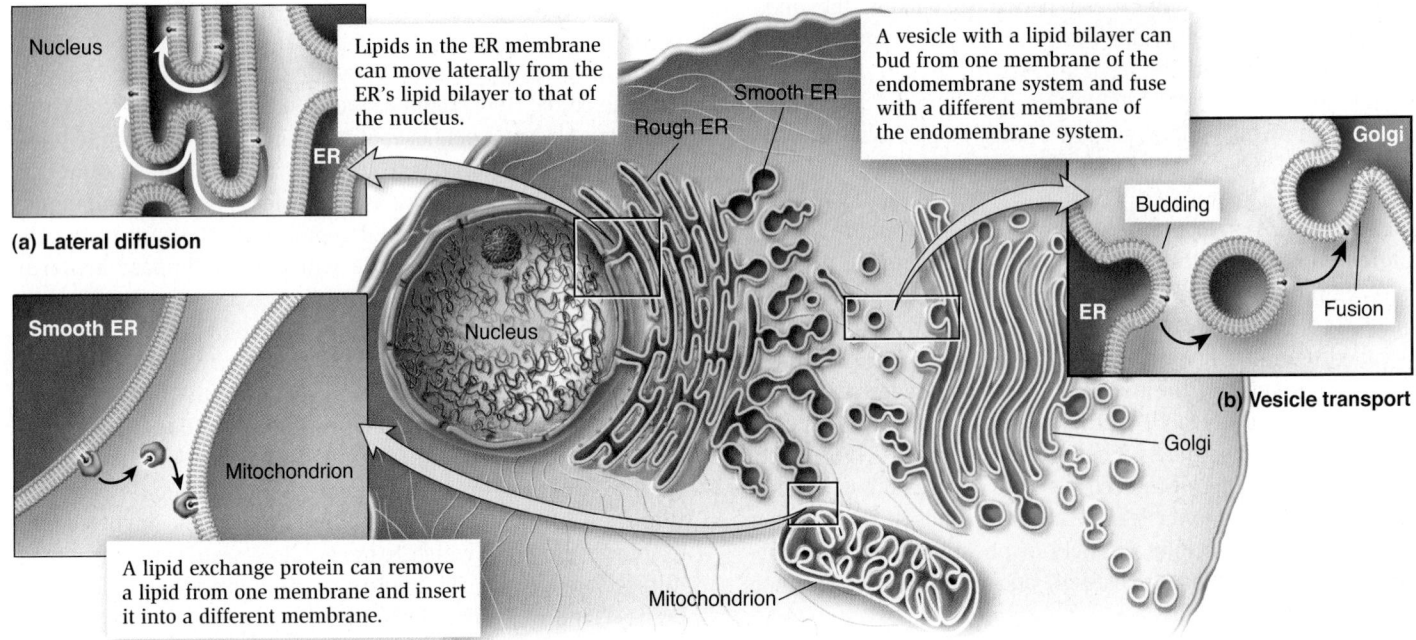

(a) Lateral diffusion

Lipids in the ER membrane can move laterally from the ER's lipid bilayer to that of the nucleus.

A vesicle with a lipid bilayer can bud from one membrane of the endomembrane system and fuse with a different membrane of the endomembrane system.

(b) Vesicle transport

A lipid exchange protein can remove a lipid from one membrane and insert it into a different membrane.

(c) Lipid exchange proteins

Figure 5.10 **Mechanisms of lipid transfer throughout a eukaryotic cell.** As shown in the enlarged inserts, lipids can be distributed throughout the cell in various ways. **(a)** Lateral diffusion occurs between the ER and nuclear envelope. **(b)** Vesicle transport occurs among the membranes of the endomembrane system. **(c)** Lipid exchange proteins can transfer lipids between any two membranes, such as between the ER and a mitochondrion.

FEATURE INVESTIGATION

Palade Demonstrated That Secreted Proteins Move Sequentially Through Organelles of the Endomembrane System

Eukaryotic cells make thousands of different proteins, each of which functions in a specific compartment within a cell. Therefore, proteins must be sorted to their correct destination. One of the first indications that proteins are systematically sorted in cells came from **pulse-chase experiments** done by George Palade and his collaborators in the 1960s. For the *pulse* researchers injected radioactive amino acids into cells. These radioactive amino acids were incorporated into polypeptides, producing radioactive proteins. A few minutes later, the cells were given a large amount of nonradioactive amino acids (*the chase*). This second step is called a chase because it greatly reduces the concentration of radioactive amino acids, effectively chasing away the ability of the cells to make radioactive proteins. The pulse-chase technique is designed to produce radioactive proteins only briefly. The location of these radioactive proteins are then monitored at successive points in time (called time points). The goal of a pulse-chase experiment is to determine where the radioactive molecules are produced, where they end up, and what routes they take to get there.

Palade chose to study the cells of the pancreas because their primary activity is protein secretion. To study the pathway for protein secretion, Palade and colleagues injected a radioactive version of the amino acid leucine into the bloodstream of guinea pigs, followed three minutes later by the chase: an injection of nonradioactive leucine (**Figure 5.11**). After the second injection, samples of pancreatic cells were removed from the animals at different time points. The cells were then prepared for transmission electron microscopy and stained with osmium tetroxide, a heavy metal that serves as a membrane stain. Next, the cell preparations were coated with a radiation-sensitive photographic emulsion. When radiation was emitted from radioactive proteins, it interacted with the emulsion in a way that caused the precipitation of silver atoms directly over the sites of the radioactive proteins. Because silver atoms are electron dense, they are visible in the transmission electron micrograph images of the cells, revealing the locations of radioactive proteins.

The electron micrograph of Figure 5.11, part 6, illustrates the results that were observed five minutes after the completion of the pulse-chase injections. Silver grains, marking the sites with radioactive proteins, were observed in the rough ER. Data collected at later time points did not show silver grains in the ER but instead showed radioactive proteins in the Golgi. Even later time points revealed radioactive proteins in secretory vesicles. In this way, Palade followed the intracellular pathway of protein movement from the ER to the Golgi to secretory vesicles. These findings caused researchers to wonder how proteins are targeted to particular organelles and how they move from one compartment to another. These topics are described next.

HYPOTHESIS Proteins that are to be secreted follow a particular intracellular pathway.

KEY MATERIALS Male guinea pigs.

Experimental level   Conceptual level

1. Inject guinea pigs with a radioactive amino acid, [3H]-leucine. After 3 minutes, inject them with nonlabeled leucine, which is called a chase.

[3H]-leucine
Nonlabelled leucine
Pancreas

2. At various times after the second injection, remove samples of pancreatic cells.

Pancreatic cell

3. Stain the sample with osmium tetroxide, which is a heavy metal that binds to membranes.

Osmium tetroxide
Sample from pancreas

4. Cut thin sections of the samples, and place a thin layer of radiation-sensitive emulsion over the sample. Allow time for radioactive emission from radiolabelled proteins to precipitate silver atoms in the emulsion.

Thin section
Add radiation-sensitive emulsion

5. Observe the sample under a transmission electron microscope.

6. **THE DATA**

Rough ER
Nucleus
Labelled proteins
Five minutes after chase

Nucleus
ER
Golgi
Secretory vesicles

Time after chase
5 min
15 min
>30 min

7. **CONCLUSION** To be secreted, proteins move from the ER to the Golgi to secretory vesicles and then to the plasma membrane, where they are released to the outside of the cell.

8. **SOURCE** Caro, L.G., and Palade, G.E (1964) Protein synthesis, storage, and discharge in the pancreatic exocrine cell. An autoradiographic study. *Journal of Cell Biology* 20:473–495.

Figure 5.11   Palade's use of the pulse-chase method to study protein secretion.

Experimental Questions

1. Explain the procedure of a pulse-chase experiment as described in Figure 5.11. Why did the investigators choose this approach?

2. Why were pancreatic cells used for the investigation in Figure 5.11?

3. What were the results of the experiment of Figure 5.11? What did the researchers conclude?

5.4 THE CELL HAS A SYSTEM TO SORT PROTEINS TO THE CORRECT CELLULAR COMPARTMENT

Learning Outcomes:

1. List the categories of proteins that are sorted cotranslationally and those that are sorted post-translationally.
2. Describe the steps that occur during the cotranslational sorting of proteins to the endoplasmic reticulum.
3. Explain how proteins are moved via vesicles through the endomembrane system.
4. Outline the steps of post-translational sorting of proteins to mitochondria or chloroplasts.

Each protein that a cell makes usually functions within one cellular compartment of the cell. How does each polypeptide reach its appropriate destination and fold into a functional protein? In eukaryotes, nuclear-encoded polypeptides have a short stretch of amino acids that helps direct them to their correct cellular location. These sequences are called **sorting signals** or **traffic signals**.

Because sorting signals are a part of the polypeptide, they must be created during the process of translation. Most eukaryotic polypeptides begin to be synthesized on ribosomes in the cytosol, as messenger RNA (mRNA) combine with ribosomal subunits and initiate translation. If the polypeptide being created is destined to function in the endoplasmic reticulum, Golgi apparatus, lysosome, vacuole, or plasma membrane, or to be secreted from the cell, then the gene that encodes it will encode a series of amino acids known as an ER **signal peptide**, which consists of 6 to 12 amino acids (most of which are hydrophobic) created near the amino terminus of the growing polypeptide. If the polypeptide is destined for the nucleus, mitochondria, or chloroplasts it will have a different peptide that constitutes a nuclear-, mitochondrial-, or chloroplast-sorting peptide, respectively. It is important to realize that sorting signal peptides are synthesized as part of the relevant polypeptide.

Some Polypeptides Are Directed Cotranslationally to the ER

Proteins that travel through the endomembrane system require an ER signal peptide. In the 1970s Günter Blobel and colleagues discovered a sorting signal in polypeptides that sends them to the ER. In 1999 Blobel won a Nobel Prize for this work.

For this sorting process, translation begins on a ribosome in the cytosol (**Figure 5.12**, step 1; this is called **cotranslational**

sorting because the first step in the sorting process begins while translation is occurring), but as the ER signal peptide is created, it attracts a protein complex known as the **signal recognition particle (SRP)**. The SRP recognizes the ER signal peptide and pauses translation (step 2). The SRP moves the entire complex—the mRNA, ribosome, and emerging signal peptide—to the membrane of the rough ER membrane. The SRP then binds to a protein receptor in the ER membrane (step 3) and in doing so docks the ribosome over a protein channel that spans the membrane and provides passage into the lumen of the ER. Now the SRP is released and translation resumes (step 4). The growing polypeptide begins to be threaded through the channel. In most cases, the ER signal peptide is removed by the enzyme signal peptidase (step 5), and after all the amino acids of the polypeptide have been added, the completed polypeptide is released into the lumen of the ER (step 6).

Most Membrane Proteins Are Inserted into the ER Membranes Cotranslationally

Membrane proteins (except those of the semiautonomous organelles) have ER signal peptides and are synthesized on ribosomes attached to the ER. But the amino acids of their ER signal peptide are not always removed, and when they persist, they become embedded within the lipid bilayer because they are hydrophobic. All membrane proteins contain at least one stretch of amino acids that are mostly hydrophobic to allow them to embed in the lipid bilayer. Some have more than one hydrophobic domain.

Transmembrane proteins span the membrane and must have at least one larger hydrophobic region of at least 20 amino acids. This hydrophobic region is large enough to embed in the membrane but reach beyond the membrane's bilayer. The amino acids of the hydrophobic segment can be adjacent to a stretch of more hydrophilic amino acids that extend beyond one or both leaflets. You can see a few examples in **Figure 5.13**. The signal peptidase protein has a transmembrane domain and a domain that extends beyond the bilayer into the lumen of the ER where it functions. The polypeptide whose synthesis is shown in Figure 5.13 has a domain at its carboxy terminus that extends out into the cytosol, a transmembrane domain anchoring it in the ER membrane, and another domain at its amino terminus extending it into the ER's lumen. Some polypeptides may contain two or more transmembrane segments. Each time a polypeptide sequence contains a stretch of 20 hydrophobic amino acids, an additional transmembrane segment is synthesized into the membrane. Once a membrane or transmembrane protein is created and positioned in the ER membrane, it can be transported to other membranes of the endomembrane system via vesicles that bud off of the ER and fuse with their destination membrane.

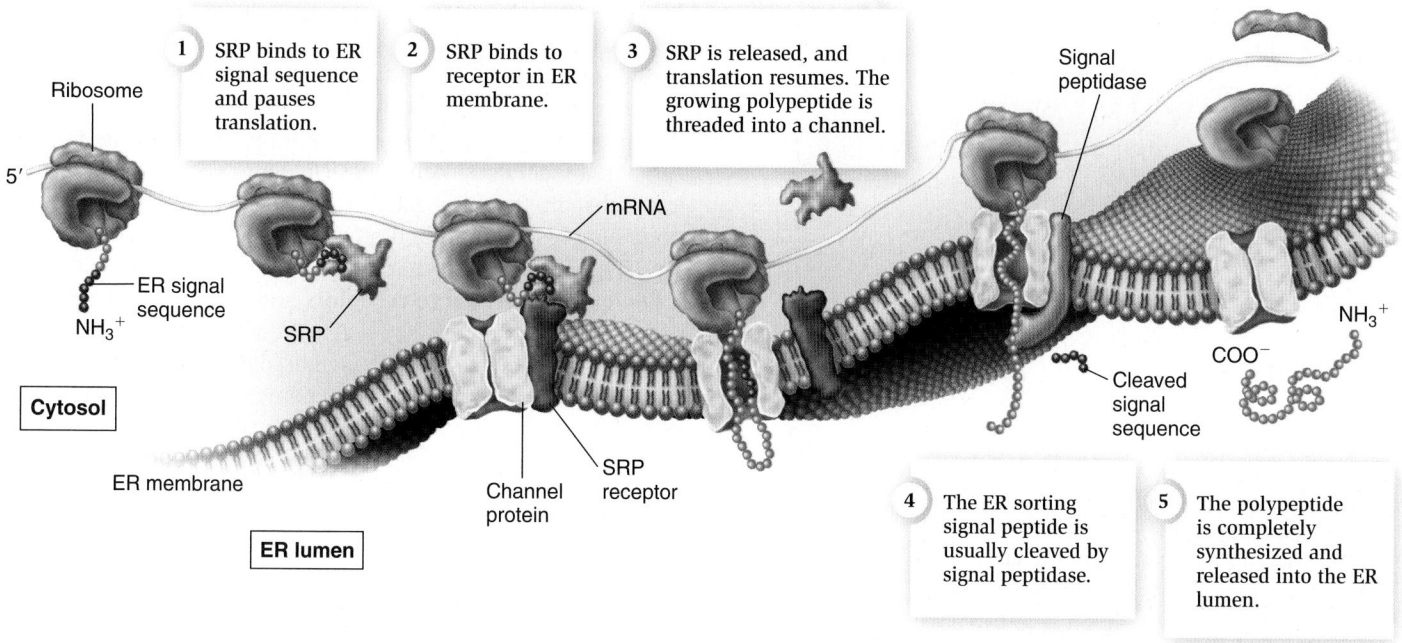

Figure 5.12   First step in cotranslational protein localization: cotranslational sorting.

Proteins Released into the ER Lumen Can Have Different Final Destinations and Different Modifications   Some proteins are meant to function in the lumen of the ER; these proteins have a stretch of amino acids that serve as an ER-retention sorting signal (different from its ER signal peptide). Those proteins that make it to the lumen of the ER but do not have an ER-retention signal are moved via vesicles to the Golgi apparatus. In the Golgi apparatus

they may undergo modifications and then move on to their final destination: lysosomes, vacuoles, or the exterior of the cell.

In the lumen of the ER many proteins have carbohydrate groups covalently linked to certain amino acids. This process is known as glycosylation. **Figure 5.14** shows an example in which a relatively large carbohydrate is transiently bound to a lipid (named dilichol) and then transferred to the amino acid

Figure 5.13   Second step in cotranslational protein localization: vesicle transport from the endoplasmic reticulum.

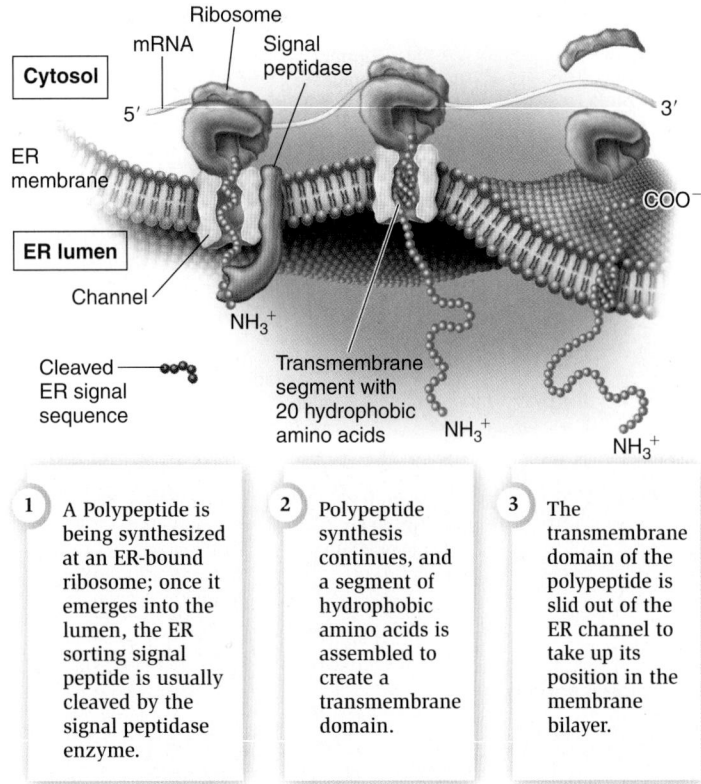

1. A Polypeptide is being synthesized at an ER-bound ribosome; once it emerges into the lumen, the ER sorting signal peptide is usually cleaved by the signal peptidase enzyme.

2. Polypeptide synthesis continues, and a segment of hydrophobic amino acids is assembled to create a transmembrane domain.

3. The transmembrane domain of the polypeptide is slid out of the ER channel to take up its position in the membrane bilayer.

Figure 5.14   Insertion of a transmembrane protein into the ER membrane.

Concept check: *What structural feature of a protein causes a region to form a transmembrane segment?*

BioConnections: *Look ahead to Figure 5.26. Discuss how transmembrane proteins are important in the binding of cells to each other and the binding of cells to the extracellular matrix.*

asparagine of a polypeptide within the ER lumen. The glycosylation is done before translation is completed. Other types of glycosylations occur after translation is completed for polypeptides shipped to the Golgi apparatus.

Glycosylation of polypeptides in the endomembrane system can have a variety of purposes. For example, proteins destined for the lysosome receive a specific type of glycosylation that serves as an additional sorting signal. Glycosylation also alters the physical properties of proteins in biologically significant ways that may allow the protein to fold into its proper final configuration and may make it more stable in the cellular environment in which it must function. Glycosylation can be a vital part of the protein's ability to complete its function. For example, membrane proteins often are glycosylated, and the particular carbohydrate that is added serves a role in cell–cell recognition. Finally, proteins that are secreted from cells are often extensively glycosylated. We call these proteins **proteoglycans**, and you will learn about them in the section of this chapter dedicated to the extracellular matrix.

Movement of Proteins in the Endomembrane System Is Done Within Transport Vesicles   Proteins that make it to the lumen of the ER are always contained within a membrane-bound vesicle as long as they are intact and within the cell. If they move within the endomembrane system, it is done as cargo in a membrane-bound vesicle. **Figure 5.15** describes vesicle transport from the ER to the Golgi, but a similar process occurs for vesicles that bud off the Golgi.

The ER membrane has two important proteins embedded in its lipid bilayer: **cargo receptors** and **v-snares** (*v* designates it as a snare protein of a vesicle). Protein molecules first bind to cargo receptors in the ER membrane in membrane regions that have v-snare proteins. The binding of protein cargo to the cargo receptor stimulates the binding of a cage-like protein shell, which helps the membrane region to bud from the ER membrane to form a vesicle. After a vesicle is released from the membrane, the protein shell is shed. The vesicle then travels through the cytosol to its destination, typically along cytoskeletal filaments. A similar type of budding process occurs when vesicles bud from the Golgi apparatus.

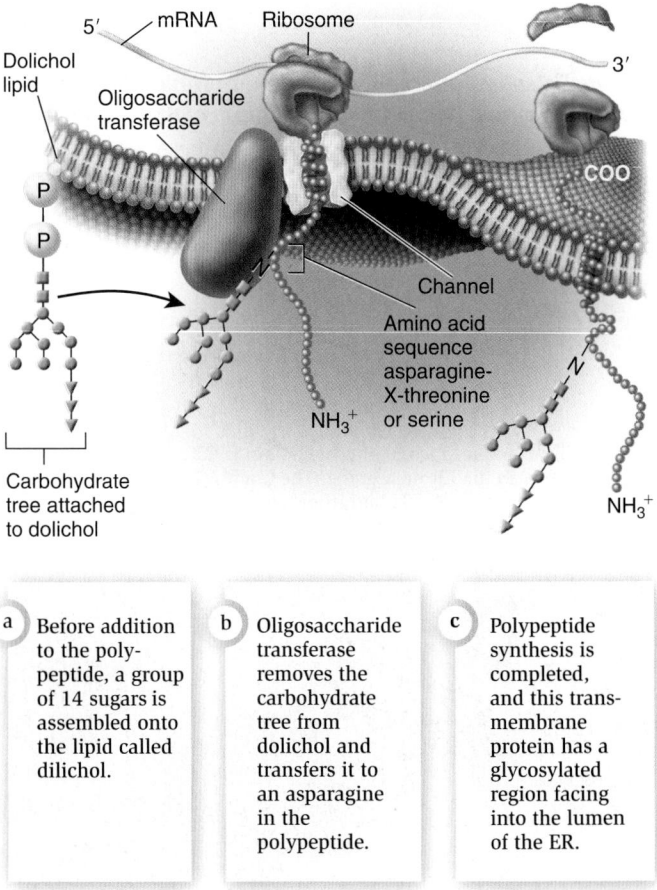

a. Before addition to the polypeptide, a group of 14 sugars is assembled onto the lipid called dilichol.

b. Oligosaccharide transferase removes the carbohydrate tree from dolichol and transfers it to an asparagine in the polypeptide.

c. Polypeptide synthesis is completed, and this transmembrane protein has a glycosylated region facing into the lumen of the ER.

Figure 5.15   N-linked glycosylation in the endoplasmic reticulum.

How is a vesicle directed to its proper final destination? The target destination has proteins called **t-snares** embedded in their membranes (*t* designates it as a snare protein of a target destination). The v-snares of the vesicle's membrane are recognized by a complementarily shaped t-snare protein embedded in the target compartment's membrane. After the v-snare recognizes a t-snare, the vesicle fuses with the membrane containing the t-snare. The recognition between v-snares and t-snares ensures that a vesicle carrying specific cargo moves to the correct target membrane in the cell.

Some Proteins Are Sorted Post-translationally to the Nucleus, Peroxisomes, Mitochondria, and Chloroplasts

The organization and function of the nucleus, peroxisomes, and semiautonomous organelles require many proteins. A few proteins of the mitochondria and chloroplast are made within those organelles, but most of their proteins and those of the peroxisome and nucleus are synthesized in the cytosol. For these organelles the movement to the correct organelle is done post-translationally (after the polypeptide has been synthesized). For this **post-translational sorting** to occur, the protein must have the appropriate sorting signal as part of its amino acid sequence. Nuclear-, mitochondrial-, chloroplast-, and peroxisome-targeting signals are different from one another and are distinct from the ER sorting signal peptides.

As one example of post-translational sorting, let's consider how a protein is directed to the innermost portion of the mitochondria—the matrix. Such a protein would have a matrix-targeting peptide as part of its structure. As shown in **Figure 5.16**, the process of protein import into the matrix involves a series of intricate protein–protein interactions. A protein that is destined for the mitochondrial matrix is first made in the cytosol, where proteins called **chaperones** work to keep it in an unfolded state. A receptor protein in the outer mitochondrial membrane recognizes the matrix-targeting signal. The protein is released from the chaperone as it is transferred to a channel in the outer mitochondrial membrane. Because it is in an unfolded state, the mitochondrial protein can be threaded through this channel and then through another channel in the inner mitochondrial membrane. These channels lie close to each other at contact sites between the outer and inner membranes. As the protein emerges in the matrix, other chaperone proteins that were already in the matrix continue to keep it unfolded. Eventually, the matrix-targeting signal is cleaved, and the entire protein is threaded into the matrix. At this stage, the chaperone proteins are released and the protein can adopt its three-dimensional active structure. Similar complex processes exist to get proteins into the nucleus, chloroplasts, and peroxisomes.

A Summary of Protein Sorting

The process of targeting a protein to its proper destination within the cell is vital and wondrously complex. Now that you have looked at the details of this process, use **Figure 5.17** to step back and get a clear overview of the cell's routing system for sorting proteins.

Figure 5.16 Post-translational sorting of a protein to the mitochondrial matrix.

Concept check: *What do you think would happen if chaperone proteins did not bind to a mitochondrial matrix protein before it was imported into the mitochondrion?*

Protein synthesis begins on ribosomes in the cytosol.

mRNA

Emerging polypeptide — NH₃⁺

Remain in cytosol

Post-translational sorting to the nucleus, mitochondria, chloroplasts, or peroxisomes

Cotranslational sorting to ER

5′

3′

mRNA   NH₃⁺

Cytosolic proteins complete their synthesis in the cytosol and remain there due to the lack of a sorting signal.

COO⁻
Completed polypeptide in cytosol

NH₃⁺

5′   3′

mRNA

ER sorting signal

NH₃⁺

ER lumen

COO⁻
Completed polypeptide in the ER

NH₃⁺

Endoplasmic reticulum (ER)

Vesicle transport to Golgi

For proteins with an ER sorting signal, translation is paused, and the protein/ribosome is sent to the ER. Some of these proteins contain ER retention signals and remain in the ER. The others are sent to the Golgi via vesicles.

5′   3′

mRNA   NH₃⁺

COO⁻
Completed polypeptide in cytosol

NH₃⁺

These proteins are completely synthesized in the cytosol. They contain sorting signals that send them to the nucleus, mitochondria, chloroplasts, or peroxisomes.

Golgi

Some of these proteins contain Golgi retention signals and remain in the Golgi. The others are sent, via vesicles, to the lysosomes, plasma membrane, or outside the cell via secretory vesicles.

Nucleus

Peroxisome

Mitochondrion

Chloroplast

Secretory vesicle

Lysosome or vacuole

Plasma membrane

Figure 5.17 Overview of protein targeting.

5.5 THE CELL HAS A SYSTEM FOR DEGRADING AND RECYCLING MACROMOLECULES

Learning Outcomes:

1. Describe the proteasome-based process of protein degradation.
2. Explain the purposes of the proteosome system.
3. Contrast the proteosome degradation system with that of the lysosome.

Thus far, we have considered how cellular components are made in response to cellular needs, assembled into machines, and moved to the location in which they must function, thereby providing organization and complex functions to living cells. But the maintenance of cell organization is a dynamic process. Except for DNA, which is stably maintained and inherited from cell to cell, the other large molecules—RNA, proteins, lipids, and polysaccharides—have finite lifespans. Biologists often speak of the half-life of molecules, which is the time it takes for 50% of the molecules to be broken down and recycled. For example, a population of mRNA molecules in prokaryotes has an average half-life of about 5 minutes, while mRNAs in eukaryotes tend to exist for longer—30 minutes to 24 hours or even several days.

The breakdown of large cellular molecules and the recycling of their building blocks occur by a variety of mechanisms. As discussed in Chapter 4, lysosomes can degrade materials in the cytosol by a process called autophagy (refer back to Figure 4.17). The components of a mitochondrion, for example, can be degraded in this manner, with building blocks returned to the cytosol, where they can be used to make new macromolecules. Lysosomes also degrade proteins that are imported into the cell via endocytosis. In addition, cytosolic enzymes break down RNA, polysaccharides, and lipids into smaller building blocks. For example, the cytosol has **ribonuclease** enzymes that degrade mRNA.

To survive and respond to environmental changes, cells must continually degrade proteins that are faulty or nonfunctional and synthesize replacements. Cells also sometimes need to degrade perfectly functional proteins that no longer serve their changing needs; this is a carefully regulated process. To be degraded, proteins are recognized by **proteases**—enzymes that cleave the bonds between adjacent amino acids. Although lysosomes in eukaryotic cells are involved in protein breakdown via autophagy and endocytosis, the primary pathway for protein degradation in archaea and eukaryotic cells is via a molecular machine called a **proteasome**. The core of the proteasome is formed from four stacked rings, each composed of seven protein subunits (**Figure 5.18**, step 1). The proteasomes of eukaryotic cells also contain cap structures at each end that control

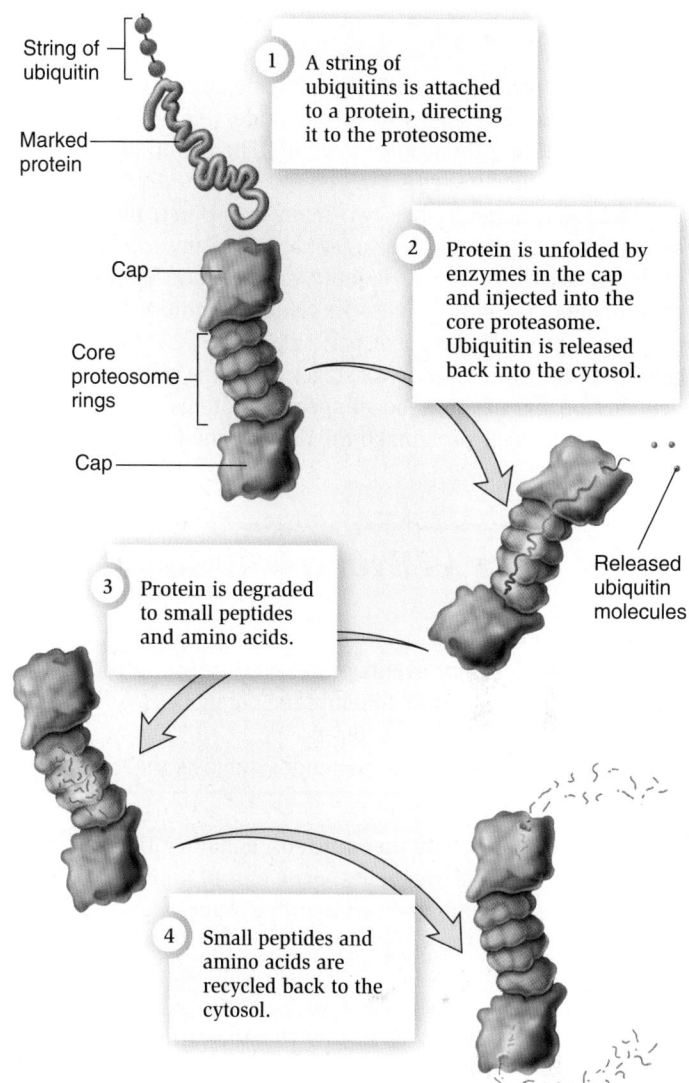

1. A string of ubiquitins is attached to a protein, directing it to the proteosome.

2. Protein is unfolded by enzymes in the cap and injected into the core proteasome. Ubiquitin is released back into the cytosol.

3. Protein is degraded to small peptides and amino acids.

4. Small peptides and amino acids are recycled back to the cytosol.

String of ubiquitin
Marked protein
Cap
Core proteosome rings
Cap
Released ubiquitin molecules

Figure 5.18   Protein degradation via the proteasome.
The proteosome consists of four complex stacked ring structures that are bracketed by a top and bottom cap.

 Principle: *Living organisms have mechanisms that maintain homeostasis. At the cellular level, the proteosome allows cells to change its proteome; this can help the organism adapt to changes to maintain homeostasis.*

the entry of proteins into the proteasome and the exit of amino acids for recycling.

In eukaryotic cells, unwanted proteins are directed to a proteasome by the covalent attachment of a small protein called **ubiquitin**. First, an enzyme recognizes a protein as either defective or unnecessary. It then covalently links several ubiquitin molecules to it (Figure 5.18, step 1). These ubiquitin molecules target the protein to the proteasome cap, which has binding sites for ubiquitin. The cap also has enzymes that unfold the protein and inject it into the internal cavity of the proteasome core (step 2). The ubiquitin proteins are removed during entry and return to the cytosol. Inside the proteasome, proteases degrade the protein into small peptides and amino acids (step 3). The process is completed when the peptides and amino acids are recycled back into the cytosol (step 4). The amino acids can be used to make new proteins.

Ubiquitin targeting has two main uses. First, the enzymes that attach ubiquitin to its target recognize improperly folded proteins, allowing cells to identify and degrade nonfunctional components. Second, changes in cellular conditions may warrant the rapid breakdown of particular proteins. For example, cell division requires a series of stages called the cell cycle, which depends on the degradation of specific proteins. Ubiquitin targeting directs these proteins to the proteasome for degradation.

5.6   CELLS AS EVOLVING UNITS OF LIFE

Learning Outcomes:

1. Describe the major events proposed to account for the evolution of the double-membrane organelles: the nucleus, mitochondria, and chloroplasts.
2. Discuss the evidence for the endosymbiosis theory.

How did eukaryotes, with their nucleus, endomembrane system, and semiautonomous organelles, evolve from a prokaryotic cell with only a cell membrane and no membrane-bound compartments? We do not know with certainty, but it is likely that the earliest eukaryotic cells first developed a nuclear compartment and the cell with a nucleus evolved from the fusion of two prokaryotic cells. DNA analyses suggest that the earliest eukaryotes' genomes have contributions from both domains of prokaryotes: Archaea and ancient Bacteria. It is thus thought that eukaryotes likely evolved after the fusion of two prokaryotic cells from these different domains, with one bacterial cell becoming the incipient nucleus and the other becoming the rest of the cell. Over time all hereditary material united into one nuclear genome. Later events led to evolution of the semiautonomous organelles.

Mitochondria and Chloroplasts Are Derived from Ancient Symbiotic Relationships

The observation that mitochondria and chloroplasts have their own genetic material was at first puzzling. The distinct genomes of mitochondria and chloroplasts can be traced to their evolutionary origin, which involved an ancient symbiotic association. **Symbiosis** occurs when two different species live in direct contact with each other. **Endosymbiosis** describes a symbiotic relationship in which the smaller species—the symbiont— lives inside (*endo* means "inside") the larger species. In 1883 Andreas Schimper proposed that chloroplasts were descended from an endosymbiotic relationship between cyanobacteria (a bacterium capable of photosynthesis) and eukaryotic cells. In 1922 Ivan Wallin also hypothesized an endosymbiotic origin for mitochondria.

In spite of these interesting ideas, the question of endosymbiosis was largely ignored until the discovery that mitochondria and chloroplasts contain their own genetic material. In 1970 Lynn Margulis revived the idea of an endosymbiotic origin of mitochondria and chloroplasts in her book *Origin of Eukaryotic Cells.* During the 1970s and 1980s the advent of molecular genetic techniques allowed researchers to analyze genes from mitochondria, chloroplasts, bacteria, and eukaryotic nuclear genomes. Researchers discovered that genes in mitochondria and chloroplasts are very similar to bacterial genes. Likewise, mitochondria and chloroplasts are strikingly similar in size and shape to certain bacterial species. These observations provided strong support for the **endosymbiosis theory**.

The endosymbiotic theory is illustrated in **Figure 5.19**. Chloroplasts likely were derived from cyanobacteria. The eukaryotic

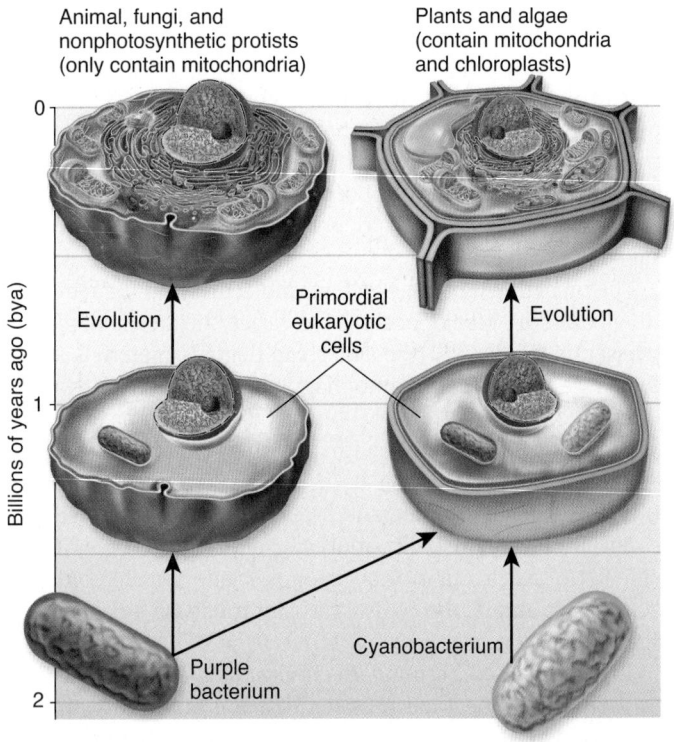

Figure 5.19 The endosymbiosis theory.   (a) According to this concept, modern mitochondria were derived from purple bacteria, also called α-proteobacteria. Through evolution, their characteristics changed into those found in mitochondria today. (b) A similar phenomenon occurred for chloroplasts, which were derived from cyanobacteria, a bacterium that is capable of photosynthesis.

 Principle: *All life is related by an evolutionary history.*

Concept check: *Discuss the similarities and differences between modern bacteria and mitochondria.*

cell that engulfed a cyanobacteria acquired the ability to harvest energy from sunlight to make ATP. Over a 2 billion year timescale, the initial "guest" bacteria evolved into the organelle we call the chloroplast. A different type of bacteria (known as purple bacteria or Proteobacteria) is thought to be the origin of mitochondria. In this case, the endosymbiotic relationship enabled eukaryotic cells to synthesize greater amounts of ATP.

Modern mitochondria and chloroplasts have lost most of the genes that still exist in present-day purple bacteria and cyanobacteria. But many similar genes now occur in eukaryotic nuclear genomes. Some researchers speculate that the movement of genes into the nucleus makes it easier for the cell to coordinate the structure, function, and division of mitochondria and chloroplasts.

5.7 | THE EXTRACELLULAR MATRIX AND CELL JUNCTIONS ALLOW MULTICELLULARITY

Learning Outcomes:

1. Explain the functional roles of the extracellular matrix in animals.
2. Outline the major structural components of the extracellular matrix in animals.
3. Describe the structure and function of plant cell walls.
4. Outline the structure and function of anchoring junctions, tight junctions, and gap junctions.
5. Describe the structure and function of middle lamella and plasmodesmata.

The first eukaryotes were single-celled organisms. From these single-celled organisms arose simple multicellular organisms, and from them evolved the more complex eukaryotes with highly specialized cell types within a multicellular body. All eukaryotes, whether single-celled or multicellular, export protective materials to the exterior side of their cell membrane. But the multicellular members of the plant and animal kingdoms do this extensively. In fact, a large portion of the body of an animal or a plant consists of a network of material that is secreted from cells and forms a complex meshwork outside of cells called the **extracellular matrix (ECM)**. The ECM is a major component of certain parts of animals and plants. For example, bones and cartilage in animals and the woody portions of plants are composed largely of ECM. Although the cells within wood eventually die, the ECM that they have produced provides a rigid structure that can support the plant for years or even centuries, as you can seen from the trunk of the majestic oak tree shown in **Figure 5.20**. Another important aspect of multicellularity is the ability of neighbouring cells to form special types of connections and to communicate with one another. These functions require specialized types of cell-to-cell direct connections that we call cell junctions. We will explore ECM and cell junctions in this section.

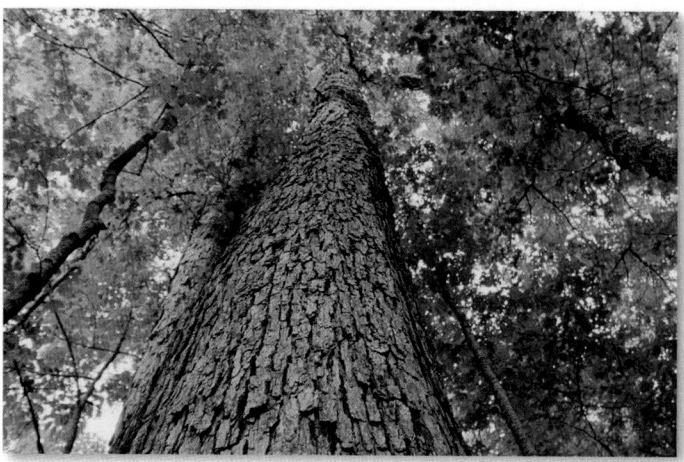

Figure 5.20 An oak tree. The wood of an oak tree is composed largely of material that is outside of cells. This material connects cells to one another and provides structural support for the tree.

 Principle: *Living organisms grow, develop, and reproduce. As the oak seedling grows, its cells divide to produce new cells with new cell walls. As the older cells mature, they develop extensive secondary cell wall materials that form the strong tree trunks that allow the tree to grow tall and sturdy.*

The Extracellular Matrix in Animals Supports and Organizes Cells and Plays a Role in Cell Signalling

Over the past few decades, cell biologists have examined the synthesis, composition, and function of the ECM in animals and plants. In this section, we will begin by examining the structure and role of the ECM in animal cells, focusing on the function of the major ECM protein and carbohydrate macromolecules. We will then explore the cell wall and the extracellular component of plant cells, and consider how it differs in structure and function from the ECM of animal cells.

The cells of animals are not surrounded by a rigid cell wall that provides structure and support. However, animal cells secrete materials to form an ECM that serves a similar purpose. Certain animal cells are completely embedded within an extensive ECM, while other cells may adhere to the ECM on only one side. **Figure 5.21** illustrates the general features of the ECM and its relationship to animal cells. The major macromolecules of the ECM are proteins and polysaccharides. The most abundant proteins are those that form large fibres; the polysaccharides create a gel-like matrix in which the proteins are found.

As you will see, the ECM in animals performs many important roles, including providing strength, structural support, organization, and cell signalling.

- Strength: The ECM is the "tough stuff" of animals' bodies. In the skin of mammals, the strength of the ECM prevents tearing. The ECM found in cartilage resists compression and provides protection to the joints.

Some cells are attached to the ECM on one side.

Some cells are embedded within the ECM.

ECM

Polysaccharides attached to a protein (a proteoglycan)

Protein fiber

Protein fibres give strength and elasticity to the ECM.

Polysaccharides help the ECM resist compression.

100 nm

20 nm

Figure 5.21   Animal cells and the extracellular matrix (ECM).

Concept check: *What are the four functions of the ECM in animals?*

Table 5.2	Proteins in the ECM of Animals	
General type	**Example**	**Function**
Adhesive	Fibronectin	Connects cells to the ECM and helps to organize components in the ECM
	Laminin	Connects cells to the ECM and helps to organize components in the basal lamina, a specialized ECM found next to epithelial cells
Structural	Collagen	Forms large fibres and interconnected fibrous networks in the ECM; provides tensile strength
	Elastin	Forms elastic fibres in the ECM that can stretch and recoil

existing cells, also suggested that all extracellular materials are made and secreted by cells. Around the same time, biologists realized that gelatin and glue, which are produced by the boiling of animal tissues, must contain a common fibrous substance. This substance was named collagen, from the Greek for "glue producing." Since that time, the advent of experimental techniques in chemistry, microscopy, and biophysics has enabled scientists to probe the structure of the ECM. We now understand that the ECM contains a mixture of several different components, including proteins, such as collagen, that form fibres.

The proteins that are found in the ECM can be grouped into adhesive proteins, such as fibronectin and laminin, and ECM structural proteins, such as collagen and elastin (**Table 5.2**). Fibronectin and laminin have multiple binding sites that bind to other components in the ECM, such as protein fibres and carbohydrates. These same proteins also have binding sites for receptors on the surfaces of cells. Adhesive proteins are so named because they adhere cells to the ECM.

Structural Proteins, Such as Collagen and Elastin, Form Large Fibres That Give the ECM Its Strength and Elasticity   As already described, proteins that are secreted from eukaryotic cells are first directed to the endoplasmic reticulum (ER) and then to the Golgi apparatus, and are subsequently secreted from the cell via vesicles that fuse with the plasma membrane. **Figure 5.22** depicts the synthesis and assembly of collagen. Individual procollagen polypeptides are first synthesized into the lumen of the ER. Three procollagen polypeptides then associate with one another to form a procollagen triple helix. The amino acid sequences at both ends of the polypeptides, termed extension peptides, serve to promote the formation of procollagen and prevent the formation of a much larger fibre. After procollagen is secreted, extracellular enzymes remove the extension peptides. Once this occurs, the protein, now called collagen, can form larger structures of the ECM. Collagen proteins assemble in a staggered way to form relatively thin collagen fibrils, which then align and create large collagen fibres.

Similarly, the ECM protects the soft parts of the body, such as the internal organs.

- Structural support: The skeletons of many animals are composed primarily of ECM. Skeletons not only provide structural support but also facilitate movement via the functioning of the attached muscles.
- Organization: The attachment of cells to the ECM plays a key role in the proper arrangement of cells throughout the body. In addition, the ECM binds together many body parts, such as tendons to bones.
- Cell signalling: A newly discovered role of the ECM is cell signalling. One way that cells in multicellular organisms sense their environment is via changes in the ECM.

Let's now consider the synthesis and structure of ECM components found in animals.

Adhesive and Structural Proteins Are Major Components of the ECM of Animals

The idea that fibres are important components of living organisms has a long history. In the Middle Ages, living organisms were thought to be composed of fibres rather than cells. This belief was eventually debunked by the cell theory. In the 1850s Rudolf Virchow, who proposed that all cells come from

A key function of collagen is to provide **tensile strength**, which is a measure of how much stretching force a material can bear without tearing apart. Collagen provides high tensile strength to many parts of the animal body. Collagen is the main protein found in bones, cartilage, tendons, and skin, and it is also found lining blood vessels and internal organs. In mammals, collagen composes more than 25% of the total protein mass, much more than any other protein. Approximately 75% of the protein in mammalian skin is composed of collagen. Leather is largely a pickled and tanned form of collagen.

Elasticity Is Provided by Elastin Proteins In addition to tensile strength, **elasticity** is needed in regions of the body, such as the lungs and blood vessels, which regularly expand and return to their original shape. In these places, the ECM contains an abundance of elastic fibres composed primarily of a protein called elastin (**Figure 5.23**). Elastin proteins form many covalent cross-links to create a fibre. In the absence of a stretching force, each protein tends to adopt a compact conformation. When subjected to a stretching force, the compact proteins extend, with the covalent cross-links keeping the fibre together. When the stretching force has ended, the proteins naturally return to their compact conformation. In this way, elastic fibres behave much like a rubber band, stretching under tension and snapping back when the tension is released.

1 Procollagen polypeptides are synthesized into the ER lumen, where they assemble into a triple helix.

ER lumen

Procollagen polypeptide (α chain)

Procollagen triple helix

Extension sequences

Collagen molecule

2 Procollagen is secreted from the cell, and the extension peptides are removed. The protein is now called collagen.

3 The removal of extension peptides allows collagen to assemble into fibrils.

Collagen fibril

4 Collagen fibrils assemble into larger collagen fibres.

Collagen fibre

Figure 5.22 **Synthesis and assembly of collagen.** Collagen is one type of structural protein found in the ECM of animal cells.

Concept check: *What prevents large collagen fibres from forming intracellularly?*

Elastic fibre

In the absence of a stretching force, the elastin proteins are in a compact conformation.

Single elastin protein

Force

When subjected to a stretching force, the elastin proteins elongate but remain attached to each other via cross links.

Force

Cross link

Figure 5.23 Elastic fibres are made of elastin, one type of structural protein found in the ECM of animal cells.

Concept check: *Suppose you treated an unstretched elastic fibre with a chemical that breaks the cross-links between adjacent elastin proteins. What would happen when the fibre was stretched?*

GENOMES AND PROTEOMES

Collagens Are a Family of Proteins That Give Animal Cells a Variety of ECM Properties

As you have seen, proteins are important constituents of the ECM of animals. By analyzing genomes and the biochemical composition of cells, researchers have determined that many different types of collagen fibres are made. These are designated type I, type II, and so on. At least 27 different types of collagens have been identified in humans. Not surprisingly, the human genome, as well as the genomes of other animals, has many different, but related, genes that encode collagen polypeptides.

All collagens have a common structure, in which three collagen polypeptides wind around one another to form a triple helix (Figure 5.22). Each polypeptide is called an α chain. In some collagens, all three α chains are identical, while in others the α chains are encoded by different collagen genes.

Each of the many different types of collagen polypeptides has a similar yet distinctive amino acid sequence that affects the structure and function of collagen fibres. For example, within the triple helix, the amino acid sequence of an α chain may cause collagen proteins to bind to each other very tightly, thereby creating a relatively stiff fibre. Such collagen fibres are found in bone and cartilage.

Amino acid side chains in the α chains influence the interactions between collagen proteins within a fibre. For example, the amino acid sequences of certain α chains may promote a looser interaction that produces a more bendable or thinner fibre. More flexible collagen fibres support the lining of your lungs and intestines. In addition, domains within the collagen polypeptide may affect the spatial arrangement of collagen proteins. The collagen shown in Figure 5.22 form fibres in which the collagen proteins align themselves in parallel arrays. Not all collagen proteins form long fibres. For example, type IV collagen proteins interact with one another in a meshwork pattern. This meshwork acts as a filtration unit around capillaries.

The genomes of bone, cartilage, lungs, intestine, and capillaries all have the same genes. But the proteome for each tissue is different because different collagen genes are transcribed to produce the mRNAs that encode specific collagen polypeptides. This differential gene expression results in different types, and amounts, of collagens being made throughout the body. Of the 27 types of collagens, **Table 5.3** lists types I to IV, each of which varies in its primary synthesis site, its structure, and its function.

Because collagens are the most abundant proteins found in animals and contribute to the structure and function of

Table 5.3	Examples of Collagen Types	
Type	Sites of synthesis*	Structure and function
I	Tendons, ligaments, bones, and skin	Forms a relatively rigid and thick fibre. Abundant. Provides most of the tensile strength to the ECM.
II	Cartilage, disks between vertebrae	Forms a fairly thick and rigid fibre but is more flexible than type I. Permits smooth movements of joints.
III	Arteries, skin, internal organs, and around muscles	Forms thin fibres, often arranged in a netlike pattern. Allows for greater elasticity in tissues.
IV	Skin, intestine, and kidneys; also found around capillaries	Does not form long fibres. Instead, proteins arranged in a meshwork pattern that provides organization and support to cell layers. Functions as a filter around capillaries.

*The sites of synthesis denote where a large amount of the collagen type is made.

most tissues, it is not surprising that many diseases are associated with alterations in collagen gene regulation and the proper synthesis, structure, processing, secretion, assembly, or degradation of the proteins themselves. For example, Alport syndrome is a genetic disorder associated with mutations in several type IV collagen genes. In Alport syndrome, loss of type IV collagens alters the ability of the cells to regulate the passage of macromolecules. Thus, waste products from the blood are not filtered properly, eventually leading to kidney failure. Hearing loss and visual impairment also can occur as the inner ear and the lens and retina of the eye also depend on type IV collagen to function properly. This is but one of many examples of human disorders that are associated with altered ECM components.

Polysaccharides Are Also Important Components of the ECM of Animals

Polysaccharides are the second major component of the ECM of animals. Among vertebrates, the most abundant types of polysaccharides in the ECM are **glycosaminoglycans (GAGs)**. These molecules are long, unbranched polysaccharides containing a repeating disaccharide unit (**Figure 5.24a**). GAGs are highly negatively charged molecules that tend to attract positively charged ions and water. The majority of GAGs in the ECM are linked to core proteins, forming **proteoglycans** (**Figure 5.24b**).

Providing resistance to compression is the primary function of GAGs and proteoglycans. Once secreted from cells, these macromolecules form a gel-like component in the ECM. Because of its high water content, the ECM is difficult to compress. GAGs and proteoglycans are abundant in regions of the body that are subjected to harsh mechanical forces, such as the joints. Two examples of GAGs are chondroitin sulphate, which

is a major component of cartilage, and hyaluronic acid, which is found in the skin, eyes, and joint fluid.

Among many invertebrates, a different important ECM component is chitin, a nitrogen-containing polysaccharide. Chitin forms the hard protective outer covering (called an exoskeleton) of insects, such as crickets and grasshoppers, and shellfish, such as lobsters and shrimp. In fact, the chitin exoskeleton is so rigid that as these animals grow, they must periodically shed this outer layer and secrete a new, larger one—a process called moulting (look ahead to Figure 30.11).

The Cell Wall Is a Plant's ECM Providing Strength and Resistance to Compression

Let's now turn our attention to the extracellular matrix of plants. Plant cells are surrounded by an organized ECM, called the **cell wall**, a protective layer that forms outside the plasma membrane of the plant cell. Like animal cells, the cells of plants are

(a) Structure of chondroitin sulfate, a glycosaminoglycan

Highly negatively charged glycosaminoglycans (GAGs)

Core protein

(b) General structure of a proteoglycan

Figure 5.24 Structures of glycosaminoglycans and proteoglycans. GAGs and proteoglycans are types of polysaccharides found in the ECM of animals cells. (a) GAGs are composed of repeating disaccharide units. They can range in length from several dozen to 25,000 disaccharide units. The GAG shown here is chondroitin sulphate, which is commonly found in cartilage. (b) Proteoglycans are composed of a long, linear core protein with many GAGs attached. Each GAG is typically 80 disaccharide units long.

 Principle: *Structure determines function. The highly charged GAGs attract water molecules forming a gel-like matrix that provides joints with protection from harsh mechanical forces.*

Concept check: *What structural feature of GAGs and proteoglycans gives them a gel-like character?*

surrounded by material that provides tensile strength and resistance to compression. The cell walls of plants, however, are usually thicker, stronger, and more rigid than the ECM found in animals. Think of the structural support needed to support the trunk, branches, and leaves of the oak tree seen in Figure 5.20. Plant cell walls provide rigidity for mechanical support, the maintenance of cell shape, and the direction of cell growth. The cell wall also constrains expansion when water enters the cell. During the evolution of land plants, these structural features of the plant cell wall may have been key factors that allowed plants to move from the water to land.

The cell walls of plants are composed of a primary cell wall and a secondary cell wall (**Figure 5.25**). The **primary cell wall** is made before the **secondary cell wall** (**Figure 5.25a**, view 2). During cell division, the primary cell wall develops between two newly made daughter cells. It is usually very flexible and allows new cells to increase in size. The main macromolecule of the primary cell wall is cellulose, a polymer made of repeating molecules of glucose attached end to end. These glucose polymers associate with each other via hydrogen bonding to form microfibrils that provide great tensile strength (**Figure 5.25b**).

Cellulose was discovered in 1838 by French chemist Anselme Payen, who was the first scientist to try to separate wood into its component parts. After treating different types of wood with nitric acid, Payen obtained a fibrous substance that was also found in cotton and other plants. His chemical analysis revealed that the fibres were made of the carbohydrate glucose. Payen called this substance cellulose, which means "consisting of cells." Cellulose is probably the single most abundant organic molecule on Earth. Wood consists mostly of cellulose, and cotton and paper are almost pure cellulose.

In addition to cellulose, other components found in the primary cell wall include hemicellulose, glycans, and pectins (see Figure 5.25a, view 3). Hemicellulose is another linear carbohydrate with a structure similar to that of cellulose, but it contains sugars other than glucose in its structure and usually forms thinner microfibrils. Glycans, carbohydrates with branching structures, are also important in cell wall structure. The cross-linking glycans bind to cellulose and provide organization to the cellulose microfibrils. Pectins, which are highly negatively charged, attract water and have a gel-like character that provides the cell wall with the ability to resist compression. Besides carbohydrates, the primary cell wall also contains small amounts of protein. Some of these proteins may increase the strength of the cell wall, while others are enzymes involved in the synthesis and organization of the carbohydrate polymers. The mechanism of cellulose synthesis via extracellular enzymes is described in Chapter 28.

The secondary cell wall is synthesized and deposited between the plasma membrane and the primary cell wall after a plant cell matures and has stopped increasing in size. It is made in layers by the successive deposition of cellulose microfibrils and other components. Although the primary wall structure is relatively similar in nearly all cell types and species, the structure of the secondary cell wall is more variable. The secondary cell wall often contains components in addition to those found in the primary cell wall. For example, phenolic compounds called **lignins** are very hard and impart considerable strength to the secondary wall structure. Lignin, a type of secondary metabolite described in Chapter 7, is found in the woody parts of plants.

Cell Junctions: The Structures That Connect the Cells of Multicellular Eukaryotes

Thus far, you have learned that the cells of animals and plants create an extracellular matrix that provides strength, support, and organization. For an organism to become multicellular, cells within the body must be linked to one another and to the ECM in specific ways that allows the cells to perform their own functions and to interact with other cells to accomplish the organism's bodily functions. In animals and plants the cell-to-cell and cell-to-ECM linkages are accomplished by specialized structures called **cell junctions**. In this section we will examine different types of cell junctions in animal and plant cells.

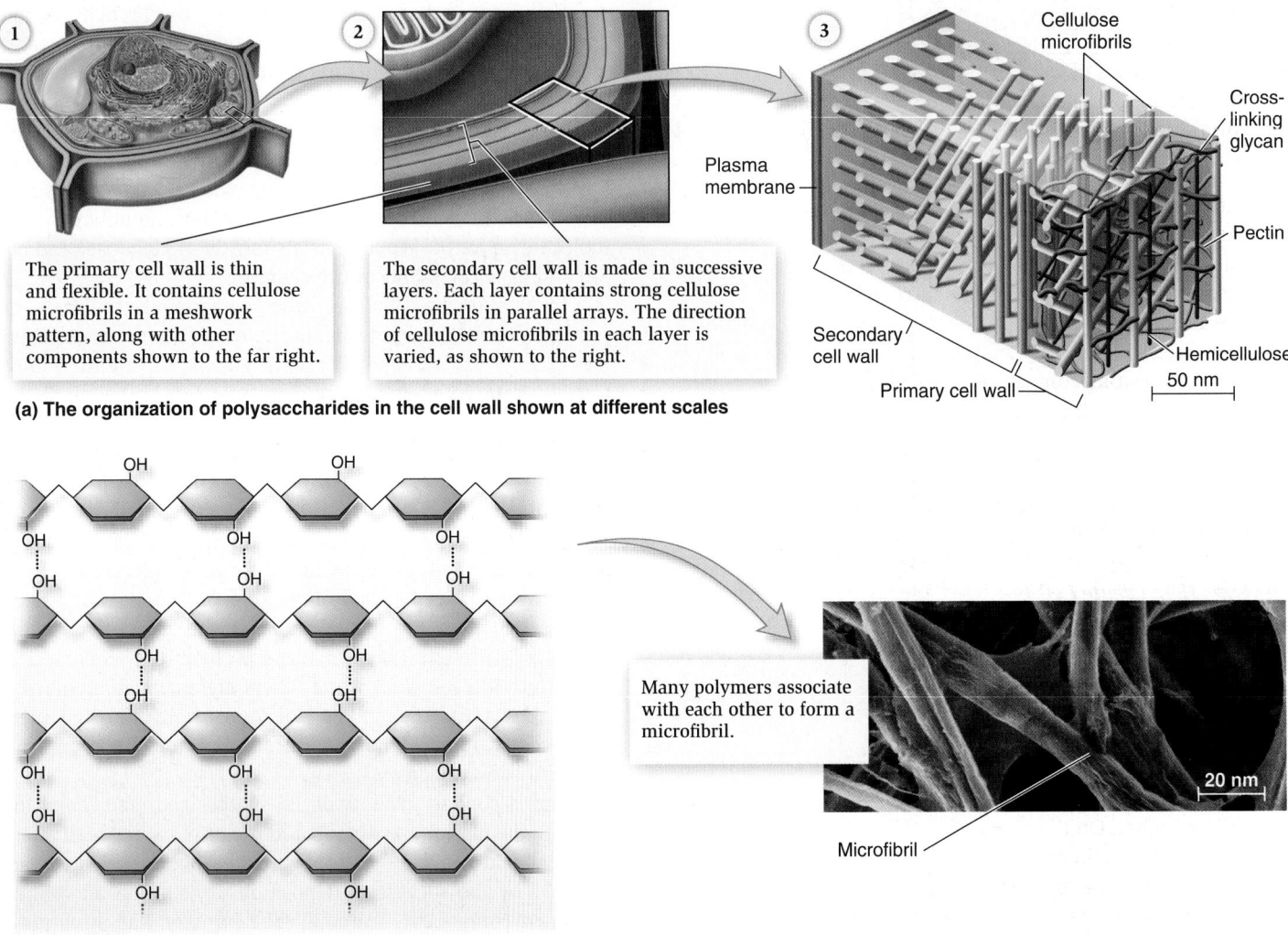

The primary cell wall is thin and flexible. It contains cellulose microfibrils in a meshwork pattern, along with other components shown to the far right.

The secondary cell wall is made in successive layers. Each layer contains strong cellulose microfibrils in parallel arrays. The direction of cellulose microfibrils in each layer is varied, as shown to the right.

(a) The organization of polysaccharides in the cell wall shown at different scales

Many polymers associate with each other to form a microfibril.

(b) Hydrogen bonding between cellulose molecules produces microfibrils

Figure 5.25   **Structure of the plant ECM.**   The primary cell wall is relatively thin and flexible. The secondary cell wall, which is produced only by certain plant cells, is made after the primary cell wall and is synthesized in successive layers.

Concept check: *With regard to cell growth, what would happen if the secondary cell wall was made too soon?*

Animal cells, which lack the structural support provided by the cell wall, have more diverse types of junctions than plant cells do. In animal cells, junctions called **anchoring junctions** play a role in anchoring cells to one another or to the extracellular matrix. In other words, they hold cells in their proper place in the body. Other junctions, termed **tight junctions**, seal cells together into a tissue that prevents small molecules from leaking through one cell layer into another. Still another type of junction known as a **gap junction** allows cells to communicate directly with each other.

In plants, cellular organization is somewhat different because plants cells are surrounded by a rigid cell wall. As you will learn, plants cells are connected to each other by a component called the middle lamella, which cements their cell walls

together. They also have junctions termed plasmodesmata that allow adjacent cells to communicate directly with each other.

Anchoring Junctions Link Animal Cells to One Another and to the ECM

The advent of electron microscopy allowed researchers to explore the types of junctions that occur between cells and within the extracellular matrix. In the 1960s Marilyn Farquhar, George Palade, and colleagues conducted several studies showing that various types of cellular junctions connect cells to one another. Over the past few decades, researchers have begun to unravel the functions and molecular structures of these anchoring junctions, which attach cells to one another and to the extracellular matrix. Anchoring junctions rely on the functioning of membrane proteins called **cell adhesion molecules (CAMs)**. Two types of CAMs are cadherin and integrin.

Anchoring junctions are grouped into four main categories, according to their functional roles and their connections to cellular components (**Figure 5.26**):

1. **Adherens junctions** connect cells to each other via cadherins. In many cases, these junctions are organized into bands around cells. In the cytosol, adherens junctions bind to cytoskeletal filaments called actin filaments.
2. **Desmosomes** also connect cells to each other via cadherins. They are spotlike points of intercellular contact that rivet.
3. **Focal adhesions** connect cells to the extracellular matrix via integrins. In the cytosol, focal adhesions bind to actin filaments.
4. **Hemidesmosomes** also connect cells to the extracellular matrix via integrins. Like desmosomes, they interact with intermediate filaments.

Caherins Help Create Cell-to-Cell Junctions Let's now consider the molecular components of anchoring junctions. **Cadherins** are CAMs that create cell-to-cell junctions (**Figure 5.27a**). Each cadherin is a dimer of identical subunits. The extracellular domains of two cadherin dimers, each in adjacent cells, bind to each other to promote cell-to-cell adhesion. This binding requires the presence of calcium ions, which change the conformation of cadherin so that cadherins in adjacent cells can bind to each other. On the inside of the cell, linker proteins connect cadherins to actin or intermediate filaments of the cytoskeleton. This promotes a more stable interaction between two cells because their strong cytoskeletons are connected to each other.

Cadherins are the major CAMs in vertebrate species. The genomes of vertebrates contain several different cadherin genes, which encode slightly different cadherin proteins. Having different types of cadherins allows similar types of cells to recognize each other. Dimer formation follows a **homophilic like-to-like binding mechanism**. To understand the concept, let's take an example. One cadherin is called E-cadherin and another is N-cadherin. E-cadherin in one cell will bind to E-cadherin if it is present in an adjacent cell. Similarly, cells with N-cadherin will bind to other cells with N-cadherin. By expressing only certain types of cadherins, each cell will bind only to other cells that express the same cadherin types. This phenomenon is important in the proper arrangement of cells throughout the body during development.

Integrins Help Create Cell-to-ECM Connections A second category of CAMs are the **integrins**, a group of cell-surface receptor proteins that create connections between cells and the ECM. In the example shown in **Figure 5.27b**, an integrin is bound to fibronectin, an ECM protein that binds to other ECM components, such as collagen fibres. Like cadherins, integrins also bind to actin or intermediate filaments in the cytosol of the cell, via linker proteins, to promote a strong association between the

In adherens junctions, cadherins connect cells to each other and to actin filaments.

In desmosomes, cadherins connect cells to each other and to intermediate filaments.

Ring of actin filaments

Intermediate filaments

Cadherins

Linker proteins

Integrin

Actin filament

ECM

In hemidesmosomes, integrins connect the ECM to intermediate filaments.

In focal adhesions, integrins connect the ECM to actin filaments.

Figure 5.26 **Types of anchoring junctions found in animals.** This figure shows the junctions on three adjacent intestinal cells.

 Principle: *Living organisms grow, develop, and reproduce. As the cells of a multicellular organism divide, they must establish the correct type of junctions with neighbouring cells or the ECM.*

Concept check: *Which junctions are cell-to-cell junctions and which are cell-to-ECM junctions?*

cytoskeleton of a cell and the extracellular matrix. Thus, integrins have an extracellular domain for the binding of ECM components and an intracellular domain for the binding of cytosolic proteins.

CAMs Have Signalling Roles When CAMs were first discovered, researchers imagined that cadherins and integrins played only a mechanical role in cell biology, holding cells to

Cadherin dimer

Cadherins link cells to each other.

Ca²⁺

Actin

Plasma membranes of adjacent cells

Linker protein

(a) Cadherins

ECM

Cytosol

Linker protein

Integrins link cells to the extracellular matrix.

Actin

Integrin

Plasma membrane

Collagen fibre

Fibronectin

ECM

(b) Integrins

Figure 5.27 Types of cell adhesion molecules (CAMs). Cadherins and integrins are CAMs that form connections in anchoring junctions. **(a)** A cadherin in one cell binds to a cadherin of an identical type in an adjacent cell. This binding requires Ca²⁺. In the cytosol, cadherins bind to actin or intermediate filaments of the cytoskeleton. **(b)** Integrins link cells to the extracellular matrix and form intracellular connections to actin or intermediate filaments.

each other or to the ECM. More recently, however, experiments have shown that cadherins and integrins are important in cell communication. When cell-to-cell and cell-to-ECM junctions are formed or broken, it affects signalling pathways within the cell. Similarly, intracellular signalling pathways can affect cadherins and integrins in ways that alter intercellular junctions and the binding of cells to ECM components.

With regard to cell signalling, integrins are particularly interesting because they are capable of both outside-in and inside-out signalling (**Figure 5.28**). Integrins are so named because they integrate changes in the ECM to changes in the cytoskeleton. When the extracellular domain of an integrin binds to components of the ECM, this causes a conformational change that affects the structure of the intracellular domain, altering its interaction with cytoskeletal proteins. This **outside-in signalling** regulates cell adhesion (the ability of cells to adhere to the ECM), cell growth, and cell migration. In addition, signals generated inside the cell can alter integrins and affect their ability to bind to components in the ECM, either lowering or increasing their affinity. This phenomenon, termed **inside-out signalling**, is also important for cell adhesion and migration, and it provides a way for cells to contribute to the organization of the ECM.

Abnormalities in CAMs, such as integrins, are often associated with the ability of cancer cells to metastasize; that is, to move to other parts of the body. Cell adhesion molecules are critical for keeping cells in their correct locations. When their function becomes abnormal because of cancer-causing mutations, cells lose their proper connections with the ECM and adjacent cells and may spread to other parts of the body. This topic is considered in more detail in Chapter 13.

Tight Junctions Prevent the Leakage of Materials Across Animal Cell Layers

In animals, tight junctions, or occluding junctions, are a second type of junction, one that forms a tight seal between adjacent cells and thereby prevents extracellular material from leaking between cells. As an example, consider the intestine. The cells that line the intestine form a sheet that is one cell thick; one side faces the intestinal lumen, while the other faces the blood (**Figure 5.29**). Tight junctions between these cells ensure that nutrients pass through the plasma membranes of the intestinal cells before entering the blood and prevent the transport of materials from the blood into the intestine.

Tight junctions are formed from the membrane proteins occludin and claudin; they form interlaced strands in the plasma membrane (see inset to Figure 5.29). These strands of proteins, each in adjacent cells, bind to each other and thereby form a tight seal between cells. Tight junctions are not mechanically strong like anchoring junctions because they do not have strong

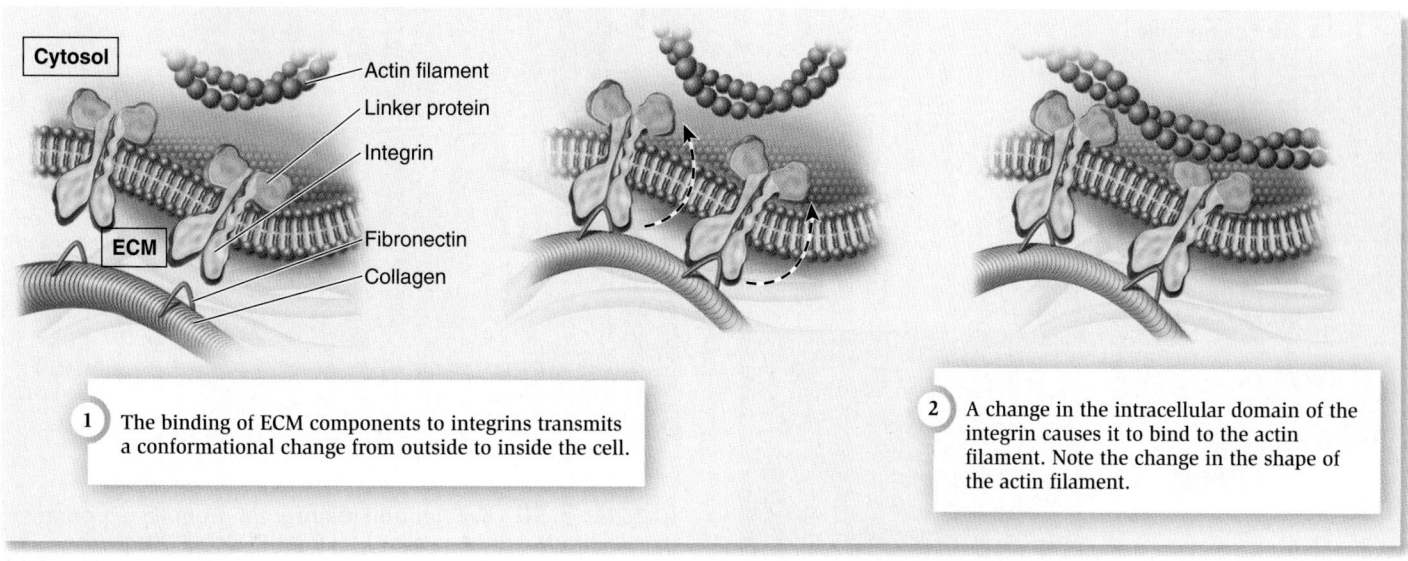

1 The binding of ECM components to integrins transmits a conformational change from outside to inside the cell.

2 A change in the intracellular domain of the integrin causes it to bind to the actin filament. Note the change in the shape of the actin filament.

(a) Outside-in signalling

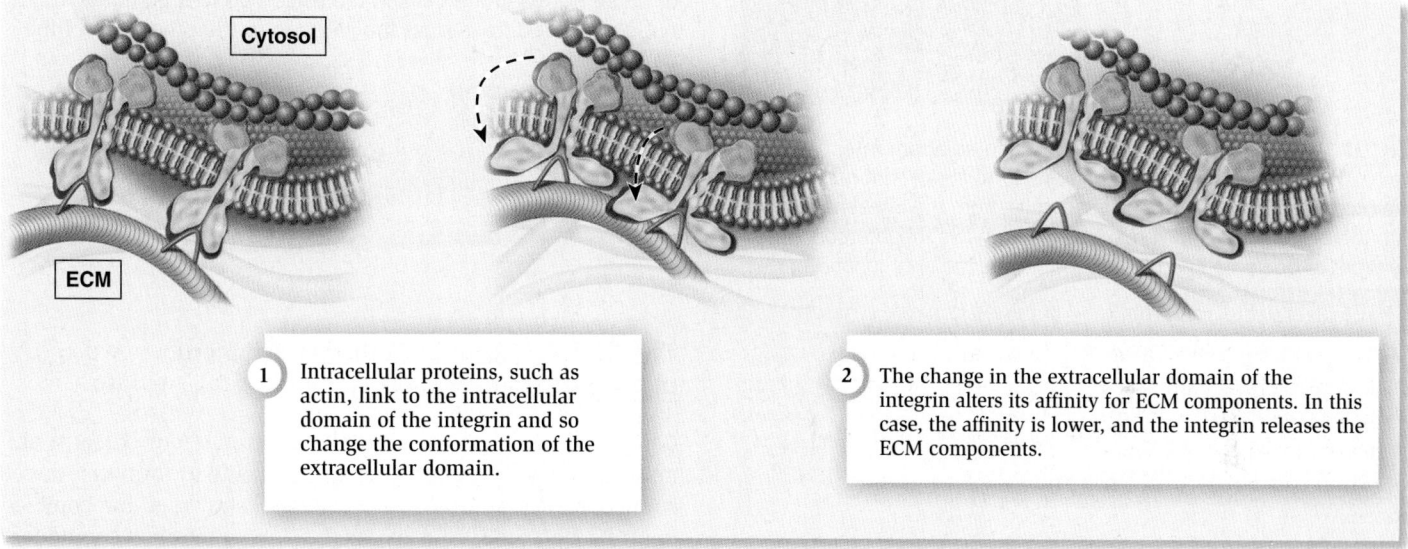

1 Intracellular proteins, such as actin, link to the intracellular domain of the integrin and so change the conformation of the extracellular domain.

2 The change in the extracellular domain of the integrin alters its affinity for ECM components. In this case, the affinity is lower, and the integrin releases the ECM components.

(b) Inside-out signalling

Figure 5.28 **Cell signalling via integrins in anchoring junctions.** (a) Outside-in signalling occurs when an integrin binds to a component in the ECM, which transmits a signal to the cytosol, thereby affecting activities inside the cell. In this example the effect is to alter the conformation of part of the cytoskeleton. (b) Inside-out signalling occurs when the cytosol affects the structure of an integrin and thereby changes its ability to bind to components in the ECM. In the example shown here, the effect is to lower the affinity for an ECM component, causing it to release from the integrin component.

Concept check: *When an animal receives a wound, this causes outside-in signalling. Explain how.*

connections with the cytoskeleton. Therefore, adjacent cells that have occluding junctions also have anchoring junctions to hold them in place.

The amazing ability of tight junctions to prevent the leakage of material across cell layers has been demonstrated by dye-injection studies. In 1972, Daniel Friend and Norton Gilula injected lanthanum, which is electron dense and can be visualized under the electron microscope, into the bloodstream of a rat. A few minutes later, a sample of a cell layer in the digestive tract was removed and visualized by electron microscopy. As seen in the micrograph in **Figure 5.30**, lanthanum diffused into the region between the cells that faces the blood, but it could not move past the tight junction to the side of the cell layer facing the lumen of the intestine.

Figure 5.29   Tight junctions between adjacent intestinal cells.   In this example, tight junctions form a seal that prevents the movement of material between cells, from the intestinal lumen into the blood, and vice versa. The inset shows the interconnected network of occludin and claudin that forms the tight junction.

Concept check: *What do you think is the role of tight junctions in the epidermal layers of your skin?*

BioConnections: *Look ahead to Figure 45.11. What problems might arise if tight junctions did not connect the cells that line your small intestine?*

Gap Junctions in Animal Cells Provide a Passageway for Intercellular Transport

A third type of junction found in animals is called a gap junction because a small gap occurs between the plasma membranes of cells connected by these junctions (**Figure 5.31**). In vertebrates, gap junctions are composed of a membrane protein called connexin. (Invertebrates have a structurally similar protein called innexin.) Six connexin proteins in one cell align with six connexin proteins in an adjacent cell to form a channel called a **connexon** (see inset to Figure 5.31).

The connexons allow the passage of ions and small molecules with a molecular mass less than 1,000 daltons. This size range includes amino acids, sugars, and small signalling molecules. Gap junctions thus allow adjacent cells to share metabolites and directly signal each other. But gap-junction channels are too small to allow the passage of macromolecules, such as mRNAs, large carbohydrates, or proteins. Therefore, cells that communicate via gap junctions maintain their own distinctive set of macromolecules.

Figure 5.30   An electron micrograph from an experiment demonstrating the function of a tight junction.   When lanthanum was injected into the bloodstream of a rat, it diffused between the cells in the region up to a tight junction but could not diffuse past the junction to the other side of the cell layer.

Concept check: *What results would you expect if a rat were fed lanthanum and then a sample of intestinal cells was observed under the EM?*

The Middle Lamella Cements Adjacent Plant Cell Walls Together

Cell junctions in plants are quite different from those in animals; plants don't use membrane proteins to form cell-to-cell connections. Plants use two different strategies for connecting adjacent cells; one of these is an additional component in the ECM called the **middle lamella**. When plant cells are dividing, the middle lamella is the first layer that is formed. Next, the primary cell wall is made inside the middle lamella (**Figure 5.32**). The middle lamella is rich in pectins, negatively charged carbohydrate polymers that are also found in the primary cell wall. These polymers attract water and make a hydrated gel. Ca^{2+} and Mg^{2+} interact with the negative charges in the carbohydrates and cement the cell walls of adjacent cells together.

The process of fruit ripening illustrates the importance of pectins in holding plant cells together. An unripened fruit, such as a green tomato, is very firm because the rigid cell walls of adjacent cells are firmly attached to each other. During ripening, the cells secrete a group of enzymes called pectinases, which digest pectins in the middle lamella and in the primary cell wall. As this process continues, the attachments between cells are broken, and the cell walls become less rigid. For this reason, a red ripe tomato is much less firm than an unripe tomato.

Figure 5.31   **Gap junctions between adjacent cells.**   Gap junctions form intercellular channels that allow the passage of small solutes. A transmembrane channel called a connexon consists of 12 proteins called connexins, 6 in each cell. The micrograph shows a gap junction between intestinal cells.

Principle: *Living organisms interact with their environment. Gap junctions between animal cells of the neuromuscular system allow rapid signalling from cell to cell that enables animals to quickly move in response to environmental changes.*

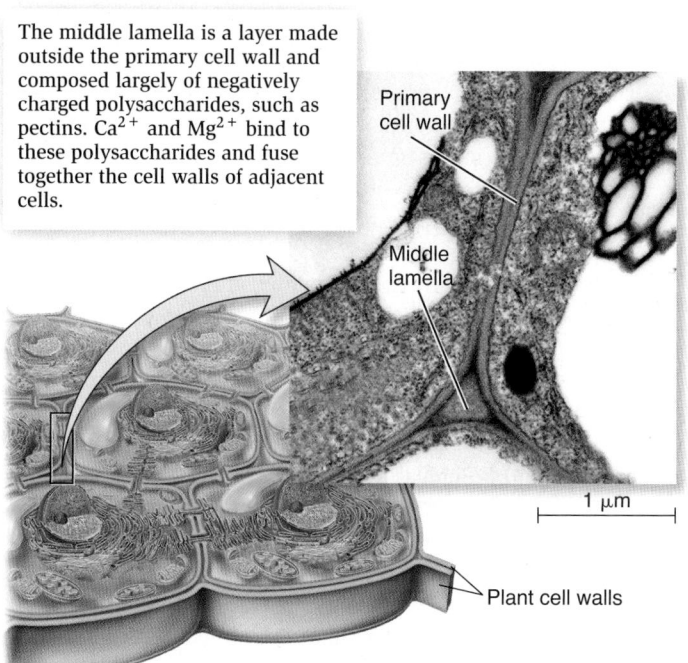

The middle lamella is a layer made outside the primary cell wall and composed largely of negatively charged polysaccharides, such as pectins. Ca^{2+} and Mg^{2+} bind to these polysaccharides and fuse together the cell walls of adjacent cells.

Figure 5.32   **Plant cell-to-cell junctions known as middle lamella.**

Concept check: *How are middle lamellae similar to the anchoring junctions and desmosomes found between animal cells? How are they different?*

Plasmodesmata Are Channels Connecting the Cytoplasm of Adjacent Plant Cells

The second type of plant junction is the plasmodesmata. In 1879 Eduard Tangl, a Russian botanist, observed intercellular cytoplasmic connections in the seeds of the strychnine tree, and he hypothesized that the cytoplasm of adjacent cells is connected by ducts in the cell walls. He first proposed that direct cell-to-cell communication integrates the functioning of plant cells. The ducts or intercellular channels that Tangl observed are now known as **plasmodesmata** (singular: plasmodesma).

Plasmodesmata are functionally similar to gap junctions in animal cells in that they allow the passage of ions, water, sugars, amino acids, and signalling molecules between cells. However, the structure of plasmodesmata is quite different from that of gap junctions. As shown in **Figure 5.33**, plasmodesmata are open channels in the cell walls of adjacent cells. At these sites, the plasma membrane of one cell is continuous with the plasma membrane of the other cell, which permits the diffusion of molecules from the cytosol of one cell to the cytosol of the other. In addition to a cytosolic connection, plasmodesmata often possess a central tubule, called a desmotubule, connecting the ER membranes of adjacent cells.

Plasmodesmata play pivotal roles in signalling between cells during early embryogenesis to establish cell fates, and recent studies have shown that their aperture can be altered to facilitate the movement of larger molecules such as specific RNAs and proteins. Some viruses have evolved proteins that allow them to use these cytoplasmic channels to infect adjacent cells.

0.6 μm

Plasmodesmata

Plasma membrane

Cell walls of adjacent plant cells

Smooth endoplasmic reticulum

Desmotubule passing through a plasmodesma

| Cytosol | | Cytosol |
Cell 1   Middle lamella   Cell 2

Figure 5.33 **Structure of plasmodesmata.** Plasmodesmata are cell junctions connecting the cytosol of adjacent plant cells. Plasmodesmata can be opened or closed; when open they allow water and small molecules to pass from cell to cell. At these sites, the plasma membrane of one cell is continuous with the plasma membrane of an adjacent cell. In addition, the ER from one cell is connected to that of the adjacent cell via a desmotubule.

5.8   CELLS AS THE BUILDING BLOCKS OF MORE COMPLEX SYSTEMS: MULTICELLULAR ORGANISMS

Learning Outcomes:

1. Determine which cell structure is important for cell migration.
2. Give examples of the type of junctions that might be found in different tissues and justify your answer.
3. Explain whether cells of the same tissue have identical or similar genomes and proteomes.

Multicellularity is seen in some protists and fungi and in all plant and animal kingdoms. The cells within different parts of the organism can be quite different in their structure and function because of their different proteomes. Clusters of cells within an organism with similar structure and function are known as **tissues**. Because tissues are fundamental units within multicellular organisms, understanding the characteristics of tissues is essential to many areas of biology, particularly plant and animal development. Plant and animal biologists are interested in understanding the genetic and morphological changes that occur as the tissues of young plants and animals develop from fertilized eggs into an adult organism. These topics will be examined in Chapters 17, 37, and 50. A multicellular organism, such as a plant or an animal, contains many cells. For example, an adult human's body has trillions of cells. Cells are organized into tissues, and tissues are organized into organs. An **organ** is a collection of two or more tissues that performs a specific function or set of functions. The heart is an organ found in the bodies of complex animals, while a leaf is an organ found in plants. We will examine the structures and functions of organs in Units VI and VII.

To create tissues and organs, cells undergo six basic processes that influence their morphology, arrangement, and number:

1. Cell division: As discussed in Chapters 10 and 14, eukaryotic cells progress through a cell cycle that leads to cell division.
2. Cell growth: Following cell division, cells take up nutrients and usually expand in volume.
3. Differentiation: During development, the cells differentiate into specialized types of cells. This differentiation results from changes in the proteome, which in turn is driven by differential expression of the genome. Cell differentiation is described in Chapter 17.
4. Migration: During embryonic development in animals, cells migrate to their appropriate positions within the body. Cell migration does not occur during plant development.
5. Apoptosis: Programmed cell death, also known as **apoptosis,** is a regulated and normal feature of plant and animal development and is necessary to produce certain morphological features of the body. For example, during development in mammals, the formation of individual fingers and toes requires the removal, by apoptosis, of the skin cells between them. It will be discussed more fully in Chapter 17.
6. Cell connections: In this chapter, you learned that cells secrete an extracellular matrix that provides strength and support. In animals, the ECM serves to organize cells within tissues and organs. In plants, the cell wall forms the ECM that shapes plant tissues. Different types of cell junctions in animal and plant cells enable cells to make physical contact and communicate with one another.

Summary of Key Concepts

5.1 An Overview of the Dynamic Interactions of the Genome, Proteome, and Environment

- In systems biology researchers study living organisms in terms of their underlying network structure—groups of structural and functional connections—rather than their individual molecular components.

- Structure determines function: this principle can be applied at the molecular, macromolecular, organelle, and cell level.

- DNA gives rise to RNA gives rise to protein. The genome (all the organism's DNA) is used selectively to create the proteome needed by a cell at a specific time. Genome and proteome interaction is dynamic. (Table 5.1)

5.2 Attaining Structure in Cells

- The maintenance of cell structure relies on the genome, functional molecules, and pre-existing organization. Other factors include the ability of certain proteins to interact with one another to form molecular machines and the dynamic turnover of cellular molecules and macromolecules.

- Interactions among proteins and RNA molecules form molecular machines that carry out complex cellular functions. (Figures 5.1, 5.2)

- The cytoskeleton is a molecular machine that provides cell organization and directs cellular movements.

- Modern cells can grow, adapt, and modify their organization, but they do not arise spontaneously from nonliving materials.

- Cell organization depends on genetic information in the cell nucleus, which produces a proteome. In turn, the proteome influences which genes will be expressed, potentially altering the proteome.

5.3 The Cell Is a System with Four Major Compartments

- In eukaryotic cells, four regions work together to produce dynamic organization. The nucleus houses the genome, which plays a key role in producing the proteome. These two regions exchange information dynamically. The cytosol is an important coordination centre for cell metabolism and organization. The organelles of the endomembrane system perform several important functions in eukaryotic cells. The semiautonomous organelles (mitochondria and chloroplasts) perform a variety of crucial functions. (Figures 5.3, 5.4, 5.5, 5.6, 5.7)

- In eukaryotic cells, the cytosol and endomembrane system work together to synthesize most lipids. The endomembrane system includes the nuclear envelope, endoplasmic reticulum, Golgi apparatus, lysosomes, vacuoles, and plasma membrane. (Figures 5.8, 5.9, 5.10)

- Palade's pulse-chase experiments demonstrated that secreted proteins move sequentially through the organelles of the endomembrane system. (Figure 5.11)

5.4 The Cell Has a System to Sort Proteins to the Correct Cellular Compartment

- Protein localization involves sorting signals and vesicle transport. (Figures 5.12, 5.13)

- Most transmembrane proteins are first inserted into the ER membrane and then transported via vesicles to other membranes of the endomembrane system. (Figure 5.14)

- Glycosylation of proteins occurs in the ER and Golgi apparatus. Glycosylation can help proteins fold properly, protect them from extracellular factors, and assist in protein sorting. (Figure 5.15)

- Most proteins are sorted to mitochondria and chloroplasts post-translationally. (Figures 5.16, 5.17)

5.5 The Cell Has a System for Degrading and Recycling Macromolecules

- The maintenance of cell organization is a dynamic process that involves breaking down molecules and recycling their building blocks. (Figure 5.18)

5.6 Cells as Evolving Units of Life

- Mitochondria and chloroplasts contain their own genetic material and divide by binary fission.

- According to the endosymbiosis theory, mitochondria and chloroplasts have evolved from bacteria that took up residence in early eukaryotic cells. (Figure 5.19)

5.7 The Extracellular Matrix and Cell Junctions Allow Multicellularity

- The extracellular matrix (ECM) is a network of material that is secreted from plant and animal cells and forms a complex meshwork outside of cells. (Figure 5.20)

- In the ECM of animals, proteins and polysaccharides are the major constituents. These materials are involved in strength, structural support, organization, and cell signalling. (Table 5.2, Figure 5.21)

- Adhesive proteins, such as fibronectin and laminin, help to adhere cells to the ECM. Structural proteins form fibres. Collagen fibres provide tensile strength, while elastic fibres allow regions of the body to stretch. (Table 5.3, Figures 5.22, 5.23)

- Glycosaminoglycans (GAGs) are polysaccharides of repeating disaccharide units that give a gel-like character to the ECM of animals. Proteoglycans consist of a core protein with attached GAGs. (Figure 5.24)

- Plant cells are surrounded by an ECM, called the cell wall. The primary cell wall is made first. It is composed largely of cellulose. The secondary cell wall is made after the primary cell wall and is often quite thick and rigid. (Figures 5.25)

- The three common types of cell junctions found in animals are anchoring, tight, and gap junctions. Plant junctions include middle lamella and plasmodesmata. (Figure 5.26, 5.27, 5.29, 5.31, 5.32, 5.33)

- Anchoring junctions involve cell adhesion molecules (CAMs), which bind cells to each other or to the ECM. The four types are adherens junctions, desmosomes, focal adhesions, and hemidesmosomes. (Figure 5.26)

- Two types of CAMs are cadherin and integrin. Cadherins link cells to one another, while integrins link cells to the ECM. In the cytosol, CAMs bind to actin or intermediate filaments. (Figure 5.27)

- Integrins can perform outside-in and inside-out signalling, which enables cells to communicate with the ECM. (Figure 5.28)

- Tight junctions, composed of occludin and claudin proteins, prevent the leakage of materials between cells. (Figures 5.29, 5.30)

- Gap junctions form channels called connexons that permit the direct passage of materials between adjacent cells. (Figure 5.31)
- The cell walls of adjacent plant cells are cemented together via middle lamella. (Figure 5.32)
- Adjacent plant cells usually have direct connections called plasmodesmata, which are open channels in the cell walls. The ER of adjacent cells is also connected via plasmodesmata. (Figure 5.33)

5.8 Cells as the Building Blocks of More Complex Systems: Multicellular Organisms

- A tissue is a group of cells that have a similar structure and function.
- An organ is composed of two or more tissues and carries out a particular function or functions.
- Six processes—cell division, cell growth, differentiation, migration, apoptosis, and cell connections—create tissues and organs.

Test to Assess Your Learning

1. The main structural elements of cells that produce cellular organization are
   a. proteins.
   b. organelles.
   c. membranes.
   d. all of the above.
   e. (a) and (c) only.

2. Which of the following statements best supports the requirements to make new cells?
   a. The formation of new cells relies solely on the presence of the genome.
   b. New cell formation requires the correct genetic information and the building blocks necessary to produce the cellular components.
   c. New cell production requires the genome, functional molecules, and pre-existing organization.
   d. The formation of new cells requires the appropriate genetic information and functional molecules for cellular activity only.
   e. All of the above.

3. Large molecular complexes that perform different cellular activities that involve changes in molecular conformation are called molecular
   a. clocks.
   b. motors.
   c. machines.
   d. proteins.
   e. proteomes.

4. Protein conformation is important to protein function. The assembly of many complex proteins relies on _____, in which surfaces of subunits recognize each other and bind together.
   a. protein sorting
   b. traffic signalling
   c. post-transcriptional changes
   d. molecular recognition
   e. proteasome activity

5. In the nucleus, proteins help maintain organization by
   a. forming a meshwork in the nucleus that organizes each chromosome into its own chromosome territory.
   b. organizing the outer nuclear membrane.
   c. organizing the inner nuclear membrane.
   d. all of the above.
   e. (a) and (c) only.

6. The cytoskeleton is an important feature of the cytosol that provides organization by
   a. determining cell shape.
   b. determining the structure of the endomembrane system.
   c. transporting proteins to the endoplasmic reticulum for protein sorting.
   d. recycling membrane-bounded proteins.
   e. all of the above.

7. Proteins that function to move lipids from one membrane to another are called
   a. lipases.
   b. membrane-bounded lipoproteins.
   c. proteases.
   d. lipid exchange proteins.
   e. phospholipids.

8. Protein sorting in the cell is possible because of
   a. sorting signals in the amino acid sequences of proteins that determine protein destinations in the cell.
   b. chaperone proteins that function to direct all proteins to the proper location inside or outside the cell.
   c. formation of protein sorting vesicles that carry proteins from the Golgi to lysosomes.
   d. DNA sequences that remain part of the proteins that determine cellular destination.
   e. all of the above.

9. Proteins that remain in the cytosol as opposed to passing through the endomembrane system are sorted
   a. before translation by pretranslational sorting.
   b. during translation by cotranslational sorting.
   c. after translation by post-translational sorting.
   d. both (b) and (c).
   e. none of the above.

10. Vesicles move to the appropriate membrane in the cell by the recognition of _____, proteins in the target membrane that act as binding sites for the vesicle.
    a. v-snares
    b. traffic signals
    c. coat proteins
    d. chaperones
    e. t-snares

11. The protein found in the ECM of animals that provides strength and resistance to tearing when stretched is
    a. elastin.
    b. cellulose.
    c. collagen.
    d. laminin.
    e. fibronectin.

12. The polysaccharide that forms the hard outer covering of many invertebrates is
    a. collagen.
    b. chitin.
    c. chondroitin sulphate.
    d. pectin.
    e. cellulose.

13. The most abundant organic molecule on Earth is _____, and it is the main macromolecule of the _____.
    a. collagen, connective tissue of animals
    b. chitin, muscle tissue of animals
    c. cellulose, primary cell wall of plants
    d. integrins, cell junctions in plants
    e. pectin, secondary cell wall of plants

14. _____ are proteins that attach animal cells to the ECM.
    a. Cadherins
    b. Integrins

c. Occludins
d. Tight junctions
e. Desmosomes

15. The gap junctions of animal cells differ from the plasmodesmata of plant cells in that
    a. gap junctions serve as communicating junctions and plasmodesmata serve as adhesion junctions.
    b. gap junctions prevent extracellular material from moving between adjacent cells, but the plasmodesmata do not.
    c. gap junctions allow for direct exchange of cellular material between cells, but plasmodesmata cannot allow the same type of exchange.
    d. gap junctions are formed by specialized proteins that form channels through the membranes of adjacent cells, but plasmodesmata are not formed by specialized proteins.
    e. all of the above.

16. Which of the following is involved in the process of tissue and organ formation in multicellular organisms?
    a. Cell division.
    b. Cell differentiation.
    c. Cell connections.
    d. Cell growth.
    e. All of the above.

Articulate to Assess Your Learning

1. Trace the path of the production of a protein, starting with the mRNA that encodes it and leading to the secretion of the protein from the cell.

2. Briefly explain how sorting signals function in protein localization.

3. Define glycosylation. What are the purposes of glycosylation?

4. List and explain the four characteristics of the extracellular matrix.

5. Distinguish between the primary cell wall and the secondary cell wall.

6. Compare and contrast plasmodesmata with tight junctions and gap junctions.

Collaborate to Assess and Extend Your Learning

1. Create a concept map that indicates the relationships among the following terms: genome, proteome, transcription, translation, transcription factors, ER localization signal, protein sorting, proteosome, cell differentiation, cell signalling.

2. Discuss the theory of how the mitochondria and chloroplast evolved. How would you explain the data on gene composition?

3. According to the cell theory all organisms are made of cells. Think about the oak tree in Figure 5.20 and about the human body. Are there any additions to or clarifications about this cell theory that you want to make?

4. Create a concept map that indicates the relationships among the following terms: cell junctions, anchoring junctions, cell adhesion molecules (CAMs), like-to-like homodimer binding mechanism, cadherins, integrins, adherens junctions, desmosomes, hemidesmosomes, cytoskeletal elements, focal adhesions, inside-out signalling, outside-in signalling, tight junctions, occludin and claudin, gap junctions, connexins, innexins, connexons, middle lamella, plasmodesmata.

5. A biological principle of life is that living organisms interact with their environment. How do the structures seen in Figure 5.8 help the organism interact successfully with its environment?

Visit McGraw-Hill Ryerson Connect™ for additional study resources.

Membrane Structure and Transport

The Shaker protein channel is illustrated here. Drawings A and B are side views of the protein channel; C and D are top views. Views A and C represent the closed configuration, and views B and D represent the open configuration that allows rapid transport of K$^+$ ions.

Chapter Outline

Cellular membranes, also known as biological membranes or biomembranes, are an essential characteristic of all living cells. As Nobel Laureate Roderick MacKinnon stated in his Nobel lecture, "The cell membrane holds the contents of a cell in one place so that the chemistry of life can occur." The **plasma membrane** separates the internal contents of a cell from its external environment. With such a role, you might imagine that the plasma membrane would be thick and rigid. Remarkably, the opposite is true. Cellular membranes are thin, typically 5 to 10 nm thick and somewhat fluid. It would take 5,000 to 10,000 membranes stacked on top of each other to equal the thickness of a piece of paper. Despite their thinness, cellular membranes are impressively dynamic structures that effectively maintain the separation between a cell and its surroundings, and they provide an interface to carry out many vital cellular activities. **Table 6.1** lists some of membranes' key roles.

In this chapter, we will begin by considering the components that provide the structure of membranes. Then, we examine one of a membrane's primary functions: **membrane transport**. Biomembranes regulate the traffic of substances into and out of the cell and its organelles. In the second part of this chapter, we will focus on the various ways to transport ions, small molecules, and large macromolecules across membranes. Chapters 7, 8, and 9 will examine other functions of membranes in detail.

Table 6.1	Important Functions of Cellular Membranes
Function	
Selective uptake and export of ions and molecules	
Cell compartmentalization	
Protein sorting	
Anchoring of the cytoskeleton	
Production of energy intermediates, such as ATP and NADPH	
Cell signalling	
Cell and nuclear division	
Adhesion of cells to one another and to the extracellular matrix	

6.1 | MEMBRANE STRUCTURE AND COMPOSITION

Learning Outcomes:

1. Describe the fluid-mosaic model of membrane structure.
2. Identify the three types of membrane proteins.
3. Describe the fluidity of membranes, how it is affected by lipid composition, and how it affects an organism's ability to adapt to its environment.
4. Explain the technique of freeze fracture electron microscopy.

One of the unifying principles of biology is that structure determines function. This principle is particularly useful when we consider how the structure of cellular membranes enables them to create compartments within cells while selectively importing and exporting vital substances. The two primary components of membranes are lipids, which form the basic matrix of a membrane, and proteins, which are embedded in the membrane or loosely attached to its surface. A third component is carbohydrates, which may be attached to membrane lipids and proteins. In this section, we are mainly concerned with the organization of these components to form a biological membrane and how they are important in the overall function of membranes. We also consider several interesting experiments that provided insight into the dynamic properties of membranes.

Biological Membranes Are a Mosaic of Lipids, Proteins, and Carbohydrates

Figure 6.1 shows the biochemical organization of cellular membranes. The basic composition of membranes is evolutionarily conserved, being similar among all living organisms. All biological membranes consist of two layers of lipids, with the most abundant lipids being phospholipids. Recall from Chapter 3 that phospholipids are amphipathic molecules, meaning they have a hydrophobic (water-fearing) region and a hydrophilic (water-loving) region. The hydrophobic tails of the lipids, referred to as fatty acyl tails, form the interior of the membrane and the hydrophilic head groups are on both exterior surfaces. A phospholipid bilayer, with its hydrophobic interior, makes it difficult for hydrophilic molecules to move across the membrane, thus providing the fundamental ability of biological membranes to form compartments. Artificial membranes can be created that consist exclusively of phospholipids bilayers, but in nature biological membranes have other essential components.

Cellular membranes always contain proteins, and most also have carbohydrates attached to lipids and proteins. The relative amounts of lipids, proteins, and carbohydrates vary among different membranes. Some membranes, such as the inner mitochondrial membrane, have no carbohydrate while the plasma membrane of eukaryotic cells can have a large amount. A typical membrane found in cell organelles contains 50% protein by mass; the remainder is mostly lipids. However, the smaller lipid molecules outnumber the proteins by about 50 to 1 because the mass of one lipid molecule is much less than the mass of a protein.

Overall, the membrane is considered a mosaic of lipid, protein, and carbohydrate molecules. The membrane structure illustrated in Figure 6.1 is referred to as the **fluid-mosaic model**, originally proposed by Jonathan Singer and Garth Nicolson in 1972. As discussed later, the membrane exhibits properties that resemble a fluid because lipids and proteins can move laterally relative to each other within the membrane. Half of a phospholipid bilayer is termed a **leaflet**. Each leaflet faces a different region. For example, the plasma (cell) membrane contains a cytosolic leaflet (facing the cytoplasm) and an extracellular leaflet (facing the cell's exterior) (Figure 6.1). With regard to lipid composition, the two leaflets of cellular membranes are highly asymmetrical. The most striking asymmetry occurs with glycolipids—lipids with attached carbohydrates. These are found primarily in the extracellular leaflet of the plasma membrane so that the carbohydrate portion of a glycolipid protrudes into the extracellular medium.

Membranes Are Semifluid

Let's now turn our attention to the dynamic properties of membranes. Although a membrane provides a critical interface between a cell and its environment, it is not a solid, rigid structure. Rather, biomembranes exhibit properties of fluidity, which

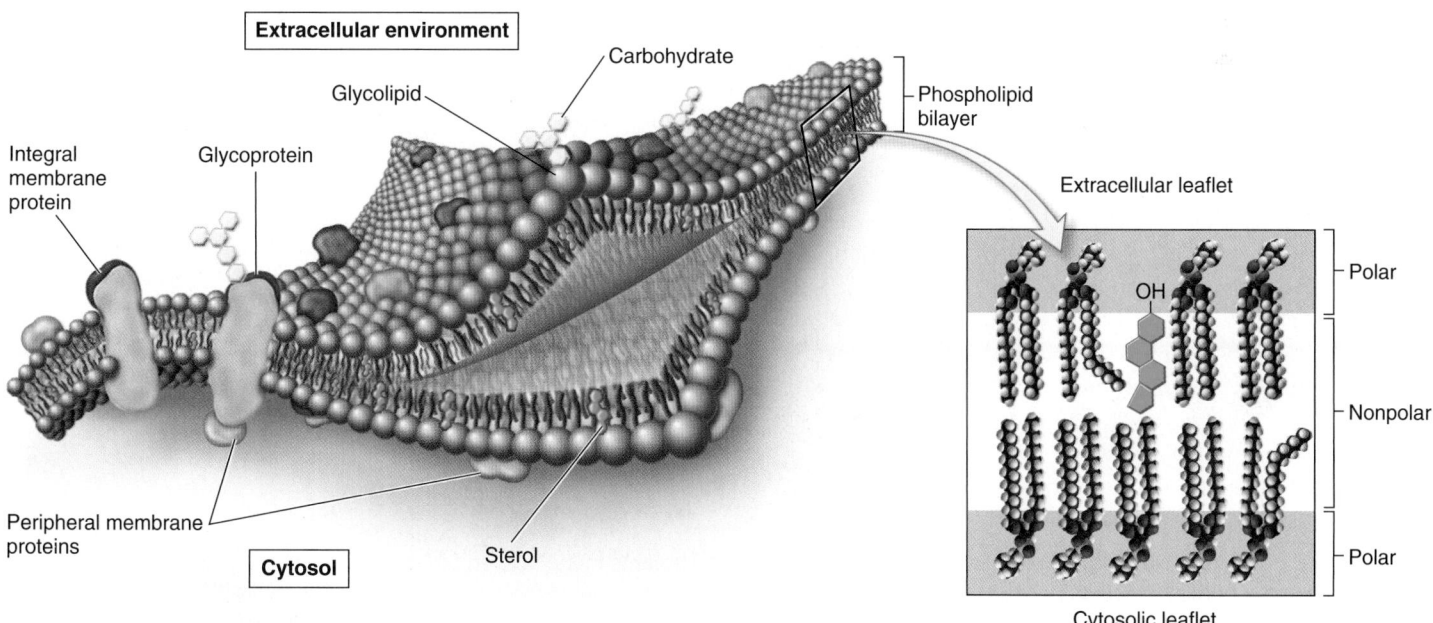

Figure 6.1 Fluid-mosaic model of membrane structure. The basic framework of a plasma membrane is a phospholipid bilayer. Proteins are inserted into the membrane and can be bound on the surface to other proteins or to lipids. Proteins and lipids, which have covalently bound carbohydrates, are called glycoproteins and glycolipids, respectively. Sterols (such as cholesterol in animal cells) can be inserted into the bilayer and modify its fluidity.

means that individual molecules remain in close association yet have the ability to readily move within the membrane. Though membranes are often described as fluid, it is more appropriate to say membranes are **semifluid**. In a fluid substance, molecules can move in three dimensions. By comparison, most lipids can move freely in only two dimensions: around their long axes and laterally within the membrane leaflet (**Figure 6.2a**). Because rotational and lateral movements keep the fatty acyl tails within the hydrophobic interior, such movements are energetically favourable. In fact, the movements of lipids within cellular membranes are quite pronounced. At 37°C, a typical lipid molecule exchanges places with its neighbours about 10^7 times per second and can be directional, moving several micrometres per second. At this rate, a lipid could traverse the length of a bacterial cell (approximately 1 μm) in only 1 second and the length of a typical eukaryotic cell in 10 to 20 seconds.

In contrast to rotational and lateral movements, movement in the third dimension—the flip-flop movement of lipids from one leaflet to the opposite leaflet—does not occur spontaneously. Energetically, such movements are extremely unfavourable because the polar head of a phospholipid would have to be transported through the hydrophobic interior. Because movement in the third dimension is limited, the two leaflets of a membrane's phospholipid bilayer can be distinct from each other in phospholipid composition. This difference relates to the biological functions that occur on the hydrophilic faces of each leaflet.

As functions change, cells can change the phospholipid composition of each leaflet by moving phospholipids from one leaflet to the other. Cells have three types of proteins embedded in membranes that can accomplish these transfers. Scramblase proteins provide a protein passageway for lipids to move across the bilayer (**Figure 6.2b**). Scramblases transfer phospholipids along a concentration gradient, from the leaflet with a higher concentration to the leaflet with a lower concentration of that lipid. The transfer does not require ATP. Two other proteins can selectively move phospholipids from one leaflet to the other

against concentration gradients. Flippases (**Figure 6.2c**) move lipids from the outer leaflet to the inner one, and floppases move lipids from the inner leaflet to the outer one (**Figure 6.2d**). Flippases and floppases both require the energy acquired from hydrolysis of ATP to accomplish their directed flipping.

The biochemical properties of sterols and phospholipids have a profound effect on the fluidity of the phospholipid bilayer (see **Table 6.2** for a summary). One key factor is the length of their fatty acyl tails, which range from 14 to 24 carbon atoms, with 18 to 20 carbons being the most common. Shorter acyl tails are less likely to interact, which makes the membrane more fluid. A second important factor is the presence of double bonds in the acyl tails. When a double bond is found, the lipid is said to be unsaturated with respect to the number of hydrogens that can be bound to the carbon atoms. A double bond creates a kink in the fatty acyl tail, making it more difficult for neighbouring tails to interact and consequently making the bilayer more fluid.

A third factor is the presence of sterols interspersed throughout the membrane, particularly the plasma membrane. In animals the dominant sterol is cholesterol (refer back to Figure 3.12a).

Table 6.2	Lipid Composition Affects Membrane Fluidity	
Lipid composition of membrane	**Affect on membrane property**
Length of fatty acyl tails of phospholipids	Shorter fatty acyl tails give greater membrane fluidity than long ones.
Double bonds in the fatty acyl tails of phospholipids	Unsaturated fats (those with double bonds in the fatty acyl tails) have greater membrane fluidity.
Sterols dispersed throughout the bilayer	Sterols, such as cholesterol, modulate membrane fluidity. At higher temperatures sterols reduce fluidity, but at lower temperatures they improve fluidity.

(a)   (b)   (c)   (d)

Figure 6.2 **Semifluidity of the lipid bilayer.** (a) Spontaneous movements in the bilayer. Lipids can move freely within their leaflet but cannot move between leaflets because the hydrophilic, polar head group would have to pass through the hydrophobic region of the bilayer. (b) Scramblase proteins provide one method of moving phospholipids between leaflets by forming a protein channel between them. (c) Flippases move lipids from the outer leaflet to the inner one with the energy provided by ATP hydrolysis. (d) Floppases also require ATP hydrolysis to move lipids from the inner leaflet to the outer one.

Principle: *Living organisms have mechanisms that maintain homeostasis. Each membrane leaflet has a distinct lipid composition, relative to the leaflet's function. But cells can use scramblases, flippases, and floppases to change that composition to meet organismal needs.*

Cholesterol tends to stabilize membranes, but its effects depend on temperature. At higher temperatures, such as those observed in mammals that maintain a constant body temperature, cholesterol makes the membrane less fluid. At lower temperatures, such as in icy water, cholesterol has the opposite effect, making the membrane more fluid and preventing it from freezing. In most plants cholesterol is not common, but other sterols, such as sitosterol and 24-methylcholesterol, regulate plant membrane fluidity and permeability, and their relative amounts may help plants adapt to changes in ambient temperature.

An optimal level of bilayer fluidity is essential for normal cell function, growth, and division. If a membrane is too fluid, which can occur at higher temperatures, it can become leaky. Conversely, if a membrane becomes too solid, which may occur at lower temperatures, the functioning of membrane proteins will be inhibited. Cells adapt to changes in temperature by altering the lipid composition of their membranes. For example, when the water temperature drops, certain fish incorporate more cholesterol in their membranes. If a plant cell is exposed to high temperatures for many hours or days, it alters its lipid composition to have longer fatty acyl tails and fewer double bonds.

Phospholipids and sterols can move laterally within their leaflet with ease. But certain membrane domains, called lipid rafts, are distinctive regions of phospholipids enriched in sterols and membrane proteins. The lipids of the **lipid raft** tend to have fatty acyl tails that are straight and hence can pack more tightly together. They are thus more stable and tend to stay clustered as a unit (raft). The name *lipid raft* derives from the fact that the phospholipid, sterols, and proteins remain associated with each other and float together in the semifluid membrane. Lipid rafts often are regions in which specific membrane proteins are inserted, especially those involved cell signalling.

Membrane Proteins Are Attached to or Embedded in the Phospholipid Bilayer

Although the phospholipid bilayer forms the basic foundation and boundary function of cellular membranes, the protein component carries out most other functions (see Table 6.1). Proteins can bind to membranes in three different ways (**Figure 6.3**).

Transmembrane proteins span the bilayer, having one or more regions that are physically embedded in the hydrophobic region of the phospholipid bilayer. The transmembrane segments are folded into α helical regions stabilized by hydrogen bonds (for review of this type of secondary structure, see Figure 3.16). These segments are stable in the membrane interior because the nonpolar amino acids interact favourably with the hydrophobic fatty acyl tails of the lipids.

A second way for proteins to associate with the membrane is via **lipid anchors**. A lipid anchor involves the covalent attachment of a lipid to an amino acid side chain within a protein. This attachment is done post-translationally after the polypeptide is created. The fatty acyl tails of the lipid anchor keep the protein firmly bound in the membrane leaflet in which it is embedded. Both transmembrane proteins and lipid-anchored proteins are classified as **integral membrane proteins**, also

Figure 6.3 **Different types of membrane proteins.** Some integral membrane proteins **(a)** have transmembrane segments that traverse the phospholipid bilayer. Such proteins usually have a series of α helical domains that contain nonpolar (hydrophobic) amino acids, shown in inset **(b)**. Other integral membrane proteins **(c)** are covalently linked to a fatty acid post-translationally. This lipid anchor allows the protein to be stably inserted in one leaflet of the membrane. Peripheral membrane proteins are associated more weakly with a membrane region. Some peripheral proteins **(d)** associate with the hydrophilic region of an integral membrane protein, other peripheral proteins form ionic interactions with the polar head groups of lipids **(e)**. The protein shown in **(b)** is bacteriorhodopsin. It contains seven transmembrane segments in an α helical structure (depicted as cylinders).

called intrinsic membrane proteins, because they cannot be released from the membrane unless the membranes are dissolved with an organic solvent or detergent—in other words, you would have to disrupt the integrity of the membrane to remove them.

Peripheral membrane proteins, also called extrinsic proteins, are a third class of membrane proteins. These proteins do not interact with the hydrophobic interior of the phospholipid bilayer. Instead, they are noncovalently bound to regions of integral membrane proteins that project out from the membrane, or they are bound to the polar head groups of phospholipids. Peripheral membrane proteins are typically bound to the membrane by hydrogen or ionic bonds. For this reason, they usually can be removed from the membrane experimentally by exposing the membrane to high salt concentrations. Researchers can use this treatment to distinguish between peripheral and integral membrane proteins.

Like lipids, many integral membrane proteins can rotate and move laterally throughout the plane of a membrane. Because membrane proteins are larger than lipids, they move through the membrane at a much slower rate. Flip-flop of integral membrane proteins does not occur because the proteins also contain hydrophilic regions that project out from the phospholipid bilayer. It would be energetically unfavourable for the hydrophilic regions of membrane proteins to pass through the hydrophobic portion of the phospholipid bilayer.

Researchers can examine the lateral movements of lipids and integral membrane proteins through a variety of methods. In 1970 Larry Frye and Michael Edidin conducted an experiment that verified the lateral movement of membrane proteins (**Figure 6.4**). Mouse and human cells were mixed together and exposed to agents that caused them to fuse. Some of these fused cells were cooled to 0°C while others were incubated at 37°C before being cooled. Both sets of cells were then exposed to fluorescently labelled antibodies that bind specifically to a mouse membrane protein called H-2. The fluorescent label was observed with a fluorescence microscope. If the fused cells were maintained at 0°C, a temperature that greatly inhibits lateral movement, the fluorescence was seen on only one portion of the fused cell (the portion originating from the mouse cell). However, the fluorescence was distributed throughout the fused cell if the fused cells were incubated for several hours at 37°C and then cooled to 0°C. This occurred because the higher temperature allowed the lateral movement of the H-2 protein throughout the plasma membrane.

A second approach to studying lateral movement, fluorescence recovery after photobleaching (FRAP), was developed in 1976 by Watt Webb and colleagues (**Figure 6.5**). In their experiment proteins on the surface of a cell were covalently labelled with a red fluorescent molecule so that the entire surface of the cell appeared red. A laser beam was then focused on a small region of the cell surface. The energy of the laser beam altered the structure of the fluorescent molecules and eliminated the red colour, a phenomenon called photobleaching. Immediately after photobleaching, a small region of the cell surface appeared white. Over time, bleached molecules within the white spot spread outward, and the white region filled in with red fluorescent molecules. These results indicate that proteins can move laterally in the membrane.

Unlike the examples shown in Figures 6.4 and 6.5, not all integral membrane proteins are capable of rotational and lateral movement. Depending on the cell type, 10% to 70% of membrane proteins may be restricted in their movement. Integral membrane proteins may be bound to components of the cytoskeleton, which restricts the proteins from moving laterally (**Figure 6.6**). Also, membrane proteins may be attached to molecules that are outside the cell, such as the interconnected network of proteins that forms the extracellular matrix of many animal cells.

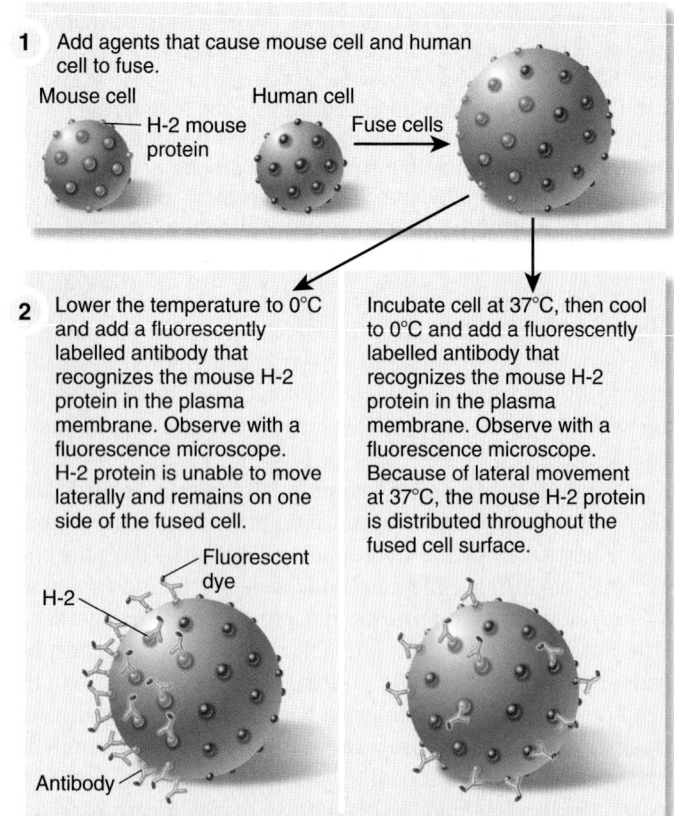

Figure 6.4   A method to measure the lateral movement of membrane proteins.

Concept check: *Explain why the H-2 proteins are found only on one side of the cell when the cells were cooled and maintained at 0°C.*

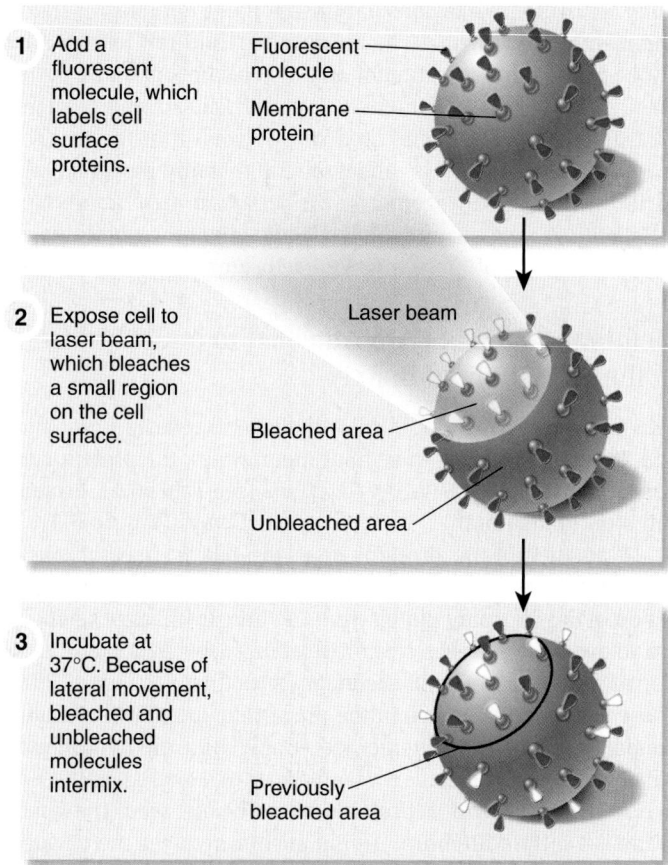

Figure 6.5   Fluorescence recovery after photobleaching (FRAP).   In this method, the surface of cells was coated with red fluorescent molecules. A laser beam bleached the small section shown in white. Over time, bleached molecules and unbleached molecules were seen to move by lateral movement.

Fibre in the extracellular matrix

Extracellular matrix

Plasma membrane

Cytosol

Linker protein

Cytoskeletal filament

Figure 6.6 **Attachment of transmembrane proteins to the cytoskeleton and extracellular matrix of an animal cell.** Some transmembrane proteins have regions that project into the cytosol and are anchored to large cytoskeletal filaments (via linker proteins), restricting lateral movement. Similarly, some integral membrane proteins bind to large, immobile components in the extracellular matrix, restricting their movement.

 Principle: *Structure determines function. The structure of the transmembrane protein allows it to bind to the extracellular matrix and the cytoskeleton.*

BioConnections: *Look back to Figure 5.29. Discuss how transmembrane proteins are important in the binding of cells to each other and the binding of cells to the extracellular matrix.*

Evolution and Adaptation of Membranes and Membrane Constituents

Eukaryotic cells have evolved a variety of different membrane-bounded compartments, each with specialized functions, from the plasma membranes of prokaryotes. The diversity of these eukaryotic membrane functions is reflected in the large number of different membrane proteins that are encoded by eukaryotic genomes. Cells also rely on differential expression of their genomes to control production of proteins that, in turn, regulate lipid biosynthesis and deployment. The lipid composition and lipid-to-protein ratio is different for different membrane compartments. As well, organisms have evolved mechanisms to allow them to adapt to changes in their environment, such as the seasonal changes in temperature, by changing the ratios of saturated to unsaturated fatty acids used in their membranes and by modulating the amount of membrane sterols. Cold-tolerant plants are thought to increase production of specialized sterols as part of the adaptation to colder temperatures. Eukaryotes also make other special lipids known as cerebrosides that can give membranes special properties. Some plants can make specific glucosylceramides that elicit defence responses against fungal attack and appear to assist plants to withstand cold stress.

The late Dr. Marilyn Griffith, Killiam research fellow and professor of biology at University of Waterloo, devoted her scientific career to understanding the biological basis of cold tolerance in plants. Her studies led to the discovery of plant antifreeze proteins that control ice formation and likely evolved from proteins used to help plants resist fungal diseases. When the dual role of these proteins was discovered, she said in an interview that she felt as though she "was staring evolution in the face."

GENOMES AND PROTEOMES

Approximately 25% of All Genes Encode Membrane Proteins

Membrane proteins participate in many important cellular processes. These include transport, energy transduction, cell signalling, secretion, cell recognition, and cell-to-cell contact. It is not surprising that cells devote a sizable fraction of their energy and metabolic machinery to the synthesis of membrane proteins. These proteins are particularly important in human medicine—approximately 70% of all medications exert their effects by binding to membrane proteins. The drugs Aspirin, ibuprofen, and acetaminophen are widely used to relieve pain and inflammatory conditions, such as arthritis. These drugs bind to cyclooxygenase, a protein in the ER membrane that is necessary for the synthesis of chemicals that play a role in inflammation and pain sensation.

Because membrane proteins are so important biologically, researchers have analyzed the genomes of many species and

asked, What percentage of genes encodes membrane proteins? They have developed tools to predict the likelihood that a gene encodes a protein that is a membrane protein. For example, the occurrence of transmembrane helices can be predicted from the amino acid sequence of a protein. All 20 amino acids can be ranked according to their preference for a hydrophobic or hydrophilic environment. With these values the amino acid sequence of a protein can be analyzed by using computer software to determine the average hydrophobicity of short amino acid sequences within the protein. A stretch of 18 to 20 amino acids in an α helix is long enough to span the membrane. If such a stretch contains a high percentage of hydrophobic amino acids, it is predicted to be a transmembrane helix. However, such computer predictions must eventually be verified by experimentation.

By using a computerized approach, research groups have attempted to calculate the percentage of genes that encode membrane proteins. The estimated percentage of membrane proteins is substantial: 20% to 30% of all genes may encode membrane proteins. This trend is found throughout all domains of life, including Archaea, Bacteria, and Eukarya. For example, in *E. coli,* approximately 30% of its genes encode membrane proteins. The genome of this bacterium contains about 4,300 genes, so roughly 1,290 genes may encode different membrane proteins. The human genome also has about 30% of genes that encode membrane proteins. However, the human genome is larger, containing 20,000 to 25,000 different genes, so the total number of genes that encode different membrane proteins is estimated at 6,000 to 7,500; the functions of many of them have yet to be determined. Identifying their functions will help researchers gain a better understanding of human biology. Likewise, medical researchers and pharmaceutical companies are interested in the identification of membrane proteins that could be targets for effective new medications.

Glycosylation of Lipids and Proteins Serves a Variety of Cellular Functions

As mentioned earlier, the third major constituent of biomembranes is carbohydrate. **Glycosylation** refers to the process of covalently attaching a carbohydrate to a protein or lipid. When a carbohydrate is attached to a lipid, this creates a **glycolipid**. Attachment to a protein produces a **glycoprotein** (see Figure 5.15 for the process).

Though the roles of carbohydrate in cell structure and function are not entirely understood, some functional consequences of glycosylation are beginning to emerge. The carbohydrates that are attached to proteins and lipids have well-defined structures that serve in some cases as recognition signals for other cellular proteins. For example, during protein targeting, proteins that are destined for the lysosome are glycosylated and have a sugar—mannose-6-phosphate—that is recognized by other proteins in the cell that target the glycosylated protein to the lysosome. Similarly, membrane glycolipids and glycoproteins often play a role in cell surface recognition. During embryonic development in animals, significant cell movement occurs. Layers of cells slide over one another to create body structures, such as the spinal cord and internal organs. The proper migration of individual cells and cell layers relies on the recognition of cell types via the carbohydrates on their cell surfaces.

In addition to its role as a recognition marker, carbohydrate can have a protective effect. The term **cell coat** or **glycocalyx** is used to describe the carbohydrate-rich zone on the cell surface that shields the cell from mechanical and physical damage (**Figure 6.7**). The carbohydrate portion of glycosylated proteins protects them from the harsh conditions of the extracellular environment and degradation by extracellular proteases, which are enzymes that digest proteins.

Membrane Structure Can Be Viewed with an Electron Microscope

Electron microscopy (Chapter 4) is a valuable tool for probing membrane structure and function. In transmission electron microscopy (TEM), a biological sample is sectioned and stained with heavy-metal dyes, such as osmium tetroxide. This compound binds tightly to the polar head groups of phospholipids, but it does not bind well to the fatty acyl tails. As shown in **Figure 6.8a**, membranes stained with osmium tetroxide resemble a railroad track. Two thin dark lines, which are the stained polar head groups, are separated by a uniform light space about 2 nm thick. This railroad track morphology is seen consistently in TEM images of cell membranes.

A specialized form of electron microscopy, freeze fracture electron microscopy (FFEM), can be used to analyze the architecture of biological membranes, most often the plasma membrane. Russell Steere invented this method in 1957. In FFEM a sample is frozen in liquid nitrogen and split open with a knife (**Figure 6.8b**). The knife fractures the frozen sample. Because of the weakness of the hydrophobic fatty acyl tails, the leaflets separate into a P layer (the leaflet in contact with the cytosol) and the E face (the leaflet of the cell membrane in contact with the extracellular matrix). Unlike the lipid bilayer, most transmembrane proteins do not break in half. They remain embedded within one of the leaflets, usually in the P layer. Integral membrane proteins that don't span the membrane stay embedded in their original leaflet. The samples are then sprayed with a heavy metal, such as platinum, that coats the sample and

Figure 6.7   A micrograph of the cell coat or glycocalyx of an animal cell.   This figure shows a lymphocyte—a type of white blood cell—stained with ethidium red, which emphasizes the thick carbohydrate layer that surrounds the cell.

Concept check: *If a heavy metal labelled the hydrophobic tails rather than the polar head groups (as osmium tetroxide does), do you think you would see a bilayer (i.e., a railroad track) under transmission electron microscopy?*

(a) Transmission electron microscopy (TEM)

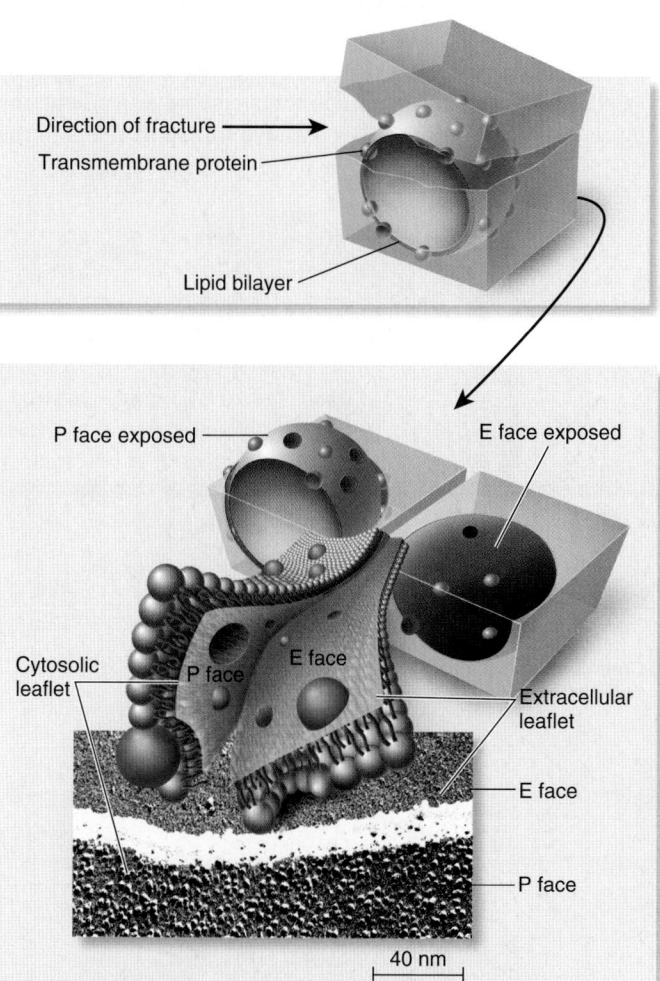

(b) Freeze fracture electron microscopy (FFEM)

Figure 6.8 Electron micrographs of a cellular membrane. **(a)** In TEM, the membrane appears as two dark parallel lines. These lines are the lipid head groups stained with osmium tetroxide. The fatty acyl tails do not stain well and appear as a light region sandwiched between the dark lines. **(b)** In freeze fracture electron microscopy, a sample is frozen in liquid nitrogen, split, and fractured. Membranes that happen to be located at the fractured region will split along their leaflets. The sample is then coated with metal and viewed with a scanning electron microscope.

reveals architectural features within each leaflet. The membrane proteins are visible as detailed contours that provide significant three-dimensional detail about their form and shape.

6.2 PHOSPHOLIPID BILAYERS OF CELLULAR MEMBRANES ARE DIFFERENTIALLY PERMEABLE

Learning Outcomes:

1. Describe the concepts of diffusion, facilitated diffusion, passive transport, gradients, and active transport.
2. Explain the process of osmosis and how it affects cell structure, relating the phenomenon to hypotonic environments.
3. Relate the presence of a cell wall to the generation of osmotic pressure.

If plasma membranes consisted of only a phospholipid bilayer, they would not permit the uptake of most nutrients and the export of waste products. But as you have already seen, biological membranes are not composed exclusively of phospholipids; they contain substantial amounts of protein. In section 6.3 we will look at the role of many of these proteins in creating selectively permeable membranes, but in this section we begin with a discussion of the phospholipid bilayer's inherent permeability and how it presents a barrier to the movement of ions and molecules. Next we consider the concepts of concentration gradients across membranes and the impact of these gradients to the movement of water into and out of cells. In contrast to many important ions and solutes, water can diffuse fairly easily through plasma membranes in a process known as osmosis.

The Phospholipid Bilayer Is a Barrier to the Diffusion of Hydrophilic Molecules

Because of their hydrophobic interiors, phospholipid bilayers present a formidable barrier to the movement of ions and hydrophilic molecules. **Diffusion** occurs when a solute (i.e., a dissolved substance) moves from a region of high concentration to a region of lower concentration. When diffusion occurs through a membrane without the aid of a transport protein, it is called **passive diffusion**. The rate of passive diffusion depends on the chemical properties of the solute and its concentration. Gases and a few small, uncharged polar molecules can passively diffuse across the bilayer. However, the rate of diffusion of ions and larger polar molecules, such as sugars and amino acids, is relatively slow. Similarly, macromolecules, such as proteins and large carbohydrates, do not readily cross a lipid bilayer. **Figure 6.9** compares the relative permeabilities of various solutes through an artificial phospholipid bilayer that does not contain any proteins or carbohydrates.

For relatively small molecules their hydrophobicity is a key determinant of how readily they can diffuse across a phospholipid bilayer. As an example, let's compare urea and diethylurea. Diethylurea is much more hydrophobic because it contains two nonpolar ethyl groups (CH_2CH_3) (**Figure 6.10**). For this reason, it can more readily pass through the hydrophobic region of the phospholipid bilayer. The rate of passive diffusion of diethylurea through a phospholipid bilayer is about 50 times as fast as urea, even though diethylurea is a little larger.

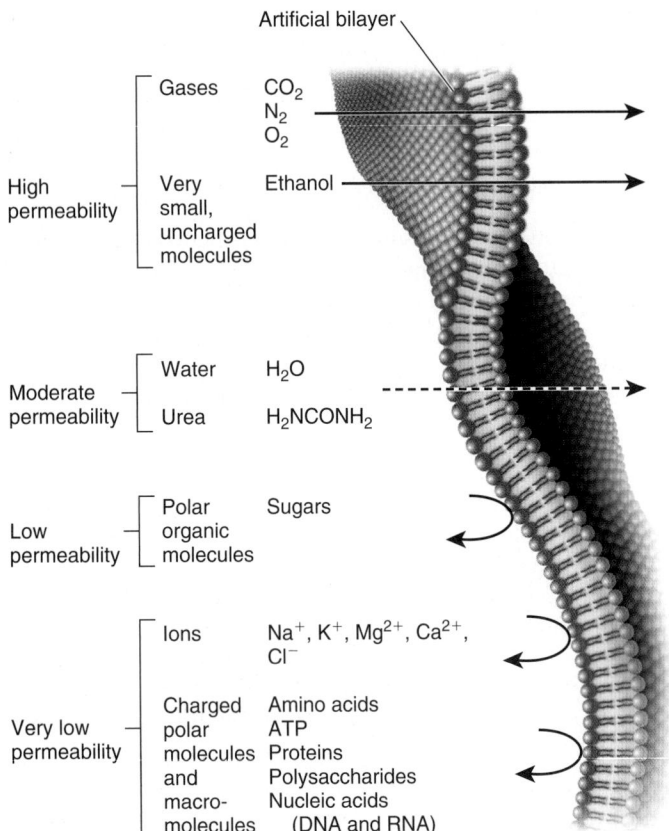

Figure 6.9   Relative permeability of an artificial phospholipid bilayer to a variety of solutes.   Solutes that easily penetrate are shown with a straight arrow that passes through the bilayer. The dotted line indicates solutes that have moderate permeability. The remaining solutes shown at the bottom are relatively impermeable.

Concept check: *Which amino acid would you expect to cross an artificial membrane more quickly: leucine or lysine?*

BioConnections: *Which amino acid, described in Chapter 3 (see Figure 3.14), would you expect to cross an artificial membrane more quickly, leucine or lysine?*

Figure 6.10   Structures of urea and diethylurea.

Cells Maintain Gradients Across Their Membranes

As you have just seen, phospholipid bilayers are impermeable to ions and most hydrophilic molecules. A hallmark of living cells is their ability to maintain a relatively constant internal environment that is distinctively different from their external environment. This involves establishing gradients of solutes across the plasma membrane and organellar membranes. When we speak of a **transmembrane gradient**, we mean that the concentration of a chemical (solute) is higher on one side of a membrane than the other (**Figure 6.11a**). For example, immediately after you eat a meal, a higher concentration of glucose is found outside your cells (in the extracellular space of the digestive tract) than inside your cells. Gradients involving ions have two components: electrical and chemical (solute). An **ion electrochemical gradient** is a dual gradient that has both an electrical gradient and a chemical gradient (**Figure 6.11b**). Let's consider a gradient involving Na^+. An electrical gradient could exist in which the amount of net positive charge outside a cell is greater than inside. At the same time, a chemical gradient could exist in which the concentration of Na^+ ions outside is greater than inside. These two gradients together constitute a Na^+ electrochemical gradient. Transmembrane gradients of ions and other solutes are a universal feature of living cells.

Cells can maintain or change transmembrane gradients by using several different processes. **Passive transport** refers to the

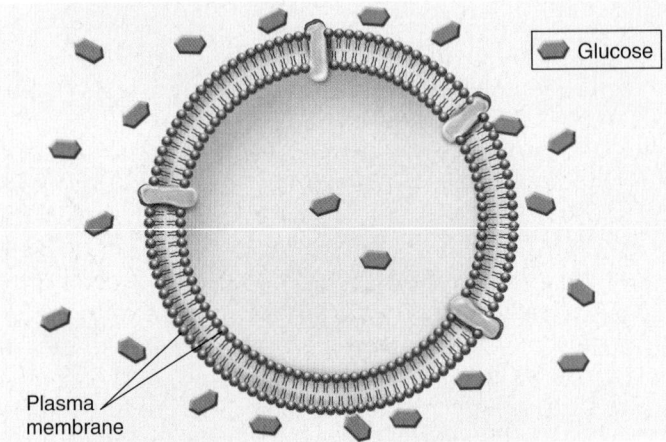

(a) Chemical gradient for glucose—a higher glucose concentration outside the cell

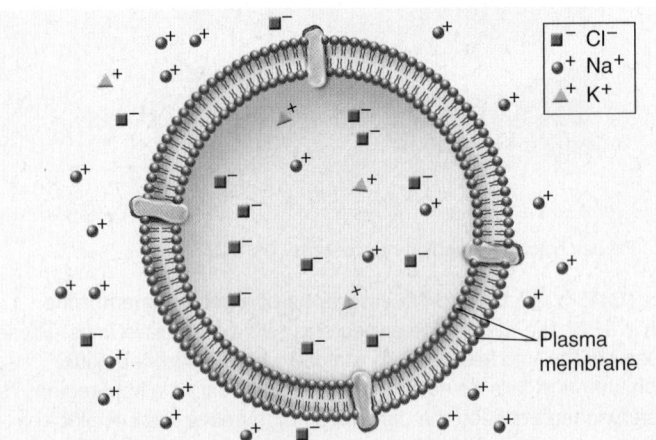

(b) Electrochemical gradient for Na⁺—more positive charges outside the cell and a higher Na⁺ concentration outside the cell

Figure 6.11   Gradients across cell membranes.

BioConnections: *Look ahead to Figure 41.10. What types of ion gradients are important for the conduction of an action potential across the plasma membrane of a neuron?*

(a) Diffusion—passive transport

(b) Facilitated diffusion—passive transport

(c) Active transport

Figure 6.12 Types of movement across a biological membrane.

diffusion of a solute across a membrane in processes that are energetically favourable (not requiring an input of energy). Passive transport mechanisms tend to dissipate a pre-existing gradient. Pay attention to the adjective *passive* because it is used to describe two different types of transport. The broad term *passive transport* means transport that does not require an input of energy. One type of passive transport is called passive diffusion, and in this case, passive means that it occurs without the aid of a transport protein. Passive diffusion is the diffusion of a solute that can move directly through the phospholipid bilayer to move across the membrane (**Figure 6.12a**). This is not a common way for solutes to move. The second type of passive transport is **facilitated diffusion**, which involves the aid of transport proteins (**Figure 6.12b**). Transport proteins facilitate the movement of various nutrients and, in some types of cells, water across the membrane. Active transport, moving molecules against a concentration gradient (**Figure 6.12c**), will be discussed in section 6.3.

Osmosis Is the Movement of Water Across Membranes in Response to Solute Concentration Gradients

We know that two solutions with different concentration of a particular solute will tend to reach equilibrium with a uniform concentration of solute. But lipid bilayers are relatively impermeable to many hydrophilic solutes; equilibrium between a cell and its environment cannot occur by diffusion of solutes because of the presence of the cell membrane. However, the cell membrane is somewhat permeable to water. Thus, in situations in which the solute cannot cross the membrane to reach equilibrium, water may move to the environment with the higher solute concentration, thereby achieving equilibrium in a different way. This movement of water has biological consequences.

When the total solute concentrations on both sides of the plasma membrane are equal, the external media and the cytosol are said to be **isotonic** (**Figure 6.13a**). However, you also have seen that transmembrane gradients commonly exist

across membranes. When the solute concentration inside the cell is lower than the cell's exterior, the solute concentration outside the cell is **hypertonic** compared the inside (**Figure 6.13b**). When the solute concentration inside the cell is higher than the cell's exterior, the solute concentration outside the cell is **hypotonic** compared to the inside (**Figure 6.13c**). If the solutes cannot move across the membrane from the region of higher concentration to the lower, water will move from the hypotonic to the hypertonic region. One method of

The solute concentration outside the cell is **isotonic** (or equal) to the inside of the cell.

Solute

(a) Outside isotonic

Cytosol

The solute concentration outside the cell is **hypertonic** to the inside of the cell.

(b) Outside hypertonic

The solute concentration outside the cell is **hypotonic** to the inside of the cell.

(c) Outside hypotonic

Figure 6.13 Relative solute concentrations outside and inside cells.

water movement, called **osmosis**, has water moving directly through the phospholipids bilayer. Organisms have evolved coping mechanisms to help them deal with the phenomenon of osmosis.

If a cell is in a hypertonic media and does not increase its internal solute concentration it will lose water to the environment and shrink (**Figure 6.14**). In animal cells this process is known as crenation; in plants and algae it is called plasmolysis. Cells generally work to have a high internal concentration of a variety of solutes, including ions, sugars, amino acids, and so on; being in a hypertonic environment is rare and only regularly occurs for organisms that live in salt water.

If cells are placed in a hypotonic environment, they will tend to take up water through osmosis. Osmosis continues unless this tendency to take up water is off set by mechanical force. **Osmotic pressure** is defined as the hydrostatic pressure needed to stop the net flow of water across a membrane because of osmosis. In organisms with a cell wall, this force can be generated. Water will enter the cell via osmosis and the cell will expand until it presses up against the cell wall.

As the cell's membrane presses on the cell wall, this generates an internal water pressure, called **turgor pressure**. This turgor pressure will counter osmosis and prevent further entry of water. Land plants thrive in a freshwater environment because they rely on turgor pressure for support and will wilt if there is an inadequate supply of fresh water (**Figure 6.15**) or if grown in a hypertonic environment (i.e., in the presence of salt water). Thus, in organisms with a cell wall, being in a hypotonic environment is not necessarily bad and may even be important for survival.

The cells of animals and some protists do not have cell walls. Without walls, these cells cannot generate osmotic pressure. Therefore, water flows into cells in hypotonic environments, increasing their volume. If this expansion continues, the cell may burst (Figure 6.14a, right side). Thus, animals and wall-less protists had to develop mechanisms to deal with hypotonic environments. Some animals move to a more favourable location; others will actively pump out water, as shown in **Figure 6.16**. Other mechanisms are considered in Chapter 47.

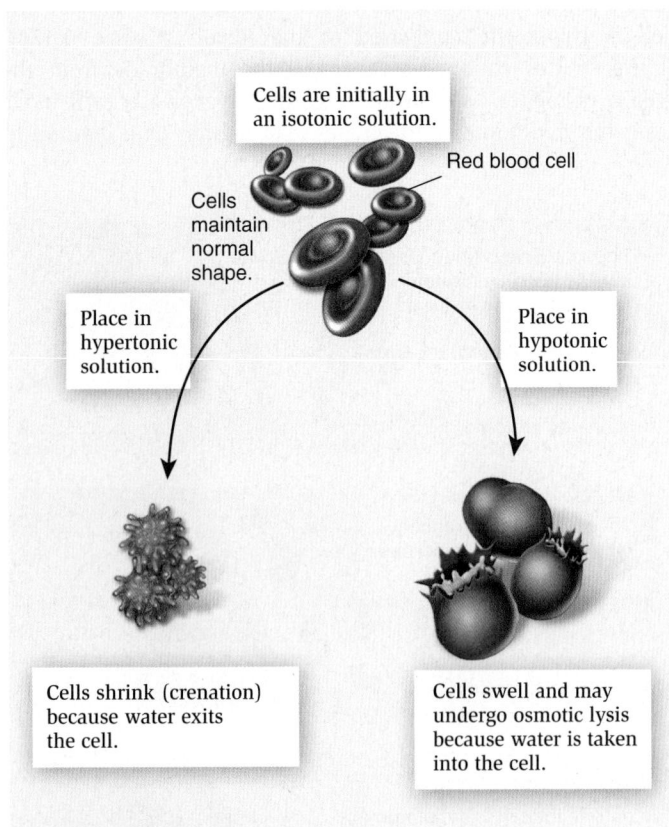

Cells are initially in an isotonic solution.

Red blood cell

Cells maintain normal shape.

Place in hypertonic solution.

Place in hypotonic solution.

Cells shrink (crenation) because water exits the cell.

Cells swell and may undergo osmotic lysis because water is taken into the cell.

(a) Osmosis in animal cells

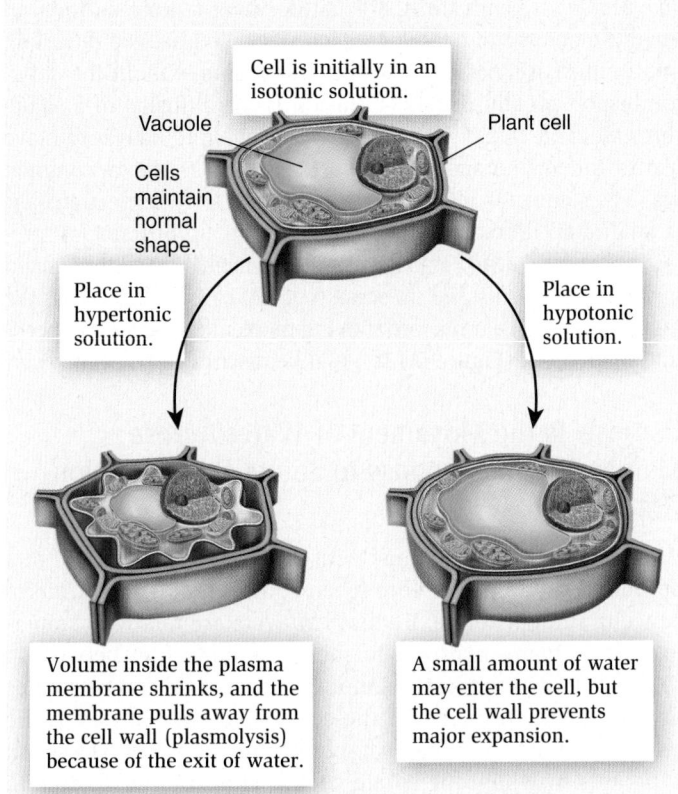

Cell is initially in an isotonic solution.

Vacuole

Plant cell

Cells maintain normal shape.

Place in hypertonic solution.

Place in hypotonic solution.

Volume inside the plasma membrane shrinks, and the membrane pulls away from the cell wall (plasmolysis) because of the exit of water.

A small amount of water may enter the cell, but the cell wall prevents major expansion.

(b) Osmosis in plant cells

Figure 6.14   **The phenomenon of osmosis.**   **(a)** In cells that lack a cell wall, such as animal cells, osmosis may promote cell shrinkage (crenation) or swelling. **(b)** In cells that have a rigid cell wall, such as plant cells, a hypertonic medium causes the plasma membrane to pull away from the cell wall, while a hypotonic medium causes only a minor amount of expansion.

Concept check: *The inside of a cell has 100 mM KCl, while the outside has 10 mM KCl. If the membrane is impermeable to KCl, in which direction will water move?*

(a) Sufficient water   **(b) Wilting**

Figure 6.15 **Wilting in plants.**   (a) When a plant has plenty of water, the slightly hypotonic surroundings cause the vacuole to store water. The increased size of the vacuole influences the volume of the cytosol, thereby exerting a turgor pressure against the cell wall. (b) Under dry conditions, water is released from the cytosol into the extracellular medium. The vacuole also shrinks, because it loses water to the cytosol. Turgor pressure is lost, which causes the plant to wilt.

Principle: *Living organisms interact with their environment. Taller plants require fresh water (a hypotonic environment) to generate the turgor pressure that supports its stems and leaves.*

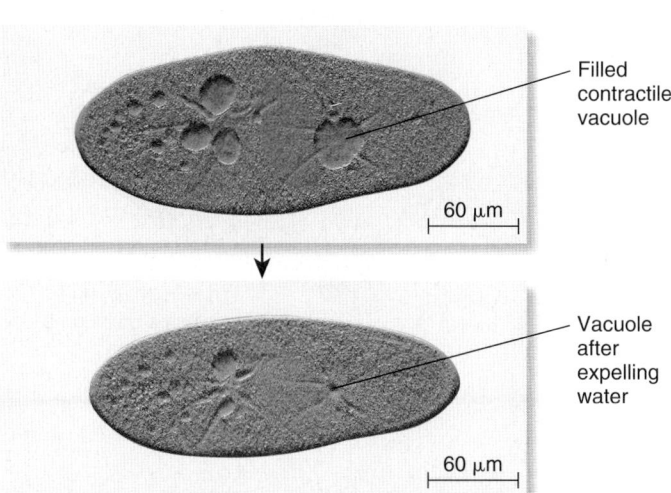

Figure 6.16 **The contractile vacuole in *Paramecium caudatum*.** In the top micrograph, a contractile vacuole is filled with water from radiating canals that collect fluid from the cytosol. The bottom micrograph shows the cell after the contractile vacuole has fused with the plasma membrane (which would be above the plane of this page) and released the water from the cell.

Concept check: *Why do freshwater protists, such as* P. caudatum, *need contractile vacuoles?*

<table>
<tr><td>**6.3**</td><td>**TRANSPORT PROTEINS BYPASS THE PHOSPHOLIPID BILAYER, ALLOWING BIOLOGICAL MEMBRANES TO BE SELECTIVELY PERMEABLE TO SMALL MOLECULES AND IONS**</td></tr>
</table>

Learning Outcomes:

1. Outline the functional differences between channels and transporters.
2. Distinguish among uniporters, symporters, and antiporters.
3. Explain the concepts of primary active transport and secondary active transport.
4. Describe the structure and function of pumps.

Because the phospholipid bilayer is a physical barrier to the passive diffusion of ions and most hydrophilic molecules, cells are able to separate their internal contents from their external environment. However, this barrier also poses a challenge because cells must take up nutrients from the environment and export waste products. Species have evolved transmembrane proteins that provide a pathway for the movement of specific ions and hydrophilic molecules across membranes. These transport proteins enable biological membranes to be selectively permeable. We can categorize transport proteins into two classes, channels and transporters.

FEATURE INVESTIGATION

Agre Discovered That Osmosis Occurs More Quickly in Cells with Transport Proteins That Allow the Facilitated Diffusion of Water

In living cells, the flow of water can occur by passive diffusion through the phospholipid bilayer. However, in the 1980s, researchers also discovered that certain cell types allow water to move across the plasma membrane at a much faster rate than would be predicted by passive diffusion. For example, water moves very quickly across the membrane of red blood cells, which causes them to shrink and swell in response to changes in extracellular solute concentrations. Likewise, bladder and kidney cells, which play a key role in regulating water balance in the bodies of vertebrates, allow the rapid movement of water across their membranes. Based on these observations, researchers speculated that certain cell types might have proteins in their plasma membranes that permit the rapid movement of water.

Peter Agre and his colleagues first identified a protein that was abundant in red blood cells and kidney cells, but not found in many other cell types. Though they initially did not know the function of the protein, its physical structure was similar to other proteins that were already known to function as transport proteins. They named this protein CHIP28, which stands for **ch**annel-forming **i**ntegral membrane **p**rotein with a molecular mass of 28,000 da. During their studies, they also identified and isolated the gene that encodes CHIP28.

In 1992 Agre and his colleagues conducted experiments to determine if CHIP28 functions in the transport of water across membranes (**Figure 6.17**). Because they already had isolated the gene that encodes CHIP28, they could make many copies of this gene in a test tube (in vitro) by using gene-cloning techniques (see Chapter 18). Starting with many copies of the gene in vitro, they added an enzyme to transcribe the gene into the RNA (called mRNA) that encodes the CHIP28 protein.

HYPOTHESIS CHIP28 may function as a water channel.

KEY MATERIALS Prior to this work, a protein called CHIP28 was identified as abundant in red blood cells and kidney cells. The gene that encodes this protein was cloned, which means that many copies of the gene were made in a test tube.

Experimental level   Conceptual level

1   Add an enzyme (RNA polymerase) and nucleotides to a test tube that contains many copies of the CHIP28 gene. This results in the synthesis of many copies of CHIP28 mRNA.

Enzymes and nucleotides

CHIP28 mRNA   RNA polymerase

CHIP28 DNA

2   Inject the CHIP28 mRNA into frog oocytes. Wait several hours to allow time for the mRNA to be translated into CHIP28 protein at the ER membrane and then moved via vesicles to the plasma membrane.

Frog oocyte
Nucleus
CHIP28 mRNA
Cytosol
CHIP28 protein is inserted into the plasma membrane.
CHIP28 protein
Ribosome

3   Place oocytes into a hypotonic medium and observe under a light microscope. As a control, also place oocytes that have not been injected with CHIP28 mRNA into a hypotonic medium and observe by microscopy.

Control
CHIP28 protein

4 THE DATA

5 CONCLUSION The CHIP28 protein, now called aquaporin, allows the rapid movement of water across the membrane.

6 SOURCE Preston, G.M., Carroll, T.P., Guggino, W.B., and Agre, P. 1992. Appearance of water channels in *Xenopus* oocytes expressing red cell CHIP28 protein. *Science* 256:385–387.

Figure 6.17 The discovery of aquaporins, water channels made of a transmembrane protein.

This RNA was then injected into frog oocytes (chosen because frog oocytes are large and easy to inject, and lack proteins in their plasma membranes that allow the rapid movement of water). The injected RNA was translated to make CHIP28 proteins that inserted into the plasma membrane of the oocytes. After allowing sufficient time for this to occur, the oocytes were placed in a hypotonic medium. As a control, oocytes that had not been injected with CHIP28 mRNA were also exposed to a hypotonic medium.

As you can see in the data, a striking difference was observed between oocytes that expressed CHIP28 versus the control. Within minutes, oocytes that contained the CHIP28 protein swelled because of the rapid uptake of water. Three to five minutes after being placed in a hypotonic medium, they actually burst. By comparison, the control oocytes did not swell as rapidly, and they did not rupture even after one hour. Taken together, these results are consistent with the hypothesis that CHIP28 functions as a transport protein that allows the facilitated diffusion of water across the membrane. Many subsequent studies confirmed this observation. Later, CHIP28 was renamed aquaporin to indicate its newly identified function of allowing water to diffuse through a pore in the membrane (**Figure 6.18**). More recently, the three-dimensional structure of aquaporin was determined (see inset to Figure 6.18). Agre was awarded the Nobel Prize in 2003 for this work.

Aquaporin is an example of a transport protein called a channel that can allow water movement that is faster than passive diffusion. Next, we will discuss the characteristics of channels and other types of transport proteins and their ability to regulate the movement of important ions and solutes.

Experimental Questions

1. What observations led to the experiment in Figure 6.17 to identify proteins that may increase water movement into the cell?

Figure 6.18 Function and structure of aquaporin. Aquaporin is a transport protein that functions by forming a channel in the membrane of certain cell types and allows the rapid diffusion of water across the membrane. The inset shows the structure of aquaporin, which was determined by X-ray crystallography.

2. How did Agre and his associates choose a candidate protein that may have functioned as a water channel in plasma membranes? What was the hypothesis tested by the researchers? Briefly explain how they were able to test their hypothesis.

3. What were the results of the experiment of Figure 6.17? Did they support the proposed hypothesis?

Channels

Protein **channels** consist of transmembrane proteins that form a passageway for the facilitated diffusion of ions or molecules across the membrane (Figure 6.18). In other words, solutes move directly through a channel to get to the other side. Aquaporin, discussed in the Feature Investigation, is a channel that allows the movement of water across the membrane. Other channels control the movement of ions or solute molecules. When a channel is open, the transmembrane movement of solutes can be extremely rapid, up to 100 million ions or molecules per second. Most channels are **gated channels**, which means they can open to allow the diffusion of solutes and close to prohibit it. The phenomenon of gating allows cells to regulate the movement of solutes. Researchers have discovered a variety of gating mechanisms (**Figure 6.19**).

Gating sometimes involves the direct binding of a molecule to the channel protein itself. **Ligand-gated channels** are controlled by the noncovalent binding of small molecules known as ligands, such as hormones or neurotransmitters (**Figure 6.19a**). These ligands are often important in the transmission of signals between nerve and muscle cells or between two nerve cells. Alternatively, intracellular proteins may bind noncovalently to channels and control their ability to open and close (**Figure 6.19b**). Another gating mechanism involves the covalent attachment of a small molecule, such as a phosphate group, to the channel protein (**Figure 6.19c**). Regulatory proteins involved in cell-signalling pathways often work by covalently attaching phosphate to proteins as a way to regulate their function. Some channel proteins are targets of these regulatory proteins. As an example, chloride channels in the human lung are opened by phosphorylation and conversely are closed by the removal of the phosphate.

Channel gating can also occur by mechanisms that do not involve the direct binding of a molecule to the channel protein. For example, some channels are **voltage-gated channels**, meaning that the channel opens and closes in response to electrical gradients (**Figure 6.19d**). Sodium and potassium channels in nerve cells are voltage-gated. The chapter-opening photo shows molecular models for the opening and closing of the voltage-gated Shaker channel, so named because animals with a defective channel have malfunctions (shaking) in their movements. Roderick MacKinnon received the Nobel Prize alongside Peter Agre in 2003 for his work elucidating the structure and function relationship of the Shaker-family of integral membrane proteins.

Another interesting gating mechanism involves **mechanosensitive channels**, which are sensitive to changes in membrane tension (**Figure 6.19e**). For example, our ability to hear depends, in part, on the functioning of mechanosensitive channels in the cells of the inner ear that are sensitive to different frequencies of sound. The opening of these ion channels in response to sound transmits signals to the brain.

Transporters

Transporters, also known as **carriers**, bind their solutes in a hydrophilic pocket and undergo a conformational change that switches the exposure of the pocket to the other side of the

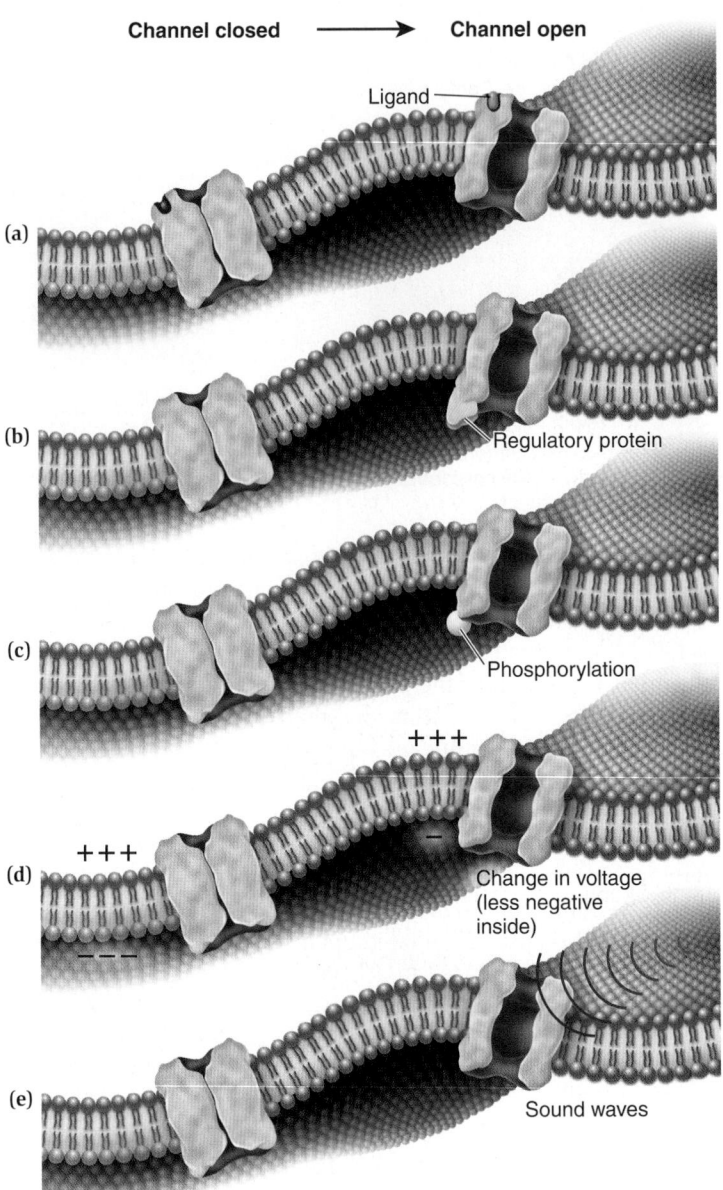

Channel closed ⟶ **Channel open**

(a) Ligand

(b) Regulatory protein

(c) Phosphorylation

(d) +++ −−− +++ − Change in voltage (less negative inside)

(e) Sound waves

Figure 6.19   Different ways that gated channels can be opened. Principle: *Living organisms interact with their environment. Cells have mechanisms to open and close channels to allow them to respond to changes in the cellular environment.*

membrane (**Figure 6.20**). Because they must undergo conformational changes to function, transporters tend to be much slower than channels. Their rate of transport is typically 100 to 1,000 ions or molecules per second. Transporters provide the principal pathway for the uptake of organic molecules, such as sugars, amino acids, and nucleotides. In animals, they also allow cells to take up certain hormones and neurotransmitters. In addition, many transporters play a key role in export. Waste products of cellular metabolism must be released from cells before they reach toxic levels. For example, one transporter removes lactic

For transport to occur, a solute binds in a hydrophilic pocket exposed on one side of the membrane. The transporter then undergoes a conformational change that switches the exposure of the pocket to the other side of the membrane, where the solute is then released.

Figure 6.20 Mechanism of transport by a transporter, also called a carrier.

acid, a by-product of muscle cells during exercise. Excessive lactic acid buildup is partly responsible for the burning sensation people feel during a strenuous workout. Other transporters, which are involved with ion transport, play an important role in cellular processes, such as regulating internal pH and controlling cell volume.

Transporters are categorized according to the number of solutes they bind and the direction of transport (**Figure 6.21**). **Uniporters** bind a single molecule or ion and transport it across the membrane. **Symporters** or **cotransporters** bind two or more different types of ions or molecules and transport them in the same direction. **Antiporters** bind two or more different types of ions or molecules and transport them in opposite directions.

A **pump** is a type of transporter protein that directly couples its conformational changes to an energy source, such as ATP hydrolysis (**Figure 6.22**). The conformational changes of pumps are energetically driven. A common category of pumps that is found in all living cells are **ATP-driven pumps**, which have a binding site for ATP. The hydrolysis of ATP provides energy that controls the sequence of conformational changes. The energy obtained from ATP hydrolysis can be used to pump solutes against a gradient. Pumps can be uniporters, symporters, or antiporters. As discussed next, pumps use energy to achieve active transport.

Active Transport Is the Movement of Substances Against a Gradient

Active transport is the movement of a solute across a membrane against its gradient—that is, from a region of low concentration to higher concentration. Active transport is energetically unfavourable and requires the input of energy. **Primary active transport** involves the functioning of pumps that directly use energy to transport a solute against a gradient. **Figure 6.23a** shows a pump that uses ATP to transport H^+ against a gradient. Such a pump can establish a large H^+ electrochemical gradient across a membrane.

A single solute moves in one direction.

(a) Uniporter

Two solutes move in the same direction.

(b) Symporter

Two solutes move in opposite directions.

(c) Antiporter

Figure 6.21 Types of transporters based on the direction of transport.

Secondary active transport, shown in **Figure 6.23b**, involves the use of an existing gradient to drive the active transport of a solute. For example, an H^+/sucrose symporter can use an H^+ electrochemical gradient, established by an ion pump, to move sucrose against its concentration gradient. For the H^+/sucrose symporter, only sucrose is actively transported. Hydrogen ions move down (with) their electrochemical gradient. H^+/solute symporters are more common in bacteria, fungi, algae, and plant cells, because H^+ pumps are found in their plasma membranes. In animal cells, a pump that exports Na^+ maintains the Na^+ gradient across the plasma membrane. Na^+/solute symporters are prevalent in animal cells.

Symport enables cells to actively import nutrients against a gradient. Symport proteins use the energy stored in the electrochemical gradient of Na^+ or H^+ to power the uphill movement of organic solutes, such as sugars, amino acids, and other needed solutes. Therefore, with symporters in their plasma membrane, cells can scavenge nutrients from the extracellular environment and accumulate high levels of them within the cytoplasm.

Figure 6.22 Transporters that function as pumps.

Principle: *Living organisms use energy. Cells use large amounts of energy for active transport across membranes.*

ATP-Driven Ion Pumps Generate Ion Electrochemical Gradients

The concept of active transport was discovered in the 1940s, based on the study of ion movements that use radioisotopes of Na^+ and K^+. After analyzing the movement of these ions across the plasma membrane of muscle cells, nerve cells, and red blood cells, researchers determined that the export of sodium ions (Na^+) is coupled with the import of potassium ions (K^+) (**Figure 6.24a**). In the late 1950s, Danish biochemist Jens Skou proposed that a single transporter is responsible for this phenomenon. By studying the membranes of nerve cells

from crabs, he was the first person to describe an ATP-driven ion pump, which was later named the Na^+/K^+ pump. He was awarded the Nobel Prize for this work in 1997. This pump can actively transport Na^+ and K^+ against their gradients by using the energy from ATP hydrolysis.

Let's take a closer look at the Na^+/K^+ pump that Skou discovered (**Figure 6.24b**). Every time one ATP is hydrolyzed, the Na^+/K^+ pump functions as an antiporter that pumps three Na^+ into the extracellular environment and two K^+ into the cytosol. Because one cycle of pumping results in the net export of one positive charge, the Na^+/K^+ pump also produces an electrical gradient across the membrane. For this reason, it is considered an **electrogenic pump**, meaning that it generates an electrical gradient. The plasma membrane of a typical animal cell contains thousands of Na^+/K^+ pumps.

By studying the interactions of Na^+, K^+, and ATP with the Na^+/K^+ pump, researchers have pieced together a molecular roadmap of the steps that direct the pumping of ions across the membrane. These steps are termed the **reaction mechanism** (Figure 6.24b). A central precept of the reaction mechanism is that the Na^+/K^+ pump can alternate between two conformations, designated E1 and E2. In E1, the ion-binding sites are accessible from the cytosol—sodium ions bind tightly to this conformation while potassium ions have a low affinity. In E2, the ion-binding sites are accessible from the extracellular environment—sodium ions have a low affinity and potassium ions bind tightly.

To examine the reaction mechanism, let's begin with the E1 conformation. Three sodium ions bind to the Na^+/K^+ pump from the cytosol (Figure 6.24b). When this occurs, ATP is hydrolyzed to ADP and phosphate. Temporarily, the phosphate is covalently bonded to the protein pump, an event called phosphorylation. Phosphorylation of the pump then triggers the switch to the E2 conformation. The sodium ions are released into the extracellular environment because they have a lower affinity for the E2 conformation, and then two potassium ions bind from the outside. The binding of K^+ causes the release of phosphate, which in turn

(a) Primary active transport

(b) Secondary active transport

Figure 6.23 Types of active transport. **(a)** During primary active transport, a pump directly uses energy, in this case from ATP, and generates a gradient. The pump uses ATP to establish an H^+ electrochemical gradient. **(b)** Secondary active transport via symport involves the use of this gradient to drive the active transport of a solute, such as sucrose.

Figure 6.24   Structure and function of the Na$^+$/K$^+$ pump.   (a) Active transport by the Na$^+$/K$^+$ pump. Each time this protein hydrolyzes one ATP molecule, it pumps out three Na and pumps in two K$^+$. **(b)** Reaction mechanism. The figure illustrates the protein conformational changes between E1 and E2. As this occurs, ATP is hydrolyzed to ADP and phosphate. During the reaction mechanism, phosphate is covalently attached to the protein but is released after potassium ions bind.

Concept check: *If a cell had ATP and sodium ions, but potassium ions were missing, how far through the reaction mechanism could the Na$^+$/K$^+$ pump proceed?*

causes a switch back to E1. Because the E1 conformation has a low affinity for K$^+$, the potassium ions are released into the cytosol. The Na$^+$/K$^+$ pump is now ready for another round of pumping.

The Na$^+$/K$^+$ pump is a key cellular enzyme in animal cells because it functions as an ion pump that maintains Na$^+$ and K$^+$ gradients across the plasma membrane. Many other types of ion pumps are also found in the plasma membrane and in organellar membranes. Ion pumps play the primary role in the formation and maintenance of ion gradients that drive many important cellular processes (**Table 6.3**). Biologists have come to understand that the transport of ions against their gradients is a never-ending activity of all living cells. ATP is commonly the source of energy to drive ion pumps, and cells typically use a substantial portion of their cellular ATP to keep them working. For example, nerve cells use up to 70% of their ATP just to operate ion pumps!

6.4 MACROMOLECULES AND LARGE PARTICLES ARE TRANSPORTED VIA ENDOCYTOSIS AND EXOCYTOSIS

Learning Outcomes:

1. Compare and contrast the mechanisms of movement molecules across membranes for endocytosis and exocytosis with the mechanism of a uniporter transport membrane protein.
2. Compare the functions of membrane transport with that of endocytosis and exocytosis.

You have seen that most small substances are transported via membrane proteins, such as pumps, transporters, and channels,

Table 6.3	Important Functions of Ion Electrochemical Gradients
Function	**Description**
Transport of ions and molecules	Symporters and antiporters use H$^+$ and Na$^+$ gradients to take up nutrients and export waste products.
Production of energy intermediates	In a mitochondrion and chloroplast, H$^+$ gradients are used to synthesize ATP.
Regulation of cytostolic pH	Transporters sense pH changes and regulate the internal pH.
Osmotic regulation	Animal cells control their internal volume by regulating ion gradients between the cytosol and extracellular fluid.
Nerve signalling	Na$^+$ and K$^+$ gradients are involved in conducting action potentials, the signals transmitted by nerve cells.
Muscle contraction	Ca^{2+} gradients regulate the ability of muscle fibres to contract.
Bacterial swimming	H$^+$ gradients drive the rotation of bacterial flagella.

Table 6.4	Examples of Exocytosis and Endocytosis
Exocytosis	**Description**
Hormones	Certain hormones, such as insulin, are composed of polypeptides. To exert its effect, insulin is secreted via exocytosis into the bloodstream from the B cells of the pancreas.
Digestive enzymes	Digestive enzymes that function in the lumen of the small intestine are secreted via exocytosis from cells of the pancreas.
Extracellular matrix	Most of the components of the extracellular matrix that surround animal cells are secreted via exocytosis.
Endocytosis	**Description**
Uptake of vital nutrients	Many important nutrients are insoluble in the bloodstream. Therefore, they are bound to proteins in the blood and then taken into cells via endocytosis. Examples include the uptake of lipids (bound to low-density lipoprotein) and iron (bound to transferrin protein).
Root nodules	Nitrogen-fixing root nodules found in certain species of plants, such as legumes, are formed by the endocytosis of bacteria. After endocytosis, the bacterial cells are contained within a membrane-enclosed compartment in the nitrogen-fixing tissue of functional nodules.
Immune system	Cells of the immune system, known as macrophages, engulf and destroy bacteria via endocytosis.

which provide a passageway for the movement of substances across the membrane. Eukaryotic cells have two other mechanisms, exocytosis and endocytosis, to transport larger molecules, such as proteins and polysaccharides and even very large particles. Both mechanisms involve the packaging of the transported substance, sometimes called the cargo, into a membrane vesicle or vacuole. The mechanisms of exocytosis and endocytosis were examined in Chapter 4. **Table 6.4** describes important examples of exocytosis and endocytosis.

Summary of Key Concepts

6.1 Membrane Structure and Composition

- Cellular membranes are dynamic structures that separate a cell from its surroundings, yet provide an interface to carry out vital cellular activities. One of their crucial functions is membrane transport. (Table 6.1)

- The accepted model of the plasma membrane is the fluid-mosaic model, and its basic framework is the phospholipid bilayer. Cellular membranes also contain proteins, and most membranes have attached carbohydrates. (Figure 6.1)

- Bilayer semifluidity is essential for normal cell function, growth, and division. The chemical properties of phospholipids, such as tail length, the presence of double bonds, and the presence of cholesterol, have a profound effect on the fluidity of the phospholipid bilayer. (Table 6.2, Figures 6.2, 6.4, 6.5)

- Proteins can bind to membranes in three different ways: as transmembrane proteins, as lipid-anchored proteins, or as peripheral membrane proteins. Transmembrane proteins and lipid-anchored proteins are classified as integral membrane proteins. Researchers are working to identify new membrane proteins and their functions because these proteins are so important biologically and medically. (Figure 6.3)

- Glycosylation, which produces glycolipids or glycoproteins, has a variety of cellular functions. Carbohydrate can serve as a recognition marker or a protective cell coat. (Figure 6.6, 6.7)

- Electron microscopy is a valuable tool for studying membrane structure and function. Freeze fracture electron microscopy (FFEM) can be used to analyze the interiors of phospholipid bilayers. (Figure 6.8)

6.2 Phospholipid Bilayers of Cellular Membranes Are Differentially Permeable

- Living cells maintain a constant internal environment that is separated from their external environment. This involves establishing transmembrane gradients across the plasma membrane and organellar membranes. (Figure 6.9, 6.10, 6.11, Table 6.3)

- Diffusion occurs when a solute moves from a region of high concentration to a region of lower concentration. Passive transport refers to the diffusion of a solute across a membrane in a process that does not require an input of energy. Passive diffusion occurs through a membrane without the aid of a transport protein. Passive transport can occur via passive diffusion or facilitated diffusion. (Figure 6.12)

- In the process of osmosis, water diffuses through a membrane from a solution that is hypotonic (lower solute concentration) into a solution that is hypertonic (higher solute concentration). Solutions with identical solute concentrations are isotonic. The tendency of water to move into any cell creates an osmotic (turgor) pressure in cells with walls. (Figures 6.13, 6.14, 6.15, 6.16, 6.17 6.18)

6.3 Transport Proteins Bypass the Phospholipid Bilayer, Allowing Biological Membranes To Be Selectively Permeable to Small Molecules and Ions

- Transport proteins enable biological membranes to be selectively permeable. The two classes of transport proteins are channels and transporters. Channels form an open passageway for the direct diffusion of solutes across the membrane; one example is aquaporin, which allows the movement of water. Most channels are gated, which allows cells to regulate the movement of solutes. Transporters (carriers), which tend to be slower than channels, bind their solutes in a hydrophilic pocket and undergo a conformational change that switches the exposure of the pocket to the other side of the membrane. A pump is a transporter that directly couples its conformational changes to an energy source. All living cells contain ATP-driven pumps. (Figures 6.17, 6.18, 6.19, 6.20, 6.21, 6.22)

- Active transport is the movement of a solute across a membrane against its gradient. Primary active transport involves pumps that directly use energy and generate a solute gradient. Secondary active transport involves the use of an existing gradient. (Figure 6.23)

- The Na^+/K^+ pump is an electrogenic ATP-driven pump. The reaction mechanism refers to the steps that direct the pumping of ions across the membrane. (Figure 6.24)

6.4 Macromolecules and Large Particles Are Transported via Endocytosis and Exocytosis

- Eukaryotic cells have two other mechanisms, exocytosis and endocytosis, to transport large molecules and particles. Exocytosis is a process in which material inside the cell is packaged into vesicles and excreted into the extracellular environment. During endocytosis, the plasma membrane folds inward to form a vesicle that brings substances into the cell. (Table 6.4)

Test to Assess Your Learning

1. Which of the following statements best describes the chemical composition of biomembranes?
   a. Biomembranes are bilayers of proteins with associated lipids and carbohydrates.
   b. Biomembranes are composed of two layers: one layer of phospholipids and one layer of proteins.
   c. Biomembranes are bilayers of phospholipids with associated proteins and carbohydrates.
   d. Biomembranes are composed of equal numbers of phospholipids, proteins, and carbohydrates.
   e. Biomembranes are composed of lipids with proteins attached to the outer surface.

2. _____ is a lipid that helps stabilize membranes of animal cells by regulating fluidity as temperature changes.
   a. Cholesterol
   b. Prostaglandin
   c. Glycerol
   d. ATP
   e. Acetone

3. The presence of double bonds in the fatty acyl tail will
   a. decrease fluidity because of the attraction between the unsaturated tails.
   b. increase fluidity because of the difficulty of the kinked acyl tail to interact.
   c. decrease fluidity by increasing the space between the phospholipids.
   d. increase fluidity by allowing more room for cholesterol to move into the membrane.
   e. decrease fluidity by decreasing the amount of proteins in the membrane.

4. Carbohydrates of the plasma membrane
   a. are associated with a protein or lipid.
   b. are located on the outer surface of the membrane.
   c. can function as cell markers for recognition by other cells.
   d. all of the above.
   e. (a) and (c) only.

5. Which of the following can easily diffuse through a lipid bilayer?
   a. Sodium ions.
   b. Amino acids.
   c. Glucose.
   d. Oxygen.
   e. DNA.

6. The tendency for Na^+ to move into the cell is due to
   a. the higher numbers of Na^+ outside the cell resulting in a chemical concentration gradient.
   b. the net negative charge inside the cell attracting the positively charged Na^+.
   c. the attractive force of K^+ inside the cell pulling Na^+ into the cell.
   d. all of the above.
   e. (a) and (b) only.

7. The hydrostatic pressure required to stop osmosis is
   a. an electrochemical gradient.
   b. filtration.
   c. tonicity.
   d. osmotic pressure.
   e. partial pressure.

8. The selectively permeable characteristic of plasma membranes is mainly due to the presence of
   a. phospholipids.
   b. transport proteins.
   c. glycolipids on the outer surface of the membrane.
   d. concentration gradients across the membrane.
   e. cholesterol.

9. During _____, materials are moved across the plasma membrane against their concentration gradient.
   a. facilitated diffusion
   b. osmosis
   c. active transport
   d. filtration
   e. simple diffusion

10. Large particles or large volumes of fluid can be brought into the cell by
    a. facilitated diffusion.
    b. active transport.
    c. endocytosis.
    d. exocytosis.
    e. all of the above.

Articulate to Assess Your Learning

1. Explain the fluid-mosaic model of membrane structure.
2. What is the difference between passive diffusion and passive transport?
3. When does a cell require active transport to move ions across a membrane? When can it use passive transport?
4. What are gated channels and how do they help cells respond to environmental changes?
5. What challenges and benefits does osmosis present to plants? To animals?

Collaborate to Assess and Extend Your Learning

1. You and your research team have been asked to design a membrane to mimic those found in cells and that would have optimal membrane fluidity at 37°C. Describe the lipids you would use. Would your answer change if the membrane was designed for 0°C? If so, how?
2. Molecules get into and out of cells in a variety of ways, as explained in this chapter. Describe a plausible mechanism or mechanisms by which each of the following items would likely get into a cell:
   a. water
   b. lysine
   c. H^+
   d. a protein
3. What is active transport? Based on what you have read in this textbook, for what different purposes might an organism use active transport?
4. Create a concept map relating the following terms: diffusion, hypertonic, hypotonic, osmosis, water movement, turgor pressure, osmotic pressure, aquaporins, and contractile vacuoles.
5. A biological principle of life is that living organisms use energy. Discuss how lipid bilayers, channels, and transporters influence the ability of cells to interact with their environment.

Visit McGraw-Hill Ryerson Connect™ for additional study resources.

Enzymes and Metabolism

Chapter Outline

Physical endurance. Conditioned athletes, like these marathon runners, have very efficient metabolism of organic molecules, such as glucose.

As discussed in Chapter 2, a **chemical reaction** is a process in which one or more substances are changed into other substances. Such reactions can result in molecules attaching to each other to form larger molecules, molecules breaking apart to form two or more smaller molecules, rearrangements of atoms within molecules, or the transfer of electrons from one atom to another. Every living cell continually performs thousands of such chemical reactions to sustain life. The term **metabolism** is used to describe the sum total of all chemical reactions that occur within an organism. The term also refers to a specific set of chemical reactions occurring at the cellular level. For example, biologists may speak of sugar metabolism or fat metabolism. Most metabolism involves the breakdown or synthesis of organic molecules.

The food we eat serves two purposes. First, it provides us with the organic materials needed to maintain cells and support the growth of new cells and tissues (e.g., the amino acids in the proteins we ingest are used to make new proteins). Second, the physiochemical properties of certain chemical bonds provide us with a source of energy. As you will see, this energy is ultimately used in a variety of ways (e.g., locomotion), but at the biochemical level, it is used to promote chemical reactions that would not occur without an input of energy. The energy can be transferred to and stored within the bonds of a molecule called ATP, which is later metabolized to release the energy to drive many processes, such as muscle contraction.

In this chapter we will begin with a general discussion of chemical reactions. We will examine the factors that control the direction of a chemical reaction and what determines its rate, paying particular attention to the role of enzymes, which act as biological catalysts. We then consider metabolism at the cellular level. First, we will examine some of the general features of chemical reactions that are vital for the energy needs of living cells. We will also explore the variety of ways in which metabolic processes are regulated and survey a group of chemical reactions that break down carbohydrates, namely, the sugar glucose. As you will learn, cells carry out an intricate series of reactions so that glucose can be used in a very controlled

fashion. Finally, the last section explores the synthesis of natural products that play specialized roles in many species.

7.1 ENERGY, CHEMICAL REACTIONS, AND ENZYMES

Learning Outcomes:

1. Describe two types of reactions based on their energy requirements.
2. Explain how ATP is used to provide energy for enzymatic reactions.

Two general factors govern any given chemical reaction in a living cell: its direction and its rate. To illustrate this point, let's consider a generalized chemical reaction:

$$a\mathrm{A} + b\mathrm{B} \rightleftharpoons c\mathrm{C} + d\mathrm{D}$$

where A and B are the reactants, C and D are the products, and *a, b, c,* and *d* are the number of moles of reactants and products. This reaction is reversible (shown by the arrow $\rightleftharpoons$), which means that A + B could be converted to C + D, or C + D could be converted to A + B. The direction of the reaction, whether C + D are made (the forward direction) or A + B are made (the reverse direction), depends on energy and on the concentrations of A, B, C, and D. In this section we will begin by examining the interplay of energy and the concentration of reactants as they govern the direction of a chemical reaction. You will learn that cells use energy intermediate molecules, such as ATP, to drive chemical reactions in a desired direction. Many types of chemical reactions, particularly those that involve organic molecules, proceed very slowly unless facilitated by a biological catalyst. In the second part of this section, we will examine how catalysts called enzymes are critical cellular components that speed up the rates of chemical reactions in living organisms.

Energy Exists in Many Forms

To understand why a chemical reaction occurs, we first need to consider **energy**, which we will define as the ability to promote change. Physicists often consider energy in two forms: kinetic energy and potential energy (**Figure 7.1**). **Kinetic energy** is energy associated with movement, such as the movement of a baseball bat from one location to another. By comparison, **potential energy** is the energy that a substance possesses because of its structure or location. The energy contained within covalent bonds in molecules is a type of potential energy called **chemical energy**. The breakage of those bonds is one way that living cells can harness this energy to perform cellular functions. **Table 7.1** summarizes chemical and other forms of energy that are important in biological systems.

An important issue in biology is the ability of energy to be converted from one form to another. The study of energy interconversions is called **thermodynamics**. Physicists have determined that two laws govern energy interconversions:

1. The **first law of thermodynamics**: The first law states that energy cannot be created or destroyed; it is also called the law of conservation of energy. However, energy can be transferred from one place to another and can be transformed from one type to another (as when, for example, chemical energy is transformed into heat).
2. The **second law of thermodynamics**: The second law states that the transfer of energy or the transformation of energy

(a) Kinetic energy   Covalent bonds in glucose store energy. **(b) Potential energy**

Figure 7.1 Examples of energy. (a) Kinetic energy, such as swinging a bat, is energy associated with motion. (b) Potential energy is stored energy. Chemical bonds in such molecules as glucose store large amounts of chemical energy.

from one form to another increases the **entropy**, or degree of disorder in a system (**Figure 7.2**). When energy is converted from one form to another, the increase in entropy causes some energy to become unusable by living organisms.

Next, you will see how these two laws place limits on the ways that living cells can use energy for their own needs.

The Change in Free Energy Determines the Direction of a Chemical Reaction or Any Other Cellular Process

From the perspective of living organisms, energy is a critical component that is necessary for life to exist. Energy powers many cellular processes, including chemical reactions; cellular movements, such as those occurring in muscle contraction; and the maintenance of cell organization. To understand how

Table 7.1	Types of Energy That Are Important in Biology	
Energy type	**Description**	**Biological example**
Light	Light is a form of electromagnetic radiation that is visible to the eye. The energy of light is packaged in photons.	During photosynthesis, light energy is captured by pigments in chloroplasts (Chapter 8). Ultimately, this energy is used to reduce carbon, thus producing organic molecules.
Heat	Heat is the transfer of kinetic energy from one object to another or from an energy source to an object. In biology, heat is often viewed as energy that can be transferred because of a difference in temperature between two objects or locations.	Many organisms, such as humans, maintain their bodies at a constant temperature. This is achieved by chemical reactions that generate heat.
Mechanical	Mechanical energy is the energy that is possessed by an object because of its motion or its position relative to other objects.	In animals, mechanical energy is associated with movements caused by muscle contraction, such as walking.
Chemical	Chemical energy is energy stored in the chemical bonds of molecules. When the bonds are broken and rearranged, they can release large amounts of energy.	The covalent bonds in organic molecules, such as glucose and ATP, store large amounts of energy. When these bonds are broken, the chemical energy released can be used to drive cellular processes.
Electrical/ion gradient	The movement of a charge or the separation of a charge can provide energy. Also, a difference in ion concentration across a membrane constitutes an electrochemical gradient, which is a source of potential energy.	High-energy electrons can release energy (that is, drop down to lower energy levels). The energy that is released can be used to drive cellular processes, such as pumping H^+ across membranes (as discussed later in this chapter).

living organisms use energy, we need to distinguish between the energy that can be used to do work (usable energy) and the energy that cannot do work (unusable energy):

total energy = usable energy + unusable energy

Why is some energy unusable? The main culprit is entropy. As stated by the second law of thermodynamics, energy transformations involve an increase in entropy, a measure of the disorder that cannot be harnessed to do work. For living organisms, the total energy is termed **enthalpy (H)** and the usable energy—the amount of available energy that can be used to do work—is called the **free energy (G)**. The letter G is in recognition of J. Willard Gibbs, who proposed the concept of free energy in 1878. The unusable energy is the system's entropy (S). Gibbs proposed that these three factors are related to each other in the following way:

$$H = G + TS$$

where T is the absolute temperature in Kelvin (K). Because our focus is on free energy, we can rearrange this equation as

$$G = H - TS$$

A critical issue in biology is whether a process will or will not occur spontaneously. For example, will glucose be broken down into carbon dioxide and water? Another way of framing this question is to ask, Is the breakdown of glucose a spontaneous reaction? A **spontaneous reaction** or process is one that will occur without an additional input of energy. However, a spontaneous reaction does not necessarily proceed quickly. In some cases, the rate of a spontaneous reaction can be quite slow.

The key way to evaluate whether a reaction is spontaneous is to determine the free energy change that occurs as a result of the chemical reaction:

$$\Delta G = \Delta H - T\Delta S$$

where delta (the Δ sign) indicates a change, such as before and after a chemical reaction. If the reaction has a negative free energy change ($\Delta G < 0$), free energy is released. Such a reaction is said to be **exergonic**. Exergonic reactions are spontaneous. Alternatively, if a reaction has a positive free energy change ($\Delta G > 0$), requiring the addition of free energy from the environment, it is termed **endergonic**. An endergonic reaction is not a spontaneous reaction.

If ΔG for a chemical reaction is negative, the reaction favours the formation of products, while a reaction with a positive ΔG favours the formation of reactants. Chemists have determined free energy changes for a variety of chemical reactions.

Less random (less entropy)

More random (more entropy)

Figure 7.2   Entropy.   Entropy is a measure of the disorder of a system. An increase in entropy means an increase in disorder, illustrated by observing a salt crystal dissolve in water.

Concept check: *Which do you think has more entropy, an ice cube or ice water?*

Adenosine triphosphate (ATP) is a molecule that is a common energy source for all cells. Let's look at the breakdown of ATP to adenosine diphosphate (ADP) and inorganic phosphate (P_i). Because water is used to remove a phosphate group, chemists refer to this as the hydrolysis of ATP (**Figure 7.3**). In the reaction of converting 1 mole of ATP to 1 mole of ADP and P_i, ΔG equals −7.3 kcal/mol.

Why does ATP hydrolysis release such a large amount of energy? In physiochemical terms the answer is complex, but we can simply state three factors that contribute to the large negative ΔG. First, ATP has four electronegative oxygen atoms, and charge repulsion is very high verses that of the products. Second, the products are better solvated than ATP. Finally, the products are more stable than ATP. This last factor is due to the delocalization of electrons on the terminal oxygens verses that of a bridging oxygen atom, which makes ATP less stable. Thus, it is not the inherent energy within the phosphate bonds that make ATP an energy-rich molecule, but rather the difference

in energy content between the reactants and the products. As discussed later in this chapter, the energy that is liberated by the hydrolysis of ATP is used to drive many cellular processes.

Even when a chemical reaction is associated with a negative free energy change, not all of the reactants are converted to products. The reaction reaches a state of **chemical equilibrium** in which the rate of formation of products equals the rate of formation of reactants. According to the generalized equation,

$$a\text{A} + b\text{B} \rightleftharpoons c\text{C} + d\text{D}$$

An equilibrium occurs, such that

$$K_{eq} = \frac{[\text{C}]^c\,[\text{D}]^d}{[\text{A}]^a\,[\text{B}]^b}$$

where K_{eq} is the equilibrium constant.

Biologists make two simplifying assumptions when determining values for equilibrium constants. First, the concentration of water does not change during the reaction and the pH remains constant at pH 7. The equilibrium constant under these conditions is designated K_{eq}'. If water is one of the reactants, as in a hydrolysis reaction, it is not included in the chemical equilibrium equation. As an example, consider the chemical equilibrium for the hydrolysis of ATP:

$$\text{ATP}^{4-} + \text{H}_2\text{O} \rightleftharpoons \text{ADP}^{2-} + \text{P}_i^{\,2-}$$

$$K_{eq}' = \frac{[\text{ADP}]\,[\text{P}_i]}{[\text{ATP}]}$$

Experimentally, the value for K_{eq}' for this reaction has been determined and found to be approximately 1,650,000 M. Such a large value indicates that the equilibrium greatly favours the formation of the products ADP and P_i.

Cells Use ATP to Drive Endergonic Reactions

An important issue that faces living organisms is that many vital processes require the addition of free energy, that is, they are endergonic and will not occur spontaneously. Fortunately, organisms have a strategy to overcome this problem. If an endergonic reaction is coupled with an exergonic reaction, the endergonic reaction will proceed spontaneously if the net free energy change for both processes combined is negative. For example, consider the following reactions:

glucose + phosphate^{2-} → glucose phosphate^{2-} + H$_2$O
$$\Delta G = +3.3 \text{ kcal/mol}$$

ATP^{4-} + H$_2$O → ATP^{2-} + P$_i^{\,2-}$ $\quad \Delta G = -7.3 \text{ kcal/mol}$

Coupled reaction:

glucose + ATP^{4-} → glucose phosphate^{2-} + ADP^{2-}
$$\Delta G = -4.0 \text{ kcal/mol}$$

The first reaction, in which phosphate is covalently attached to glucose, is endergonic, while the second, the hydrolysis of ATP, is exergonic. By itself, the first reaction would not be spontaneous. If the two reactions are coupled, however, the net free energy change for both reactions combined is exergonic

Adenine (A)

Phosphate groups

Adenosine triphosphate (ATP)

Hydrolysis of ATP

Ribose

Adenosine diphosphate (ADP)　　　**Phosphate (P$_i$)**

$\Delta G = -7.3 \text{ kcal/mol}$

Figure 7.3 **ATP hydrolysis.** The hydrolysis of ATP to ADP and P_i is exergonic. As shown in this figure, ATP has a net charge of −4, while ADP and P_i are shown with net charges of −2 each. When these compounds are shown in chemical reactions with other molecules, the net charges will also be shown. Otherwise, these compounds will simply be designated ATP, ADP, and P_i. Note also that at neutral pH, ADP^{2-} will dissociate to ADP^{3-} and H$^+$. Likewise, P$_i^{\,2-}$ also dissociates to P$_i^{\,3-}$ and H$^+$ at neutral pH.

(**Figure 7.4**). In the coupled reaction, a phosphate is directly transferred from ATP to glucose by the enzyme hexokinase; this coupled reaction proceeds spontaneously because the net free energy change is negative. As discussed later, the transfer of phosphate from ATP to glucose is a first step in the breakdown of glucose to smaller molecules. Exergonic reactions, such as the breakdown of ATP, are commonly coupled to cellular processes that would otherwise be endergonic.

Enzymes Increase the Rates of Chemical Reactions

Thus far we have examined aspects of energy and considered how the laws of physics are related to the direction of chemical reactions. If a chemical reaction has a negative free energy change, the reaction will be spontaneous; it will tend to proceed in the direction of reactants to products. Although thermodynamics governs the direction of an energy transformation, it does not control the rate of a chemical reaction. For example, the breakdown of the molecules in gasoline to smaller molecules is a highly exergonic reaction. Even so, we could place gasoline and oxygen in a container and nothing much would happen (provided it wasn't near a flame). If we came back several days later, we would find the gasoline essentially unchanged. Perhaps if we came back in a few million years, the gasoline would have been broken down. On a timescale of months or a few years, however, the chemical reaction would proceed very slowly.

For most chemical reactions in cells to proceed at a rapid pace, a catalyst is needed. A **catalyst** is an agent that speeds up the rate of a chemical reaction without being consumed during the reaction. In living cells, is the most common catalyst is an **enzyme**, a protein molecule that accelerates chemical reactions.

The term was coined in 1876 by a German physiologist, Wilhelm Kühne, who discovered the enzyme trypsin in pancreatic juice. A few biological catalysts are RNA molecules called **ribozymes**. Some of these RNAs act as nucleases in self-splicing reactions, while others conduct such activities as catalyzing the formation of bonds that link amino acids to one another during protein synthesis. The discovery of ribozymes has stimulated research in numerous areas of molecular biology and medicine. Canadian Sidney Altman shared the Nobel Prize in Chemistry in 1989 for his contributions to ribozyme research.

Why are catalysts necessary to speed up a chemical reaction? When a covalent bond is broken or formed, this process initially involves the straining or contortion of one or more bonds in the starting molecule(s), and it may involve the positioning of two molecules so that they interact with each other properly. Let's consider the reaction in which ATP is used to attach a phosphate to glucose:

$$\text{glucose} + \text{ATP}^{4-} \rightarrow \text{glucose phosphate}^{2-} + \text{ADP}^{2-}$$

For a reaction to occur between glucose and ATP, they must collide in the correct orientation and possess enough energy so that chemical bonds can be changed. As glucose and ATP approach each other, their electron clouds cause repulsion. To overcome this repulsion, an initial input of energy, called the **activation energy**, is required (**Figure 7.5**). Activation energy allows the molecules to get close enough to cause a rearrangement of bonds. With the input of activation energy, glucose and ATP can achieve a **transition state** in which the original bonds are stretched to their limit. Once the reactants have reached the transition state, the chemical reaction can readily proceed to the formation of products.

The activation energy required to achieve the transition state is a barrier to the formation of products. This barrier is the reason that the rate of many chemical reactions is very slow. There are two common ways to overcome this barrier and thereby accelerate a chemical reaction. First, the reactants could be exposed to a large amount of energy (e.g., heat). As we noted previously, if gasoline is sitting at room temperature, nothing much happens. However, if the gasoline is exposed to a flame or spark, it breaks down rapidly, perhaps at an explosive rate! Alternatively, a second strategy is to lower the activation energy barrier. Enzymes lower the activation energy to a point at which a small amount of available energy can push the reactants to a transition state.

How do enzymes work to lower the activation energy threshold to promote chemical reactions? One barrier to achieving the transition state is the inherent entropy of the reactants. By binding to the reactants, enzymes largely nullify these entropic forces, which lowers the energy requirements for the reaction to proceed. Additionally, because enzymes are proteins that bind to relatively small reactants (Figure 7.5), specific chemical bonds of the reactants are strained to foster an instability that favours reactivity and the conversion of reactants to products. Charged amino acids in the active site of enzymes often facilitate a reaction by changing the local chemical environment of the reactants. In some cases, enzymes lower the

ATP hydrolysis provides the energy to drive endergonic reactions

Figure 7.4 **The ATP cycle and coupled reactions.** Living cells continually recycle ATP. The breakdown of food molecules is used to synthesize ATP from ADP and P_i. The hydrolysis of ATP to ADP and P_i is used to drive many different endergonic reactions (the action of hexokinase in converting glucose to glucose-6-phosphate is shown) and to power other cellular processes (e.g., muscle contraction).

Figure 7.5 **Activation energy of a chemical reaction.** An exergonic reaction: activation energy is needed for molecules to achieve a transition state. One way that enzymes lower the activation energy is by straining the reactants so that less energy is required to attain the transition state. A second way is by binding two reactants so that they are close to each other and in a favourable orientation.

Concept check: *How does lowering the activation energy affect the rate of a chemical reaction? How does it affect the direction of the reaction?*

activation energy by directly participating in the chemical reaction. For example, certain enzymes that hydrolyze ATP form a covalent bond between phosphate and an amino acid in the enzyme. However, this condition is temporary. The covalent bond between phosphate and the amino acid is quickly broken, releasing phosphate and returning the amino acid back to its original condition. An important example of such an enzyme is Na^+/K^+-ATPase, used in the Na^+/K^+ pump described in Chapter 6 (refer back to Figure 6.24).

Enzymes Recognize Their Substrates with High Specificity and Undergo Conformational Changes

Thus far, we have considered how enzymes lower the activation energy of a chemical reaction and thereby increase its rate. Let's consider some other features of enzymes that enable them to serve as effective catalysts in chemical reactions. The **active site** is the location in an enzyme where the chemical reaction takes place. The **substrates** for an enzyme are the reactant molecules and ions that bind to an enzyme at the active site and participate in the chemical reaction. For example, hexokinase is an enzyme whose substrates are glucose and ATP (**Figure 7.6**). The binding between an enzyme and a substrate produces an **enzyme-substrate complex**.

A key feature of nearly all enzymes is that they bind their substrates with a **high affinity** or high degree of specificity. For example, because hexokinase binds glucose very well, we say it has a high affinity for glucose. By comparison, hexokinase has a low affinity for other sugars, such as fructose and galactose, which have similar structures to glucose. In 1894 the German scientist Emil Fischer proposed that the recognition of a substrate by an enzyme resembles the interaction between a lock and key: only the right-sized key (the substrate) will fit into the keyhole (active site) of the lock (the enzyme). Further research

| 1 | ATP and glucose bind to enzyme (hexokinase). | 2 | Enzyme undergoes conformational change that binds the substrates more tightly. This induced fit strains chemical bonds within the substrates and/or brings them closer together. | 3 | Substrates are converted to products. | 4 | Products are released. Enzyme is reused. |

Figure 7.6 **The steps of an enzyme-catalyzed reaction.** The example shown here involves the enzyme hexokinase, which binds glucose and ATP. The products are glucose-phosphate and ADP, which are released from the enzyme.

revealed that the interaction between an enzyme and its substrates also involves movements or conformational changes in the enzyme itself. As shown in Figure 7.6, these conformational changes cause the substrates to bind more tightly to the enzyme, a phenomenon called **induced fit**. Only after this conformational change takes place does the enzyme catalyze the conversion of reactants to products.

Some enzymes require additional nonprotein molecules to carry out their functions. Such **cofactors** can be grouped into three classes. Metal ions, such as Fe^{2+} or Zn^{2+} often participate in organizing the structure of a protein or assist in carrying out enzymatic reactions (e.g., iron is necessary to bind oxygen in the protein hemoglobin). **Coenzymes**, including NADH, discussed later in this chapter, transiently associate with some enzymes and are often involved in group or electron transfer reactions. Many coenzymes are derived from vitamins, emphasizing the importance of proper nutrition in supporting biochemical processes. Finally, **prosthetic groups** are nonprotein molecules that bind very tightly to their protein partners to aid their function (e.g., the heme group that binds to the protein called globin to produce hemoglobin).

The ability of enzymes to speed catalysis is very sensitive to perturbations in the local environment. In particular, temperature and pH are critical factors that dictate the structure of the protein and hence its ability to selectively bind to its substrate(s). Although these requirements are nearly always supported in higher eukaryotic cells, lower eukaryotes, such as yeast, and single-celled prokaryotes are often exposed to relatively extreme environmental conditions that can compromise enzyme function.

7.2 OVERVIEW OF METABOLISM

Learning Outcomes:

1. Distinguish between catabolic and anabolic reactions.
2. Give an example of a redox reaction involving a coenzyme.

In the previous section, we examined the underlying factors that govern individual chemical reactions. In living cells, chemical reactions are often coordinated with each other and occur in a sequence called a **metabolic pathway**, each step of which is catalyzed by a specific enzyme (**Figure 7.7**). These pathways are categorized according to whether the reactions lead to the breakdown or synthesis of substances. **Catabolic reactions** result in the breakdown of molecules into smaller molecules. Such reactions are often exergonic. By comparison, **anabolic reactions** promote the synthesis of larger molecules from smaller precursor molecules. This process usually is endergonic and, in living cells, must be coupled to an exergonic reaction. In this section, we will survey the general features of catabolic and anabolic reactions, and explore the ways in which these metabolic pathways are controlled.

Initial substrate Intermediate 1 Intermediate 2 Final product

Figure 7.7 **A metabolic pathway.** In a metabolic pathway, a series of different enzymes catalyze the changes in the structure of a molecule, beginning with a starting substrate and ending with a final product.

Catabolic Reactions Recycle Organic Building Blocks and Produce Energy Intermediates, Such As ATP and NADH

Catabolic reactions involve the breakdown of macromolecules or smaller organic molecules. One reason for the breakdown of these molecules is to recycle the building blocks needed to construct new macromolecules. For example, proteins are polymers composed of a chain of amino acids. When a protein is improperly folded or is no longer needed by a cell, the peptide bonds between amino acids in such a protein are broken by enzymes called proteases. This generates amino acid monomers that can be used in the construction of new proteins.

$$\text{protein} \xrightarrow{\quad\text{proteases}\quad} \text{many individual amino acids}$$

Similarly, the breakdown of RNA by enzymes called nucleases produces nucleotides that can be used in the synthesis of new RNA molecules.

$$\text{RNA} \xrightarrow{\quad\text{nucleases}\quad} \text{many individual nucleotides}$$

The breakdown of macromolecules, such as unneeded proteins and RNA molecules, allows a cell to recycle the building blocks that compose those macromolecules and use them to make new macromolecules.

A second reason for the breakdown of macromolecules and smaller organic molecules is to obtain energy that can be used to drive endergonic processes in the cell. Covalent bonds store a large amount of energy. However, when cells break covalent bonds in such organic molecules as carbohydrates and proteins, they do not directly use the energy that is released in this process. Instead, the released energy is stored in **energy intermediates**, such molecules as ATP and NADH, that are directly used to drive endergonic reactions in cells.

As an example, let's consider the breakdown of glucose into two molecules of pyruvate. As we'll discuss later in this chapter, the breakdown of glucose to pyruvate involves a catabolic pathway called glycolysis. Some of the energy that is released during the breakage of covalent bonds in glucose is harnessed to synthesize ATP. However, this does not occur in a single step. Rather, glycolysis involves a series of steps in which covalent bonds are broken and rearranged. This process creates molecules that can readily donate a phosphate group to ADP, thereby creating ATP. For example, phosphoenolpyruvate consists of a phosphate group attached to pyruvate. Because of the arrangement of bonds in phosphoenolpyruvate, this phosphate bond is easily broken. Therefore, the phosphate can be readily transferred to ADP:

$$\text{phosphoenolpyruvate} + \text{ADP} \rightarrow \text{pyruvate} + \text{ATP}$$
$$\Delta G = -7.5 \text{ kcal/mol}$$

This is an exergonic reaction and therefore favours the formation of products. In this step of glycolysis, the breakdown of an organic molecule, namely, phosphoenolpyruvate, results in the synthesis of an energy intermediate molecule, ATP, which can then be used by a cell to drive endergonic reactions. This way of synthesizing ATP, termed **substrate-level phosphorylation**, occurs when an enzyme directly transfers a phosphate from one molecule to a different molecule. In this case, a phosphate is transferred from phosphoenolpyruvate to ADP. Another way to make ATP is via **chemiosmosis**. In this process, energy stored in an ion electrochemical gradient is used to make ATP from ADP and P_i. We will consider this mechanism later in the chapter.

An important event that can occur during the breakdown of small organic molecules is **oxidation**, a process that involves the removal of electrons. This event is called oxidation because oxygen frequently is involved in chemical reactions that remove electrons from other molecules. By comparison, **reduction** is the addition of electrons to an atom or a molecule. Reduction is so named because the addition of a negatively charged electron reduces the net charge of a molecule. Reduction of organic compounds also frequently involves reducing the number of double (or triple) bonds in a molecule, as is illustrated in **Figure 7.8a**.

Electrons do not exist freely in solution. When an atom or a molecule is oxidized, the electron that is removed must be transferred to another atom or molecule, which becomes reduced. This type of reaction is termed a **redox reaction**, which is short for a reduction–oxidation reaction. Redox reactions, in addition to powering cells with most of their free energy, are used in a wide variety of metabolic pathways to facilitate the interconversion of compounds. The enzymes that participate in redox reactions are often targets of therapeutic drugs. For example, the drug Lipitor is a competitive inhibitor (discussed in the next section) of the enzyme HMG-CoA reductase, which is involved in the production of cholesterol.

As a generalized equation, an electron can be transferred from molecule Y to molecule X as follows:

$$Ye^- + X \rightarrow Y + Xe^-$$

As shown in Figure 7.8a, Y has been oxidized (that is, had an electron removed) and X has been reduced (that is, had an electron added). In general, a substance that has been oxidized has less energy, while a substance that has been reduced has more energy.

During the oxidation of organic molecules, such as glucose, the electrons are used to create energy intermediates, such as

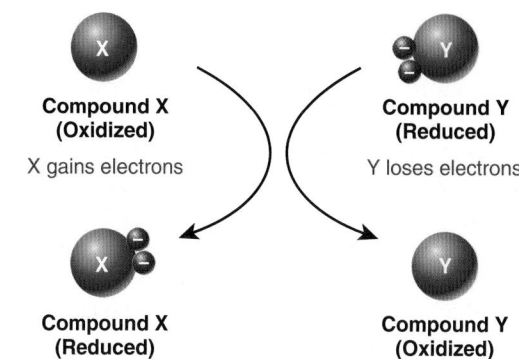

(a) A coupled redox reaction

(b) The reduction of NAD⁺ to create NADH

Figure 7.8 Redox reactions. **(a)** Oxidized compound X receives electrons from reduced compound Y. In this case, Y serves as a reducing agent, and on donating its electrons, it becomes oxidized. Y can now serve as an oxidizing agent, capable of receiving electrons from a reduced compound (not necessarily X). **(b)** NAD⁺ is composed of two nucleotides, one with an adenine base and one with a nicotinamide base. The oxidation of organic molecules releases electrons that can bind to NAD⁺ and (along with a hydrogen ion) result in the formation of NADH. The two electrons and H⁺ are incorporated into the nicotinamide ring. Note: The actual net charges of NAD⁺ and NADH are minus one and minus two, respectively. They are designated NAD⁺ and NADH to emphasize the net charge of the nicotinamide ring, which is involved in many oxidation–reduction reactions.

NADH (**Figure 7.8b**). In this process, an organic molecule has been oxidized and **NAD$^+$ (nicotinamide adenine dinucleotide)** has been reduced to NADH. Cells use NADH in two common ways. First, as you will see, the oxidation of NADH is a highly exergonic reaction that can be used to make ATP. Second, NADH can donate electrons to other organic molecules and thereby energize them. Such energized molecules can more readily form covalent bonds. Therefore, as described next, NADH is often needed in anabolic reactions that involve the synthesis of larger molecules through the formation of covalent bonds between smaller molecules.

Anabolic Reactions Require an Input of Energy to Make Larger Molecules

Anabolic reactions are also called **biosynthetic reactions**, because they are necessary to make larger molecules and macromolecules. We will examine the synthesis of macromolecules in several chapters of this textbook. For example, RNA and protein biosynthesis are described in Chapter 11. Cells also need to synthesize small organic molecules, such as amino acids and fats, if they are not readily available from food sources. Such molecules are made by the formation of covalent linkages between precursor molecules. For example, glutamate (an amino acid) is made by the covalent linkage between α-ketoglutarate (a product of sugar metabolism) and ammonium.

$$
\begin{array}{c}
COO^- \\
| \\
CH_2 \\
| \\
CH_2 \\
| \\
C{=}O \\
| \\
COO^-
\end{array}
+ NH_4^+ + NADH \longrightarrow
\begin{array}{c}
COO^- \\
| \\
CH_2 \\
| \\
CH_2 \\
| \\
H_3N^+{-}C{-}COO^- \\
| \\
H
\end{array}
+ NAD^+ + H_2O
$$

α-ketoglutarate   Ammonium   Glutamate

Another amino acid, glutamine, is made from glutamate and ammonium.

$$
\begin{array}{c}
COO^- \\
| \\
CH_2 \\
| \\
CH_2 \\
| \\
H_3N^+{-}C{-}COO^- \\
| \\
H
\end{array}
+ NH_4^+ + ATP^{4-} + H_2O \longrightarrow
\begin{array}{c}
O{=}C{-}NH_2 \\
| \\
CH_2 \\
| \\
CH_2 \\
| \\
H_3N^+{-}C{-}COO^- \\
| \\
H
\end{array}
+ ADP^{2-} + P_i^{2-}
$$

Glutamate Ammonium   Glutamine

In both reactions, an energy intermediate molecule, such as NADH or ATP, is needed to drive the reaction forward.

GENOMES AND PROTEOMES

Many Proteins Use ATP as a Source of Energy

Over the past several decades researchers have studied the functions of many types of proteins and discovered numerous examples in which a protein uses ATP to drive a cellular process (**Table 7.2**). In humans a typical cell uses millions of ATP molecules per second. At the same time the breakdown of food molecules releases energy that allows us to make more ATP from ADP and P$_i$. The turnover of ATP occurs at a remarkable pace. An average person hydrolyzes about 45 kg of ATP per day, yet we do not have 45 kg of ATP in our bodies. For this to happen, each ATP undergoes about 10,000 cycles of hydrolysis and resynthesis (from ADP and P$_i$) during an ordinary day.

Table 7.2	Examples of Proteins That Use ATP for Energy
Type	**Description**
Metabolic enzymes	Many enzymes use ATP to catalyze endergonic reactions. For example, hexokinase uses ATP to attach phosphate to glucose.
Transporters	Ion pumps, such as the Na$^+$/K$^+$ pump, use ATP to pump ions against a gradient (see Chapter 6).
Motor proteins	Motor proteins, such as myosin, use ATP to facilitate cellular movement, such as muscle contraction (see Chapter 44).
Chaperones	Chaperones are proteins that use ATP to aid in the folding and unfolding of cellular proteins (see Chapter 5).
DNA-modifying enzymes	Many proteins, such as helicases and topoisomerases, use ATP to modify the conformation of DNA (see Chapter 10).
Aminoacyl-tRNA synthetases	These enzymes use ATP to attach amino acids to tRNAs (see Chapter 11).
Protein kinases	Protein kinases are regulatory proteins that use ATP to attach a phosphate to proteins, thereby affecting the function of the phosphorylated protein (see Chapter 9).

By studying the structures of many proteins that use ATP, biochemists have discovered that particular amino acid sequences within proteins function as ATP-binding sites. This information has allowed researchers to predict whether a newly discovered protein uses ATP or not. When an entire genome sequence of a species is experimentally determined, the genes that encode proteins can be analyzed to find out whether the encoded proteins have ATP-binding sites in their amino acid sequences. By using this approach, researchers have been able to analyze proteomes—all the proteins that a given cell can make—and estimate the percentage of proteins that are able to bind ATP. (Most of these proteins are expected to use ATP as a source of energy, though some of them may simply bind ATP without hydrolyzing it to ADP and P_i.) This approach has been applied to the proteomes of Bacteria, Archaea, and Eukarya. On average, more than 20% of all proteins bind ATP. However, this number is likely to be an underestimate of the total percentage of ATP-using proteins because we may not have identified all the types of ATP-binding sites in proteins. In humans, who have an estimated 20,000 to 25,000 different genes, a minimum of 4,000 to 5,000 of those genes encode proteins that use ATP. From these numbers, you can see the enormous importance of ATP as a source of energy for living cells.

Metabolic Pathways Are Regulated in Three General Ways

Before we end our general discussion of metabolism, let's consider the various ways in which chemical reactions are regulated in living cells. The regulation of catabolic pathways is important, so that a cell breaks down organic molecules when energy is needed but conserves them when an adequate supply of energy intermediates is available. The control of anabolic pathways is essential so that a cell does not waste energy making too much of the products of such pathways. The regulation of catabolic and anabolic pathways occurs at the genetic, cellular, and biochemical levels.

Gene Regulation   Because enzymes in every metabolic pathway are encoded by genes, one way that cells control chemical reactions is via gene regulation. For example, if a bacterial cell is not exposed to a particular sugar in its environment, it will turn off the genes that encode the enzymes that are needed to break down that sugar. Alternatively, if the sugar becomes available, the genes are switched on. Chapter 12 examines the steps of gene regulation in detail.

Cellular Regulation   Metabolism is also coordinated at the cellular level. Cells integrate signals from their environment and adjust their chemical reactions to adapt to those signals. As discussed in Chapter 9, cell-signalling pathways often lead to the activation of protein kinases that covalently attach a phosphate group to target proteins. For example, when people are frightened, they secrete a hormone called epinephrine into their bloodstream. This hormone binds to the surface of muscle cells and stimulates an intracellular pathway that leads to the phosphorylation and activation of several intracellular proteins, including enzymes involved in carbohydrate metabolism. These activated enzymes promote the breakdown of carbohydrates, an event that supplies the frightened individual with more energy. Epinephrine is sometimes called the "fight-or-flight" hormone because the added energy prepares an individual to either stay and fight or run away. After a person is no longer frightened, hormone levels drop and other enzymes called phosphatases remove the phosphate groups from enzymes, thereby restoring the original level of carbohydrate metabolism.

Biochemical Regulation   A third and very prominent way that metabolic pathways are controlled is at the biochemical level. In this case, the binding of a molecule to an enzyme directly regulates its function. Biochemical regulation is typically categorized according to the site where the regulatory molecule binds. Let's consider two types that involve regulatory molecules that inhibit enzyme function.

Competitive inhibitors are molecules that bind to the active site of an enzyme and inhibit the ability of the substrate to bind. In other words, such inhibitors compete with the substrate for the ability to bind to the enzyme. Competitive inhibitors usually have a structure that mimics the structure of the enzyme's substrate. As mentioned earlier, the drug Lipitor is structurally similar to the substrate of HMG-CoA reductase, and as a result of this competition, less cholesterol is produced.

Noncompetitive inhibitors bind to an enzyme at a location that is outside the active site and inhibit the enzyme's function. An example is a form of regulation called **feedback inhibition**, in which the product of a metabolic pathway inhibits an enzyme that acts early in the pathway, thus preventing the overaccumulation of the product (**Figure 7.9**). Many metabolic pathways use feedback inhibition as a form of biochemical regulation. In such cases, the inhibited enzyme has two binding sites. One is the active site, where the reactants are converted to products. The other, for enzymes that are controlled by feedback inhibition, is an **allosteric site**, where a molecule can bind noncovalently and affect the function of the active site. The binding of a molecule to an allosteric site causes a conformational change in the enzyme that inhibits its catalytic function.

Allosteric sites are often found in the enzymes that catalyze the early steps in a metabolic pathway. Such allosteric sites typically bind molecules that are the products of the metabolic pathway. When the products bind to these sites, they inhibit the function of these enzymes and thereby prevent the formation of too much product.

Initial substrate   Intermediate 1   Intermediate 2   Final product

Active site

Enzyme 1

Allosteric site

Enzyme 2

Enzyme 3

Conformational
change

Feedback Inhibition:
If the concentration of the final product becomes high,
it will bind to enzyme 1 and cause a conformational
change that inhibits its ability to convert the initial
substrate into intermediate 1.

Final product

Figure 7.9 **Feedback inhibition.** In this process, the product of a metabolic pathway inhibits an enzyme that functions in the pathway, thereby preventing the overaccumulation of the product.

Cellular and biochemical regulation are important and rapid ways to control chemical reactions in a cell. But when considering a metabolic pathway composed of several enzymes, which enzyme in a pathway should be controlled? In many cases, a metabolic pathway has a **rate-limiting step**, which is the slowest step in a pathway. If the rate-limiting step is inhibited or occurs at a faster rate, such changes will have the greatest impact on the formation of the product of the metabolic pathway. Rather than affecting all the enzymes in a metabolic pathway, cellular and biochemical regulation are often directed at the enzyme that catalyzes the rate-limiting step. This is an efficient and rapid way to control the amount of product of a pathway.

7.3 CELLULAR RESPIRATION

Learning Outcomes:

1. Describe the four metabolic pathways that are used to break down glucose into CO_2.
2. Describe why oxygen is needed to efficiently convert glucose to cellular energy.
3. Outline the three phases of glycolysis and the net products.
4. Describe the series of enzymatic reactions that constitute glycolysis.
5. Discuss the concept of a metabolic cycle.
6. Identify the initial reactants, the final products, and the net products of the citric acid cycle.
7. Explain how the electron transport chain produces an H^+ electrochemical gradient.
8. Explain how ATP synthase uses the H^+ electrochemical gradient to synthesize ATP.
9. Describe and interpret the results of the experiment that showed that the ATP synthase is a rotary machine.

Cellular respiration is a process by which living cells obtain energy from organic molecules. A primary aim of cellular respiration is to make the energy intermediates ATP and NADH. When oxygen (O_2) is used, this process is termed **aerobic respiration**. During aerobic respiration, O_2 is consumed and CO_2 is released. When we breathe, we inhale the oxygen that is needed for aerobic respiration and exhale the CO_2 that is a byproduct of the process. For this reason, the term respiration has a second meaning, which is the act of breathing.

Different types of organic molecules, such as carbohydrates, proteins, and fats, can be used as energy sources to drive aerobic respiration:

$$\text{organic molecules} + O_2 \rightarrow CO_2 + H_2O + \text{energy}$$

In this section, we will largely focus on the use of glucose as an energy source for cellular respiration:

$$\underset{\text{(glucose)}}{C_6H_{12}O_6} + 6\,O_2 \rightarrow 6\,CO_2 + 6\,H_2O + \text{energy intermediates} + \text{heat}$$
$$\Delta G = -686 \text{ kcal/mol}$$

We will focus on the breakdown of glucose in a eukaryotic cell in the presence of oxygen. Certain covalent bonds within glucose store a large amount of chemical bond energy. When glucose is broken down via oxidation, ultimately to CO_2 and water, the energy within those bonds is released and used to make three types of energy intermediates: ATP, NADH, and $FADH_2$. This process involves four metabolic pathways: (1) glycolysis, (2) the breakdown of pyruvate, (3) the citric acid cycle, and (4) oxidative phosphorylation (**Figure 7.10**).

1. In glycolysis, glucose (6 C, meaning a compound with six carbon atoms) is broken down in the cytosol to two pyruvate molecules (3 C each), producing a net gain of two ATP molecules, via substrate-level phosphorylation, and two NADH molecules. In eukaryotes, glycolysis occurs in the cytosol.

Figure 7.10 **An overview of cellular respiration.** (1) Glycolysis occurs in the cytosol and results in the oxidation of glucose into two pyruvates, producing two ATP and two NADH molecules. The two pyruvates enter the mitochondrial matrix (2), where they are oxidized, thereby producing two acetyl groups (each attached to CoA) and two CO_2 molecules. Two molecules of NADH are made in the process. (3) The two acetyl groups then enter the citric acid cycle, where they are incorporated into organic molecules. Four CO_2 molecules are then released and two ATP, six NADH, and two $FADH_2$ are synthesized. (4) Oxidative phosphorylation occurs along the cristae, which are formed from inner mitochondrial membrane. The NADH and $FADH_2$ molecules that are made during these various steps are then used during oxidative phosphorylation to synthesize more ATP molecules. The maximum yield of ATP is 34 to 38 molecules for every glucose that is completely broken down.

Concept check: *The breakdown of glucose produces a lot of NADH. What is NADH mostly used for?*

2. In the breakdown of pyruvate to an acetyl group, the two pyruvate molecules enter the mitochondrion, where each one is broken down to an acetyl group (2 C) and one CO_2 molecule. For each pyruvate broken down via oxidation, one NADH molecule is made by the reduction of NAD^+.

3. In the citric acid cycle, each acetyl group is incorporated into an organic molecule, which is later oxidized to liberate two CO_2 molecules. One ATP, three NADH, and one $FADH_2$ are made in this process. Because there are two acetyl groups (one from each pyruvate), the total yield is four CO_2, two ATP via substrate-level phosphorylation,

six NADH, and two $FADH_2$. This process occurs in the mitochondrial matrix.

4. In oxidative phosphorylation, the NADH and $FADH_2$ made in the three previous stages contain high-energy electrons that can be readily transferred in a redox reaction to other molecules. Once removed from NADH or $FADH_2$, these high-energy electrons release some energy; through an electron transport chain, that energy is harnessed to produce an H^+ electrochemical gradient. In chemiosmosis, energy stored in the H^+ electrochemical gradient is used to synthesize ATP from ADP and P_i. The overall process of electron transport

Figure 7.11 Overview of glycolysis.

BioConnections: *Look ahead to Table 45.1. With regard to oxygen needs, what is an advantage of glycolytic muscle fibers?*

Figure 7.12 **A detailed look at the steps of glycolysis.** The pathway begins with a six-carbon molecule (glucose), which is eventually broken down into two molecules that contain three carbons each. The notation × 2 in the figure indicates that two of these three-carbon molecules are produced from each glucose molecule.

Principle: *Living organisms have mechanisms that maintain homeostasis. To maintain a relatively constant level of ATP in the cytosol, the activity of phosphofructokinase is controlled by feedback inhibition. A high level of ATP inhibits its function.*

and ATP synthesis is called **oxidative phosphorylation** because NADH and $FADH_2$ have been oxidized and ADP has become phosphorylated to make ATP. Approximately 30 to 34 ATP molecules are made via oxidative phosphorylation for each glucose molecule consumed. In eukaryotes, oxidation phosphorylation occurs along the cristae, which are invaginations of the inner mitochondrial membrane. The invaginations greatly increase the surface area of the inner membrane and thereby increase the amount of ATP that can be made. In Bacteria and Archaea, oxidative phosphorylation occurs along the plasma membrane.

Now let's examine in detail the chemical and enzymatic activities that take place in each of the four stages of cellular respiration.

Stage 1: Glycolysis Is a Metabolic Pathway That Breaks Down Glucose to Pyruvate

Glycolysis (from the Greek *glykos,* meaning "sweet," and *lysis,* meaning "splitting") involves the breakdown of glucose, a simple sugar. This process can occur in the presence or absence of oxygen; that is, under aerobic or anaerobic conditions. During the 1930s several German biochemists, including Gustav Embden, Otto Meyerhof, and Jacob Parnas, determined that the process involved 10 steps, each one catalyzed by a different enzyme. The elucidation of these steps was a major achievement in the field of biochemistry. Researchers have since discovered that glycolysis is the common pathway for glucose breakdown in Bacteria, Archaea, and Eukarya. Remarkably, the steps of glycolysis are virtually identical in nearly all living species, suggesting that glycolysis arose very early in the evolution of life on our planet.

The 10 steps of glycolysis are grouped into three phases (**Figure 7.11**). The first phase (steps 1–3) involves an energy investment. Two ATP molecules are hydrolyzed, and the phosphates from those ATP molecules are attached to glucose, which is converted to fructose-1,6-bisphosphate. The energy investment phase raises the free energy of glucose and thereby allows later reactions to be exergonic. The cleavage phase (steps 4–5) breaks the six-carbon molecule into two molecules of glyceraldehyde-3-phosphate. The third phase (steps 6–10) liberates energy. The two glyceraldehyde-3-phosphate molecules are broken down to two pyruvate molecules. This produces two molecules of NADH and four molecules of ATP. Because two molecules of ATP are used in the energy investment phase, the net yield of ATP is two molecules. **Figure 7.12**

6 Glyceraldehyde-3-phosphate is oxidized to 1,3-bisphosphoglycerate. NADH is produced. In 1,3-bisphosphoglycerate, the phosphate group in the upper left is destabilized, meaning that the bond will break in a highly exergonic reaction.

7 A phosphate is removed from 1,3-bisphosphoglycerate to form 3-phosphoglycerate. The removed phosphate is transferred to ADP to make ATP via substrate-level phosphorylation.

8 The phosphate group in 3-phosphoglycerate is moved to a new location, creating 2-phosphoglycerate.

9 A water molecule is removed from 2-phosphoglycerate to form phosphoenolpyruvate. In phosphoenolpyruvate, the phosphate group is destabilized, meaning that the bond will break in a highly exergonic reaction.

10 A phosphate is removed from phosphoenolpyruvate to form pyruvate. The removed phosphate is transferred to ADP to make ATP via substrate-level phosphorylation.

describes the details of the 10 reactions of glycolysis. The net reaction of glycolysis is

$$C_6H_{12}O_6 + 2\ NAD^+ + 2\ ADP^{2-} + 2\ P_i^{2-} \rightarrow$$
glucose

$$2\ CH_3(C{=}O)COO^- + 2\ H^+ + 2\ NADH + 2\ ATP^{4-} + 2\ H_2O$$
pyruvate

When a cell has a sufficient amount of ATP, feedback inhibition occurs in glycolysis. At high concentration, ATP binds to an allosteric site in phosphofructokinase, which catalyzes the third step in glycolysis and is thought to be the rate-limiting step. When ATP binds to this allosteric site, a conformational change occurs that renders the enzyme functionally inactive. This prevents the further breakdown of glucose and thereby inhibits the overproduction of ATP. Alternatively, if ADP binds to this enzyme, its function is stimulated, thereby increasing the rate of glycolysis.

Stage 2: Pyruvate Enters the Mitochondrion and Is Broken Down to an Acetyl Group and CO₂

In eukaryotes, glycolysis in the cytoplasm generates pyruvate, which is then transported into the mitochondrion. Once in the mitochondrial matrix (see Figure 4.26), pyruvate molecules are broken down by an enzyme complex called pyruvate dehydrogenase (**Figure 7.13**). A molecule of CO_2 is removed from each pyruvate and the remaining acetyl group is attached to an

organic molecule called coenzyme A (CoA) to create acetyl CoA. (In chemical equations, CoA is depicted as CoA-SH to emphasize how the SH group participates in the chemical reaction.) During this process, two high-energy electrons are removed from pyruvate and transferred to NAD^+ and together with H^+ create a molecule of NADH. For each pyruvate, the net reaction is

$$\begin{array}{cc} O & O \\ \parallel & \parallel \end{array}$$
$$^-O{-}C{-}C{-}CH_3 + CoA\text{-}SH + NAD^+ \rightarrow$$
Pyruvate   CoA

$$\begin{array}{c} O \\ \parallel \end{array}$$
$$CoA{-}S{-}C{-}CH_3 + CO_2 + NADH$$
Acetyl CoA

The acetyl group is attached to CoA via a covalent bond to a sulphur atom. The hydrolysis of this bond releases a large amount of free energy, making it possible for the acetyl group to be transferred to other organic molecules. As described next, the acetyl group attached to CoA enters the citric acid cycle.

Stage 3: During the Citric Acid Cycle, Reducing Power and ATP Are Generated and CO₂ Is Released

The third stage of sugar metabolism introduces a new concept: the **metabolic cycle**. During a metabolic cycle, particular molecules enter the cycle while others leave; the process is cyclical because it involves a series of organic molecules that are regenerated with each turn of the cycle. The idea of a metabolic cycle was first proposed in the early 1930s by German biochemist Hans Krebs. While studying carbohydrate metabolism, he analyzed cell extracts from pigeon muscle and determined that citric acid and other organic molecules participated in a cycle that resulted in the breakdown of carbohydrates to carbon dioxide. This cycle is called the **citric acid cycle** or the Krebs cycle, in honour of Krebs, who was awarded the Nobel Prize in 1953.

An overview of the citric acid cycle is shown in **Figure 7.14**. At the beginning of the cycle, the acetyl group is removed from acetyl CoA and attached to oxaloacetate (4 C) to form citrate (6 C), also called citric acid. In a series of steps, two CO_2 molecules are released. As this occurs, three molecules of NADH, one molecule of FADH₂, and one molecule of GTP are made. The GTP is used to make ATP. After eight steps, oxaloacetate is regenerated so that the cycle can begin again, provided acetyl CoA is available. **Figure 7.15** shows a more detailed view of the citric acid cycle. For each acetyl group attached to CoA, the net reaction of the citric acid cycle is as follows:

$$acetyl\text{-}CoA + 3\ H_2O + 3\ NAD^+ + FAD + GDP^{2-} + P_i^{2-} \rightarrow$$
$$CoA\text{-}SH + 2\ CO_2 + 3\ NADH + FADH_2 + GTP^{4-}$$

Regulation of the Citric Acid Cycle How is the citric acid cycle controlled? The rate of the cycle is largely regulated by the availability of substrates, such as acetyl-CoA and NAD^+,

Pyruvate is made in the cytosol by glycolysis. It travels through a channel in the outer membrane and an H^+/pyruvate symporter in the inner membrane to reach the mitochondrial matrix.

Pyruvate is oxidized via pyruvate dehydrogenase to an acetyl group and CO_2. NADH is made. During this process, the acetyl group is transferred to coenzyme A (CoA) and is later removed and enters the citric acid cycle.

Figure 7.13   Breakdown of pyruvate and the attachment of an acetyl group to CoA.   Pyruvate enters the mitochondrion by travelling through a channel in the outer membrane and then through an H^+/pyruvate symporter in the inner membrane.

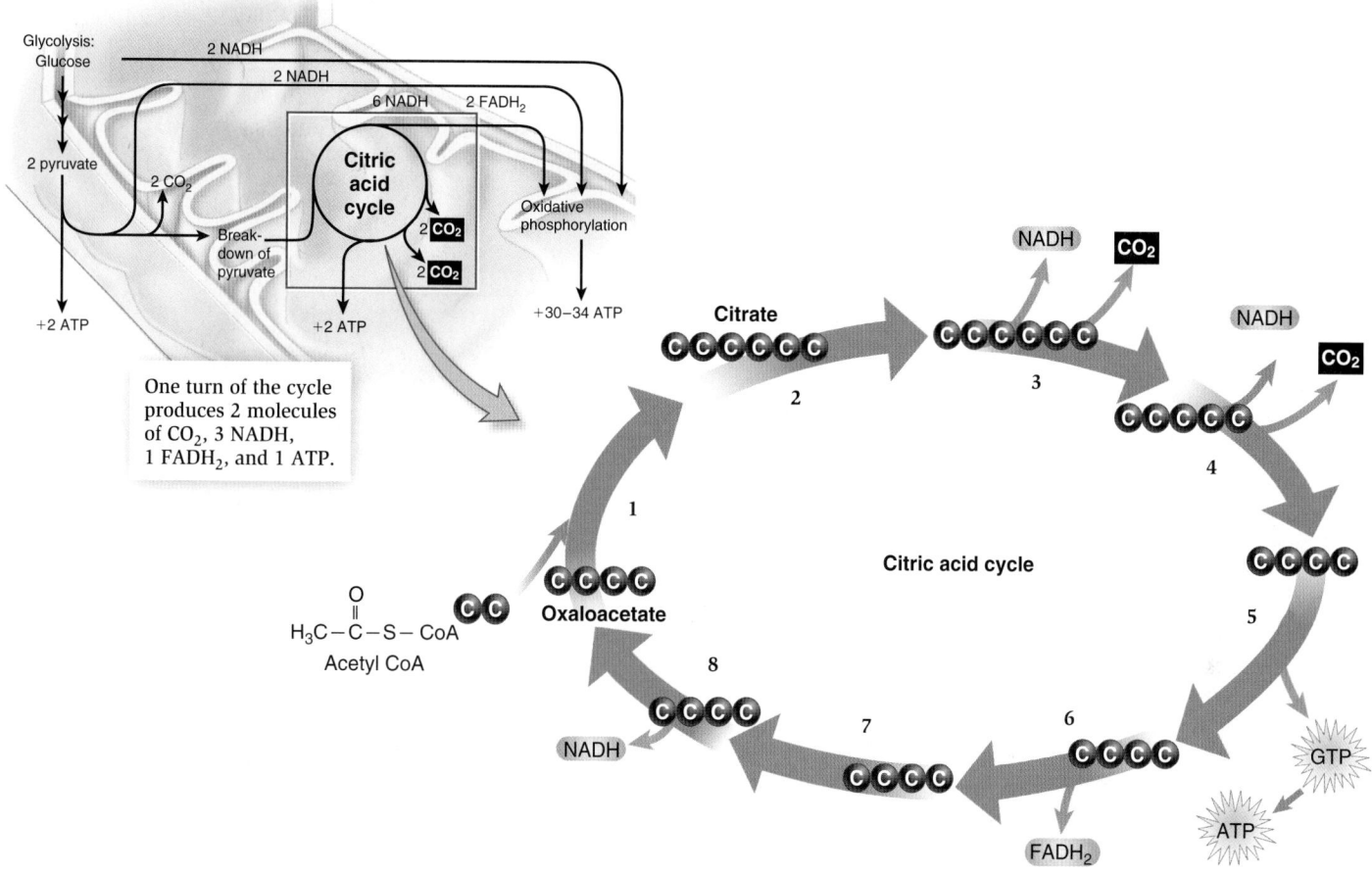

Figure 7.14 Overview of the citric acid cycle.

and by feedback inhibition. The three steps in the cycle that are highly exergonic are those catalyzed by citrate synthase, isocitrate dehydrogenase, and α-ketoglutarate dehydrogenase (Figure 7.15). Each of these steps can become rate-limiting under certain circumstances, and the way that each enzyme is regulated varies among different species. Let's consider an example. In mammals, NADH and ATP act as feedback inhibitors of isocitrate dehydrogenase, whereas NAD^+ and ADP act as activators. In this way, the citric acid cycle is inhibited when NADH and ATP levels are high, but it is stimulated when NAD^+ and ADP levels are high.

Stage 4: During Oxidative Phosphorylation, NADH and FADH$_2$ Are Used to Make More ATP

During the first three stages of glucose metabolism, the oxidation of glucose has yielded six molecules of CO_2, four molecules of ATP, 10 molecules of NADH, and two molecules of $FADH_2$. Let's now consider how high-energy electrons are removed from NADH and $FADH_2$ to make more ATP. This process is called oxidative phosphorylation because NADH and $FADH_2$ are oxidized through the removal of electrons, and ATP is made by the phosphorylation of ADP (**Figure 7.16**). Oxidative phosphorylation usually occurs under aerobic conditions, which means that

it typically requires oxygen. As described next, the oxidative process involves the electron transport chain, while the phosphorylation occurs via the ATP synthase.

The Electron Transport Chain Establishes an Electrochemical Gradient The **electron transport chain (ETC)** consists of a group of protein complexes and small organic molecules embedded in the inner mitochondrial membrane. These components are referred to as an electron transport chain because the components can accept and donate electrons to each other in a linear manner (Figure 7.16). Most of the members of the ETC are protein complexes (designated I to IV) that have prosthetic groups, which are small molecules attached to the surface of the proteins, that aid in their function. For example, cytochrome oxidase contains two prosthetic groups, each with an iron atom. The iron in each prosthetic group can readily accept and release an electron. One member of the electron transport chain, ubiquinone (Q), is not a protein. Rather, ubiquinone is a small organic molecule that can accept and release an electron and can diffuse through the lipid bilayer.

The red line in Figure 7.16 shows the path of electrons as they flow along the ETC. This path is a series of redox reactions in which electrons are transferred to components with

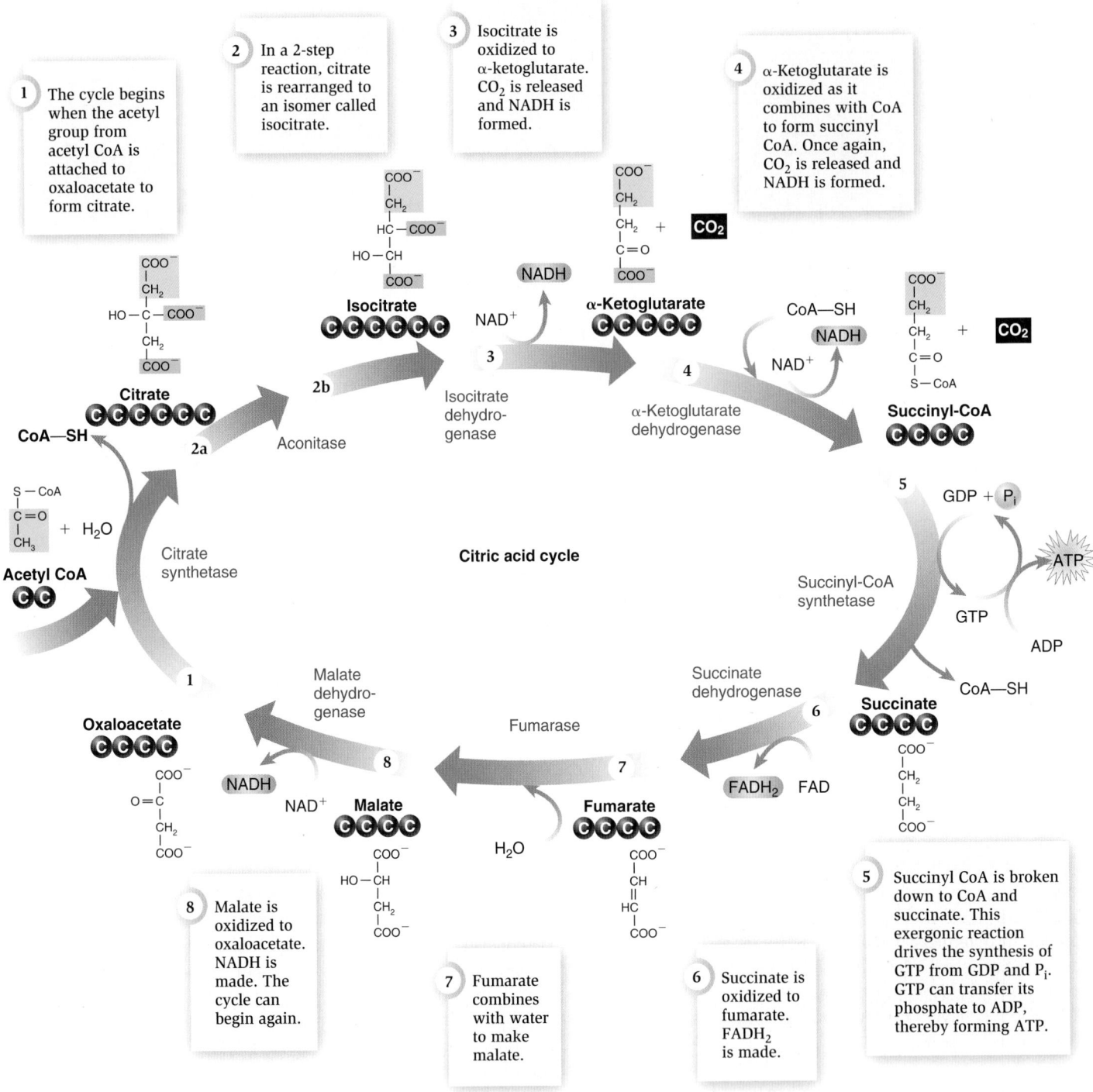

Figure 7.15 **A detailed look at the steps of the citric acid cycle.** The blue boxes indicate the location of the acetyl group which is oxidized at step 6. The green boxes indicate the locations where CO_2 molecules are removed.

increasingly higher electronegativity. As discussed in Chapter 2, electronegativity is a measure of an atom's ability to attract electrons. At the beginning of the chain, a pair of high-energy electrons from NADH are transferred one at a time to NADH dehydrogenase (complex I), and then to ubiquinone (Q), cytochrome b-c_1 (complex III), cytochrome c, cytochrome oxidase (complex IV), and finally O_2. At the end of the chain, two electrons, $2H^+$, and $\frac{1}{2}O_2$ combine to form a molecule of water.

Similarly, $FADH_2$ transfers electrons to succinate reductase (complex II), and electrons then move along the electron transport chain, ultimately to oxygen.

The electron transport chain is also called the **respiratory chain** because the oxygen we breathe is used in this process. One component of the electron transport chain, cytochrome oxidase (complex IV), is inhibited by both carbon monoxide and cyanide. The deadly effects of these poisons occur because

1a NADH is oxidized to NAD^+. High-energy electrons are transferred to NADH dehydrogenase. Some of the energy is harnessed to pump H^+ into the intermembrane space. Electrons are then transferred to ubiquinone.

1b $FADH_2$ is oxidized to FAD. High-energy electrons are transferred to succinate reductase and then to ubiquinone.

2 From ubiquinone, electrons travel to cytochrome b-c_1. Some of the energy is harnessed to pump H^+ into the intermembrane space. Electrons are transferred to cytochrome c.

3 From cytochrome c, electrons are transferred to cytochrome oxidase. Some of the energy is harnessed to pump H^+ into the intermembrane space. Electrons are transferred to oxygen, and water is produced.

4 Steps 1–3 produce a H^+ electrochemical gradient. As H^+ flow down their electrochemical gradient into the matrix through ATP synthase, the energy within this gradient causes the synthesis of ATP from ADP and P_i.

KEY
- - - - H^+ movement
——— e^- movement

NADH dehydrogenase

NADH

NAD^+ + H^+

Succinate reductase

$FADH_2$

FAD + 2 H^+

Q Ubiquinone

Cytochrome b-c_1

Matrix

Cytochrome c

c

2 H^+ + ½ O_2

Cytochrome oxidase

H_2O

H^+

ADP + P_i

ATP

Inner mitochondrial membrane

Matrix

Intermembrane space

Electron transport chain

ATP synthase

Intermembrane space

Figure 7.16 **Oxidative phosphorylation.** This process consists of two distinct events involving the electron transport chain and the ATP synthase. The electron transport chain removes electrons from NADH or $FADH_2$ and pumps H^+ across the inner mitochondrial membrane. In chemiosmosis, ATP synthase uses the energy in this H^+ electrochemical gradient to phosphorylate ADP and thereby synthesize ATP. In this figure, an O_2 atom is represented as ½O_2 to emphasize that the electron transport chain reduces oxygen when it is in its molecular (O_2) form.

Concept check: *Can you explain the name of cytochrome oxidase? Can you think of another appropriate name?*

the electron transport chain is shut down, preventing cells from making enough ATP for survival.

As shown in Figure 7.16, the movement of electrons results in the pumping of H$^+$ across the inner mitochondrial membrane to establish a large **H$^+$ electrochemical gradient** in which the concentration of H$^+$ is higher outside the matrix, and an excess of positive charge exists outside the matrix. Because hydrogen ions consist of protons, the H$^+$ electrochemical gradient is also called the **proton-motive force**. NADH dehydrogenase, cytochrome b-c$_1$, and cytochrome oxidase are H$^+$ pumps. While travelling along the electron transport chain, electrons release free energy, and some of this energy is captured by these proteins to pump H$^+$ out of the matrix into the intermembrane space. Because the electrons from FADH$_2$ enter the chain at an intermediate step, fewer hydrogen ions are pumped out of the matrix compared with the release of electrons from NADH.

Why do electrons travel from NADH or FADH$_2$ to O$_2$? As you might expect, the answer lies in free energy changes and electronegativity of the respiratory complexes. The electrons found on the energy intermediates have a high amount of potential energy. As they travel along the electron transport chain to acceptors of higher electronegativity, free energy is released (**Figure 7.17**). The movement of one electron from NADH to O$_2$ results in a very negative free energy change of approximately −25 kcal/mol. That is why the process is spontaneous and proceeds in the forward direction. The movement of electrons is a highly exergonic reaction, and some of the free energy released can be harnessed to do cellular work. In this case, some energy is used to pump H$^+$ across the inner mitochondrial membrane and establish an H$^+$ electrochemical gradient that is then used to power ATP synthesis.

Figure 7.17 The relationship between free energy and electron movement along the electron transport chain. As electrons hop from one site to another along the electron transport chain, they release energy. Some of this energy is harnessed to pump H$^+$ across the inner mitochondrial membrane. The total energy released by a single electron is approximately −25 kcal/mol.

ATP Synthase Makes ATP via Chemiosmosis The second event of oxidative phosphorylation is the synthesis of ATP by an enzyme called **ATP synthase**. The H$^+$ electrochemical gradient across the inner mitochondrial membrane is a source of potential energy. How is this energy used? The flow of H$^+$ back into the matrix is an exergonic process. The lipid bilayer is relatively impermeable to H$^+$. However, H$^+$ can pass through the membrane-embedded portion of the ATP synthase. This enzyme harnesses some of the free energy that is released as the ions flow through its membrane-embedded region to synthesize ATP from ADP and P$_i$ (see Figure 7.16). This is an example of an energy conversion: energy in the form of an H$^+$ electrochemical gradient, or proton-motive force, is converted to chemical bond energy in ATP. The chemical synthesis of ATP by pushing H$^+$ across a membrane is called chemiosmosis (from the Greek *osmos*, meaning "to push"). The theory behind it was proposed by Peter Mitchell, a British chemist who was awarded the Nobel Prize in 1978.

For each molecule of NADH that is oxidized and each molecule of ATP that is made, the two chemical reactions of oxidative phosphorylation can be represented as follows:

$$NADH + H^+ + \frac{1}{2} O_2 \rightarrow NAD^+ + H_2O$$
$$ADP^{2-} + P_i^{2-} \rightarrow ATP^{4-} + H_2O$$

The oxidation of NADH to NAD$^+$ results in an H$^+$ electrochemical gradient in which more hydrogen ions are in the intermembrane space compared with the matrix. The synthesis of one ATP molecule is thought to require the movement of three to four ions into the matrix, down their H$^+$ electrochemical gradient.

When we add up the maximal amount of ATP that can be made by oxidative phosphorylation, most researchers agree that it is in the range of 30 to 34 ATP molecules for each glucose molecule that is broken down to CO$_2$ and water. However, the maximum amount of ATP is rarely achieved for two reasons. First, although 10 NADH and 2 FADH$_2$ are available to create the H$^+$ electrochemical gradient across the inner mitochondrial membrane, a cell may use some of these molecules for anabolic pathways. For example, NADH is used in the synthesis of organic molecules, such as glycerol (a component of phospholipids) and lactic acid (which is secreted from muscle cells during strenuous exercise). Second, the mitochondrion may use some of the H$^+$ electrochemical gradient for other purposes. For example, the gradient is used for the uptake of pyruvate into the matrix via an H$^+$/pyruvate symporter. Therefore, the actual amount of ATP synthesis is understandably less than the maximum number of 30 to 34. Even so, by comparing the amount of ATP that can be made by glycolysis (2), the citric acid cycle (2), and oxidative phosphorylation (30–34), we see that oxidative phosphorylation provides a cell with a much greater capacity to make ATP.

Experiments with Purified Proteins in Membrane Vesicles Verified Chemiosmosis

To show experimentally that the ATP synthase actually uses an H$^+$ electrochemical gradient to make ATP, researchers needed to purify the enzyme and study its function in vitro. In 1974

Ephraim Racker and Walther Stoeckenius purified the ATP synthase and another protein called bacteriorhodopsin, which is found in certain species of Archaea. Previous research had shown that bacteriorhodopsin is a light-driven H^+ pump. Racker and Stoeckenius took both purified proteins and inserted them into membrane vesicles (**Figure 7.18**). The ATP synthase was oriented so that its ATP synthesizing region was on the outside of the vesicles. Bacteriorhodopsin was oriented so that it would pump H^+ into the vesicles. They added ADP and P_i on the outside of the vesicles. In the dark, no ATP was made. However, when they shone light on the vesicles, a substantial amount of ATP was made. Because bacteriorhodopsin was already known to be a light-driven H^+ pump, these results convinced researchers that the ATP synthase uses an H^+ electrochemical gradient as an energy source to make ATP.

1 ATP synthase and bacteriorhodopsin were incorporated into membrane vesicles.

ATP synthase

Vesicle

Bacteriorhodopsin (light-driven H^+ pump)

2 ADP and P_i were added on the outside of the vesicles.

ADP

P_i

3a One sample was kept in the dark. No ATP was made.

No H^+ gradient

3b One sample was exposed to light. ATP was made.

Light rays

H^+ gradient

ATP

Figure 7.18 The Racker and Stoeckenius experiment showing that an H^+ electrochemical gradient drives ATP synthesis via the ATP synthase.

Concept check: *Is the functioning of the electron transport chain always needed to make ATP via the ATP synthase?*

The ATP Synthase Is a Rotary Machine That Makes ATP as It Spins

The structure and function of the ATP synthase are particularly intriguing and have received much attention over the past few decades (**Figure 7.19**). The ATP synthase is a rotary machine. The region embedded in the membrane is composed of three types of subunits called *a*, *b*, and *c*. Approximately 10 to 14 *c* subunits form a ring in the membrane. Each *c* subunit is an H^+ channel. One *a* subunit is bound to this ring, and two *b* subunits are attached to the a subunit and protrude out of the membrane. The non-membrane-embedded subunits are designated with Greek letters. One ε and one γ subunit bind to the ring of *c* subunits. The γ subunit forms a long stalk that pokes into the centre of another ring of three α and three β subunits. The β subunits are the catalytic site where ATP is made. Finally, the δ subunit forms a connection between the ring of α and β subunits and the two *b* subunits.

When hydrogen ions pass through a narrow channel at the contact site between a *c* subunit and the *a* subunit, a conformational change causes the γ subunit to turn clockwise (when viewed from the intermembrane space). Each time the γ subunit turns 120 degrees it changes its contacts with the three β subunits, which in turn causes the β subunits to change their conformations. How do these conformational changes promote ATP synthesis? The answer is that the conformational changes occur in a way that favours ATP synthesis and release. As shown in **Figure 7.20**, the conformational changes in the β subunits happen in the following order:

- Conformation 1: ADP and P_i bind with good affinity.
- Conformation 2: ADP and P_i bind so tightly that ATP is made.
- Conformation 3: ATP (and ADP and P_i) bind very weakly, and ATP is released.

The nonmembrane-embedded portion consists of 1 ε, 1 γ, 1 δ, 3 α, and 3 β subunits. Movement of H^+ between a *c* subunit and the *a* subunit causes the γ subunit to rotate. The rotation, in 120° increments, causes the β subunits to progress through a series of 3 conformational changes that lead to the synthesis of ATP from ADP and P_i.

The membrane-embedded portion consists of a ring of 9–12 *c* subunits, 1 *a* subunit, and 2 *b* subunits. H^+ move between the *c* and *a* subunits.

ADP + P_i

ATP

δ

b

α

β

α

H^+ Matrix

γ

ε

c   *c*   *c*

a

Intermembrane space

H^+

Figure 7.19 The subunit structure and function of the ATP synthase.

Conformation 1: ADP and P_i bind with good affinity.

Conformation 2: ADP and P_i bind so tightly that ATP is made.

Conformation 3: ATP binds very weakly and is released.

β Subunit

ADP + P_i

β Subunit

β Subunit

Rotation of the γ subunit

Rotation of the γ subunit

Rotation of the γ subunit

Figure 7.20 **Conformational changes that result in ATP synthesis.** For simplicity, the α subunits are not shown. This figure emphasizes the conformational changes in the β subunit shown at the top. The other two β subunits also make ATP. All three β subunits alternate between three conformational states because of their interactions with the γ subunit.

FEATURE INVESTIGATION

Yoshida and Kinosita Demonstrated That the γ Subunit of the ATP Synthase Spins

In 1997 Masasuke Yoshida, Kazuhiko Kinosita, and their colleagues set out to experimentally visualize the rotary nature of the ATP synthase (**Figure 7.21**). The membrane-embedded region of the ATP synthase can be separated from the rest of the protein by treatment of mitochondrial membranes with a high concentration of salt, releasing the portion of the protein containing the one γ, three α, and three β subunits. The researchers adhered the $\gamma\alpha_3\beta_3$ complex to a glass slide so that the γ subunit was protruding upward. Because the γ subunit is too small to be seen with a light microscope, it is not possible to

visualize the rotation of the γ subunit directly. To circumvent this problem, the researchers attached a large, fluorescently labelled actin filament to the γ subunit via a linker protein. The fluorescently labelled actin filament is very long compared with the γ subunit and can be readily seen with a fluorescence microscope.

Because the membrane-embedded portion of the protein was missing, the researchers added ATP to get the γ subunit to rotate. Although the normal function of the ATP synthase is to make ATP, it can run backward. In other words, the ATP synthase can hydrolyze ATP. As shown in the data for Figure 7.21, when the researchers added ATP, the fluorescently labelled actin filament was observed to rotate counterclockwise, which

HYPOTHESIS ATP synthase is a rotary machine.

KEY MATERIALS Purified complex containing 1 γ, 3 α, and 3 β subunits.

Experimental level   Conceptual level

1   Adhere the purified $\gamma\alpha_3\beta_3$ complex to a glass slide so the base of the γ subunit is protruding upward.

Add purified complex.

γ

$\gamma\alpha_3\beta_3$ complex

α   β   α

Slide

2   Add linker proteins and fluorescently labelled actin filaments. The linker protein recognizes sites on both the γ subunit and the actin filament.

Add linker proteins and fluorescent actin filaments.

γ   Linker proteins

Fluorescent actin filament

α   β   α

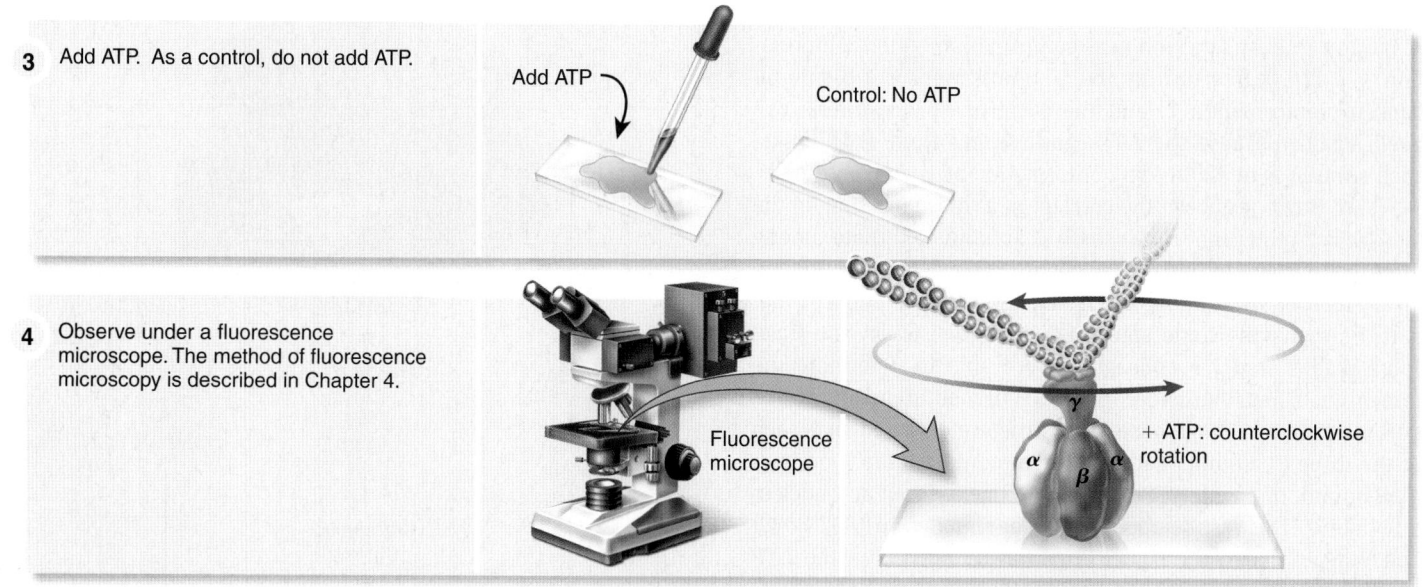

3 Add ATP. As a control, do not add ATP.

Add ATP

Control: No ATP

4 Observe under a fluorescence microscope. The method of fluorescence microscopy is described in Chapter 4.

Fluorescence microscope

+ ATP: counterclockwise rotation

γ

α β α

5 **THE DATA**

Results from step 4:

ATP	Rotation
No ATP added	No rotation observed.
ATP added	Rotation was observed as shown below. This is a time-lapse view of the rotation in action.

Row 1

Row 2

6 **CONCLUSION** The γ subunit rotates counterclockwise when ATP is hydrolyzed. It would be expected to rotate clockwise when ATP is synthesized.

7 **SOURCE** Reprinted by permission from Macmillan Publishers Ltd. Noji, H., Yasuda, R.,Yoshida, M., and Kinosita, K. 1997. Direct observation of the rotation of F_1-ATPase. *Nature* 386:299–303.

Figure 7.21 Evidence that the ATP synthase is a rotary machine.

is opposite to the direction that the γ subunit rotates when ATP is synthesized. In fact, actin filaments were observed to make more than 100 revolutions in the presence of ATP. These results convinced the scientific community that the ATP synthase is indeed a rotary machine.

Experimental Questions

1. The components of the ATP synthase are too small to be visualized by light microscopy. For the experiment in Figure 7.21, how did the researchers observe the movement of the ATP synthase?

2. In the experiment in Figure 7.21, what observation did the researchers make that indicated that the ATP synthase is a rotary machine? What was the control of this experiment? What did it indicate?

3. Were the rotations seen by the researchers in the data of Figure 7.21 moving in the same direction as expected in the mitochondria during ATP synthesis? Why or why not?

Each time the γ subunit turns 120 degrees, it causes a β subunit to change to the next conformation. After conformation 3, a 120-degree turn by the γ subunit returns a β subunit back to conformation 1, and the cycle of ATP synthesis can begin again. Because the ATP synthase has three β subunits, each subunit is in a different conformation at any given time.

Paul Boyer proposed the concept of a rotary machine in the late 1970s. In his model the three β subunits alternate among three conformations, as described previously. Boyer's original idea was met with great skepticism, because the concept that part of an enzyme could spin was very novel, to say the least. John Walker and his colleagues were able to determine the three-dimensional structure of the non-membrane-embedded portion of the ATP synthase. The structure revealed that each of the three β subunits had a different conformation: one with ADP bound, one with ATP bound, and one without any nucleotide bound. This result supported Boyer's model. In 1997 Boyer and Walker shared the Nobel Prize for their work on the ATP synthase. As described in the Feature Investigation, researchers subsequently visualized the rotation of the γ subunit.

Metabolic Pathways for Carbohydrate Metabolism Are Interconnected to Pathways for Amino Acid and Fat Metabolism

Thus far, we have focused our attention on the stages of glucose breakdown that result in the release of CO_2 and the production of NADH, $FADH_2$, and ATP. In addition, cells use other organic molecules as a source of energy. When you eat a meal, it is likely to contain not only carbohydrates (including glucose) but also proteins and fats. Proteins and fats are also broken down by the enzymes involved with glucose metabolism.

As shown in **Figure 7.22**, proteins and fats can enter into glycolysis, or the citric acid cycle, at different points. Proteins are first acted on by enzymes, either in digestive juices or within cells, that cleave the bonds connecting individual amino acids. Because the 20 amino acids differ in their side chains, amino acids and their breakdown products can enter at different points in the pathway. Breakdown products of amino acids can enter glycolysis, or an acetyl group can be removed from certain amino acids and become attached to CoA. Other amino acids can be modified and enter the citric acid cycle. Similarly, fats can be broken down to glycerol and fatty acids. Glycerol can be modified to glyceraldehyde-3-phosphate and enter glycolysis at step 5 (see Figure 7.12). Fatty acyl tails can have two carbon acetyl units removed, which bind to CoA, and then enter the citric acid cycle. By using the same pathways for the breakdown of sugars, amino acids, and fats, cells are more efficient because they can use the same enzymes for the breakdown of different starting molecules.

Likewise, carbohydrate metabolism is connected to the metabolism of other cellular components at the anabolic level. Cells can use carbohydrates to manufacture parts of amino acids, fats, and nucleotides. For example, glucose-6-phosphate of glycolysis is used to construct the sugar and phosphate portion of nucleotides, while oxaloacetate of the citric acid cycle

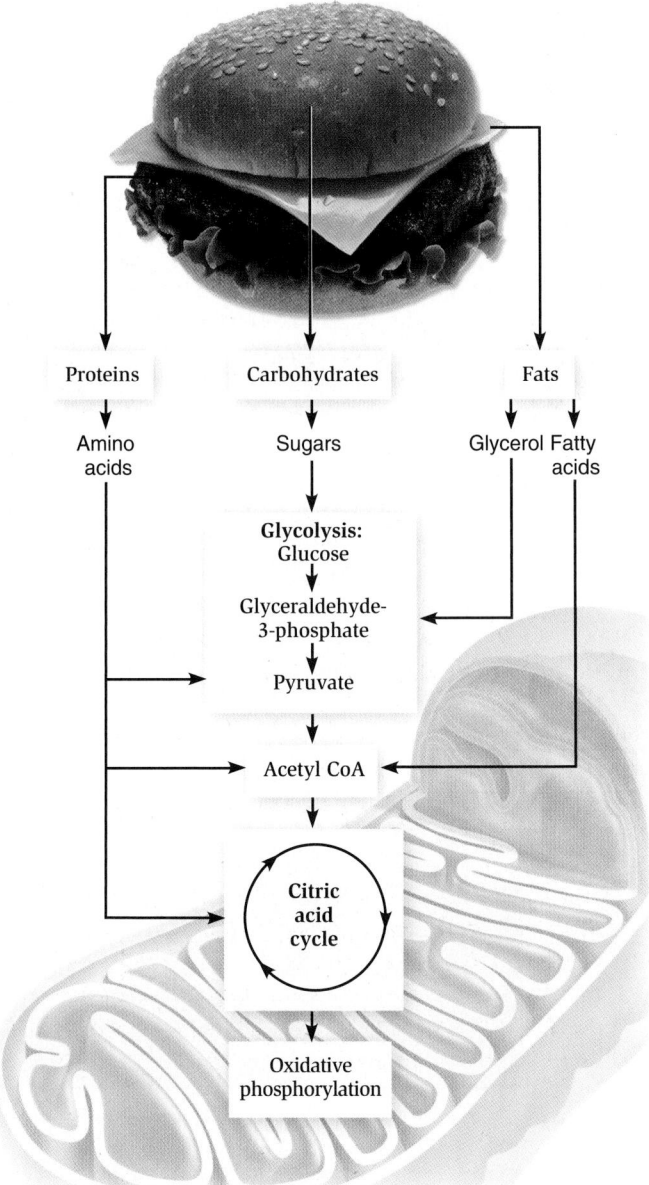

Figure 7.22 Integration of protein, carbohydrate, and fat metabolism.   Breakdown products of amino acids and fats can enter the same pathway that is used to break down carbohydrates. The energy densities (in kcal/g) of fats, proteins, and carbohydrates are 9, 4, and 4, respectively.

Concept check: *What is a cellular advantage of integrating protein, carbohydrate, and fat metabolism? Why are fats more energy dense than proteins or carbohydrates?*

can be used as a precursor for the biosynthesis of purine and pyrimidine bases. Portions of amino acids can be made from products of glycolysis (for example, pyruvate) and components of the citric acid cycle (oxaloacetate). In addition, many other catabolic and anabolic pathways are found in living cells that connect the metabolism of carbohydrates, proteins, fats, and nucleic acids.

7.4 ANAEROBIC RESPIRATION AND FERMENTATION

Learning Outcomes:

1. Describe how certain microorganisms make ATP by using a final electron acceptor of their electron transport chain that is not oxygen.
2. Explain how muscle and yeast cells use fermentation to synthesize ATP under anaerobic conditions.

Thus far, we have surveyed catabolic pathways that result in the complete breakdown of glucose in the presence of oxygen. Cells also commonly metabolize organic molecules in the absence of oxygen. The term **anaerobic** is used to describe an environment that lacks oxygen. Some microorganisms, such as bacteria and fungi, exist in anaerobic environments but still have to oxidize organic molecules to obtain sufficient amounts of energy. Examples include microbes living in the intestinal tract and those living deep in the soil. Similarly, when a person exercises strenuously, the rate of oxygen consumption by muscle cells may greatly exceed the rate of oxygen delivery. Under these conditions, the muscle cells become anaerobic and must obtain sufficient energy in the absence of oxygen to maintain their level of activity.

Organisms have evolved two different strategies to metabolize organic molecules in the absence of oxygen, a process called **anaerobic respiration**. One mechanism is to use a substance other than O_2 as the final electron acceptor of an electron transport chain. A second approach is to produce ATP only via substrate-level phosphorylation. In this section we will consider examples of both strategies.

Figure 7.23 An example of anaerobic respiration in *E. coli.* When oxygen is absent, *E. coli* can use nitrate instead of oxygen as the final electron acceptor in an electron transport chain. This generates an H^+ electrochemical gradient that is used to make ATP via chemiosmosis. Note: As shown in this figure, ubiquinone (Q) picks up H^+ on one side of the membrane and deposits it on the other side. A similar event happens during aerobic respiration in mitochondria (described in Figure 7.16), except that ubiquinone transfers H^+ to cytochrome b-c_1, which pumps it into the intermembrane space.

Some Microorganisms Carry Out Anaerobic Respiration

At the end of the electron transport chain discussed earlier in Figure 7.16, cytochrome oxidase recognizes O_2 and catalyzes its reduction to H_2O. The final electron acceptor of the chain is O_2. Many species of bacteria that live under anaerobic conditions have evolved enzymes that function similarly to cytochrome oxidase but recognize molecules other than O_2 and use them as the final electron acceptor.

For example, *Escherichia coli*, a bacterial species found in your intestinal tract, produces an enzyme called nitrate reductase under anaerobic conditions. This enzyme uses nitrate (NO_3^-) as the final electron acceptor of an electron transport chain. **Figure 7.23** shows a simplified electron transport chain in *E. coli* in which nitrate is the final electron acceptor. In *E. coli* and other bacterial species, the electron transport chain is in the plasma membrane (also called the cytoplasmic or inner membrane). Electrons travel from NADH to NADH dehydrogenase to ubiquinone (Q) to cytochrome b and then to nitrate reductase. At the end of the chain, nitrate is converted to nitrite (NO_2^-).

This process generates an H^+ electrochemical gradient in three ways. First, NADH dehydrogenase pumps H^+ out of the cytoplasm. Second, ubiquinone picks up H^+ in the cytoplasm and carries it to the other side of the membrane. Third, the synthesis of nitrate consumes H^+ ions in the cytoplasm. The generation of an H^+ gradient via these three processes allows *E. coli* cells to make ATP via chemiosmosis under anaerobic conditions.

Fermentation Is the Breakdown of Organic Molecules without Net Oxidation

Many organisms, including animals and yeast, can use only O_2 as the final electron acceptor of their electron transport chains. When confronted with anaerobic conditions, these organisms must have a different way of producing sufficient ATP. One strategy is to make ATP via glycolysis, which can occur under anaerobic or aerobic conditions. Under anaerobic conditions, the cells do not use the citric acid cycle or the electron transport chain but make ATP only via glycolysis.

A key issue is that glycolysis requires NAD⁺ and generates NADH. Under aerobic conditions, oxygen acts as a final electron acceptor, and the high-energy electrons from NADH can be used to make more ATP. To make ATP, NADH is oxidized to NAD⁺. However, this cannot occur under anaerobic conditions in yeast and animals and, as a result, NADH builds up and NAD⁺ decreases. This is a potential problem for two reasons. First, at high concentrations, NADH will haphazardly donate its electrons to other molecules and promote the formation of free radicals, highly reactive chemicals that can damage DNA and cellular proteins. For this reason, yeast and animal cells that are exposed to anaerobic conditions must have a way to remove the excess NADH generated from the breakdown of glucose. The second problem is the decrease in NAD⁺. Cells need to regenerate NAD⁺ to keep glycolysis running and make ATP via substrate-level phosphorylation.

How do muscle cells cope with the buildup of NADH and decrease in NAD⁺? When a muscle is working strenuously and becomes anaerobic, as in high-intensity exercise, the pyruvate from glycolysis is reduced to make lactate. (The uncharged, or protonated, form is called lactic acid.) The electrons to reduce pyruvate are derived from NADH, which is oxidized to NAD⁺ (**Figure 7.24a**). Therefore, this process decreases NADH and reduces its potentially harmful effects. It also increases the levels of NAD⁺, thereby allowing glycolysis to continue. The lactate is secreted from muscle cells. Once sufficient oxygen is restored, the lactate produced during strenuous exercise can be taken up by cells, converted back to pyruvate, and used for energy, or it may be used by the liver and other tissues to make glucose.

Yeast cells can cope with anaerobic conditions differently. During wine making, a yeast cell metabolizes sugar under anaerobic conditions. The pyruvate is broken down to CO_2 and a two-carbon molecule called acetaldehyde. The acetaldehyde is then reduced to make ethanol while NADH is oxidized to NAD⁺ (**Figure 7.24b**). Similar to lactate production in muscle cells, this decreases NADH and increases NAD⁺, thereby preventing the harmful effects of NADH and allowing glycolysis to continue.

The term **fermentation** is used to describe the breakdown of organic molecules to harness energy without any net oxidation (that is, without any removal of electrons). The breakdown of glucose to lactate or ethanol is an example of fermentation. Although electrons are removed from an organic molecule, such as glucose, to make pyruvate and NADH, the electrons are donated back to an organic molecule in the production of lactate or ethanol. Therefore, no net removal of electrons from an organic molecule occurs. Compared with oxidative phosphorylation, fermentation produces far less ATP for two reasons. First, glucose is not oxidized completely to CO_2 and water.

Glucose is oxidized to 2 pyruvate molecules. Two pyruvates are reduced to 2 lactate molecules.

(a) Production of lactic acid

Glucose is oxidized to 2 pyruvate molecules. Two acetaldehyde molecules are reduced to 2 ethanol molecules.

(b) Production of ethanol

Figure 7.24 Examples of fermentation. In these examples, NADH is produced by the oxidation of an organic molecule, and then the NADH is used up by donating electrons to a different organic molecule, such as pyruvate **(a)** or acetaldehyde **(b)**.

Second, the NADH that is made during glycolysis cannot be used to make more ATP. Overall, the complete breakdown of glucose in the presence of oxygen yields 34 to 38 ATP molecules. By comparison, the anaerobic breakdown of glucose to lactate or ethanol yields only two ATP molecules.

7.5 / SECONDARY METABOLISM

Learning Outcomes:

1. Explain why many plants have evolved to produce secondary metabolites.

Primary metabolism is the synthesis and breakdown of molecules and macromolecules that are found in all forms of life and are essential for cell structure and function. These include such compounds as lipids, sugars, nucleotides, and amino acids and the macromolecules that are derived from them. Cellular respiration, which you learned about earlier in this chapter, is an example of primary metabolism. By comparison, **secondary metabolism** involves the synthesis of molecules—**secondary metabolites**—that are not essential for cell structure and growth. Any given secondary metabolite is unique to one species or group of species and is not usually required for survival. Secondary metabolites, also called secondary compounds, are commonly made in plants, bacteria, and fungi, where they play a variety of roles. Many secondary metabolites taste or smell bad. When produced in a plant, for example, such a molecule can prevent animals from eating the plant. In some cases, secondary metabolites are toxic. Such molecules can act as a chemical weapon that inhibits the growth of nearby organisms. In addition, many secondary metabolites produce a strong smell or bright colour that attracts or repels other organisms. For example, the scent of a rose is due to secondary metabolites, and the scent attracts insects that aid in pollination.

Biologists have discovered thousands of different secondary metabolites, though any given species tends to produce only one or a few types. As you will learn, many of these have been put to practical use by humans, including the spices that are used in cooking, phytochemicals that are used as pharmacological drugs, and antibiotics that inhibit the growth of pathogenic microorganisms. Plants are particularly diverse in the types of secondary metabolites they produce, perhaps because they need clever ways to defend themselves. Bacteria and fungi also produce a large array of these compounds, while animals tend to produce relatively few. You may have seen the 1992 movie *Medicine Man* starring Sean Connery as a scientist who travels the world looking for plants that might hold the cure for cancer. In a similar vein, the late Neil Towers of the University of British Columbia had a long and distinguished career of investigating secondary metabolites in many plants and microorganisms for their phytoprotectant and pharmacological properties. In this section we will survey four categories of secondary metabolites: phenolics, alkaloids, terpenoids, and polyketides.

Phenolic Compounds Are Antioxidants That Have Intense Flavours and Bright Colours

The **phenolic** compounds all contain a cyclic ring of carbon with three double bonds, known as a benzene ring, within their structure. When a benzene ring is covalently linked to a single hydroxyl group, the compound is known as phenol.

Phenol is the simplest of the phenolic compounds, though free phenol is not significantly accumulated in living organisms. However, more complex molecules that are derived from phenol are made in cells. Such phenolic compounds are synthesized by using the side groups of the amino acids phenylalanine (which has a benzene ring) or tyrosine (which has a phenol ring). Common categories of phenolics are the flavonoids, tannins, and lignins. The tannins and lignins are large polymeric molecules composed of many phenolic units.

Flavonoids are produced by many plant species and create a variety of flavours and smells. These can play a role as deterrents to eating a plant or as attractants that promote pollination. The flavours of chocolate and vanilla largely come from a mixture of flavonoid molecules. Vanilla is produced by several species of perennial vines of the genus *Vanilla* native to Mexico and tropical America (**Figure 7.25a**). The primary source of commercial vanilla comes from *V. planifolia.* Vanilla extract is obtained from the seed capsules. Another role of flavonoids is pigmentation. Anthocyanins (from the Greek *anthos,* meaning "flower," and *kyanos,* meaning "blue") produce the red, purple, and blue colours of many flowers, fruits, and vegetables (**Figure 7.25b**).

Biochemists have discovered that flavonoids have remarkable antioxidant properties that prevent the formation of damaging free radicals. In plants, flavonoids are thought to act as powerful antioxidants, helping to protect plants from ultraviolet (UV) damage. In recent times, nutritionists have advocated the consumption of fruits and vegetables that have high amounts of flavonoids, such as broccoli and spinach. Dark chocolate is also rich in these antioxidants.

Tannins are large phenolic polymers, so named because they combine with the protein of animal skins to form leather. This process, known as tanning, also imparts a tan colour to animal skins. Tannins are found in many plant species and typically act as a deterrent to animals, either because of a bitter taste or because of toxic effects. They also can inhibit the enzymes found in the digestive tracts of animals, if consumed in large amounts. Tannins are found abundantly in grape skins and play a key role in the flavour of red wine. Aging breaks down tannins, making the wine less bitter.

Lignins are also large phenolic polymers synthesized by plants. Lignin is found in plant cell walls and makes up about

Vanillin

Pelargonidin — an anthocyanin

(a) Flavonoids in vanilla provide flavour

(b) Anthocyanins, such as pelargonidin, give red colour

Figure 7.25 Phenolic compounds as secondary metabolites. The two examples shown here are flavonoids, which are a type of phenolic compound. **(a)** The flavour of vanilla is largely produced by flavonoids, an example of which is vanillin. Commercially, vanillin is extracted from the seed capsule of *Vanilla planifolia.* **(b)** Another group of flavonoids that causes red, blue, or purple colour are anthocyanins. The red colour of strawberries is caused by pelargonidin, an anthocyanin.

one-quarter to one-third of the weight of dry wood. The lignins form polymers that bond with other plant wall components, such as cellulose. This strengthens plant cells and enables a plant to better withstand the rigors of environmental stress. To make paper, which is much more malleable than wood, the lignin is removed.

Alkaloids Form a Large Group of Bitter-Tasting Molecules That Also Provide Defence Mechanisms

Alkaloids are a group of structurally related molecules that all contain nitrogen and usually have a cyclic, ringlike structure. More than 12,000 different alkaloids have been discovered. Their name is derived from the observation that they are basic or alkaline molecules. Alkaloids are usually synthesized from amino acids precursors. Alkaloids are commonly made in plant species and occasionally in fungi (mushrooms) and animals (shellfish). Familiar examples include caffeine, nicotine, atropine, morphine, ergot, and quinine.

Like phenolics, many alkaloids serve a defence function in plants. Alkaloids are bitter-tasting molecules and often have an unpleasant odour. These features may prevent an animal from eating a plant or its fruit. For example, an alkaloid in chile peppers called capsaicin elicits a burning sensation. This molecule is so potent that one part per million can be detected by the human tongue. Capsaicin discourages some mammals from eating the

peppers. Interestingly, however, birds do not experience the burning sensation of capsaicin and help the plant by dispersing the seeds.

Other alkaloids are poisonous, like the alkaloid **atropine**, a potent toxin derived from the deadly nightshade plant (**Figure 7.26a**). Animals that eat this plant and consequently ingest atropine become very sick and may die. It is unlikely that an animal that eats deadly nightshade and survives would choose to eat it a second time. Atropine acts by interfering with nerve transmission. In humans, for example, atropine causes the heart to speed up to dangerous rates, because the nerve inputs that normally keep a check on heart rate are blocked by atropine. Despite the potential toxicity of atropine, it is used in a variety of human-health-related applications, some of which include dilation of the pupils for ophthalmic purposes and treatment of cardiac arrest. It is also used as an antidote to poisoning by organophosphate insecticides and nerve agents.

Vincenzo De Luca of Brock University in Ontario has been instrumental in elucidating the cell types of the Madagascar periwinkle (**Figure 7.26b**) that produce vindoline, a precursor to more complex alkaloids, such as vincristine and vinblastine. These compounds are anticancer drugs that disrupt microtubule function and thus inhibit cell division.

Terpenoids Are Molecules with Intense Smells and Colour

A third major class of secondary metabolites are the **terpenoids**, of which more than 25,000 have been identified, more than any other family of naturally occurring products. Terpenoids are synthesized from five-carbon isoprene units (shown below) and are also called isoprenoids.

Isoprene units are linked to form larger compounds with multiples of five-carbon atoms. In many cases, the isoprene units form cyclic structures.

Terpenoids have a wide array of functions in plants. Notably, because many terpenoids are volatile (they become gases), they are responsible for the odours emitted by many types of plants, such as menthol produced by mint. The odours of terpenoids may attract pollinators or repel animals that eat plants. In addition, terpenoids often impart an intense flavour to plant tissues. Many of the spices used in cooking are rich in different types of terpenoids. Examples include cinnamon, fennel, cloves, cumin, caraway, and tarragon. Terpenoids are found in many traditional herbal remedies and are under medical investigation for potential pharmaceutical effects.

Other terpenoids, like the carotenoids, are responsible for the coloration of many species. An example is β-carotene, which gives carrots their orange colour. Carotenoids are also found in leaves, but their colour is masked by chlorophyll, which is green. In the autumn, when chlorophyll breaks down, the colour of the

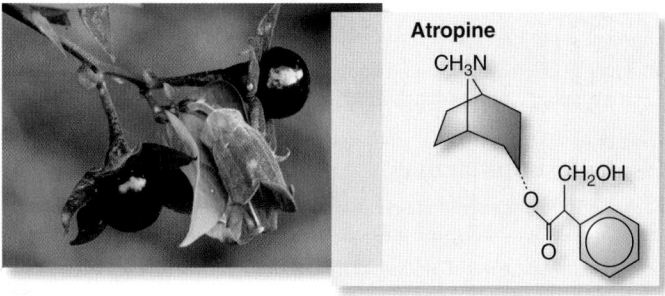

(a) Deadly nightshade (*Hyoscyamus niger*)

R = Me: (+) - vinblastine (1)
R = CHO: (+) - vincristine (2)

(−) - vindoline (3)

(b) Madagaskar periwinkle (*Cantharanthus roseus*)

Figure 7.26 **Alkaloids as secondary metabolites.**
(a) Atropine is an alkaloid produced by the plant called deadly nightshade (*Hyoscyamus niger*). Atropine is toxic because it interferes with nerve transmission, but its properties also make it a useful therapeutic agent under certain circumstances.
(b) The Madagascar periwinkle (*Catharanthus roseus*) produces the alkaloid vindoline, which is used to synthesize the anticancer drugs vincristine and vinblastine.

carotenoids becomes evident. Carotenoids give colour to animals, such as salmon, goldfish, and flamingos (**Figure 7.27**). Another role of terpenoids is cell signalling. All steroid hormones, which function as signalling molecules in animals and plants (as we will discuss in Chapter 9), are derived from terpenoids.

Polyketides Are Often Used as Chemical Weapons to Kill Competing Organisms

Polyketides are a group of secondary metabolites that are produced by bacteria, fungi, plants, insects, dinoflagellates, molluscs, and sponges. They are synthesized by the polymerization

Flamingo (*Phoenicopterus ruber*)

Figure 7.27 **Terpenoids as secondary metabolites.** Carotenoids are a type of brightly coloured terpenoid. The example here is β-carotene, which gives many organisms an orange colour. Flamingos (*Phoenicopterus ruber*) receive β-carotene in their diet, primarily from eating shellfish.

of acetyl (CH_3COOH) and propionyl (CH_3CH_2COOH) groups to create a diverse collection of molecules, often with many ringed structures. Polyketides are usually secreted by the organism that makes them and are often highly toxic to other organisms. For example, the polyketide known as streptomycin is made by the soil bacterium *Streptomyces griseus* (**Figure 7.28**). It is secreted by this bacterium and taken up by other species, where it disrupts protein synthesis and thereby inhibits their growth.

Streptomyces griseus, a soil bacterium

Figure 7.28 **Polyketides as secondary metabolites.** Streptomycin, whose structure is shown here, is an antibiotic produced by *Streptomyces griseus,* a soil bacterium. The scanning electron micrograph shows *S. griseus*.

In this way, *S. griseus* is able to kill or inhibit the growth of other species in its vicinity. This is an advantage for *S. griseus* because other species may be using limited resources that the bacterium could use for its own growth.

During the past several decades, more than 10,000 polyketides have been identified and analyzed. Familiar examples include streptomycin, erythromycin, and tetracycline. The toxic effects of polyketides are often very selective, making them valuable medical tools. For example, streptomycin disrupts protein synthesis in many bacterial species, but it does not adversely affect protein synthesis in mammalian cells. Therefore, it has been used as an antibiotic to treat or prevent bacterial infections in humans and other mammals. Similarly, other polyketides inhibit the growth of fungi, parasites, and insects. More recently, researchers have even discovered that certain polyketides inhibit the growth of cancer cells. The production and sale of polyketides to treat and prevent diseases and as pesticides is an enormous industry.

Summary of Key Concepts

7.1 Energy, Chemical Reactions, and Enzymes

- The fate of a chemical reaction is determined by its direction and rate.
- Energy, the ability to promote change, exists in many forms. According to the first law of thermodynamics, energy cannot be created or destroyed, but it can be converted from one form to another. The second law of thermodynamics states that energy interconversions involve an increase in entropy. (Figures 7.1, 7.2, Table 7.1)
- Free energy is the amount of available energy that can be used to do work. Spontaneous reactions release free energy, which means they have a negative free energy change. (Figure 7.3)
- An exergonic reaction has a negative free energy change, while an endergonic reaction has a positive change. Chemical reactions proceed until they reach a state of chemical equilibrium, where the rate of formation of products equals the rate of formation of reactants.
- Cells use energy intermediates, such as ATP, to drive endergonic reactions (Figure 7.4).
- Proteins that speed up the rate of a chemical reaction are called enzymes. They lower the activation energy that is needed to achieve a transition state. (Figure 7.5)
- Enzymes recognize the reactants, also called substrates, with a high specificity. Conformational changes are involved in lowering the activation energy for a chemical reaction. (Figure 7.6)

7.2 Overview of Metabolism

- Metabolism is the sum of the chemical reactions in a living organism. Enzymes often function in pathways that lead to the formation of a particular product. (Figure 7.7)
- Catabolic reactions involve the breakdown of larger molecules into smaller ones. These reactions regenerate small molecules that are used as building blocks to make new molecules. The small molecules are also broken down to make energy intermediates, such as ATP and NADH. Such reactions are often redox reactions in which electrons are transferred from one molecule to another. (Figure 7.8)
- Anabolic reactions involve the synthesis of larger molecules and macromolecules.

- Estimates from genome analysis indicate that more than 20% of a cell's proteins use ATP. (Table 7.2)
- Metabolic pathways are controlled by gene regulation, cell signalling, and feedback inhibition. (Figure 7.9)

7.3 Cellular Respiration

- Cells obtain energy via cellular respiration, which involves the breakdown of organic molecules.
- The breakdown of glucose occurs in four stages: glycolysis, pyruvate breakdown, citric acid cycle, and oxidative phosphorylation. (Figure 7.10)
- During glycolysis, which occurs in the cytosol, glucose is split to two molecules of pyruvate, with a net yield of two molecules of ATP and two of NADH. ATP is made by substrate-level phosphorylation. (Figures 7.11, 7.12)
- Pyruvate is broken down to CO_2, and an acetyl group that becomes attached to CoA. NADH is made during this process. (Figure 7.13)
- During the citric acid or Krebs cycle, an acetyl group is removed from acetyl CoA and attached to oxaloacetate to make citrate. In a series of steps, two CO_2 molecules, three NADH, one $FADH_2$, and one ATP are made, after which the cycle begins again. (Figures 7.14, 7.15)
- Oxidative phosphorylation involves two events. The electron transport chain oxidizes NADH or $FADH_2$ and generates an H^+ electrochemical gradient. This gradient is used by the ATP synthase to make ATP via chemiosmosis. (Figures 7.16, 7.17)
- Racker and Stoeckenius showed that the ATP synthase uses an H^+ gradient by reconstituting the ATP synthase with a light-driven H^+ pump. (Figure 7.18)
- The ATP synthase is a rotary machine. The rotation is caused by the movement of H^+ through the *c* subunits that cause the γ subunit to spin, resulting in three conformational changes in the γ subunits that promote ATP synthesis. (Figures 7.19, 7.20)
- Yoshida and Kinosita experimentally demonstrated rotation of the γ subunit by attaching a fluorescently labelled actin filament and watching it spin in the presence of ATP. (Figure 7.21)
- Proteins and fats can enter into glycolysis or the citric acid cycle at different points. These nutrients have different energy densities. (Figure 7.22)

7.4 Anaerobic Respiration and Fermentation

- Anaerobic respiration occurs in the absence of oxygen. Certain microorganisms can carry out anaerobic respiration in which the final electron acceptor of the electron transport chain is a substance other than oxygen, such as nitrate. (Figure 7.23)
- During fermentation, organic molecules are broken down without any net oxidation (that is, without any removal of electrons). Examples include lactate production in muscle cells and ethanol production in yeast. (Figure 7.24)

7.5 Secondary Metabolism

- Secondary metabolites are not usually necessary for cell structure and function, but they provide an advantage to an organism that may involve their taste, smell, or colour, or a poison. The four categories of secondary metabolites are phenolic compounds, alkaloids, terpenoids, and polyketides. (Figures 7.25, 7.26, 7.27, 7.28)
- Secondary compounds have many important practical uses in industry and medicine.

Test to Assess Your Learning

1. According to the second law of thermodynamics,
   a. energy cannot be created or destroyed.
   b. each energy transfer decreases the disorder of a system.
   c. energy is constant in the universe.
   d. each energy transfer increases the level of disorder in a system.
   e. chemical energy is a form of potential energy.

2. _____ reactions release free energy.
   a. Exergonic
   b. Spontaneous
   c. Endergonic
   d. All of the above
   e. Both (a) and (b)

3. Enzymes speed up reactions by
   a. providing chemical energy to fuel a reaction.
   b. lowering the activation energy necessary to initiate the reaction.
   c. causing an endergonic reaction to become an exergonic reaction.
   d. substituting for one of the reactants necessary for the reaction.
   e. none of the above.

4. Which of the following factors will alter the function of enzymes?
   a. pH.
   b. Temperature.
   c. Cofactors.
   d. All of the above.
   e. (b) and (c) only.

5. In biological systems, ATP functions by
   a. providing the energy necessary for an endergonic reaction by coupling it with an exergonic reaction.
   b. acting as an enzyme and lowering the activation energy of certain reactions.
   c. adjusting the pH of solutions to maintain optimal conditions for enzyme activity.
   d. regulating the speed at which endergonic reactions proceed.
   e. interacting with enzymes as a cofactor to stimulate chemical reactions.

6. During redox reactions, the molecule that donates an electron is said to be
   a. reduced.
   b. phosphorylated.
   c. oxidized.
   d. catabolized.
   e. methylated.

7. Scientists are identifying proteins that use ATP as an energy source by
   a. determining whether those proteins function in anabolic or catabolic reactions.
   b. determining whether the protein has a known ATP-binding site.
   c. predicting the free energy necessary for the protein to function.
   d. determining whether the protein has an ATP synthase subunit.
   e. all of the above.

8. During glycolysis, ATP is produced by
   a. oxidative phosphorylation.
   b. substrate-level phosphorylation.
   c. redox reactions.
   d. all of the above.
   e. both (a) and (b).

9. When a muscle becomes anaerobic during strenuous exercise, why is it necessary to convert pyruvate to lactate?
   a. To decrease NAD^+ and increase NADH.
   b. To decrease NADH and increase NAD^+.
   c. To increase NADH and increase NAD^+.
   d. To decrease NADH and decrease NAD^+.
   e. To keep oxidative phosphorylation running.

10. Secondary metabolites
    a. help deter predation of certain organisms by causing the organism to taste bad.
    b. help attract pollinators by producing a pleasant smell.
    c. help organisms compete for resources by acting as a poison to competitors.
    d. provide protection from DNA damage.
    e. all of the above.

Articulate to Assess Your Learning

1. Distinguish between endergonic reactions and exergonic reactions.

2. Define *feedback inhibition*.

3. The electron transport chain is so named because electrons are transported from one component to another. Describe the purpose of the electron transport chain.

Collaborate to Assess and Extend Your Learning

1. Discuss several ways in which metabolic pathways are controlled or regulated.

2. Discuss the advantages and disadvantages of aerobic respiration, anaerobic respiration, and fermentation.

3. Discuss the roles of secondary metabolites in biology. Such compounds have a wide variety of practical applications. If you were going to start a biotechnology company that produced secondary metabolites for sale, which would you focus on? How might you go about discovering new secondary metabolites that could be profitable?

4. A principle of biology is that living organisms have mechanisms that maintain homeostasis. How is glucose breakdown regulated to maintain homeostasis? What would be some potentially harmful consequences if glucose metabolism were not regulated properly?

Visit McGraw-Hill Ryerson Connect™ for additional study resources.

Photosynthesis

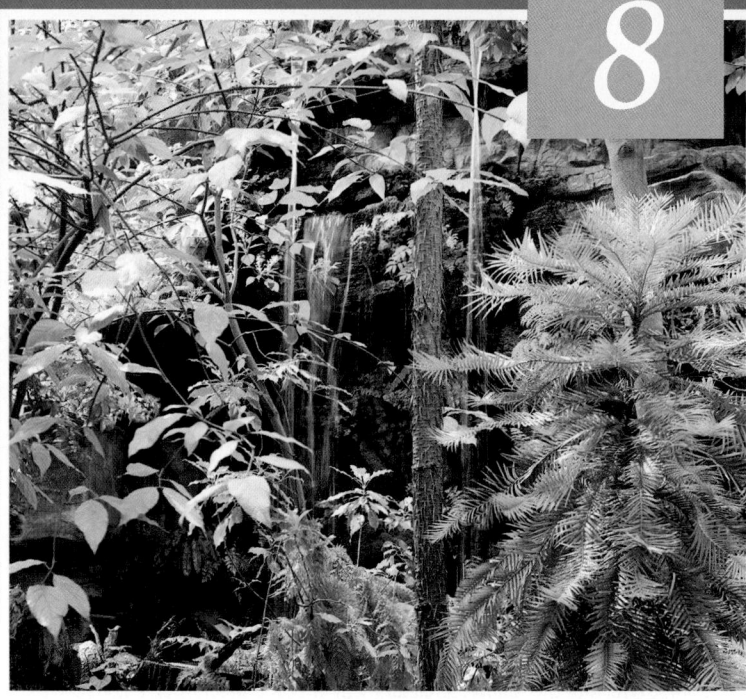

Chapter Outline

A tropical rain forest in the Amazon. Plant life in tropical rain forests carries out a large amount of the world's photosynthesis and supplies the atmosphere with a sizable fraction of its oxygen.

Take a deep breath. Nearly all of the oxygen in every breath you take is made by the abundant plant life, algae, and cyanobacteria on Earth. More than 20% of the world's oxygen is produced in the Amazon rain forest in South America alone (see the chapter-opening photo). Biologists are alarmed about the rate at which these forests are being destroyed by human activities, such as agriculture and resource extraction. Rain forests once covered 14% of Earth's land surface; now they occupy less than 6%. At their current rate of destruction, rain forests may be nearly eliminated in fewer than 40 years. Such an event may lower the level of oxygen in the atmosphere and thereby have a global, harmful impact on living organisms.

In rain forests and across Earth, the most visible colour on land is green. The green colour of plants is due to a pigment called chlorophyll. This pigment provides the starting point for the process of **photosynthesis**, in which the energy from light is captured and used to synthesize glucose and other organic molecules. Nearly all living organisms ultimately rely on photosynthesis for their nourishment, either directly or indirectly. Photosynthesis is also responsible for producing the oxygen that makes up a large portion of Earth's atmosphere. Therefore, all aerobic organisms rely on photosynthesis for cellular respiration.

We begin this chapter with an overview of photosynthesis, emphasizing how it occurs in green plants. We will then explore the two stages of photosynthesis: the light reactions, in which light energy is captured by the chlorophyll pigments within plants and converted to chemical energy in the form of two compounds, ATP and NADPH; and the Calvin cycle, a series of steps in which these compounds drive the incorporation of CO_2 into carbohydrates. We conclude with a consideration of the variations in photosynthesis that occur in plants living in hot and dry conditions.

8.1 | OVERVIEW OF PHOTOSYNTHESIS

Learning Outcomes:

1. Write the general equations that represent the process of photosynthesis.
2. Outline how photosynthesis powers the biosphere.
3. Describe the general structure of chloroplasts.
4. Explain how photosynthesis occurs in two phases: the light reactions and carbon fixation.

In the mid-seventeenth century a Flemish physician, Jan Baptista Van Helmont, conducted an experiment in which he transplanted the shoot of a young willow tree into a bucket of soil of known weight. He watered the tree and allowed it to grow for five years. After this time, the willow tree had added about 74 kg to its original weight, but the soil had lost only 57 g. Van Helmont correctly concluded that the willow tree did not get most of its nutrients from the soil. He also hypothesized that the mass of the tree came from the water he had added over the five years. This hypothesis was partially correct, but we now know that CO_2 from the air is also a major contributor to the growth and mass of plants.

In the 1770s Jan Ingenhousz, a Dutch physician, immersed green plants underwater and discovered that they released bubbles of oxygen. Ingenhousz determined that sunlight was necessary for oxygen production. During this same period Jean Senebier, a Swiss botanist, found that CO_2 is required for plant growth, and Nicolas-Théodore de Saussure, a Swiss chemist, showed that water is also essential. With this accumulating information Julius von Mayer, a German physicist, proposed in 1845 that plants convert light energy from the sun into chemical energy.

For the next several decades, plant biologists studied photosynthesis in prokaryotes, algae, and green plants. Researchers discovered that some photosynthetic bacteria could use hydrogen sulphide (H_2S) instead of water (H_2O) for photosynthesis and that these organisms released sulphur instead of oxygen. In the 1930s, based on this information, Dutch American microbiologist Cornelis van Niel proposed a general equation for photosynthesis that applies to plants, algae, and photosynthetic bacteria alike:

$$CO_2 + 2\,H_2A + \text{light energy} \rightarrow CH_2O + 2A + H_2O$$

where A is oxygen (O) or sulphur (S) and CH_2O is the general formula for a carbohydrate. This is a redox reaction in which H_2A is oxidized and CO_2 is reduced.

In green plants, A is oxygen and 2A is a molecule of oxygen that is designated O_2. Therefore, this equation becomes

$$CO_2 + 2\,H_2O + \text{light energy} \rightarrow CH_2O + O_2 + H_2O$$

When the carbohydrate that is produced is glucose, we multiply each side of the equation by six to obtain:

$$6\,CO_2 + 12\,H_2O + \text{light energy} \rightarrow C_6H_{12}O_6 + 6\,O_2 + 6\,H_2O$$
$$\text{glucose}$$
$$\Delta G = +685 \text{ kcal/mol}$$

In this redox reaction CO_2 is reduced during the formation of glucose, and H_2O is oxidized during the formation of O_2. The free energy change required for the production of 1 mol of glucose from carbon dioxide and water is a whopping +685 kcal/mol! To put this into perspective, a similar amount of energy would be used by an average-sized person mountain biking for one hour. As we learned in Chapter 7, endergonic reactions are driven forward by coupling the reaction with an exergonic process, a process that releases free energy. In this case, the energy from light ultimately drives the synthesis of glucose.

In this section, we will survey the general features of photosynthesis as it occurs in green plants. Later sections will examine the various steps in this process.

Photosynthesis Powers the Biosphere

The term **biosphere** describes the regions on the surface of Earth and in the atmosphere where living organisms exist. Organisms can be categorized as heterotrophs and autotrophs. **Heterotrophs** must consume food—organic molecules from their environment—to sustain life. Most species of bacteria and protists, as well as all species of fungi and animals, are heterotrophs. By comparison, **autotrophs** sustain themselves by producing organic molecules from inorganic sources, such as CO_2 and H_2O. **Photoautotrophs** are autotrophs that use light as a source of energy to make organic molecules. These include green plants, algae, and some bacterial species, such as cyanobacteria.

Life in the biosphere is largely driven by the photosynthetic power of green plants and algae. The existence of most species relies on a key energy cycle that involves the interplay between organic molecules (such as glucose) and inorganic molecules, namely, O_2, CO_2, and H_2O (**Figure 8.1**). Photoautotrophs, such as plants, make a large proportion of Earth's organic molecules via photosynthesis, by using light energy, CO_2, and H_2O. During this process, they also produce O_2. To supply their energy needs, photoautotrophs (and heterotrophs) metabolize the organic molecules via cellular respiration.

As we examined in Chapter 7, cellular respiration involves the breakdown of organic molecules to produce energy intermediates, such as ATP. When glucose is broken down to CO_2, the net reaction of cellular respiration in the presence of oxygen can be summarized as

$$C_6H_{12}O_6 + 6\,O_2 \rightarrow 6\,CO_2 + 6\,H_2O + \text{energy}$$

The net reaction of photosynthesis (in which only six net molecules of H_2O are consumed) can be viewed as the opposite of respiration:

$$6\,CO_2 + 6\,H_2O + \text{energy} \rightarrow C_6H_{12}O_6 + 6\,O_2$$

The breakdown of glucose during cell respiration is an energy-releasing process that drives the synthesis of ATP. By comparison, the energy that is needed to synthesize glucose during photosynthesis ultimately comes from sunlight.

Plants make a large proportion of Earth's organic molecules via photosynthesis. At the same time, they also produce O_2. These organic molecules are metabolized by the plants themselves as well as by heterotrophs, such as animals and fungi. This metabolism generates CO_2, which is released into the atmosphere and can be used by plants to make more organic molecules, such as glucose. In this way, a cycle exists between photosynthesis and cellular respiration that sustains life on our planet.

Figure 8.1 **Energy cycle of the biosphere.** Photosynthesis uses light, CO_2, and H_2O to produce O_2 and organic molecules. These organic molecules can be broken down to CO_2 and H_2O via cellular respiration to supply energy in the form of ATP.

Concept check: *Which types of organisms carry out cellular respiration? Is it heterotrophs, autotrophs, or both?*

In Plants and Algae, Photosynthesis Occurs in the Chloroplast

Chloroplasts are organelles found in plant cells and algae that carry out photosynthesis. These organelles contain large quantities of **chlorophyll**, a pigment that gives plants their green colour. All green parts of a plant contain chloroplasts and are capable of photosynthesis, although the majority of photosynthesis occurs in the leaves (**Figure 8.2**). The tissue in the central part of the leaf, called the **mesophyll**, contains cells with chloroplasts. For photosynthesis to occur, the mesophyll cells must obtain water and carbon dioxide. The water is taken up by the roots of the plant and is transported to the leaves by small veins. Carbon dioxide gas enters the leaf, and oxygen exits, via pores called **stomata** (singular: stoma), from the Greek, meaning "mouth." The anatomy of leaves will be examined further in Chapter 33.

Like a mitochondrion, a chloroplast contains an outer and inner membrane, with an intermembrane space lying between the two. A third membrane, called the **thylakoid membrane**, contains pigment molecules, including chlorophyll. The thylakoid membrane forms many flattened, fluid-filled tubules called the **thylakoids**, which enclose a single, convoluted compartment known as the **thylakoid lumen**. Thylakoids stack on top of each other to form a structure called a **granum** (plural: grana). The **stroma** is the fluid-filled region of the chloroplast between the thylakoid membrane and the inner membrane.

Photosynthesis Occurs in Two Stages: Light Reactions and the Calvin Cycle

The process of photosynthesis can be divided into two stages called the **light reactions** and the **Calvin cycle**. The term photosynthesis is derived from the association between these two stages. The prefix *photo* refers to the light reactions that capture the energy needed for the synthesis of carbohydrates that occurs in the Calvin cycle. Each stage occurs at specific sites in the chloroplast: the light reactions take place at the thylakoid membrane, and the Calvin cycle occurs in the stroma (**Figure 8.3**).

The light reactions involve an amazing series of energy conversions, starting with light energy and ending with chemical energy in the form of covalent bonds. The light reactions produce three chemical products: ATP, NADPH, and O_2. ATP and NADPH are energy intermediates that provide the needed energy and electrons to drive the Calvin cycle. Like NADH, **NADPH (nicotinamide adenine dinucleotide phosphate)** is an electron carrier; its structure differs from NADH by the presence of an additional phosphate group. In the Calvin cycle, atmospheric carbon dioxide is incorporated into organic molecules, some of which are converted to carbohydrates.

O_2 is another important product of the light reactions. As described in Chapter 7, this molecule is vital to the process of aerobic respiration. Nearly all the O_2 in the atmosphere is produced by photosynthesis from plants, algae, and some aquatic

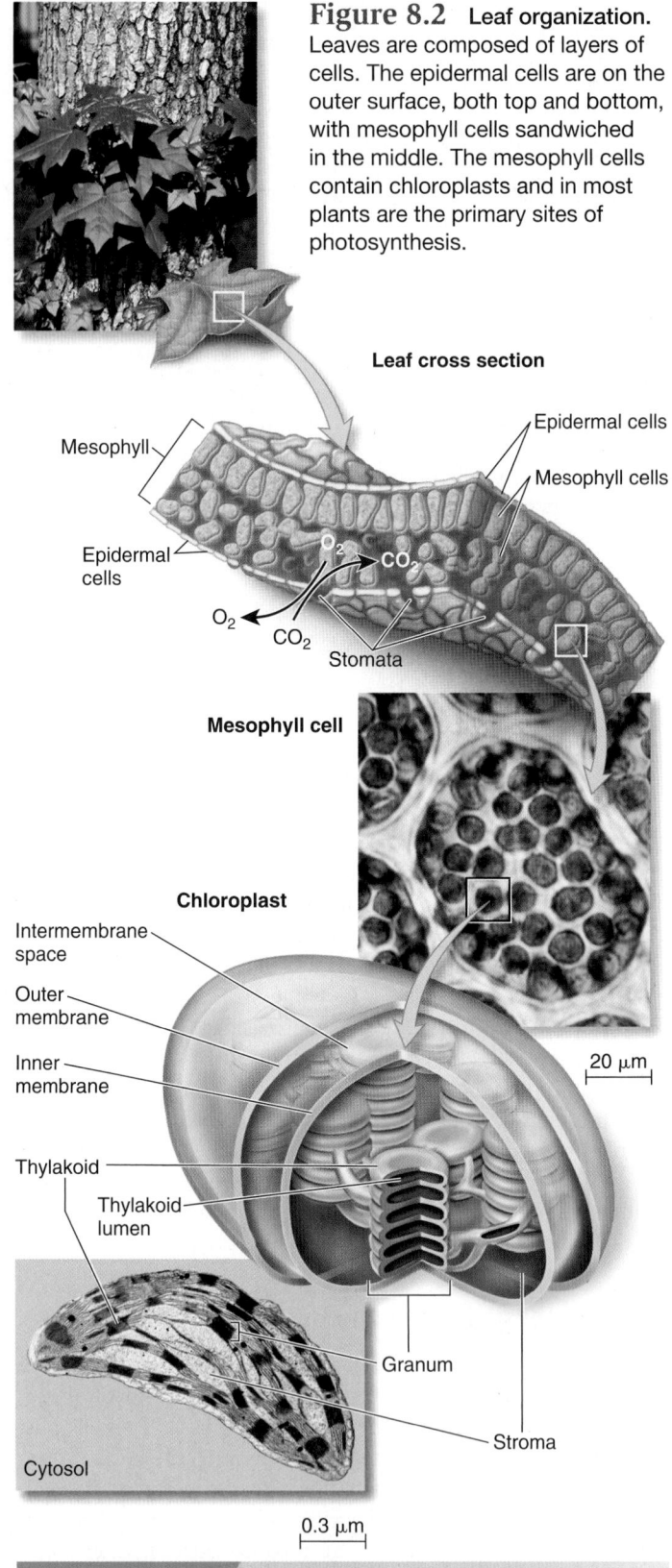

Figure 8.2   Leaf organization. Leaves are composed of layers of cells. The epidermal cells are on the outer surface, both top and bottom, with mesophyll cells sandwiched in the middle. The mesophyll cells contain chloroplasts and in most plants are the primary sites of photosynthesis.

Leaf cross section

Mesophyll
Epidermal cells
O_2
CO_2
O_2
CO_2
Stomata
Epidermal cells
Mesophyll cells

Mesophyll cell

Chloroplast
Intermembrane space
Outer membrane
Inner membrane
Thylakoid
Thylakoid lumen
Granum
Stroma

Cytosol

20 μm

0.3 μm

BioConnections: *Look ahead to Figure 36.17. How many guard cells comprise a stoma (plural, stomata)?*

The light reactions in the thylakoid membrane produce ATP, NADPH, and O_2.

The Calvin cycle in the stroma uses CO_2, ATP, and NADPH to make carbohydrates.

Figure 8.3 An overview of the two stages of photosynthesis: light reactions and the Calvin cycle. The light reactions, through which O_2, ATP, and NADPH are made, occur at the thylakoid membrane. The Calvin cycle, in which enzymes use ATP and NADPH to incorporate CO_2 into carbohydrate, occurs in the stroma.

microorganisms. More than 20% of the world's oxygen is produced in the Amazon rain forest in South America. Similarly, about 50% of all oxygen is produced by phytoplankton, which are typically single-celled prokaryotes and algae. Thus, stewardship of oceans, lakes, and other waterways is critical to maintaining a healthy environment. Degradation of ecosystems can lead to loss of habitats and a decline in the amount of oxygen produced could have serious consequences for all aerobic organisms.

8.2 | REACTIONS THAT HARNESS LIGHT ENERGY

Learning Outcomes:

1. Define the general properties of light.
2. Describe how pigments absorb light energy, and describe the types of pigments found in plants and green algae.
3. Outline the steps in which photosystem II and I capture light energy and produce O_2, ATP, and NADPH.
4. Explain the process of cyclic photophosphorylation in which only ATP is made.

According to the first law of thermodynamics discussed in Chapter 7, energy cannot be created or destroyed, but it can be transferred from one place to another and transformed from one form to another. During photosynthesis, energy in the form of light is transferred from the sun, some 148 million km away, to a pigment molecule in a photosynthetic organism, such as a plant. What follows is an interesting series of energy transformations in which light energy is transformed into electrochemical energy and then into energy stored within chemical bonds.

In this section we will explore this series of transformations, collectively called the light reactions of photosynthesis. We begin by examining the unique properties of light and then consider the features of chloroplasts that allow them to capture light energy. The remaining sections focus on how the light reactions of photosynthesis create three important products: O_2, ATP, and NADPH.

Light Energy Is a Form of Electromagnetic Radiation

Light is a critical phenomenon that is essential to supporting life on Earth. Light is a type of electromagnetic radiation, so named because it consists of energy in the form of electric and magnetic fields. Electromagnetic radiation travels as waves caused by the oscillation of the electric and magnetic fields. The **wavelength** is the distance between the peaks in a wave pattern. The **electromagnetic spectrum** encompasses all possible wavelengths of electromagnetic radiation, from relatively short wavelengths (gamma rays) to much longer wavelengths (radio waves) (**Figure 8.4**). Visible light is the range of wavelengths that are detected by the human eye, commonly in the range from 380 to 740 nm. As discussed later, visible light provides the energy to drive photosynthesis.

Physicists have also discovered that light exhibits behaviours that are characteristic of particles. Albert Einstein formulated the photon theory of light in which he proposed that

Figure 8.4 The electromagnetic spectrum. The bottom portion of this figure emphasizes visible light, the wavelengths of electromagnetic radiation that are visible to the human eye. Light in the visible portion of the electromagnetic spectrum drives photosynthesis.

light is composed of discrete particles called **photons**—massless particles each travelling in a wavelike pattern and moving at the speed of light. Each photon contains a specific amount of energy. An important difference between the various types of electromagnetic radiation described in Figure 8.4 is the amount of energy found in the photons. Shorter wavelength radiation carries more energy per unit of time than longer wavelength radiation.

The sun radiates the entire spectrum of electromagnetic radiation. The atmosphere prevents much of this radiation from reaching Earth's surface. For example, the ozone layer forms a thin shield in the upper atmosphere, protecting life on Earth from much of the sun's ultraviolet (UV) rays. Even so, a substantial amount of electromagnetic radiation does reach Earth's surface. The effect of light on living organisms is critically dependent on the energy of the photons. The photons found in gamma rays, X-rays, and UV rays have very high energy. When molecules in cells absorb such energy, the effects can be devastating. These types of radiation can cause mutations in DNA and even lead to cancer. By comparison, the energy of photons found in visible light is much milder. Molecules can absorb this energy in a way that does not cause permanent harm. Let's now consider how molecules in living cells absorb the energy within visible light.

Photosynthetic Pigments Absorb Light Energy

When light strikes an object, one of three things can happen. First, light may simply pass through an object, a phenomenon called transmission. Second, the object may change the path of light toward a different direction (reflection). Third, the object may absorb the light (absorption). The term **pigment** is used to describe a molecule that can absorb light energy. When light strikes a pigment, some of the wavelengths of light energy are absorbed, while others are reflected. For example, we perceive that leaves are green because they are reflecting radiant energy of the green wavelength. Various pigments in the leaves absorb the other light energy wavelengths. At the extremes of colour reflection are white and black. A white object reflects nearly all the light energy falling on it, whereas a black object absorbs nearly all the light energy.

What do we mean when we say that light energy is absorbed? In the visible spectrum, light energy is usually absorbed by boosting electrons to higher energy levels (**Figure 8.5**). Recall from Chapter 2 that electrons are located around the nucleus of an atom. The location in which an electron is likely to be found is called its orbital. Electrons in different orbitals possess different amounts of energy. For an electron to absorb light energy and be boosted to an orbital with a higher energy, it must overcome the difference in energy between the orbital it is in and the orbital to which it is going. For this to happen, an electron must absorb a photon that contains precisely that amount of energy. Among different pigment molecules a variety of electrons exist that can be shifted to different energy levels. Therefore, the wavelength of light that a pigment absorbs depends on

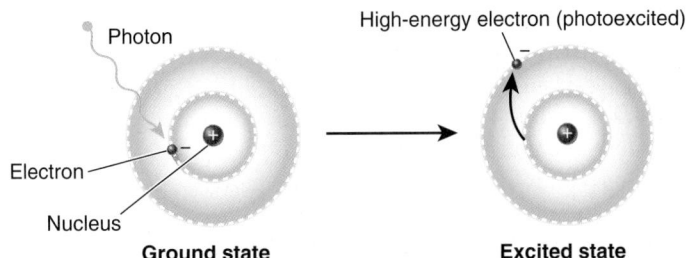

Figure 8.5 **Absorption of light energy by an electron.** When a photon of light of the correct amount of energy strikes an electron, the electron is boosted from the ground (unexcited) state to a higher energy level. When this occurs, the electron occupies an orbital that is farther away from the nucleus of the atom. At this farther distance, the electron is held less firmly and is considered unstable.

Concept check: *Describe three things that could happen to an excited electron.*

the amount of energy that is needed to boost an electron to a higher orbital.

After an electron absorbs energy, it is said to be in an excited state. Usually, this is an unstable condition. The electron may release the energy in different ways. First, when an excited electron drops back down to a lower energy level, it may release heat. For example, on a sunny day, the sidewalk heats up because it absorbs light energy that is released as heat. A second way that an electron can release energy is in the form of light. Certain organisms, such as jellyfish, possess molecules that make them glow. This glow is due to the release of light when electrons drop down to lower energy levels, a phenomenon called fluorescence.

In the case of photosynthetic pigments, however, a different event happens that is critical for the process of photosynthesis. At a particular step, an excited electron in a photosynthetic pigment is removed from that molecule and transferred to another molecule where the electron is more stable. When this occurs, the energy in that electron is said to be "captured" because the electron does not drop down to a lower energy level through the release of heat or light.

Plants Contain Different Types of Photosynthetic Pigments

In plants, several different pigment molecules absorb the light energy used to drive photosynthesis. Two types of chlorophyll pigments, termed **chlorophyll *a*** and **chlorophyll *b***, are found in green algae and plants. Their structure was determined in the 1930s by German chemist Hans Fischer (**Figure 8.6a**). In the chloroplast, both chlorophylls *a* and *b* are bound to integral membrane proteins in the thylakoid membrane.

The chlorophylls contain a porphyrin ring and a phytol tail. A magnesium ion (Mg^{2+}) is bound to the porphyrin ring. An electron in the porphyrin ring follows a path in which it spends some of its time around several different atoms. Because this electron isn't restricted to a single atom, it is called a delocalized electron. The delocalized electron can absorb light energy. The phytol tail in chlorophyll is a long hydrophobic hydrocarbon structure. Its function is to anchor the pigment to the surface of hydrophobic proteins within the thylakoid membrane of chloroplasts.

Carotenoids are another type of pigment found in chloroplasts (**Figure 8.6b**). These pigments impart a colour that ranges from yellow to orange to red. Carotenoids are often the major pigments in flowers and fruits. In leaves, the more abundant chlorophylls usually mask the colours of carotenoids. In climates where the leaves change colours, the quantity of chlorophyll in the leaf declines during autumn. The carotenoids become readily visible and produce the yellows and oranges of autumn foliage.

An **absorption spectrum** is a diagram that depicts the wavelengths of electromagnetic radiation that are absorbed by a pigment. Each of the pigments shown in **Figure 8.6c** absorbs light in different regions of the visible spectrum. The absorption spectra of chlorophylls *a* and *b* are slightly different, though both chlorophylls absorb light most strongly in the red and violet parts of the visible spectrum and absorb green light poorly. Green light is reflected, which is why leaves appear green. Carotenoids absorb light in the blue and blue-green regions of the visible spectrum, reflecting yellow and red.

Why do plants have different pigments? Having different pigments allows plants to absorb light at many different wavelengths. In this way, plants are more efficient at capturing the energy in sunlight. This phenomenon is highlighted in an **action spectrum**, which describes the rate of photosynthesis plotted as a function of different wavelengths of light (**Figure 8.6d**). The highest rates of photosynthesis correlate with the wavelengths that are strongly absorbed by the chlorophylls and carotenoids. Photosynthesis is poor in the green region of the spectrum, because these pigments do not readily absorb this wavelength of light.

Figure 8.6   Structures and properties of pigment molecules.   (a) The structure of chlorophylls *a* and *b*. As indicated, chlorophylls *a* and *b* differ only at a single site, at which chlorophyll *a* has a —CH$_3$ group and chlorophyll *b* has a —CHO group. **(b)** The structure of β-carotene, an example of a carotenoid. The shaded areas are the regions in which a delocalized electron can hop from one atom to another. **(c)** Absorption spectra that show the absorption of light by chlorophyll *a*, chlorophyll *b*, and β-carotene. **(d)** An action spectrum of photosynthesis depicting the relative rate of photosynthesis in green plants at different wavelengths of light.

Two Photosystems Work Together to Produce ATP and NADPH

As noted previously, photosynthetic organisms have the unique ability not only to absorb light energy but also to capture that energy in a stable way. Many organic molecules can absorb light energy. For example, on a sunny day, molecules in your skin absorb light energy and release the energy as heat. The heat that is released, however, cannot be harnessed to do useful work. A key feature of photosynthesis is the ability of pigments to capture light energy and transfer it to other molecules that can hold on to the energy in a stable fashion and ultimately produce energy intermediate molecules that can do cellular work.

Let's now consider how chloroplasts capture light energy. The thylakoid membranes of the chloroplast contain two distinct complexes of proteins and pigment molecules called photosystem I (PSI) and photosystem II (PSII) (**Figure 8.7**). PSI was discovered before PSII, but PSII is the initial step in photosynthesis. We will consider the structure and function of PSII in greater detail later in this chapter.

As described in steps 1 and 2 of Figure 8.7, light excites electrons in pigment molecules, such as chlorophylls, which are located in regions of PSII and PSI called light-harvesting complexes. Rather than releasing their energy in the form of heat, the excited electrons follow a path shown by the red arrow. The combined action of PSII and PSI is termed **noncyclic electron flow** because the electrons move linearly from PSII to PSI and ultimately reduce $NADP^+$ to NADPH.

Initially, the excited electrons move from a pigment molecule called P680 in PSII to other electron carriers called pheophytin (Pp), Q_A, and Q_B. The excited electrons are moved out of PSII by Q_B. PSII also oxidizes water, which generates O_2 and adds H^+ into the thylakoid lumen. The electrons released from the oxidized water molecules are used to replenish the electrons that leave PSII via Q_B.

After a pair of electrons reaches Q_B, each one enters an **electron transport chain (ETC)**—a series of electron carriers—located in the thylakoid membrane. The electron transport chain functions similarly to the one found in mitochondria. From Q_B, an electron goes to a cytochrome complex; then to plastocyanin (Pc), a small protein; and then to PSI. Along its journey from

Figure 8.7 The synthesis of O_2, ATP, and NADPH by the concerted actions of photosystems I and II. The linear process of electron movement from photosystem II to photosystem I to NADPH is called noncyclic electron flow.

Concept check: *Are ATP, NADPH, and O_2 produced in the stroma or the thylakoid lumen?*

PSII to PSI, the electron releases some of its energy at particular steps and is transferred to the next component that has a higher electronegativity. The energy released is harnessed to pump H⁺ into the thylakoid lumen.

A key role of PSI is to make NADPH (Figure 8.7, step 3). When light strikes the light-harvesting complex of PSI, this energy is also transferred to a reaction centre, where a high-energy electron is removed from a pigment molecule, designated P700, and transferred to a primary electron acceptor. A protein called ferredoxin (Fd) can accept two high-energy electrons, one at a time, from the primary electron acceptor. Fd then transfers the two electrons to the enzyme NADP⁺ reductase. This enzyme transfers the two electrons to NADP⁺ and together with an H⁺ produces NADPH. The formation of NADPH results in fewer H⁺ in the stroma.

The synthesis of ATP in chloroplasts is achieved by a chemiosmotic mechanism called **photophosphorylation**, which is similar to that used to make ATP in mitochondria. In chloroplasts, ATP synthesis is driven by the flow of H⁺ from the thylakoid lumen into the stroma via ATP synthase (Figure 8.7, step 4). An H⁺ electrochemical gradient is generated in three ways: (1) the splitting of water, which places H⁺ in the thylakoid lumen; (2) the movement of high-energy electrons from PSII to PSI, which pumps H⁺ into the thylakoid lumen; and (3) the formation of NADPH, which consumes H⁺ in the stroma.

A key difference between PSII and PSI is how the pigment molecules receive electrons. As discussed in more detail later, P680⁺ receives an electron from water. By comparison, P700⁺—the oxidized form of P700—receives an electron from Pc. Therefore, PSI does not need to split water to reduce P700⁺ and does not generate oxygen.

In summary, the steps of the light reactions of photosynthesis produce three chemical products: O_2, NADPH, and ATP:

1. O_2 is produced in the thylakoid lumen by the oxidation of water by PSII. Two electrons are removed from water, which produces 2 H⁺ and ½ O_2. The two electrons are transferred to P680⁺ molecules.
2. NADPH is produced in the stroma from high-energy electrons that start in PSII and are boosted a second time in PSI. Two high-energy electrons and one H⁺ are transferred to NADP⁺ to produce NADPH.
3. ATP is produced in the stroma via ATP synthase that uses an H⁺ electrochemical gradient.

Cyclic Electron Flow Produces Only ATP

The mechanism of harvesting light energy, described in Figure 8.7, is called noncyclic electron flow because electrons begin at PSII and eventually are transferred to NADP⁺. The electron flow is a linear process that produces ATP and NADPH in roughly equal amounts. However, as you will see, the Calvin cycle uses more ATP than NADPH. Therefore, in some photosynthetic organisms, excited electrons take an alternative path as a way to make more ATP. In 1959 Daniel Arnon discovered a pattern of electron flow that is cyclic and generates ATP alone (**Figure 8.8**).

Figure 8.8 Cyclic photophosphorylation. In this process, an electron follows a cyclic path that is powered by photosystem I. This contributes to the formation of an H⁺ electrochemical gradient, which is then used to make ATP by ATP synthase.

Concept check: *Why is having cyclic photophosphorylation an advantage to a plant over having only noncyclic electron flow?*

GENOMES AND PROTEOMES

The Cytochrome Complexes of Mitochondria and Chloroplasts Contain Evolutionarily Related Proteins

The endosymbiont theory, presented in Chapter 5, suggested that mitochondria and chloroplasts of extant organisms were derived from ancient prokaryotic cells. A recurring theme in cell biology is that evolution has resulted in groups of genes that encode proteins that play similar but specialized roles in cells. When two or more genes are similar because they are derived from the same ancestral gene, they are called **homologous genes**. As discussed in Chapter 21, homologous genes encode proteins that have similar amino acid sequences and perform similar functions.

A comparison of the electron transport chains of mitochondria and chloroplasts reveals homologous genes. In particular, let's consider the cytochrome complex found in the thylakoid membrane of plants and algae, called cytochrome b_6-f (**Figure 8.9a**) and cytochrome b-c_1, which is found in the electron transport chain of mitochondria (**Figure 8.9b**; refer back to Figure 7.16). Both cytochrome b_6-f and cytochrome b-c_1 are composed of several protein subunits. One of those proteins is called cytochrome b_6 in cytochrome b_6-f and cytochrome b in cytochrome b-c_1.

By analyzing the gene sequences, researchers discovered that cytochrome b_6 and cytochrome b are homologous proteins. These proteins carry out similar functions: both of them accept electrons from a quinone (Q_B or ubiquinone) and both donate an electron to another protein within their respective complexes (cytochrome f or cytochrome c_1). Likewise, both of these proteins function as H^+ pumps that capture some of the energy that is released from electrons to transport H^+ across the membrane. In this way, evolution has produced a family of cytochrome b-type proteins that play similar but specialized roles.

(a) Cytochrome b_6-f in the chloroplast

(b) Cytochrome b-c_1 in the mitochondrion

Figure 8.9 Homologous proteins in the electron transport chains of chloroplasts and mitochondria. **(a)** Cytochrome b_6-f is a complex involved in electron and H^+ transport in chloroplasts, and **(b)** cytochrome b-c_1 is a complex involved in electron and H^+ transport in mitochondria. These complexes contain homologous proteins designated cytochrome b_6 in chloroplasts and cytochrome b in mitochondria. The inset shows the three-dimensional structure of cytochrome b, which was determined by X-ray crystallography. It is an integral membrane protein with several transmembrane helices and two heme groups, which are prosthetic groups involved in electron transfer. The structure of cytochrome b_6 has also been determined and found to be very similar.

Principle: *Populations of organisms evolve from one generation to the next. The process of evolution has generated divergent genes encoding proteins with similar but specialized functions.*

Concept check: *Explain why the three-dimensional structures of cytochrome b and cytochrome b$_6$ are very similar.*

Arnon termed the process **cyclic photophosphorylation** because (1) the path of electrons is cyclic, (2) light energizes the electrons, and (3) ATP is made via the phosphorylation of ADP. Because of the path of the electrons, the mechanism is also called **cyclic electron flow**.

When light strikes PSI, high-energy electrons are sent to the primary electron acceptor and then to ferredoxin (Fd). The key difference in cyclic photophosphorylation is that the high-energy electrons are transferred from ferredoxin to Q_B. From Q_B the electrons then go the cytochrome complex, then to plastocyanin (Pc), and back to PSI. As the electrons travel along this cyclic route, they release energy, and some of this energy is used to transport H^+ into the thylakoid lumen. The resulting H^+ gradient drives the synthesis of ATP via the ATP synthase. However, NADPH is not produced.

Cyclic electron flow is favoured when the level of $NADP^+$ is low and NADPH is high. Under these conditions, there is sufficient NADPH to run the Calvin cycle, which is described later. Alternatively, when $NADP^+$ is high and NADPH is low, noncyclic electron flow is favoured, so more NADPH can be made. Cyclic electron flow is also favoured when ATP levels are low.

Figure 8.10   A closer look at how PSII harvests light energy and oxidizes water.   Note that two electrons are released during the oxidation of water, but they are transferred one at a time to P680$^+$.

8.3 / MOLECULAR FEATURES OF PHOTOSYSTEMS

Learning Outcomes:

1. Describe how the light-harvesting complex absorbs light energy and how resonance energy transfer occurs.
2. Diagram the path of electron flow through photosystem II.
3. Explain how O_2 is produced by photosystem II.

The previous section provided an overview of how chloroplasts absorb light energy and produce ATP, NADPH, and O_2. As you have learned, two photosystems, namely PSI and PSII, play critical roles in two aspects of photosynthesis. First, both PSI and PSII absorb light energy and capture that energy in the form of excited electrons. Second, PSII oxidizes water and thereby produces O_2. In this section, we will take a closer look at how these events occur at the molecular level.

Photosystem II Captures Light Energy and Produces O_2

PSI and PSII have two main components: a light-harvesting complex and a reaction centre. **Figure 8.10** shows how these components function in PSII. In 1932 Robert Emerson and an undergraduate student, William Arnold, originally discovered the **light-harvesting complex** in the thylakoid membrane. It is composed of several dozen pigment molecules that are anchored to transmembrane proteins. The role of the complex is to directly absorb photons of light. When a pigment molecule absorbs a photon, an electron is boosted to a higher energy level. As shown in Figure 8.10, the energy (not the electron itself) is transferred to adjacent pigment molecules by a process called **resonance energy transfer**. The energy may be transferred among multiple pigment molecules until it is eventually transferred to a special pigment molecule designated P680, which is located within the reaction centre of PSII. The P680 pigment is so named because it can directly absorb light at a wavelength of 680 nm. However, P680 is more commonly excited by resonance energy transfer from another chlorophyll pigment. In either case, when an electron in P680 is excited, it is designated P680*. The light-harvesting complex is also called the **antenna complex** because it acts like an antenna that absorbs energy from light and funnels that energy to P680 in the reaction centre.

A high-energy (photoexcited) electron in a pigment molecule is relatively unstable. It may abruptly release its energy by giving off heat or light. Unlike the pigments in the light-harvesting complex that undergo resonance energy transfer, P680* can actually release its high-energy electron and become P680+.

$$P680^* \rightarrow P680^+ + e^-$$

The role of the reaction centre is to quickly remove the high-energy electron from P680* and transfer it to another molecule, where the electron will be more stable. This molecule is called the **primary electron acceptor** (Figure 8.10). The transfer of the electron from P680* to the primary electron acceptor is remarkably fast. It occurs in less than a few picoseconds! (One picosecond equals one-trillionth of a second, also noted as 10^{-12} s.) Because this occurs so quickly, the excited electron does not have much time to release its energy in the form of heat or light.

After the primary electron acceptor has received this high-energy electron, the light energy has been captured and can be used to perform cellular work. As discussed earlier, the work it performs is to synthesize the energy intermediates ATP and NADPH.

Let's now consider what happens to P680+, which has given up its high-energy electron. After P680+ is formed, it is necessary to replace the electron so that P680 can function again. Therefore, another role of the reaction centre is to replace the electron that is removed when P680* becomes P680+. This missing electron of P680+ is replaced with a low-energy electron from water (Figure 8.10).

$$H_2O \rightarrow 2 H^+ + \tfrac{1}{2} O_2 + 2 e^-$$
$$2 P680^+ + 2 e^- \rightarrow 2 P680$$
(from water)

The oxidation of water results in the formation of oxygen gas (O_2), which is used by many organisms for cellular respiration. PSII is the only known protein complex that can oxidize water, resulting in the release of O_2 into the atmosphere.

Photosystem II Is an Amazing Redox Machine

All cells rely on redox reactions to store and use energy and to form covalent bonds in organic molecules. PSII is a particularly remarkable example of a redox machine. As we have learned, this complex of proteins removes high-energy electrons from a pigment molecule and transfers them to a primary electron acceptor. Perhaps even more remarkable is that PSII can remove low-energy electrons from water—a very stable molecule that holds onto its electrons tightly. The removal of electrons from water results in the formation of oxygen (O_2).

Many approaches have been used to study how PSII works. In recent years, much effort has been aimed at determining the biochemical composition of the protein complex and the roles of its individual components. The number of protein subunits varies somewhat from species to species and may vary due to environmental changes. Typically, PSII is composed of approximately 19 different protein subunits. Two subunits, designated D1 and D2, contain the reaction centre, which carries out the redox reactions (**Figure 8.11**). Two other subunits, called CP43 and CP47, bind the pigment molecules that form the light-harvesting complex. Many additional subunits regulate the function of PSII and provide structural support.

Figure 8.11 illustrates the pathway of electron movement through PSII. The red arrows indicate the movement of a high-energy electron, and the black arrows show the path of a low-energy electron. Let's begin with a high-energy electron. When the electron on P680 is boosted to a higher energy level, usually by resonance energy transfer, this high-energy electron then moves to the primary electron acceptor, which is a chlorophyll molecule lacking Mg^{2+}, called pheophytin (Pp). Pheophytin is permanently bound to PSII and transfers the electron to a plastoquinone molecule, designated Q_A, which is also permanently bound to PSII. Next, the electron is transferred to another plastoquinone molecule designated Q_B, which can accept two high-energy electrons and bind two H^+. As shown earlier in Figure 8.7, Q_B can diffuse away from the reaction centre.

Let's now consider the path of a low-energy electron. The oxidation of water occurs in a region called the **manganese cluster**. This site is located on the side of D1 that faces the thylakoid lumen. The manganese cluster has four Mn^{2+}, one Ca^{2+}, and one Cl^-. Two water molecules bind to this site. D1 catalyzes the removal of four low-energy electrons from the two water molecules to produce O_2 and four H^+. Each low-energy electron is transferred, one at a time, to an amino acid in D1 (a tyrosine, Tyr) and then to P680+ to produce P680.

KEY
→ Low-energy electron
→ High-energy electron

The path of electron flow through photosystem II

Water is oxidized at the manganese cluster, and its electrons travel one at a time along the path shown by the arrows.

Figure 8.11 **The molecular structure of photosystem II.** Schematic drawing showing the path of electron flow from water to Q_B. The CP43 and CP47 protein subunits wrap around D1 and D2. Pigments in CP43 and CP47 can transfer energy to P680 by resonance energy transfer.

 Principle: *Structure determines function. The structural arrangement of the manganese cluster, P680, pheophytin, Q_A, and Q_B provides a pathway of electron movement from photosystem II to the electron transport chain.*

The Use of Light Flashes of Specific Wavelengths Provided Experimental Evidence for the Existence of PSII and PSI

An experimental technique that uses light flashes at particular wavelengths has been important in helping researchers to understand the function of photosystems. In this method, pioneered by Robert Emerson, a photosynthetic organism is exposed to a particular wavelength of light, after which the rate of photosynthesis is measured by the amount of CO_2 consumed or the amount of O_2 produced. In the 1950s, Emerson performed a particularly intriguing experiment that greatly stimulated photosynthesis research (**Figure 8.12**). He subjected algae to light flashes of different wavelengths and obtained a mysterious result. When he exposed algae to a wavelength of 680 nm, he observed a low rate of photosynthesis. A similarly low rate of photosynthesis occurred when he exposed algae to a wavelength of 700 nm.

Figure 8.12 **The enhancement effect observed by Emerson.** When photosynthetic organisms, such as green plants and algae, are exposed to 680-nm and 700-nm light simultaneously, the resulting rate of photosynthesis is much more than double the rate produced by each wavelength individually.

Concept check: *Would the enhancement effect be observed if two consecutive flashes of light occurred at 680 nm?*

However, when he exposed the algae to both wavelengths of light simultaneously, the rate of photosynthesis was more than double the rate observed at only one wavelength. This phenomenon was termed the **enhancement effect**. We know now that it occurs because light of 680-nm wavelength can readily activate the pigment (P680) in the reaction centre in PSII but is not very efficient at activating pigments in PSI. In contrast, light of 700-nm wavelength is optimal at activating the pigments in PSI but not those in PSII. When algae are exposed to both wavelengths, however, the pigments in both photosystems are maximally activated.

When researchers began to understand that photosynthesis results in the production of both ATP and NADPH, Robin Hill and Fay Bendall proposed that photosynthesis involves two photoactivation events. According to their model, known as the Z scheme, an electron proceeds through a series of energy changes during photosynthesis (**Figure 8.13**). The Z refers to the zigzag shape of this energy curve. Based on our modern understanding of photosynthesis, we now know these events involve increases and decreases in the energy of an electron as it moves from PSII through PSI to $NADP^+$ during noncyclic electron flow. An electron on a nonexcited pigment molecule in photosystem II has the lowest energy. In PSII, light boosts an electron to a much higher energy level. As the electron travels from PSII to PSI, some of the energy is released. The input of light in PSI boosts the electron to an even higher energy than it attained in PSII. The electron releases a little energy before it is eventually transferred to $NADP^+$.

Figure 8.13 The Z scheme, showing the energy of an electron moving from photosystem II to NADP⁺. The oxidation of water releases two electrons that travel one at a time from photosystem II to NADP⁺. As seen here, the input of light boosts the energy of the electron twice. At the end of the pathway, two electrons are used to make NADPH.

Concept check: *During its journey from photosystem II to NADP⁺, at what point does an electron have the highest amount of energy?*

8.4 SYNTHESIZING CARBOHYDRATES VIA THE CALVIN CYCLE

Learning Outcomes:

1. Outline the three phases of the Calvin cycle.
2. Explain how Calvin and Benson identified the components of the Calvin cycle.

In the previous section, we learned how the light reactions of photosynthesis produce O₂, ATP, and NADPH. We will now turn our attention to the second phase of photosynthesis, the Calvin cycle, in which ATP and NADPH are used to make carbohydrates. The Calvin cycle consists of a series of steps that occur in a metabolic cycle. In plants and algae, it occurs in the stroma of chloroplasts. In cyanobacteria, the Calvin cycle occurs in the cytoplasm of the bacterial cells.

The Calvin cycle takes CO_2 from the atmosphere and incorporates the carbon into organic molecules, namely, carbohydrates. As mentioned earlier, carbohydrates are critical for two reasons. First, these organic molecules provide the precursors to make the organic molecules and macromolecules of nearly all living cells. The organic molecules in your body are ultimately derived from the operation of the Calvin cycle in algae and plants. The second key reason why the Calvin cycle is important involves the storage of energy. Recall that such molecules as glucose contain large amounts of chemical energy in

their covalent bonds. The Calvin cycle produces carbohydrates, which store energy. These carbohydrates are accumulated inside plant cells. When a plant is in the dark and not carrying out photosynthesis, the stored carbohydrates can be used as a source of energy. Similarly, when an animal consumes a plant, it can use the carbohydrates as an energy source.

In this section, we will examine the three phases of the Calvin cycle and their components. We will also explore the experimental approach of Melvin Calvin and his colleagues that enabled them to elucidate the steps of this cycle.

The Calvin Cycle Incorporates CO_2 into Carbohydrate

The Calvin cycle, also called the Calvin-Benson cycle, was determined by chemists Melvin Calvin, Andrew Adam Benson, and their colleagues in the 1940s and 1950s. This cycle requires a massive input of energy. For every six carbon dioxide molecules that are incorporated into carbohydrate such as glucose, 18 ATP molecules are hydrolyzed and 12 NADPH molecules are oxidized:

$$6CO_2 + 12\ H_2O \rightarrow C_6H_{12}O_6 + 6\ O_2 + 6\ H_2O$$
gulcose

$$18\ ATP + 18\ H_2O \rightarrow 18\ ADP + 18\ P_i$$
$$12\ NADPH \rightarrow 12\ NADP^+ + 12\ H^+ + 24\ e^-$$

Although biologists commonly describe glucose as a product of photosynthesis, glucose is not directly made by the Calvin cycle. Instead, products of the Calvin cycle are used as starting materials for the synthesis of glucose and other molecules, including sucrose. After glucose molecules are made, they can be linked to form a polymer of glucose called starch, which is stored in the chloroplast for later use. Alternatively, the disaccharide sucrose may be made and transported out of the leaf to other parts of the plant.

The Calvin cycle can be divided into three phases: carbon fixation, reduction and carbohydrate production, and regeneration of ribulose bisphosphate (RuBP) (**Figure 8.14**).

Carbon Fixation (Phase 1) During **carbon fixation**, CO_2 becomes incorporated into ribulose bisphosphate (RuBP), a five-carbon sugar. The term *fixation* means that the carbon has been removed from the atmosphere and fixed into an organic molecule that is not a gas. The product of the reaction is a six-carbon intermediate that immediately splits to form two molecules of 3-phosphoglycerate (3PG). The enzyme that catalyzes this step is RuBP carboxylase/oxygenase, or **Rubisco**. This enzyme, which constitutes approximately 50% of the total protein in chloroplasts, is likely to be the most abundant protein on Earth. This observation underscores the massive amount of carbon fixation that occurs in the biosphere.

$$CO_2 + RuBP \xrightarrow{\text{Rubisco}} 2 \times \text{3-phosphoglycerate}$$

Reduction and Carbohydrate Production (Phase 2) In the second phase ATP is used to convert 3PG to 1,3-bisphosphoglycerate. Next, electrons from NADPH reduce 1,3-bisphosphoglycerate to glyceraldehyde-3-phosphate (G3P). G3P is a carbohydrate with three carbon atoms. The key difference between 3PG and G3P is that G3P has a C—H bond, while the analogous carbon in 3PG forms a C—O bond (Figure 8.14). The C—H bond can occur because the G3P molecule has been

Figure 8.14 **The Calvin cycle.** This cycle has three phases: (1) carbon fixation, (2) reduction and carbohydrate production, and (3) regeneration of RuBP.

Concept check: *Why is NADPH needed during this cycle?*

FEATURE INVESTIGATION

The Calvin Cycle Was Determined by Isotope Labelling Methods

The steps in the Calvin cycle involve the conversion of one type of molecule to another, eventually regenerating the starting material, RuBP. In the 1940s and 1950s, Calvin and his colleagues used ^{14}C, a radioisotope of carbon, as a way to label and trace molecules produced during the cycle (**Figure 8.15**). They injected ^{14}C-labelled CO_2 into cultures of the green algae

Chlorella pyrenoidosa grown in an apparatus called a "lollipop" (because of its shape). The *Chlorella* cells were given different lengths of time to incorporate the ^{14}C-labelled carbon, ranging from fractions of a second to many minutes. After this incubation period, the cells were abruptly placed into a solution of alcohol to inhibit enzymatic reactions and thereby stop the cycle.

The researchers separated the newly made radiolabelled molecules by a variety of methods. The most commonly used method was two-dimensional paper chromatography. In this

GOAL The incorporation of CO_2 into carbohydrate involves a biosynthetic pathway. The aim of this experiment was to identify the steps.

KEY MATERIALS The green alga *Chlorella pyrenoidosa* and ^{14}C-labelled CO_2.

Experimental level   **Conceptual level**

1   Grow *Chlorella* in an apparatus called a "lollipop." Add ^{14}C-labelled CO_2 and incubate for various lengths of time (from fractions of a second to many minutes). Stop the Calvin cycle by placing a sample of cells into a solution of alcohol.

Addition of $^{14}CO_2$

Chlorella

Lamp

Lollipop

Alcohol solution

$^{14}CO_2$

Calvin cycle

Alcohol

Cycle stopped

2   Take a sample of the internal cell contents and spot on the corner of chromatography paper. This spot is called the origin.

Origin

1,3-BPG

3PG

G3P

RuBP

3   Place edge of paper in a solvent, such as phenol-water, and allow time for solvent to rise and separate the mixture of molecules that were spotted at the origin.

Solvent

1,3-BPG

G3P

3PG

RuBP

4   Dry paper, turn 90°, and then place the edge in a different solvent such as butanol-propionic acid-water. Allow time for solvent to rise.

1,3-BPG

G3P

3PG

RuBP

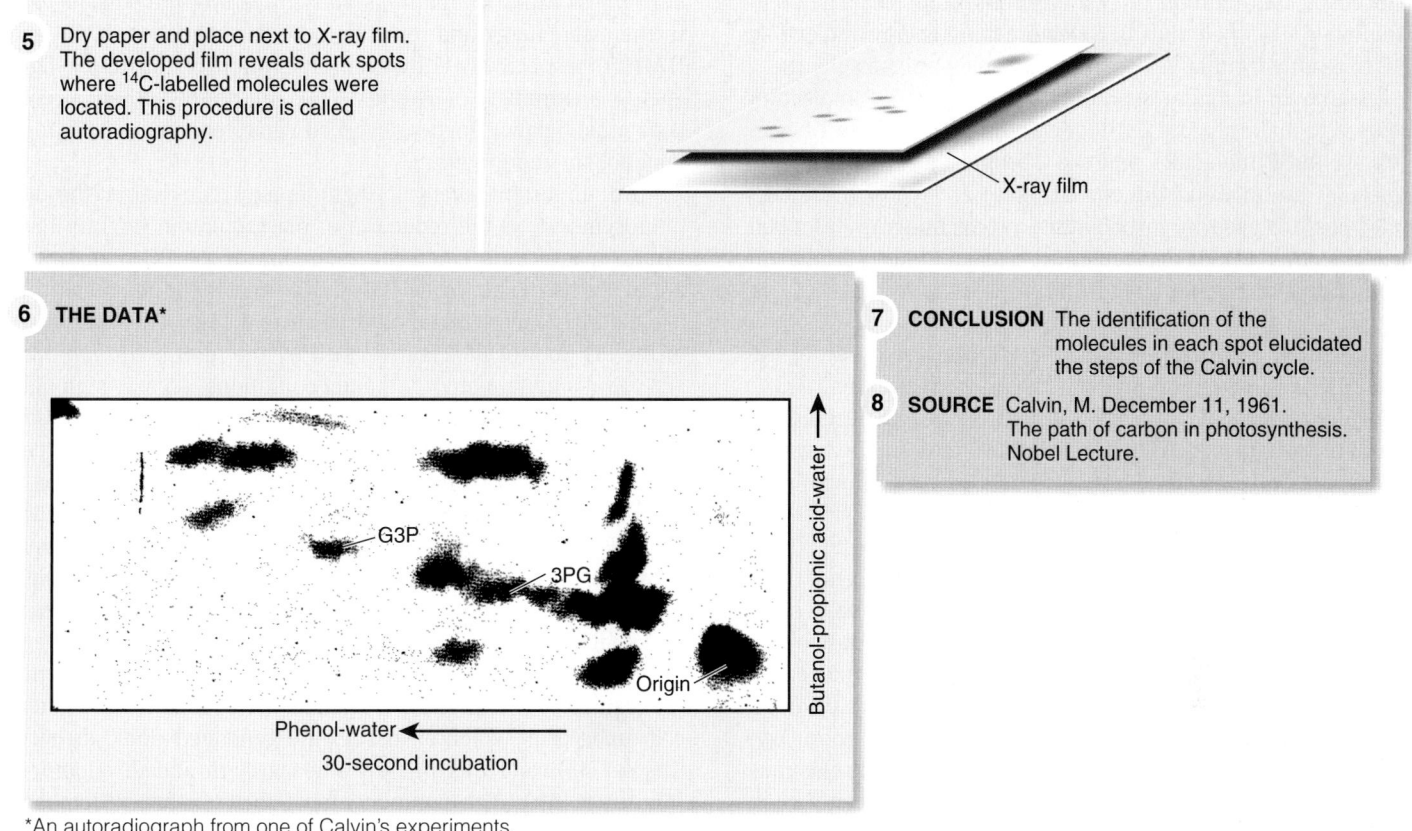

5   Dry paper and place next to X-ray film. The developed film reveals dark spots where ^{14}C-labelled molecules were located. This procedure is called autoradiography.

X-ray film

6   **THE DATA***

Butanol-propionic acid-water

G3P

3PG

Origin

Phenol-water ←

30-second incubation

7   **CONCLUSION** The identification of the molecules in each spot elucidated the steps of the Calvin cycle.

8   **SOURCE** Calvin, M. December 11, 1961. The path of carbon in photosynthesis. Nobel Lecture.

*An autoradiograph from one of Calvin's experiments.

Figure 8.15   The determination of the Calvin cycle by using labelling of CO_2 with ^{14}C.

approach, a sample containing radiolabelled molecules was spotted onto a corner of the paper at a location called the origin. The edge of the paper was placed in a solvent, such as phenol-water, and the solvent would ascend to the top of the paper. As the solvent rose through the paper, so did the radiolabelled molecules. The rate at which they rose depended on their structures, which determine how soluble they are in the solvent and how strongly they interact with the fibres in the paper. This step separated the mixture of molecules spotted onto the paper at the origin. The paper was then dried and turned 90 degrees, and then the edge was placed in a different solvent, such as butanol-propionic acid-water. Again, the solvent would rise through the paper, thereby separating molecules in a second dimension. Note that a specific molecule could be very soluble in one of the solvents and much less so in the second solvent. After this second separation step, the paper was dried and exposed to X-ray film, a procedure called autoradiography. Radioactive emission from the ^{14}C-labelled molecules caused dark spots to appear on the film.

The pattern of spots changed, depending on the length of time that the cells were incubated with ^{14}C-labelled CO_2. If the incubation period was short, only molecules that were made in the first steps of the Calvin cycle were seen, while longer incubations revealed molecules synthesized in later steps. For example, after short incubations, 3-phosphoglycerate (3PG) and 1,3-bisphosphoglycerate (1,3-BPG) were observed, while longer

incubations showed glyceraldehyde-3-phosphate (G3P) and ribulose bisphosphate (RuBP).

A challenge for Calvin and his colleagues was to identify the chemical nature of each spot. This was achieved by a variety of chemical methods. For example, a spot could be cut out of the paper, the molecule within the paper could be washed out, or eluted, and then the eluted molecule could be subjected to the same procedure that included a radiolabelled molecule whose structure was already known. If the unknown molecule and known molecule migrated to the same spot in the paper, this indicated that they were the same molecule. During the late 1940s and 1950s, Calvin and his colleagues identified all the ^{14}C-labelled spots and the order in which they appeared. In this way, they were able to determine the series of reactions of what we now know as the Calvin cycle. For this work, Calvin was awarded the Nobel Prize in Chemistry in 1961.

Experimental Questions

1. What was the purpose of the study conducted by Calvin and his colleagues?

2. In Calvin's experiments shown in Figure 8.15, why did the researchers use ^{14}C? Why did they examine samples at several different time periods? How were the different molecules in the samples identified?

3. What were the results of Calvin's study?

reduced by the addition of two electrons from NADPH. Compared with 3PG, the bonds in G3P store more energy and enable G3P to readily form larger organic molecules, such as glucose.

As shown in Figure 8.14, only some of the G3P molecules are used to make glucose or other carbohydrates. Phase 1 began with six RuBP molecules and six CO_2 molecules. Twelve G3P molecules are made at the end of phase 2. Two of these G3P molecules are used in carbohydrate production. As described next, the other 10 G3P molecules are needed to keep the Calvin cycle turning by regenerating RuBP.

Regeneration of RuBP (Phase 3) In the last phase of the Calvin cycle, a series of enzymatic steps converts the 10 G3P molecules (10 × 3C) into six RuBP (6 × 5C) molecules, by using six molecules of ATP. As each RuBP molecule is regenerated, it can serve as an acceptor for CO_2, thereby allowing the cycle to continue.

As we have just seen, the Calvin cycle begins by using carbon from an inorganic source, that is, CO_2, and ends with organic molecules that will be used by the plant to make other compounds. You may be wondering why it is not possible to directly link the CO_2 molecules to form these larger molecules. The answer lies in the number of electrons that orbit carbon atoms. In CO_2, the carbon atom is considered electron poor. Oxygen is a very electronegative atom that monopolizes the electrons it shares with other atoms. In a covalent bond between carbon and oxygen, the shared electrons are closer to the oxygen atom.

By comparison, in an organic molecule, the carbon atom is electron rich. During the Calvin cycle, ATP provides energy and NADPH donates high-energy electrons so that the carbon originally in CO_2 has been reduced. The Calvin cycle combines fewer electronegative atoms with carbon atoms so that C—H and C—C bonds are formed. This allows the eventual synthesis of larger organic molecules, including glucose, amino acids, and other essential compounds. In addition, the covalent bonds within these molecules are capable of storing large amounts of energy.

8.5 | ENVIRONMENTAL EXTREMES AND VARIATIONS IN PHOTOSYNTHESIS

Learning Outcomes:

1. Explain how photostasis can be achieved when plants are exposed to extreme environmental conditions.
2. Explain the concept of photorespiration.
3. Describe how C_4 and CAM plants avoid photorespiration and conserve water.

Thus far, we have considered the process of photosynthesis as it occurs in the chloroplasts of green plants and algae. Photosynthesis is a two-stage process in which the light reactions produce O_2, ATP, and NADPH, and the Calvin cycle uses the ATP and NADPH in the synthesis of carbohydrates and for other enzymatic reactions of metabolism. This two-stage process is a universal feature of photosynthesis in all green plants, algae, and cyanobacteria. The photosynthetic apparatus is remarkably efficient at capturing photons and converting the solar energy to chemical energy and reducing power in the form of ATP and NADPH, respectively. However, absorption of too much light energy is extremely dangerous. Thus, all photosynthetic organisms must balance energy absorbed verses energy used through metabolism and growth.

An important event in light energy conversion through photosynthesis is the reduction of plastoquinone (PQ) by PSII. **Photostasis** occurs when the reduction of the PQ pool is balanced by its oxidation by PSI and by metabolic reactions that use the high energy metabolites (**Figure 8.16a**). The redox state of the PQ pool of PSII is described by the term *excitation pressure*. Under certain environmental conditions, such as high light intensity, adverse temperatures, nutrient depletion, and water deficit, the excitation pressure is high, and this situation can pose problems for cells. Norman Hüner and his colleagues at the University of Western Ontario have shown that the redox state of the photosynthetic apparatus is a sensor of environmental stress. In many species of cyanobacteria, algae, and plants, changes in excitation pressure result in signalling processes that enable these organisms to alter their metabolism and gene expression to cope with suboptimal conditions. In higher plants, the regulatory network can also affect meristematic cells, a stem cell cache from which all tissues are generated (look ahead to Chapter 33), and this in turn alters growth and development (**Figure 8.16b**). The components of this sensing system and the elucidation of the signalling pathways are current areas of interest in the Hüner lab, and it is anticipated that these studies will have implications for increasing plant tolerance to myriad stresses, such as cold, drought, and elevated CO_2, and for enhancing the efficiency of light energy conversion into biomass and seed yield in agriculturally important crops.

Although plants have many ways in which they can alter their biochemistry to survive during periods of adversity, over a longer evolutionary scale several variations of photosynthesis have evolved to enable plants to cope with daily extremes in their environments. We conclude Chapter 8 with a description of two variations of photosynthesis that help to maximize photosynthetic efficiency in hot and dry environments.

Photorespiration Decreases the Efficiency of Photosynthesis

In the previous section you learned that Rubisco adds a CO_2 molecule to an organic molecule, RuBP, to produce two molecules of 3-phosphoglycerate (3PG):

$$\text{RuBP} + CO_2 \rightarrow 2 \text{ 3PG}$$

For most species of plants, the incorporation of CO_2 into RuBP is the only way for carbon fixation to occur. Because 3PG is a three-carbon molecule, these plants are called **C_3 plants**, which account for approximately 90% of all terrestrial plants.

Researchers have discovered that the active site of Rubisco can also function as an oxygenase. As mentioned earlier, that is why it is called Rubisco, which stands for RuBP carboxylase/oxygenase. When Rubisco adds an O_2 molecule to RuBP, this creates only one molecule of 3-phosphoglycerate and a two-carbon molecule called phosphoglycolate. The phosphoglycolate is then dephosphorylated

(a) The redox state of the PQ pool is a sensor of environmental change

(b) Environmental sensing by the chloroplast generates signals that influence growth

Figure 8.16   Photostasis and excitation pressure.   (a) The redox pool of plastoquinone (PQ) is a sensor of environmental conditions. Photostasis occurs when energy inputs are balanced by energy consumption (or heat loss). Imbalances alter the excitation pressure on PSII and result in redox signalling to adjust gene expression and metabolism in the short term or may have more profound developmental consequences if unfavourable conditions persist **(b).**

Principle: *Living organisms have mechanisms that maintain homeostasis. Photostasis centres on how photoautotrophs manage the energy flow from the sun, using it to drive growth and metabolism when conditions are optimal, and sometimes dissipating it through heat loss or other mechanisms if conditions are not conducive to growth.*

to glycolate and released from the chloroplast. In a series of steps the two-carbon glycolate is eventually oxidized in other organelles to produce an organic molecule and a molecule of CO_2:

$$RuBP + O_2 \rightarrow 3\text{-phosphoglycerate} + \text{phosphoglycolate}$$

$$\text{phosphoglycolate} \rightarrow \text{glycolate} \rightarrow \rightarrow \rightarrow CO_2$$

This process, called **photorespiration**, uses O_2 and liberates CO_2. Photorespiration is considered wasteful because it reverses the effects of photosynthesis, thereby reducing the ability of a plant to make carbohydrates, which limits plant growth.

Photorespiration is more likely to occur when plants are exposed to a hot and dry environment. To conserve water, the stomata of the leaves close, inhibiting the uptake of CO_2 from the air and trapping the O_2 that is produced by photosynthesis. When the level of CO_2 is low and O_2 is high, photorespiration is favoured. If C_3 plants are subjected to hot and dry environmental conditions, as much as 25% to 50% of their photosynthetic work is reversed by the process of photorespiration.

Why do plants carry out photorespiration? The answer is not entirely clear. One common view is that photorespiration does not offer any advantage and is an evolutionary relic. When Rubisco first evolved some 3 billion years ago, the atmospheric oxygen level was low, and phosphorespiration would not have been a problem. Another view is that photorespiration may have a protective advantage. On hot and dry days, CO_2 levels within a plant can fall and O_2 levels can rise. Under these conditions, highly toxic oxygen-containing molecules, such as free radicals, may be produced that could damage the plant. Therefore, plant biologists have hypothesized that the role of photorespiration may be to protect the plant against the harmful effects of such toxic molecules by consuming O_2 and releasing CO_2. In addition, photorespiration affects the metabolism of other compounds in plants. David Canvin and his colleagues at Queen's University showed that such respiratory processes provide the reductant needed for nitrogen assimilation and highlighted the importance of biochemical regulation among different organelles in coordinating nitrogen and carbon metabolism.

C_4 Plants Have Evolved a Mechanism to Minimize Photorespiration

Certain species of plants have developed an interesting way to prevent photorespiration. In the early 1960s Hugo Kortschak discovered that the first product of photosynthesis in sugarcane is not 3-phosphoglycerate but instead is a compound with four carbon atoms. Such species as sugarcane are thus called **C_4 plants** because the first step in carbon fixation produces a four-carbon compound. Later, Marshall Hatch and Roger Slack confirmed this result and identified the compound as oxaloacetate. For this reason, the pathway is sometimes called the Hatch-Slack pathway.

Some C_4 plants have a unique leaf anatomy that allows them to avoid photorespiration (**Figure 8.17**). An interior layer in the leaves of many C_4 plants has a two-cell organization composed of mesophyll cells and bundle-sheath cells. CO_2 from the atmosphere enters the mesophyll cells via stomata. Once inside, the enzyme **PEP carboxylase** adds CO_2 to phosphoenolpyruvate (PEP) to produce the four-carbon compound oxaloacetate. PEP carboxylase

does not recognize O_2. Therefore, unlike Rubisco, PEP carboxylase does not promote photorespiration when CO_2 is low and O_2 is high. Instead, PEP carboxylase continues to fix CO_2.

A key feature of these types of C_4 plants is that a four-carbon compound is transferred between cells. As shown in Figure 8.17, the compound oxaloacetate is converted to the four-carbon compound malate, which is transported into the bundle-sheath cell. Malate is then broken down into pyruvate and CO_2. The pyruvate returns to the mesophyll cell, where it is converted to PEP via ATP, and the cycle in the mesophyll cell can begin again. The CO_2 enters the Calvin cycle in the chloroplasts of the bundle-sheath cells. Because the mesophyll cell provides the bundle-sheath cell with a steady supply of CO_2, the concentration of CO_2 remains high in the bundle-sheath cell. Also, the mesophyll cells shield the bundle sheath cells from high levels of O_2. This strategy minimizes photorespiration, which requires low CO_2 and high O_2 levels to proceed.

Which is better—being a C_3 or a C_4 plant? The answer is that it depends on the environment. In warm and dry climates, C_4 plants have an advantage because during the day they can keep their stomata partially closed to reduce water vaporization from the leaf and thereby conserve water. Furthermore, they avoid photorespiration. C_4 plants are well adapted to habitats with high daytime temperatures and intense sunlight. Some examples of C_4 plants include crabgrass, corn, and sugarcane. In cooler climates, C_3 plants have the edge because it takes less energy for them to fix carbon dioxide. The process of carbon fixation that occurs in C_4 plants uses ATP to regenerate PEP from pyruvate (Figure 8.17), which C_3 plants do not have to expend.

CAM Plants Are C_4 Plants That Take Up Carbon Dioxide at Night

You have just learned that certain C_4 plants prevent photorespiration by pumping CO_2 into the bundle-sheath cells, where the Calvin cycle occurs. Another strategy followed by other C_4 plants called **CAM plants** is to separate these processes in time. CAM stands for crassulacean acid metabolism, because the process was first studied in members of the plant family Crassulaceae. CAM plants are water-storing succulents, such as cacti, bromeliads (including pineapple), and sedums. To avoid water loss, CAM plants keep their stomata closed during the day and open them during the night, when it is cooler and the relative humidity is higher.

How, then, do CAM plants carry out photosynthesis? **Figure 8.18** compares CAM plants with the other type of C_4 plants we considered in Figure 8.17. Photosynthesis in CAM plants occurs entirely within mesophyll cells but the synthesis of a C_4 molecule and the Calvin cycle occur at different times. During the night the stomata of CAM plants open, thereby allowing the entry of CO_2 into mesophyll cells, where it joins with PEP to form the four-carbon compound oxaloacetate. This is converted to malate, which accumulates during the night in the central vacuoles of the cells. In the morning, the stomata close to conserve moisture. The accumulated malate in the mesophyll cells leaves the vacuole and is broken down to release CO_2, which then drives the Calvin cycle during the daytime.

Mesophyll cells: Form a protective layer around bundle-sheath cells so they are not exposed to high O_2.

Bundle-sheath cells: Site of Calvin cycle.

High O_2 and low CO_2 diffuses around the mesophyll cells.

O_2
O_2 O_2
O_2 O_2
CO_2

Stomata

Vein

Epidermal cells

Mesophyll cell—exposed to high O_2 and low CO_2

PEP carboxylase

PEP 3 C

AMP + PP$_i$

Oxaloacetate 4 C

ATP + P$_i$

Malate 4 C

Pyruvate 3 C

CO_2

Calvin cycle

Bundle-sheath cell—accumulates CO_2, not exposed to high O_2 levels

Vein

Sugar

Figure 8.17   Leaf structure and its relationship to the C_4 cycle. C_4 plants have mesophyll cells that initially take up CO_2 and bundle-sheath cells, where much of the carbohydrate synthesis occurs. Compare this leaf structure with the structure of C_3 leaves shown in Figure 8.2.

Concept check: *How does this cellular arrangement minimize photorespiration?*

BioConnections: *Look ahead to Figure 36.9. How do plants get water needed for photosynthesis into their leaves?*

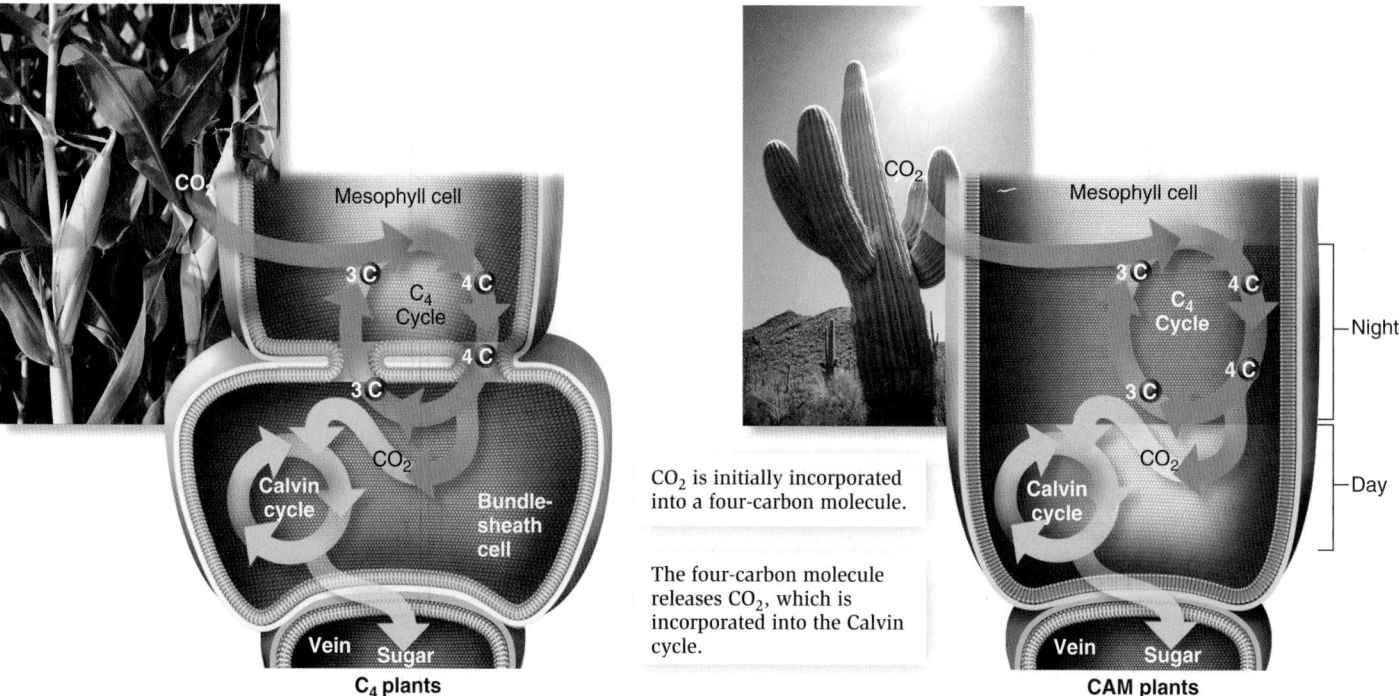

CO_2

Mesophyll cell

3 C   4 C
C_4 Cycle
4 C
3 C

CO_2

Calvin cycle

Bundle-sheath cell

Vein   Sugar

C_4 plants

CO_2

Mesophyll cell

3 C   4 C
C_4 Cycle
4 C
3 C

Night

CO_2

Calvin cycle

Day

Vein   Sugar

CAM plants

CO_2 is initially incorporated into a four-carbon molecule.

The four-carbon molecule releases CO_2, which is incorporated into the Calvin cycle.

Figure 8.18   A comparison of C_4 and CAM plants. C_4 plants are those plants in which the first organic product of carbon fixation is a four-carbon compound. Using this definition, CAM plants are a type of C_4 plant because they produce a four-carbon molecule when CO_2 is initially taken up. CAM plants, however, do not separate the functions of making a four-carbon molecule and the Calvin cycle into different types of cells. Instead, they make a four-carbon molecule at night and break down that molecule during the day, so that the CO_2 can be incorporated via the Calvin cycle.

Concept check: *What are the advantages and disadvantages of C_3, C_4, and CAM plants?*

Summary of Key Concepts

8.1 Overview of Photosynthesis

- Photosynthesis is the process by which plants, algae, and cyanobacteria capture light energy to synthesize carbohydrates. (Figure 8.1)

- Heterotrophs must obtain organic molecules in their food, while autotrophs can make organic molecules from inorganic sources. Photoautotrophs use the energy from light to make organic molecules. (Figure 8.1)

- Photosynthesis uses carbon dioxide, water, and energy to generate carbohydrates and oxygen.

- An energy cycle occurs in the biosphere in which photosynthesis uses light, CO_2 and H_2O to make organic molecules (anabolic reaction), and the organic molecules are broken back down to CO_2 and H_2O via cellular respiration to supply energy in the form of ATP (catabolic reactions). (Figure 8.1)

- In plants and algae, photosynthesis occurs within chloroplasts, which have an outer membrane, inner membrane, and thylakoid membrane. The stroma is found between the thylakoid membrane and inner membrane. In plants the leaves are the major site of photosynthesis. (Figure 8.2)

- The light reactions of photosynthesis capture light energy to make ATP, NADPH, and O_2. These reactions occur at the thylakoid membrane. Carbohydrate synthesis happens in the stroma and uses ATP and NADPH from the light reactions. (Figure 8.3)

8.2 Reactions That Harness Light Energy

- Light is a form of electromagnetic radiation that travels in waves and is composed of photons with discrete amounts of energy. (Figure 8.4)

- Electrons can absorb light energy and be boosted to a higher energy level. (Figure 8.5)

- Photosynthetic pigments include chlorophylls a and b and carotenoids. These pigments absorb light energy in the visible spectrum. (Figure 8.6)

- During noncyclic electron flow, electrons from photosystem II follow a pathway along an electron transport chain in the thylakoid membrane. This pathway generates an H^+ gradient that is used to make ATP. In addition, light energy striking photosystem I boosts an electron to a very high energy level that allows the synthesis of NADPH. (Figure 8.7)

- During cyclic photophosphorylation, electrons are activated in PSI and flow from Fd to Q_B to the cytochrome complex to Pc and back to PSI. This cyclic electron route produces an H^+ gradient that is used to make ATP. (Figure 8.8)

- Cytochrome b in mitochondria and cytochrome b_6 in chloroplasts are homologous proteins, both of which are involved in electron transport and H^+ pumping. (Figure 8.9)

8.3 Molecular Features of Photosystems

- In the light-harvesting complex of photosystem II, pigment molecules absorb light energy that is transferred to the reaction centre via resonance energy transfer. A high-energy electron from P680* is transferred to a primary electron acceptor. An electron from water is then used to replenish the electron that is lost from P680*. (Figures 8.10, 8.11)

- Emerson showed that, compared with single light flashes at 680 nm and 700 nm, light flashes at both wavelengths more than doubled the amount of photosynthesis. This occurred because these wavelengths activate pigments in PSII and PSI, respectively. (Figure 8.12)

- The Z scheme proposes that an electron absorbs light energy twice, at both PSII and PSI, losing some of that energy as it flows along the electron transport chain in the thylakoid membrane. (Figure 8.13)

8.4 Synthesizing Carbohydrates via the Calvin Cycle

- The Calvin cycle can be divided into three phases: carbon fixation, reduction and carbohydrate production, and regeneration of ribulose bisphosphate (RuBP). During this process, ATP is used as a source of energy and NADPH is used as a source of high-energy electrons so that CO_2 can be incorporated into carbohydrate. (Figure 8.14)

- Calvin and Benson used radioisotope labelling and chromatography to identify the products of the Calvin cycle and to determine the series of steps in the biochemical pathway. (Figure 8.15)

8.5 Environmental Extremes and Variations in Photosynthesis

- C_3 plants can incorporate CO_2 into organic molecules only via RuBP to make 3PG, a three-carbon molecule.

- Photostasis occurs when the energy and reductive power harnessed by photosynthesis are counterbalanced by the energy and reducing power of the Calvin cycle and by other metabolic reactions (Figure 8.16)

- Photorespiration can occur under conditions of high O_2 and low CO_2, which occur under hot and dry conditions. During this process, some CO_2 is liberated and O_2 is used.

- Some C_4 plants avoid photorespiration because CO_2 is first incorporated, via PEP carboxylase, into a four-carbon molecule, which is pumped from mesophyll cells into bundle-sheath cells. This maintains a high concentration of CO_2 in the bundle-sheath cells, where the Calvin cycle occurs. The high CO_2 concentration minimizes photorespiration. (Figure 8.17)

- CAM plants prevent photorespiration by fixing CO_2 into a four-carbon molecule at night and then running the Calvin cycle during the day with their stomata closed to reduce water loss. (Figure 8.18)

Test to Assess Your Learning

1. The water necessary for photosynthesis
   a. is split into H_2 and O_2.
   b. is directly involved in the synthesis of carbohydrate.
   c. provides the electrons to replace lost electrons in photosystem II.
   d. provides H^+ needed to synthesize G3P.
   e. does none of the above.

2. The reaction centre pigment differs from the other pigment molecules of the light-harvesting complex in that
   a. the reaction centre pigment is a carotenoid.
   b. the reaction centre pigment absorbs light energy and transfers that energy to other molecules without the transfer of electrons.
   c. the reaction centre pigment transfers excited electrons to other molecules.
   d. the reaction centre pigment does not transfer excited electrons to the primary electron acceptor.
   e. the reaction centre acts as an ATP synthase to produce ATP.

When the ligand concentration is above the K_d value, most of the receptors are likely to have ligand bound to them. In contrast, if the ligand concentration is substantially below the K_d value, most receptors will not be bound by their ligand. The K_d values for many different ligands and their receptors have been experimentally determined. How is this information useful? It allows researchers to predict when a signalling molecule is likely to cause a cellular response. If the concentration of a signalling molecule is far below the K_d value, a cellular response is not likely because relatively few receptors will form a complex with the signalling molecule.

Unlike enzymes, which convert their substrates into products, receptors do not usually alter the structure of their ligands. Instead, the ligands alter the structure of their receptors, causing a conformational change (**Figure 9.5**). After binding, the hormone • receptor complex is called an activated receptor, because the binding of the hormone to its receptor has changed the receptor in a way that will initiate a cellular response.

The binding of a ligand to its receptor is a reversible process, and when dissociation of the ligand occurs, the receptor is no longer in the activated state.

Cells Contain a Variety of Cell Surface Receptors That Respond to Extracellular Signals

Most signals, either environmental agents or signals that are secreted from cells, are small hydrophilic molecules or large molecules that do not readily pass through the plasma membrane of cells. To respond to such extracellular signals, cells possess several different types of **cell surface receptors**—receptors that are found in the plasma membrane and thus strategically positioned to monitor the external environment. A typical cell

Ligand (signalling molecule)

Ligand binding

Inactive receptor

Activated receptor

The binding of a ligand to its receptor causes a conformational change in the receptor, resulting in receptor activation.

Cytosol

Figure 9.5   Receptor activation.

BioConnections: *Look back at Figure 7.6. How is the binding of a ligand to its receptor similar to the binding of a substrate to an enzyme? How are they different?*

often possesses dozens or even hundreds of different cell surface receptors (present singly or in multiple copies) that enable the cell to respond to different kinds of signalling molecules. By analyzing the functions of cell surface receptors from many different organisms, researchers have determined that most fall into one of three categories: enzyme-linked receptors, G-protein-coupled receptors, and ligand-gated channels, which are described next.

Enzyme-Linked Receptors   Receptors known as **enzyme-linked receptors** are found in all living species. Many human hormones bind to this type of receptor. For example, when insulin binds to an enzyme-linked receptor in muscle cells, it enhances their ability to use glucose. Enzyme-linked receptors typically have two important domains: an extracellular domain, which binds a signalling ligand, and an intracellular domain, which has a catalytic function (**Figure 9.6a**). When a signalling molecule binds to the extracellular domain, a conformational change is transmitted through the membrane-embedded portion of the protein that affects the conformation of the intracellular catalytic domain. In most cases this conformational change causes the catalytic domain to become functionally active.

Most types of enzyme-linked receptors function as **protein kinases**, enzymes that transfer a phosphate group from ATP to specific amino acids in a protein (**Figure 9.6b**). For example, tyrosine kinases attach phosphate to the amino acid tyrosine, whereas serine/threonine kinases attach phosphate to the amino acids serine and threonine. In the absence of a signalling molecule, the catalytic domain of the receptor remains inactive. However, when a signal binds to the extracellular domain, the catalytic domain is activated. Under these conditions, the receptor may phosphorylate itself or it may phosphorylate intracellular proteins. The attachment of a negatively charged phosphate changes the structure of a protein and thereby can alter its function. Later in this chapter we will explore how this event leads to a cellular response, such as the activation of enzymes that affect cell function.

G-Protein-Coupled Receptors   Receptors called **G-protein-coupled receptors (GPCRs)** are found in the cells of all eukaryotic species. GPCRs typically contain seven transmembrane segments that wind back and forth through the plasma membrane. The receptors interact with intracellular proteins called **G proteins**, which are so named because of their ability to bind **g**uanosine **tri**phosphate (GTP) and **g**uanosine **di**phosphate (GDP). GTP is similar in structure to ATP except it has guanine as a base instead of adenine. In the 1970s the existence of G proteins was first proposed by Martin Rodbell and colleagues, who found that GTP was needed for certain hormone receptors to cause an intracellular response. Later, Alfred Gilman and his co-workers used genetic and biochemical techniques to identify and purify a G protein. In 1994 Rodbell and Gilman won the Nobel Prize for their pioneering work. The importance of

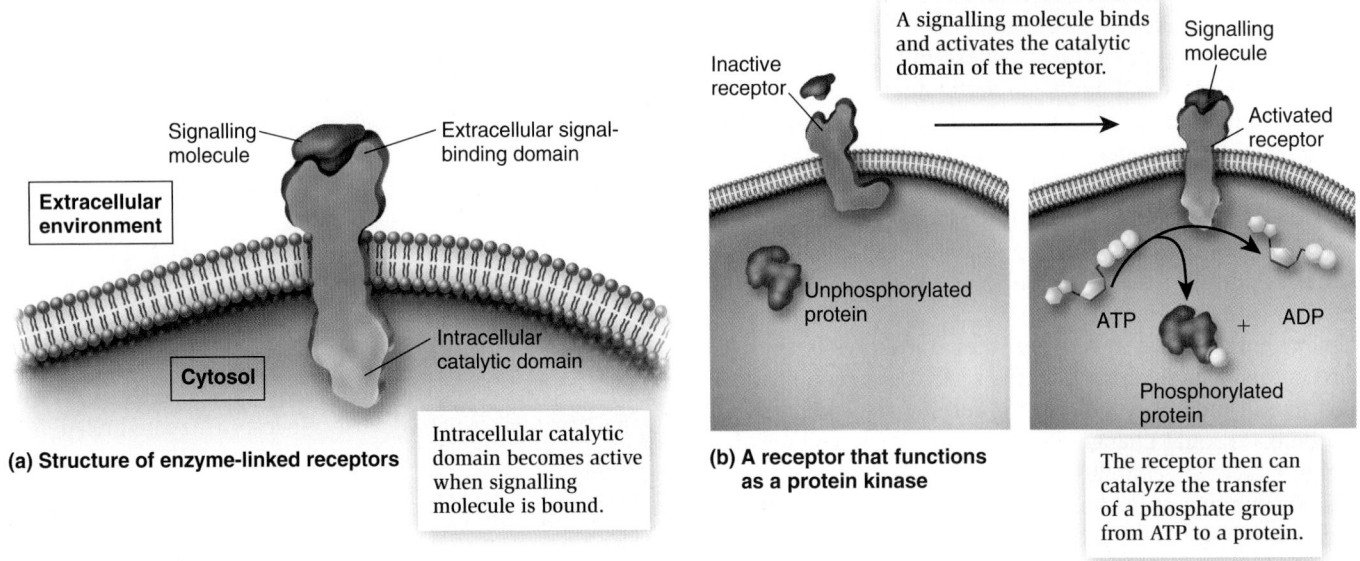

(a) **Structure of enzyme-linked receptors**

Intracellular catalytic domain becomes active when signalling molecule is bound.

(b) **A receptor that functions as a protein kinase**

The receptor then can catalyze the transfer of a phosphate group from ATP to a protein.

Figure 9.6   Enzyme-linked receptors.

Concept check: *Based on your understanding of ATP as an energy intermediate, is the phosphorylation of a protein via a protein kinase an exergonic or endergonic reaction? How is the energy of protein phosphorylation used—what does it accomplish?*

Figure 9.7   The activation of G-protein-coupled receptors and G proteins.

Concept check: *What has to happen for the α and β/γ subunits of the G protein to reassociate with each other?*

G-protein-coupled pathways in cellular metabolism and signalling is underscored by the fact that many human disorders (central nervous system, cardiac and metabolic disorders, pain, allergic responses) are caused by alterations in components of these pathways, and nearly half of all pharmaceuticals influence G-protein-coupled pathways.

Figure 9.7 shows how a GPCR and G protein interact. At the cell surface, a signalling molecule binds to a GPCR, causing a conformational change that activates the receptor which in turn causes it to bind to a G protein. The G protein, which is a lipid-anchored protein, releases GDP and binds GTP instead. GTP binding changes the conformation of the G protein, causing it to dissociate into its α subunit and a β/γ dimer. Later in this chapter we will examine how the α subunit interacts with other proteins in a signal transduction pathway to elicit a cellular response. The β/γ dimer can also play a role in signal transduction. For example, it can regulate the function of ion channels in the plasma membrane.

When a signalling molecule and GPCR dissociate, the GPCR is no longer activated, and the cellular response is reversed. For the G protein to return to the inactive state, the α subunit first hydrolyzes its bound GTP to GDP and P_i. After this occurs, the α and β/γ subunits reassociate with each other to form an inactive G protein complex.

Ligand-Gated Channels   Ion channels are proteins that allow the diffusion of ions across cellular membranes. **Ligand-gated channels** are a third type of cell surface receptor found in the plasma membrane of animal, plant, and fungal cells. When a signalling molecule (ligand) binds to this type of receptor, the channel opens and allows the flow of ions through the membrane, changing the concentrations of ions in the cell (**Figure 9.8**).

In animals, ligand-gated channels are important in the transmission of signals between neurons and muscle cells and between two neurons. In addition, ligand-gated channels in the plasma membrane allow the uptake of Ca^{2+} into the cytosol. As discussed later in this chapter changes in the cytosolic concentration of Ca^{2+} often play an important role in signal transduction.

Cells Also Have Intracellular Receptors Activated by Signalling Molecules That Pass Through the Plasma Membrane

Although most receptors for signalling molecules are located in the plasma membrane, some are found inside the cell. In these cases, the signalling molecule must pass through the plasma membrane to gain access to its receptor. For example, two types of signalling molecules—steroids and auxins—diffuse into the cell, where they bind to intracellular receptors.

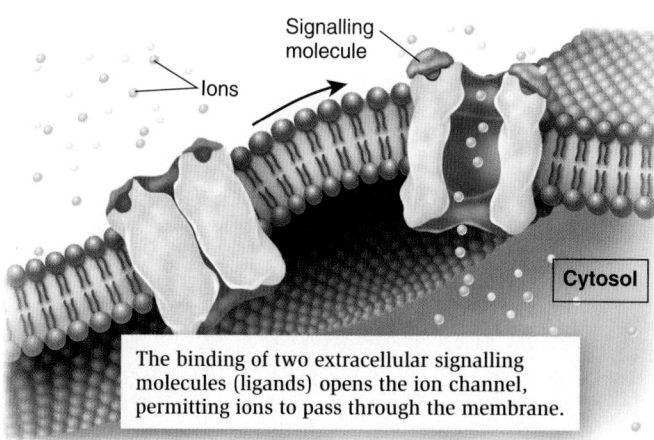

The binding of two extracellular signalling molecules (ligands) opens the ion channel, permitting ions to pass through the membrane.

Figure 9.8   The function of a ligand-gated ion channel.

As described in Chapter 49, steroid hormones, such as estrogens and androgens, are secreted into the bloodstream from cells of endocrine glands. The behaviour of estrogen is typical of many steroid hormones (**Figure 9.9a**). Because estrogen is hydrophobic, it can diffuse through the plasma membrane of a target cell and bind to a receptor in the cell. Some steroids bind to receptors in the cytosol, which then travel into the nucleus, while other steroid hormones, such as estrogen, bind to receptors that are in the nucleus. After binding, the estrogen • receptor complex undergoes a conformational change that enables it to form a dimer with another estrogen • receptor complex. The dimer then binds to the DNA and activates the transcription of specific genes. The estrogen receptor is an example of a transcription factor—a protein that regulates the transcription of genes. The expression of specific genes changes cell structure and function in a way that results in a cellular response to the hormone.

A second example of an intracellular receptor is the receptor for a group of related plant hormones called auxins, which are important in many plant signalling pathways, including the growth of shoots toward light (see Figure 9.2), the growth of roots into the soil, and the flowering process. In 2005 a research group led by Canadian Mark Estelle determined that auxin binds to an intracellular receptor called TIR1 (TIR stands for transport inhibitor response, so named because mutations in this receptor alter the response of drugs that inhibit auxin transport in plants). Auxin binds to TIR1 in the cytosol. This activates TIR1, which then travels to the nucleus (**Figure 9.9b**). Like steroid receptors, TIR1 also causes the activation of specific genes. However, TIR1 does not do this directly. After auxin binds, the receptor causes the breakdown of a protein that inhibits several genes. When this inhibitory protein is broken down, the gene inhibition is relieved and the genes are transcribed into mRNA.

Estrogen

2 Estrogen receptors form a dimer, bind next to specific genes, and activate their transcription. The mRNAs are then translated into proteins that affect the structure and function of the cell.

Active estrogen receptor dimer

Protein that affects cell structure and function

1 Estrogen diffuses across the plasma membrane, enters the nucleus, and binds to the estrogen receptors. The receptors undergo a conformational change.

Inactive estrogen receptor

Chromosomal DNA

mRNA

Nucleus

(a) Estrogen receptor

Auxin

Proteins that inhibit certain genes that are involved with cell division

2 Activated TIR1 enters the nucleus and causes the breakdown of a protein that inhibits several genes that are needed for cell division. These genes are then transcribed into mRNA, and the mRNA is translated into proteins that promote cell division.

TIR1

1 Auxin enters the cell and binds to TIR1 in the cytosol, thereby activating it.

Nucleus

DNA

mRNA

Protein that promotes cell division

(b) Auxin receptor

Figure 9.9   Examples of intracellular receptors.

9.3 SIGNAL TRANSDUCTION AND THE CELLULAR RESPONSE

Learning Outcomes:

1. For signalling molecules that bind to a receptor tyrosine kinase receptor or a G-protein-coupled receptor, describe the signal transduction pathways and how those pathways lead to a cellular response.
2. Relate the function of second messengers to signal transduction pathways.
3. List some examples of second messengers and explain how they exert their effects.

We now turn our attention to the intracellular events that enable a cell to respond to a signalling molecule that binds to a cell surface receptor. In most cases, the binding of a signalling molecule to its receptor stimulates a signal transduction pathway. We begin by examining a pathway that is controlled by an enzyme-linked receptor. We will then examine pathways and cellular responses that are controlled by G-protein-coupled receptors. As you will learn, these pathways sometimes involve the production of intracellular signals called second messengers.

Receptor Tyrosine Kinases Activate Signal Transduction Pathways Involving a Protein Kinase Cascade that Alters Gene Transcription

Receptor tyrosine kinases are a category of enzyme-linked receptors that are found in all animals and also in choanoflagellates, which are the protists that are most closely related to animals (see Chapter 26). However, they are not found in bacteria, archaea, or other eukaryotic species (bacteria do have receptor histidine kinases, and all eukaryotes have receptor serine/threonine kinases). The human genome contains about 60 different genes that encode receptor tyrosine kinases that recognize various types of signalling molecules, such as hormones.

Figure 9.10 describes a simplified signal transduction pathway for epidermal growth factor (EGF). A **growth factor** is a protein ligand that acts as a signalling molecule that stimulates cell growth or division. This protein ligand is secreted from endocrine cells, travels through the bloodstream, and binds to a receptor tyrosine kinase called the EGF receptor. EGF is responsible for stimulating epidermal cells, such as skin cells, to divide. Following receptor activation, the three general parts of the signal transduction pathway are also activated: (1) relay proteins (also called adaptor proteins) activate a protein kinase cascade; (2) the protein kinase cascade phosphorylates several transcription factors; and (3) the phosphorylated transcription factors stimulate gene transcription. Next, we will consider the details of this pathway.

EGF Receptor Activation   For receptor activation to occur, two EGF receptor subunits each bind a molecule of EGF. The binding of EGF causes the subunits to dimerize and phosphorylate each other on tyrosines within the receptors, which is why they are named receptor tyrosine kinases. Next comes the signal transduction pathway.

Relay Proteins   The phosphorylated form of the EGF receptor is first recognized by a relay protein of the signal transduction pathway called Grb. This interaction changes the conformation of Grb so that it binds to another relay protein in the signal

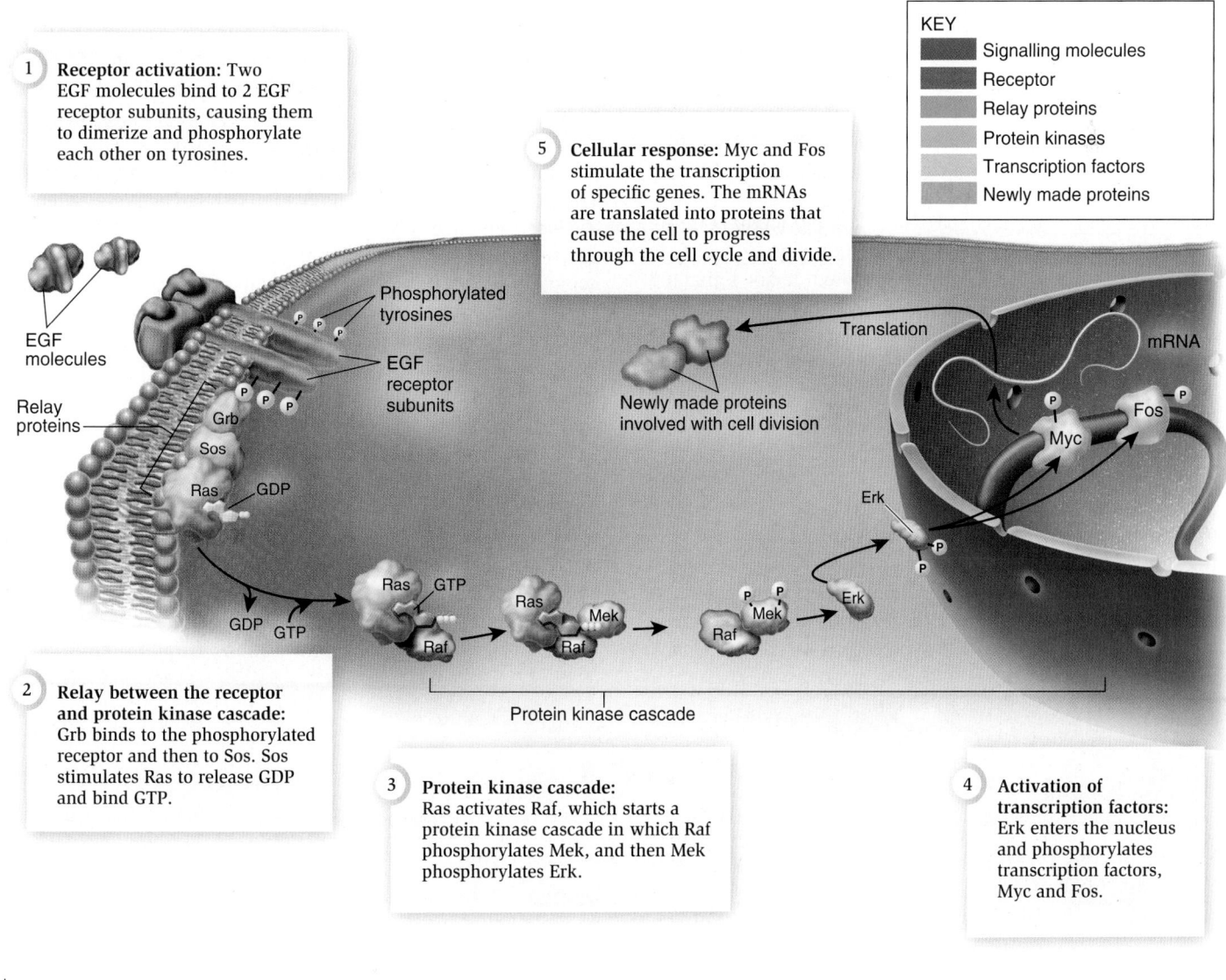

Figure 9.10   The epidermal growth factor (EGF) pathway that promotes cell division.

transduction pathway termed Sos and thereby changes the conformation of Sos. The activation of Sos causes a third relay protein called Ras to release GDP and bind GTP. The GTP form of Ras is the active form.

Protein Kinase Cascade   The function of Grb, Sos, and Ras is to relay a cellular signal to additional proteins in the signal transduction pathway that form a **protein kinase cascade**. This cascade involves the sequential activation of multiple protein kinases. Activated Ras binds to Raf, the first protein kinase in the cascade. Raf then phosphorylates Mek, which becomes active and, in turn phosphorylates Erk. Raf, Mek, and Erk, the protein kinase cascade, are all examples of **mitogen-activated protein kinases (MAP kinases)**. This type of protein kinase was first discovered because it is activated in the presence of mitogens—agents that cause a cell to divide. EGF is an example of a mitogen.

Activation of Transcription Factors and the Cellular Response   The phosphorylated form of Erk enters the nucleus and phosphorylates transcription factors, such as Myc and Fos. What is the cellular response? Once these transcription factors are phosphorylated, they stimulate the expression of genes that encode proteins that promote cell division. After these proteins are made, the cell will be stimulated to divide.

Growth factors, such as EGF, cause a rapid increase in the expression of many genes in mammals, perhaps as many as 100. As we will discuss in Chapter 13, growth factor signalling pathways are often involved in cancer. Mutations that cause proteins in these pathways to become hyperactive result in cells that divide uncontrollably.

Second Messengers, Such as Cyclic AMP, Are Key Components of Many Signal Transduction Pathways

Let's now turn to examples of signal transduction pathways and cellular responses that involve G-protein-coupled receptors (GPCRs). Extracellular signalling molecules that bind to a cell surface receptor are referred to as first messengers. After first messengers bind to receptors such as GPCRs, many signal transduction pathways lead to the production of **second messengers**—small molecules or ions that relay signals inside the cell. The signals that result in second messenger production often act quickly, in a matter of seconds or minutes, but the duration of their action is usually short. Therefore, such signalling is typically used when a cell needs a quick and short cellular response.

Production of cAMP   Mammalian and plant cells make several different types of G protein α subunits. One type of α subunit binds to **adenylyl cyclase**, an enzyme in the plasma membrane. This interaction stimulates adenylyl cyclase to synthesize **cyclic adenosine monophosphate (cyclic AMP or cAMP)** from ATP (**Figure 9.11**). The molecule cAMP is an example of a second messenger.

Signal Transduction Pathway Involving cAMP   Let's explore a signal transduction pathway in which the G-protein-coupled receptor recognizes the hormone epinephrine (also called adrenaline). This hormone is sometimes called the "fight-or-flight" hormone. Epinephrine is produced when an individual is confronted with a stressful situation, and it helps the person deal with a perceived threat or danger.

First, epinephrine binds to its receptor and activates a G protein (**Figure 9.12**). The α subunit then activates adenylyl cyclase, which catalyzes the production of cAMP from ATP. One effect of cAMP is to activate protein kinase A (PKA), which is composed of four subunits: two catalytic subunits that phosphorylate specific cellular proteins, and two regulatory subunits that inhibit the catalytic subunits when they are bound to each other. Cyclic AMP binds to the regulatory subunits of PKA. The binding of cAMP separates the regulatory and catalytic subunits, which allows each catalytic subunit to be active.

Cellular Response via PKA   How does PKA activation lead to a cellular response? The catalytic subunit of PKA phosphorylates specific cellular proteins, such as enzymes, structural proteins, and transcription factors. The phosphorylation of enzymes and structural proteins will influence the structure and function of the cell. Likewise, the phosphorylation of transcription factors

Figure 9.11   The synthesis and break-down of cyclic AMP.   Cyclic AMP (cAMP) is a second messenger formed from ATP by adenylyl cyclase, an enzyme in the plasma membrane. cAMP is inactivated by the action of an enzyme called phosphodiesterase, which converts cAMP to AMP.

Figure 9.12 A signal transduction pathway involving cAMP. The pathway leading to the formation of cAMP and subsequent activation of PKA, which is mediated by a G-protein-coupled receptor (GPCR).

Concept check: *In this figure, which part is the signal transduction pathway, and which is the cellular response?*

leads to the synthesis of new proteins that affect cell structure and function.

As a specific example of a cellular response, **Figure 9.13** shows how a skeletal muscle cell responds to elevated levels of epinephrine. When PKA becomes active, it phosphorylates two enzymes: phosphorylase kinase and glycogen synthase. Both of these enzymes are involved with the metabolism of glycogen, which is a polymer of glucose that is used to store energy. When phosphorylase kinase is phosphorylated, it becomes activated. The function of phosphorylase kinase is to phosphorylate another enzyme in the cell called glycogen phosphorylase, which then becomes activated. This enzyme causes glycogen breakdown by phosphorylating glucose units at the ends of a glycogen polymer, which releases individual glucose molecules from glycogen:

$$\text{glycogen}_n + P_i \xrightarrow{\substack{\text{glycogen} \\ \text{phosphorylase}}} \text{glucogen}_{n-1} + \text{glucose phosphate}$$

where n is the number of glucose units in glycogen.

When PKA phosphorylates glycogen synthase, the function of this enzyme is inhibited rather than activated (Figure 9.13). The function of glycogen synthase is make glycogen. Therefore, the effect of cAMP is to prevent glycogen synthesis.

Taken together, the effects of epinephrine in skeletal muscle cells are to stimulate glycogen breakdown and inhibit

glycogen synthesis. This provides these cells with more glucose molecules, which they can use for the energy needed for muscle contraction. In this way, such muscles are better prepared to fight or flee.

Terminating the Cellular Response As mentioned, signalling that involves second messengers is typically of short duration. Several factors are important for inactivating the signalling pathway. When the signalling molecule is no longer produced and its level falls, a larger percentage of the receptors are not bound by their ligands. When a ligand dissociates from the GPCR, it becomes deactivated. Intracellularly, the α subunit hydrolyzes its GTP to GDP, and the α subunit and β/γ dimer reassociate to form an inactive G protein (see step 3, Figure 9.7). The level of cAMP decreases because of the action of an enzyme called **phosphodiesterase**, which converts cAMP to AMP.

As the cAMP level falls, the regulatory subunits of PKA release cAMP, and the regulatory and catalytic subunits

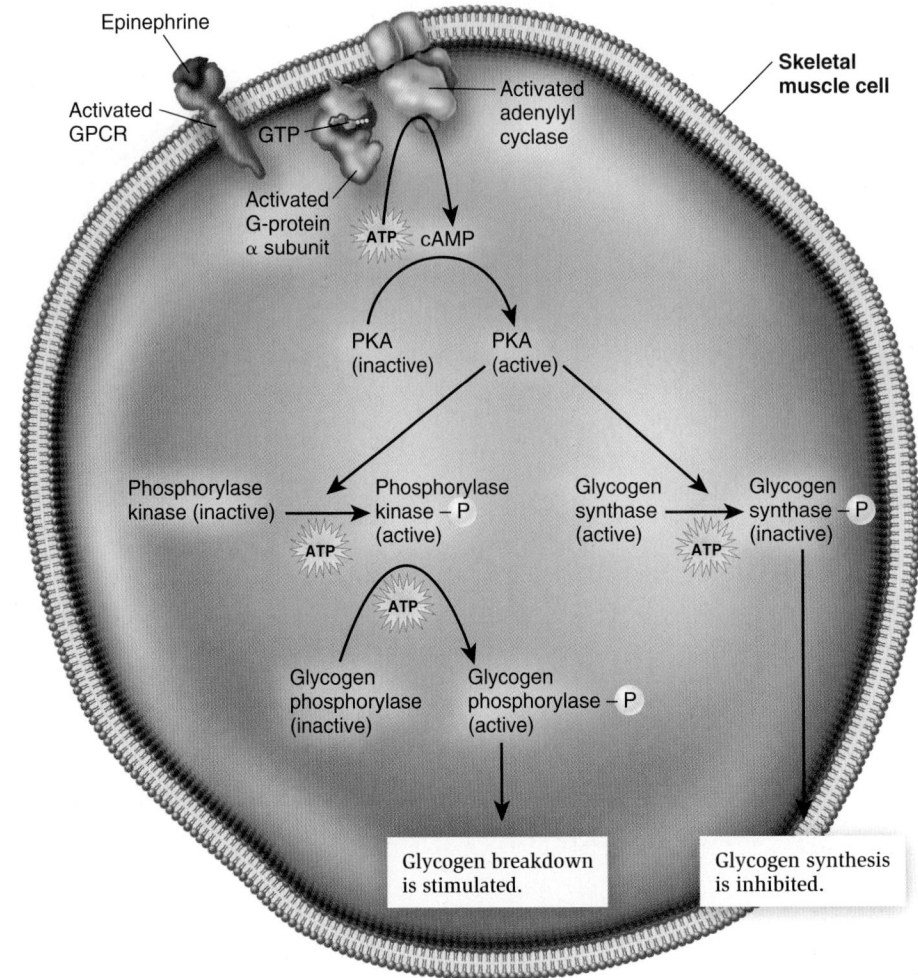

Figure 9.13 The cellular response of skeletal muscle cells to epinephrine.

Concept check: *Explain whether phosphorylation activates or inhibits enzyme function.*

reassociate, thereby inhibiting PKA. Finally, enzymes called **protein phosphatases** are responsible for removing phosphate groups from proteins, which reverses the effects of PKA.

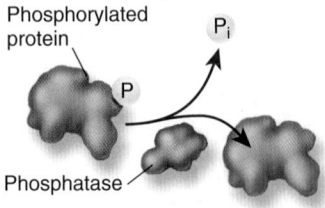

The Main Advantages of Second Messengers Are Amplification and Speed In the 1950s Earl Sutherland determined that many different hormones cause the formation of cAMP in a variety of cell types. This observation, for which he won the Nobel Prize in Physiology or Medicine in 1971, stimulated great interest in the study of signal transduction pathways. Since Sutherland's discovery, the production of second messengers, such as cAMP, has been found to have two important advantages: amplification and speed.

Amplification of the signal involves the synthesis of many cAMP molecules, which, in turn, activate many PKA proteins (**Figure 9.14**). Likewise, each PKA protein can phosphorylate many target proteins in the cell to promote a cellular response.

A second advantage of second messengers, such as cAMP, is speed. Because second messengers are relatively small and water soluble, they can diffuse rapidly through the cytosol. For example, Brian Bacskai and his colleagues studied the response of neurons to a signalling molecule called serotonin, which is a neurotransmitter that binds to a GPCR. In humans, low serotonin is believed to play a role in depression, anxiety, and other behavioural disorders. To monitor cAMP levels, neurons grown in a laboratory were injected with a fluorescent protein that changes its fluorescence when cAMP is made. As shown in the right micrograph in **Figure 9.15**, such cells made a substantial amount of cAMP within 20 seconds after the addition of serotonin.

Figure 9.14   **Signal amplification.**   An advantage of a signal transduction pathway is the amplification of a signal. In this case, a single signalling molecule leads to the phosphorylation of many, perhaps hundreds or thousands, of target proteins.

Concept check: *In the case of signalling pathways involving hormones, why is signal amplification an advantage?*

Figure 9.15   **The rapid speed of cAMP production.**   The micrograph on the left shows a neuron before its exposure to serotonin, while the micrograph on the right shows the same cell 20 seconds after exposure. Blue indicates a low level of cAMP, yellow is an intermediate level, and red/purple is a high level.

Signal Transduction Pathways Can Also Lead to the Production of Second Messengers, Such as Diacylglycerol, Inositol Trisphosphate, and Calcium   Cells use several different types of second messengers, and more than one type can be used at the same time. Let's now consider a second way that an activated G protein can influence a signal transduction pathway and produce second messengers. This pathway produces the second messengers diacylglycerol (DAG) and inositol trisphosphate (IP$_3$), and ultimately it can cause cellular effects by altering the levels of calcium (Ca$^+$) in the cell.

Production of DAG and IP$_3$ To start this pathway, a signalling molecule binds to its GPCR, which, in turn, activates a G protein. However, rather than activating adenylate cyclase,

as described earlier in Figure 9.12, the α subunit of this G protein activates an enzyme called phospholipase C, which breaks a covalent bond in a plasma membrane phospholipid called PIP$_2$, producing the two second messengers DAG and IP$_3$ (**Figure 9.16**). Many molecules of DAG and IP$_3$ are produced when phospholipase C becomes active, thereby leading to signal amplification.

Release of Ca^{2+} into the Cytosol   Because of active transport via a Ca^{2+}-ATPase, the lumen of the ER contains a very high concentration of Ca^{2+} compared with the cytosol. After IP$_3$ is released into the cytosol, it binds to a ligand-gated ion channel in the ER membrane. The binding of IP$_3$ causes the channel to open, releasing many Ca^{2+} ions into the cytosol, which further amplifies the signal. Calcium ions act as second messengers to elicit a cellular response in a variety of ways, two of which are shown in Figure 9.16 and described next.

Cellular Response via Protein Kinase C   Ca^{2+} and DAG can bind to protein kinase C (PKC), which activates the kinase. Once activated, PKC can phosphorylate specific cellular proteins, thereby altering their function and leading to a cellular response. In smooth muscle cells, for example, protein kinase C phosphorylates proteins that are involved with contraction.

Cellular Response via Calmodulin   Ca^{2+} also can bind to a protein called calmodulin, which is a calcium-modulated protein. The Ca^{2+}-calmodulin complex then interacts with specific cellular proteins and alters their functions. For example, calmodulin regulates proteins involved in carbohydrate breakdown in liver cells.

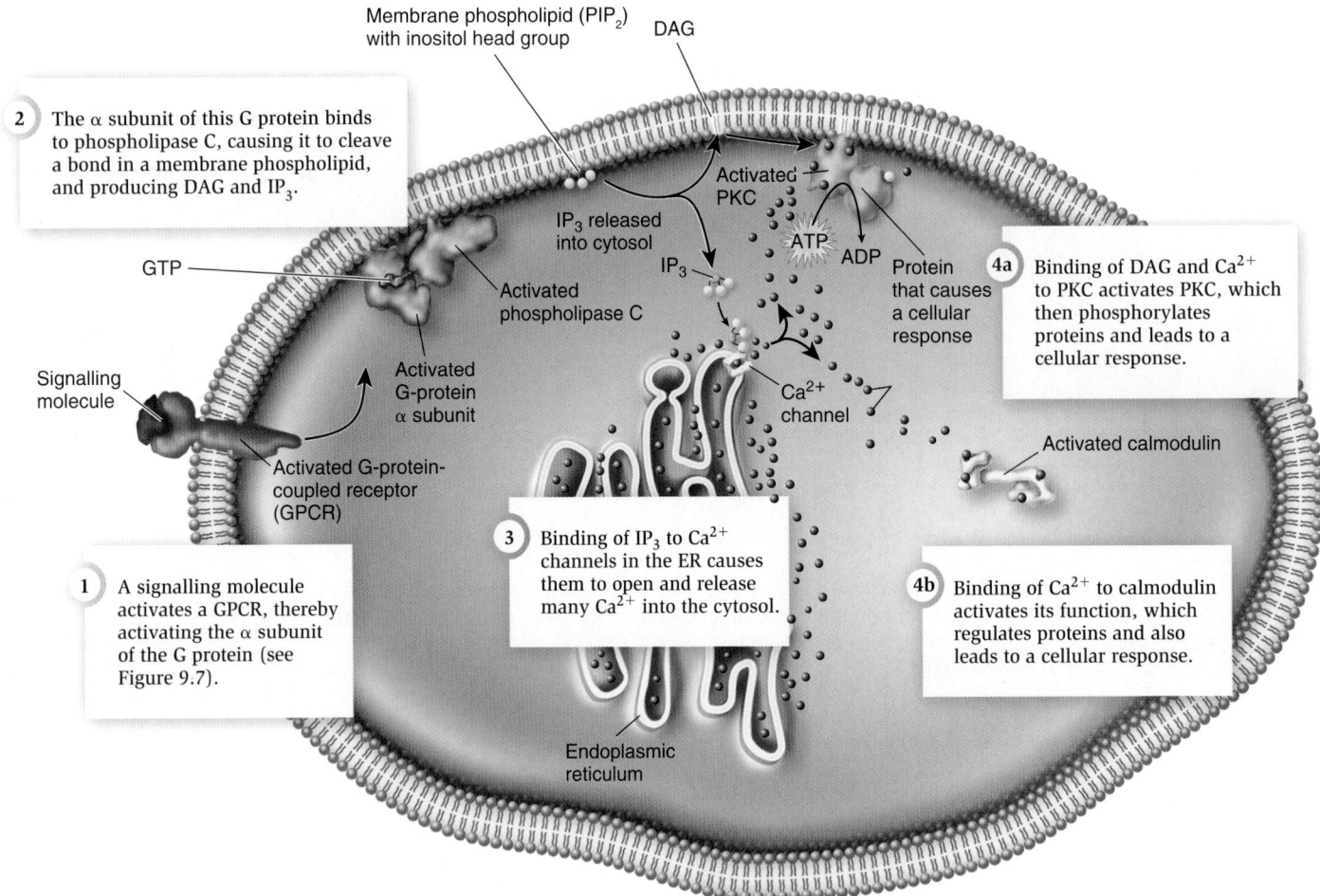

Membrane phospholipid (PIP₂) with inositol head group

DAG

2 The α subunit of this G protein binds to phospholipase C, causing it to cleave a bond in a membrane phospholipid, and producing DAG and IP₃.

Activated PKC

IP₃ released into cytosol

GTP

ATP

ADP

IP₃

Protein that causes a cellular response

4a Binding of DAG and Ca²⁺ to PKC activates PKC, which then phosphorylates proteins and leads to a cellular response.

Activated phospholipase C

Signalling molecule

Activated G-protein α subunit

Ca²⁺ channel

Activated calmodulin

Activated G-protein-coupled receptor (GPCR)

3 Binding of IP₃ to Ca²⁺ channels in the ER causes them to open and release many Ca²⁺ into the cytosol.

1 A signalling molecule activates a GPCR, thereby activating the α subunit of the G protein (see Figure 9.7).

4b Binding of Ca²⁺ to calmodulin activates its function, which regulates proteins and also leads to a cellular response.

Endoplasmic reticulum

Figure 9.16 A signal transduction pathway involving diacylglycerol (DAG), inositol trisphosphate (IP₃), and changing Ca²⁺ levels.

9.4 HORMONAL SIGNALLING IN MULTICELLULAR ORGANISMS

Learning Outcomes:

1. Explain how the cellular response to a particular hormone can vary among different cell types.
2. Describe how a cell's response to a hormone depends on the types of proteins that it makes.

Thus far, we have considered how signalling molecules bind to particular types of receptors, thereby activating a signal transduction pathway that leads to a cellular response. In this section we will consider how hormones in multicellular organisms exert a variety of responses. As you will learn, the type of cellular response that is caused by a particular hormone depends on the type of cell. Each cell type responds to a particular hormone in its own unique way. The variation in a cellular response is determined by the types of proteins,

such as receptors and signal transduction proteins, that each cell type produces.

The Cellular Response to a Given Hormone Varies Among Different Cell Types

As you have seen, signalling molecules usually exert their effects on cells via signal transduction pathways that control the functions and/or synthesis of specific proteins. In multicellular organisms, one of the amazing effects of hormones is their ability to coordinate cellular activities. One example is epinephrine, which is secreted from endocrine cells. As mentioned, epinephrine is also called the fight-or-flight hormone because it quickly prepares the body for strenuous physical activity. Epinephrine is also secreted into the bloodstream when someone is exercising vigorously.

Epinephrine has different effects throughout the body (**Figure 9.17**). We have already discussed how it promotes the breakdown of glycogen in skeletal muscle cells (see Figure 9.13). In the lungs, it relaxes the airways, allowing a

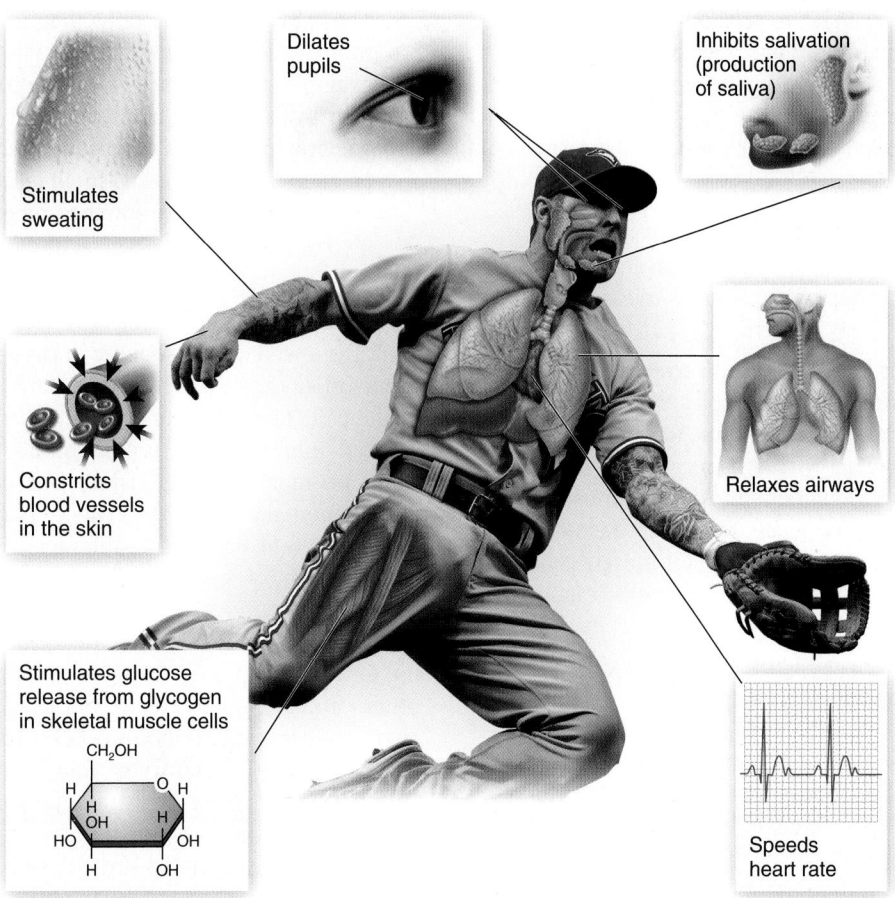

Stimulates
sweating

Dilates
pupils

Inhibits salivation
(production
of saliva)

Constricts
blood vessels
in the skin

Relaxes airways

Stimulates glucose
release from glycogen
in skeletal muscle cells

Speeds
heart rate

Figure 9.17   **The effects of epinephrine in humans.**   Excitement and physical exertion result in epinephrine release, triggering physiological changes that enable the body to respond to challenges.

Principle: *New properties emerge from complex interactions. Because different cell types respond to epinephrine in different ways, an emergent property of epinephrine production is that a multicellular organism can respond to this hormone in a very complex way, preparing it to fight or flee from a perceived threat.*

person to take in more oxygen. In the heart, epinephrine stimulates heart muscle cells so the heart beats faster. Interestingly, one of the effects of caffeine can be explained by this mechanism. Caffeine inhibits phosphodiesterase, which converts cAMP to AMP. When phosphodiesterase is inhibited by caffeine, cAMP persists for a longer time and prolongs the effects of signalling molecules, such as epinephrine. Therefore, even low levels of epinephrine will have a greater effect. This is one of the reasons why drinks containing caffeine, including coffee and many energy drinks, provide a feeling of vitality and energy.

GENOMES AND PROTEOMES

A Cell's Response to Hormones and Other Signalling Molecules Depends on Its Proteome

As Figure 9.17 shows, a hormone, such as epinephrine, produces diverse responses throughout the body. How do we explain the fact that various cell types can respond so differently to the same hormone? The answer lies primarily in **differential gene regulation**. As a multicellular organism develops from a fertilized egg, the cells of the body become differentiated into particular types, such as heart and lung cells. The mechanisms that underlie this differentiation process are described in Chapter 17. Although different cell types, such as heart and lung cells, contain the same set of genes—the same genome—they are not expressed in the same pattern. Certain genes that are turned off in heart cells are turned on in lung cells, while some genes that are turned on in heart cells are turned off in lung cells. Remember that the proteome is defined by the genes that are actively expressed. Thus, the gene expression pattern in a given cell type both coordinates and limits the types of signalling events that can occur. The following are examples of how differential gene regulation affects the cellular response:

1. A cell may or may not express a receptor for a particular signalling molecule. For example, not all cells of the human body express a receptor for epinephrine. These cells are not affected when epinephrine is released into the bloodstream.

2. Different cell types have different cell surface receptors that recognize the same signalling molecule. In humans, a signalling molecule called acetylcholine has two different types of receptors. One acetylcholine receptor is a ligand-gated ion channel that is expressed in skeletal muscle cells. Another acetylcholine receptor is a G-protein-coupled receptor (GPCR) that is expressed in heart muscle cells. Because of this, skeletal and heart muscle cells respond differently to acetylcholine.

3. Two (or more) receptors can work the same way in different cell types but have different affinities for the same signalling molecule. Two different GPCRs may recognize the same hormone, but a receptor expressed in liver cells may have a higher affinity (that is, a lower K_d) for a hormone compared with a receptor expressed in muscle cells. In this case, the liver cells will respond to a lower hormone concentration than the muscle cells will.

4. The expression of proteins involved in intracellular signal transduction pathways can vary in different cell types. For example, one cell type may express the proteins that are needed to activate PKA, while another cell type may not.

5. The expression of proteins that are controlled by signal transduction pathways can vary in different cell types. For example, the presence of epinephrine in skeletal muscle cells leads to the activation of glycogen phosphorylase, an enzyme involved in glycogen breakdown. However, this enzyme is not expressed in all cells of the body. Glycogen breakdown will be stimulated by epinephrine only if glycogen phosphorylase is expressed in that cell.

Although the perception of the signalling ligand is of critical importance in initiating any changes in cellular metabolism, the speed and specificity of the response and the number of metabolic processes influenced are dictated by the proteome of the cell. As highlighted earlier, signalling involves the coordinated interaction of protein molecules, and such interactions are most easily envisioned as two structures that have complementary surfaces. These complementary structures allow different proteins to interact with one another through the strength of many weak noncovalent interactions (e.g., hydrogen bonding). As such interactions occur, this leads to changes in protein structure and hence the potential for creating new conformations capable of additional interactions with other proteins. Collectively, the associations that foster biochemical processes define the **interactome** of the cell. Recent research in the laboratory of Tony Pawson at the University of Toronto has focused on cataloguing the myriad interactions that occur and are responsible for coordinating cell division, axon guidance, regulated proteolysis, and carcinogenesis. Our understanding of the modular nature of interacting surfaces may suggest strategies for protein engineering to permit biochemical pathways and processes to be controlled or redirected, which has many potential (e.g., human therapeutics) applications.

9.5   APOPTOSIS: PROGRAMMED CELL DEATH

Learning Outcomes:

1. Explain the relationship between cell signalling and programmed cell death.
2. Outline the extrinsic pathway of apoptosis.

We will end our discussion of signal transduction pathways and cellular responses by considering one of the most dramatic responses that eukaryotic cells exhibit: **apoptosis**, or programmed cell death. During this process a cell orchestrates its own destruction. The cell first shrinks and forms a rounder shape caused by the internal destruction of its nucleus and cytoskeleton (**Figure 9.18**). The plasma membrane then forms irregular extensions that eventually become blebs—small cell fragments that break away from the cell as it destroys itself.

Cell biologists have discovered that apoptosis plays many important roles. During embryonic development in animals, it is needed to sculpt the tissues and organs. For example, the fingers on a human hand are initially webbed but become separated during embryonic development when the cells between the fingers undergo apoptosis (see Chapter 17, Figure 17.4). Apoptosis is also necessary in adult organisms to maintain the proper cell number in tissues and organs, and it eliminates cells that have become worn out or infected by viruses, or have the potential to cause cancer. In this section we will examine the pioneering work that led to the discovery of apoptosis and explore its molecular mechanism.

Intrinsic and Extrinsic Signal Transduction Pathways Lead to Apoptosis   Since these early studies on apoptosis, cell biologists have discovered that apoptosis plays many important roles. We have already discussed how apoptosis is important for development and sculpting of certain tissues and organs, such as human hands, and how it is necessary in adult organisms to maintain the

1. Cell beginning apoptosis.
2. Condensation of nucleus and cell shrinkage.
3. Multiple extensions of the plasma membrane.
4. Further blebbing.

Figure 9.18 Stages of apoptosis.

FEATURE INVESTIGATION

Kerr, Wyllie, and Currie Found That Hormone Signals May Control Apoptosis

How was apoptosis discovered? One line of evidence involved the microscopic examination of tissues in mammals. In the 1960s British pathologist John Kerr microscopically examined liver tissue that was deprived of oxygen. Within hours of oxygen deprivation, he observed that some cells underwent a process that involved cell shrinkage. Around this time, similar results had been noted by other researchers, such as Scottish pathologists Andrew Wyllie and Alastair Currie, who had studied cell death in the adrenal glands. In 1973 Kerr, Wyllie, and Currie joined forces to study this process further.

Before their collaboration, other researchers had already established that certain hormones affect the growth of the adrenal glands, which sit atop the kidneys. Adrenocorticotropic hormone (ACTH) was known to increase the number of cells in the adrenal cortex, which is the outer layer of the adrenal glands. By contrast, prednisolone was shown to suppress the synthesis of ACTH and cause a decrease in the number of cells in the cortex. In the experiment described in **Figure 9.19**, Kerr, Wyllie, and Currie wanted to understand how these hormones exerted their effects. They subjected rats to four types of treatments: (1) control rats were injected with saline (salt water), and other rats were injected with (2) prednisolone alone, (3) prednisolone plus ACTH, or (4) ACTH alone.

After two days samples of adrenal cortex were obtained from the rats and observed by using light microscopy. Even in control samples, the researchers occasionally observed cell death via apoptosis (see the micrograph in the Data section).

However, in prednisolone-treated rats, the cells in the adrenal cortex were found to undergo a dramatically higher rate of apoptosis. Multiple cells undergoing apoptosis were found in 9 out of every 10 samples observed under the light microscope. Such a high level of apoptosis was not observed in control samples or in samples obtained from rats treated with both prednisolone and ACTH or ACTH alone. Therefore, ACTH appears to prevent apoptosis.

The results of Kerr, Wyllie, and Currie are important for two reasons. First, their results indicated that tissues decrease their cell number via a mechanism that involves cell shrinkage and eventually blebbing. Second, they showed that cell death could follow a program that, in this case, was induced by the presence of prednisolone (which decreases ACTH). They coined the term *apoptosis* to describe this process.

Experimental Questions

1. In the experiment of Figure 9.19, explain the effects on apoptosis in the control rats (saline injected) versus those injected with prednisolone alone, prednisolone and ACTH, or ACTH alone.
2. Prednisolone inhibits the production of ACTH in rats. Do you think it inhibited the ability of rats to make their own ACTH when they were injected with both prednisolone and ACTH? Explain.
3. Of the four groups—control, prednisolone alone, prednisolone and ACTH, and ACTH alone—which would you expect to have the lowest level of apoptosis? Explain.

HYPOTHESIS Hormones may affect cell number in the adrenal gland by controlling the rate of apoptosis.

KEY MATERIALS Laboratory rats, purified prednisolone, and ACTH.

Experimental level   **Conceptual level**

1 As a control, inject rats with saline. Also inject rats with prednisolone alone, prednisolone plus ACTH, or ACTH alone. Note: Five rats were injected in each case.

Previous studies predicted that prednisolone alone may promote apoptosis by lowering ACTH levels.

2 After two days, obtain samples of adrenal tissue from all 20 rats.

Adrenal gland

Cell undergoing apoptosis

3 Observe the samples via light microsocopy, which is described in Chapter 4.

4 **THE DATA**

Micrograph of adrenal tissue showing occasional cells undergoing apoptosis (see arrow)

Treatment	Number of animals	Glands with enhanced apoptosis*/ Total number of animals
Saline	5	0/10
Prednisolone	5	9/10
Prednisolone + ACTH	5	0/10
ACTH	5	0/10

*Samples from two adrenal glands were removed from each animal. Enhanced apoptosis means that cells undergoing apoptosis were observed in every sample under the light microscope.

5 **CONCLUSION** Prednisolone alone, which lowers ACTH levels, causes some cells to undergo apoptosis. During this process, the cells shrink and form blebs as they kill themselves. Apoptosis is controlled by hormones.

6 **SOURCE** Wyllie, A.H., Kerr, J.F.R., Macaskill, I.A.M., and Currie, A.R. (1973) Adrenocortical cell Deletion: The Role of ACTH. *Journal of Pathology* 111, 85–94.

Figure 9.19 Discovery of apoptosis in the adrenal cortex by Kerr, Wyllie, and Currie.

proper cell number in tissues and organs, eliminating cells that have become worn out, have become infected by viruses or intracellular bacteria, or have the potential to cause cancer. In mammals, apoptosis is also important in the proper functioning of the immune system that wards off infections. The immune system is composed of a variety of cell types, such as B cells and T cells, that can fight infectious agents and eliminate damaged cells. For this to occur, the immune system creates a large pool of B and T cells, and then uses apoptosis to weed out those that are potentially damaging to the body or ineffective at fighting infection.

Apoptosis involves the activation of cell signalling pathways. One pathway, called the intrinsic or mitochondrial pathway, is stimulated by internal signals, such as DNA damage that could cause cancer. Proteins on the surface of the mitochondria play a key role in eliciting the response. Alternatively, extracellular signals can promote apoptosis. This is called the extrinsic or death receptor pathway.

Let's consider how an extracellular signal causes apoptosis. The extrinsic pathway of apoptosis begins with the activation of **death receptors** on the surface of the cell. Death receptors, such as Fas, stimulate a pathway that leads to apoptosis when they become bound to an extracellular ligand. **Figure 9.20** shows a simplified pathway for this process. In this example, the extracellular ligand is a protein composed of three

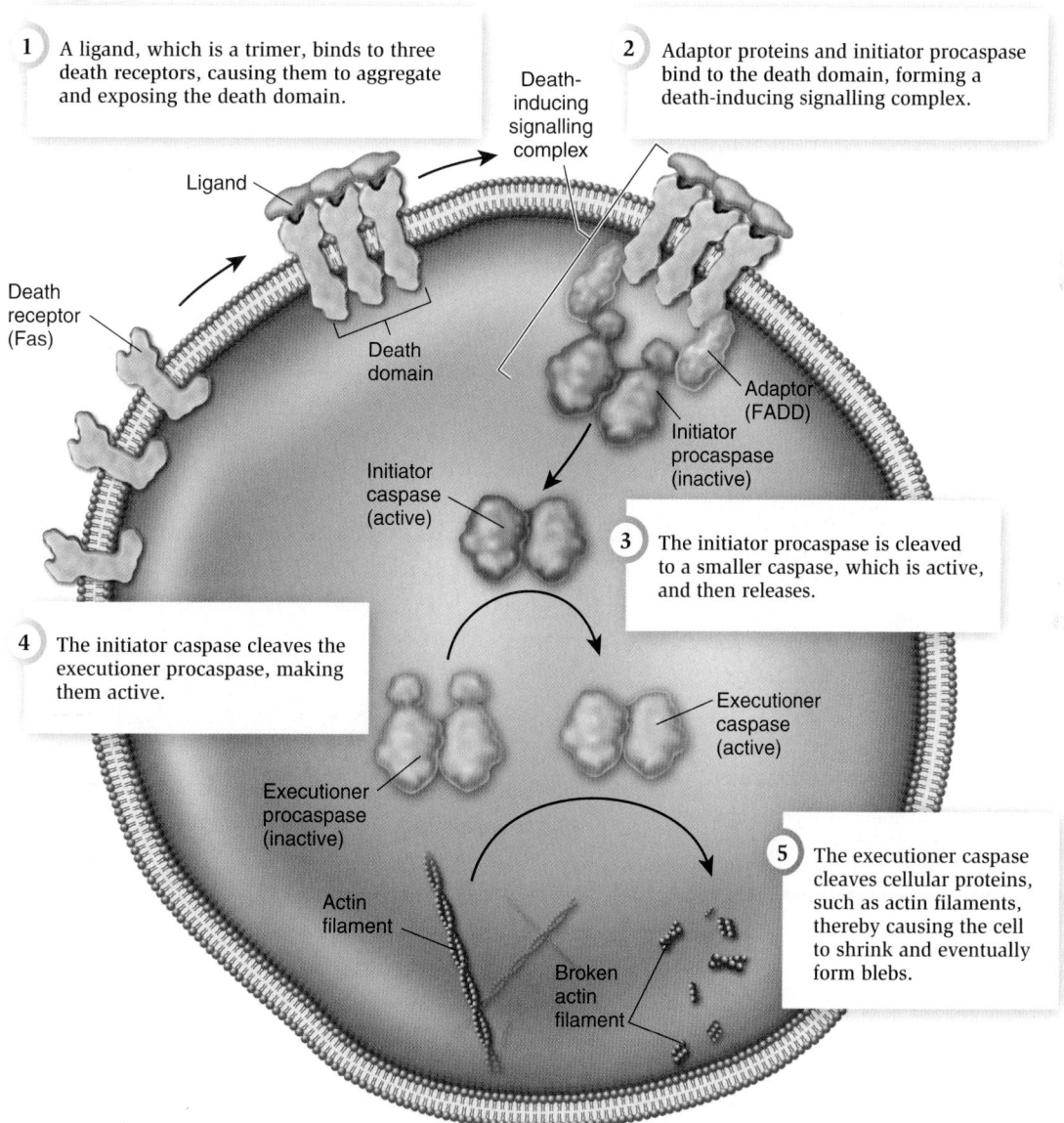

1 A ligand, which is a trimer, binds to three death receptors, causing them to aggregate and exposing the death domain.

2 Adaptor proteins and initiator procaspase bind to the death domain, forming a death-inducing signalling complex.

Death-inducing signalling complex

Ligand

Death receptor (Fas)

Death domain

Adaptor (FADD)

Initiator procaspase (inactive)

Initiator caspase (active)

3 The initiator procaspase is cleaved to a smaller caspase, which is active, and then releases.

4 The initiator caspase cleaves the executioner procaspase, making them active.

Executioner caspase (active)

Executioner procaspase (inactive)

Actin filament

Broken actin filament

5 The executioner caspase cleaves cellular proteins, such as actin filaments, thereby causing the cell to shrink and eventually form blebs.

Figure 9.20   **The extrinsic pathway for apoptosis in mammals.**   This simplified pathway leads to apoptosis when cells are exposed to an extracellular signal that causes cell death.

Concept check: *How are the roles of the initiator and the executioner caspases different in this process?*

Concept check: *A human disorder called syndactyly involves webbing between one or more fingers and toes. How might this disorder be related to apoptosis?*

identical subunits—a trimeric protein. Such trimeric ligands that promote cell death are typically produced on the surface of cells of the immune system that recognize abnormal cells and target them for destruction. For example, when a cell is infected with a virus, cells of the immune system will target the infected cell for apoptosis. The trimeric ligand binds to three death receptors, which causes them to aggregate into a trimer. This results in a conformational change that exposes the death domain in the cytosol. Once the death domain is exposed, it binds to an adaptor, such as FADD, which then binds to a procaspase. (FADD is an abbreviation for Fas-associated protein with death domain). The complex between the death receptors, FADD, and procaspase is called the **death-inducing signalling complex (DISC)**.

Once the procaspase, which is inactive, is part of the death-inducing signalling complex, it is converted by proteolytic cleavage to caspase, which is active. An active **caspase** functions as a protease—an enzyme that digests other proteins. After it is activated, the caspase is then released from the DISC. This caspase is called an initiator caspase because it initiates the activation of many other caspases in the cell. These other caspases are called executioner or effector caspases because they are directly responsible for digesting intracellular proteins and causing the cell to die. The executioner caspases digest a variety of intracellular proteins, including the proteins that constitute the cytoskeleton and nuclear lamina as well as proteins involved with DNA replication and repair. In this way, the executioner caspases cause the cellular changes described earlier in Figure 9.18. The caspases also activate an enzyme called DNase that chops the DNA in the cell into small fragments. This event may be particularly important for eliminating virally infected cells because it will also destroy viral genomes that are composed of DNA.

Summary of Key Concepts

9.1   General Features of Cell Communication

- A signal is an agent that can influence the properties of cells. A signal binds to a receptor to elicit a cellular response. Cell signalling is needed so that cells can sense environmental changes and communicate with one another. (Figures 9.1, 9.2)
- Cell-to-cell communication also allows cells to adapt, as when plants grow toward light. (Figure 9.2)
- Cell-to-cell communication can vary in the mechanism and distance that a signal travels. Signals are relayed between cells in five common ways: direct intercellular, contact-dependent, autocrine, paracrine, and endocrine signalling. (Figure 9.3)
- Cell signalling is usually a three-stage process involving receptor activation, signal transduction, and a cellular response. A signal transduction pathway is a group of proteins that convert an initial signal to a different signal inside the cell. (Figure 9.4)

9.2   Cellular Receptors and Their Activation

- A signalling molecule, also called a ligand, binds to a receptor with an affinity that is measured as a dissociation constant or K_d value.

The binding of a ligand to a receptor is usually very specific and alters the conformation of the receptor. (Figure 9.5)

- Enzyme-linked receptors have some type of catalytic function. Many of them are protein kinases that can phosphorylate proteins. (Figure 9.6)
- G-protein-coupled receptors (GPCRs) interact with G proteins to initiate a cellular response. (Figure 9.7)
- Some receptors are ligand-gated channels that allow the flow of ions across cellular membranes. (Figure 9.8)
- While most receptors involved in cell signalling are found on the cell surface, some receptors, such as the estrogen receptor and auxin receptor, are intracellular receptors. (Figure 9.9)

9.3   Signal Transduction and the Cellular Response

- Signalling pathways influence whether or not a cell will divide. An example is the pathway that is stimulated by epidermal growth factor, which binds to a receptor tyrosine kinase. (Figure 9.10)
- Second messengers, such as cAMP, play a key role in signal transduction pathways, such as those that occur via G-protein coupled receptors. These pathways are reversible once the signal is degraded. (Figures 9.11, 9.12)
- An example of a pathway that uses cAMP is found in skeletal muscle cells responding to elevated levels of epinephrine, the "fight-or-flight" hormone. Epinephrine enhances the function of enzymes that increase glycogen breakdown and inhibits enzymes that cause glycogen synthesis. (Figure 9.13)
- Second messenger pathways amplify the signal and occur with great speed. (Figures 9.14, 9.15)
- Diacylglycerol (DAG), inositol trisphosphate (IP_3), and Ca^{2+} ions are other examples of second messengers involved in signal transduction. (Figure 9.16)

9.4   Hormonal Signalling in Multicellular Organisms

- Hormones, such as epinephrine, exert different effects throughout the body. (Figure 9.17)
- The way in which any particular cell responds to a signalling molecule depends on the types of proteins it makes. These include the types of receptors, proteins involved in signalling transduction pathways, and proteins that carry out the cellular response. The amounts of these proteins are controlled by differential gene regulation.
- The interactome is the collection of all interactions between signalling (and other) molecules that coordinate cellular metabolism. Identification and characterization of interacting domains is an active area of research and may suggest strategies for protein engineering to alter signalling pathways.

9.5   Apoptosis: Programmed Cell Death

- Apoptosis is the process of programmed cell death in which the nucleus and cytoskeleton break down, and eventually the cell breaks apart into blebs. (Figure 9.18)
- Microscopy studies by Kerr, Wyllie, and Currie, in which they studied the effects of hormones on the adrenal cortex, were instrumental in the discovery of apoptosis. (Figure 9.19)
- Apoptosis plays many important roles in multicellular organisms, including sculpting tissues and organs during embryonic development, maintaining the proper cell number in tissues and organs, eliminating cells that have become worn out or have the potential to cause cancer, and helping the immune system function properly.
- Apoptosis can occur via intrinsic or extrinsic pathways. (Figure 9.20)

Test to Assess Your Learning

1. An agent that allows a cell to respond to changes in its environment is termed
   a. a cell surface receptor.
   b. an intracellular receptor.
   c. a structural protein.
   d. a signal.
   e. apoptosis.

2. When a cell secretes a signalling molecule that binds to receptors on neighbouring cells as well as the same cell, this is called _____ signalling.
   a. direct intercellular
   b. contact-dependent
   c. autocrine
   d. paracrine
   e. endocrine

3. Which of the following does not describe a typical cellular response to signalling molecules?
   a. Activation of enzymes within the cell.
   b. Change in the function of structural proteins that determine cell shape.
   c. Alteration of levels of certain proteins in the cell by changing the level of gene expression.
   d. Change in a gene sequence that encodes a particular protein.
   e. All of the above.

4. A cell's ability to respond to a particular signal depends on
   a. whether or not the cell possesses the appropriate receptor for the signal.
   b. the chemical nature of the signal molecule.
   c. whether or not the signal molecule is water soluble.
   d. the concentration of ATP in the cell.
   e. none of the above.

5. _____ bind to receptors inside cells
   a. Steroid hormones
   b. Ions
   c. Auxins
   d. All of the above
   e. Both (a) and (c)

6. Small molecules, such as cAMP, that relay signals within the cell are called
   a. secondary metabolites.
   b. ligands.
   c. G proteins.
   d. second messengers.
   e. transcription factors.

7. The benefit of second messengers in signal transduction pathways is
   a. an increase in the speed of a cellular response.
   b. duplication of the ligands in the system.
   c. amplification of the signal.
   d. all of the above.
   e. both (a) and (c).

8. All cells of a multicellular organism may not respond in the same way to a particular ligand (signalling molecule) that binds to a cell surface receptor. The difference in response may be due to
   a. the type of receptor for the ligand that the cell expresses.
   b. the affinity of the ligand for the receptor of a given cell type.
   c. the type of signal transduction pathways that the cell expresses.
   d. the type of target proteins that the cell possesses.
   e. all of the above.

9. Apoptosis is the process of
   a. cell migration.
   b. cell signalling.
   c. signal transduction.
   d. signal amplification.
   e. programmed cell death.

10. Which statement best describes the extrinsic pathway for apoptosis?
    a. Caspases recognize an environmental signal and expose their death domain.
    b. Death receptors recognize an environmental signal that then leads to the activation of caspases.
    c. Initiator caspases digest the nuclear lamina and cytoskeleton.
    d. Executioner caspases are part of the death-inducing signalling complex (DISC).
    e. All of the above.

Articulate to Assess Your Learning

1. What are the two general reasons that cells need to communicate?

2. What are the three stages of cell signalling? What stage does not occur when the estrogen receptor is activated?

3. What would be some of the harmful consequences if apoptosis did not occur?

Collaborate to Assess and Extend Your Learning

1. Discuss and compare several different types of cell-to-cell communication. What are some advantages and disadvantages of each type?

2. How does differential gene regulation enable various cell types to respond differently to the same signalling molecule? Why is this useful to multicellular organisms?

3. Certain mutations can alter the structure of the Ras protein so it will not hydrolyze GTP. Such mutations cause cancer. Explain why.

4. A principle of biology is that living organisms interact with their environment. Discuss how cell signalling helps organisms to interact with their environment.

Visit McGraw-Hill Ryerson Connect™ for additional study resources.

An interview with Dr. Julie Forman-Kay from Toronto's Hospital for Sick Children, by Zeba Siddiqui, a third-year student at the University of Toronto—Scarborough.

Dr. Julie Forman-Kay is a senior research scientist at Sick Kids Hospital (Toronto) and a Professor of Biochemistry at the University of Toronto.

What brought you to research?

Many people are interested in understanding things, but at a certain point, they get content. I guess I never got content. Everybody has an inherent curiosity, which is often beaten out of them. The reason I am in research is because it hasn't been beaten out of me.

Why did you choose molecular structure and function as your area?

I am mostly fascinated by the human body and how it works. In my mind the best way to study those is not at the deep physics level of subatomic particles, but studying at the physiological level is not deep enough. You really need to know at the molecular level. Physical chemistry of biological macromolecules—to me, that is where the answers really lie.

What is cystic fibrosis (CF) and what causes it?

CF is a genetic disease in which a protein, CFTR, has been mutated. CFTR is a membrane protein that is a co-regulator of ion balance in the cell. Primarily, it is a chloride channel, but it regulates other ions and ion homeostasis is absolutely essential in epithelial cells, which is where it is found—on the surface of epithelial cells. If ion balance is destroyed in the case of CF, then, simplistically, one thing happens: there is not enough fluid in the extracellular space. This leads to a thick buildup of mucus, which can trap things like bacteria. So, that is what causes the disease on one level, but ion homeostasis imbalance also leads to other effects that could be thought of as contributing to the disease. Calcium homeostasis is a huge regulator of many things in the cell and, now, it is thought that CFTR plays a role in calcium homeostasis. Disturbance of calcium homeostasis leads to many problems. That is a piece of it as well. So, what causes the disease? It is that this particular protein doesn't function properly. It doesn't get to the membrane to a large part, and it doesn't do its job if it gets there.

What do you imagine will happen if CFTR is overactive?

Actually, there are diseases for which treatment could inhibit CFTR function, for example, diarrhea. I said one of the biggest problems with CF is that there is not enough fluid coming into the extracellular space. The opposite of that is when there is too much fluid. If the epithelial cells with this problem are lining the intestines, then this leads to diarrhea.

Why aren't other properly functioning chloride ion channels able to overcome the problems caused by defect in CFTR?

They aren't able to communicate with the other regulatory ion channels. I think the regulatory system has been broken, in a sense. It would be great to have a sensor to show how much chloride is going out of a cell and, if there is not enough, to go back and activate other chloride channels, but that is not what the cell does. The cell doesn't do that because it doesn't have that sensory system. But it is a possible approach for therapeutics.

Does mutation ΔF508 in the CFTR gene render the protein product (CFTR) completely dysfunctional? Or does it just lower its activity?

The biggest effect of the deletion of Phe508 is that the protein doesn't get to the cell surface. It gets trapped in the endoplasmic reticulum by the ER quality-control machinery. If you can get the protein to the membrane, and there are drugs that can do that, it is still impaired in its channel activity. It is not completely dysfunctional; it is just not as good a channel. So, the therapeutic approach is twofold. You have to first correct channel trafficking and bring it to membrane and then potentiate its activity. The magic drug would be dual-acting corrector-potentiator.

I can't help but wonder if targeting ubiquitin ligase specific to CFTR could be a possible approach to augmenting the amount of CFTR available in a cell. What do you think about it?

There is something wrong with the way CFTR is assembled. Even if it doesn't get degraded, it is not going to be functional. If you manage to not degrade it, it might shift the equilibrium a little bit and you might get a little more on the plasma membrane, but the defect inherent in the protein hasn't been directly addressed. It is not just that the protein can't get to the membrane; it can't get to the membrane because it fails quality control. Why is it failing quality control? It is not properly folded. You have to first fix it so that it folds properly to get it to the membrane.

❯ What are some other consequences of improperly functioning ion channels?

There are so many effects of ion homeostasis imbalance, it is absolutely astounding. One major consequence would be problems with nerve transduction because ions are key. This would lead to loss of muscle control. Ions, in terms of the nervous system, are hugely important. Neurotransmitters in the brain all bind to ion channels. A chloride channel in an epithelial cell has a more localized effect but, in the nervous system, ion balance is more global.

❯ What is your dream research project?

The thing that motivates me as a scientist is understanding the biophysics of biological function but specifically as it relates to highly dynamic proteins: intrinsically disordered proteins. They are often the regulatory elements of proteins in a cell. Often, people ignore them, but if you show them that this is a major element of cell biology or a major element of cell cycle control, they get thinking and are interested. To me, that is exciting because I like to make people think and make them get out of their ruts of old paradigms for understanding things. So, the dream project is the one that shakes people out of old paradigms with something that helps explain biology from the standpoint of fundamental physical mechanisms of disordered proteins.

❯ Where do we currently stand in CFTR research?

We have made significant advances but we are really not there yet. In terms of understanding things at the molecular level, the regulation, we are not as far along as we are with CF

therapeutics. There are already therapeutics that have major effects. CF used to be a pediatric disease. Patients used to die before they became adults. Now, CF patients are getting married and having kids. The lifestyle for them is very challenging. But at the end of the day, with all the drugs, with all the physical therapy, with all the supplements, people are living and dealing with CF. We are much further than we used to be but there is no cure, yet.

❯ What is next?

There is a lot of focus on trying to get a structure of CFTR so rational drug design can be done. And even in the absence of a structure of full length, you can take models of CFTR and structures of individual domains and use those to do rational drug design. Then there is a huge focus on chaperones. The chaperone network maintains the health of proteins, that is, maintaining proteostasis, which is homeostasis for proteins. So, the thought is if you can shift proteostasis boundary in people with CF, then you can get the chaperone network to deal with $\Delta F508$ or other mutations more effectively. In summary, there is rational drug design and there is an attempt to control proteostasis.

❯ Where do you see yourself in 10 years?

I am really interested in proteins in neurobiology and there are tons of disordered proteins in neurobiology. I see myself looking at biologically relevant proteins with big disordered regions and trying to understand important biological principles. I am really tied to understanding biophysical mechanisms of regulation of biology. My focus on understanding biophysics of dynamics and disorder, protein interaction, regulation, phosphorylation, other posttranslational protein modifications is unlikely to change.

UNIT III
Genetics

Genetics is the branch of biology that deals with heredity—the transmission of characteristics from parents to offspring. We begin this unit by examining the structure of the genetic material, namely, DNA, at the molecular and cellular levels. We will explore the structure and replication of DNA in Chapter 10. We then consider how genes work at the molecular level and how the information within genes is made into products such as RNA and proteins (Chapters 11 and 12). The expression of genes is largely responsible for the characteristics of living organisms. We will also examine how mutations can alter the properties of genes and even lead to diseases, such as cancer (Chapter 13).

In Chapter 14 we turn our attention to the mechanisms of how genes are transmitted from parent to offspring. This topic begins with a discussion of how the DNA of eukaryotes is packaged into chromosomes. Next we consider how chromosomes are sorted and transmitted during mitotic or meiotic cell division. Chapter 15 explores the relationships between the transmission of genes and the outcome of an offspring's traits. We will look at fundamental genetic patterns called Mendelian inheritance, after the nineteenth-century biologist who discovered them, as well as more complex patterns that could not have been predicted from Mendel's work.

Chapters 10 through 15 focus on the fundamental properties of the genetic material and heredity. The remaining chapters in this unit explore additional specialized topics of genetics. In Chapter 16 we will examine some of the unique genetic properties of bacteria and viruses. Chapter 17 considers how genes play a fundamental role in the development of animals and plants from a fertilized egg to an adult. We end this unit by exploring genetic technologies that are used by researchers, clinicians, and biotechnologists to unlock the mysteries of genes and provide tools and applications that benefit humans (Chapters 18 and 19).

 ## Certain biology principles will be emphasized in this unit:

- *The genetic material, DNA, provides a dynamic plan for sustaining life.* Throughout this unit you will see how the genetic material carries the information to sustain life.

- *Structure determines function.* In Chapters 10 through 15 we will examine how the structures of DNA, RNA, genes, and chromosomes underlie their functions.

- *Living organisms interact with their environment.* In Chapters 12 and 15 we will explore the interactions between an organism's genes and its environment.

- *Living organisms grow, develop, and reproduce.* In Chapter 17 we will consider how a genetic program is involved in the developmental stages of animals and plants.

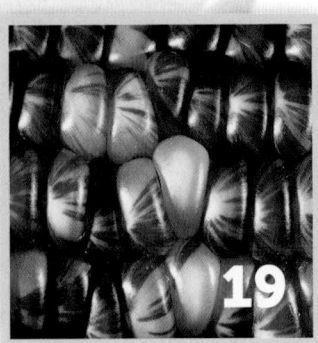

Nucleic Acid Structure and DNA Replication

Models of replicated DNA double helices that occur within duplicated chromosomes (micrograph of a duplicated human chromosome).

Throughout Unit 3 you will be thinking about DNA, genes, and chromosomes. The chapter-opening photo on this page will help you visualize the fact that chromosomes are composed of DNA. We begin our survey of **genetics** by examining DNA at the molecular level. Once you understand how DNA works at this level, it becomes easier to see how DNA function affects the properties of cells and, ultimately, the characteristics or traits of organisms. The past several decades have seen exciting advances in techniques and approaches to investigate and even to alter the genetic material. These advances have not only greatly expanded our understanding of molecular genetics, but also such technologies are widely used in related disciplines, such as biochemistry, cell biology, and microbiology.

To a large extent our understanding of genetics comes from our knowledge of the molecular structure of DNA (deoxyribonucleic acid) and RNA (ribonucleic acid). In this chapter we begin by considering some classic experiments that were consistent with the theory that DNA is the genetic material. We will then survey the molecular features of DNA, which will allow you to appreciate how DNA can store information and be accurately copied. The ability to make a copy of DNA is one of the key elements of its structure that allow it to function as the hereditary material.

10.1 BIOCHEMICAL IDENTIFICATION OF THE GENETIC MATERIAL

Learning Outcomes:

1. List the four key criteria that the genetic material must fulfill.
2. Describe and interpret the results of the experiments that identified DNA as the genetic material.

The genetic material functions as a dynamic blueprint for the construction of living organisms. In addition, the genetic material allows organisms to survive in their native environments. For example, an individual's DNA provides the dynamic blueprint that encodes information to make the enzymes that are needed to metabolize food. To fulfill its role, the genetic material must meet several criteria:

1. *Information:* The genetic material must contain the information necessary to construct an entire organism.
2. *Transmission:* The genetic material must be passed from parent to offspring. It also must be passed from cell to cell during cell division.
3. *Replication:* For transmission to occur, the genetic material must be accurately copied.
4. *Variation:* Differences in the genetic material must account for the known variation within each species and among different species.

The quest to identify the genetic material really began in 1883 when August Weismann and Karl Nägeli championed the idea that a chemical substance exists within living cells that is responsible for the transmission of traits from parents to offspring. During the next 30 years the search for the hereditary material centred on the behaviour of **chromosomes** of plants and animals. The term *chromosomes* literally means "coloured" (*chromo*) "body" (*soma*), referring to the observation by early microscopists that the chromosomes are easily stained by coloured dyes. Attention was drawn to the chromosomes because these structures could be seen to double and then divide as one cell divided to produce a daughter cell or cells. Because the transmission patterns of chromosomes from cell to cell and from parent to offspring corresponded precisely to that expected of the hereditary material, researchers became convinced that chromosomes carry the biomolecules that dictate cell and organismal structure and function.

The study of the chemical composition of chromosomes initially misled researchers. Chromosomes contain two classes of macromolecules: proteins and DNA. Scientists of that era viewed proteins as the likely hereditary material because of their complexity; proteins adopt a wide range of three-dimensional shapes and are made from 20 different amino acids. By comparison, DNA seemed less complex because it contains only four types of repeating units, each of which is called **nucleotide**. Therefore, from the 1920s to the 1940s most scientists expected that research studies would reveal that proteins were the genetic material. Contrary to this expectation, however, the experiments described in this section were pivotal in showing that DNA carries out this critical role.

Griffith's Bacterial Transformation Experiments Indicated the Existence of a Biochemical Genetic Material

Studies in microbiology were important in developing an experimental strategy to identify the genetic material. In the late 1920s, Frederick Griffith studied a type of bacterium known then as pneumococci and now classified as *Streptococcus pneumoniae*. Some strains of *S. pneumoniae* secrete a polysaccharide capsule, while other strains do not. When carefully transferred onto Petri plates containing a solid growth medium, capsule-secreting strains have a smooth colony morphology. Those strains unable to secrete a capsule have a colony morphology that looks rough. Smooth strains of *S. pneumoniae* can cause pneumonia and other symptoms in mammals. In mice, such infections are often fatal.

As shown in **Figure 10.1**, Griffith injected live and heat-killed bacteria into mice and then observed whether the mice died. He investigated the effects of two strains of *S. pneumoniae*, type S for smooth and type R for rough. When injected into a mouse, the living smooth strain killed the mouse (Figure 10.1, step 1). We now know that the capsule is necessary for this to occur because it prevents the mouse's immune system from killing the bacterial cells. Following the death of the mouse, many type S bacteria were found in the mouse's blood. By comparison, when living type R bacteria were injected into a mouse, they did not kill the mouse and living bacteria were not found in the live mouse's blood (Figure 10.1, step 2). This established the link between the smooth strain's ability to make a capsule and its **pathogenicity**: the ability to cause a disease in the host cell.

In a follow-up to these results, Griffith also heat-killed the smooth bacteria and then injected them into the mouse. As expected, the dead smooth colony bacteria could not cause disease in the mouse (Figure 10.1, step 3). A surprising result occurred when Griffith mixed live nonpathogenic type R bacteria with heat-killed type S bacteria and then injected them into a mouse—the mouse died (Figure 10.1, step 4). The blood from the dead mouse contained living type S bacteria! These results indicated that a substance from dead type S bacteria was transforming the type R bacteria into type S. Griffith called this process **transformation**, and he termed the unidentified material that was responsible for this phenomenon the *transformation principle*. The mechanism of transformation will be considered in Chapter 16. For now let's consider the significance of Griffith's experiments. According to Griffith's results,

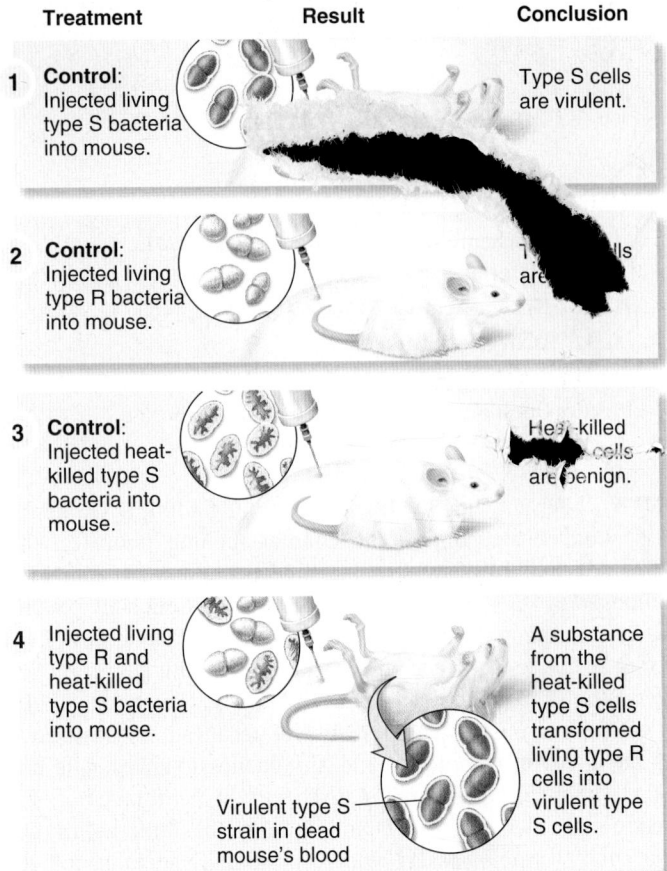

Treatment	Result	Conclusion
1 Control: Injected living type S bacteria into mouse.		Type S cells are virulent.
2 Control: Injected living type R bacteria into mouse.		...lls are...
3 Control: Injected heat-killed type S bacteria into mouse.		Heat-killed ...cells are benign.
4 Injected living type R and heat-killed type S bacteria into mouse.	Virulent type S strain in dead mouse's blood	A substance from the heat-killed type S cells transformed living type R cells into virulent type S cells.

Figure 10.1 Griffith's experiments that showed the transformation of bacteria by a "transformation principle."

Concept check: *Let's suppose that the type R strain used by Griffith was resistant to being killed by an antibiotic, while the type S strain lacked this trait. For the experiment described in step (4), would you expect the living type S bacteria found in the dead mouse's blood to be resistant to the antibiotic?*

BioConnections: *Look ahead to Figure 18.18. How does bacterial transformation play a role in the transfer of genes, such as antibiotic resistance genes, from one bacterial species to another?*

the transformed bacteria had acquired the *information* to make a capsule from the heat-killed cells. For the transformed bacteria to have proliferated and thereby killed the mouse, the substance conferring the ability to make a capsule must have been *replicated* and *transmitted* from mother to daughter cells. Taken together, these observations are consistent with the idea that the formation of a capsule is governed by genetic material, because it meets the four criteria described at the beginning of this section. Thus, the experiment of Figure 10.1, step (4) was consistent with the idea that genetic material from the dead bacteria had been transferred to the living rough bacteria and provided those bacteria with a gelatine capsule, a new trait. At the time of his studies, however, Griffith could not determine the biochemical composition of the transforming substance.

FEATURE INVESTIGATION

Avery, MacLeod, and McCarty Used Purification Methods to Reveal That DNA Is the Genetic Material

Exciting discoveries sometimes occur when researchers recognize that another scientist's experimental approach can be modified and then used to dig deeper into a scientific question. In the 1940s Oswald Avery, Colin MacLeod, and Maclyn McCarty were also interested in the process of bacterial transformation. During their studies they realized that Griffith's observations could be used to devise an experimental strategy to biochemically identify the genetic material. They asked the question, What substance is being transferred from the dead type S bacteria to the live type R?

Avery, MacLeod, and McCarty used established biochemical procedures to purify classes of macromolecules, such as

proteins, DNA, and RNA, from a type S streptococcal strain. Initially, they discovered that only the purified DNA could convert type R bacteria into type S. To further verify that DNA is the genetic material, they performed the investigation outlined in **Figure 10.2**. They purified DNA from a type S strain and mixed it with type R bacteria. After allowing time for DNA uptake, they added an antibody that aggregated any untransformed type R bacteria, which were removed by centrifugation. The remaining bacteria were incubated overnight on Petri plates.

When they mixed their DNA extract with type R bacteria, some of the bacteria were converted to type S (see plate B in step 5 of Figure 10.2). As a control, if no DNA extract was added, no type S bacterial colonies were observed on the Petri plates (see plate A in step 5). Though this result was consistent with the idea that DNA is the genetic material, a careful biochemist might argue that the DNA extract may not have

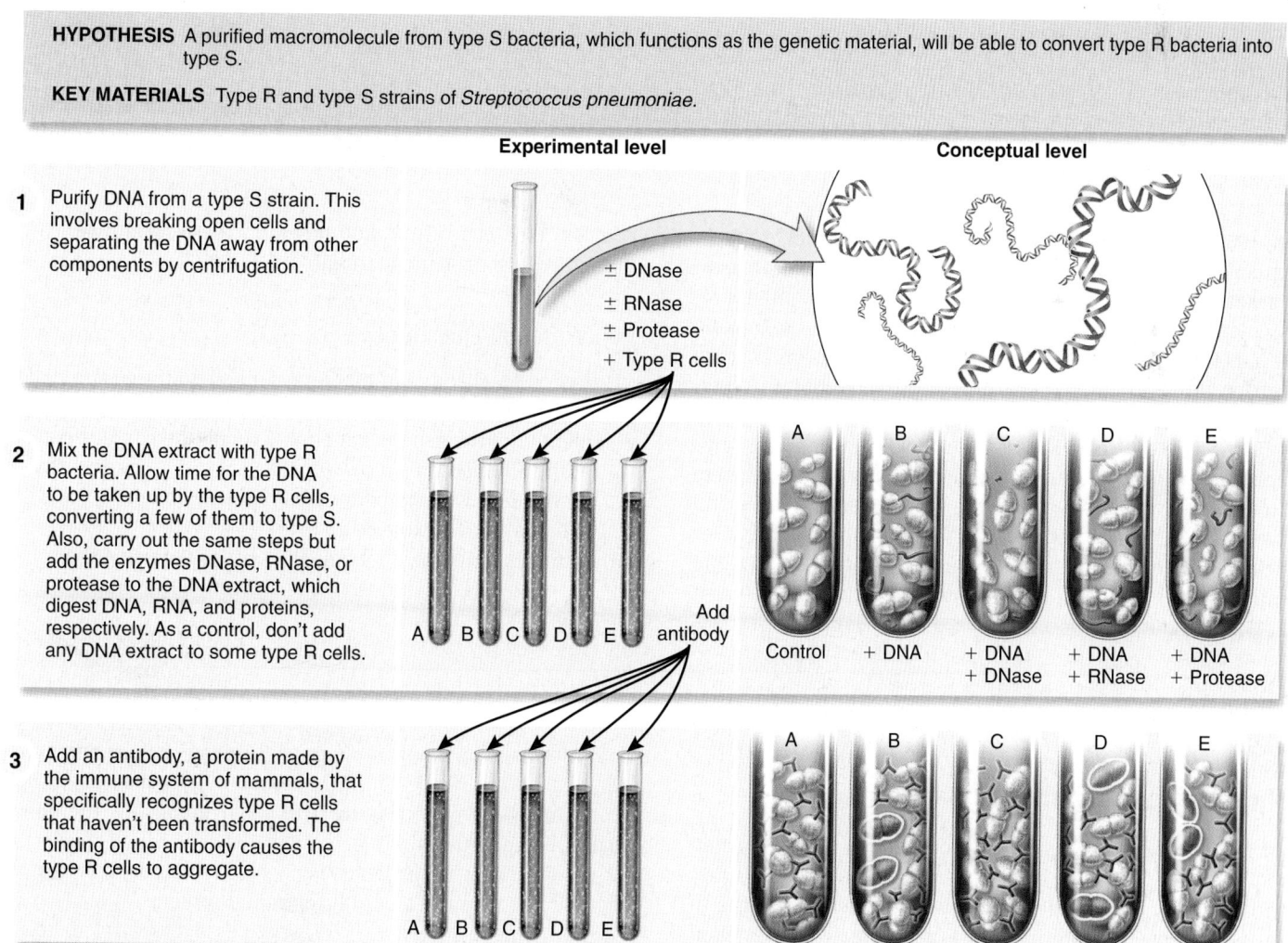

HYPOTHESIS A purified macromolecule from type S bacteria, which functions as the genetic material, will be able to convert type R bacteria into type S.

KEY MATERIALS Type R and type S strains of *Streptococcus pneumoniae*.

Experimental level   **Conceptual level**

1 Purify DNA from a type S strain. This involves breaking open cells and separating the DNA away from other components by centrifugation.

± DNase
± RNase
± Protease
+ Type R cells

2 Mix the DNA extract with type R bacteria. Allow time for the DNA to be taken up by the type R cells, converting a few of them to type S. Also, carry out the same steps but add the enzymes DNase, RNase, or protease to the DNA extract, which digest DNA, RNA, and proteins, respectively. As a control, don't add any DNA extract to some type R cells.

Add antibody

| A | B | C | D | E |
| Control | + DNA | + DNA + DNase | + DNA + RNase | + DNA + Protease |

3 Add an antibody, a protein made by the immune system of mammals, that specifically recognizes type R cells that haven't been transformed. The binding of the antibody causes the type R cells to aggregate.

Figure 10.2   The Avery, MacLeod, and McCarty experiments that identified DNA as Griffith's transformation principle—the genetic material.

Figure 10.2 *(Continued)*

4   Remove type R cells by centrifugation. Plate the remaining bacteria (if any) that are in the supernatant onto petri plates. Incubate overnight.

Centrifuge

Type S cells in supernatant

Type R cells in pellet

5   **THE DATA**

A

Control

B

DNA extract

C

DNA extract + DNase

D

DNA extract + RNase

E

DNA extract + protease

6   **CONCLUSION** DNA is responsible for transforming type R cells into type S cells.

7   **SOURCE** Avery, O.T., MacLeod, C.M., and McCarty, M. 1944. Studies on the Chemical Nature of the Substance Inducing Transformation of Pneumococcal Types. *Journal of Experimental Medicine* 79:137–156.

been 100% pure. Realistically, any purified extract is likely to contain small traces of other substances. For this reason the researchers realized that a small amount of contaminating material in the DNA extract could actually be the genetic material. The most likely contaminating substances in this case would be protein or RNA. To address this possibility, Avery, MacLeod, and McCarty treated the DNA extract with enzymes that digest DNA (called DNase), RNA (RNase), or protein (protease) (see Figure 10.2, step 2). When the DNA extracts were treated with RNase or protease, the type R bacteria were still converted into type S, suggesting that contaminating RNA or protein in the extract was not acting as the genetic material (see plates D and E). Moreover, when the extract was treated with DNase, its ability to convert type R bacteria into type S

was lost (see plate C). Taken together, these results indicated that DNA is the genetic material.

Experimental Questions

1. Avery, MacLeod, and McCarty worked with two strains of *Streptococcus pneumoniae* to determine the biochemical identity of the genetic material. Explain the characteristics of the *Streptococcus pneumoniae* strains that made them particularly well suited for such an experiment
2. What is a DNA extract?
3. In the experiment what was the purpose of using the protease, RNase, and DNase if only the DNA extract caused transformation?

Hershey and Chase Determined That DNA Is the Genetic Material of T2 Bacteriophage

Although the work of Avery, MacLeod, and McCarty was consistent with the idea that DNA is the genetic material, further experimentation was needed to determine whether the use of DNA as the genetic material was a widespread phenomenon in biology. In 1952 the efforts of Alfred Hershey and Martha Chase centred on the study of a virus named T2. This virus infects the *Escherichia coli* bacteria and is therefore known as a

bacteriophage or simply a **phage**. A T2 phage has an outer covering called the phage coat that contains a capsid, sheath, tail fibres, and base plate (**Figure 10.3**). Biochemically, the phage coat is composed entirely of protein. DNA is found inside the T2 capsid. From a biochemical perspective T2 is very simple because it is composed of only DNA and proteins.

The genetic material of T2 provides a blueprint to make new phages. However, all viruses must introduce their genetic material into the cytoplasm of a living host cell to have it replicated. In the case of T2, the tail is attached to the bacterial cell wall and then the genetic material is injected into the cytoplasm (Figure 10.3).

Hershey and Chase devised a method to separate the phage coat, which is attached to the outside of the bacterium, from the genetic material, which is injected into the cytoplasm. They detached the coat from the bacterium with the high shear forces produced by a blender. In addition, they used radioisotopes to label the DNA and proteins separately. Sulphur atoms are found in proteins but not in DNA, whereas phosphorus atoms are found in DNA but not in phage proteins. They exposed T2-infected bacterial cells to ^{35}S (a radioisotope of sulphur) or to ^{32}P (a radioisotope of phosphorus). These infected cells produced phages that had incorporated ^{35}S into their proteins or ^{32}P into their DNA. The labelled phages were then used in the experiment shown in **Figure 10.4**.

(a) Schematic drawing of T2 bacteriophage

(b) An electron micrograph of T2 bacteriophage infecting _E. coli_

Figure 10.3   **The structure of T2 bacteriophage.**   The colourized electron micrograph in part (b) shows T2 phages attached to an _E. coli_ cell and injecting their genetic material into the cell.

Hershey and Chase took samples of T2 phages, one labelled with ^{35}S and the other with ^{32}P, and mixed them in separate tubes with _E. coli_ cells for a short time. This allowed the phages enough time to inject their genetic material into the bacteria. The samples were then subjected to shearing forces in a blender

Figure 10.4   Hershey and Chase experiment showing that the genetic material of T2 phage is DNA.

Concept check: _In these experiments, which isotope do you expect to find in the pellet: ^{32}P or ^{35}S?_

for up to eight minutes. This treatment removed the phage coat from the surface of the bacterial cell without causing cell lysis. Each sample was then subjected to centrifugation at a speed that caused the heavier bacterial cells to form a pellet at the bottom of the tube, while the lighter phage coats remained in the supernatant, which is the solution above the pellet. The amount of radioactivity in the supernatant (emitted from either ^{35}S or ^{32}P) was determined by using an instrument called a scintillation counter.

As you can see in the data of Figure 10.4, most of the ^{35}S isotope (80%) was found in the supernatant. Because the shearing force removed only the phage coat, this result indicates that the empty phages contain primarily protein. In contrast, only about 35% of the ^{32}P was found in the supernatant, indicating that most of the phage DNA was located within the bacterial cells in the pellet. Taken together, these results suggest that the phage DNA is injected into the bacterial cytoplasm during infection, giving the expected outcome if DNA is the genetic material of T2.

10.2 NUCLEIC ACID STRUCTURE

Learning Outcomes:

1. Describe the structure of nucleotides, a DNA strand, and the DNA double helix.
2. Discuss and interpret the work of Franklin, Chargaff, and Watson and Crick.

The two sets of experiments provided compelling evidence to support the role of DNA as the genetic material. Although strong evidence suggested that DNA was the hereditary material, scientists were baffled as to how DNA, with only four types of nucleotides, could contain all the information needed to provide the blueprint for life. When biologists want to understand the function of a material at the molecular and cellular level, they focus some of their efforts on investigating its biochemical structure. An understanding of DNA structure has proven to be particularly informative because the structure makes it easy to understand how DNA can store information, how variation in structure can occur, and how DNA can be replicated for future generations.

DNA and its molecular cousin, RNA, are known as **nucleic acids**. This term is derived from the discovery of DNA by Friedrich Miescher in 1869. He isolated a novel phosphorus-containing substance from the nuclei of white blood cells found in waste surgical bandages. He named this substance nuclein. As the chemistry of DNA and RNA structure became better understood, it was found that they are acidic molecules, releasing hydrogen ions (H$^+$) in solution and having a net negative charge at neutral pH. Thus, DNA and RNA nucleins were renamed as nucleic acids.

The Building Blocks of Nucleic Acid Polymers Are Nucleotides

DNA is a very large macromolecule composed of smaller building blocks. DNA and RNA are both polymers that are assembled step by step by combining their monomer units through a series of dehydration (condensation) reactions. The monomer units for DNA and RNA are known as **nucleotides**. The structures of nucleotides were determined by P. A. Levene in the 1920s. A nucleotide has three components: a phosphate group, a pentose (five-carbon) sugar, and a nitrogenous base. The nitrogenous base and phosphate group are attached to the sugar to form a nucleotide (**Figure 10.5**). The nucleotides found in DNA and RNA contain different sugars. Deoxyribose is found in DNA, while ribose is found in RNA. Compared with ribose, deoxyribose is missing a single oxygen atom; the prefix *deoxy* (meaning "without oxygen") refers to this missing atom.

Five different nitrogenous bases are found in nucleotides, although any given nucleotide contains only one nitrogenous base. The five nitrogenous bases are subdivided into two categories: the purines and the pyrimidines (Figure 10.5). The **purine** nitrogenous bases, **adenine (A)** and **guanine (G)**, have

(a) DNA nucleotide

(b) RNA nucleotide

Figure 10.5   **Nucleotides and their components.**   For simplicity, the carbon atoms in the ring structures are not shown.

a double-ring structure; the **pyrimidine** nitrogenous bases, **cytosine (C)**, **thymine (T)**, and **uracil (U)**, have a single-ring structure. Thymine is found only in DNA; uracil is found only in RNA. Adenine, guanine, and cytosine are found in both DNA and RNA.

A conventional numbering system has been created to describe the attachment sites of the nitrogenous base and phosphate to the sugar molecule (**Figure 10.6**). In the sugar ring, carbon atoms are numbered in a clockwise direction starting with the carbon atom to the right of the ring oxygen atom. The fifth carbon is outside the ring. The prime symbol (′) is used to distinguish the numbering of carbons in the sugar, while the atoms in the ring structures of the nitrogenous bases are not given the prime designation. The sugar carbons are designated 1′ ("one prime"), 2′, 3′, 4′, and 5′. Within a nucleotide, the nitrogenous base is attached to the sugar's 1′ carbon and the phosphate group is attached to the sugar's 5′ carbon. An —OH group is found off the 3′ carbon. Thus, each sugar of a nucleotide has a geometric polarity based on the fact that a phosphate is attached to the fifth carbon, which projects in the opposite direction as the —OH group off the third carbon. This polarity is important for the ability of DNA to form its final three-dimensional structure and is extremely important for us in understanding how DNA replication occurs. To assist us in visualizing this geometric polarity, **Figure 10.7**, far left shows a simplified representation of a nucleotide as an arrowhead, with the point representing the 5′ end with the phosphate group.

Once a nucleotide is part of a nucleic acid polymer, it occurs as a nucleotide with a single phosphate group (Figure 10.6a). The nucleotide monomers that will be incorporated into polymers actually contain three phosphate groups and are called nucleotide triphosphates (Figure 10.6b). During the polymerization process some of the energy stored in the extra phosphate group's bonds is used to create the covalent bonds that connect the individual nucleotides into a polymer. We will look at this process next.

A Nucleic Acid Polymer Strand Is a Linear Linkage of Nucleotides with Directionality

The next level of nucleic acid structure occurs as nucleotides are covalently attached to each other in a linear fashion to form a polymer. In nucleic acids each polymer is called a strand. Figure 10.7 depicts a short strand of DNA with four nucleotides. The type of covalent bond that forms is a phosphoester bond (a covalent bond between phosphorus and oxygen) involving the

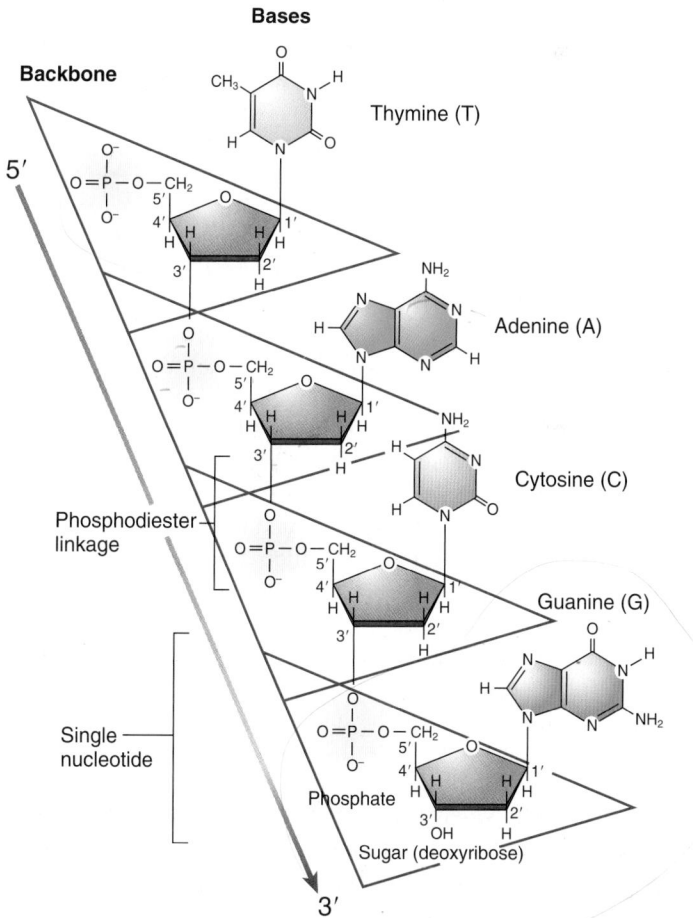

Figure 10.7 **The structure of a DNA strand.** Nucleotides are covalently bonded to each other in a linear manner. Notice the directionality of the strand and the fact that it carries a particular sequence of bases. An RNA strand has a very similar structure, except that the sugar is ribose rather than deoxyribose, and uracil is substituted for thymine.

Figure 10.6 **Conventional numbering in a DNA nucleotide.** (a) A nucleotide as it occurs in a polymer with one phosphate group. A triangle is used to emphasize a nucleotide's polarity. (b) A nucleotide triphosphate, the starting monomer for nucleic acid polymerization.

sugar molecule in one nucleotide and the phosphate group of the next nucleotide. Another way of viewing the linkage between two nucleotides is to notice that a phosphate group connects two sugar molecules. The linkage in DNA and RNA strands is called a **phosphodiester linkage** and is composed of *two* phosphoester bonds. As you will see in our discussions of the structure of DNA in cells, the nucleotides are oriented in space such that the phosphates and sugar molecules form the **backbone** of a DNA or an RNA strand, while the nitrogenous bases project from the backbone. The backbone is negatively charged because of the negative charges of the phosphate groups.

You have already seen that each nucleotide has a geometric asymmetry. This asymmetry also affects the orientation of the nucleotides within a strand. Each phosphate in a phosphodiester linkage is covalently bound to the 5′ carbon in one nucleotide and to the 3′ carbon in the other. In a strand, all sugar molecules are oriented in the same direction. For example, in the strand shown in Figure 10.7, all the 5′ carbons in every sugar molecule are above the 3′ carbons. A strand has a *directionality* based on the orientation of the sugar molecules within that strand. In Figure 10.7, going from top to bottom, the direction of the strand is said to be 5′ to 3′. The 5′ end of a DNA strand has a phosphate group, while the 3′ end has an —OH group.

A Few Key Experiments Paved the Way to Solving the Structure of DNA

In 1953 James Watson and Francis Crick, along with collaborator Maurice Wilkins, determined the structure of the DNA double helix. Before their work DNA was already known to be composed of nucleotides. However, scientists did not know how the nucleotides were bonded. Watson and Crick wanted to determine the structure of DNA because they thought this knowledge would provide insights into how it could function as the genetic material.

To solve the structure of DNA, Watson and Crick drew on the approach to solving structure used by Linus Pauling, the X-ray diffraction data of Rosalind Franklin and Maurice Wilkins, and the nitrogenous base composition studies of Erwin Chargaff. Let's see how they put this knowledge together to determine the structure of DNA.

Linus Pauling had determined that proteins could form regions of α helix. To determine the structure of the α helix, Pauling built large models by linking together simple ball-and-stick units. In this way, he could see whether atoms fit together properly in a complicated three-dimensional structure. This approach is still widely used today, except that now researchers construct three-dimensional models by using computers. Watson and Crick used a ball-and-stick approach to solve the structure of the DNA double helix.

X-ray diffraction was also a key experimental tool in the discovery of the DNA double helix. When a substance is exposed to radiation, such as X-rays, the atoms in the substance will scatter the X-rays (**Figure 10.8a**). If the substance has a repeating structure, the pattern of scattering, known as the diffraction pattern, is mathematically related to the structural arrangement of the atoms causing the scattering. The diffraction pattern is

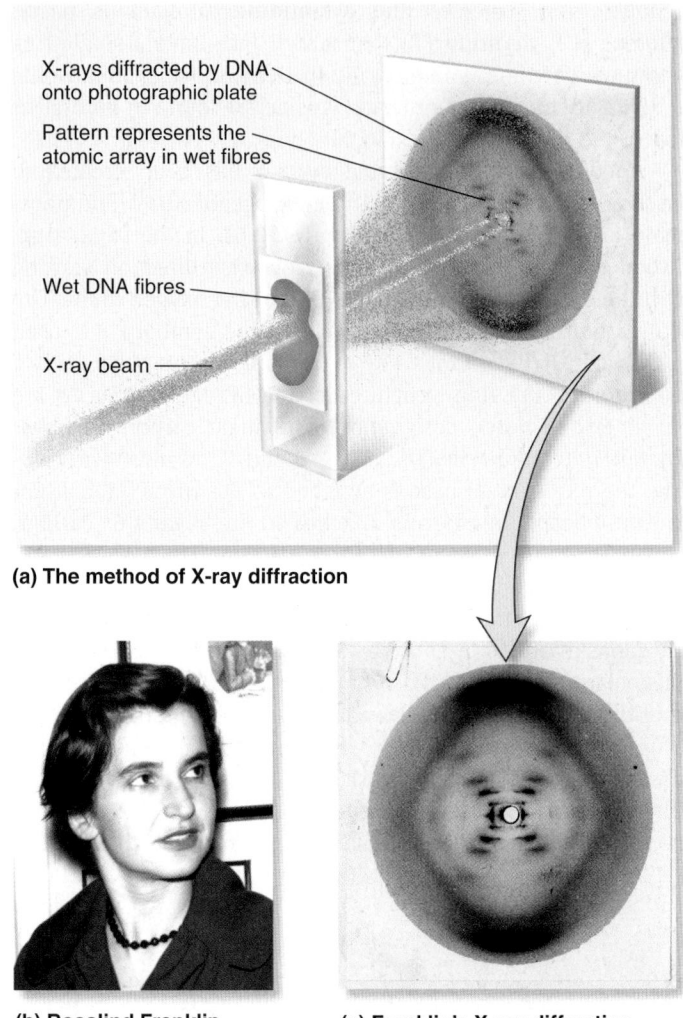

(a) The method of X-ray diffraction

X-rays diffracted by DNA onto photographic plate

Pattern represents the atomic array in wet fibres

Wet DNA fibres

X-ray beam

(b) Rosalind Franklin

(c) Franklin's X-ray diffraction pattern of wet DNA fibres

Figure 10.8   Rosalind Franklin and X-ray diffraction applied to DNA wet fibres.   **(a)** The exposure of X-rays to DNA causes the X-rays to be scattered. **(b)** Rosalind Franklin. **(c)** Because the DNA forms a repeating structure, the X-rays are scattered in a way that produces an X-ray diffraction pattern.

analyzed by using mathematical theory to provide information regarding the three-dimensional structure of the molecule. Rosalind Franklin (**Figure 10.8b**), working in the same laboratory as Maurice Wilkins, was a gifted experimentalist who made marked advances in X-ray diffraction techniques involving DNA. The diffraction pattern of DNA fibres produced by Franklin is shown in **Figure 10.8c**. This pattern suggested a helical structure with a diameter that is relatively uniform but too wide to be formed by a single-strand of DNA. The pattern also provided information regarding the number of nucleotides per turn and was consistent with the spacing of 2 nm (nanometres) between the strands. These observations were instrumental in solving the structure of DNA.

The other piece of information that proved critical for the determination of the double helix structure came from Erwin

Chargaff. He pioneered many of the biochemical techniques for the isolation, purification, and measurement of nucleic acids from living cells. Chargaff analyzed the nitrogenous base composition of DNA isolated from many different species. He consistently observed that the amount of adenine in each sample was similar to thymine and the amount of cytosine was similar to guanine. As you will see, this observation became crucial evidence that helped Watson and Crick develop the double helix model of DNA.

Watson and Crick Deduced the Double Helix Structure of DNA

Pulling together knowledge from their colleagues' experimental approaches, Watson and Crick began their experimental studies. They assumed that nucleotides were linked together in a linear fashion and that the chemical linkage between two nucleotides was always the same. Then, they set out to build ball-and-stick models that incorporated all the experimental observations.

Modelling of chemical structures often involves trial and error. Watson and Crick initially considered several incorrect models. One model was a double helix in which the nitrogenous bases were on the outside of the helix. Another model showed the nitrogenous bases forming hydrogen bonds with the identical nitrogenous base in the opposite strand (that is, A with A, T with T, G with G, and C with C). However, the model building revealed that the nitrogenous bases could not fit together this way. Finally, they realized that the hydrogen bonding of adenine to thymine was structurally similar to that of cytosine to guanine. In both cases, a purine (A or G) bonds with a pyrimidine (T or C). With an interaction between A and T and between G and C, the ball-and-stick models showed that the two strands would form a double helix structure in which all atoms would fit together properly. This ball-and-stick model was consistent with all the known data (**Figure 10.9**).

Figure 10.9   Watson and Crick and their model of the DNA double helix.

Watson, Crick, and Wilkins proposed the structure of DNA, which was published in the journal *Nature* in 1953. In 1962 they were awarded a Nobel Prize. Unfortunately, Rosalind Franklin had died in 1958, and the Nobel Prize is not awarded posthumously.

DNA Has a Repeating, Antiparallel Helical Structure Formed by the Complementary Base Pairing of Nucleotides

The configuration that Watson and Crick proposed is a double-stranded repeating helical structure with the sugar-phosphate backbone on the outside and the nitrogenous bases on the inside (**Figure 10.10a**). The double-stranded DNA helix consists of two polymers (strands) of deoxyribonuleotides. The helical structure is stabilized by hydrogen bonding between the nitrogenous bases of the two strands; we call the hydrogen bonding that occurs between the nitrogenous bases **base pairing**. The hydrogen bonding is possible because the nitrogenous bases of each strand project inward toward each other. A distinguishing feature of DNA base pairing is its specificity. Optimum hydrogen bonding occurs as an adenine base in one strand forms two hydrogen bonds with a thymine base in the opposite strand, and a guanine base of one strand forms three hydrogen bonds with a cytosine base of the opposite strand (**Figure 10.10b**). With adenine (a single-ringed pyrimidine) always paired with the double-ringed purine thymine, and the double-ringed guanine always paired with the single-ringed cytosine, the base pairs of a helix all have the same width, giving the double helix a uniform structure. One complete turn of the double helix is composed of 10 base pairs. The physical basis of the **AT/GC rule** derives from optimization of hydrogen bonding and the uniform width that occurs when a purine pairs with pyrimidine. The AT/GC rule (also known as Chargaff's rule) explains Chargaff's data in which he found equal amounts of A and T, and equal amounts of G and C, in DNA. One very important feature of DNA's structure is that the stable helix can form only when the two strands have opposite directionality. We use the term **antiparallel** to describe this opposite directionality. Watson and Crick proposed an antiparallel structure in their original DNA model because this is the only orientation that allows optimum base pairing across the helix.

Because of the AT/GC rule, the base sequences of two DNA strands are **complementary**. That is, we can predict the sequence in one DNA strand if we know the sequence in the opposite strand. For example, if one strand has the sequence of 5′–GCGGATTT–3′, the opposite strand must be 3′–CGCCTAAA–5′. With regard to their 5′ and 3′ directionality, the two strands of a DNA double helix are antiparallel. As shown in Figure 10.10, one strand runs in the 5′ to 3′ direction from top to bottom, while the other strand is oriented 3′ to 5′ from top to bottom. Watson and Crick proposed an antiparallel structure in their original DNA model because this is the only orientation that allows optimum base pairing across the helix.

Figure 10.10   Structure of the DNA double helix.   (a) DNA is a helix composed of two antiparallel strands. **(b)** The AT/GC base pairing holds the strands together via hydrogen bonds.

Concept check: *If one DNA strand is 5'–GATTCGTTC–3', what is the complementary strand?*

The DNA model shown in Figure 10.10a is called a ribbon model, which clearly shows the components of the DNA molecule. However, other models are also used to visualize DNA. The model for the DNA double helix shown in **Figure 10.11** is a space-filling model in which the atoms are depicted as spheres. This type of structural model emphasizes the surface of DNA. As you can see in this model, the sugar-phosphate backbone is on the outermost surface of the double helix. In a living cell, the backbone has the most direct contact with water. The atoms of the nitrogenous bases are more internally located within the double-stranded structure. The inner regions where the atoms of the nitrogenous bases make contact with the surrounding water are termed **grooves**. Two grooves, called the **major groove** and the **minor groove**, spiral around the double helix. As discussed in later chapters, the major groove provides a location in which

a protein can bind to a particular sequence of nitrogenous bases and affect the expression of a gene.

The double-stranded model for DNA with nitrogenous base complementarity immediately suggests how DNA might be used as a template to make a copy of itself. We will look more closely at this in the next section. The realization that the nitrogenous bases of adjacent nucleotides form the sequential linear rungs of the helix suggested the order of nitrogenous bases might be a code. From the perspective of information content, a key feature of DNA and RNA structure is that a strand contains a specific sequence of nitrogenous bases. In Figure 10.7, the sequence of nitrogenous bases is thymine–adenine–cytosine–guanine. This sequence is abbreviated TACG. To indicate its directionality, the strand is abbreviated as 5'–TACG–3'. Because the nucleotides within a strand are attached to each other by stable covalent

Minor groove Major groove Minor groove Major groove

Figure 10.11 **A space-filling model of the DNA double helix.** In the sugar-phosphate backbone, sugar molecules are shown in red and phosphate groups are shown in yellow. This backbone is on the outermost surface of the double helix. The atoms of the bases, shown in green, are more internally located within the double-stranded structure. Notice the major and minor grooves that are formed by this arrangement.

 Principle: *Structure determines function. The major groove provides a binding site for proteins that control the expression of genes.*

bonds, the sequence of nitrogenous bases cannot shuffle around and become rearranged. Therefore, the sequence of nitrogenous bases in a DNA strand will remain the same over time, except in rare cases when mutations occur. By convention we shorten the cumbersome phrase "the sequence of the nitrogenous bases along a polymer" to "the base sequence." The base sequence of DNA and RNA is the critical feature that allows them to store and transmit information.

10.3 DNA REPLICATION

Learning Outcomes:

1. Discuss and interpret the experiments of Meselson and Stahl.
2. Describe how the AT/GC rule underlies the ability of DNA to be replicated semiconservatively.
3. Describe how the synthesis of new DNA strands begins at an origin of replication.
4. List the functions of helicase, topoisomerase, single-strand binding protein, primase, and DNA polymerase at the replication fork.
5. Outline the key differences between the synthesis of the leading and lagging strands.
6. List three reasons that DNA replication is very accurate.
7. Explain how DNA replication occurs at telomeres in eukaryotic chromosomes.

In this section we will begin by looking at an early experiment that helped to determine the method of DNA replication. Next, we will examine the structural characteristics that enable a double helix to be faithfully copied. Finally, we will consider the proteins involved in DNA replication; many cellular proteins are needed to initiate DNA replication and allow it to proceed accurately and quickly.

Replication Overview

In the previous section, we considered the structure of the genetic material: DNA is a double helix that obeys the AT/GC rule. From this structure, Watson and Crick were able to suggest a mechanism by which DNA is copied. They proposed that during this process, known as **DNA replication**, the original DNA strands are used as templates for the synthesis of new DNA strands.

Meselson and Stahl Used Density Gradients to Show That DNA Replication Is a Semiconservative Process Watson and Crick's model of DNA's structure immediately suggested a mechanism for DNA replication—the two strands separate and are used as a template to make a new strand. In 1958, Matthew Meselson and Franklin Stahl devised an investigational approach that gave us the first experimental details to support this notion. An important feature of their research was the use of isotope labelling. Nitrogen occurs in a common light (^{14}N) form and a rare heavy (^{15}N) form. Meselson and Stahl studied DNA replication in the bacterium *E. coli*. They grew *E. coli* cells for many generations in a medium that contained only the ^{15}N form of nitrogen (**Figure 10.12**). This produced a population of bacterial cells in which all the DNA nitrogenous bases had the ^{15}N isotope. Then, they transferred the bacteria to a medium that contained only ^{14}N as its nitrogen source. The cells were allowed to divide, and samples were collected after each round of DNA replication. Because the bacteria were doubling in a medium that contained only ^{14}N, all the newly made DNA strands would be labelled with ^{14}N, while the original strands would remain labelled with the heavy form, ^{15}N.

Meselson and Stahl used **density gradient centrifugation** to separate DNA molecules based on differences in density. Samples were placed on the top of a solution that contained a cesium chloride salt gradient. A double helix containing all nitrogenous bases with ^{15}N would have the highest density and would move to the bottom of the gradient. In contrast, if both DNA strands contained ^{14}N, the DNA would have the lightest density and remain closer to the top of the gradient. If one strand contained ^{14}N and the other strand contained ^{15}N, the DNA would be half-heavy and have an intermediate density, ending up near the middle of the gradient.

Meselson and Stahl found that after one round of DNA replication, all DNA molecules exhibited a density that was half-heavy (Figure 10.12, step 5). After two rounds of replication, DNA of two densities were observed: both light DNA and half-heavy DNA. Taken together, the results of the Meselson and Stahl experiment strongly suggest that for DNA replication the two strands of DNA are each used as a template to make a complementary strand, which then base pairs with the template strand. Thus, after DNA replication the two double-stranded DNA helices each consist of one intact old strand and one newly created complementary strand. We describe this attribute of DNA replication as **semiconservative replication**. Meselson and Stahl showed the semiconservative mechanism for DNA

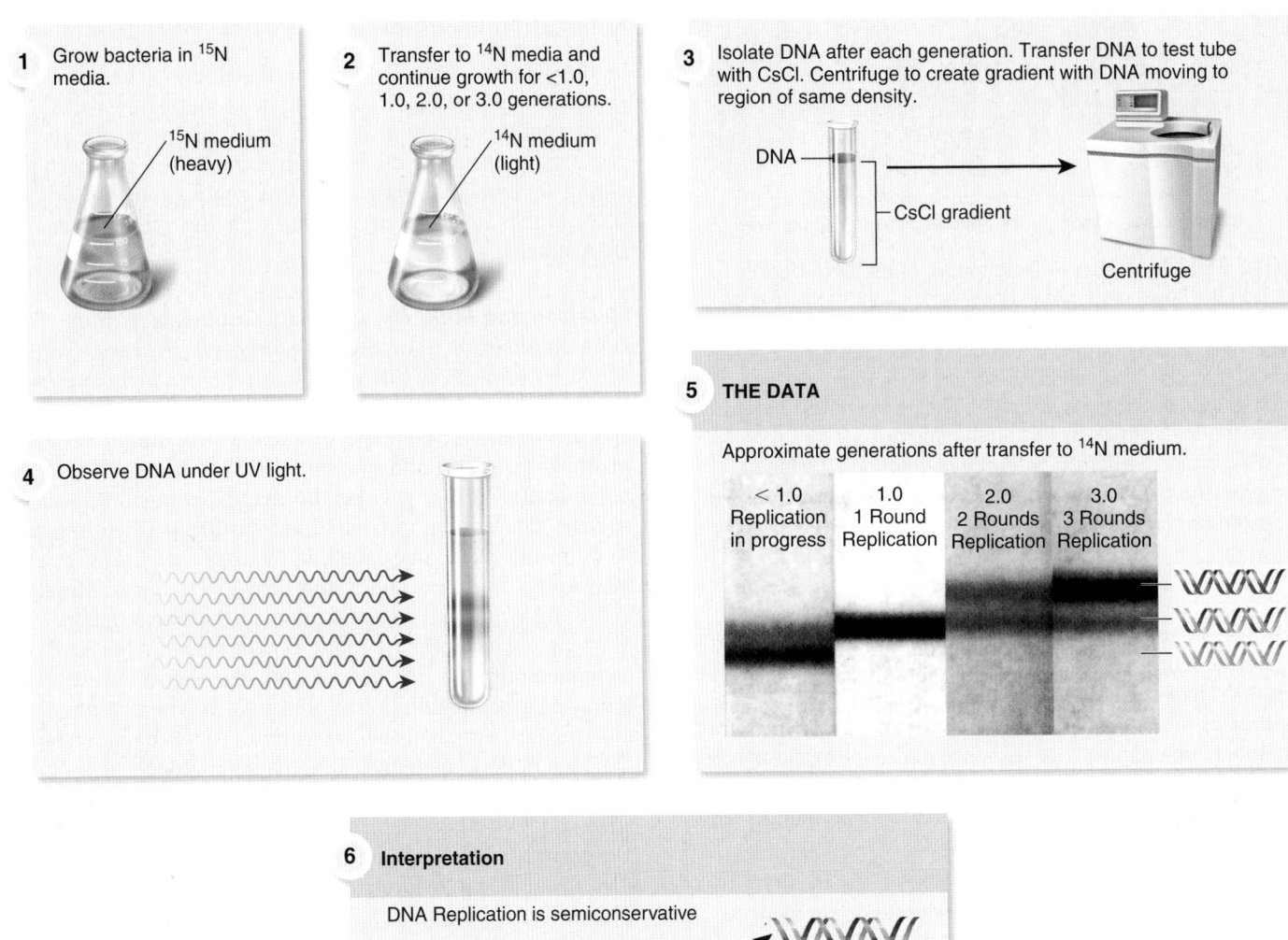

Figure 10.12 The Meselson and Stahl experiment showing that DNS replication is semiconservative.

Concept check: *If this experiment were conducted for four rounds of DNA replication (that is, four generations), what would be the expected fractions of light DNA and half-heavy DNA, according to the semiconservative model?*

replication in the prokaryote *E. coli.* A year later, Herbert Taylor showed that the DNA of eukaryotic chromosomal DNA also appears to be replicated semiconservatively.

Semiconservative DNA Replication Proceeds According to the AT/GC Rule

Semiconservative DNA replication relies on the complementarity of DNA strands according to the AT/GC rule. During the replication process the two complementary strands of DNA separate and serve as template strands for the synthesis of new strands of DNA (**Figure 10.13**). After the double helix has separated, individual nucleotides have access to the template strands. Hydrogen bonding between individual nucleotides and the template strands must obey the AT/GC rule. A covalent bond is formed between the phosphate of one nucleotide and the sugar of the previous nucleotide. The result is that two double helices are made that have the same nitrogenous base sequence as the original DNA molecule. This is a critical feature of DNA replication, because

① Sequence of a DNA double helix before DNA replication.

② DNA strands separate. Nucleotides bind to the parental strands according to the AT/GC rule and are linked together to form daughter strands.

③ The process continues to produce two double helices with the same base sequence.

Figure 10.13   DNA replication according to the AT/GC rule.
Principle: *The genetic material, DNA, provides a dynamic plan for sustaining life. The covalent linkage of a sequence of bases allows DNA to store information.*

it enables the replicated DNA molecules to retain the same information (that is, the same nitrogenous base sequence) as the original molecule.

DNA Replication Begins at an Origin of Replication and Continues in Both Directions Creating Replication Bubbles

Prokaryotes have DNA polymers that consist of thousands of nucleotides, and eukaryotes can have DNA helices that have millions of nucleotides. For cells to divide in a timely fashion,

they must be able to quickly and correctly replicate their DNA; they must also coordinate DNA replication with cell division. In large measure the control of DNA replication occurs at specific sites on the DNA helix known as **origins**. An **origin of replication** is a site within a chromosome that serves as a starting point for DNA replication. At the origin, the base pairing across the helix is disrupted, to allow the two DNA strands to unwind. Now each strand is available to serve as a template and a replication bubble is created (**Figure 10.14a**). DNA replication proceeds outward from the origin in both directions, a process termed **bidirectional replication**. The number of origins of replication varies among different organisms. Bacteria, which have one relatively small, circular chromosome, have a single origin of replication (**Figure 10.14b**). Bidirectional replication starts at the origin of replication, forming a replication bubble that continuously expands until the new strands meet on the opposite side of the chromosome (Figure 10.14b). Eukaryotes have larger chromosomes that are linear. They require multiple origins of replication so that the DNA can be replicated in a reasonable time (**Figure 10.14c**). For eukaryotes the replication bubbles expand until the newly made strands from each origin eventually meet, and replication reaches the end of the linear chromosomes.

Challenges of Bidirectional DNA Replication

Now that you understand the structure of DNA and the role of complementarity for DNA replication, we will look in detail at this complex process. Several important biological realities determine the bidirectionally of DNA replication:

- The two strands of a DNA helix are always oriented antiparallel to each other.
- The new strand being created must be antiparallel to the strand that serves as its template.
- The DNA polymerase enzymes that can bring deoxyribo-nucleotides to a growing strand of DNA can add a nucleotide only to the —OH group that occurs at the 3′ end of the new strand. We say DNA synthesis occurs in a 5′ to 3′ direction.

The antiparallel nature of the two strands and the fact that DNA synthesis occurs only in the 5′ to 3′ direction make the geometry of bidirectional DNA replication complicated, especially so in eukaryotes. To understand the complications of DNA replication, do the following "thought experiment." Imagine a linear single-stranded DNA that is one of the two strands created from unwinding a double helix. Imagine that this strand's directionality, left to right, is 5′ to 3′. The origin of replication (the start point) is in the centre of this.

(a) Bidirectional replication **(b) Single origin of replication in bacteria** **(c) Multiple origins of replication in eukaryotes**

Figure 10.14 **Origins of replication in the chromosomes of different organisms.** (a) Bidirectional replication starts at the origin of replication. (b) Bacteria have a single origin of replication. (c) A eukaryotic chromosome has multiple origins.

We want to proceed bidirectionally as DNA synthesis occurs. What problems do we encounter in our thought experiment? The first problem is that DNA polymerases can add only to the 3′ —OH of an existing nucleotide, but at the very beginning there is no existing nucleotide for the new strand. How do cells get around this problem? Cells first create a small segment of RNA at the origin by using the existing segment of DNA as a template. This works because RNA polymerases, enzymes that create RNA, can lay down a nucleotide with only DNA as a template. But in choosing a nucleotide to create, RNA polymerases also rely on complementarity and hence must orient the nucleotide antiparallel to the template strand. RNA polymerases also work only in the 5′ to 3′ direction, hence the directionality shown here:

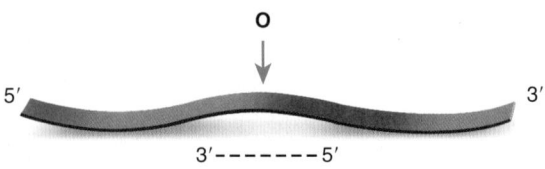

Now we have what is know, as an RNA primer to start the new strand. What is possible now? Can we add

deoxyribonucleotides to both ends of this primer? No, we cannot. Remember that DNA polymerases can add a nucleotide only to the —OH group that occurs at the 3′ end of the new strand. Thus, DNA polymerase can complete DNA synthesis from the 3′ end but not from the 5′ end.

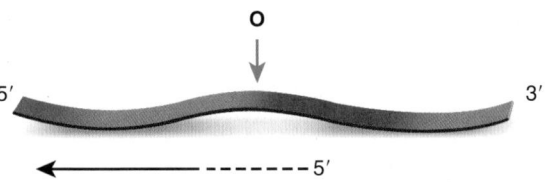

So how can cells perform bidirectional DNA replication from an origin? After a brief delay, a second RNA primer is created at a distance from the first, and DNA replication proceeds from the second primer.

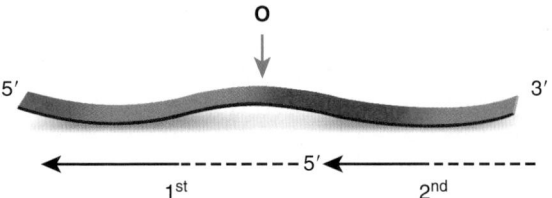

This thought experiment was designed to show the geometric complications that occur in DNA replication. It will also help you realize that the term *bidirectional* can be misleading. Even though overall it is true that DNA replication spreads out in both directions from origins, the directionality of synthesis is always the same, 5′ to 3′ as nucleotides are added to the 3′ —OH of a nucleotide. The complexity of DNA replication increases when we realize that there are two parental strands that each serve as templates for DNA replication (here we looked at only one). Now that we have established the complexity of the process, let's look at how the DNA and proteins interact for the molecular events of DNA replication for both parental strands.

Molecular Events of DNA Replication

DNA replication requires the coordinated action of a large collection of proteins and enzymes that have specific roles in the process. **Table 10.1** provides a summary of these proteins and their functions. For DNA replication to occur, the two strands of the double helix must be separated, creating a replication bubble with two forks (**Figure 10.15**). For simplicity we often will consider events of replication at

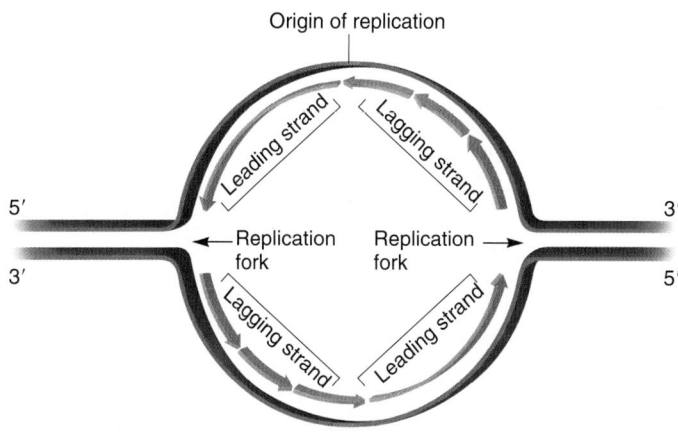

Replication from an origin

Figure 10.15   Bidirectional DNA synthesis creates two forks, each with one continuous leading strand and a lagging strand composed initially of Okazaki fragments.   This diagram illustrates the locations of RNA primers and the leading and lagging strands that are made during bidirectional DNA replication from one origin of replication.

Concept check: *Which strand, the leading or lagging strand, is made discontinuously in the direction opposite to the movement of the replication fork?*

Table 10.1	Proteins Involved in DNA Replication
Common name	**Function**
Origin-binding protein	Binds at origins and creates a small replication bubble
DNA helicase	Separates double-stranded DNA into single strands
Single-strand binding protein	Binds to single-stranded DNA and prevents it from re-forming a double helix
Topoisomerase	Removes tightened coils ahead of the replication fork
DNA primase	Synthesizes short RNA primers
DNA polymerase	Synthesizes DNA in the leading and lagging strands, removes RNA primers, and fills in the gaps
DNA polymerase III (*E. coli*)	Synthesizes DNA for leading strands and Okazaki fragments with its 5′ to 3′ polymerization function, corrects mistakes with its 3′ to 5′ exonuclease function, removes RNA primers, and fills in gaps
DNA polymerase I (*E. coli*)	Removes RNA primers at origins and for Okazaki fragments with its 5′ to 3′ exonuclease function, synthesizes DNA for the resulting gap with its 5′ to 3′ polymerization function, corrects mistakes with its 3′ to 5′ exonuclease function
Clamp protein	Holds the DNA polymerase in place on the DNA
DNA ligase	Creates a phosphodiester linkage to connect DNA segments created after RNA primer removal (connects adjacent Okazaki fragments)

only one fork, but you must always remember that because DNA replication is bidirectional, two forks emanate from each origin. Let's now look at how proteins carry out DNA replication.

Origin Binding Proteins, Helicase, Topoisomerase, and Single-Strand Binding Proteins: Formation and Movement of the Replication Fork   When it's time for DNA replication to occur, origins of replication bind with regulatory proteins that unwind DNA at the origin, creating a small replication bubble. At a replication bubble two DNA helicase proteins bind and, acting as wedges, begin moving in opposite directions, creating a replication fork in each direction. Each DNA helicase uses energy from ATP to separate the DNA strands and keep the fork moving forward. The action of DNA helicase generates additional coiling just ahead of the replication fork that is alleviated by another enzyme called DNA topoisomerase. After the two parental DNA strands have been separated by helicase, **single-strand binding proteins** bind to the single strands of parental DNA and prevent them from re-forming a double helix. In this way, the nitrogenous bases within the parental strands are kept exposed until DNA polymerase can use them as templates for the synthesis of complementary strands. The positioning of these three early-acting proteins is shown in **Figure 10.16**.

DNA topoisomerase travels slightly ahead of the replication fork and alleviates coiling caused by the action of helicase.

Single-strand binding proteins coat the DNA strands to prevent them from re-forming a double helix.

DNA helicase travels along one DNA strand in the 5′ to 3′ direction and separates the DNA strands.

Direction of replication fork

Figure 10.16 Proteins that facilitate the formation and movement of a replication fork. DNA helicases travel along each fork on one DNA strand in the 5′ to 3′ direction and separate the parental DNA strands. After they are separated, single-strand binding proteins coat the parental DNA strands to prevent them from re-forming a double helix. Topoisomerase travels slightly ahead on each fork and alleviates coiling that is caused by the action of helicase.

DNA polymerase is able to covalently link nucleotides together from a primer.

DNA polymerase can link nucleotides only in the 5′ to 3′ direction because it can add a new nucleotide only to the free 3′ —OH of the last nucleotide.

RNA primer

(a) Need for a primer

(b) 5′ to 3′ direction of synthesis

Figure 10.17 Enzymatic feature of DNA polymerase. (a) DNA polymerase needs a primer to begin DNA synthesis. (b) Once begun, DNA polymerase can synthesize DNA only in the 5′ to 3′ direction.

Primase and DNA Polymerases: Initial Synthesis of the Leading and Lagging Strands Because DNA polymerases cannot start DNA replication, an enzyme called DNA primase initiates synthesis by making a complementary primer that is actually a short segment of RNA, typically 10 to 12 nucleotides long (**Figure 10.17**). These short RNA strands prime the process of DNA replication. At a later stage in DNA replication, these RNA primers will need to be removed and replaced with DNA.

Once a primer is made, DNA synthesis can occur from the free 3′ —OH group of the ribose sugar of the primer. A category of enzyme known as DNA polymerase is responsible for covalently linking nucleotides to form DNA strands. The structure of DNA polymerase in action resembles a human hand with the DNA threaded through it (**Figure 10.18a**). As DNA polymerase slides along the DNA, free nucleotides with three phosphate groups, called deoxynucleoside triphosphates, hydrogen bond to the exposed complementary nitrogenous bases of the template strand according to the AT/GC rule. At its catalytic site, DNA polymerase breaks a bond at the middle phosphate of the nucleotide triphosphate and then attaches the resulting nucleotide with one phosphate group (a deoxynucleoside monophosphate) to the 3′ end of a growing strand via a phosphoester bond. The breakage of the covalent bond that releases pyrophosphate (two phosphate groups) is

an exergonic reaction that provides the energy to covalently connect adjacent nucleotides (**Figure 10.18b**). The rate of synthesis is truly remarkable. In bacteria, DNA polymerase can synthesize DNA at a rate of 500 nucleotides per second, while eukaryotic species can make DNA at a rate of about 50 nucleotides per second.

Each replication fork has DNA synthesis occurring for two newly created strands. Each fork is creating a leading strand and, with a slight delay, a lagging strand. The leading strand of each fork is the one in which the 5′ to 3′ direction is moving in the same direction as the continuously opening fork. In the leading strand DNA primase makes one RNA primer at the origin (**Figure 10.19**, step 1), and then DNA polymerase attaches nucleotides in a 5′ to 3′ direction as it slides toward the opening of the replication fork (Figure 10.19, step 2). DNA synthesis is continuously occurring as the fork continuously opens. In *E. coli* this DNA polymerase is known as DNA polymerase III and is associated with a clamp protein to assist its correct positioning on the DNA.

Continuous replication is not possible for the lagging strand because for it the required 5′ to 3′ direction is back toward the origin. Therefore, synthesis for the lagging strand regularly must wait for a primer to be made (Figure 10.19, step 3), after which short segments of DNA can be synthesized (Figure 10.19, step 4). These short segments are called **Okazaki fragments**, after the scientists who first isolated them. Each Okazaki fragment contains a short RNA primer made by DNA primase at the 5′ end and the remainder of the fragment is a strand of DNA made by DNA polymerase.

DNA polymerases have the ability to add a nucleotide to the 3′ —OH group of the previously added nucleotide. We call this its 5′ to 3′ polymerization function. Additionally all DNA polymerases have another enzymatic function, a **proofreading** 3′ to 5′ exonuclease function. After a DNA polymerase has

(a) Action of DNA polymerase

Figure 10.18 **Enzymatic synthesis of DNA.**
(a) DNA polymerase recognizes free nucleotides called deoxynucleoside triphosphates and attaches a deoxynucleoside monophosphate to the 3′ end of a growing strand. **(b)** DNA polymerase breaks the bond at the middle phosphate in a deoxynucleoside triphosphate, causing the release of pyrophosphate. This provides the energy to form a covalent phosphoester bond between the resulting deoxynucleoside monophosphate and the previous nucleotide in the growing strand.

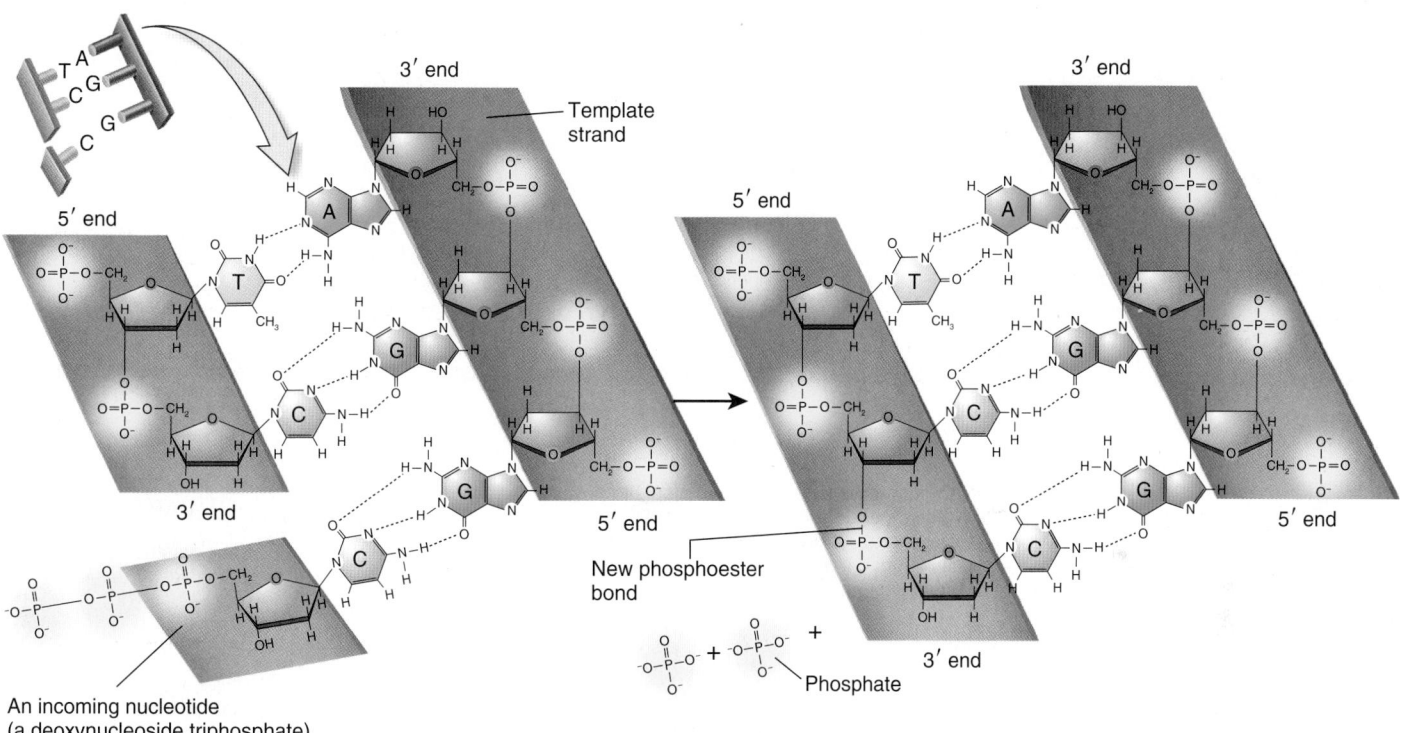

(b) Chemistry of DNA replication

Principle: *Living organisms use energy. The energy in the deoxyribonucleoside triphosphate is used to create the phosphoester bonds that are part of the phosphodiester linkages that hold the nucleotides together.*

added a nucleotide, it assesses the correctness of the base pairing across the helix. If the base pairing is incorrect, it removes the incorrect nucleotide by using the 3′ to 5′ exonuclease function to break the phosphodiester bond it just created. After the incorrect nucleotide has been removed, the DNA polymerase tries again to add the correct deoxyribonucleotide. Thus, on both the leading and lagging strands, DNA polymerase checks and corrects as it moves along.

A Special DNA Polymerase and DNA Ligase: Processing of Okazaki Fragments
To complete DNA synthesis, all the RNA primers must be removed and all the discontinuous segments

created on the lagging strands must be connected. These two operations are done by the combined action of a special DNA polymerase and an enzyme known as DNA ligase. The special DNA polymerase, called DNA polymerase I in *E. coli*, binds at the 5′ end of an RNA primer (Figure 10.19, step 4). This special DNA polymerase has an enzymatic function not seen in other DNA polymerases. It can remove nucleotides from the 5′ end of a segment by using a 5′ to 3′ exonuclease function. As each ribonucleotide is removed from the 5′ end of the primer, this same polymerase replaces it with an deoxyribonucleotide, but it adds the deoxyribonucleotide to the 3′ end of the adjacent DNA segment (Figure 10.19, step 4). The DNA polymerase then

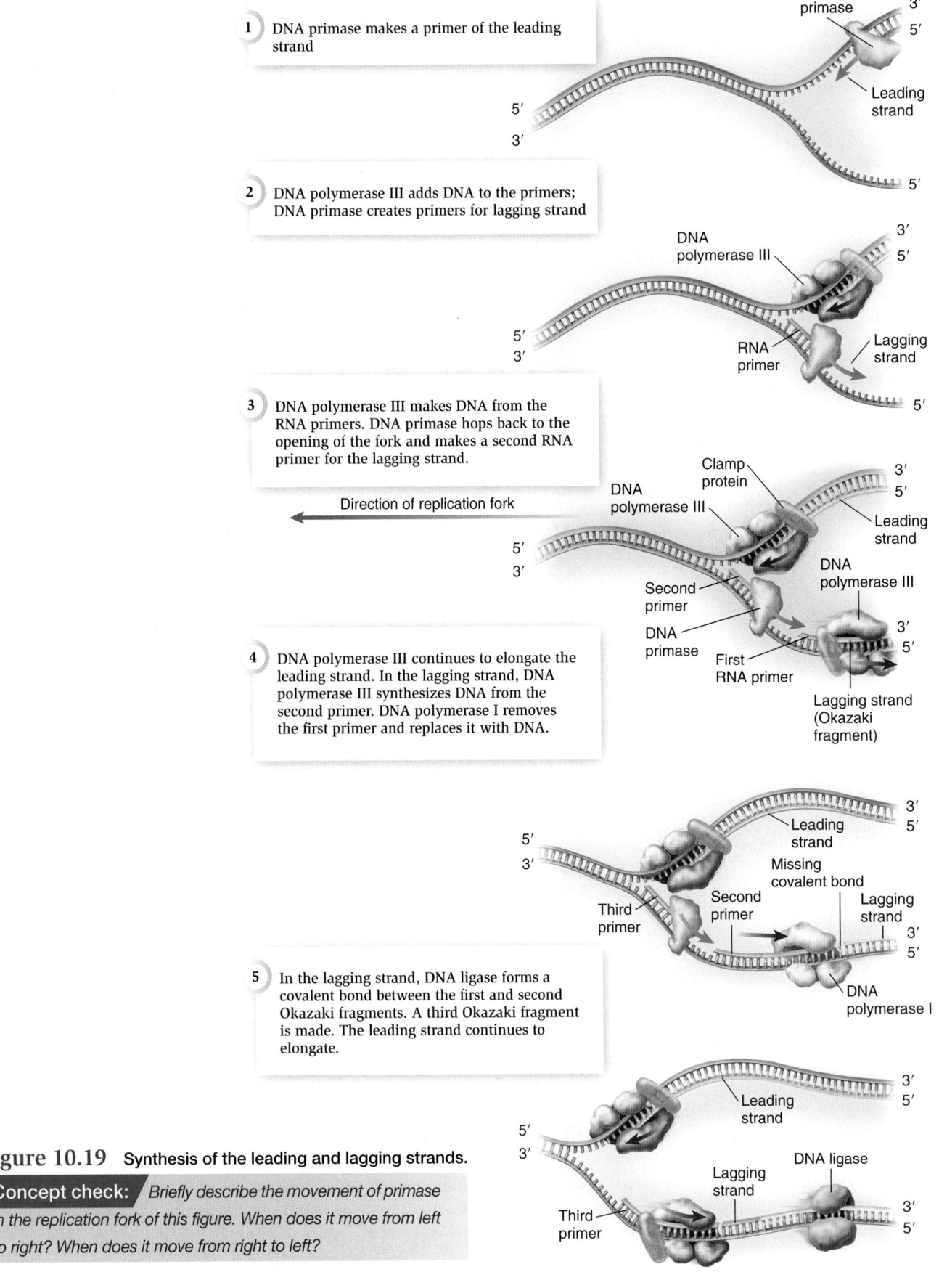

1 DNA primase makes a primer of the leading strand

2 DNA polymerase III adds DNA to the primers; DNA primase creates primers for lagging strand

3 DNA polymerase III makes DNA from the RNA primers. DNA primase hops back to the opening of the fork and makes a second RNA primer for the lagging strand.

Direction of replication fork

4 DNA polymerase III continues to elongate the leading strand. In the lagging strand, DNA polymerase III synthesizes DNA from the second primer. DNA polymerase I removes the first primer and replaces it with DNA.

5 In the lagging strand, DNA ligase forms a covalent bond between the first and second Okazaki fragments. A third Okazaki fragment is made. The leading strand continues to elongate.

Figure 10.19   Synthesis of the leading and lagging strands.

Concept check: *Briefly describe the movement of primase in the replication fork of this figure. When does it move from left to right? When does it move from right to left?*

proofreads to be sure the correct nucleotide was added. Once the entire RNA primer is replaced, the newly synthesized DNA is connected to the DNA originally created next to the primer by the action of DNA ligase, which creates the missing phosphodiester bond (Figure 10.19, step 5).

DNA Replication Is Very Accurate

Although errors can happen during DNA replication, permanent mistakes are extraordinarily rare. For example, during bacterial DNA replication only 1 mistake occurs per 100 million nucleotide additions. This high level of **fidelity** occurs for several reasons. First, hydrogen bonding between A and T or between G and C is more stable than between mismatched pairs. Second, the active site of DNA polymerase is unlikely to catalyze bond formation between adjacent nucleotides if a mismatched base pair is formed. Third, DNA polymerase minimizes mistakes with its proofreading function. In addition to DNA polymerases, living cells possess several other enzymes

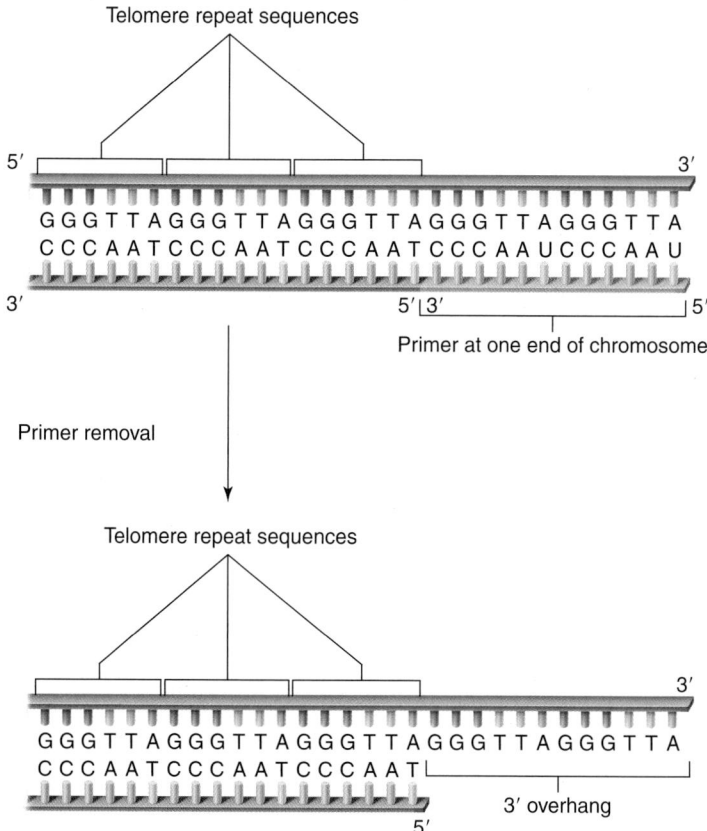

Figure 10.20 **Telomere sequences at the end of a human chromosome.** The telomere sequence shown here is found in humans and other mammals. The length of the 3′ overhang is variable among different species and cell types.

that function solely to repair abnormalities in DNA. If such lesions are not fixed, a permanent change in the genetic material, namely, a mutation, can occur. Mutations can lead to cancer in the organism and to birth defects in the next generation if they occur in sperm or egg. These topics are considered in Chapter 13.

Linear Chromosomes Require Special Mechanisms to Replicate Their Ends

Some special problems associated with replicating the ends of eukaryotic chromosomes do not occur in circular chromosomes. We will end our discussion of DNA replication by considering a specialized form that happens only in eukaryotic cells, as a consequence of their linear chromosomes. This unusual form of DNA replication occurs at the ends of eukaryotic chromosomes in regions called **telomeres**. Telomeres of all of an organism's chromosomes are composed of a series of the same repeated DNA sequences and the special proteins that are bound to those sequences. Telomeric sequences consist of a short sequence that is repeated a few dozen to a few hundred times in a row (**Figure 10.20**). A telomere also has a region at the 3′ end that is termed a 3′ overhang because it does not have a complementary strand. The repeat sequence shown here, 5′–GGGTTA–3′, is the sequence found in human telomeres. Other organisms have different repeat sequences. For example, the sequence found in the telomeres of maize is 5′–GGGTTA–3′.

As discussed previously, DNA polymerase synthesizes DNA only in a 5′ to 3′ direction and requires a primer. For these reasons, DNA polymerase cannot copy the tip of the DNA strand with a 3′ end. At this location the parental DNA strand has no place for an upstream primer to be made. Conceivably, an RNA primer could be made that is complementary to the very tip of this DNA strand. However, after such a primer is removed by DNA polymerase, it would still leave a short, unreplicated region. Therefore, if this replication problem continued, a linear chromosome would become progressively shorter with each round of DNA replication.

In 1984 Carol Greider and Elizabeth Blackburn discovered an enzyme called **telomerase** that prevents chromosome shortening. It attaches many copies of a repeated DNA sequence to the ends of chromosomes (**Figure 10.21**). The telomerase enzyme contains both protein and RNA. The RNA part of telomerase has a sequence that is complementary to the DNA sequence found in the telomeric repeat. This allows telomerase to bind to the 3′ overhang region of the telomere. Following binding the RNA sequence beyond the binding site functions as a template, allowing telomerase to synthesize a six-nucleotide sequence at the end of the DNA strand. The enzyme then moves to the new end of this DNA strand and attaches another six nucleotides to the end. This occurs many times and thereby greatly lengthens the 3′ end of the DNA in the telomeric region. This lengthening

1 Telomerase binds to a DNA repeat sequence.

Repeat sequence

5′   3′
TAGGGTTAGGGTTAGGGTTA   GGGTTA
ATCCCAAT   AAUCCCAAU
3′   5′

RNA in telomerase

Telomerase

2 Telomerase synthesizes a 6-nucleotide repeat sequence.

TAGGGTTAGGGTTAGGGTTAGGGTTAGGGT   T   A
ATCCCAAT   AAUCCCAAU

3 Telomerase moves six nucleotides to the right and begins to make another repeat.

TAGGGTTAGGGTTAGGGTTAGGGTTAGGGT   T
ATCCCAAT   AAUCCCAAU

4 Primase makes an RNA primer near the end of the telomere, and DNA polymerase synthesizes a complementary strand in the 5′ to 3′ direction. The RNA primer is eventually removed.

5′   3′
TAGGGTTAGGGTTAGGGTTAGGGTTAGGGTTA
ATCCCAATCCCAATCCCAAUCCCAAUCCC
3′   RNA primer that is 5′
                      eventually removed

5 RNA primer is removed, the newly synthesized telomeric DNA folds over, and special trip strand pairing occurs.

TAGGGTTAGGGTTAGGGTTA
ATCCCAATCCCAATCCCAA

Figure 10.21   Mechanism of DNA replication by telomerase.

provides an upstream site for an RNA primer to be made. DNA polymerase then synthesizes the complementary DNA strand. In this way the progressive shortening of eukaryotic chromosomes is prevented.

Researchers have discovered an interesting connection between telomeres and cellular aging. In humans and other mammals the different cell types of the body have a predetermined number of times they can divide. For example, if a small sample of skin is removed from a person's body and grown in the laboratory, the cells will double a finite number of times. Furthermore, the number of doublings depends on the age of the person from whom the sample is taken. If a sample is from an infant, the cells will typically double about 80 times, while if a sample is from an older person, the cells will double only 10 to 20 times before division ceases. Cells that have doubled many times and have reached a point where they have lost the capacity to divide any further are termed **senescent**.

The progressive shortening of telomeres is correlated with cellular senescence, although the relationship between the two phenomena is not well understood. The telomerase enzyme is normally present in germ-line cells, which give rise to gametes, and in many rapidly dividing somatic cells. However, telomerase function is typically reduced as an organism ages. In 1998 Andrea Bodnar and her colleagues inserted a gene that encodes a highly active telomerase into human cells grown in the laboratory, using techniques described in Chapter 18. The results were amazing. The expression of telomerase prevented telomere shortening and cellular senescence. The cells expressing telomerase continued to divide, just like younger, healthy cells.

Telomerase function is also associated with cancer. When cells become cancerous, they continue to divide uncontrollably. In 90% of all types of human cancers, telomerase has been found to be present at high levels in the cancerous cells. This prevents telomere shortening and may play a role in the continued growth of cancer cells. The mechanism whereby cancer cells are able to increase the function of telomerase is not well understood and is a topic of active research. For example, with funding from the Canadian Foundation for Innovation, Dr. Peter M. Lansdorp, professor of medicine at the University of British Columbia and member of the BC Cancer Agency, Terry Fox Lab, and Canadian Stem Cell Network, is working with colleagues to develop novel tools to measure the telomere length in individual cells and in chromosomes to address questions about the role of telomeres in normal aging; tumour progression; and specific genetic, hematological, and immune disorders.

GENOMES AND PROTEOMES

DNA Polymerases Are a Family of Enzymes with Specialized Functions

Thus far, we have examined the general properties of DNA replication. Three important issues are speed, fidelity, and completeness. DNA replication must proceed quickly and with great accuracy, and RNA and gaps should not be left in the newly made strands. To ensure that these three requirements are met, nearly all living species produce more than one type of DNA polymerase. Each type differs in the rate of DNA synthesis, the accuracy of replication, and the ability to prevent the formation of DNA gaps. Let's first consider how evolution produced these different forms of DNA polymerase and then examine how their functions are finely tuned to the process of DNA replication.

The genomes of most species have several DNA polymerase genes because of the phenomenon of gene duplication, which is described in Chapter 19. During evolution, independent genetic changes have altered the properties of each gene to produce a family of DNA polymerase enzymes with more specialized (and hence more efficient) functions. These changes are suited to the organism in which they are found. For comparison, let's consider the bacterium *E. coli* and humans. *E. coli* has five different DNA polymerases, designated I, II, III, IV, and V. In humans more than a dozen different DNA polymerases have been identified (**Table 10.2**). Why does *E. coli* need five DNA polymerases while humans need 12 or more? The answer lies in specialization and the unique functional needs of each species.

In *E. coli,* DNA polymerase III is responsible for the majority of DNA replication. This enzyme is composed of multiple subunits, each with its own functional role. In addition to the catalytic subunit that actually synthesizes DNA, DNA polymerase III has other subunits that allow it to clamp onto the template DNA and synthesize new DNA very rapidly and with high fidelity. By comparison, DNA polymerase I is composed of a single subunit. Its role during DNA replication is to rapidly remove the RNA primers and fill in the short vacant regions with DNA. DNA polymerases II, IV, and V are involved in repairing DNA and in replicating damaged DNA. DNA polymerases I and III stall when they encounter DNA damage and may be unable to make a complementary strand at such a site. By comparison, DNA polymerases II, IV, and V don't stall. Therefore, though their rate of synthesis is not as rapid as DNA polymerases I and III, they ensure that DNA replication is complete.

Table 10.2	DNA Polymerases in *E. coli* and Humans
Polymerase types*	**Function**
E. coli	
III	Replicates most of the DNA during cell division
I	Removes RNA primers and fills the gaps
II, IV, and V	Repairs damaged DNA and replicates over DNA damage
Humans	
α (alpha)	Primes DNA and synthesizes short DNA strands
δ (delta), ε (epsilon)	Displaces DNA polymerase and then replicates DNA at a rapid rate
γ (gamma)	Replicates the mitochondrial DNA
η (eta), κ (kappa), ι (iota), ζ (zeta)	Replicates over damaged DNA
α, β (beta), δ, ε, σ (sigma), λ (lambda), μ (mu), φ (phi), θ (theta)	Repairs DNA or has other functions

Certain DNA polymerases may have more than one function.

In human cells the DNA polymerases are designated with Greek letters (Table 10.2). DNA polymerase α (alpha) has its own built-in primase subunit. It synthesizes short RNA regions, followed by short DNA regions. Two other DNA polymerases, δ (delta) and δ (epsilon), then extend the DNA at a faster rate. DNA polymerase γ (gamma) functions in the mitochondria to replicate mitochondrial DNA.

Certain DNA polymerases function as lesion-replicating enzymes. As with DNA polymerases I and III in *E. coli,* when the general DNA polymerases (α, δ, or ε) encounter abnormalities in DNA structure (that is, a lesion), they may be unable to replicate over the damage. If this happens, lesion-replicating polymerases are attracted to the damaged DNA. These polymerases have special properties that enable them to synthesize a complementary strand over the abnormal region. Each type of lesion-replicating polymerase may be able to replicate over different kinds of DNA damage. Similarly, other human DNA polymerases play an important role in DNA repair. The need for multiple repair enzymes is rooted in the various ways that DNA can be damaged, as described in Chapter 13. Multicellular organisms must be particularly vigilant about DNA repair because changes in DNA sequence (mutations) can lead to birth defects and cancer.

Summary of Key Concepts

10.1 Biochemical Identification of the Genetic Material

- The genetic material carries information to produce the traits of organisms. It is replicated and transmitted from cell to cell and generation to generation, and it has differences that explain the variation among different organisms.

- Griffith's work with type R and type S bacteria was consistent with the transfer of genetic material, which he called the transformation principle. (Figure 10.1)

- Avery, MacLeod, and McCarty used biochemical methods to show that DNA is the transformation principle. (Figure 10.2)

- Hershey and Chase labelled T2 phages with ^{35}S and ^{32}P and determined that the ^{32}P-labelled DNA was the genetic material of this phage. (Figures 10.3, 10.4)

10.2 Nucleic Acid Structure

- DNA is composed of nucleotides, which covalently link to form DNA strands. Two DNA strands are held together by hydrogen bonds between the nitrogenous bases. Chromosomes are made of DNA and proteins.

- Nucleotides are composed of a phosphate, a sugar, and a nitrogenous base. The sugar can be deoxyribose (DNA) or ribose (RNA). The purine bases are adenine and guanine, and the pyrimidine bases are thymine (DNA only), cytosine, and uracil (RNA only). (Figure 10.5)

- The atoms in a nucleotide are numbered in a conventional way. (Figure 10.6)

- In a strand of DNA (or RNA), the sugars are connected by covalent bonds in a 5′ to 3′ direction. (Figure 10.7)

- Watson, Crick, and Wilkins used Franklin's X-ray diffraction data, Chargaff's biochemical data (that is, A = T, G = C), and Pauling's modelling approach to construct ball-and-stick models to reveal the double helix structure of DNA. (Figures 10.8, 10.9)

- DNA is a double helix in which the DNA strands are antiparallel and obey the AT/GC rule. (Figures 10.10, 10.11)

10.3 DNA Replication

- Meselson and Stahl used ^{15}N- and ^{14}N-isotope labelling methods to show that DNA is replicated by a semiconservative mechanism in which the product of DNA replication is one original strand and one new strand. (Figures 10.12)

- New DNA strands are made according to the AT/GC rule in which parental strands serve as templates for the synthesis of new daughter strands. (Figure 10.13)

- Within chromosomes DNA replication begins at sites known as origins of replication, where the DNA unwinds to make replication forks. Bacterial chromosomes have a single origin, while eukaryotic chromosomes have many. (Figure 10.14)

- DNA synthesis occurs bidirectionally from an origin of replication. The synthesis of new DNA strands happens near each replication fork. The leading strand is made continuously, in the same direction that the fork is moving. The lagging strand is made in the opposite direction as short Okazaki fragments that are connected together. (Figure 10.15)

- DNA helicase separates DNA strands, single-strand binding proteins keep them separated, and DNA topoisomerase alleviates coiling ahead of the fork. (Figure 10.16, Table 10.1)

- DNA polymerase requires a primer and can make new DNA strands only in the 5′ to 3′ direction. (Figure 10.17, Table 10.1)

- Deoxynucleoside triphosphates bind to the template strands, and DNA polymerase catalyzes the formation of a phosphoester bond between the 3′ end of the strand and a deoxynucleoside monophosphate. Pyrophosphate is released. (Figure 10.18, Table 10.1)

- DNA primase makes one primer in the leading strand and multiple primers in the lagging strand. DNA polymerase extends these primers with DNA and removes the primers when they are no longer needed. DNA ligase connects adjacent Okazaki fragments. (Figure 10.19, Table 10.1)

- The ends of linear eukaryotic chromosomes have telomeres composed of repeat sequences. DNA polymerase cannot synthesize the tip of one of these DNA strands. (Figures 10.20, 10.21)

- Telomerase binds to the telomere repeat sequence and synthesizes a six-nucleotide repeat. This happens many times in a row to lengthen one DNA strand of the telomere. DNA primase, DNA polymerase, and DNA ligase are needed to synthesize the complementary DNA strand. (Figure 10.21)

- Living organisms have several different types of DNA polymerases with specialized functions. DNA polymerases proofread to correct nucleotide addition mistakes. Cells also have other repair systems to minimize the error rate because mistakes in DNA synthesis can lead to mutation, which can lead to birth defects and cancer. (Table 10.2)

Test to Assess Your Learning

1. Why did researchers initially believe the genetic material was a protein?
   a. Proteins are more biochemically complex than DNA.
   b. Proteins are found only in the nucleus, but DNA is found in many areas of the cell.
   c. Proteins are much larger molecules and can store more information than DNA.
   d. All of the above.
   e. Both (a) and (c).

2. Considering the components of a nucleotide, what component always determines whether the nucleotide will be incorporated into a DNA strand or an RNA strand?
   a. phosphate group
   b. pentose sugar
   c. nitrogenous base
   d. Both (b) and (c)

3. Which of the following equations would be correct when considering DNA base composition?
   a. %A + %T = %G + %C
   b. %A = %G
   c. %A = %G = %T = %C
   d. %A + %G = %T + %C

4. If the sequence of a section of DNA is 5′–CGCAACTAC–3′, what is the correct sequence for the opposite strand?
   a. 5′–GCGTTGATG–3′
   b. 3′–ATACCAGCA–5′
   c. 5′–ATACCAGCA–3′
   d. 3′–GCGTTGATG–5′

5. Of the following statements, which is correct when considering the process of DNA replication?
   a. New DNA molecules are composed of two completely new strands.
   b. New DNA molecules are composed of one strand from the old molecule and one new strand.

c. New DNA molecules are composed of strands that are a mixture of sections from the old molecule and sections that are new.

d. None of the above.

6. Meselson and Stahl were able to demonstrate semiconservative replication in *E. coli* by

a. using radioactive isotopes of phosphorus to label the old strand and visually determining the relationship of old and new DNA strands.

b. using different enzymes to eliminate old strands from DNA.

c. using isotopes of nitrogen to label the DNA and determining the relationship of old and new DNA strands by density differences of the new molecules.

d. labelling viral DNA before it was incorporated into a bacterial cell and visually determining the location of the DNA after centrifugation.

7. During replication of a DNA molecule, the daughter strands are not produced in exactly the same manner. One strand, the leading strand, is made toward the replication fork, while the lagging strand is made in fragments in the opposite direction. This difference in the synthesis of the two strands is the result of which of the following?

a. DNA polymerase is not efficient enough to make two strands of DNA.

b. The two parental strands are antiparallel, and DNA polymerase makes DNA only in the 5′ to 3′ direction.

c. The lagging strand is the result of DNA breakage caused by UV light.

d. The cell does not contain enough nucleotides to make two complete strands.

8. Considering the different proteins involved in DNA replication and their functions, which of the following does *not* represent an accurate relationship?

a. DNA helicase unwinds the DNA molecule.

b. DNA primase produces the Okazaki fragments of the lagging strand.

c. DNA topoisomerase reduces the coiling ahead of the replication fork.

d. Single-strand binding proteins prevent the double helix from re-forming.

9. Which of the following does *not* promote the fidelity of DNA replication?

a. DNA polymerase will not form bonds between nucleotides if there is a mismatched base.

b. DNA polymerase has the ability to recognize mismatched bases and remove them.

c. Hydrogen bonds that hold the two strands together are more stable in correctly matched bases than between mismatched bases.

d. All of the above are correct.

10. Most organisms have more than one form of DNA polymerase. Some forms play specific roles in replication, while others play roles in DNA repair. What is the proposed mechanism for the evolution of the multiple forms of DNA polymerase?

a. Increased copies of polymerase genes caused by chromosome number change over several generations.

b. Species hybridization may introduce new forms of polymerases.

c. Gene duplication followed by mutations alters the activity of the polymerase.

d. Mutations change other genes into DNA polymerases.

Articulate to Assess Your Learning

1. List and explain the four characteristics of the genetic material.

2. Explain or describe the essential features of the Watson and Crick model of the structure of DNA.

3. Explain the function of telomerase and why it is needed.

Collaborate to Assess and Extend Your Learning

1. Discuss the reasons that very few errors are made during DNA replication.

2. What was Frederick Griffith's contribution to the study of DNA and why was it so important?

3. (a) **Reality**: Draw an origin actively being used for DNA replication. Draw both leading and lagging strands. Label all free 3′ and 5′ ends. Label the first two primers created for the leading strands. Label three Okazaki fragments per lagging strand. For these Okazaki fragments label each as occurring first, second, or third in time.

(b) **Hypothetical**: Now imagine that a new and novel DNA polymerase has evolved in a eukaryote. Imagine that it can create DNA *de novo* (without needing a primer) and it can work from either a 5′ or 3′ end. Draw an active origin being used for DNA replication with the same amount of synthesis as in questions 3(a). Label all free 3′ and 5′ ends. Does it have leading and lagging strands?

4. Create a concept map relating the following terms and processes:
DNA polymerases have a 5′ to 3′ polymerization function
DNA polymerases have a 3′ to 5′ exonuclease function
Some DNA polymerases have a 5′ to 3′ exonuclease function
antiparallel
complementarity
creating DNA on leading strands
creating DNA on lagging strands
proofreading
removing RNA primers
replacing the nucleotides of the RNA primer with DNA

5. A biological principle of life is that structure determines function. Discuss how the structure of DNA underlies different aspects of its function.

Visit McGraw-Hill Ryerson Connect™ for additional study resources.

Gene Expression at the Molecular Level

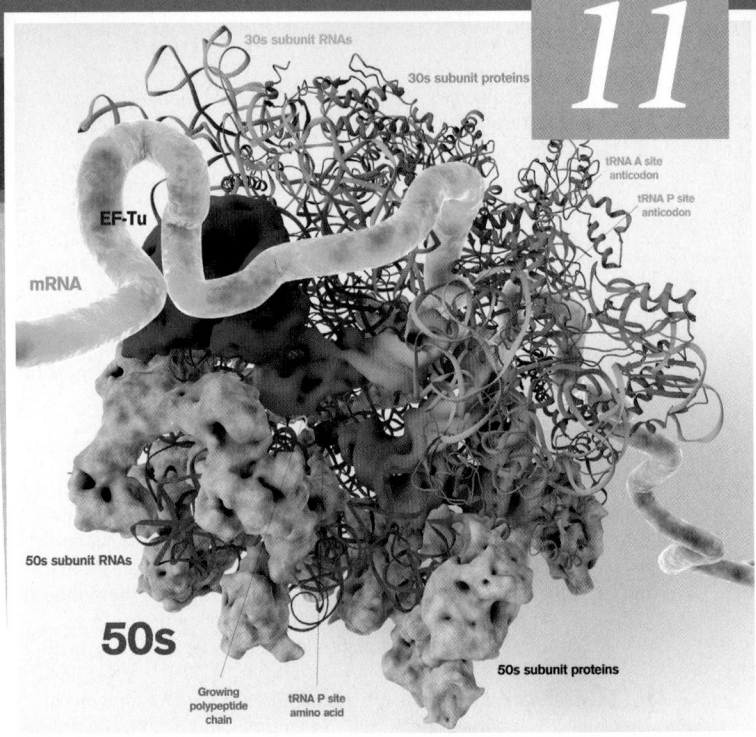

11

Chapter Outline

This model of an active ribosome shows the associated mRNA (aquamarine), tRNAs (thick lime green), rRNA (slender yellow-green [30S] and magenta [50S] ribbons), and ribosomal proteins (orange [30S] and light purple [50S]).

In Chapter 10 we looked at how genes are duplicated during the process of chromosomal DNA replication; in this chapter we explore how genes are used to make proteins. You will learn how DNA sequences are organized into genes, how these genes are used as templates to make RNA molecules, and how a set of RNAs working together ultimately lead to the synthesis of functional proteins. The term **gene expression** can refer to gene function both at the trait level and at the molecular level, and the two phenomena are intricately woven together. The expression of genes at the molecular level affects the structure and function of cells, which, in turn, determine the traits that an organism expresses.

We first consider how researchers came to realize that most genes encode the information to make proteins and how other genes aid in the decoding process. Then, we explore the steps of gene expression as they occur at the molecular level. These steps include the use of a gene as a template to make an RNA molecule, the processing of the RNA into a functional molecule, and the use of RNA molecules to make proteins.

11.1 **GENES CONTROL BIOCHEMICAL REACTIONS BY ENCODING THE POLYPEPTIDE COMPONENTS OF ENZYMES**

Learning Outcomes:

1. Explain Garrod's contribution to our understanding of genes and phenotypes, and describe the observations that sparked his hypothesis.
2. Describe and interpret the results of the experiments of Beadle and Tatum.

Even before genes were known to be segments of DNA, scientists had asked, How do genes function to create the traits of living organisms? The first approach that was successful in addressing this question involved the study of mutations, which are inheritable changes in the genetic material. A **mutation** can affect gene function by altering the gene itself. Research that was focused on the effects of mutations proved instrumental in determining the relationship between normal genes and functional proteins, and mutated abnormal genes and nonfunctional proteins. In these first studies of gene function, inheritable changes in genes were found to be associated with changes in metabolic activity caused by defective enzymes.

In this section we will begin by considering two early studies in which researchers examined the effects of mutations in humans and in a bread mould. Even though they involved very different organisms, both studies led to the conclusion that the role of certain genes is to encode enzymes. In later sections we will examine the general features of gene expression at the molecular level.

The Study of Inborn Errors of Metabolism Suggested Genes Encode Enzymes

In 1908 Archibald Garrod, a British physician, proposed a relationship between genes and the production of enzymes. Before his work, biochemists had studied many metabolic pathways that consist of a series of conversions of one molecule to another, each step catalyzed by an enzyme. **Figure 11.1** illustrates part of the metabolic pathway for the breakdown of phenylalanine, an amino acid commonly found in human diets. While phenylalanine is an essential amino acid, too much is toxic. Normally when there is an excess of phenylalanine, the enzyme phenylalanine hydroxylase catalyzes the conversion of phenylalanine to tyrosine, another amino acid. A different enzyme, tyrosine aminotransferase, converts tyrosine into the next molecule, called *p*-hydroxyphenylpyruvic acid. In each case, a specific enzyme catalyzes a single chemical reaction.

Garrod studied patients with defects in the ability to metabolize certain compounds. Much of his work centred on the inherited disease alkaptonuria, in which the patient's body accumulates abnormal levels of homogentisic acid (also called alkapton). This compound, which is bluish black, results in discoloration of the skin and cartilage and causes the urine to appear black. Garrod hypothesized that the defect in these patients was due to an accumulation of homogentisic acid, which in turn was due to a missing or defective enzyme, namely, homogentisic acid oxidase (Figure 11.1a, last panel). Because, he already knew that alkaptonuria is an inherited condition, Garrod proposed a relationship between the inheritance of a mutant (defective) gene, the presence of a defective enzyme, and a metabolic disease. Garrod described alkaptonuria as an **inborn error of metabolism.** At the turn of the twentieth century, this was a particularly insightful idea, because the structure and function of the genetic material was completely unknown.

Beadle and Tatum Proposed the One Gene–One Enzyme Hypothesis

Although Garrod published a book and several papers on inherited metabolic disorders, his work was largely ignored until the early 1940s, when George Beadle and Edward Tatum rediscovered it. Beadle and Tatum were also interested in the relationships among genes, enzymes, and traits. They decided to study the genetics of *Neurospora crassa,* a common bread mould. *Neurospora* is easily grown in the laboratory and has few nutritional requirements. The minimum requirements for growth are a carbon source (namely, sugar), inorganic salts, and one vitamin known as biotin. Otherwise, *Neurospora* has many different cellular enzymes that can synthesize the small molecules, such as carbohydrates, lipids, nucleotides, amino acids and many vitamins, that are essential to make the large macromolecules needed for growth. Beadle and Tatum focused on the genetics of *Neurospora*'s normal ability to synthesize its own amino acids.

Hypothesizing that genes encode enzymes, Beadle and Tatum reasoned that a mutation or change in a gene might cause a defect in an enzyme that is needed for the synthesis of an amino acid. A mutant strain (one that carries such a mutation) would be unable to grow unless that amino acid was supplemented in the growth medium. Strains without a mutation are called wild-type strains. We will look at one of Beadle and Tatum's experiments that examined the genetics of the synthesis of the amino acid arginine. At that time, the pathway leading to arginine synthesis was thought to involve certain precursor molecules, including ornithine and citrulline. A simplified pathway for arginine synthesis is shown in **Figure 11.2a**.

(a)

(b)

Figure 11.1 The metabolic pathway to break down phenylalanine and its relationship to genetic diseases. (a) Each step in the pathway is catalyzed by a different enzyme, as shown in the boxes on the right. If one of the enzymes is not functioning, the previous compound builds up, causing the conditions named in the boxes on the left. In this pathway defects in phenylalanine hydroxylase, hydroxyphenylpyruvate oxidase, and homogentisic acid oxidase cause phenylketonuria, tyrosinosis, and alkaptonuria, respectively. (b) A blood sample is collected from newborns to do phenylketonuria (PKU) screening.

Beadle and Tatum proposed that a different enzyme catalyzes each step in a **biochemical pathway** and that a different gene controlled the production of each different enzyme. To test their hypothesis, they first exhaustively collected different mutant strains that all required arginine for growth. They reasoned that if the pathway has three precursor molecules, then three enzymes should be required and three genes should be involved, one for each enzyme. As they zeroed in on this pathway, they expected to find only three groups of mutations. One group of mutations would produce a defective enzyme 1, the second group of mutations would produce defective enzyme 2, and the third group of mutations would produce defective enzyme 3. They hypothesized that each category of mutant strain would be blocked at only a single step in the consecutive series of reactions that lead to arginine synthesis. To test this hypothesis, they examined mutant strains for their ability to grow in the presence of ornithine, citrulline, and arginine. A simplified depiction of the results is shown in **Figure 11.2b.**

Based on their growth properties, each mutant strain did fall into one of the three groups. Group 1 mutants were missing enzyme 1, needed for the conversion of a precursor molecule into ornithine. They could grow if ornithine or either of the later intermediates (citrulline or arginine) was added to the growth medium. Group 2 mutants were missing the second enzyme in this pathway needed for the conversion of ornithine into citrulline. The group 2 mutants would not grow if only ornithine was added but could grow if citrulline or arginine was added. Finally, the group 3 mutants were missing the enzyme needed for the conversion of citrulline into arginine. These mutants could grow only if arginine was added. Based on these results, the researchers were able to order the functions of the genes involved in arginine synthesis in the following way:

Group 1	Group 2	Group 3
→	→	→
	Ornithine	Citrulline	Arginine

These experiments provided valuable insights into how many genes exert their influence on cells. From these experiments we learned that many genes function by encoding the information to make enzymes. Beadle and Tatum's experiments also laid the foundation for using genetic approaches to study fundamental biology processes. By searching exhaustively for mutations, and determining how many different functional groups they fall into, a biologist can find a major clue as to the number of biological steps required for a particular biological trait. For example, one approach used to identify the number of proteins involved in DNA replication was to look for mutations in DNA replication and see how many different groups the mutations fell into.

From their studies Beadle and Tatum concluded that a single gene controlled the synthesis of a single enzyme. This was referred to as the *one gene–one enzyme hypothesis.* As our understanding of gene expression has improved, we have had to modify the one gene–one enzyme hypothesis. Enzymes are only one category of cellular proteins. Not all proteins function as enzymes. In addition, some proteins are composed of two or more different polypeptides. Therefore, a more accurate statement is that one gene encodes a polypeptide, which is a linear sequence of amino acids. Proteins are composed of one or more polypeptides. An example of a protein composed of different polypeptides is hemoglobin, the protein that carries oxygen in

(a) Simplified pathway for arginine synthesis

(b) Growth of strains on minimal and supplemented growth media

Figure 11.2   An example of an experiment that supported Beadle and Tatum's one gene–one enzyme hypothesis.   (a) A simplified pathway for arginine synthesis. (b) Growth of wild-type (WT) and mutant *Neurospora* groups (groups 1, 2, and 3) in the presence of ornithine, citrulline, or arginine. As shown on the left, the mutant strains do not grow on a minimal medium lacking arginine. However, all mutants can grow if arginine is added, and specific mutants can grow when the pathway intermediates (ornithine or citrulline) are added.

Concept check: *What type of enzyme function is missing in group 2 mutants?*

red blood cells. It is composed of two α-globin and two β-globin polypeptides. In this case, the expression of two genes (that is, the α-globin and β-globin genes) is needed to create a functional protein. Based on this more recent information, the original concept proposed by Beadle and Tatum has been modified to the **one gene–one polypeptide theory.** As you will see later, even this hypothesis requires modification.

11.2 POLYPEPTIDE PRODUCTION IS A MULTISTEP PROCESS REQUIRING AT LEAST THREE MAJOR CATEGORIES OF GENES

Learning Outcomes:

1. Outline the central dogma of genetics, including a list of the three major classes of RNAs and their specific roles.
2. Explain how proteins are largely responsible for determining an organism's characteristics.

Thus far, we have considered two classic studies that led researchers to conclude that genes encode enzymes or, more broadly, that genes encode polypeptides. Let's now consider the two general steps of gene expression at the molecular level.

The first step, known as **transcription,** produces an RNA copy of a gene, also called an RNA transcript. Most genes are structural genes, which serve as templates to produce an RNA molecule that, through its sequences of bases, contains the information to specify a polypeptide with a specific amino acid sequence. This type of RNA is termed **messenger RNA (mRNA),** because its job is to carry information from the chromosomal DNA to the ribosomes in the cytosol. As discussed

later, **ribosomes** play a key role in the synthesis of polypeptides. Functional ribosomes are composed of RNA and proteins; the RNA of the ribosomes is another category of RNA known as **ribosomal RNA (rRNA).** The second step for molecular gene expression, termed **translation,** is the process of synthesizing a specific polypeptide on a ribosome. The term *translation* is used because a nucleotide base sequence in mRNA is "translated" into an amino acid sequence of a polypeptide. However, the ribosome and mRNAs cannot do the translation alone; another group of RNAs, known as **transfer RNA (tRNA),** is essential. They are called tRNAs because they bring an amino acid to the ribosome, interact specifically with a region of mRNA, and then transfer the amino acid to the growing polypeptide. Thus, the transcription of three categories of genes is required to produce polypeptides: mRNA encoding structural genes, rRNA genes, and tRNA genes. (Look back to Figure 5.4 to visualize these different genes and their products, and examine the chapter-opening photo to see how tightly organized these components are on the ribosome during translation.)

The transcription of DNA into mRNA and the translation of mRNA into a polypeptide have been called the **central dogma** of gene expression at the molecular level. This central dogma applies equally to prokaryotes and eukaryotes. However, in prokaryotes transcription and translation both occur in the cytosol of the cell, and translation begins as soon as a region of mRNA has been transcribed (**Figure 11.3a**). In contrast the nuclear genes of eukaryotes are transcribed and then undergo a step called **RNA processing** to create the mature forms of mRNA, rRNA, and tRNA. Once processed, mRNAs and tRNAs leave the nucleus via nuclear pores. The rRNAs associate with their partner ribosomal proteins and then also leave the nucleus through the nuclear pores. In the cytosol mRNA, tRNAs, and ribosomal subunits all combine to initiate the process of translation (**Figure 11.3b**).

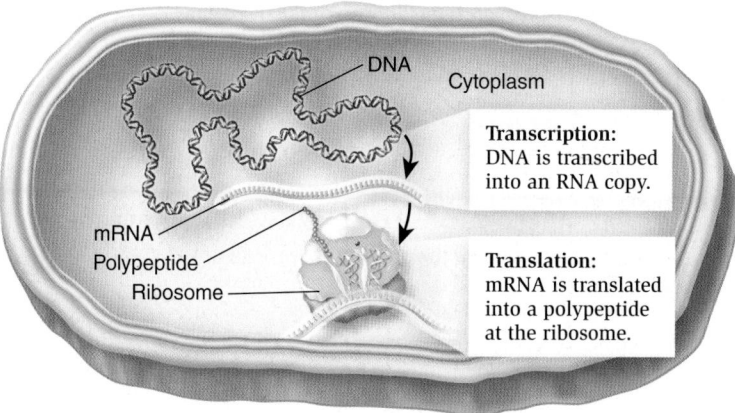

(a) Molecular gene expression in prokaryotes

Figure 11.3 The central dogma of genetics at the molecular level. (a) In bacteria that lack a cell nucleus, transcription and translation occur in the cytoplasm. Because of this lack of spatial separation, translation of an mRNA can begin before its transcription is complete. (b) In eukaryotes, transcription and RNA processing occur in the nucleus, while translation takes place in the cytosol. Thus, transcription and RNA processing are completed before translation begins.

(b) Molecular gene expression in eukaryotes

The Protein Products of Genes Determine an Organism's Characteristics

The genes that constitute the genetic material provide a dynamic blueprint for the characteristics of every organism. They contain the information necessary to create an organism and allow it to favourably interact with its environment. Each structural gene stores the information for the production of a polypeptide, which then becomes a unit within a functional protein. The activities of proteins determine the structure and function of cells, either by serving as structural components themselves or by controlling the production and localization of other important categories of macromolecules. Furthermore, the traits or characteristics of all organisms are rooted in the activities of cellular proteins. One extreme example is the genetic disease of phenylketonuria. Individuals with this inborn error of metabolism do not produce a functional version of the important enzyme phenylalanine hydroxylase (refer back to Figure 11.1a). Without this enzyme and with a normal diet, the person accumulates high levels of phenylalanine that in turn are converted to phenylpyruvate. Phenylpyruvate at high levels prevents normal brain development. With knowledge of the basis of this disease, researchers created a diet that lacks phenylalanine. Routine infant testing (see Figure 11.1b) now identifies affected individuals early to prevent toxic levels of phenylpyruvate and hence prevent disease symptoms.

The main function of the genetic material is to encode the production of proteins in the correct cell, at the proper time, and in suitable amounts. This is an intricate task, because living cells make thousands of different kinds of proteins. Refer back to Table 3.2 to review the many different cellular roles of proteins.

11.3 TRANSCRIPTION

Learning Outcomes:

1. Describe how a gene is organized for transcription into RNA.
2. Outline the three stages of transcription and the role of RNA polymerase in this process.
3. Explain how genes within the same chromosome vary with regard to their direction of transcription.
4. Compare and contrast transcription in bacteria and eukaryotes.

DNA is used as a template to make RNA, which in turn, is used to make polypeptides. Let us now look at the important process of making RNA, a process known as transcription. Our understanding of transcription initially came from studies involving bacteria and bacteriophages (viruses that infect bacterial cells). In 1956 Eliot Volkin and Lazarus Astrachan infected *E. coli* cells with a bacteriophage; they discovered that the viral RNA made immediately after infection had a base composition that was very similar to the base composition of the viral DNA. They suggested that the viral DNA was used as a stored template to make viral RNA.

We now know that the DNA of genes is indeed the long-term storage site of the information needed to make polypeptides. But rather than being used directly to make polypeptides, a working copy of the DNA, composed of RNA, is made. This occurs by the process of transcription, in which a DNA sequence is copied into an RNA sequence. Importantly, transcription does not permanently alter the structure of DNA. Therefore, the same DNA can continue to store information even after an RNA copy has been made. In this section we will examine the steps that are necessary for genes to act as transcriptional units. We also will consider some differences in these steps between prokaryotes and eukaryotes.

At the Molecular Level, a Gene Can Be Transcribed and Produces a Functional Product

Let's look now at the gene as a unit of function. One molecular definition of a gene is an organized unit of DNA sequences that is transcribed into RNA and ultimately results in the formation of a functional product. A **structural gene** is one that is transcribed to produce an mRNA that specifies the amino acid sequence of a polypeptide. In this case the polypeptide is considered the functional product, while the mRNA is an intermediary in polypeptide synthesis. Among all species more than 90% of all genes are structural genes. However, for nonstructural genes, the functional product is the RNA itself. The RNA from a nonstructural gene is never translated. Two important products of nonstructural genes are tRNAs and rRNAs: tRNAs help decode the language of mRNA into that of amino acids, while rRNAs are important components of ribosomes, as discussed earlier.

A gene is composed of specific base sequences organized in a way that allows the DNA to be used as a template to make RNA. **Figure 11.4** shows the general organization of sequences

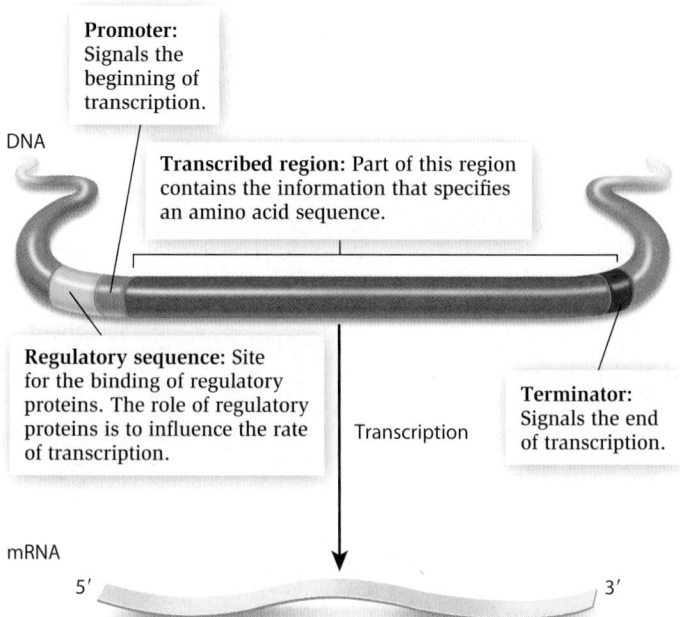

Promoter: Signals the beginning of transcription.

DNA

Transcribed region: Part of this region contains the information that specifies an amino acid sequence.

Regulatory sequence: Site for the binding of regulatory proteins. The role of regulatory proteins is to influence the rate of transcription.

Transcription

Terminator: Signals the end of transcription.

mRNA

5′   3′

Figure 11.4 A structural gene as a transcriptional unit.

Concept check: *If a terminator were removed from a gene, how would this affect transcription? Where would transcription end?*

that are needed for a structural gene. Transcription begins near a site in the DNA called the **promoter.** As you will see, the promoter region of a gene is not used as a template; instead, it positions the RNA polymerase at the transcription start site. The promoter region is followed by the transcribed region that ends with a termination signal region of a gene, or **terminator,** that specifies the end of transcription. As shown in Figure 11.4, the DNA is transcribed into RNA from the end of the promoter through the coding sequence (for mRNA) through the terminator region.

Other DNA sequences are involved in the regulation of transcription. These **regulatory sequences** function as sites for binding regulatory proteins. When a regulatory protein binds to a regulatory sequence, this affects the rate of transcription. Some regulatory proteins enhance the rate of transcription, while others inhibit it. We'll consider this topic in Chapter 12. Now let's look at the process of transcription in prokaryotes.

During Transcription, RNA Polymerase Uses a DNA Template to Make RNA

Transcription occurs in three stages called initiation, elongation, and termination (**Figure 11.5**). The **initiation stage** begins with a recognition step. In bacteria, such as *E. coli,* a protein called **sigma factor** binds to **RNA polymerase,** the enzyme

that synthesizes strands of RNA. Sigma factor also recognizes the base sequence of a promoter and binds there. In this way sigma factor causes RNA polymerase to recognize a promoter sequence.

RNA polymerase synthesizes the RNA transcript during the **elongation stage.** Before elongation can occur, sigma factor is released to allow RNA polymerase to slide along the DNA in a way that separates the DNA strands, forming a small bubble-like structure known as the **open complex** (or transcription bubble) that is approximately 10 to 15 base pairs long. The DNA strand that is used as a template for RNA synthesis is called the DNA **template** or **noncoding strand.** The opposite DNA strand is called the **coding strand** because, for structural genes, it has the same sequence as the mRNA (excepting thymidine instead of uracil) and serves as the code to make polypeptides.

The complementarity rules that were required for DNA replication are also used for transcription, except that uracil substitutes for thymine in RNA. Because base pairing is required, the newly created RNA must be oriented antiparallel to the DNA template. The enzymes that use ribonucleotide triphosphate monomers to create strands of RNA are called RNA polymerases; they follow the rule of adding the next nucleotide onto the 3′ OH group of the preceding ribonucleotide. Therefore, as shown in Figure 11.5, the new molecule of RNA is synthesized in the 5′ to

1 Initiation:
The promoter functions as a recognition site for sigma factor. RNA polymerase is bound to sigma factor, which causes it to bind to the promoter. Following binding, the DNA is unwound to form an open complex.

2 Elongation/synthesis of the RNA transcript:
Sigma factor is released and RNA polymerase slides along the DNA in an open complex to synthesize RNA.

3 Termination:
When RNA polymerase reaches the terminator, it and the RNA transcript dissociate from the DNA.

Figure 11.5 **Stages of transcription in prokaryotes.** Transcription can be divided into initiation, elongation, and termination phases. The inset emphasizes the direction of RNA synthesis and base pairing between the DNA template strand and RNA.

BioConnections: *Look back at DNA polymerase described in Figures 10.16 to 10.18. What are similarities and differences between the function of DNA polymerase and RNA polymerase?*

3′ direction. For example, an RNA with a sequence of nucleotides reading 5′–AUGUUACAUCGG–3′ will have been transcribed from a DNA template with a sequence of 3′–TACAATGTAGCC–5′.

In contrast to DNA replication, RNA polymerases do not proofread or remove primers; therefore, they do not have any exonuclease functions. Once RNA transcription is underway, the rate of RNA synthesis in bacteria is about 40 nucleotides per second. Eventually, RNA polymerase receives a termination signal, which causes it and the newly made RNA transcript to dissociate from the DNA. This event constitutes the **termination stage** of transcription. The termination portion of a gene in prokaryotes is sometimes a portion of the transcript that folds back on itself. This folded region disrupts RNA polymerase's association with the DNA, terminating transcription. In other cases in prokaryotes the terminal region of the transcript attracts a protein called rho that causes the RNA polymerase to fall off the DNA. In both cases the termination region of the DNA is itself actually transcribed.

The catalytic portion of RNA polymerase that is responsible for the synthesis of RNA has a similar structure in all species, both prokaryotes and eukaryotes. RNA polymerase contains a cavity that allows it to slide along the DNA. The DNA strands enter at the side of the protein and are separated at a region where the cavity makes a right-angle turn. Individual ribonucleotide triphosphates can enter this region through a small pore and be used to make a strand of RNA in a 5′ to 3′ direction.

When considering the transcription of multiple genes along the chromosomes of double-stranded DNA, the DNA strand that is used as a template can vary for these different genes. **Figure 11.6** shows three adjacent genes within a chromosome. Genes A and B are transcribed from left to right, using the bottom DNA strand as a template. By comparison, gene C is transcribed from right to left, using the top DNA strand as a template. Notice that in all three cases the synthesis of the RNA transcript occurs in a 5′ to 3′ direction, and the template strand is read in the 3′ to 5′ direction. The choice of strands is determined by the position of key promoter DNA sequences; the strand that is near these key DNA sequences and can be read in the 3′ to 5′ direction will be the template strand.

Eukaryotic Transcription Is Fundamentally Similar to Prokaryotic Except That More Proteins Are Involved in the Process

The basic features of transcription are identical between prokaryotic and eukaryotic organisms. Eukaryotic genes also have promoters, and the transcription process involves initiation, elongation, and termination. However, in eukaryotes, each step tends to involve a greater complexity of protein components. For example, three forms of RNA polymerase are found in eukaryotes, designated I, II, and III. RNA polymerase II is responsible for transcribing the mRNA from eukaryotic structural genes, while RNA polymerases I and III transcribe nonstructural genes, such as the genes that encode tRNAs and rRNAs. By comparison, bacteria have a single type of RNA polymerase that transcribes all genes.

For the initiation of transcription, the eukaryotic process also is more complex. Recall that bacteria, such as *E. coli,* use a single protein, sigma factor, to recognize the promoter of genes. By comparison, RNA polymerase II of eukaryotes always requires five general transcription factors to initiate transcription. **Transcription factors** are proteins that influence the ability of RNA polymerase to transcribe genes. In addition to these five general transcription factors, the transcription of specific genes requires additional specific transcription factors. We'll look at this topic in the next chapter. Termination of transcription in eukaryotes also requires more proteins than does prokaryotic transcription, and transcription termination in eukaryotes also usually is linked with additional processing of RNA, as we will see in the next section.

Both prokaryotes and eukaryotes modify their primary transcripts. The initial transcripts of the three major categories of RNA—tRNAs, rRNAs, and mRNAs—undergo processing. For tRNAs and rRNAs the processing is minimal and involves large primary transcripts being cut into several different, smaller final RNA products. Professor Mark Bayfield of York University studies tRNA processing; his work is featured in our Unit 3 interview that follows Chapter 19. Prokaryotic precursor mRNAs have very little modification. But as you will see in the next section, eukaryotic mRNAs are extensively processed.

Figure 11.6   The transcription of three different genes that are found in the same chromosome.   RNA polymerase synthesizes each RNA transcript in a 5′ to 3′ direction, sliding along a DNA template strand in a 3′ to 5′ direction. However, the use of the template strand can vary from gene to gene. For example, genes *A* and *B* use the bottom strand, while gene *C* uses the top strand.

11.4 / RNA PROCESSING

Learning Outcomes:

1. Describe the processing that occurs for tRNA and rRNA in prokaryotes and eukaryotes.
2. Describe the addition of the 5′ cap and 3′ poly A tail to eukaryotic mRNA.
3. Explain the process of splicing that produces mature eukaryotic mRNA.

During the 1960s and 1970s the physical structure of the gene became well established based largely on studies of bacterial genes. Most bacterial mRNAs can be translated into polypeptides as soon as they are made. By comparison, eukaryotic mRNA transcripts undergo splicing before proper translation can occur. In eukaryotes, transcription of each structural gene produces a longer RNA, pre-mRNA, which undergoes certain processing events before it exits the nucleus. The final product is called a **mature mRNA.** Transcription and RNA processing occur in the nucleus of eukaryotes, but translation occurs in the cytoplasm. Thus, in eukaryotes, transcription is separated from translation in both time and space. As you will see in this section, three major categories of processing are regularly done to eukaryotic primary transcripts: 5′-capping, 3′-poly A tail addition, and splicing to remove introns. An overview of these processes and their relationship to the gene is shown in **Figure 11.7.**

RNA Processing Includes Adding a 5′ Cap and a 3′ Poly A Tail to the Ends of Eukaryotic mRNAs

Mature mRNAs of eukaryotes have a 7-methylguanosine molecule covalently attached at the 5′ end, an event known as **capping** (**Figure 11.8a**). Capping occurs while RNA polymerase is still creating the pre-mRNA, usually when the primary transcript is only 20 to 25 nucleotides long. The 7-methylguanosine cap structure, called a **5′ cap,** is recognized by cap-binding proteins, which are needed for the proper exit of mRNA from the nucleus. Once an mRNA is in the cytosol, the 5′ cap structure is recognized by other cap-binding proteins that enable the mRNA to bind to a ribosome for translation.

As transcription proceeds past the coding region of the gene, two important noncoding regions are transcribed at the 3′ end of the primary transcript. One region is the transcription terminator region, and the other is typically a segment of RNA with the sequence 5′–AAUAAA–3′. The terminator region binds a protein that causes RNA polymerase II to fall off the gene, ending transcription. The 5′–AAUAAA–3′ sequence attracts an enzyme complex that cuts the primary transcript just after the 5′–AAUAAA–3′ sequence and, with a poly A polymerase function, adds a series of adenine-containing nucleotides, one by one, to all mRNA transcripts. Typically 100 to 200 adenine-nucleotides are added, and this structure is called a **poly A tail** (**Figure 11.8b**). DNA does not have a corresponding series of thymidine-containing nucleotides; the poly A tail is not encoded in the gene sequence. The

Figure 11.7 Modifications to eukaryotic pre-mRNA are needed to create a functional (mature) mRNA molecule.

Concept check: *If a terminator were removed from a gene, how would this affect transcription? Where would transcription end?*

(a) Cap structure at the 5′ end of eukaryotic mRNA

(b) Addition of a poly A tail at the 3′ end of eukaryotic mRNA

Figure 11.8 Modifications that occur at the ends of mRNA in eukaryotic cells. (a) A 7-methylguanosine cap is attached to the 5′ end. (b) A poly A tail is added to the 3′ end.

long poly A tail makes eukaryotic mRNA more stable, allowing them to exist for a longer time in the cytosol. Interestingly, new research has shown that some bacterial mRNAs also have poly A tails attached to them. However, the poly A tail has an opposite effect in bacteria: it causes the mRNA to be rapidly degraded.

Splicing Involves the Removal of Introns and the Linkage of Exons

When the experimental tools became available to study eukaryotic genes at the molecular level, the scientific community was astonished by the discovery that the coding sequences within many eukaryotic structural genes are interrupted by large segments of DNA sequences that are transcribed but not translated into protein. The coding regions of an mRNA are called **exons,** while the intervening sequences that are not translated are called **introns.** To create a functional eukaryotic mRNA, the **precursor RNA** undergoes a process known as **splicing** in which the introns are removed and the remaining exons are covalently linked to each other (**Figure 11.9a**).

In the late 1970s several research groups, including those of Pierre Chambon, Bert O'Malley, and Philip Leder, investigated the presence of introns in eukaryotic structural genes. Leder's experiments used electron microscopy to identify introns in the

(a) Schematic drawing of mature mRNA binding to DNA containing an intron

(b) Results after electron microscopy

Figure 11.9   Leder's experiment showing the binding of mRNA to DNA that contains an intron.   (a) The steps in the experimental procedure. (b) A micrograph of the results.

Concept check: *Explain why the double-stranded intron loops out of the structure shown in part (b).*

β-globin gene. β-globin is a polypeptide that is a subunit of hemo-globin. To identify introns, Leder used a strategy that involved the binding of mRNA to DNA. In this approach the double-stranded DNA of the β-globin gene was first separated into single strands and then mixed with mature mRNA from the β-globin gene that had been isolated from red blood cells. The mature mRNA, which already had its intron removed, was allowed to bind to the template strand of DNA, causing the intron in the DNA to loop out. Next, the coding strand was allowed to bind to the template strand, although it could not bind in places where the RNA was already bound. Leder and his colleagues then examined this DNA/RNA mixture with an electron microscope and recovered images like the one in **Figure 11.9b.** They realized that such images could result from spliced mRNA binding to a region of a gene containing one intron that occurs between two exons (Figure 11.9a, step 2). The intervening double-stranded region occurs because an intron has been spliced out of the mature mRNA, and the mRNA cannot bind to this segment of the gene. Chambon and O'Malley obtained similar results for other structural genes. Thus, electron microscopy, combined with molecular techniques, was used to determine the location of introns in genes.

Since these initial discoveries, introns have been found in many eukaryotic genes. Splicing is less frequent among uni-cellular eukaryotic species, such as yeast, but is a widespread phenomenon among more complex eukaryotes. In mammals and flowering plants, most structural genes have one or more introns. As an extreme example, the human dystrophin gene, which harbours a mutation in people with Duchenne muscular dystrophy, has 79 exons punctuated by 78 introns. Introns are also found in a few bacterial genes, but they are generally very rare in prokaryotic species.

Introns are removed from eukaryotic pre-mRNA by a large complex called a **spliceosome** that is composed of several sub-units known as snRNPs (pronounced "snurps"). Each snRNP contains small nuclear RNA and a set of proteins. This small nuclear RNA is the product of a nonstructural gene. Intron RNA is defined by particular sequences within the intron and at the intron–exon boundaries (**Figure 11.10**). These include a 5′ splice site, a branch site, and a 3′ splice site. Spliceosome subunits bind to specific sequences at these three locations. This binding causes the intron to loop outward, and the two exons are brought closer together. The 5′ splice site is then cut, and the 5′ end of the intron becomes covalently attached to the branch site. In the final step, the 3′ splice site is cut, and then the exons are covalently attached to each other. The intron is released and will eventually be degraded.

In some cases the function of the spliceosome can be regu-lated so that the splicing of exons for a given mRNA can occur in two or more ways to produce the possibility of alternative splic-ing. When alternative splicing occurs, a given pre-mRNA can be spliced in more than one way to produce more than one type of mature mRNA that encode a somewhat different polypeptide. Thus, the one gene–one polypeptide theory is not always true. You will see in the next chapter how alternative splicing occurs.

Although primarily in mRNAs, introns can be found in rRNA and tRNA molecules of certain species. These introns, however,

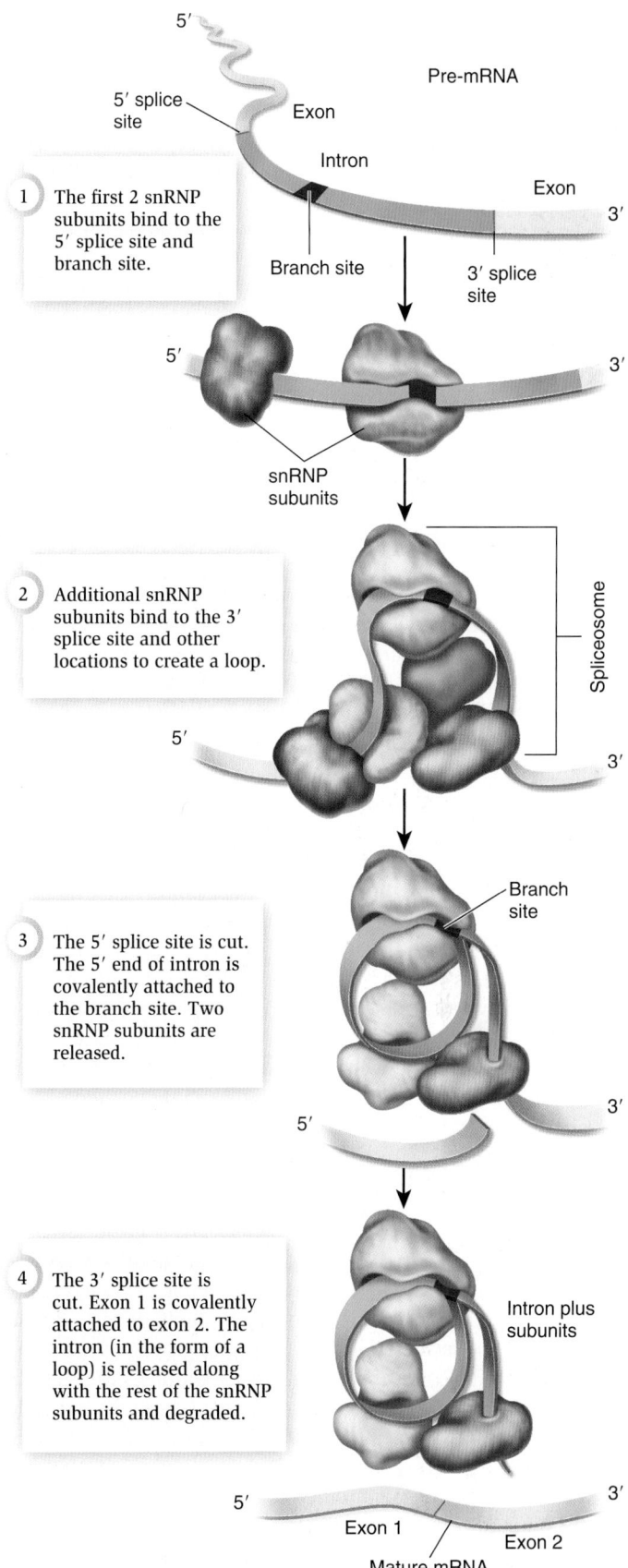

Figure 11.10 The splicing of a eukaryotic pre-mRNA by a spliceosome.

are not removed by the action of a spliceosome. Instead, rRNAs and tRNAs are **self-splicing,** which means that the RNA itself can catalyze the removal of its own intron. Portions of the RNA act like an enzyme to cleave the covalent bonds at the intron–exon boundaries and connect the exons together. RNA molecules that catalyze chemical reactions are called **ribozymes.**

11.5 TRANSLATION AND THE GENETIC CODE

Learning Outcomes:

1. Explain how the genetic code specifies the relationship between the sequence of codons in mRNA and the amino acid sequence of a polypeptide.
2. Describe the experiments that led to the deciphering of the genetic code.

In the two previous sections, we considered how an RNA transcript is made and how eukaryotes process that transcript. Now we will begin to examine the next process, that of translation, at the molecular level. In 1960 Matthew Meselson and Francois Jacob found that proteins are synthesized on cellular structures known as ribosomes. One year later Francois Jacob and Jacques Monod proposed that RNA, which is transcribed from DNA, provides the information for protein synthesis at ribosomes. This type of RNA, which they named messenger RNA (mRNA), carries information from the DNA to the ribosome, where proteins are made during the process of translation.

Translation involves an interpretation of one language into another. In this case, the language of mRNA, which is a nucleotide sequence, is translated into the language of a polypeptide, which is an amino acid sequence. To understand the process of translation, we will first examine the **genetic code,** which specifies the relationship between the sequence of nucleotides in the mRNA and the sequence of amino acids in a polypeptide.

During Translation, the Genetic Code Is Used to Make a Polypeptide with a Specific Amino Acid Sequence

The ability of mRNA to be translated into a polypeptide relies on the genetic code. This code is contained in the sequence of bases in an mRNA molecule. The code is read in groups of three consecutive ribonucleotide bases known as **codons** (**Table 11.1**). The sequence of three bases in most codons specifies a particular amino acid. For example, the codon CCC specifies the amino acid proline, while the codon GGC encodes the amino acid glycine. From the analysis of many different species, including bacteria, protists, fungi, plants, and animals, researchers have found that the genetic code is nearly universal. Only a few rare exceptions to the genetic code have been noted (see note to Table 11.1).

Because there are 20 different amino acids, at least 20 codons are needed to specify each type. With four types of bases in mRNA (A, U, G, and C), a genetic code containing two

Table 11.1 The Genetic Code*

		Second position			
	U	**C**	**A**	**G**	
U	UUU ⎫ Phe UUC ⎭ UUA ⎫ Leu UUG ⎭	UCU ⎫ UCC ⎪ Ser UCA ⎪ UCG ⎭	UAU ⎫ Tyr UAC ⎭ UAA Stop UAG Stop	UGU ⎫ Cys UGC ⎭ UGA Stop UGG Trp	U C A G
C	CUU ⎫ CUC ⎪ Leu CUA ⎪ CUG ⎭	CCU ⎫ CCC ⎪ Pro CCA ⎪ CCG ⎭	CAU ⎫ His CAC ⎭ CAA ⎫ Gln CAG ⎭	CGU ⎫ CGC ⎪ Arg CGA ⎪ CGG ⎭	U C A G
A	AUU ⎫ AUC ⎪ Ile AUA ⎭ AUG Met/ start	ACU ⎫ ACC ⎪ Thr ACA ⎪ ACG ⎭	AAU ⎫ Asn AAC ⎭ AAA ⎫ Lys AAG ⎭	AGU ⎫ Ser AGC ⎭ AGA ⎫ Arg AGG ⎭	U C A G
G	GUU ⎫ GUC ⎪ Val GUA ⎪ GUG ⎭	GCU ⎫ GCC ⎪ Ala GCA ⎪ GCG ⎭	GAU ⎫ Asp GAC ⎭ GAA ⎫ Glu GAG ⎭	GGU ⎫ GGC ⎪ Gly GGA ⎪ GGG ⎭	U C A G

First position (left column); Third position (right column)

Exceptions to the genetic code are sporadically found among various species. For example, AUA encodes methionine in yeast and mammalian mitochondria; UGA encodes tryptophan in mammalian mitochondria; CUU, CUA, CUC, and CUG encode threonine in yeast mitochondria; AGA and AGG act as stop codons in ciliated protozoa, yeast, and mammalian mitochondria; and UAA and UAG encode glutamine in ciliated protozoa.

bases in a codon would not be sufficient, because only 4^2, or 16, different codons would be possible. By comparison, a three-base codon system can specify 4^3, or 64, different codons; this is more than enough (Table 11.1). For example, the codons GGU, GGC, GGA, and GGG all specify the amino acid glycine. Because some amino acids are specified by more than one codon, the genetic code is said to be **degenerate,** meaning more than one codon can specify the same amino acid.

Let's look at the organization of a eukaryotic mature mRNA to see how translation occurs (**Figure 11.11**). The 5′ end of the mRNA contains a cap that serves as the ribosomal binding site. Beyond the cap, there is a 5′ region that precedes the start codon. This is called the 5′ untranslated leader region. Next is a large portion of an mRNA that functions as the coding sequence specifying the amino acid sequence of a polypeptide. This coding sequence consists of a series of codons. The **start codon,** which is only a few nucleotides from the ribosomal-binding site, is usually AUG. This codon specifies methionine. The many codons that follow the start codon dictate the linear sequence of amino acids within a given polypeptide. A typical polypeptide is a few hundred amino acids long. Finally, one of three **stop codons** signals the end of translation. These codons, also known as **termination codons** or **nonsense codons,** are UAA, UAG, and UGA. Typically, the stop codon is followed by region called the 3′ untranslated trailer.

The start codon also defines the **reading frame** of an mRNA. Beginning at the start codon, each adjacent codon is read as a group of three bases, that is, a triplet, in the 5′ to 3′ direction. For example, look at the following two mRNA sequences and their corresponding amino acid sequences.

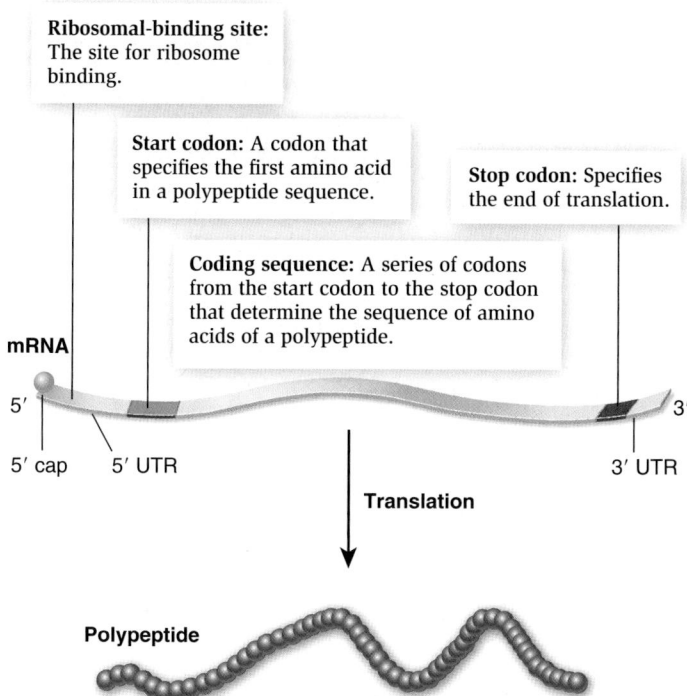

Ribosomal-binding site: The site for ribosome binding.

Start codon: A codon that specifies the first amino acid in a polypeptide sequence.

Stop codon: Specifies the end of translation.

Coding sequence: A series of codons from the start codon to the stop codon that determine the sequence of amino acids of a polypeptide.

mRNA

5′

5′ cap   5′ UTR   3′ UTR   3′

Translation

Polypeptide

Figure 11.11 **The organization of mRNA as a translational unit.** The 5′ untranslated leader sequence (5′ UTR) occurs after the 5′ cap and before the translation start site; hence, it is noncoding. Similarly the 3′ UTR occurs after the translation stop codon and is also noncoding.

Principle: *The genetic material, DNA, provides a dynamic blueprint for sustaining life. Transcription is the first step in accessing the information that is stored in DNA.*

	Ribosome binding	Start codon

mRNA 5′ cap–<u>AUAAGGAGG</u>UUACG(AUG)(CAG)(CAG)(GGC)(UUU)(ACC)–polyA tail–3′

Polypeptide   Met - Gln - Gln - Gly - Phe - Thr

	Ribosome binding	Start codon

mRNA 5′ cap–<u>AUAAGGAGG</u>UUACG (AUG)(UCA)(GCA)(GGG)(CUU)(UAC)C–polyA tail–3′

Polypeptide   Met - Ser - Ala - Gly - Leu - Tyr

The first sequence shows how the mRNA codons would be correctly translated into amino acids. In the second sequence, an additional U has been added to the same sequence after the start codon. The addition of just one base shifts the reading frame for the rest of the mRNA and thereby changes all the codons after the U as they occur in the 5′ to 3′ direction. This one base addition results in the creation of polypeptides with five different amino acids.

From this comparison, you can also see that the genetic code is nonoverlapping, which means that for a given mRNA each base functions within a single codon.

The relationships among the coding sequence of a gene, the codons in mRNA, and a polypeptide sequence are shown schematically in **Figure 11.12**. For simplicity, the DNA sequence of introns is not shown in the DNA. The coding strand of DNA corresponds to the mRNA strand, except that U in the mRNA is substituted for T in the DNA. The template strand is used to make mRNA. Figure 11.12 also depicts another key category of RNA: the tRNAs. Transfer RNA functions as the translator or intermediary between an mRNA codon and an amino acid. To translate a nucleotide sequence of mRNA into an amino acid sequence, recognition occurs between mRNA and tRNA molecules via base pairing. The **anticodon** region of a tRNA allows it to base pair with a complementary codon in mRNA. Furthermore, the tRNA must carry the amino acid specified by the genetic code of the codon/anticodon. For example, if the anticodon in a tRNA is 3′–AAG–5′, it is complementary to the 5′–UUC–3′ codon. According to the genetic code, a UUC codon specifies phenylalanine. Therefore, a tRNA with a 3′–AAG–5′ anticodon must carry phenylalanine. As another example, a tRNA with a 3′–GGG–5′ anticodon is complementary to a 5′–CCC–3′ codon, which specifies proline. This tRNA must carry proline.

Synthetic RNA Helped to Decipher the Genetic Code

Now let's look at some early experiments that allowed scientists to decipher the genetic code. During the early 1960s, the genetic code was determined by the collective efforts of several research groups headed by Marshall Nirenberg, Severo Ochoa, H. Gobind Khorana, and Philip Leder. Before their studies other scientists had discovered that bacterial cells can be broken open and components from the cytoplasm can synthesize polypeptides. This is termed an in vitro or cell-free translation system. Nirenberg and Ochoa made synthetic RNA molecules by using an enzyme that covalently connects nucleotides. Then, by using this synthetic mRNA, they determined which amino acids were incorporated into polypeptides. For example, if an RNA molecule had only adenine-containing nucleotides (for example, 5′–AAAAAAAAAAAAAAAAAAAA–3′), a polypeptide was produced that contained only lysine. This result indicated that the AAA codon specifies lysine.

Khorana and his collaborators developed a novel method to synthesize RNA. They first created short RNA molecules that were two to four nucleotides long and had a defined sequence. For example, RNA molecules with the sequence 5′–AUC–3′ were synthesized chemically. These short RNAs were then linked enzymatically, in a 5′ to 3′ manner, to create a longer RNA molecule:

5′–AUCAUCAUCAUCAUCAUCAUCAUCAUC–3′

Depending on whether the reading frame begins with the first, second, or third base in this sequence, this RNA contains three different codons: AUC (isoleucine), UCA (serine), and CAU (histidine). Using a cell-free translation system, this RNA encoded a polypeptide containing only isoleucine, serine, and histidine.

Another method used to decipher the genetic code involved the chemical synthesis of short RNA molecules, as described in the Feature Investigation.

Figure 11.12   Relationship among the coding sequence of a gene, the codon sequence of an mRNA, the anticodons of tRNA, and the amino acid sequence of a polypeptide.   For simplicity, the DNA sequence of introns is not shown in the DNA.

Concept check: *If an anticodon in a tRNA molecule has the sequence 3′–ACC–5′, which amino acid does it carry?*

FEATURE INVESTIGATION

Nirenberg and Leder Found That RNA Triplets Can Promote the Binding of tRNA to Ribosomes

In 1964 Nirenberg and Leder discovered that RNA molecules containing any three nucleotides (that is, any triplet) can stimulate ribosomes to bind a tRNA molecule. In other words, an RNA triplet can act like a codon within an mRNA molecule. Ribosomes bind RNA triplets, and a tRNA with the appropriate anticodon subsequently binds to the ribosome.

To establish the relationship between triplet sequences and specific amino acids, Nirenberg and Leder began with samples containing ribosomes and a particular triplet (**Figure 11.13**). For example, in one experiment they began with a sample of ribosomes that were mixed with 5′–CCC–3′ triplets. The triplets became bound to the ribosomes just as mRNA binds to a ribosome; we'll go through the whole process of translation later in the chapter, but for now just keep in mind that tRNAs

interact with mRNA on a ribosome during the synthesis of polypeptides. This sample was divided into 20 tubes. To each tube, the researchers next added a mixture of cellular tRNAs that already had amino acids attached to them. However, each mixture of tRNAs had only one type of radiolabelled amino acid. For example, one mixture of tRNAs had only proline that was radiolabelled; a second mixture of tRNAs had only serine that was radiolabelled; and so on. The tRNA with the anticodon that was complementary to the added triplet would bind to the triplet, which was already bound to the ribosome. For example, if the triplet was 5′–CCC–3′, a tRNA with a 3′–GGG–5′ anticodon would be bound to the triplet/ribosome complex. This tRNA carries proline.

To determine which tRNA had bound, the samples from each tube were poured through a filter that trapped the large ribosomes but did not trap tRNAs that were not bound to ribosomes. The researchers then determined the amount of radioactivity on each filter. If the tRNA carrying the radiolabelled amino acid was bound to the triplet/ribosome complex, radioactivity would be trapped on the filter. Because only one amino acid was radiolabelled in each tRNA sample, the scientists could determine which triplet corresponded to which amino acid. In the example shown here, CCC corresponds to proline. Therefore, the tRNA sample containing radiolabelled proline showed a large amount of radioactivity on the filter. By

HYPOTHESIS   An RNA triplet can bind to a ribosome and promote the binding of the tRNA that carries the amino acid that the RNA triplet specifies.

KEY MATERIALS   The researchers made 20 in vitro translation systems, which included ribosomes, tRNAs, and 20 amino acids. The 20 translation systems differed with regard to which amino acid was radiolabelled. For example, in 1 translation system, radiolabelled glycine was added, and the other 19 amino acids were unlabelled. In another system, radiolabelled proline was added, and the other 19 amino acids were unlabelled. The in vitro translation systems also contained the enzymes that attach amino acids to tRNAs.

Experimental level   **Conceptual level**

1   Mix together RNA triplets of a specific sequence and 20 in vitro translation systems. In the example shown here, the triplet is 5′ – CCC – 3′. Each translation system contained a different radiolabelled amino acid. (Note: Only 3 tubes are shown here.)

In vitro translation system with 1 radiolabelled amino acid (for example, proline)

Tubes containing an RNA triplet

Proline

Ribosome

2   Allow time for the RNA triplet to bind to the ribosome and for the appropriate tRNA to bind to the RNA triplet.

Radiolabelled proline
Proline tRNA
RNA triplet that specifies proline

3   Pour each mixture through a filter that allows the passage of unbound tRNA but does not allow the passage of ribosomes.

Ribosomes trapped on filter

Filter

Filter

tRNAs not bound to a ribosome

4   Count radioactivity on the filter.

Scintillation counter

5   **THE DATA**

Triplet	Radiolabelled amino acid trapped on the filter	Triplet	Radiolabelled amino acid trapped on the filter
5′ – AAA – 3′	Lysine	5′ – GAC – 3′	Aspartic acid
5′ – ACA – 3′	Threonine	5′ – GCC – 3′	Alanine
5′ – ACC – 3′	Threonine	5′ – GGU – 3′	Glycine
5′ – AGA – 3′	Arginine	5′ – GGC – 3′	Glycine
5′ – AUA – 3′	Isoleucine	5′ – GUU – 3′	Valine
5′ – AUU – 3′	Isoleucine	5′ – UAU – 3′	Tyrosine
5′ – CCC – 3′	Proline	5′ – UGU – 3′	Cysteine
5′ – CGC – 3′	Arginine	5′ – UUG – 3′	Leucine
5′ – GAA – 3′	Glutamic acid		

Figure 11.13   Nirenberg and Leder's use of triplet binding assays to decipher the genetic code.

Figure 11.13   *(Continued)*

> **6**   **CONCLUSION**   This method enabled the researchers to identify many of the codons of the genetic code.
>
> **7**   **SOURCES**   Leder, Philip, and Nirenberg, Marshall W. 1964. RNA Codewords and Protein Synthesis, III. On the nucleotide sequence of a cysteine and a leucine RNA codeword. *Proceedings of the National Academy of Sciences* 52:1521–1529.

studying triplets with different sequences, Nirenberg and Leder could identify many codons of the genetic code.

Since 61 codons specify amino acids, you might expect there to be 61 different tRNAs. But most species have somewhat fewer because of the phenomenon of *wobble* in the third position of the codon–anticodon base pairing. The tolerance of the wobble in the third position is largely due to modification of the bases of the tRNA that allow it to form hydrogen bonds with more than one base of the mRNA.

Experimental Questions

1. Briefly explain how studying the pathway that leads to arginine synthesis allowed Beadle and Tatum to conclude that one gene encodes one enzyme.
2. What was the benefit of using radiolabelled amino acids in the Nirenberg and Leder experiment?
3. Predict the results that Nirenberg and Leder would have found for the following triplets: AUG, UAA, UAG, UGA.

11.6   THE MACHINERY AND STAGES OF TRANSLATION

Learning Outcomes:

1. Describe the structure and function of each important region of tRNA molecules.
2. Explain how aminoacyl-tRNA synthetases attach amino acids to tRNAs.
3. Outline the structural features of bacterial and eukaryotic ribosomes.
4. Discuss how ribosomal RNA (rRNA) is used to evaluate evolutionary relationships among different species.

Let's now turn our attention to the components found in living cells that are needed to use the genetic code and translate mRNA into polypeptides. Earlier in this chapter we considered the first step in gene expression, namely, transcription. To transcribe an RNA molecule, an existing DNA template strand is used to make a complementary RNA strand. A single enzyme, RNA polymerase, can catalyze this reaction. By comparison, translation requires more components because the sequence of codons in an mRNA molecule must be translated into a sequence of amino acids according to the genetic code. A single protein cannot accomplish such a task. Instead, many different proteins and RNA molecules must interact in an intricate series of steps to synthesize a polypeptide.

Because of its complexity, translation is a costly process from an energy point of view. A cell must make many different components, including mRNAs, tRNAs, ribosomes, and translation factors, so that polypeptides can be made (**Table 11.2**). The synthesis of these components uses a great deal of cellular energy. In addition, the mechanism for the translation process itself also uses a large amount of energy. Though the estimates vary from cell to cell and from species to species, most cells use a substantial amount of their energy to translate mRNA into polypeptides. In *E. coli*, for example, approximately 90% of cellular energy is used for this process. This value underscores the complexity and importance of translation in living organisms. In this section we will first focus on the components of the translation machinery and then we'll examine the steps of translation.

Transfer RNAs Share Common Structural Features

To understand how tRNAs act as carriers of the correct amino acids during translation and function as the translators, researchers have examined the structural characteristics of tRNAs. The tRNAs of both prokaryotes and eukaryotes share common features. As originally proposed by Robert Holley in 1965, the two-dimensional structure of tRNAs exhibits a cloverleaf pattern. The structure has three

Table 11.2	Components of the Translation Machinery
Component	**Function**
mRNA	Contains the information for a polypeptide sequence according to the genetic code.
tRNA	A molecule with two functional sites. One site, termed the anticodon, recognizes a codon in mRNA. A second site has the appropriate amino acid attached to it.
Ribosomes	Composed of many proteins and rRNA molecules. The ribosome provides a location where mRNA and tRNA molecules can properly interact. The ribosome also catalyzes the formation of covalent bonds between adjacent amino acids so that a polypeptide can be made.
Translation factors	Three categories of translation factors are needed for the three stages of translation that are described in the last section of this chapter. Initiation factors are required for the assembly of mRNA, the first tRNA, and ribosomal subunits. Elongation factors are needed to synthesize the polypeptide. Release factors are needed to recognize the stop codon and disassemble the translation machinery. Several translation factors use GTP as an energy source to carry out their functions.

stem-loops and a 3′ single-stranded region (**Figure 11.14a**). The three-dimensional structure of tRNA molecules involves additional folding to produce the secondary structure seen in **Figure 11.14b**. The stems are regions where the RNA is double stranded because of intrastrand complementary base pairing, while the loops are regions without base pairing. The 3′ single-stranded region is called the acceptor stem because it accepts the attachment of an amino acid. The anticodon is located in the loop of the second stem-loop region. The cells of every organism make many different tRNA molecules, each encoded by a different gene. A tRNA is named according to the amino acid it carries. For example, tRNA^ser will carry a serine. Because the genetic code contains six different serine codons, a cell produces more than one type of tRNA^ser.

Aminoacyl-tRNA Synthetases Help Translate the Code by Attaching an Appropriate Amino Acid to Each tRNA

To perform its role during translation, a tRNA must have the appropriate amino acid attached to its 3′ end. The enzymes that catalyze the attachment of amino acids to tRNA molecules are known as **aminoacyl-tRNA synthetases.** Cells make 20 distinct aminoacyl-tRNA synthetase enzymes, one for each of the 20 different amino acids. Each aminoacyl-tRNA synthetase is named for the specific amino acid it attaches to tRNA. For example, alanine-tRNA synthetase recognizes a tRNA with an alanine anticodon (that is, tRNA_ala) and attaches an alanine to it.

Aminoacyl-tRNA synthetases catalyze two chemical reactions involving an amino acid, a tRNA molecule, and ATP (**Figure 11.15**). After an amino acid and ATP have bound to the enzyme, the amino acid is activated by the covalent attachment of an AMP molecule. Pyrophosphate is released. Next, the activated amino acid is covalently attached to the 3′ end of the appropriate tRNA molecule, and AMP is released. Finally, the tRNA with its attached amino acid, called a **charged tRNA** or an **aminoacyl tRNA,** is released from the enzyme.

The ability of each aminoacyl-tRNA synthetase to recognize an appropriate tRNA has been called the second genetic code. A precise recognition process is necessary to maintain the fidelity of genetic information. If the wrong amino acid were attached to a tRNA, the amino acid sequence of the translated polypeptide would be incorrect. To prevent this from happening, aminoacyl-tRNA synthetases are amazingly accurate enzymes. The wrong amino acid is attached to a tRNA fewer than 1 in 100,000 attempts. The anticodon region of the tRNA is usually important for recognition by the correct aminoacyl-tRNA synthetase. In addition, the acceptor stem and base sequences in other stem-loop regions may facilitate binding to the correct type of aminoacyl t-RNA synthetase.

Ribosomes Are Assembled from rRNA and Proteins

As described earlier in Figure 11.12, the act of translation involves an interaction between mRNA and tRNA molecules. The ribosome can be thought of as a macromolecular arena in which translation takes place. Bacterial cells have one type of ribosome, which translates all mRNAs in the cytoplasm. However, because

(a) Two-dimensional structure of tRNA

(b) Three-dimensional structure of tRNA

Figure 11.14 Structure of tRNA. (a) The two-dimensional or secondary structure is that of a cloverleaf. Notice the anticodon on the second of the three stem-loop structures. The single-stranded region (acceptor stem) is where an amino acid can attach. (b) The actual three-dimensional structure folds in on itself.

Principle: *Structure determines function. The structure of tRNA has two functional sites: a 3′ single-stranded region where an amino acid is attached and an anticodon that binds to a codon on mRNA.*

Concept check: *How does the existence of functional RNAs, such as tRNAs, require a modification of the one gene–one polypeptide theory?*

eukaryotic cells are compartmentalized into cellular organelles that are bounded by membranes, their translation machinery is more complex. Biochemically distinct ribosomes are found in different cellular compartments. The most abundant type of eukaryotic ribosome functions in the cytosol. In addition, all eukaryotic cells have ribosomes in their mitochondria. Plant and algal cells also have ribosomes in their chloroplasts. The compositions of mitochondrial and chloroplast ribosomes are more similar to bacterial ribosomes than they are to eukaryotic cytosolic ribosomes.

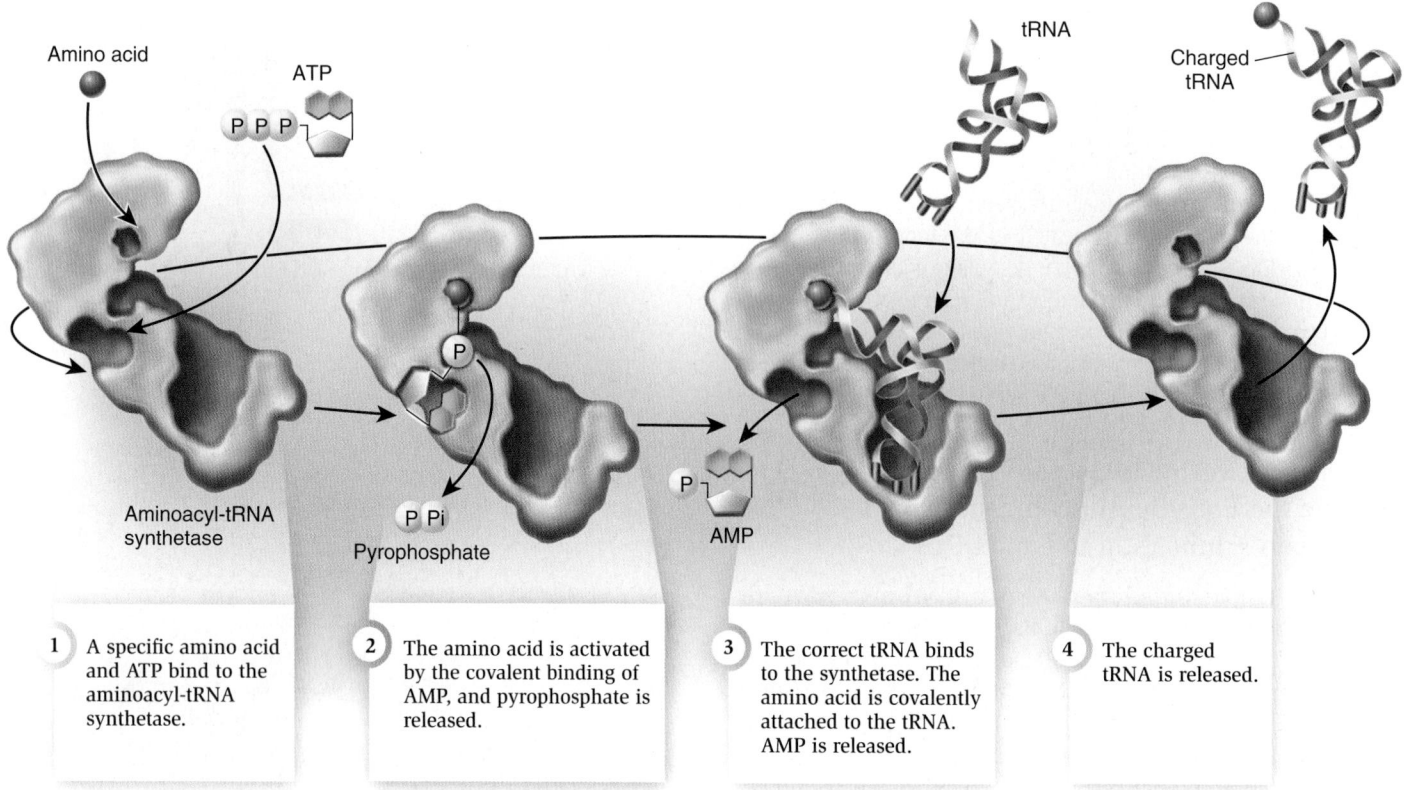

Figure 11.15 Aminoacyl-tRNA synthetase charging a tRNA.

Principle: *Living organisms use energy. The process of translation uses a sizable amount of a cell's energy.*

BioConnections: *Look back at Figure 7.3, which describes the hydrolysis of ATP. Why is ATP needed to charge a tRNA?*

Unless otherwise noted, the term *eukaryotic ribosome* refers to ribosomes in the cytosol, not to those found in organelles.

A ribosome is a large complex composed of structures called the large and small subunits. The term *subunit* is perhaps misleading, because each ribosomal subunit is itself formed from the assembly of many different proteins and RNA molecules. In ribosomes found in the bacterium *E. coli*, the small subunit is called 30S, and the large subunit is 50S (**Figure 11.16a**). The designations 30S and 50S refer to the rate at which these subunits sediment when subjected to a centrifugal force. This rate is described as a sedimentation coefficient in Svedberg units (S) in honour of Theodor Svedberg, who invented the ultracentrifuge. The 30S subunit is formed from the assembly of 21 different ribosomal proteins and one 16S rRNA molecule. The 50S subunit contains 34 different proteins and two different rRNA molecules, called 5S and 23S (Figure 11.16a). Together, the 30S and 50S subunits form a 70S ribosome (Svedberg units don't add up linearly because they are a function of weight, size, and shape). In bacteria, the ribosomal proteins and rRNA molecules are synthesized in the cytoplasm, and the ribosomal subunits are assembled there as well. At Dalhousie University, the research group of Canada Research Chair Dr. Michael Gray is studying the ribosomal RNAs in the mitochondria of the early diverging unicellular eukaryote *Euglena gracilis*. The goal is to better understand how the complex assemblage of ribosomal RNAs and proteins evolved to facilitate the process of translation.

Eukaryotic ribosomes consist of subunits that are slightly larger than their bacterial counterparts (**Figure 11.16b**). In eukaryotes, 40S and 60S subunits are combined to form an 80S ribosome. The 40S subunit is composed of 33 proteins and an 18S rRNA. The 60S subunit has 49 proteins and 5S, 5.8S, and 28S rRNAs. The synthesis of eukaryotic rRNA occurs in the nucleolus, a region of the nucleus that is specialized for that purpose. The ribosomal proteins are made in the cytosol and imported into the nucleus. The rRNAs and ribosomal proteins are then assembled to make the 40S and 60S subunits within the nucleolus. The 40S and 60S subunits are exported via the nuclear pores into the cytosol, where they associate to form an 80S ribosome during translation.

Because of structural differences between bacterial and eukaryotic ribosomes, certain chemicals can bind to bacterial ribosomes but not to eukaryotic ribosomes, and vice versa. Some **antibiotics,** which are chemicals that inhibit the growth of certain microorganisms, bind only to bacterial ribosomes and inhibit translation. Examples include erythromycin and chloramphenicol. Because these chemicals do not inhibit eukaryotic ribosomes, they have been effective drugs for the treatment of bacterial infections in humans and domesticated animals.

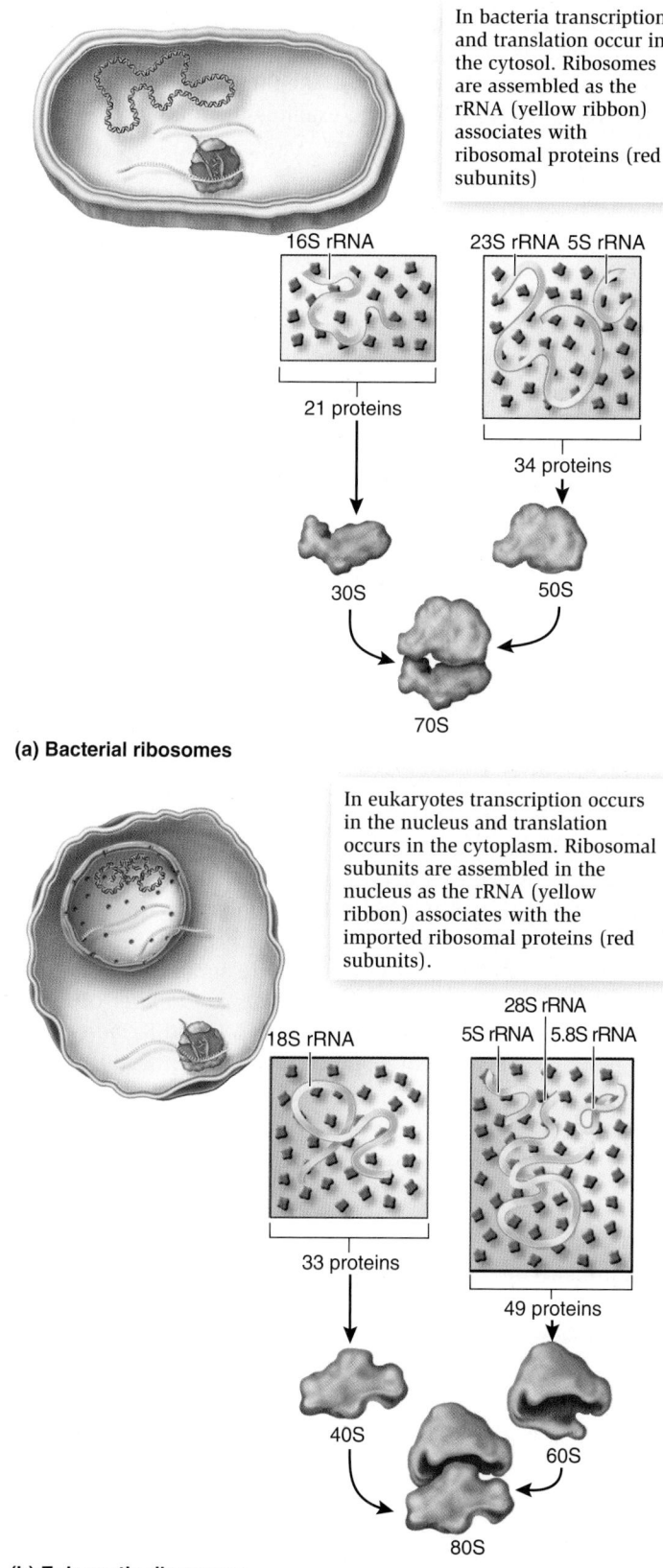

In bacteria transcription and translation occur in the cytosol. Ribosomes are assembled as the rRNA (yellow ribbon) associates with ribosomal proteins (red subunits)

16S rRNA

23S rRNA   5S rRNA

21 proteins

34 proteins

30S

50S

70S

(a) Bacterial ribosomes

In eukaryotes transcription occurs in the nucleus and translation occurs in the cytoplasm. Ribosomal subunits are assembled in the nucleus as the rRNA (yellow ribbon) associates with the imported ribosomal proteins (red subunits).

28S rRNA

18S rRNA

5S rRNA   5.8S rRNA

33 proteins

49 proteins

40S

60S

80S

(b) Eukaryotic ribosomes

Figure 11.16   Mature ribosomes are composed of proteins and rRNA.   (a) Bacterial ribosomes. (b) Eukaryotic ribosomes found in the cytosol.

50S subunit

E site

P site

A site

30S subunit

(a) Bacterial ribosome model based on X-ray diffraction studies

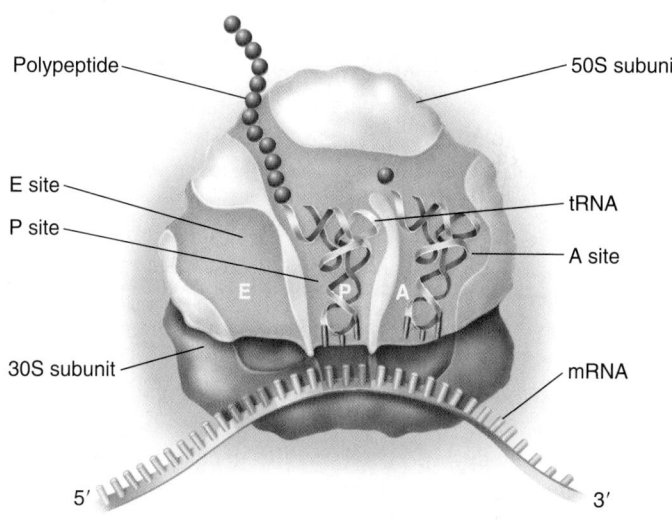

Polypeptide

50S subunit

E site

P site

tRNA

A site

30S subunit

mRNA

E   P   A

5′

3′

(b) Schematic model for ribosome structure

Figure 11.17   Ribosome structure.   (a) A model for the structure of the ribosome based on X-ray diffraction studies, showing the large and small subunits and the major binding sites. The rRNA is shown in yellow (large and small subunit), while the ribosomal proteins are light orange (large subunit) and dark orange (small subunit). (b) A schematic model emphasizing functional sites in the ribosome and showing bound mRNA and tRNA with an attached polypeptide.

Components of Ribosomal Subunits Form Functional Sites for Translation

To understand the structure and function of the ribosome at the molecular level, researchers have determined the locations and functional roles of the individual ribosomal proteins and rRNAs. In recent years a few research groups have succeeded in purifying ribosomes and causing them to crystallize in a test tube. By using the technique of X-ray diffraction, the crystallized ribosomes provide detailed information about ribosome structure. **Figure 11.17a** shows a model of a bacterial ribosome. The overall shape of each subunit is largely determined by the structure of the rRNAs, which constitute most of the mass of the ribosome.

During bacterial translation the mRNA lies on the surface of the 30S subunit, within a space between the 30S and 50S subunits (**Figure 11.17b**). As a polypeptide is synthesized, it exits through a hole within the 50S subunit. Ribosomes contain discrete sites where tRNAs bind and the polypeptide is synthesized. In 1964 James Watson proposed a two-site model for tRNA binding to the ribosome. These sites are known as the **peptidyl site (P site)** and **aminoacyl site (A site).** In 1984 Knud Nierhaus and Hans-Jorg Rheinberger expanded this to a three-site model (Figure 11.17b). The third site is known as the **exit site (E site).** Later we will examine the roles of these sites in the synthesis of a polypeptide.

GENOMES AND PROTEOMES

Comparisons of Small Subunit rRNAs Among Different Species Provide a Basis for Establishing Evolutionary Relationships

Translation is a fundamental process that is vital for the existence of all living species. The components needed for translation arose very early in the evolution of life on our planet. In fact, they arose in an ancestor that gave rise to all known living species. For this reason all organisms have translational components that are evolutionarily related to each other. For example, the rRNA found in the small subunit of ribosomes is similar in all forms of life, though it is slightly larger in eukaryotic species (18S) than in bacterial species (16S). In other words, the gene for the small subunit rRNA (SSU rRNA) is found in the genomes of all organisms.

One way that geneticists explore evolutionary relationships is by comparing the sequences of evolutionarily related genes. At the molecular level gene evolution involves changes in DNA sequences. After two different species have diverged from each other during evolution, the genes of each species have an opportunity to accumulate changes, or mutations, that alter the sequences of those genes. After many generations, evolutionarily related species contain genes that are similar but not identical, because each species will accumulate different mutations. In general, if a very long time has elapsed since two species diverged evolutionarily, their genes tend to be quite different. In contrast, if two species diverged relatively recently on an evolutionary time scale, their genes tend to be more similar.

Figure 11.18 compares a portion of the sequence of the small subunit rRNA gene from three mammalian and three bacterial species. The colours highlight different types of comparisons. The sequences shaded in yellow are identical in five or six species. Sequences that are identical in different species are said to be evolutionarily conserved. Presumably, these sequences were found in the primordial gene that gave rise to modern species, and because these sequences may have some critical function, they have not been able to change over evolutionary time. Those sequences shaded in green are identical in all three mammals, but differ when compared with one or more bacterial species. By scanning the mammalian species you may notice that all three sequences are identical in this region. The sequences shaded in red are identical in two or three bacterial species but differ compared with the mammalian small subunit rRNA genes. The sequences from *E. coli* and *Serratia marcescens* are more similar to each other than the sequence from *Bacillus subtilis* is to either of them. This is consistent with the idea that *E. coli* and *S. marcescens* are more closely related evolutionarily than either of them is to *B. subtilis*.

Figure 11.18 Comparison of small subunit rRNA gene sequences from three eukaryotes and three bacterial species. Note the many similarities (yellow) and differences (green and red) among the sequences.

The Stages of Translation

Like transcription, the process of translation occurs in three stages called initiation, elongation, and termination. **Figure 11.19** provides an overview of the process. During initiation, mRNA, the first tRNA, and ribosomal subunits assemble into a complex. Next, in the elongation stage, the ribosome moves from the start codon in the mRNA toward the next codon, synthesizing a polypeptide according to the sequence of codons in the mRNA. Finally, the process is terminated when the ribosome reaches a stop codon and the complex disassembles, releasing the completed polypeptide. Let's examine the steps in this process as they occur in living cells.

Translation Is Initiated with the Assembly of mRNA, tRNA, and the Ribosomal Subunits

During translation initiation in prokaryotes, mRNA, the first tRNA, and the ribosomal subunits assemble into a functional complex. In all species this assembly requires the help of proteins called **ribosomal initiation factors** that facilitate the interactions between these components (see Table 11.2). The assembly also requires an input of energy. Guanosine triphosphate (GTP) is hydrolyzed by the initiation factors to provide the necessary energy.

In the absence of translation the small and large ribosomal subunits exist separately. To begin assembly in bacteria, mRNA binds to the small ribosomal subunit (**Figure 11.20**). The binding of mRNA to this subunit is facilitated by a short ribosomal-binding sequence near the 5′ end of the mRNA. This sequence is complementary to a portion of the 16S rRNA within the small ribosomal subunit. For this reason the mRNA and rRNA hydrogen bond to each other by base pairing. The start codon is usually just a few nucleotides downstream (that is, toward the 3′ end) from the ribosomal-binding sequence. A specific tRNA, which functions as the **initiator tRNA,** recognizes the start codon AUG in mRNA and binds to it. To complete the initiation stage, the large ribosomal subunit associates with the small subunit. At the end of this stage, the initiator tRNA is located in the P site of the ribosome.

In eukaryotic species the initiation phase has two differences compared with that of their bacterial counterparts. First, instead of a ribosomal-binding sequence, eukaryotic mRNAs have a 7-methylguanosine cap at their 5′ end. This cap is recognized by cap-binding proteins, which promote the binding of the mRNA to the small ribosomal subunit. Also, unlike bacteria, in which the start codon is very close to a ribosomal-binding sequence, the location of start codons in eukaryotes is more variable. To identify a start codon, Marilyn Kozak proposed in

1 **Initiation:** mRNA, tRNA, and the ribosomal subunits form a complex.

2 **Elongation:** The ribosome travels in the 5′ to 3′ direction and synthesizes a polypeptide.

3 **Termination:** The ribosome reaches a stop codon, and all of the components disassemble, releasing a completed polypeptide.

Figure 11.19   An overview of the stages of translation.

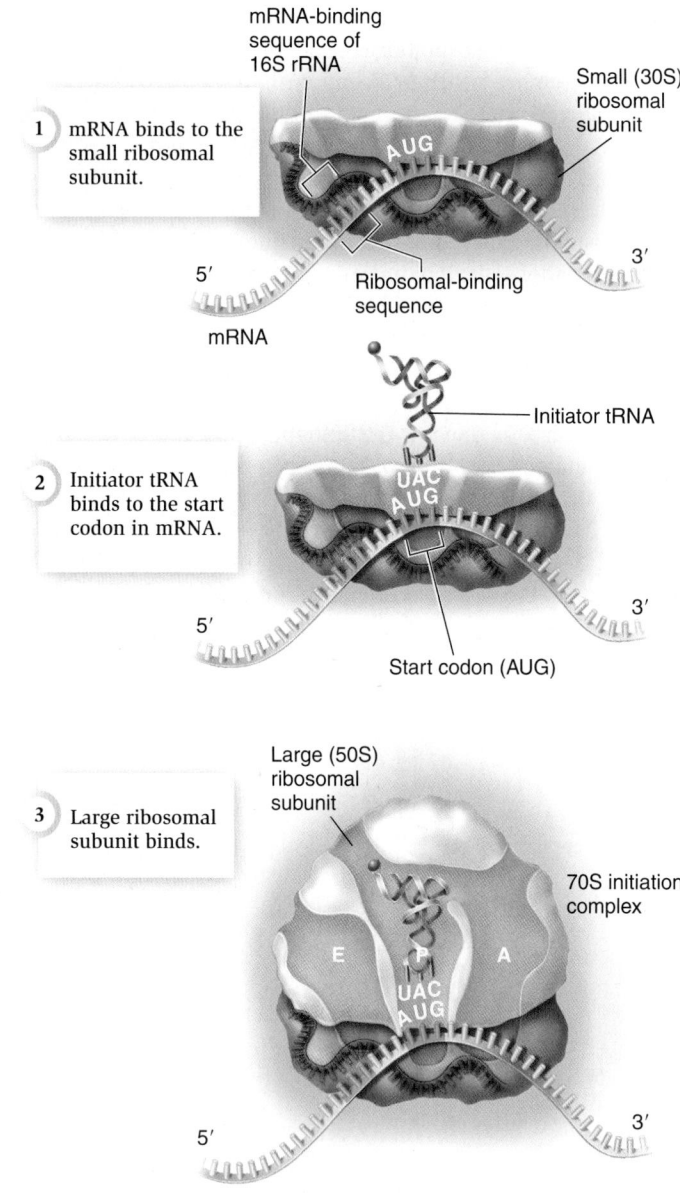

Figure 11.20 Initiation stage of translation in bacteria.

1978 that the small ribosomal subunit begins at the 5′ end and then scans along the mRNA in the 3′ direction in search of an AUG sequence. In many, but not all, cases the first AUG codon is used as a start codon. By analyzing the sequences of many eukaryotic mRNAs, Kozak and her colleagues discovered that the sequence around an AUG codon is important for it to be used as a start codon. The sequence for optimal start codon recognition is shown here:

Upstream of start codon	Start codon	Downstream coding region
. . . G C C (A or G) C C	(**A U G**)	G . . . .

Aside from an AUG codon itself, a guanosine just past the start codon and the sequence of six bases directly upstream from the start codon are important for helping the small subunit of the ribosome recognize the AUG codon as a start codon.

If an AUG codon is within a site that deviates markedly from this optimal sequence, the small subunit may not recognize this AUG as a start codon and instead may move past it, using another AUG codon farther downstream. Once the small subunit selects a start codon, an initiator tRNA binds to the start codon, and the large ribosomal subunit then associates with the small subunit to complete the assembly process.

Polypeptide Synthesis Occurs During the Elongation Stage

As its name suggests, the elongation stage involves the covalent bonding of amino acids, one at a time, to create a polypeptide. Even though this process involves several different components, translation occurs at a remarkable rate. Under normal cellular conditions the translation machinery can elongate a polypeptide chain at a rate of 15 to 18 amino acids per second in bacteria and 6 amino acids per second in eukaryotes.

To elongate a polypeptide by one amino acid, a tRNA brings a new amino acid to the ribosome, where it is attached to the end of a growing polypeptide chain. In **Figure 11.21** (step 1) translation has already proceeded to a point where a short polypeptide is attached to the tRNA located in the P site of the ribosome. This is called peptidyl tRNA. In the first step of elongation, an aminoacyl tRNA carrying a single amino acid binds to the A site. This binding occurs because the anticodon in the tRNA is complementary to the codon in the mRNA. The hydrolysis of GTP by proteins that function as **elongation factors** provides the energy for the binding of the tRNA to the A site (see Table 11.2). At this stage of translation, a peptidyl tRNA is at the P site and an aminoacyl tRNA is at the A site, which is how the P and A sites came to be named.

In the next step a **peptide bond** is formed between the amino acid at the A site and the amino acid last added to the growing polypeptide chain, thereby lengthening the chain by one amino acid. As this occurs, the polypeptide is removed from the tRNA in the P site and transferred to the amino acid at the A site, an event termed a **peptidyl transfer reaction.** This reaction is catalyzed by a region of the 50S subunit known as the peptidyltransferase complex, which is composed of several proteins and rRNA. Thomas Steitz, Peter Moore, and their colleagues proposed that the rRNA is responsible for catalyzing bond formation between adjacent amino acids. In other words the ribosome is a ribozyme.

After the peptidyl transfer reaction is complete, the next step involves the movement or **translocation** of the ribosome toward the 3′ end of the mRNA by exactly one codon. This shifts the tRNAs at the P and A sites to the E and P sites, respectively. Notice that the next codon in the mRNA is now exposed in the unoccupied A site. The uncharged tRNA exits the E site. At this point, the next charged tRNA can enter the empty A site, and the same series of steps will add the next amino acid to the polypeptide chain.

Termination Occurs When a Stop Codon Is Reached in the mRNA

When a stop codon is found in the A site of a ribosome, translation is ended. The three stop codons, UAA, UAG, and UGA, do

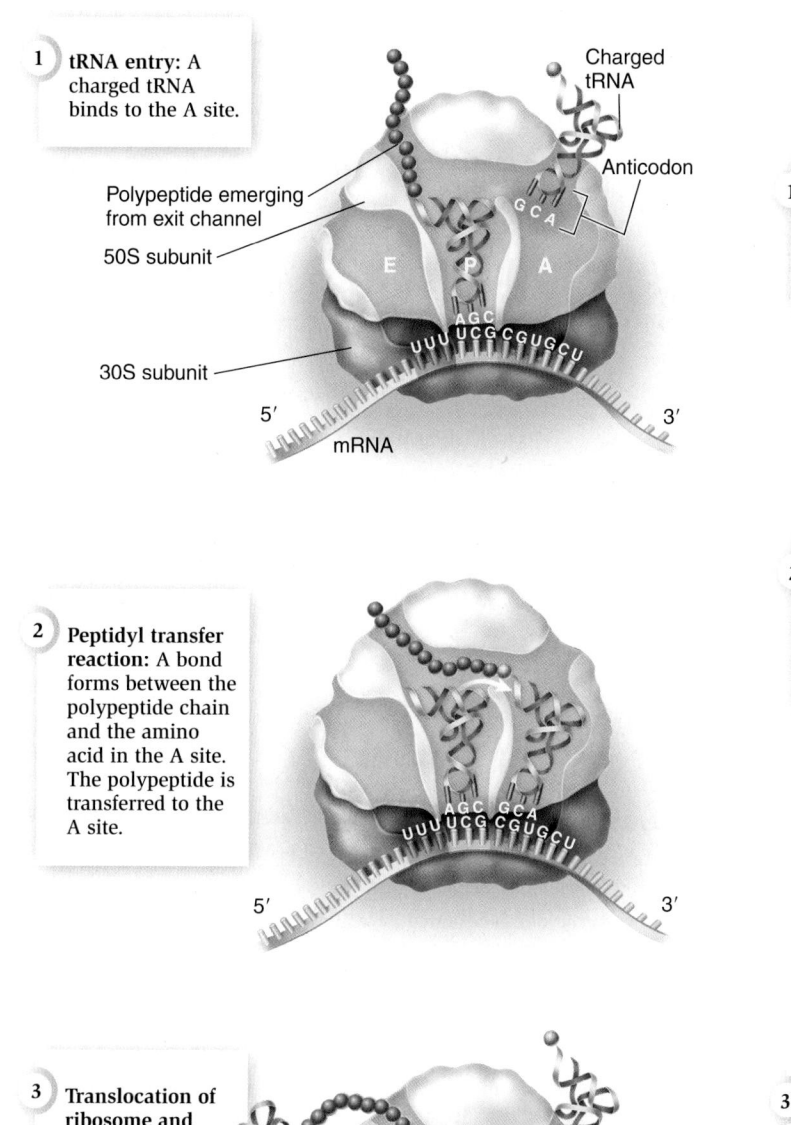

1 **tRNA entry:** A charged tRNA binds to the A site.

Polypeptide emerging from exit channel

50S subunit

30S subunit

Charged tRNA

Anticodon

mRNA

2 **Peptidyl transfer reaction:** A bond forms between the polypeptide chain and the amino acid in the A site. The polypeptide is transferred to the A site.

3 **Translocation of ribosome and release of tRNA:** The ribosome translocates 1 codon to the right. The uncharged tRNA is released from the E site. This process is repeated again and again until a stop codon is reached.

Figure 11.21 Elongation stage of translation in bacteria.

Principle: *Living organisms use energy. The process of translation uses a sizable amount of a cell's energy.*

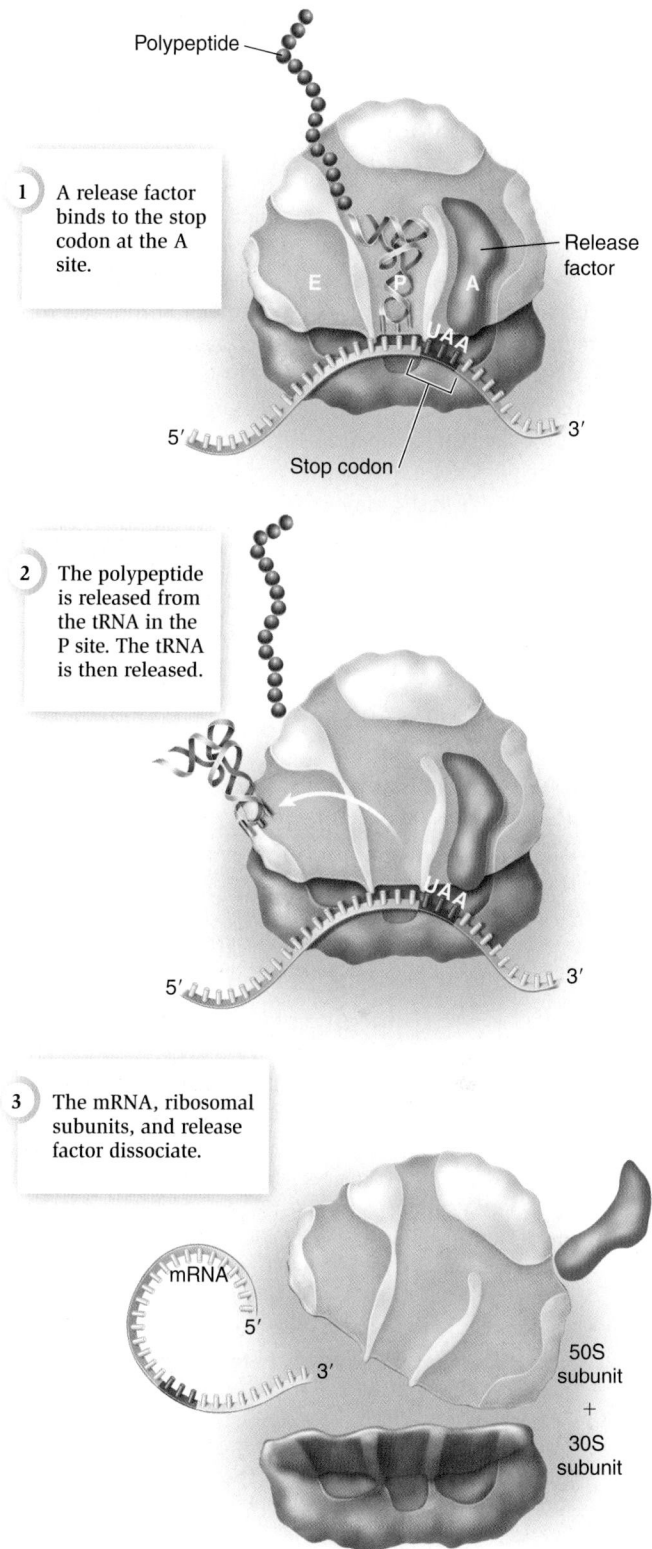

Polypeptide

1 A release factor binds to the stop codon at the A site.

Release factor

Stop codon

2 The polypeptide is released from the tRNA in the P site. The tRNA is then released.

3 The mRNA, ribosomal subunits, and release factor dissociate.

mRNA

50S subunit

+

30S subunit

Figure 11.22 Termination stage of translation in bacteria.

not have tRNAs with complementary sequences. Instead, stop codons are recognized by proteins, known as **release factors** (see Table 11.2). Interestingly, the three-dimensional structure of a release factor protein mimics the structure of tRNAs.

Figure 11.22 illustrates the termination stage of translation. In step (1) of this figure, the completed polypeptide chain is attached to a tRNA in the P site. A stop codon is located at the A site. In the first step a release factor binds to the stop codon at the A site. In the second step the bond between the polypeptide and the tRNA is hydrolyzed, causing the polypeptide and tRNA to be released from the ribosome.

Finally, in the third step the ribosomal subunits, mRNA, and release factor dissociate.

A Polypeptide Chain Has Directionality from Its Amino End to Its Carboxyl End

Polypeptide synthesis has a directionality that parallels the 5′ to 3′ orientation of mRNA. **Figure 11.23** compares the sequence of a very short polypeptide with the mRNA that encodes it. The first amino acid is said to be at the **N-terminus** or **amino terminus** of the polypeptide; the amino terminus has a free amino group. Peptide bonds connect the amino acids. These bonds form between the carboxyl group of the previous amino acid and the amino group of the next amino acid. The last amino acid in a completed polypeptide does not have another amino acid attached to its carboxyl group. This last amino acid is said to be located at the **C-terminus** or **carboxyl terminus**. A carboxyl group (COOH) is always found at this end of the polypeptide chain. Note: At neutral pH, the amino group is positively charged (NH_3^+), while the carboxyl group is negatively charged (COO^-).

Figure 11.23   The directionality of a polypeptide compared to an mRNA.

Concept check: *Is the codon for the last amino acid in a polypeptide closer to the 5′ or 3′ end of the mRNA?*

Summary of Key Concepts

11.1 Genes Control Biochemical Reactions by Encoding the Polypeptide Components of Enzymes

- Based on his studies of inborn errors of metabolism, Garrod hypothesized that genes encode enzymes. (Figure 11.1)
- By studying the nutritional requirements of bread mould, Beadle and Tatum proposed the one gene–one enzyme hypothesis. Later this idea was expanded to the one gene–one polypeptide theory. (Figure 11.2)

11.2 Polypeptide Production Is a Multistep Process Requiring at Least Three Major Categories of Genes

- A polypeptide is a unit of structure. A protein, composed of one or more polypeptides, is a unit of function.
- At the molecular level, the central dogma of genetics states that most genes are transcribed into mRNA, and then the mRNA is translated into polypeptides. Eukaryotes modify their RNA transcripts to make them functional. (Figure 11.3)
- The molecular expression of genes is fundamental to the characteristics of an organism's traits.

11.3 Transcription

- The promoter of a gene signals the beginning of transcription, while the terminator specifies where transcription will end for a given gene. Regulatory sequences control whether a gene is turned on or off. (Figure 11.4)
- In bacteria, sigma factor binds to RNA polymerase and to a promoter, thereby promoting the initiation of transcription. The RNA transcript is made during the elongation stage because of base pairing of nucleotides to the template strand of DNA. RNA polymerase is released from the DNA at the termination site. (Figure 11.5)

- The genes along a chromosome are transcribed in different directions. (Figure 11.6)

11.4 RNA Processing

- Eukaryotic mRNA is first made as a pre-mRNA that is capped, spliced, and given a poly A tail. (Figures 11.7, 11.8)
- Eukaryotic genes often have introns. These are intervening sequences that are found in between the coding sequences, which are called exons. Microscopy studies with mature mRNA revealed the presence of introns in eukaryotic genes. (Figure 11.9)
- Introns are removed from eukaryotic pre-mRNA by a spliceosome. The components of a spliceosome first recognize the intron boundaries and the branch site, and then remove the intron and connect the adjacent exons. (Figure 11.10)

11.5 Translation and the Genetic Code

- The genetic code is found in mRNA molecules and determines the amino acid sequences of polypeptides. Each of the 64 codons specifies a start codon (methionine), other amino acids, or a stop codon. (Table 11.1, Figure 11.12)
- The template strand of DNA is used to make mRNA with a series of codons. Recognition between mRNA and many tRNA molecules determines the amino acid sequence of a polypeptide. (Figure 11.12)
- Nirenberg and Leder used the ability of RNA triplets to promote the binding of tRNA to ribosomes as a way to determine many of the codons of the genetic code. (Figure 11.13)

11.6 The Machinery and Stages of Translation

- Translation requires mRNA, tRNAs, ribosomes, and many translation factors. (Table 11.2)
- tRNA molecules have a cloverleaf structure. Two important sites are the 3′ end, which covalently binds an amino acid, and the anticodon, which base pairs with a codon in mRNA. (Figure 11.14)

- The enzyme aminoacyl-tRNA synthetase attaches the correct amino acid to a tRNA molecule. (Figure 11.15)
- Ribosomes are composed of rRNA molecules and many proteins to produce a small and large subunit. Bacterial and eukaryotic ribosomes differ in their composition. (Figure 11.16)
- Ribosomes have three sites called the A, P, and E sites, which are locations for the binding and release of tRNA molecules. (Figure 11.17)
- The gene that encodes the small subunit rRNA has been extensively used in the evolutionary comparisons of different species. (Figure 11.18)
- Translation occurs in three stages called initiation, elongation, and termination. (Figure 11.19)
- During initiation of translation, the mRNA assembles with the ribosomal subunits and the first tRNA molecule. (Figure 11.20)
- Polypeptide synthesis occurs during the elongation stage, one amino acid at a time. (Figure 11.21)
- During the termination of translation the binding of a release factor to the stop codon causes the release of the completed polypeptide and the disassembly of the mRNA and ribosomal subunits. (Figure 11.22)
- A polypeptide has a directionality in which the first amino acid is at the N- or amino terminus, while the last amino acid is at the C- or carboxyl terminus. (Figure 11.23)

Test to Assess Your Learning

1. Which of the following best represents the central dogma of gene expression?
   a. During transcription, DNA codes for polypeptides.
   b. During transcription, DNA codes for RNA, which codes for polypeptides during translation.
   c. During translation, DNA codes for RNA, which codes for polypeptides during transcription.
   d. During replication, DNA is used to make RNA.
   e. None of the above.

2. Transcription of a gene begins at a site on DNA called _____ and ends at a site on DNA known as _____.
   a. an initiation codon, the termination codon
   b. a promoter, the termination codon
   c. an initiation codon, the terminator
   d. a promoter, the terminator
   e. an initiator, the terminator

3. The product of transcription of a structural gene is
   a. tRNA.
   b. mRNA.
   c. rRNA.
   d. polypeptide.
   e. (a), (b), and (c).

4. In eukaryotic RNA processing, the nontranslated sequences that are removed are called
   a. exons.
   b. introns.
   c. promoters.
   d. codons.
   e. ribozymes.

5. Ribozymes are
   a. the organelles in which translation takes place.
   b. the RNA molecules that are components of ribosomes.
   c. the proteins that are components of ribosomes.
   d. the portions of the pre-mRNA that are removed.
   e. RNA molecules that catalyze chemical reactions.

6. The _____ is the organelle where the translation process takes place.
   a. mitochondria
   b. nucleus
   c. ribosome
   d. lysosome
   e. ribozyme

7. The region of the tRNA that is complementary to the triplet on the mRNA is
   a. the acceptor stem.
   b. the codon.
   c. the peptidyl site.
   d. the anticodon.
   e. the adaptor loop.

8. During the initiation step of translation, the first codon, _____, will enter the _____ and associate with the initiator tRNA.
   a. UAG, A site
   b. AUG, A site
   c. UAG, P site
   d. AUG, P site
   e. AUG, E site

9. The movement of the polypeptide from the tRNA in the P site to the tRNA in the A site is referred to as
   a. peptide bonding.
   b. aminoacyl binding.
   c. translation.
   d. peptidyl transfer reaction.
   e. elongation.

10. The synthesis of a polypeptide occurs during which stage of translation?
    a. initiation
    b. elongation
    c. termination
    d. splicing
    e. None of the above.

Articulate to Express Your Learning

1. Define *mutation* and explain the role of mutation in the development of Garrod's and Beadle and Tatum's thinking.

2. Imagine that the promoter binds RNA polymerase in a position such that transcription is going in the direction of the arrow. Which strand (A or B) is used as the template? Explain your choice.

3. Explain the one gene–one enzyme hypothesis and list all the more modern modifications of this hypothesis.

4. What is the function of an aminoacyl-tRNA synthetase?

Collaborate to Assess and Extend Your Learning

1. What amino acid sequence would be generated by the following mRNA? Explain your answer to a classmate.

   5'..........GCC-ACC-AUG-GAA-CGU-CGU-CAA-CUC-UGA-GUA..........3'

2. Diagram the double helix for a structural gene of a prokaryote. Label the promoter region, transcription start site, transcription termination site, translation start site, and translation stop site. Now do the same exercise for a eukaryotic structural gene.

3. How can we analyze rRNA to establish evolutionary relationships between different species of organisms?

4. How do differences in cell structure between prokaryotes and eukaryotes generate differences in gene expression?

5. Create a concept map by using the following terms: mutation, theory one gene, one enzyme, genetic code, triplet code, codons, anticodons, aminoacyl-tRNA synthetases, charged tRNAs, uncharged tRNAs, base pairing rules.

6. A biological principle of life is that genetic material provides a blueprint for sustaining life. Explain how the information within the blueprint is accessed at the molecular level.

Visit McGraw-Hill Ryerson Connect™ for additional study resources.

Gene Regulation

Chapter Outline

A model for a protein that binds to DNA and regulates genes. The catabolite activator protein (CAP), shown in dark and light blue, is binding to the DNA double helix, shown in orange and white. This protein, described later in Figure 12.10, activates gene transcription.

At the molecular level, **gene expression** is the process by which the information within a gene is made into a functional product, such as an RNA molecule or a protein. The majority of genes in all species are regulated so that the proteins they specify are produced at appropriate times and in specific amounts. The term **gene regulation** refers to the ability of cells to control their own level of gene expression. By comparison other genes have essentially constant levels of expression in all conditions over time. These are called **constitutive genes**. Typically, constitutive genes, also referred to as housekeeping genes, encode proteins that are necessary for the survival of an organism.

The importance of gene regulation is underscored by the number of genes devoted to this process in an organism. A sizable portion of the genomes of complex organisms, such as plants and animals, is devoted to the process of gene regulation. For example, in *Arabidopsis thaliana*, a plant that has been studied as a model organism by plant geneticists, more than 5% of its genome (about 1500 genes) encodes proteins that regulate the transcription of other genes.

In this chapter we will begin with an overview that emphasizes the benefits of gene regulation and the general mechanisms that achieve such regulation. Later sections will describe how bacteria regulate gene expression in the face of environmental change and will detail the complex nature of gene regulation in eukaryotes.

12.1 OVERVIEW OF GENE REGULATION

Learning Outcomes:

1. Discuss the various ways that organisms benefit from gene regulation.
2. Identify where gene regulation can occur in the pathway of gene expression for bacteria and eukaryotes.

Living organisms derive many benefits from regulating genes. This process ensures that proteins will be produced only when they are required. For example, certain proteins help an organism to survive environmental stress, such as drastic changes in temperature or exposure to ultraviolet (UV) light. Because these proteins are required only when the organism is confronted with the stress, a cell conserves energy and resources if such proteins are made only when the stressor is present. In addition some proteins function in the metabolism of small molecules that may or may not be present in the environment. For example, certain proteins are needed for a bacterium to take up and metabolize particular sugars. These proteins are required only when the bacterium is exposed to such sugars in its environment.

Like bacteria, eukaryotic organisms need to adapt to changes in their environment. For example, all eukaryotic species can respond to environmental stresses, such as UV radiation, by turning on genes that provide protection against this harmful environmental agent. In humans exposure to UV light turns on genes that result in the production of melanin, a pigment that acts as a photoprotectant.

In addition to responding to environmental conditions, eukaryotes also regulate genes when cells are dividing and specializing, and when they are going through developmental stages. For example, some proteins are needed just for cell division. In multicellular organisms certain proteins are made only in particular cell types or their amounts may vary from cell to cell. In humans, for example, some proteins are needed in muscle cells but not in nerve cells, and vice versa. Similarly, in multicellular organisms that progress through different developmental stages (fertilized egg, embryo, and adult), certain proteins are needed only at particular stages of development. In this section we will examine a few examples that illustrate the important consequences of gene regulation. We will also illustrate how gene expression can be regulated at several levels: these are termed *transcriptional, post-transcriptional, translational,* and *post-translational control.* The evolution of multiple levels of control has enabled complex organisms to carefully control their proteome by sensing extrinsic (environmental) and intrinsic (internal) signals and integrating these inputs to fine-tune the levels of individual proteins.

Bacteria Regulate Genes to Respond to Nutrients in Their Environment

The bacterium *E. coli* can use many types of sugars as food sources, thereby increasing its chances of survival. Let's consider the process of how it uses lactose, which is the sugar found in milk. *E. coli* can use lactose because it carries genes that code for proteins that enable it to take up lactose and metabolize it.

Figure 12.1 illustrates the effects of lactose on the regulation of those genes. Lactose use requires a transporter, called lactose permease, that facilitates the uptake of lactose into the cell, and an enzyme, called β-galactosidase, that catalyzes the breakdown of lactose. When lactose is not present in the environment, an *E. coli* cell makes very little of these proteins. However, when lactose becomes available, gene regulation causes the synthesis of many more copies of these proteins, enabling the bacterium to efficiently use lactose from its environment. Eventually, all the lactose in the environment will be used up.

At this point the genes encoding these proteins will be shut off, and most of the proteins will be degraded. Therefore, this mode of gene regulation conserves the cell's energy because it ensures that the proteins needed for lactose usage are made only when lactose is present in the environment.

Eukaryotic Gene Regulation Produces Different Cell Types in a Single Organism

One of the most amazing examples of gene regulation is the phenomenon of **cell differentiation**. In multicellular organisms, such as plants and animals, cells become specialized, or differentiated, into particular types. In humans, for example, cells may become specialized into muscle cells, neurons, skin cells, or other types. **Figure 12.2** shows micrographs of three types of cells found in humans. Their morphologies are strikingly different. Likewise, their functions within the body are also quite different. Muscle cells are important in body movements, neurons function in synaptic signalling, and skin cells form a protective outer surface for the body.

Gene regulation is responsible for creating different types of cells within a multicellular organism. The three cell types shown in Figure 12.2 contain the same genome, meaning they carry the same set of genes. However, their proteomes—the collection of proteins they produce from the genome—are quite different because of gene regulation. Certain proteins are found in particular cell types but not in others. Alternatively, a protein may be present in all three cell types, but the relative amounts of the protein may be different. The amount of a given protein

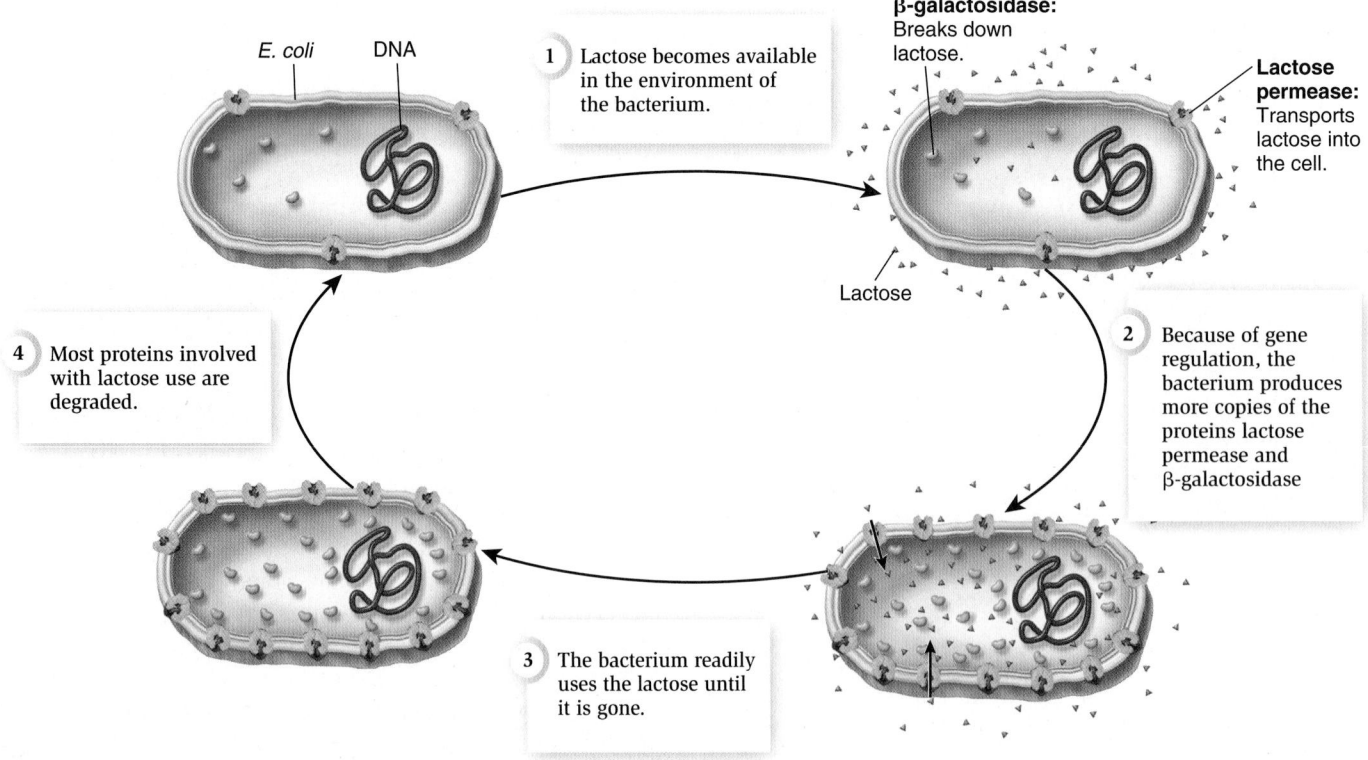

β-galactosidase: Breaks down lactose.

1 Lactose becomes available in the environment of the bacterium.

E. coli   DNA

Lactose permease: Transports lactose into the cell.

Lactose

4 Most proteins involved with lactose use are degraded.

2 Because of gene regulation, the bacterium produces more copies of the proteins lactose permease and β-galactosidase

3 The bacterium readily uses the lactose until it is gone.

Figure 12.1 Gene regulation of lactose use in *E. coli.*

Concept check: *What is the advantage to E. coli of regulating the genes involved with lactose use?*

(a) Skeletal muscle cell   **(b) Neuron**   **(c) Skin cell**

Figure 12.2   Examples of different cell types in humans.   These cells have the same genetic composition. Their unique morphologies are due to differences in the proteins they make.

Concept check: *How does gene regulation underlie the different morphologies of these cells?*

depends on many factors, including how strongly the corresponding gene is transcribed and how much protein is synthesized from mRNA. Gene regulation at the level of transcription and translation plays a major role in determining the proteome of each cell type. We'll discuss these forms of gene regulation later in this chapter. In addition other factors described in Unit II, such as protein degradation, post-translational modifications, and feedback inhibition, are important in controlling the functions and relative amounts of proteins in a cell.

Eukaryotic Gene Regulation Enables Multicellular Organisms to Progress Through Developmental Stages

In multicellular organisms that progress through developmental stages, certain genes are expressed at one stage of development but not another. This topic is discussed further in Chapter 17. For now let's consider an example of such developmental gene regulation in mammals. Early stages of mammalian embryo and fetal development occur in the uterus of female mammals. In humans the embryonic stage lasts from fertilization to eight weeks. During this stage of development, differentiation of cells sculpts all major tissues and organs, and the body plan is established. The fetal stage occurs from eight weeks to birth (41 weeks). This stage is characterized by continued refinement of body parts and a large increase in size.

The oxygen demands of a rapidly growing embryo and fetus are quite different from the needs of the mother. Gene regulation plays a vital role in ensuring that an embryo and fetus get the proper amount of oxygen. As described in Chapter 45, hemoglobin is a protein that delivers oxygen to the cells of a mammal's body. A hemoglobin protein is composed of four globin polypeptides, two encoded by one globin gene and two encoded by another globin gene (**Figure 12.3**). The genomes of mammals carry several genes (designated with Greek letters) that encode slightly different globin polypeptides. During the embryonic stage of development the (epsilon) ε-globin and (zeta) ζ-globin genes are turned on. At the fetal stage these genes are turned off, and the (alpha) α-globin and (gamma)

	Embryo	Fetus	Adult
Hemoglobin protein	2 ζ-globins 2 ε-globins	2 α-globins 2 γ-globins	2 α-globins 2 β-globins
Oxygen affinity	Highest	High	Moderate
Gene expression α-globin gene β-globin gene γ-globin gene ζ-globin gene ε-globin gene	Off Off Off On On	On Off On Off Off	On On Off Off Off

Figure 12.3   Developmental regulation of human globin genes.

Principle: *Living organisms grow, develop, and reproduce. Gene regulation is an important process that allows organisms to proceed through developmental stages.*

γ-globin genes are turned on. Finally, at birth the γ-globin gene is turned off, and the (beta) β-globin gene is turned on.

How do the embryo and fetus acquire oxygen from their mother's bloodstream? The hemoglobin that is produced during the embryonic and fetal stages has a much higher binding affinity for oxygen than does the hemoglobin produced after birth. Therefore, the embryo and fetus can remove oxygen from the mother's bloodstream very efficiently and use that oxygen for their own needs. This occurs across the placenta, where the mother's bloodstream is adjacent to the bloodstream of the embryo or fetus. In this way gene regulation enables mammals to develop internally, even though the embryo and fetus are not breathing on their own.

Gene Regulation Can Occur at Different Points in the Process from DNA to Protein

Thus far you have learned that gene regulation can have a dramatic impact on the ability of organisms to respond to environmental changes, produce different types of cells, and progress through developmental stages. For genes that encode proteins, the regulation of gene expression can occur at any of the steps that are needed to produce a functional protein.

In bacteria gene regulation most commonly occurs at the level of transcription, which means that bacteria regulate how much mRNA is made from most genes (**Figure 12.4a**). When geneticists say a gene is "turned off," they mean that no mRNA is made from that gene, whereas a gene that is "turned on" is transcribed into mRNA. A second way for bacteria to regulate gene expression is to control the rate at which mRNA is translated into protein. Because transcription is the first step in gene expression, transcriptional regulation is a particularly efficient way to regulate genes as cells avoid wasting energy when the product of the gene is not needed. A second way for bacteria to regulate gene expression is to control the ability of an mRNA to be translated into protein. This form of gene regulation is less common in bacteria. Last, gene expression can be regulated at the protein or post-translational level.

In eukaryotes, gene regulation occurs at many levels, including transcription, RNA processing, translation, and after translation is complete (**Figure 12.4b**). As it is in their bacterial counterparts, transcriptional regulation is a prominent form of gene regulation in eukaryotes. As discussed later in this chapter, eukaryotic genes are transcriptionally regulated in several

different ways, some of which are not found in bacteria. Also, as discussed in Chapter 11, eukaryotes process their mRNA transcripts in ways that do not commonly occur in bacteria. For example, RNA splicing is a widespread phenomenon in eukaryotes. Later in this chapter we will examine how this process is regulated to create two or more different types of mRNA from a single gene. Eukaryotes also regulate mRNA after its modification. The amount of mRNA can be regulated by controlling its degradation. In addition the translation of mRNA may be regulated by small inhibitory RNA molecules or by RNA-binding proteins that prevent translation from occurring.

As in prokaryotes, proteins can be regulated by eukaryotes in a variety of ways other than gene regulation, including feedback inhibition, post-translational modification, and degradation via the proteasome. These mechanisms are discussed in Unit II. Now, let's look at transcriptional regulation in bacteria.

12.2 REGULATION OF TRANSCRIPTION IN BACTERIA

Learning Outcomes:

1. Explain how regulatory transcription factors and small effector molecules are involved in the regulation of transcription.
2. Describe the organization of the *lac* operon and how it is under negative and positive control.
3. Interpret the results of the experiments by Jacob, Monod, and Pardee.
4. Describe how the *trp* operon is under negative control.

Because of gene regulation, bacteria can respond specifically to changes in their cellular and environmental conditions. As you have seen, when a bacterium is exposed to a particular nutrient in its environment, such as a sugar, genes are expressed that encode proteins needed for the uptake and metabolism of that sugar. In addition, bacteria have enzymes that synthesize cellular molecules, such as particular amino acids. It is to the bacteria's advantage to turn off the genes that encode those enzymes when a sufficient amount of the amino acid is present in the cytoplasm. In this section we will examine the underlying molecular mechanisms that bring about transcriptional regulation in bacteria.

Transcriptional Regulation Usually Involves Regulatory Transcription Factors and Small Effector Molecules

In most cases transcriptional regulation involves the actions of **regulatory transcription factors**, proteins that bind to DNA near a promoter and affect the rate of transcription of one or more nearby genes. These transcription factors can either decrease or increase the rate of transcription of a gene. **Repressors** are regulatory transcription factors that bind to DNA and decrease the rate of transcription. This is a form of regulation called **negative control**. **Activators** bind to DNA and increase the rate of transcription, a form of regulation termed **positive control** (**Figure 12.5a**).

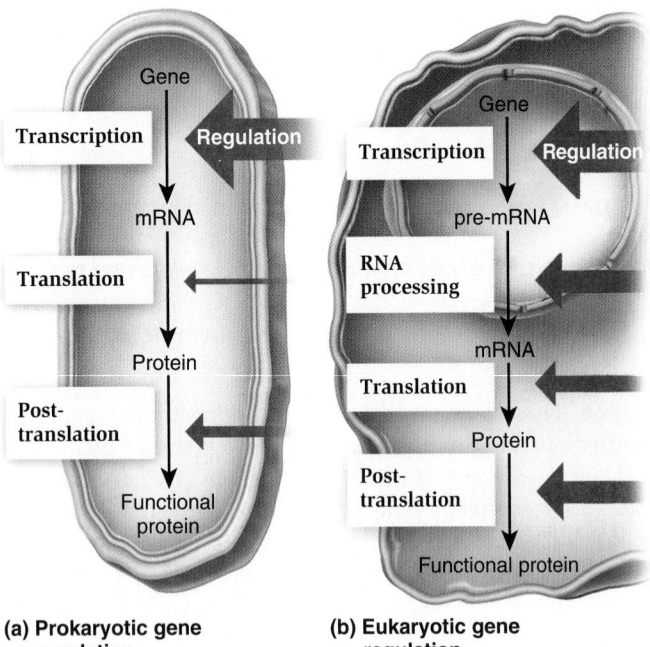

(a) Prokaryotic gene regulation

(b) Eukaryotic gene regulation

Figure 12.4 Overview of points of control for gene regulation in (a) prokaryotes and (b) eukaryotes. The relative sizes of the red arrows indicate the prominence with which regulation at that point is used to control the production of functional proteins.

In conjunction with regulatory transcription factors, molecules called **small effector molecules** often play a critical role in transcriptional regulation. A small effector molecule exerts its effects by binding to a regulatory transcription factor and causing a conformational change in the protein. In many cases the effect of the conformational change determines whether the protein can bind to the DNA. **Figure 12.5b** illustrates an example involving a repressor. When the small effector molecule is absent, the repressor binds to the DNA and inhibits transcription. However, later when the small effector molecule is synthesized or becomes available, it will bind to the repressor and cause a conformational change that inhibits the ability of the protein to bind the DNA. Transcription can occur because the repressor is not able to bind to the DNA. Repressors and activators that respond to small effector molecules have two functional regions called **domains**. One domain is a site at which the protein binds to the DNA. The other domain is the binding site for the small effector molecule.

The *lac* Operon Contains Genes That Encode Proteins Involved in Lactose Metabolism

In bacteria, structural genes are sometimes clustered together in units that are under the transcriptional control of a single promoter. This gene cluster, known as an **operon**, is transcribed into an mRNA, called a **polycistronic mRNA**, an mRNA that encodes more than one protein. What is the advantage of such an arrangement? An operon organization allows a bacterium to coordinately regulate a group of genes that encode proteins that operate in a common biochemical pathway.

The genome of *E. coli* carries an operon called the *lac* **operon**, which contains the genes for the enzymes we discussed earlier that allow it to metabolize lactose (see Figure 12.1). **Figure 12.6a** shows the organization of this operon as it is found in the *E. coli* chromosome, as well as the polycistronic mRNA that is transcribed from it. The *lac* operon contains a promoter, *lacP*, that is used to transcribe three structural genes: *lacZ*, *lacY*, and *lacA*. *LacZ* encodes β-galactosidase, which as you may remember is an enzyme that breaks down lactose (**Figure 12.6b**). As a side reaction, β-galactosidase also converts a small percentage of lactose into allolactose, a structurally similar sugar or lactose analogue. As described later allolactose is important in the regulation of the *lac* operon. The *lacY* gene encodes lactose permease, which is a membrane protein required for the transport of lactose into the cytoplasm of the bacterium. The *lacA* gene encodes galactoside transacetylase, which covalently modifies lactose and

Negative control: A repressor inhibits transcription.

Positive control: An activator promotes transcription.

(a) Actions of regulatory transcription factors

The repressor protein is bound to the promoter region when the small effector molecule is not present.

The binding of the small effector molecule causes a conformational change in the repressor protein that prevents it from binding to the DNA.

(b) Action of a small effector molecule on a repressor protein

Figure 12.5 Actions of regulatory transcription factors and small effector molecules.   (a) Regulatory transcription factors can exert positive or negative control. (b) One way that a small effector molecule can exert its effects is by preventing a repressor protein from binding to the DNA.

(a) Organization of DNA sequences in the *lac* region of the *E. coli* chromosome

(b) Functions of lactose permease and β-galactosidase

Figure 12.6   **The *lac* operon.**   **(a)** This diagram depicts a region of the *E. coli* chromosome that contains the *lacI* regulatory gene and the adjacent *lac* operon, as well as the polycistronic mRNA transcribed from the operon. **(b)** Function of lactose permease and β-galactosidase. Lactose permease cotransports H⁺ with lactose. Bacteria maintain an H⁺ gradient across their cytoplasmic membrane that drives the active transport of lactose into the cytoplasm. β-galactosidase cleaves lactose into galactose and glucose. As a side reaction, it can also convert lactose into allolactose.

lactose analogues by attaching an acetyl group (—COCH₃). Although the functional necessity of this enzyme remains unclear, the attachment of acetyl groups to nonmetabolizable lactose analogues may prevent their buildup to toxic levels in the cytoplasm.

Near the *lac* promoter are two regulatory sites designated the operator and the CAP site (see Figure 12.6a). The **operator**, or *lacO* site, is a sequence of nucleotides that provides a binding site for a repressor protein. The **CAP site** is a DNA sequence recognized by an activator protein.

Adjacent to the *lac* operon is the *lacI* gene, which encodes the **lac repressor**. This repressor protein is important for the regulation of the *lac* operon. The *lacI* gene, which is constitutively expressed at fairly low levels, has its own promoter called the *i* promoter. It is considered to be a **regulatory gene** because the sole function of the encoded protein is to regulate the expression of other genes. Because the *lacI* gene has its own promoter it is not considered a part of the *lac* operon. Let's now take a look at how the *lac* operon is regulated by the *lac* repressor.

The *lac* Operon Is Under Negative Control by a Repressor Protein

In the late 1950s the first researchers to investigate genetic regulation were Francois Jacob and Jacques Monod at the Pasteur Institute in Paris, France. Their focus on gene regulation stemmed from an interest in the phenomenon known as enzyme adaptation, which had been identified early in the twentieth century. Enzyme adaptation refers to the observation that a particular enzyme appears within a living cell only after the cell has been exposed to the substrate for that enzyme. Jacob and Monod studied lactose metabolism in *E. coli* to investigate this phenomenon. When they exposed bacteria to lactose, the levels of lactose-using enzymes in the cells increased by 1,000- to 10,000-fold. After lactose was removed, the synthesis of the enzymes abruptly stopped.

The first mechanism of regulation that Jacob and Monod discovered involved the *lac* repressor protein, which binds to the sequence of nucleotides found at the *lac* operator site. Once bound, the *lac* repressor prevents RNA polymerase from transcribing the *lacZ, lacY,* and *lacA* genes (**Figure 12.7a**).

When lactose is absent from the environment, allolactose is not made and the lac repressor is free to bind to the *lac* operator. The transcription of the operon is inhibited.

lac regulatory gene

lac operon

RNA polymerase

lac promoter

Operator

lacI   *lacP*   *lacO*   *lacZ*   *lacY*   *lacA*

mRNA

Lac repressor binds to the operator and inhibits transcription.

Lac repressor (active)

(a) Lactose absent from the environment

When lactose is present, allolactose is made inside the cell. The binding of allolactose to the lac repressor prevents it from binding to the *lac* operator site. This permits the transcription of the *lac* operon.

RNA polymerase

lacI   *lacP*   *lacO*   *lacZ*   *lacY*   *lacA*

Transcription

mRNA

Polycistronic mRNA

Translation

β-Galactosidase

Lactose permease

Galactoside transacetylase

Allolactose

Conformational change

The binding of allolactose to the lac repressor causes a conformational change that prevents the lac repressor from binding to the operator site.

Lac repressor (inactive)

(b) Lactose present

Figure 12.7   Negative control of an inducible set of genes: function of the *lac* repressor in regulating the *lac* operon.

Concept check: *With regard to regulatory proteins and small effector molecules, explain the meaning of the terms* negative control *and* inducible.

FEATURE INVESTIGATION

Jacob, Monod, and Pardee Studied a Constitutive Bacterial Mutant to Determine the Function of the *lac* Repressor

You have learned that the *lac* repressor binds to the *lac* operator site to exert its effects. Let's now take a look at experiments that helped researchers to determine the function of the *lac* repressor. Our understanding of *lac* operon regulation came from studies involving *E. coli* strains that showed abnormalities in the process of lactose use. In the 1950s Jacob and Monod and their colleague Arthur Pardee had identified a few rare mutant bacteria that exhibited this phenomenon. The mutants expressed the genes of the *lac* operon constitutively, meaning that the *lacZ*, *lacY*, and *lacA* genes were expressed even in the absence of lactose in the environment. The researchers discovered that some mutations that caused this abnormality had occurred in the *lacI* region of the DNA. Such strains were termed *lacI⁻* to indicate that the *lacI* region was not functioning properly. Normal or wild-type *lacI* strains of *E. coli* are called *lacI⁺*.

The researchers hypothesized that the *lacI* gene encoded an enzyme that degraded an internal inducer of the *lac* operon. The *lacI⁻* mutation was thought to inhibit this enzyme and thereby allow the internal inducer to always be synthesized. In this way, the *lacI⁻* mutation would make it unnecessary for cells to be exposed to lactose for induction. However, during this study and in later studies they eventually arrived at the hypothesis that the *lacI* gene encodes a repressor protein, which proved to be correct (**Figure 12.8**). A mutation in the *lacI* gene that eliminates the synthesis of a functional lac repressor would prevent the *lac* repressor protein from inhibiting transcription. At the

time of their work, however, the function of the *lac* repressor was not yet known.

To further understand the nature of the *lacI⁻* mutation, Jacob, Monod, and Pardee applied a genetic approach. Although bacterial conjugation is described in Chapter 16, let's briefly examine this process to understand this experiment. The earliest studies of Jacob, Monod, and Pardee in 1959 involved matings between recipient cells, termed F⁻, and donor cells, which were Hfr strains that transferred a portion of the bacterial chromosome to a recipient cell. Later experiments in 1961 involved the transfer of circular segments of DNA known as F factors. We will consider this later type of experiment here. Sometimes an F factor also carries genes that were originally found within the bacterial chromosome. These types of F factors are called F′ factors (F prime factors). A strain of bacteria containing F′ factor genes is called a **merozygote**, or partial diploid. The production of merozygotes was instrumental in allowing Jacob, Monod, and Pardee to elucidate the function of the *lacI* gene.

As shown in **Figure 12.9**, these researchers studied the *lac* operon in a bacterial strain carrying a *lacI⁻* mutation that caused constitutive expression of the *lac* operon. In addition the mutant strain was subjected to mating to create a merozygote that also carried a normal *lac* operon and normal *lacI⁺* gene on an F′ factor. The merozygote contained both *lacI⁺* and *lacI⁻* genes. The constitutive mutant and corresponding merozygote were allowed to grow separately in a liquid medium and were then divided into two tubes each. In half the tubes the cells were incubated with lactose to determine whether lactose was needed to induce the expression of the operon. In the other tubes lactose was omitted. To monitor the expression of the *lac* operon, the cells were broken open and then tested for the amount of β-galactosidase they released by measuring its ability to convert a colourless compound into a yellow product.

The Data section of Figure 12.9 summarizes the effects of this constitutive mutation and its analysis in a merozygote. As Jacob, Monod, and Pardee already knew, the *lacI⁻* mutant strain expressed the *lac* operon constitutively, in the presence and absence of lactose. However, when a normal *lac* operon and *lacI⁺* gene were introduced on an F′ factor into a cell harbouring the mutant *lacI⁻* gene on the chromosome, the normal *lacI⁺* gene could regulate both operons. In the absence of lactose, both operons were shut off. This occurred because a single *lacI⁺* gene on the F′ factor can produce enough repressor protein to bind to both operator sites. Furthermore, this protein is diffusible (can spread through the cytoplasm) and can bind to *lac* operons that are on the F′ factor and on the bacterial chromosome. Taken together, the data indicated that the normal *lacI* gene encodes a diffusible protein that represses the *lac* operon.

The interactions between regulatory proteins and DNA sequences illustrated in this experiment have led to the definition of two genetic terms. A ***cis*-acting element** or ***cis*-effect** is a DNA segment that must be adjacent to the gene(s) that it

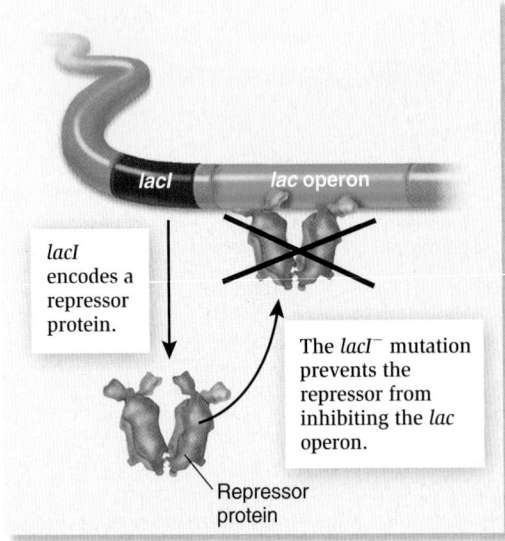

Figure 12.8 Jacob, Monod, and Pardee's hypothesis for the function of the *lacI* region.

HYPOTHESIS The *lacI⁻* mutation inhibits the lac repressor and thereby allows the constitutive expression of the *lac* operon. Note: This correct hypothesis actually arose from the results of this study and other studies.

KEY MATERIALS A constitutive *lacI⁻* mutant strain was already characterized. An F′ factor carrying a normal *lacI⁺* gene and *lac* operon was introduced into this strain to produce a merozygote strain. Note: POZ⁺Y⁺A⁺ refers to a normal *lac* operon.

9   **SOURCE** Jacob, Francois, and Monod, Jacques. 1961. Genetic regulatory mechanisms in the synthesis of proteins. *Journal of Molecular Biology* 3:318–356.

Figure 12.9   The experiment performed by Jacob, Monod, and Pardee to study a *lacI* constitutive mutant.

regulates. The *lac* operator site is an example of a *cis*-acting element. In contrast, a **trans-effect** is a form of genetic regulation that can occur even though two DNA segments are not physically adjacent. The action of the *lac* repressor on the *lac* operon is a *trans*-effect. A *trans*-effect is mediated by genes that encode diffusible regulatory proteins, whereas a *cis*-effect is mediated by DNA sequences that bind regulatory proteins.

Experimental Questions

1. What were the key observations made by Jacob, Monod, and Pardee that led to the development of their hypothesis regarding the *lacI* gene and the regulation of the *lac* operon?

2. What was the eventual hypothesis proposed by the researchers to explain the function of the *lacI* gene and the regulation of the *lac* operon?

3. How did Jacob, Monod, and Pardee test the hypothesis? What were the results of the experiment? How do these results support the idea that the *lacI* gene produces a repressor protein?

RNA polymerase can bind to the promoter when the *lac* repressor is bound to the operator site, but RNA polymerase cannot move past the operator to transcribe the *lacZ*, *lacY*, and *lacA* genes.

Whether or not the *lac* repressor binds to the operator site depends on allolactose, which is the previously mentioned side product of the β-galactosidase enzyme (see Figure 12.6b). How does allolactose control the *lac* repressor? Allolactose is an example of a small effector molecule. The *lac* repressor protein contains four identical subunits, each one recognizing a single allolactose molecule. When four allolactose molecules bind to the *lac* repressor, this causes a conformational change that prevents the repressor from binding to the operator site. Under these conditions, RNA polymerase is free to transcribe the operon (**Figure 12.7b**).

The regulation of the *lac* operon enables *E. coli* to conserve energy because lactose-using proteins are made only when lactose is present in the environment. Allolactose is an **inducer**, a small effector molecule that increases the rate of transcription, and the *lac* operon is said to be an **inducible operon**. When the bacterium is not exposed to lactose, no allolactose is available to bind to the *lac* repressor. Therefore, the *lac* repressor binds to the operator site and inhibits transcription. In reality, the repressor does not completely inhibit transcription, and very small amounts of β-galactosidase, lactose permease, and galactoside transacetylase are made. Even so, the levels are far too low for the bacterium to readily use lactose. When the bacterium is exposed to lactose, a small amount can be transported into the cytoplasm via lactose permease, and β-galactosidase will convert some of it to allolactose (see Figure 12.6b). The cytoplasmic level of allolactose will gradually rise until allolactose binds to the *lac* repressor, which induces the *lac* operon and promotes the transcription of the *lacZ*, *lacY*, and *lacA* genes. Translation of the encoded polypeptides will produce the proteins needed for lactose uptake and metabolism, as described previously in Figure 12.1.

The *lac* Operon Is Also Under Positive Control by an Activator Protein

In addition to negative control by a repressor protein, the lac operon is also positively regulated by an activator protein called the **catabolite activator protein (CAP)**. CAP is controlled by a small effector molecule, **cyclic adenosine monophosphate (cyclic AMP or cAMP)**, which is produced from ATP via an enzyme known as adenylyl cyclase. Gene regulation involving CAP and cAMP is an example of positive control (**Figure 12.10**). When cAMP binds to CAP, the cAMP-CAP complex binds to the CAP site near the *lac* promoter. This causes a bend in the DNA that enhances the ability of RNA polymerase to bind to the promoter. In this way, the rate of transcription is increased.

The key functional role of CAP is to allow *E. coli* to choose between different sources of sugar. In a process known as **catabolite repression**, the presence of a preferred energy source inhibits the use of other energy sources. In this case transcription of the *lac* operon is inhibited by the presence of glucose, which is a catabolite (it is broken down—catabolized—inside the cell). This gene regulation allows *E. coli* to preferentially use glucose compared with other sugars, such as lactose. How does this occur? Glucose inhibits the production of cAMP and thereby prevents the binding of CAP to the DNA. In this way, glucose blocks the activation of the *lac* operon and thereby inhibits transcription. Though it may seem puzzling, the term *catabolite repression* was coined before the action of the cAMP-CAP complex was understood at the molecular level. Historically, the primary observation of researchers was that glucose (a catabolite) inhibited (repressed) lactose metabolism. Further experimentation revealed that CAP is an activator protein.

Let's now consider how the concerted actions of the *lac* repressor and CAP allow bacteria to use the sugars in their environment most efficiently. When a bacterium is exposed to glucose, the uptake of glucose into the cell inhibits adenylyl cyclase, which causes cAMP levels to drop. Without cAMP, CAP cannot bind to the CAP site. When a bacterium is exposed to lactose, allolactose levels in the cytoplasm rise. The binding of allolactose prevents the *lac* repressor from binding to the operator site. With these ideas in mind, **Figure 12.11** considers the four possible environmental conditions that an *E. coli* bacterium might experience with regard to these sugars.

When both lactose and glucose levels are high, the *lac* operon is shut off, because CAP does not activate transcription (**Figure 12.11a**). Under these conditions, the bacterium uses

Figure 12.10 Positive regulation of the *lac* operon by the catabolite activator protein (CAP). When cAMP is bound to CAP, CAP binds to the DNA and causes it to bend. This bend facilitates the binding of RNA polymerase.

BioConnections: *Look back at Figure 9.12. What is the function of cAMP in eukaryotic cells?*

glucose rather than lactose. Greater efficiency is achieved if the bacterium uses one type of sugar at a time. At another time, if lactose levels are high and glucose is low, the *lac* operon is turned on because CAP is bound to the CAP site and the *lac* repressor is not bound to the operator site (**Figure 12.11b**). Under these conditions the bacterium catabolizes lactose. When lactose levels are low, the *lac* repressor prevents transcription of the *lac* operon, whether glucose levels are high or low (**Figure 12.11c, 12.11d**).

The *trp* Operon Is Also Under Negative Control by a Repressor Protein

So far in this section we have examined the regulation of the *lac* operon. Let's now consider an example of an operon that encodes enzymes involved in biosynthesis rather than degradation. Our example is the ***trp* operon** of *E. coli*, which encodes

(a) Lactose high, glucose high

(b) Lactose high, glucose low

(c) Lactose low, glucose high

(d) Lactose low, glucose low

Figure 12.11   Effects of lactose and glucose on the expression of the *lac* operon.

Concept check: *What are the advantages of having both an activator and a repressor protein?*

enzymes that are required to make the amino acid tryptophan, a building block of cellular proteins. More specifically, the *trpE, trpD, trpC, trpB,* and *trpA* genes encode enzymes that are involved in a pathway that leads to tryptophan synthesis.

The *trp* operon is regulated by a repressor protein that is encoded by the *trpR* gene. The binding of the repressor to the *trp* operator site inhibits transcription. The ability of the *trp* repressor to bind to the *trp* operator is controlled by tryptophan, which is the product of the enzymes that are encoded by the operon. When tryptophan levels within the cell are very low, the *trp* repressor cannot bind to the operator site. Under these conditions RNA polymerase readily transcribes the operon (**Figure 12.12a**). In this way the cell expresses the genes that encode enzymes that result in the synthesis of tryptophan, which is in short supply. Alternatively, when the tryptophan levels within the cell are high, tryptophan turns off the *trp* operon. Tryptophan acts as a small effector molecule or **corepressor** by binding to the *trp* repressor protein. This causes a conformational change in the repressor that allows it to bind to the *trp* operator site, inhibiting the ability of RNA polymerase to transcribe the operon (**Figure 12.12b**). Therefore, the bacterium does not waste energy making tryptophan when it is abundant.

The actions of the small effector molecules of the *lac* and *trp* operons are quite different. The *lac* repressor binds to its

operator in the absence of its small effector molecule, while the *trp* repressor binds to its operator only in the presence of its small effector molecule. The *lac* operon is categorized as inducible because allolactose, its small effector molecule, induces transcription. By comparison, the *trp* operon is considered to be a **repressible** operon because its small effector molecule, tryptophan, represses transcription.

Repressible Operons Usually Encode Anabolic Enzymes, and Inducible Operons Encode Catabolic Enzymes

Thus far you have seen that bacterial operons can be transcriptionally regulated in a positive or negative way—or sometimes both. By comparing the mechanisms of regulation among many bacterial operons, geneticists have noticed a general trend. When the genes in an operon encode proteins that function in the breakdown, or **catabolism**, of a substance, the substance to be broken down (or a related compound) often acts as the inducer. This keeps the genes turned off unless the appropriate substance is available. For example, allolactose, which is a product of lactose metabolism, acts as an inducer of the *lac* operon. An inducible form of regulation allows the bacterium to express the appropriate genes only when they are needed to metabolize lactose.

When tryptophan levels are low, the *trp* repressor is inactive, allowing the entire *trp* operon to be transcribed.

RNA polymerase

trpR

P   O

trpE trpD trpC trpB trpA

Transcription

mRNA

Trp repressor

Inactive *trp* repressor cannot bind to the operator site.

(a) Low tryptophan

When tryptophan levels are high, tryptophan (the corepressor) binds to the *trp* repressor, enabling it to bind to the operator site, which prevents transcription.

trpE trpD trpC trpB trpA

trpR   P   O

Tryptophan

Binding of corepressor causes a conformational change in the *trp* repressor that allows it to bind to the operator site. This blocks RNA polymerase from transcribing the operon.

(b) High tryptophan

Figure 12.12   Negative control of a repressible set of genes: function of the *trp* repressor and corepressor (tryptophan) in regulating the *trp* operon.

Concept check: *How are the functions of the* lac *repressor and* trp *repressor similar, and how are they different?*

Other cellular enzymes are important for synthesizing organic molecules, a process termed **anabolism**. Because these molecules are generally needed for the functioning of the cell, the genes that encode these anabolic enzymes tend to be regulated by a repressible mechanism, allowing the genes to be transcribed unless they are turned off. The small effector molecule is commonly a product of the enzymes' biosynthetic activities. For example, as you learned, tryptophan is produced by the enzymes that are encoded by the *trp* operon. When enough of this amino acid has been made, tryptophan itself acts as a corepressor, turning off the genes required for tryptophan biosynthesis. Therefore, a repressible form of regulation provides the bacterium with a way to prevent the overproduction of the product of a biosynthetic pathway. Now let's look at how transcription is regulated in eukaryotes.

12.3 REGULATION OF TRANSCRIPTION IN EUKARYOTES: ROLES OF TRANSCRIPTION FACTORS AND MEDIATOR

Learning Outcomes:

1. Explain the concept of combinatorial control.
2. Describe how RNA polymerase and general transcription factors initiate transcription at the core promoter.
3. Discuss how activators, coactivators, repressors, TFIID, and mediator play a role in gene regulation.

Transcriptional regulation in eukaryotes follows some of the same principles as those found in prokaryotes. For example, activator and repressor proteins are involved in regulating genes by influencing the ability of RNA polymerase to initiate transcription. In addition many eukaryotic genes are regulated by small effector molecules. However, some important differences also occur. In eukaryotic species genes are almost always organized individually, not in operons. Eukaryotic gene regulation also tends to be more intricate, because eukaryotes are faced with complexities that differ from their prokaryotic counterparts. For example, eukaryotes have more complicated cell structures that include many more proteins and a variety of cell organelles. Most eukaryotes are multicellular and contain different cell types. As discussed earlier in this chapter, animal cells can differentiate into a variety of cell types. Furthermore, animals and plants progress through developmental stages that require changes in gene expression.

By studying transcriptional regulation, researchers have discovered that most eukaryotic genes, particularly those found in multicellular species, are regulated by many factors. This phenomenon is called **combinatorial control** because the combination of many factors determines the expression of any given gene. At the level of transcription, common factors that contribute to combinatorial control include the following:

1. One or more activators can stimulate the ability of RNA polymerase to initiate transcription.
2. One or more repressors can inhibit the ability of RNA polymerase to initiate transcription.
3. The function of activators and repressors can be modulated in several ways, which include the binding of small effector molecules, protein-protein interactions, and covalent modifications.
4. Activators are necessary to alter the chromatin structure in the region where a gene is located, thereby making it easier for RNA polymerase to bind to the gene and initiate transcription.

5. DNA methylation usually inhibits transcription, either by preventing the binding of an activator protein or by recruiting proteins that inhibit transcription.

All five of these factors can contribute to the regulation of a single gene, or possibly only three or four will play a role. In most cases transcriptional regulation is aimed at controlling the initiation of transcription at the promoter. In this section we will survey these basic kinds of gene regulation in eukaryotic species.

Eukaryotic Structural Genes Have a Core Promoter and Response Elements

To understand gene regulation in eukaryotes, we first need to consider the DNA sequences that are needed to initiate transcription. For eukaryotic structural genes that encode proteins, three features are found in most promoters: a **transcriptional start site**, a **TATA box**, and **response elements** (**Figure 12.13**). The TATA box and transcriptional start site form the **core promoter**. The transcriptional start site is the place in the DNA where transcription actually begins. The TATA box, which is a 5′–TATAAAA–3′ sequence, is usually about 25 base pairs upstream from a transcriptional start site. The TATA box is important in determining the precise starting point for transcription. If it is missing from the core promoter, transcription may start at a variety of different locations. The core promoter, by itself, results in a low level of transcription that is termed **basal transcription**.

Regulatory elements (or regulatory sequences) are DNA segments that regulate eukaryotic genes. As described later, regulatory elements are recognized by regulatory transcription factor proteins that control the ability of RNA polymerase to initiate transcription at the core promoter. Some response elements, known as **enhancers**, play a role in the ability of RNA polymerase to begin transcription and thereby enhance the rate

Figure 12.13 A common organization of sequences for the promoter of a eukaryotic structural gene. The core promoter is made up of a TATA box and a transcriptional start site. The TATA box sequence is 5′–TATAAAA–3′. The sequence of the transcriptional start site in the 5′ to 3′ direction is two pyrimidines (C or T), then CA, then five pyrimidines. The A marks the site of the first A in the RNA transcript. The sequences shown for the TATA box and transcriptional start site are those found in the coding strand. Py refers to pyrimidine, cytosine, or thymine. Regulatory elements, such as enhancers and silencers, are usually found upstream from the core promoter.

of transcription. When enhancers are not functioning, most eukaryotic genes have very low levels of basal transcription. Other response elements, known as **silencers**, prevent transcription of a given gene when its expression is not needed. When these sequences function, the rate of transcription is decreased.

A common location for regulatory elements is the region that is 50 to several hundred base pairs upstream from the transcriptional start site (Figure 12.13). However, the locations of response elements are quite variable among different eukaryotic genes. Regulatory elements can be quite distant from the promoter, even 100,000 base pairs away, yet exert strong effects on the ability of RNA polymerase to initiate transcription at the core promoter. They do so by looping to come into close proximity to the promoters that they modulate. Adaptor proteins often connect proteins that are bound to the enhancer with proteins that are bound to the promoter region.

RNA Polymerase II, General Transcription Factors, and Mediator Are Needed to Transcribe Eukaryotic Structural Genes

As discussed in Chapter 11, three forms of RNA polymerases, designated I, II, and III, are found in eukaryotes. RNA polymerase II transcribes structural genes that encode proteins. By studying transcription in a variety of eukaryotic species, researchers have identified three types of proteins that play a role in initiating transcription at the core promoter of structural genes: RNA polymerase II, five different proteins called **general transcription factors (GTFs)**, and a large protein complex called **mediator**.

RNA polymerase II and the GTFs must come together at the TATA box of the core promoter so transcription can be initiated. A series of interactions must occur between these proteins so that RNA polymerase II can bind to the DNA. The completed assembly of RNA polymerase II and GTFs at the TATA box is known as the **preinitiation complex** (**Figure 12.14**).

The third component needed for transcription in eukaryotes is the mediator protein complex. **Mediator** is composed of many proteins that bind to each another to form an elliptical-shaped complex that partially wraps around RNA polymerase II and the GTFs. Mediator derives its name from the observation that it mediates interactions between RNA polymerase II and regulatory transcription factors, such as activators or repressors that bind to enhancers or silencers. The function of mediator is to control the rate at which RNA polymerase can begin to transcribe RNA at the transcriptional start site.

Activators and Repressors Can Influence the Function of GTFs or Mediator

In eukaryotes regulatory transcription factor proteins called activators and repressors bind to enhancers or silencers, respectively, and regulate the rate of transcription of a nearby gene. Activators and repressors commonly regulate the function of RNA polymerase II by binding to GTFs or mediator. As shown in **Figure 12.15**, some activators bind to an enhancer and then influence the function of GTFs. For example, an activator may

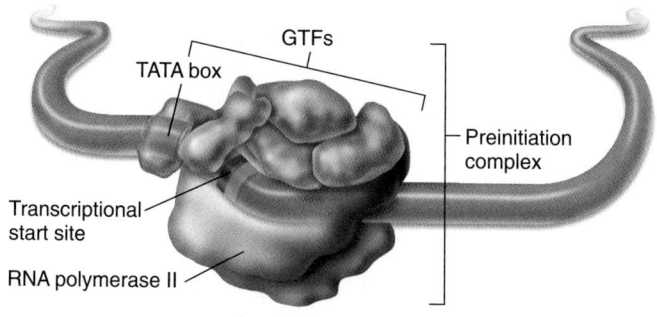

Figure 12.14 **The preinitiation complex.** General transcription factors (GTFs) and RNA polymerase II assemble into the preinitiation complex at the core promoter in eukaryotic structural genes.

improve the ability of a GTF called TFIID to initiate transcription. The function of TFIID is to recognize the TATA box and begin the assembly process. An activator may recruit TFIID to the TATA box, thereby promoting the assembly of GTFs and RNA polymerase II into the preinitiation complex. In contrast, repressors can inhibit the function of TFIID. Certain repressors exert their effects by preventing the binding of TFIID to the

TATA box or by inhibiting the ability of TFIID to assemble other GTFs and RNA polymerase II at the core promoter.

In addition to affecting general transcription factors, a second way that regulatory transcription factors control RNA polymerase II is via mediator (**Figure 12.16**). In this example an activator also interacts with a **coactivator**—a protein that increases the rate of transcription but does not directly bind to the DNA itself. The activator/coactivator complex stimulates the function of mediator and thereby causes RNA polymerase II to proceed to the elongation phase of transcription more quickly. Alternatively, repressors have the opposite effect to those seen in Figure 12.16. When a repressor inhibits mediator, RNA polymerase II cannot progress to the elongation stage.

A third way that regulatory transcription factors influence transcription is by recruiting proteins that affect the compaction or packing of DNA to the promoter region. As described in Chapter 14, the DNA found in eukaryotic chromosomes is highly compacted. To be accessible to RNA polymerase II and GTFs, the DNA must be loosened up. This process is described later in the chapter.

The Specificity of Binding of Regulatory Transcription Factors to DNA Is Governed by Multiple Weak Interactions

Double-stranded DNA is an antiparallel helix, but the helix is an irregular spiral that has alternating major and minor grooves (**Figure 12.17a**). The major groove averages about

1. An activator binds to an enhancer.

Activator

Enhancer

2. The activator enhances the ability of a GTF called TFIID to bind to the TATA box.

TFIID

TATA box

3. TFIID promotes the assembly of the preinitiation complex.

TFIID

TATA box

Preinitiation complex

Figure 12.15 **Effect of an activator via TFIID, a general transcription factor.**

Enhancer

Mediator

Preinitiation complex

1. Mediator binds to the preinitiation complex, but transcriptional initiation does not occur.

2. An activator binds to a distant enhancer and a coactivator binds to the activator. A bend in the DNA allows the activator/coactivator complex to interact with mediator. This interaction causes RNA polymerase to proceed to the elongation stage of transcription.

Coactivator

Enhancer Activator

Figure 12.16 **Effect of an activator via mediator.**

(a) The major and minor grooves of DNA

(b) Functional groups

(c) The interaction of a transcription factor with DNA

(d) Functional groups within the major groove

Figure 12.17 **Interaction of transcription factors with DNA.**   **(a)** The major and minor grooves of DNA result from the helical twist of the antiparallel DNA strands. **(b)** Functional groups of nitrogenous bases extend into the major groove. The green highlighting shows a hydrogen bond acceptor. Yellow is a hydrogen bond donor. Purple represents a methyl group, and red is a hydrogen atom. **(c)** The interaction of a transcription factor with DNA depends on multiple weak interactions between amino acid side chains and functional groups of the nitrogenous bases. **(d)** Functional groups within the major groove define a code that denotes sequence-specific binding by transcription factors; two sequences are shown: 5′–CATGCATG–3′ is a sequence found in the promoters of seed-storage protein genes in many plants; 5′–TCCTAATCCC–3′ is a sequence found in some *Drosophila* promoters that is recognized by the bicoid transcription factor.

22 Angstroms (Å) wide, while the minor groove is approximately 12 Å wide. The nitrogenous bases are stacked in the centre of the helix, but their edges extend into the grooves, where the functional groups can be recognized by sequence-specific DNA binding proteins (transcription factors).

How can a protein, such as a transcription factor, distinguish one type of DNA sequence from another? Two aspects of protein structure are important for sequence-specific binding. First, most types of transcription factors have (alpha) α-helical domains (refer back to Figure 3.16) that can fit into the major groove of DNA. Second, the specificity of DNA binding is dictated by the primary amino acid sequence of the α helix and how it interacts with the functional groups of the nitrogenous bases along the major groove of DNA (**Figure 12.17b**). Remember that of the 20 common amino acids, some side chains are polar and can participate in hydrogen bonding with other nearby molecules. Other side chains can also interact with DNA, for example, through hydrophobic interactions between aromatic amino acids and the ring structures of the nitrogenous bases. The functional groups of the nitrogenous bases consist of hydrogen bond donors and acceptors, as well as hydrogen atoms and methyl groups. Figure 12.17b shows the AT and CG base pairs with their functional groups highlighted. When a transcription factor α helix slides along the major groove of DNA, several adjacent weak interactions (typically hydrogen-bonding pairs) can occur between the amino acid side chains of the protein and the functional groups of the nitrogenous bases along a contiguous stretch of DNA (**Figure 12.17c**).

Multiple weak interactions result in strong sequence-specific binding. When such an interaction occurs, the transcription factor/DNA helix assumes a specific conformation that controls the expression of the gene. In some instances other transcriptional activators/RNA polymerase components are assembled and the gene is activated. In other cases a structure or complex is formed that represses transcription. The coordinated binding of a region of a promoter and a specific transcription factor is thus governed by multiple weak interactions between amino acid side chains and nucleotides, both of which are in a precise sequence arrangement. **Figure 12.17d** shows two different recognition sequences, one for a plant-seed-specific promoter and the other for a developmentally regulated gene in *Drosophila*. As you can see, the arrangement of the specific nucleotides results in major grooves that have distinct binding properties and therefore are bound by specific transcription factors that govern the expression of the genes.

12.4 / REGULATION OF TRANSCRIPTION IN EUKARYOTES: CHANGES IN CHROMATIN STRUCTURE AND DNA METHYLATION

Learning Outcomes:

1. Describe how eukaryotic genes are flanked by nucleosome-free regions and how nucleosomes are altered during gene transcription.
2. Explain how DNA methylation affects transcription.

In eukaryotes, DNA is associated with proteins to form a structure called **chromatin**—the complex of DNA and protein that makes up eukaryotic chromosomes. DNA is compacted by wrapping itself around a group of proteins called **histones**. A repeating structural unit of eukaryotic chromatin is the **nucleosome**, which is 11 nanometres (nm) in diameter and composed of 146 or 147 bp (base pairs) of DNA wrapped around an octamer of histone proteins. Each octamer contains two molecules of four types of histone proteins: H2A, H2B, H3, and H4. Histone proteins are very basic proteins because they contain a large number of positively charged lysine and arginine amino acids. The negative charges found in the phosphates of DNA are attracted to the positive charges on histone proteins. The amino terminal tail of each histone protein protrudes from the histone octamer. These tails can be covalently modified and play a key role in gene regulation.

The nucleosomes are connected by linker regions of DNA that vary in length from 20 to 100 bp, depending on the species and cell type. A particular histone named histone H1 is bound to the linker region, as are other types of proteins. The overall structure of connected nucleosomes resembles beads on a string. This structure shortens the length of the DNA molecule about sevenfold.

Nucleosome units are organized into a more compact structure that is 30 nm in diameter, known as the **30-nm fibre**. Histone H1 and other proteins are important in the formation of the 30-nm fibre, which shortens the nucleosome structure another sevenfold. The structure of the 30-nm fibre has proven difficult to determine because the conformation of the DNA may be substantially altered when extracted from living cells. A current model for the 30-nm fibre was proposed by Rachel Horowitz and Christopher Woodcock in the 1990s. According to their model, linker regions in the 30-nm structure are variably bent and twisted, with little direct contact observed between nucleosomes. The 30-nm fibre forms an asymmetric, three-dimensional zigzag of nucleosomes. At this level of compaction, the overall picture of chromatin that emerges is an irregular, fluctuating structure with stable nucleosome units connected by bendable linker regions.

How does the structure of chromatin affect gene transcription? Nucleosomes are composed of DNA wrapped around an octamer of histone proteins. Depending on the locations and arrangements of nucleosomes, a region containing a gene may be in a **closed conformation**, and transcription may be difficult or impossible without changes in chromatin structure that allow transcription factors to gain access to and bind to the DNA in the promoter region. Such chromatin, said to be in an **open conformation**, is accessible to GTFs and RNA polymerase II, and transcription can take place. In this section we will examine how chromatin is converted from a closed to an open conformation. We will also explore how **DNA methylation**—the attachment of methyl groups to the base cytosine—affects chromatin conformation and gene expression.

Transcription Is Controlled by Changes in Chromatin Structure

In recent years geneticists have been trying to identify the steps that promote the interconversion between the closed and open conformations of chromatin. One way to change chromatin structure is through **ATP-dependent chromatin remodelling complexes**, which are a group of proteins that alter chromatin structure. Such complexes use energy from ATP hydrolysis to drive a change in the locations and/or compositions of nucleosomes, thereby making the DNA more or less amenable to transcription. Therefore, chromatin remodelling is important for both the activation and the repression of transcription.

In what ways do ATP-dependent chromatin remodelling complexes change chromatin structure? Three effects are possible. One result is that ATP-dependent chromatin remodelling complexes bind to chromatin and change the locations of nucleosomes (**Figure 12.18a**). This may involve a shift of the relative positions of a few nucleosomes or a change in the relative spacing of nucleosomes over a long stretch of DNA. A second effect is that remodelling complexes evict histone octamers from the DNA, thereby creating gaps without nucleosomes (**Figure 12.18b**). A third possibility is that chromatin remodelling complexes change the composition of nucleosomes by removing standard histone proteins from an octamer and replacing them with histone variants (**Figure 12.18c**). A **histone variant** is a histone protein that has a slightly different amino acid sequence compared with the standard histone proteins described earlier. Some histone variants promote gene transcription, whereas others inhibit it.

Histone Modifications Affect Gene Transcription

In recent years researchers have learned that the amino terminal tails of histone proteins are subject to several types of covalent modifications. For example, an enzyme called **histone acetyltransferase** attaches acetyl groups ($-COCH_3$) to the amino terminal tails of histone proteins. When acetylated, histone proteins do not bind as tightly to the DNA, which aids in transcription. More than 50 enzymes have been identified in mammals that selectively modify amino terminal tails. **Figure 12.19** shows an example in the amino terminal tails of histone proteins H2A, H2B, H3, and H4 that can be modified by acetyl, methyl, and phosphate groups.

What are the effects of covalent modifications of histones? First, modifications may directly influence interactions between DNA and histone proteins, and between adjacent nucleosomes. As mentioned, the acetylation of histones loosens their binding to DNA and aids in transcription. Second, histone modifications provide binding sites that are recognized by other proteins. According to the **histone code hypothesis**, proposed by Brian Strahl and David Allis in 2000, the pattern of histone modification is recognized by proteins much like a language or code. One pattern of histone modification may attract proteins that inhibit transcription. Alternatively, a different combination of histone modifications may attract proteins, such as ATP-dependent chromatin remodelling complexes, that promote gene transcription. In this way, the histone code plays a key role in accessing the information within the genomes of eukaryotic species.

(a) **Change in nucleosome position**

Chromatin-remodelling complex (not shown) changes the relative positions of a few nucleosomes.   or   Changes the spacing of nucleosomes over a long distance.

Histone octamers are removed by a chromatin-remodelling complex.

(b) **Histone eviction**

Standard histones are replaced with variant histones by a chromatin-remodelling complex.

(c) **Replacement with variant histones**

Figure 12.18 ATP-dependent chromatin remodelling. Chromatin-remodelling complexes may (a) change the locations of nucleosomes, (b) remove histones from the DNA, or (c) replace standard histones with variant histones. The chromatin remodelling complex, which is composed of a group of proteins, is not shown in this figure.

Eukaryotic Genes Are Flanked by Nucleosome-Free Regions

Studies over the past 10 years or so have revealed that many eukaryotic genes show a common pattern of nucleosome organization (**Figure 12.20**). For active genes or those genes that

Figure 12.19 **Examples of covalent modifications that occur to the amino terminal tails of histone proteins.** The amino acids are numbered from the N-terminus or amino end. The modifications shown here are m for methylation, p for phosphorylation, and ac for acetylation. Many more modifications can occur to the amino terminal tails. These modifications are reversible.

Concept check: *What are the two opposing effects that histone modifications can have with regard to chromatin structure?*

can be activated, the core promoter is found at a **nucleosome-free region (NFR)**, which is a site that is missing nucleosomes. The NFR is typically 150 bp long. Although the NFR may be required for transcription, it is not, by itself, sufficient for gene activation. At any given time in the life of a eukaryotic

cell, many genes that contain an NFR are not being actively transcribed. The NFR is flanked by two nucleosomes that are termed the −1 and +1 nucleosomes. These nucleosomes often contain histone variants that promote transcription. The nucleosomes downstream from the +1 nucleosome tend to be evenly spaced near the beginning of a eukaryotic gene, but their spacing becomes less regular farther downstream. The end of many eukaryotic genes is followed by another NFR. This arrangement at the end of genes may be important for transcriptional termination.

Transcriptional Activation Involves Changes in Nucleosome Locations, Composition, and Histone Modifications

A key role of certain activators is to recruit ATP-dependent chromatin-remodelling complexes and histone-modifying enzymes to the promoter region of eukaryotic genes. Though the order of recruitment may differ among specific activators, this appears to be critical for transcriptional initiation and elongation. In the scenario shown in **Figure 12.21**, an activator binds to an enhancer in the NFR. The activator then recruits chromatin remodelling complexes and histone-modifying enzymes to this region. The chromatin remodelling complex may shift nucleosomes or temporarily evict nucleosomes from the promoter region. Nucleosomes containing certain histone variants are thought to be more easily removed from the DNA than those containing the standard histones. Histone-modifying enzymes, such as histone acetyltransferase, covalently modify histone proteins and may affect nucleosome contact with the DNA (see Figure 12.21, step 2). The actions of chromatin remodelling complexes and histone-modifying enzymes facilitate the binding of general transcription factors and RNA polymerase II to the core promoter, thereby allowing the formation of a preinitiation complex (see Figure 12.21, step 3).

Further changes in chromatin structure are necessary for elongation to occur. RNA polymerase II cannot transcribe DNA that is tightly wrapped in nucleosomes. For transcription to occur, histones are evicted, partially displaced, or destabilized

A nucleosome-free region (NFR) is found at the beginning and end of many genes. Nucleosomes tend to be precisely positioned near the beginning and end of a gene, but are less regularly distributed elsewhere.

Figure 12.20 **Nucleosome arrangements near a eukaryotic structural gene.**

BioConnections: *Look ahead to Figure 14.1. What are the components of a nucleosome?*

Many genes are flanked by nucleosome-free regions (NFR) and well-positioned nucleosomes.

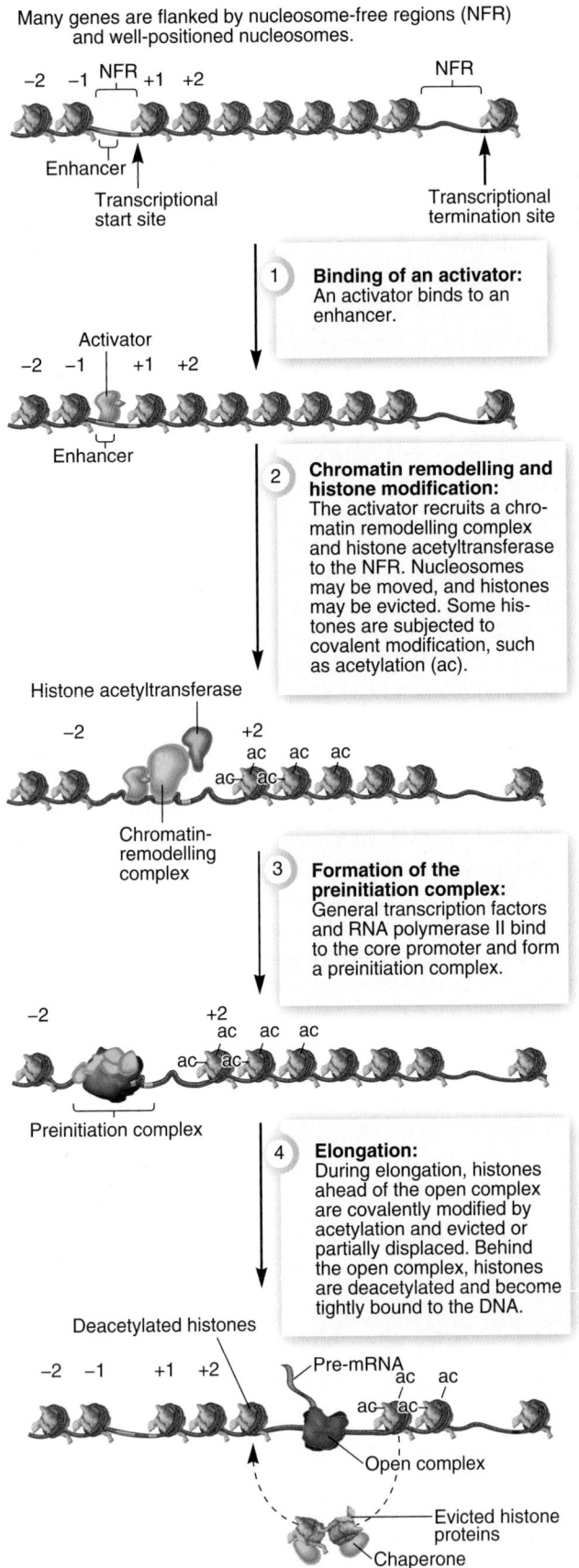

1 Binding of an activator:
An activator binds to an enhancer.

2 Chromatin remodelling and histone modification:
The activator recruits a chromatin remodelling complex and histone acetyltransferase to the NFR. Nucleosomes may be moved, and histones may be evicted. Some histones are subjected to covalent modification, such as acetylation (ac).

3 Formation of the preinitiation complex:
General transcription factors and RNA polymerase II bind to the core promoter and form a preinitiation complex.

4 Elongation:
During elongation, histones ahead of the open complex are covalently modified by acetylation and evicted or partially displaced. Behind the open complex, histones are deacetylated and become tightly bound to the DNA.

Figure 12.21   A simplified model for the transcriptional activation of a eukaryotic structural gene.

so that RNA polymerase II can pass. Evicted histones are then reassembled by chaperone molecules and placed back on the DNA behind the moving RNA polymerase II (see Figure 12.21, step 4). These histones may be deacetylated—have had their acetyl groups removed—so they bind more tightly to the DNA.

DNA Methylation Inhibits Gene Transcription

Let's now turn our attention to a mechanism that usually silences gene expression. DNA structure can be modified by the covalent attachment of methyl groups ($-CH_3$) by an enzyme called **DNA methylase**. This modification, termed DNA methylation, is common in some eukaryotic species but not all. For example, yeast and *Drosophila* have little or no detectable methylation of their DNA, whereas DNA methylation in vertebrates and plants is relatively abundant. In mammals, approximately 5% of DNA is methylated. Eukaryotic DNA methylation occurs on the cytosine base at the 5 position, to create 5-methyl cytosine, shown below.

Cytosine (C)   **5-Methyl Cytosine (5mC)**

DNA methylation usually inhibits the transcription of eukaryotic genes, particularly when it occurs near the promoter. In vertebrates and flowering plants, many genes contain sequences called **CpG islands** near their promoters. CpG refers to the nucleotides of C and G in DNA that are connected by a phosphodiester linkage. A CpG island is a cluster of CpG sites. Unmethylated CpG islands are usually correlated with active genes, whereas repressed genes contain methylated CpG islands. In this way DNA methylation may play an important role in the silencing of particular genes.

How does DNA methylation inhibit transcription? This can occur in two general ways. First, methylation of CpG islands can prevent an activator from binding to an enhancer element, thus inhibiting the initiation of transcription. A second way that methylation inhibits transcription is by altering chromatin structure. Proteins known as **methyl-CpG-binding proteins** bind methylated sequences. Once bound to DNA, the methyl-CpG-binding protein recruits other proteins to the region that inhibit transcription. As discussed in Chapter 15, DNA methylation is also associated with an inheritance pattern called **epigenetic inheritance** in which gene expression is altered in a way that is fixed during an individual's lifetime. Such epigenetic changes may affect the phenotype of the individual, but they are not permanent over two or more generations.

REGULATION OF RNA PROCESSING AND TRANSLATION IN EUKARYOTES

Learning Outcomes:

1. Outline the process of alternative splicing and how it increases protein diversity.
2. Describe how RNA interference is used to regulate the expression of genes.
3. Explain how RNA-binding proteins can regulate the translation of specific mRNAs, using the regulation of iron absorption in mammals as an example.

In the preceding sections of this chapter we focused on the regulation of gene transcription in prokaryotes and eukaryotes. Unlike in bacteria, gene expression in eukaryotes is commonly regulated at the levels of RNA processing and translation. These added levels of regulation provide benefits that are important to eukaryotic species. First, by regulating RNA processing, eukaryotes can produce more than one mRNA transcript from a single gene. This allows a gene to encode two or more polypeptides and thereby increases the complexity of eukaryotic proteomes. Second, transcriptional regulation in eukaryotes takes time before its effects are observed at the cellular level. During transcriptional regulation, (1) the chromatin must be converted to an open conformation, (2) the gene must be transcribed, (3) the RNA must be processed and exported from the nucleus, and (4) the protein must be made via translation. All these steps take several minutes. One way to achieve faster regulation is to control steps that occur after an RNA transcript is made. In eukaryotes, translational regulation provides a faster way to regulate the levels of gene products, namely, proteins. A small RNA molecule or RNA-binding protein can bind to an mRNA and affect the ability of the mRNA to be translated into a polypeptide.

During the past few decades, many critical advances have been made in our knowledge of the regulation of RNA processing and translation. Even so, molecular geneticists are still finding new forms of regulation, making this an exciting area of modern research. In this section we will survey a few of the known mechanisms of RNA processing and translational regulation.

Alternative Splicing of pre-mRNAs Creates Protein Diversity

In eukaryotes a pre-mRNA transcript is processed before it becomes a mature mRNA (see Figure 11.7). When a pre-mRNA has multiple introns and exons, splicing may occur in more than one way, resulting in the production of two or more different polypeptides. Such **alternative splicing** is a form of gene regulation that allows an organism to use the same gene to make different proteins at different stages of development, in different cells types, or in response to a change in the environmental conditions. Alternative splicing is an important form of gene regulation in complex eukaryotes, such as animals and plants. An advantage of alternative splicing is that two or more different polypeptides can be derived from a single gene, thereby increasing the size of the proteome while minimizing the size of the genome.

Let's consider an example of alternative splicing for a mammalian pre-mRNA that encodes a protein known as tropomyosin, which functions in the regulation of cell contraction in animals. It is located along the thin filaments found in smooth muscle cells, such as those in the uterus and small intestine, and in striated muscle cells that are found in cardiac and skeletal muscle. α-tropomyosin is also synthesized in many types of nonmuscle cells but in lower amounts. Within a multicellular organism different types of cells must regulate their contractibility in subtly different ways. One way this may be accomplished is by the production of different forms of α-tropomyosin.

Figure 12.22 shows the intron–exon structure of the rat α-tropomyosin pre-mRNA and two ways that the pre-mRNA

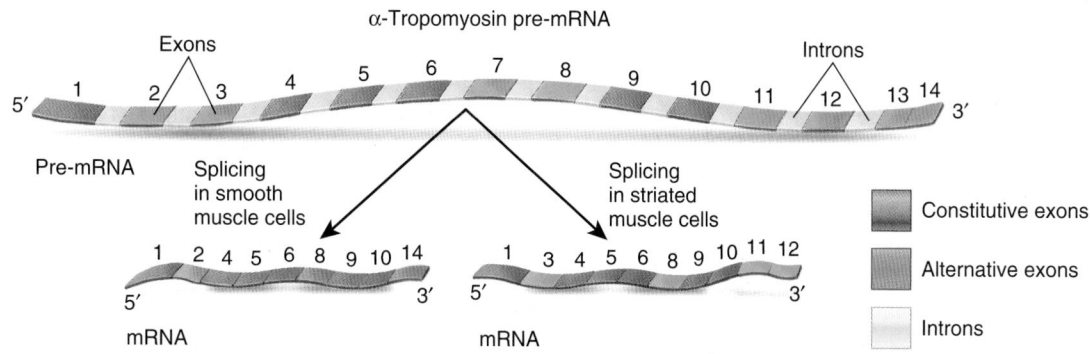

Figure 12.22 Alternative splicing of the rat α-tropomyosin pre-mRNA. The top part of this figure depicts the structure of the rat α-tropomyosin pre-mRNA. Exons are shown as coloured boxes, and introns are illustrated as connecting black lines. The lower part of the figure describes the final mRNA products in smooth and striated muscle cells after alternative splicing. Note: Exon 8 is found in the final mRNA of smooth and striated muscle cells, but not in the mRNA of certain other cell types. The junction between exons 13 and 14 contains a 3′ splice site that enables exon 13 to be separated from exon 14.

Concept check: *What is the biological advantage of alternative splicing?*

GENOMES AND PROTEOMES

Alternative Splicing Tends to Be More Prevalent in Complex Eukaryotic Species

In the past few decades many technical advances have improved our ability to analyze the genomes and proteomes of many different species. Researchers have been able to determine the amount of DNA from several species and estimate the total number of genes. In addition scientists can also estimate the number of polypeptides if information is available concerning the degree of alternative splicing in a given species.

Table 12.1 compares six species, a bacterium (*Escherichia coli*), a eukaryotic single-celled organism (yeast—*Saccharomyces cerevisiae*), a small nematode worm (*Caenorhabditis elegans*), a fruit fly (*Drosophila melanogaster*), a small flowering plant (*Arabidopsis thaliana*), and a human (*Homo sapiens*). As a general trend less complex organisms tend to have fewer genes. For example, unicellular organisms have only a few thousand genes, whereas multicellular species have tens of thousands. Even so, the trend is by no means a linear one. If we compare *C. elegans* and *D. melanogaster*, the fly actually has fewer genes even though it is morphologically more complex. In addition, larger genomes do not necessarily have more genes. For example, the human genome is more than 20 times the size of the *Arabidopsis* genome, but they encode a comparable number of genes. The record holder is the trillium relative *Paris japonica*, with a genome size nearly 60 times that of humans.

A second trend in Table 12.1 concerns alternative splicing. This phenomenon does not occur in bacteria and is rare in *S. cerevisiae*. The frequency of alternative splicing increases from worms to flies to humans. For example, the level of alternative

Table 12.1	Gene Number and Biological Complexity			
Species	**Level of complexity**	**Genome size (million base pairs)**	**Approximate number of genes**	**Percentage of genes alternatively spliced**
Escherichia coli	A unicellular prokaryote	4.2	4,000	0
Saccharomyces cerevisiae	A unicellular eukaryote	12	6,000	<1
Caenorhabditis elegans	A tiny worm (about 1,000 cells)	97	19,000	2
Drosophila melanogaster	An insect	137	14,000	7
Arabidopsis thaliana	A flowering plant	142	26,000	11
Homo sapiens	A complex mammal	3,000	25,000	70

splicing in humans is 10 times that than in *Drosophila*. This trend can partially explain the increase in biological complexity among these species, as the number of different proteins produced by translation of alternatively spliced RNAs dramatically increases the proteome size. Even though humans have only about 25,000 different genes, they can make more than 100,000 different proteins because most genes are alternatively spliced in multiple ways.

can be spliced. The pre-mRNA contains 14 exons, 6 of which are constitutive exons (shown in red), which are always found in the mature mRNA from all cell types. Presumably, constitutive exons encode polypeptide segments of the α-tropomyosin protein that are necessary for its general structure and function. By comparison, alternative exons (shown in green) are not always found in the mRNA after splicing has occurred. The polypeptide sequences encoded by alternative exons may subtly change the function of α-tropomyosin to meet the needs of the cell type in which it is found. For example, Figure 12.22 shows the predominant splicing products found in smooth muscle cells and striated muscle cells. Exon 2 encodes a segment of the α-tropomyosin protein that alters its function to make it suitable for smooth muscle cells. By comparison, the α-tropomyosin mRNA found in striated muscle cells does not include exon 2. Instead, this mRNA contains exon 3, which is more suitable for that cell type.

RNA Interference Blocks the Expression of mRNA

Let's now turn our attention to regulatory mechanisms that affect translation. **MicroRNAs (miRNAs)** and **short-interfering RNAs (siRNAs)** are RNA molecules that are processed to a small size, typically 22 nucleotides long, and silence the expression of pre-existing mRNAs. The precursors of miRNAs are encoded by genes and usually form a hairpin structure. In most cases miRNAs are partially complementary to certain cellular mRNAs and inhibit their translation. By comparison, short-interfering RNAs are derived from RNA molecules that come together to form a double-stranded region. For example, a cellular RNA may bind to an RNA that is transcribed from viral genome. The siRNAs are usually a perfect match to specific mRNAs and cause the mRNAs to be degraded.

Insight into the mechanism of miRNA inhibition came from the surprising results of Andrew Fire and Craig Mello, who

Figure 12.23 Mechanism of action of microRNA (miRNA). Pre-siRNAs are also acted on by dicer, but siRNAs are derived from two RNA molecules that form a double-stranded region rather than one RNA molecule that forms a hairpin.

Principle: *Structure determines function. Because the structure of an miRNA or siRNA is complementary to an mRNA, it is able to inhibit the function of the mRNA.*

(a) Low iron levels

(b) High iron levels

Figure 12.24 Translational regulation of ferritin mRNA by the iron regulatory protein (IRP).

Concept check: *Poisoning can occur if a small child finds a bottle of vitamins, such as those that taste like candy, and eats a large number of them. One of the toxic effects involves the ingestion of too much iron. How does the IRP protect people from the toxic effects of too much iron?*

discovered the mechanism of action of miRNA (**Figure 12.23**). A pre mi-RNAs is first synthesized as single stranded molecule, which forms a hairpin structure because of intrastrand complementary base pairing. (A pre-siRNA, which is not shown in this figure, is composed of two RNA molecules that come together to form a double-stranded region.) The double-stranded region is trimmed to a sequence of around 22 base pairs by an enzyme called dicer. The 22-bp sequence becomes part of a complex called the **RNA-induced silencing complex (RISC)**, which also includes several proteins. One of the RNA strands is then degraded. The miRNA or siRNA in the complex binds to a target mRNA with a complementary sequence.

Two things may happen on binding. When the miRNA and mRNA are not a perfect match or are only partially complementary,

translation is inhibited. Alternatively, when an siRNA and mRNA are a perfect match or highly complementary, the mRNA is cut into two pieces and then degraded. Both miRNA and siRNA have the same effect—the expression of the mRNA is silenced. Fire and Mello called this **RNA interference (RNAi)**, because the miRNA interferes with the proper expression of an mRNA.

Since this study, researchers have discovered that genes encoding miRNAs are widely found in animals and plants. In humans, for example, approximately 200 different genes encode miRNAs. RNAi represents an important mechanism of gene regulation that results in mRNA silencing. In 2006 Fire and Mello were awarded the Nobel Prize for their studies of RNAi.

Translational Regulation by mRNA Binding Proteins

Another way to regulate translation involves RNA-binding proteins that directly affect translational initiation. The regulation of iron absorption provides a well-studied example. Iron is a vital cofactor for many cellular enzymes; however, it is toxic at high levels. To prevent toxicity, mammalian cells synthesize a protein called ferritin, which forms a hollow, spherical complex that can store excess iron.

The mRNA that encodes ferritin is controlled by an RNA-binding protein known as the **iron regulatory protein (IRP)**. When iron levels in the cytosol are low and more ferritin is not needed, IRP binds to a response element within the ferritin mRNA known as the **iron regulatory element (IRE)**. The IRE is located upstream from the start codon in a region called the 5′–untranslated region (5′–UTR). Through base pairing it forms a stem-loop structure. The binding of IRP to the IRE inhibits translation of the ferritin mRNA (**Figure 12.24a**). However, when iron is abundant in the cytosol, the iron binds directly to IRP and prevents it from binding to the IRE. Under these conditions the ferritin mRNA is translated to make more ferritin protein (**Figure 12.24b**).

Why is translational regulation of ferritin mRNA an advantage over transcriptional regulation of the ferritin gene? This mechanism of translational control allows cells to rapidly respond to changes in their environment. When cells are confronted with high levels of iron, they can quickly make more ferritin protein to prevent the toxic buildup of iron. This mechanism is faster than transcriptional regulation, which would require the activation of the ferritin gene and the transcription of ferritin mRNA before the synthesis of more ferritin protein.

Many examples exist of regulation at the translational level. In the case of the ferritin gene, regulation leads to a specific response involving a single protein; however, more global regulators also influence the physiology and behaviour of an organism. Consider the work of Nahum Sonenberg of McGill University. In the late 1970s Sonenberg and Aaron Shatkin discovered the eIF4E protein, which binds to the 5′ cap of mRNA molecules and thus can mediate a variety of mRNA regulatory processes (e.g., export from the nucleus, translational control). Sonenberg's more recent work has focused on the regulatory control of translation, mediated by proteins that bind to eIF4E. For example, to study the role of the 4E-BP1 protein, his team created mice with a mutation in the 4E-BP1 gene that inhibited the protein's expression. The result was that the mice were much leaner than normal mice. Further investigations showed that 4E-BP1 inhibits the process that turns white fat (normally stored by the body) into brown fat (which the body burns). This discovery could help lead to the creation of a drug to inhibit 4E-BP1 function in humans as a way to treat obesity. Similarly, a different 4E binding protein, 4E-BP2, seems to play a role in the brain in promoting memory; mice deficient in 4E-BP2 demonstrated poorer performance in a variety of memory and learning tests. These studies point to translational control of mRNAs as a key regulatory step that underpins normal metabolism; loss of that control may lead to disease states.

Summary of Key Concepts

12.1 Overview of Gene Regulation

- Most genes are regulated so that the levels of gene expression can vary under different conditions. By comparison, constitutive genes are expressed at constant levels.

- Gene regulation ensures that gene products are made only when they are needed. An example is the synthesis of the gene products needed for lactose use in bacteria. (Figure 12.1)

- Multicellular eukaryotes regulate genes to produce different cell types, such as muscle, nerve, and skin cells. (Figure 12.2)

- Eukaryotes also regulate genes so that gene products are produced at different developmental stages. An example is the group of globin genes in mammals. (Figure 12.3)

- All organisms regulate gene expression at a variety of levels, including transcription, translation, and post-translation. Eukaryotes also regulate RNA processing. (Figure 12.4)

12.2 Regulation of Transcription in Bacteria

- Repressors and activators are regulatory proteins that bind to the DNA and regulate the transcription of genes. Small effector molecules control the ability of regulatory proteins to bind to DNA. (Figure 12.5)

- The *lac* operon found in *E. coli* is an arrangement of three structural genes controlled by a single promoter. The operon is transcribed into a polycistronic mRNA. The operator and CAP site are involved with gene regulation via the *lac* repressor and CAP, respectively. (Figure 12.6)

- The *lac* repressor binds to the operator site and prevents RNA polymerase from transcribing the operon. When allolactose binds to the repressor, this causes a conformational change that prevents the repressor from binding to the operator site. (Figure 12.7)

- By constructing a merozygote, Jacob, Monod, and Pardee determined that *lacI* encodes a diffusible protein that represses the *lac* operon. (Figure 12.8, 12.9)

- Positive control of the *lac* operon occurs when the catabolite activator protein (CAP) binds to the CAP site in the presence of cAMP This causes a bend in the DNA, which allows RNA polymerase to bind to the promoter. (Figure 12.10)

- Glucose inhibits cAMP production. This inhibits the expression of the *lac* operon because CAP cannot bind to the CAP site. This form of regulation provides bacteria with a more efficient use of their resources because the bacteria use one sugar at a time. (Figure 12.11)

- The *trp* operon is repressible. The presence of tryptophan causes the *trp* repressor to bind to the *trp* operator and stop transcription. This prevents the excessive buildup of tryptophan in the cell, which would be a waste of energy. (Figure 12.12)

12.3 Regulation of Transcription in Eukaryotes: Roles of Transcription Factors and Mediator

- Eukaryotic genes exhibit combinatorial control, meaning that many factors control the expression of a single gene.

- Eukaryotic promoters consist of a core promoter (containing a TATA box and transcriptional start site) and response elements, such as enhancers or silencers, that regulate the rate of transcription. (Figure 12.13)

- General transcription factors (GTFs) are needed for RNA polymerase II to bind to the core promoter. (Figure 12.14)
- Activators and repressors can regulate RNA polymerase II by interacting with GTFs, such as TFIID, or via mediator, a protein complex that wraps around RNA polymerase II. (Figures 12.15, 12.16)
- The double-stranded DNA helix has an irregular spiral and alternating major and minor grooves. The nitrogenous bases are stacked in the centre of the helix, but their edges extend into the grooves, where the functional groups can be recognized by transcription factors. (Figure 12.17)

12.4 Regulation of Transcription in Eukaryotes: Changes in Chromatin Structure and DNA Methylation

- ATP-dependent chromatin remodelling complexes change the positions and compositions of nucleosomes. (Figure 12.18)
- The pattern of covalent modification of the amino terminal tails of histone proteins, also called the histone code, can inhibit or promote transcription. (Figure 12.19)
- Eukaryotic genes are usually flanked by nucleosome-free regions. (Figure 12.20)
- For eukaryotic genes a pre-initiation complex forms at a nucleosome-free region. During elongation, nucleosomes are displaced ahead of RNA polymerase and re-form after RNA polymerase has passed. (Figure 12.21)
- DNA methylation, which occurs at CpG islands near promoters, usually inhibits transcription by (1) preventing the binding of activator proteins or (2) promoting the binding of proteins that inhibit transcription.

12.5 Regulation of RNA Processing and Translation in Eukaryotes

- In alternative splicing, a single type of pre-mRNA can be spliced in more than one way, producing polypeptides with somewhat different sequences. This is a common way for complex eukaryotes to increase the size of their proteomes. (Figure 12.22, Table 12.1)
- MicroRNAs (miRNAs) and short-interfering RNAs (siRNAs) inhibit mRNAs by inhibiting translation or by promoting the degradation of mRNAs, respectively. (Figure 12.23)
- RNA-binding proteins can regulate the translation of specific mRNAs. An example is the regulation of iron absorption, in which the iron regulatory protein (IRP) regulates the translation of ferritin mRNA. (Figure 12.24)

Test to Assess Your Learning

1. Genes that are expressed at all times at relatively constant levels are known as _____ genes.
   a. inducible
   b. repressible
   c. positive
   d. constitutive
   e. structural

2. Which of the following is *not* considered a level of gene regulation in prokaryotes?
   a. transcriptional
   b. RNA processing
   c. translational
   d. post-translational
   e. All the above are levels at which prokaryotes are able to regulate gene expression.

3. Transcription factors that bind to DNA and stimulate transcription are
   a. repressors.
   b. small effector molecules.
   c. activators.
   d. promoters.
   e. operators.

4. In prokaryotes the unit of DNA that contains multiple structural genes under the control of a single promoter is called _____. The mRNA produced from this unit is referred to as _____ mRNA.
   a. an operator, a polycistronic
   b. a template, a structural
   c. an operon, a polycistronic
   d. an operon, a monocistronic
   e. a template, a monocistronic

5. For the *lac* operon, what would be the expected effects of a mutation in the operator site that prevented the binding of the repressor protein?
   a. The operon would always be turned on.
   b. The operon would always be turned off.
   c. The operon would always be turned on, except when glucose is present.
   d. The operon would be turned on only in the presence of lactose.
   e. The operon would be turned on only in the presence of lactose and the absence of glucose.

6. The presence of _____ in the medium prevents the CAP from binding to the DNA, resulting in _____ in transcription of the *lac* operon.
   a. lactose, an increase
   b. glucose, an increase
   c. cAMP, a decrease
   d. glucose, a decrease
   e. lactose, a decrease

7. The *trp* operon is considered _____ operon because the structural genes necessary for tryptophan synthesis are not expressed when the levels of tryptophan in the cell are high.
   a. an inducible
   b. a positive
   c. a repressible
   d. a negative
   e. both (c) and (d)

8. Response elements that function to increase transcription levels in eukaryotes are called
   a. promoters.
   b. silencers.
   c. enhancers.
   d. transcriptional start sites.
   e. activators.

9. DNA methylation in many eukaryotic organisms seems to relate to
   a. increased translation levels.
   b. introns that will be removed.
   c. regions of DNA that do not contain structural genes.
   d. decreased transcription levels.
   e. response elements that are not necessary for transcription.

10. _____ refers to the phenomenon where a single type of pre-mRNA can give rise to multiple mRNAs because of different patterns of intron and exon removal.
    a. Spliceosomes
    b. Variable expression
    c. Alternative splicing
    d. Polycistronic mRNA
    e. Induced silencing

Articulate to Assess Your Learning

1. Explain the difference between inducible and repressible operons. Give an example of each.

2. Explain how transcription factors interact with specific DNA sequences.

3. Transcriptional regulation often involves a regulatory protein that binds to a segment of DNA and a small effector molecule that binds to the regulatory protein. Do the following terms apply to a regulatory protein, a segment of DNA, or a small effector molecule? (a) repressor, (b) inducer, (c) operator site, (d) corepressor, and (e) activator.

Collaborate to Assess and Extend Your Learning

1. Discuss the advantages and disadvantages of genetic regulation at the different levels described in Figure 12.4.

2. Discuss the advantages and disadvantages of combinatorial control of eukaryotic genes.

3. Why is mammalian DNA methylation typically found in the CG doublet as opposed to another type of sequence (e.g., CT)?

4. A principle of biology is that *the genetic material, DNA, provides a dynamic plan for sustaining life.* Explain how gene regulation is an important mechanism for sustaining life

Visit McGraw-Hill Ryerson Connect™ for additional study resources.

Mutation, DNA Repair, Cell Cycle Regulation, and Cancer

Chapter Outline

During the past two decades, more than 25% of the beluga whales in Canada's St. Lawrence Seaway have died of cancer.
Biologists speculate that these deaths are caused by cancer-causing pollutants, such as polycystic aromatic hydrocarbons (PAHs).

At a summer camp the children enjoy ice cream, horseback riding, hay rides, swimming, and learning about the habits of owls. Not such an unusual camp, you might be thinking. However, what makes Camp Sundown unique is that the outdoor fun begins at dusk and runs all night. The children at this camp have inherited a disorder called xeroderma pigmentosum (XP), which makes them highly sensitive to the sun. Their skin will blister or freckle on minimum sun exposure. Of great concern is skin cancer. People with XP may have a 1,000-fold greater risk of developing skin cancer, though such a risk is greatly decreased if sun exposure is minimized.

What explains the symptoms of xeroderma pigmentosum? XP individuals are highly susceptible to **mutation**, which is defined as a heritable change in the genetic material. When a mutation occurs, the order of nucleotide bases in a DNA molecule, its base sequence, is changed permanently, and this alteration can be passed from mother to daughter cells during cell division. Mutations that lead to cancer cause particular genes to be expressed in an abnormal way. For example, a mutation could affect the transcription of a gene, or it could alter the functional properties of the polypeptide specified by a gene.

Should we be afraid of mutations? Yes and no. On the positive side, mutations are essential to the continuity of life. They supply the variation that enables species to evolve and become better adapted to their environments. Mutations provide the foundation for evolutionary change. On the negative side, however, new mutations are more likely to be harmful than beneficial to the individual. The genes within modern species are the products of billions of years of evolution and have evolved to work properly. Random mutations are more likely to disrupt genes than to enhance their function. As you will see in this chapter, mutations can cause cancer. In addition many forms of inherited diseases, such as XP, cystic fibrosis, and sickle-cell anemia, are caused by gene mutations. For this and many other reasons understanding the molecular nature of mutations is a compelling area of research.

Because mutations can be quite harmful, all species have evolved several ways to repair damaged DNA. Such **DNA repair systems** reverse DNA damage before a permanent mutation can occur. DNA repair systems are vital to the survival of all organisms. If these systems did not exist, mutations would be so prevalent that few species, if any, would survive. People with XP have an impaired DNA repair system, which is the underlying cause of their disorder. DNA damage from sunlight is normally repaired. In people with XP, damaged DNA often remains unrepaired, which can lead to cancer. In this chapter we will examine how such DNA repair systems operate. But first, let's explore the molecular basis of mutation.

13.1 MUTATION

Learning Outcomes:

1. List the different ways that mutations can alter the amino acid sequence of a polypeptide.
2. Describe and interpret the replica plating experiments of the Lederbergs.
3. Distinguish between mutations in somatic cells and in germ-line cells.
4. Discuss the difference between spontaneous and induced mutations.
5. Describe the Ames test for determining if a substance is a mutagen.

How do mutations affect traits? To answer this question at the molecular level, we must understand how changes in DNA structure can ultimately affect DNA function. Most of our understanding of mutation has come from the study of experimental organisms, such as bacteria and *Drosophila*. Researchers can expose these organisms to environmental agents that cause mutations and then study the consequences of the mutations that arise. In addition, because these organisms have a short generation time, researchers can investigate the effects of mutations when they are passed from parent to offspring over many generations.

The structure and amount of genetic material can be altered in a variety of ways. For example, chromosome structure and number can change. These types of genetic changes will be considered in Chapter 14. In this section we will focus on **gene mutations**, which are relatively small changes in the sequence of DNA in a particular gene. We will be primarily concerned with the ways that mutations can affect the expression of single genes. We will also consider how the timing of new mutations during an organism's development has important consequences. Finally, we will explore how environmental agents may bring about mutations and examine a testing method that is used to determine whether an agent causes mutations.

Gene Mutations Alter the DNA Sequence of a Gene

Mutations can cause two basic types of changes to a gene: (1) the base sequence within a gene can be changed, and (2) one or more base pairs can be added to or removed from the gene. A **point mutation** affects only a single base pair within the DNA. For example, the DNA sequence shown here has been altered by a **base substitution** in which a T (in the top strand) has been replaced by a G:

5′—CCCGCTAGATA—3′   5′—CCCGCGAGATA—3′
        | | | | | | | | | | | | | | | | | | | | | |
3′—GGGCGATCTAT—5′   3′—GGGCGCTCTAT—5′

A point mutation can also involve the addition of a single base pair to or the deletion of a single base pair from a DNA sequence. For example, in the following sequence, a single base pair has been added to the DNA:

5′—GGCGCTAGATC—3′   5′—GGCAGCTAGATC—3′
        | | | | | | | | | | | | | | | | | | | | |
3′—CCGCGATCTAG—5′   3′—CCGTCGATCTAG—5′

Though point mutations may seem like small changes to a DNA sequence, they can have important consequences when genes are expressed, as you will see next.

Gene Mutations Can Affect the Amino Acid Sequence of a Polypeptide

If a mutation occurs within the region of a structural gene that specifies the amino acid sequence, it can alter that sequence in a variety of ways. **Table 13.1** considers the potential effects of point mutations. **Silent mutations** do not alter the amino acid sequence of the polypeptide, even though the nucleotide sequence has changed. Remember that the genetic code is a triplet code, with three contiguous nucleotides specifying each amino acid of a protein. Because the genetic code is degenerate, silent mutations can occur in the third base within most

Table 13.1	Consequences of Point Mutations Within the Coding Sequence of a Structural Gene

Mutation in the DNA	Effect on polypeptide	Example*
None	None	ATGGCCGGCCCGAAAGAGACC — Met Ala Gly Pro Lys Glu Thr
Base substitution	Silent: causes no change	ATGGCCGGCCCCAAAGAGACC — Met Ala Gly Pro Lys Glu Thr
Base substitution	Missense: changes one amino acid	ATGCCCGGCCCGAAAGAGACC — Met Pro Gly Pro Lys Glu Thr
Base substitution	Nonsense: changes to a stop codon	ATGGCCGGCCCGTAAGAGACC — Met Ala Gly Pro STOP
Addition (or deletion) of single base	Frameshift: produces a different amino acid sequence	ATGGCCGGCACCGAAAGAGACC — Met Ala Gly Thr Glu Arg Asp

*DNA sequence in the coding strand. This sequence is the same as the mRNA sequence, except that RNA contains uracil (U) instead of thymine (T).

codons without changing the type of amino acid it encodes. Silent mutations are also considered **neutral mutations** because they do not affect the function of the encoded protein.

A **missense mutation** is a base substitution that changes a single amino acid in a polypeptide sequence. A missense mutation may not alter protein function because it changes only a single amino acid within a polypeptide that is typically hundreds of amino acids long. When a missense mutation has no detectable effect on protein function, it is also referred to as a neutral mutation. A missense mutation that substitutes an amino acid whose chemical properties are similar to the original amino acid is likely to be neutral (refer back to Figure 3.14 for a comparison of the chemical properties of the 20 amino acids). For example, a missense mutation in which a glutamic acid is replaced by an aspartic acid may not alter protein function because both amino acids are negatively charged and have similar side chain structures.

Alternatively, some missense mutations have a dramatic effect on protein function. A striking example of such a missense mutation occurs in the human disease known as **sickle-cell anemia**. This disease involves a mutation in the β-globin gene, which encodes one of the polypeptide subunits that make up hemoglobin, the oxygen-carrying protein in red blood cells. Because less oxygen is carried to tissues, patients often experience pain and muscle fatigue, and the long-term depletion of oxygen can cause deterioration of some tissues (e.g., retinal damage that can result in blindness). In the most common form of this disease, a missense mutation alters the polypeptide sequence so that the sixth amino acid is changed from a glutamic acid to a valine. Because glutamic acid is hydrophilic but valine is hydrophobic, this single amino acid substitution alters the structure and function of the hemoglobin protein. The mutant hemoglobin subunits tend to stick to one another when the oxygen concentration is low. The aggregated proteins form fibrelike structures within red blood cells, which causes the cells to lose their normal morphology and become sickle shaped (**Figure 13.1**). It's rather amazing that a single amino acid substitution could have such a profound effect on the structure and function of cells.

Two other types of point mutations cause more dramatic changes to a polypeptide sequence. A **nonsense mutation** involves a change from a normal codon to a stop or termination codon. This causes translation to be terminated earlier than expected, producing a truncated polypeptide (see Table 13.1). Compared with a normal polypeptide, a shorter polypeptide is much less likely to function properly. Finally, a **frameshift mutation** involves the addition or deletion of nucleotides that are not multiples of three nucleotides. Because the codons are read in multiples of three, this shifts the reading frame so that a completely different amino acid sequence occurs downstream from the mutation (see Table 13.1). Such a large change in polypeptide structure is also likely to inhibit protein function.

Except for silent mutations, new mutations are more likely to produce polypeptides that have reduced rather than enhanced function. However, mutations can occasionally produce a polypeptide that has an enhanced function. Although these favourable mutations are relatively rare, they can result in an organism with a greater likelihood of surviving and reproducing. The favourable effect of a mutation can cause it to increase in frequency in a population over many generations. This topic is discussed in Chapter 22.

Gene Mutations Can Occur Outside of Coding Sequences and Influence Gene Expression

Thus far we have focused on mutations in the coding regions of structural genes. In Chapters 11 and 12 we learned how other DNA sequences play important roles during gene expression. A mutation can occur within noncoding sequences and affect gene expression (**Table 13.2**). For example, a mutation can alter the sequence within the promoter of a gene and thereby affect the rate of transcription. A mutation that improves the ability of transcriptional activators to bind to the DNA may enhance transcription, whereas other mutations may block their binding and thereby inhibit transcription.

Mutations in transcriptional response elements or operator sites can alter the regulation of gene transcription. For example,

Figure 13.1 A missense mutation causes red blood cells to sickle in sickle-cell anemia. Scanning electron micrographs of (a) normal red blood cells and (b) sickled red blood cells. As shown above the micrographs, a missense mutation in the β-globin gene (which codes for a subunit of hemoglobin) changes the sixth amino acid in the β-globin polypeptide from a glutamic acid to a valine. (c) This micrograph shows how this alteration to the structure of β-globin causes the formation of abnormal fibrelike structures. In normal cells, hemoglobin proteins do not form fibres.

Concept check: *Based on the fibrelike structures seen in part (c), what aspect of hemoglobin structure does a glutamic acid at the sixth position in β-globin prevent? Speculate on how the charge of this amino acid may play a role.*

 Principle: *Structure determines function. A single amino acid change in hemoglobin severely compromises the structure and function of hemoglobin as an oxygen carrier.*

Table 13.2	Effects of Mutations in Gene Regulatory Elements
Sequence	**Effect of mutation**
Promoter	May increase or decrease the rate of transcription
Transcriptional response element/ operator site	May alter the regulation of transcription
Splice junctions	May alter the ability of pre-mRNA to be properly spliced
Translational response element	May alter the ability of mRNA to be translationally regulated

in Chapter 11, we considered the roles of regulatory sequences, such as the *lac* operator site in *E. coli*, which is recognized by the *lac* repressor protein (refer back to Figure 11.7). Mutations in the *lac* operator site can disrupt the proper regulation of the *lac* operon. An operator mutation can change the DNA sequence so that the *lac* repressor protein does not bind to it. This mutation would cause the operon to be constitutively expressed even in the absence of lactose.

Mutations can also occur in other noncoding regions of a gene and alter gene expression in a way that may affect the encoded polypeptide sequence or its expression. For example, in Chapter 11 we discussed the splicing of RNA during RNA processing in eukaryotes (refer back to Figure 11.10). Mutations can occur at the boundaries between introns and exons and prevent proper splicing. When this occurs, the mRNA may not contain the correct order and number of exons. In Chapter 12 we also discussed response elements that are recognized by proteins that control translation. For example, the iron regulatory protein recognizes response elements within the mRNA that encodes ferritin (refer back to Figure 12.24). A mutation that alters this response element can prevent the proper translational regulation of ferritin.

FEATURE INVESTIGATION

The Lederbergs Used Replica Plating to Show That Mutations Are Random Events

Thus far we have considered how mutations can affect the expression of genes. Let's now ask, How do mutations occur? This question has an interesting history. For hundreds of years biologists wondered whether mutations that affect the traits of an individual occur as a result of existing circumstances or whether they are unplanned events that happen randomly in any gene of any individual. In the nineteenth century French naturalist Jean Baptiste Lamarck proposed that physiological events (for example, use and disuse) determine whether traits are passed along to offspring. For example, his hypothesis suggested that an individual who practised and became adept at a physical activity, such as the long jump, would pass that quality on to his or her offspring. Geneticists in the early twentieth century suggested that genetic variation occurs as a matter of chance and that natural selection results in the differential reproductive success of organisms that are better adapted to their environments. According to this view individuals whose genes happen to contain beneficial mutations are more likely to survive and to pass those genes to their offspring.

These opposing views were tested in bacterial studies in the 1940s and 1950s. One such study, by Joshua and Esther Lederberg, focused on the occurrence of mutations in bacteria (**Figure 13.2**). First, the researchers placed a large number of *E. coli* bacteria onto a plate of growth medium that was incubated overnight so that each bacterial cell divided many times to form a bacterial colony of millions of cells. This was called the master plate. Using a technique known as **replica plating**, the researchers used a sterile piece of velvet cloth to lightly touch the plate and pick up a few bacterial cells from each colony. They then transferred this replica to two secondary plates that contained an agent that selected for the growth of bacterial cells with a particular mutation.

In the example shown in Figure 13.2, the secondary plates contained T1 bacteriophages, or phages, which are viruses that infect bacteria and cause them to burst or lyse. On these plates only those rare cells that had acquired a mutation conferring resistance to T1 infection, termed *ton^r*, could grow. All other cells were lysed by the proliferation of phages in the bacterial cytoplasm. Therefore, only a few colonies were observed on the secondary plates. Strikingly, these colonies occupied the same locations on each plate. How did the Lederbergs interpret these results? The data indicated that the *ton^r* mutations occurred randomly while the bacterial cells were forming colonies on the nonselective master plate. The presence of T1 bacteriophages in the secondary plates did not cause the mutatons. Rather the T1 bacteriophages simply selected for the growth of *ton^r* mutants that were already in the population. These results supported the idea that mutations are random events.

Experimental Questions

1. Explain the difference between the opposing views of mutation before the Lederbergs' study.
2. What hypothesis were the Lederbergs testing? What were the results of the experiment?
3. How did the Lederbergs' results support or refute the hypothesis?

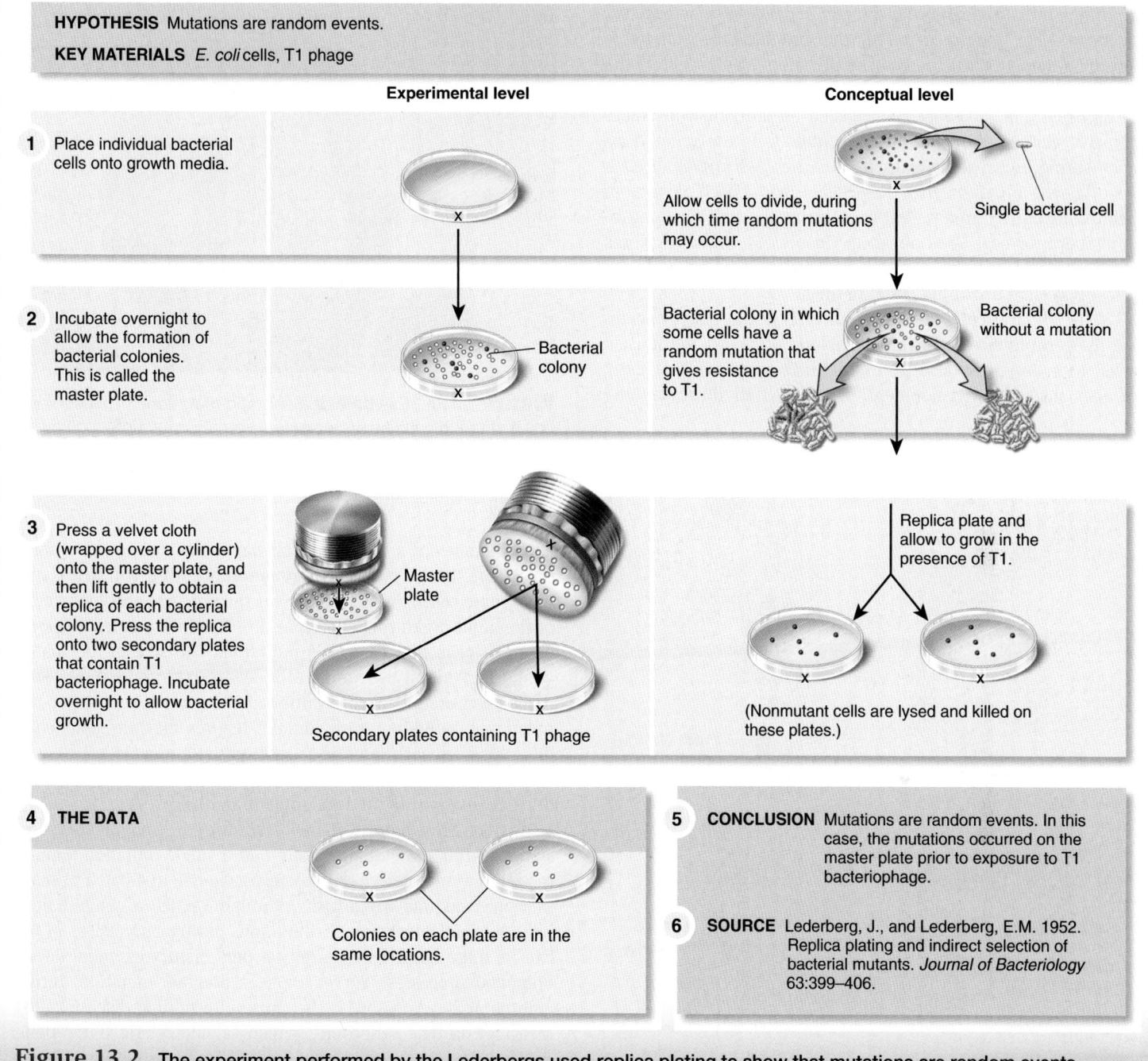

HYPOTHESIS Mutations are random events.

KEY MATERIALS *E. coli* cells, T1 phage

Experimental level | Conceptual level

1 Place individual bacterial cells onto growth media.

Allow cells to divide, during which time random mutations may occur.

Single bacterial cell

2 Incubate overnight to allow the formation of bacterial colonies. This is called the master plate.

Bacterial colony

Bacterial colony in which some cells have a random mutation that gives resistance to T1.

Bacterial colony without a mutation

3 Press a velvet cloth (wrapped over a cylinder) onto the master plate, and then lift gently to obtain a replica of each bacterial colony. Press the replica onto two secondary plates that contain T1 bacteriophage. Incubate overnight to allow bacterial growth.

Master plate

Secondary plates containing T1 phage

Replica plate and allow to grow in the presence of T1.

(Nonmutant cells are lysed and killed on these plates.)

4 **THE DATA**

Colonies on each plate are in the same locations.

5 **CONCLUSION** Mutations are random events. In this case, the mutations occurred on the master plate prior to exposure to T1 bacteriophage.

6 **SOURCE** Lederberg, J., and Lederberg, E.M. 1952. Replica plating and indirect selection of bacterial mutants. *Journal of Bacteriology* 63:399–406.

Figure 13.2 The experiment performed by the Lederbergs used replica plating to show that mutations are random events.

Mutations Can Occur in Germ-Line or Somatic Cells

Let's now consider how the timing of a mutation can have an important impact on its potential effects. Multicellular organisms begin their lives as a single fertilized egg cell, and through cell division they produce the many cells of the adult organism. For example, humans begin as a single fertilized egg and become an adult with approximately 10 trillion to 50 trillion cells. When a mutation occurs in a single gene, however, the mutation may or may not be found in all the cells A mutation can occur in any cell of the body, either very early in life, such as in a gamete (eggs or sperm) or a fertilized egg, or later in life, such as in the embryonic or adult stages. The exact time and location of a mutation is critical both to the severity of the genetic effect and to whether the mutation can be passed on to offspring.

Geneticists classify the cells of animals into two types: germ-line and somatic cells. The term **germ line** refers to cells that give rise to gametes, such as egg and sperm cells. A germ-line mutation can occur directly in a sperm or an egg cell, or it can occur in a precursor cell that produces the gametes. If a mutant gamete participates in fertilization, all the cells of the resulting offspring will contain the mutation, as indicated in red in **Figure 13.3a**. Likewise, when such an individual produces gametes, the mutation can be transmitted to future generations of offspring. Because an individual carries two copies of each gene, a new mutation in a single gene has a 50% chance of being transmitted from parent to offspring through the contributed sperm or egg. Look ahead to Chapter 14, which explores the process of meiosis and the fundamentals of **heredity**, to fully appreciate how traits are inherited.

The **somatic cells** constitute all cells of the body, excluding the germ-line cells. Examples include skin cells and muscle cells. Mutations can also occur within somatic cells at early or late stages of development. **Figure 13.3b** illustrates the

Figure 13.4   **Example of a somatic mutation.**   This person has a streak of white hair because a somatic mutation occurred in a single cell during embryonic development that prevented pigmentation of the hair. This cell continued to divide to produce a streak of white hair.

consequences of a mutation that happened during the embryonic stage. In this example a mutation occurred within a single embryonic cell. This single cell was the precursor for many cells of the adult organism. Therefore, in the adult, a patch of tissue contains cells that carry the mutation. The size of any patch would depend on the timing of a new mutation. In general the earlier a mutation occurs during development, the larger the patch. An individual with somatic regions that are genetically different from each other is called a **genetic mosaic**.

Figure 13.4 shows a person who had a somatic mutation during an early stage of development. In this case, the person has a streak of white hair while the rest of the hair is pigmented. Presumably, this individual initially had a single mutation happen in an embryonic cell that ultimately gave rise to a patch of scalp that produced the white hair. Although a patch of white hair is not a harmful consequence, mutations during early stages of life can be quite harmful, especially if they disrupt essential developmental processes. For example, a somatic mutation during embryonic development is the cause of a human disease called McCune-Albright syndrome, which is characterized by bone defects, hormonal imbalances, and skin abnormalities. Therefore, even though it is sensible to avoid environmental agents that cause mutations during all stages of life, the possibility of somatic mutations is a rather compelling reason to avoid such agents during the early stages of life, such as during embryonic and fetal development, infancy, and early childhood. In part this is the logic behind public health education initiatives for expectant mothers, who are urged to carefully monitor their diet and environment and to avoid things such as alcohol and smoking.

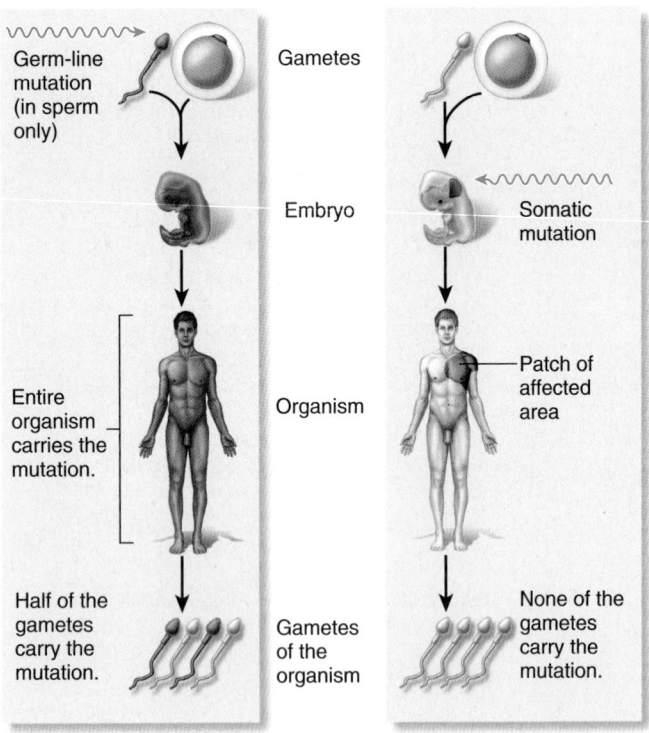

(a) Germ-line mutation   (b) Somatic cell mutation

Figure 13.3   **The effects of germ-line versus somatic cell mutations.**   Red indicates which cells carry the mutation. **(a)** If a mutation is passed via gametes, such germ-line mutations occur in every cell of the body. Because humans have two copies of most genes, a germ-line mutation in one of those two copies will be transmitted to only half the gametes. **(b)** Somatic mutations affect a limited area of the body and are not transmitted to offspring.

Principle: *Living organisms grow, develop, and reproduce.* As a multicellular organism grows and develops, a germ-line mutation will exist in all cells of the body, whereas a somatic mutation will be found only in a particular region.

Concept check: *Why are somatic mutations not transmitted to offspring?*

Mutations Can Be Spontaneous or Induced

Biologists categorize the causes of mutation as being either spontaneous or induced. **Spontaneous mutations** result from abnormalities in biological processes (**Table 13.3**). Spontaneous

Table 13.3	Some Common Causes of Gene Mutations
Common causes of mutations	**Description**
Spontaneous	
Errors in DNA replication	A mistake by DNA polymerase can cause a point mutation.
Toxic metabolic products	The products of normal metabolic processes may be reactive chemicals, such as free radicals, that can alter the structure of DNA.
Spontaneous changes in nucleotide structure	On rare occasions, the linkage between purines and deoxyribose can spontaneously break. Changes in base structure (isomerization) can cause mispairing during DNA replication.
Transposons	As discussed in Chapter 19, transposons are small segments of DNA that can insert at various sites in the genome. If they insert into a gene, they can inactivate the gene.
Induced	
Chemical agents	Chemical substances, such as benzo (a)pyrene, a chemical found in cigarette smoke, can cause changes in the structure of DNA.
Physical agents	Physical agents, such as UV (ultraviolet) light and X-rays, can damage the DNA.

Table 13.4	Examples of Mutagens
Mutagen	**Effect(s) on DNA structure**
Chemical	
Nitrous acid	Deaminates bases
5-Bromouracil	Acts as a base analogue
2-Aminopurine	Acts as a base analogue
Nitrogen mustard	Alkylates bases
Ethyl methanesulphonate	Alkylates bases
Proflavin	Inserts next to bases in the DNA double helix and causes additions or deletions
Physical	
X-rays	Causes base deletions, single nicks in DNA strands, cross-linking, and chromosomal breaks
UV light	Promotes pyrimidine dimer formation, which involves covalent bonds between adjacent pyrimidines (C or T)

mutations occur because biology isn't perfect. Enzymes, for example, can function abnormally. In Chapter 10 you learned that DNA polymerase can make a mistake during DNA replication by putting the wrong base in a newly synthesized daughter strand. Though such errors are rare, they do occur at a low rate. In addition normal metabolic processes within the cell produce many chemicals that may react with the functional groups of the nitrogenous bases of DNA to alter the structure of the DNA double helix. Finally, the structure of nucleotides is not absolutely stable. On occasion spontaneous isomerizations occur, and such a change can cause a mutation if it occurs immediately before DNA replication. (Structural isomers are discussed in Chapter 3.)

The rates of mutations vary from species to species and from gene to gene. Larger genes are usually more likely to incur a mutation than are smaller genes. A common rate of spontaneous mutation is approximately one mutation for every 1 million genes per cell division. As the human genome contains approximately 25,000 genes, many replication cycles could occur before a mutation arises, but replication errors are not the only source of mutations.

Induced mutations are caused by environmental agents that enter the cell and then alter the structure of DNA. They cause the mutation rate to be higher than the spontaneous mutation rate. Chemical substances and physical agents that are known to cause mutation and lead to changes in DNA structure are called **mutagens** (Table 13.4). We will consider their effects in the next section.

Mutagens Alter DNA Structure in Different Ways

Researchers have discovered that an enormous array of agents can act as mutagens to permanently alter the structure of DNA. We often hear in the news media that we should avoid these agents in our foods and living environments. We even use products, such as sunscreens, to help us avoid the mutagenic effects of these agents, such as ultraviolet (UV) light from the sun. The public is concerned about mutagens for two important reasons. First, mutagenic agents are often involved in the development of human cancers. Second, because new mutations can be harmful, people want to prevent gene mutations that may have damaging effects on their future offspring.

How do mutagens affect DNA structure? Some chemical mutagens act by covalently modifying the structure of nucleotides. For example, nitrous acid (HNO_2) deaminates bases by replacing amino groups with keto groups ($-NH_2$ to $=O$). This can change cytosine to uracil. When this altered DNA replicates, the modified base does not pair with the appropriate base in the newly made strand. Instead, uracil pairs with adenine (**Figure 13.5**).

Similarly, 5-bromouracil and 2-aminopurine, which are called base analogues, have structures that are similar to particular bases in DNA and can substitute for them. When incorporated into DNA, they also cause errors in DNA replication. Other chemical mutagens can disrupt the appropriate pairing between nucleotides by alkylating bases within the DNA. During alkylation, methyl or ethyl groups are covalently attached to the bases. Examples of alkylating agents include nitrogen mustards (used as a chemical weapon during World War I) and ethyl methanesulfonate (EMS), which is a commonly used mutagen in laboratory experiments.

Some chemical mutagens exert their effects by interfering with DNA replication. For example, benzo(a)pyrene, which is found in automobile exhaust, cigarette smoke, and charbroiled

Template strand | After replication

Figure 13.5 Deamination and mispairing of modified bases by a chemical mutagen. Nitrous acid changes cytosine to uracil by replacing NH_2 with an oxygen. During DNA replication, uracil will pair with adenine and thereby creates a mutation in the newly replicated strand.

food, is metabolized to a compound (benzopyrene diol epoxide) that inserts between the bases of the double helix, thereby distorting the helical structure. When DNA is replicated in the presence of such a mutagen, single nucleotide additions and deletions can occur in the newly made strands.

DNA molecules are also sensitive to physical agents, such as radiation. In particular, radiation of short wavelength and high energy, called ionizing radiation, is known to alter DNA structure. Ionizing radiation includes X-rays and gamma rays. This type of radiation can penetrate deeply into biological materials, where it creates free radicals. These molecules can alter the structure of DNA in a variety of ways. Exposure to high doses of ionizing radiation can cause base deletions, breaks in one DNA strand, or even a break in both DNA strands.

Nonionizing radiation, such as UV light, contains less energy and penetrates only the surface of biological materials, such as the skin. Nevertheless, UV light is known to cause DNA mutations. For example, UV light can cause the formation of a **thymine dimer**, one type of pyrimidine dimer, which is a site at which two adjacent thymine bases become covalently cross-linked (**Figure 13.6**). A thymine dimer within a DNA strand may cause a mutation when that DNA strand is replicated. When DNA polymerase attempts to replicate over a thymine dimer, proper base pairing does not occur between the template strand and the incoming nucleotides. This mispairing can cause gaps in the newly made strand or the incorporation of incorrect bases. Plants, in particular, must have effective ways to prevent UV damage because they are exposed to sunlight throughout the day.

Testing Methods Can Determine Whether an Agent Is a Mutagen

Researchers have developed testing methods that can ascertain whether or not an agent is a mutagen. One commonly used

Figure 13.6 Formation and structure of a thymine dimer. Sunlight contains harmful UV radiation that can damage DNA and lead to skin cancer.

test is the **Ames test**, which was developed by Bruce Ames in the 1970s. This test uses a strain of a bacterium, *Salmonella typhimurium*, that cannot synthesize the amino acid histidine. This strain contains a point mutation within a gene that encodes an enzyme required for histidine biosynthesis. The mutation renders the enzyme inactive. The bacteria cannot grow unless histidine has been added to the growth medium. However, a second mutation can correct the first mutation (a process called *reversion*), restoring the ability to synthesize

1 Mix together the *Salmonella typhimurium* strain, rat liver extract, and suspected mutagen and incubate. The suspected mutagen is omitted from the control sample. The rat liver extract is added because liver enzymes sometimes convert chemicals into mutagens.

Control

Rat liver extract

Rat liver extract

Suspected mutagen

S. typhimurium strain (requires histidine)

S. typhimurium strain (requires histidine)

2 Plate the mixtures onto petri plates that lack histidine. Incubate overnight to allow bacterial growth.

A large number of colonies suggests that the suspected mutagen causes mutation.

Figure 13.7 **The Ames test for mutagenicity.** In this example 2 million bacterial cells were placed on each plate. Two colonies were observed from the control sample while 44 were observed from the sample exposed to a suspected mutagen.

Concept check: *Based on the results shown in this figure, what is the rate of mutation caused by the suspected mutagen?*

histidine and enabling the revertant to grow on a medium that lacks histidine. The Ames test monitors the rate at which this second mutation occurs and thereby indicates whether the chemical agent increases the mutation rate above the spontaneous rate.

Figure 13.7 outlines the steps in the Ames test. The suspected mutagen is mixed with a rat liver extract and the bacterial strain of *S. typhimurium,* which cannot synthesize histidine. Why would a rat liver extract be used? Such an extract contains many enzymes involved in various metabolic pathways. Ames knew that some chemicals themselves are not mutagenic but are converted by mammalian enzymes into potent mutagens. Thus, this step improves the ability to identify agents that can cause mutation in mammals. As a control, bacteria that have not been exposed to the mutagen are also tested. After an incubation period in which mutations may occur, a large number of bacteria are plated on a growth medium that does not contain histidine. The *Salmonella* strain is not expected to grow on these plates. However, if a mutation has occurred that allows a cell to synthesize histidine, these revertants will multiply during an overnight incubation period to form a visible bacterial colony.

To estimate the mutation rate researchers count and compare the colonies that grow in the absence of histidine with the total number of bacterial cells that were originally placed on

the plate for both the test and the control. The control condition is a measure of the spontaneous mutation rate, while the test condition monitors the rate of mutation in the presence of the suspected mutagen. As an example let's suppose that 2 million bacteria were placed in both the control and the suspected mutagen tubes. In the control experiment, two bacterial colonies were observed. The spontaneous mutation rate is calculated by dividing 2 (the number of mutants) by 2 million (the number of original cells). This equals 1 in 1 million, or 1×10^{-6}. By comparison 44 colonies were observed in the test condition (Figure 13.7). In this case the mutation rate is 44 divided by 2 million, which equals 2.2×10^{-5}. The mutation rate in the presence of the mutagen is more than 20 times the spontaneous mutation rate.

How do we determine if an agent is a mutagen? Researchers compare the mutation rate in the presence and absence of the suspected mutagen. The Ames test is conducted several times. If the statistics reveal that the mutation rate in the suspected-mutagen sample is significantly higher than in the control sample, the researchers may tentatively conclude that the agent is a mutagen. Interestingly, many studies have used the Ames test to compare the urine from cigarette smokers with that from nonsmokers. This research has shown that urine from smokers contains much higher levels of mutagens.

13.2 / DNA REPAIR

Learning Outcomes:

1. List the general features of DNA repair systems.
2. Describe the steps of nucleotide excision repair.
3. Explain the connection between defects in DNA repair systems and the inherited human disease xeroderma pigmentosum.

In the previous section we considered the causes and consequences of mutation. As you have seen, mutations are random events that often have negative consequences. To minimize mutation, all living organisms have evolved the ability to repair changes that occur in the structure of DNA. Such DNA repair systems have been studied extensively in many organisms, particularly *E. coli*, yeast, and mammals. In this section we will examine DNA repair systems that can detect abnormalities in DNA structure and repair them. The importance of these systems becomes evident when they are missing. For example, as discussed at the beginning of this chapter, people with xeroderma pigmentosum are highly susceptible to the harmful effects of sunlight because they are missing a single DNA repair system.

How do organisms minimize the occurrence of mutations? Cells contain several DNA repair systems that can fix different types of DNA alterations (**Table 13.5**). Each repair system is composed of one or more proteins that play specific roles in the repair mechanism. DNA repair requires two coordinated events. In the first step, one or more proteins in the repair system detect an irregularity in DNA structure. In the second step the abnormality is repaired. In some cases the change in DNA structure can be directly repaired. For example, sometimes DNA is modified by the attachment of an alkyl group, such as $-CH_2CH_3$, to a base. In **direct repair**, an enzyme removes this alkyl group,

Table 13.5	Common Types of DNA Repair Systems*
System	**Description**
Direct repair	A repair enzyme recognizes an incorrect structure in the DNA and directly converts it back to a correct structure.
Base excision and nucleotide excision repair	An abnormal base or nucleotide is recognized and a portion of the strand containing the abnormality is removed. The complementary DNA strand is then used as a template to synthesize a normal DNA strand.
Methyl-directed mismatch repair	This is similar to excision repair except that the DNA defect is a base pair mismatch in the DNA, not an abnormal nucleotide. The mismatch is recognized, and a strand of DNA in this region is removed. The complementary strand is used to synthesize a normal strand of DNA.

*Other types of repair systems exist; these are common examples.

thereby restoring the structure of the original base. More commonly, however, the altered DNA is removed and a new segment of DNA is synthesized. In this section we will examine nucleotide excision repair as an example of how such systems operate. This system, which is found in all species, is an important mechanism of DNA repair.

Nucleotide Excision Repair Systems Remove Segments of Damaged DNA

In **nucleotide excision repair (NER)** a region encompassing several nucleotides in the damaged strand is removed from the DNA, and the intact undamaged strand is used as a template for the resynthesis of a normal complementary strand. NER can fix many different types of DNA damage, including UV-induced damage, chemically modified bases, missing bases, and various types of cross-links (such as thymine dimers). The system is found in all species, although its molecular mechanism is better understood in bacteria.

In *E. coli* the NER system is composed of four key proteins: UvrA, UvrB, UvrC, and UvrD. They are named Uvr because they are involved in ultraviolet light repair of pyrimidine dimers, although these proteins are also important in repairing chemically damaged DNA. DNA polymerase and DNA ligase are also required to complete the repair process.

How does the NER system work? Two UvrA proteins and one UvrB protein form a complex that tracks along the DNA (**Figure 13.8**). Damaged DNA has a distorted double helix, which the UvrA-UvrB complex can sense. When it identifies a damaged segment, the two UvrA proteins are released and UvrC binds to UvrB at the site. The UvrC protein makes incisions in one DNA strand on both sides of the damaged site. After this incision process, UvrC is released. UvrD binds to UvrB. UvrD then begins to separate the DNA strands, and UvrB is released. The action of UvrD unwinds the DNA, which removes a short DNA strand that contains the damaged region. UvrD is released. After the damaged DNA strand is removed, a gap is left in the double helix. DNA polymerase fills in the gap by using the undamaged strand as a template. Finally, DNA ligase makes the last covalent connection between the newly made DNA and the original DNA strand.

Human Genetic Diseases Occur When a Component of the NER System Is Missing

Thus far we have considered the NER system in *E. coli*. In humans NER systems were discovered by the analysis of genetic diseases that affect DNA repair. These include xeroderma pigmentosum (XP), Cockayne's syndrome (CS), and PIBIDS. (PIBIDS is an acronym for a syndrome with symptoms that include photosensitivity [increased sensitivity to sunlight], ichthyosis [a skin disorder], brittle hair, intellectual impairment, decreased fertility, and short stature.) Photosensitivity is a common characteristic in all three syndromes because of an inability to repair UV-induced lesions. Therefore, people with these syndromes must avoid prolonged exposure to sunlight, and mitosis. However, we now know that these are critical stages of the cell cycle. In actively dividing cells the G_1, S, and G_2 phases are collectively known as **interphase**. Alternatively, cells may exit the cell cycle and remain for long periods in a stage called G_0. The G_0 stage is a substitute for G_1. A cell in the G_0 phase has postponed making a decision about whether to divide or, in the case of terminally differentiated cells (such as nerve cells in an adult animal), has made a decision to never divide again.

The length of the cell cycle varies considerably among different cells types, ranging from several minutes in quickly growing embryos to several months in slow-growing adult cells. For fast-dividing mammalian cells in adults, the length of the cycle is typically about 24 hours. The various stages within the cell cycle also vary in length. G_1 is often the longest and also the most variable phase, while M phase is the shortest. For a cell that divides in 24 hours, the following lengths for each phase are typical:

- G_1 phase: 11 hours
- S phase: 8 hours
- G_2 phase: 4 hours
- M phase: 1 hour

During the G_1 phase the cell makes a decision regarding its progression into the S phase. Depending on the environmental conditions and the presence of signalling molecules, a cell in the G_1 phase may satisfy certain biochemical criteria that position it at a special control point called the **restriction point**. Once past the restriction point, a cell is committed to advancing to the S phase, during which the chromosomes are replicated. After replication, the two duplicated chromosomes are still joined and are referred to as a pair of **sister chromatids**. When the S phase is completed, a cell actually has twice as many chromatids as the number of chromosomes in the G_1 phase. For example, a human cell in the G_1 phase has 46 distinct chromosomes (two pairs of 23 chromosomes), but after having replicated the DNA in the S phase, the same cell in G_2 has 46 pairs of chromosomes, for a total of 92 chromatids.

During the G_2 phase a cell synthesizes proteins that are necessary for chromosome sorting and cell division. It then progresses into the M phase of the cell cycle, when **mitosis** occurs. The primary purpose of mitosis is to divide one cell nucleus into two nuclei, distributing the duplicated chromosomes so that each daughter cell will receive the same complement of chromosomes. For example, a human cell in the G_2 phase has 92 chromatids, which are found in 46 pairs. During mitosis, these pairs of chromatids are separated and sorted so that each daughter cell will receive a complete genetic complement of 46 chromosomes (23 pairs). Mitosis is the name given to this sorting process. In most cases, mitosis is followed by **cytokinesis**, which is the division of the cytoplasm to produce two distinct daughter cells. The decision to divide is based on external factors, such as environmental conditions and signalling molecules, and internal controls, including cell cycle control molecules and checkpoints, as we will discuss next.

Environmental Conditions and Signalling Molecules Affect the Decision to Divide

In unicellular organisms the decision to divide is based largely on environmental conditions. For example, if yeast cells are supplied with a sufficient amount of nutrients and are exposed to the correct temperature and pH, they are likely to divide. In multicellular organisms, such as plants and animals, the decision to divide is more complex. Although nutrient availability, temperature, and pH are important to the cells in a multicellular organism, other factors also influence the process of cell division. As development proceeds in a multicellular organism, genetic factors come into play. In mammals, for example, most nerve cells in the adult have lost the capacity to divide because of a genetic program that begins during embryonic development. This is one reason that it is difficult to recover from certain injuries to the nervous system, such as those that affect the spinal cord.

Multicellular organisms rely on signalling molecules to coordinate cell division throughout the body. In plants hormones play a key role in promoting cell division. For example, small molecules called **cytokinins**—so named because their presence causes cytokinesis—promote cell division in plants. These compounds have a structure that is similar to adenine. Cytokinins are secreted at the growing tips of plants. In animals **growth factor**, a type of protein that stimulates certain cells to grow and divide, is secreted into the bloodstream. As described in Chapter 9, growth factors bind to transmembrane receptors on the target cells, initiating one or more signal transduction pathways. Often, certain transcription factors are produced or activated that then lead to the expression of genes that promote cell cycle progression.

As we will discuss in the next section, growth factor signalling pathways are often involved in cancer. Mutations that cause proteins in these pathways to become hyperactive result in cells that divide uncontrollably. These genes encode proteins that are necessary for a cell to divide, including proteins called cyclins, whose function is described next.

The Cell Cycle Is Controlled by Checkpoint Proteins

The progression through the cell cycle is a highly regulated process that ensures that the nuclear genome is intact and that the conditions are appropriate for a cell to divide. Proteins called **cyclins** and **cyclin-dependent kinases (cdks)** are responsible for advancing a cell through the phases of the cell cycle. Cyclins are so named because their levels oscillate with the cell cycle. To be active, the kinases controlling the cell cycle must bind to (are dependent on) a cyclin. The number of cyclins and cdks varies from species to species.

Figure 13.11 gives a simplified description of how cyclins and cdks work together to advance a cell through G_1 and mitosis. During G_1 the amount of a particular cyclin called G_1 cyclin increases. The G_1 cyclin binds to cdk to form an activated G_1 cyclin/cdk complex. This complex phosphorylates proteins that are needed to advance the cell to the next stage in the cell cycle. For example, certain proteins involved with DNA synthesis are

G₁ checkpoint (restriction point): Determines if conditions are favourable for cell division and if the DNA is damaged. G₁ cyclin is made in response to sufficient nutrients and growth factors.

G₁ cyclin is degraded after cell enters S phase.

Mitotic cyclin

Activated G₁ cyclin/cdk complex

G₁ cyclin

G₂ checkpoint: Checks for DNA damage, determines if all the DNA is replicated, and monitors the levels of proteins needed for M phase.

Activated mitotic cyclin/cdk complex

Metaphase checkpoint: Determines if all chromosomes are attached to the spindle apparatus.

Mitotic cyclin is degraded as cell progresses through mitosis.

Figure 13.11   Checkpoints in the cell cycle.   This is a general diagram of the eukaryotic cell cycle. Progression through the cell cycle requires the formation of activated cyclin/cdk complexes. There are different types of cyclin proteins, which are typically degraded after the cell has progressed to the next phase. The formation of activated cyclin/cdk complexes is regulated by checkpoint proteins.

phosphorylated and activated, thereby allowing the cell to carry on events in the S phase. When the cell passes into the S phase, G₁ cyclin is degraded. Similar events advance the cell through other stages of the cell cycle. A different cyclin, called mitotic cyclin, accumulates late in G₂. It binds to cdk to form an activated mitotic cyclin/cdk complex. This complex phosphorylates proteins that are needed to advance into the M phase.

Three critical regulatory points called **checkpoints** are found in the cell cycle of eukaryotic cells (Figure 13.11). At these checkpoints a variety of proteins, referred to as **checkpoint proteins**, act as sensors to determine whether a cell is in the proper condition to divide. The G₁ checkpoint, which is the restriction point, determines whether conditions are favourable for cell division. G₁ checkpoint proteins can also sense whether the DNA has incurred damage. If it has, these checkpoint proteins will prevent the formation of active cyclin/cdk complexes and thereby stop the progression of the cell cycle. A second checkpoint exists in G₂. This checkpoint also checks the DNA for damage and ensures that all the DNA has been replicated. The G₂ checkpoint also monitors the levels of proteins that are needed

to progress through the M phase. A third checkpoint, called the metaphase checkpoint, senses the integrity of the spindle apparatus. As you will see in Chapter 14, the spindle apparatus is involved in chromosome sorting. Metaphase is a step in mitosis during which all the chromosomes should be attached to the spindle apparatus. If a chromosome is not correctly attached, the metaphase checkpoint will stop the cell cycle. This checkpoint prevents cells from incorrectly sorting their chromosomes during division.

Checkpoint proteins delay the cell cycle until problems are fixed or even prevent cell division when problems cannot be fixed. A primary aim of checkpoint proteins is to prevent the division of a cell that may have incurred DNA damage or that harbours abnormalities in chromosome number. When the functions of checkpoint genes are lost through mutation, cell division may not be directly accelerated. However, as discussed in the last section of this chapter, the loss of checkpoint protein function increases the likelihood that undesirable genetic changes will occur that can cause mutation and cancerous growth.

FEATURE INVESTIGATION

Masui and Markert's Study of Oocyte Maturation Led to the Identification of Cyclin and Cyclin-Dependent Kinase

During the 1960s researchers were intensely searching for the factors that promote cell division. In 1971 Yoshio Masui of the University of Toronto and Clement Markert of Yale University developed a way to test whether a substance causes a cell

to progress from one phase of the cell cycle to the next. They chose to study frog oocytes—cells produced by female frogs that develop or mature into egg cells. At the time of their work researchers had already determined that frog oocytes naturally become dormant in the G₂ stage of the cell cycle for up to eight months (**Figure 13.12**). During mating season female frogs produce a hormone called progesterone. After progesterone binds to receptors in dormant egg cells, they progress from G₂ to the

Oocyte dormant in the G₂ phase.

Oocyte advances to the beginning of M phase where chromosomes condense (maturation).

Progesterone

Figure 13.12 Oocyte maturation in certain species of frogs.

beginning of the M phase, where the chromosomes condense and become visible under the microscope. This phenomenon is called maturation. When a sperm fertilizes the egg, the M phase is completed, and the zygote continues to undergo cellular divisions.

Progesterone is a signalling molecule, so Masui and Markert speculated that this hormone affects the functions or amounts of proteins that trigger the oocyte to undergo maturation. To test this hypothesis, they developed the procedure described in **Figure 13.13** by using the oocytes of the leopard frog (*Rana pipiens*). They began by exposing oocytes to progesterone *in vitro* and then incubating these oocytes for 2 hours or 12 hours. As a control they also used oocytes that had not been exposed to progesterone. These three types of cells were called the donor oocytes.

Next, they used a micropipette to transfer a small amount of cytosol from the three types of donor oocytes to recipient

HYPOTHESIS Progesterone induces the synthesis of a factor(s) that advances frog oocytes through the cell cycle from G₂ to M phase.

KEY MATERIALS Oocytes from *Rana pipiens*.

Experimental level	Conceptual level

1 Expose oocytes to progesterone, then incubate for 2 or 12 hours. As a control, also use oocytes that have not been exposed to progesterone. All three types are donor oocytes.

Progesterone Progesterone No progesterone (control)
02:00   12:00

Donor oocytes

Progesterone — Activates intracellular receptor

Factors are made that advance oocyte to M phase. One such factor is called maturation promoting factor (MPF).

Donor oocyte

2 Using a micropipette, transfer some cytosol from the three types of donor oocytes to recipient oocytes that have not been exposed to progesterone.

Donor cytosol

Micropipette tip

Donor oocytes   Recipient oocyte

Recipient oocyte

MPF

Recipient oocyte received MPF from donor oocyte if donor oocyte was incubated for 12 hours with progesterone.

3 Incubate for several hours, and observe the recipient oocytes under the microscope to determine if the recipient oocytes advance to M phase. Advancement to M phase can be determined by the condensation of the chromosomes.

Recipient oocyte that had received cytosol containing MPF from donor oocyte.

Condensed chromosomes

4 THE DATA

Donor oocytes	Recipient oocytes proceeded to M phase?
Control, no progesterone exposure	No
Progesterone exposure, incubation for 2 hours	No
Progesterone exposure, incubation for 12 hours	Yes

5 CONCLUSION Exposure of oocytes to progesterone for 12 hours results in the synthesis of a factor(s) that advances frog oocytes through the cell cycle from G_2 to M phase.

6 SOURCE Masui, Y., and Markert, C.L. 1971. Cytoplasmic control of nuclear behavior during meiotic maturation of frog oocytes. *Journal of Experimental Zoology* 177:129–145.

Figure 13.13   The experimental approach used by Masui and Markert to identify cyclin and cyclin-dependent kinase (cdk).

oocytes that had not been exposed to progesterone. Masui and Markert observed that the recipient oocytes that had been injected with cytosol from the control donor oocytes or from oocytes that had been incubated with progesterone for only two hours did not progress to M phase. However, cytosol from donor oocytes that had been incubated with progesterone for 12 hours caused the recipient oocytes to advance to the M phase. The scientists concluded that a cytosolic factor that required more than two hours to be synthesized after progesterone treatment had been transferred to the recipient oocytes and induced maturation. The factor that caused the oocytes to progress (or mature) from G_2 to the M phase was originally called the **maturation promoting factor (MPF)**.

After MPF was discovered in frogs, it was found in all eukaryotic species that researchers studied. MPF is important in the division of all types of cells, not just oocytes. It took another 17 years before Manfred Lohka, Marianne Hayes, and James Maller were able to purify the components that make up MPF.

This was a difficult undertaking because these components are found in very small amounts in the cytosol, and they are easily degraded during purification procedures. We now know that MPF is a complex made of mitotic cyclin and cyclin-dependent kinase (cdk), as described in Figure 13.11.

Experimental Questions

1. At the time of Masui and Markert's study shown in Figure 13.13, what was known about the effects of progesterone on oocytes?
2. What hypothesis did Masui and Markert propose to explain the function of progesterone? Explain the procedure used to test the hypothesis.
3. How did the researchers explain the difference between the results obtained by using donor oocytes exposed for 2 hours versus donor oocytes exposed for 12 hours?

13.4 CANCER

Learning Outcomes:

1. Outline the general steps in the development of cancer.
2. Describe the general functions of oncogenes.
3. List the four common types of genetic changes that convert proto-oncogenes into oncogenes
4. Identify the two general functions of the proteins encoded by tumour-suppressor genes.
5. Describe three common ways that tumour-suppressor genes are silenced.

Cancer is a disease of multicellular organisms that is characterized by uncontrolled cell division. More than 1.5 million people in North America are diagnosed with cancer each year, and about half that number will die from the disease. In about 10% of cancers a higher predisposition to develop the disease is an inherited trait. Most cancers, though, perhaps 90%, do not involve genetic changes that are passed from parent to offspring. Rather, cancer is usually an acquired condition that typically occurs later in life. At least 80% of all human cancers are related to exposure to **carcinogens**, which are agents that increase the likelihood of developing cancer. Most carcinogens, such as UV light and certain chemicals in cigarette smoke, are mutagens that promote genetic changes in somatic cells. These DNA alterations can lead to effects on gene expression that ultimately affect cell division and thereby lead to cancer. In this section we will explore such genetic abnormalities.

How does cancer occur? In most cases the development of cancer is a multistep process (**Figure 13.14**). Cancers originate from a single cell. This single cell and its lineage of daughter cells undergo a series of mutations that cause the cells to grow

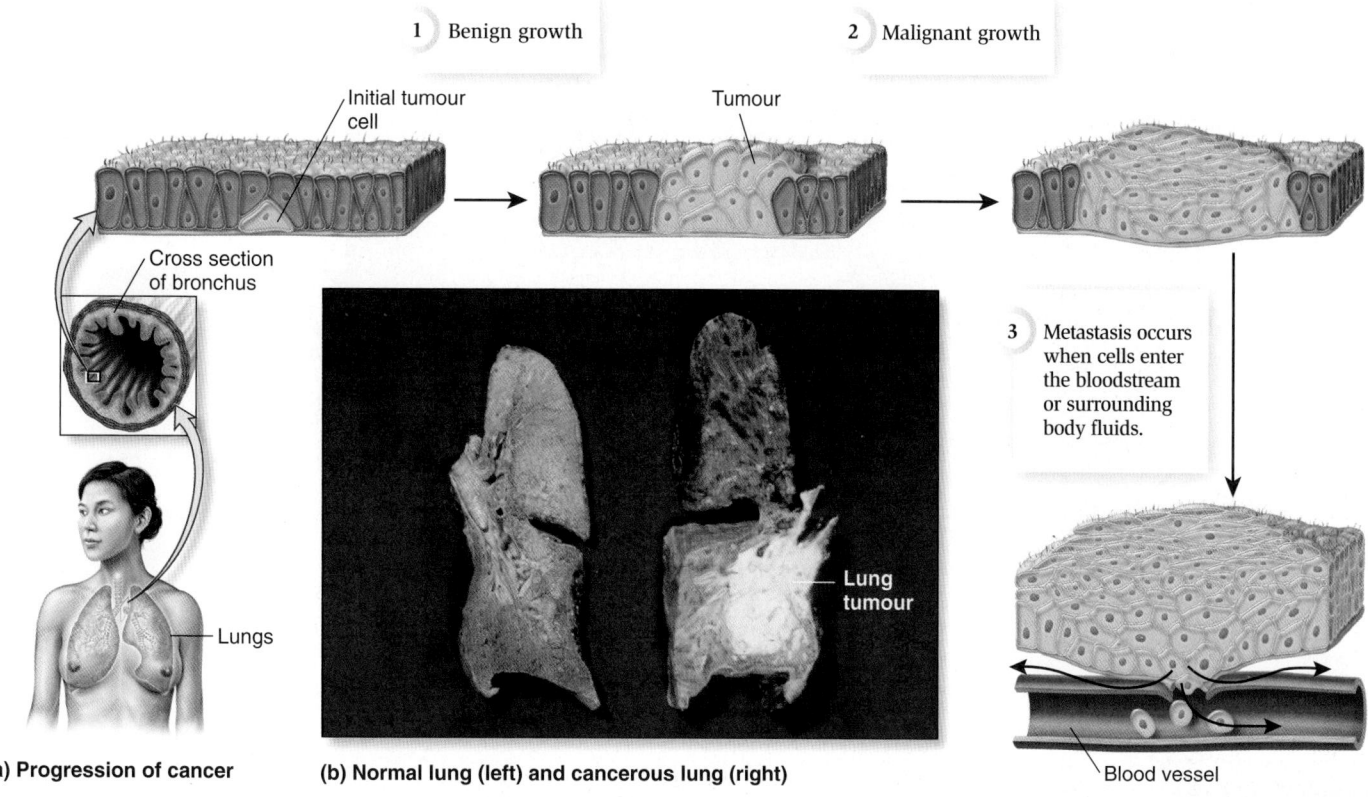

1 Benign growth

1 Benign growth   2 Malignant growth

Initial tumour cell   Tumour

Cross section of bronchus

3 Metastasis occurs when cells enter the bloodstream or surrounding body fluids.

Lungs

Lung tumour

Blood vessel

(a) Progression of cancer   **(b) Normal lung (left) and cancerous lung (right)**

Figure 13.14   The progression and effects of cancer.   (a) In a healthy individual an initial gene mutation converts a normal cell into a tumour cell. This tumour cell divides to produce a benign tumour. Additional genetic changes in the tumour cells may occur, leading to a malignant tumour. At a later stage in malignancy the tumour cells will invade surrounding tissues, and some malignant cells may metastasize by travelling through the bloodstream to other parts of the body. **(b)** On the left is a photo of a human lung that was obtained from a healthy nonsmoker. The lung shown on the right has been ravaged by lung cancer. This lung was taken from a person who was a heavy smoker.

abnormally. At an early stage, the cells form a **tumour**, which is an overgrowth of cells. For most types of cancer a tumour begins as a precancerous or **benign** growth. Such tumours do not invade adjacent tissues and do not spread throughout the body. This may be followed by additional mutations that cause some cells in the tumour to lose their normal growth regulation and become **malignant**. Such tumours invade healthy tissues and spread through the bloodstream or surrounding body fluids, a process called **metastasis**. If left untreated, malignant cells will cause the death of the organism.

Over the past few decades researchers have identified many genes that promote cancer when they are mutant. By comparing the function of each mutant cancer-causing gene with the corresponding nonmutant gene found in healthy cells, these genes have been placed into two categories. In some cases a mutation causes a gene to be expressed at higher levels than normal (hyperactivity). This hyperactivity contributes to the uncontrolled cell growth that is observed in cancer cells. This type of mutant gene is called an **oncogene**. Alternatively, when a **tumour-suppressor gene** is normal (that is, not mutant), it encodes a protein that prevents cancer. However, when a mutation eliminates its function, cancer may occur. Thus, the two categories of cancer-causing genes are based on the effects of

mutations. Oncogenes are the result of mutations that cause hyperactivity, while loss-of-function mutations in tumour-suppressor genes promote cancer. In this section we will begin with a discussion of oncogenes and then consider tumour-suppressor genes.

Oncogenes Cause the Hyperactivity of Proteins That Promote Cell Division

Researchers have identified many oncogenes, a large number of which encode proteins that function in cell growth-signalling pathways. Cell division is regulated, in part, by growth factors, which are molecules that regulate cell division. A growth factor binds to a receptor, which results in receptor activation (**Figure 13.15**). This stimulates an intracellular signal transduction pathway that activates transcription factors. In this way the transcription of specific genes is activated in response to a growth factor. After they are made, the gene products promote cell division.

Eukaryotic species produce many different growth factors that play a role in cell division. Likewise, cells have several different types of signal transduction pathways, which are composed of proteins that respond to growth factors and

Signal transduction pathway

Figure 13.15 General features of a growth factor or hormone signalling pathway that promotes cell division.

Concept check: *How does the presence of a growth factor ultimately affect the function of the cell?*

BioConnections: *Look back at Figure 9.10. Could drugs that inhibit protein kinases be used to combat cancer? Explain.*

promote cell division. Mutations in the genes that encode these signal transduction proteins can change them into oncogenes (**Table 13.6**).

How does an oncogene promote cancer? In some cases an oncogene may keep a cell division signalling pathway in a permanent "on" position. One way oncogenes keep cell division turned on is by producing a functionally overactive protein. As a specific example, let's consider how a mutation alters an intracellular signalling protein called Ras (refer back to Figure 9.10). The Ras protein is a GTPase that hydrolyzes GTP to GDP + P_i

(**Figure 13.16**). When a signal transduction pathway is activated, the Ras protein releases GDP and binds GTP. When GTP is bound, the activated Ras protein promotes cell division. The Ras protein returns to its inactive state by hydrolyzing its bound

Table 13.6	Examples of Growth Factor Pathway Oncogenes
Gene*	**Cellular function**
erbB	Growth factor receptor for EGF (epidermal growth factor)
ras	GTP/GDP-binding protein
raf	Serine kinase
myc	Transcription factor
fos	Transcription factor
jun	Transcription factor

*The genes described in this table are found in humans and other vertebrate species. Most of the genes have been given three-letter names that are abbreviations for the type of cancer the oncogene causes or the type of virus in which the gene was first identified.

Ras releases GDP and then binds GTP to become active.

Inactive Ras protein

Active Ras protein

The active Ras protein participates in a signal transduction pathway that promotes cell division.

GTP hydrolysis returns Ras to an inactive state.

Figure 13.16 The function of Ras, a protein that is part of signal transduction pathways. When GTP is bound, the activated Ras protein promotes cell division. When GTP is hydrolyzed to GDP and P_i, Ras is inactivated and cell division is inhibited.

GTP, and cell division is inhibited. Mutations that convert the normal *ras* gene into an oncogenic *ras* either decrease the ability of Ras protein to hydrolyze GTP or increase the rate of exchange of bound GDP for GTP. Both of these functional changes result in a greater amount of the active GTP-bound form of the Ras protein. In this way, these mutations keep the signalling pathway turned on when it should not be, and uncontrolled cell division results.

Mutations in Proto-oncogenes Convert Them to Oncogenes

Thus far we have examined the functions of proteins that cause cancer when they become overactive. In some cases the amount of the protein increases, while in other cases the activity of the protein increases. Such hyperactivity promotes uncontrolled cell division. Let's now consider the common types of genetic changes that create such oncogenes. Proto-oncogenes are normal genes that are important for many aspects of cell cycling. However, four common genetic changes can convert a proto-oncogene into an oncogene (**Figure 13.17**): missense mutations, gene amplifications, chromosomal translocations, and retroviral insertions.

Missense Mutation A missense mutation (**Figure 13.17a**), which changes a single amino acid in a protein, alters the function of the encoded protein in a way that promotes cancer. An example is a mutation in the *ras* gene that changes a specific glycine to a valine in the Ras protein. This mutation decreases the ability of the Ras protein to hydrolyze GTP, which promotes cell division (see Figure 13.16). Experimentally, chemical mutagens have been shown to cause this missense mutation and thereby lead to cancer.

Gene Amplification Another genetic event that occurs in some cancer cells is an increase in the number of copies of a proto-oncogene (see **Figure 13.17b**). An abnormal increase in copy number results in too much of the encoded protein. In 1982 Mark Groudine discovered that the *myc* gene, which encodes a transcription factor, was amplified in a human leukemia.

Chromosomal Translocation A third type of genetic alteration that can lead to cancer is a chromosomal translocation (see **Figure 13.17c**). This occurs when two different chromosomes break, and the ends of the broken chromosomes fuse with each other incorrectly. Very specific types of chromosomal translocations have been identified in certain types of tumours. In 1960 Peter Nowell discovered that a form of leukemia called chronic myelogenous leukemia (CML)—a type of cancer involving blood cells—was correlated with the presence of a shortened version of a human chromosome. This shortened chromosome is the result of a chromosome translocation in which two different chromosomes, chromosomes 9 and 22, exchange pieces. This activates a proto-oncogene, *abl*, in an unusual way (**Figure 13.18**). In healthy individuals the *bcr* gene and the *abl*

A change in the amino acid sequence of a proto-oncogene protein may cause it to function in an abnormal way. For example, missense mutations can convert *ras* genes into oncogenes.

(a) Missense mutation

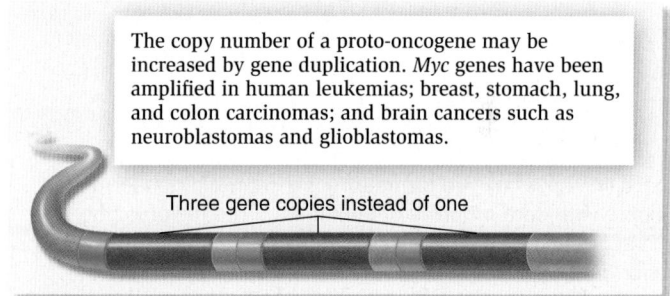

The copy number of a proto-oncogene may be increased by gene duplication. *Myc* genes have been amplified in human leukemias; breast, stomach, lung, and colon carcinomas; and brain cancers such as neuroblastomas and glioblastomas.

(b) Gene amplification

A piece of chromosome may be translocated to another chromosome and affect the expression of genes at the breakpoint site. In one form of leukemia, for example, a translocation causes parts of the *bcr* and *abl* genes to fuse, thereby creating a chimeric oncogene.

(c) Chromosomal translocation

When a virus integrates into the chromosome, viral regulatory elements may enhance the expression of a nearby proto-oncogene, converting it to an oncogene.

(d) Retroviral insertion

Figure 13.17 Genetic changes that convert proto-oncogenes to oncogenes.

Normal chromosomes

Chromosome 9

abl

Breakage and fusion

bcr

Chromosome 22

Chromosomes with translocations

bcr
abl

This chimeric gene causes chronic myelogenous leukemia.

Figure 13.18   **The formation of a chimeric gene found in people with certain forms of leukemia.**   The fusion of the *bcr* and *abl* genes creates a chimeric gene that encodes an abnormal fusion protein, leading to leukemia. The blue regions are the promoters for the *bcr* and *abl* genes.

Concept check: *The* bcr *gene is normally expressed in blood cells. Explain how this observation is related to the type of cancer that the translocation causes.*

gene are located on different chromosomes. In CML these chromosomes break and rejoin in a way that causes the promoter and the first part of *bcr* to fuse with part of *abl*. This abnormal fusion event produces a **chimeric gene** composed of two gene fragments. This chimeric gene acts as an oncogene that encodes an abnormal fusion protein whose functional overactivity leads to leukemia.

Retroviral Insertion   Finally, certain types of viruses can convert proto-oncogenes into oncogenes during the viral replication cycle (see **Figure 13.17d**). Retroviruses insert their DNA into the chromosomal DNA of their host cell. The viral genome contains promoter and response elements that cause a high level of expression of viral genes. On occasion, the viral DNA inserts into a host chromosome next to a proto-oncogene. This can result in the overexpression of the proto-oncogene, thereby promoting cancer. This is one way for a virus to

cause cancer. Alternatively, a virus may cause cancer because it carries an oncogene in the viral genome. This phenomenon is described next.

Some Types of Cancer Are Caused by Viruses

The great majority of cancers are caused by mutagens that alter the structure and expression of genes that are found in cells. A few viruses, however, are known to cause cancer in plants, animals, and humans (**Table 13.7**).

In 1911 the first cancer-causing virus to be discovered was isolated from chicken sarcomas by Peyton Rous. A **sarcoma** is a tumour of connective tissue, such as bone or cartilage. During the 1970s Rous sarcoma virus (RSV) research led to the identification of a viral gene that acts as an oncogene. Researchers investigated RSV by using it to infect chicken cells grown in the laboratory. This caused the chicken cells to grow like cancer cells, continuously and in an uncontrolled manner. Researchers identified mutant RSV strains that infected and proliferated within chicken cells without transforming them into malignant cells. These RSV strains were missing a gene that is found in the form of the virus that does cause cancer. This gene was named the *src* gene because it causes sarcoma.

Harold Varmus and Michael Bishop, in collaboration with Peter Vogt, later discovered that normal (nonviral, uninfected) cells contain a copy of the *src* gene in their chromosomes. It is a proto-oncogene. Researchers have speculated that RSV may have acquired the *src* gene during a previous viral replication cycle. An RSV may have integrated next to the *src* gene in a host cell and later brought the *src* gene along with the viral DNA during the excision process. Once incorporated into a viral genome, the *src* gene is overexpressed because it is

Table 13.7	Examples of Viruses That Cause Cancer
Virus	**Description**
Rous sarcoma virus	Causes sarcomas in chickens
Simian sarcoma virus	Causes sarcomas in monkeys
Abelson leukemia virus	Causes leukemia in mice
Hardy-Zuckerman-4 feline sarcoma virus	Causes sarcomas in cats
Hepatitis B	Causes liver cancer in several species, including humans
Papillomavirus	Causes benign tumours and malignant carcinomas in several species including humans; causes cervical cancer in humans
Epstein-Barr virus	Causes Burkitt's lymphoma, which primarily occurs in immunosuppressed individuals such as AIDS patients

transcribed from a very active viral promoter. This ultimately produces too much of the Src protein and promotes uncontrolled cell division.

Tumour-Suppressor Genes Prevent Mutation or Cell Proliferation

We have examined the first category of genes that can promote cancer, namely, oncogenes. We now turn our attention to the second category: tumour-suppressor genes. The role of a normal (nonmutant) tumour-suppressor gene is to prevent cancerous growth. The proteins encoded by tumour-suppressor genes usually have one of two functions: they act in the maintenance of genome integrity or as negative regulators of the cell cycle (**Table 13.8**).

Maintenance of Genome Integrity   Some tumour-suppressor genes encode proteins that maintain the integrity of the genome, acting to either monitor or repair alterations in the genome. The proteins encoded by these genes are vital for the prevention of abnormalities, such as gene mutations, DNA breaks, and improperly segregated chromosomes. Therefore, when these proteins are functioning properly, they minimize the chance that a cancer-causing mutation will occur. In some cases the proteins will prevent a cell from progressing through the cell cycle if an abnormality

is detected. As described earlier in the chapter, these checkpoint proteins check the integrity of the genome and prevent a cell from progressing past a certain point in the cell cycle. Checkpoint proteins are not usually required to regulate normal, healthy cell division, but they can stop cell division if an abnormality is detected.

As discussed previously, proteins called cyclins and cyclin-dependent protein kinases (cdks) are responsible for advancing a cell through the four phases of the cell cycle. The formation of activated cyclin/cdk complexes can be stopped by checkpoint proteins. A specific example of a tumour-suppressor gene that encodes a checkpoint protein is *p53*, discovered in 1979 by Arnold Levine. Its name refers to the molecular mass of the p53 protein, which is 53 kDa (kilodaltons). About 50% of all human cancers are associated with defects in this gene, including malignant tumours of the lung, breast, esophagus, liver, bladder, and brain, as well as leukemias and lymphomas (cancer of the lymphatic system).

As shown in **Figure 13.19**, p53 is a G_1 checkpoint protein that controls the ability of cells to progress from the G_1 stage of the cell cycle to the S phase. The expression of the *p53* gene is induced when DNA is damaged. The p53 protein is a regulatory transcription factor that activates several different genes, leading to the synthesis of proteins that stop the cell cycle and other proteins that repair the DNA. When p53 is activated, a cell cannot progress from G_1 into the S phase. If the DNA is eventually repaired, a cell may later proceed through the cell cycle.

Table 13.8	Functions of Selected Tumour-Suppressor Genes	
---	---	
Gene	**Function of encoded protein**	
	Maintain genome integrity	
p53	p53 is a transcription factor that positively regulates a few specific target genes and negatively regulates others in a general manner. It acts as a sensor of DNA damage. It can prevent the progression through the cell cycle and also can promote apoptosis.	
BRCA-1, BRCA-2	BRCA-1 and BRCA-2 proteins are both involved in cellular defence against DNA damage. They can play a role in sensing DNA damage, or they can act to facilitate DNA repair. These genes are sometimes mutant in persons with inherited forms of breast cancer.	
XPD	This represents several different genes whose products function in DNA repair. These genes are defective in people with xeroderma pigmentosum.	
	Inhibit cell division (negative regulators)	
Rb	The Rb protein is a negative regulator that represses the transcription of genes required for DNA replication and cell division.	
NF1	The NF1 protein stimulates Ras to hydrolyze its GTP to GDP. Loss of NF1 function causes the Ras protein to be overactive, which promotes cell division.	
p16	A negative regulator of cyclin-dependent protein kinase.	

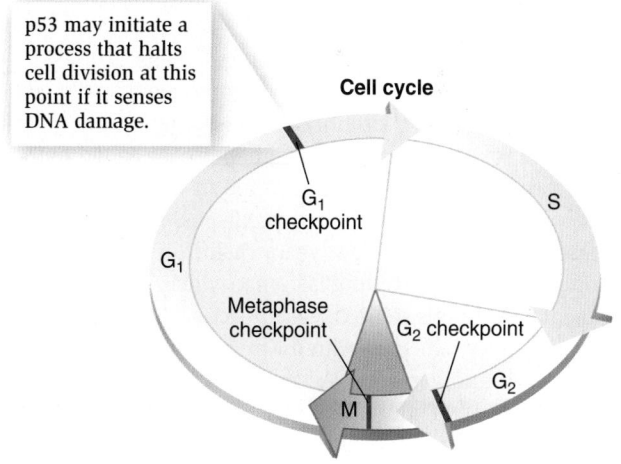

p53 may initiate a process that halts cell division at this point if it senses DNA damage.

Figure 13.19   The cell cycle and checkpoints.   Eukaryotic cells progress through a cell cycle composed of G_1, S, G_2, and M phases. The red bars indicate common checkpoints that will stop the cell cycle if genetic abnormalities are detected. The p53 protein will stop a cell at the G_1 checkpoint if it senses DNA damage.

Concept check: *Why is it an advantage for an organism to have checkpoints that can stop the cell cycle?*

Alternatively, if the DNA damage is too severe, the p53 protein will also activate other genes that promote programmed cell death. This process, called **apoptosis**, involves cell shrinkage and DNA degradation. As described in Chapter 9, an enzyme known as **caspase** is activated during apoptosis (refer back to Figure 9.20). Caspases function as proteases that are sometimes called the executioners of the cell. Caspases digest selected cellular proteins, such as microfilaments, which are components of the cytoskeleton. Eventually, the cell membrane loses its integrity and the cell dies, but the remnants are phagocytized by cells of the immune system. It is obviously beneficial for a multicellular organism to occasionally destroy some of its own cells that have become cancerous.

When checkpoint genes, such as *p53*, are rendered inactive by mutation, the division of normal healthy cells may not be adversely affected. For example, mice that are missing the *p53* gene are born healthy. This indicates that checkpoint proteins, such as p53, are not necessary for normal cell growth and division. However, these mice are very sensitive to mutagens, such as UV light, and easily develop cancer. This result suggests that checkpoint proteins are needed to stop cell division only when there is a strong likelihood that a mutation may have occurred. The loss of checkpoint protein function makes it more likely that undesirable genetic changes will occur that could cause cancerous growth.

Negative Regulators of Cell Division   A second type of tumour-suppressor gene encodes proteins that are negative regulators or inhibitors of cell division. Their function is necessary to properly halt cell division. If their function is lost, cell division is abnormally accelerated.

An example of a tumour-suppressor gene is the *Rb* gene, which encodes a protein that is a negative regulator of cell division. *Rb* was the first tumour-suppressor gene to be identified in humans by studying patients with a disease called retinoblastoma, a cancerous tumour that occurs in the retina of the eye. Some people have an inherited predisposition to develop this disease within the first few years of life. By comparison, the noninherited form of retinoblastoma, which is caused by environmental agents, is more likely to occur later in life. Based on these differences, in 1971 Alfred Knudson proposed a "two-hit" model for retinoblastoma. According to this idea, retinoblastoma requires two mutations to occur. As diploid organisms, humans have two copies of the *Rb* gene, one from each parent. Individuals with the inherited form of the disease already have received one mutant gene from one of their parents. They need only one additional mutation to develop the disease. Individuals with the noninherited form of the disease must have two mutations (one in each copy of the two *Rb* genes) in the same retinal cell to cause the disease. Because two mutations are much less likely than a single mutation, the noninherited form of this disease is expected to occur much later in life and to occur only rarely. Since Knudsen's original hypothesis, molecular studies have confirmed the two-hit hypothesis.

The Rb protein negatively controls a regulatory transcription factor called E2F that activates genes required for cell cycle progression from G_1 to the S phase. The binding of the Rb protein to E2F inhibits its activity and prevents cell division (**Figure 13.20**). When a normal cell is supposed to divide, cyclins bind to cyclin-dependent protein kinases. This binding activates the kinases, which then leads to the phosphorylation of the Rb protein. The phosphorylated form of the Rb protein is released from E2F, thereby allowing E2F to bind to enhancers and activate genes needed to progress through the cell cycle. When both copies of Rb are defective, the E2F protein is always active. This explains why uncontrolled cell division occurs in retinoblastoma.

Gene Mutations, Chromosome Loss, and DNA Methylation Can Inhibit the Expression of Tumour-Suppressor Genes

Cancer biologists would like to understand how tumour-suppressor genes are inactivated, because this knowledge may ultimately help them to prevent cancer. So how are tumour-suppressor genes silenced? The function of tumour-suppressor

1 When E2F is bound to Rb, E2F is inhibited, and cell division is prevented.

2 Phosphorylation of Rb, via cyclin-dependent kinases, causes it to dissociate from E2F.

3 Unbound E2F becomes activated and can then bind to DNA, causing target gene transcription.

Activated

Target gene

Gene product promotes cell division.

Figure 13.20   **Function of the Rb protein.**   The Rb protein inhibits the function of a regulatory transcription factor called E2F that turns on genes that cause a cell to divide. When cells are supposed to divide, Rb is phosphorylated by cyclin-dependent protein kinases, which allows E2F to function. If Rb protein is not made or is not functional because of a mutation, E2F will always be active, and the cell will be stimulated to divide uncontrollably.

genes is lost in three common ways. First, a mutation can occur specifically within a tumour-suppressor gene to inactivate its function. For example, a mutation could abolish the function of the promoter for a tumour-suppressor gene or introduce a premature stop codon in its coding sequence. Either of these would prevent the expression of a functional protein. Chromosome loss is a second way that the function of a tumour-suppressor gene is lost. Chromosome loss may contribute to the progression of cancer if the missing chromosome carries one or more tumour-suppressor genes.

Recently, researchers have discovered a third way that these genes may be inactivated. Tumour-suppressor genes found in cancer cells are sometimes abnormally methylated. As discussed in Chapter 12, transcription is inhibited when CpG islands near a promoter region are methylated. Such methylation near the promoters of tumour-suppressor genes has been found in many types of tumours, suggesting that this form of gene inactivation plays an important role in the formation or progression of malignancy.

Most Forms of Cancer Are Caused by a Series of Genetic Changes That Progressively Alter the Growth Properties of Cells

The discovery of oncogenes and tumour-suppressor genes has allowed researchers to study the progression of certain forms of cancer at the molecular level. Cancer usually requires multiple genetic changes, perhaps 10 or more, to the same cell. Many cancers begin with a benign genetic alteration that, over time and with additional mutations, leads to malignancy. Furthermore, a malignancy can continue to accumulate genetic changes that make it even more difficult to treat because the cells divide faster or invade surrounding tissues more readily.

Lung cancer is one type of cancer that progresses through different stages of abnormal cell proliferation. Worldwide, more than 1.2 million cases are diagnosed every year. Nearly 90% of these cases are caused by smoking and are thus preventable. Unlike other cancers for which early diagnosis is possible, lung cancer is usually detected only after it has become advanced and is difficult if not impossible to cure. The five-year survival rate for lung cancer patients is less than 15%.

Most cancers in the lung are **carcinomas**—cancers of epithelial cells (**Figure 13.21a**). Epithelial cells are described in Chapter 5. The top images in this figure show the normal epithelium found in a healthy lung. The rest of the figure shows the progression of cancer that is due to mutations in basal cells—a type of epithelial cell. Keep in mind that cancer occurs through the accumulation of mutations in a cell lineage, beginning with an initial mutant cell that then divides multiple times to produce a population of many daughter cells (refer back to Figure 13.14). As mutations accumulate in basal cells, their numbers increase dramatically. This causes a thickening of the epithelium, a condition called hyperplasia. The proliferation of basal cells causes the loss of the ciliated columnar epithelial cells that normally line the airways. As additional mutations accumulate, the basal cells develop more abnormal morphologies, a condition known as dysplasia. In the early stages of dysplasia, the abnormal basal cells are precancerous. If the source of chronic irritation (usually cigarette smoke) is eliminated, the abnormal cells are likely to disappear. Alternatively, if smoking continues, these abnormal cells may accumulate additional genetic changes and lose the ability to stop dividing. Such cells have become cancerous—the person has basal cell carcinoma.

The basement membrane is a sheetlike layer of extracellular matrix components that provides a barrier between the lung cells and the bloodstream. If the cancer cells have not yet metastasized by penetrating the basement membrane, they will not have spread into the blood and to other parts of the body. If the tumour is removed at this stage, the patient should be cured. The lower images in Figure 13.21a show a tumour that has broken through the basement membrane. The metastasis of these cells to other parts of the body will likely kill the patient, usually within a year of being diagnosed.

The cellular changes that lead to lung cancer are correlated with genetic changes. These include the occurrence of mutations that create oncogenes and inhibit tumour-suppressor genes. The order of mutations is not absolute. It takes time for such multiple changes to accumulate, so cancer is usually a disease of older people. Reducing your exposure to mutagens throughout your lifetime will minimize the risk of mutations to your genes that could promote cancer.

GENOMES AND PROTEOMES

Mutations in Approximately 300 Human Genes May Promote Cancer

Researchers have identified a large number of genes that are mutated in cancer cells. Though not all of these mutant genes have been directly shown to affect the growth rate of cells, such mutations are likely to be found in tumours because they provide some type of growth advantage for the cell population from which the cancer developed. For example, certain mutations can enable cells to metastasize to neighbouring locations. These mutations may not affect growth rate, but they provide a growth advantage in that cancer cells are not limited to growing in a particular location; they can migrate to new locations.

How many genes can contribute to cancer when they become mutant? Researchers have estimated that about 300 different genes may play a role in the development of human cancer. Humans have an estimated 20,000 to 25,000 genes, and therefore approximately 1% of our genes have the potential to promote cancer if their function is altered by a mutation.

Normal lung epithelium

Hyperplasia

Loss of ciliated cells

Dysplasia (initially precancerous, then cancerous)

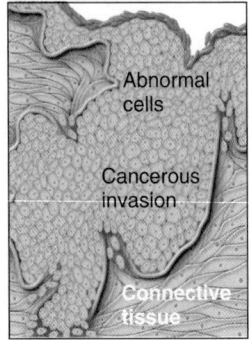

Invasive cancerous cells that can metastasize

(a) Cellular changes

Genes that are commonly mutated in lung cancer include

Oncogenes	**Tumour-suppressor genes**
erbB—epidermal growth factor receptor	*p53*—checkpoint
ras—cell signalling	*XPD*—DNA repair
myc—transcription factor	*Rb*—negative regulator
Cyclin D1—promotes the cell cycle	*p16*—negative regulator

(b) Genetic changes

Figure 13.21 Progression of changes leading to lung cancer. Lung tissue is largely composed of different types of connective tissue and epithelial cells, including columnar and basal cells. **(a)** A progression of cellular changes in basal cells caused by the accumulation of mutations leads to basal cell carcinoma, a common type of lung cancer. **(b)** Mutations in several different genes contribute to lung cancer.

Summary of Key Concepts

13.1 Mutation

- A mutation is a heritable change in the genetic material.
- Point mutations, which affect a single nucleotide, can alter the coding sequence of genes in several ways. These include silent, missense, nonsense, and frameshift mutations. (Table 13.1)
- Sickle-cell anemia is caused by a missense mutation that changes a single amino acid in hemoglobin. (Figure 13.1)
- Gene mutations can also alter gene function by changing DNA sequences that are not within the coding region. (Table 13.2)
- The Lederbergs used replica plating and showed that mutations are random events. (Figure 13.2)
- Germ-line mutations affect gametes while somatic mutations affect only a part of the body and cannot be passed to offspring. (Figures 13.3, 13.4)
- Spontaneous mutations are the result of errors in natural biological processes, while induced mutations are due to agents in the environment that cause changes in DNA structure. (Table 13.3)
- Mutagens are chemical or physical agents that lead to mutations in the DNA. (Table 13.4, Figures 13.5, 13.6)
- Testing methods, such as the Ames test, can determine whether an agent is a mutagen. (Figure 13.7)

13.2 DNA Repair

- DNA repair systems involve proteins that sense DNA damage and repair it before a mutation occurs. (Table 13.5)

- Nucleotide excision repair systems recognize various types of DNA damage, such as thymine dimers. A region in the damaged strand is excised, and a new strand is synthesized, using the intact strand as a template. (Figure 13.8)

- Certain inherited diseases in humans are due to defects in nucleotide excision repair. (Figure 13.9)

13.3 Cell Cycle Regulation

- The eukaryotic cell cycle consists of four phases called G_1 (first gap), S (synthesis of DNA), G_2 (second gap), and M phase (mitosis and cytokinesis). The G_1, S, and G_2 phases are collectively known as interphase. (Figure 13.10)

- An interaction between cyclin and cyclin-dependent kinase is necessary for cells to progress through the cell cycle. Checkpoint proteins sense the environmental conditions and the integrity of the genome, and they control whether the cell progresses through the cell cycle. (Figure 13.11)

- Masui and Markert studied the maturation of frog oocytes to identify a substance that was necessary for oocytes to progress through the cell cycle. This substance was later identified as a complex of mitotic cyclin and cyclin-dependent kinase and called maturation promoting factor (MPF). (Figures 13.12, 13.13)

13.4 Cancer

- Cancer is caused by the accumulation of mutations in a line of cells that leads to uncontrolled cell growth. (Figure 13.14)

- Oncogenes often encode proteins involved in cell-signalling pathways that promote cell division. (Figures 13.15, 13.16, Table 13.6)

- A mutation that inhibits the ability of the Ras protein to hydrolyze its GTP converts the *ras* gene into an oncogene. (Figure 13.16)

- Four common types of genetic changes—missense mutations, gene amplifications, chromosomal translocations, and retroviral insertions—can convert proto-oncogenes into oncogenes. (Figure 13.17)

- A chromosome translocation that fuses parts of the *bcr* gene and the *abl* gene also creates an oncogene that causes leukemia. (Figure 13.18)

- Some types of cancer are caused by viruses. (Table 13.7)

- The normal function of tumour-suppressor genes is to prevent cancer. Loss-of-function mutations in such genes can promote cancer. Tumour-suppressor genes often encode proteins that maintain the integrity of the genome or function as negative regulators of cell division. (Table 13.8)

- Checkpoint proteins monitor the integrity of the genome and prevent the cell from progressing through the cell cycle if abnormalities are detected. (Figure 13.19)

- The Rb protein is a negative regulator of cell division because it inhibits E2F, a transcription factor that promotes cell division. (Figure 13.20)

- Tumour-suppressor genes can be inactivated by gene mutations, chromosome loss, and DNA methylation.

- Most forms of cancer, such as lung cancer, involve multiple genetic changes that lead to malignancy. (Figure 13.21)

- More than 300 human genes, or about 1% of our genes, are known to be associated with cancer when they become mutant.

Test to Assess Your Learning

1. Point mutations that do not alter the amino acid sequence of the resulting gene product are called _____ mutations.
   a. frameshift
   b. natural
   c. silent
   d. nonsense
   e. missense

2. Some point mutations will lead to an mRNA that produces a much shorter polypeptide. This type of mutation is known as a _____ mutation.
   a. neutral
   b. silent
   c. missense
   d. nonsense
   e. chromosomal

3. The type of mutation that alters the entire amino acid sequence from the site of the mutation is known as a _____ mutation.
   a. neutral
   b. silent
   c. missense
   d. nonsense
   e. frameshift

4. Mutagens can cause mutations by
   a. chemically altering DNA nucleotides.
   b. disrupting DNA replication.
   c. altering the genetic code of an organism.
   d. all of the above.
   e. (a) and (b) only.

5. The mutagenic effect of UV light is
   a. the alteration of cytosine bases to adenine bases.
   b. the formation of purine dimers that interfere with genetic expression.
   c. the breaking of the sugar-phosphate backbone of the DNA molecule.
   d. the formation of pyrimidine dimers that disrupt DNA replication.
   e. the deletion of thymine bases along the DNA molecule.

6. The Ames test
   a. provides a way to determine if any type of cell has experienced a mutation.
   b. provides a way to determine the mutagenic effect of certain types of agents.
   c. allows researchers to experimentally disrupt gene activity by causing a mutation in a specific gene.
   d. provides a way to repair mutations in bacterial cells.
   e. all of the above.

7. Xeroderma pigmentosum
   a. is a genetic disorder that results in uncontrolled cell growth.
   b. is a genetic disorder in which normal NER systems are not fully functional.
   c. is a genetic disorder that results in the loss of pigment in certain patches of skin.
   d. results from the lack of DNA polymerase proofreading.
   e. both (b) and (d).

8. If a mutation eliminated the function of UvrC, which aspect of nucleotide excision repair would not work?
   a. sensing a damaged DNA site
   b. endonuclease cleavage of the damaged strand
   c. removal of the damaged strand

d. synthesis of a new strand, using the undamaged strand as a template
e. none of the above

9. Whether or not a cell divides depends on
   a. nutrient availability.
   b. environmental conditions.
   c. the presence of signal molecules that regulate cell division.
   d. cellular proteins that regulate cell division.
   e. all of the above.

10. Checkpoints during the cell cycle are important because they
    a. allow the organelle activity to catch up to cellular demands.
    b. ensure the integrity of the cell's DNA.
    c. allow the cell to generate sufficient ATP for cellular division.
    d. are the only time DNA replication can occur.
    e. all of the above.

11. Cancer cells are said to be metastatic when they
    a. begin to divide uncontrollably.
    b. invade healthy tissue.
    c. migrate to other parts of the body.
    d. cause mutations in other healthy cells.
    e. all of the above.

12. Oncogenes can be produced by
    a. missense mutations.
    b. gene amplification.
    c. chromosomal translocation.
    d. retroviral insertion.
    e. all of the above.

Articulate to Assess Your Learning

1. Explain the difference between a missense mutation and a nonsense mutation.

2. Explain how a frameshift mutation can lead to premature termination of a polypeptide.

3. Is a random mutation more likely to be beneficial or harmful? Explain your answer.

4. Distinguish between spontaneous and induced mutations. Which are more harmful? Which are avoidable?

Collaborate to Assess and Extend Your Learning

1. Discuss some advantages and some disadvantages of mutations.

2. Some mutations of proto-oncogenes give rise to oncogenes that are expressed in tissues where the proto-oncogene was silent or give rise to elevated levels of the encoded protein. Discuss the nature of these mutations and how they would be different from mutations in which a hyperactive protein is produced.

3. Suppose that a mutation occurs in the *p53* gene that leads to it becoming overexpressed. What impact would this have on the general physiology of the cell and on its potential for becoming malignant?

4. A large amount of research is aimed at studying mutations, particularly with respect to cancer. However, research dollars are finite. Where would you put your money for mutation research and why? (a) testing potential mutagens; (b) investigating molecular effects of mutagens; (c) investigating DNA repair mechanisms; (d) some other place.

5. Would cancer occur if both copies of the *Rb* gene and both copies of the *E2F* gene were rendered inactive because of mutations?

6. A principle of biology is that the genetic material, DNA, provides a dynamic plan for sustaining life. Explain how mutations may cause alterations to the genetic material that are detrimental to sustaining life.

Visit McGraw-Hill Ryerson Connect™ for additional study resources.

Eukaryotic Chromosomes, Mitosis, and Meiosis

14

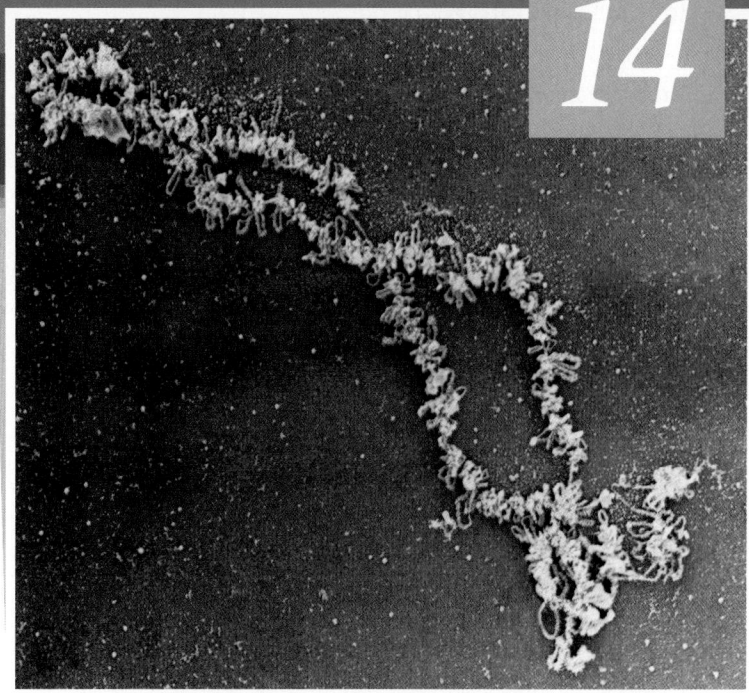

A giant lampbrush chromosome displays its looped domains

Chapter Outline

The focus of Unit III is the genetic material—its structure and function. The primary function of the genetic material is to store the information needed to produce the characteristics of an organism. To fulfill this role at the molecular level, DNA sequences are (1) used as templates to synthesize RNA, (2) used as templates for their own replication, (3) precisely associated with chromosomal proteins and compacted into structures we call chromosomes that can fit within living cells, and (4) segregated (after being replicated and packaged into chromosomes) between dividing cells. In this chapter, we will examine the last two of these characteristics of the DNA; this requires that we change our perspective.

Genes are functional units of the hereditary material, discrete segments of much larger DNA molecules. In Chapters 10 to 13 our perspective has been at the level of the DNA or RNA, and how these macromolecules are produced (DNA replication in Chapter 10, RNA transcription in Chapter 11), how DNA and RNA work together for the production of the proteins the cell needs (Chapters 11 and 12), and how DNA can be damaged and repaired (Chapter 13). At the end of Chapter 13 we considered the cell cycle.

In this chapter we will again look at the cell cycle but now from the perspective of the chromosomes. We also will begin to think of the DNA from the perspective of the chromosome and how the DNA is organized into chromosomes to function at the different phases of the cell cycle. Once we have the big picture clearly in mind, we will focus our attention on the M phase, the division phase of the cell cycle, and think of how this phase of the cell cycle serves the needs of the organism. We also will consider how organismal development and reproduction require two different types of M phase to meet the needs of the organism. Last, we will examine variation in the structure and number of chromosomes that is seen in nature.

14.1 / CHROMOSOME STRUCTURE AND FUNCTION, AND THE CELL CYCLE

Learning Outcomes:

1. Describe the structure of nucleosomes and the 30-nm fibre, and how the 30-nm fibre forms radial loop domains.
2. Relate the level of chromosome condensation to the stages of the cell cycle and the ability to do transcription.
3. Outline the various levels of compaction that lead to a metaphase chromosome.

In this section we will look at how eukaryotic chromosomes are associated with proteins and organized to function in eukaryotic cells. Most eukaryotic cells are only 10 to 100 μm (micrometres) in diameter, and the cell nucleus is only about 2 to 4 μm in diameter. A typical eukaryotic chromosome contains a single linear, double-stranded DNA molecule that may be hundreds of millions of base pairs long. If the DNA from a single set of human chromosomes were stretched from end to end, it would be more than 1 m long but only 2 nm (nanometres) in diameter. Therefore, to fit inside the nucleus lengthwise, the incredibly slender DNA molecules are shortened but are made wider as they are carefully packaged with proteins into the functional structures we know as **chromosomes**.

The word *chromosome* literally means "coloured body." The name is derived from early studies of chromosomes done at the phase in the cell cycle when the chromosomes are most condensed and most visible when stained with dyes. But chromosomes are found in this highly compacted state only for a brief time in the cell cycle. Chromosomes are very dynamic structures that change their protein composition and configuration as they alternate between highly and loosely condensed states in response to changes in the cell cycle and developmental state.

(a) Electron micrograph of chromatin with histone H1 removed to produce 'beads on a string' configuration

Nucleosome:
8 histone proteins +
146–147 nucleotide
base pairs of DNA

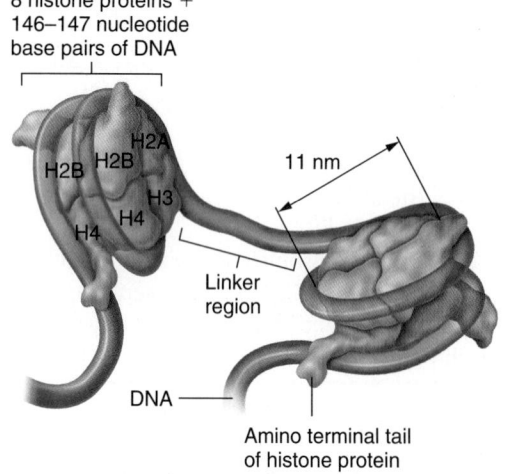

H2A

H2B H2B

H3

H4

H4

11 nm

Linker region

DNA

Amino terminal tail of histone protein

(b) Structure and components of each nucleosome

Figure 14.1 Structure of a nucleosome. (a) Electron micrograph of chromatin with histone H1 removed to produce a "beads on a string" configuration. (b) A nucleosome is composed of double-stranded DNA wrapped around an octamer of histone proteins. A linker region of DNA runs between two adjacent nucleosomes.

Let's now examine how DNA is associated with chromosomal proteins and packaged into functional chromosomes.

DNA Wraps Around Histone Proteins to Form Nucleosomes

The first level of chromosome organization is the wrapping of the DNA helix around a protein complex known as a **nucleosome**. Each nucleosome is composed of the DNA plus an octamer that consists of two molecules of histone H2A, two molecules of histone H2B, two molecules of histone H3, and two molecules of histone H4. All the histone proteins contain a large number of positively charged lysine and arginine amino acids. This is very important because these positive charges attract the negative charges that are found in the phosphate group backbone of the DNA helices. **Figure 14.1** depicts the organization of the histone proteins and shows how the DNA is wrapped around the exterior surface of the octamer, with 146 to 147 base pairs (bp) making 1.65 turns around the histone octamer. While the main portion of the histone octamer is approximately spherical, the individual histone molecules each have a tail region that extends from the sphere. As we discuss later, covalent modifications of these tails likely are one way to control the degree of chromatin compaction. The nucleosome, which is the association of DNA and histones together, is sometimes referred to as the **11-nm fibre** because the nucleosome is 11 nm in diameter.

Not all chromosomal DNA is wrapped around the histone octamer; small "linker" regions of DNA that vary in length from 20 to 100 bp run between the octamers. This first level of organization—nucleosomes and linkers—is collectively known as the "beads on a string" level of organization, with the nucleosomes as the beads and the linker DNA as the string. This level of chromosomal organization shortens the length of the DNA molecule about sevenfold. The evidence supporting a beads-on-a-string structure is described in the Feature Investigation. The Feature Investigation involves biochemical treatment of the chromosomal DNA and the disruption of its higher-order structure. When we use this biochemical perspective, we often refer to the DNA and its associated proteins as **chromatin**, because it is no longer organized in its native state.

Nucleosomes Compact to Form a 30-Nanometre Fibre

In living cells the beads-on-a-string organization is followed by another level of packaging. The linker DNA is normally associated with another histone, histone H1, creating a more compact structure 30 nm in diameter (known as the **30-nm fibre**) that shortens the chromosomal DNA another sevenfold. **Figure 14.3a** shows an electron micrograph of the 30-nm fibre extracted from nuclei. The precise structure of the 30-nm fibre in vivo is not known with certainty, but one model proposed by Rachel Horowitz and Christopher Woodcock in the 1990s is

FEATURE INVESTIGATION

Noll Confirmed Kornberg's Beads-on-a-String Model by Digestion of the Linker Region

Roger Kornberg proposed the beads-on-a-string model in 1974. Markus Noll decided to test Kornberg's model by digesting chromatin with DNase-I, an enzyme that breaks the phosphodiester bonds of the DNA. Noll reasoned that if the model was correct, the linker region of DNA would be more accessible to DNase-I than would the 146-bp region that is tightly bound to the histones. Therefore, he expected incubation with DNase-I to make cuts in the linker region and produce DNA pieces that would be approximately 200 bp long, given that the DNA used had linker regions of about 50 bp. (Note: The size of the DNA fragments was expected to vary somewhat, since the linker region is not of constant length and the cut within the linker region can occur at different sites.)

Figure 14.2 describes Noll's experimental protocol. He began with nuclei from rat liver cells and incubated them

HYPOTHESIS DNA wraps around histone proteins in a regular, repeating pattern.

KEY MATERIAL Nuclei from rat liver cells.

Experimental level   **Conceptual level**

1   Incubate nuclei with low, medium, and high concentrations of DNase-I. The conceptual level shows a low DNase-I concentration.

DNase-I

37°C   37°C   37°C

Low   Medium   High

Before digestion (beads on a string)

After digestion (DNA is cut in linker region)

Treat with detergent and add phenol.

2   Extract the DNA from the cell nucleus by dissolving the membranes with detergent and adding phenol. DNA goes into aqueous phase.

Aqueous phase (contains DNA)

Phenol phase (contains membranes and proteins)

Marker   Low   Medium   High

DNA in aqueous solution (low DNase-I)

3   Load the DNA into a well of a gel and separate the DNA according to size. The marker lane contains a mixture of DNA fragments of known sizes.

Gel

Low

600 bp

400 bp

200 bp

bp = base pairs

4   Visualize the DNA fragments by staining the DNA with ethidium bromide, which binds to DNA and is fluorescent when excited by UV light.

5   **THE DATA**

Results from the experiment:

DNase-I concentration: 30 units mL^{-1} 150 units mL^{-1} 600 units mL^{-1}
bp = base pairs

6   **CONCLUSION**   DNA was digested in a pattern that strongly supports the nucleosome model for chromatin structure.

7   **SOURCE**   Noll, M. 1974. Subunit Structure of Chromatin. *Nature* 251: 249–251.

Figure 14.2   **Noll's DNase-I digestion experiment, which verified the beads-on-a-string model of DNA compaction.**

beads-on-a-string model. At lower DNase-I concentrations, longer pieces were observed that were in multiples of 200 bp (400, 600, and so on). These longer pieces resulted from occasional uncut linker regions. For example, a DNA piece might contain two nucleosomes and be 400 bp in length. Taken together, these results strongly supported the nucleosome model for chromatin structure.

with low, medium, or high concentrations of DNase-I. At high concentrations the enzyme should make a cut in every linker region, while at medium and low concentrations, DNase-I may occasionally miss cutting a linker region, which would produce larger DNA fragments in multiples of 200 bp. Following digestion the DNA was extracted from the cell nuclei and then analyzed by gel electrophoresis to determine the sizes of the DNA fragments. (Gel electrophoresis is described in detail in Chapter 18.)

As shown in the data, at high DNase-I concentrations, the chromosomal DNA was digested into fragments of approximately 200 bp in length. This result is consistent with the

Experimental Questions

1. What is DNase-I and why was it used in this experiment?
2. Noll hypothesized that DNA fragments of 200 bp would support the beads-on-a-string model of nucleosome structure for this particular species. Explain the rationale for this particular fragment length.
3. The experiment consisted of three assays with differing concentrations of DNase-I. How did the different concentrations of DNase-I affect the results?

shown in **Figure 14.3b**. According to their model, linker regions in the 30-nm structure are associated with interacting histone H1 proteins and variably bent and twisted; there is little direct contact between nucleosomes. The 30-nm fibre forms an asymmetric, three-dimensional zigzag of nucleosomes. At this level of compaction the overall picture of chromatin that emerges is an irregular, fluctuating structure with stable nucleosome

units connected by bendable linker regions. We know that histone H1 and other nonhistone proteins are important in the formation of the 30-nm fibre, because if histone H1 and the nonhistones are extracted, the 30-nm fibre is lost and only the beads on a string remain. Thus far, we have examined two mechanisms that compact eukaryotic DNA, the formation of nucleosomes and their arrangement into a 30-nm fibre. Taken

(a) Micrograph of a 30-nm fibre

30 nm

(b) Three-dimensional zigzag model

Figure 14.3   The 30-nm fibre.   (a) A photomicrograph of the 30-nm fibre. **(b)** In this three-dimensional zigzag model, the linker DNA forms a bendable structure with little contact between adjacent nucleosomes.

together, these two events shorten the folded DNA by about 49 times its original size.

The Nucleosomal Fibre Is Organized into Loops That Are Anchored to the Nuclear Matrix

A third level of organization occurs as the nucleosomal DNA is organized into looped domains (**Figure 14.4a**). Formation of the looped domains involves interactions between the 30-nm fibres and a filamentous network of proteins in the nucleus called the **nuclear matrix**. From Chapter 4 you will recall that the nuclear matrix consists of the **nuclear lamina** (a collection of protein fibres that line the inner nuclear membrane) that is connected to a network of related fibrous proteins that run through the interior of the nucleus. (**Figure 14.4b**). Regions of the nucleosomal DNA interact with specific proteins; these proteins in turn bind the nucleosomal DNA to the nuclear matrix proteins. In this way, loop domains, which are often 25,000 to 200,000 bp, are organized and anchored to the nuclear matrix.

Nuclear lamina

Nuclear matrix

Nuclear pore

(a) Proteins that form the nuclear matrix

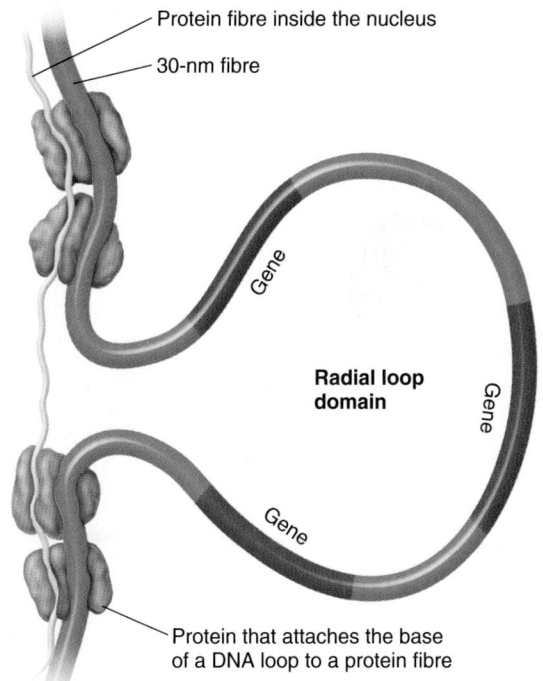

Protein fibre inside the nucleus

30-nm fibre

Gene

Radial loop domain

Gene

Gene

Protein that attaches the base of a DNA loop to a protein fibre

(b) Radial loop domain bound to a protein fibre

Figure 14.4   Structure of the nuclear matrix and its attachment to the 30-nm fibre.   (a) The nucleus contains a fibrous protein network with the nuclear lamina (yellow) along the periphery and the nuclear matrix (blue) projecting into the interior. The nuclear matrix provides a structural framework for anchoring looped domains (the looped domains are not shown in this cut out of the nucleus). **(b)** Special proteins (shown in blue) interact with both the 30-nm nucleosomal fibres and the nuclear matrix network.

Interphase Chromosomes Are Heterogenous in the Level of Condensation

So far we have examined the first three levels of organization that are present for all chromosome regions throughout the cell cycle: "DNA helix" organized into "beads on string" organized into the "30-nm fibre" organized into "looped domains".

During the processes of DNA replication and transcription, individual looped domains may briefly loosen their histones' association with the DNA when a region of DNA needs to be replicated or transcribed. But this is done very locally and fleetingly such that at any given moment the vast majority of the chromosomal DNA exists as intact 30-nm fibres organized into looped domains.

There are additional levels of chromosome organization, but once we go beyond the first three levels of chromosome packaging, we need to think about additional levels of compaction in the context of the cell cycle. **Figure 14.5** contains a simplified version of the cell cycle that highlights the activity and organization of chromosomal DNA at each major stage of the cell cycle. The cell cycle consists of G_1, the S phase, G_2, and the M phase. G_1, the S phase, and G_2 are collectively known as interphase because their appearance in microscopy images is similar; all three stages also undergo both transcription and translation. The last stage, the M phase, is much briefer and has the dramatic condensation of chromosomes.

During interphase all regions of the chromosomes have the first three levels of organization. But the compaction level of

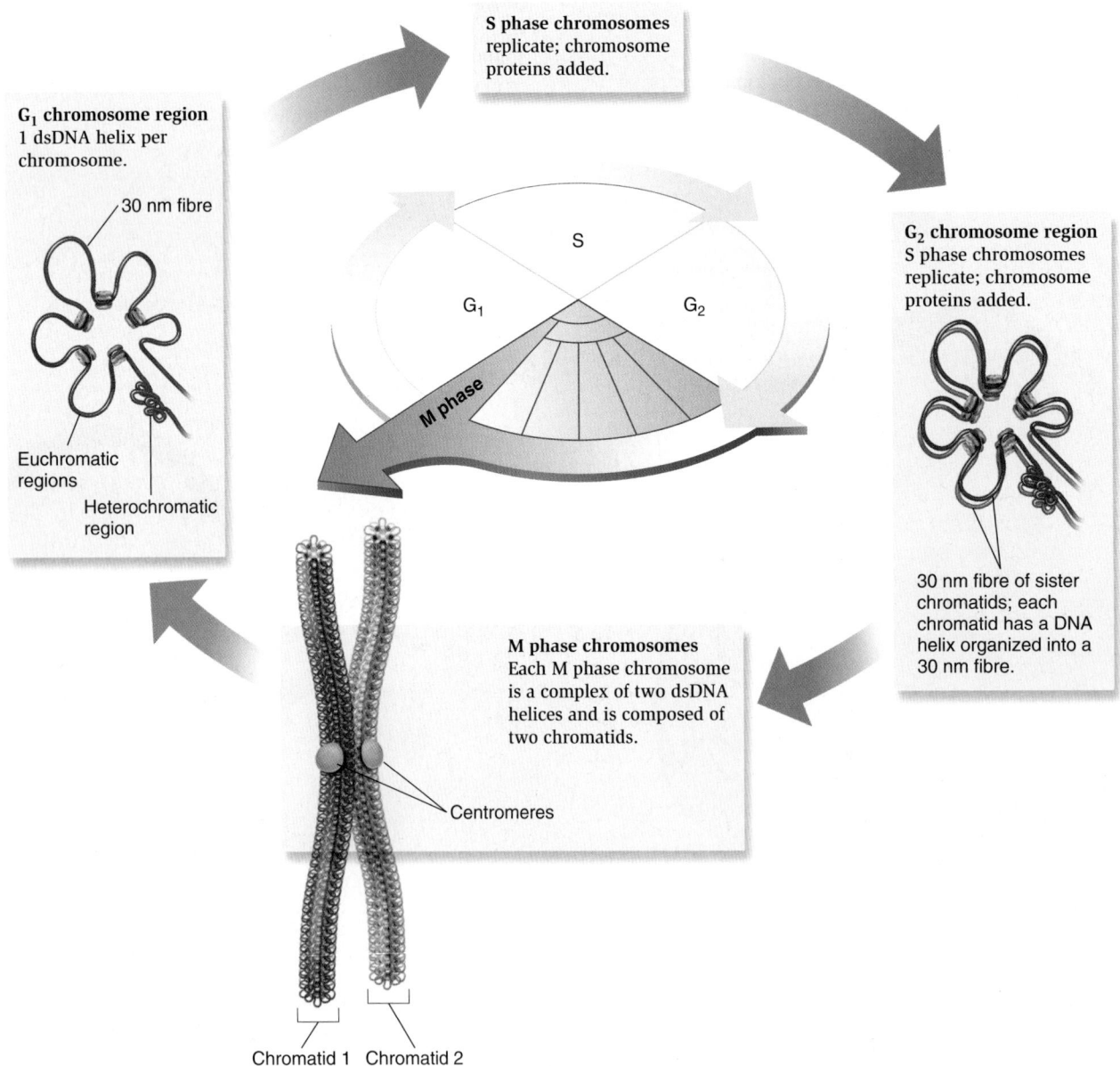

Figure 14.5   Structure of chromosomal DNA throughout the cell cycle.

Principle: *Structure determines function. Euchromatic regions are capable of being used as a template for transcription while the more condensed heterochromatin is not.*

chromosomes in the cell nucleus during interphase is not uniform because some chromosome regions are additionally compacted. **Euchromatin** refers to chromosome regions that occur as looped domains of 30-nm fibre that are not compacted further during interphase. Euchromatic chromosome regions are accessible to the transcription machinery and hence are capable of being transcribed during interphase. Euchromatic regions also readily can be used as a template during the S phase portion of interphase as the chromosomes are replicated. In contrast the term **heterochromatin** is used to describe regions of chromosomes in which the looped domains are tightly packed together. In general, these regions are transcriptionally *inactive* because of their highly compacted conformation, which prevents the transcription machinery from gaining access. These heterochromatic regions also are the last regions of chromosomes to be replicated because special mechanisms are required to decondense them enough to serve as templates for DNA replication. It is not possible with normal chromosome stains to see distinct chromosomes during interphase, because the moderately condensed euchromatin regions are too slender to be distinguished from each other clearly.

Interphase Activity from the Chromosomal Perspective

Transcription and translation occur during G1, S, and G2. In G1 the proteins that are produced via translation are largely geared to cell growth and organismal functions. In the S phase the dominant cellular activity is replication of the chromosomal DNA; some new transcription and translation also occur. But most of the translational activity is for creating the histones and other chromosomal proteins needed to organize the newly replicated chromosomal DNA. When the cell moves from the S phase into G2, each chromosome is composed of two identical DNA helices associated with chromosomal proteins. We call the two tightly associated, packaged DNA helices sister chromatids. During G2 sister chromatids are held together all along their length by special chromosome proteins known as cohesins. Because each sister chromatid mostly is composed of euchromatic regions, we can not see the chromatids and chromosomes as distinct entities, but they still occupy separate chromatin domains and can, when appropriate, be used as templates for transcription. Transcription and translation also occur in G2, and some is directed toward the cell's functions for the organism. But the majority of the new proteins being produced in G2 are stockpiled for use in the last stage of the cell cycle—the M phase—when both the chromosomes and the cytoplasmic contents must be carefully partitioned into the resulting two cells.

For the M Phase the Chromosomes Must Undergo Additional Compaction

The M phase of the cell cycle is the phase when a cell divides to produce daughter cells. The most complex part of cell division is the division of the nucleus because each chromosome must now segregate sister chromatids, sending one to each daughter cell. To segregate these chromatids, the final level of chromosome condensation must be done. For this process all the looped domains are coiled into tightly compressed spirals.

Figure 14.6 The steps in eukaryotic chromosomal compaction leading to the metaphase chromosome.

BioConnections: *Look ahead to Figure 15.9. Why do you think it is necessary for the chromosomes to become compact in preparation for cell division?*

Figure 14.6 illustrates the successive levels of compaction that chromosomal DNA undergoes as it is replicated and then packaged into an M phase chromosome. As the chromosomes are condensing, they lose most of the cohesin molecules that were holding sister chromatids together, except in one specialized region known as the centromere. Each chromosome is composed

GENOMES AND PROTEOMES

The Histone Code Hypothesis for Controlling Chromatin Compaction

We just have discussed how the chromosomal DNA of eukaryotic species are highly organized and compacted to fit inside the cell's nucleus. Even euchromatin is compacted to such a degree that it is difficult for transcription factors and RNA polymerase to access and transcribe genes; the association of DNA with the nucleosomes must be loosened so that genes can be transcribed into RNA.

Each of the histone proteins consists of a globular domain and a flexible, charged amino terminus called an amino terminal tail. The DNA wraps around the globular domains, as depicted in Figure 14.1, and the amino terminal tails protrude from the chromatin. Recently, researchers, such as Michael Kobor and M. C. Lorincz of the University of British Columbia, have been studying how particular amino acids in the amino terminal tails are subject to several types of covalent modifications, including acetylation, methylation, and phosphorylation. More than 50 different enzymes that selectively modify amino terminal tails have been identified in mammals. **Figure 14.7** shows examples of sites in the tails of H2A, H2B, H3, and H4 that can be modified.

These tail modifications can have two effects. First, they can directly influence interactions between nucleosomes. Second, histone modifications provide binding sites that are recognized by proteins. According to the histone code hypothesis, proposed by Brian Strahl and David Allis in 2000, the pattern of histone modification is recognized by particular proteins, much like a language or code. For example, one pattern might involve phosphorylation of the serine at the first amino acid in H2A and acetylation of the fifth and eighth amino acids in H4, which are lysines. A different pattern could involve acetylation of the fifth amino acid, a lysine, in H2B and methylation of the third amino acid in H4, which is an arginine.

The pattern of covalent modifications of amino terminal tails provides binding sites for proteins that subsequently affect the degree of chromatin compaction. One pattern of histone modification may attract proteins that cause the chromatin to become even more compact. This would silence the transcription of genes in the region. Alternatively, a different

Figure 14.7 **Examples of covalent modifications that occur to the amino terminal tails of histone proteins.** The amino acids are numbered from the amino terminus. The modifications shown here are m for methylation, p for phosphorylation, and ac for acetylation. Many more modifications can occur to the amino terminal tails; the ones shown here represent common examples.

combination of histone modifications may attract proteins, such as chromatin remodelling enzymes discussed in Chapter 12, that serve to loosen the chromatin and thereby promote gene transcription. In this way the histone code plays a key role in accessing the information within the genomes of eukaryotic species. Researchers are trying to unravel which patterns of histone modifications promote compaction and which promote a loosening of chromatin structure. In other words, they are trying to decipher the histone code.

of two sister chromatids that continue to be held together in the region of their centromeres. The highly condensed M phase chromosome cannot readily undergo transcription. Therefore, most transcriptional activity ceases as the M phase progresses.

14.2   MITOTIC CELL DIVISION

Learning Outcomes:

1. Describe the changes that chromosomes undergo as they move from the G2 phase of the cell cycle to the M phase.

2. Explain the structure and function of the mitotic spindle.
3. Outline the key events that occur during the phases of mitosis, and indicate what the products of mitosis are.

Now that we have looked at the changes that chromosomes undergo in structure as they move through the cell cycle, we are ready to turn our attention to the M phase of the cell cycle and the mechanism of cell division. There are, in fact two, different types of M phases. The primary one is called **mitotic cell division**. During the process of mitotic cell division, a cell divides to produce two new cells that are genetically identical to the original cell. By convention, the original cell is usually called the mother cell, and the new cells are the two daughter cells. Mitotic cell division involves division of the nuclear contents, called **mitosis**, and **cytokinesis**, which is the division of the contents of the cytoplasm.

One purpose of mitotic cell division is **asexual reproduction**. Certain unicellular eukaryotic organisms, such as baker's yeast (*Saccharomyces cerevisiae*) and the amoeba, increase their numbers in this manner. For asexual reproduction, a single-celled organism undergoes a mitotic division to produce two cells from the original mother cell. A second equally important reason for mitotic cell division is the production and maintenance of multicellularity. Multicellular organisms, such as plants, animals, and most fungi, rely on mitotic cell division to produce a multicellular organism from a single-celled zygote. Humans, for example, begin as a single fertilized egg, and repeated cellular divisions produce an adult with several trillion cells. As you might imagine, the precise transmission of chromosomes is critical during every cell division so that all cells of the body receive the correct amount of genetic material.

In this section, we will explore how the process of mitotic cell division requires the sorting of chromosomes. Once the chromosomes are sorted, cytokinesis finishes the work of cell division by dividing the cytoplasmic contents.

The Events of Mitosis

To understand the chromosomal composition of cells and the behaviour of chromosomes during cell division, scientists observe chromosomes with the use of microscopes. **Mitosis** is the sorting process that ensures that each daughter cell will obtain the correct number and types of chromosomes. Mitosis was first observed microscopically in the 1870s by a German biologist named Walter Flemming, who coined the term *mitosis* (from the Greek *mitos*, meaning "thread"). He studied the large, transparent skin cells of salamander larvae as they were dividing and noticed that chromosomes are constructed of "threads" that are doubled along their length. These double threads divided and moved apart, one going to each of the two daughter nuclei. By this mechanism, Flemming pointed out, the two daughter cells receive an identical group of threads, the same as the number of threads in the mother cell. Mitosis in a real animal cell is shown in **Figure 14.8b–f** (top portion), accompanied by an explanatory diagram below it.

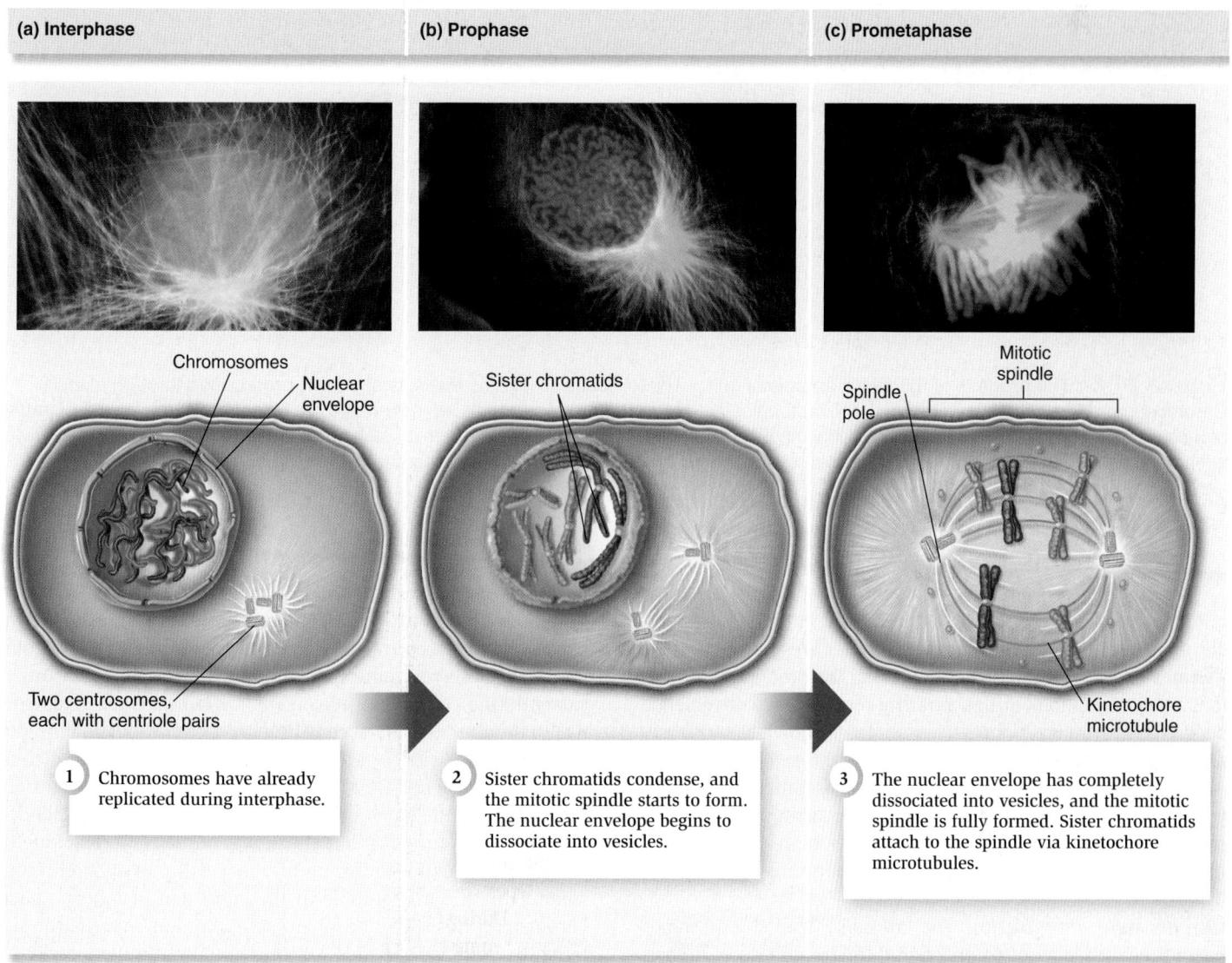

(a) Interphase

Chromosomes
Nuclear envelope
Two centrosomes, each with centriole pairs

1 Chromosomes have already replicated during interphase.

(b) Prophase

Sister chromatids

2 Sister chromatids condense, and the mitotic spindle starts to form. The nuclear envelope begins to dissociate into vesicles.

(c) Prometaphase

Mitotic spindle
Spindle pole
Kinetochore microtubule

3 The nuclear envelope has completely dissociated into vesicles, and the mitotic spindle is fully formed. Sister chromatids attach to the spindle via kinetochore microtubules.

(d) Metaphase

(e) Anaphase

(f) Telophase and cytokinesis

Metaphase plate

Individual chromosomes

Cleavage furrow

Polar microtubule

4 Sister chromatids align along the metaphase plate.

5 Sister chromatids separate, and individual chromosomes move toward the poles as kinetochore microtubules shorten. Polar microtubules lengthen and push the poles apart.

6 Chromosomes decondense, and the nuclear envelope re-forms. Cytokinesis separates the mother cell into two daughter cells, which begins with a cleavage furrow in animal cells.

Figure 14.8   The process of mitosis in an animal cell.   The top panel illustrates the cells of a newt progressing through mitosis. Chromosomes are stained purple, and the microtubules are green. The bottom panels are schematic drawings that emphasize the sorting and separation of the chromosomes. (The original diploid cell had six chromosomes, three in each set). At the start of mitosis, these have already replicated into 12 chromatids. The final result is two daughter cells, each containing six chromosomes.

Principle: *Living organisms grow, develop, and reproduce. To grow, multicellular organisms must increase the number of their cells and therefore must undergo mitosis.*

We now know that Flemming's threads are the sister chromatids that are produced by DNA replication and packaged with chromosomal proteins during the S phase. We also know that during G2, the cell was busily producing the proteins it needed for mitosis. Let's look at this amazing process. For convenience we divide the process of mitosis into phases known as prophase, metaphase, anaphase, and telophase. As the cell leaves G2, it enters the first stage of mitosis, known as prophase. During prophase two parallel sets of events are occurring: the chromosomes are getting into the configuration required for segregation, and the mitotic spindle apparatus is forming.

Chromosome Preparation for Mitosis   The chromosomes begin their last level of compaction during prophase of mitosis

and show the threadlike structure noted by Flemming and seen in the top portion of Figure 14.8b–f). As the chromosomes condense, the sister chromatids lose the cohesins that were holding them closely together, becoming distinct from each other, except in the centromere region (where cohesins are retained). Each chromosome has a **centromere**, a region of the chromosome with special DNA sequences and a greater degree of compaction. The special DNA of the centromere region can attract the proteins of the kinetochore. As you will see, the **kinetochore** is a complex of proteins that attach microtubules to each kinetochore and contain a motor protein that will move the chromosome along the microtubule in the latter half of mitosis. Each chromatid forms an active kinetochore. But importantly, the sister chromatids are still held together in the centromere region.

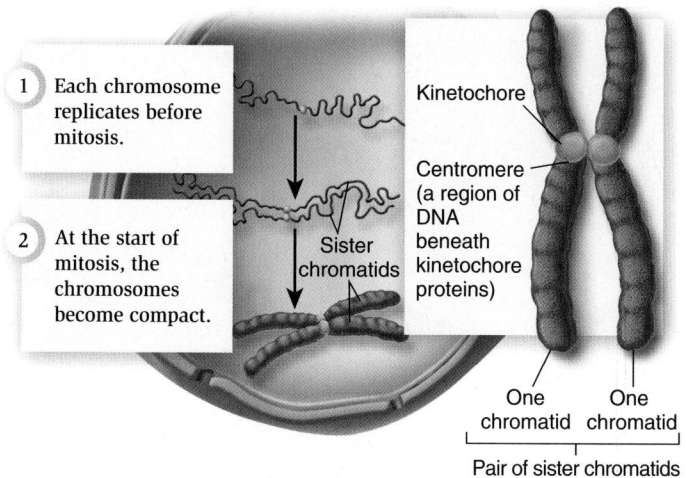

(a) Chromosome replication and compaction within the nucleus

1 Each chromosome replicates before mitosis.

2 At the start of mitosis, the chromosomes become compact.

Sister chromatids

Kinetochore

Centromere (a region of DNA beneath kinetochore proteins)

One chromatid   One chromatid

Pair of sister chromatids

(b) Schematic drawing of a metaphase chromosome within the nucleus

Figure 14.9 **Replication and compaction of chromosomes into pairs of sister chromatids.**   (a) Chromosomal replication producing a pair of sister chromatids. While the chromosomes are elongated, they are replicated to produce two copies that are connected and lie parallel. This is a pair of sister chromatids. Later, when the cell is preparing to divide, the sister chromatids condense into more compact structures that are easily seen with a light microscope. (b) A schematic drawing of a metaphase chromosome. This structure has two chromatids that lie side by side. The two chromatids are held together by cohesion proteins in their centromere region.

By the end of prophase the chromosomes are visible under a microscope and each chromosome can be seen to be composed of two chromatids, each with a functional kinetochore (**Figure 14.9**). In the simplified diagrams shown along the bottom of Figure 14.8 (b–f), the original mother cell contains six condensed chromosomes, with each chromosome composed of two sister chromatids.

Spindle Apparatus Preparation for Mitosis As the chromosomes are condensing and forming their kinetochores within the nucleus, the **mitotic spindle apparatus** (also known simply as the **mitotic spindle**) is being assembled in the cytoplasm. To understand the mitotic spindle, you must first recall that interphase cells have a cytoskeleton. One important part of the cytoskeleton is the microtubule array. At the onset of mitosis, there is one major microtubule organizing centre (MTOC) near one side of the nucleus, from which originate an array of microtubules. An example in an animal cell can be seen in **Figure 14.8a**. In animal cells the MTOC is associated with additional proteins that form a contractile band that functions during cytokinesis. In animal cells the MTOC and contractile proteins are visible as a structure known as a centrosome. Plants and fungi do not use a contractile band for cytokinesis; they have just the MTOC, which is detectable only as the location from which microtubules originate.

As the cell enters the prophase of mitosis, the MTOC duplicates, and in animal cells we can now see two centrosomes (Figure 14.8b). As prophase proceeds, the two MTOCs move

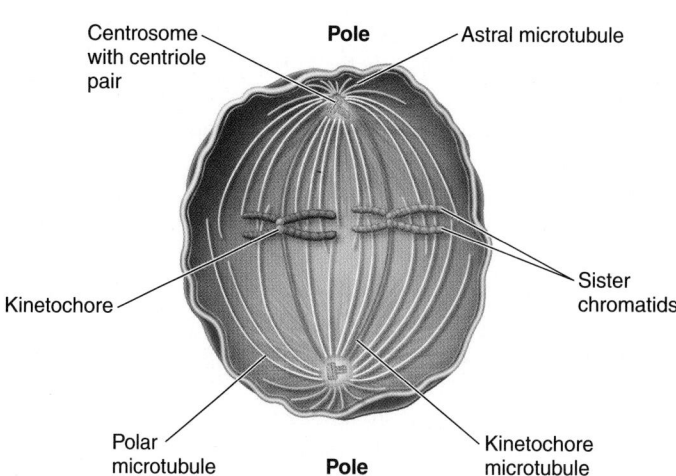

Centrosome with centriole pair

Pole

Astral microtubule

Kinetochore

Sister chromatids

Polar microtubule

Pole

Kinetochore microtubule

Figure 14.10   **The structure of the mitotic spindle.**   The mitotic spindle is formed by the microtubule organizing regions from three types of microtubules. The astral microtubules emanate away from the region between the poles. The polar microtubules project into the region between the two poles. The kinetochore microtubules are attached to the kinetochores of sister chromatids.

apart, positioning themselves on opposite sites of the nucleus. Even as they are moving, the two MTOCs are functional and are organizing an array of microtubules. After they have separated, each MTOC is positioned at one pole of the spindle apparatus.

As we noted, the spindle is formed from protein fibres called microtubules that grow out from the MTOCs. Each MTOC organizes the construction of the microtubules by rapidly polymerizing tubulin proteins. There are three types of spindle microtubules: astral, polar, and kinetochore microtubules (**Figure 14.10**). The **astral microtubules** are those microtubules that extend away from the nucleus; they are important for positioning the spindle apparatus within the cell. The other two types of the microtubules project toward the nucleus. We will look at these in the next section.

Chromosome and Spindle Interactions Now that we have looked at chromosome and spindle preparations, you are ready to think about how these two sets of preparations lead to separation of the chromosomes during mitosis. At the end of prophase the nuclear envelope disassembles. This marks the end of prophase and the beginning of the next stage, metaphase. Now that there is no nuclear envelope, the forming spindle invades the region where the chromosomes are. **Polar microtubules** project across the region defined by the two MTOC poles and meet up with microtubules originating from the opposite pole. Polar microtubules that overlap with a microtubule from the other pole are stabilized and play a role in the separation of the two poles. Finally, microtubules that bump into a kinetochore are attached to the kinetochore and become **kinetochore microtubules**; they will provide a track along which chromosomes move to the poles at the appropriate time.

Prometaphase (Figure 14.8c) is a term sometimes used to describe the first part of metaphase when the spindle fibres are invading the nuclear region and interacting with the kinetochores of chromatids. Because the kinetochores of sister chromatids are facing in opposite directions, they will ultimately attach microtubules from opposite poles. Eventually, as cells move beyond prometaphase, all the chromosomes will be lined up in the midregion, called the **metaphase plate**, with sister chromatids facing opposite poles (Figure 14.8d). This configuration results from the fact that sister chromatids are attached to microtubules from opposite poles, and all chromosomes are pushed to the centre. When microtubules that are polymerizing toward the centre zone bump into the noncentromere regions of chromosomes, they push them to the centre. When this alignment is complete, the cell is in the **metaphase** of mitosis (Figure 14.8d). Now that all pairs of sister chromatids are facing opposite poles, they are ready to be equally distributed into two daughter cells.

The next step in the sorting process occurs during **anaphase** (Figure 14.8e). At this stage the cohesin proteins that were retained at the centromeres are now removed and the connections between sister chromatids in the centromere regions are lost. Each chromatid, now considered to be an individual chromosome, is linked to one of the two poles by kinetochore microtubules. As anaphase proceeds, motor proteins within the kinetochore move along the kinetochore microtubule toward the pole, carrying the chromosome along with it.

The separation of the chromosomes is thus accomplished in part by the movement of the chromosomes to the poles. But the process is also assisted by a second mechanism because as the chromosomes are moving toward the pole, the two poles are moving apart. This occurs because the overlapping polar microtubules lengthen and push against each other, thereby pushing the poles farther apart. During the last part of mitosis, called **telophase**, the chromosomes have reached their respective poles, and the nuclear membranes now re-form to produce two separate nuclei, and the chromosomes decondense. In the explanatory diagram of Figure 14.8f, you can see that two nuclei are produced that each contain six chromosomes.

Cytokinesis In most cases, mitosis is quickly followed by cytokinesis, the process by which the two nuclei are segregated into two daughter cells, each containing a portion of the cytoplasmic contents. Although the stages of mitosis are similar between plant and animal cells, the process of cytokinesis is quite different. In animal cells cytokinesis involves a contractile band of proteins in the centrosome known as a **cleavage furrow**, which constricts like a drawstring to separate the cells (**Figure 14.11a**). In plants, the mother cell has a cell wall; the two daughter cells are separated by the formation of new cell wall material, called the **cell plate** (**Figure 14.11b**), that forms between the two daughter cells.

The Importance of M Phase Mitosis and cytokinesis ultimately produce two daughter cells having the same number of chromosomes as the mother cell. Unless a mistake went uncorrected during DNA replication, or a mistake occurred during mitosis, the two daughter cells are genetically identical both to each other and to the mother cell from which they were derived. Thus, the critical consequence of this sorting process

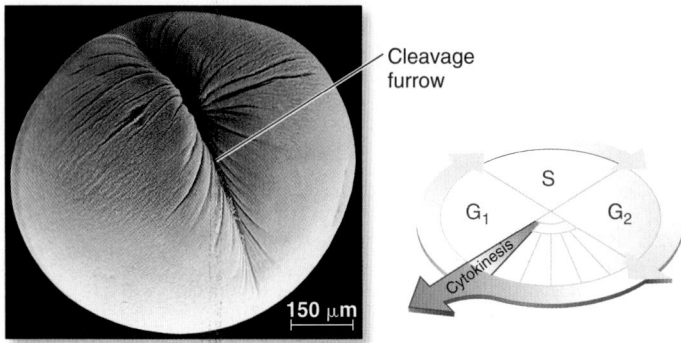

(a) Cleavage of an animal cell

(b) Formation of a cell plate in a plant cell

Figure 14.11 Micrographs showing cytokinesis in animal and plant cells.

is to ensure genetic consistency from one cell to the next. Asexual reproduction and multicellularity both rely on the repeated M phase processes of mitosis and cytokinesis.

14.3 EUKARYOTIC CHROMOSOMES ARE INHERITED IN SETS

Learning Outcomes:

1. Describe the features of chromosomes and how sets of chromosomes are examined microscopically and organized into a karyotype.
2. Distinguish sister chromatids from homologous chromosomes.
3. Explain the level of similarity and difference between the DNA sequences of homologous chromosomes.

You have just seen that when a cell prepares to divide, the chromosomes become more tightly compacted, which shortens them and increases their diameter. A consequence of this shortening is that during the M phase chromosomes take on distinctive shapes, and the numbers of chromosomes in a cell can be determined with relatively simple microscopy techniques. **Cytogenetics** is the field of genetics that involves the microscopic examination of chromosomes. Cytogeneticists have found that a given species has a characteristic number of chromosomes, each with a specific size and centromere location.

M Phase Chromosomes Can Be Organized into a Karyotype

Figure 14.12 shows the general procedure for preparing and viewing M phase chromosomes from a eukaryotic cell. In this example the cells are obtained from human blood. In particular, the chromosomes within the lymphocytes (a type of white blood cell) are examined. A sample of the blood cells is obtained and treated with drugs that stimulate the cells to divide. The actively dividing cells are centrifuged to concentrate them and then mixed with a hypotonic solution that makes the cells swell. The expansion in cell structure causes the chromosomes to spread out, making it easier to see each individual chromosome. Next, the cells are concentrated by a second centrifugation and

treated with a fixative that preserves their structure. The cells are then exposed to a chemical dye that binds to the chromosomes and stains them. As we will learn later, this gives chromosomes a distinctive banding pattern that greatly enhances their contrast and ability to be uniquely identified. The cells are then placed on a slide and viewed with a light microscope. In a cytogenetics laboratory the microscopes are equipped with a digital camera to photograph the chromosomes. On a computer screen the chromosome images can be organized in a standard way, usually from largest to smallest. A photographic representation of the chromosomes, as in the photograph in step (5) of Figure 14.12, is called a **karyotype**. A karyotype reveals how many chromosomes are found within the cell and allows the identification of all the chromosomes of the set.

By studying the karyotypes of many species, scientists have discovered that eukaryotic chromosomes occur in sets; each set is composed of several different types of chromosomes. For example, one set of human chromosomes contains 23 different

1 A sample of blood is collected and treated with drugs that stimulate cell division. The sample is then subjected to centrifugation.

Supernatant

Blood cells — Pellet

2 The supernatant is discarded, and the cell pellet is suspended in a hypotonic solution. This causes the cells to swell and the chromosomes to spread out from one another.

Hypotonic solution

3 The sample is subjected to centrifugation a second time to concentrate the cells. The cells are suspended in a fixative, stained, and placed on a slide.

Fix   Stain

Blood cells

4 The slide is viewed by a light microscope equipped with a camera; the sample is seen on a computer screen. The chromosomes can be photographed and arranged electronically on the screen.

5

A pair of sister chromatids

G band

Homologues

For a diploid human cell, two complete sets of chromosomes from a single cell constitute a karyotype of that cell.

Figure 14.12   The procedure for making a karyotype.

Concept check: *Researchers usually treat cells with drugs that stimulate them to divide before the procedure for making a karyotype. Why would this be useful?*

types of chromosomes. By convention, the chromosomes are numbered according to size, with the largest chromosomes having the smallest numbers. For example, human chromosomes 1, 2, and 3 are relatively large, whereas 21 and 22 are the two smallest (Figure 14.12). This numbering system does not apply to sex chromosomes. Many animal species have sex chromosomes—one pair of chromosomes that are different in males and females and determine the sex of the individual. Sex chromosomes are designated with the letters X and Y in humans.

A second feature of many eukaryotic cells is that the cell may contain two complete sets of chromosomes. Again, if we consider humans as an example, the karyotype shown in Figure 14.12 contains two sets of chromosomes, with 23 different chromosomes in each set. Therefore, this human cell contains 46 chromosomes. A person's cells have 46 chromosomes each because the individual inherited one set from the father and one set from the mother. When the cells of an organism carry two sets of chromosomes, that organism is said to be **diploid**. Geneticists use the designation $2n$ to represent the number of chromosomes found in the zygote (typically the diploid number). For example, humans are $2n$, where $2n = 46$. Most human cells are diploid. The exceptions are **gametes**—sperm and egg cells. The designation $1n$ indicates the number of chromosomes in the gametes (called the haploid number). In humans $1n = 23$. In diploid organisms the $1n$ number symbolizes that one set of chromosomes is present in a gamete. For humans there are 23 chromosomes in one complete set.

When an organism is diploid, there are pairs of chromosomes for each chromosome type in the set. The two chromosomes of a pair of chromosomes are called homologous chromosomes or **homologues** for simplicity. As illustrated in Figure 14.12, a diploid cell has a pair of chromosome #1, a pair of chromosome #2, and so forth. For each pair, the chromosome on the left is a homologue to the one on the right and vice versa. What is the source of the pair of chromosomes? Diploid organisms typically have pairs of chromosomes because they originate from a zygote that received one complete set of chromosomes from the parental sperm and the other complete set from the parental egg.

If the egg and sperm originate from members of the same species, the homologous chromosomes should be very similar. Each of the two chromosomes of a homologous pair are usually nearly identical in size and contain a similar composition of genetic material, having the same set of genes distributed along their length. The two versions of the same gene (one from the sperm and one from the egg) need not be identical in DNA sequence. As an example, consider an eye colour gene in humans. One homologous chromosome that originates from the mother's egg might carry a version of the eye colour gene associated with brown eyes, while the gene on the homologue that originated from the father's sperm might be associated with blue eyes. Thus the two versions of the gene on homologues might be very similar in DNA sequence, but not identical; this is not surprising given that the DNA helices of the homologues originated from two different parents. This is in sharp contrast to the same gene that is carried on the two sister chromatids that originated from replication of the same one DNA helix.

The DNA sequences on homologous chromosomes are very similar. In most cases, the sequence of bases on one homologue differs by less than 1% from the sequence on the other homologue. For example, the DNA sequence of chromosome 1 that you inherited from your mother would be greater than 99% identical to the DNA sequence of chromosome 1 that you inherited from your father. Nevertheless, keep in mind that the sequences are not identical. The slight differences in DNA sequence provide important variation in gene function. Again, if we use an eye colour gene as an example, a minor difference in DNA sequence distinguishes two forms of the gene: brown versus blue.

As you will see in Chapter 15 some species have **sex chromosomes** that have a role in determining the sex of individuals. The striking similarity between homologous chromosomes does *not* apply to the sex chromosomes (for example, the X and Y chromosomes of mammals). These sex chromosomes differ in size and genetic composition. Certain genes that are found on the X chromosome are not found on the Y chromosome, and vice versa. The X and Y chromosomes are not considered homologous chromosomes, although they do have short regions of homology.

Homologous Chromosomes Are Not Associated During Mitotic M Phase, But Are Associated During Meiotic M Phase

So far we have looked at the most commonly used M phase—mitosis. When we discussed mitosis, it was not necessary to consider homologous chromosomes because each chromosome acts independently during mitosis. The key event of a mitotic nuclear division is to separate the genetically identical sister chromatids. As you will see in the next section, some organisms have a phase in their life cycle when they consist of haploid cells (or have a sector of their body with haploid cells) as well as a phase in their life cycle when they consist of diploid cells. Mitosis can work well for either haploid or diploid cells, as long as the chromosomes have been replicated and consist of two sister chromatids. The purpose of mitosis, as we have discussed, is to produce two genetically identical daughter cells from one original mother cell. This is quite different from the other type of M phase, a process known as meiosis. For meiosis the purpose is to reduce the chromosome number, and for this it is essential that homologous chromosomes become temporarily, but intimately, associated.

14.4 / MEIOSIS AND SEXUAL REPRODUCTION

Learning Outcomes:

1. Contrast the role of meiosis with that of mitosis and relate this to the differences between prophase I of meiosis and the prophase of mitosis.
2. Describe the processes of synapsis and crossing over.
3. Outline the key events that occur during the phases of meiosis.
4. Compare and contrast mitosis and meiosis, focusing on key steps that account for the different outcomes of these two processes.

We now turn our attention to the special M phase known as meiosis and its role in the process of sexual reproduction. As discussed earlier, a diploid cell contains two homologous sets of chromosomes. For example, a diploid human cell contains 23 pairs of chromosomes for a total of 46 chromosomes. A **haploid** cell contains a single set of chromosomes; a human haploid cell (sperm or egg cell) contains only 23 chromosomes. **Sexual reproduction** requires a **fertilization** event in which two haploid gametes unite to re-create the diploid number of chromosomes in the **zygote**. In the case of many multicellular species, the zygote then grows and divides by mitosis to produce a multicellular organism with many diploid cells.

Meiosis is the special nuclear division that produces haploid cells from a diploid reproductive cell. The term *meiosis* literally means "to make smaller," referring to the smaller number of chromosomes found in cells following this process. For meiosis the chromosomes must be correctly sorted and distributed in a way that reduces the chromosome number to half its original diploid value but ensures that the haploid cell has one complete set. In the case of human gametes, for example, each gamete must receive half the total number of chromosomes, but not just any 23 chromosomes will do. A gamete must receive one chromosome from each of the 23 pairs. For this to happen, two rounds of divisions are necessary; the two rounds are called meiosis I and meiosis II (**Figure 14.13**). In the first meiotic division (called the reductional division) homologous chromosomes become associated and then are separated and segregated into daughter nuclei. The second meiotic division (called the equational division) occurs in both daughter nuclei and separates sister chromatids. When a cell begins meiosis, it contains homologous pairs. When meiosis is complete, the starting diploid cell will have produced four haploid cells. In this section we will examine the cellular events of meiosis that reduce the chromosome number, typically from diploid to haploid. In addition we will briefly consider how this process plays a role in the life cycles of fungi, plants, and animals.

The First Meiotic Division, Meiosis I, Separates Homologous Chromosomes

Like mitosis, meiosis begins after a cell has progressed through the G_1, S, and G_2 phases of the cell cycle. But unlike mitosis, the sorting that occurs during **meiosis I** separates homologues. This event is unique to meiosis and requires that homologous chromosomes first become associated. In prophase I the replicated chromosomes begin to condense; some important differences exist in the chromosome organization of meiotic (compared with mitotic) chromosomes. For the prophase of meiosis I, sister chromatids are held together all along their length and must share one functional kinetochore (unlike mitosis, in which each chromatid forms its own kinetochore). While still relatively decondensed, homologous chromosomes accomplish two key events that do not occur in mitosis. In the first event, homologous chromosomes (each consisting of a pair of sister chromatids) become very closely associated to form a **bivalent** (**Figure 14.14**). The process of forming a bivalent is termed **synapsis**. In most eukaryotic species an elaborate protein structure known as the synaptonemal complex is formed between homologous chromosomes.

The second meiosis-specific event that occurs early in meiosis is **crossing over**, which involves a physical, reciprocal

Figure 14.13 **How the process of meiosis reduces chromosome number.** This simplified diagram emphasizes the reduction in chromosome number as a diploid cell divides by meiosis to produce four haploid cells.

exchange between chromosome pieces of homologous (nonsister) chromatids (Figure 14.14). As discussed in the next chapter, crossing over can increase the genetic variation of a species. As prophase I continues, the chromosomes continue to condense. By the end of prophase I the synaptonemal complex breaks down and homologous chromosomes tend to separate except at the sites of crossovers; at crossovers the connection between homologues persists and is reinforced with chromosomal proteins. This connection is called a **chiasma** (plural: chiasmata), because it physically resembles the Greek letter chi, Χ. Chiasmata result from a combination of two factors: (1) the reciprocal exchange that now connects nonsister chromatids into one DNA helix, and (2) the fact that sister chromatids

1 Homologous chromosomes condense.

Synaptonemal complex forming

2 Synapsis begins.

Bivalent

3 Bivalents form.

Chiasma

4 Crossing over occurs.

5 Chiasma becomes visible as homologous chromosomes lose the synaptonemal complex.

Figure 14.14   Formation of a bivalent and crossing over during meiosis I.   At the beginning of meiosis, homologous chromosomes pair up to form a bivalent, usually with a synaptonemal complex between them. Crossing over occurs between homologous, nonsister chromatids within the bivalent. During this process homologues exchange segments of chromosomes. For simplicity the two homologous chromosomes are shown side by side, with two nonsister chromatids close and two much farther apart. In real cells, however, the homologous chromosomes actually lie on top of each other; hence, both nonsister chromatids of homologous chromosomes are equivalent distances apart.

 Principle: *Structure determines function. Homologous chromosomes must become intimately associated to exchange chromosome segments.*

are still held together all along their length by cohesin proteins. The number of crossovers is carefully controlled by cells and depends on the number and sizes of the chromosomes. Variation in the total number of reciprocal exchanges per homologous chromosome and per nucleus exists among species and often even between sexes of the same species. By the end of prophase I, bivalents are condensed and chiasmata are visible. Now that you have an understanding of bivalent formation and crossing over, you are ready to consider the remaining phases of meiosis (**Figure 14.15**).

As the homologous chromosomes form bivalents within the nucleus, the first meiotic spindle is forming outside the nucleus (**Figure 14.15a**). As in mitosis there are astral microtubules, polar microtubules, and kinetochore microtubules. At the end of the first prophase, the nuclear membrane disassembles, allowing the spindle apparatus to invade the region containing the condensing chromosomes (**Figure 14.15b**). In prometaphase I microtubules can interact with kinetochores. Recall that for the first meiotic division sister chromatids share one kinetochore. Thus, for prometaphase it is the two kinetochores of homologous chromosomes that capture microtubules oriented to opposite poles and ultimately are aligned in the mid-region between the poles. At metaphase I the bivalents are organized along the metaphase plate. It is important to notice that each bivalent (consisting of paired homologous chromosomes) aligns on the metaphase plate independently of all of the other bivalents. For example, in one meiosis, the homologous chromosomes originating from one parent (whose chromosome contributions are shown with dark red, dark green, and dark blue chromosomes) may be facing the pole on the right, and the homologous chromosomes from the other parent (represented with light red, light green, and light blue chromosomes) might go to the pole on the left. But in other meiosis in the same individual (for example, **Figure 14.15c**) you could have the dark red chromosomes moving to the same pole as the light green and light blue chromosomes, while the light red moves to the same pole as the dark green and dark blue ones. In yet other meiotic cells from the same individual, homologues could be arranged differently along the metaphase plate (for example, dark red, dark blue, and light green to one pole and light red, light blue, and dark green to the other pole). Because eukaryotic species typically have many chromosomes per set, bivalents can be randomly aligned along the metaphase plate in a variety of ways. For example, consider that humans have 23 chromosomes per set. The possible number of different, random alignments is 2^n, where n equals the number of chromosomes per set. Thus, in humans, this equals 2^{23}, or more than 8 million possibilities. Because the homologues are genetically similar but not identical, the random relative alignment of homologous chromosomes (to one or the other pole) provides a mechanism to promote a vast amount of genetic diversity among the resulting haploid cells. When meiosis is complete, it is very unlikely that any two human gametes will have the same combination of homologous chromosomes.

The segregation of homologous chromosomes occurs during anaphase I (**Figure 14.15d**). At this time sister chromatids lose their connections to each other except in the region of the centromere. This allows the chiasmata to come apart, removing the connections between homologues. The still-connected sister

Meiosis I

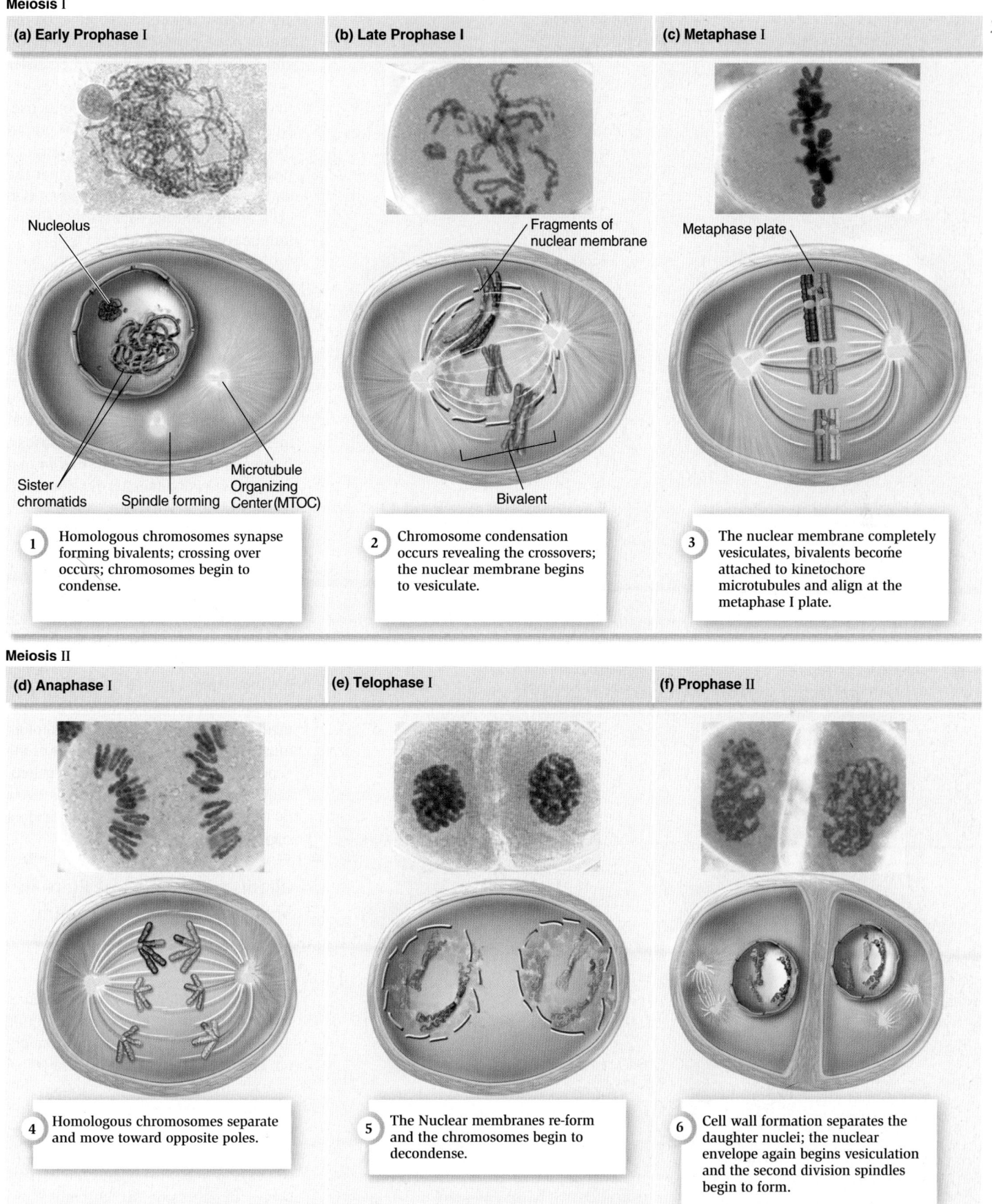

(a) Early Prophase I

Nucleolus

Sister chromatids

Spindle forming

Microtubule Organizing Center (MTOC)

1 Homologous chromosomes synapse forming bivalents; crossing over occurs; chromosomes begin to condense.

(b) Late Prophase I

Fragments of nuclear membrane

Bivalent

2 Chromosome condensation occurs revealing the crossovers; the nuclear membrane begins to vesiculate.

(c) Metaphase I

Metaphase plate

3 The nuclear membrane completely vesiculates, bivalents become attached to kinetochore microtubules and align at the metaphase I plate.

Meiosis II

(d) Anaphase I

4 Homologous chromosomes separate and move toward opposite poles.

(e) Telophase I

5 The Nuclear membranes re-form and the chromosomes begin to decondense.

(f) Prophase II

6 Cell wall formation separates the daughter nuclei; the nuclear envelope again begins vesiculation and the second division spindles begin to form.

Figure 14.15 **The stages of meiosis in a plant cell.** The top portion of each panel shows micrographs of nuclei of the Easter lily ($2n = 24$) progressing through the indicated stages of meiosis. The lower panel gives a diagrammatic representation of the comparable event in a simpler nucleus ($2n = 6$).

(g) Metaphase II

⑦ Nuclear membrane completely vesiculates. Sister chromatids attach to spindle via kinetochore microtubules and align along the metaphase plate.

(h) Anaphase II

⑧ Sister chromatids separate and individual chromosomes move toward poles as kinetochore microtubules shorten. Polar microtubules lengthen and push poles apart.

(i) Telophase II

⑨ Chromosomes decondense and nuclear membranes reform.

(j) Tetrad with cytokinesis

Four haploid cells

⑩ Cell walls form around each nucleus, but all four cells remain enclosed in a common wall, forming a tetrad.

chromatids migrate to one pole via the motor protein on their shared kinetochore. Finally, at telophase I, the sister chromatids have reached their respective poles, and they then decondense. Nuclear membranes now form around the two chromosome sets to produce two separate nuclei. If we consider the end result of meiosis I, we see that two cells are produced, each with half the number of chromosomes.

The Second Meiotic Division, Meiosis II, Separates Sister Chromatids

Meiosis I is followed by cytokinesis and then **meiosis II** (see Figure 14.15). No S phase occurs between meiosis I and meiosis II. The sorting events of meiosis II are similar to those of mitosis in that during the second meiotic division, each chromatid forms its own kinetochore; sister chromatids are connected only in the region of their centromeres; sister chromatids are lined up on the metaphase plate, facing opposite poles; and, finally, sister chromatids go to opposite poles during the second anaphase. The nuclear envelope reforms at telophase II. Four haploid nuclei are produced by the end of the second meiotic division. If meiosis is done correctly, all four haploid nuclei will have one complete set of the genetic material but will not be genetically identical because of the crossovers that have occurred and the independent segregation of each bivalent.

Changes in a Few Key Steps in Meiosis and Mitosis Account for the Different Outcomes of These Two Processes

If we compare the outcome of meiosis with that of mitosis, the results are quite different. Mitosis produces two daughter cells that are genetically identical to each other and to the mother cell. In our example shown in Figure 14.8, the starting cell has six chromosomes (three homologous pairs of chromosomes), and both daughter cells have copies of the same six chromosomes.

Table 14.1	A Comparison of Mitosis, Meiosis I, and Meiosis II		
Event	**Mitosis**	**Meiosis I**	**Meiosis II**
Synapsis during prophase	No	Yes, bivalents are formed	No
Crossing over during prophase	Rarely	Commonly	Rarely
Attachment to poles at prometaphase	Sister chromatids are attached to kinetochores from opposite poles.	A pair of sister chromatids is attached to the same pole.	A pair of sister chromatids is attached to opposite poles.
Alignment on the metaphase plate	Sister chromatids	Bivalents	Sister chromatids
Type of separation at anaphase	Sister chromatids separate. A single chromatid, now called a chromosome, moves to one pole.	Homologues of each bivalent separate to opposite poles. The sister chromatids of each homologue move together to the same pole.	Sister chromatids separate. A single chromatid, now called a chromosome, moves to one pole.

By comparison, meiosis reduces the number of sets of chromosomes. In the example shown in Figure 14.15, the starting cell has six chromosomes, while the four daughter cells have only three chromosomes each. These daughter cells do not contain a random mix of three chromosomes: each haploid daughter cell contains one complete set of chromosomes, while the original diploid mother cell has two complete sets. **Table 14.1** emphasizes the differences between certain key steps in meiosis and mitosis that account for the different outcomes of these two processes.

14.5 MITOSIS, MEIOSIS, AND FERTILIZATION ALLOW SEXUALLY REPRODUCING SPECIES TO PRODUCE HAPLOID AND DIPLOID CELLS AT DIFFERENT TIMES IN THEIR LIFE CYCLES

Learning Outcomes:

1. Distinguish among the life cycles of diploid-dominant species, haploid-dominant species, and species that exhibit an alternation of generations.
2. Describe the roles of meiosis, fertilization, and mitosis in the life cycle of each type of species.

Let's now turn our attention to the relationship among mitosis, meiosis, and sexual reproduction in the life cycles of animals, plants, fungi, and protists. For any given species the sequence of events that produces another generation of organisms is known as a **life cycle**. For sexually reproducing organisms, this involves a shift between haploid cells or organisms and diploid cells or organisms (**Figure 14.16**).

Most animal species are diploid, and their haploid gametes are considered to be a specialized type of cell destined for fertilization. For this reason animals are viewed as **diploid-dominant species** (**Figure 14.16a**). By comparison many fungi and some protists use an opposite strategy. They are **haploid-dominant species** (**Figure 14.16b**). In fungi, such as bread mould, the multicellular organism is haploid ($1n$). During sexual reproduction haploid cells unite to create a diploid zygote, which then immediately proceeds through meiosis to create four haploid cells called spores. Each spore goes through mitotic divisions to create a multicellular haploid organism.

Plants and some algae have life cycles that are intermediate between the extreme cases of diploid or haploid dominance. Such species exhibit an **alternation of generations** (**Figure 14.16c**). These organisms alternate between multicellular diploid forms, called **sporophytes**, and multicellular haploid forms, called **gametophytes**. Meiotic cells within the sporophyte produce haploid spores, which divide by mitosis to produce the male and female gametophytes. Special cells within the male and female gametophytes differentiate into haploid gametes—sperm and egg, respectively. Fertilization occurs between two gametes, producing a diploid zygote that then undergoes repeated mitotic cell divisions to create the new sporophyte.

Among different plant species, the *relative* sizes of the gametophyte and sporophyte vary greatly. In simpler plants, such as mosses, the haploid gametophyte is a small but visible multicellular organism, while the diploid sporophyte is tiny and survives within the haploid organism. In more complex plants, such as ferns, as shown in Figure 14.16c, both the diploid sporophyte and the haploid gametophyte can grow independently. The sporophyte is considerably larger and is the organism that we commonly think of as a fern. In the most complex, seed-bearing plants, such as roses and oak trees, the diploid sporophyte is the large multicellular plant, while the gametophyte is composed of only a few cells formed within the sporophyte.

When comparing animals, plants, and fungi, it's interesting to consider how gametes are made. In animals the gametes are the direct products of meiosis. In contrast, in plants the meiotic products divide by mitosis to produce the multicellular haploid gametophyte. Within the multicellular gametophyte, certain cells become specialized as gametes.

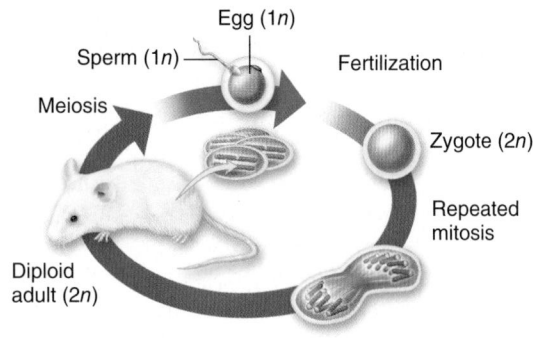

(a) Animal life cycle (mouse)—diploid dominant

(b) Fungal life cycle (bread mould)—haploid dominant

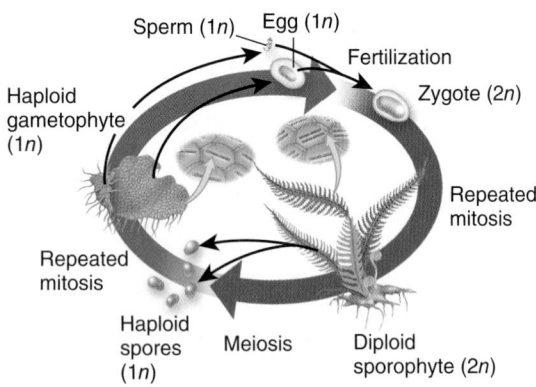

(c) Plant life cycle (fern)—alternation of generations

Figure 14.16 **A comparison of three types of sexual life cycles.** Meiosis produces haploid cells, fertilization creates diploid zygotes, and mitosis will occur variably depending on the type of life cycle.

 Principle: *Living organisms grow, develop, and reproduce. To grow multicellularly, organisms must have cells that undergo mitosis. For sexual reproduction some special cells must undergo meiosis, and egg and sperm must combine via fertilization.*

Concept check: *What is the main reason for meiosis? What is the reason for mitosis in animals, in plants, and in fungi?*

14.6 VARIATION IN CHROMOSOME STRUCTURE AND NUMBER

Learning Outcomes:

1. Describe how chromosomes can vary in size, centromere location, and number.
2. Identify the four types of chromosome rearrangements that can occur through large-scale chromosome mutations.
3. Compare and contrast aneuploid with euploidy changes and allopolyploid and autopolyploid changes.
4. Give examples of how changes in chromosome number affect the characteristics of animals and plants.

In the previous sections of this chapter, we examined two important features of chromosomes: their structure, and the two sorting processes (mitosis and meiosis) that maintain the normal species chromosome number following cell division. In this section we will examine how the organization of genes along a chromosome and the numbers of chromosomes within an organism can vary within and between species.

The study of chromosomal variation is important for several reasons. Not surprisingly, geneticists have discovered that variations in chromosome organization and number can have major effects on the characteristics of an organism. For example, we now know that several human genetic diseases and cancers are caused by such changes. In addition, changes in chromosome organization and number have been an important force in the evolution of new species. This topic is considered in Chapter 23.

Natural Variation Exists in Chromosome Structure and Number

Before we examine chromosome variation, we need to return to the concept of the karyotype. To determine the normal karyotype of a species, a cytogeneticist microscopically examines the chromosomes from several members of the species and then describes the set of chromosomes. Cytogeneticists strive to identify each different chromosome of a species' set. Cytogeneticists have various ways to classify and identify chromosomes in their metaphase form. The three most commonly used features are size, location of the centromere, and banding patterns that are revealed when the chromosomes are treated with stains. Based on centromere location, each chromosome is classified as **metacentric** (near the middle), **submetacentric** (off centre), **acrocentric** (near one end), or **telocentric** (very near the end, followed only by telomeric DNA sequences) (**Figure 14.17a**). Because the centromere is never exactly in the centre of a chromosome, each chromosome has a short arm and a long arm. The short arm is designated with the letter *p* (from the French *petite*); the long arm is designated with the letter *q*. In telocentric chromosomes the short arm may be nearly invisible, consisting only of telomeric DNA sequences required to stabilize the end. Using the mentioned criteria, a karyotype is generated from a chromosome preparation by placing the largest chromosomes

(a) A comparison of centromeric locations

Metacentric   Submetacentric   Acrocentric   Telocentric

A pair of sister chromatids

Centromere

G-band

Homologous chromosomes each existing as a pair of sister chromatids

(b) Giemsa staining of human chromosomes

Figure 14.17 Features of normal metaphase chromosomes. (a) A comparison of centromeric locations. (b) Illustrations of human chromosomes that have been treated and then stained with Giemsa to show G bands.

first with the short arms on top and the long arms on the bottom (**Figure 14.17**).

Because different chromosomes of a species often have similar sizes and centromeric locations, cytogeneticists must use additional methods to accurately identify each chromosome within a karyotype. For detailed identification, chromosomes are treated with stains to produce characteristic banding patterns. Cytogeneticists use several different staining procedures to identify specific chromosomes. An example is Giemsa stain, which, when combined with specific pretreatment of the chromosomes, can produce **G banding** (**Figure 14.17b**). The alternating pattern of G bands is unique for each type of chromosome.

The karyotype for a given species tends to be relatively constant. In most cases normal individuals of the same species will have the same number and types of chromosomes; different species will have their own distinctive karyotype. For example, the normal chromosome composition of human cells is two sets of 23 chromosomes for a total of 46. Other diploid species can have different numbers of chromosomes. Dogs have 78 chromosomes (39 per haploid set), fruit flies have 8 chromosomes (4 per set), and tomatoes have 24 chromosomes (12 per set).

The inspection of karyotypes is useful in two ways. Karyotype analysis can be used diagnostically to identify chromosomal mutations that can be associated with disease. Karyotype analysis is also useful in understanding evolutionary relationships and the role of chromosomal mutation in the evolution of new species. We will now look at some of the types of chromosome mutations that are rare but nonetheless found in natural populations.

Large-Scale Mutations Can Rearrange Chromosome Segments

Let's now consider how the organization of genes along normal chromosomes can be modified by chromosomal mutations. Chromosomal mutations are distinguished from simpler mutations in that they typically affect more than one gene. The chromosomal mutations we will consider are also called chromosome rearrangements; the four categories are deficiencies, duplications, inversions, and translocations (**Figure 14.18**). A major source of these rearrangements is DNA binding chemicals or ionizing radiation that can break the phosphodiester backbones of chromosomes. Cells have mechanisms to detect and repair these breaks, but sometimes the broken chromosomes are put back together incorrectly, causing the rearrangement.

Deficiencies and duplications are changes in the total amount of genetic material in a single chromosome. When a **deficiency** occurs, a segment of chromosomal material is missing. In other words the affected chromosome is deficient in a significant amount of genetic material. The term **deletion** is also used to describe a missing region of a chromosome. In contrast in a **duplication** a section of a chromosome occurs two or more times in a row or is duplicated in more than one chromosome region.

The consequences of a deficiency or duplication depend on the size of the affected region and whether the region was rich in genes that are vital to the development of the organism. When deficiencies or duplications have an effect, they are usually detrimental. Larger changes in the amount of genetic material tend to be more harmful because more genes are missing or duplicated. Also it is generally the case that the more complex the body plan of the organism, the less it tolerates deletions and duplications. Thus, plants tolerate these chromosomal mutations more than do vertebrate animals.

Inversions and translocations are chromosomal mutations that do not change the total number of genes, but create rearrangements of genes. An **inversion** is a change in the direction of the genetic material along a single chromosome. When a segment of one chromosome has been inverted, the order of G bands is opposite to that of a normal chromosome (see Figure 14.18). A **translocation** occurs when one segment of a chromosome becomes attached to a different chromosome. In a **simple translocation** a single piece of chromosome is attached

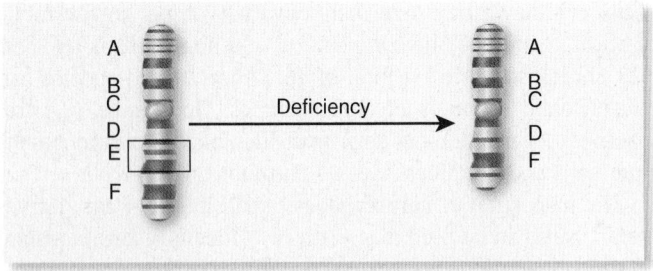

(a) Deletion: Removes a segment of chromosome.

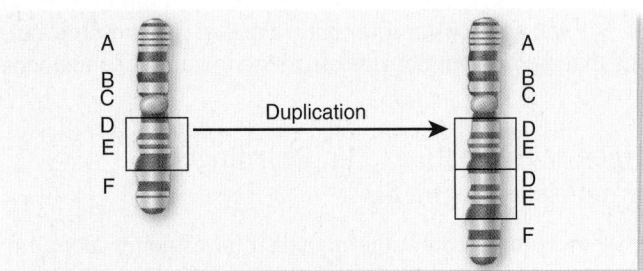

(b) Duplication: Doubles a particular region.

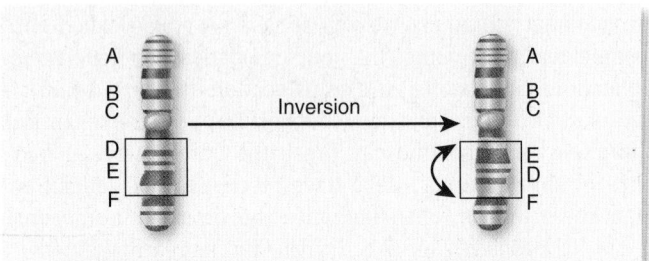

(c) Inversion: Flips a region to the opposite orientation.

(d) Simple translocation: Moves a segment of 1 chromosome to another chromosome.

(e) Reciprocal translocation: Exchanges pieces between 2 different chromosomes.

Figure 14.18   Types of changes in chromosome structure.

to another chromosome. In a **reciprocal translocation** two different types of chromosomes exchange pieces, thereby producing two abnormal chromosomes carrying translocations. If no genetic material is lost as the inversion or translocation occurs, then the individual with the inversion or translocation may not suffer any reduction in viability. But the rearrangement will usually cause problems during meiosis and hence the individual with the rearrangement will have some reduction in fertility.

Variation Occurs in the Number of Individual Chromosomes and in the Number of Chromosome Sets

Let's now turn to changes in the chromosome number. Variations in chromosome number can be categorized in two ways: variation in the number of sets of chromosomes, and variation in the number of particular chromosomes within a set. The suffix *-ploid* or *-ploidy* refers to a complete set of chromosomes. Organisms that are **euploid** (the prefix *eu-* means "true") have complete sets of chromosomes. For example, in a species that is diploid, a euploid organism would have two sets of chromosomes in its somatic cells. In *Drosophila melanogaster,* for example, a normal individual has eight chromosomes. The species is diploid, having two sets of four chromosomes (**Figure 14.19a**). Organisms can vary with regard to the number of sets of chromosomes they have. For example, on rare occasions, an abnormal fruit fly can be produced with three sets of four chromosomes each (for a total of 12 chromosomes) (**Figure 14.19b**). Such organisms are still euploid but since they have more than two complete sets, they are called **tetraploid**. A diploid organism's ploidy level is referred to as $2X$, a **triploid** organism's as $3X$, a tetraploid organism's as $4X$, and so forth. In diploids the number of chromosomes in the zygote $(2n) = 2X$, but in polyploids the number of chromosomes in the zygote $(2n)$ can be higher, such as in tetraploids, for example, which are $2n = 4X$.

The second way that chromosome number can vary is a phenomenon called **aneuploidy**. This refers to an alteration in the number of particular chromosomes, so that the total number of chromosomes is not an exact multiple of a set. For example, an abnormal fruit fly could contain nine chromosomes instead of eight because it had three copies of chromosome 2 instead of the normal two copies (**Figure 14.19c**). Such an animal is said to have trisomy 2 or to be **trisomic**. Instead of being perfectly diploid, a trisomic animal is $2n + 1$. By comparison, a fruit fly could be lacking a single chromosome, such as chromosome 1, and contain a total of seven chromosomes $(2n - 1)$. This fruit fly is **monosomic** and would be described as having monosomy 1.

Nondisjunction and Interspecies Breeding Are Common Mechanisms That Change Chromosome Number

Variations in chromosome number both within and between species are fairly widespread and have a significant impact on the characteristics of plants and animals. For these reasons researchers have wanted to understand the mechanisms that

Figure 14.19 Types of variation in chromosome number. **(a)** The normal diploid number of chromosomes in *Drosophila*. The X chromosome is also called chromosome 1. Examples of chromosomes of polyploid fly karyotype **(b)** and aneuploid fly karyotype **(c)**.

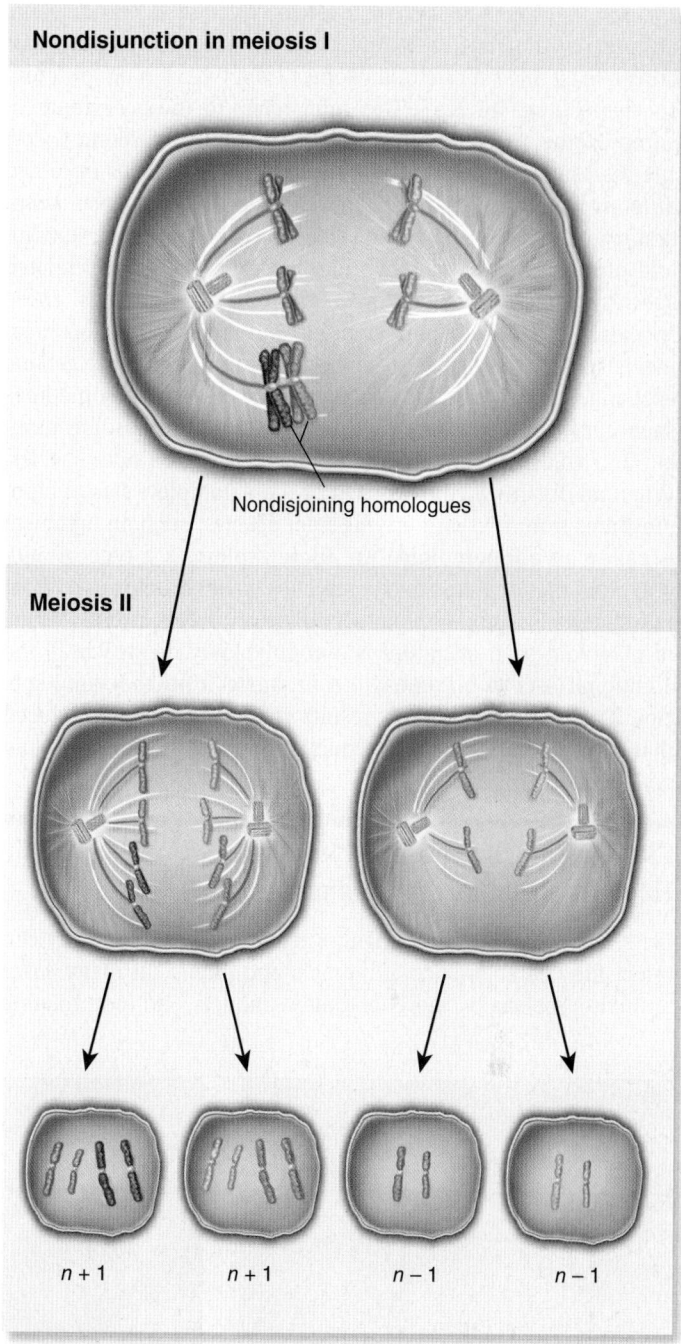

Figure 14.20 Nondisjunction during the formation of haploid cells. The cell on the left is diploid, containing three pairs of chromosomes. During the formation of haploid cells, one copy of each chromosome should be sorted into each cell. Nondisjunction, however, can produce a cell with too many or too few chromosomes.

Concept check: *Could nondisjunction produce a polyploid individual?*

cause these variations. In some cases a change in chromosome number is the result of the abnormal sorting of chromosomes during cell division. The term **nondisjunction** refers to an event in which the chromosomes do not sort properly during cell division. Mitotic nondisjunction can occur if sister chromatids fail to go to opposite poles. Meiotic nondisjunction can occur during meiosis I (**primary nondisjunction**) or meiosis II (**secondary nondisjunction**) and produce haploid cells that have too many or too few chromosomes. If such a gamete fuses with a normal gamete during fertilization, the resulting organism will be aneuploid and will have an abnormal chromosomal composition in all its cells. Because of the complex events that must be accomplished for proper disjunction at the first meiotic division (synapsis, crossing over, bivalent orientation on the

metaphase I plate), primary nondisjunction (**Figure 14.20**) is far more common than either meiotic secondary nondisjunction or mitotic nondisjunction.

Another mechanism that leads to variation in chromosome number is interspecies breeding. An **alloploid** organism contains a least one set of chromosomes from two or more different species (**Figure 14.21a**). This term refers to the occurrence of chromosome sets (*ploidy*) from the genomes of different (*allo-*) species. An alloploid that has one set of chromosomes from two different species is an **allodiploid**. Species that are close evolutionary relatives are most likely to breed and produce allodiploid offspring, or species hybrids. For example, closely related species of grasses may interbreed to produce allodiploids. These species hybrids are often vigorous but have difficulties with meiosis (not being able to undergo normal reciprocal genetic exchange) and hence are usually sterile. However, sometimes such cells will spontaneously double their chromosome number and will then contain two complete sets from both species. When an organism contains two or more complete sets of chromosomes from two or more different species, such an organism is called an **allopolyploid**. An **allotetraploid** is a type of allopolyploid that contains two complete sets of chromosomes from two species for a total of four sets (**Figure 14.21b**). Another type of polyploid seen in nature is autopolyploidy, in which all the additional sets of chromosomes originate from the same species. Autopolyploidy usually results when gametes are produced that have not undergone a reductional division, and a diploid gamete is produced.

Changes in Chromosome Number Have Important Consequences

Let's now consider how changes in chromosome number can affect the characteristics of animals and plants. In many cases animals, especially more complex animals, do not tolerate

(a) Alloploidy (allodiploid, species hybrid)

(b) Allopolyploidy (allotetraploid)

Figure 14.21   A comparison of alloploidy (seen in species hybrids) and new allopolyploid species.

(a) Octaploid strawberries (left) and diploid strawberries (right)

(b) Diploid daylilies (left) and tetraploid relative (right)

(c) Bread wheat

Figure 14.22   **Polyploidy has been an important factor in the evolution of plants.**   (a) The octaploid strawberry on the left has eight sets of chromosomes and is much larger than diploid strawberry on the right. (b) The diploid daylily on the left, with two sets of chromosomes, is smaller than its tetraploid relative on the right, which has four chromosome sets. (c) Bread wheat, *Triticum aestivum,* is an allohexaploid. Its six sets of chromosomes are the result of two separate species hybridizations and subsequent chromosome doublings.

  Principle: *All life is related by an evolutionary history. New species can evolve from related ones through polyploidization.*

deviations from diploidy well. For example, polyploidy in mammals is generally a lethal condition. However, a few cases of naturally occurring variations from diploidy do occur in animals. Male bees, which are called drones, contain a single set of chromosomes. They are produced from unfertilized eggs. By comparison, female bees are diploid. A few examples of vertebrate polyploid animals have been discovered. On rare occasions animals that are morphologically very similar can be found as a diploid species and as a separate polyploid species. This situation occurs among certain amphibians and reptiles.

In contrast to animals, plants tolerate polyploidy well and polyploidy is frequently seen in the plant kingdom. Among ferns and flowering plants, about 30%–35% of species are polyploid. Polyploidy is also important in agriculture. In many instances, polyploid strains of plants display characteristics that are helpful to humans. They are often larger and more robust (**Figure 14.22a, 14.22b**). These traits are clearly advantageous in the production of food. Many of the fruits and grains we eat are produced from polyploid plants. For example, the species of wheat that we use to make bread, *Triticum aestivum,* is an allohexaploid (containing six sets of chromosomes) that likely arose from the union of diploid genomes from three closely related species (**Figure 14.22c**). During its evolution two diploid species must have interbred to create a sterile allodiploid species hybrid that underwent spontaneous chromosome doubling to create a fertile allotetraploid. Later, this tetraploid wheat hybridized with a third diploid species to create a sterile allotriploid species hybrid that then underwent another doubling to create an allohexaploid wheat that is the ancestor of modern hexaploid wheat. Plant polyploids tend to exhibit greater adaptability, which allows them to withstand harsher environmental conditions. Other examples of important polyploid crops are maize, potatoes, and cotton. Polyploid ornamental plants commonly produce larger flowers than their diploid counterparts (Figure 14.22b).

Although polyploidy is often beneficial, especially in plants, aneuploidy in all eukaryotic species usually has detrimental consequences to the organism. To understand why, consider the relationship between gene expression and chromosome number. For many but not all genes, the level of gene expression is correlated with the number of copies of the gene per cell. Consider the case for a cell that is normally diploid. Two units of expression will occur for genes on paired chromosomes for all genes that are expressed in proportion to the number of chromosome copies in the cell. But three units of expression will occur for genes carried on a chromosome that has three copies in a cell. This discrepancy in relative amounts of gene expression will usually cause metabolic imbalances within a cell. Similarly, metabolic imbalances will occur if only one unit of expression occurs for all the genes of a particular chromosome because the organism is deficient in that chromosome. Therefore, in trisomic and monosomic individuals, an imbalance in the level of gene expression occurs that interferes with the proper functioning of cells.

One important reason that geneticists are so interested in aneuploidy is its relationship to certain inherited disorders in humans. Even though most people are born with a normal number of chromosomes, alterations in chromosome number occur with surprising frequency during gamete formation. About 5%–10% of all fertilized human eggs result in an embryo with an abnormality in chromosome number. In most cases, these abnormal embryos do not develop properly and result in a spontaneous abortion very early in pregnancy. Approximately 50% of all spontaneous abortions are due to alterations in chromosome number.

In general, in mammals, monosomy (missing one chromosome) is lethal; the only tolerated monosomies in mammals are for a sex chromosome. The impact of extra chromosomes is more variable, with some trisomics producing live births in mammals. Again the greatest tolerance in mammals is for extra sex chromosomes. Aside from the sex chromosomes, the most common observed trisomies in live births are for chromosomes 21, 18, and 13 (**Table 14.2**). Trisomies of the other human chromosomes and most monosomies are presumed to be lethal and have been found only in spontaneously aborted embryos and fetuses.

Table 14.2   Aneuploid Conditions in Humans

Condition	Frequency (# of live births)	Syndrome	Characteristics
Autosomal			
Trisomy 21	1/800	Down	Mental retardation, abnormal pattern of palm creases, slanted eyes, flattened face, short stature, early death
Trisomy 18	1/6,000	Edward	Mental and physical retardation, facial abnormalities, extreme muscle tone, early death
Trisomy 13	1/15,000	Patau	Mental and physical retardation, wide variety of defects in organs, large triangular nose, early death
Sex chromosomal			
XXY	1/1,000 (males)	Klinefelter	Sexual immaturity (no sperm), breast swelling in males
XYY	1/1,000 (males)	Jacobs	Tall
XXX	1/1,500 (females)	Triple X	Tall and thin, menstrual irregularity
XO	1/5,000 (females)	Turner	Short stature, webbed neck, sexually undeveloped

Summary of Key Concepts

14.1 Chromosome Structure and Function, and the Cell Cycle

- Chromosomes are structures that carry the genetic material in living cells.

- Chromatin is the name given to the lower levels of organization of DNA-protein complexes that underlie chromosomes.

- In eukaryotic chromosomes, the DNA is wrapped around histone proteins to form nucleosomes. (Figure 14.1)

- Noll tested the nucleosome model for chromatin structure by using DNase-I to digest chromosomes and showing that the DNA was obtained in multiples of 200 bp. (Figure 14.2)

- Nucleosomes are further compacted into 30-nm fibres because the linker regions are variably twisted and bent into a zigzag pattern. (Figure 14.3)

- A third level of compaction of eukaryotic chromosomes involves the formation of radial loop domains in which the bases of 30-nm fibres are anchored to a network of proteins called the nuclear matrix. This level of compaction is called euchromatin. In heterochromatin, the loops are even more closely packed together. (Figure 14.4)

- Interphase chromosomes are organized into looped domains of 30-nm fibres, but the M phase requires additional chromosome condensation (compaction). (Figures 14.5, 14.6)

- Gene expression is controlled by the level of compaction of the chromatin. The pattern of covalent modification of the amino terminal tails of histone proteins, also called the histone code, is is thought to be one way to control the level of compaction. (Figure 14.7).

14.2 Mitotic Cell Division

- The cell cycle is a series of stages during which cells grow and do specific functions for the health of the organism (G_1 phase), replicate and package the hereditary material (S phase), prepare for cell division (G_2 phase) and divide to produce new cells (M phase).

- During the S phase eukaryotic chromosomes are replicated to produce a pair of identical sister chromatids that remain attached to each other.

- Mitosis is a particular type of nuclear division that can occur during M phase. It consists of four major phases called prophase, metaphase, anaphase, and telophase. During prophase the chromosomes condense and the nuclear membrane fragments. The spindle apparatus is completely formed by the end of prometaphase. During metaphase the chromosomes are aligned in a single row along the metaphase plate. At anaphase the sister chromatids separate from each other and move to opposite poles; the poles themselves also move farther apart. During telophase the chromosomes decondense and the nuclear membranes re-form. (Figure 14.8)

- During the prophase of mitosis the chromosomes condense further and form kinetochores. (Figure 14.9)

- The mitotic spindle is composed of astral, kinetochore, and polar microtubules. The spindle organizes the process of cell division and plays a central role in chromosome sorting. (Figure 14.10)

- Cytokinesis in animal cells involves the formation of a cleavage furrow. In plant cells, two separated cells are produced by the formation of a cell plate. (Figure 14.11)

14.3 Eukaryotic Chromosomes Are Inherited in Sets

- Cytogeneticists examine cells microscopically to determine their chromosome composition. A micrograph that shows the alignment of chromosomes from a given cell is called a karyotype. (Figure 14.12)

- Diploid cells have two sets of chromosomes while haploid cells have only one set.

14.4 Meiosis and Sexual Reproduction

- The process of meiosis begins with a diploid cell and produces four haploid cells with one set of chromosomes each. (Figure 14.13)

- During the prophase of meiosis, homologous pairs of sister chromosomes synapse, and crossing over occurs. After crossing over chiasmata can be seen. (Figure 14.14)

- Meiosis is divided into meiosis I and II, each composed of prophase, prometaphase, metaphase, anaphase, and telophase. During meiosis I the homologues are separated to different cells, and during meiosis II the sister chromatids are separated to different cells. (Figure 14.15, Table 14.1)

14.5 Mitosis, Meiosis, and Fertilization Allow Sexually Reproducing Species to Produce Haploid and Diploid Cells at Different Times in Their Life Cycles

- The life cycle of animals is diploid dominant, while many fungi and protists show a haploid-dominant life cycle. Plants alternate between diploid and haploid forms. (Figure 14.16)

14.6 Variation in Chromosome Structure and Number

- Chromosomes are named metacentric, submetacentric, acrocentric, and telocentric according to their centromere location. Each type of chromosome can be uniquely identified by its banding pattern after staining. (Figure 14.17)

- Deficiencies, duplications, inversions, and translocations are different ways to alter chromosome structure. (Figure 14.18)

- A euploid organism has the correct number of chromosomes. A polyploid organism has three or more sets of chromosomes. An aneuploid organism has one too many (trisomy) or one too few (monosomy) chromosomes. (Figure 14.19)

- Nondisjunction and interspecies matings can alter chromosome number. An alloploid has chromosome sets from two or more different species. (Figures 14.20, 14.21)

- Polyploid animals are relatively rare, but polyploid plants are common and tend to be more robust than their diploid counterparts. (Figure 14.22)

- Aneuploidy in humans is responsible for several types of human genetic diseases, including Down syndrome. (Table 14.2)

Test to Assess Your Learning

1. In eukaryotic cells, chromosomes consist of
   a. DNA and RNA.
   b. DNA only.
   c. RNA and proteins.
   d. DNA and proteins.
   e. RNA only.

2. A nucleosome is
   a. a dark-staining body composed of RNA and proteins found in the nucleus.
   b. a protein that helps organize the structure of chromosomes.
   c. another word for a chromosome.
   d. a structure composed of eight histones wrapped with DNA.
   e. the short arm of a chromosome.

3. Compaction of chromosomes is not uniform. Some areas are more compact than others. Which of the following statements is true about the differing levels of organization in the eukaryotic chromosome?
   a. More compact areas of the chromosome are called euchromatin and contain genes that are not expressed.
   b. More compact areas of the chromosome are called heterochromatin and contain genes that are not expressed.
   c. More compact areas of the chromosome are called heterochromatin and contain genes that are expressed at high levels.
   d. More compact areas of the chromosome are called euchromatin and contain genes that are expressed at high levels.
   e. None of the above is correct.

4. Which of the following is a reason for mitotic cell division?
   a. reproduction
   b. gamete formation in animals
   c. multicellularity
   d. all of the above
   e. both (a) and (c)

5. A replicated chromosome is composed of
   a. two homologous chromosomes held together at the centromere.
   b. four sister chromatids held together at the centromere.
   c. two sister chromatids held together at the centromere.
   d. four homologous chromosomes held together at the centromere.
   e. one chromosome with a centromere.

6. Which of the following is *not* an event of anaphase of mitosis?
   a. The nuclear envelope breaks down.
   b. Sister chromatids separate.
   c. Kinetochore microtubules shorten, pulling the chromosomes to the pole.
   d. Polar microtubules push against each other, moving the poles farther apart.
   e. All of the above occur during anaphase.

7. A student is looking at cells under the microscope. The cells are from an organism that has a diploid number of 14. For one particular slide, the cell has seven replicated chromosomes aligned at the metaphase plate of the cell. Which of the following statements accurately describes this particular cell?
   a. The cell is in metaphase of mitosis.
   b. The cell is in metaphase I of meiosis.
   c. The cell is in metaphase II of meiosis.
   d. All of the above are correct.
   e. Both (b) and (c) are correct.

8. Which of the following statements accurately describes a difference between meiosis and mitosis?
   a. Mitosis produces diploid cells and meiosis produces haploid cells.
   b. Homologous chromosomes synapse during meiosis but do not synapse during mitosis.
   c. Crossing over commonly occurs during meiosis, but it does not commonly occur during mitosis.

d. All of the above are correct.
e. Both (a) and (c) are correct.

9. During crossing over in meiosis I,
   a. homologous chromosomes are not altered.
   b. homologous chromosomes exchange genetic material.
   c. chromosomal damage occurs.
   d. genetic information is lost.
   e. cytokinesis occurs.

10. Aneuploidy is the result of
    a. the duplication of a region of a chromosome.
    b. the inversion of a region of a chromosome.
    c. nondisjunction during meiosis.
    d. interspecies breeding.
    e. all of the above.

Articulate to Assess Your Learning

1. Distinguish between heterochromatin and euchromatin.
2. Explain the histone code hypothesis.
3. Distinguish between homologous chromosomes and sister chromatids.
4. Describe all the events that must occur to ensure that homologous chromosomes will orient to opposite poles at metaphase I, including the role of cohesins.

Collaborate to Assess and Extend Your Learning

1. Discuss several variations in chromosome structure and number. Use the terms *euploidy, polyploidy,* and *aneuploidy,* and explain how they occur and what their genetic consequences are.
2. What is crossing over, when does it occur, and what is its significance?
3. Sexual reproduction is a source of genetic variation. List all the sources of genetic variation that arise in a sexually reproducing organism.
4. Create a concept map with the following terms: histone H1, histones H2a, H2b, H3, H4, linker DNA, 11-nm fibre, 30-nm fibre, nuclear matrix, looped domains, euchromatin, heterochromatin, M phase chromosomes, transcription, and segregation.
5. A biological principle of life is that cells are the simplest unit of life. Explain how mitosis is a key process in the formation of new cells.

Visit McGraw-Hill Ryerson Connect™ for additional study resources.

Inheritance and Phenotype Determination

15

Seed colour in lentils is determined by gene interaction

Long before people knew anything about cells or chromosomes, they observed patterns of heredity and speculated about them. The ancient Greek physician Hippocrates provided the first known explanation for the transmission of hereditary traits (ca. 400 BCE). He suggested that "seeds" produced by all parts of the body are collected and transmitted to offspring at the time of conception and that these seeds cause offspring to resemble their parents. This idea, known as **pangenesis**, influenced the thinking of scientists for many centuries.

Plant breeder Joseph Kolreuter carried out the first systematic genetic crosses between 1761 and 1766. Kolreuter crossed different strains of tobacco plants and found that the offspring were usually intermediate in appearance between the two parents. He concluded that parents make equal genetic contributions to their offspring and that their genetic material blends together as it is passed to the next generation. This interpretation was consistent with the concept known as **blending inheritance**, which was widely accepted at that time. In the early nineteenth century Jean-Baptiste Lamarck, a French naturalist, hypothesized that species change over the course of many generations by adapting to new environments. According to Lamarck, behavioural changes modify traits, and such modified traits were inherited by offspring. For example, an individual who became adept at archery would pass that skill to his or her offspring. Overall the prevailing view before the nineteenth century was that hereditary traits were rather malleable and could change and blend over the course of one or two generations.

In the last chapter we considered the process of cell division and how chromosomes are transmitted during mitosis and meiosis. Observations of these processes in the second half of the nineteenth century provided compelling evidence for **particulate inheritance**—the idea that the determinants of hereditary traits are transmitted intact from one generation to the next. Remarkably, this idea was first proposed in the 1860s by a researcher who knew nothing about chromosomes. Gregor Mendel (**Figure 15.1**) is remembered today as the "father of genetics"; he used statistical analysis of carefully designed breeding experiments to arrive at the concept of a gene. Forty years later, through the convergence of Mendel's work and that of cell biologists, this concept became the foundation of the modern science of genetics.

In this chapter we will consider how genes are inherited to produce the genetic makeup (**genotype**) of offspring and then consider how the offspring's genotype leads to their physical characteristics (**phenotypes**). In the first section we consider the fundamental genetic patterns known as Mendelian inheritance and the relationship of these patterns to the behaviour of chromosomes during meiosis. In the second section we examine the distinctive inheritance patterns of genes located on the X chromosome, paying special attention to the work of Thomas Hunt Morgan, whose investigation of these patterns confirmed that genes are on chromosomes. In the third section we look at why genes on the same chromosome often do not yield Mendelian results. In sections four and five we discuss how gene products work to produce phenotypes, and you will get a glimpse of how biologically complex the production of phenotypes can be. In the sixth section we look at how organelle genes are inherited. Finally, in the last section we examine how DNA can be modified in ways that do not alter the genetic code but do alter a gene's ability to be expressed in a manner that can be transmitted as the cell replicates and divides its genetic material.

Figure 15.1 **Gregor Johann Mendel, the father of genetics.** Mendel published his founding work for modern genetics in 1866, seven years after Darwin published his book *The Origin of Species*. Had Darwin known of Mendel's work it would have helped him understand one important source of genetic variation.

15.1 MENDEL'S LAWS AND THE CHROMOSOME THEORY OF INHERITANCE

Learning Outcomes:

1. List the advantages of using the garden pea to study inheritance.
2. Describe the difference between dominant and recessive traits.
3. Distinguish between genotype and phenotype.
4. Define Mendel's law of segregation and law of independent assortment.
5. Relate the behaviour of chromosomes during meiosis to Mendel's laws of inheritance.
6. Use a Punnett square to predict the outcome of a genetic cross.
7. Relate the use of probability to predict outcomes to the use of a Punnett Square and to Mendel's laws.
8. Apply pedigree analysis to deduce inheritance patterns in humans, distinguishing between recessively inherited disorders and dominantly inherited disorders.

Gregor Johann Mendel (1822–1884) was raised on a farm and entered the Augustinian monastery of St. Thomas in Brno (Czech Republic) at the age of 21. He was ordained a priest and worked for a short time as a substitute teacher, but he failed the licensing exam because of his answers to the physics and natural history questions. So he enrolled at the University of Vienna to expand his knowledge in these areas. Mendel's training in physics and mathematics taught him to perceive the world as an orderly place, governed by natural laws that could be stated as simple mathematical relationships.

In 1856 Mendel began his historic studies on pea plants. For eight years, he analyzed thousands of pea plants grown on a small plot in his monastery garden. He kept careful records that included quantitative data concerning the outcome of his studies. He published his work, entitled "Experiments on Plant Hybrids," in 1866. This paper was largely ignored by scientists at that time, partly because of its title and because it was published in a rather obscure journal, *The Proceedings of the Brünn Society of Natural History*. Mendel was also clearly ahead of his time. Biology had not yet become a quantitative, experimental science. Before his death in 1884 Mendel reflected, "My scientific work has brought me a great deal of satisfaction and I am convinced that it will be appreciated before long by the whole world." Sixteen years later three European biologists with interests in plant genetics—Hugo de Vries, Carl Correns, and Erich von Tschermak—rediscovered Mendel's work. Within a few years, the impact of Mendel's studies was felt around the world.

As you can see from the learning outcomes, this section is extremely important for understanding inheritance. We will examine Mendel's experiments and how they led to the formulation of the basic genetic principles we call Mendel's laws. These principles apply not only to the pea plants Mendel studied but also to a wide variety of sexually reproducing organisms, including humans. We then consider how the study of chromosomes in the late nineteenth and early twentieth centuries provided a physical explanation for Mendel's laws. At the end of this section we will briefly examine the laws of probability on which Mendel based his analysis and how they are used to predict simple patterns of inheritance.

Analysis of Inheritance Patterns in Pea Plants Led Mendel to Formulate Two Basic Laws of Genetics

When two individuals with different characteristics are mated to or crossed with each other, this is called a **hybridization** experiment, and the offspring are referred to as hybrids. For example, a hybridization experiment could involve a cross between a purple-flowered plant and a white-flowered plant. Mendel was particularly intrigued by the consistency with which offspring of such crosses showed characteristics of one or the other parent in successive generations. His intellectual foundation in physics and the natural sciences led him to consider that this regularity might be rooted in natural laws that could be expressed mathematically. To uncover these laws, he carried out quantitative hybridization experiments in which he carefully analyzed the numbers of offspring carrying specific traits. This analysis led him to formulate two fundamental genetic principles, known today as the law of segregation of alleles and the law of independent assortment.

Mendel chose the garden pea, *Pisum sativum*, because several properties of this species were particularly advantageous for genetic study. First, it had many readily available varieties that differed in visible characteristics, such as the appearance of seeds, pods, flowers, and stems. Such features of an organism are called **characters** or **traits**. **Figure 15.2** illustrates the seven characters that Mendel eventually chose to follow in his

Character	Variants	

Flower colour — Purple / White

Flower position — Axial / Terminal

Seed colour — Yellow / Green

Seed shape — Round / Wrinkled

Pod colour — Green / Yellow

Pod shape — Smooth / Constricted

Height — Tall / Dwarf

Figure 15.2 The seven traits that Mendel studied.

breeding experiments. Each trait had two variants. For example, one trait he followed was height, which had variants known as tall and dwarf. Another was seed colour, which had the variants yellow and green.

A second important feature of garden peas is that they are normally self-fertilizing. In **self-fertilization**, a female gamete is fertilized by a male gamete from the same plant. Like many flowering plants, peas have male and female sex organs in the same flower (**Figure 15.3**). Male gametes (sperm cells) are produced within pollen grains, which are formed in the male structures called stamens. Female gametes (egg cells) are produced in structures called ovules that form within an organ called an ovary. For fertilization to occur, a pollen grain must land on the receptacle called a stigma, enabling a sperm to migrate to an ovule and fuse with an egg cell. The stamens and ovaries of pea plants each are enclosed by a modified petal. This arrangement greatly favours self-fertilization. Self-fertilization makes it easy to produce plants that breed true for a given trait, meaning that the trait does not vary from generation to generation. For example, if a pea plant with yellow seeds breeds true for seed colour, then all the plants that grow from these seeds will also produce yellow seeds. A variety that continues to exhibit the same trait after several generations of self-fertilization is called a **true-breeding line**. Before conducting the studies described in this chapter, Mendel had already established that the seven traits that he chose to study were true breeding in the strains of pea plants he had obtained. Using true-breeding lines was an important feature of his studies.

A third reason for using garden peas in hybridization experiments was the ease of making crosses: the flowers are

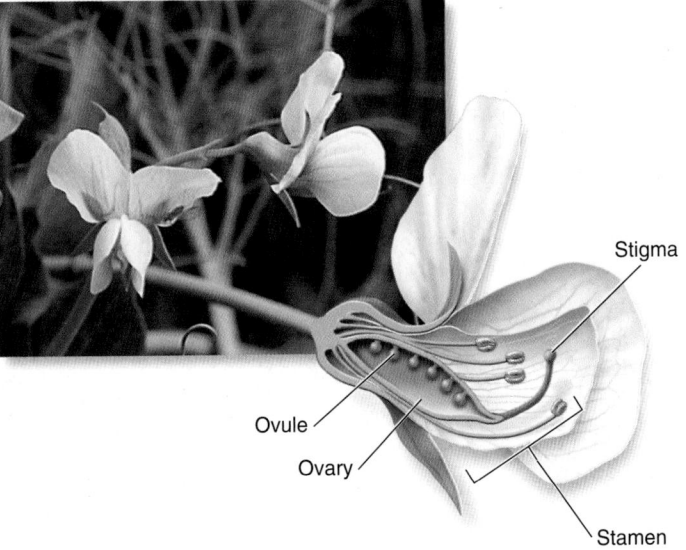

Figure 15.3 Flower structure in pea plants. The pea flower produces both male and female gametes. Sperm form in the pollen produced within the stamens; egg cells form in ovules within the ovary. A modified petal encloses the stamens and stigma, encouraging self-fertilization.

quite large and easy to manipulate. In some cases Mendel wanted his pea plants to self-fertilize, but in others he wanted to cross plants that differed with respect to some trait, a process called **cross-fertilization** or hybridization. In garden peas, cross-fertilization requires placing pollen from one plant on the stigma of another plant's flower. Mendel's cross-fertilization procedure is shown in **Figure 15.4**. He would pry open an immature flower and remove the stamens before they produced pollen, so that the flower could not self-fertilize. He then used a paintbrush to transfer pollen from another plant to the stigma of the flower that had its stamens removed. In this way, Mendel was able to cross-fertilize any two of his true-breeding pea plants and obtain any type of hybrid he wanted.

Following the Inheritance Pattern of Single Traits, Mendel Developed the Law of Segregation of Alleles

Mendel began his investigations by studying the inheritance patterns of pea plants that differed with regard to a single trait. A cross in which an experimenter follows the variants of only one trait is called a **single-factor cross**. As an example, we will consider a single-factor cross in which Mendel followed the tall and dwarf variants for height (**Figure 15.5a**). The left side of Figure 15.5a shows his experimental approach. The true-breeding parents are termed the **P generation** (parental generation), and a cross of these plants is called a P cross. The first-generation offspring of a P cross are the **F$_1$ generation** (first filial generation, from the Latin *filius*, meaning "son"). When the true-breeding parents differ with regard to a single trait, their F$_1$ offspring are called single-trait hybrids, or **monohybrids**. When Mendel crossed true-breeding tall and dwarf plants, he observed that all plants of the F$_1$ generation were tall.

Next, Mendel followed the transmission of this trait for a second generation. To do so, he allowed the F$_1$ monohybrids to self-fertilize, producing a generation called the **F$_2$ generation** (second filial generation). The dwarf trait reappeared in the F$_2$ offspring: three-fourths of the plants were tall and one-fourth

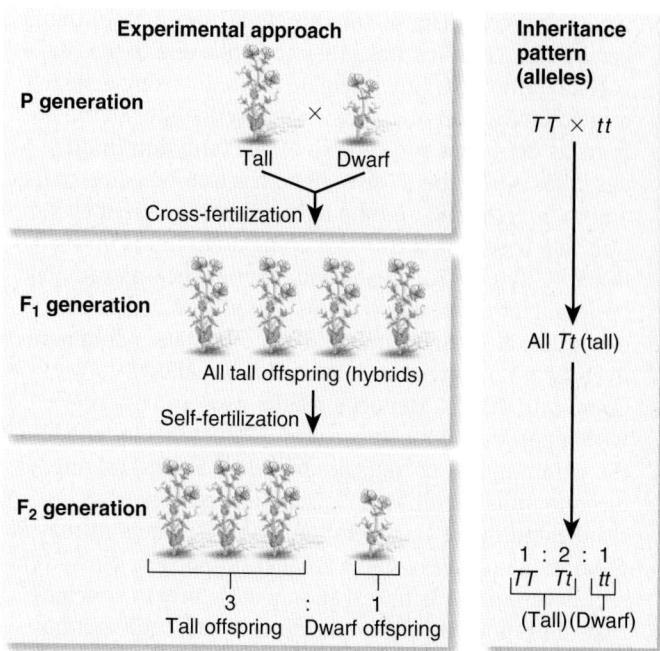

(a) **Mendel's protocol for making monohybrid crosses**

THE DATA

P cross	F$_1$ generation	F$_2$ generation	Ratio
Purple × white flowers	All purple	705 purple, 224 white	3.15:1
Axial × terminal flowers	All axial	651 axial, 207 terminal	3.14:1
Yellow × green seeds	All yellow	6,022 yellow, 2,001 green	3.01:1
Round × wrinkled seeds	All round	5,474 round, 1,850 wrinkled	2.96:1
Green × yellow pods	All green	428 green, 152 yellow	2.82:1
Smooth × constricted pods	All smooth	882 smooth, 299 constricted	2.95:1
Tall × dwarf stem	All tall	787 tall, 277 dwarf	2.84:1
Total	**All dominant**	**14,949 dominant, 5,010 recessive**	**2.98:1**

(b) **Mendel's observed data for all seven traits**

Figure 15.5 Mendel's analyses of single-factor crosses.

were dwarf. Mendel obtained similar results for each of the traits that he studied, as shown in the data of **Figure 15.5b**. A quantitative analysis of his data allowed Mendel to postulate three important ideas regarding the properties and transmission of these traits from parents to offspring:

1. *Dominant and recessive traits.* Perhaps the most surprising outcome of Mendel's work was that the data argued strongly against the prevailing notion of a

1 | Remove stamens from purple flower.

2 | Transfer pollen from stamens of white flower to the stigma of a purple flower.

Figure 15.4 Mendel's procedure for cross-fertilizing pea plants.

blending mechanism of heredity. In all seven cases the F$_1$ generation displayed traits distinctly like one of the two parents rather than intermediate traits. By using genetic terms that Mendel originated, we describe the alternative traits as dominant and recessive. The term **dominant** describes a trait that is seen in both a true-breeding parent and in its F$_1$ hybrid and the term **recessive** describes a trait that is seen in a true-breeding parent but is masked in the F$_1$ hybrid. Tall stems and green pods are examples of dominant traits; dwarf stems and yellow pods are examples of recessive traits. We say that tall is dominant over dwarf and green is dominant over yellow.

2. *Genes and alleles.* Mendel's results were consistent with a particulate mechanism of inheritance, in which the determinants of traits are inherited as unchanging, discrete units. In all seven cases the recessive trait reappeared in the F$_2$ generation: some F$_2$ plants displayed the dominant trait, while a smaller proportion showed the recessive trait. This observation led Mendel to conclude that the genetic determinants of traits are "unit factors" that are passed intact from generation to generation. These unit factors are now called **genes**, a term coined by the botanist Wilhelm Johannsen in 1911. Mendel postulated that every individual carries two versions of a gene for a given trait and that the gene for each trait may have variant forms, which we now call **alleles**. For example, the gene controlling height in Mendel's pea plants occurs in two variants: the dominant tall allele that is associated with the tall trait and the recessive allele associated with the dwarf trait. The right side of Figure 15.5a shows Mendel's conclusions and uses genetic symbols (letters) that were adopted later. The letters *T* and *t* represent the alleles of the gene for plant height. By convention, the uppercase letter represents the dominant allele (in this case, tall) and the same letter in lowercase represents the recessive allele.

3. *Segregation of alleles.* When Mendel compared the number of F$_2$ offspring exhibiting dominant and recessive traits, he noticed a recurring pattern. Although some experimental variation occurred, he observed approximately a 3:1 ratio between the dominant and the recessive trait (Figure 15.5b). This observation allowed him to conclude that the two copies of a gene (alleles) carried by an F$_1$ plant **segregate** (separate) from each other so that each sperm or egg carries only one allele. The diagram in **Figure 15.6** shows that segregation of the F$_1$ alleles should result in equal numbers of gametes carrying the dominant allele (*T*) and the recessive allele (*t*). If these gametes combine randomly at fertilization, as shown in the figure, this would account for the 3:1 ratio of the F$_2$ generation. Note that the genotype *Tt* can be produced by two different combinations of alleles—the *T* allele can come from the male gamete and the *t* allele from the female gamete, or vice versa. This accounts for the fact that the *Tt* genotype is produced twice as often as either *TT* or *tt*. The idea that the two copies of a gene segregate from

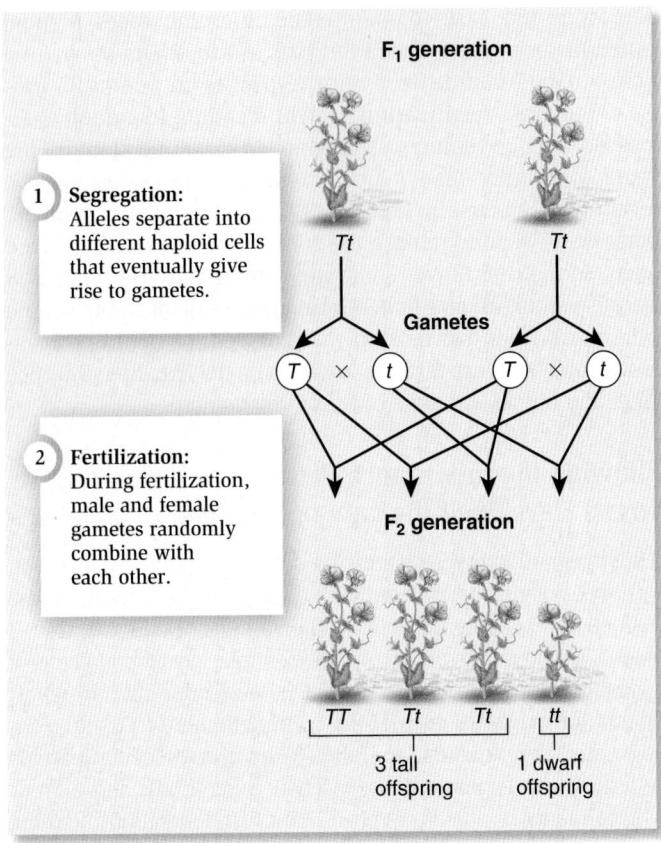

Figure 15.6 How the law of segregation of alleles explains Mendel's observed ratios.   The segregation of alleles in the F$_1$ generation gives rise to gametes that carry just one of the two alleles. These gametes combine randomly during fertilization, producing the allele combinations *TT, Tt,* and *tt* in the F$_2$ offspring. The combination *Tt* occurs twice as often as either of the other two combinations because it can be produced in two different ways. The *TT* and *Tt* offspring are tall, while the *tt* offspring are dwarf.

 Principle: *Living organisms grow, develop, and reproduce. Mendel used the natural reproductive cycle of peas to understand the inheritance of traits.*

each other during transmission from parent to offspring is known today as Mendel's **law of segregation of alleles**.

Genotype Describes an Organism's Genetic Makeup, and Phenotype Describes Its Characteristics

To continue our discussion of Mendel's results, we need to define some genetic terms. As noted, the term *genotype* refers to the genetic composition of an individual. In the example shown earlier in Figure 15.5a, *TT* and *tt* are the genotypes of the P generation and *Tt* is the genotype of the F$_1$ generation. In a P cross, both parents are true-breeding plants. In pea plants true-breeding plants are individuals with two identical copies of a gene; they are said to be **homozygous** with respect to that gene. In the specific P cross we are considering, the tall plant is homozygous for *T* and the dwarf plant is homozygous for *t*.

In contrast, a **heterozygous** individual carries two different alleles of the same gene. Plants of the F$_1$ generation are heterozygous, with the genotype *Tt*, because every individual carries one copy of the tall allele and one copy of the dwarf allele. The F$_2$ generation includes both homozygous individuals (homozygotes *TT* and *tt*) and heterozygous individuals (heterozygotes *Tt*).

As also noted earlier, the term *phenotype* refers to the characteristics of an organism that we can see as the result of its genotype. In the example in Figure 15.5a, one of the parent plants has the tall phenotype and the other has the dwarf phenotype. Although the F$_1$ offspring are heterozygous (*Tt*), their phenotypes are tall because each has a copy of the dominant tall allele. In contrast, some F$_2$ plants are tall and others dwarf in a ratio of 3 (tall):1 (dwarf).

A Punnett Square Can Be Used to Predict the Outcome of Crosses

A common way to predict the outcome of simple genetic crosses is to make a **Punnett square**, a method originally proposed by the British geneticist Reginald Punnett. To construct a Punnett square, you must know the genotypes of the parents. What follows is a step-by-step description of the Punnett square approach that uses a cross of heterozygous tall plants.

Step 1. Write down the genotypes of both parents. In this example a heterozygous tall plant is crossed to another heterozygous tall plant. The plant providing the pollen is considered the male parent and the plant providing the eggs, the female parent. (In self-pollination, a single individual produces both types of gametes.)

Male parent: *Tt*
Female parent: *Tt*

Step 2. Write down the possible gametes that each parent can make. Remember that the law of segregation of alleles tells us that a gamete contains only one copy of each gene.

Male gametes: *T* or *t*
Female gametes: *T* or *t*

Step 3. Create an empty Punnett square. The number of columns equals the number of male gametes, and the number of rows equals the number of female gametes. Our example has two rows and two columns. Place the male gametes across the top of the Punnett square and the female gametes along the side.

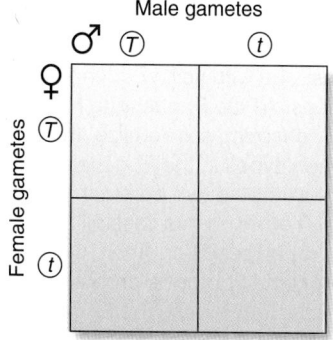

Step 4. Fill in the possible genotypes of the offspring by combining the alleles of the gametes in the empty boxes.

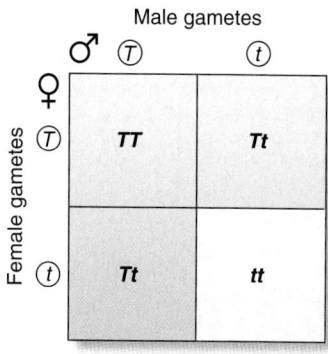

Step 5. Determine the relative proportions of genotypes and phenotypes of the offspring. The genotypes are obtained directly from the Punnett square. In this example, the genotypes are *TT*, *Tt*, and *tt* in a 1:2:1 ratio. To determine the phenotypes, you must know which allele is dominant. For plant height, *T* (tall) is dominant to *t* (dwarf). The genotypes *TT* and *Tt* are tall; the genotype *tt* is dwarf. Therefore, our Punnett square shows that the ratio of phenotypes is expected to be 3:1, or 3 tall plants to 1 dwarf plant. Keep in mind, however, that these are predicted ratios for large numbers of offspring. If only a few offspring are produced, the observed ratios could deviate significantly from the predicted ratios. We will examine the question of sample size and genetic prediction later in this chapter. Construction of a Punnett Square is the reverse of the mental processing Mendel did. Mendel looked at the cross outcomes and thought of what must have been in the "boxes" to give the ratios he saw. Then he thought about how an organism could produce the gametes that allowed fertilization to create the genotypes in the boxes of the Punnett Square.

A Testcross Can Be Used to Determine an Individual's Genotype

When a trait has two variants, one of which is dominant over the other, we know that an individual with a recessive phenotype has no copy of the dominant allele. A dwarf pea plant, for example, must have the genotype *tt*. But an individual with a dominant phenotype can be either homozygous or heterozygous—a tall pea plant can have the genotype *TT* or *Tt*. To distinguish between these two possibilities, Mendel devised a method called a **testcross** that is still used today. In a testcross the researcher crosses the individual of interest to an individual that can donate only the recessive allele and observes the phenotypes of the offspring. **Figure 15.7** shows how this procedure can be used to determine the genotype of a tall pea plant. If the testcross produces some dwarf offspring, as shown on the right side of the figure, these offspring must have two copies of the recessive allele, one inherited from each parent. Therefore, the tall parent must be a heterozygote, with the genotype *Tt*. Alternatively, if all of the offspring are tall, as shown on the left, the tall parent is likely to be a homozygote, with the genotype *TT*.

example the allele for yellow seeds (Y) might be inherited with the allele for round seeds (R), as shown in **Figure 15.8a**. The recessive alleles are green seeds (y) and wrinkled seeds (r). A second possibility was that the two genes are independent so that their alleles are randomly distributed into gametes (**Figure 15.8b**). By following the transmission pattern of two traits simultaneously, Mendel could distinguish between these two possibilities and

Figure 15.7 **A testcross.** The purpose of this experiment is to determine whether the organism with the dominant phenotype, in this case a tall pea plant, is a homozygote (TT) or a heterozygote (Tt).

Concept check: *Suppose we had a plant with purple flowers and unknown genotype and conducted a testcross to determine its genotype. We obtained 41 plants, 20 of which had white flowers and 21 of which had purple flowers. What was the genotype of the original purple-flowered plant?*

Analyzing the Inheritance Pattern of Two Traits Simultaneously Demonstrated the Law of Independent Assortment

Mendel's analysis of single-factor crosses suggested that traits are inherited as discrete units and that the alleles for a given gene segregate during the formation of haploid cells. To obtain additional insights into how genes are transmitted from parents to offspring, Mendel conducted crosses in which he simultaneously followed the inheritance of two different traits. A cross of this type is called a two-factor cross. We will examine a two-factor cross in which Mendel simultaneously followed the inheritance of seed colour and seed shape (**Figure 15.8**). He began by crossing pea plants from strains that were homozygous for both traits. The plants of one strain had yellow, round seeds and plants of the other strain had green, wrinkled seeds. He then allowed the F_1 offspring to self-fertilize and observed the phenotypes of the F_2 generation.

One possible outcome might have been that the two genes would segregate together and always be inherited together. In our

(a) Hypothesis: Linked assortment

(b) Hypothesis: Independent assortment

P Cross	F_1 generation	F_2 generation
Yellow, round seeds × Green, wrinkled seeds	Yellow, round seeds	315 yellow, round seeds
		101 yellow, wrinkled seeds
		108 green, round seeds
		32 green, wrinkled seeds

(c) The data observed by Mendel

Figure 15.8 **Two hypotheses for the assortment of two different genes.** This figure shows a cross between two true-breeding pea plants, one with yellow, round seeds and one with green, wrinkled seeds. All the F_1 offspring have yellow, round seeds. When the F_1 offspring self-fertilize, the two hypotheses predict different phenotypes in the F_2 generation. **(a)** The linkage hypothesis proposes that the two parental alleles always stay associated with each other. In this case all the F_2 offspring will have either yellow, round seeds or green, wrinkled seeds. **(b)** The independent assortment hypothesis proposes that each allele assorts independently. In this case the F_2 generation will display four different phenotypes. **(c)** Mendel's observations supported the independent assortment hypothesis.

determine whether the genes that determine seed shape and seed colour **assort** (are distributed) together or independently.

What experimental results could Mendel predict for each of these two models? He predicted that the F_1 would be the same in either case. The homozygous P generation would produce only two kinds of gametes, *YR* and *yr*, so in either case the F_1 offspring would be heterozygous for both traits; that is, they would have the genotypes *YyRr*. Because Mendel knew from his earlier experiments that yellow was dominant to green and round was dominant to wrinkled, he could predict that all the F_1 plants would have yellow, round seeds. In contrast, as shown in Figure 15.8, the ratios he obtained in the F_2 generation would depend on whether the two genes segregated together or independently.

If the parental traits segregated together, as in Figure 15.8a, the F_1 plants could produce only gametes that are *YR* or *yr*. These gametes would combine to create offspring with the genotypes *YYRR* (yellow, round), *YyRr* (yellow, round), or *yyrr* (green, wrinkled). The ratio of phenotypes would be 3 yellow, round to 1 green, wrinkled. Every F_2 plant would be phenotypically like one P-generation parent or the other; none would display a new combination of the parental traits. However, if the alleles segregated independently, the F_2 generation would show a wider range of genotypes and phenotypes, as shown by the large Punnett square in Figure 15.8b. In this case each F_1 parent produces four kinds of gametes—*YR*, *Yr*, *yR*, and *yr*—instead of two, so the square is constructed with four rows on each side and shows 16 possible genotypes. The F_2 generation includes plants with yellow, round seeds; yellow, wrinkled seeds; green, round seeds; and green, wrinkled seeds, in a ratio of 9:3:3:1.

The actual results for this two-factor cross are shown in **Figure 15.8c**. Crossing the true-breeding parents produced **dihybrid** offspring—offspring that are hybrids with respect to both traits. These F_1 dihybrids all had yellow, round seeds, confirming that yellow and round are dominant traits. This result was consistent with either hypothesis. However, the data for the F_2 generation were consistent only with the independent assortment hypothesis. Mendel observed four phenotypically different types of F_2 offspring, in a ratio that was reasonably close to 9:3:3:1.

Mendel's results were similar for every pair of traits he studied. His data supported the idea, now called the **law of independent assortment**, that the alleles of different genes segregate independently during sexual reproduction. Independent assortment means that a specific allele for one gene can be found in a gamete regardless of which allele for a different gene is found in the same gamete. In our example, the yellow and green alleles assort independently of the round and wrinkled alleles. The union of gametes from F_1 plants carrying these alleles produces the F_2 genotypic and phenotypic ratios shown in Figure 15.8b.

The Chromosome Theory of Inheritance Relates Mendel's Observations to the Behaviour of Chromosomes

Mendel's studies with pea plants led to the concept of a unit of heredity, which is the foundation for our understanding of inheritance. However, at the time of Mendel's work the physical nature and location of genes was a mystery. In fact, the idea that inheritance has a physical basis was not even addressed until 1883, when biologist August Weismann and botanist Carl Nägeli championed the idea that a substance in living cells is responsible for the transmission of hereditary traits. Nägeli also suggested that parents contribute equal amounts of this substance to their offspring. Several scientists, including Eduard Strasburger and Walter Flemming, observed dividing cells under the microscope and suggested that the chromosomes are the carriers of the genetic material.

In the early twentieth century the idea that chromosomes carry the genetic material dramatically unfolded as researchers continued to study the processes of fertilization, mitosis, and meiosis. It became increasingly clear that the characteristics of organisms are rooted in the continuity of cells during the life of an organism and from one generation to the next. Several scientists noted striking parallels between the segregation and assortment of traits noted by Mendel and the behaviour of chromosomes during meiosis. Among these scientists were Theodor Boveri and Walter Sutton, who independently proposed the chromosome theory of inheritance. According to this theory the inheritance patterns of traits could be explained by the transmission of chromosomes during meiosis and fertilization. Thomas Hunt Morgan's studies of fruit flies, which we will examine later in this chapter, were instrumental in creating a general consensus supporting this theory.

The **chromosome theory of inheritance** consists of five fundamental principles:

1. Chromosomes contain the genetic material, which is transmitted from parent to offspring and from cell to cell. Genes are found in the chromosomes.
2. Chromosomes are replicated and passed from parent to offspring. They are also passed from cell to cell during the multicellular development of an organism. Each type of chromosome retains its individuality during cell division and gamete formation.
3. The nucleus of a diploid cell contains two sets of chromosomes, which are found as homologous pairs. One member of each pair is inherited from the mother and the other from the father. The maternal and paternal sets of homologous chromosomes are functionally equivalent; each set carries a full complement of genes (the exception is sex chromosomes, as we will discuss in a later section).
4. At meiosis, one member of each chromosome pair segregates into one daughter nucleus and its homologue segregates into the other daughter nucleus. Each of the resulting haploid cells contains only one set of chromosomes. During the formation of haploid cells, the members of different chromosome pairs segregate independently.
5. Gametes are haploid cells that combine to form a diploid cell during fertilization, with each gamete transmitting one set of chromosomes to the offspring. In animals one set comes from the mother and the other set comes from the father.

Now that you have the basic tenets of the chromosome theory, let's relate these ideas to Mendel's laws.

Gene locus—site on chromosome where a gene is found. A gene can exist as two or more different alleles.

Pair of homologous chromosomes

T—Tall allele

Genotype: *Tt* (heterozygous)   *t*—Dwarf allele

Figure 15.9 A gene locus. The locus (location) of a gene is the same for each member of a homologous pair, whether the individual is homozygous or heterozygous for that gene. This individual is heterozygous (*Tt*) for a gene for plant height in peas.

BioConnections: *Look back at Figure 14.12 and explain the relationship between diploidy and homologous chromosomes.*

Chromosomes and Segregation Mendel's law of segregation of alleles can be explained by the pairing and subsequent segregation of homologous chromosomes during meiosis. Before we examine this idea, it will be helpful to introduce another genetic term. The physical location of a gene on a chromosome is called the gene's **locus** (plural: loci). As shown in **Figure 15.9** each member of a homologous chromosome pair carries an allele of the same gene at the same locus. The individual in this example is heterozygous (*Tt*), so each homologue has a different allele.

Figure 15.10 follows a homologous chromosome pair through the events of meiosis. This example involves a pea plant, heterozygous for height, *Tt*. The top of Figure 15.10 shows the two homologues before DNA replication. When a cell prepares to divide, the homologues each replicate to produce pairs of sister chromatids. Each chromatid carries a copy of the allele found on the original homologue, either *T* or *t*. The homologues, each consisting of two sister chromatids, pair during prophase I, align facing opposite poles during metaphase I, and then segregate at anaphase I. Next the two daughter nuclei each subsequently undergo the second meiotic division. The end result of meiosis is that each haploid cell has a copy of just one of the two original homologues. Two of the cells have a chromosome carrying the *T* allele, while the other two have a chromosome carrying the *t* allele at the same locus. If the haploid cells shown at the bottom of Figure 15.10 combine randomly during fertilization, they produce diploid offspring with the genotypic and phenotypic ratios shown earlier in Figure 15.6.

Chromosomes and Independent Assortment The law of independent assortment can also be explained by the behaviour of chromosomes during meiosis. **Figure 15.11** shows the segregation of two pairs of homologous chromosomes in a pea plant. One pair carries the gene for seed colour: the yellow allele (*Y*) is on one chromosome, and the green allele (*y*) is on its homologue. The other pair of chromosomes carries the gene for seed shape: one member of the pair has the round allele (*R*), while its

Heterozygous (*Tt*) cell from a tall plant

Diploid cell

1 **Chromosomes replicate and cell progresses to metaphase of meiosis I.**

Metaphase I

2 **Homologues segregate into separate cells during anaphase of meiosis I.**

Sister chromatids

Homologues paired with each other

3 **Sister chromatids separate during anaphase of meiosis II.**

Four haploid cells

Figure 15.10 The chromosomal basis of allele segregation. This example shows a pair of homologous chromosomes in a cell of a pea plant. The dark red chromosome was inherited from the male parent and the light red chromosome was inherited from the female parent. This individual is heterozygous for a height gene (*Tt*). The two homologues segregate from each other during meiosis, leading to segregation of the tall allele (*T*) and the dwarf allele (*t*) into different haploid cells.

Concept check: *When we say that alleles segregate, what does the word* segregate *mean? How is this related to meiosis, described in Chapter 14?*

BioConnections: *When we say that alleles segregate, what does the word segregate mean? How is this related to meiosis, shown in Figure 14.15, step 4?*

homologue carries the wrinkled allele (*r*). Thus, this individual is heterozygous for both genes, with the genotype *YyRr*.

At metaphase I of meiosis the two different pairs of chromosomes independently align themselves along the metaphase plate. This alignment can occur in two equally probable ways, shown on the two sides of the figure. On the left the chromosome carrying the *y* allele is aligned on the same side of the metaphase plate as the chromosome carrying the *R* allele; *Y* is aligned with *r*. On the right the opposite has occurred: *Y* is aligned with *R* and *y* is with *r*. In each case the chromosomes that aligned on the same side of the metaphase plate segregate into the same daughter cell. In this

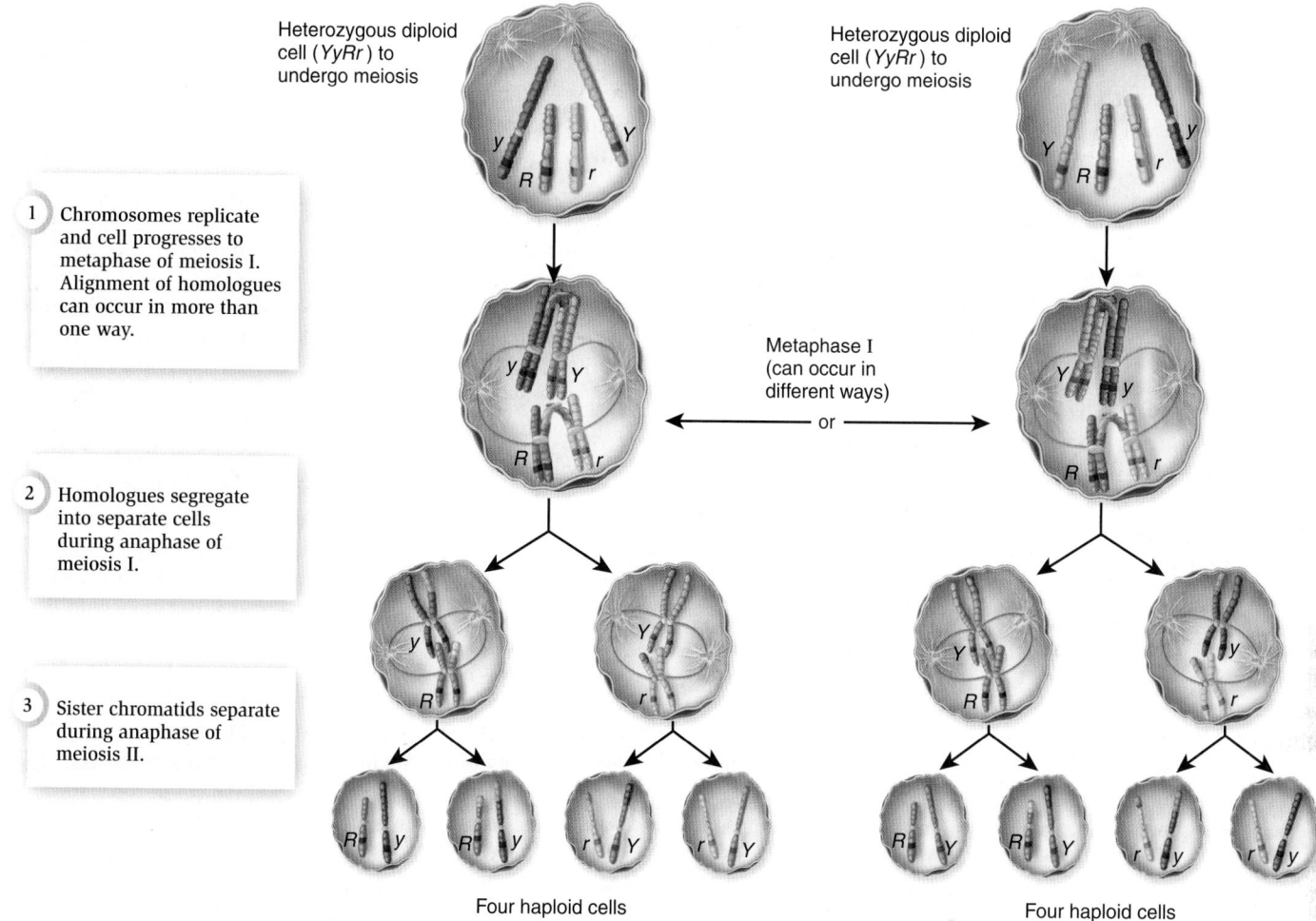

Figure 15.11 The chromosomal basis of independent assortment. The genes for seed colour (*Y* or *y*) and seed shape (*R* or *r*) in peas are on different chromosomes. During the metaphase of meiosis I different arrangements of the two chromosome pairs can lead to different combinations of the alleles in the resulting haploid cells. On the left, the chromosome carrying the dominant *R* allele has segregated with the chromosome carrying the recessive *y* allele; on the right, the two chromosomes carrying the dominant alleles (*R* and *Y*) have segregated together.

way the random alignment of chromosome pairs during meiosis I leads to the independent assortment of alleles found on different chromosomes. For two loci found on different chromosomes, each with two variant alleles, meiosis produces four allele combinations in equal numbers, as seen at the bottom of the figure.

If a *YyRr* (dihybrid) plant undergoes self-fertilization, any two gametes can combine randomly during fertilization. Because four kinds of gametes are made, this allows for 16 possible allele combinations in the offspring. These genotypes, in turn, produce four phenotypes in a 9:3:3:1 ratio, as seen earlier in Figure 15.8. This ratio is the expected outcome when a heterozygote for two genes on different chromosomes undergoes self-fertilization.

Eukaryotic chromosomes usually are the home of many genes. What if two genes are located on the same chromosome; will they sort independently? When two genes occur on the same DNA helix, at the time of anaphase I they cannot sort independently and must go to the same daughter nucleus. Thus, the transmission pattern for genes on homologous chromosomes may not conform to the law of independent assortment. We will discuss this phenomenon, known as linkage, in a later section.

Genetic Predictions Are Based on Probability

As you have seen, Mendel's laws of inheritance can be used to predict the outcome of genetic crosses. This is useful in many ways. In agriculture, for example, plant and animal breeders use predictions about the types of offspring their crosses will produce to develop commercially important crops and livestock. In addition, people are often interested in the potential characteristics of their future children. This information is particularly important to individuals who carry alleles that cause inherited diseases. Of course, no one can see into the future and definitively predict what will happen. Nevertheless, genetic counsellors can often help couples by predicting the likelihood of having an affected child. This probability is one factor that can influence a couple's decision about whether to have children.

Genetic predictions are based on the mathematical rules of probability. The chance that an event will have a particular outcome is called the **probability** of that outcome. The probability of a given outcome depends on the number of possible outcomes. For example, if you draw a card at random from a 52-card deck, the probability that you will get the jack of diamonds is 1 in 52, because there are 52 possible outcomes for the draw, and only 1 jack of diamonds. In contrast, only two outcomes are possible when you flip a coin, so the probability is one in two (1/2 or 0.5 or 50%) that the heads side will be showing when the coin lands. The general formula for the probability (P) that a random event will have a specific outcome is

$$P = \frac{\text{number of times an event occurs}}{\text{total number of possible outcomes}}$$

Thus, for a single coin toss, the chance of getting heads is

$$P_{\text{heads}} = \frac{1 \text{ heads}}{(1 \text{ heads} + 1 \text{ tails})} = \frac{1}{2}$$

Earlier in this chapter we considered the use of Punnett squares to predict the fractions of offspring with a given genotype or phenotype. Our example was self-fertilization of a pea plant that was heterozygous for the height gene (Tt), and our Punnett square predicted that one-fourth of the offspring would be dwarf. We can make the same prediction by using a probability calculation:

$$P_{\text{dwarf}} = \frac{1 \text{ } tt}{(1 \text{ } TT + 2Tt + 1 \text{ } tt)} = \frac{1}{4}$$

Probability and Sample Size A probability calculation allows us to predict the likelihood that a future event will have a specific outcome. However, the accuracy of this prediction depends to a great extent on the number of events we observe or, in other words, on the size of our sample. For example, if we toss a coin six times, the calculation we just presented for P_{heads} suggests that we should get heads three times and tails three times. However, each coin toss is an independent event, meaning that every time we toss the coin there is a random chance that it will come up heads or tails, regardless of the outcome of the previous toss. With only six tosses we would not be too surprised if we got four heads and two tails. The deviation between the observed and expected outcomes is called the random sampling error. With a small sample the random sampling error can cause the observed data to be quite different from the expected outcome. By comparison, if we flipped a coin 1,000 times, the percentage of heads would be fairly close to the predicted 50%. With a larger sample, we expect the sampling error to be smaller.

Earlier in this chapter we examined Mendel's data for pea plants and learned that his observations were very close to the outcome that we would predict from a Punnett square. Mendel counted a large number of pea plants, which made his sampling error quite small. However, when we apply probability to humans, the small size of human families can cause the observed data to be quite different from the expected outcome. Consider, for example, a couple who are both heterozygous for an allele that affects eye colour (Bb). The dominant allele is brown, so both of these parents have brown eyes. We can use a Punnett square to predict that one-fourth of their offspring will have blue eyes, which is the recessive phenotype for a *bb* homozygote. However, the genotype or phenotype of each child

is independent of each other. Each child has one chance in four of having the recessive phenotype; the birth of a blue-eyed child does not make it more or less likely that the next child will have blue eyes. Thus, in a family with four children, we would not be too surprised if two of them had blue eyes—twice the predicted number. In this case a large deviation occurs between the observed outcome (50% blue-eyed children) and the expected outcome (25% blue-eyed children). This large random sampling error can be attributed to the small sample size.

The Product Rule and the Sum Rule Punnett squares allow us to predict the likelihood that a genetic cross will produce an offspring with a particular genotype or phenotype. Alternatively, to predict the likelihood of producing multiple offspring with particular genotypes or phenotypes, we can use the **product rule**, which states that the probability that two or more independent events will occur is equal to the product of their individual probabilities. As we have already discussed, events are independent if the outcome of one event does not affect the outcome of another. In our previous coin-toss example, each toss is an independent event—if one toss comes up heads, another toss still has an equal chance of coming up either heads or tails. If we toss a coin twice, what is the probability that we will get heads both times? The product rule says that it is equal to the probability of getting heads on the first toss (1/2) times the probability of getting heads on the second toss (1/2), or one in four ($1/2 \times 1/2 = 1/4$).

To see how the product rule can be applied to a genetics problem, let's consider a rare, recessive human trait known as congenital analgesia. (*Congenital* refers to a condition present at birth; *analgesia* means "insensitivity to pain.") People with this trait can distinguish between such sensations as sharp and dull or hot and cold, but they do not perceive extremes of sensation as painful. The first known case of congenital analgesia, described in 1932, was a man who made his living entertaining the public as a "human pincushion." For a phenotypically normal couple each heterozygous for the recessive allele causing congenital analgesia, we can ask, What is the probability that their first three offspring will have the disorder? To answer this question, we must first determine the probability of a single offspring having the abnormal phenotype. By using a Punnett square, we would find that the probability of an individual offspring being homozygous recessive is 1/4. Thus, each of this couple's children has one chance in four of having the disorder.

We can now use the product rule to calculate the probability of this couple having three affected offspring in a row. The phenotypes of the first, second, and third offspring are independent events; that is, the phenotype of the first offspring does not affect the phenotype of the second or third offspring. The product rule tells us that the probability of all three children having the abnormal phenotype is

$$\frac{1}{4} \times \frac{1}{4} \times \frac{1}{4} = \frac{1}{64} = 0.016$$

The probability of the first three offspring having the disorder is 0.016, or 1.6%. In other words, we can say that this couple's chance of having three children in a row with congenital analgesia is very small—only 1.6 out of 100. The phenotypes of the first, second, and third child are independent of each other.

Let's now consider a second important rule of probability (the sum rule) that is useful in predicting outcomes of particular crosses. In a cross between two heterozygous (*Tt*) pea plants, we may want to know the probability of a particular offspring being a homozygote. In this case we are asking, What is the chance that this individual will be either homozygous *TT* or homozygous *tt*? To answer an "either/or" question, we use the sum rule, which applies to events with mutually exclusive outcomes. When we say that outcomes are mutually exclusive, we mean that they cannot occur at the same time. A pea plant can be tall or dwarf, but not both at the same time: the tall and dwarf phenotypes are mutually exclusive. Similarly, a plant with the genotype *TT* cannot be *Tt* or *tt*. Each genotype is mutually exclusive. Often for the sum rule we are dealing with at least two different fertilizations; in our example we need to consider the fertilization that could give *TT* and the fertilization that could give *tt*. These are mutually exclusive events; a given fertilization can be one or the other but not both. According to the **sum rule** the probability that one of two or more mutually exclusive outcomes will occur is the sum of the probabilities of the possible outcomes. This means that to find the probability that an offspring will be either homozygous *TT* or homozygous *tt*, we add the probability that it will be *TT* and the probability that it will be *tt*. By using a Punnett square, we find that the probability for each of these genotypes is one in four. We can now use the sum rule to determine the probability of an individual having one of these genotypes:

$$\frac{1}{4} \quad + \quad \frac{1}{4} \quad = \quad \frac{1}{2}$$

(probability of *TT*) + (probability of *tt*) = (probability of either *TT* or *tt*)

This calculation predicts that in crosses of two *Tt* parents, half of the offspring will be homozygotes—either *TT* or *tt*.

Pedigree Analysis Examines the Inheritance of Human Traits

As you have seen, Mendel conducted experiments by making selective crosses of pea plants and analyzing large numbers of offspring. Later geneticists also relied on crosses of experimental organisms, especially fruit flies. Obviously, geneticists studying human traits cannot use this approach, for ethical and practical reasons. Instead, human geneticists must rely on information from family trees or pedigrees. In this approach, called **pedigree analysis**, an inherited trait is analyzed over a few generations in one family. The results of this method may be less definitive than the results of breeding experiments because the small size of human families can lead to large sampling errors. Nevertheless, a pedigree analysis can often provide important clues concerning human inheritance.

Pedigree analysis has been used to understand the inheritance of genetic diseases that follow simple Mendelian patterns. Many genes exist in at least two forms—the normal allele and an abnormal allele that has arisen by mutation. Disease

symptoms can occur as a result of the mutant allele. Pedigree analysis allows us to determine whether the mutant allele is dominant or recessive and to predict the likelihood of an individual being affected.

We have already considered one human abnormality caused by a recessive allele, congenital analgesia. We will use another recessive condition to illustrate pedigree analysis. The pedigree in **Figure 15.12** concerns a human genetic disease known as cystic fibrosis (CF). Worldwide, approximately 3% of people of European descent are heterozygous carriers of the recessive CF allele. These heterozygous carriers are phenotypically normal. Individuals who are homozygous for the CF allele (about 0.03%) exhibit the disease symptoms, which include abnormalities of the pancreas, intestine, sweat glands, and lungs. (You will see how a single gene can have such far-reaching effects when we discuss the molecular basis of Mendelian inheritance later in the chapter.) A human pedigree like the one in Figure 15.12 shows the oldest generation (designated by the Roman numeral I) at the top, with later generations (II and III) below it. A man (represented by a square) and a woman (represented by a circle) who

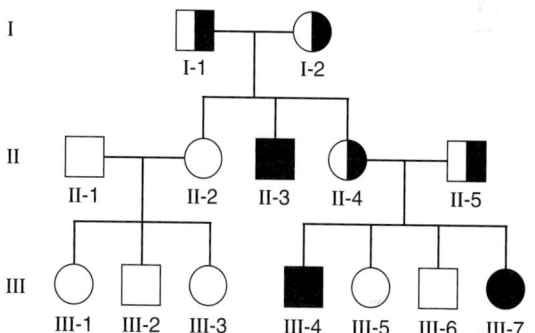

(a) Human pedigree showing cystic fibrosis

○♀	Female
□♂	Male
○ □	Unaffected individual
● ■	Affected individual
◐ ◨ ⊙	Presumed heterozygote (the dot notation indicates sex-linked traits)

(b) Symbols used in a human pedigree

Figure 15.12 A family pedigree of a recessive trait. Some members of the family in this pedigree have cystic fibrosis. I represents the first generation recorded, II the second, and III the third. Phenotypically normal individuals I-1, I-2, II-4, and II-5 are presumed to be heterozygotes because they have produced affected offspring.

Concept check: *Suppose a genetic disease is caused by a mutant allele. If two affected parents produce an unaffected offspring, can the mutant allele be recessive?*

produce offspring, are connected by a horizontal line; a vertical line connects parents with their offspring. Siblings (brothers and sisters) are denoted by downward projections from a single horizontal line, from left to right in the order of their birth. For example, individuals I-1 and I-2 are the parents of individuals II-2, II-3, and II-4, who are all siblings. Individuals who have the disease, such as individual II-3, are depicted by filled symbols.

The pattern of affected and unaffected individuals in this pedigree is consistent with a recessive mode of inheritance for CF: two unaffected individuals produce one or more affected offspring. Such individuals are presumed to be heterozygotes (designated by a half-filled symbol). However, the same unaffected parents can also produce unaffected offspring, because an individual must inherit two copies of the mutant allele to exhibit the disease. A recessive mode of inheritance is also characterized by the observation that all the offspring of two affected individuals will be affected. However, for genetic diseases like CF that limit survival or fertility, there may rarely or never be cases where two affected individuals produce offspring.

Although many of the alleles causing human genetic diseases are recessive, some are known to be dominant. **Figure 15.13** shows a family pedigree involving Huntington disease, a condition that causes the degeneration of brain cells involved in emotions, intellect, and movement. If you examine this pedigree, you will see that every affected individual has one affected parent. This pattern is characteristic of most dominant disorders. The symptoms of Huntington disease, which usually begin to appear when people are 30 to 50 years old, include uncontrollable jerking movements of the limbs, trunk, and face; progressive loss of mental abilities; and the development of psychiatric problems. In 1993 researchers identified the gene involved in this disorder. The normal allele encodes a protein called huntingtin, which functions in nerve cells. The mutant allele encodes an abnormal form of the protein, which aggregates within nerve cells in the brain. Further research is needed to determine how this aggregation contributes to the disease.

Most human genes are found on chromosomes called **autosomes**. Autosomes are pairs of homologous chromosomes

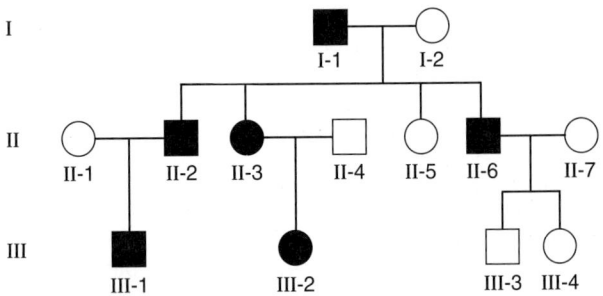

Figure 15.13   A family pedigree of a dominant trait. Huntington disease is caused by a dominant allele. Note that each affected offspring in this pedigree has an affected parent.

 Principle: *The genetic material, DNA, provides a dynamic plan for sustaining life. When mutated, the genes can cause abnormal phenotypes that lead to death.*

that both sexes have. Mendelian inheritance patterns are associated with these autosomal genes. Huntington disease is an example of a trait with an autosomal dominant inheritance pattern, whereas cystic fibrosis illustrates the pattern called autosomal recessive. However, some human genes are located on sex chromosomes, which are different in males and females. These genes have their own characteristic inheritance patterns, which we will consider in the next section.

15.2   SEX CHROMOSOMES AND X-LINKED INHERITANCE PATTERNS

Learning Outcomes:

1. Outline the principles of the chromosome theory of inheritance and Morgan's contribution to it.
2. Describe different systems of sex determination in animals and plants.
3. Predict the outcome of crosses when genes are located on sex chromosomes.
4. Explain why X-linked recessive traits are more likely to occur in males.

In the first part of this chapter we discussed Mendel's experiments, which established the basis for understanding how traits are transmitted from parents to offspring. We also examined the chromosome theory of inheritance, which provided a framework for explaining Mendel's observations. Mendelian patterns of gene transmission are observed for many genes located on autosomes in a wide variety of eukaryotic species.

We will now turn our attention to genes located on **sex chromosomes**. As you learned in Chapter 14, this term refers to a distinctive pair of chromosomes that are different in males and females. Sex chromosomes are found in many but not all species with separate sexes. The study of sex chromosomes proved pivotal in confirming the chromosome theory. The distinctive transmission patterns of genes on sex chromosomes helped early geneticists show that particular genes are located on particular chromosomes.

In this section we will consider several mechanisms by which the presence or composition of sex chromosomes determines an individual's sex in different species. We will then examine some of the early research involving sex chromosomes that provided convincing evidence for the chromosome theory of inheritance. Finally, we will consider the inheritance patterns of genes on sex chromosomes and why recessive traits are seen more frequently in one sex than the other.

In Many Species, Sex Differences Are Due to the Presence of Sex Chromosomes

According to the chromosome theory of inheritance, chromosomes carry the genes that determine an organism's traits. Some early evidence supporting this theory involved a consideration of sex determination. In 1901 American biologist C. E. McClung, who studied fruit flies, suggested that male and female sexes in insects are due to the inheritance of particular chromosomes. Following McClung's initial observations several mechanisms of sex determination were found in different species of animals. Some examples are described in **Figure 15.14**. All these mechanisms involve chromosomal differences between the sexes, and most involve a difference in a single pair of sex chromosomes.

In the mammalian X-Y system of sex determination, the somatic cells of males have one X and one Y chromosome, while female somatic cells contain two X chromosomes (**Figure 15.14a**). For example, the 46 chromosomes carried by human cells consist of one pair of sex chromosomes (either XY or XX) and 22 pairs of autosomes. The presence of the Y chromosome causes maleness in mammals. This is known from the analysis of rare individuals who carry chromosomal abnormalities. For example, mistakes that occasionally occur during meiosis may produce an individual who carries two X chromosomes and one Y chromosome. Such an individual develops into a male. A gene called the *SRY* gene located on the Y chromosome of mammals is known to play a key role in the developmental pathway that leads to maleness. How the *SRY* gene initiates the development of maleness is not fully understood. Researchers, such as Dr. Teruko Taketo of McGill University, are studying this process.

Many insects (**Figure 15.14b**) also have sex chromosomes. In one system females have a pair of sex chromosomes and are designated XX, and it is the ratio of the number of X chromosomes to sets of autosomes that determines sex:

$$2 \text{ (Xs)}/2 \text{ (sets of autosomes)} = \text{female}$$

The male has only one sex chromosome, the X, and is designated XO. Crickets (Figure 15.14b) are one example of this system. In other insect species, such as *Drosophila melanogaster*, the male has both an X chromosome and a Y chromosome and is designated XY. Unlike the Y chromosome of mammals, the Y chromosome of *Drosophila* does not determine maleness and has only one known gene that determines sperm motility.

Thus far, we have considered examples in which females are the **homogametic sex**, meaning all normal gametes receive a copy of the same type of sex chromosome, and males are the **heterogametic sex**, producing two types of gametes: one for female offspring and another for male offspring. However, in some animal species, such as birds and some fish, the males are the homogametic sex (**Figure 15.14c**). When the male is the homogametic sex, the sex determination is called the Z-W system to distinguish it from the X-Y system found in mammals. The male is ZZ and the female is ZW.

Not all chromosomal mechanisms of sex determination involve a special pair of sex chromosomes. An interesting mechanism, known as the haplo-diploid system, is found in bees (**Figure 15.14d**). Unfertilized eggs are haploid and can be stimulated to develop into haploid male bees, called drones, without being fertilized. All males are haploid and produce haploid sperm by mitosis. If a haploid egg is fertilized by a haploid sperm, it will have two chromosome sets and hence be diploid. It will develop into a female.

(a) The X-Y system in mammals

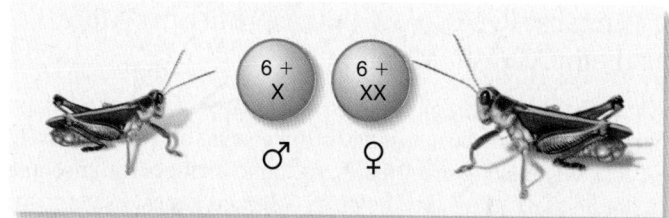

(b) The X-O system in certain insects

(c) The Z-W system in birds

(d) The haplo-diploid system in bees

Figure 15.14 Different mechanisms of sex determination in animals. The numbers shown in the circles indicate the numbers of autosomes.

Concept check: *If a person is born with only one X chromosome and no Y chromosome, would you expect that person to be a male or a female? Explain your answer.*

Although sex determination is controlled by sex chromosomes in many species, other mechanisms are also known. In certain reptiles and fish sex is controlled by environmental factors, such as temperature. For example, in the American alligator (*Alligator mississippiensis*), temperature controls sex development. When eggs of this alligator are incubated at 33°C, 100% of them produce male individuals. When the eggs are incubated at a temperature below 33°C, they produce 100% females, while at a temperature above 33°C, they produce 95% females.

Most species of flowering plants, including pea plants, have a single type of diploid, or sporophyte, that makes both male and female gametophytes. However, the sporophytes of some species have two sexually distinct types of individuals, one with flowers that produce male gametophytes, and the other with flowers that produce female gametophytes. Examples include hollies, willows, poplars, and date palms. Sex chromosomes, designated X and Y, are responsible for sex determination in many such species. The male plant is XY, while the female plant is XX. However, in some species with separate sexes, microscopic examination of the chromosomes does not reveal distinct types of sex chromosomes.

In Humans, Recessive X-Linked Traits Are More Likely to Occur in Males

In humans the X chromosome is rather large and carries many genes, while the Y chromosome is quite small and has relatively few genes. Therefore, many genes are found on the X chromosome but not on the Y; these are known as **X-linked genes**. By comparison, only a few genes are known to be Y linked, meaning that they are found on the Y chromosome but not on the X. The term **sex linked** refers to genes that are found on one sex chromosome but not on the other. Because few genes are found on the Y chromosome, the term *sex-linked genes* usually refers to X-linked genes.

In mammals a male cannot be described as being homozygous or heterozygous for an X-linked gene, because these terms describe genes that are present in two copies. Instead, the term **hemizygous** is used to describe the single copy of an X-linked gene in a male. Many recessive X-linked mutant alleles cause diseases in humans, and these diseases occur more frequently in males than in females. Why?

As an example, consider the X-linked recessive disorder called classical hemophilia (hemophilia A). In individuals with hemophilia, blood does not clot normally and a minor cut can bleed for a long time. Small bumps can lead to large bruises because broken capillaries leak blood profusely into surrounding tissues before the capillaries are repaired. Common accidental injuries pose a threat of severe internal or external bleeding for people with hemophilia. Hemophilia A is caused by a recessive X-linked disease allele that encodes a defective form of a clotting protein. If a mother is a heterozygous carrier of hemophilia A, each of her children has a 50% chance of inheriting the recessive allele. A Punnett square shows a cross between a normal father and a heterozygous mother. X^{h-A} is the chromosome that carries the recessive allele for hemophilia A.

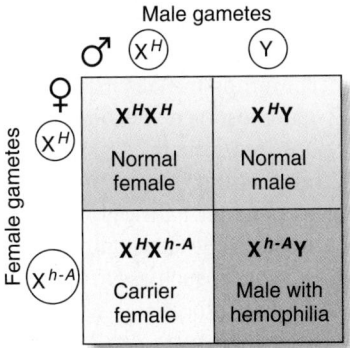

Although each child has a 50% chance of inheriting the hemophilia allele from the mother, only sons will exhibit the disorder. Because sons do not inherit an X chromosome from their fathers, a son who inherits the abnormal allele from his mother will have hemophilia. However, a daughter who inherits the hemophilia allele from her mother will also inherit a normal allele from her father. This daughter will have a normal phenotype, but if she passes the abnormal allele to her sons, they will have hemophilia.

FEATURE INVESTIGATION

Morgan's Experiments Showed a Correlation Between a Genetic Trait and the Inheritance of a Sex Chromosome in *Drosophila*

The distinctive inheritance pattern of X-linked recessive alleles provides a way to demonstrate that a specific gene is on an X chromosome. In fact, an X-linked gene was the first gene to be located on a specific chromosome. In 1910 American geneticist Thomas Hunt Morgan began work on a project in which he reared large populations of fruit flies, *Drosophila melanogaster,* in the dark to determine if their eyes would atrophy from disuse and disappear in future generations. Even after many consecutive generations, the flies showed no noticeable changes. After two years, however, Morgan finally obtained an interesting result: a true-breeding line of *Drosophila* produced a male fly with white eyes rather than the normal red eyes. The white-eye trait must have arisen from a new mutation that converted the normal red-eye allele into a white-eye allele.

By using an approach similar to Mendel's, Morgan studied the inheritance of the white-eye trait by making crosses and quantitatively analyzing the outcomes. In the experiment described in **Figure 15.15**, Morgan crossed his white-eyed male to a red-eyed female. All the F_1 offspring had red eyes, suggesting that red is dominant to white. The F_1 offspring were then mated to each other to obtain an F_2 generation. As seen in the data table, this self-cross of the F_1 produced 2,459 red-eyed females, 1,011 red-eyed males, and 782 white-eyed males. Surprisingly, no white-eyed females were observed in the F_2 generation.

Morgan's results suggested a connection between the alleles for eye colour and the sex of the offspring. As shown in the conceptual column of Figure 15.15 and in the Punnett square, the data are consistent with the idea that the eye-colour alleles in *Drosophila* are located on the X chromosome. X^{w+} is the chromosome carrying the normal allele

GOAL A quantitative analysis of genetic crosses may reveal the pattern of inheritance of a particular gene.

KEY MATERIALS A true-breeding line of red-eyed fruit flies plus one white-eyed male fly that was discovered in the population.

1. Cross the white-eyed male to a red-eyed female.

Experimental level — P generation — ♂ × ♀

Conceptual level — ♂ × ♀ — $X^w Y \times X^{w^+} X^{w^+}$

2. Record the results of the F_1 generation. This involves noting the eye colour and sexes of the offspring.

F_1 generation — ♂ : ♀

$X^{w^+} Y : X^{w^+} X^w$

3. Cross F_1 offspring with each other to obtain F_2 generation of offspring.

♂ × ♀

$X^{w^+} Y \times X^{w^+} X^w$

4. Record the eye colour and sex of F_2 offspring.

F_2 generation — ♂ : ♂ : ♀ : ♀

$X^{w^+} Y : X^w Y : X^{w^+} X^{w^+} : X^{w^+} X^w$

5. **THE DATA**

Cross	Results
Original white-eyed male to a red-eyed female	F_1 generation All red-eyed flies
F_1 males to F_1 females	F_2 generation 1,011 red-eyed males 782 white-eyed males 2,459 red-eyed females 0 white-eyed females

6. **CONCLUSION** The data are consistent with an inheritance pattern in which an eye-colour gene is located on the X chromosome.

7. **SOURCE** Morgan, Thomas H. 1910. Sex limited inheritance in *Drosophila*. *Science* 32:120–122.

Figure 15.15 Morgan's crosses of red-eyed and white-eyed *Drosophila*.

for red eyes, and X^w is the chromosome carrying the mutant allele for white eyes.

The Punnett square predicts that the F_2 generation will not have any white-eyed females, a prediction that was confirmed by Morgan's experimental data. However, it should also be pointed out that the experimental ratio of red eyes to white eyes in the F_2 generation is $(2{,}459 + 1{,}011){:}782$, which equals 4.4:1. This ratio deviates significantly from the ratio of 3:1 predicted in the Punnett square. The lower than expected number of white-eyed flies is explained by a decreased survival of white-eyed flies.

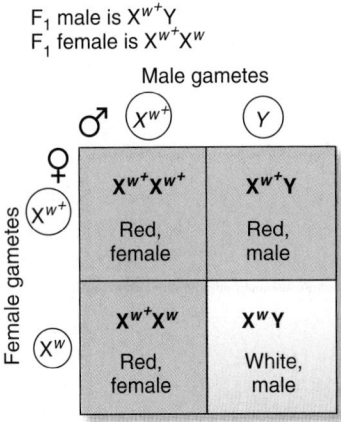

F$_1$ male is X^{w+}Y
F$_1$ female is X^{w+}X^w

Following this initial discovery Morgan carried out many experimental crosses that located specific genes on the *Drosophila* X chromosome. As more geneticists did experimental crosses, many more sex-linked genes were discovered; all have deviations from Mendelian 3:1 ratio in reciprocal crosses. These deviations are due to deviation from Mendel's first law of segregation of alleles because one sex (males in mammals and flies) has only one version of the sex-linked genes, not two. Morgan's research showing how differences in chromosomes are associated with differences in inheritance provided some of the most persuasive evidence for the chromosome theory of inheritance. In recognition of this contribution, in 1933 Morgan became the first geneticist to receive a Nobel Prize.

Trying to understand why some genes did not follow Mendel's first law brought scientists to a better understanding of inheritance. As geneticists did more crosses to create and study dihybrids, they noted that Mendel's second law of independent assortment did not always hold either. We will now explore why some genes do not sort independently.

Experimental Questions

1. What was the original purpose of Morgan's experiments with *Drosophila?*
2. How was Morgan able to demonstrate that red eye colour is dominant over white eye colour?
3. What results led Morgan to conclude that eye colour was associated with the sex of the individual?

15.3 GENES ON THE SAME CHROMOSOME: LINKAGE, RECOMBINATION, AND MAPPING

Learning Outcomes:

1. Describe how linkage violates the law of independent assortment.
2. Explain how experimental crosses can demonstrate linkage.
3. Calculate the distance between genes that are linked on the same chromosome.

In all the inheritance patterns we have studied so far, the alleles segregate and assort independently as predicted by Mendel's laws. But for some inheritance patterns the outcome of a cross violates Mendel's second law. In this section we focus on transmission patterns that do not conform to the law of independent assortment. We will begin by examining Morgan's first experimental cross that demonstrated this pattern. Morgan proposed that genes located close on the same chromosome tend to be inherited as a group. Finally, we will see how crossing over between such genes provided the first method of mapping genes on chromosomes.

Bateson and Punnett's Crosses of Sweet Peas Showed That Genes Do Not Always Assort Independently

You have learned that the independent assortment of alleles is due to the independent alignment of homologous chromosomes during meiosis (refer back to Figure 15.11). But what happens when the alleles of different genes are on the same chromosome? A typical chromosome contains many hundreds or even a few thousand different genes. When two genes are close together on the same chromosome, they tend to be transmitted as a unit, a phenomenon known as **linkage**. A group of genes that usually stay together are said to be linked. In a two-factor cross, linked genes do not follow the law of independent assortment.

The first study showing linkage between two different genes was a cross of sweet peas carried out by William Bateson and Reginald Punnett in 1905. A surprising result occurred when they conducted a cross involving two different traits: flower colour and pollen shape (**Figure 15.16**). One of the parent plants had purple flowers (*PP*) and long pollen (*LL*); the other had red flowers (*pp*) and round pollen (*ll*). As Bateson and Punnett expected, the F$_1$ plants all had purple flowers and long pollen (*PpLl*). The unexpected result came in the F$_2$ generation. Although the offspring displayed the four phenotypes predicted by Mendel's laws, the observed numbers of offspring did not conform to the predicted 9:3:3:1 ratio. Rather, as seen in the data in Figure 15.16, the F$_2$ generation had a much higher proportion of the two phenotypes found in the parental generation: purple flowers with long pollen, and red flowers with round pollen. These results did not support the law of independent assortment. Bateson and Punnett suggested that the transmission of flower colour and pollen shape was somehow coupled, so that these traits did not always assort independently. Although the law of independent assortment applies to many

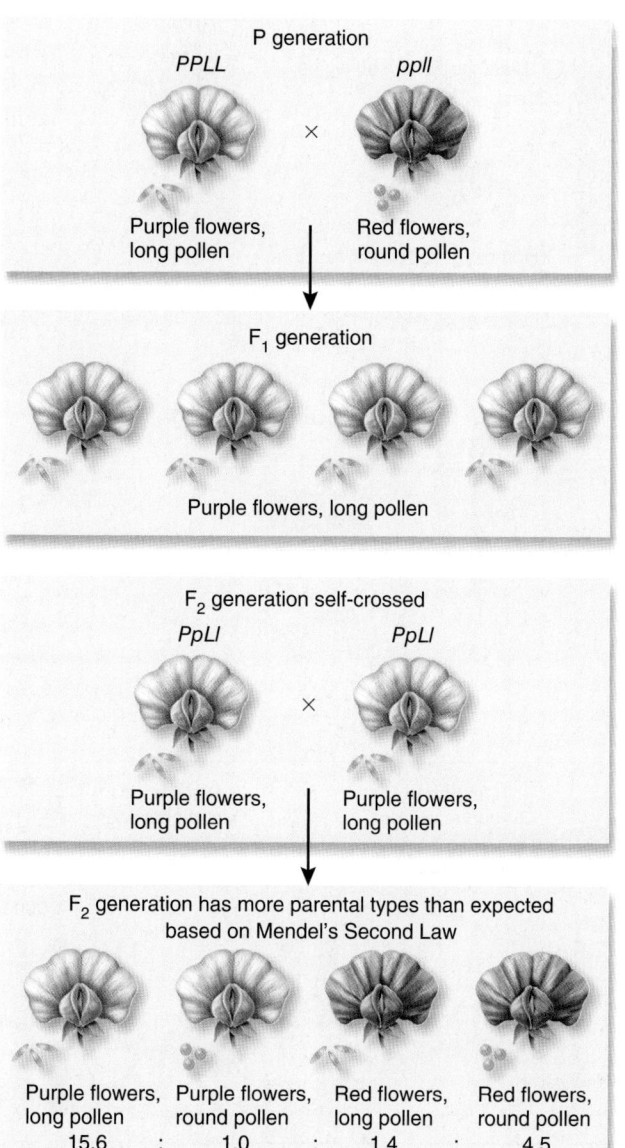

Figure 15.16 A cross of sweet peas showing that independent assortment does not always occur.

other genes, in this example, the hypothesis of independent assortment was rejected.

Linkage and Crossing Over Produce Parental and Recombinant Phenotypes

Although Bateson and Punnett realized their results did not conform to Mendel's law of independent assortment, they did not provide a clear explanation for their data. A few years later Thomas Hunt Morgan obtained similar results in crosses of fruit flies while studying the transmission pattern of genes located on the X chromosome. Like Bateson and Punnett, Morgan observed many more F$_2$ offspring with the parental combination of traits than would be predicted on the basis of independent

assortment. Morgan was again successful because he brought together genetic data with observations of chromosomes. He linked his genetic data to the crossover configurations seen with meiotic chromosomes (e.g., Figure 14.14). To explain his data, Morgan proposed three ideas:

1. When different genes are located on the same chromosome, the genes are likely to be inherited together.
2. Because of crossing over during meiosis, homologous chromosomes can exchange pieces of chromosomes and create new combinations of alleles.
3. The likelihood of crossing over depends on the distance between two genes. Crossovers between homologous chromosomes are much more likely to occur between two genes that are farther apart in the chromosome, compared with two genes that are closer together.

To illustrate the first two of these ideas, **Figure 15.17** considers a series of crosses involving two genes that are linked on the same chromosome in *Drosophila*. The P generation cross is between flies that are homozygous for alleles that affect body colour and wing shape. The female is homozygous for the wild-type alleles that produce grey body colour (b^+b^+) and straight wings (c^+c^+); the male is homozygous for mutant alleles that produce black body colour (bb) and curved wings (cc). Note that the symbols for the genes are based on the name of the mutant allele; the wild-type allele is indicated by a superscript plus sign ($^+$). The chromosomes next to the flies in Figure 15.17 show the arrangement of these alleles. If the two genes are on the same chromosome, we know the arrangement of alleles in the P-generation flies because these flies are homozygous for both genes ($b^+b^+c^+c^+$ or $bbcc$). In the P-generation female on the left, b^+ and c^+ are linked, while b and c are linked in the male on the right.

Let's now look at the outcome of the crosses in Figure 15.17. As expected, the F$_1$ offspring (b^+bc^+c) all had grey bodies and straight wings, confirming that these are the dominant traits. In the next cross F$_1$ females were mated to males that were homozygous for both recessive alleles ($bbcc$). A cross in which an individual with a dominant phenotype is mated with a homozygous recessive individual is called a *testcross*, as described earlier. In the crosses we are discussing here, the purpose of the testcross is to determine whether the genes for body colour and wing shape are linked. If the genes were on different chromosomes and assorted independently, this testcross should have produced equal numbers of F$_2$ offspring with the four possible phenotypes. The observed numbers, shown above the F$_2$ phenotypes, clearly conflict with this prediction based on independent assortment. The two most abundant phenotypes are those with the combinations of characteristics in the P generation: grey bodies and straight wings or black bodies and curved wings. These offspring are **nonrecombinants** because their combination of traits has not changed from the parental generation. They are also termed **parental types**. The smaller number of offspring that have a different combination of traits—grey

P

♀ Grey body, straight wings

b^+ b^+

c^+ c^+

Homozygous dominant
$b^+b^+c^+c^+$

×

♂ Black body, curved wings

b b

c c

Homozygous recessive
$bbcc$

F₁

♀ Grey body, straight wings

b^+ b

c^+ c

b^+bc^+c

Testcross
×

♂ Black body, curved wings

b b

c c

$bbcc$

F₂

	Grey body, straight wings	Black body, curved wings	Grey body, curved wings	Black body, straight wings	Total
Number observed	371	359	133	137	1,000
Number expected based on independent assortment	250	250	250	250	1,000

b^+bc^+c $bbcc$ b^+bcc bbc^+c

Nonrecombinants   Recombinants

Figure 15.17 **Linkage and recombination of alleles.** An experimenter crossed $b^+b^+c^+c^+$ and $bbcc$ flies to produce F₁ heterozygotes. F₁ females were then testcrossed to $bbcc$ males. The large number of parental phenotypes in the F₂ generation suggests that the two genes are linked on the same chromosome. F₂ recombinant phenotypes occur because the alleles can be rearranged by crossing over.

BioConnections: *Look back at Figure 14.15. When does crossing over occur?*

bodies and curved wings or black bodies and straight wings—are **recombinants** or **nonparental types**.

How do we explain the occurrence of recombinants when genes are linked on the same chromosome? This relates to Morgan's second point. As shown beside the flies of the F₂ generation in Figure 15.17, each recombinant individual has a chromosome that is the product of a crossover. The crossover occurred while the F₁ female fly was making egg cells. As shown below, four different egg cells are possible:

Because of crossing over, two of the four egg cells produced by meiosis have recombinant chromosomes. What happens

Crossover

b^+ b^+ b b

c^+ c^+ c c

Homologues in F₁ female

Meiosis

b^+
c^+

b^+
c

b
c

b
c^+

Nonrecombinant chromosomes   Recombinant chromosomes

when eggs containing such chromosomes are fertilized in the testcross? Each of the male fly's sperm cells carries a chromosome with the two recessive alleles. If the egg contains the recombinant chromosome carrying the b^+ and c alleles, the testcross will produce an F_2 offspring with a grey body and curved wings. If the egg contains the recombinant chromosome carrying the b and c^+ alleles, F_2 offspring will have a black body and straight wings. Therefore, crossing over in the F_1 female can explain the occurrence of both types of F_2 recombinant offspring.

Morgan's ideas about linkage and crossing over were based on similar data, derived from his studies of genes on the X chromosome. The idea that linked genes tend to be inherited together explained the high frequency of parental combinations of traits in certain crosses. The suggestion that crossing over produces chromosomes with new allele combinations accounted for the occurrence of recombinant phenotypes. Morgan's third idea regarding linkage was that the frequency of crossing over between linked genes depends on the distance between them. This suggested a method for determining the relative positions of genes on a chromosome, as you will see next.

GENOMES AND PROTEOMES

Recombination Frequencies Provide a Method for Mapping Genes Along Chromosomes

The oldest approach to studying the arrangement of genes along chromosomes, and for determining which genes are on which chromosomes, is called **genetic linkage mapping** (also known as gene mapping or chromosome mapping). This experimental method is used to determine the linear order of genes that are linked to each other along the same chromosome. As depicted in **Figure 15.18**, this linear arrangement is shown in a chart known as a **genetic linkage map**. Each gene has its own unique locus at a particular site within a chromosome. For example, the gene for black body colour (*b*) that we discussed earlier is located near the middle of the chromosome, while the gene for curved wings (*c*) is closer to one end. Alfred Sturtevant, an undergraduate who spent time in Morgan's laboratory, created the first genetic linkage map, showing five genes on the *Drosophila* X chromosome in 1911. All the genes of the chromosome are part of the same linkage group.

Genetic linkage mapping allows us to estimate the relative distances between linked genes based on the likelihood that a crossover will occur between them. This likelihood is proportional to the distance between the genes, as Morgan first proposed. If the genes are very close together, a crossover is unlikely to begin in the region between them. However, if the genes are very far apart, a crossover is more likely to be initiated between them and thereby recombine their alleles. Therefore, in a cross involving two genes on the same chromosome, the percentage of recombinant offspring is correlated with the distance between the genes. This correlation provides the experimental basis for gene mapping. If a two-factor testcross produces many recombinant offspring, the experimenter concludes that the genes are far apart. If very few recombinant offspring are observed, the genes must be close together.

To find the distance between two genes, the experimenter must determine the frequency of crossing over between them, called their **recombination frequency**. This is accomplished by conducting a testcross. As an example let's refer back to the *Drosophila* testcross described in Figure 15.17. As we discussed, the genes for body colour and wing shape are on the same chromosome; the recombinant offspring are the result of crossing over during egg formation in the F_1 female. We can use the data from the testcross shown in Figure 15.17 to estimate the distance between these two genes. The **map distance** between two linked genes is defined as the number of recombinant offspring divided by the total number of offspring times 100.

Map units	Mutant phenotype	Wild-type phenotype
0.0	Aristaless, *al*	Long aristae
13.0	Dumpy wings, *dp*	Long wings
48.5	Black body, *b*	Grey body
54.5	Purple eyes, *pr*	Red eyes
67.0	Vestigial wings, *vg*	Long wings
75.5	Curved wings, *c*	Straight wings
104.5	Brown eyes, *bw*	Red eyes

Figure 15.18 A simplified genetic linkage map. This map shows the relative locations of a few genes along a chromosome in *Drosophila melanogaster*. The name of each gene is based on the mutant phenotype. The numbers on the left are map units (mu). The distance between two genes, in map units, corresponds to their recombination frequency in testcrosses.

$$\text{map distance} = \frac{\text{number of recombinant offspring}}{\text{total number of offspring}} \times 100$$

$$= \frac{133 + 137}{371 + 359 + 133 + 137} \times 100$$

$$= 27.0 \text{ map units}$$

The units of distance are called **map units (mu)**, or sometimes **centimorgans (cM)**, in honour of Thomas Hunt Morgan. One map unit is equivalent to a 1% recombination frequency. In this example 270 out of 1,000 offspring are recombinants, so the recombination frequency is 27% and the two genes are 27.0 mu apart.

Genetic linkage maps were first useful for analyzing the genes of organisms that are easily crossed and produce many offspring in a short time. Genetic linkage mapping is also the only technique that can reveal the frequency of recombinant types between two genes. This information is useful in plant and animal breeding projects and in interpreting pedigrees that follow linked genes. Genetic mapping has been used to establish the linkage maps of many agriculturally important plants and animals, and all the important model organisms.

In many animals, such as humans, genetic mapping has been challenging because of family sizes and the fact that we don't do controlled matings. However, with the advent of **molecular phenotypes**, ones that can be detected in vitro, from a single cell from the organism, it is possible to create detailed linkage maps in humans, and this knowledge has been essential to successfully determining the DNA sequence of the human genome and to identifying particular DNA sequences as the genes associated with particular human genetic disorders. You will learn more about this in Chapter 18.

15.4 VARIATIONS IN PHENOTYPIC RATIOS AND THEIR MOLECULAR BASIS

Learning Outcomes:

1. Relate dominant and recessive traits to protein function.
2. Describe pleiotropy and explain why it occurs.
3. Predict the outcome of crosses that exhibit incomplete dominance and codominance.
4. Discuss how the environment plays a critical role in determining the outcome of traits.

The term **Mendelian inheritance** describes the inheritance patterns of genes that segregate and assort independently. In the first section of this chapter we considered the inheritance pattern of traits affected by a single gene that is found in two variants, one of which is completely dominant over the other. This pattern is called **simple Mendelian inheritance** because the phenotypic ratios in the offspring clearly demonstrate Mendel's laws. In the second section, we examined **X-linked inheritance**, the pattern displayed by pairs of dominant and recessive alleles located on X chromosomes. Early geneticists observed these Mendelian inheritance patterns without knowing why one trait was dominant over another. In the third section we looked at how genes on the same chromosome can be linked and not show independent assortment.

In this section we discuss the molecular basis of dominant and recessive traits, and you will see how the molecular expression of a gene can have widespread effects on an organism's phenotype. In addition, we examine the inheritance patterns of genes that segregate and assort independently but do not display a simple dominant-recessive relationship. The transmission of these genes from parents to offspring does not usually produce the ratios of phenotypes we would expect on the basis of Mendel's observations. This does not mean that Mendel was wrong. Rather, the inheritance patterns of many traits are more intricate and interesting than the simple patterns he chose to study. As described in **Table 15.1**, our understanding of gene function at the molecular level explains both simple Mendelian inheritance and other more complex inheritance patterns for single genes. This modern knowledge also sheds light on the role of the environment in producing an organism's phenotype, which we will discuss at the end of the section.

Protein Function Explains the Phenomenon of Dominance

As you learned at the beginning of this chapter, Mendel studied seven traits that were found in two variants each. The dominant variants are the common alleles for these traits in pea plants. For any given gene, geneticists refer to a prevalent allele in a population as a **wild-type allele** (see Figure 15.2). In most cases a wild-type allele encodes a protein that is made in the proper amount and functions normally. By comparison, alleles that have been altered by mutation are called **mutant alleles**; these tend to be rare in natural populations. In the case of Mendel's seven traits the recessive alleles are due to rare mutations.

By studying genes and their gene products at the molecular level, researchers have discovered that a mutant allele is often defective in its ability to express a functional protein. In other words mutations that produce mutant alleles are likely to decrease or eliminate the synthesis or functional activity of a protein. Such mutations are often inherited in a recessive fashion. To understand why many defective alleles are recessive, we need to take a quantitative look at protein function.

In a simple dominant-recessive relationship, the recessive allele does not affect the phenotype of the heterozygote. In this type of relationship, a single copy of the dominant (wild-type) allele is sufficient to mask the effects of the recessive allele. But if the recessive allele cannot produce a functional protein, how do we explain the dominant phenotype of the heterozygote? **Figure 15.19** considers the example of flower colour in a pea plant. As shown at the top of this figure, the gene encodes an enzyme that is needed to make a purple pigment. The *P* allele is dominant because one *P* allele encodes enough of the functional protein—50% of the amount found in a normal homozygote—to provide a normal phenotype. Thus, the *PP* homozygote and the *Pp* heterozygote both make enough of the purple pigment to yield purple flowers. The *pp* heterozygote cannot make any of the functional enzyme required for pigment synthesis, so its flowers are white.

Table 15.1	Different Types of Single-Gene Nuclear Inheritance Patterns and Their Molecular Basis

Type	Description
Simple Mendelian inheritance	**Inheritance pattern:** The pattern of traits is determined by a pair of alleles that display a dominant/recessive relationship and are located on an autosome. The presence of the dominant allele masks the presence of the recessive allele.
	Molecular basis: In many cases, the amount of protein produced by a heterozygote, which may be 50% of that produced by a dominant homozygote, is sufficient to produce the dominant trait.
X-linked inheritance	**Inheritance pattern:** The pattern of traits is determined by genes that display a dominant-recessive relationship and are located on the X chromosome. In mammals and fruit flies males are hemizygous for X-linked genes. In these species X-linked recessive traits occur more frequently in males than in females.
	Molecular basis: In a female with one recessive X-linked allele (a heterozygote), the protein encoded by the dominant allele is sufficient to produce the dominant trait. A male with a recessive X-linked allele (a hemizygote) does not have a dominant allele and does not make any of the functional protein.
Incomplete dominance	**Inheritance pattern:** This pattern occurs when the heterozygote has a phenotype intermediate to the phenotypes of the dominant and recessive homozygotes, as when a cross between red-flowered and white-flowered plants produces pink-flowered offspring.
	Molecular basis: 50% of the protein encoded by the normal (wild-type) allele is not sufficient to produce the normal trait.
Codominance	**Inheritance pattern:** This pattern that occurs when the heterozygote expresses both alleles simultaneously. For example, a human carrying the A and B alleles for the ABO antigens of red blood cells produces both the A and the B antigens (has an AB blood type).
	Molecular basis: The codominant alleles encode proteins that function slightly differently from each other. In a heterozygote the function of each protein affects the phenotype uniquely.
Sex-influenced inheritance	**Inheritance pattern:** This pattern occurs when an allele is recessive in one sex and dominant in the other. An example is pattern baldness in humans.
	Molecular basis: Sex hormones affect the molecular expression of genes, which can have an impact on the phenotype.

The explanation that "50% of the normal protein is enough" is true for many wild-type alleles. In such cases the normal homozygote is making much more of the wild-type protein than necessary, so if the amount is reduced to 50%, as it is in the heterozygote, the individual still has plenty of this protein to accomplish whatever cellular function it performs. In other cases, however, an allele may be dominant because the heterozygote actually produces more than 50% of the normal amount of functional protein. This increased production

Protein P functions as an enzyme. The amount of functional protein P is the molecular connection between the genotype and the phenotype. The normal (dominant) allele encodes a functional enzyme.

Genotype	*PP*	*Pp*	*pp*
Amount of functional protein P produced	100%	50%	0%
Phenotype	**Purple**	**Purple**	**White**

The relationship of the normal (dominant) and mutant (recessive) alleles displays simple Mendelian inheritance.

Colourless precursor molecule → Protein P → Purple pigment

Figure 15.19 How genes produce proteins that determine traits in a simple dominant-recessive relationship. In many cases the amount of protein encoded by a single dominant allele is sufficient to produce the normal phenotype. In this example the normal phenotype is purple flower colour in a pea plant. The normal allele (*P*) encodes protein P, an enzyme needed for the synthesis of purple pigment. A plant with one or two copies of the normal allele produces enough pigment to produce purple flowers. In a *pp* homozygote, the complete lack of the normal protein results in white flowers.

is due to the phenomenon of gene regulation, which was discussed in Chapter 12. The normal gene is up-regulated in the heterozygote to compensate for the lack of function of the defective allele.

Single-Gene Mutations May Cause Inherited Diseases and May Have Pleiotropic Effects

The idea that recessive alleles usually cause a substantial decrease in the expression of a functional protein is supported by analyses of many human genetic diseases. Keep in mind that a genetic disease is caused by a rare mutant allele. **Table 15.2** lists several examples of human genetic diseases in which a recessive allele fails to produce a specific cellular protein in its active form.

More than 7,000 human disorders are caused by mutations in single genes. With a human genome size of 20,000 to 25,000 genes, this means that roughly one-third of our genes, when disrupted by mutation, can cause some kind of abnormality. Any particular single-gene disorder is relatively rare. But taken together, about 1 individual in 100 has a disorder that is due to a single-gene mutation. Such diseases generally have simple inheritance patterns in family pedigrees. Although the majority of these diseases follow a recessive inheritance pattern, some

Table 15.2	Examples of Recessive Human Genetic Diseases	
Disease	**Protein produced by the normal gene***	**Description**
Phenylketonuria	Phenylalanine hydroxylase	Inability to metabolize phenylalanine. Can lead to severe intellectual disability and physical degeneration. The disease can be treated by following a phenylalanine-free diet beginning early in life.
Cystic fibrosis	A chloride-ion transporter	Inability to regulate ion balance in epithelial cells. Leads to a variety of abnormalities, including production of thick lung mucus and chronic lung infections.
Tay-Sachs disease	Hexosaminidase A	Defect in lipid metabolism. Leads to paralysis, blindness, and early death.
Alpha-1 antitrypsin deficiency	Alpha-1 antitrypsin	Inability to prevent the activity of protease enzymes. Causes liver damage and emphysema.
Hemophilia A	Coagulation factor VIII	A defect in blood clotting caused by a missing clotting factor. An accident can cause excessive bleeding or internal hemorrhaging.

Individuals who exhibit the disease are homozygous (or hemizygous) for a recessive allele that results in a defect in the amount or function of the normal protein.

are known to be dominant. We have already discussed Huntington disease as an example of a dominant human disorder (see Figure 15.13). Other examples of diseases caused by dominant alleles include achondroplasia (a form of dwarfism) and osteogenesis imperfecta (brittle bone disease).

Single-gene disorders often illustrate the phenomenon of **pleiotropy**, which means that a mutation in a single gene can have multiple effects on an individual's phenotype. Pleiotropy occurs for several reasons:

1. The expression of a single gene can affect cell function in more than one way. For example, a defect in a microtubule protein can affect cell division and cell movement.
2. A gene can be expressed in different cell types in a multicellular organism.
3. A gene can be expressed at different stages of development.

In this genetics unit we tend to discuss genes as they affect a single trait. This educational approach allows you to appreciate how genes function and how they are transmitted from parents to offspring. However, this focus can also obscure how complex gene function is. In all or nearly all cases the expression of a gene is pleiotropic with regard to the characteristics of an organism. The expression of any given gene influences the expression of many other genes in the genome, and vice versa. Pleiotropy is revealed when researchers study the effects of gene mutations.

As an example of a pleiotropic mutation, let's consider cystic fibrosis (CF), which we considered earlier as an example of a recessive human disorder (see Figure 15.12). The normal allele encodes a protein called the cystic fibrosis transmembrane conductance regulator (CFTR) that regulates ionic balance by allowing the transport of chloride ions (Cl^-) across epithelial-cell membranes. The mutation that causes CF diminishes the function of this Cl^- transporter, affecting several parts of the body in different ways. Because the movement of Cl^- affects water transport across membranes, the most severe symptom of CF is thick mucus in the lungs, which occurs because of a water imbalance. In sweat glands the normal Cl^- transporter has the function of recycling salt out of the glands and back into the skin before it can be lost to the outside world. Persons with CF have excessively salty sweat because of their inability to recycle salt back into their skin cells. A common test for CF is measurement of salt on the skin. Another effect is seen in the reproductive systems of males who are homozygous for the CF allele. Most males with CF are infertile because the vas deferens, the tubules that transport sperm from the testes, are absent or undeveloped. Presumably, a normally functioning Cl^- transporter is needed for the proper development of the vas deferens in the embryo. You can see that a defect in CFTR has multiple effects throughout the body.

Incomplete Dominance Results in an Intermediate Phenotype

For certain traits a heterozygote that carries two different alleles exhibits a phenotype that is intermediate between the corresponding homozygous individuals. This phenomenon is known as **incomplete dominance**. In 1905 Carl Correns discovered this pattern of inheritance for alleles affecting flower colour in the four-o'clock plant (*Mirabilis jalapa*). **Figure 15.20** shows a cross between two four-o'clock plants: a red-flowered homozygote and a white-flowered homozygote. The allele for red flower colour is designated C^R and the white allele is C^W. These alleles are designated with superscripts rather than upper-case and lower-case letters because neither allele is dominant. The offspring of this cross have pink flowers—that is, they are C^RC^W heterozygotes with an intermediate phenotype. If these F_1 offspring are allowed to self-fertilize, the F_2 generation shows a ratio of 1/4 red-flowered plants, 1/2 pink-flowered plants, and 1/4 white-flowered plants. As noted in the Punnett square, this is a 1:2:1 phenotypic ratio rather than the 3:1 ratio observed for simple Mendelian inheritance. Thus, although the genotypic ratios are those predicted by Mendel, the phenotypic ratio is not. This is because in the heterozygotes, 50% of the protein encoded by the C^R gene is not sufficient to produce the red-flower phenotype.

The degree to which we judge an allele to exhibit incomplete dominance may depend on how closely we examine an

Figure 15.20 **Incomplete dominance in the four-o'clock plant.** When red-flowered and white-flowered homozygotes (C^RC^R and C^WC^W) are crossed, the resulting heterozygote (C^RC^W) has an intermediate phenotype of pink flowers.

individual's phenotype. An example is an inherited human disease called phenylketonuria (PKU). This disorder is caused by a rare mutation in a gene that encodes an enzyme called phenylalanine hydroxylase. This enzyme is needed to metabolize the amino acid phenylalanine. If left untreated, homozygotes carrying the mutant allele suffer severe symptoms, including intellectual disabilities, seizures, microcephaly (small head), poor development of tooth enamel, and decreased body growth. By comparison heterozygotes appear phenotypically normal. For this reason geneticists consider PKU to be a recessive disorder. However, biochemical analysis of the blood of heterozygotes shows that they typically have a phenylalanine blood level double that of an individual carrying two normal copies of the gene. Therefore, at this closer level of examination, heterozygotes exhibit incomplete dominance.

ABO Blood Type Provides an Example of Multiple Alleles and of Codominance

Although normal diploid individuals have at most two copies of each gene, many genes have three or more variants in the population. We describe such a gene as having **multiple alleles**. The phenotype of an individual depends on which two alleles an individual inherits. ABO blood types in humans are an example of phenotypes produced by multiple alleles.

As shown in **Table 15.3**, human red blood cells have structures on their plasma membrane known as surface antigens, which are constructed from several sugar molecules that are connected to form a carbohydrate tree. Antigens are substances (in this case, carbohydrates) that are recognized as foreign by antibodies produced by the immune system. Three types of surface molecules, known as A, B, and O, found on red blood cells serve as potential antigens. The synthesis of the A, B, and O antigens is determined by enzymes, which are encoded by a gene that has three alleles designated I^A, I^B, and i, respectively. The i allele is recessive to both I^A and I^B. A person who is homozygous ii will have red blood cells with the surface molecule O (blood type O; the O surface molecule does not serve as a new antigen). The red blood cells of an I^AI^A homozygous or I^Ai heterozygous individual will have a surface molecule that is antigen A (blood type A). Similarly, a homozygous I^BI^B or heterozygous I^Bi individual will produce a surface molecule that is antigen B (blood type B). A person who is I^AI^B heterozygous makes both antigens, expressing A and B, on every red blood cell (blood type AB). The phenomenon in which a single individual expresses both alleles in a way that leads to both traits in the phenotype is called **codominance**.

What is the molecular explanation for codominance for the I^A and I^B alleles? Biochemists have analyzed the carbohydrate tree produced in people of differing blood types. The differences are shown schematically in Table 15.3. In type O, the carbohydrate tree is smaller than in type A or type B because a sugar has not been attached to a specific site on the tree. People with blood type O have a loss-of-function mutation in the gene that encodes the enzyme that attaches a sugar at this site. This enzyme, called a glycosyltransferase, is inactive in type O individuals. In contrast the type A and type B antigens have sugars attached to this site, but each of them has a different sugar. This difference occurs because the enzymes encoded by the I^A allele and I^B alleles have slightly different active sites. As a result the enzyme encoded by the I^A allele attaches a sugar called N-acetylgalactosamine to the carbohydrate tree, while the enzyme encoded by the I^B allele attaches galactose. N-acetylgalactosamine is represented by an orange hexagon in Table 15.3, and galactose, by a green triangle.

The attachment of two different sugars gives surface antigens A and B significantly different molecular structures. Such differences in shape allow antibodies to recognize and bind very specifically to certain antigens. The blood of type A individuals has antibodies, called serum antibodies, that bind to the B antigen. Similarly, type B individuals produce antibodies against the A antigen. Type O individuals produce both kinds of antibodies, and type AB individuals produce neither. (No antibodies are produced against antigen O.) When a person receives a blood

Table 15.3   The ABO Blood Group

Blood type	O	A	B	AB
Genotype	ii	$I^A I^A$ or $I^A i$	$I^B I^B$ or $I^B i$	$I^A I^B$
Surface antigen	Neither A nor B	A	B	A and B
Serum antibodies	Against A and B	Against B	Against A	None

transfusion, the donor's blood must be an appropriate match with the recipient's blood to avoid a dangerous antigen:antibody reaction. For example, if a person with type O blood is given type A blood, the recipient's anti-A antibodies will react with the donated blood cells and cause them to agglutinate (clump together). This situation is life threatening because it will cause the blood vessels to clog. Identification of the donor and recipient blood types, called blood typing, is essential for safe transfusions.

The Expression of Certain Traits Is Influenced by the Sex of the Individual

Certain autosomal genes are expressed differently in heterozygous males and females. The term **sex-influenced inheritance** refers to the phenomenon in which an allele is dominant in one sex but recessive in the other. Pattern baldness is an example of a sex-influenced trait in humans. This trait is characterized by a balding pattern in which hair loss occurs on the front and top of the head but not on the sides (**Figure 15.21**). A woman who is homozygous for the baldness allele will develop the trait (although in women it is usually characterized by a significant thinning of the hair that occurs relatively late in life). A male who is heterozygous for the pattern-baldness allele (designated B) will become bald, but a heterozygous female will not. In other words the baldness allele is recessive in females but dominant in males:

Sex		**Genotype**	
	BB	Bb	bb
Male	Bald	Bald	Nonbald
Female	Bald	Nonbald	Nonbald

As you can see from the pedigree in Figure 15.21, a bald male may have inherited the baldness allele from either parent. Thus, a striking observation is that fathers with pattern baldness can pass this trait to their sons. This could not occur if the trait was X-linked, because fathers transmit only Y chromosomes to their sons.

The sex-influenced nature of pattern baldness is related to the production of the male sex hormone testosterone. The gene that affects pattern baldness encodes an enzyme called 5-α-reductase, which converts testosterone to 5-α-dihydrotestosterone (DHT). DHT binds to cellular receptors and affects the expression of many genes, including those in the cells of the scalp. The allele

that causes pattern baldness results in an overexpression of this enzyme. Because mature males normally make more testosterone than females do, this allele has a greater phenotypic impact in males. However, a rare tumour of the adrenal gland can cause the secretion of abnormally large amounts of testosterone in females. If this occurs in a woman who is heterozygous Bb, she will become bald. If the tumour is removed surgically, her hair will return to its normal condition.

The Environment Plays a Vital Role in the Making of a Phenotype

In this chapter we have been concerned mainly with the effects of genes on phenotypes. However, phenotypes are shaped by an organism's environment as well as by its genes. An organism cannot exist without its genes or without an environment

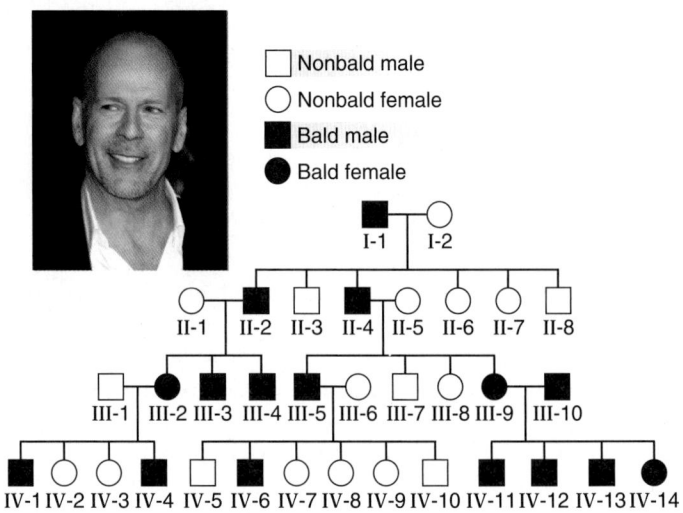

Figure 15.21   Pattern baldness.   Pattern baldness, shown in an adult male in the photograph, is an example of the sex-influenced expression of an autosomal gene. Bald individuals are represented by filled symbols in the pedigree.

Concept check: *With regard to baldness, which phenotypes have a single genotype?*

in which to live. Both are indispensable for life. An organism's genotype provides the information for environmental conditions to create a phenotype.

The term **norm of reaction** refers to the effects of environmental variation on a phenotype. Specifically, it is the phenotypic range seen in individuals with a particular genotype. To evaluate the norm of reaction, researchers study members of true-breeding strains that have the same genotypes and subject them to different environmental conditions. For example, **Figure 15.22** shows the norm of reaction for genetically identical plants raised at different temperatures. As shown in the figure, these plants attain a maximal height when raised at 20°C. At 10°C and 30°C the plants are substantially shorter. Growth cannot occur below 0°C or above 35°C.

The norm of reaction can be quite dramatic when we consider environmental influences on certain inherited diseases. A striking example is the human genetic disease phenylketonuria (PKU). As we discussed earlier in the chapter, this disorder is caused by a rare mutation in the gene for phenylalanine hydroxylase, an enzyme needed to metabolize the amino acid phenylalanine. People with one or two functional copies of the gene can eat foods containing the amino acid phenylalanine and metabolize it correctly. However, homozygotes for the defective allele cannot metabolize phenylalanine. When these individuals eat a standard diet containing phenylalanine, this amino acid accumulates within their bodies and becomes highly toxic. Under these conditions, PKU homozygotes manifest a variety of detrimental symptoms, including intellectual disabilities, underdeveloped teeth, and foul-smelling urine. In contrast, when these individuals are identified at birth and given a restricted diet that is free of phenylalanine, they develop normally (**Figure 15.23**). This is

Figure 15.23   Environmental influences on the expression of PKU within a single family.   All three children in this photo have inherited the alleles that cause PKU. The child in the middle was raised on a phenylalanine-free diet and developed normally. The other two children, born before the benefits of such a diet were known, were raised on diets containing phenylalanine. These two children have symptoms of PKU, including intellectual disabilities.

a dramatic example of how genes and the environment can interact to determine an individual's phenotype. In Canada newborns are tested for PKU, which occurs in about 1 in 20,000 babies. A newborn who is found to have this disorder can be raised on a phenylalanine-free diet and develop normally.

15.5 | GENE PRODUCTS FREQUENTLY INTERACT IN DETERMINING COMPLEX PHENOTYPES

Learning Outcomes:

1. Describe how the alleles of one gene can mask or be epistatic to the alleles of a different gene.
2. Explain why polygenic traits usually show a continuum of phenotype variation.

The study of single genes whose mutant alleles had strong, obvious effects on individual traits was pivotal in establishing the science of genetics. This focus allowed Mendel to formulate the basic laws of inheritance for traits with a simple dominant-recessive inheritance pattern. Likewise, this approach helped later researchers understand inheritance patterns involving incomplete dominance and codominance, as well as traits that are influenced by an individual's sex. In reality most traits are the result of the interaction of many genes' products. For example, in both plants and animals the trait of height is affected by genes that encode proteins involved in the production of growth hormones, cell division, the uptake of nutrients, metabolism, and many other functions. A defect in any of these genes is likely to have a negative impact on an individual's height.

Figure 15.22   The norm of reaction.   The norm of reaction is the range of phenotypes that an organism with a particular genotype exhibits under different environmental conditions. In this example genetically identical plants were grown at different temperatures in a greenhouse and then measured for height.

   Principle: *Living organisms interact with their environment. Environmental factors contribute to the range of phenotypes seen for a continuous trait.*

Given that many genes control height, you may be wondering how Mendel was able to study the effects of a single gene that produced tall or dwarf pea plants. The answer lies in the genotypes of his strains. Although many genes affect the height of pea plants, Mendel chose true-breeding strains that differed with regard to only one of these genes. As a hypothetical example, let's suppose that pea plants have 10 genes affecting height, which we will call *K, L, M, N, O, P, Q, R, S,* and *T*. The genotypes of two hypothetical strains of pea plants may be

Tall strain: *KK LL MM NN OO PP QQ RR SS TT*
Dwarf strain: *KK LL MM NN OO PP QQ RR SS tt*

In this example the tall and dwarf strains differ at only a single locus. One strain is *TT* and the other is *tt,* and this accounts for the difference in their height. If we cross tall and dwarf plants, the genotypes of the F₂ offspring will differ with regard to only one gene; the other nine genes will be identical in all of them. This approach allows a researcher to study the effects of a single gene even though many genes may affect a single trait.

In this section we will examine situations in which one trait is controlled by the products of two or more genes, each of which has two or more alleles. This phenomenon is called a **gene interaction**. As you will see, allelic variation at two or more loci may affect the outcome of traits in different ways. First we will look at interactions in which a defective allele of one gene prevents the action of a functional allele of a different gene. Then we will discuss interactions in which multiple genes have additive effects on a single trait. These additive effects, together with environmental influences, account for the continuous phenotypic variation that we see for most traits.

An Epistatic Gene Interaction Occurs When the Allele of One Gene Masks the Phenotypic Effects of a Different Gene

In some gene interactions the alleles of one gene mask the expression of the alleles of another gene. This phenomenon is called **epistasis** (Greek *ephistanai,* which means "stopping"). An example is the unexpected gene interaction discovered by William Bateson and Reginald Punnett in the early twentieth century, when they were studying crosses involving the sweet pea, *Lathyrus odoratus*. A cross between a true-breeding purple-flowered plant and a true-breeding white-flowered plant produced an F₁ generation with all purple-flowered plants and an F₂ generation with a 3:1 ratio of purple- to white-flowered plants. Of course, Mendel's laws predicted this result. The surprise came when the researchers crossed two different varieties of white-flowered sweet peas (**Figure 15.24**). All the F₁ generation plants had purple flowers! When these plants were allowed to self-fertilize, the F₂ generation had purple-flowered and white-flowered plants in a 9:7 ratio. This result does not meet the expectation of a Mendelian ratio. If the white plants were both mutants of the same gene, we would have expected the mutant trait in both the F₁ and the F₂. The reappearance of

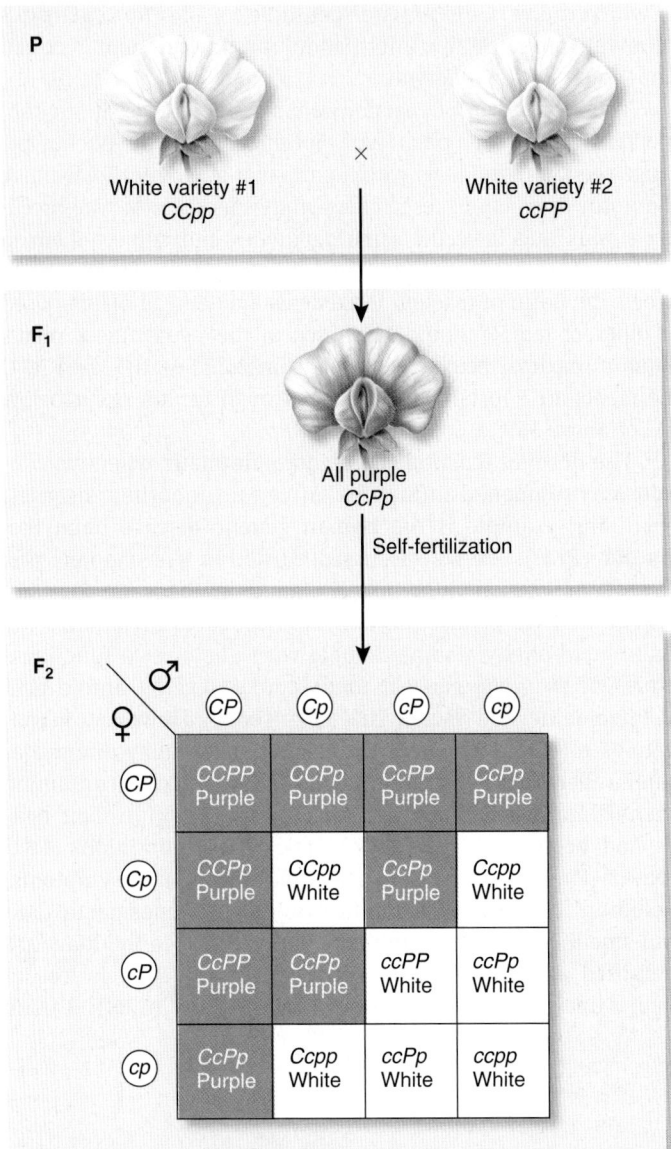

Figure 15.24 Epistasis in the sweet pea. The colour of the sweet pea flower is controlled by two genes, each with a dominant and a recessive allele. Each of the dominant alleles (*C* and *P*) encodes an enzyme required for the synthesis of purple pigment. A plant that is homozygous recessive for either gene (*cc* or *pp*) cannot synthesize the pigment and will have white flowers.

Concept check: *In a Ccpp individual which functional enzyme is missing? Is it the enzyme encoded by the C or P gene?*

the wild-type purple flowers led Bateson and Punnett to deduce that two genes were involved in determining purple flowers and that their F₁ were dihybrids. But if the F₁ are dihybrids, a Mendelian result would have been a 9:3:3:1 ratio of phenotypes in the F₂. Bateson and Punnett recognized that their 9:7 ratio was a variation of the 9:3:3:1 ratio in which the 3:3:1 all had the same phenotype: white. Thus, from their data they deduced that two different genes were involved in flower colour determination; to get purple flowers, a plant must have at least one dominant allele for each of these genes. The relationships among the alleles are as follows:

C (one allele for purple) is dominant to c (white)

P (an allele for purple of a different gene) is dominant to p (white)

cc masks P, or pp masks C, in either case producing white flowers

A plant that was homozygous for either c or p would have white flowers even if it had a purple-producing allele at the other locus.

Epistatic interactions often arise because two or more different proteins are involved in a single cellular function. For example, two or more proteins may be part of an enzymatic pathway leading to the formation of a single product. This is the case for the formation of a purple pigment in the sweet pea strains we have been discussing:

$$\text{Colourless precursor} \xrightarrow{\text{Enzyme C}} \text{Colourless intermediate} \xrightarrow{\text{Enzyme P}} \text{Purple pigment}$$

In this example the action of two different enzymes is required to produce the purple pigment. Gene C encodes a functional protein, enzyme C, that converts the colourless precursor into a different colourless intermediate. The recessive c allele results in a lack of production of enzyme C in the homozygote. Gene P encodes the functional enzyme P, which converts the colourless intermediate into the purple pigment (enzyme P cannot work on the colourless precursor). Like the c allele, the p allele results in an inability to produce a functional protein. A plant that is homozygous for either of the recessive alleles will not make any functional enzymes C or P. When either of these enzymes is missing, the plant cannot make the purple pigment and has white flowers.

Labrador retrievers have three common coat colours: yellow, chocolate, and black (**Figure 15.25**). Coat colour in Labrador retrievers is an example of another type of epistasis. Gene B encodes an enzyme that produces a black pigment. The protein encoded by its allele, gene b, produces a brown pigment. A functional copy of another gene, gene E, is required to deposit the pigment into the hair shaft; individuals of genotype ee will have a yellow coat regardless of whether they are genotype BB, Bb, or bb because they cannot deposit the pigment into the hair shaft. The ee genotype is epistatic to the B gene.

Polygenic Inheritance and Environmental Influences Produce Continuous Phenotypic Variation

As you have just seen, an epistatic interaction causes the alleles of one gene to mask the effects of a different gene. Let's now turn to another way that the alleles of different genes can affect the phenotype of a single trait. In many cases the effects of

Figure 15.25   Epistasis in coat colour of Labrador retrievers.   This mother Labrador retriever has genotype *bb ee*. She has a litter of pups some of which are yellow, some chocolate, and some black.

Concept check: *Considering the mother's genotype, the phenotypes of her pups, and the fact that the B allele is dominant to b, and the E allele is dominant to e, what was the genotype of the father?*

alleles are additive. This has been observed for many traits, particularly those that are quantitative in nature.

Until now we have discussed the inheritance of traits with clearly defined phenotypic variants, such as red or white eyes in fruit flies. These are known as discrete traits, or **discontinuous traits**, because the phenotypes do not overlap. For most traits, however, the phenotypes cannot be sorted into discrete categories. The majority of traits in all organisms are **continuous traits**, also called **quantitative traits**, which show continuous variation over a range of phenotypes. In humans quantitative traits include height, weight, skin colour, metabolic rate, and heart size, to mention a few. In the case of domestic animals and plant crops, many of the traits that people consider desirable are quantitative in nature, such as the number of eggs a chicken lays, the amount of milk a cow produces, and the number of apples on an apple tree. Consequently, much of our modern understanding of quantitative traits comes from agricultural research.

Quantitative traits are **polygenic**, which means that several or many genes contribute to the outcome of the trait. For many polygenic traits genes contribute to the phenotype in an additive way. Another important factor is the environment. As you saw earlier in this chapter, the environment plays a vital role in the phenotypic expression of genes. Environmental factors often have a major impact on quantitative traits. For example, an animal's diet affects its weight, and the amounts of rain and sunlight that fall on an apple tree affect how many apples it produces.

Because quantitative traits are polygenic and greatly influenced by environmental conditions, the phenotypes among different individuals can vary substantially in any given population. As an example, let's consider skin pigmentation in people. This trait is influenced by several genes, which tend to interact in an additive way. As a simplified example, let's consider a population in which this trait is controlled by three genes, which we will designate A, B, and C. Each gene has a dark allele, designated A^D, B^D, or C^D, and a light allele, designated A^L, B^L, or C^L, respectively. All the alleles encode enzymes that cause the synthesis of skin pigment, but the enzymes encoded by dark alleles cause more pigment synthesis than the enzymes encoded by light alleles. **Figure 15.26** considers a hypothetical case in which people who were heterozygous for all three genes produced a large population of offspring. The bar graph shows the genotypes of the offspring, grouped according to the total number of dark alleles. As shown by the shading of the figure, skin pigmentation increases as the number of dark alleles increases. Offspring who have no dark alleles and those who have no light alleles—that is, who are homozygous for all three genes—are fewer in number than those with some combination of dark and light alleles. As seen in the bell-shaped curve above the bar graph, the phenotypes of the offspring fall along a continuum. This continuous phenotypic variation, which is typical of quantitative traits, is produced by genotypic differences together with environmental effects. A second bell-shaped curve (the dashed line) depicts the expected phenotypic range if the same population of offspring had been raised in a sunnier environment, which increases pigment production. These two curves illustrate how the environment can also have a significant influence on the range of phenotypes.

In our discussion of genetics we have tended to focus on discrete traits because this makes it easier to relate a specific genotype with a phenotype. This is usually not possible for continuous traits. For example, as depicted in the middle bar of Figure 15.26, seven different genotypes can produce individuals with a medium amount of pigmentation. Nevertheless, it is important to emphasize that the majority of traits in all organisms are continuous, not discrete. Most traits are influenced by the allele combinations of several genes and by the internal and external environment.

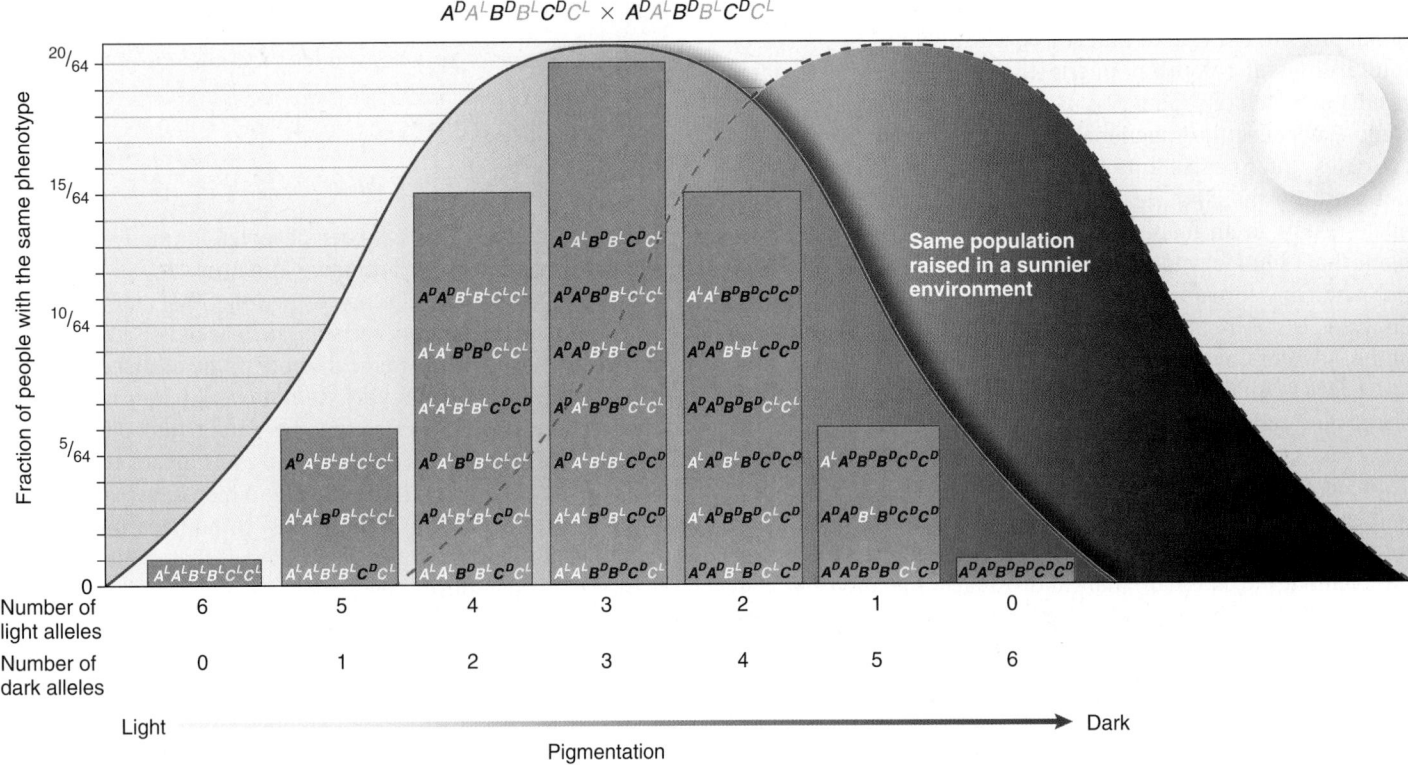

Figure 15.26 **Continuous variation in a polygenic trait.** Skin colour is a polygenic trait that can display a continuum of phenotypes. The bell curve on the left (solid line) shows the range of skin pigmentation in a hypothetical human population. The bar graph within the curve shows the additive effects of three genes that affect pigment production in this population; each bar shows the fraction of people with a particular number of dark alleles (A^D, B^D, and C^D) and light alleles (A^L, B^L, and C^L). The bell curve on the right (dashed line) represents the expected range of phenotypes if the same population was raised in a sunnier environment.

 Principle: *Living organisms interact with their environment. Sunlight affects the range of skin tones observed in a population.*

<table>
<tr><td>

15.6 / EXTRANUCLEAR INHERITANCE: ORGANELLE GENOMES

Learning Outcomes:

1. Describe the general features of mitochondrial and chloroplast genomes.
2. Explain why chloroplast and mitochondrial genes usually exhibit maternal inheritance.
3. List human diseases associated with mutations in mitochondrial genes.

</td></tr>
</table>

In a previous section we examined the inheritance patterns of linked genes that violate the law of independent assortment. In this section we will explore inheritance patterns that violate the law of segregation of alleles. Gene transmission can defy this law because some genes are not found on the chromosomes in the cell nucleus. The segregation pattern of nuclear genes is explained by the pairing and segregation of homologous chromosomes during meiosis; genes found elsewhere in the cell do not segregate in the same way. The transmission of genes that are located outside the cell nucleus is called **extranuclear inheritance**.

Two important types of extranuclear inheritance patterns involve genes that are found in mitochondria and chloroplasts (**Figure 15.27**). Extranuclear inheritance is also called **cytoplasmic inheritance** because these organelles are in the cytoplasm of the cell. As we discussed in Chapter 5, mitochondria and chloroplasts are found in eukaryotic cells because of an ancient endosymbiotic relationship. They contain their own genetic material or genomes. Although these organelle genomes are much smaller than nuclear genomes, researchers have discovered that they are critically important in the phenotypes of organisms. In plants, for example, the chloroplast genome carries many genes that are vital for photosynthesis. Mitochondrial genes are critical for respiration. In humans mutations in the mitochondrial genome can cause inherited diseases. In this section we will examine the transmission patterns observed for genes found in the chloroplast and mitochondrial genomes and consider how mutations in these genes can affect an individual's traits.

Chloroplast Genomes Are Often Maternally Inherited

In 1909 Carl Correns carried out one of the first experiments showing an extranuclear inheritance pattern. He discovered that leaf pigmentation in the four-o'clock plant (*Mirabilis jalapa*) follows a pattern of inheritance that does not obey Mendel's law of segregation of alleles. Four-o'clock leaves can be green, white, or variegated, as shown in **Figure 15.28**. Correns observed that the pigmentation of the offspring depended solely on the pigmentation of the maternal parent, a phenomenon called **maternal inheritance**. If the female parent had white leaves, all the offspring had white leaves. Similarly, if the female was green, so were all the offspring. The offspring of a variegated female parent could be green, white, or variegated.

At the time Correns did not understand that chloroplasts contain some genes. We now know that the pigmentation of

(a) An animal cell

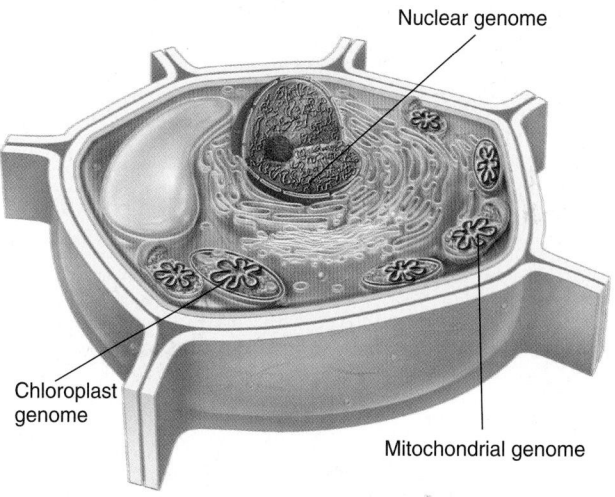

(b) A plant cell

Figure 15.27 **The locations of genetic material in animal and plant cells.** The chromosomes in the cell nucleus are collectively known as the nuclear genome. Mitochondria and chloroplasts have small circular chromosomes, which are called the mitochondrial and chloroplast genomes.

> **BioConnections:** *Look back at Figure 5.19. What is the evolutionary origin of mitochondria and chloroplasts in eukaryotic cells?*

four-o'clock leaves can be explained by the occurrence of genetically different types of chloroplasts in the leaf cells. As discussed in Chapter 8, chloroplasts are the site of photosynthesis, and their green colour is due to the presence of the pigment called chlorophyll. Certain genes required for chlorophyll synthesis are found within the chloroplast DNA. The green phenotype is due to the presence of chloroplasts that have normal genes and synthesize the usual quantity of chlorophyll. The white phenotype is caused by a mutation in a gene within the chloroplast DNA that prevents the synthesis of most of the chlorophyll. (Enough chlorophyll is made for the plant to survive.) The variegated phenotype occurs in leaves that have a mixture of the two types of chloroplasts.

Leaf pigmentation follows a maternal inheritance pattern because the chloroplasts in four o'clocks are inherited only

Correns' crosses

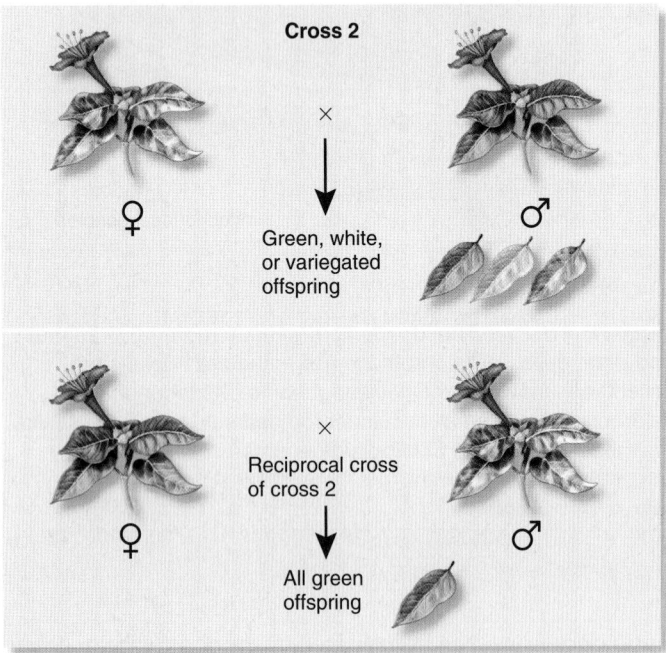

Figure 15.28   Maternal inheritance in the four-o'clock plant.   The genes for green pigment synthesis in plants are part of the chloroplast genome. The white phenotype in four o'clocks is due to chloroplasts with a mutant allele that greatly reduces green pigment production. The variegated phenotype is due to a mixture of normal and mutant chloroplasts. In four o'clocks, the egg contains all the plastids that are inherited by the offspring, so the phenotype of the offspring is determined by the female parent.

Concept check: *In this example where is the gene located that causes the green colour of four-o'clock leaves? How is this gene transmitted from parent to offspring?*

through the cytoplasm of the egg (**Figure 15.29**). During plant fertilization, a sperm cell from a pollen grain fertilizes an egg cell to create a zygote, which eventually develops into a plant. In four o'clocks, the egg cell contains several proplastids that are inherited by the offspring, while the sperm cell does not contribute any proplastids. As discussed in Chapter 4, proplastids develop into various types of plastids, including chloroplasts. Thus, the phenotype of a four-o'clock plant depends on the types of proplastids it inherits from the maternal parent. If the maternal parent transmits only normal proplastids, all offspring will have green leaves (**Figure 15.29a**). Alternatively, if the maternal parent transmits only mutant proplastids, all offspring will have white leaves (**Figure 15.29b**). The genetic composition of the paternal parent does not affect the outcome. Because an egg cell contains several proplastids, an offspring from a variegated maternal parent may inherit only normal proplastids, only mutant proplastids, or a mixture of normal and mutant proplastids. Consequently, the offspring of a variegated maternal parent can be green, white, or variegated individuals (**Figure 15.29c**).

The variegated phenotype is due to segregation events that occur after fertilization. As a zygote containing both types of chloroplasts divides to produce a multicellular plant, some cells

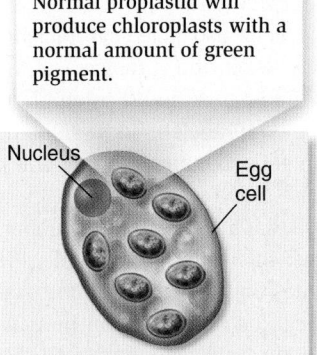

Normal proplastid will produce chloroplasts with a normal amount of green pigment.

(a) Egg cell from a maternal parent with green leaves

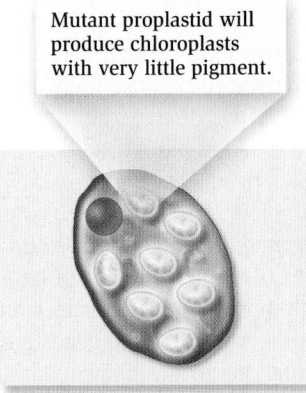

Mutant proplastid will produce chloroplasts with very little pigment.

(b) Egg cell from a maternal parent with white leaves

(c) Possible egg cells from a maternal parent with variegated leaves

Figure 15.29   Plastid composition of egg cells from green, white, and variegated four-o'clock plants.   In this drawing of four-o'clock egg cells, normal proplastids are represented as green and mutant proplastids as white. Proplastids do not differentiate into chloroplasts in egg cells, and they are not actually green. **(a)** A green plant produces eggs carrying normal proplastids. **(b)** A white plant produces eggs carrying mutant proplastids. **(c)** A variegated plant produces eggs that can contain either or both types of proplastids.

may receive mostly normal chloroplasts. Further division of these cells gives rise to a patch of green tissue. Alternatively, as a matter of chance, other cells may receive mostly mutant chloroplasts that are defective in chlorophyll synthesis. This results in a patch of tissue that is white.

In most species of plants the egg cell provides most of the zygote's cytoplasm, while the much smaller male gamete often provides little more than a nucleus. Therefore, chloroplasts are most often inherited via the egg. In seed-bearing plants maternal inheritance of chloroplasts is the most common transmission-pattern. However, certain species exhibit a pattern called **biparental inheritance**, in which both the pollen and the egg contribute chloroplasts to the offspring. Others exhibit **paternal inheritance**, in which only the pollen contributes these organelles. For example, most types of pine trees show paternal inheritance of chloroplasts.

Mitochondrial Genomes Are Maternally Inherited in Humans and Most Other Species

Mitochondria are found in nearly alleukaryotic species. Similar to the transmission of chloroplasts in plants, maternal inheritance is the most common pattern of mitochondrial transmission in eukaryotic species, and it is for the same reason. The egg cell usually donates its nucleus and its cytoplasm (with mitochondria) and the sperm donates only a nucleus. A few species do exhibit biparental or paternal inheritance of the mitochondrial genome. The mitochondrial genome of many mammalian species has been analyzed and usually contains a total of 37 genes. Twenty-four genes encode tRNAs and rRNAs, which are needed for translation inside the mitochondrion. Thirteen genes encode proteins that are involved in oxidative phosphorylation. As discussed in Chapter 7, the primary function of the mitochondrion is the synthesis of ATP via oxidative phosphorylation.

In humans, as in most species, mitochondria are maternally inherited. Researchers have discovered that mutations in human mitochondrial genes can cause a variety of rare diseases. These are usually chronic, degenerative disorders that affect the brain, eyes, heart, muscle, kidney, and endocrine glands. For example, Leber's hereditary optic neuropathy (LHON) affects the optic nerve. It can lead to the progressive loss of vision in one or both eyes. LHON can be caused by a mutation in one of several different mitochondrial genes.

15.7 EPIGENETIC EFFECTS: X INACTIVATION, GENOMIC IMPRINTING, AND MATERNAL EFFECTS

Learning Outcomes:

1. Describe the process of X-inactivation and how it affects the phenotype of heterozygous females.
2. Explain the molecular basis of genomic imprinting and how it affects inheritance patterns.

We will end our discussion of complex inheritance patterns by considering examples in which the timing and control of gene expression create inheritance patterns that are determined by the sex of the individual or by the sex of the parents. The first two patterns, called X inactivation and genomic imprinting, are types of **epigenetic inheritance**. In epigenetic inheritance, modification of a gene or chromosome during egg formation, sperm formation, or early stages of embryo growth alters gene expression in a way that is fixed during an individual's lifetime. Epigenetic changes permanently affect the phenotype of the individual, but they are not permanent over many generations, and they do not change the actual DNA sequence. For example, a gene can undergo an epigenetic change that inactivates it for an individual's entire life, so that it is never expressed in that individual. However, when the same individual makes gametes, the gene can become activated and remain active during the lifetime of an offspring that inherits the gene.

At the end of this section we will also consider genes that exhibit a bizarre inheritance pattern called the **maternal effect**, in which the genotype of the mother directly determines the phenotype of her offspring. Surprisingly, for maternal effect genes, the genotypes of the father and of the offspring themselves do not affect the offspring's phenotype. As you will learn, this phenomenon is explained by the accumulation of gene products that the mother provides to her developing eggs.

In Female Mammals, One X Chromosome Is Inactivated in Each Somatic Cell

In 1961 British geneticist Mary Lyon proposed the phenomenon of **X inactivation**, in which one X chromosome in the somatic cells of female mammals is inactivated, meaning that its genes are not expressed. The **Lyon hypothesis**, as X inactivation also came to be known, was based on two lines of evidence. The first evidence came from microscopic studies of mammalian cells. In 1949 Murray Barr and Ewart Bertram identified a highly condensed structure in the cells of female cats that was not found in the cells of male cats. This structure was named a **Barr body** after one of its discoverers (**Figure 15.30**). In 1960 Susumu Ohno correctly proposed that a Barr body is a highly condensed X chromosome. Lyon's second line of evidence was

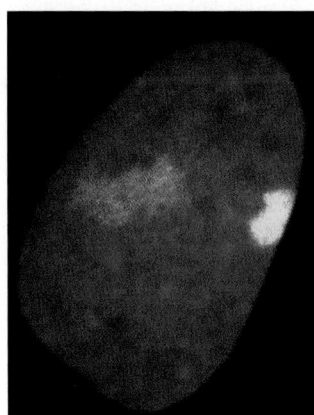

Figure 15.30
X chromosome inactivation in female mammals produces the Barr Body. The Barr body can be seen at the periphery of this cell as a dense yellow object. In this micrograph the staining was done with a yellow fluorescent probe that recognizes the X chromosome in both its active form and the highly condensed, inactive Barr body.

 Principle: *Structure determines function. The highly condensed X chromosome is inactive, without gene expression.*

the inheritance pattern of variegated coat colours in certain mammals. A classic case is the calico cat, which has randomly distributed patches of black and orange fur (**Figure 15.31a**).

According to the Lyon hypothesis, the calico pattern is explained by the permanent inactivation of one X chromosome in each cell that forms a patch of the cat's skin, as shown in **Figure 15.31b.** The gene involved is an X-linked gene that occurs as an orange allele, X^O, and a black allele, X^B. A female cat that is heterozygous for this gene will be calico. (The white underside is due to a dominant allele of a different autosomal gene.) At an early stage of embryonic development, one of the two X chromosomes is randomly inactivated in each of the cat's somatic cells, including those that will give rise to the hair-producing skin cells. As the embryo grows and matures, the pattern of X inactivation is maintained during subsequent cell divisions. For example, skin cells derived from a single embryonic cell in which the X^B-carrying chromosome has been inactivated will produce a patch of orange fur, because they express only the X^O allele that is carried on the active chromosome. Alternatively, a group of skin cells in which the chromosome carrying X^O has been inactivated will express only the X^B allele, producing a patch of black fur. Because the primary event of X inactivation is a random process that occurs at an early stage of development, the result is an animal with randomly distributed patches of black and orange fur.

In female mammals that are heterozygous for X-linked genes, approximately half of their somatic cells will express one allele, while the rest of their somatic cells will express the other allele. These heterozygotes are called **mosaics** because they are composed of two types of cells, analogous to the different-coloured pieces in the pictures called mosaics. The phenomenon of mosaicism is readily apparent in calico cats, in which the alleles affect fur colour. Likewise, human females who are heterozygous for X-linked genes are mosaics, with one allele expressed in some cells and the alternative allele in other cells. Women who are heterozygous for recessive X-linked alleles usually show the dominant trait because the expression of the dominant allele in 50% of their cells is sufficient to produce the dominant phenotype.

On rare occasions a female who is heterozygous for a recessive X-linked disease-causing allele may show mild or even severe disease symptoms. Because the pattern of X-chromosome inactivation is random, there will be a small percentage of heterozygous women who happen to inactivate the X chromosome carrying the normal allele in a large percentage of their cells, as a matter of bad luck. As an example let's consider the recessive X-linked form of hemophilia that we discussed earlier. This type of hemophilia is caused by a defect in a gene that encodes a blood-clotting factor, called factor VIII, that is made by cells in the liver and secreted into the bloodstream. X inactivation in humans occurs when an embryo is 10 days old. At this stage, the liver contains only about a dozen cells. In most females who are heterozygous for the normal and hemophilia alleles, roughly half of their liver cells will express the normal allele. However, on rare occasions, all or most of the dozen embryonic liver cells might happen to inactivate the X chromosome carrying the

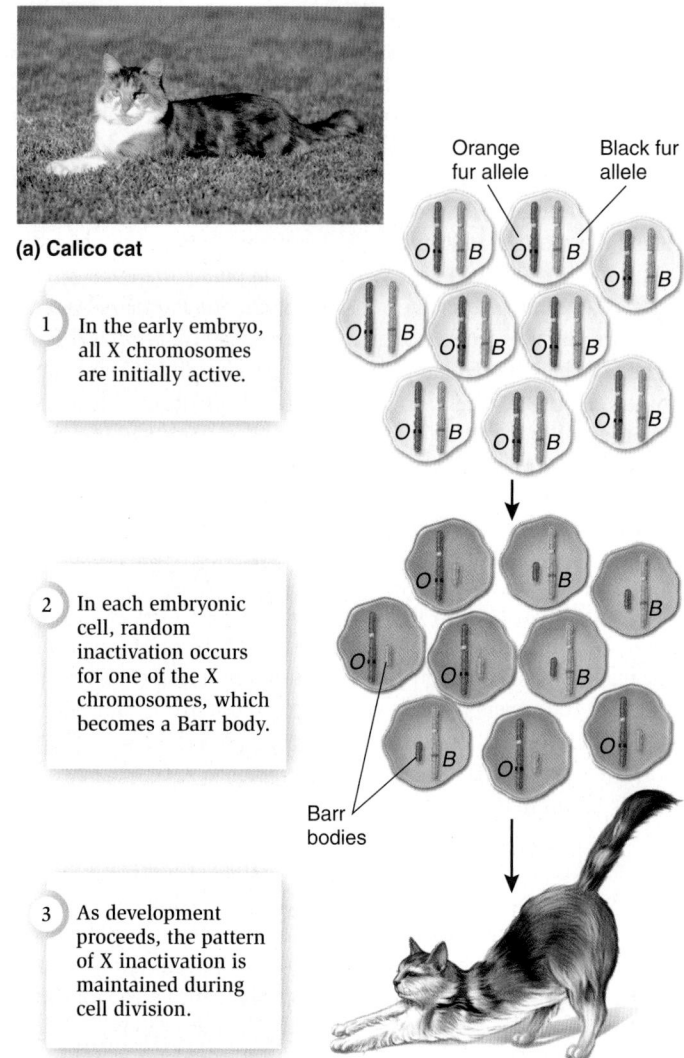

(a) Calico cat

1. In the early embryo, all X chromosomes are initially active.

2. In each embryonic cell, random inactivation occurs for one of the X chromosomes, which becomes a Barr body.

Barr bodies

3. As development proceeds, the pattern of X inactivation is maintained during cell division.

(b) Process of X inactivation

Figure 15.31 Random X-chromosome inactivation in a calico cat. **(a)** A calico cat. **(b)** X inactivation during embryonic development. The calico pattern is due to random X-chromosome inactivation in a female that is heterozygous for the X-linked gene with black and orange alleles. The cells at the top of this figure represent a small mass of cells making up the very early embryo. In these cells, both X chromosomes are active. At an early stage of embryonic development, one X chromosome is randomly inactivated in each cell. The initial inactivation pattern is maintained in the descendents of each cell as the embryo matures into an adult. The pattern of orange and black fur in the adult cat reflects the pattern of X inactivation in the embryo.

Concept check: *If a female cat is homozygous for the orange allele, would it show a calico phenotype?*

dominant normal allele. Following growth and development, such a female will have a very low level of factor VIII and as a result will show symptoms of hemophilia.

At this point you may be wondering why X inactivation occurs. Researchers have proposed that X inactivation achieves **dosage compensation** between male and female mammals.

The X chromosome carries many genes, while the Y chromosome has only a few. The inactivation of one X chromosome in the female reduces the number of expressed copies (doses) of X-linked genes from two to one. As a result the expression of X-linked genes in females and males is roughly equal.

The X Chromosome Has an X Inactivation Centre That Controls Compaction into a Barr Body

After the Lyon hypothesis was confirmed, researchers became interested in the genetic control of X inactivation. The cells of humans and other mammals have the ability to count their X chromosomes and allow only one of them to remain active. Additional X chromosomes are converted to Barr bodies. In normal females two X chromosomes are counted and one is inactivated. In normal males one X chromosome is counted and none inactivated. On occasion, however, people are born with abnormalities in the number of their sex chromosomes. In these disorders, known as Turner syndrome, Triple X syndrome, and Klinefelter syndrome, the cells inactivate the number of X chromosomes necessary to leave a single active chromosome.

Phenotype	Chromosome composition	Number of Barr bodies
Normal female	XX	1
Normal male	XY	0
Turner syndrome (female)	XO	0
Triple X syndrome (female)	XXX	2
Klinefelter syndrome (male)	XXY	1

Although the genetic control of inactivation is not entirely understood at the molecular level, a short region on the X chromosome called the **X-inactivation centre (Xic)** is known to play a critical role. Eeva Therman and Klaus Patau identified Xic from its key role in X inactivation. The counting of human X chromosomes is accomplished by counting the number of Xics. The Xic on each X chromosome is necessary for inactivation to occur. Therman and Patau found that in cells with two X chromosomes, if one of them is missing its Xic because of a chromosome mutation, neither X chromosome will be inactivated. This is a lethal condition for a human female embryo.

The expression of a specific gene within the X inactivation centre is required for compaction of the X chromosome into a Barr body. This gene, discovered in 1991, is named *Xist* (for X inactive specific transcript). The *Xist* gene product is a long RNA molecule that does not encode a protein. Instead, the role of *Xist* RNA is to coat one of the two X chromosomes during the process of X inactivation. The *Xist* gene on the inactivated X chromosome continues to be expressed after other genes on this chromosome have been silenced.

The process of X inactivation can be divided into three phases: initiation, spreading, and maintenance (**Figure 15.32**). During initiation one of the X chromosomes is targeted for inactivation. This chromosome is inactivated during the spreading phase, so called because inactivation begins near the X inactivation centre and spreads in both directions along the chromosome. Spreading requires the transcription of the *Xist* gene and coating of the X chromosome with *Xist* RNA. After coating, proteins associate with the *Xist* RNA and promote compaction of the chromosome into a Barr body. Maintenance refers to replication of the compacted chromosome during subsequent cell divisions. Although initiation and spreading occur only during embryonic development, maintenance occurs throughout the individual's life. Continued activity of the *Xist* gene on an inactivated X chromosome maintains this chromosome as a Barr body during cell division. Whenever a somatic cell divides in a female mammal, the Barr body is replicated to produce two Barr bodies.

The Transcription of an Imprinted Gene Depends on the Sex of the Parent

As you have seen, X inactivation is a type of epigenetic inheritance in which a chromosome is modified in the early embryo, permanently altering gene expression in that individual. Other

1. Initiation: Occurs during embryonic development. The X inactivation centres (Xics) are counted and one of the X chromosomes is targeted for inactivation.

2. Spreading: Occurs during embryonic development. It begins at the Xic and progresses toward both ends until the entire chromosome is inactivated. The Xist gene, located within the Xic, encodes an RNA that coats the X chromosome and promotes its compaction into a Barr body.

3. Maintenance: Occurs from embryonic development through adult life. The inactivated X chromosome is maintained as a Barr body during subsequent cell divisions.

Figure 15.32 The process of X inactivation.

types of epigenetic inheritance occur in which genes or chromosomes are modified in the gametes of a parent, permanently altering gene expression in the offspring. **Genomic imprinting** refers to a phenomenon in which a segment of DNA is **imprinted**, or marked, in a way that affects gene expression throughout the life of the individual who inherits that DNA.

Genomic imprinting occurs in numerous species, including insects, plants, and mammals. Imprinting may involve a single gene, a part of a chromosome, an entire chromosome, or even all of the chromosomes inherited from one parent. It is permanent in the somatic cells of a given individual, but the marking of the DNA is altered from generation to generation. Imprinted genes do not follow a Mendelian pattern of inheritance because imprinting causes the offspring to distinguish between maternally and paternally inherited alleles. Depending on how a particular gene is marked by each parent, the offspring will express either the maternal or the paternal allele but not both.

Let's consider a specific example of imprinting that involves a gene called *Igf2* that is found in mice and other mammals. This gene encodes a growth hormone called insulin-like growth factor 2 that is needed for proper growth. If a normal copy of this gene is not expressed, a mouse will be dwarf. The *Igf2* gene is known to be located on an autosome, not on a sex chromosome. Because mice are diploid, they have two copies of this gene, one from each parent.

Researchers have discovered that mutations can occur in the *Igf2* gene that block the function of the Igf2 hormone. When mice carrying normal or mutant alleles are crossed to each other, a bizarre result is obtained (**Figure 15.33**). If the male parent is homozygous for the normal allele and the female is homozygous for the mutant allele, all the offspring grow to a normal size. In contrast if the male is homozygous for the mutant allele and the female is homozygous for the normal allele, all

the offspring are dwarf. The reason this result is so surprising is that the normal and dwarf offspring have the same genotype but different phenotypes! These phenotypes are not the result of any external influence on the offspring's development. Rather, the allele that is expressed in their somatic cells depends on which parent contributed which allele. In mice the *Igf2* gene inherited from the mother is imprinted in such a way that it cannot be transcribed into mRNA. Therefore, only the paternal gene is expressed. The mouse on the left side of Figure 15.33 is normal because it expresses a functional paternal gene. In contrast the mouse on the right is dwarf because the paternal gene is a mutant allele that results in a nonfunctional hormone. In both cases, the maternal gene is inactive due to imprinting.

Why is the maternal gene not transcribed into mRNA? To answer this question, we need to consider the molecular function of genes. As discussed in Chapter 12, the attachment of methyl (—CH₃) groups to the bases of DNA can alter gene transcription. For most genes methylation silences gene expression by causing the DNA to become more compact. For a few genes methylation can enhance gene expression by attracting activator proteins to the promoter. Researchers have discovered that DNA methylation is the marking process that occurs during the imprinting of certain genes, including the *Igf2* gene.

Figure 15.34 shows the imprinting process in which a maternal gene is methylated. The left side of the figure follows the marking process during the life of a female individual; the right side follows the same process in a male. Both individuals received a methylated gene from their mother and a nonmethylated copy of the same gene from their father. Via cell division the zygote develops into a multicellular organism. Each time a somatic cell divides, enzymes in the cell maintain the methylation of the maternal gene, while the paternal gene remains unmethylated. If the methylation inhibits transcription of this

	♀	♂		♀	♂
Parents	*Igf2⁻ Igf2⁻* (homozygous dwarf)	× *Igf2 Igf2* (homozygous normal)		*Igf2 Igf2* (homozygous normal)	× *Igf2⁻ Igf2⁻* (homozygous dwarf)
Offspring genotype		*Igf2* ● *Igf2⁻* ▲ (heterozygous)			*Igf2* ▲ *Igf2⁻* ● (heterozygous)
Allele that is transcribed in offspring		*Igf2* (normal)			*Igf2⁻* (nonfunctional)
Phenotype		Normal			Dwarf

Igf2   Normal allele
Igf2⁻   Mutant allele
▲   Silenced allele (from female parent)
●   Expressed allele (from male parent)

Figure 15.33 **An example of genomic imprinting in the mouse.** In the cross on the left, a homozygous male with the normal *Igf2* allele is crossed to a homozygous female carrying a defective allele, *Igf2⁻*. An offspring is phenotypically normal because the paternal allele is expressed. In the cross on the right, a homozygous male carrying the defective allele is crossed to a homozygous normal female. In this case an offspring is dwarf because the paternal allele is defective and the maternal allele is not expressed.

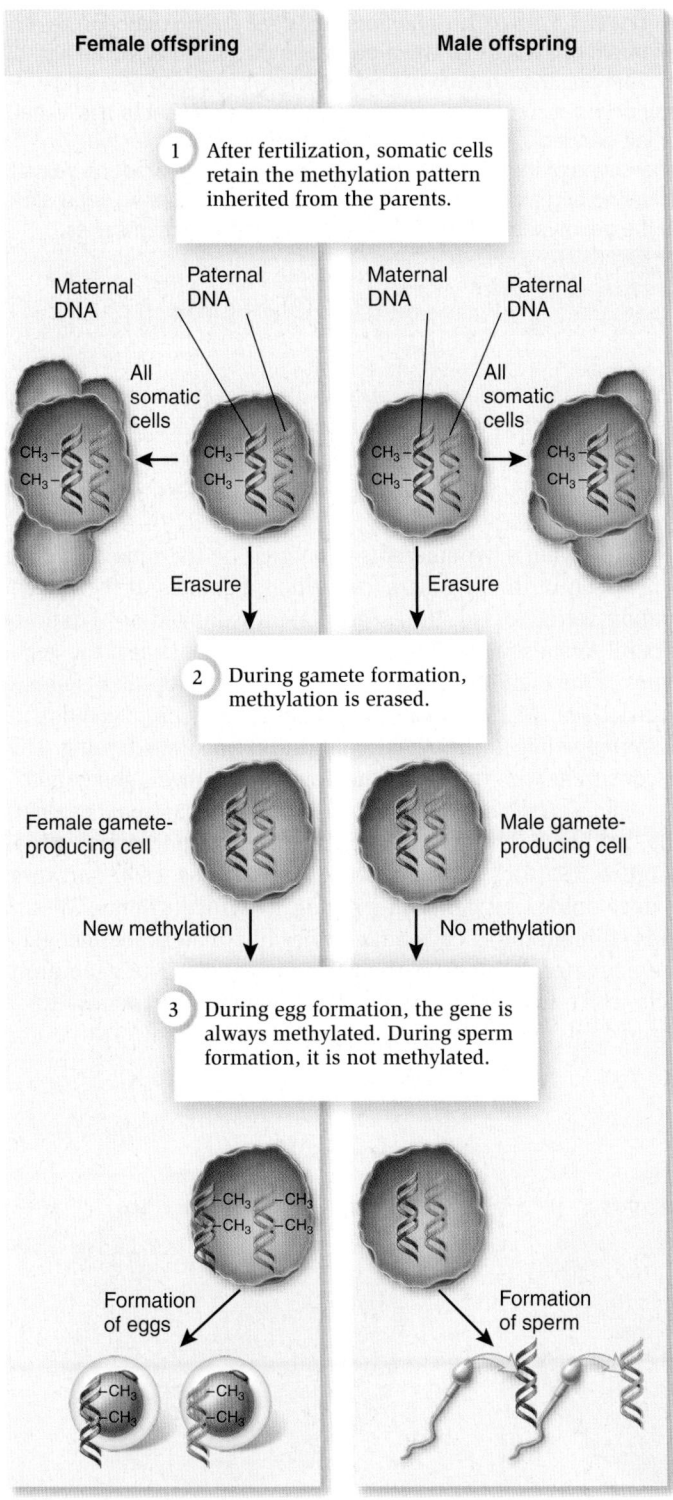

Female offspring   **Male offspring**

1 After fertilization, somatic cells retain the methylation pattern inherited from the parents.

Maternal DNA   Paternal DNA   Maternal DNA   Paternal DNA

All somatic cells   All somatic cells

CH_3 CH_3 CH_3 CH_3
CH_3 CH_3 CH_3 CH_3

Erasure   Erasure

2 During gamete formation, methylation is erased.

Female gamete-producing cell   Male gamete-producing cell

New methylation   No methylation

3 During egg formation, the gene is always methylated. During sperm formation, it is not methylated.

CH_3 CH_3
CH_3 CH_3

Formation of eggs   Formation of sperm

CH_3 CH_3
CH_3 CH_3

Figure 15.34 **Genomic imprinting via DNA methylation.** The cells at the top of this figure have a methylated gene inherited from the mother and a nonmethylated version of the same gene inherited from the father. This pattern of methylation is the same in male and female offspring and is maintained in their somatic cells. The methylation is erased during gamete formation, but in females the gene is methylated again at a later stage in the formation of eggs. Therefore, females always transmit a methylated, transcriptionally silent copy of this gene, while males transmit a nonmethylated, active copy.

gene, only the paternal copy will be expressed in the somatic cells of both the male and female offspring.

The methylation state of an imprinted gene can be altered when individuals make gametes. First, as shown in Figure 15.34, the methylation is erased. Next, the gene may be methylated again, but that depends on whether the individual is female or male. In females making eggs, both copies of the gene are methylated; in males making sperm, neither copy is methylated. When we consider the effects of methylation over two or more generations, we can see how this phenomenon creates an epigenetic transmission pattern. The male in Figure 15.34 has inherited a methylated gene from his mother that is transcriptionally silenced in his somatic cells. Although he does not express this gene during his lifetime, he can pass on an active, nonmethylated copy of this exact same gene to his offspring.

Genomic imprinting is a recently discovered phenomenon that has been shown to occur for a few genes in mammals. For some genes, such as *Igf2*, the maternal allele is silenced; for other genes the paternal allele is silenced. Biologists are still trying to understand the reason for this curious marking process.

For Maternal Effect Genes, the Genotype of the Mother Determines the Phenotype of the Offspring

In epigenetic inheritance, genes are altered in ways that affect their expression in an individual or the individual's offspring. As you have seen, some of these alterations produce strange inheritance patterns in which organisms with the same genotype have different phenotypes. Another strange inheritance pattern, with a very different explanation, involves a category of genes called **maternal effect genes**.

A. E. Boycott first identified inheritance patterns caused by maternal effect genes in the 1920s, in his studies of the freshwater snail *Lymnaea peregra*. In this species the shell and internal organs can be arranged in either a right-handed (dextral) or a left-handed (sinistral) direction. The dextral orientation is more common and is dominant to the sinistral orientation. Whether a snail's body curves in a dextral or a sinistral direction depends on the pattern of cell division immediately following fertilization. **Figure 15.35** shows the results of Boycott's crosses of true-breeding strains of snails with either a dextral or a sinistral orientation. When a dextral female (*DD*) was crossed to a sinistral male (*dd*), all the offspring were dextral. However, crossing a sinistral female (*dd*) to a dextral male (*DD*) produced the opposite result: all the offspring were sinistral. These seemingly contradictory outcomes could not be explained in terms of Mendelian inheritance.

Alfred Sturtevant later suggested that snail coiling is due to a maternal effect gene that exists as a dextral (*D*) and a sinistral (*d*) allele. In the genetic cross shown on the left, the P generation female is dextral (*DD*) and the male is sinistral (*dd*). In the cross shown on the right, the female is sinistral (*dd*) and the male is dextral (*DD*). In either case the F_1 offspring are *Dd*. When the F_1 individuals from these two crosses are mated to each other, a genotypic ratio of 1 *DD*:2 *Dd*:1 *dd* is predicted for the F_2 generation. Because the *D* allele is dominant to the *d* allele, a Mendelian inheritance pattern would produce a 3:1 phenotypic ratio of dextral to sinistral snails. Instead, the snails of the F_2 generation were

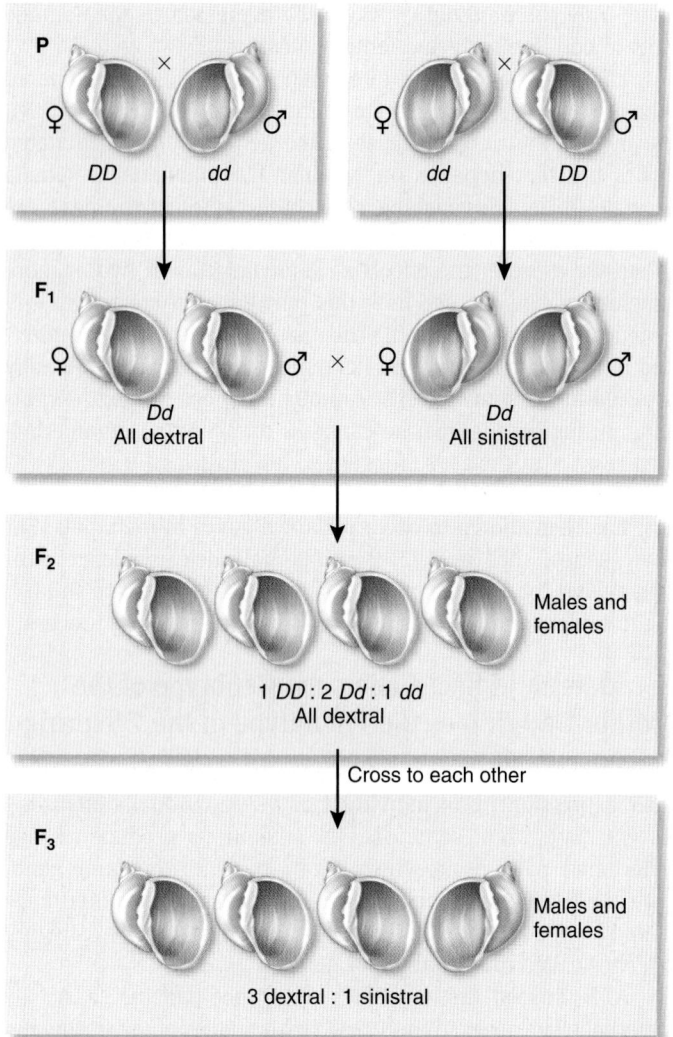

Figure 15.35 The inheritance of snail coiling direction as an example of a maternal effect gene.   In the snails shown in this experiment, the direction of body coiling is controlled by a single pair of genes. *D* (dextral, or right-handed) is dominant to *d* (sinistral, or left-handed). The genotype of the mother determines the phenotype of the offspring. A *DD* or *Dd* mother will produce dextral offspring and a *dd* mother will produce sinistral offspring, regardless of the genotypes of the father and of the offspring themselves.

Concept check: *An offspring has a genotype of Dd and coils to the left. What is the genotype of its mother?*

all dextral. To explain this observed result, Sturtevant proposed that the phenotype of the F_2 offspring depended solely on the genotype of the F_1 mother. Because the F_1 mothers were *Dd,* and the *D* allele is dominant, the F_2 offspring were dextral even if their genotype was *dd!*

Sturtevant's hypothesis is supported by the ratio of phenotypes seen in the F_3 generation. When members of the F_2 generation were crossed, the F_3 generation exhibited a 3:1 ratio of dextral to sinistral snails. These F_3 phenotypes reflect the genotypes of the F_2 mothers. The ratio of genotypes for the F_2 females was 1 *DD:*2 *Dd:*1 *dd.* The *DD* and *Dd* females produced dextral offspring, while the *dd* females produced sinistral offspring. This is consistent with the 3:1 phenotypic ratio in the F_3 generation.

The process of egg maturation in female animals explains the peculiar inheritance pattern of maternal effect genes (**Figure 15.36**). Maternal cells called nurse cells surround a developing egg cell and provide it with nutrients. Within these diploid nurse cells both copies of a maternal effect gene are activated to produce their gene products. The gene products are transported into the egg, where they persist for a significant time during embryonic development. The *D* and

All offspring are dextral because the egg received the gene products of the *D* allele.

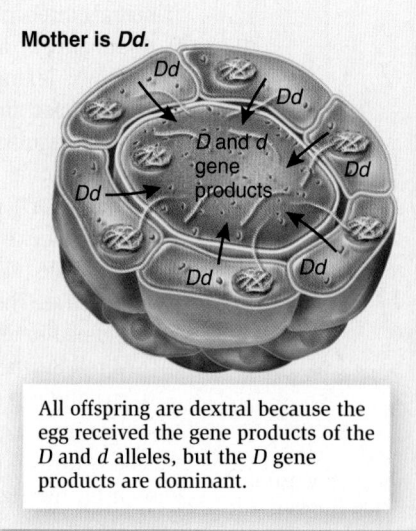

All offspring are dextral because the egg received the gene products of the *D* and *d* alleles, but the *D* gene products are dominant.

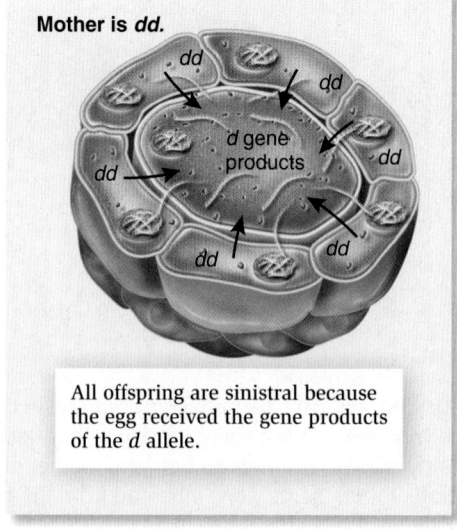

All offspring are sinistral because the egg received the gene products of the *d* allele.

Figure 15.36 The mechanism of maternal effect in snail coiling.   In this simplified diagram the mother's diploid nurse cells transfer gene products to the egg as it matures. These gene products persist after fertilization, affecting development of the early embryo. If the nurse cells are *DD* or *Dd,* they will transfer the dominant *D* gene product to the egg, causing the offspring to be dextral. If the nurse cells are *dd,* only the *d* gene product will be transferred to the egg and the offspring will be sinistral.

d gene products influence the pattern of cell division during the early stages of the snail's embryonic development. If an egg receives only the *D* gene product, the snail will develop a dextral orientation, while an egg that receives only the *d* gene product will produce a snail with a sinistral orientation. If an egg receives both *D* and *d* gene products, the snail will be dextral because the *D* gene product is dominant over *d*. In this way the gene products of nurse cells, which are determined by the mother's genotype, influence the development of the offspring.

Several dozen maternal effect genes have been identified in experimental organisms, such as *Drosophila*. Recently, they have also been found in mice and humans. As we will discuss in

Chapter 17, the products of maternal effect genes are critically important in the early stages of animal development.

Summary of Inheritance Patterns

Now that we have looked at the diverse processes that influence the genotypic ratios seen in offspring and the remarkable biological process that translate these genotypes into phenotypes, we can marvel at the process by which geneticists have unravelled the biological basis of inheritance and are beginning to understand phenotypes. **Table 15.4** summarizes the variety of phenotype-derived patterns of inheritance that geneticists have synthesized from a wealth of genetic studies.

Table 15.4	Inheritance Patterns from Simple to Complex	
Type	**Description**	**Examples**
Single Genes	**Transmission Pattern**	
Mendelian (autosomal)	Inheritance patterns in which a single gene affects a single trait, and the parents have two versions of the genes (alleles) that can segregate	*T/t* alleles for tall/dwarf plants (Figure 15.5)
Sex linked	Inheritance pattern in which a single gene affects a single trait but one sex is hemizygous, having only one version of most sex chromosome genes	Red X^{w+}/white X^w alleles eye colour in *Drosophila* (Figure 15.15)
Maternal (extranuclear) inheritance	Transmission pattern of genes that are inherited independently of genes in the nucleus and do not segregate during meiosis; usually these genes are inherited from the mother	Chloroplast and mitochondrial genes (Figure 15.27)
Multiple Genes	**Transmission Patterns**	
Assort independently	Two genes that segregate independently of each other	The yellow and round genes of peas (Figure 15.8)
Linkage	Two sets of alleles for two genes, that segregate dependently and tend to be inherited in parental combinations	b^+c^+ and *bc* in *Drosophila* (Figure 15.7)
One Gene	**Phenotype Determination: Dominance Relationships of Alleles**	
	Simple dominant-recessive allele: one allele completely determines phenotype	Tall/short *T/t* in peas (Figure 15.5) I^A/i blood group alleles (Table 15.3)
	Incomplete dominance between alleles: both alleles contribute to an intermediate phenotype	White flowers: C^wC^w Red flowers: C^RC^R Pink flowers: C^wC^R (Figure 15.20)
	Codominance between alleles: phenotype associated with both alleles is seen	I^A and I^B alleles in I^AI^B individual human blood types (Table 15.3)
More Than One Gene	**Phenotype(s) Determination**	
Independent action	The two genes each affect a different trait without their gene products interacting	The yellow and round genes of peas (Figure 15.8)
Epistasis	A type of gene interaction in which the alleles of one gene mask the effects of all alleles of another gene	*C* locus and *P* locus of sweet peas (Figure 15.24)
Multiple genes interacting in a positive way to create continuous traits	Inheritance pattern in which the offspring display a continuous range of phenotypes; this pattern is produced by the additive interactions of several genes, together with environmental influences	Height, intelligence, and skin colour are a few examples of traits determined by many genes interacting with each other and the environment (Figure 15.26)
Epigenetic Factors	**Phenotype Determination**	
X inactivation	Phenomenon of female mammals in which one X chromosome is inactivated in every somatic cell, producing a mosaic phenotype; most genes on the inactivated X chromosome are not expressed	Barr bodies in mammals (Figures 15.30 and 15.31)
Genomic imprinting	Inheritance pattern in which an allele from one parent is inactivated in the somatic cells of the offspring, while the allele from the other parent is expressed	Imprinting via methylation (Figure 15.33)
Maternal effect	Inheritance pattern in which the genotype of the mother determines the phenotype of the offspring; occurs because maternal effect genes of the mother provide gene products to developing eggs	Snail shell coiling (Figure 15.35)

Summary of Key Concepts

15.1 Mendel's Laws and the Chromosome Theory of Inheritance

- Mendel focused his attention on seven characters or traits found in garden peas that existed in two variants each. (Figures 15.1, 15.2)

- Mendel could allow his peas to self-fertilize or he could carry out cross-fertilization, also known as hybridization. (Figures 15.3, 15.4)

- By following the inheritance pattern of a single trait (a single-factor cross) for two generations, Mendel determined the law of segregation of alleles. This law tells us that two alleles of a gene segregate from each other when passed from parents to offspring. (Figures 15.5, 15.6)

- The genotype is the genetic makeup of an organism. Alleles are alternative versions of the same gene. A phenotype is a description of the traits that an organism displays. The genotype describes an organism's genetic makeup, while the phenotype describes its characteristics.

- A Punnett square can be constructed to predict the outcome of crosses when the genotypes of the parents are known.

- A testcross can be conducted to determine if an individual displaying a dominant trait is a homozygote or heterozygote. (Figure 15.7)

- By conducting a dihybrid cross, Mendel determined the law of independent assortment, which says that the alleles for two different genes assort independently of each other. In a dihybrid cross, this yields a 9:3:3:1 ratio in the F_2 generation. (Figure 15.8)

- The chromosome theory of inheritance explains how the steps of meiosis account for the inheritance patterns observed by Mendel. Each gene is located at a particular locus on a chromosome. (Figures 15.9, 15.10, 15.11)

- The product rule and sum rule allow us to predict the outcome of crosses based on probability. Random sampling error is the deviation between observed and predicted values.

- Instead of conducting crosses, the inheritance patterns in humans are determined from a pedigree analysis. (Figures 15.12, 15.13)

15.2 Sex Chromosomes and X-Linked Inheritance Patterns

- Many species of animals and a few species of plants have separate male and female sexes. In many cases sex is determined by differences in sex chromosomes. (Figure 15.14)

- In mammals, recessive X-linked traits are more likely to occur in males. An example is hemophilia.

- Morgan carried out crosses that showed that an eye-colour gene in *Drosophila* is located on the X chromosome. (Figure 15.15)

15.3 Genes on the Same Chromosome: Linkage, Recombination, and Mapping

- When two different genes are on the same chromosome, they are in the same linkage group. Linked genes tend to be inherited as a unit, unless crossing over separates them. Dihybrids produce fewer than 50% recombinant-type gametes (Figures 15.16, 15.17)

- The percentage of offspring produced in a two-factor testcross can be used to map the relative locations of genes along a chromosome. (Figure 15.18)

15.4 Variations in Phenotypic Ratios and Their Molecular Basis

- Several inheritance patterns have been discovered that obey Mendel's laws but yield differing phenotypic ratios of offspring compared with Mendel's crosses. (Table 15.1)

- Recessive inheritance of mutant alleles is often due to a loss-of-function allele. The wild-type allele will be dominant if the normal protein is produced in sufficient amounts to produce the normal phenotype. The mutant allele will be dominant if the mutant allele blocks the function of the wild-type allele or if the wild-type allele cannot compensate for the mutant allele and there are no intermediate phenotypes. (Figure 15.19)

- Mutant genes are responsible for many inherited diseases in humans. In many cases the effects of a mutant gene are pleiotropic, meaning that the gene affects several different aspects of bodily structure and function. (Table 15.2)

- Incomplete dominance occurs when a heterozygote has a phenotype that is intermediate between either homozygote. This occurs because 50% of the normal protein is not enough to give the same phenotype as a normal homozygote, but the phenotype of the heterozygote is intermediate. (Figure 15.20)

- ABO blood type is an example of multiple alleles in which a gene exists in three alleles in a population. The A and B alleles are codominant, which means that both are expressed in the same individual. These alleles encode enzymes with different specificities for attaching sugar molecules to make antigens. (Table 15.3)

- Pattern baldness in people is a sex-influenced trait that is dominant in males and recessive in females. This pattern occurs because sex hormones influence the expression of certain genes. (Figure 15.21)

- All traits are influenced by the environment. The norm of reaction is a description of how a trait can change, depending on the environmental conditions. (Figures 15.22, 15.23)

15.5 Gene Products Frequently Interact in Determining Complex Phenotypes

- When the alleles of one gene mask the effects of the alleles of a different gene, this type of gene interaction is called epistasis. (Figures 15.24, 15.25)

- Quantitative traits, such as height and weight, are polygenic, which means that several genes govern the trait. Often, the alleles of such genes contribute in an additive way to the phenotype. This produces continuous variation in the trait, which is graphed as a bell curve. (Figure 15.26)

15.6 Extranuclear Inheritance: Organelle Genomes

- Mitochondria and chloroplasts carry a small number of genes. The inheritance of such genes is called extranuclear inheritance. (Figure 15.27)

- Chloroplasts in the four-o'clock plant are transmitted via the egg, a pattern called maternal inheritance. (Figures 15.28, 15.29)

15.7 Epigenetic Effects: X Inactivation, Genomic Imprinting, and Maternal Effects

- Epigenetic inheritance refers to patterns in which a gene is inactivated during the life of an organism but not over many generations.

- X inactivation in mammals occurs when one X chromosome is randomly inactivated in females. If the female is heterozygous for an X-linked gene, this can lead to a variegated phenotype. (Figures 15.30, 15.31)

- X inactivation occurs in three phases: initiation, spreading, and maintenance. (Figure 15.32)

- Imprinted genes are inactivated in one parent, but not in both. The offspring expresses only one of the two alleles. (Figure 15.33)

- During gamete formation, methylation of a gene from one parent is a mechanism to achieve imprinting. (Figure 15.34)

- For maternal effect genes the genotype of the mother determines the phenotype of the offspring. This is explained by the phenomenon of the mother's nurse cells contributing gene products to egg cells that are needed for early stages of development. (Figures 15.35, 15.36)

- Several types of gene transmission are known to occur. Genes work together and are influenced by the environment and by epigenetic factors and maternal effects. (Table 15.4)

Test to Assess Your Learning

1. Based on Mendel's experimental crosses, what is the expected F_2 phenotypic ratio of a monohybrid cross?
   a. 1:2:1
   b. 2:1
   c. 3:1
   d. 9:3:3:1
   e. 4:1

2. If a dihybrid is testcrossed, what is the expected phenotypic ratio of the offspring if the two genes are sorting independently?
   a. 1:2:1
   b. 2:1
   c. 3:1
   d. 9:3:3:1
   e. 1:1:1:1

3. An individual who has two different alleles of a particular gene is said to be
   a. dihybrid.
   b. recessive.
   c. homozygous.
   d. heterozygous.
   e. hemizygous.

4. Which of Mendel's laws cannot be observed in a monohybrid cross?
   a. segregation
   b. dominance-recessiveness
   c. independent assortment
   d. codominance
   e. All of the above can be observed in a monohybrid cross.

5. During a _____ cross an individual with the dominant phenotype and unknown genotype is crossed with a _____ individual to determine the unknown genotype.
   a. monohybrid, homozygous recessive
   b. dihybrid, heterozygous
   c. test, homozygous dominant
   d. monohybrid, homozygous dominant
   e. test, homozygous recessive

6. In humans males are said to be _____ at X-linked loci.
   a. dominant
   b. homozygous
   c. recessive
   d. heterozygous
   e. hemizygous

7. A gene that affects more than one phenotypic trait is said to be
   a. dominant.
   b. wild type.
   c. dihybrid.
   d. pleiotropic.
   e. heterozygous.

8. A hypothetical flowering plant species produces red, pink, and white flowers. To determine the inheritance pattern, the following crosses were conducted, with the results indicated:
   red × red → all red
   white × white → all white
   red × white → all pink
   What type of inheritance pattern does this represent?
   a. dominance-recessiveness
   b. X linked
   c. codominance
   d. incomplete dominance
   e. pleiotropy

9. Genes located on a sex chromosome are said to be
   a. X linked.
   b. dominant.
   c. hemizygous.
   d. sex linked.
   e. sex influenced.

10. Genes that are expressed differently depending on whether the individual is male or female are
    a. sex linked.
    b. pleiotropic.
    c. sex influenced.
    d. incomplete dominant.
    e. hemizygous.

11. Quantitative traits, such as height and weight, are governed by several genes that usually contribute in an additive way to the trait. This is called
    a. independent assortment.
    b. discontinuous inheritance.
    c. maternal inheritance.
    d. linkage.
    e. polygenic inheritance.

12. Based on the ideas proposed by Morgan, which of the following statements concerning linkage is *not* true?
    a. Traits determined by genes located on the same chromosome are likely to be inherited together.
    b. Crossing over between homologous chromosomes can create new gene combinations.
    c. Crossing over is more likely to occur between genes that are closer together.
    d. The probability of crossing over depends on the distance between the genes.
    e. All but one of the above statements are correct.

13. In genetic linkage mapping 1 map unit is equivalent to
    a. 100 base pairs.
    b. 1 base pair.
    c. 10% recombination frequency.
    d. 1% recombination frequency.
    e. 1% the length of the chromosome.

14. Suppose a man was heterozygous for two genes both known to reside on chromosome 3. By using molecular techniques, scientists genotyped his sperm and determined that 40 of every one 1,000 of his gametes were recombinant type. What is the map distance between the two genes?
    a. 40 cM
    b. 4 cM
    c. 2 cM
    d. 20 cM
    e. 400 cM

15. Colour-blindness is determined by a recessive X-linked allele. A women who is colour-blind marries a man with normal vision. What is the probability of their having a daughter who is colour-blind?
    a. 1/4
    b. 1/2

c. 3/4
d. 1
e. 0

16. In most organisms the egg contributes the mitochondria for the zygote; the sperm does not. This phenomenon is known as
    a. biparental inheritance.
    b. paternal inheritance.
    c. maternal effect.
    d. maternal inheritance.
    e. both (c) and (d).

17. Modification of a gene during gamete formation or early development that alters the way the gene is expressed during the individual's lifetime is called
    a. maternal inheritance.
    b. epigenetic inheritance.
    c. epistasis.
    d. multiple allelism.
    e. alternative splicing.

18. When a gene is inactivated during gamete formation and that gene is maintained in an inactivated state in the somatic cells of offspring, such an inheritance pattern is called
    a. linkage.
    b. X inactivation.
    c. maternal effect.
    d. genomic imprinting.
    e. polygenic inheritance.

19. A calico coat pattern in cats is the result of
    a. X inactivation.
    b. epistasis.
    c. organelle heredity.
    d. genomic imprinting.
    e. maternal inheritance.

20. Maternal effect inheritance can be explained by
    a. gene products that are given to an egg by the nurse cells.
    b. the methylation of genes during gamete formation.
    c. the spreading of X inactivation from the Xic locus.
    d. the inheritance of alleles that contribute additively to a trait.
    e. none of the above.

Articulate to Assess Your Learning

1. What is a testcross and why would a geneticist usually want to do one?

2. Compare and contrast the purposes of a Punnett square and a family pedigree analysis.

3. Imagine three mutant alleles, for three different genes that each are completely nonfunctional (i.e., they produce a completely nonfunctional protein). The biological situation for each of the three genes is described below. For each gene, indicate whether you would expect the *mutant* allele to be dominant, incompletely dominant, or recessive to the wild-type allele. Explain your decisions.
    a. For gene 1: 100 units of enzymatic function are required to get the normal wild-type phenotype; any value less than that has the same mutant phenotype. One wild-type allele can produce 100 units of activity. The mutant allele for gene 1 will be _____ to the wild-type allele.
    b. For gene 2: 100 units of enzymatic function are required to get a normal phenotype; any value less than that has the same mutant phenotype. One wild-type allele can produce 75 units of activity. The mutant allele for gene 2 will be _____ to the wild-type allele.
    c. For gene 3: 0–49 units of enzyme function give phenotype 1, 50–99 units of enzyme function give phenotype 2, and 100 or

more units of enzymatic function give phenotype 3. One wild-type allele can produce 75 units of activity. The mutant allele for gene 2 will be _____ to the wild-type allele.

4. Explain why recessive X-linked traits in humans are more likely to occur in males and dominant X-linked traits are more likely to occur in females.

5. Explain how linkage is determined and give the biological basis for it.

6. Compare and contrast the terms *epigenetic* and *genetic inheritance*.

Collaborate to Assess and Extend Your Learning

1. Discuss Mendel's two laws and why they are important. Explain how documented exceptions to each of the laws led to a better understanding of inheritance.

2. Suppose that a man is affected with a dominant genetic disease; his wife does not carry any copy of the disease allele. He and his wife decide to have a child and want an assessment of the risks. Indicate the probability of the following:
    a. He will have an affected son if the disease allele resides on the mitochondrial chromosome.
    b. He will have an affected son if the disease allele resides on the X chromosome.
    c. He will have an affected son if the disease allele resides on an autosomal chromosome.
    d. He will have an affected daughter if the disease allele resides on the mitochondrial chromosome.
    e. He will have an affected daughter if the disease allele resides on the X chromosome.
    f. He will have an affected daughter if the disease allele resides on an autosomal chromosome.

3. Two individuals are each *AaBb* heterozygotes and they are mated.
    a. What is the expected genotypic ratio for the next generation if the two genes are sorting independently?
    b. What is the expected *phenotypic* ratio for the same mating as in (a) for the next generation if the two genes are sorting independently and *A* is dominant to *a*, and *B* is dominant to *b*?
    c. What is the expected phenotypic ratio for the same mating for the next generation if the two genes are sorting independently and *A* is dominant to *a*, but *B* and *b* display codominance?
    d. What would be the expected *genotypic* ratio if the *A* and *B* genes were so tightly linked that they never had a cross over between them during meiosis?

4. Discuss two types of gene interactions. For each, tell whether or not you would expect a 9:3:3:1 ratio if a dihybrid of the two genes was self-crossed.

5. Consider gene *a*, gene *b*, gene *c*, gene *d* and gene *e*, all in the same organism. Genes *a*, *b* and *c* are nuclear genes. Genes *a* and *b* are close together on chromosome 1, gene *c* is on chromosome 2, gene *e* is on an X chromosome. Gene *d* is a chloroplast gene. Create a concept map showing the relationships of these genes to the following terms: Mendelian inheritance, independent assortment, linkage, X-linkage, maternal inheritance, cytoplasmic inheritance.

6. A biological principle of life is that living organisms interact with their environment. Discuss how the environment plays a key role in determining the outcome of an individual's traits.

Genetics of Viruses and Bacteria

Chapter Outline

This bacterium is a common cause of meningitis—a serious infection that causes inflammation of the tissues lining the spinal cord and the brain.

While studying for his calculus test, Jason was having trouble concentrating. The brightness of his desk light was hurting his eyes. He had a severe headache and fever, and he thought he must be coming down with a cold. He had taken some Aspirin, but it didn't seem to be helping. He wondered if a snack would help. As he was eating some potato chips, he dropped one. When he tried to look down to see where it had landed, he realized that his neck was extremely stiff; he could barely tilt his head to look forward. During the evening, Jason became confused and lethargic, and his roommate urged him to see a doctor. Fortunately, Jason took his advice and went to the university medical centre. The diagnosis was bacterial meningitis—an inflammation of the protective membranes that cover the brain and spinal cord, collectively called the meninges. Although it's a relatively rare disease, bacterial meningitis is up to six times more common among people living in close quarters, such as university dormitories. Because Jason sought help early enough, his disease was treated with antibiotics. Had he not gotten help, the disease could have caused severe brain damage and even death.

Jason's story highlights a primary reason biologists are so interested in viruses and bacteria. Infectious diseases caused by viruses and bacteria are a leading cause of human suffering and death, accounting for one-quarter to one-third of deaths worldwide. The spread of infectious diseases results from human behaviour, and it has been accelerated by changes in land-use patterns, increased trade and travel, and the inappropriate use of antibiotic drugs. Although the incidence of fatal infectious diseases in Canada is low compared with the worldwide average, an alarming increase in more deadly strains of viruses and bacteria has occurred over the past few decades. Since 1980, the number of deaths in Canada caused by infectious diseases has approximately doubled.

In this chapter we turn our attention to the genetic analyses of viruses and bacteria. We will begin by examining viruses and other nonliving particles that infect living cells. All organisms are susceptible to infection by one or more types of viruses, which use the host's cellular machinery to replicate their own genome. Once a cell is infected, the genetic material of a virus orchestrates a series of events that ultimately produces new virus particles. We will consider the biological complexity of viruses and explore viral reproductive cycles. We will also examine some of the simplest and smallest infectious agents, called viroids and prions.

In the other sections of this chapter we will examine the bacterial genome and the methods used in its investigation. Like their eukaryotic counterparts, bacteria have genetic differences that affect their cellular traits, and the techniques of modern microbiology make many of these differences, such as sensitivity to antibiotics and differences in nutritional requirements, easy to detect. Although bacteria reproduce asexually by cell division, their genetic variety is enhanced by a process called gene transfer, in which genes are passed from one bacterial cell to another. Like sexual reproduction in eukaryotes, gene transfer enhances the genetic diversity observed among bacterial species. In this chapter we will explore three interesting ways that bacteria can transfer genetic material.

16.1   GENETIC PROPERTIES OF VIRUSES

Learning Outcomes:

1. Compare and contrast how viruses differ with regard to their host range, structure, and genomes.
2. List the six steps in viral reproductive cycles, and distinguish between the lysogenic and lytic cycles.
3. Describe how emerging viruses, such as HIV, arise and spread through populations.
4. Explain how an understanding of virus structure and reproduction can aid in the development of drugs to combat viruses.
5. Outline two hypotheses regarding the origin of viruses.

Viruses are nonliving particles with nucleic acid genomes. Why are viruses considered nonliving? They do not exhibit all seven properties that are associated with living organisms (refer back

Figure 16.1 A plant infected with tobacco mosaic virus.

to Figure 1.2). Viruses are not composed of cells, and, by themselves, they do not carry out metabolism, use energy, maintain homeostasis, or even reproduce. A virus or its genetic material must be taken up by a living cell to replicate.

The first virus to be discovered was tobacco mosaic virus (TMV). This virus infects several species of plants and causes mosaic-like patterns in which normal-coloured patches are interspersed with light green or yellowish patches on the leaves (**Figure 16.1**). TMV damages leaves, flowers, and fruit but almost never kills the plant. In 1883 German scientist Adolf Mayer determined that this disease could be spread by spraying the sap from one plant onto another. Sap that had been passed through filters with pores small enough to prevent the passage of bacterial cells was still able to spread the disease. At first some researchers suggested the agent was a chemical toxin. However, Dutch botanist Martinus Beijerinck ruled out this possibility by showing that sap could continue to transmit the disease after many plant generations. A toxin would have been diluted after many generations, but Beijerinck's results indicated the disease agent was multiplying in the plant. Around the same time, animal viruses were discovered in connection with a disease of cattle called foot-and-mouth disease. In 1900 the first human virus, the virus that causes yellow fever, was identified.

Since these early studies, microbiologists, geneticists, and molecular biologists have taken a great interest in the structure, genetic composition, and replication of viruses. In this section we will discuss the structure of viruses and examine viral reproductive cycles in detail, paying particular attention to human immunodeficiency virus (HIV), the virus that causes acquired immune deficiency syndrome (AIDS) in humans.

Viruses Are Remarkably Varied, Despite Their Simple Structure

A **virus** is a small infectious particle that consists of nucleic acid enclosed in a protein coat. Researchers have identified and studied more than 4,000 different types of viruses. Although all viruses share some similarities, such as small size and the reliance on a living cell for replication, they vary greatly in their characteristics, including their host range, their structure, and their genome composition. Some of the major differences are described next, and the characteristics of selected viruses are shown in **Table 16.1**.

Differences in Host Range A cell that is infected by a virus is called a **host cell**, and a species that can be infected by a specific virus is called a host species for that virus. Viruses differ greatly in their **host range**—the number of species and cell types they can infect. Table 16.1 lists a few examples of viruses with widely different ranges of host species. Tobacco mosaic virus, which we discussed earlier, has a broad host range. TMV is known to infect more than 150 different species of plants. By comparison, other viruses have a narrow host range, with some infecting only a single species, such as humans. Furthermore, a virus may infect only a specific cell type in a host species. **Figure 16.2** shows some viruses that infect particular human cells and cause disease.

Structural Differences Viruses cannot be seen by using even the best light microscope. Although the existence of viruses was postulated in the 1890s, viruses were not observed until the 1930s, when the electron microscope was invented. Viruses range in size from about 20 to 400 nm in diameter (1 nanometre = 10^{-9} metres). For comparison, a typical bacterium is 1,000 nm in diameter, and the diameter of most eukaryotic cells is 10 to 1,000 times that of a bacterium. Adenoviruses, which cause infections of the respiratory and gastrointestinal tracts, have an average diameter of 75 nm. More than 50 million adenoviruses could fit into an average-sized human cell.

What are the common structural features of all viruses? As shown in **Figure 16.3**, all viruses have a protein coat called a **capsid** that encloses a genome consisting of one or more molecules of nucleic acid. Capsids are composed of one or several different proteins and have a variety of shapes, including helical and polyhedral. **Figure 16.3a** shows the structure of TMV, which has a helical capsid made of identical protein subunits. **Figure 16.3b** shows an adenovirus, which has a polyhedral capsid. Protein fibres with a terminal knob are located at the corners of the polyhedral capsid. Many viruses that infect animal cells, such as the influenza virus shown in **Figure 16.3c**, have a **viral envelope** enclosing the capsid. The envelope consists of a lipid bilayer that is derived from a cellular membrane of the host cell and is embedded with virally encoded glycoproteins called spikes or spike glycoproteins.

In addition to encasing and protecting the genetic material, the capsid and envelope enable viruses to infect their hosts. In many viruses the capsids or envelopes have specialized proteins, such as protein fibres with a knob (Figure 16.3b) and spike glycoproteins (Figure 16.3c), that help them bind to the surface of a host cell. A virus that infects a bacterium, called a **bacteriophage (phage)**, may have much more complex capsids, with accessory structures used for anchoring the virus to a host cell and injecting the viral nucleic acid (**Figure 16.3d**). As we will discuss later, the tail fibres of such bacteriophages are needed to attach the virus to the bacterial cell wall.

Table 16.1 Hosts and Characteristics of Selected Viruses

Virus or group of viruses	Host	Effect on host	Nucleic acid*	Genome size (kb)[†]	Number of genes[†]
Phage fd	E. coli	Slows growth	ssDNA	6.4	10
Phage λ	E. coli	Causes lysis	dsDNA	48.5	71
Phage T4	E. coli	Causes lysis	dsDNA	169	288
Phage Qβ	E. coli	Slows growth	ssRNA	4.2	4
Tobacco mosaic virus (TMV)	Many plants	Causes mottling and necrosis of leaves and other plant parts	ssRNA	6.4	6
Cauliflower mosaic virus	A few plants	Similar to TMV	dsDNA	8	1
Baculoviruses	Insects	Most baculoviruses are species specific; they usually kill the insect	dsDNA	133.9	154
Parvovirus	Mammals	Causes respiratory, flulike symptoms	ssDNA	5	5
Influenza virus	Mammals/birds	Causes classic flu, with fever, cough, sore throat, and headache (examples are H1N1 and H5N1)	ssRNA	13.5	11
Epstein-Barr virus	Humans	Causes mononucleosis, with fever, sore throat, and fatigue	dsDNA	172	80
Coronavirus	Mammals/birds	Causes fever, respiratory symptoms (an example is severe acute respiratory syndrome [SARS])	ssRNA	30	16
Adenovirus	Humans	Cause respiratory symptoms and diarrhea	dsDNA	34	35
Flaviviruses	Mammals/insects	Cause fever, headache, jaundice, hemorrhagic illness (examples include yellow fever, encephalitis, West Nile virus, hepatitis C)	ssRNA	12	10
Herpes simplex type II	Humans	Causes blistering sores on the genital region	dsDNA	158.4	77
HIV (type I)	Humans	Causes AIDS, an immunodeficiency syndrome eventually leading to death	ssRNA	9.7	9

*The abbreviations ss and ds refer to single stranded and double stranded, respectively.
[†]Several of the viruses listed in this table are found in different strains that show variation with regard to genome size and number of genes. The numbers reported in this table are typical values. The abbreviation kb refers to kilobase, which equals 1,000 bases.

Genome Differences   The genetic material in a virus is called a **viral genome**. The composition of viral genomes varies markedly among different types of viruses, as suggested by the examples in Table 16.1. The nucleic acid of some viruses is DNA, while in others it is RNA. These are referred to as DNA viruses and RNA viruses, respectively. It is striking that some viruses use RNA for their genome, whereas all living organisms use DNA. In some viruses the nucleic acid is single stranded, whereas in others it is double stranded. The genome can be linear or circular, depending on the type of virus. Some kinds of viruses have more than one copy of the genome.

Viral genomes also vary considerably in size, ranging from a few thousand to more than a hundred thousand nucleotides (see Table 16.1). For example, the genomes of some simple viruses, such as phage Qβ, are only a few thousand nucleotides long and contain only a few genes. Other viruses, particularly those with a complex structure, such as phage T4, contain many more genes. These extra genes encode many different proteins, some of which are involved in the formation of the elaborate capsid shown in Figure 16.3d.

Viruses Reproduce by Causing Their Host Cells to Produce New Viruses   When a virus infects a host cell, the expression of viral genes leads to a series of steps, called a **viral reproductive cycle**, which results in the production of new viruses. The details of the steps may be quite different among various types of viruses, and even the same virus may have the capacity to follow alternative cycles. Even so, by studying the reproductive cycles of hundreds of different viruses, researchers have determined that the viral reproductive cycle consists of five or six basic steps.

To illustrate the general features of viral reproductive cycles, **Figure 16.4** considers these steps for two types of viruses. **Figure 16.4a** shows the cycle of phage λ (lambda), a bacteriophage with double-stranded DNA as its genome, while **Figure 16.4b** depicts the cycle of HIV, an enveloped animal virus containing single-stranded RNA. The descriptions that follow compare the reproductive cycles of these two very different viruses.

Step 1: Attachment   In the first step of a viral reproductive cycle, the virus must attach to the surface of a host cell. This attachment is usually specific for one or just a few types of cells because proteins in the virus recognize and bind to specific molecules on the cell surface. In the case of phage λ, the phage tail fibres bind to proteins in the outer bacterial cell membrane of E. coli cells. In the case of HIV, spike glycoproteins in the viral envelope bind to protein receptors in the plasma membrane of human blood cells called helper T cells.

Brain and CNS:
Flavivirus—yellow fever, West Nile virus
Rhabdovirus—rabies

Skin:
Herpes simplex I—cold sores
Variola virus—smallpox

Respiratory tract:
Influenza virus—flu
Coronavirus—SARS
Rhinovirus—common cold

Immune system:
Rubella virus—measles
Human immunodeficiency virus—AIDS
Epstein-Barr virus—mononucleosis

Digestive system:
Hepatitis B virus—viral hepatitis
Rotavirus—viral gastroenteritis
Norwalk virus—viral gastroenteritis

Reproductive system:
Herpes simplex II—genital herpes
Papillomavirus—warts, cervical cancer

Blood:
Ebola virus—hemorrhagic fever
Hantavirus—hemorrhagic fever
with renal syndrome

Figure 16.2 **Some viruses that cause human diseases.** Most viruses that cause disease in humans infect cells of specific tissues, as illustrated by the examples in this figure. Note: Herpes simplex I and II infect nerve cells of the peripheral nervous system that are found in the skin and genital region, respectively.

Step 2: Entry After attachment the viral genome enters the host cell. Attachment of phage λ stimulates a conformational change in the phage coat proteins, so that the shaft (also called the sheath) contracts and the phage injects its DNA into the bacterial cytoplasm. In contrast, the envelope of HIV fuses with the plasma membrane of the host cell, so both the capsid and its contents are released into the cytosol. Some of the HIV capsid proteins are then removed by host cell enzymes, releasing the viral RNA and an enzyme called reverse transcriptase into the cytosol. As discussed shortly, reverse transcriptase is needed for step (3).

Once a viral genome has entered the cell, one or several viral genes are expressed immediately because of the action of host cell enzymes and ribosomes. Expression of these key genes leads quickly to either step (3) or step (4) of the reproductive cycle, depending on the specific virus. The genome of some viruses, including both phage λ and HIV, can integrate into a chromosome of the host cell. For such viruses, the cycle may

proceed from step (2) to step (3) as described next, delaying the production of new viruses. Alternatively, the cycle can proceed directly from step (2) to step (4) and quickly lead to the production of new viruses.

Step 3: Integration Viruses that are capable of integration carry a gene that encodes an enzyme called **integrase**. For integration to occur, this gene is expressed soon after entry so that integrase protein is made. Integrase cuts the host's chromosomal DNA and inserts the viral genome into the chromosome. In the case of phage λ the double-stranded DNA that entered the cell can be directly integrated into the double-stranded DNA of the chromosome. Once integrated, the phage DNA in a bacterium is called a **prophage**. While it exists as a prophage, this type of viral reproductive cycle is called the **lysogenic cycle**. As discussed later, new phages are not made during the lysogenic cycle and the host cell is not destroyed. On occasion a prophage can be excised from the bacterial chromosome and proceed to step (4).

How can an RNA virus integrate its genome into the host cell's DNA? For this to occur, the viral genome must be copied into DNA. HIV accomplishes this by means of a viral enzyme called **reverse transcriptase**, which is carried within the capsid and released into the host cell, along with the viral RNA. Reverse transcriptase uses the viral RNA strand to make a complementary copy of DNA, and it then uses the DNA strand as a template to make double-stranded viral DNA. This process is called reverse transcription because it is the reverse of the usual transcription process, in which a DNA strand is used to make a complementary strand of RNA. The viral double-stranded DNA enters the host cell nucleus and is inserted into a host chromosome via integrase. Once integrated, the viral DNA in a eukaryotic cell is called a **provirus**. Viruses that follow this mechanism are called **retroviruses**.

Step 4: Synthesis of Viral Components The production of new viruses by a host cell involves the replication of the viral genome and the synthesis of capsid proteins that make up the viral coat. In the case of a bacteriophage that has been integrated into the host chromosome, the prophage must be excised as described in step (3) before synthesis of new viral components can occur. An enzyme called excisionase is required for this process. Following excision, host cell enzymes make many copies of the phage DNA and transcribe the genes within these copies into mRNA. Host cell ribosomes translate this viral

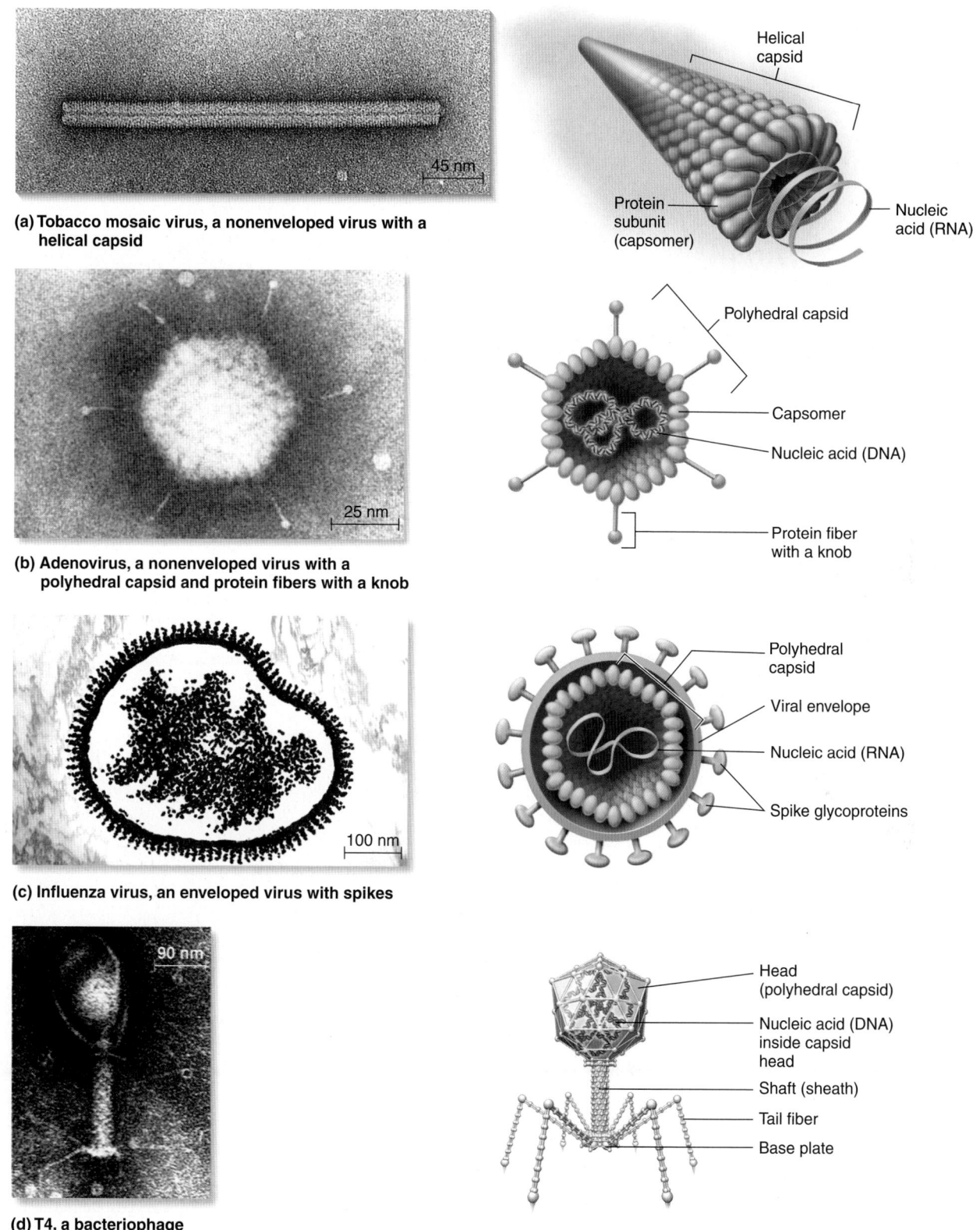

(a) Tobacco mosaic virus, a nonenveloped virus with a helical capsid

Helical capsid

Protein subunit (capsomer)

Nucleic acid (RNA)

(b) Adenovirus, a nonenveloped virus with a polyhedral capsid and protein fibers with a knob

Polyhedral capsid

Capsomer

Nucleic acid (DNA)

Protein fiber with a knob

(c) Influenza virus, an enveloped virus with spikes

Polyhedral capsid

Viral envelope

Nucleic acid (RNA)

Spike glycoproteins

(d) T4, a bacteriophage

Head (polyhedral capsid)

Nucleic acid (DNA) inside capsid head

Shaft (sheath)

Tail fiber

Base plate

Figure 16.3 **Variations in the structure of viruses.** All viruses contain nucleic acid (DNA or RNA) surrounded by a protein capsid. They may or may not have an outer envelope surrounding the capsid. **(a)** Tobacco mosaic virus has a capsid made of 2,130 identical protein subunits, helically arranged around a strand of RNA. **(b)** Adenoviruses have polyhedral capsids containing fibre proteins with a knob. **(c)** Many animal viruses, including the influenza virus, have an envelope composed of a lipid bilayer and spike glycoproteins. The lipid bilayer is obtained from the host cell when the virus buds from the plasma membrane. **(d)** Some bacteriophages, such as T4, have capsids with accessory structures that facilitate invasion of a bacterial cell.

Concept check: *What features vary among different types of viruses?*

1 Attachment:
The phage binds specifically to proteins in the outer bacterial cell membrane.

(a) Reproductive cycle of phage λ

2 Entry:
The phage injects its DNA into the bacterial cytoplasm.

3 Integration:
Phage DNA may integrate into the bacterial chromosome via integrase. The host cell carrying a prophage may then undergo repeated divisions, which is called the lysogenic cycle. To end the lysogenic cycle and switch to the lytic cycle, the phage DNA is excised. Alternatively, the reproductive cycle may completely skip the lysogenic cycle and proceed directly to step 4.

1 Attachment:
Spike glycoproteins bind to receptors on the host cell plasma membrane.

(b) Reproductive cycle of HIV

2 Entry:
The viral envelope fuses with the host cell membrane, releasing the capsid and its contents into the cytosol. Some capsid proteins are removed by cellular enzymes, a process called uncoating. This releases the RNA and reverse transcriptase into the cytosol.

3 Integration:
Viral RNA is reverse transcribed into double-stranded DNA and then integrated into the host cell chromosome, via integrase. The integrated provirus may remain latent for a long period of time.

Figure 16.4 Comparison of the steps of two viral reproductive cycles.   (a) The reproductive cycle of phage λ, a bacteriophage with a double-stranded DNA genome. (b) The reproductive cycle of HIV, an enveloped animal virus with a single-stranded RNA genome.

BioConnections: *Look back at Figure 4.15. How does the release of HIV resemble exocytosis?*

4 **Synthesis of viral components:**
In the lytic cycle, phage DNA directs the synthesis of viral components. During this process, the phage DNA circularizes, and the host chromosomal DNA is degraded.

5 **Viral assembly:**
Phage components are assembled with the help of noncapsid proteins to make many new phages.

6 **Release:**
The viral enzyme called lysozyme causes cell lysis, and new phages are released from the broken cell.

Capsid proteins

Spike glycoproteins

Reverse transcriptase

Viral RNA

4 **Synthesis of viral components:**
Proviral DNA directs the synthesis of viral components.

5 **Viral assembly:**
Capsid proteins enclose 2 RNA molecules and 2 molecules of reverse transcriptase. Capsid assembles with spike glycoproteins during budding.

6 **Release:**
Virus buds from the plasma membrane of the host cell and is released. The new viral envelope is derived from a portion of the host cell plasma membrane.

mRNA into viral proteins. The expression of phage genes leads to the degradation of the host chromosomal DNA.

In the case of HIV the DNA provirus is not excised from the host chromosome. Instead, it is transcribed in the nucleus to produce many copies of viral RNA. These viral RNA molecules enter the cytosol, where they are used to make viral proteins and serve as the genome for new viral particles.

Step 5: Viral Assembly   After all the necessary components have been synthesized, they must be assembled into new viruses. Some viruses with a simple structure self-assemble, meaning that viral components made by the host cell spontaneously bind to each other to form a complete virus particle. An example of a self-assembling virus is TMV, which we examined earlier (see Figure 16.3a). TMV capsid proteins assemble around a TMV RNA molecule, which becomes trapped inside the hollow capsid.

Other viruses, including the two shown in Figure 16.4, have more complicated structures that do not self-assemble. The correct assembly of phage λ requires the help of noncapsid proteins not found in the completed phage particle. Some of these noncapsid proteins function as enzymes that modify capsid proteins, while others serve as scaffolding for the assembly of the capsid.

The assembly of an HIV virus occurs in two stages. First, capsid proteins assemble around two molecules of HIV RNA and two molecules of reverse transcriptase. Next, the newly formed capsid acquires its outer envelope in a budding process. This second phase of assembly occurs during step (6), as the virus is released from the cell.

Step 6: Release   The final stage of a viral reproductive cycle is the release of new viruses from the host cell. The release of bacteriophages is a dramatic event. Because bacteria are surrounded by a rigid cell wall, the phages must burst, or lyse, their host cell to escape. After the phages have been assembled, a phage-encoded enzyme called lysozyme digests the bacterial cell wall, causing the cell to burst. Lysis releases many new phages into the environment, where they can infect other bacteria and begin the cycle again. Collectively, steps (1), (2), (4), (5), and (6) are called the **lytic cycle** because they lead to cell lysis.

The release of enveloped viruses from an animal cell is far less dramatic. This type of virus escapes by a mechanism called budding that does not lyse the cell. In the case of HIV a newly assembled virus particle associates with a portion of the plasma membrane containing HIV spike glycoproteins. The membrane enfolds the viral capsid and eventually buds from the surface of the cell. This is how the virus acquires its envelope, which is a piece of host cell membrane studded with viral glycoproteins.

Latency in Bacteriophages   As you saw in step (3), viruses can integrate their genomes into a host chromosome. In some cases the prophage or provirus may remain inactive, or **latent**,

for a long time. Most of the viral genes are silent during latency, and the viral reproductive cycle does not progress to step (4).

Latency in bacteriophages is also called lysogeny. When this occurs, both the prophage and its host cell are said to be lysogenic. When a lysogenic bacterium prepares to divide, it copies the prophage DNA along with its own, so each daughter cell inherits a copy of the prophage. A prophage can be replicated repeatedly in this way without killing the host cell or producing new phage particles. As mentioned earlier, this is called the lysogenic cycle.

Bacteriophages that can alternate between lysogenic and lytic cycles are called **temperate phages** (**Figure 16.5**). Phage λ is an example of a temperate phage. On infection it can either enter the lysogenic cycle or proceed directly to the lytic cycle. Other phages, called **virulent phages**, have only lytic cycles. The genome of a virulent phage is not capable of integration into a host chromosome. Phage T2, which we examined in Chapter 10, is a virulent phage that infects *E. coli*. Unlike phage λ, which can coexist harmlessly with *E. coli*, T2 always lyses the infected cell.

For temperate phages, such as λ, environmental conditions influence whether or not viral DNA is integrated into a host chromosome and how long the virus remains in the lysogenic cycle. If nutrients are readily available, phage λ usually proceeds directly to the lytic cycle after its DNA enters the cell. Alternatively, if nutrients are in short supply, the lysogenic cycle is often favoured because sufficient material may not be available to make new viruses. If more nutrients become available later, this may cause the prophage to become activated. At this point the viral reproductive cycle will switch to the lytic cycle, and new viruses will be made, assembled, and released.

Latency in Human Viruses   Latency among human viruses can occur in two different ways. For HIV, latency occurs because the virus has integrated into the host genome and remained dormant for a long time. The genomes of other viruses can exist as an **episome**—a genetic element that can replicate independently of the chromosomal DNA but also can occasionally integrate into chromosomal DNA. Examples of viral genomes that can exist as episomes include different types of herpesviruses that cause cold sores (herpes simplex type I), genital herpes (herpes simplex type II), and chickenpox (varicella zoster). A person infected with a type of herpesvirus may have periodic outbreaks of disease symptoms when the virus switches from the latent episomal form to the active form that produces new virus particles.

As an example, consider the herpesvirus called varicella zoster. The initial infection by this virus causes chickenpox, after which the virus can remain latent for many years as an episome. The disease called shingles occurs when varicella zoster switches from the latent state and starts making new virus particles. Shingles begins as a painful rash that eventually erupts into blisters. The blisters follow the path of the neurons that carry the latent varicella zoster virus. The blisters often

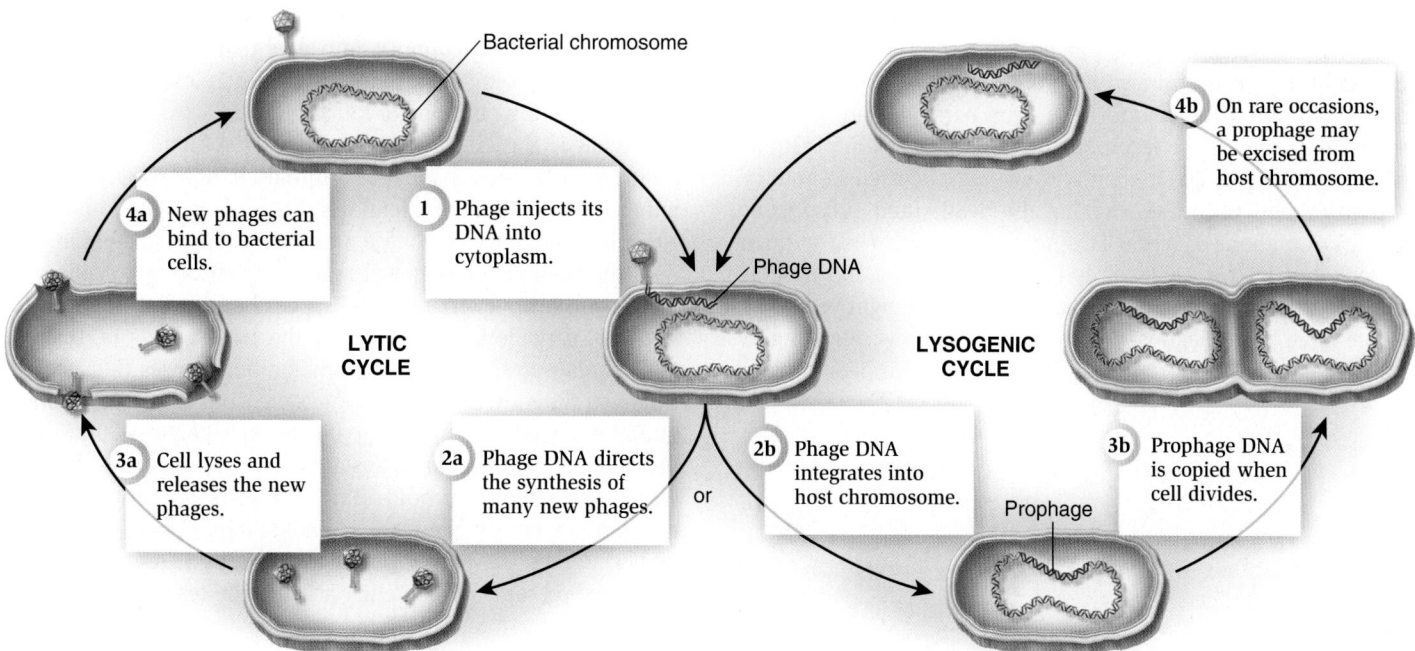

Figure 16.5 **Lytic and lysogenic cycles of bacteriophages.** Some phages, such as phage λ, may follow either a lytic or a lysogenic reproductive cycle. During the lytic cycle new phages are made and the bacterial cell is destroyed. During the lysogenic cycle the integrated phage DNA, or prophage, is replicated along with the DNA of the host cell. Environmental conditions influence how long the phage remains in the lysogenic cycle. Other phages, such as T2, follow only lytic cycles.

Concept check: *From the perspective of the virus, what are the primary advantages of the lytic and lysogenic cycles?*

form a ring around the back of the patient's body. The disease is called shingles because the blisters line up like the shingles on a house.

Emerging Viruses, Such as H5N1, Have Arisen Recently and Can Rapidly Spread Through a Population

A primary reason researchers are interested in viral reproductive cycles is the ability of many viruses to cause diseases in humans and other hosts. Some examples of disease-causing viruses in humans were presented in Figure 16.2. New viruses, called **emerging viruses**, have arisen recently and their likelihood of causing infection is greatly increasing. Such viruses often cause public alarm and can lead to a significant loss of human life.

Severe acute respiratory syndrome (SARS) is an emerging virus that causes a potentially life-threatening illness. Shortly after an epidemic occurred in 2002–2003, a consortium of researchers at the University of British Columbia and the National Microbiology Laboratory in Winnipeg mapped and sequenced the viral genome, providing clues on the number of genes and their encoded proteins, and enabling comparisons to other genomes by using bioinformatics tools (which are discussed more fully in Chapter 19). The SARS virus is a member

of the coronavirus group and appears to have originated in the horseshoe bat, infected a cat-like animal called a civet, and mutated to expand its host range to include humans.

Influenza A viruses are a group of viruses that cause a variety of symptoms in humans that most of us associate with the seasonal "flu." These include fever and chills, sore throat, coughing, fatigue, headache, and general malaise. In some cases the infected individual experiences mild symptoms or even no symptoms. Influenza viruses can be classified according to the properties of their hemagglutinin (H) and neuaminidase (N) glycoproteins. There are 16 known hemagglutinin subtypes and 9 known neuraminidase subtypes. For example, the H1N1 strain that caused the 1918 Spanish flu pandemic (which is estimated to have killed between 40 million and 100 million people) and the 2009 swine flu is a combination of the H1 hemagglutinin and the N1 neuraminidase.

Do the terms "bird flu" or "swine flu," used by the media, imply that the influenza came from birds or pigs? The answer is yes. Most influenza viruses have a fairly broad host range, infecting both avian and mammalian species. The viral genome consists of eight single-stranded RNA molecules that can encode 11 different viral proteins. Viral coat proteins can be **antigens**—molecules that stimulate the immune system to produce antibodies. Simultaneous infection of a cell by two different influenza viruses leads to reassortment of the viral RNAs, creating a unique viral strain (**Figure 16.6**). This phenomenon is known as antigenic shift. For example, if a cell is infected with an H5N2 virus and also with an H1N1 virus, the reassortment of the viral RNAs into new virus particles can generate both H5N1 and H1N2 recombinant viruses. The H5N1 strain gained notoriety in 2004 when an outbreak occurred in poultry in many Asian countries, causing the death (and subsequent culling) of millions of birds. This new strain is believed to have passed directly from wild birds to poultry flocks, and it soon acquired the ability to infect humans. In the past eight years 583 people have been diagnosed with H5N1 infections, resulting in 344 deaths, a 59% mortality rate. Many of these people were

in good health before their infection. Should the H5N1 virus further mutate, for example, in a way that makes it more easily transmissible or infectious, a global pandemic could occur, potentially killing billions of humans.

What is the effect of random mutations and how do they occur? You learned in Chapter 13 that changes to DNA can be induced by a variety of chemicals, by ionizing radiation, and as a result of the reactivity of the nitrogenous bases in combination with the millions of chemical reactions that occur in cells on a daily basis. However, most cells possess efficient DNA repair systems, capable of using one of the two strands of DNA as the template to repair the mutated strand. Viruses that possess single-stranded RNA genomes must use both host enzymes and virally encoded enzymes to replicate their genomes and make the mRNAs that then are translated into viral proteins. Because there is no effective proofreading system (see Chapter 10) and no complementary template strand to repair new mutations, viral genomes are highly prone to mutating. Thus, the H and N surface proteins, which elicit an immune response to combat the infection, can rapidly change and become unrecognizable to the immune system. This phenomenon is known as antigenic drift. Both antigenic drift and antigenic shift are responsible for the constant changes that alter the influenza genome, its host range, and its transmissibility; these are some of the reasons that medical science has not created a vaccine for the common cold or for influenza. The seasonal flu shot is a cocktail of three influenza viruses that induce an immune response, and the composition of the mixture is a best guess based on the prevalence of influenza subtypes in a particular year.

New strains of influenza virus, such as H1N1, arise fairly regularly because of new mutations. In Canada, despite vaccination attempts to minimize the spread of influenza, more than 20,000 people are hospitalized with the disease each year, and 4,000 die. Medical professionals are very concerned that the H5N1 bird flu will mutate and increase its transmissability, resulting in a global pandemic that would cause widespread human mortality and severe health care and economic problems. Recently, several groups of scientists reported the creation of new strains of H5N1 supervirus in the laboratory. Superficially, such research might seem unwise or even unethical, but an increased knowledge of specific mutations that affect the viral life cycle and infection are critical to identifying and tracking potential pandemic strains and may enable the production of an effective vaccine against them.

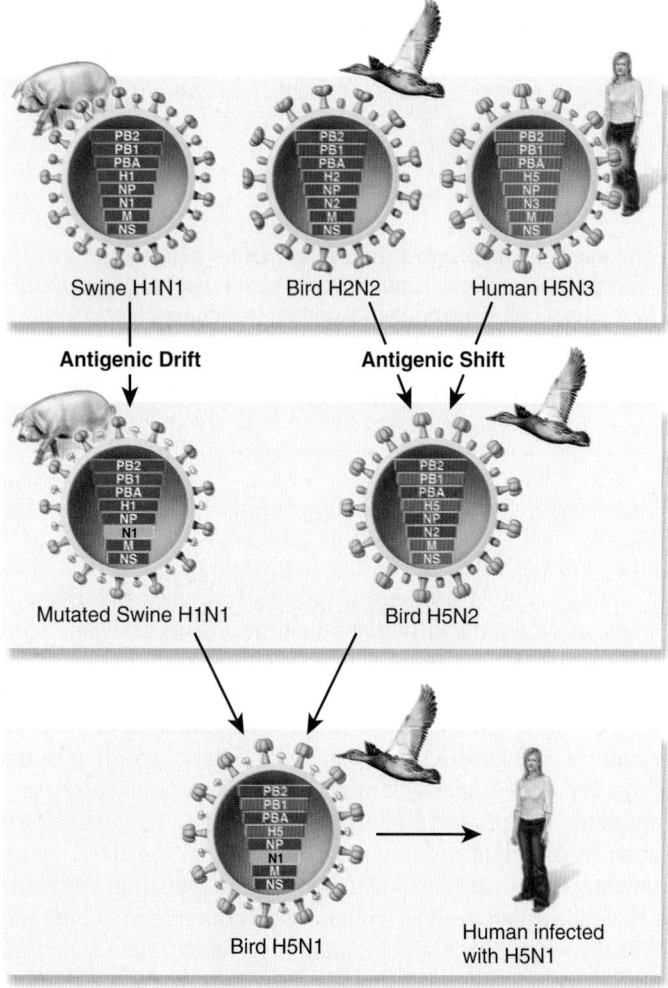

Figure 16.6 Antigenic shift and antigenic drift in influenza viruses. Humans, birds, and pigs are common hosts for many influenza viruses. The genome consists of eight RNA molecules (represented by the coloured rectangles within the viral particle), two of which (H and N) encode surface proteins. Infection of a common host by two different viruses can lead to the production of recombinant viruses, a phenomenon known as antigenic shift. Mutations within the viral genome segments can lead to changes in the protein component, a phenomenon known as antigenic drift. A generic pathway is shown that illustrates the possible evolution of the deadly H5N1 bird flu virus.

Several Hypotheses Have Been Proposed to Explain the Origin of Viruses

Because viruses are such small particles, we have no fossil record of their evolution, and researchers must rely on analyses of modern viruses to develop hypotheses about their origin. Viral genomes follow the same rules of gene expression as the genomes of their host cells. Viral genes have promoter sequences that are similar to those of their host cells, and the translation of viral proteins relies on the genetic code. Viruses depend entirely on host cells for their proliferation. No known virus makes its own ribosomes or generates the energy it requires to make new viruses. Therefore, many biologists have argued that cells must have evolved before viruses.

How did viruses come into existence? A common hypothesis for the origin of viruses is they evolved from macromolecules inside living cells. The precursors of the first viruses may have been plasmids—small, circular DNA molecules that exist independently of chromosomal DNA. (Plasmids are described later in this chapter.) Biologists have hypothesized that such DNA molecules may have acquired genes that code for proteins that facilitate their own replication. Though many biologists favour the idea that viruses originated from primitive plasmids or other chromosomal elements, some have suggested they are an example of regressive evolution—the reduction of a trait or traits over time. This hypothesis proposes that viruses are degenerate cells that have retained the minimal genetic information essential for reproduction.

A new and interesting hypothesis is that viruses did not evolve from living cells but instead evolved in parallel with cellular organisms. As we discuss in Chapter 20, the precursors of cellular DNA genomes may have been RNA molecules that could replicate independently of cells. This stage of evolution, termed the RNA world, could have involved the parallel evolution of both viruses and cellular organisms.

16.2 VIROIDS AND PRIONS

Learning Outcomes:

1. Distinguish between a viroid and a virus.
2. Describe the structure of prions, and explain how they cause disease.

Some nonliving infectious agents are even simpler then viruses. Viroids are composed solely of RNA and prions are composed solely of protein. In this section we will begin by examining viroids, infectious agents that cause diseases in plants. Next, we will discuss infectious proteins known as prions, which cause devastating neurological diseases in humans and other mammals. Unlike other agents of infection, prions have no genes and cannot be copied by the replication machinery of a cell. Instead, they increase their numbers by inducing changes in other protein molecules within living cells.

Viroids Are RNA Particles That Infect Plant Cells

In 1971 Theodor Diener discovered that the agent of potato spindle tuber disease is a small RNA molecule devoid of any protein. He coined the term **viroid** for this newly discovered infectious particle. Viroids are composed solely of a single-stranded circular RNA molecule that is a few hundred nucleotides long.

Viroids infect plant cells, where they depend entirely on host enzymes for their replication. Some viroids are replicated in the host cell nucleus, others in the chloroplast. In contrast

to viral genomes the RNA genomes of viroids do not code for any proteins. How do viroids affect plant cells? The RNA of some viroids is known to possess ribozyme activity, and some researchers think this activity can damage plants by interfering with the function of host cell molecules. However, the mechanism by which viroids induce disease is not well understood.

Since Diener's initial discovery many more viroids have been characterized as the agents of diseases affecting many economically important plants, including potato, tomato, cucumber, orange, coconut, grape, avocado, peach, apple, pear, and plum (**Figure 16.7**). Some viroids have devastating effects, as illustrated by the case of the coconut cadang-cadang viroid, which has killed more than 20 million coconut trees in Southeast Asia. Other viroids produce less severe damage, causing necrosis on leaves; shortening of stems; bark cracking; and delays in foliation, flowering, and fruit ripening. A few viroids induce mild symptoms or no symptoms at all.

Prions Are Infectious Proteins That Cause Neurodegenerative Diseases

Before we end our discussion of nonliving infectious particles, let's consider an unusual mechanism in which agents known as **prions** cause a group of rare, fatal brain diseases affecting humans and other mammals. Until the 1980s, biologists thought that any infectious agent, whether living or nonliving, must have genetic material. It seemed logical that genetic material is needed to store the information to create new infectious particles.

In the 1960s British researchers Tikvah Alper and John Stanley Griffith discovered that preparations from animals with certain neurodegenerative diseases remained infectious even after exposure to radiation that would destroy any DNA or RNA. The researchers suggested that the infectious agent was a

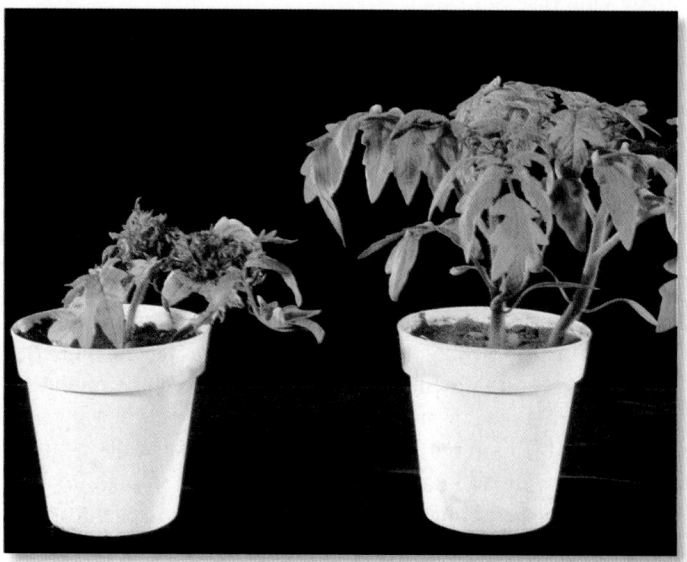

Figure 16.7 Effects of the tomato apical stunt viroid.
The plant on the left is infected; the one on the right is healthy.

protein. Furthermore, they speculated that the protein usually preferred one folding pattern, but it could sometimes misfold and then catalyze other proteins to misfold, creating a chain reaction of misfolding. In the early 1970s Stanley Prusiner, moved by the death of a patient from such a neurodegenerative disease, began to search for the causative agent. In 1982 Prusiner isolated a disease-causing particle composed entirely of protein, which he called a prion. The term was based on his characterization of the particle as a proteinaceous infectious agent. Further experiments carried out by Prusiner and others conclusively demonstrated the particle's infectious character. In 1997 Prusiner was awarded the Nobel Prize in Medicine for his work on prions.

Prion diseases arise from the ability of the prion protein to induce abnormal folding in normal protein molecules (**Figure 16.8**). The prion protein exists in a disease-causing conformation designated PrP^{Sc}. The superscript Sc refers to scrapie, an example of a prion disease. A normal conformation of this same protein, which does not cause disease, is termed PrP^C. The superscript C stands for cellular. The normal protein is encoded by an individual's genome, and the protein is expressed at low levels in certain types of neurons.

How does someone contract a prion disease? A healthy person can acquire the abnormal protein by eating meat or organs of an animal with the disease. Unlike most other proteins in the diet, the prion protein is not digested in the stomach and small intestine and is absorbed into the bloodstream. After being taken up by nerve cells, the prion protein gradually converts the cell's normal proteins to the abnormal conformation. As a prion disease progresses, the PrP^{Sc} proteins are deposited as dense aggregates that form tough fibrils in the cells of the brain and peripheral nervous tissues, causing the disease symptoms. Some of the abnormal prion proteins are also excreted from infected cells, where they travel through the bloodstream. In this way, a prion disease can spread through the body like many viral diseases.

Prions are now known to cause several types of fatal neurodegenerative diseases affecting humans, livestock, and wildlife (**Table 16.2**). As a group, prion diseases are termed transmissible spongiform encephalopathies (TSE). The postmortem examination of the brains of affected individuals reveals a substantial destruction of brain tissue. The brain has a spongy appearance. Most prion diseases progress fairly slowly. Over several months to a few years, symptoms proceed from a loss of motor control to dementia, paralysis, wasting, and eventually death. These symptoms are correlated with an increase in the level of prion protein in the neurons of infected individuals. No current treatment can halt the progression of any of the TSEs. For this reason great public alarm occurs when an outbreak of a TSE is reported. For example, in May 2003 a single report of bovine spongiform encephalitis, also known as mad cow disease, was confirmed in Alberta, leading several countries to restrict the import of Canadian beef. The government of Canada responded by funding PrioNet Canada, whose mission is to promote basic, applied, and social science research to better understand prion diseases.

1. A prion protein in the PrP^{Sc} conformation enters the cell and binds to a normal protein in the PrP^C conformation.

2. The prion protein in the PrP^{Sc} conformation converts a PrP^C protein into a PrP^{Sc} protein.

Original PrP^{Sc} molecule

PrP^{Sc} converted from PrP^C

3. The two PrP^{Sc} proteins bind to two PrP^C proteins (these will be converted to PrP^{Sc}).

4. Over time, many PrP^C proteins will be converted to PrP^{Sc} proteins, and fibrils will form.

Fibril

Figure 16.8 **A proposed molecular mechanism of prion diseases.** A healthy neuron normally contains only the PrP^C conformation of the prion protein. The abnormal PrP^{Sc} conformation catalyzes the conversion of PrP^C proteins into PrP^{Sc} proteins. Over time the amount of PrP^{Sc} proteins reaches high levels, thereby causing the symptoms of prion diseases.

 Principle: *Structure determines function. The two conformations of prion proteins have different structures. The abnormal conformation has the functional ability to convert normal prion proteins to the abnormal conformation.*

Table 16.2	Examples of Neurodegenerative Diseases Caused by Infectious Prions
Disease	**Description**
Kuru	A human disease that was once common in certain native tribes of New Guinea. It begins with a loss of coordination, usually followed by dementia. Infection was spread by ritual cannibalism, a practice that ended in 1958.
Scrapie	A disease of sheep and pigs characterized by intense itching in which the animals tend to scrape themselves against trees or other objects. Neurodegeneration follows.
Mad cow disease	A disease of cows that begins with changes in posture and temperament, followed by loss of coordination and then neurodegeneration.
Chronic wasting disease	A disease of deer (genus *Odocoileus*) and Rocky Mountain elk (*Cervus elaphus nelsoni*). A consistent symptom is weight loss over time. The disease is progressive and fatal.

Figure 16.9 Nucleoids within the bacterium *Bacillus subtilis.* In the light micrograph shown here, the nucleoids are fluorescently labelled and seen as bright, oval-shaped regions within the bacterial cytoplasm. Two or more nucleoids are usually found within each cell.

Concept check: *How many nucleoid regions are in the bacterial cell to the far right?*

16.3 GENETIC PROPERTIES OF BACTERIA

Learning Outcomes:

1. Outline the key features of a bacterial chromosome.
2. Describe the two processes that compact the bacterial chromosome.
3. Outline the structure and functions of plasmids.
4. Diagram the process of cell division in bacteria.

Bacteria are usually unicellular organisms. Individual cells can exist as single units or remain associated with each other after cell division, forming pairs, chains, or clumps. Bacteria are widespread on Earth, and numerous species are known to cause various types of infectious diseases. We begin this section by exploring the structure and replication of the bacterial genome and the organization of DNA sequences along a bacterial chromosome. We then examine how the chromosome is compacted to fit inside a bacterium and how it is transmitted during asexual reproduction.

Bacteria Typically Have Circular Chromosomes That Carry a Few Thousand Genes

The genes of bacteria are found within structures known as bacterial chromosomes. Although a bacterial cell usually has a single type of chromosome, it can have more than one copy of that chromosome. The number of copies depends on the bacterial species and on growth conditions, but a bacterium typically has one to four identical chromosomes. Each bacterial chromosome is tightly packed within a distinct **nucleoid** region of the cell (**Figure 16.9**). Unlike the eukaryotic nucleus, the bacterial nucleoid is not a separate cellular compartment bounded by a membrane, and the DNA in the nucleoid is in direct contact with the cytoplasm of the cell.

Like eukaryotic chromosomes, bacterial chromosomes contain molecules of double-stranded DNA, along with many different proteins. Unlike eukaryotic chromosomes, however, bacterial chromosomes are usually circular and tend to be much shorter, typically only a few million base pairs (bp) long. For example, the chromosome of *Escherichia coli* has approximately 4.6 million bp, and the *Hemophilus influenzae* chromosome has roughly 1.8 million bp. By comparison, an average eukaryotic chromosome may be 100 million bp long.

A typical bacterial chromosome contains a few thousand unique genes that are found throughout the chromosome. Structural gene sequences, nucleotide sequences that encode proteins, account for the largest part of bacterial DNA. Other nucleotide sequences in the chromosome influence DNA replication, gene expression, and chromosome structure. One of these sequences is the origin of replication, which is a few hundred bp long. Bacterial chromosomes have a single origin of replication that functions as an initiation site for the assembly of several proteins that are required for DNA replication (refer back to Figure 10.14a).

The Formation of Chromosomal Loops and DNA Supercoiling Makes the Bacterial Chromosome Compact

Bacterial cells are much smaller than most eukaryotic cells (refer back to Figure 4.1). *E. coli* cells, for example, are approximately 1 μm wide and 2 μm long. To fit within a bacterial cell, the DNA of a typical bacterial chromosome must be compacted about 1,000-fold. How does this occur? The

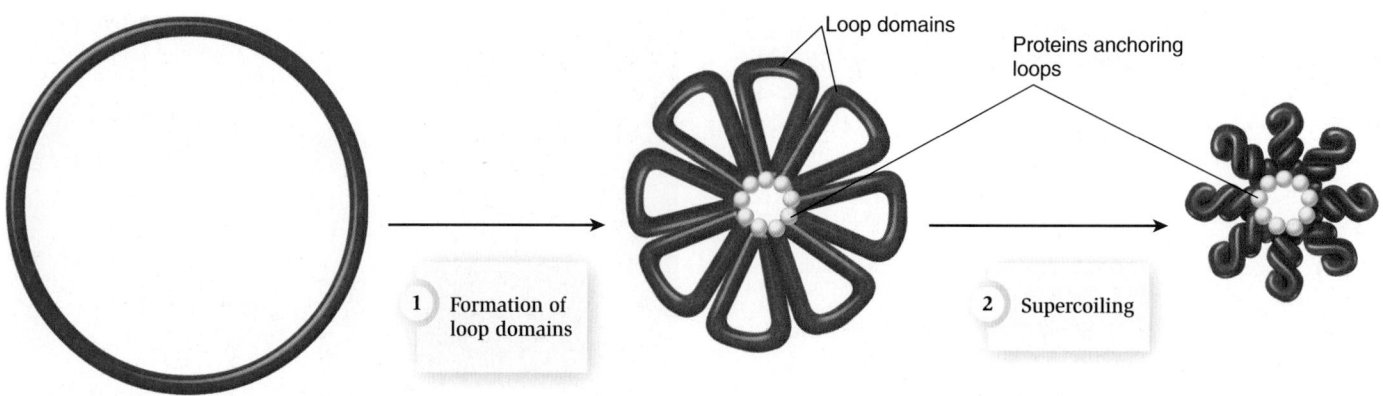

Circular chromosomal DNA   Looped chromosomal DNA with associated proteins   Supercoiled and looped DNA

Figure 16.10 **The compaction of a bacterial chromosome.**   As a way to compact the large, circular chromosome, segments are organized into smaller loop domains by binding to proteins at the bases of the loops. These loops are made more compact by DNA supercoiling.

Concept check: *Describe how the loop domains are held in place.*

compaction process, shown in **Figure 16.10**, occurs through two processes: by the formation of loops and by the supercoiling of the looped DNA.

Unlike eukaryotic DNA, bacterial DNA is not wound around histone proteins to form nucleosomes. However, the binding of proteins to bacterial DNA is important in the formation of **loop domains**—chromosomal segments that are folded into loops. As shown in Figure 16.10, DNA-binding proteins anchor the bases of the loops in place. The number of loops varies according to the size of a bacterial chromosome and the species. The *E. coli* chromosome has 50 to 100 loop domains, each with about 40,000 to 80,000 bp. This looping compacts the circular chromosome about 10-fold. A similar process of loop-domain formation occurs in eukaryotic chromatin compaction, which was described in Chapter 14.

DNA **supercoiling** is a second important way of compacting the bacterial chromosome. Because DNA is a long, thin molecule, twisting can dramatically change its conformation. This compaction is similar to what happens to a rubber band if you twist it in one direction. Because the two strands of DNA already coil around each other, the formation of additional coils through twisting is referred to as supercoiling. Bacterial enzymes called topoisomerases twist the DNA and control the degree of DNA supercoiling.

Plasmids Are Small Pieces of Extrachromosomal DNA

In addition to chromosomal DNA, bacterial cells commonly contain **plasmids**, small, circular pieces of DNA that exist separately from the bacterial chromosome (**Figure 16.11**). Plasmids occur naturally in many strains of bacteria and in a few types of eukaryotic cells, such as yeast. The smallest plasmids consist

of just a few thousand base pairs and carry only a gene or two. The largest are in the range of 100,000 to 500,000 bp and carry several dozen or even hundreds of genes. A plasmid has its own origin of replication that allows it to be replicated independently of the bacterial chromosome. The DNA sequence of the origin of replication influences how many copies of the plasmid are found within a cell. Some origins are said to be very strong because they result in many copies of the plasmid, perhaps as many as 100 per cell. Other origins of replication have sequences that are much weaker, so the number of copies is relatively low, such as one or two per cell.

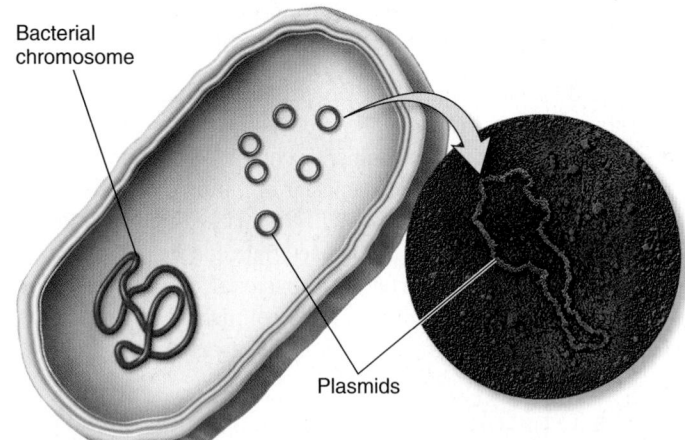

Figure 16.11 **Plasmids in a bacterial cell.**   Plasmids are small, circular DNA molecules that exist independently of the bacterial chromosome.

Concept check: *Describe the similarities and differences between a bacterial chromosome and a plasmid.*

Why do bacteria have plasmids? Certain genes within a plasmid usually provide some type of growth advantage to the cell or aid in survival under certain conditions. By studying plasmids in many different species, researchers have discovered that most plasmids fall into five different categories:

1. Resistance plasmids, also known as R factors, contain genes that confer resistance against antibiotics and other types of toxins.
2. Degradative plasmids carry genes that enable the bacterium to digest and use an unusual substance. For example, a degradative plasmid may carry genes that allow a bacterium to digest an organic solvent, such as toluene.
3. Col-plasmids contain genes that encode colicins, which are proteins that kill other bacteria.
4. Virulence plasmids carry genes that turn a bacterium into a pathogenic strain.
5. Fertility plasmids, also known as F factors, allow bacteria to mate, a topic described later in this chapter.

On occasion a plasmid may integrate into the bacterial chromosome. Plasmids that can integrate or remain independent of the chromosome are also termed episomes.

Most Bacteria Reproduce Asexually by Binary Fission

Thus far, we have considered the genetic material of bacteria and how the bacterial chromosome is compacted to fit inside the cell. Let's now turn our attention to the process of cell division. The capacity of bacteria to divide is astounding. The cells of some species, such as *E. coli*, can divide every 20–30 minutes. When placed on a solid growth medium in a Petri dish, an *E. coli* cell and its daughter cells will undergo repeated cellular divisions and form a clone of genetically identical cells called a **bacterial colony** (**Figure 16.12**). Starting with a single cell that is invisible to the naked eye, a visible bacterial colony containing 10 million to 100 million cells will form in less than a day!

As described in Chapter 14, the division of eukaryotic cells requires a sorting process called mitosis, because eukaryotic chromosomes occur in sets and each daughter cell must receive the correct number and types of chromosomes. By comparison a bacterial cell usually has only a single type of chromosome. Cell division occurs by a much simpler process called **binary fission**. **Figure 16.13** shows this process for a cell with a single chromosome. Before it divides, the cell replicates its DNA. This produces two identical copies of the chromosome. Next, the cell's plasma membrane is drawn inward and deposits new cell wall material, separating the two daughter cells. Each daughter cell receives one copy of the original chromosome. Therefore, except when a mutation occurs, each daughter cell contains an identical copy of the mother cell's genetic material. Like other

Figure 16.12 Growth of a bacterial colony. Through successive cell divisions, a single bacterial cell of *E. coli* forms a genetically identical group of cells called a bacterial colony.

Concept check: *Let's suppose a bacterial strain divides every 30 minutes. If a single cell is placed on a plate, how many cells will be in the colony after 16 hours?*

types of asexual reproduction, binary fission does not involve genetic contributions from two different parents.

If a bacterial cell contains plasmids, these will replicate independently of the bacterial chromosome. During binary fission, the plasmids are distributed to daughter cells so that each daughter cell usually receives one or more copies of the plasmid.

Mother cell

Plasma membrane — Cell wall

Chromosome

1 Bacterial chromosome replicates.

2 Cell begins to divide.

3 A cell wall is formed between the two cells.

4 Cell division is completed.

Two daughter cells

Figure 16.13 Bacterial cell division. Bacteria reproduce by a type of cell division called binary fission. Before a bacterium divides, the bacterial chromosome is replicated to produce two identical copies. These two copies segregate from each other during cell division, with one copy going to each daughter cell.

 Principle: *Living organisms grow, develop, and reproduce. After cell division a bacterial cell increases in size.*

16.4 GENE TRANSFER BETWEEN BACTERIA

Learning Outcomes:

1. Compare and contrast the three forms of gene transfer in bacteria: conjugation, transformation, and transduction.
2. Describe the experiments of Lederberg and Tatum and how they led to the discovery of conjugation.
3. Define the process of horizontal gene transfer.

Even though bacteria reproduce asexually, they exhibit a great deal of genetic diversity. Within a given bacterial species, the term **strain** refers to a lineage that has genetic differences compared with another strain. For example, one strain of *E. coli* may be resistant to an antibiotic, whereas another strain may be sensitive to the same antibiotic.

How does genetic diversity arise in an asexual species? It comes primarily from two sources. First, mutations can occur that alter the bacterial genome and affect the traits of bacterial cells. Second, diversity can arise by gene transfer, also called **genetic transfer**, in which genetic material is transferred from one bacterial cell to another. Through gene transfer, an advantageous gene that arises in one bacterium can be spread to new strains and even to other species. For example, an antibiotic-resistance gene may be transferred from a resistant strain to a sensitive strain.

Gene transfer occurs in three different ways: conjugation, transformation, and transduction (**Table 16.3**). **Conjugation** involves a direct physical interaction between two bacterial

Table 16.3	**Three Mechanisms of Gene Transfer Found in Bacteria**
Mechanism	**Description**
Conjugation: Donor cell Recipient cell 	Requires direct contact between a donor and a recipient cell. The donor cell transfers a strand of DNA to the recipient. In the example shown here, DNA from a plasmid is transferred to the recipient cell. Both donor and recipient cells end up with a plasmid.
Transformation: Donor cell Recipient cell (dead)	When a bacterial cell dies, it can release a fragment of its DNA into the environment. This DNA fragment is taken up by a recipient cell, which incorporates the DNA into its chromosome.
Transduction: Donor cell Recipient cell (infected by a virus) 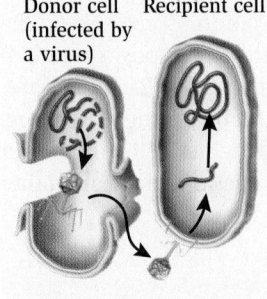	When a virus infects a donor cell, it may incorporate a fragment of bacterial chromosomal DNA into a newly made virus particle. The virus then transfers this fragment of DNA to a recipient cell.

FEATURE INVESTIGATION

Lederberg and Tatum's Work with *E. coli* Demonstrated Gene Transfer Between Bacteria and Led to the Discovery of Conjugation

In 1946 and 1947 Joshua Lederberg and Edward Tatum carried out the first experiments that clearly demonstrated gene transfer from one bacterial strain to another (**Figure 16.14**). The researchers studied strains of *E. coli* that had different nutritional requirements for growth. They designated one strain

$met^+bio^+thr^+pro^+$ because its growth required that the amino acid methionine (met) and the vitamin biotin (bio) be added to the growth medium. This strain did not require the amino acids threonine (thr) or proline (pro) for growth. Another strain, designated $met^+bio^+thr^-pro^-$, had just the opposite requirement. It needed threonine and proline in its growth medium, but not methionine or biotin. These differences in nutritional requirements correspond to allelic differences between the two strains. The $met^-bio^-thr^+pro^+$ strain had defective genes

---

HYPOTHESIS Genetic material can be transferred from one bacterial strain to another.

KEY MATERIALS Two bacterial strains, one that was $met^-bio^-thr^+pro^+$ and the other that was $met^+bio^+thr^-pro^-$.

	Experimental level	Conceptual level

1 In three separate tubes, add either the $met^-bio^-thr^+pro^+$ strain, the $met^+bio^+thr^-pro^-$ strain, or a mixture of both strains.

Incubate several hours.

$met^-bio^-thr^+pro^+$ $met^+bio^+thr^-pro^-$

2 Remove 10^8 cells from each tube and spread onto plates that lack methionine, biotin, threonine, and proline.

10^8 10^8 10^8

Nutrient agar plates lacking amino acids and biotin

Genetic material was transferred between the two strains.

3 Incubate overnight to allow growth of bacterial colonies.

No colonies   Bacterial colonies ($met^+bio^+thr^+pro^+$)   No colonies

---

4 THE DATA

Strain	Number of colonies after overnight growth
$met^-bio^-thr^+pro^+$	0
$met^+bio^+thr^-pro^-$	0
Both strains together	~10

5 CONCLUSION Gene transfer has occurred from one bacterial strain to another.

6 SOURCE Lederberg, Joshua, and Tatum, Edward L. 1946. Novel genotypes in mixed cultures of biochemical mutants of bacteria. *Cold Spring Harbor Symposia on Quantitative Biology* 11:113–114.

Tatum, Edward L., and Lederberg, Joshua. 1947. Genetic recombination in the bacterium *Escherichia coli*. *Journal of Bacteriology* 53:673–684.

Figure 16.14 Experiment of Lederberg and Tatum demonstrating gene transfer in *E. coli*.

encoding enzymes necessary for methionine and biotin synthesis, whereas the *met⁺bio⁺thr⁻pro⁻* strain had defective genes for the enzymes required to make threonine and proline.

Figure 16.14 compares the results of mixing the two *E. coli* strains with the results when they were not mixed. The tube shown on the left contained only *met⁻bio⁻thr⁺pro⁺* cells, and the tube on the right had only *met⁺bio⁺thr⁻pro⁻* cells. The middle tube contained a mixture of the two kinds of cells. In each case the researchers applied about 100 million (10⁸) cells to plates containing a growth medium lacking amino acids and the vitamin biotin. When the unmixed strains were applied to these plates, no colonies were observed to grow. This result was expected because the plates did not contain the methionine and biotin that the *met⁻bio⁻thr⁺pro⁺* cells needed for growth, or the threonine and proline that the *met⁺bio⁺thr⁻pro⁻* cells required. The striking result occurred when the researchers plated 10⁸ cells from the tube containing the mixture of the two strains. In this case approximately 10 cells multiplied and formed visible bacterial colonies on the plates. Because these cells were able to reproduce without supplemental amino acids or vitamins, their genotype must have been *met⁺bio⁺thr⁺pro⁺*. Mutation cannot account for the occurrence of this new genotype because colonies were not observed on the other two plates, which had the same number of cells and also could have incurred mutations.

To explain the results of their experiment, Lederberg and Tatum hypothesized that some genetic material had been transferred between the two strains when they were mixed. This transfer could have occurred in two ways. One possibility is that the genes providing the ability to synthesize threonine and proline (*thr⁺pro⁺*) were transferred to the *met⁺bio⁺thr⁻pro⁻* strain. Alternatively, the genes providing the ability to synthesize methionine and biotin (*met⁺bio⁺*) may have been transferred to the *met⁻bio⁻thr⁺pro⁺* cells. The experimental results cannot distinguish between these two possibilities, but they provide compelling evidence that at least one of them occurred.

How did the bacteria in Lederberg and Tatum's experiment transfer genes between strains? Two mechanisms seemed plausible. Either genetic material was released from one strain and taken up by the other, or cells of the two different strains made contact and directly transferred genetic material. To distinguish these two scenarios, Bernard Davis conducted experiments using the same two strains of *E. coli*. The apparatus he used, known as a U-tube, is shown in **Figure 16.15**. The tube had a filter with pores big enough for pieces of DNA to pass through but too small to permit the passage of bacteria. After filling the tube with a liquid medium, Davis added *met⁻bio⁻thr⁺pro⁺* bacteria on one side of the filter and *met⁺bio⁺thr⁻pro⁻* bacteria on the other. The application of pressure or suction promoted the movement of liquid through the pores. Although the two kinds of bacteria could not mix, any genetic material released by one of them would be available to the other.

After allowing the bacteria to incubate in the U-tube, Davis placed cells from each side of the tube on growth plates lacking methionine, biotin, threonine, and proline. No bacterial colonies

Figure 16.15   **A U-tube apparatus like the one used by Bernard Davis.**   Bacteria of two different strains were suspended in the liquid in the tube and separated by a filter. The liquid was forced through the filter by alternating suction and pressure. The pores in the filter were too small for the passage of bacteria, but they allowed the passage of DNA.

Concept check: *Would the results have been different if the pore size were larger and allowed the passage of bacterial cells?*

grew on these plates. How did Davis interpret these results? He proposed that without physical contact, the two *E. coli* strains could not transfer genetic material from one to the other. The conceptual level of Figure 16.14, step (1), shows the physical connection that explains Lederberg and Tatum's results. Conjugation is the process of gene transfer that requires direct cell-to-cell contact. It has been subsequently observed in other species of bacteria. Many, but not all, species of bacteria can conjugate.

Experimental Questions

1. What was the hypothesis tested by Lederberg and Tatum?
2. During the Lederberg and Tatum experiment, the researchers compared the growth of mutant strains under two scenarios: mixed strains or unmixed strains. When the unmixed strains were plated on the experimental growth medium, why did no colonies grow? When the mixed strains were plated on the experimental growth medium, 10 colonies were observed. What was the significance of these colonies?
3. The gene transfer seen in the Lederberg and Tatum experiment could have occurred in one of two ways: taking up DNA released into the environment or contact between two bacterial cells allowing for direct transfer. Bernard Davis conducted an experiment to determine the correct process. Explain how his results indicated the correct gene transfer process.

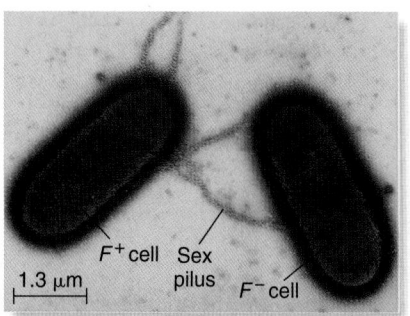

1.3 μm

F⁺ cell   Sex pilus   F⁻ cell

(a) Micrograph of conjugating cells

Figure 16.16   Bacterial conjugation.   **(a)** Two *E. coli* cells conjugating. The cell on the left, designated *F⁺*, is the donor; the cell on the right, designated *F⁻*, is the recipient. The two cells make contact via sex pili made by the *F⁺* cell. **(b)** The transfer of an F factor during conjugation. At the end of conjugation, both the donor cell and the recipient cell are *F⁺*.

Concept check: *If a donor cell has only one F factor, explain how the donor and recipient cell both contain one F factor following the transfer of an F factor during conjugation.*

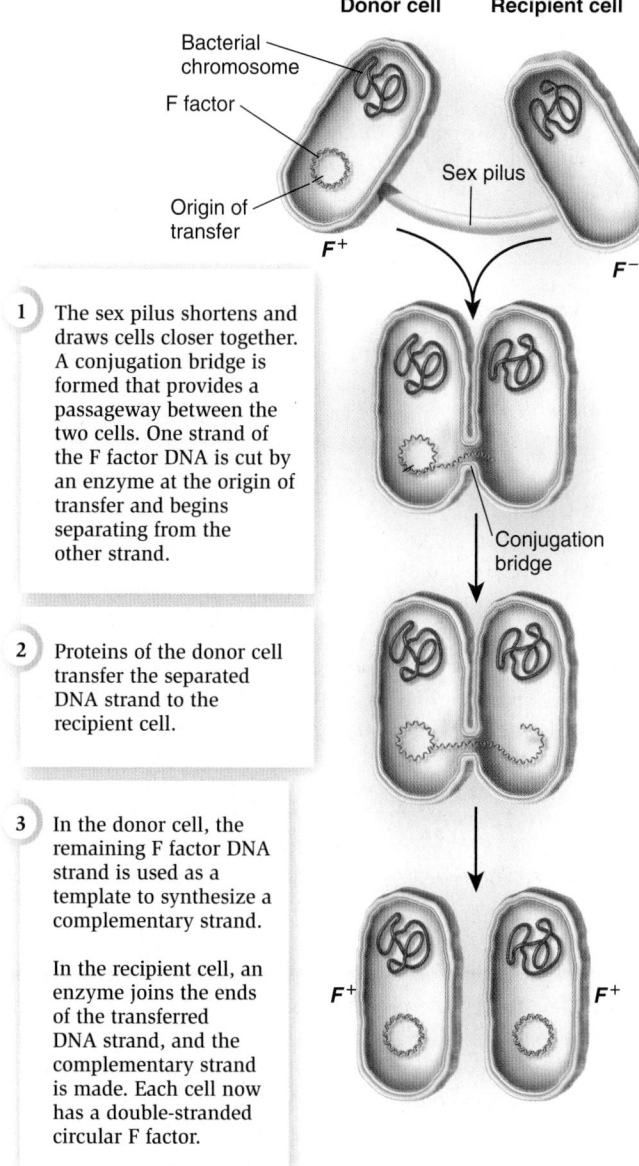

Donor cell   Recipient cell

Bacterial chromosome

F factor

Origin of transfer

Sex pilus

F⁺   *F⁻*

1   The sex pilus shortens and draws cells closer together. A conjugation bridge is formed that provides a passageway between the two cells. One strand of the F factor DNA is cut by an enzyme at the origin of transfer and begins separating from the other strand.

Conjugation bridge

2   Proteins of the donor cell transfer the separated DNA strand to the recipient cell.

3   In the donor cell, the remaining F factor DNA strand is used as a template to synthesize a complementary strand.

In the recipient cell, an enzyme joins the ends of the transferred DNA strand, and the complementary strand is made. Each cell now has a double-stranded circular F factor.

F⁺   *F⁺*

(b) Transfer of an F factor

cells. During conjugation one bacterium acts as a donor and transfers DNA to a recipient cell. In **transformation**, DNA that is released into the environment when a bacterium dies is taken up by another bacterial cell. **Transduction** occurs when

a virus infects a bacterial cell and then transfers some of that cell's DNA to another bacterium. These three types of gene transfer have been extensively investigated in research laboratories, and their molecular pathways continue to be studied with great interest. In this section we will examine these mechanisms in greater detail and consider the experiments that led to their discovery.

During Conjugation, DNA Is Transferred from a Donor Cell to a Recipient Cell

In the early 1950s Joshua and Esther Lederberg, William Hayes, and Luca Cavalli-Sforza independently discovered that only certain bacterial strains can donate genetic material during conjugation. For example, only about 5% of *E. coli* strains can act as donor strains. Further research showed that a strain that is incapable of acting as a donor can acquire this ability after being mixed with a donor strain. Hayes correctly proposed that donor strains contain a type of plasmid called a fertility factor, or **F factor**, that can be transferred to recipient strains. Other donor *E. coli* strains were later identified that can transfer portions of the bacterial chromosome at high frequencies. After a segment of the chromosome is transferred, it then inserts, or recombines, into the chromosome of the recipient cell. Such donor strains were named Hfr (for <u>h</u>igh <u>f</u>requency of <u>r</u>ecombination). In our discussion we will focus on donor strains that carry F factors.

The micrograph in **Figure 16.16a** shows two conjugating *E. coli* cells. The cell on the left is designated *F⁺*, meaning that it has an F factor. This donor cell is transferring genetic material to the recipient cell on the right, which lacks an F factor and is designated *F⁻*. F factors carry several genes that are required for conjugation and also can carry genes that confer a growth advantage for the bacterium.

Figure 16.16b describes the events that occur during conjugation in *E. coli*. The process is similar in other bacteria that are capable of conjugating, although the details vary somewhat from one species to another. Contact between donor and recipient cells is often a key step that initiates the conjugation process. Recall from Chapter 4 that many bacteria have appendages called pili that allow them to attach to surfaces and to each other. **Sex pili** are made by *F⁺* cells that bind specifically to *F⁻* cells. They are so named because conjugation has sometimes been called bacterial mating or bacterial sex. However, these terms are a bit misleading because the process does not involve equal genetic contributions from two gametes and it does not produce offspring. Instead, bacterial mating is a form of gene transfer that alters the genetic composition of the recipient cell. Donor strains have genes responsible for the formation of sex pili. In F^+ strains the genes are located on the F factor. In *E. coli* and some other species, F^+ cells make very long pili that attempt to make contact with nearby F^- cells. Once contact is made, the pili shorten, drawing the donor and recipient cells closer together.

Successful contact stimulates the donor cell to begin the transfer process. Genes within the F factor encode proteins that promote the transfer of one strand of F factor DNA. This DNA strand is cut at the origin of transfer, and then the strand travels through the pilus into the recipient cell. The other strand remains in the donor cell and the complementary strand is synthesized, thereby restoring the F factor DNA to its original double-stranded condition. In the recipient cell the two ends of the newly acquired F factor DNA strand are joined to form a circular molecule, and its complementary strand is synthesized to produce a double-stranded F factor. The end result of conjugation is that the recipient cell has acquired an F factor, converting it from an F^- to an F^+ cell. The genetic composition of the donor strain has not been changed.

In Transformation, Bacteria Take Up DNA from the Environment

In contrast to conjugation, the process of gene transfer known as bacterial transformation does not require direct contact between bacterial cells. Frederick Griffith first discovered this process in 1928 while working with strains of *Streptococcus pneumoniae*. He called the unknown substance that transferred properties of one strain to another the transformation principle. Experimental work in the 1940s and 1950s showed that the transformation principle is DNA and that transformation involves the transfer of genes. We discussed some of these important experiments in Chapter 10 (Figures 10.1 and 10.2).

How does a bacterial cell become transformed? First, it imports a strand of DNA that another bacterium released into the environment when it died. This DNA strand may then insert or recombine into the bacterial chromosome, so that the live bacterium is now carrying genes from the dead bacterium—the live bacterium has been transformed. Not all bacterial strains have the ability to take up DNA. Those that do have this ability are described as naturally **competent**, and they have genes that encode proteins called competence factors. Competence factors facilitate the binding of DNA fragments to the bacterial cell surface, the uptake of DNA into the cytoplasm, and the incorporation of the imported DNA into the bacterial chromosome. Temperature, ionic conditions, and the availability of nutrients also affect whether or not a bacterium will be competent to take up genetic material.

In recent years biologists have unravelled some of the steps that occur when competent bacterial cells are transformed by taking up genetic material from the environment. In the example shown in **Figure 16.17**, the DNA released from a dead bacterium carries a gene, *tet*^{R}, that confers resistance to the

1. A DNA fragment containing the *tet*^{R} gene binds to a cell surface receptor.

2. Bacterial enzymes cut the DNA into smaller fragments.

3. One strand is degraded, and a single strand is imported into the cell by a DNA uptake system.

4. The imported DNA is incorporated into the bacterial chromosome, and the complementary strand is made.

Transformed cell that is resistant to the antibiotic tetracycline

Figure 16.17   The steps of bacterial transformation.   This process has transformed a bacterium that was sensitive to the antibiotic tetracycline into one that can grow in the presence of this antibiotic.

BioConnections: *Look back at Figures 10.1 and 10.2. How did the phenomenon of transformation allow researchers to demonstrate that DNA is the genetic material?*

antibiotic tetracycline. First, a large fragment of the DNA binds to a surface receptor on the outside of a bacterial cell that is sensitive to tetracycline. Enzymes secreted by the bacterium cut this large fragment into fragments small enough to enter the cell. The next step is for a small DNA fragment to begin its entry into the bacterial cytoplasm. One of the two DNA strands of this fragment is degraded. The other strand enters the bacterial cytoplasm via a DNA uptake system that transports the DNA across the plasma membrane. Finally, the imported DNA strand is incorporated into the bacterial chromosome and the complementary strand is synthesized. Following transformation, the recipient cell has been transformed from a tetracycline-sensitive to a tetracycline-resistant cell.

GENOMES AND PROTEOMES

Horizontal Gene Transfer Is the Transfer of Genes Between the Same or Different Species

So far we have considered gene transfer from one bacterial strain to another strain of the same species. In addition, conjugation, transformation, and transduction occasionally occur between cells of different bacterial species. The term **horizontal gene transfer** refers to a process in which an organism incorporates genetic material from another organism without being the offspring of that organism (refer back to Figure 1.7). Conjugation, transformation, and transduction are examples of horizontal gene transfer. In contrast, vertical gene transfer occurs when genes are passed from one generation to the next—from parents to offspring and from mother cells to daughter cells.

Why is horizontal gene transfer important? In recent years, analyses of bacterial genomes have shown that a sizable fraction of bacterial genes are derived from horizontal gene transfer. For example, roughly 17% of the genes of *E. coli* and of *Salmonella typhimurium* have been acquired from other species by horizontal transfer during the past 100 million years. Many of these acquired genes are for traits that give cells a selective advantage, including genes that confer antibiotic resistance, the ability to degrade toxic compounds, and the ability to withstand extreme environments. Some horizontally transferred genes confer pathogenicity, turning a harmless bacterial strain into one that can cause disease. Geneticists have suggested that horizontal gene transfer has played a major role in the evolution of different bacterial species. In many cases the acquisition of new genes allows a bacterium to survive in a new type of environment and can eventually lead to the formation of a new species.

A second reason that horizontal gene transfer is important is its medical relevance. Let's consider antibiotic resistance. Antibiotics are widely prescribed to treat bacterial infections in humans and domestic animals. They are also used in agriculture to increase the growth of livestock and to control bacterial diseases of high-value fruits and vegetables. Unfortunately, the widespread and uncontrolled use of antibiotics has greatly increased the prevalence of antibiotic-resistant strains of bacteria, strains that have a selective advantage over those that are susceptible to antibiotics. Resistant strains carry genes that counteract the action of antibiotics in various ways. A resistance gene may encode a protein that breaks down the drug, pumps it out of the cell, or prevents it from inhibiting cellular processes.

The term **acquired antibiotic resistance** refers to the common phenomenon of a previously susceptible strain becoming resistant to a specific antibiotic. This change may result from genetic alterations in the bacteria's own genome, but it is often due to the horizontal transfer of resistance genes from a resistant strain. As often mentioned in the news media, antibiotic resistance has increased dramatically worldwide over the past few decades, with resistant strains reported in almost all pathogenic strains of bacteria. For example, the most common cause of pneumonia is infection by *Streptococcus pneumoniae*. In many countries, nearly 50% of all *S. pneumoniae* strains are now penicillin resistant, with resistance to other drugs increasing as well. Some of the most severe antibiotic resistance problems occur in hospitals. The widespread use (and misuse) of antibiotics in a relatively closed environment contributes to bacterial resistance, and as hospital bacteria undergo conjugation, transformation, and transduction, resistance (perhaps to more than one antibiotic) spreads among the population. Resistant strains of *Klebsiella pneumoniae* and *Enterococcus faecium* are significant causes of infection and death among critically ill patients in intensive care units, and methicillin-resistant *Staphylococcus aureus* (MRSA), a so-called superbug that is resistant to a number of antibiotics, is becoming an increasing concern worldwide.

In Transduction, Viruses Transfer Genetic Material from One Bacterium to Another

Perhaps the most curious method of gene transfer is transduction, in which viruses that infect bacteria transfer bacterial genes from one bacterium to another. As discussed earlier in this chapter, certain viruses are DNA-containing particles that use the cellular machinery of bacteria for their own replication. The new viral particles made in this way usually contain only viral genes. On rare occasions, however, a virus may pick up a piece of DNA from the bacterial chromosome. When a virus carrying a segment of bacterial DNA infects another bacterium, it transfers this segment into the chromosome of its new bacterial host.

The mechanism of transduction is actually due to an error in a phage lytic cycle, as shown in **Figure 16.18**. In this example a phage called P1 infects an *E. coli* cell that has a gene (*his*$^+$) for histidine synthesis. Phage P1 causes the host cell chromosome to degrade into small pieces. When new phage viruses are assembled, coat proteins may accidentally enclose a piece of host DNA that carries this gene. This produces a phage carrying bacterial chromosomal DNA. In the example shown in Figure 16.18, this transducing phage is released and binds to an *E. coli* cell that lacks the *his*$^+$ gene. It inserts the bacterial DNA fragment into the recipient cell, which then integrates this fragment into its own chromosome (refer back to Figure 16.4a, step 3). In this case gene transfer by transduction converts a *his*$^-$ strain of *E. coli* to a *his*$^+$ strain.

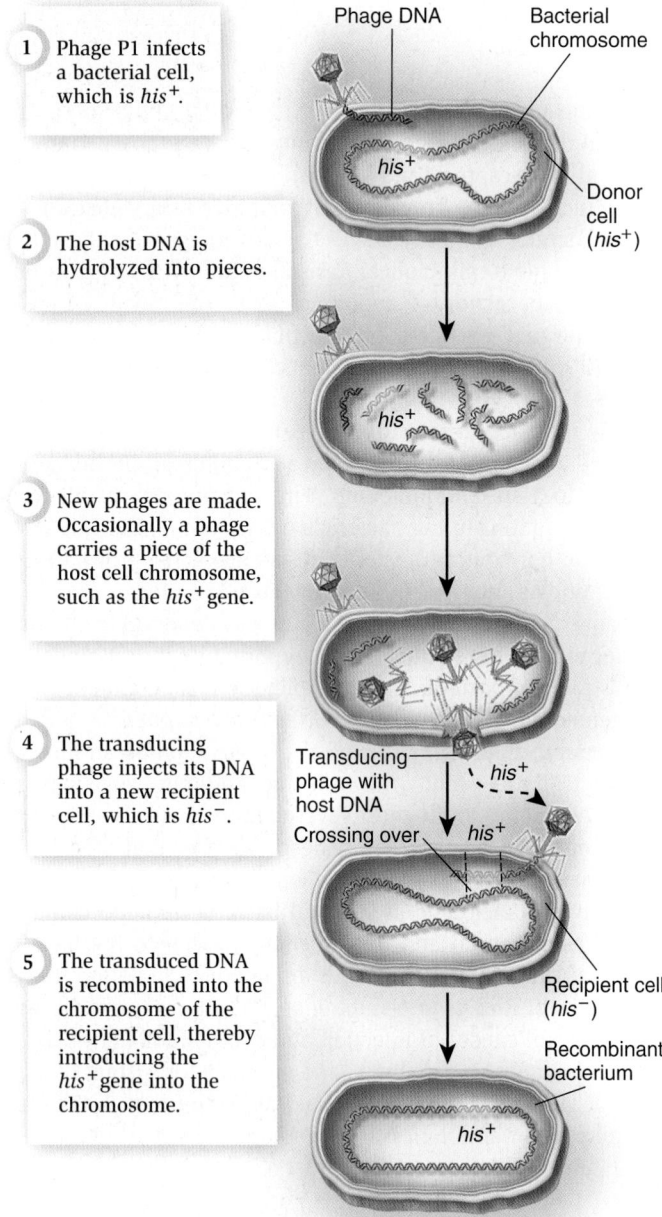

1 Phage P1 infects a bacterial cell, which is *his*+.

Phage DNA

Bacterial chromosome

his+

Donor cell (*his*+)

2 The host DNA is hydrolyzed into pieces.

his+

3 New phages are made. Occasionally a phage carries a piece of the host cell chromosome, such as the *his*+ gene.

4 The transducing phage injects its DNA into a new recipient cell, which is *his*−.

Transducing phage with host DNA

his+

Crossing over

his+

5 The transduced DNA is recombined into the chromosome of the recipient cell, thereby introducing the *his*+ gene into the chromosome.

Recipient cell (*his*−)

Recombinant bacterium

his+

The recombinant bacterium has a genotype (*his*+) that is different from the original recipient bacterial cell (*his*−).

Figure 16.18 Bacterial transduction by P1 phage.

Concept check: *Is transduction a normal part of the phage life cycle? Explain.*

Summary of Key Concepts

16.1 Genetic Properties of Viruses

- Viruses are nonliving particles that do not exhibit all of the properties associated with living organisms. A virus or its genetic material must be taken up by a living cell to replicate. Tobacco mosaic virus (TMV) was the first virus to be discovered. (Figure 16.1)

- Viruses vary with regard to their host range, structure, and genome composition. (Table 16.1, Figures 16.2, 16.3)

- The viral reproductive cycle consists of five or six basic steps, including attachment, entry, integration, synthesis, assembly, and release. (Figure 16.4)

- Some bacteriophages can alternate between two reproductive cycles: the lytic cycle and lysogenic cycle. (Figure 16.5)

- Influenza viruses have a broad host range and can change quickly by both antigenic shift and antigenic drift. (Figures 16.6)

16.2 Viroids and Prions

- Viroids are RNA molecules that infect plant cells. (Figure 16.7)

- Prions are proteins that exist in an abnormal conformation and can cause disease. (Figure 16.8, Table 16.2)

16.3 Genetic Properties of Bacteria

- Bacteria typically have a single type of circular chromosome found in the nucleoid region of the cell. The chromosome contains many genes and a single origin of replication. (Figures 16.9)

- The bacterial chromosome is made more compact by the formation of loops and by DNA supercoiling. (Figure 16.10)

- Plasmids are small, circular DNA molecules that exist independently of the bacterial chromosome. Examples are resistance, degradative, virulence, and fertility plasmids and col-plasmids. (Figure 16.11)

- When placed on a solid growth medium, a single bacterial cell will divide many times to produce a colony composed of many cells. (Figure 16.12)

- Bacterial cells reproduce by asexual reproduction in a process called binary fission, during which a cell divides into two identical daughter cells. (Figure 16.13)

16.4 Gene Transfer Between Bacteria

- Three common modes of gene transfer among bacteria are conjugation, transformation, and transduction. (Table 16.3)

- Lederberg and Tatum's work demonstrated the transfer of bacterial genes between different strains of *E. coli* by conjugation. Davis showed that direct contact was needed for this type of gene transfer. (Figures 16.14, 16.15)

- During conjugation, a strand of DNA from an F factor is transferred from a donor to a recipient cell through a sex pilus. (Figure 16.16)

- Transformation is the process in which a segment of DNA from the environment is taken up by a competent cell and incorporated into the bacterial chromosome. (Figure 16.17)

- Bacterial transduction is a form of gene transfer in which a bacteriophage transfers a segment of bacterial chromosomal DNA to another cell. (Figure 16.18)

- Horizontal gene transfer is a process in which an organism incorporates genetic material from another organism without being the offspring of that organism. It has played a large role in the evolution of bacterial species.

Test to Assess Your Learning

1. The _____ is the protein coat of a virus that surrounds the genetic material.
   a. host
   b. prion

c. capsid

d. viroid

e. capsule

2. Among the viruses identified, the characteristics of their genomes show many variations. Which of the following does *not* describe a typical characteristic of viral genomes?

a. The genetic material can be DNA or RNA.

b. The nucleic acid can be single stranded or double stranded.

c. The genome can carry just a few genes or several dozen.

d. The number of copies of the genome can vary.

e. All of the above describe typical variation in viral genomes.

3. During viral infection, attachment is usually specific to a particular cell type because

a. the virus is attracted to the appropriate host cells by proteins secreted into the extracellular fluid.

b. the virus recognizes and binds to specific molecules in the cytoplasm of the host cell.

c. the virus recognizes and binds to specific molecules on the surface of the host cell.

d. the host cell produces channel proteins that provide passageways for viruses to enter the cytoplasm.

e. the virus releases specific proteins that make holes in the membrane large enough for the virus to enter.

4. HIV, a retrovirus, has a high mutation rate because

a. the DNA of the viral genome is less stable than other viral genomes.

b. the viral enzyme reverse transcriptase has a high likelihood of making replication errors.

c. the viral genome is altered every time it is incorporated into the host genome.

d. antibodies produced by the host cell mutate the viral genome when infection occurs.

e. all of the above.

5. A _____ is an infectious agent composed solely of RNA, whereas a _____ is an infectious agent composed solely of protein.

a. retrovirus, bacteriophage

b. viroid, virus

c. prion, virus

d. retrovirus, prion

e. viroid, prion

6. Genetic diversity is maintained in bacterial populations by all of the following except

a. binary fission.

b. mutation.

c. transformation.

d. transduction.

e. conjugation.

7. Bacterial cells divide by a process known as

a. mitosis.

b. cytokinesis.

c. meiosis.

d. binary fission.

e. glycolysis.

8. Gene transfer, whereby a bacterial cell takes up bacterial DNA from the environment, is called

a. conjugation.

b. binary fission.

c. recombination.

d. transformation.

e. transduction.

9. A bacterial cell can donate DNA during conjugation when it

a. produces competence factors.

b. contains an F factor.

c. is virulent.

d. has been infected by a bacteriophage.

e. all of the above.

10. A bacterial species that becomes resistant to certain antibiotics may have acquired the resistance genes from another bacterial species. The phenomenon of acquiring genes from another organism without being the offspring of that organism is known as

a. hybridization.

b. integration.

c. horizontal gene transfer.

d. vertical gene transfer.

e. competence.

Articulate to Assess Your Learning

1. How are viruses similar to living cells and how are they different?

2. What are three mechanisms of gene transfer in bacteria? Discuss the evolutionary and medical significance of horizontal gene transfer.

Collaborate to Assess and Extend Your Learning

1. Discuss the possible origin of viruses. Which ideas do you think are the most likely?

2. Conjugation is sometimes called *bacterial mating*. Discuss how conjugation is similar to sexual reproduction in eukaryotes and how it is different.

3. If you mix an equal number of F^+ and F^- cells, how would you expect the proportions to change over time? Do you expect an increase in the relative proportions of F^+ and F^- cells? Explain your answer.

4. A principle of biology is the genetic material provides the blueprint for sustaining life. Discuss how horizontal gene transfer alters the blueprint.

Visit McGraw-Hill Ryerson Connect™ for
additional study resources.

Developmental Genetics

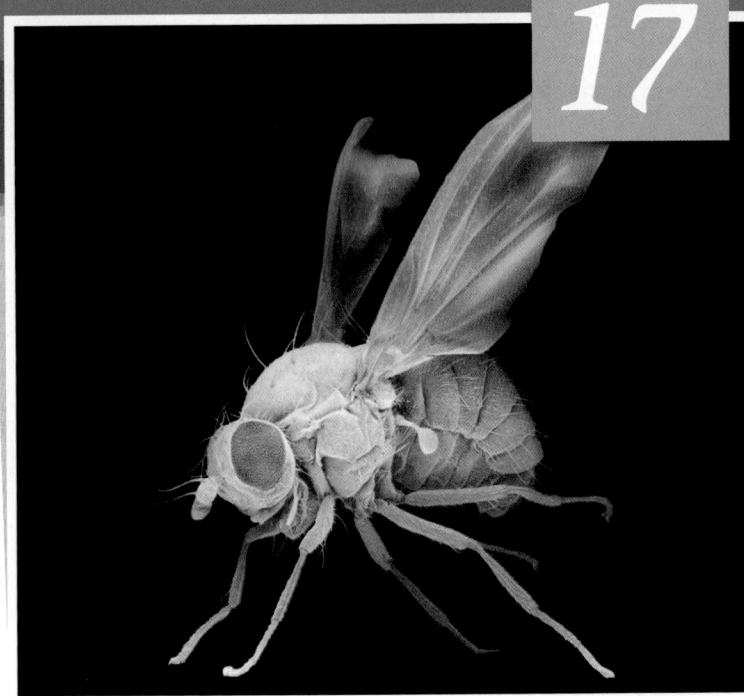

Drosophila melanogaster, the fruit fly, has served as a model organism to study animal development.

Chapter Outline

I n biology the term **development** refers to a series of changes in the state of a cell, a tissue, an organ, or an organism. Development is the underlying process that gives rise to the structure and function of living organisms. In complex multicellular organisms this remarkable process begins from a single cell (fertilized egg), and as development proceeds, the elaboration of many diverse tissues and cell types generates the embryo, the fetus, and finally the adult. The structure or form of an organism is called its morphology. As you have learned throughout this textbook, an important paradigm in biology is that structure (morphology) determines function. Scientists interested in biological functions are called physiologists. Development is of great importance to physiologists because the functions of a specialized cell, such as a nerve cell, and a complex organ, such as a heart, are the result of development.

Biologists came to realize that plants and animals undergo amazing changes in development to create the structure and function that is found in adult organisms. Such observations motivated researchers to uncover the underlying processes that promote these developmental changes. Since the 1940s, genetics has emerged as the fundamental driving force behind research in developmental biology. It is currently one of the most intensely researched fields of biology.

Developmental genetics aims to understand how gene expression controls the process of development. In this chapter we will learn how the sequential actions of genes provide a program for the development of an organism from a fertilized egg to an adult. The last few decades have seen exciting advances in our understanding of developmental genetics at the molecular level. Scientists have chosen a few experimental organisms, such as the fruit fly, a nematode worm, the mouse, and the plant *Arabidopsis,* and worked toward the identification and characterization of the genes required for running their developmental programs. In certain organisms, notably the fruit fly, most of the genes that play a critical role in the embryonic stages of development have been identified. Researchers are now exploring how the proteins encoded by these genes control the course of development. In this chapter we begin with an overview that emphasizes the general principles of development. We will then examine the details of development in

plants and animals, with an emphasis on genetics. Chapters 37 and 50 also consider plant and animal development, with an emphasis on structure and function.

17.1 GENERAL THEMES IN DEVELOPMENT

Learning Outcomes:

1. List several invertebrate, vertebrate, and plant model organisms and describe the reasons that biologists study them.
2. Outline the process of pattern formation in plants and animals.
3. Describe the four ways that cells respond to positional information.
4. Explain how morphogens and cell-to-cell contacts convey positional information.
5. Outline how development in animals occurs in four phases that are controlled by transcription factors.

Development begins when sperm and egg unite to produce a **zygote**, a diploid cell that divides and develops into an **embryo** and eventually into an adult organism. During the early stages of development, cells divide and begin to arrange themselves into ordered units. As this occurs, each cell also becomes **determined**, which means it is destined to become a particular cell type, such as a muscle or intestinal cell. This commitment occurs long before a cell becomes **differentiated**, meaning that the cell's morphology and function have changed, usually permanently, into a highly specialized cell type. In an adult each cell type plays its own particular role for the good of the entire individual. In animals, for example, muscle cells allow an organism to move, while intestinal cells facilitate the absorption of nutrients. This division of labour among various cells of an organism works to promote its survival.

The genomes of living organisms contain a set of genes that orchestrate the program of development. In unicellular species the program controls the structure and function of the cell. In multicellular organisms the program not only controls cellular features but also determines the arrangement of cells in the organisms. In this section we will examine some of the general issues associated with the development of multicellular species. Later sections will focus on specific examples of development in animals and plants.

Developmental Biologists Have Chosen a Few Model Organisms to Study Development

The development of even a simple multicellular organism involves many types of changes in form and function. For this reason the research community has focused its efforts on only a few model organisms, with the expectation that knowledge of the developmental programs in these model organisms will apply to many other species. For animal development the two organisms that have been the most extensively investigated are two invertebrate species: the fruit fly *Drosophila melanogaster* and the nematode worm *Caenorhabditis elegans* (**Figures 17.1a, 17.1b**). Why have these two organisms been chosen as models to investigate development? *Drosophila* has been studied for a variety of reasons. First, researchers have exposed this organism to mutagens and identified many mutant organisms with altered developmental pathways. The techniques for generating and analyzing mutants in this organism are more advanced than in any other animal. Second, in all of its life stages, *Drosophila* is large enough and has distinct enough morphological features to easily identify the effects of mutations, yet it is small enough to determine where particular genes are expressed at critical stages of development. *C. elegans* is used by developmental geneticists for its simplicity.

The adult organism is a small transparent worm composed of only about a thousand somatic cells. Starting with a fertilized egg, the pattern of cell division and the fate of each cell within the embryo are completely known.

Embryologists have also studied the morphological features of development in many vertebrate species. Historically, amphibians and birds have been studied extensively, because their eggs are rather large and easy to manipulate. From a morphological point of view, the developmental stages of the chicken (*Gallus gallus*) and the African clawed frog (*Xenopus laevis*) have been described in detail. More recently, several vertebrate species have been the subject of genetic studies of development. These include the house mouse (*Mus musculus*) and the small aquarium zebrafish (*Brachydanio rerio*) (**Figure 17.1c, 17.1d**).

In the study of plant development, the model organism for genetic analysis is thale cress (*Arabidopsis thaliana*), more commonly called *Arabidopsis* by researchers (**Figure 17.1e**). *Arabidopsis* is a small annual weed that belongs to the wild mustard family but is closely related to important crop plants, such as canola. It occurs naturally throughout temperate regions of the world. *Arabidopsis* has a short generation time of about two months and a small genome size of 14×10^7 bp, which is similar to *Drosophila* and *C. elegans*. The small stature of the plant permits efficient large-scale propagation of *Arabidopsis* in a laboratory setting and its self-fertility facilitates genetic analyses and seed production.

Both Animals and Plants Develop by Pattern Formation

Development in plants and animals produces a body plan or pattern. At the cellular level the body pattern is due to the arrangement of cells and their differentiation. The coordination of these events leads to the formation of a body with a particular pattern, a process called **pattern formation**. The result of

(a) *Drosophila melanogaster*

(c) *Mus musculus*

(b) *Caenorhabditis elegans*

(d) *Danio rerio*

(e) *Arabidopsis thaliana*

Figure 17.1   Model organisms used to study the genetics of development.

animal development is usually the formation of an adult body pattern organized along three axes: the **dorsoventral axis**, the **anteroposterior axis**, and the **right-left axis** (**Figure 17.2a**). In addition many animal bodies are then **segmented** into separate sections containing specific body parts, such as wings or legs.

By comparison the body pattern of plants is quite different, being formed along a root-shoot axis in the embryo but having post-embryonic vegetative development that is reiterative, generating new leaves, stems, and flowers at specific intervals along the main axis. Although the stems are often radially symmetrical, lateral organs have a distinct polarity, with surfaces that face the main axis (adaxial) or are oriented away from the main axis (abaxial). Generally, the abaxial-adaxial sidedness can be loosely equated with the dorsal-ventral type of symmetry that is observed in many animals (**Figure 17.2b**). The root and shoot axes are determined at the first division of the fertilized egg, and growth occurs in a radial pattern around those axes. As you'll see later, the identification of mutant alleles that disrupt development has permitted great insight into the genes controlling pattern formation.

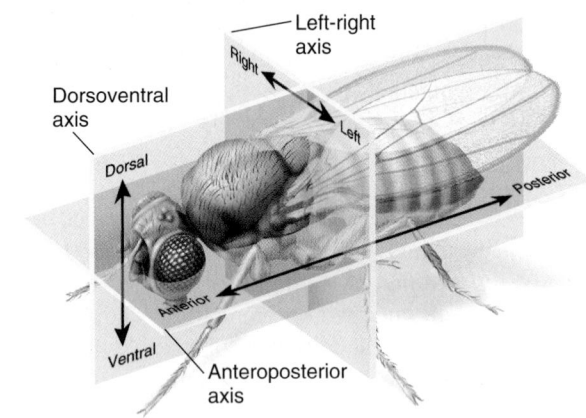

(a) Body plan found in many animals

(b) Body plan found in many seed-bearing plants

Figure 17.2   Body plan axes in animals and plants.

Pattern Formation Depends on Positional Information

Before we examine how genes affect pattern formation, let's consider a central concept in developmental biology: **positional information**. For an organism to develop the correct morphological features or pattern, each cell of the body must become the appropriate cell type based on its position relative to other cells. Each cell receives positional information that provides it with instructions on where to go and what type of cell to become. Later in this chapter we will examine how the expression of genes and the function of gene products provide this information.

A cell can respond to positional information in one of four ways: cell division, cell migration, cell differentiation, and cell death (**Figure 17.3**). First, positional information may

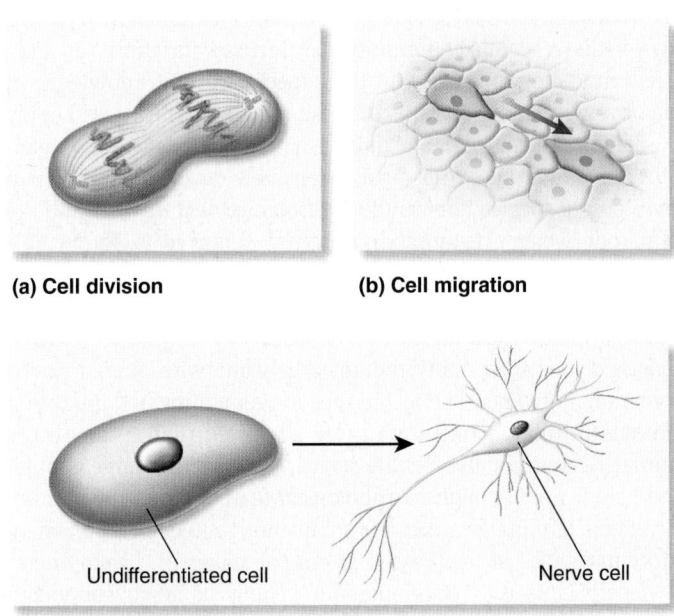

(a) Cell division   **(b) Cell migration**

Undifferentiated cell   Nerve cell

(c) Cell differentiation

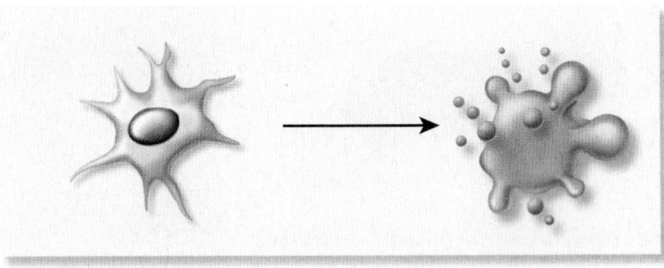

(d) Cell death (apoptosis)

Figure 17.3   Four types of cellular responses to positional information in animals.

Concept check: *Which of these four responses do you expect to be more prevalent in the early stages of development, and which would become more prevalent in later stages?*

BioConnections: *Look back at Figure 9.18. What are the stages of apoptosis?*

stimulate a cell to divide. Second, positional information in animals may cause the migration of a cell or group of cells in a particular direction from one region of the embryo to another. Third, it may cause a cell to differentiate into a specific cell type, such as a nerve cell. Finally, positional information may promote **apoptosis**, or programmed cell death, described in Chapter 9. Apoptosis plays a key role in sculpting the bodies of animals. In vascular plants certain cells undergo programmed cell death to form tracheids, specialized cells that function in water transport.

As an example of how the coordination of these four processes is required for pattern formation, let's consider the development of the vertebrate limb. **Figure 17.4a** shows the growth and development of a human arm during the embryonic stage. Cell division with accompanying cell growth increases the size of the limb (**Figure 17.4b**). Cell migration is also important in this process. For example, embryonic cells that eventually form

muscles in the arm and hand must migrate long distances to reach their correct location within the limb.

As development proceeds, cell differentiation produces the tissues that will eventually be found in the fully developed limb. Some cells will become nerve cells, others will be muscle cells, and still others will form the outer layer of skin. Finally, apoptosis is important in the formation of fingers. If apoptosis did not occur, a human hand would have webbed fingers.

Morphogens and Cell-to-Cell Contacts Convey Positional Information

How does positional information lead to the development of a body plan? Two main molecular mechanisms are used to communicate positional information. One of these mechanisms involves molecules called morphogens. **Morphogens** impart positional information and promote developmental changes

(a) Limb development in a human embryo

1. Cell division promotes the growth of the limb.

Limb bud

2. Cell migration causes cells to reach their correct location.

3. Cell differentiation produces specialized cells, such as muscle cells.

4. Apoptosis eliminates cells in between the fingers.

(b) Four cellular processes that promote limb formation

Figure 17.4 Limb development in humans. (a) Photographs of limb development in human embryos. The limb begins as a protrusion called a limb bud that eventually forms an arm and hand. (b) The development of a human limb from an embryonic limb bud.

Concept check: *How would finger formation be affected if apoptosis did not occur?*

at the cellular level. A morphogen influences the fate of a cell by promoting cell division, cell migration, cell differentiation, or apoptosis. A key feature of morphogens is that they act in a concentration-dependent manner. At a high concentration a morphogen will restrict a cell into a particular developmental pathway, while at a lower concentration it will not. There is often a critical **threshold concentration** above which the morphogen will exert its effects but below which it is ineffective.

Morphogens typically are distributed asymmetrically along a concentration gradient. This can happen at one of two times during early development. First, morphogenic gradients can be established in the oocyte, a cell that matures into an egg cell (**Figure 17.5a**). Second, a morphogenic gradient can be established in the embryo by secretion and transport (**Figure 17.5b**). A certain cell or group of cells can synthesize and secrete a morphogen at a specific stage of development. After secretion the morphogen is transported to neighbouring cells. The concentration of the morphogen is usually highest

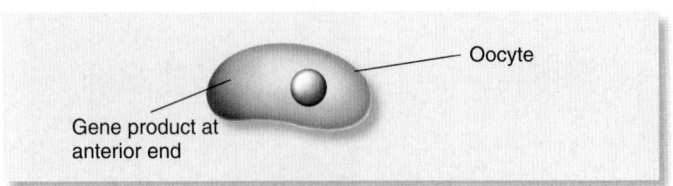

(a) Asymmetric distribution of morphogens in the oocyte

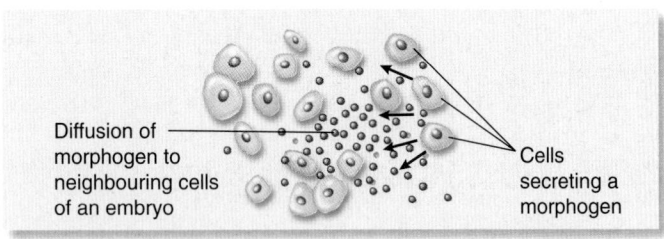

(b) Induction: Asymmetric synthesis and extracellular distribution of a morphogen

(c) Cell adhesion: Cell-to-cell contact conveys positional information

Figure 17.5 Molecular mechanisms that convey positional information. Asymmetrical distribution of a morphogen in the **(a)** oocyte or **(b)** embryo. **(c)** Positional information can also be obtained by cell-to-cell contact.

BioConnections: *Look back at Chapter 9. Discuss the role of cell receptors in responding to positional information.*

near the cells that secrete it. The morphogen can then influence the developmental fate of cells that are exposed to it in a process called **induction**.

Another mechanism used to convey positional information involves **cell adhesion** (**Figure 17.5c**). Each cell makes its own collection of surface receptors that enable it to adhere to other cells. Such receptors, which are known as **cell adhesion molecules (CAMs)**, are described in Chapter 5. The positioning of a cell within a multicellular organism is strongly influenced by the combination of contacts it makes with other cells and with the extracellular matrix.

The phenomenon of cell adhesion and its role in multicellular development was first recognized by H. V. Wilson in 1907. He took multicellular sponges and separated them into individual cells. Remarkably, the cells actively migrated until they adhered to one another to form a new sponge, complete with the chambers and canals that characterize a sponge's internal structure. When sponge cells from different species were mixed, they sorted themselves properly, adhering only to cells of the same species. Overall, these results indicate that cells possess specific CAMs, which are critical in cell-to-cell recognition. Cell adhesion plays an important role in governing the position that a cell will adopt during development. Together, the actions of morphogens and CAMs convey positional information to the cells in a developing organism.

Pattern Formation Occurs in Phases That Are Controlled by Transcription Factors

The formation of a body, both in plants and in animals, occurs in a series of overlapping organizational phases. As an overview of this process, we will consider four general phases of pattern development in an animal (**Figure 17.6**). While this example involves human development, research suggests that pattern formation in all complex animals follows a similar plan. The first phase is to organize the body along major axes. The anteroposterior axis determines the organization from head to tail, the dorsoventral axis governs the structure from front (ventral) to back (dorsal), and the right-left axis provides organization from side to side. During the second phase the body becomes organized into smaller regions, a process called segmentation. In insects these regions form well-defined segments. In mammals, some segmentation of the body is apparent during embryonic development, but defined boundaries are lost as the embryo proceeds to the fetal and adult stages. In the third phase the cells within the segments organize themselves in ways that will produce particular body parts. Finally, during the fourth phase the cells themselves change their morphologies and differentiate. This final phase of development produces an organism with many types of tissues, organs, and other body parts with specialized functions. The phases of development do overlap. For example, cell differentiation begins to occur as the cells are adopting their correct locations.

How does genetics underlie the phases of animal development? Geneticists have discovered a parallel between the expression of specific transcription factors, which are described in Chapter 12, and the four major phases of animal development. As noted in

Hierarchy of transcription factors

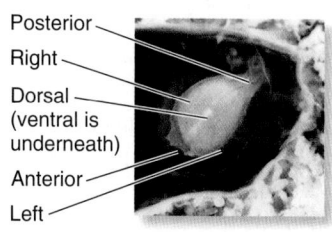

Posterior
Right
Dorsal (ventral is underneath)
Anterior
Left

1 **Phase 1:**
Transcription factors determine the formation of the body axes and control the expression of transcription factors of phase 2.

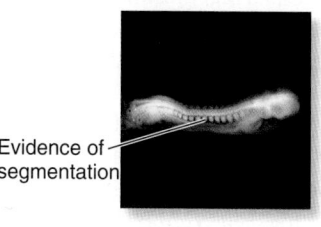

Evidence of segmentation

2 **Phase 2:**
Transcription factors cause the embryo to become subdivided into regions that have properties of individual segments. They also control transcription factors of phase 3.

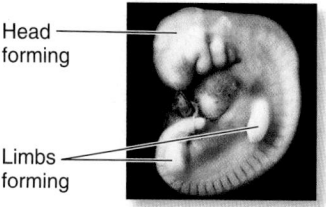

Head forming

Limbs forming

3 **Phase 3:**
Transcription factors cause each segment and groups of segments to develop specific characteristics. They also control transcription factors of phase 4.

4 **Phase 4:**
Transcription factors cause cells to differentiate into specific cell types, such as skin, nerve, and muscle cells.

Figure 17.6 Pattern development in a human embryo. As shown here, pattern formation in animals occurs in four phases that are controlled by a hierarchy of transcription factors. The example shown here involves human development, although research suggests that pattern formation in all complex animals follows a similar plan. The ideas in this scenario are based largely on analogies between pattern formation in mammals and *Drosophila*. Many of the transcription factors that are likely to control the early phases of pattern formation in mammals have yet to be identified. Note that the phases of development are overlapping. For example, cell differentiation begins to occur as the cells are adopting their correct locations.

Concept check: *During which of the four phases of development would you expect cell division and cell migration to be the most prevalent?*

Figure 17.6, a hierarchy of transcription factors controls whether or not certain genes are expressed at a specific phase of development in a particular cell type, a phenomenon called **differential gene regulation**. Many morphogens, particularly those that act during early phases of development, function as transcription factors.

17.2 DEVELOPMENT IN ANIMALS

Learning Outcomes:

1. Describe how animal development occurs in four overlapping phases.
2. Explain how the analysis of mutants has been an important tool in our understanding of development in animals.
3. Distinguish the functions of maternal effect genes, segmentation genes, and homeotic genes in animal development.
4. Define the general properties of stem cells.
5. Describe how transcription factors control cell differentiation.

In this section we will begin by examining the general stages of *Drosophila* development and then focus our attention on embryonic development. During this stage the overall body plan is determined. You will see how the differential expression of particular genes and the localization of positional information within the embryo control the developmental processes of pattern formation and segmentation. The roles of genes in the organization of mammalian embryos are not as well understood as they are in *Drosophila*. Even so, the analysis of the genomes of mammals and many other species has revealed many interesting parallels in the developmental program of all animals.

This section will end with an examination of cell differentiation. This process is better understood in mammals than in *Drosophila* because researchers have been studying mammalian cells in the laboratory for many decades. To explore cell differentiation, we will consider mammals as our primary example.

Embryonic Development Determines the Pattern of Structures in the Adult

As a way to appreciate the phases of pattern formation in animals, we will largely focus on development in *Drosophila*. **Figure 17.7** illustrates a simplified sequence of events in *Drosophila* development. Let's examine these steps before we consider the differential gene regulation that causes them to happen.

The oocyte is critical to establishing the pattern of development that will ultimately produce an adult organism. It is an elongated cell that contains positional information. As shown in **Figure 17.7a**, the fertilized egg already has anterior and posterior ends that correspond to those found in the adult (compare Figure 17.7a and 17.7e).

A key process in *Drosophila* embryonic development is the formation of a segmented body pattern. The embryo is subdivided into visible segments grouped into three general areas: the head, the thorax, and the abdomen. **Figure 17.7b** shows the segmented pattern of a *Drosophila* embryo about 10 hours after fertilization. A *Drosophila* embryo then develops into a **larva** (**Figure 17.7c**), a free-living organism that is morphologically very different from the adult. Many animal species do not have larval stages. *Drosophila* undergoes three successive larval stages. After the third larval stage, the organism becomes a **pupa** (**Figure 17.7d**), a transitional stage between the larva and the adult. Through a process known as **metamorphosis**, the larva transforms into a pupa and then a pupa becomes a mature adult that emerges from the pupal case (**Figure 17.7e**). Each segment in the adult has its own characteristic structures. For example, the wings are on a thoracic segment. From beginning to end this process takes about 10 days.

Phase 1 Pattern Development: Maternal Effect Genes Promote the Formation of the Main Body Axes

The first phase in *Drosophila* embryonic pattern development is the establishment of the body axes, which occurs before the embryo becomes segmented (see Figure 17.6). The morphogens necessary to establish these axes are distributed before

fertilization. In most invertebrates and some vertebrates, certain morphogens that are important in early developmental stages are deposited asymmetrically within the egg as it develops. Later, after the egg has been fertilized and development begins, these morphogens will initiate developmental programs that govern the formation of the body axes of the embryo.

As an example of one morphogen that plays a role in axis formation, let's consider the product of a gene in *Drosophila* called *bicoid*. Its name is derived from the observation that a mutation that inactivates the gene results in a larva with two posterior ends (**Figure 17.8**). During normal egg development, the *bicoid* gene product accumulates in the anterior region of the oocyte, causing the development of the anterior end of the embryo.

How does the *bicoid* gene product accumulate in the anterior region of the oocyte? The answer involves specialized nurse cells that are found next to the oocyte in the ovaries of female flies. As discussed in Chapter 15, nurse cells supply the products (for example, mRNA) of **maternal effect genes**. These genes cause an unusual pattern of inheritance called **maternal effect** (refer back to Figure 15.36). In *Drosophila* the nurse cells are located toward the anterior end of the oocyte rather than the posterior end. The *bicoid* gene is transcribed in the nurse cells, and *bicoid* mRNA is then transported into the anterior end of the oocyte and trapped there (**Figure 17.9a**). Before fertilization, the *bicoid* mRNA is highly concentrated near the anterior side of the oocyte (**Figure 17.9b**). After fertilization, the *bicoid* mRNA is translated and a gradient of Bicoid protein is established across the zygote (**Figure 17.9c**). This gradient starts a progression of

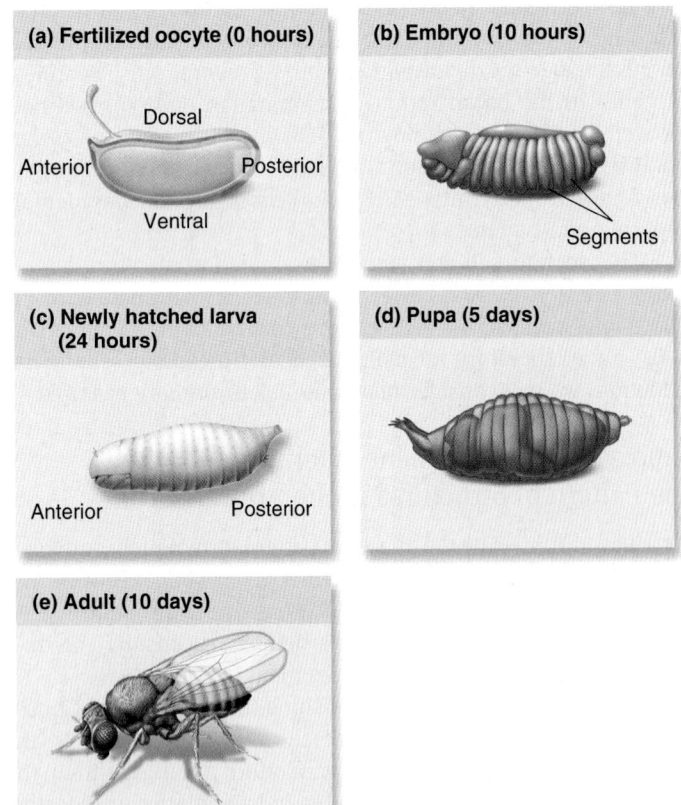

(a) Fertilized oocyte (0 hours)

Dorsal

Anterior   Posterior

Ventral

(b) Embryo (10 hours)

Segments

(c) Newly hatched larva (24 hours)

Anterior   Posterior

(d) Pupa (5 days)

(e) Adult (10 days)

Figure 17.7   Developmental stages of the fruit fly *Drosophila.*

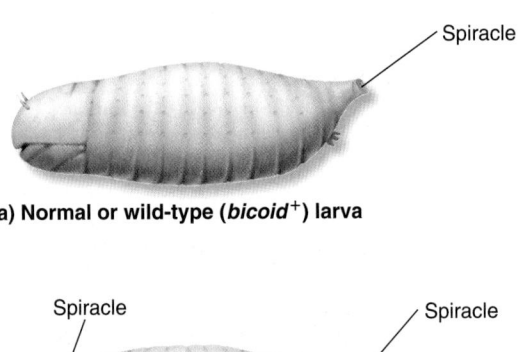

Spiracle

(a) Normal or wild-type (*bicoid*⁺) larva

Spiracle   Spiracle

(b) Mutant (*bicoid*⁻) larva

Figure 17.8   The *bicoid* mutation in *Drosophila*.   (a) A normal *bicoid*⁺ embryo. (b) A *bicoid*⁻ embryo, in which both ends of the larva develop posterior structures. For example, both ends develop a spiracle, which normally is found only at the posterior end.

Concept check: *What would you expect the phenotype to be of a larva in which the bicoid gene was expressed in both the anterior region and the posterior region of the oocyte?*

(b) Staining of *bicoid* mRNA in an oocyte

(c) Staining of Bicoid protein in an early embryo

Nurse cell

Follicle cell

Anterior end
of oocyte

Oocyte

bicoid mRNA

Follicle

**(a) Transport of maternal effect gene
products (*bicoid* mRNA) into the oocyte**

Figure 17.9 Asymmetrical localization of gene products during egg development in *Drosophila.* **(a)** The nurse cells transport maternal effect gene products, such as *bicoid* mRNA, into the anterior end of the developing oocyte. **(b)** Staining of *bicoid* mRNA in an oocyte before fertilization. The *bicoid* mRNA is trapped near the anterior end. **(c)** Staining of Bicoid protein after fertilization. The Bicoid protein forms a gradient, with its highest concentration near the anterior end.

developmental events that will provide the positional information that causes the end of the zygote with a high Bicoid protein concentration to become the anterior end of the embryo.

The Bicoid protein is a morphogen that functions as a transcription factor to activate particular genes at specific times. The ability of Bicoid to activate a given gene is tuned exquisitely to its concentration. Because of its asymmetrical distribution, the Bicoid protein will activate genes only in certain regions of the embryo. For example, a high concentration of Bicoid stimulates the expression of a gene called *hunchback* (that also encodes a transcription factor) in the anterior half of the embryo, but its concentration is too low in the posterior half to activate the *hunchback* gene. The ability of Bicoid to activate genes in certain regions but not others plays a role in the second phase of pattern formation: segmentation.

The Study of* Drosophila *Mutants Has Identified Genes That Control the Development of Segments As described in Figure 17.6, the second phase of pattern formation is the development of segments. The normal *Drosophila* embryo is subdivided into 15 segments: three head segments, three thoracic segments, and nine abdominal segments (**Figure 17.10**). Each segment of the embryo gives rise to unique morphological features in the adult. For example, the second thoracic segment (T2) produces a pair of legs and a pair of wings.

In the 1970s Christiane Nüsslein-Volhard and Eric-Wieschaus undertook a systematic search for *Drosophila* mutants with disrupted development. In particular they focused their search on genes that alter the segmentation pattern of the *Drosophila* embryo and larva, called **segmentation genes**. Based on the characteristics of abnormal larva, they identified three classes of segmentation genes: gap genes, pair-rule genes, and segment-polarity genes When a mutation inactivates a **gap gene**, several adjacent segments are missing in the larva—a gap occurs. Thus, the gap genes

encode determinants of an early stage of development, leading to the proper patterning of entire regions of the body. A defect in a **pair-rule gene** can cause alternating segments or parts of segments to be deleted, implying that these genes regulate smaller domains of the developing organism. Finally, **segment-polarity gene** mutations cause portions of segments to be missing either an anterior or a posterior region and cause adjacent regions to become mirror images of each other. Such genes control the orientation and identity of regions within the domains.

Phase 2 Pattern Development: Segmentation Genes Act Sequentially to Divide the *Drosophila* Embryo into Segments

The study of segmentation genes has provided information regarding the process by which segments are formed. To create a segment, a group of genes acts sequentially to govern the fate of a given region of the body. A simplified scheme of gene

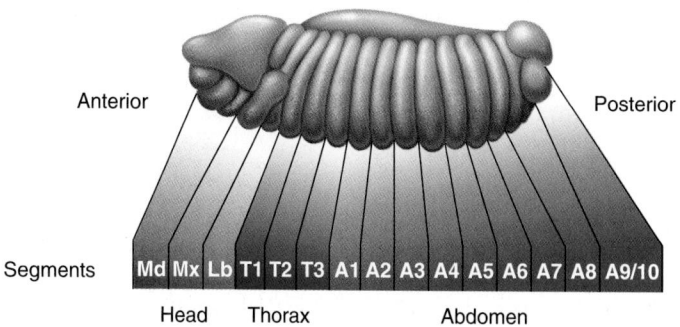

Anterior

Posterior

Segments

Md Mx Lb T1 T2 T3 A1 A2 A3 A4 A5 A6 A7 A8 A9/10

Head   Thorax   Abdomen

Figure 17.10 The organization of segments in the *Drosophila* embryo.

expression that leads to a segmented pattern in the *Drosophila* embryo is shown in **Figure 17.11**. Many more genes are actually involved in this process.

Generally, maternal effect genes, which promote phase 1 pattern development, activate gap genes; this activation is seen as broad bands of gap gene expression in the embryo (Figure 17.11, step 2). The gap genes and maternal effect genes then activate the pair-rule genes in alternating stripes in the embryo (Figure 17.11, step 3). Once the pair-rule genes are activated, their gene products then regulate the segment-polarity genes. As you follow the progression from maternal effect genes to segment-polarity genes, notice that a body pattern is emerging in the embryo that matches the segmentation pattern found in the larva and adult animal. As you can see in step (4) of Figure 17.11, the 15 locations where a segment-polarity gene is expressed correspond to portions of segments in the adult fly. To appreciate this phenomenon, notice that the embryo at this stage is curled up and folded back on itself. If you imagine that the embryo was stretched out linearly, the 15 stripes seen in this embryo correspond to portions of the 15 segments of an adult fly.

Phase 3 Pattern Development: Homeotic Genes Control the Development of Segment Characteristics

Thus far we have considered how the *Drosophila* embryo becomes organized along axes and then into a segmented body pattern. During the third phase of pattern development, each segment begins to develop unique characteristics (see Figure 17.6). Geneticists use the term **cell fate** to describe the ultimate morphological features that a cell or group of cells will adopt. For example, the fate of cells in segment T2 is to develop into a thoracic segment containing two legs and two wings. In *Drosophila* the cells in each segment of the body have their fate determined at a very early stage of embryonic development, long before the morphological features become apparent.

Our understanding of developmental fate has been greatly aided by the identification of mutant genes that alter cell fates. In animals the first mutant of this type was described by the German entomologist G. Kraatz in 1876. He observed a sawfly (*Cimbex axillaris*) in which part of an antenna was replaced with a leg. During the late nineteenth century, English zoologist William Bateson collected many of these types of observations and published them in a book. He coined the term homeotic to describe changes in which one body part is replaced by another. These abnormalities are caused by mutant alleles of **homeotic genes**—genes that specify the fate of a particular segment or region of the body.

As an example, **Figure 17.12** shows a normal fly and one with mutations in a complex of homeotic genes called the *bithorax* complex. A normal fly has two wings on the second thoracic segment and two halteres, which together function as a balancing organ that resembles a pair of miniature wings, on the third thoracic segment. In this mutant fly the third thoracic segment has the characteristics of the second, so the fly has no

Phase 1	Phase 2		
Asymmetric localization of maternal effect gene products	Gap gene expression	Pair-rule gene expression	Segment-polarity gene expression

① **Maternal effect genes** encode proteins that establish the anteroposterior and dorsoventral axes. These proteins activate gap genes.

② **Gap genes** produce broad bands of proteins that act as transcription factors to activate pair-rule genes. These transcription factors bind to enhancers that are located adjacent to pair-rule genes.

③ **Pair-rule genes** are expressed in alternating stripes. Each stripe of protein is found in a portion of every other segment. Proteins encoded by pair-rule genes regulate segment-polarity genes.

④ **Segment-polarity genes** are expressed in a portion of every segment. At this stage, all of the segments of the body are defined.

Figure 17.11 Overview of segmentation in *Drosophila.*   The micrographs depict the progression of *Drosophila* development during the first few hours following fertilization. The micrographs also show the expression of protein products of a maternal effect gene (step 1) and segmentation genes (steps 2–4). In step (1), the protein is stained brown and is found in the left side of the early embryo, which is the anterior end. In step (2), one protein encoded by a gap gene is stained in green and another is stained in red. The yellow region is where the two different gap proteins overlap. In step (3), a protein encoded by a pair-rule gene is stained in light blue. In step (4), a protein encoded by a segment-polarity gene is stained pink. When comparing steps (3) and (4), note that the embryo has undergone a 180° turn, folding back on itself.

(a) Normal fly with two wings

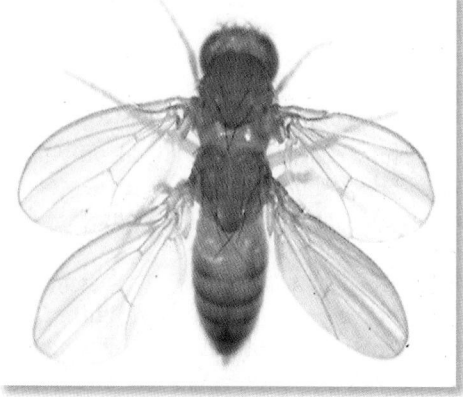

(b) Mutant fly with four wings

Figure 17.12   The *bithorax* mutation in *Drosophila*.   **(a)** A normal fly has two wings on the second thoracic segment and two halteres on the third thoracic segment. **(b)** This fly carries mutations in a complex of genes called the *bithorax* complex. In this fly the third thoracic segment has the same characteristics as the second thoracic segment, thereby producing a fly with four wings instead of two.

halteres and four wings. The term *bithorax* refers to the duplicated characteristics of the second thoracic segment. Edward Lewis, a pioneer in the genetic study of development, became interested in the *bithorax* phenotype and began investigating it in 1946. He discovered that the mutant chromosomal region contains a complex of genes that play a role in the third phase of development.

Homeotic genes encode homeotic proteins that function as transcription factors. The coding sequence of homeotic genes contains a 180-bp sequence known as a **homeobox**. The homeobox encodes a region of the protein called a **homeodomain**, which functions in binding to the DNA. The primary function of homeotic proteins is to activate the transcription of specific genes that promote developmental changes in the animal. The homeodomain binds to enhancer sequences, which are described in Chapter 12. These enhancers are found near specific genes that control development. Most homeotic proteins also contain a transcriptional activation domain. After the homeodomain binds an enhancer, the transcriptional activation domain assists the assembly of proteins to promote transcription. However, it should be noted that some homeotic proteins also function as repressors of transcription of some genes.

GENOMES AND PROTEOMES

A Homologous Group of Homeotic Genes Is Found in All Animals

As you have learned, mutations are often detrimental to organisms, but they are also drivers of evolution and the complexity of organisms. Although single nucleotide changes can alter the expression of a gene or result in minor changes to the amino acid sequence (though this can have major implications, as was illustrated by the example of sickle-cell anemia in Figure 13.1), more substantive changes can quickly alter the rate of evolution. In particular, the phenomenon of gene **duplication**, which will be discussed in greater detail in Chapter 19, essentially creates two identical copies of the gene. One gene copy is needed to encode the original protein, but the other is essentially free to accumulate mutations that alter the function of the encoded protein. In this way, the original protein function is retained (original gene), but the organism has extra genetic material (the duplicated gene) that, when mutated, can produce proteins with slightly different functions. **Figure 17.13** illustrates two cycles of gene duplication in which a duplication event produces two copies of a gene, one of which may undergo mutations to produce a protein that allows the individual to outcompete others of the species. Over time this selective advantage results in a few individuals prevailing and eventually

Original chromosome

Gene duplication

Mutation/divergence

Gene duplication

Mutation/divergence

Figure 17.13   Gene duplication increases genetic complexity.   Gene duplication results in an additional, identical copy of a specific gene. Over many generations, mutation followed by selection alters the sequence of one or both genes; expression results in the synthesis of proteins that may have novel functions that confer advantages to the organisms. Multiple rounds of this process generate gene families that are similar in sequence but have diverged to serve specific functions.

dominating the species. Gene duplication is the first step in the evolution of a **gene family**: a collection of similar, but not identical, genes that contribute to the success and complexity of organisms. This theme in evolution is well illustrated by the segmentation genes.

As you will learn in Chapter 18, molecular genetic technologies allow genes to be mapped, cloned, and sequenced. It is the complementary nature of the two strands of DNA that underpins hybridization techniques wherein a single strand of DNA from one organism (termed the *probe*) can base pair with the complementary DNA strand of a homologous gene, whether in the same organism or from a different organism. The strength of binding is directly correlated with the degree to which the two DNA strands can interact. Direct DNA sequencing and computer comparisons of sequence data from different organisms is used to determine the percentage identity of two sequences. The management and analysis of huge datasets has resulted in the birth of a new subdiscipline in molecular biology, **bioinformatics**, which is one of the subjects of Chapter 19.

Such comparisons have identified the evolutionary relationships between genes and have established that the homeotic genes of *Drosophila* have cognates in higher organisms, such as mice and humans.

The general approach of using *Drosophila* genes as probes to identify homologous vertebrate genes has been quite successful. The *Antennapedia* complex contains five genes, designated *lab, pb, Dfd, Scr,* and *Antp*. The *bithorax* complex has three genes, *Ubx, abd-A,* and *Abd-B*. Both of these complexes are located on the same chromosome, but a long stretch of DNA separates them (**Figure 17.14**). Researchers have found complexes of homeotic genes in vertebrate species that bear striking similarities to those in the fruit fly. In the mouse these groups of adjacent homeotic genes are called *Hox* **complexes**. The mouse has four *Hox* complexes, designated *HoxA, HoxB, HoxC,* and *HoxD*. Thirty-eight genes are found in the four complexes, which represent 13 different gene types. You can see from Figure 17.14 that several of the homeotic genes in fruit flies and mammals are evolutionarily related. Among the first six types of *Hox* genes, five of them

Figure 17.14 **Conservation and colinearity of homeotic genes.** The hypothetical progenitor organism has a chromosome with several homeotic genes that are similar but not identical. Additional gene duplication and selection events led to new speciation events and eventually led to the evolution of *Drosophila,* having the two clusters of *Antennapedia* and *bithorax* genes, and the mouse, having four clusters of *Hox* genes located on four different chromosomes. The order of expression of the genes is correlated with the specification of the anterior to posterior segments of each organism, a phenomenon called colinearity.

are homologous to genes found in the *Antennapedia* complex of *Drosophila*. Among the last seven (genes numbered 7–13), three are homologous to the genes of the *bithorax* complex.

Interestingly, the order of homeotic genes along the chromosome correlates with their expression along the anteroposterior axis of the body. This phenomenon is called the **colinearity rule**. In both the mouse and *Drosophila*, the arrangement of *Hox* genes along the chromosome follows the colinearity rule, reflecting their pattern of expression from the anterior to the posterior end (Figure 17.14). Mutations in these genes affect the formation of structures along this axis. These results indicate that the *Hox* genes play a role in determining the fates of regions along the anteroposterior axis. Nevertheless, additional research will be necessary to understand the individual role that each of the 38 *Hox* genes plays during embryonic development.

Hox genes are present in all animals. Sponges, which are a primitive type of animal, have a single *Hox* gene. The study of *Hox* genes in many different animal species has shown that the *Hox* cluster, with its colinear expression and its role of determining the anteroposterior axis, originated very early in the evolution of animals. At the level of genetics, fundamental similarities are observed in the ways that animals, such as worms, fruit flies, and mammals, undergo embryonic development. Researchers have suggested that a universal body plan exists for animal development. A portion of the genome of all animals is devoted to the execution of this plan. The biological diversity that we see among animals is due to deviation from this common plan.

Phase 4 Pattern Development: Stem Cells Can Divide and Differentiate into Specialized Cell Types

Thus far we have focused our attention on patterns of gene expression that occur during the early stages of development. These genes control the basic body plan of the organism. During the fourth phase of pattern development, the emphasis shifts to cell differentiation (see Figure 17.6). But how do cells differentiate into the necessary cell types? For example, how does an undifferentiated mesodermal cell differentiate into a specialized muscle cell, or how does an ectodermal cell differentiate into a nerve cell?

Although invertebrates have been instrumental in our understanding of pattern formation in animals, cell differentiation has been studied more extensively in mammals. One reason is that researchers have been able to grow mammalian cells in the laboratory for many decades. The availability of laboratory-grown cells makes it much easier to analyze the process of cell differentiation.

By studying mammalian cells in the laboratory, geneticists have determined that the profound morphological differences between two different types of differentiated cells, such as muscle and neurons, arise through gene regulation. Though muscle cells and neurons contain the same set of genes, they regulate the expression of their genes in very different ways. Certain genes that are transcriptionally active in muscle cells are inactive in nerve cells, and vice versa. Therefore, nerve and muscle cells express different proteins that affect the morphological and physiological characteristics of the respective cells in distinct ways. In this manner differential gene expression underlies cell differentiation.

General Properties of Stem Cells To understand the process of cell differentiation in a multicellular organism, we need to consider the special properties of **stem cells**, which divide and supply the cells that construct the bodies of all animals and plants. Stem cells have two common characteristics. First, they have the capacity to divide, and second, their daughter cells can differentiate into one or more specialized cell types. The two daughter cells that are produced from the division of a stem cell may have different fates (**Figure 17.15**). One cell may remain an undifferentiated stem cell, while the other daughter cell may differentiate into a specialized cell type. With this asymmetrical division-differentiation pattern, the population of stem cells remains constant, yet stem cells provide a population of specialized cells. For example, in mammals this mechanism is needed to replenish cells that have a finite lifespan, such as skin cells and red blood cells.

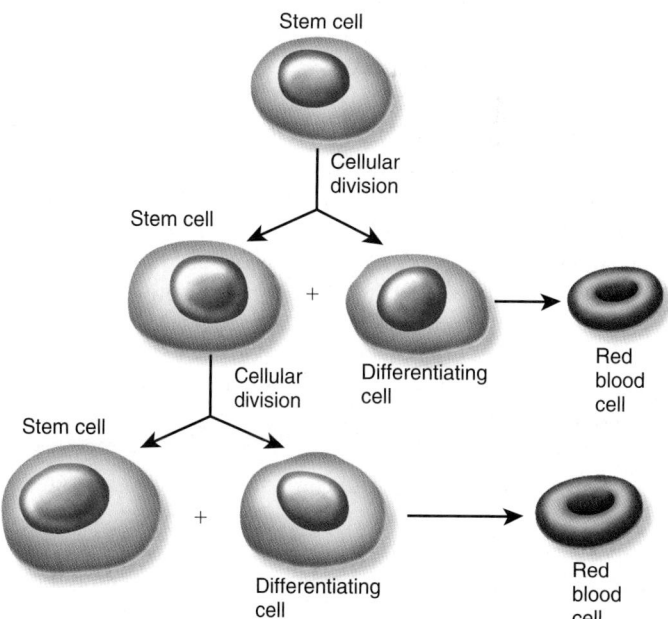

Figure 17.15 **Growth pattern of stem cells.** When a stem cell divides, one of the two daughter cells may remain a stem cell, while the other cell may differentiate into a specialized cell type, such as the red blood cells shown here.

Concept check: *What are the two key features of stem cells?*

Stem Cells During Development   In mammals stem cells are commonly categorized according to their developmental stage and their ability to differentiate (**Figure 17.16**). The ultimate stem cell is the fertilized egg, which, via multiple cellular divisions, can give rise to an entire organism. A fertilized egg is considered **totipotent** because it can produce all the cell types in the adult organism. The early mammalian embryo contains **embryonic stem cells (ES cells)**, which are initially found in the inner cell mass of the blastocyst. The blastocyst stage of embryonic development occurs before uterine implantation. Embryonic stem cells are **pluripotent**, which means they can also differentiate into almost every cell type of the body. However, a single embryonic stem cell has lost the ability to produce an entire, intact individual. At the early fetal stage of development, the cells that later give rise to sperm or eggs cells, known as the **embryonic germ cells (EG cells)**, also are pluripotent.

During the embryonic and fetal stages of development, cells lose their ability to differentiate into a wide variety of cell types. Adults have both multipotent and unipotent stem cells. A **multipotent** stem cell can differentiate into several cell types, but far fewer than a pluripotent embryonic stem cell. For example, hematopoietic stem cells (HSCs) found in the bone marrow can give rise to multiple blood cell types (**Figure 17.17**). Multipotent HSCs can follow a pathway in which cell division produces a myeloid progenitor cell, which then differentiates into various cells of the blood and immune systems. Alternatively, an HSC can follow a path in which it becomes a lymphoid progenitor cell that differentiates into different blood cell types. Other stem cells found in adults seem to be **unipotent**, or able to produce only daughter cells that differentiate into one cell type. For example, stem cells in the testes produce daughter cells that differentiate only into sperm.

Stem Cells in Medicine   Why are researchers so interested in stem cells? A compelling medical reason is the potential to treat human diseases or injuries that cause cell and tissue damage. This application has already become a reality in certain cases. For example, bone marrow transplants are used to treat patients with certain forms of cancer. When bone marrow from a healthy person is injected into the body of a patient who has had his immune system wiped out via radiation, the stem cells within the transplanted marrow have the ability to proliferate and differentiate into various types of blood cells within the body of the patient.

Renewed interest in the use of stem cells in the potential treatment of many other diseases was fostered by studies in 1998 that showed researchers can obtain ES cells from blastocysts and EG cells from aborted fetuses and successfully propagate them in the laboratory. As mentioned, ES and EG cells are pluripotent. Therefore, they have the capacity to produce many different kinds of tissue. Samuel Weiss and his colleagues at the University of Calgary discovered a central nervous system stem cell that can be induced to divide and differentiate into neurons, astrocytes, or oligodendrocytes. Further research in this area may enable scientists to use these stem cells to repair damaged brain or spinal tissue, as well as to treat neurodegenerative

Figure 17.16   Occurrence of stem cells at different stages of mammalian development.

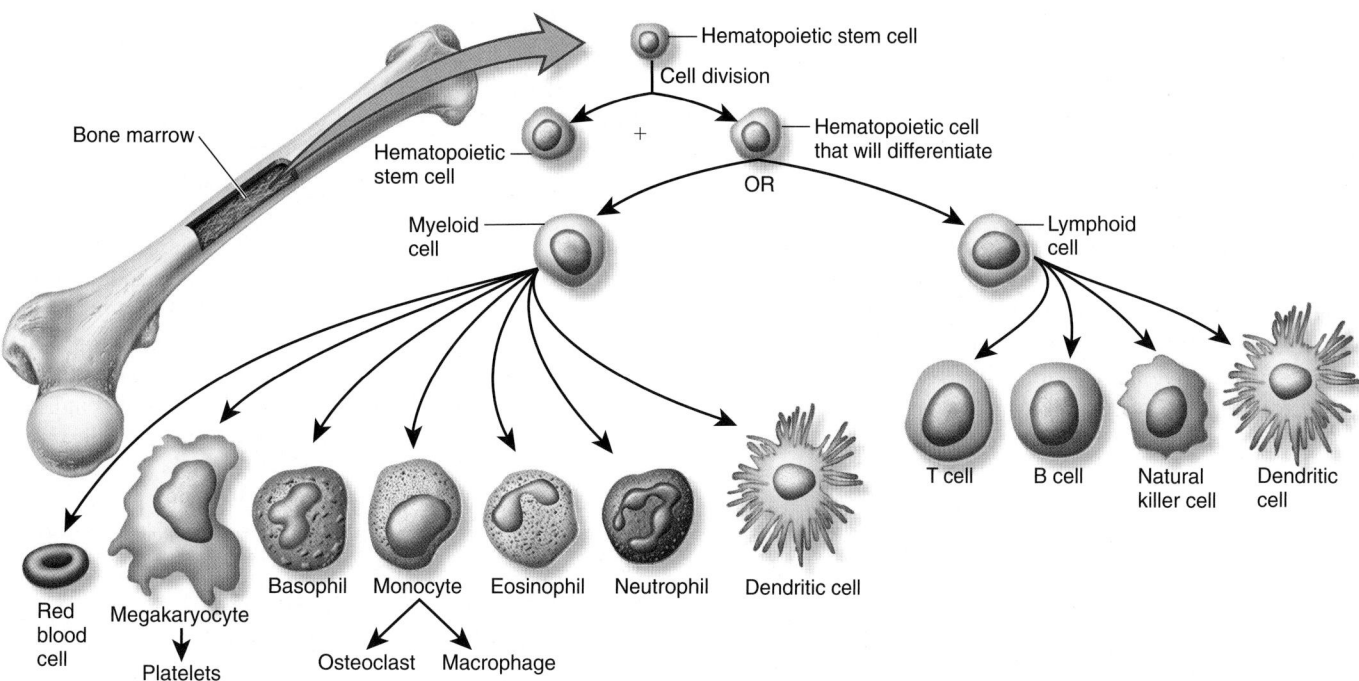

Figure 17.17 **Fates of hematopoietic stem cells (HSCs).** HSCs can follow two pathways in which cell division produces a myeloid cell and one that produces a lymphoid cell. Each develops into different blood cell types.

Concept check: *Are hematopoietic stem cells totipotent, pluripotent, multipotent, or unipotent?*

diseases. Embryonic cells could potentially be used to treat a wide variety of diseases associated with cell and tissue damage (**Table 17.1**). Much progress has been made in testing the use of stem cells in animal models. However, more research will need to be done before the use of stem cells to treat such diseases in humans is realized.

Despite the pluripotent nature of stem cells, finding ways to control their differentiation remains elusive. Recently,

Table 17.1	Some Potential Uses of Stem Cells to Treat Diseases
Cell or tissue type	**Disease treatment**
Nerve	Implantation of cells into the brain to treat Parkinson's disease
	Treatment of injuries, such as those to the spinal cord
Skin	Treatment of burns and skin disorders
Cardiac	Repair of heart damage associated with heart attacks
Cartilage	Repair of joints damaged by injury or arthritis
Bone	Repair of damaged bone or replacement with new bone
Liver	Repair or replacement of liver tissue damaged by injury or disease
Skeletal/muscle	Repair or replacement of damaged muscle

a team of researchers from the University of Toronto and McMaster University, led by Janet Rossant, demonstrated that overexpression of two genes called *SOX7* and *SOX17* can have profound effects on cell differentiation. *SOX17* induction resulted in endodermal lineages that differentiated toward liver and pancreatic identities. Such reprogramming of stem cells is important from a basic research prospective to allow scientists to more fully understand the signalling pathways that control differentiation. These studies also represent an early step toward reprogramming a person's own stem cells for use in treating disease and tissue damage, without the complications of tissue rejection that often occur when donor cells are isolated from another individual, and without raising ethical concerns.

From an ethical perspective the primary issue that raises debate is the source of stem cells for research and potential treatments. Most ES cells have been derived from human embryos that were produced from in vitro fertilization, a method of assisted conception in which fertilization occurs outside the mother's body and a limited number of the resulting embryos are transferred to the uterus. Most EG cells are obtained from aborted fetuses, either those that were spontaneously aborted (miscarried) or those in which the decision to abort was not related to donating the fetal tissue to research. Some feel that it is morally wrong to use this tissue in the research or treatment of disease. Furthermore, some people fear that this technology could lead to intentional abortions to obtain fetal tissues for transplantation. Conversely, others feel that these embryos and fetuses were not going to become living individuals; therefore, it is beneficial to study these cells and to use them in a positive way to treat human diseases and injury. It is not clear whether these two opposing viewpoints can reach a common ground. Many governments are enacting laws that limit or prohibit the use of embryos or fetuses to obtain stem cells but permit the use of stem cell lines that are already available in research laboratories. In Canada, for example, the Assisted Human Reproduction Act allows research to be conducted by using IVF embryos but does not allow for the creation of embryos for research. In the United States federal law prohibits the use of government funding for research projects that involve the destruction of embryos to obtain stem cells. However, government-sponsored research can be done on stem cell lines that were created before this legislation was enacted.

If stem cells could be obtained from adult cells and propagated in the laboratory, the ethical dilemma may be avoided, because most people do not have serious moral objections to current procedures, such as bone marrow transplantation. In 2006 work by Shinya Yamanaka and colleagues showed that adult mouse fibroblasts (a type of connective tissue cell) could become pluripotent through the introduction of four genes that encode transcription factors. In 2007 Yamanaka's laboratory and two other research groups were able to show that such induced pluripotent stem cells can differentiate into all cell types when injected into mouse blastocysts and grown into baby mice. These results indicate that adult cells can be reprogrammed to become embryonic stem cells.

FEATURE INVESTIGATION

Davis, Weintraub, and Lasser Identified Genes That Promote Muscle Cell Differentiation

A key question regarding the study of stem cells is, What causes a stem cell to differentiate into a particular cell type? Though the answer is not understood in great detail, researchers have discovered that certain proteins function as master transcription factors that cause a cell to differentiate into a specific cell type. The investigation described here was one of the first studies to reveal this phenomenon.

In 1987 Robert Davis, Harold Weintraub, and Andrew Lasser conducted a study to identify genes that promote muscle cell differentiation. The initial strategy for their experiments was to identify genes that are expressed only in differentiating muscle cells, not in nonmuscle cells. Though methods of gene cloning are described in Chapter 18, let's briefly consider these scientists' cloning methods so we can understand their approach. They began with two different laboratory cell lines that could differentiate into muscle cells. From these two cell lines, they identified about 10,000 different genes that were transcribed into mRNA. Next, they compared the expressed genes in these two muscle cell lines with genes that were expressed in a nonmuscle cell line. Davis, Weintraub, and Lasser's comparison revealed 26 genes that were expressed only in the two muscle cell lines and not in the nonmuscle cell line. To narrow their search further, they examined the expression of these 26 genes in other nonmuscle cell lines they had available. Among the 26, only 3 of them were not expressed in other nonmuscle cell lines. Based on these criteria, they were left with three different cloned genes, which they termed *MyoA*, *MyoD*, and *MyoH*.

In the experiment shown in **Figure 17.18**, the scientists' goal was to determine whether any of these three cloned genes could cause nonmuscle cells to differentiate into muscle cells.

By using molecular techniques described in Chapter 18, the coding sequence of each cloned gene was placed next to an active promoter, and then the genes were introduced into fibroblasts, which are a type of cell that normally differentiates into osteoblasts (bone cells), chrondrocytes (cartilage cells), adipocytes (fat cells), and smooth muscle cells but, in vivo, never differentiates into skeletal muscle cells. However, when the cloned *MyoD* gene was expressed in fibroblast cells in a laboratory, the fibroblasts differentiated into skeletal muscle cells. These cells contained large amounts of myosin, which is a protein that is expressed in muscle cells. The other two cloned genes (*MyoA* and *MyoH*) did not cause muscle cell differentiation or promote myosin production.

Since this initial discovery researchers have found that *MyoD* belongs to a small group of genes termed **myogenic bHLH genes** that initiate muscle development. Myogenic bHLH genes encode transcription factors that contain a basic domain and a helix-loop-helix domain (bHLH). They are found in all vertebrates, and they have been identified in several invertebrates, such as *Drosophila* and *C. elegans*. In all cases, myogenic bHLH genes are activated during skeletal muscle cell development.

Experimental Questions

1. What was the goal of the research conducted by Davis, Weintraub, and Lassar?
2. How did Davis, Weintraub, and Lassar's research identify the candidate genes for muscle differentiation?
3. Once the researchers identified the candidate genes for muscle differentiation, how did they test the effect of each gene on cell differentiation? What were the results of the study?

HYPOTHESIS Muscle differentiation is induced by particular genes.

KEY MATERIALS Three cloned genes had been identified that were expressed only in differentiating muscle cell lines. The researchers also had fibroblast cell lines, which do not normally differentiate into muscle cells.

Experimental level — Conceptual level

1. In three separate tubes, add each of the three cloned genes, designated *MyoA*, *MyoD*, and *MyoH*.

MyoA   *MyoD*   *MyoH*

DNA

2. Add fibroblast cells to the tubes and incubate in the presence of calcium phosphate ($CaPO_4$), which promotes the uptake of DNA into the cells.

1. Fibroblast cells
2. $CaPO_4$

Fibroblast — DNA taken up by cell

3. Plate the cells on solid growth media. Allow the cells to grow for three to five days. Cells will express the cloned gene.

MyoD
MyoA   *MyoH*

4. Examine the cells under a microscope to determine if they have the morphology of differentiating muscle cells.

Now looks like a muscle cell

Still look like a fibroblast

5. Also, determine if the cells are synthesizing myosin, which is a protein that is abundantly made in muscle cells. This is done by adding a labelled antibody that recognizes myosin and determining the amounts of antibody that bind.

Colony labelled with myosin antibody

MyoD
MyoA   *MyoH*

Antibodies

Figure 17.18 Davis, Weintraub, and Lasser and the promotion of muscle cell differentiation in fibroblasts by the expression of *MyoD*.

Figure 17.18 *(Continued)*

6 THE DATA

Results from step (4):

DNA added	Microscopic morphology of cells
MyoA	Fibroblasts
MyoD	Muscle cells
MyoH	Fibroblasts

Results from step 5:

DNA added	Colonies labelled with antibody that binds to myosin?
MyoA	No
MyoD	Yes
MyoH	No

7 CONCLUSION The *MyoD* gene encodes a protein that causes cells to differentiate into skeletal muscle cells.

8 SOURCE Davis, Robert L., Weintraub, Harold, and Lassar, Andrew B. 1987. Expression of a single transfected cDNA converts fibroblasts to myoblasts. *Cell* 51:987–1000.

17.3 DEVELOPMENT IN PLANTS

Learning Outcomes:

1. Outline the stages of pattern development in plants.
2. Explain the ABC model for flower development.

Because all eukaryotic organisms share an evolutionary history, animals and plants have many common features, including the types of events that occur during development. However, the general morphology of plants is quite different from animals. Plant morphology exhibits two key features (see Figure 17.2b). The first is the root-shoot axis. Most plant growth occurs via cell division near the tips of the shoots and the bottoms of the roots. Second, this growth occurs in a well-defined radial pattern. For example, early in *Arabidopsis* growth, a rosette of leaves is produced from leaf buds that emanate in a spiral pattern directly from the main shoot (**Figure 17.19**). Later, the shoot generates branches that produce leaf buds as they grow. Overall, the radial pattern in which a plant shoot generates buds is an important mechanism that determines much of the general morphology of the plant.

At the cellular level, too, plant development differs markedly from animal development. For example, cell migration does not occur during plant development. In plants an entirely new individual can be regenerated from many types of somatic cells. Certain somatic cells of plants are totipotent, with the ability to produce an entire individual.

In spite of these apparent differences, the underlying molecular mechanisms of pattern formation in plants still share some similarities with those in animals. Like animals, plants use the mechanism of differential gene expression to coordinate the development of a body plan. Like their animal counterparts, a plant's developmental program relies on the use of transcription factors that determine spatial, temporal, and quantitative

aspects of gene expression. In this section we will consider pattern formation in plants and examine how transcription factors play a key role in plant development.

Plant Development Occurs from Meristems That Are Formed in the Embryo

Before we discuss genes that control plant development, let's examine pattern formation in the early development of the plant embryo. **Figure 17.20** illustrates a common sequence of events

Figure 17.19 **Radial pattern of shoot growth in plants.** Early in development, as shown here in *Arabidopsis,* a single shoot promotes the formation of early leaves on the plant. Later, buds will form from the main shoot that will go on to form branches. The buds that produce the branches and the leaves that form on the branches are also produced in a radial manner.

that takes place in the embryonic development of seed plants, such as *Arabidopsis.* After fertilization the first cell division is asymmetrical and produces a smaller apical cell and a larger basal cell (**Figure 17.20a**). The apical cell will give rise to most of the embryo and later develop into the shoot of the plant. In *Arabidopsis,* the basal cell will give rise to the root, along with a structure called the suspensor, which will channel nutrients from the parent plant to the young embryo (**Figure 17.20b**).

At the heart stage, which is composed of only about 100 cells, the basic organization of the plant has been established (**Figure 17.20c**). Plants have organized groups of actively dividing stem cells called **meristems**. As discussed earlier in this chapter, stem cells retain the ability to divide and their daughter cells differentiate into multiple cell types. The meristem produces offshoots of proliferating and differentiating cells. The **root apical meristem** gives rise only to the root, while the **shoot apical meristem** produces all aerial parts of the plant, which include the stem and lateral structures, such as leaves and flowers.

The heart stage then progresses to the formation of a seedling that has two cotyledons, which are embryonic leaves that store nutrients for the developing embryo and seedling. In the seedling shown in **Figure 17.20d**, you can see three main regions. The **apical region** produces the leaves and flowers of the plant. The **central region** gives rise to stem tissue. Finally, the **basal region** produces the roots. Each of these three regions develops differently, as indicated by their unique cell division patterns and distinct morphologies.

As you can see in the inset to Figure 17.20d, the shoot meristem is organized into three areas called the organizing centre, the central zone, and the peripheral zone. The **organizing centre** ensures the proper organization of the meristem and preserves the correct number of actively dividing stem cells. The **central zone** is an area in which undifferentiated stem cells are always maintained. As these cells divide, some are pushed out into the **peripheral zone**, where they will acquire positional information that determines their fate as lateral branches, leaves, or flowers.

By analyzing mutants that disrupt the developmental process, researchers have discovered that the apical, central, and basal regions of a growing plant express different sets of genes. G. Jürgens and his colleagues began a search to identify a category of genes known as the **apical-basal-patterning genes**, which are important in early stages of plant development. A few examples are described in **Table 17.2**. Defects in apical-basal-patterning genes cause dramatic effects in one of these

Figure 17.20 **Developmental steps in the formation of a plant embryo.** **(a)** The two-cell stage consists of the apical cell and basal cell. **(b)** The eight-cell stage consists of a pro-embryo and a suspensor. The suspensor gives rise to extra embryonic tissue that is needed for seed formation. **(c)** At the heart stage all the plant tissues have begun to form. Note that the shoot meristem is located between the future cotyledons, while the root meristem is on the opposite side. **(d)** A seedling showing basal, central, and apical regions. The inset shows the organization of the shoot meristem. Note: The steps shown in parts (a), (b), and (c) occur during seed formation, and the embryo would be enclosed within a seed.

Principle: *Living organisms grow, develop, and reproduce. This diagram depicts how cell division and differentiation transform the zygote into a multicellular seedling.*

Table 17.2	Examples of Arabidopsis Apical-Basal-Patterning Genes
Region: *Gene*	**Description**
Apical	
Gurke	Mutations that cause minor loss of function in the *Gurke* gene produce seedlings with highly reduced or no cotyledons. Complete loss of function eliminates the entire shoot.
Aintegumenta	Encodes a transcription factor that is also expressed in the peripheral zone. Its expression maintains the growth of lateral buds.
Central	
Scarecrow	Encodes a transcription factor that plays a role in the asymmetrical division that produces the radial pattern of growth in the stem. Note: The Scarecrow protein also affects cell division patterns in roots and plays a role in sensing gravity.
Basal	
Monopterous	Encodes a transcription factor. When this gene is defective, the plant embryo cannot initiate the formation of root structures, but root structures can be formed post-embryonically under the correct growth conditions. This gene seems to be required for organizing root formation in the embryo but is not required for root formation per se.

three regions. For example, the *gurke* gene is necessary for apical development. When it is defective, the embryo lacks apical structures.

Plant Homeotic Genes Control Flower Development

Although William Bateson coined the term *homeotic* to describe such mutations in animals, the first known homeotic genes were described in plants. Naturalists in ancient Greece and Rome, for example, recorded their observations of double flowers in which stamens were replaced by petals. In current research geneticists are studying these types of mutations to better understand developmental pathways in plants. Many homeotic mutations affecting flower development have been identified in *Arabidopsis* and also in the snapdragon (*Antirrhinum majus*).

A normal *Arabidopsis* flower is composed of four concentric whorls of structures (**Figure 17.21a**). The first outer whorl contains four **sepals**, which protect the flower bud before it opens. The second whorl is composed of four **petals**, and the third whorl contains six stamens. The **stamens** are structures that make the male gametophyte, pollen. Finally, the fourth, innermost whorl contains two carpels that are fused together. The **carpels** produce, enclose, and nurture the female gametophytes.

By analyzing the effects of many different homeotic mutations in *Arabidopsis*, Enrico Coen and Elliot Meyerowitz proposed the ABC model for flower development in 1991. In this model three classes of genes, called *A*, *B*, and *C*, govern the formation of sepals, petals, stamens, and carpels. More recently, a fourth category of genes called the *E* genes was found to also be required for this process. In *Arabidopsis* Figure 17.21a illustrates how these genes affect normal flower

development. In whorl 1, gene *A* product is made. This promotes sepal formation. In whorl 2, *A*, *B*, and *E* gene products are made, which promotes petal formation. In whorl 3 the expression of genes *B*, *C*, and *E* causes stamens to be made. Finally, in whorl 4 the products of *C* and *E* genes promote carpel formation.

Now let's consider what happens in certain homeotic mutants that undergo transformations of particular whorls. According to the original ABC model, genes *A* and *C* repress each other's

Figure 17.21   Normal and mutant homeotic gene action in *Arabidopsis*.   (a) A normal flower composed of four concentric whorls of structures: sepals, petals, stamens, and carpels. To the right is the ABC model of homeotic gene action in *Arabidopsis*. This is a revised model based on the recent identification of *E* genes. (b) A homeotic mutant defective in gene *A* in which the sepals have been transformed into carpels, and the petals have been transformed into stamens. (c) A triple mutant defective in the *A*, *B*, and *C* genes, producing a flower with all leaves.

Concept check: *What pattern would you expect if the B gene was expressed in whorls 2, 3, and 4?*

expression, and gene *B* functions independently. In a mutant defective in gene *A* expression, gene *C* will also be expressed in whorls 1 and 2. This produces a carpel-stamen-stamen-carpel arrangement in which the sepals have been transformed into carpels and the petals into stamens (**Figure 17.21b**). When gene *B* is defective, a flower cannot make petals or stamens. Therefore, a gene *B* defect yields a flower with a sepal-sepal-carpel-carpel arrangement. When gene *C* is defective, gene *A* is expressed in all four whorls. This results in a sepal-petal-petal-sepal pattern. If the expression of *E* genes is defective, the flower consists entirely of sepals. Note, too, that determinacy is compromised: instead of the flower terminating in a specific floral organ (usually a fused carpel), the program of development reiterates, giving rise to flowers with many whorls.

Overall, the genes described in Figure 17.21 promote a pattern of development that leads to sepal, petal, stamen, or carpel structures. But what happens if genes *A*, *B*, and *C* are all defective? This produces a flower that is composed entirely of leaves (**Figure 17.21c**). These results indicate that the leaf structure is the default pathway and that the *A*, *B*, *C*, and *E* genes cause development to deviate from a leaf structure to make something else. In this regard the sepals, petals, stamens, and carpels can be viewed as modified leaves. With astonishing insight, Johann Goethe, a German poet, novelist, playwright, and natural philosopher, originally proposed this idea more than 200 years ago.

Like the *Drosophila* homeotic genes, plant homeotic genes are part of a hierarchy of gene regulation. Many plant homeotic genes belong to a family of genes called MADS box genes, which encode transcription factor proteins that contain a DNA-binding domain called a MADS domain. The *Arabidopsis* homeotic genes do not contain a sequence similar to the homeobox found in animal homeotic genes.

Summary of Key Concepts

17.1 General Themes in Development

- Development refers to a series of changes in the state of a cell, a tissue, an organ, or an organism. Developmental genetics seeks to understand how gene expression controls the development process.
- A cell's fate becomes determined before the cell differentiates into a specialized cell type.
- *Drosophila, C. elegans,* the mouse, zebrafish, and *Arabidopsis* are model organisms studied by developmental geneticists. (Figure 17.1)
- The process that gives rise to a plant or an animal with a particular body structure is called pattern formation. (Figure 17.2)
- Pattern formation depends on positional information. Four responses to positional information are cell division, cell migration, cell differentiation, and apoptosis. (Figures 17.3, 17.4)
- Positional information is conveyed by morphogens and cell adhesion. (Figure 17.5)
- Transcription factors control the program of development in animals and plants. In animals this program occurs in four phases. (Figure 17.6)

17.2 Development in Animals

- Embryonic development in *Drosophila* occurs in a series of steps, starting with a zygote, then an embryo, a larvae, a pupa, and an adult. The basic body plan is established in the embryo. (Figure 17.7)
- Maternal effect genes control the formation of body axes. (Figures 17.8, 17.9)
- In the second phase of pattern formation, the sequential expression of three categories of segmentation genes divides the embryo into segments. Mutations that alter *Drosophila* development have allowed scientists to understand the normal process. (Figures 17.10, 17.11)
- During the third phase of pattern formation, each segment begins to develop its own unique characteristics. Homeotic genes control the development of a particular segment or group of segments. (Figures 17.12, 17.13, 17.14)

- Gene duplication events result in additional copies of genes and create/expand gene families. (Figure 17.13)
- Invertebrates, such as *Drosophila*, and vertebrates, such as the mouse, both have a homologous set of homeotic genes. In mammals, these are called the *Hox* genes. (Figure 17.14)
- In the fourth phase of pattern formation, stem cells divide and differentiate into specialized cell types. (Figure 17.15)
- Stem cells are categorized according to their developmental stage and their ability to differentiate. In mammals a fertilized egg is totipotent; certain embryonic and fetal cells are pluripotent; and stem cells in the adult are multipotent or unipotent. (Figures 17.16, 17.17)
- Stem cells have the potential to treat a variety of human disorders. (Table 17.1)
- Certain master transcription factors control the cell differentiation process. An example is *MyoD*, which Davis, Weintraub, and Lasser showed experimentally can cause a cell to differentiate into a muscle cell. (Figure 17.18)

17.3 Development in Plants

- Plants grow in a radial pattern along a root and shoot axis. (Figure 17.19)
- Plant meristems contain dividing cells that promote the development of plant structures, such as roots, stems, leaves, and flowers. (Figure 17.20)
- The apical, central, and basal regions of the growing plant express different sets of pattern formation genes. (Table 17.2)
- Four classes of homeotic genes in plants, *A, B, C,* and *E*, control flower development. (Figure 17.21)

Test to Assess Your Learning

1. The process whereby a cell's morphology and function have changed is called
   a. determination.
   b. cell fate.
   c. differentiation.
   d. genetic engineering.
   e. both (a) and (c).

2. Pattern formation in plants is along the _____ axis.
   a. dorsoventral
   b. anteroposterior
   c. right-left
   d. root-shoot
   e. all of the above

3. Positional information is important in determining the destiny of a cell in a multicellular organism. Cells respond to positional information by
   a. dividing.
   b. migrating.
   c. differentiating.
   d. undergoing apoptosis.
   e. all of the above.

4. Morphogens are
   a. molecules that disrupt normal development.
   b. molecules that convey positional information.
   c. mutagenic agents that cause apoptosis.
   d. receptors that allow cells to adhere to the extracellular matrix.
   e. both (a) and (c).

5. What group of molecules plays a key role in controlling the program of developmental changes?
   a. motor proteins
   b. transporters
   c. transcription factors
   d. restriction endonucleases
   e. cyclins

6. Use the following list of events to determine the proper sequence for animal development:
   1. Formation of tissues, organs, and other body structures in each segment.
   2. Axes of the entire animal are determined.
   3. Cells become differentiated.
   4. The entire animal is divided into segments.
   a. 2, 3, 4, 1
   b. 1, 2, 4, 3
   c. 2, 4, 3, 1
   d. 3, 2, 4, 1
   e. 2, 4, 1, 3

7. The homeotic genes in *Drosophila*
   a. determine the structural and functional characteristics of different segments of the developing fly.
   b. encode motor proteins that transport morphogens throughout the embryo.
   c. are dispersed apparently randomly throughout the genome.
   d. are expressed in similar levels in all parts of the developing embryo.
   e. both (a) and (c).

8. Which of the following genes do *not* play a role in the process whereby segments are formed in the fruit fly embryo?
   a. homeotic genes
   b. gap genes
   c. pair-rule genes
   d. segment-polarity genes
   e. All of the above play a role in segmentation.

9. An embryonic stem cell that can give rise to any type of cell of an adult organism but cannot produce an entire intact individual is called
   a. totipotent.
   b. pluripotent.
   c. multipotent.
   d. unipotent.
   e. antipotent.

10. During plant development, the leaves and the flowers of the plant are derived from
    a. the central region.
    b. the basal region.
    c. the suspensor.
    d. the apical region.
    e. both (a) and (d).

Articulate to Assess Your Learning

1. If you observed fruit flies with the following developmental abnormalities, would you guess that a mutation has occurred in a segmentation gene or a homeotic gene? Explain your guess.
   a. Three abdominal segments are missing.
   b. One abdominal segment has legs.

2. What is a meristem? Explain the role of meristems in plant development.

Collaborate to Assess and Extend Your Learning

1. Developmental genetics is based on a complex network of gene regulation. Starting with maternal effect genes and ending with master transcription factors, draw or describe how this network is structured for *Drosophila*. How many genes do you think are necessary to describe a complete developmental network for the fruit fly? How many genes do you think are needed for a network to specify one segment?

2. Is it possible for a phenotypically normal female fly to be homozygous for a loss-of-function allele in the *bicoid* gene? What would be the phenotype of the offspring that such a fly would produce if it were mated to a male that was homozygous for the normal *bicoid* allele?

3. The *MyoD* gene in mammals plays a role in muscle cell differentiation, while the *Hox* genes are homeotic genes that play a role in the differentiation of particular regions of the body. Explain how the functions of these genes are similar and different.

4. A principle of biology is that living organisms grow, develop, and reproduce. Discuss how maternal effect genes, segmentation genes, and homeotic genes control the process of development in animals.

Visit McGraw-Hill Ryerson Connect™ for additional study resources.

Genetic Technology

Chapter Outline

Copycat, the first cloned pet. In 2002 the cat shown here, called Copycat or CC (for carbon copy), was produced by cloning, a procedure described later in this chapter.

Sabrina was diagnosed with type I diabetes, once called juvenile diabetes, when she was 13 years old. Since then she's been giving herself regular injections of insulin, a protein hormone that is normally made by cells in the pancreas. Sabrina's pancreas doesn't make this hormone. Her prescription insulin says Humulin on the bottle, which stands for human insulin. You might be surprised to learn that her insulin is not made by human cells. It's actually made by a laboratory strain of the bacterium *Escherichia coli* that has been genetically modified to synthesize a hormone identical in structure to human insulin. This is just one example of how researchers have been able to apply **recombinant DNA technology**—the use of laboratory techniques to isolate and manipulate fragments of DNA—to benefit humans. Such technology produces recombinant DNA, which refers to any DNA molecule that has been manipulated so it contains DNA from two or more sources.

In the early 1970s the first successes in making recombinant DNA molecules were accomplished independently by two groups at Stanford University: David Jackson, Robert Symons, and Paul Berg; and Peter Lobban and A. Dale Kaiser. Both groups were able to isolate and purify pieces of DNA in a test tube, and then covalently link together two or more DNA fragments. Shortly thereafter, these recombinant DNA molecules were introduced into living cells. Once inside a host cell the recombinant molecules are replicated to produce many identical copies, a process known as cloning. When copies contain a gene of interest, the technique is called **gene cloning**. In the first part of the chapter we will explore recombinant DNA technology and gene cloning, techniques that have enabled geneticists to probe relationships between gene sequences and phenotypic consequences. Such studies have been fundamental to our understanding of gene structure and function.

Later in this chapter we will consider the topic of genomics, the molecular analysis of the entire genome of a species. In recent years molecular techniques have progressed to the point where researchers can study the structure and function of many genes as large integrated networks. For example, the expression of all genes in a genome can be analyzed simultaneously under different conditions, such as in normal versus cancer cells. This information can help us to understand how changes in gene expression can cause uncontrolled cell proliferation.

In the last section of this chapter we will explore the topic of **biotechnology**—the use of living organisms or the products of living organisms for human benefit. **Genetic engineering**, the direct manipulation of genes for practical purposes, is playing an ever-increasing role in the creation of strains of microorganisms, plants, and animals that have characteristics that are useful to people. These include bacteria that make human insulin, crops that make their own insecticides, and farm animals that make human medicines.

18.1 GENE CLONING

Learning Outcomes:

1. Outline the steps of gene cloning using vectors.
2. Distinguish between a genomic library and a cDNA library.
3. Explain how gel electrophoresis is used to separate DNA fragments.
4. Describe the steps of gene cloning using polymerase chain reaction (PCR).

Molecular biologists want to understand how the molecules within living cells contribute to cell structure and function. Because proteins are the workhorses of cells, many researchers focus their attention on the structure and function of proteins, or the genes that encode them. In a laboratory it is common to study just one or perhaps a few different genes or proteins. At the molecular level this is a daunting task. Most eukaryotes have 25,000 to 30,000 genes, making the identification and characterization of any single gene or protein akin to finding a needle in a haystack. To overcome this truly formidable obstacle, researchers frequently take the approach of cloning the genes that encode their proteins of interest.

As mentioned, the term gene cloning refers to procedures that lead to the formation of many copies of a particular gene. **Figure 18.1** provides an overview of the steps and goals of gene cloning. The process is usually done for one of two reasons: (1) a researcher needs to make many copies of the gene, perhaps to study the DNA directly or to use the DNA as a tool, or (2) the researcher needs to obtain lots of the gene product—mRNA or protein. For example, biochemists use gene cloning to obtain large amounts of proteins to study their structure and function. In modern molecular biology the many uses for gene cloning are remarkable. Gene cloning has provided the foundation for critical technical advances in a variety of disciplines, including genetics, cell biology, microbiology, biochemistry, and medicine. In this section we will examine the procedures that are used to copy genes.

Step 1: Vector DNA and Chromosomal DNA Are the Starting Materials to Clone a Gene

In the first step of gene cloning, a key material is a type of DNA known as a **vector** (from a Latin term meaning "one who carries") (Figure 18.1). In cloning experiments a vector can carry a small segment of chromosomal DNA, perhaps only a single gene. By comparison, a chromosome carries many more genes, perhaps a few thousand. When a vector is introduced into a living cell, it can replicate, and the DNA that it carries is also replicated. This produces many identical copies of the inserted gene.

The vectors commonly used in gene cloning experiments were derived originally from two natural sources: plasmids or viruses. Some vectors are **plasmids**, which are small circular pieces of DNA. As discussed in Chapter 16 plasmids are found naturally in many strains of bacteria and also occasionally in eukaryotic cells. Commercially available plasmids have been genetically engineered for effective use in cloning experiments. They contain unique sites into which scientists can easily insert pieces of DNA. An alternative type of vector used in cloning experiments is a **viral vector**. Viruses can infect living cells and propagate themselves by taking control of the host cell's metabolic machinery. When a chromosomal gene is inserted into a viral vector, the gene will be replicated whenever the viral DNA is replicated. Therefore, viruses can be used as vectors to carry other pieces of DNA. Note that only certain parts of naturally occurring plasmids and viruses are used in the construction of vectors, a feature that limits or negates their natural pathogenicity. For example, a vector must contain an origin of DNA replication such that the host cell metabolic machinery will recognize this sequence and replicate the molecule.

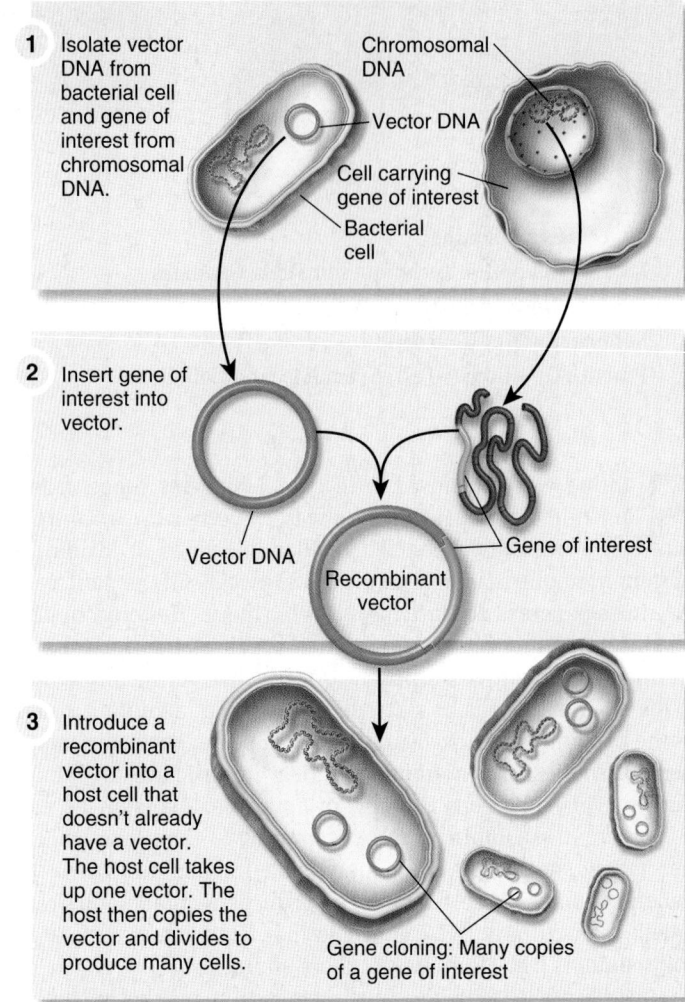

1. Isolate vector DNA from bacterial cell and gene of interest from chromosomal DNA.

Chromosomal DNA
Vector DNA
Cell carrying gene of interest
Bacterial cell

2. Insert gene of interest into vector.

Vector DNA
Recombinant vector
Gene of interest

3. Introduce a recombinant vector into a host cell that doesn't already have a vector. The host cell takes up one vector. The host then copies the vector and divides to produce many cells.

Gene cloning: Many copies of a gene of interest

Gene cloning is done to achieve one of two main goals:

Producing large amounts of DNA of a specific gene	Expressing the cloned gene to produce the encoded protein
Examples	*Examples*
• Cloned genes provide enough DNA for DNA sequencing. The sequence of a gene can help us understand how a gene works and identify mutations that cause diseases.	• Large amounts of the protein can be purified to study its structure and function.
• Cloned DNA can be used as a probe to identify the same gene or similar genes in other organisms.	• Cloned genes can be introduced into bacteria or livestock to make pharmaceutical products such as insulin.
	• Cloned genes can be introduced into plants and animals to alter their traits.
	• Cloned genes can be used to treat diseases—a clinical approach called gene therapy.

Figure 18.1 Gene cloning. The process of gene cloning allows a single gene to be isolated and produced in large numbers, facilitating a variety of investigations into gene structure and function.

Another material needed to clone a gene is the gene itself, which we will call the gene of interest. The source of the gene is the chromosomal DNA of the organism of interest. The preparation of chromosomal DNA involves breaking open cells and extracting and purifying the DNA by using biochemical techniques, such as chromatography and centrifugation.

Step 2: Cutting Chromosomal and Vector DNA into Pieces and Linking Them Together Produces Recombinant DNA molecules

The second step in a gene cloning experiment is the insertion of chromosomal DNA into the vector (Figure 18.1). DNA fragments must be cut and pasted to produce recombinant vectors. To cut DNA researchers use enzymes known as **restriction enzymes** or restriction endonucleases. These enzymes, which were discovered by Werner Arber, Hamilton Smith, and Daniel Nathans in the 1960s and 1970s, are made naturally by many different species of bacteria. Restriction enzymes protect bacterial cells from invasion by foreign DNA, particularly that of bacteriophages. Currently, several hundred restriction enzymes from various bacterial species have been identified and are available commercially to molecular biologists.

The restriction enzymes used in cloning experiments bind to a specific base sequence and then cleave the DNA backbone at two defined locations, one in each strand. The sequences recognized by restriction enzymes are called **restriction sites**. Most restriction enzymes recognize sequences that are palindromes, which means that the sequence is identical when read in the opposite direction in the complementary strand (**Table 18.1**). For example, the sequence recognized by the restriction enzyme EcoRI is 5′–GAATTC–3′ in the top strand. Read in the opposite direction in the bottom strand, this sequence is also 5′–GAATTC–3′. Certain restriction enzymes are useful in cloning because they digest DNA into fragments with **sticky ends**. Such DNA fragments have single-stranded ends that will hydrogen bond to other DNA fragments cut with the same enzyme, because the sticky ends have complementary sequences.

Figure 18.2 shows the action of a restriction enzyme and the insertion of a gene into a vector. This vector also carries the *ampR* and *lacZ* genes, whose functions will be discussed later. The restriction enzyme binds to specific sequences in both the vector and the chromosomal DNA. It then cleaves the DNA backbones, producing DNA fragments with sticky ends (Figure 18.2, step 1). The sticky ends of a piece of chromosomal DNA and the vector DNA then hydrogen bond with each other (Figure 18.2, step 2). However, this interaction is not stable because it involves only a few hydrogen bonds between complementary bases. To establish a permanent connection between two DNA fragments, the sugar-phosphate backbones of the DNA strands must be covalently linked. This linkage is catalyzed by DNA ligase, an enzyme that catalyzes

Table 18.1	Examples of Restriction Enzymes Used in Gene Cloning	
Restriction enzyme*	**Bacterial source**	**Sequence recognized†**
*Bam*HI	*Bacillus amyloliquefaciens* H	↓ 5′–GGATCC–3′ 3′–CCTAGG–5′ ↑
*Eco*RI	*Escherichia coli* RY13	↓ 5′–GAATTC–3′ 3′–CTTAAG–5′ ↓
*Sac*I	*Streptomyces achromonogenes*	↓ 5′–GAGCTC–3′ 3′–CTCGAG–5′ ↑

* Restriction enzymes are named according to the species in which they are found. The first three letters are italicized because they indicate the genus and species names. Since a species can produce more than one restriction enzyme, the enzymes are designated I, II, III, and so on, to indicate the order in which they were discovered in a given species.
† The arrows show the locations in the upper and lower DNA strands where the restriction enzymes cleave the DNA backbone.

the formation of a covalent bond between adjacent DNA fragments. (Figure 18.2, step 3).

In some cases the two ends of the vector will simply ligate back together, restoring it to its original circular structure; this forms what is called a recircularized vector. In other cases a fragment of chromosomal DNA can become ligated to both ends of the vector. When this happens, a segment of chromosomal DNA has been inserted into the vector, resulting in a **recombinant vector** or a hybrid vector. The recombinant vector is then ready to be cloned. A recombinant vector may contain the gene of interest or it may contain a different piece of chromosomal DNA.

Step 3: Putting Recombinant Vectors into Host Cells and Allowing Those Cells to Propagate Achieves Gene Cloning

The procedure in Figure 18.2 inserts a chromosomal gene into a plasmid vector. The vector already carries an antibiotic-resistance gene called the *ampR* gene. Such a gene is called a **selectable marker** because the presence of the antibiotic selects for the growth of cells expressing the *ampR* gene. The *ampR* gene encodes an enzyme known as β-lactamase that degrades the antibiotic ampicillin, which normally kills bacteria. Bacteria containing the *ampR* gene can grow on media containing ampicillin because they can degrade it. In a cloning experiment in which the *ampR* gene is found within the plasmid, the growth of cells in the presence of ampicillin identifies bacteria that contain the plasmid.

The third step in gene cloning is the actual cloning of the gene of interest. In this step, the goal is for the recombinant vector carrying the desired gene to be taken up by bacterial cells treated with agents that render them permeable to DNA

Figure 18.2   Step 2 of gene cloning: The actions of a restriction enzyme and DNA ligase to produce a recombinant vector.   The restriction enzyme binds to a specific sequence in both the chromosomal DNA and the vector DNA. It then cleaves the DNA backbones, producing DNA fragments. The complementary single-stranded ends of the DNA fragments hydrogen bond with each other. The enzyme DNA ligase then covalently links these fragments, producing a recombinant vector.

Concept check: *In the experiment shown in this figure, has the gene of interest been cloned?*

BioConnections: *Look back at Figure 16.11. What are the general properties of plasmids?*

molecules (**Figure 18.3**). This procedure is called **transformation**, when a plasmid vector is used, or **transfection**, when a viral vector is introduced into a cell. During transformation some cells take up a single plasmid while most cells fail to take up a plasmid. The bacteria are then plated onto Petri plates with a bacterial growth medium containing ampicillin. In the experiment shown here, the bacterial cells were originally sensitive to ampicillin. Bacteria that have not taken up a plasmid will be killed by the antibiotic. In contrast any bacterium that has taken up a plasmid carrying the *amp^R* gene will grow and divide many times to form a bacterial colony containing millions of cells. Because each cell in a single colony is derived from the same original cell that took up a single plasmid, all cells within a colony contain the same type of plasmid DNA.

In the experiment shown in Figure 18.3, the experimenter can distinguish bacterial colonies that contain a recombinant vector from those containing a recircularized vector—and therefore no chromosomal DNA. In a recombinant vector a piece of chromosomal DNA carrying a desired gene has been inserted into a region of the vector that contains the *lacZ* gene, which encodes the enzyme β-galactosidase. The insertion of

chromosomal DNA into the vector disrupts the *lacZ* gene. By comparison, a recircularized vector has a functional *lacZ* gene. The functionality of *lacZ* can be determined by providing the growth medium with a colourless compound, X-Gal, which is cleaved by β-galactosidase into a blue dye. Bacteria grown in the presence of X-Gal will form blue colonies if they have a functional β-galactosidase enzyme and white colonies if they do not. In this experiment, therefore, bacterial colonies containing recircularized vectors will form blue colonies, while colonies containing recombinant vectors will be white.

The net result of gene cloning is amplification of a single recombinant molecule into an enormous number of copies. During transformation a single bacterial cell usually takes up a single recombinant vector. Two subsequent events lead to the production of many copies of the cloned gene. First, because the vector has a highly active origin of replication, the bacterial host cell produces many copies of the recombinant vector per cell. Second, the bacterial cells divide approximately every 20 minutes. Following overnight growth, a population of many millions of bacteria will be obtained from a single cell. Each of these bacterial cells will contain many copies of the cloned gene. For example, a bacterial colony may comprise 10 million

1 Mix plasmid DNA with many *E. coli* cells that have been treated with agents that make them permeable to DNA.

Gene of interest

Part of *lacZ*

Part of *lacZ*

amp^R

Origin of replication

In this example, the gene of interest was inserted into a plasmid. This disrupts the *lacZ* gene and renders it nonfunctional. It is also possible for any other chromosomal DNA fragment to be inserted into the plasmid, or the plasmid may recircularize without an insert.

This shows a bacterial cell that has taken up the plasmid carrying the gene of interest. Many bacterial cells fail to take up a plasmid.

2 Plate cells on media containing ampicillin and X-Gal. Incubate overnight. Note: The *amp^R* gene allows bacteria to grow in the presence of ampicillin. The *lacZ* gene encodes β-galactosidase that degrades X-Gal to produce a blue colour.

Blue colony

White colony

Each bacterial colony is derived from a single cell; so all the cells in a colony are genetically identical.

Recircularized vector without an insert—*lacZ* gene is functional and produces blue colour.

Recombinant vector with an insert—*lacZ* gene is nonfunctional.

Figure 18.3 **Step 3 of gene cloning: The cloning of a recombinant vector.** For cloning to occur, a recombinant vector is introduced into a host cell, which copies the vector and divides to produce many cells. This produces many copies of the gene of interest.

cells, with each cell containing 50 copies of the recombinant vector. Therefore, this bacterial colony would have 500 million copies of the cloned gene.

A DNA Library Is a Collection of Many Different DNA Fragments

In our previous discussion of gene cloning we focused on the insertion of a particular gene into a vector, and its introduction into a host cell. But how do we know that a vector contains the gene of interest? In a typical cloning experiment, such as the one described in Figures 18.2 and 18.3, the treatment of chromosomal DNA with restriction enzymes actually yields tens of thousands of different DNA fragments. Therefore, after the DNA fragments are ligated individually to vectors, a researcher has a collection of many recombinant vectors, with each vector containing a particular fragment of chromosomal DNA. This collection of vectors is known as a **DNA library** (**Figure 18.4**). Researchers make DNA libraries by using the methods shown

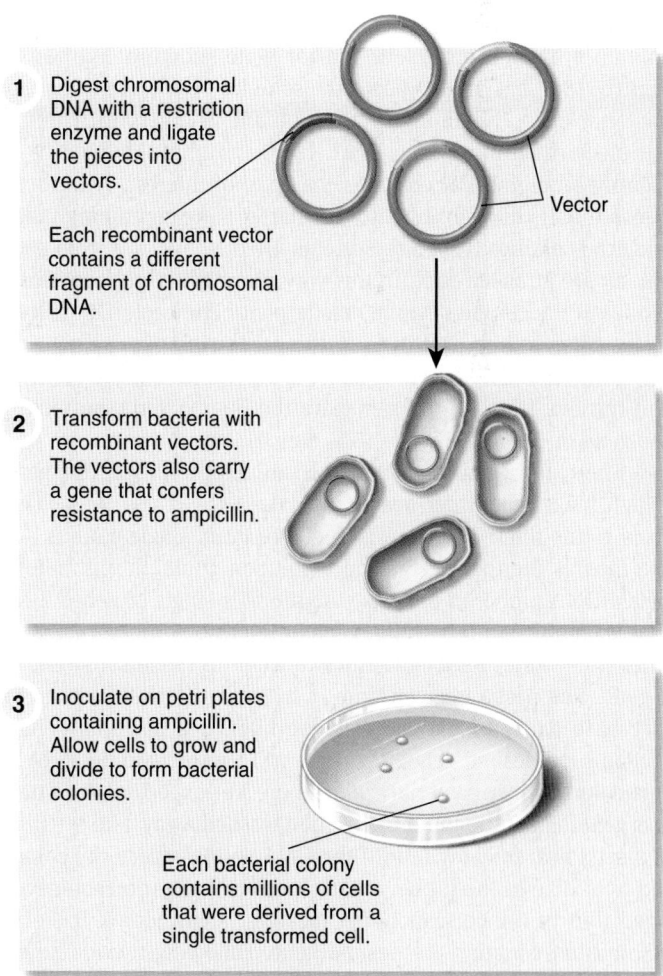

1 Digest chromosomal DNA with a restriction enzyme and ligate the pieces into vectors.

Each recombinant vector contains a different fragment of chromosomal DNA.

Vector

2 Transform bacteria with recombinant vectors. The vectors also carry a gene that confers resistance to ampicillin.

3 Inoculate on petri plates containing ampicillin. Allow cells to grow and divide to form bacterial colonies.

Each bacterial colony contains millions of cells that were derived from a single transformed cell.

Figure 18.4 **A DNA library.** Each colony in a DNA library contains a vector with a different piece of chromosomal DNA.

in Figures 18.2 and 18.3 and then use those libraries to identify clones of genes in which they are interested.

Two types of DNA libraries are commonly made. The library is called a **genomic library** when the inserts are derived from chromosomal DNA, and they represent the entire genome of the organism. Alternatively, researchers can isolate mRNA and use the enzyme reverse transcriptase, described in Chapter 16, to make DNA molecules with mRNA as a starting material. Such DNA is called **complementary DNA (cDNA)**. A **cDNA library** is a collection of recombinant vectors that have cDNA inserts, which represent all the genes expressed in the original sample. It is important to appreciate that genomic libraries prepared from mouse liver or brain tissues will be essentially identical, whereas cDNA libraries cloned from liver and brain tissues are composed of clones that are similar (for example, genes encoding proteins that are found in all tissues) and clones that are unique to one tissue or the other (for example, the gene encoding aldolase B is expressed in liver but not in the brain).

In many cloning experiments the ultimate goal is to clone a specific gene. After making a DNA library, how is it possible to identify those rare colonies that happen to contain the gene of interest? One way is through **colony hybridization**, in which a researcher uses a probe to identify colonies that contain a desired gene. The master plate shown at the top of **Figure 18.5** has many bacterial colonies, each composed of bacterial cells containing a recombinant vector with a different piece of chromosomal DNA. In this example the goal is to identify a colony that contains the gene of interest. A nitrocellulose filter is laid gently onto the master plate containing many bacterial colonies. When the filter is lifted, some cells from each colony are attached to it. In this way, the filter paper contains a replica of the colonies on the master plate. The bacteria attached to the filter will be destroyed in the processing of the filter, but the location of a colony of interest is preserved and the scientist can retrieve from the master plate the live bacteria containing the gene of interest (Figure 18.5, step 4).

The cells attached to the filter are exposed to a detergent, which makes them permeable, and the DNA inside the cells is fixed to the filter. The DNA is denatured into single strands and the filter is then submerged in a solution containing a radiolabelled DNA probe. In this case the probe is single-stranded DNA that is complementary to the gene of interest. A probe that is 15 to 20 nucleotides long is usually sufficient to specifically bind to a gene. The probe is given time to hybridize (form complementary base pairs) to the DNA on the filter. If a bacterial colony contains the desired gene, the probe will hybridize to the DNA in this colony. Most bacterial colonies are not expected to contain this gene. The unbound probe is then washed away, and the filter is placed next to X-ray film. If the DNA within a bacterial colony did hybridize to the probe, a dark spot will appear on the developed film in the corresponding location, identifying a bacterial colony that contains the desired gene. Following the identification of labelled colonies, the researcher can go back to the master plate to select and grow bacteria containing the cloned gene.

1 A filter is gently laid onto the master plate and lifted, yielding a replica of the master plate.

Master plate with a DNA library

Each bacterial colony has a recombinant vector with a different piece of chromosomal DNA. The goal in this experiment is to identify colonies that have the gene of interest as an insert.

Nitrocellulose filter

2 The lifted filter is treated with detergent to make the bacteria permeable and the DNA is fixed to the filter. The DNA is then denatured into single strands, and a radioactively labelled probe is added that is complementary to the gene of interest.

Radiolabelled probe

5′ | / 3′

3′ ⅃⅃⅃⅃⅃⅃⅃⅃⅃⅃⅃ 5′

Single strand of the gene of interest in a bacterial colony

3 After allowing time for the probe to hybridize with the desired gene, the filter is washed to remove unbound probe and then placed next to X-ray film.

X-ray film

4 Based on the orientation of the filter and X-ray film (the X on both mark where they match), the colonies containing the gene of interest are identified on the master plate.

Master plate (see above)

Colonies containing the cloned gene of interest

Figure 18.5 Identifying a cloned gene by colony hybridization. This method can be used to identify rare colonies containing the gene of interest from a DNA library.

Blotting Methods Can Reveal Sequence Homology and Identify Gene Families

As you have just seen, blotting methods, such as colony hybridization, can allow us to detect a gene within a DNA library. Another blotting method, **Southern blotting**, can detect the presence of a particular gene within a mixture of many chromosomal DNA fragments separated on a gel. This method, developed by Edwin Southern in 1975, can be used to determine the number of copies of a gene within the genome of an organism. For example, Southern blotting has revealed that rRNA genes are found in multiple copies, whereas protein-encoding genes are usually unique. In the study of human genetic diseases, Southern blotting can also detect small gene deletions. Another common use of Southern blotting is to identify gene families, in which two or more genes are derived from the same ancestral gene. The members of a gene family are homologous, having similar but not identical DNA sequences. Southern blotting can distinguish the homologous members of a gene family within a single species or identify homologous genes among different species.

Before we discuss the Southern blotting method further, we first need to examine **gel electrophoresis**, a technique that is used to separate macromolecules on a gel. In the example shown in **Figure 18.6**, gel electrophoresis was used to separate different fragments of chromosomal DNA based on their masses. The gel is a semisolid agarose matrix, with depressions at the top called wells to which samples are added. An electric field is applied to the gel, causing charged molecules to migrate from the top of the gel toward the bottom—a process called electrophoresis. DNA is negatively charged and moves toward the positive end of the gel, which is at the bottom in this figure. Smaller DNA fragments move more quickly through the gel polymer and therefore are located closer to the bottom of the gel compared with larger ones. At the end of the electrophoretic run, fragments that differ in size have been separated from one another. The DNA fragments in each band can then be stained with a dye for identification.

In a Southern blotting experiment a strand of DNA from a gene of interest is labelled (for example, radiolabelled) in vitro, and the labelled strand is used as a probe to detect the presence of the gene within a mixture of many DNA fragments obtained from chromosomal DNA. The basis for a Southern blotting experiment, as with other hybridization experiments, is that two DNA fragments will bind to each other only if they have complementary sequences. In such an experiment a labelled strand of the probe will pair specifically with a complementary DNA strand from a chromosomal fragment. To begin a Southern blotting experiment, the chromosomal DNA is isolated and digested with a restriction enzyme (**Figure 18.7**). Because the restriction enzyme cuts the chromosomal DNA at many different sites within the chromosomes, this step produces thousands of DNA pieces of different sizes. The chromosomal pieces are loaded onto a gel that separates them according to their masses. The DNA pieces

1 Load samples of DNA fragments into wells at the top of the gel.

Samples

Wells

Electrodes

Gel

2 Apply an electric field.

3 Wait additional time.

Higher-mass molecules

Each band is a group of DNA fragments with the same mass.

Lower-mass molecules

Figure 18.6 Separation of molecules by gel electrophoresis. In this example, samples containing many fragments of DNA are loaded into wells at the top of the gel and then subjected to an electric field that causes the fragments to move toward the bottom of the gel. This separates the fragments according to their masses, with the smaller DNA fragments near the bottom of the gel.

Concept check: *One DNA fragment contains 600 bp and another has 1,300 bp. Following electrophoresis, which would be closer to the bottom of a gel?*

within the gel are denatured into single-stranded molecules and then transferred from the gel to a nitrocellulose filter, a process called blotting. At this point, the filter contains many unlabelled DNA strands that have been separated according to mass.

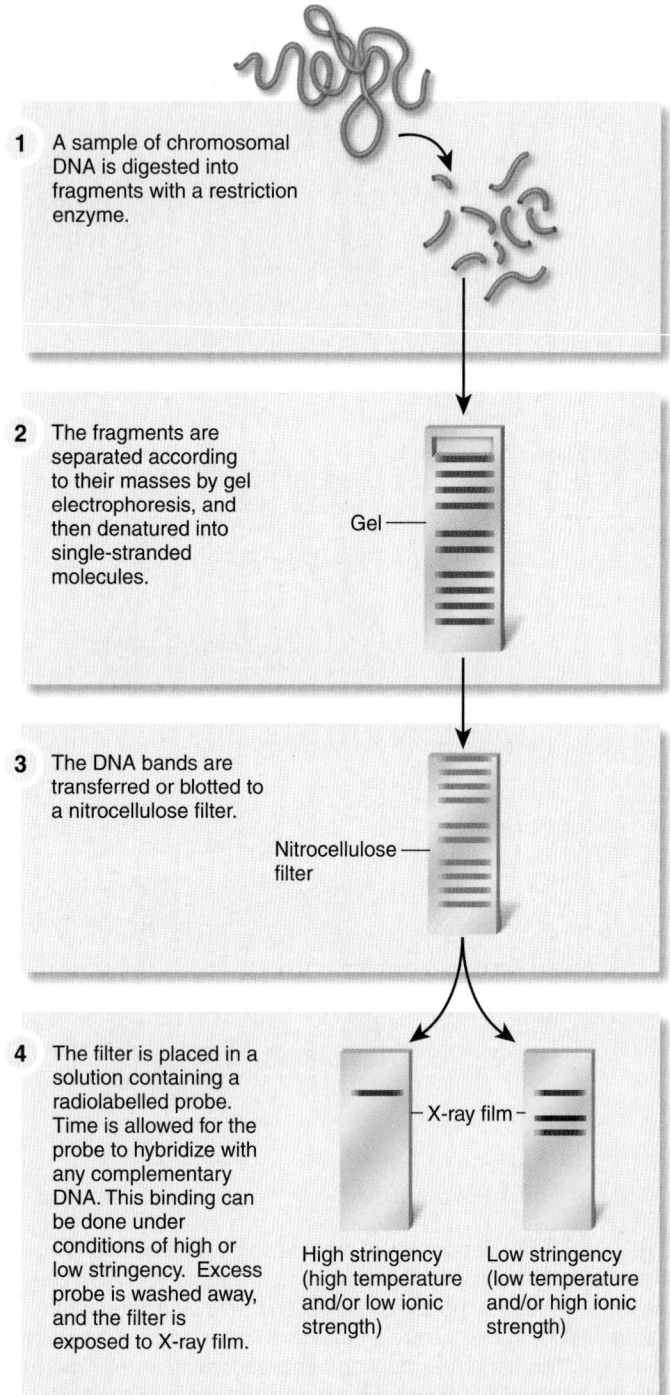

1 A sample of chromosomal DNA is digested into fragments with a restriction enzyme.

2 The fragments are separated according to their masses by gel electrophoresis, and then denatured into single-stranded molecules.

Gel

3 The DNA bands are transferred or blotted to a nitrocellulose filter.

Nitrocellulose filter

4 The filter is placed in a solution containing a radiolabelled probe. Time is allowed for the probe to hybridize with any complementary DNA. This binding can be done under conditions of high or low stringency. Excess probe is washed away, and the filter is exposed to X-ray film.

X-ray film

High stringency (high temperature and/or low ionic strength)

Low stringency (low temperature and/or high ionic strength)

The next step is to determine if any of these unlabelled strands contain sequences complementary to a probe. The filter, which has the unlabelled chromosomal DNA attached to it, is submerged in a solution containing the radiolabelled probe. If the labelled probe and a strand of chromosomal DNA are complementary, they will hydrogen bond to each other. Any unbound radiolabelled probe is then washed away, and the filter is exposed to X-ray film. Locations where the labelled probe is bound appear as dark bands on the developed X-ray film.

Important variables in the Southern blotting procedure are temperature and the ionic strength of the hybridization and wash steps. If these steps are done at high temperatures or at low salt concentrations, the probe and chromosomal DNA must be very complementary—nearly a perfect match—to hybridize. This condition is called high stringency and is used to detect a close match between the probe and a chromosomal DNA fragment. If the temperature is lower or the ionic strength is higher, DNA sequences that are similar but not necessarily identical can hybridize to the probe. This is called low stringency and can be used to detect homologous genes. In the results shown in Figure 18.7, conditions of high stringency reveal that the probe, which is a strand of DNA from a gene of interest, binds to a single chromosomal DNA fragment, indicating that the gene is found in a single copy in the genome. At low stringency, however, two additional bands are detected. These results suggest that this gene is a member of a gene family composed of three distinct members. In earlier chapters we introduced gene families, such as those encoding histones and globins. The Southern blotting technique can be used to inform the researcher of related sequences in the genome of interest.

The Polymerase Chain Reaction (PCR) Can Also Be Used to Make Many Copies of DNA

Thus far we have examined cloning methods in which the gene of interest was inserted into a vector and then introduced into a host cell. Another way to copy DNA without the aid of vectors and host cells is a technique called the **polymerase chain reaction (PCR)** that was developed by Kary Mullis in 1985 (**Figure 18.8**). The goal of PCR is to make many copies of a specific target DNA, perhaps encompassing a gene or part of a gene. Several reagents are required for synthesis of the DNA. First, two different primers are needed that are complementary

Figure 18.7 **The technique of Southern blotting.** This technique is used to identify genes that are complementary to a labelled DNA probe from a known gene. Thousands of restriction fragments of all sizes are separated on the gel (panel 2), and upon blotting these fragments are transferred in the same order (panel 3). These fragments cannot be seen on the filter, and bands are shown on the gel and the filter paper only to reinforce the notion that the banding pattern is the same on both. Under conditions of low stringency the probe can bind to genes that are similar but not identical to the probe, thereby identifying homologous genes that constitute a gene family.

Concept check: *The globin gene family is described in Chapter 19 (look ahead to Figure 19.8). Suppose you started with human chromosomal DNA and a probe that is complementary to the β-globin gene. How many bands would you see under conditions of high stringency? How many under low stringency?*

to sequences at each end of the DNA region to be amplified. These primers are usually about 20 nucleotides long. One primer is called the forward primer, and the other is the reverse primer. PCR also requires all four deoxynucleoside triphosphates (dNTPs) and a heat-stable form of DNA polymerase called *Taq* polymerase (isolated from the bacterium *Thermus aquaticus,* which lives in hot springs). A heat-stable form of DNA polymerase is necessary because PCR involves heating steps that would inactivate most other natural forms of DNA polymerase.

To make copies, a sample of chromosomal DNA, called the template DNA, is denatured into single-stranded molecules by heat treatment and then the primers bind to the DNA as the temperature is lowered. The binding of the primers to the specific sites in the template DNA is called annealing. Once the primers have annealed, *Taq* polymerase will catalyze the synthesis of complementary DNA strands, thereby doubling the amount of DNA in the region between the two primers. The sequential process of denaturation-annealing-synthesis is then repeated to double the amount of template DNA many times over. This method is called a chain reaction because the products of each previous step are used as reactants in subsequent steps. A device that controls the temperature and automates the timing of each step, known as a thermocycler, is used to carry out PCR. The PCR technique can amplify the sample of DNA by a staggering amount. After 30 cycles of denaturation, primer annealing, and primer extension, a DNA sample will increase 2^{30}-fold, which is approximately a billionfold, in a few hours!

The PCR reaction shown in Figure 18.8 seeks to amplify a particular DNA segment. The sequences of the PCR primers are complementary to two specific sequences within the DNA. Therefore, the two primers bind to these sites and the intervening region is replicated. To conduct this type of PCR experiment, the researcher must have prior knowledge about the sequence of the DNA to design primers that are complementary to the ends of the DNA sequence. When specific primers can be constructed, PCR can amplify a specific region of DNA from a complex mixture of DNA or from a small amount of DNA. For example, PCR is routinely used in crime investigations to amplify DNA from small samples of cells that may have

Figure 18.8 **Polymerase chain reaction (PCR).** During each PCR cycle, short DNA sequences that are complementary to the ends of the targeted DNA sequence bind to the DNA and act as primers for the synthesis of this DNA region (see small illustrations next to arrows in cycle 1). The primers used in actual PCR experiments are usually 20 to 25 nucleotides long. The region between the two primers is typically hundreds of nucleotides long, not just several nucleotides as shown here. The net result of PCR is the exponential amplification of DNA that is flanked by the two primers.

BioConnections: *Look back at Figure 10.17. Why are primers needed in a PCR experiment?*

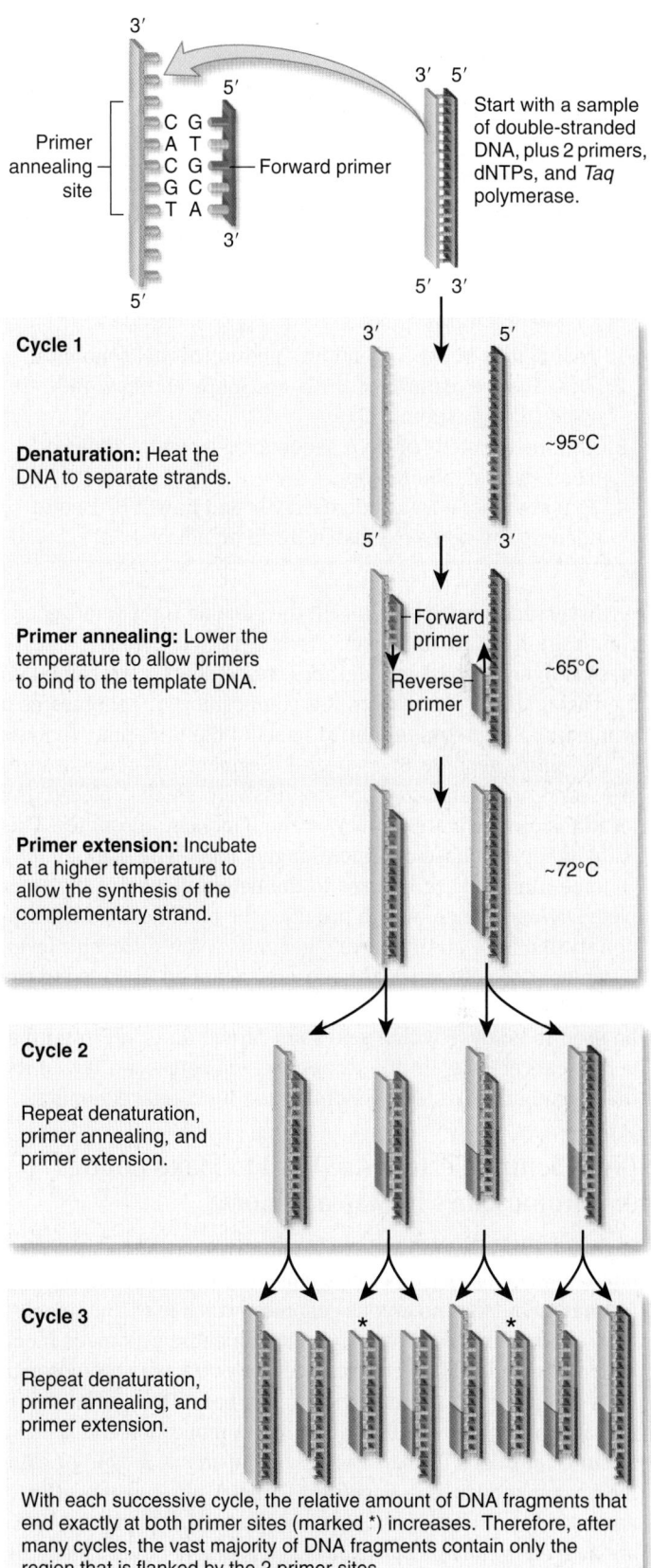

been left behind at a crime scene. This generates an amount of DNA sufficient for analysis by other molecular methods (e.g., sequencing) so that the DNA evidence can be compared with that of the victim and the suspects.

18.2 GENOMICS: TECHNIQUES TO STUDY GENOMES

Learning Outcomes:

1. Distinguish between genomics and functional genomics.
2. Describe the features of BACs and YACs and how they are used to map chromosomes.
3. Outline the steps of DNA sequencing using the dideoxy chain-termination method.
4. Explain what a DNA microarray is and how it is used to identify the genes expressed by an organism.

As discussed throughout Unit III, the genome is the total genetic composition of an organism. As genetic technology has progressed over the past few decades, researchers have gained an increasing ability to analyze the composition of genomes as a whole unit. The term **genomics** refers to the molecular analysis of the entire genome of a species. Segments of chromosomes are cloned and analyzed in progressively smaller pieces, the locations of which are known on the intact chromosomes. This is the mapping phase of structural genomics. The mapping of a genome ultimately progresses to the determination of the complete DNA sequence, which provides the most detailed description available of an organism's genome at the molecular level. By comparison, **functional genomics** is aimed at studying the expression of a genome. For example, functional genomics can be used to analyze which genes are turned on or off in normal versus cancer cells. In this section we will consider a few of the methods that are used in genomics and functional genomics.

BAC Cloning Vectors Are Used to Make Contigs of Chromosomes to Map a Genome

In general most plasmid and viral vectors can accommodate inserts only a few thousand to perhaps tens of thousands of nucleotides in length. For large eukaryotic genomes, which may contain more than 1 billion bp (base pairs), cloning an entire genome is much easier when a cloning vector can accept very large chromosomal DNA inserts. If a plasmid or viral vector has a DNA insert that is too large, it will have difficulty with DNA replication and is likely to suffer deletions in the insert. By comparison, a type of cloning vector known as a **bacterial artificial chromosome (BAC)** can reliably contain much larger inserted DNA fragments. BACs are derived from large plasmids called F factors (see Chapter 16). They can typically contain inserts of up to 500,000 bp. BACs are used in genomic research in the same way as other types of vectors. Similarly, YACs, yeast artificial chromosomes, are used as vectors in yeast. An insert in a YAC can be several hundred thousand to perhaps 2 million nucleotides long.

The term **mapping** refers to the process of determining the relative locations of genes or other DNA segments along a chromosome. After many large fragments of chromosomal DNA have been inserted into BACs or YACs, the first step of mapping is to determine the relative locations of the inserted chromosomal pieces as they would occur in an intact chromosome. This is called physical mapping. Each vector contains a clone with regions that overlap those of its neighbours (**Figure 18.9**).

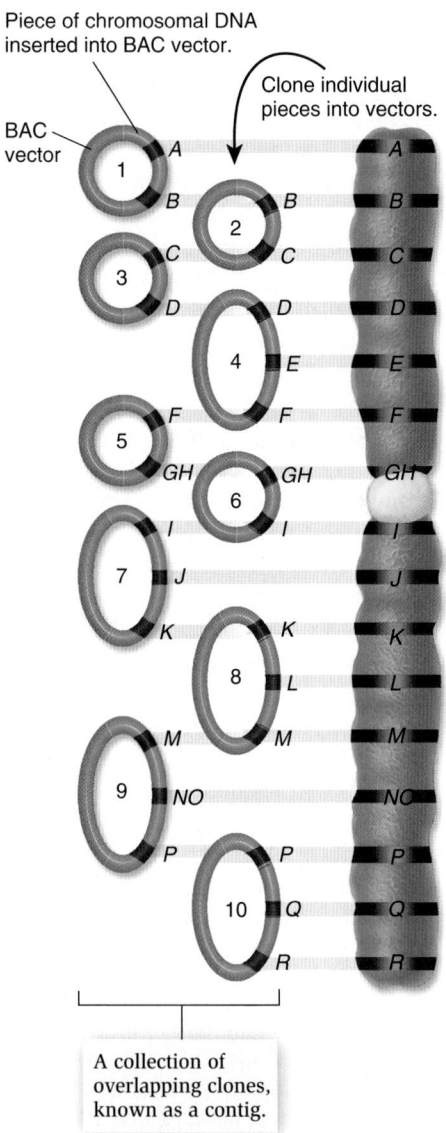

A collection of overlapping clones, known as a contig.

Figure 18.9 **A contig.** As shown here, a contig is a collection of clones that have overlapping pieces of DNA from a particular chromosome. The numbers denote the order of the members of the contig. The chromosome is labelled with letters that denote the locations of particular genes. The members of the contig have overlapping regions that share some of the same genes, which allows researchers to order them.

Concept check: *What does it mean when we say that two members of a contig have overlapping regions?*

For example, clones 7 and 8 both carry gene K. These overlapping regions allow researchers to identify the order of the clones along the chromosome. To obtain a complete physical map of a chromosome, researchers assemble the clones into a series of contiguous overlapping DNA fragments known as a **contig**.

The Dideoxy Chain-Termination Method Is Used to Determine the Base Sequence of DNA

Once researchers have cloned DNA into vectors and obtained a physical map, the next phase of genomic research is **DNA sequencing**, which is a method to determine the base sequence of DNA. Scientists can learn a great deal about the function of a gene if its nucleotide sequence is known. For example, the investigation of genetic sequences has been vital in our understanding of the genetic basis of human diseases.

A commonly used method for DNA sequencing, developed in 1977 by Frederick Sanger and colleagues, is known as the **dideoxy chain-termination method**, or more simply, **dideoxy sequencing**. Dideoxy sequencing is based on our knowledge of DNA replication. As described in Chapter 10, DNA polymerase connects adjacent deoxynucleotides by catalyzing a covalent linkage between the 5′–phosphate on one nucleotide and the 3′—OH group on the previous nucleotide. Chemists, however, can synthesize nucleotides, called dideoxynucleoside triphosphates (ddNTPs), that are missing the —OH group at the 3′ position (**Figure 18.10**). Note: The prefix *dideoxy-* refers to the fact that there are two (di) removed (de) oxygens (oxy) compared with ribose, which has —OH groups at both the 2′ and 3′ positions. Sanger reasoned that if a dideoxynucleotide is added to a growing DNA strand, the strand can no longer grow because the 3′—OH group is missing, which results in chain termination.

Before describing the steps of this DNA sequencing protocol, we need to discuss the DNA segments that are used in a sequencing experiment. The segment of DNA to be sequenced must be obtained in large amounts by using the gene cloning or PCR techniques that were described earlier in this chapter. In **Figure 18.11** the segment of DNA to be sequenced was inserted into a vector next to a primer-annealing site, the site where the primer will bind. The target DNA is initially double stranded, but **Figure 18.11a** shows the DNA after it has been denatured into a single strand by heat treatment.

Let's now examine the steps involved in DNA sequencing. Many copies of this single-stranded DNA are placed into a tube and mixed with primers that bind to the primer-annealing site. DNA polymerase and all four types of regular deoxynucleotides (dNTPs) are also added. In addition a low concentration of each of the four dideoxynucleotides (ddGTP, ddATP, ddTTP, or ddCTP) is added. Each type of ddNTP is tagged with a different coloured fluorescent molecule; typically ddA is green, ddT is red, ddG is yellow, and ddC is blue. The tube is then incubated to allow DNA polymerase to make strands complementary to one strand of the target DNA sequence. However, the incorporation of a ddNTP will occasionally cause DNA synthesis to terminate early, preventing further elongation of the strand. For example, let's consider ddTTP. Synthesis of new DNA strands will stop at the sixth or thirteenth position after the annealing site if a ddTTP, instead of a dTTP, is incorporated into the growing DNA strand (Figure 18.11a). This means the target DNA has a complementary A at the sixth and thirteenth positions. Eventually, a set of fluorescently tagged strands results, with the colour of the ddNTP representing the last nucleotide added to the strand.

After the samples have been incubated for several minutes, the newly made DNA strands are separated according to their lengths by subjecting them to gel electrophoresis. This can be done by using a slab gel, as shown in Figure 18.11a, or more commonly by running them through a gel-filled capillary tube. The shorter strands move to the bottom of the gel more quickly than the longer strands. Electrophoresis is continued until each band emerges from the bottom of the gel, where a laser excites the fluorescent dye. A fluorescence detector records the amount of fluorescence emission at four wavelengths, corresponding to the four dyes.

An example of a printout from a fluorescence detector is shown in **Figure 18.11b**. The peaks of fluorescence correspond to the DNA sequence that is complementary to the target DNA. The height of the fluorescent peaks is not always the same, because ddNTPs are incorporated at certain sites more readily than at other sites. Note that ddG is usually labelled with a yellow dye, but it is converted to black ink on the printout for ease of reading. Though improvements in automated sequencing continue to be made, a typical sequencing run can provide a DNA sequence that is approximately 700 to 900 bases long, and perhaps even longer.

Figure 18.10   Structure of a dideoxynucleotide. This figure shows the structure of dideoxyguanosine triphosphate, abbreviated ddGTP. It has a hydrogen, shown in red, instead of a hydroxyl group at the 3′ position. The prefix, dideoxy-, means it has two (di) missing (de) oxygens (oxy) compared with ribose, which has —OH groups at both the 2′ and 3′ positions.

A Microarray Can Identify Which Genes Are Transcribed by a Cell

Let's now turn our attention to functional genomics. Researchers have developed an exciting new technology, called **DNA microarrays** (or gene chips), that is used to monitor the expression of thousands of genes simultaneously. A DNA microarray is a small silica, glass, or plastic slide that

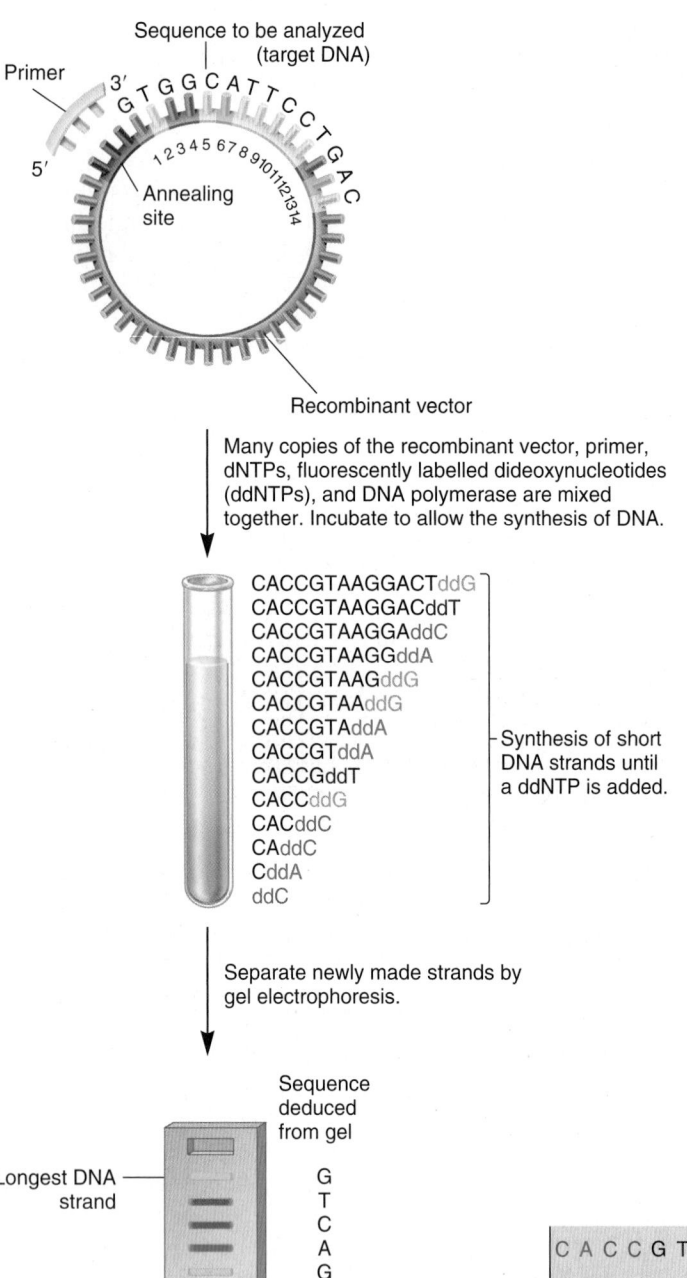

Sequence to be analyzed (target DNA)

Primer

Annealing site

Recombinant vector

Many copies of the recombinant vector, primer, dNTPs, fluorescently labelled dideoxynucleotides (ddNTPs), and DNA polymerase are mixed together. Incubate to allow the synthesis of DNA.

CACCGTAAGGACTddG ⎤
CACCGTAAGGACddT ⎥
CACCGTAAGGAddC ⎥
CACCGTAAGGddA ⎥
CACCGTAAGddG ⎥
CACCGTAAddG ⎥ Synthesis of short
CACCGTAddA ⎬ DNA strands until
CACCGTddA ⎥ a ddNTP is added.
CACCGddT ⎥
CACCddG ⎥
CACddC ⎥
CAddC ⎥
CddA ⎥
ddC ⎦

Separate newly made strands by gel electrophoresis.

Sequence deduced from gel

Longest DNA strand

G
T
C
A
G
G
A
A
T
G
C
C
A
C

Laser beam

Fluorescence detector

(a) Dideoxy DNA sequencing method

CACCGTAAGGACTG

(b) Output from automated sequencing

Figure 18.11   DNA sequencing by the dideoxy method.   (a) The procedure of dideoxy sequencing using fluorescently labelled ddNTPs. (b) This method uses a fluorescence detector that measures the four kinds of ddNTPs as they emerge from the gel.

Concept check: *What happens when a ddNTP is incorporated into a growing DNA strand?*

is dotted with many different sequences of single-stranded DNA, each corresponding to a short sequence within a known gene. Each spot contains multiple copies of a specific DNA sequence. For example, one spot in a microarray may correspond to a sequence within the β-globin gene, while another spot could correspond to a different gene, such as a gene that encodes an iron transporter. A single slide contains tens of thousands of different spots in an area the size of a postage stamp. The DNA sequences of each spot are known. These microarrays are typically produced by using spotting technologies that are quite similar to the way that an inkjet printer deposits ink on paper.

What is the purpose of using a DNA microarray? In the experiment shown in **Figure 18.12**, the goal is to determine which genes are transcribed into mRNA from a particular sample of cells. In other words, which genes in the genome are expressed? To conduct this experiment mRNA was isolated from a sample of cells and then used to make fluorescently labelled cDNA. The labelled cDNAs were then incubated with a DNA microarray. The DNA in the microarray is single stranded and corresponds to the sense strand—the strand that has a sequence like mRNA. Those cDNAs that are complementary to the DNAs in the microarray will hybridize and thereby remain bound to the microarray. The array is washed to remove unhybridized probes and then analyzed by using a microscope equipped with a computer that scans the fluorescence intensity for each spot. If the fluorescence intensity in a spot is high, a large amount of cDNA in the sample hybridized to the DNA at this location. For example, if the β-globin gene was expressed in the cells being tested, a large amount of cDNA for this gene would be made, and the fluorescence intensity for that spot would be high. Because the DNA sequence of each spot is already known, a fluorescent spot identifies cDNAs that are complementary to those DNA sequences. Furthermore, because the cDNA was generated from mRNA, this technique identifies genes that have been transcribed in a particular cell type under a given set of conditions. Thus far, the most common use of microarrays is to study gene expression patterns. In addition the technology of DNA microarrays has found many other important uses (**Table 18.2**).

1 Isolate mRNA from cells of interest. Add reverse transcriptase along with fluorescent nucleotides.

In this example, the cells make 3 different mRNAs, labelled A, D, and F.

DNA microarray

This process produces fluorescently labelled cDNA that is complementary to the mRNA.

Each spot contains single-stranded DNA molecules that correspond to a short sequence of a particular gene.

2 Hybridize cDNAs to the microarray, and wash away any unbound cDNAs.

3 Place the hybridized fluorescent DNA on the microarray into a scanning fluorescence microscope.

4 A computer generates an image that indicates the relative fluorescence intensity of each spot. In this case, spots A, D, and F are highly fluorescent.

Actual microarray

Figure 18.12 Identifying transcribed genes within a DNA microarray. In this simplified example only three cDNAs specifically hybridize to spots on the microarray. Those genes were expressed in the cells from which the mRNA was isolated. In an actual experiment, the array typically has hundreds or thousands of different cDNAs and tens of thousands of different spots.

Table 18.2	Applications of DNA Microarrays
Application	**Description**
Cell-specific gene expression	A comparison of microarray data that uses cDNAs derived from mRNA of different cell types can identify genes that are expressed in a cell-specific manner.
Gene regulation	Environmental conditions play an important role in gene regulation. A comparison of microarray data that uses cDNA derived from mRNA isolated from cells exposed to two different environmental conditions may reveal genes that are induced under one set of conditions and repressed under another set of conditions.
Elucidation of metabolic pathways	Genes that encode proteins that participate in a common metabolic pathway are often expressed in a parallel manner and can be revealed from a microarray analysis.
Tumour profiling	Different types of cancer cells exhibit striking differences in their profiles of gene expression, which can be revealed by a DNA microarray analysis. This approach is gaining widespread use to classify tumours that are sometimes morphologically indistinguishable.
Genetic variation	A mutant allele may not hybridize to a spot on a microarray as well as a wild-type allele. Therefore, microarrays are gaining widespread use as a tool to detect genetic variation. This application has been used to identify disease-causing alleles in humans and to elucidate mutations that contribute to quantitative traits in plants and other species.
Microbial strain identification	Microarrays can distinguish between closely related bacterial species and subspecies.

18.3 BIOTECHNOLOGY

Learning Outcomes:

1. Describe how recombinant microorganisms are used to make medicines and reduce pollutants in the environment.
2. Distinguish between a gene knockout versus a gene replacement, and explain how both are used in the study of human diseases.
3. Give examples of using transgenic livestock to make medical products.
4. Describe the method of using *Agrobacterium tumefaciens* to produce transgenic plants.
5. Outline the steps to produce Dolly, the first cloned mammal.
6. Explain the technique of DNA fingerprinting and list its common uses.
7. Describe the technique of gene therapy.

Biotechnology is the use of living organisms, or products from living organisms, to benefit humans. Although the term has become associated with molecular genetics, biotechnology is not a new topic. Its use began about 12,000 years ago when humans began to domesticate animals and plants for the production of food. Since that time many species of microorganisms, plants, and animals have become routinely used by people. More recently, the term *biotechnology* has become associated with molecular genetics. Since the 1970s molecular genetic tools have provided new ways to make use of living organisms to benefit humans.

In this section we will consider genetic techniques to alter the characteristics of microorganisms, plants, and animals. Examples include bacteria that can degrade pollutants in the environment and livestock that make human hormones. We will also examine several topics that are often in the news. We will explore the technical side of mammalian cloning and also touch on the ethical issues. Another newsworthy topic is DNA fingerprinting, a common method used to analyze the DNA from an individual. Like conventional fingerprinting, this technique can be used for identification purposes, such as in a crime investigation. Finally, we will explore a remarkable technology, site-directed mutagenesis, in our Feature Investigation. This discovery achieved much acclaim and resulted in a Nobel Prize for Canadian Michael Smith in 1993. The refined protocol is a widely used analytical tool in genetics and molecular biology.

Many Important Medicines Are Produced by Recombinant Microorganisms

In 1983 Health Canada approved the sale of human insulin made by recombinant bacteria. In healthy individuals, insulin is produced by the beta cells of the pancreas. Insulin functions to regulate several physiological processes, particularly the uptake of glucose into fat and muscle cells (see Chapter 47). People with insulin-dependent diabetes cannot synthesize an adequate amount of insulin because of a defect in their beta cells. Today, people with this disorder are usually treated with human insulin that is made by genetically engineered bacteria. Before 1983 insulin was isolated from pancreases removed from cattle and pigs. Unfortunately, in some cases, people with diabetes became allergic to cow insulin. These allergic patients had to use expensive combinations of insulin from human cadavers and other animals. Now, they can use human insulin made by recombinant bacteria.

As shown in **Figure 18.13**, insulin is a hormone composed of two polypeptides, called the A and B chains, held together by disulphide bonds. To produce this hormone by using bacteria, the coding sequence of the A or B chains is inserted into a plasmid vector next to the coding sequence of the *E. coli* protein, β-galactosidase. After transforming bacteria with such vectors, the cells produce many copies of a fusion protein comprising β-galactosidase and the A or B chain. This step is necessary because the A and B chains are rapidly degraded when expressed in bacterial cells by themselves; the fusion proteins, however, are not. These fusion proteins are then extracted from the bacterial cells and treated with a chemical, cyanogen bromide (CNBr), that cleaves after methionine to separate β-galactosidase from

Figure 18.13   The use of bacteria to make human insulin.

the A or B chain. The A and B chains are purified and mixed together under conditions in which they will fold and associate with each other to form a functional insulin hormone molecule.

Microorganisms Can Reduce Environmental Pollutants

Bioremediation is the use of living organisms, typically microorganisms or plants, to detoxify pollutants in the environment. As its name suggests, it is a biological remedy for pollution. During microbial bioremediation, enzymes produced by a microorganism modify a toxic pollutant by altering or transforming its structure. In many cases the toxic pollutant is degraded, yielding less complex, nontoxic metabolites.

Since the early twentieth century microorganisms have been used in the treatment and degradation of sewage. More recently, the field of bioremediation has expanded into the treatment of hazardous and refractory chemical wastes (i.e., chemicals that are difficult to degrade), usually associated with chemical and industrial activity. These pollutants include heavy metals, petroleum hydrocarbons, and halogenated organic compounds, such as those with chlorine atoms, as well as pesticides, herbicides, and organic solvents. Many new applications that use microorganisms to degrade these pollutants are being tested. The field of bioremediation has been fostered by better knowledge of how pollutants are degraded by microorganisms, the identification of new and useful strains of microbes, and the ability to enhance bioremediation through genetic engineering.

In 1980 in a landmark case (*Diamond v. Chakrabarty*), the U.S. Supreme Court ruled that a live, recombinant microorganism is patentable as a "'manufacture' or 'composition of matter.'" The first recombinant microorganism to be patented was a bacterium that contained a laboratory-constructed plasmid and was capable of breaking down crude oil. This strain can oxidize the hydrocarbons commonly found in petroleum. It grew faster on crude oil than did any of the natural strains that were tested. However, it has not been a commercial success because this recombinant strain metabolizes only a limited number of toxic compounds. Unfortunately, the strain did not degrade many higher-molecular-weight compounds that tend to persist in the environment.

Bioremediation is a developing industry. In the future recombinant microorganisms may provide an effective way to decrease the levels of toxic chemicals within our environment. However, this approach will require careful studies to demonstrate that recombinant organisms are effective at reducing pollutants and safe when released into the environment.

Gene Replacements and Knockouts in Mice Can Be Used to Understand Gene Function and Human Disease

Let's now turn our attention to the genetic engineering of animals. Researchers can introduce a cloned gene into a fertilized egg or embryonic cells and create animals that carry the cloned gene. The term **transgenic** is used to describe an organism that carries genes that were introduced by using molecular techniques, such as gene cloning. Transgenics are also called **genetically modified organisms (GMOs)**.

Such GMOs are typically made in two ways. In some cases, the cloned gene will insert randomly into the genome and result in **gene addition**—the insertion of cloned gene into the genome. In rare cases the cloned gene will recombine with the normal gene on a chromosome, a phenomenon called **gene replacement**.

For eukaryotic species that are diploid, only one of the two copies is initially replaced. In other words the initial gene replacement creates a heterozygote carrying one normal copy of the gene and one copy that has been replaced with a cloned gene. Heterozygotes can be crossed to each other to obtain homozygotes, which carry both copies of the cloned gene. If the cloned gene carries a mutation that inactivates the normal gene's function, such a homozygote, is said to have undergone a **gene knockout**. The inactive cloned gene has replaced both copies of the normal gene. In this way the function of the normal gene has been "knocked out." Scientists can also employ RNA interference, discussed in Chapter 12, to create knockouts, or knockdowns if gene expression is not completely abolished. Gene replacements and gene knockouts have become powerful tools for understanding gene function.

A particularly exciting avenue of gene replacement research is its application in the study of human disease. As an example, let's consider cystic fibrosis (CF), which is one of the most common and severe inherited human disorders. In humans the defective gene that causes CF has been identified. Likewise, the homologous gene in mice was later identified. Using the technique of gene replacement, researchers produced mice that are homozygous for the same type of mutation that is found in humans with CF. Such mice exhibit disease symptoms resembling those found in humans, namely, respiratory and digestive abnormalities. Why is this approach useful? These mice can be used as model organisms to study this human disease. Furthermore, these mice models have been used to test the effects of various therapies in the treatment of the disease.

Biotechnology Holds Promise in Producing Transgenic Livestock

The technology of creating transgenic mice has been extended to other animals, and much research is under way to develop transgenic species of livestock including fish, sheep, pigs, goats, and cattle. A novel avenue of research involves the production of medically important proteins in the mammary glands of livestock to facilitate isolation of the proteins in milk. This approach is sometimes called **molecular pharming**. (The word *pharming* refers to the use of farm animals to make pharmaceuticals.) Several human proteins have been successfully produced in the milk of domestic livestock, such as goats, sheep, and cattle. These include Factor IX to treat a certain type of hemophilia, tissue plasminogen activator to dissolve blood clots, and α-1-antitrypsin for the treatment of emphysema.

How are human proteins, such as hormones, made in such a way that they are produced in the milk of livestock? As we learned in Chapter 12, gene regulation promotes the expression of genes in certain cell types and under certain conditions. Researchers have identified several genes that are transcribed only in lactating mammary cells. One example is β-lactoglobulin, a protein that is specifically found in milk. To express a human hormone into a domestic animal's milk, the promoter for a milk-specific gene is linked to the coding sequence of a human hormone gene and inserted into a plasmid vector (**Figure 18.14**). In addition to the promoter, a short signal sequence may also be necessary so that the protein hormone will be secreted from the mammary cells and into the milk. Such a recombinant vector is then injected into an oocyte, such as a sheep oocyte, where it integrates into the

1 Clone a human hormone gene into a plasmid vector next to a sheep β-lactoglobulin promoter. This promoter is functional only in mammary cells, so the protein product is secreted into the milk.

Human hormone gene

β-lactoglobulin promoter

Plasmid vector

2 Inject this recombinant plasmid into a sheep oocyte. The plasmid DNA will integrate into the chromosomal DNA, resulting in the addition of the hormone gene into the sheep's genome.

Sheep oocyte

3 The oocyte is fertilized and implanted into a female sheep, which then gives birth to a transgenic sheep offspring.

Transgenic sheep

4 Obtain milk from a female transgenic sheep. The milk contains a human hormone.

Milk containing human hormone

5 Purify the hormone from the milk.

Figure 18.14   Molecular pharming.   This procedure is used for expressing human genes in a domestic animal's milk. The β-lactoglobulin promoter is normally expressed in mammary cells, whereas the human hormone gene is not. In transgenic sheep, the recombinant DNA is expressed in mammary cells and the protein (hormone) is secreted into the milk, facilitating its isolation by biochemical techniques.

genome. The egg is then fertilized by exposure to sperm and then implanted into the uterus of a female sheep. The resulting offspring carries the cloned gene. If the offspring is a female, the protein encoded by the human gene will be expressed within the mammary gland and secreted into the milk. The milk can then be obtained from the animal, and the human protein isolated and purified.

Compared with the production of proteins in bacteria, molecular pharming has an advantage: certain proteins are more likely to function properly when expressed in mammals. This may be due to post-translational modifications of proteins that occur in mammals but not in bacteria. In addition certain proteins may be degraded rapidly or folded improperly when expressed in bacteria. Furthermore, the yield of recombinant proteins in milk can be quite large. Each dairy cow, for example, produces about 10,000 litres of milk per year. In some cases a transgenic cow can produce approximately 1 g/L of the transgenic protein in its milk.

Agrobacterium tumefaciens Can Be Used to Make Transgenic Plants

The production of transgenic plants is somewhat easier than the production of transgenic animals because many somatic tissues from plants are totipotent, which means that an entire organism can be regenerated from such cells. Therefore, a transgenic plant can be made by the introduction of cloned genes into somatic tissue, such as the tissue of a leaf. After the cells of a leaf have become transgenic, an entire plant can be regenerated by treating the leaf with plant growth hormones that cause it to form roots and shoots. The result is an entire plant that is transgenic.

Molecular biologists often use the bacterium *Agrobacterium tumefaciens,* which naturally infects plant cells and causes tumours, to produce transgenic plants. A plasmid from the bacterium is known as the **Ti plasmid**, for tumour-inducing plasmid. This plasmid contains a region called the T DNA (for transferred DNA) that is transferred from the bacterium into the plant cell's genome. After this occurs genes within the T DNA that encode plant growth hormones cause uncontrolled plant cell growth and produce a crown gall tumour, a bulbous growth on the plant. Natural strains of *A. tumefaciens* infect many different species of plants and researchers have developed newer strains that have an even greater capacity to infect different plant species.

Researchers have disarmed the Ti plasmid by removing the genes that encode the plant growth hormones, and these modified Ti plasmids are now routinely used as vectors to introduce cloned genes into plant cells. The mechanism by which the T DNA is taken up into plant cells and integrated into the plant chromosomal DNA remains intact and can be exploited to introduce foreign genes. In addition, a selectable marker gene has been inserted into the T DNA to allow selection of plant cells that have taken up the T DNA. A gene that provides resistance to the antibiotic kanamycin, called *Kan^R*, is a commonly used selectable marker. Finally, the Ti plasmid used in cloning experiments has been modified to contain unique restriction enzyme recognition sites for the convenient insertion of any gene of interest.

Figure 18.15 shows the general strategy for producing transgenic plants via T DNA–mediated gene transfer. A desired gene is inserted into the T DNA of a genetically engineered Ti plasmid and then transformed into *A. tumefaciens*. Plant cells are exposed to the transformed *A. tumefaciens* carrying the Ti plasmid. After allowing time for infection the plant cells are grown on a solid medium that contains kanamycin and carbenicillin. Carbenicillin kills *A. tumefaciens,* and kanamycin kills any plant cells that have not taken up the T DNA. Therefore, the only surviving cells are those plant cells that have integrated the T DNA into their genome. Because the T DNA also contains the cloned gene of interest, the selected plant cells are expected to have received this cloned gene as well. The cells are then transferred to a medium that contains the plant growth hormones necessary for the regeneration of entire plants.

Many transgenic plants have been approved for human consumption. Their production has become routine practice for many agriculturally important plant species, including alfalfa, corn, cotton, soybean, tobacco, and tomato. Transgenic plants can be given characteristics that are agriculturally useful, such as those that improve plant quality and protection. For example, crop yields are reduced significantly by pests, such as insects and bacterial and fungal pathogens. For many years, crop dusters conducted aerial spraying of fields with chemicals and with spores of the bacterium *Bacillus thuringiensis* (BT). It was known that these spores were effective on certain *Lepidopteran* insects, which cause extensive damage to the plant and create routes for infection by other bacteria and fungal pathogens that may not cause problems in the absence of wounding. Scientists have learned that it is the CRY protein of the BT proteome that is responsible for this protection. The protein is synthesized as a nontoxic precursor, and after ingestion by feeding *Lepidopteran* larvae, it is exposed to an alkaline environment, which results in cleavage of the protein and activation of the toxin. In addition, the insect gut has a receptor for this protein and binding of the toxin to the receptor results in breakdown of the gut membrane; the larvae die from bacterial septicemia.

Transgenic plants expressing the CRY protein are under widespread cultivation and some (e.g., maize) are consumed by humans. Is it safe to eat these crops? Apparently so, based on differences in the physiology and biochemistry of different species. Humans have an acidic gut; thus, ingested CRY is not cleaved into the active toxin. Moreover, humans don't have the receptor that binds the active toxin. The CRY protein can either be passed through the digestive tract, or, like other ingested proteins, be partially or totally destroyed by processes that transform the food we eat into nutritive value. Proponents of this technology point out that BT crops reduce pesticide usage, fuel consumption, and labour costs, and they have little or no effect on other types of insects, plants,

or animals. In addition, the reduction in fungal infections reduces mycotoxins in the food supply. **Figure 18.16** shows that more than half of the acreage of both corn and cotton are now BT varieties.

1 Gene of interest is inserted into the T DNA of the Ti plasmid.

Ti plasmid
Gene of interest
T DNA
Kan^R
Site where restriction enzyme cuts
Recombinant Ti plasmid

2 The recombinant Ti plasmid is transformed into *A. tumefaciens*.

A. tumefaciens
Recombinant Ti plasmid

3 Plant cells are exposed to *A. tumefaciens*. The T DNA is transferred into a plant cell and incorporated into the plant cell's chromosome.

Plant cell
Inserted T DNA carrying gene of interest

4 The plant cells are placed in a medium containing kanamycin and carbenicillin. Kanamycin kills plant cells that have not taken up T DNA. Carbenicillin kills *A. tumefaciens*. The surviving plant cells are transferred to growth media that has plant hormones necessary for regenerating an entire plant.

Plant with cloned gene

Figure 18.15 Using the Ti plasmid and *Agrobacterium tumefaciens* to make transgenic plants.

(a) A field of Bt corn

(b) Bt corn and Bt cotton usage since 1996

Figure 18.16 **The production of transgenic crops.**
(a) A field of transgenic corn carrying a gene from *Bacillus thuringiensis*. The plants have increased resistance to major insect pests. (b) This graph shows the rapid increase in the use of transgenic crops since 1996.

Research into transgenic plants has also led to the development of novel products, such as biodegradable plastics and molecules for industrial and medical applications. For example, transgenic plants have been modified to produce vaccines against many human and animal diseases, including hepatitis B, cholera, and malaria. Transgenic plants have been made that produce a variety of medicines, such as human epidermal growth factor for wound repair and human interferon to fight viral diseases and cancer.

Researchers Have Succeeded in Cloning Mammals from Somatic Cells

We now turn our attention to cloning as a way to genetically manipulate plants and animals. The term *cloning* has many different meanings. At the beginning of this chapter we discussed gene cloning, which involves methods that produce many copies of a gene or its protein product. The cloning of an entire organism is a different matter. This happens in nature by accident. Identical twins are genetic clones that began from the same fertilized egg. Similarly, researchers can take mammalian embryos at an early stage of development (for example, the two-cell to eight-cell stage), separate the cells, implant them into the uterus of a female, and obtain multiple births of genetically identical individuals.

As noted earlier, the reproductive cloning of new individuals is relatively easy in the case of plants, which can be cloned from somatic cells. Until recently, this approach had not been possible with mammals. For several decades scientists believed that chromosomes within the somatic cells of mammals had incurred irreversible genetic changes that rendered them unsuitable for reproductive cloning. However, this hypothesis has been disproven. In 1996 Ian Wilmut and his colleagues at the Roslin Institute in Edinburgh, Scotland, created clones of sheep by using the genetic material from somatic cells. As you may have heard, they named the first cloned lamb Dolly.

Figure 18.17 illustrates how Dolly was created. The researchers removed mammary cells from an adult female sheep and grew them in the laboratory. The researchers then extracted the nucleus from a sheep oocyte and fused a diploid mammary cell with the enucleated oocyte cell. Fusion was promoted by electric pulses. After fusion the zygote was implanted into the uterus of an adult sheep. One hundred and forty-eight days later, Dolly was born.

Dolly was (almost) genetically identical to the sheep that donated a mammary cell to create her. Dolly and the donor sheep were (almost) genetically identical in the same way that identical twins are. They carry the same set of genes and look remarkably similar. However, Dolly and her somatic cell donor had some minor genetic differences because of possible differences in their mitochondrial DNA and exhibited some phenotypic differences because of maternal effect genes. Interestingly, Dolly died at age six, while most sheep live to be 12 to 15 years old. Some people speculated that Dolly's genome was six years old when she was born (that was the age of the sheep that donated the mammary cells), and Dolly's telomeres were found to be about 20% shorter than normal. Recall that progressive telomere shortening is associated with cellular senescence and aging (Chapter 10), but it is unclear if this was a determinant in Dolly's premature death.

Mammalian cloning is still at an early stage of development. Nevertheless, creating Dolly was a breakthrough that showed that it is technically possible. In recent years, cloning by using somatic cells has been achieved in several mammalian species, including sheep, cows, mice, goats, pigs, and cats. In 2002 the first pet was cloned, which was named Copycat (see the chapter-opening photo). The cloning of mammals provides the potential for many practical applications. Cloning livestock would enable farmers to use the somatic cells from their best animals to create genetically homogeneous herds. This could be advantageous in terms of agricultural yield, although such a genetically homogeneous herd may be more susceptible to certain diseases.

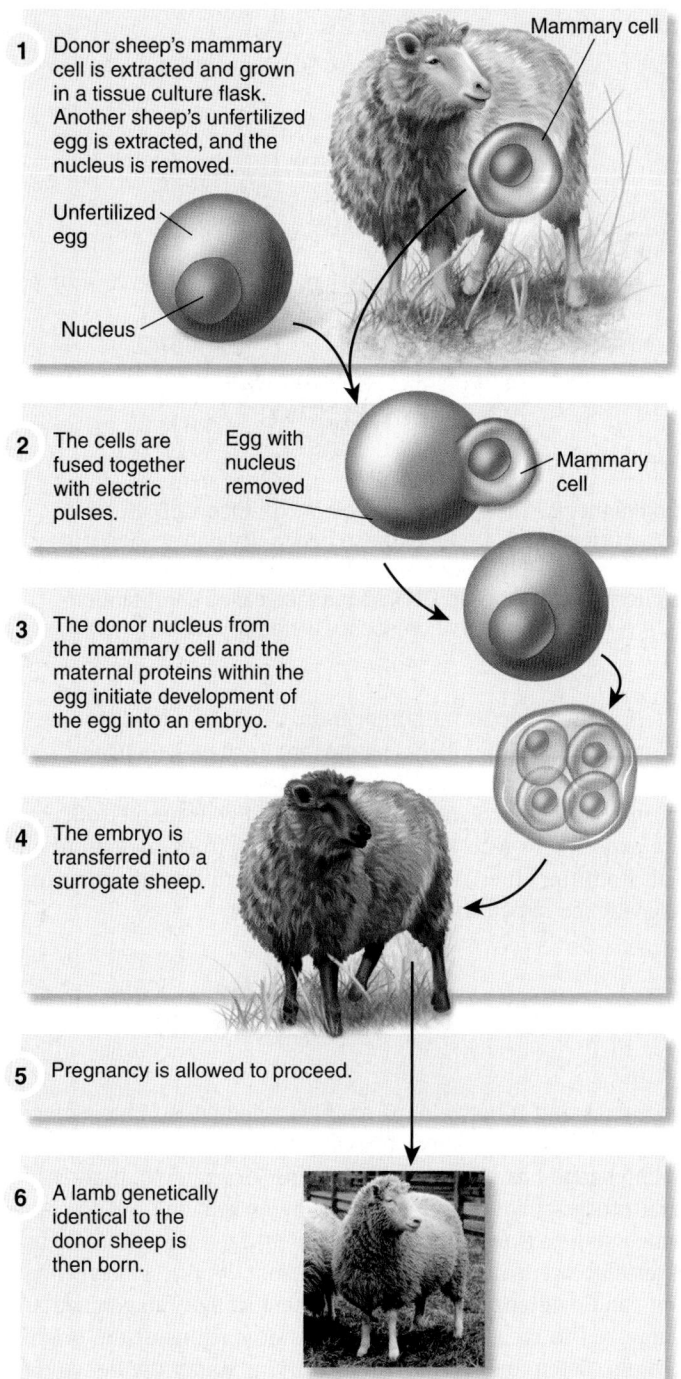

1. Donor sheep's mammary cell is extracted and grown in a tissue culture flask. Another sheep's unfertilized egg is extracted, and the nucleus is removed.

Mammary cell

Unfertilized egg

Nucleus

2. The cells are fused together with electric pulses.

Egg with nucleus removed

Mammary cell

3. The donor nucleus from the mammary cell and the maternal proteins within the egg initiate development of the egg into an embryo.

4. The embryo is transferred into a surrogate sheep.

5. Pregnancy is allowed to proceed.

6. A lamb genetically identical to the donor sheep is then born.

Figure 18.17 Protocol for the successful cloning of sheep. In this protocol the genetic material from a somatic cell is used to make a cloned mammal, in this case the sheep Dolly.

Although reproductive cloning may have practical uses in the field of agriculture, people have become greatly concerned with the possibility of human cloning. This prospect has raised serious ethical questions. Some people feel that it is morally wrong and threatens the basic fabric of parenthood and family. Others feel that it is a modern technology that offers a new avenue for reproduction, one that could be offered to infertile couples, for example. Human cloning is a complex subject with many more viewpoints than these two. In the public sector the sentiment toward human cloning has been generally negative. Indeed, many countries have issued a complete ban on human cloning, while others permit limited research in this area. In the future our society will have to wrestle with the legal and ethical aspects of cloning as it applies not only to animals but also to people.

DNA Fingerprinting Is Used for Identification and Relationship Testing

DNA fingerprinting, also known as DNA profiling, is a technology that identifies individuals and distinguishes among individuals based on variations in their DNA. Like the human fingerprint, the DNA of each individual is a distinctive characteristic that provides a means of identification. When subjected to DNA fingerprinting, the selected fragments of chromosomal DNA produce a series of bands on a gel (**Figure 18.18a**). The unique pattern of these bands is a distinguishing feature of each individual.

DNA fingerprinting is now done by using PCR, which amplifies **short tandem repeat sequences (STRs)**—short DNA sequences that are repeated many times in a row. Such tandem repeat sequences, which are noncoding regions of chromosomal DNA, are found at specific locations in the genomes of all species. The number of repeats at each location tends to vary from one individual to the next. This variation provides a way to distinguish one individual from another. Using primers that are complementary to DNA sequences that flank each STR, the STRs from a sample of DNA are amplified by PCR and then separated by gel electrophoresis according to their molecular masses. As in DNA sequencing the amplified STR fragments are fluorescently labelled. A laser excites the fluorescent molecule within an STR, and a detector records the amount of fluorescence emission for each STR. The DNA fingerprint yields a series of peaks, each peak having a characteristic molecular mass (**Figure 18.18b**). In this automated approach the pattern of peaks is an individual's DNA fingerprint.

Within the past decade or so the uses of DNA fingerprinting have expanded in many ways. DNA fingerprinting has gained acceptance as a precise method of identification. In medicine it is used to identify different species of bacteria and fungi, and it can even distinguish among closely related strains of the same species. This is useful so that clinicians can treat patients with the appropriate antibiotic or fungicide.

A second common use is in forensics—providing evidence in a criminal case. DNA fingerprinting can be used as evidence that an individual was at a crime scene. Forensic DNA was first used in the Canadian court system in 1988. When a sample taken from a crime scene matches the DNA fingerprint of an individual, the probability that a match could occur simply by chance can be calculated. Each STR size is given a probability score based on its observed frequency within a reference human population (Caucasian, Asian, etc.). An automated DNA fingerprint contains many peaks, and the probability scores for

(a) Traditional DNA fingerprinting

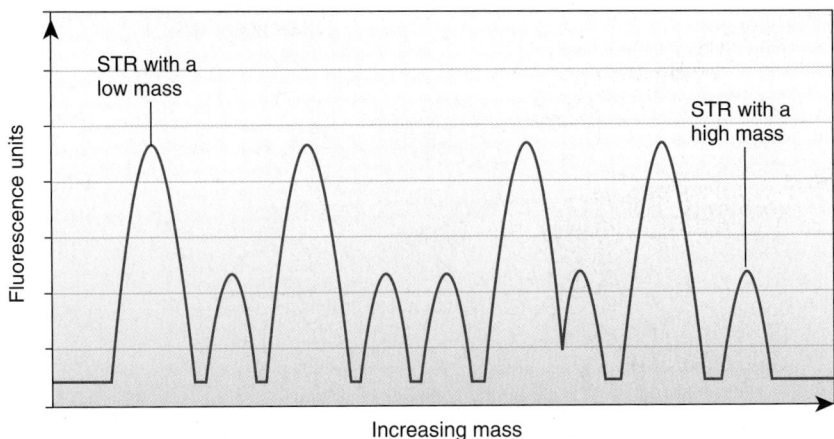

(b) Automated DNA fingerprinting

Figure 18.18   DNA fingerprinting.   (a) Chromosomal DNA from two different individuals was subjected to traditional DNA fingerprinting. Their DNA appears as a series of bands on a gel. The dissimilarities in the patterns of these bands distinguish individuals, much as the differences in physical fingerprint patterns can be used for identification. DNA evidence at a crime scene (E) matches suspect 2 (S2) but not suspect 1 (S1). **(b)** Automated DNA fingerprinting compares fluorescently labelled DNA sequences called short tandem repeat sequences (STRs), which differ in length among various individuals. A printout from the fluorescence detector is shown here.

each peak are multiplied together to arrive at the likelihood that a particular pattern of peaks would be observed. For example, if a DNA fingerprint contains 20 fluorescent peaks, and the probability of an individual having each peak is 1/4, then the likelihood of having that pattern would be $(1/4)^{20}$, or roughly 1 in 1 trillion. Therefore, a match between two samples is rarely a matter of random chance.

Another important application of DNA fingerprinting is relationship testing. People who are related genetically have some peaks in common. The number they share depends on the closeness of their genetic relationship. For example, offspring are expected to receive half of their peaks from one parent and half from the other. Therefore, DNA fingerprinting can be used as evidence in paternity cases.

FEATURE INVESTIGATION

Michael Smith's In Vitro Site-Specific Mutagenesis

In 1976 Professor Michael Smith took a sabbatical from the University of British Columbia to work in the laboratory of Fred Sanger, a pioneer in DNA sequencing technology (for which Sanger won his second Nobel Prize in 1980). There, Smith collaborated with Clyde Hutchinson of the University of North Carolina, and his team cleverly showed that specific mutations could be induced in a target gene. The technique became known as site-directed mutagenesis. Nearly 30 years after the landmark work, the technique has been highly refined to facilitate mutagenesis experiments, which are commonly used to alter specific sequences of known genes.

To appreciate the importance of this technology, place it in the context of an industrial application. The active site of an enzyme is generated by precise three-dimensional folding of the polypeptide chain, bringing reactive amino acids into close proximity. Scientists can now alter the nucleotide sequence of codons, changing them and thus the amino acids that they encode. Changes in specific amino acids, followed by analysis of the function of the mutant enzyme, often are used to investigate the role of particular residues. On a grander scale, automated

processes and robotics have enabled scientists to change every amino acid of a particular enzyme and investigate what effects each change has on enzyme function. For example, if an industrial process might be undertaken by an enzyme but for other processing reasons this must occur at an acidic pH (where a naturally occurring enzyme would not work), genes encoding candidate enzymes can be systematically mutagenized and expressed to create many thousands of versions of the original protein. Often, one is capable of working under the demanding conditions required. Thus, both basic and applied research has embraced this technology. For his pioneering efforts, Michael Smith was awarded the Nobel Prize in 1993.

Smith and his collaborators used the bacteriophage φX174 as their experimental system (**Figure 18.19**). The lysis *E* gene had been investigated and was known to be associated with lysis of the bacterial host cell. Mutants of the bacteriophage also existed that led to lysis only under certain conditions. To set the stage for understanding Smith's work, first let us briefly review the life cycle of a bacteriophage (refer back to Figure 16.5). Lytic phages cause their hosts to die, releasing progeny viruses. Infected cells serve to propagate the phage, and after

GOAL To introduce specific changes in the nucleotide sequence of DNA.

STARTING MATERIALS φX174 bacteriophage, wildtype and supressor *E.coli,* oligonucleotides of defined sequence, DNA polymerase, and DNA ligase.

Experimental level

Conceptual level

1 Bacterial growth and the concept of a "lawn"

No dilution → Plate onto agar media → Incubate overnight → Undiluted; uniformly covered 'lawn'

Bacterial culture

Diluted 1000X → → 1000X diluted; discrete colonies

2 Infection by bacteriophages leads to plaque formation

φX174 phage

Undiluted bacteria

Allow infection Spread on agar media → Incubate overnight → Phage infect and lyse cells, subsequent infection and lysis of neighbouring cells generates a hole (plaque) in the bacterial lawn.

3 Targeting of a mutation in the φX174 lysisE gene

Wildtype DNA	5′ CGC TGG ACT TTG TGG GAT ACC
Decoded polypeptide	Arg Trp Thr Leu Trp Asp Thr
Mutant oligonucleotide	5′ T TTG T AG GAT AC 3′OH
Change in protein sequence	**STOP**

3′OH

DNA polymerase → Heteroduplex

Infection and Replication →

Bacteria contain two distinct types of phage DNAs

Wild–type + Mutant

DNA replication generates equal proportions of wild-type and mutant viral DNAs

4 Infect su⁺ host: both wild-type and mutant virus form plaques

Mixed viral population

Su⁺ bacteria

Plate on agar media → Plaque formation

Su⁺ cells suppress the TAG stop codon by incorporating Tryptophan

Su⁺ strain

Ribosome Su⁻ strain

mRNA

ACT TTG TAG TAG

Leu Trp
Thr

Translation continues past stop codon, functional lysisE protein produced

ACT TTG TAG TAG

Leu
Thr

Stop codon recognized, short polypeptide released, lysisE protein nonfunctional

Figure 18.19 In vitro oligonucleotide site-directed mutagenesis.

Figure 18.19 *(Continued)*

5 Analysis of individual cored plaques

Individual plaque cored from plate with pipette

Plaque formation indicates phage in core were wildtype

Infect su⁻ bacteria

No plaque formation indicates phage in core were mutant

Wild–type lysisE gene produces normal protein that functions in cell lysis after infection, leading to plaque formation

Mutant lysisE gene contains a stop codon; a short, non–functional lysisE protein is produced, but lysis does not occur

6 **CONCLUSION** Using synthetic oligonucleotides of defined sequence, it is possible to alter gene sequences in a site–directed matter to create mutations (and to repair them!).

7 **SOURCE** Hutchinson, C.A., Phillips, S., Edgell, M.H., Gillam, S., Jahnke, P., and Smith, M. Mutagenesis at a specific position in a DNA sequence, *Journal of Biological Chemistry* 253: 6551-6560 (1978).

lysis nearby hosts can become infected. Ordinarily, if a scientist plates a large number of bacteria on a nutrient medium in a Petri dish, the cells accumulate such a high density that individual colonies cannot be distinguished; rather, a dense and uniform "lawn" of bacteria is seen. If at some point before plating, the molecular biologist were to infect the cells with some phage particles, some cells would be infected and undergo lysis. Early in the process, or at low infectivity ratios, there are no visible consequences. Later, after the first round of lysis, nearby cells are infected and they in turn lyse. Eventually, after multiple rounds of infection and lysis, a small cleared area in the bacterial lawn is observed. This is termed a *plaque*.

The lysis *E* gene of phage φX174 encodes a protein involved in host cell lysis. The wild-type gene encodes a protein containing a tryptophan residue at position 587. Tryptophan is encoded by the codon UGG in mRNA, shown in Figure 18.19 as the coding strand of DNA. To read the triplets, remember that it is DNA and replace the thymidines (T, a base found only in DNA) with uracils (U, a base found only in RNA). Smith and his colleagues synthesized two 12-mer oligonucleotides, one of wild-type and the other with a single base change that alters the TGG codon to TAG. Examination of the genetic code (see Table 11.1) reveals that this codon does not specify an amino acid but rather signals termination of the protein chain (stop). Thus, such a mutant makes an mRNA, which is then translated, but the lysis *E* protein produced is truncated and nonfunctional, compromising the ability of the mutant virus to lyse the cell.

Smith's plan was to anneal the oligonucleotide to single-stranded, circular wild-type viral DNA and to synthesize a new viral strand in a test tube with purified enzymes (DNA polymerase and DNA ligase). The resulting heterduplexes (one wild-type strand and one mutant strand) could be used to infect

bacteria, and the resulting viral progeny would be of two distinct types: one wild-type and competent to lyse cells, and the other mutant and lysis defective. After infecting the bacteria, the scientists chemically lysed the cells and collected the mixture of viral particles. They then infected a type of bacteria called su⁺, which is genetic nomenclature for suppressor, wild-type. This strain, when encountering the UAG terminator codon, instead inserts tryptophan into the growing amino acid chain. This effectively suppresses the viral mutation at position 587 and allows both mutant and wild-type virus to grow and lyse the cells, forming plaques.

A plaque is derived from a single infection event, so the viral DNA should be derived from a single viral particle. Recall that the mixture contained both wild-type and mutant viral DNAs, so some plaques should be caused by wild-type virus and some should be caused by mutant virus. To test this researchers can core out individual plaques from a plate, wash out the virus particles, and reinfect other cells. The investigators did this, elegantly proving their point by challenging both su⁺ and su⁻ cells with the individual isolates. When su⁻ cells were infected, all isolates gave rise to plaques. However, when infection of su⁻ cells was performed, some of the isolates that did produce plaques on the su⁺ cells did not lyse the su⁻ cells. In the su⁻ cells, the protein synthesis machinery recognized UAG as a stop codon and produced defective lysis E proteins, prohibiting plaque formation.

To provide additional supporting evidence for their claim of site-directed mutagenesis, the investigators isolated DNA from a number of viral isolates and sequenced it, directly proving that position 587 contained the A in mutants unable to form plaques on su⁻ cells. Finally, a complementary approach was taken in which mutant DNA was used as the starting material and the process was repeated, this time beginning with an oligonucleotide primer with a G at position 587 to restore the wild-type coding sequence. As you might predict, this resulted in a proportion of the viruses that had regained the ability to produce a functional lysis E protein.

In his Nobel lecture, Smith quoted another Nobel laureate, Joshua Lederberg: "The *ignis fatuus* of genetics has been the specific mutagen, the reagent that would penetrate to a given gene, recognize and modify it in a specific way." Indeed, Smith and his colleagues provided that tool with the discovery of site-directed mutagenesis. Its use has led to many profound discoveries and likely will be instrumental in achieving others, such as gene replacement therapy.

Experimental Questions

1. What is mutagenesis?
2. In the investigation in Figure 18.19, how did the researchers generate new DNA molecules with specific alterations in the sequence?
3. How were suppressor mutations useful to Smith in validating his experiments?

Summary of Key Concepts

18.1 Gene Cloning

- Recombinant DNA technology is the use of laboratory techniques to isolate and manipulate fragments of DNA.

- Gene cloning is the process of making multiple copies of a gene. The procedure is used to obtain large amounts of the DNA that encodes a particular gene or to obtain large amounts of the gene product. (Figure 18.1)

- Plasmid and viral vectors are used in gene cloning. To obtain recombinant DNA, a vector and chromosomal DNA are cut with restriction enzymes. The DNA fragments bind to each other via their sticky ends, and the pieces are linked together via DNA ligase. (Table 18.1, Figure 18.2)

- When a recombinant vector is introduced into a bacterial cell, the cell replicates the vector and also divides to produce many cells. This achieves gene cloning. (Figure 18.3)

- A collection of recombinant vectors, each with a particular piece of chromosomal DNA, is introduced into bacterial cells to create a genomic DNA library. If the DNA inserts are derived from cDNA, which is made from mRNA, this is a cDNA library. (Figure 18.4)

- Colony hybridization is a method that uses a labelled probe that recognizes a specific gene to identify that gene in a DNA library. (Figure 18.5)

- Gel electrophoresis is used to separate macromolecules by using an electric field that causes them to pass through a gel matrix. Gel electrophoresis typically separates molecules according to their masses. (Figure 18.6)

- In a Southern blotting experiment, a labelled probe, which is a strand of DNA from a specific gene, is used to identify that gene in a mixture of many chromosomal DNA fragments. (Figure 18.7)

- Polymerase chain reaction (PCR) is another technique to make many copies of a gene. Primers are used that flank the region of DNA to be amplified. (Figure 18.8)

18.2 Genomics: Techniques to Study Genomes

- Genomics is the study of genomes as whole units; functional genomics studies the expression of a genome.

- For genomics, large fragments of chromosomal DNA are cloned into vectors such as BACs. One goal of structural genomics is to make a contig, which is a collection of clones that cover a contiguous region of a chromosome. This is a type of mapping—determining the relative locations of genes or other DNA segments along a chromosome. (Figure 18.9)

- The dideoxy method of DNA sequencing uses dideoxynucleotides to determine the base sequence of a segment of DNA. (Figures 18.10, 18.11)

- An important technique in functional genomics is a microarray that contains a group of spots, each with a specific type of DNA. It is used as a hybridization tool to study the expression of groups of genes. (Figure 18.12, Table 18.2)

18.3 Biotechnology

- Microorganisms can be genetically engineered to produce human products, such as insulin. (Figure 18.13)

- Microorganisms are also used to reduce pollutants in the environment, a phenomenon called bioremediation.

- Transgenic organisms, also called genetically modified organisms, are made via gene replacement or gene addition.

- Transgenic livestock can be genetically engineered to produce human hormones in their milk. (Figure 18.14)

- The Ti plasmid in *Agrobacterium tumefaciens* has been extensively used to produce transgenic plants, which can be used to produce food, fibre, oil, or other products of agronomic, industrial, or medical importance. (Figures 18.15, 18.16)

- The cloning of mammals can be achieved by fusing a somatic cell with an egg that has had its nucleus removed. The possibility of human cloning raises serious ethical questions. (Figure 18.17)

- DNA fingerprinting is a method of identification based on the occurrence of segments of DNA in the genomes of all individuals, such as STRs, that are variable in length among different individuals. (Figure 18.18)

- Site-directed mutagenesis enables specific changes to be made to cloned DNA sequences, enabling scientists to test the role of particular sequences in gene expression and in protein structure and function. (Figure 18.19)

Test to Assess Your Learning

1. Vectors used to clone genes were derived originally from
   a. proteins.
   b. plasmids.
   c. viruses.
   d. all of the above.
   e. (b) and (c) only.

2. Restriction enzymes
   a. are used to cut DNA into pieces for gene cloning.
   b. are naturally produced by bacteria cells to prevent viral infection.
   c. produce sticky ends on DNA fragments.
   d. all of the above.
   e. (a) and (c) only.

3. A DNA library produced by isolating mRNA from a cell and using reverse transcriptase to make DNA molecules is called a _____ library.
   a. genomic
   b. mRNA
   c. proteonomic
   d. cDNA
   e. chromosomal

4. Researchers can identify the colonies that contain the vector with the gene of interest by
   a. screening the different colonies by using a probe that is complementary to the gene of interest.
   b. keeping records of the particular colonies that were supposedly inoculated with the particular probe.
   c. using PCR to determine the gene sequence of the DNA in the different colonies.
   d. using DNA fingerprinting techniques to identify the particular gene of interest.
   e. none of the above.

5. A method used to detect a particular DNA sequence within a mixture of many DNA fragments is
   a. PCR.
   b. colony hybridization.
   c. DNA fingerprinting.
   d. DNA sequencing.
   e. Southern blotting.

6. Why is *Taq* polymerase used in PCR rather than other DNA polymerases?
   a. *Taq* polymerase is a synthetic enzyme that produces DNA strands at a faster rate than natural polymerases.
   b. *Taq* polymerase is a heat-stable form of DNA polymerase that can function after exposure to the high temperatures that are necessary for PCR.
   c. *Taq* polymerase is easier to isolate than other DNA polymerases.
   d. *Taq* polymerase is the DNA polymerase commonly produced by most eukaryotic cells.
   e. All of the above.

7. Let's suppose you want to clone a gene that has never been analyzed before by DNA sequencing. Which of the following statements do you agree with the most?
   a. Do PCR to clone the gene because it is much faster.
   b. Do PCR to clone the gene because it is very specific and gives a high yield.
   c. You can't do PCR because you can't make forward and reverse primers.
   d. Do cloning by insertion into a vector because it will give you a higher yield.
   e. Do cloning by insertion into a vector because it is easier than PCR.

8. During bioremediation, microorganisms are used to
   a. clone genes from eukaryotic organisms.
   b. introduce correct genes into individuals with genetic diseases.
   c. decrease pollutants in the environment.
   d. produce useful products, such as insulin.
   e. all of the above.

9. Organisms that carry genes that were introduced by using molecular techniques are called
   a. transgenics.
   b. clones.
   c. mutants.
   d. genetically modified organisms.
   e. both (a) and (d).

10. DNA fingerprinting is used
    a. to provide a means of precise identification of an organism, such as the identification of specific strains of bacteria.
    b. as a forensics tool to provide evidence in a criminal case.
    c. to determine genetic relationships between individuals.
    d. to determine the identity of an individual.
    e. all of the above.

Articulate to Assess Your Learning

1. Explain how using one restriction enzyme to cut both a plasmid and a gene of interest will allow the gene to be inserted into the plasmid.

2. Explain and draw the structural feature of a dideoxyribonucleotide that causes chain termination.

3. Explain how gel electrophoresis separates DNA fragments.

Collaborate to Assess and Extend Your Learning

1. Discuss the use of microorganisms for bioremediation.
2. Discuss the process of molecular pharming.
3. Discuss the ethical issues associated with genetic engineering, stem cell research, and the cloning of mammals.
4. A principle of biology is that all life is related by an evolutionary history. Describe the molecular techniques that are used in gene cloning, genomics, and creating recombinant organisms that are based on this principle.

Visit McGraw-Hill Ryerson Connect™ for additional study resources.

Genomes, Proteomes, and Bioinformatics

Chapter Outline

The unifying theme of biology is evolution. The genome of every living species is the product of more than 3.5 billion years of evolution. We can understand the unity of modern organisms by realizing that all species evolved from an interrelated group of ancestors. Most chapters in this book contain the Genomes and Proteomes feature to help you see the evolutionary connections among all forms of life and to understand how the genetic material produces the form and function of living organisms. By now, you are familiar with the concept of a **genome**, which is the complete genetic makeup of a cell or an organism. The genome of each species is critical to its existence in several ways:

- The genome stores information in the form of genes, which provide a blueprint to produce the characteristics of organisms.
- The genome is copied and transmitted from generation to generation.
- The accumulation of genetic changes over many generations produces the evolutionary changes that alter species and create new species.

An extension of genome analysis is the study of **proteomes**, which refers to the entire complement of proteins that a cell or an organism can make. The function of most genes is to encode proteins, which are the key participants in maintaining cell structure and in carrying out most cell functions. Analyzing the proteome of a single species and comparing the proteomes of different species allow biologists to understand the structure and function of cells, multicellular organisms, and the interactions between organisms and their environment.

The terms *genomes* and *proteomes* are sometimes confused with the terms genomics and proteomics. When we speak of genomes and proteomes, we are talking about characteristics of living organisms. By comparison, genomics and proteomics are experimental approaches to studying genomes and proteomes, respectively. An exciting advance in biology has been the ability to analyze the DNA sequence of genomes and the expression of groups of genes. This technology is genomics. Likewise, other tools have been invented to study large groups of proteins; this technology is proteomics. The techniques of genomics and proteomics were discussed in Chapter 18.

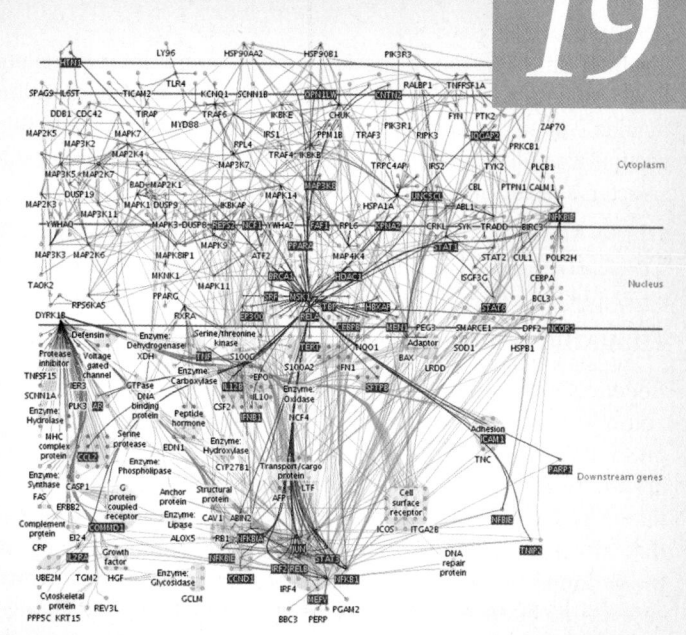

The bioinformatics age. The amount of data derived from the analyses of genomes and proteomes is so staggering in size and complexity that researchers have turned to computers to organize, analyze, and display how components are related to one another and how they interact. This information explosion has led to the development of bioinformatics.

In the first two sections of this chapter our focus will be primarily on biology, not on experimental techniques. We will consider the sizes and compositions of the genomes and proteomes of prokaryotic and eukaryotic species. As you will learn, genomes and proteomes are full of surprises. For example, did you know that most of your DNA has no known function? From a molecular perspective, genomes and proteomes contain extensive and intriguing information, which has challenged researchers to study them by using computer technology. In the last section of this chapter we will consider how the field of bioinformatics, which uses computers to study biological information, has been critical in the study of genomes and proteomes.

19.1 / BACTERIAL AND ARCHAEAL GENOMES

Learning Outcomes:

1. List the key characteristics of bacterial and archaeal genomes.
2. Describe the method of shotgun DNA sequencing.
3. Explain how metagenomics might be used to examine the biodiversity of a community.

The past decade has seen remarkable advances in our overall understanding of the entire genomes of many species. As genetic technology has progressed, researchers have increasingly become able to analyze the composition of genomes as a whole unit. For many species we now know their complete DNA sequence, which provides the most detailed description available of an organism's genome at the molecular level. In this section we will survey the sizes and composition of genomes in selected species of bacteria and archaea.

The Genomes of Bacteria and Archaea Typically Consist of a Circular Chromosome with a Few Thousand Genes

Geneticists have made great progress in the study of bacterial and archaeal genomes. Some of the key features of prokaryotic chromosomes are described in Chapter 16. Researchers are interested in the genomes of prokaryotic species for three main reasons. First, bacteria cause many different diseases that affect humans, as well as plants and animals. Studying the genomes of bacteria reveals important clues about the process of infection and also may help us find ways to combat bacterial infection. A second reason for studying prokaryotic and archaeal genomes is that the information we learn about these microscopic organisms often applies to larger and more complex organisms. For example, basic genetic mechanisms, such as DNA replication and gene regulation, were first understood in *Escherichia coli*. That knowledge provided a critical foundation to understanding how these processes work in humans and other eukaryotic species. A third reason is evolution. The origin of the first eukaryotic cell probably involved a union between an archaeal and a bacterial cell. The study of prokaryotic genomes helps us understand how all living species evolved. Finally, another reason to study the genomes of bacteria is their use as tools in research and biotechnology, which was discussed in Chapter 18.

As of 2011 the genomes of more than 700 bacterial and archaeal species have been completely sequenced and analyzed. The chromosomes of prokaryotes are usually a few million base pairs (bp) long. Genomic researchers refer to 1 million bp as 1 megabase pair, abbreviated Mbp or Mb. Most bacteria and archaea contain a single type of chromosome, though multiple copies may be present in a single cell. However, some bacteria are known to have different chromosomes. For example, *Vibrio cholerae,* the bacterium that causes the diarrheal disease of cholera, has two different chromosomes in each cell, one 2.9 Mb and the other 1.1 Mb.

Bacterial and archaeal chromosomes are often circular. For example, the two chromosomes in *V. cholerae* are circular, as is the single type of chromosome found in *E. coli*. However, linear chromosomes are found in some prokaryotic species, such as *Borrelia burgdorferi,* which is the bacterium that causes Lyme disease, the most common tick-borne disease in Canada and the United States. Certain bacterial species can even contain both linear and circular chromosomes. *Agrobacterium tumifaciens,* which infects plants and causes a disorder called crown gall disease (look ahead to Figure 25.3) disease, has one linear chromosome (2.1 Mb) and one circular chromosome (3.0 Mb).

Table 19.1 compares the sequenced genomes from several prokaryotic species. They range in size from 1.7 to 5.2 Mb. The total number of genes is correlated with the total genome size. Roughly 1,000 genes are found for every Mb of DNA. Compared with eukaryotic genomes, bacterial and archaeal genomes are less complex. Their chromosomes lack centromeres and telomeres, and they have a single origin of replication. Also, chromosomes of bacteria and archaea have relatively little repetitive DNA, whereas repetitive sequences are usually abundant in eukaryotic genomes.

In addition to one or more chromosomes, bacteria often have plasmids, usually circular pieces of DNA that exist independently of the bacterial chromosome. Plasmids are typically small, in the range of a few thousand to tens of thousands of base pairs in length, though some can be quite large, even hundreds of thousands of base pairs (the *Agrobacterium* Ti plasmid is about 200kbp). The various functions of plasmids are described in Chapter 16. Their use as vectors in genetic engineering is discussed in Chapter 18.

Table 19.1	Examples of Prokaryotic Genomes That Have Been Sequenced*		
Species	**Genome size (Mb)†**	**Number of genes‡**	**Description**
Methanobacterium thermoautotrophicum	1.7	1,869	An archaeon that produces methane
Haemophilus influenzae	1.8	1,753	One of several different bacterial species that causes respiratory illness and meningitis
Sulfolobus solfataricus	3.0	3,032	An archaeon that metabolizes sulphur-containing compounds
Lactobacillus plantarum	3.3	3,052	A type of lactic acid bacterium used in the production of cheese and yogurt
Mycobacterium tuberculosis	4.4	4,294	The bacterium that causes the respiratory disease tuberculosis
Escherichia coli	4.6	4,289	A common intestinal bacterium; certain strains can cause human illness
Bacillus anthracis	5.2	5,439	The bacterium that causes the disease anthrax

* Prokaryotic species often exist as different strains that may differ slightly in their genome size and number of genes. The data are from common strains of the indicated species. The species shown in this table have only one type of chromosome.
† Mb equals 1 million base pairs.
‡ The number of genes is an estimate based on the analysis of genome sequences.

FEATURE INVESTIGATION

Venter, Smith, and Colleagues Sequenced the First Complete Genome, That of *Haemophilus influenza*, in 1995

The first genome to be entirely sequenced was that of the bacterium *Haemophilus influenzae*. This bacterium causes a variety of diseases in humans, including respiratory illnesses and bacterial meningitis. *H. influenzae* has a relatively small genome size, approximately 1.8 Mb.

A common strategy for sequencing an entire genome is called **shotgun DNA sequencing**. In this approach, researchers use the technique of dideoxy sequencing to randomly sequence many DNA fragments from the genome. As a matter of chance some of the fragments overlap—the end of one fragment contains the same DNA region as the beginning of another fragment. Computers are used to align the overlapping regions and assemble the DNA fragments into a contiguous sequence identical to that found in the intact chromosome (refer back to Figure 18.9). The advantage of shotgun DNA sequencing is that it does not require extensive genetic mapping, which can be time-consuming. A disadvantage is that researchers will waste time sequencing the same region of DNA more times than necessary to assemble the sequence correctly.

To obtain a complete sequence of a genome with the shotgun approach, how do researchers decide how many fragments to sequence? With the following equation we can calculate the probability that a base will not be sequenced by using this approach:

$$P = e^{-m}$$

where P is the probability that a base will be left unsequenced, e is the base of the natural logarithm ($e = 2.72$), and m is the number of bases sequenced divided by the total genome size. For example, in the case of *H. influenzae*, with a genome size of 1.8 Mb, if researchers sequenced 9.0 Mb, $m = 5$ (i.e., 9.0 Mb/1.8 Mb):

$$P = e^{-m} = e^{-5} = 0.0067 \text{ or } 0.67\%.$$

This means that if we randomly sequence 9.0 Mb, which is five times the length of a single genome, we are likely to miss only 0.67% of the genome. With a genome size of 1.8 Mb, we would miss about 12,060 nucleotides out of approximately 1.8 million. Such missed sequences are typically on small DNA fragments that—as a matter of random chance—did not happen to be sequenced. The missing links in the genome can be sequenced later by using mapping methods.

In their discovery-based investigation, Craig Venter, Hamilton Smith, and colleagues used a shotgun DNA sequencing approach (**Figure 19.1**). The researchers isolated chromosomal DNA from *H. influenzae* and broke the DNA into small fragments, approximately 2,000 bp in length. These fragments were randomly cloned into vectors that allow the DNA to be propagated in *E. coli*. Each *E. coli* clone carried a vector with a different piece of DNA from *H. influenzae*. As discussed in Chapter 18, this collection of clones is called a DNA library. The researchers then subjected many of these clones to the procedure of DNA sequencing. They sequenced a total of approximately 10.8 Mb of DNA.

The outcome of this genome-sequencing project was a very long DNA sequence. In 1995, Venter, Smith, and colleagues published the entire DNA sequence of *H. influenzae*.

GOAL The goal is to obtain the entire genome sequence of *Haemophilus influenzae*. This information will reveal its genome size and also which genes the organism has.

KEY MATERIALS A strain of *H. influenzae*.

Experimental level   **Conceptual level**

1 Purify DNA from a strain of *H. influenzae*. This involves breaking open cells and adding phenol. Most protein components go into the phenol phase. DNA remains in the aqueous (water) phase.

DNA in aqueous (water) phase
Proteins in phenol phase

H. influenzae chromosomal DNA

2 Sonicate the DNA to break it into small fragments of about 2,000 bp in length.

Sound waves   Sound waves

DNA fragments in aqueous phase

Figure 19.1 Determination of the complete genome sequence of *Haemophilus influenzae* by Venter, Smith, and colleagues.

Figure 19.1 *(Continued)*

3 Clone the DNA fragments into vectors. The procedures for cloning are described in Chapter 18. This produces a DNA library.

Refer back to Figures 18.2 and 18.3.

Vector DNA

Piece of *H. influenzae* DNA

A DNA library

4 Subject many clones to the procedure of dideoxy DNA sequencing, also described in Chapter 18. A total of 10.8 Mb was sequenced.

Refer back to Figure 18.11.

Produces a large number of overlapping sequences.

...CCAGTCCCATGCCATGGCCCAGTCCC

5 Use tools of bioinformatics, described in the last section of this chapter, to identify various types of genes in the genome.

CCATGCCATGGCCCC

Explores the genome sequence and identifies and characterizes genes.

6 THE DATA

1,600,000

1

400,000

1,830,137 bp
~1,800 genes

1,200,000

800,000

Functions of Proteins Encoded by Genes

% of genome			% of genome		
6.8		Amino acid biosynthesis	5.3		Metabolism of purines, pyrimidines, nucleosides, and nucleotides
5.4		Biosynthesis of cofactors, prosthetic groups, carriers			
8.3		Cell envelope	6.3		Regulatory functions
5.3		Cellular processes	8.6		Replication
3.0		Central intermediary metabolism	12.2		Transport and binding proteins
10.4		Energy metabolism	14.0		Translation
2.5		Fatty acid/phospholipid metabolism	2.7		Transcription
			9.2		Other categories

7 CONCLUSION *H. influenzae* has a genome size of 1.83 Mb with approximately 1,800 genes. The functions of many of those genes could be inferred by comparing them to genes in other species.

8 SOURCE Fleischmann et al. 1995. Whole-genome random sequencing and assembly of *Haemophilus influenzae* Rd. *Science* 269:496–512.

The researchers then analyzed the genome sequence by computer to obtain information about the properties of the genome. Questions that they asked included these: How many genes does the genome contain? What are the likely functions of those genes? Later in this chapter, we will learn how scientists can answer such questions with the use of computers. The data in Figure 19.1 summarize the results that the researchers obtained. The *H. influenzae* genome is composed of 1,830,137 bp of DNA. The computer analysis predicted 1,743 genes. Based on their similarities to known genes in other species, the researchers also predicted the functions of nearly two-thirds of these genes. What about the genes whose function is unknown? These are gaps in our knowledge of what types of proteins the genes encode and their normal roles in the *H. influenzae* cell, but they also afford specific opportunities to investigate the unknown. The diagram shown in the data of Figure 19.1 places genes in various categories based on their predicted function. These results gave the first complete "genome picture" of a living organism!

Experimental Questions

1. What was the goal of the experiment conducted by Venter, Smith, and colleagues?
2. How does shotgun DNA sequencing differ from procedures that involve mapping? Name an advantage and a disadvantage of the shotgun DNA sequencing approach.
3. What were the results of the study described in Figure 19.1?

Metagenomics and Synthetic Genomics

High throughput sequencing techniques have permitted examinations of DNA sequences present in environmental samples, an approach that has been termed **metagenomics** or environmental genomics. Numerous applications can be anticipated from this technology. For example, scientists can estimate the biodiversity of insect populations by analyzing DNA from windshield splatter, the particulate matter from insects striking the windscreen of a moving car. Large-scale sequencing of DNA from these samples, followed by comparisons to sequence databases (discussed in section 21.4), reveals both the number of species and their relative abundance in the original sample. Similarly, metagenomics is a discovery tool to identify known species in samples (for example, from various ocean depths, in runoff from mining operations, in thermal springs) and to reveal the existence of unknown sequences (and thus the likelihood of unknown species or genes) in these samples. Such knowledge has many potential benefits, such as discovering genes that encode enzymes of industrial or medical importance and enabling bioremediation of contaminated soil or water by identifying and employing specific microbes that are capable of decontaminating toxic substances.

Synthetic genomics is a branch of genomics that employs chemically synthesized genes and even entire genomes to ultimately construct living organisms. The first synthetic genome, that of the bacterium *Mycoplasma mycoides,* was successfully synthesized in 2010 and shown to encode all functions to support the replication and physiology of the bacterium. The importance of this technology is threefold. First, it enables scientists to determine the minimal genome capable of sustaining life. Second, the development of the technology will enable cassettes of numerous genes (potentially encoding an entire biochemical pathway) to be transferred into a host organism to confer new properties. In this regard it is anticipated that synthetic genomics will enable numerous biotechnological advances in fields such as biofuel research and vaccine production. Despite the potential benefits of synthetic genomics, there are unknown risks associated with the creation of new life forms, and this area will undoubtedly fuel many lively discussions on both the biological and ethical issues.

19.2 EUKARYOTIC GENOMES

Learning Outcomes:

1. Describe the key features of eukaryotic genomes.
2. Name the two major types of transposable elements and describe how they differ.
3. Explain how gene duplications can occur and lead to the formation of gene families.
4. Outline the goals and results of the Human Genome Project.

Thus far we have examined bacterial and archaeal genomes. In this section we turn to eukaryotes, which include protists, fungi, animals, and plants. As you will learn, their genomes are larger and more complex than their bacterial and archaeal counterparts. In addition to genes, eukaryotic genomes often have abundant amounts of noncoding sequences, whose function is largely unknown. For example, eukaryotic genomes typically have a substantial amount of short repeated sequences called repetitive DNA. We will explore how certain types of repetitive DNA sequences are formed by a process called transposition. We will also examine how the duplication of genes can lead to families of related genes.

The Nuclear Genomes of Eukaryotes Are Sets of Linear Chromosomes That Vary Greatly in Size and Composition Among Different Species

As discussed in Chapter 14, the genome located in the nucleus of eukaryotic species is usually found in sets of linear chromosomes. In humans, for example, one set contains 23 linear chromosomes—22 autosomes and one sex chromosome, X or Y. In addition, certain organelles in eukaryotic cells contain a small amount of DNA. These include the mitochondrion, which plays a role in ATP synthesis, and the chloroplast (found in plants and algae), which carries out photosynthesis. The genetic material in these organelles is referred to as the mitochondrial or the chloroplast genome to distinguish it from the nuclear genome, which is located in the cell nucleus. In this chapter, we will focus on the nuclear genome of eukaryotes.

Sizes of Nuclear Genomes In the past decade or so the DNA sequence of entire nuclear genomes has been determined for several eukaryotic species (**Table 19.2**). The genomes of simpler eukaryotes, such as yeast, carry a few thousand different genes, while the genomes of more complex eukaryotes contain tens of thousands of genes. Motivation to sequence these genomes comes from four main sources. First, the work of researchers can greatly benefit from genome sequences that allow them to identify and characterize the genes of model organisms. This has been the impetus for genome projects involving baker's yeast (*Saccharomyces cerevisiae*), the fruit fly (*Drosophila melanogaster*), a nematode worm (*Caenorhabditis elegans*), the simple plant called thale cress (*Arabidopsis thaliana*), and the mouse (*Mus musculus*). A second reason for genome sequencing is to gather more information to identify and treat human diseases, which is an important aim of sequencing the human genome. Researchers hope that the DNA sequence of the human genome will help to identify genes in which mutation plays a role in disease. Third, by sequencing the genomes of agriculturally important species, new strains of livestock and plant species with improved traits can be developed. Finally, evolutionary biologists are interested in genome sequences as a way to establish evolutionary relationships.

Relationship between Genome Sizes and Repetitive Sequences Eukaryotic genomes are generally larger than prokaryotic genomes in terms of both the number of genes and the genome size (Table 19.2). The genomes of simpler eukaryotes, such as yeast, contain several thousand different genes,

Table 19.2	Examples of Eukaryotic Nuclear Genomes That Have Been Sequenced		
Species	**Nuclear genome size (Mb)**	**Number of genes**	**Description**
Saccharomyces cerevisiae (baker's yeast)	12.1	6,294	One of the simplest eukaryotic species; it has been extensively studied by researchers to understand eukaryotic cell and molecular biology.
Caenorhabditis elegans (nematode worm)	100	~19,000	A model organism used to study animal development.
Drosophila melanogaster (fruit fly)	180	~14,000	A model organism used to study many genetic phenomena, including development.
Arabidopsis thaliana (thale cress)	120	~26,000	A model organism studied by plant biologists.
Oryza sativa (rice)	440	~40,000	A cereal grain with a relatively small genome; it is very important worldwide as a food crop.
Mus musculus (mouse)	2,500	~20,000–25,000	A model mammalian organism used to study genetics, cell biology, and development.
Homo sapiens (humans)	3,200	~20,000–25,000	Our own genome, the sequencing of which will help to elucidate our inherited traits and to aid in the identification and treatment of diseases.

(a) Genome size

(b) *Echinops bannaticus*

(c) *Echinops nanus*

Figure 19.2   Genome sizes among selected groups of eukaryotes.   (a) Genome sizes among various groups of eukaryotes are shown on a log scale. As an example for comparison, two closely related species of globe thistle are pictured: *Echinops bannaticus* in **(b)** and *Echinops nanus* in **(c)**. These species have similar characteristics, but *E. bannaticus* has nearly double the amount of DNA that *E. nanus* does because of the accumulation of repetitive DNA sequences.

Concept check: *What are two reasons that the groups of species shown in (a) have variation in their total amount of DNA?*

whereas the genomes of more complex eukaryotes contain tens of thousands of genes. Note that the number of genes is not the same as genome size. When we speak of genome size, this means the total amount of DNA, often measured in megabase pairs. The relative sizes of nuclear genomes vary dramatically among different eukaryotic species (**Figure 19.2a**). Generally, increases in the amount of DNA are correlated with increases in cell size, cell complexity, and body complexity. For example, yeast have smaller genomes than animals. However, major variations in genome sizes are observed among organisms that are similar in form and function. For example, the total amount of DNA found within different species of amphibians varies over 100-fold.

The DNA content of closely related species can also vary. As an example, let's consider two closely related species of the plant called the globe thistle, *Echinops bannaticus* and *Echinops nanus* (**Figure 19.2b, 19.2c**). These species have similar

numbers of chromosomes, but *E. bannaticus* has nearly double the amount of DNA as *E. nanus*. What is the explanation for the larger genome of *E. bannaticus*? The genome of *E. bannaticus* is not likely to contain twice as many genes. Rather, its genome composition includes many **repetitive sequences**, which are short DNA sequences that are present in many copies throughout the genome. Repetitive sequences are often abundant in eukaryotic species.

Types of Repetitive Sequences   Repetitive sequences fall into two broad categories: moderately repetitive and highly repetitive. **Moderately repetitive sequences** are found a few hundred to several thousand times in the genome. In some cases these sequences are multiple copies of the same gene. For example, the genes that encode ribosomal RNA (rRNA) are found in many copies. The cell needs a large amount of rRNA for its cellular ribosomes, which is accomplished by having and expressing multiple copies of the genes that encode rRNA. In addition other types of functionally important sequences can be moderately repetitive. For example, multiple copies of origins of replication are found in eukaryotic chromosomes. Other moderately repetitive sequences may play a role in the regulation of gene transcription and translation.

Highly repetitive sequences are those that are found tens of thousands or even millions of times throughout the genome. Each copy of a highly repetitive sequence is relatively short, ranging from a few nucleotides to several hundred nucleotides in length. Most of these sequences have no known function, and whether they benefit the organism is a matter of debate. A widely studied example is the *Alu* family of sequences found in humans and other primates. The *Alu* sequence is approximately 300 bp long. This sequence derives its name from the observation that it contains a site for cleavage by a restriction endonuclease known as *Alu*I. It represents about 10% of the total human DNA and occurs approximately every 5,000 to 6,000 bases. Evolutionary studies suggest that the *Alu* sequence arose 65 million years ago from a section of a single ancestral gene known as the 7SL RNA gene. Remarkably, during 65 million years the *Alu* sequence has been copied and inserted into the human genome so often that it now appears more than 1 million times. The mechanism for the proliferation of *Alu* sequences will be described later.

Some highly repetitive sequences, like the *Alu* family, are interspersed throughout the genome. Other highly repetitive sequences are clustered in a tandem array in which a very short nucleotide sequence is repeated many times in a row. In *Drosophila*, for example, 19% of the chromosomal DNA is highly repetitive DNA found in tandem arrays. An example is shown here:

```
A A T A T A A T A T A T A A T A T A A T A T A A T A T A T
T T A T A T T A T A T A T T A T A T T A T A T T A T A T A
```

In this particular tandem array, two related sequences, AATAT and AATATAT, are repeated many times. Highly repetitive sequences, which contain tandem arrays of short sequences, are commonly found in centromeric regions of chromosomes and can be quite long, sometimes more than 1 million bp in length!

Figure 19.3 shows the composition of the relative classes of DNA sequences found in the nuclear genome of humans. Surprisingly, exons, the coding regions of structural genes, and the genes that give rise to rRNA and tRNA, make up only about 2% of our genome. The other 98% is composed of noncoding sequences. Though we often think of genomes as being the repository of sequences that code for proteins, most eukaryotic genomes are largely composed of other types of sequences. Intron DNA is the second most common category at 24%. Unique noncoding DNA, whose function is largely unknown, constitutes 15%. Repetitive DNA makes up 59% of the DNA in the genome. Much of the repetitive DNA is derived from transposable elements, which are described next.

Transposable Elements Can Move from One Chromosomal Location to Another

As you have seen, genomes are composed of several types of DNA sequences. Such sequences include not just the coding sequences of genes but also other sequences, including introns and repetitive sequences. Much of the moderately repetitive and highly repetitive DNA that is found in genomes is derived from a process called **transposition**, in which a short segment of DNA moves within a cell from its original site to a new site

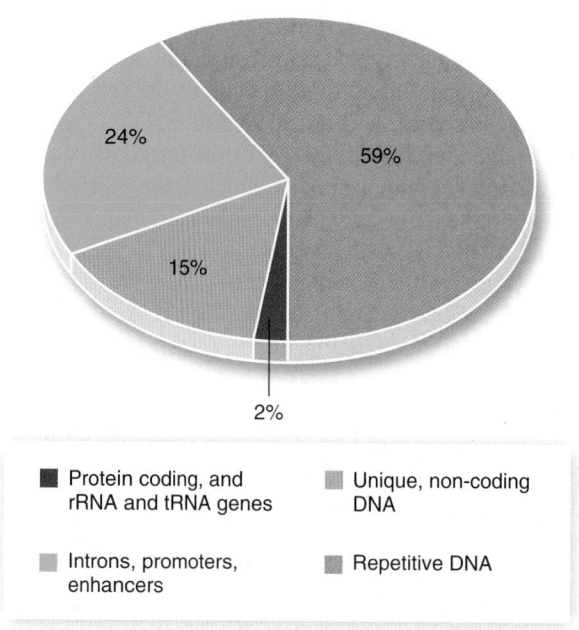

Figure 19.3   The composition of DNA sequences that are found in the nuclear genome of humans.   Note that only about 2% of our genome codes for proteins; most of our genome is made up of repetitive sequences.

in the genome. The DNA segments that transpose themselves are known as **transposable elements (TEs)**. They range from a few hundred to several thousand base pairs in length. TEs have sometimes been referred to as "jumping genes," because they are inherently mobile. Barbara McClintock first identified transposable elements in the late 1940s from her studies with corn plants (**Figure 19.4**). She identified a segment of DNA that could move into and out of a gene that affected the colour of corn kernels, producing a speckled appearance. Since that

(a) Barbara McClintock

(b) Speckled corn kernels caused by transposable elements

Figure 19.4   Barbara McClintock, who discovered transposable elements.   As shown in part **(b)**, when a transposable element is found within a pigment gene in corn, its frequent movement causes the kernel colour to be speckled.

time biologists have discovered many different types of TEs in prokaryotes, protists, fungi, plants, and animals—transposable elements have been found in all species examined.

Though Barbara McClintock identified TEs in corn in the late 1940s, her work was met with great skepticism because many researchers had trouble believing that DNA segments could be mobile. The advent of molecular technology in the 1960s and 1970s allowed scientists to understand more about the characteristics of TEs that enable their movement. Most notably, research involving bacterial TEs eventually progressed to a molecular understanding of the transposition process. In 1983, more than 30 years after her initial discovery, McClintock was awarded the Nobel Prize.

Researchers have studied TEs from many species, including bacteria, archaea, and eukaryotes. They have discovered that TEs fall into two groups, based on different mechanisms of movement.

DNA Transposons Transposable elements that move via a DNA molecule are called **DNA transposons**. Both ends of DNA transposons usually have inverted repeats (IRs)—DNA sequences that are identical (or very similar) but run in opposite directions (**Figure 19.5a**), such as the following:

5′—CTGACTCTT—3′   and   5′—AAGAGTCAG—3′

3′—GACTGAGAA—5′   3′—TTCTCAGTC—5′

Depending on the particular transposable element, inverted repeats range from 9 to 40 base pairs in length. In addition, TEs may contain a central region that encodes **transposase**, an enzyme that facilitates transposition.

As shown in **Figure 19.5b**, one type of transposition occurs by a cut-and-paste mechanism. Transposase first recognizes the inverted repeats in the TE and then removes the sequence from its original site. Next, the transposase/TE complex moves to a new location, and transposase then inserts the sequence into the chromosome. Transposition can occur when a cell is in the process of DNA replication. If a transposable element is removed from a site that has already replicated and is inserted into a chromosomal site that has not yet replicated, the TE will increase in number after DNA replication is complete. This is one way for TEs to become more numerous in a genome.

Retroelements Another category of transposable elements moves via an RNA intermediate. This form of transposition is very common but is found only in eukaryotic species. These types of elements are known as **retroelements** or **retrotransposons**. The *Alu* sequence in the human genome is an example of a retroelement. Some retroelements contain genes that encode the enzymes reverse transcriptase and integrase, which are needed in the transposition process (**Figure 19.6a**). Recall from Chapter 16 that reverse transcriptase uses RNA as a template to synthesize a complementary copy of DNA. Retroelements may also contain repeated sequences called terminal repeats at each end that facilitate their recognition.

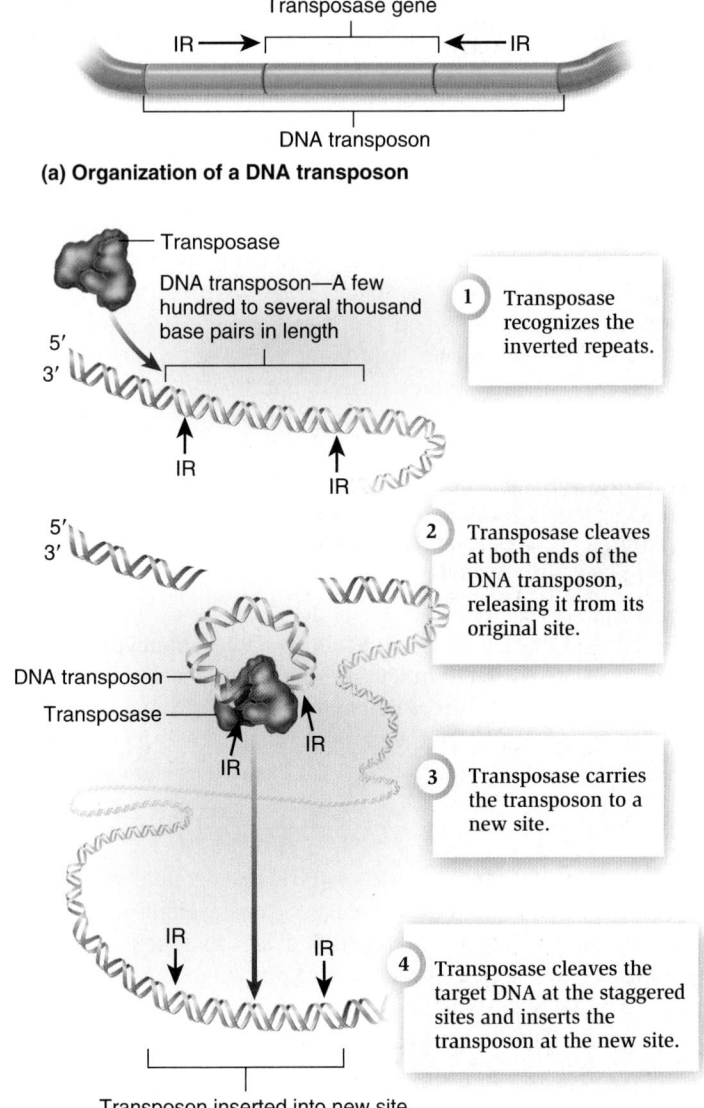

(a) Organization of a DNA transposon

Transposase gene

IR   IR

DNA transposon

Transposase

DNA transposon—A few hundred to several thousand base pairs in length

5′
3′

IR   IR

5′
3′

DNA transposon
Transposase

IR
IR

IR   IR

IR   IR

Transposon inserted into new site

1 Transposase recognizes the inverted repeats.

2 Transposase cleaves at both ends of the DNA transposon, releasing it from its original site.

3 Transposase carries the transposon to a new site.

4 Transposase cleaves the target DNA at the staggered sites and inserts the transposon at the new site.

(b) Cut-and-paste mechanism of transposition

Figure 19.5 Simple transposable elements and their mechanism of transposition. **(a)** Simple transposable elements (TEs) contain inverted repeat (IR) sequences at each end and a gene that encodes transposase in the middle. **(b)** Simple transposition occurs by a cut-and-paste mechanism.

The mechanism of retroelement movement is shown in **Figure 19.6b**. First, the element is transcribed into RNA by the enzyme RNA polymerase. Reverse transcriptase uses this RNA as a template to synthesize a double-stranded DNA molecule. The ends of the double-stranded DNA are then recognized by integrase, which catalyzes the insertion of the DNA into the host chromosomal DNA. The integration of retroelements can occur at many locations within the genome. Furthermore, because a single retroelement can be copied into many RNA transcripts, retroelements may accumulate rapidly within a genome. This explains how the *Alu* element in the human genome was able to proliferate and constitute 10% of our genome.

(a) Organization of a retroelement

1 RNA polymerase transcribes the retroelement into RNA.

2 Reverse transcriptase uses the RNA as a template to synthesize a double-stranded DNA molecule.

3 Integrase inserts this retroelement DNA into the chromosome.

4 The chromosome now contains two copies of the retroelement.

(b) Mechanism of movement of a retroelement

Figure 19.6 **Retroelements and their mechanism of transposition.** Retroelements are found only in eukaryotic species. **(a)** Some retroelements contain terminal repeats and can contain genes that encode the enzymes reverse transcriptase and integrase, which are needed in the transposition process. **(b)** The process that adds a copy of a retroelement into a host chromosome.

Concept check: *Based on their mechanism of movement, which type of TEs do you think would proliferate more rapidly in a genome: simple TEs (see Figure 19.5b) or retroelements?*

Role of Transposable Elements

What is the biological significance of TEs? The answer is unclear. According to the **selfish DNA hypothesis**, TEs exist because they have the characteristics that allow them to insert themselves into the host cell DNA. In other words, they resemble parasites in the sense that they inhabit the host without offering any advantage. They can proliferate within the host as long as they do not harm the host to the extent that they significantly disrupt survival. However, TEs can do harm. For example, if they jump into the middle of an important gene and thereby disrupt its function, this may have a negative impact on the phenotype of an organism.

Other biologists have argued that TEs may provide benefits to a given species. For example, bacterial TEs often carry an antibiotic-resistance gene that provides the organism with a survival advantage. In addition, TEs may cause greater genetic diversity by promoting chromosomal rearrangements. As discussed next, such rearrangements can cause a misaligned crossover during meiosis and promote the formation of a gene family.

Gene Duplications Provide Additional Material for Genome Evolution, Sometimes Leading to the Formation of Gene Families

Let's now turn our attention to a way that the number of genes in a genome can increase. Small chromosomal duplications are important because they provide raw material for the addition of more genes into a species' genome. Such duplications can create **homologous genes**—two or more similar genes that are derived from a single ancestral gene (**Figure 19.7a**). Over many generations each version of the gene accumulates different mutations, resulting in genes with similar, but not identical, DNA sequences.

How do duplications occur? One mechanism that produces gene duplications is a misaligned crossover (**Figure 19.7b**). In this example two homologous chromosomes have paired with each other during meiosis, but the homologs are misaligned. If a crossover occurs, this produces one chromosome with a gene duplication, one with a deletion, and two normal chromosomes. Each of these chromosomes will be segregated into different haploid cells (gametes). If a gamete carrying the chromosome with the gene duplication participates in fertilization with another gamete, an offspring with a gene duplication is produced. In this way gene duplications can form and be transmitted to future generations. The presence of multiple copies of the same transposable element in a genome can foster this process, because the chromosomes can misalign while attempting to align TEs that are at different locations in the same chromosome.

During evolution gene duplications can occur numerous times. Two or more homologous genes within a single species are also called **paralogs** or paralogous genes. Multiple gene duplication followed by sequence divergence can result in a gene family composed of two or more paralogous genes that carry out related functions. A well-studied example is the globin gene family found in animals. The globin genes encode polypeptides that are subunits of proteins that function in oxygen binding. Hemoglobin, which is made in red blood cells, carries oxygen throughout the body. In humans the globin gene family is composed of 14 paralogs that were originally derived from a single ancestral globin gene (**Figure 19.8**). According to an evolutionary analysis the ancestral globin gene duplicated between 500 million and 600 million years ago. Since that time, additional duplication events and chromosomal rearrangements have occurred to produce the current number of 14 genes on

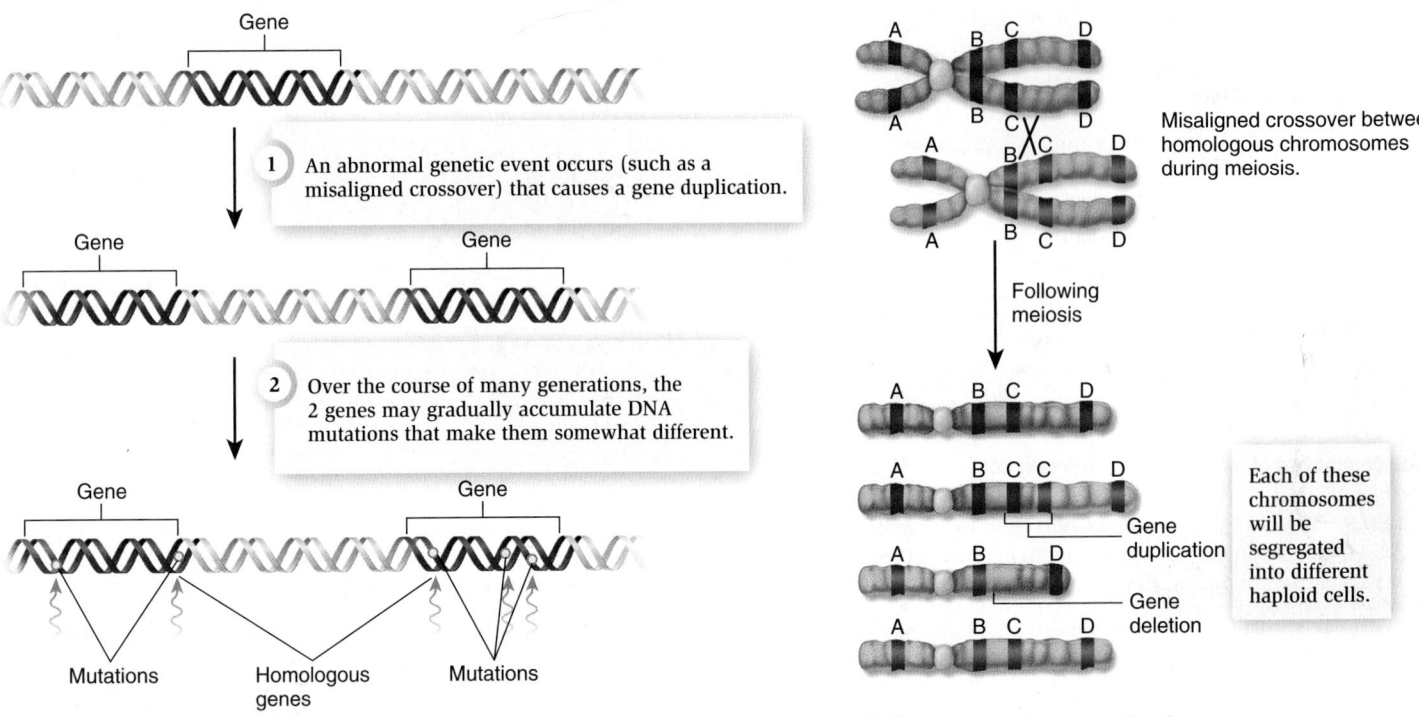

(a) Gene duplication and the formation of homologous genes

(b) Mechanism of gene duplication

Figure 19.7   Gene duplication and the evolution of homologous genes.   (a) Gene duplication produces two copies of the same gene. Over time, these copies accumulate different random mutations, which results in homologous genes with similar, but not identical, DNA sequences. (b) Mechanism of gene duplication. If two homologous chromosomes misalign during meiosis, a crossover will produce a chromosome with a gene duplication and one with a corresponding deletion (which may be lethal).

BioConnections: *Look back to Figure 17.13. How are multigene families formed?*

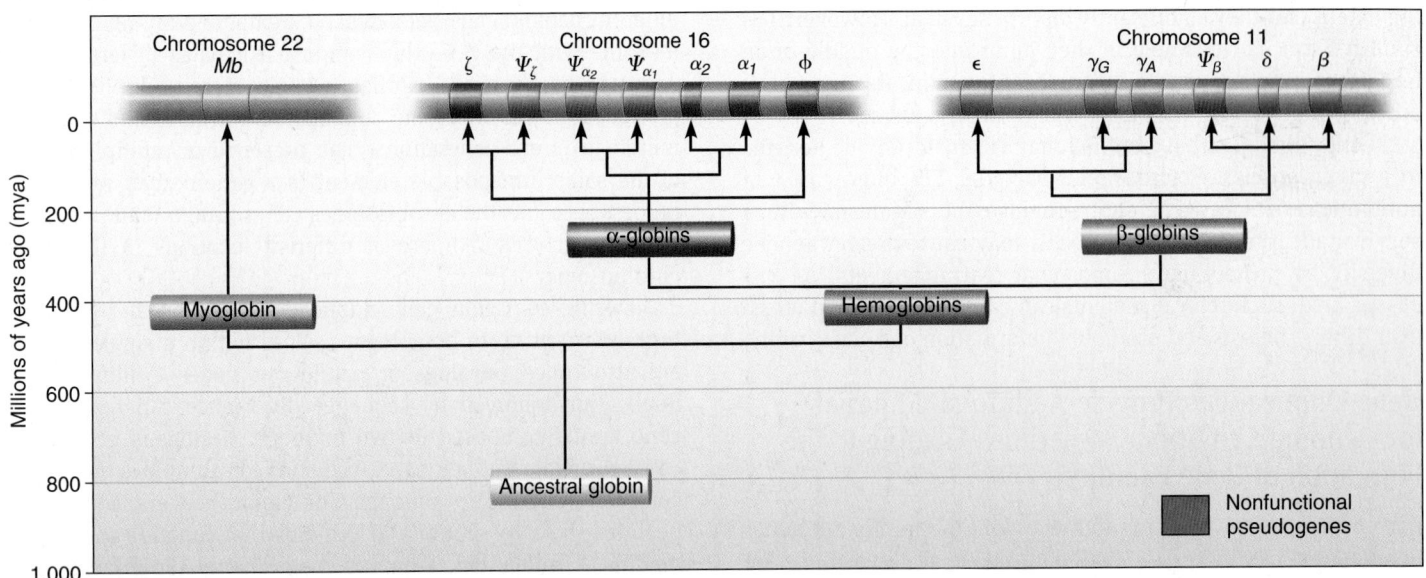

Figure 19.8   The evolution of the globin gene family in humans.   The globin gene family evolved from a single ancestral globin gene. The first gene duplication produced two genes that accumulated mutations and became the genes encoding myoglobin and the family of hemoglobins. The modern myoglobin gene is found on chromosome 22. An ancestral hemoglobin gene duplicated to produce the α- and β-globins. Further duplications of ancestral α-globin and β-globin genes produced several homologous genes on chromosomes 16 and 11, respectively. The four genes shown in grey are nonfunctional pseudogenes.

Concept check: *What is the advantage of a gene family?*

BioConnections: *Look back to Figure 12.3. How do different gene family members vary in their affinity for oxygen?*

three different human chromosomes. Four of these are pseudogenes, which are genes that have been produced by gene duplication but have accumulated mutations that make them nonfunctional so they are not transcribed into RNA.

Gene families have been important in the evolution of complex traits. Even though all the globin polypeptides are subunits of proteins that play a role in oxygen binding, the accumulation of different mutations in the various family members has created globins that are more specialized in their function. For example, myoglobin is better at binding and storing oxygen in muscle cells, whereas the hemoglobins are better at binding and transporting oxygen via the red blood cells. Also, different globin genes are expressed during different stages of human development. For instance, the (epsilon) ε-globin and (zeta) ζ-globin genes are expressed very early in embryonic life. During the second trimester of gestation the (alpha) α-globin and (gamma) γ-globin genes are turned on. Following birth the γ-globin genes are turned off and the (beta) β-globin gene is turned on. These differences in the expression of the globin genes reflect the differences in the oxygen transport needs of humans during the embryonic, fetal, and postpartum stages of life (refer back to Figure 12.3).

The Human Genome Project Has Stimulated Genomic Research

Before ending our discussion of genomes, let's consider the **Human Genome Project**, a research effort to identify and map all human genes. Scientists had been discussing how to undertake this project since the mid-1980s. In 1988, the National Institutes of Health in Bethesda, Maryland, established an Office of Human Genome Research with James Watson as its first director. The Human Genome Project, which officially began on October 1, 1990, was a 13-year effort coordinated by the U.S. Department of Energy and the National Institutes of Health, with research performed in Canada, the United States, New Zealand, and Britain. Scientists from China, France, Germany, Japan, and the United Kingdom were also part of an international consortium. From its outset, the Human Genome Project had the following goals:

1. To identify all human genes. This involved mapping the locations of genes throughout the entire genome. The data from the Human Genome Project suggest that humans have about 20,000 to 25,000 different genes.
2. To obtain the DNA sequence of the entire human genome. The first draft of a nearly completed DNA sequence was published in February 2001, and a second draft was published in 2003. The entire genome is approximately 3.2 billion nucleotides long. If the entire human genome were typed in a textbook like this, with about 3,000 letters per page, it would be nearly 1 million pages long.
3. To develop technology for the generation and management of human genome information. Some of the efforts of the Human Genome Project have involved improvements in molecular genetic technology, such as gene cloning, DNA sequencing, and so forth. The Human Genome Project has also developed computer tools to allow scientists to easily access up-to-date information from the project and analytical tools to interpret genomic information.
4. To analyze the genomes of model organisms. These include *E. coli, S. cerevisiae, D. melanogaster, C. elegans, A. thaliana,* and *M. musculus.*
5. To develop programs focused on understanding and addressing the ethical, legal, and social implications of the results obtained from the Human Genome Project. An important question is, Who should have access to genetic information? Should employers, insurance companies, law enforcement agencies, and schools know our genetic makeup? The answer is complex and will require discussion among many groups. Another controversial topic is gene patenting. In the United States genes can be patented for a variety of reasons. For example, the patenting of genes has been associated with the commercial development of diagnostic tests for genetic diseases. Some argue that patenting fosters greater investment into research and development; others say it can impede basic research and scientific innovation.

A great benefit expected from the characterization of the human genome is the ability to identify our genes. A complete DNA sequence has made it profoundly easier for researchers to locate such genes. Furthermore, the DNA sequence of the human genome provides researchers with insight into the types of proteins encoded by these genes. Some current and potential applications of the Human Genome Project include the improved diagnosis and treatment of genetic diseases, such as cystic fibrosis, Huntington disease, and Duchenne muscular dystrophy. The project may also enable researchers to identify the genetic basis of common disorders, such as cancer, diabetes, and heart disease, which involve alterations in several genes.

In 2000, the Government of Canada approved the creation of a nonprofit organization called Genome Canada to develop and implement a national strategy to support large-scale genomics projects. There are six genome centres, located across the country, which direct project development and provide competitive research grant funding for regional mandates. These centres also afford numerous opportunities for student involvement in research and actively promote public outreach and education on genomics and proteomics.

19.3   PROTEOMES

Learning Outcomes:

1. Distinguish between a proteome and a genome.
2. List the major categories of proteins in a proteome.
3. Explain how the number of proteins in an organism's proteome can be greater than the number of genes in its genome.

Thus far in this chapter we have considered the genome characteristics of many different species, including humans. Because most genes encode proteins, a logical next step is to examine the functional roles of the proteins that a species can make. As mentioned, the entire collection of proteins that a cell or an organism produces is called a proteome. A key challenge facing molecular biologists is the study of proteomes. Much like the study of genomes, this requires the collective contributions of many research scientists, as well as improvements in technologies that are aimed at explaining the complexities of the proteome. In this section, we will begin by considering the functional categories of proteins and examining their relative abundance in the proteome. We will also explore the molecular mechanisms that cause an organism's proteome to be much larger than its genome.

The Proteome Is a Diverse Array of Proteins with Many Kinds of Functions

The genomes of simple, unicellular organisms, such as bacteria and yeast, contain thousands of structural genes, while the genomes of complex multicellular organisms contain tens of thousands. Such genome sizes can produce proteomes with tens of thousands to hundreds of thousands of different proteins. To bring some order to this large amount of complex information, researchers often organize proteins into different categories based on their functions.

Table 19.3 describes some general categories of protein function and provides examples of each type. Many approaches are used to categorize proteins. The categories listed in Table 19.3 are just one of the more general ways to evaluate protein function. For example, the data of Figure 19.1 categorize protein function in a different, more detailed way.

The relative abundance of proteins can be viewed at two levels. First, we can consider abundance in the genome—the numbers of genes in the genome that encode a particular type or category of protein. For example, if an entire genome encodes 10,000 different types of proteins and 1,500 of these are different types of transporters, we would say that 15% of the genome is composed of transporters. However, such an analysis ignores the phenomenon that genes are expressed at different levels. In other words, various proteins are made in different amounts. Therefore, a second way to view protein abundance is to consider abundance in the cell—the amount of a given protein or protein category that is actually made by a living cell. For example, less than 1% of human genes encode proteins, such as collagen, that are found in the extracellular matrix (ECM). Even so, these genes are highly expressed in certain cells, so a large amount of this type of protein is made compared to other types.

Figure 19.9 presents a general comparison of protein abundance in two cell types in humans: liver and muscle cells. The liver plays a key role in metabolism, while muscles are involved in bodily movements. Both liver and muscle cells have the same genome and the same set of genes. Therefore, at the level of the genome, the percentages of genes encoding the different protein categories are identical. However, at the cellular level, the relative abundance of certain protein categories is quite different.

Table 19.3	Categories of Proteins Found in the Proteome	
Function		**Examples**
Metabolic enzymes		Hexokinase: Phosphorylates glucose during the first step in glycolysis
		Glycogen synthetase: Uses glucose to synthesize a large carbohydrate known as glycogen
Structural proteins		Tubulin: Forms cytoskeletal structures known as microtubules
		Collagen: Found abundantly in the extracellular matrix of animals
Motor proteins		Myosin: Involved in muscle cell contraction
		Kinesin: Involved in the movement of chromosomes during cell division
Cell-signalling proteins		Insulin: Influences target cell metabolism and growth
		Insulin receptor: Recognizes insulin and initiates a cellular response
Transport proteins		Lactose permease: Transports lactose across the bacterial cell membrane
		Hemoglobin: Found in red blood cells and transports oxygen throughout the body
Gene expression and regulatory proteins		Transcription factors: Regulate the expression of genes
		Ribosomal proteins: Make up the structure of ribosomes, which are needed for the synthesis of new proteins
Protective proteins		Antibodies: Fight viral and bacterial infections in vertebrate species
		Antiviral proteins: Prevent viruses from binding to cells or successfully infecting cells in plants and animals

Liver cells make a large number of different enzymes that play a role in the metabolism of fats, proteins, and carbohydrates. By comparison their level of structural and motor proteins is relatively small. In contrast muscle cells have fairly low levels of enzymes, but they have a high percentage of structural and motor proteins. These differences in protein composition between liver in muscle cells is largely due to differential gene regulation.

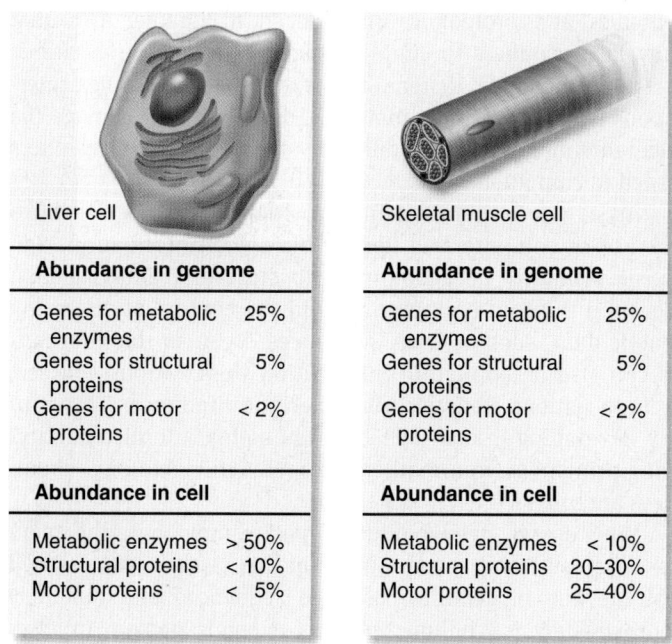

Figure 19.9 A comparison of the proteomes in human liver and skeletal muscle cells. Because all cells of the human body carry the same genome, the percentages of proteins that are encoded in the genome are the same in each cell type. However, the relative amounts of proteins that are actually made in different cell types can be vastly different, as is the case between liver and skeletal muscle cells.

Concept check: *What genetic process explains the differences in protein abundance in liver cells versus muscle cells?*

The Number of Different Proteins in a Species' Proteome Is Larger Than the Number of Genes in Its Genome

From the sequencing and analysis of genomes, researchers can identify all or nearly all the genes that a species has. For example, the human genome is predicted to contain between 20,000 and 25,000 different genes that encode proteins. Even so, humans can make many more than 25,000 different types of proteins. The larger size of the proteome relative to the genome is primarily due to two types of cellular processes, as described next.

Alternative Splicing Because of **alternative splicing**, different mRNA molecules can be produced from the same pre-mRNA transcript (refer back to Figure 12.22). For many genes a single pre-mRNA can be spliced in more than one way, resulting in the production of two or more polypeptides with different amino acid sequences (**Figure 19.10a**). The splicing is often cell specific, or it may be related to environmental conditions. Alternative splicing is widespread, particularly among more complex eukaryotes (refer back to Table 12.1). It can lead to the

(a) Alternative splicing

Each of these 3 polypeptides has segments with different amino acid sequences.

(b) Post-translational covalent modification

Figure 19.10 Cellular mechanisms that increase protein diversity. **(a)** During alternative splicing, the pattern of exons that remains in a mature mRNA can be different, creating multiple types of transcripts from the same gene. **(b)** In post-translational covalent modification, after a protein is made, it can be modified in a variety of ways, some of which are permanent and some reversible.

BioConnections: *Look back at Figure 9.13. How is reversible phosphorylation used in cell signaling?*

production of several or perhaps dozens of different polypeptide sequences from the same type of pre-mRNA. This greatly increases the number of potential proteins in the proteome, while minimizing the size of the genome.

Post-translational Covalent Modification   A second process that greatly diversifies the composition of a proteome is the phenomenon of **post-translational covalent modification**, the modification of the structure of a protein after its translation (**Figure 19.10b**). Such modifications can be permanent or reversible. Permanent modifications are primarily involved with the assembly and construction of functional proteins. These alterations include proteolytic processing (the cleavage of a polypeptide to a smaller unit); disulphide bond formation; and the attachment of prosthetic groups (such as heme, a component of hemoglobin), sugars, or lipids. In Chapter 5 we also considered the attachment of ubiquitin to a protein, which targets it for degradation. By comparison, reversible modifications, such as phosphorylation, acetylation, and methylation, often transiently affect the function of a protein (Figure 19.10b). Molecules are covalently attached and later removed by cellular enzymes. Because a given type of protein may be subjected to several different types of modifications, this can greatly increase the forms of a particular protein that are found in a cell at any given time.

It has been estimated that some human cells may contain hundreds of thousands of different proteins because of these mechanisms that expand the coding capacity of the genome. Proteomics researchers are heavily engaged in determining the protein components of many cell types and how external stimuli (e.g., drugs) alter the proteome.

19.4   BIOINFORMATICS

Learning Outcomes:

1. Describe how scientists use bioinformatics.
2. Define database.
3. Explain how the BLAST program works and why it is useful.

In the previous sections you learned that the number of genes in a genome and the number of proteins that are made by a given cell type are extremely large. In the 1960s and 1970s, when the tools of molecular biology first became available, researchers tended to focus on the study of just one or a few genes and proteins at a time. Although this is a useful approach, scientists realized that nearly every cellular or organismal process or behaviour is dictated by complex interactions involving the expression of many genes and the functioning of many different proteins. Such an awareness challenged researchers to invent new tools to study many genes and many proteins at the same time. These tools involved experimental procedures,

genomics and proteomics (introduced in Chapter 18), that allowed researchers to simultaneously investigate the various parts of a biological system. The study of such complex interactions is called **systems biology**. To analyze and manage the huge amounts of data produced by these studies, researchers turned to computers.

As a very general definition, **bioinformatics** describes any use of computers to handle biological information. Scientists primarily use computers to store and analyze data. We often think of bioinformatics in the context of analyzing genetic data, such as DNA sequences. Even so, bioinformatics can also be applied to information from various sources, such as patient statistics and scientific literature. This rapidly developing branch of biology is highly interdisciplinary, using principles from mathematics, statistics, biology, chemistry, and physics.

Why do we need bioinformatics? Simply put, the main issues are size and speed. Earlier in this chapter, you learned that the human genome has been sequenced and that it is approximately 3.2 billion bp long. A single person, or even a group of talented mathematicians, cannot, in a reasonable time, analyze such an enormous amount of data. Instead, the data are put into computers and then scientists devise computational procedures to study and evaluate them. Computers' ability to analyze data at a rate of millions or even billions of operations per second makes it possible to solve biological problems that were thought intractable a few decades ago. Biologists have made many important discoveries by using a bioinformatic approach. For example, we can compare the entire genome sequences of different organisms, which contain millions or even billions of base pairs, and identify genes that are homologous in two or more different species. We can also compare genes in the same species and discover how mutations in particular genes are correlated with the development of diseases, such as cancer and diabetes.

In this section we will consider the branch of bioinformatics that focuses on the use of molecular information to study biology. This area, also called **computational molecular biology**, uses computers to characterize the molecular components of living things. Molecular genetic data, which come in the form of a DNA, RNA, or protein sequence, are particularly amenable to computer analysis. In this section we will first survey the fundamental concepts that underlie the analysis of genetic sequences. We will then consider how these methods are used to provide knowledge about how biology works at the molecular level.

Sequence Files Are Stored and Analyzed by Computers

The first step in bioinformatics is to collect and store data in a computer. As an example let's consider a gene sequence as a type of data. The gene sequence must first be determined experimentally by using the technique of DNA sequencing.

After the sequence is obtained, the next step is to put that data into a computer. To store data in a computer, a scientist creates a computer data file and enters the data into the file. For short genetic sequences, fewer than a few hundred nucleotides, this can be done by using a keyboard to type the DNA sequence into the file. For very long genetic sequences, however, like those obtained in genome-sequencing projects, keyboarding data would be a tedious and error-prone process. Typically, genetic sequence data are entered into a computer file by laboratory instruments that can read experimental data—such as data from a DNA-sequencing experiment—and enter the sequence directly into a computer.

Genetic sequence data in a computer data file can be investigated in many different ways, corresponding to the many questions a researcher might ask about the sequence and its functional significance, including the following:

1. Does a sequence contain a gene?
2. Does a gene sequence contain a mutation that might cause a disease?
3. Where are functional sequences, such as promoters, regulatory sites, and splice sites, located within a particular gene?
4. From the sequence of a structural gene, what is the amino acid sequence of the polypeptide encoded by that gene?
5. Is a genetic sequence similar to any other known sequences?
6. What is the evolutionary relationship between two or more genetic sequences?

To answer these and many other questions, computer programs have been written to analyze genetic sequences in particular ways. As an example let's consider a computer program aimed at decoding a DNA sequence into an amino acid sequence. **Figure 19.11** shows a short computer data file of a DNA sequence that is presumed to be part of the coding sequence of a structural gene. In this figure only the coding strand of DNA is shown. A computer program can analyze this sequence and print out the possible amino acid sequences that this DNA sequence would encode. The program relies on the triplet genetic code (refer back to Table 11.1). In the example in Figure 19.11 a computer program would show the results for all three possible translational reading frames, beginning at nucleotide 1, 2, or 3, respectively. Recall that the genetic code is a triplet code and thus three reading frames are possible depending on whether we begin at the first, second, or third nucleotide of the DNA sequence. In a newly obtained DNA sequence, a researcher would not know which was the correct reading frame, and so the computer program provides all three. Reading frames 2 and 3 include several stop codons, while reading frame 1 does not. From these results, reading frame 1 is likely correct. For a new DNA sequence, a researcher also may not know which DNA strand is the coding strand. Therefore, the sequence of the other DNA strand, which is not shown in this figure, would also be analyzed by the computer program. Algorithms to detect open reading frames (ORFs) exist that can locate a translational start codon, and then conduct conceptualized translation in that reading frame until a stop codon is found. The length of the ORF can be specified to increase the probability that the ORF actually encodes a protein.

The Scientific Community Has Collected Computer Data Files and Stored Them in Large Computer Databases

Over the past several decades, the amount of genetic information generated by researchers and clinicians has become enormous. The Human Genome Project, for example, has produced

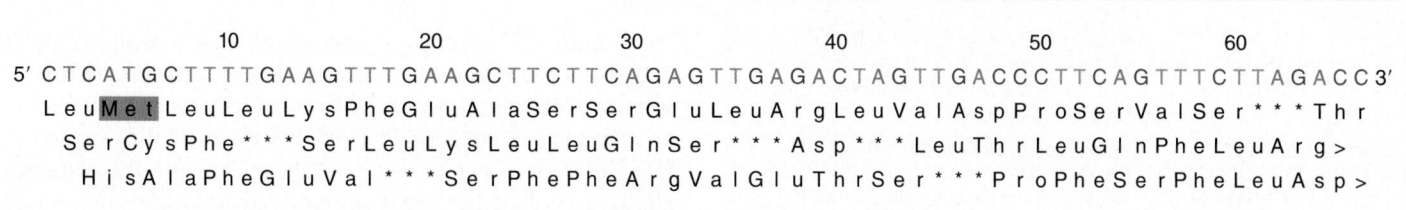

Figure 19.11 Conceptualized translation of a DNA sequence. The top line shows a short nucleotide sequence that a researcher might obtain from either a computer database or direct DNA sequencing. Assuming that this is the coding strand, which has the same sequence as the mRNA derived from it (with the exception that the T's in DNA are transcribed into U's in the mRNA), the DNA can be decoded by the computer to yield the polypeptide sequence. The three-letter names represent the amino acids encoded by specific triplets of the nucleotide sequence (codons in mRNA) and the asterisks represent termination signals specified by stop codons. Note that three reading frames are possible, depending on the starting point, and thus three hypothetical protein products are possible. Normally, protein chains begin with a methionine reside (highlighted in green) and are terminated by a stop codon. For the sequence given above, an open reading frame exists that would encode a polypeptide of 19 amino acids.

more data than any other undertaking in the history of biology. With these advances, scientists have realized that another critical use of computers is as storage for the staggering amount of data produced from genetic research.

When a large number of computer data files are collected, stored in a single location, and organized for rapid search and retrieval, this collection is called a **database**. The files within databases are often annotated, which means they contain a concise description of each gene sequence, the name of the organism from which the sequence was obtained, and the function of the encoded protein, if it is known. The file may also describe other features of significance and provide a published reference that contains the sequence.

The research community has collected genetic information from thousands of research labs and created several large databases. **Table 19.4** describes some of the major genetic databases in use worldwide. These databases enable researchers to access and compare genetic sequences that are obtained by many laboratories. Later in this chapter, we will learn how researchers can use databases to analyze genetic sequences.

Table 19.4	Examples of Major Computer Databases
Type	**Description**
Nucleotide sequence	DNA sequence data are collected into three internationally collaborating databases: GenBank (a U.S. database), EMBL (European Molecular Biology Laboratory Nucleotide Sequence Database), and DDBJ (DNA Data-bank of Japan). These databases receive sequence and sequence annotation data from genome projects, sequencing centres, individual scientists, and patent offices. These databases are accessed via the Internet and on CD-ROM.
Amino acid sequence	Amino acid sequence data are collected into a few international databases, including Swiss-Prot (Swiss protein database), PIR (Protein Information Resource), Genpept (translated peptide sequences from the GenBank database), and TrEMBL (translated sequences from the EMBL database).
Three-dimensional structure	PDB (Protein Data Bank) collects the three-dimensional structures of biological macro-molecules, with an emphasis on protein structure. These are primarily structures that have been determined by X-ray crystallography and nuclear magnetic resonance (NMR), but some models are included in the database. These structures are stored in files that can be viewed on a computer screen.

From: Persson, B. 2000. Bioinformatics in protein analysis. *EXS* 88:215–31.

The databases described in Table 19.4 collect genetic information from many different species. Scientists have also created more specialized databases, called relational databases, that focus on the genetic characteristics of a single species. Genome databases have been created for most model organisms, such as bacteria (*E. coli*), yeast (*S. cerevisiae*), worms (*C. elegans*), fruit flies (*D. melanogaster*), plants (*A. thaliana*), mice (*M. musculus*), and humans (*H. sapiens*). The primary aim of genome databases is to organize the information from sequencing and mapping projects for a single species. Genome databases identify the known genes within an organism and describe their map locations in the genome. In addition a genome database may provide information concerning gene alleles, available mutants, RNA splicing and protein data, microarray data, bibliographic information, links to relevant resources for more detailed analyses, and other pertinent information.

Many programs are available over the Internet to use the information within databases. For example, the National Center for Biotechnology Information (NCBI), which is a part of the U.S. National Institutes of Health, manages a Website called Tools for Data Mining, where anyone can run various types of programs that are used to analyze genetic sequences (www.ncbi.nlm.nih.gov/Tools). Like conventional mining, in which a precious mineral is extracted from a large area of land, data mining is the extraction of useful information and often previously unknown relationships from sequence files and large databases.

Computer Programs Can Identify Homologous Sequences

Let's now turn our attention to the use of computer technology to identify genes that are evolutionarily related. Organisms that are closely related evolutionarily tend to have genes with similar DNA sequences. As an example, let's consider the gene that encodes β-globin. As described earlier in Figure 19.8, β-globin is a polypeptide found in hemoglobin, which carries oxygen in red blood cells. The β-globin gene is found in humans and other vertebrates.

Figure 19.12a compares a short region of the β-globin gene from the laboratory mouse (*Mus musculus*) and laboratory rat (*Rates norvegicus*). As you can see, the gene sequences are similar but not identical. In this 60-nucleotide sequence, five differences are observed. The reason for the sequence similarity is that the genes are derived from the same ancestral gene. This idea is shown schematically in **Figure 19.12b**. An ancestral gene was found in a rodent species that is a common ancestor to both mice and rats. During evolution this ancestral species diverged into different species, which eventually gave rise to several modern rodent species, including mice and rats. Following divergence the β-globin genes accumulated distinct mutations that produced somewhat different nucleotide sequences for this gene. Therefore, in mice and

(a) A comparison of one DNA strand of the mouse and rat β-globin genes

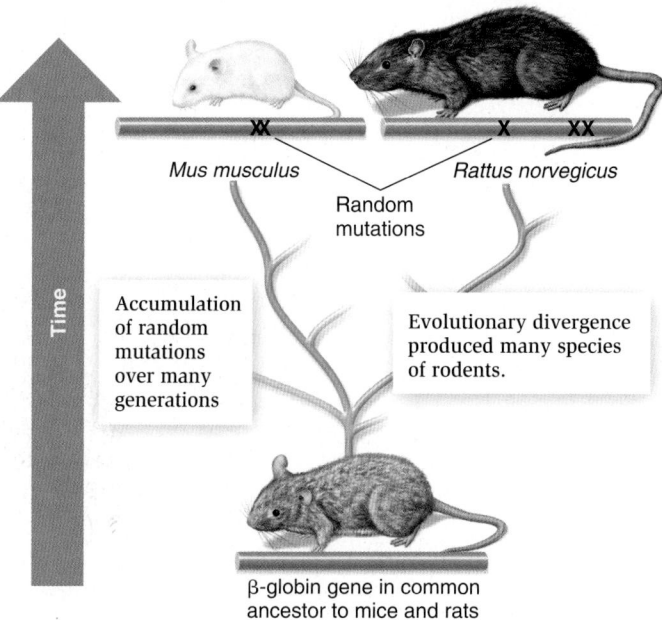

(b) The formation of homologous β-globin genes during evolution of mice and rats

Figure 19.12 Structure and formation of the homologous β–globin genes in mice and rats. (a) A comparison of a short region of the gene that encodes β-globin in laboratory mice (*Mus musculus*) and rats (*Rattus norvegicus*). Only one DNA strand is shown. Bases that are identical between the two sequences are connected by a vertical line. The β-globin genes are similar because they are derived from the same ancestral gene, but they are not identical because each species has accumulated a few different random mutations since the divergence of its latest common ancestor. (b) The formation of these homologous β-globin genes during evolution. An ancestral β-globin gene was found in a rodent species that was a common ancestor to both mice and rats. This ancestral species later diverged into different species, which gave rise to modern rodent species, such as mice and rats. During this process, the β-globin genes accumulated different random mutations, causing the DNA sequences of these two homologous genes to be slightly different.

rats, the β-globin genes have homologous sequences—their sequences are similar because they are derived from the same ancestral gene, but they are not identical because each species has accumulated a few different random mutations. Homologous genes in different species are also called **orthologs**. Analyzing orthologs helps biologists understand the evolutionary

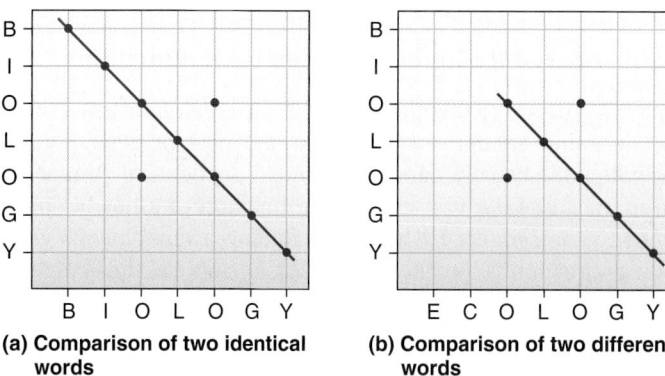

(a) Comparison of two identical words

(b) Comparison of two different words

Figure 19.13 The use of a simple dot matrix. In these comparisons, a diagonal line indicates sequence similarity. (a) The word BIOLOGY is compared with itself. Dots are placed where the same letter occurs at the two corresponding positions. Notice the diagonal line that is formed. (b) Two similar but different sequences, BIOLOGY and ECOLOGY are compared with each other. Notice that only a partial line is formed by this comparison. Clearly the two terms are related (the suffix -logy is the study of a particular topic determined by the initial word stem) but are not identical.

relationships among modern species, a topic that we will consider in more detail in Units IV and V.

How do researchers, with the aid of computers, determine whether two genes are homologous? To evaluate the similarity between two sequences, they can construct a matrix. **Figure 19.13** illustrates the use of a simple dot matrix to evaluate two sequences. In **Figure 19.13a**, the word BIOLOGY is compared with itself. Each point in the grid corresponds to one position of each sequence. The matrix allows all such pairs to be compared simultaneously. Dots are placed where the same letter occurs at the two corresponding positions. Sequences that are alike produce a diagonal line on the matrix. In contrast **Figure 19.13b** compares two similar but different sequences: BIOLOGY and ECOLOGY. This comparison produces only a partial diagonal line. The key observation is that regions of similarity are distinguished by the occurrence of many dots along a diagonal line within the matrix. This same concept holds true when base sequences of homologous genes are compared with each other.

To discover whether homology exists between two genes, researchers must compare relatively long DNA sequences. For such long sequences a simple dot matrix approach is not adequate. Instead, dynamic computer programming methods are used to identify similarities between genetic sequences. This approach was proposed originally by Saul Needleman and Christian Wunsch in 1970. Dynamic programming methods are theoretically similar to a dot matrix, but they involve mathematical operations that are beyond the scope of this textbook. In their original work Needleman and Wunsch demonstrated that whale myoglobin and human β-globin genes have similar sequences.

A Database Can Be Searched to Identify Homologous Sequences and Thereby Identify Gene Function

Why is it useful to identify homology between different genes? Because they are derived from the same ancestral gene, homologous genes usually carry out similar or identical functions. In many cases the first clue to the function of a newly determined gene sequence is given by finding a homologous gene whose function is already known. An example is the gene that is altered in people with cystic fibrosis. After this gene was identified in humans, bioinformatic methods revealed that it is homologous with several genes found in other species. A few of the homologous genes were already known to encode proteins that function in the transport of ions and small molecules across the plasma membrane. This observation provided an important clue that cystic fibrosis involves a defect in membrane transport.

The ability of computer programs to identify homology between genetic sequences provides a powerful tool for predicting the function of genetic sequences. In 1990 Stephen Altschul, David Lipman, and their colleagues developed an approach called a **basic local alignment search tool**, or **BLAST**. The BLAST program has been described by many biologists as the single most important tool in computational molecular biology. This computer program can start with a particular genetic sequence—either a nucleotide or an amino acid sequence—and then locate homologous sequences within a large database.

As an example of how the BLAST program works, let's consider the human enzyme phenylalanine hydroxylase, which functions in the metabolism of phenylalanine, an amino acid. Recessive mutations in the gene that encodes this enzyme are responsible for the disease called phenylketonuria (PKU). The computational experiment shown in **Table 19.5** started with the amino acid sequence of this protein and used the BLAST program to search the Swiss-Prot database, which contains hundreds of thousands of different protein sequences. The BLAST program can determine which sequences in the Swiss-Prot database are the closest matches to the amino acid sequence of human phenylalanine hydroxylase. Table 19.5 shows the results, which includes 10 of the best matches to human phenylalanine hydroxylase that were identified by the program. Because this enzyme is found in nearly all eukaryotic species, the program identified phenylalanine hydroxylase from many different species. The column to the right of the match number shows the percentage of amino acids that are identical between the species indicated and the human sequence. Because the human phenylalanine hydroxylase sequence is already in the Swiss-Prot database, the closest match of human phenylalanine hydroxylase is to itself. The next nine sequences are in order of similarity. The next most similar sequence is from the orangutan, a close relative

| Table 19.5 | Results from a BLAST Program Comparing Human Phenylalanine Hydroxylase with Database Sequences |

Match	Percentage of identical* amino acids	Species	Function of sequence†
1	100	Human (*Homo sapiens*)	Phenylalanine Hydroxylase
2	99	Orangutan (*Pongo pygmaeus*)	Phenylalanine Hydroxylase
3	95	Mouse (*Mus musculus*)	Phenylalanine Hydroxylase
4	95	Rat (*Rattus norvegicus*)	Phenylalanine Hydroxylase
5	89	Chicken (*Gallus gallus*)	Phenylalanine Hydroxylase
6	82	Pipid frog (*Xenopus tropicalis*)	Phenylalanine Hydroxylase
7	82	Green pufferfish (*Tetradon nigroviridis*)	Phenylalanine Hydroxylase
8	82	Zebrafish (*Danio rerio*)	Phenylalanine Hydroxylase
9	80	Japanese pufferfish (*Takifugu rubripes*)	Phenylalanine Hydroxylase
10	75	Fruit fly (*Drosophila melanogaster*)	Phenylalanine Hydroxylase

* The number indicates the percentage of amino acids that are identical with the amino acid sequence of human phenylalanine hydroxylase.
† In some cases the function of the sequence was determined by biochemical assay. In other cases the function was inferred because of the high degree of sequence similarity with other species.

of humans. This is followed by two mammals, the mouse and rat, and then five vertebrates that are not mammals. The 10th best match is from *Drosophila*, an invertebrate.

You can see two trends in Table 19.5. First, the order of the matches follows the evolutionary relatedness of the various species to humans. The similarity between any two sequences is related to the time that has passed since they diverged from a common ancestor. Among the species listed in this table, humans are most similar to themselves, followed by the orangutan, other mammals, other vertebrates, and finally invertebrates. The second trend is that several of the matches involve species that are important from a research, a medical, or an agricultural perspective. Currently, our databases are biased toward organisms that are of interest to humans, particularly model organisms, such as mice and *Drosophila*. Over the next several decades, the sequencing of genomes from many different species will lessen this bias.

Overall, Table 19.5 is an example of the remarkable computational abilities of computer technology. In less than a minute, the amino acid sequence of human phenylalanine hydroxylase can be compared with hundreds of thousands of different sequences to yield the data shown in the table. The main power of the BLAST program is its use with newly identified sequences, in which a researcher does not know the function of a gene or an encoded protein. When the BLAST program identifies a match to a sequence whose function is already known, it is likely that the newly identified sequence has an identical or a similar function.

Bioinformatic Algorithms Are Essential to Data Mining

As discussed in Chapter 18, microarray analyses are routinely used to monitor the expression of every gene in a genome. This information can be used as a comparative quantitative tool to study gene expression during the normal course of development or in response to a particular stimulus (e.g., the addition of a drug). Nicholas Provart and his colleagues at the University of Toronto created the Bio-Array Resource (BAR), a suite of bioinformatics tools that facilitates gene sequence and expression analyses by interfacing with several public domain databases containing huge datasets. Programs in the BAR suite permit the identification of genes whose patterns of expression can be correlated (either positively or negatively). It is possible to search for commonalities in promoter sequences, examine potential protein interactions, and examine gene expression patterns in development or in response to various chemical, hormone, biotic, and abiotic stresses; light regimes; and other stimuli. A common visualization tool presents expression levels in a heatmap format, overlaying these data onto schematics of tissues (in this case, tissues from the model plant *Arabidopsis*). Regions in which gene expression is high are denoted as red; regions of low expression are in yellow. **Figure 19.14a** shows an example in which the *AFO* gene, encoding a transcription factor, was the subject of a query that asked for the identification of genes that negatively correlate with *AFO*. Such genes might be targets of *AFO*, which could act to repress their transcription. **Figure 19.14b** shows expression data as an eFP (electronic fluorescent pictograph) for *AFO* and one of its possible targets. Data mining of this nature permits researchers to quickly correlate information in large datasets and to focus their studies on genes and proteins of interest to them.

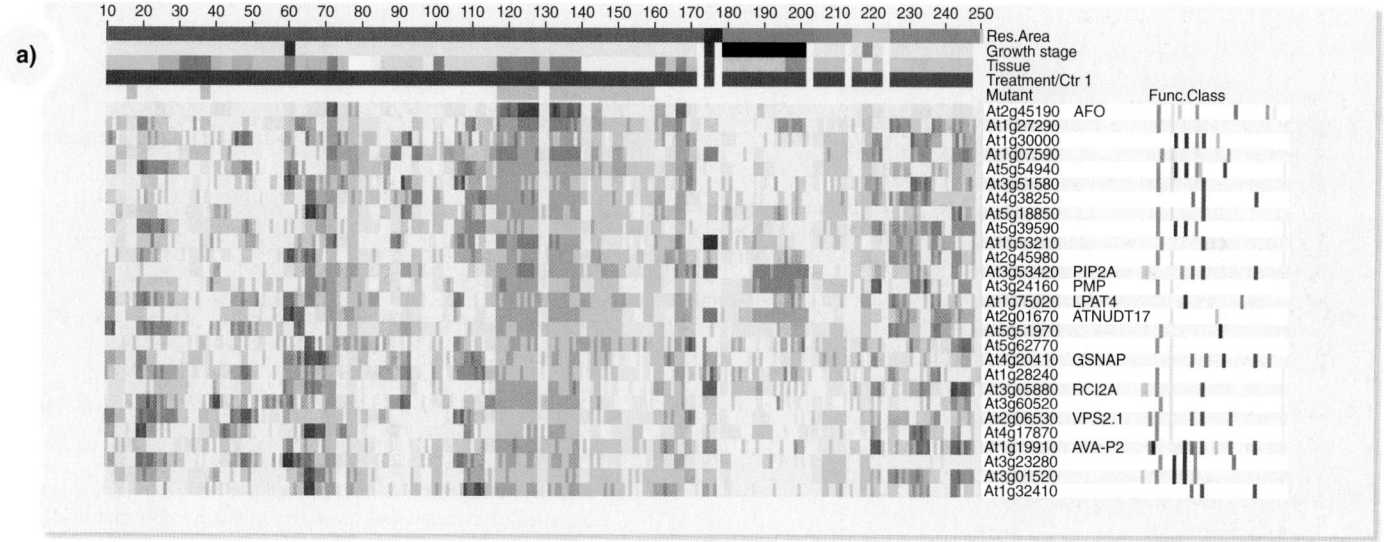

Figure 19.14 Bioinformatics tools at the BAR (Bio-Array Resource). DNA sequence and microarray datasets are used by algorithms that permit the investigator to ask questions about a gene of interest. (a) The display shows that 250 different datasets were consulted, which represent a number of experiments involving different tissues, growth conditions, treatments, and mutants. The colour-coded bars identify the sample, but the legend has been removed for simplicity. The heatmap shows the expression of *AFO* in these samples. The algorithm was asked to find genes whose expression negatively correlates with that of *AFO*. These genes may be targets that are repressed by *AFO*. (b) Electronic fluorescent pictograph (eFP) representation of *AFO* expression during development. (c) eFP representation of the expression of one of the possible *AFO* targets. Note that in tissues in which *AFO* expression is high, the target gene expression tends to be low, and vice versa.

Figure 19.14   *(Continued)*

Summary of Key Concepts

19.1 Bacterial and Archaeal Genomes

- The genome is the complete genetic makeup of a cell, an organism, or a species.

- Bacterial and archaeal genomes are typically a single circular chromosome that has several hundred thousand to a few million base pairs of DNA. Such genomes usually have a few thousand different genes. Bacteria often have extrachromosomal DNA molecules called plasmids. (Table 19.1)

- Venter, Smith, and colleagues used a shotgun DNA-sequencing strategy to determine the first sequence of a prokaryotic genome, that of *Haemophilus influenzae.* (Figure 19.1)

- Metagenomics employs high throughput DNA sequencing followed by database comparisons to determine the number and relative frequency of sequences (and thus species) in an environmental sample.

19.2 Eukaryotic Genomes

- The nuclear genomes of eukaryotic species are composed of sets of linear chromosomes with a total length of several million to billions of base pairs. They typically contain several thousand to tens of thousands of genes. (Table 19.2)

- Genomes' sizes vary among eukaryotic species. In many cases this variation is due to the accumulation of noncoding regions of DNA, particularly repetitive DNA sequences. (Figures 19.2, 19.3)

- Much of the repetitive DNA is derived from transposable elements, segments of DNA that can move from one site to another through a process called transposition. (Figure 19.4)

- Transposable elements fall into two groups that move by two different molecular mechanisms. DNA transposons move by a cut-and-paste mechanism facilitated by the enzyme transposase. Retroelements move to new sites in the genome via RNA intermediates. (Figures 19.5, 19.6)

- Gene duplication may occur by a misaligned crossover during meiosis. This is one mechanism that can produce a gene family, two or more homologous genes in a species that have related functions. (Figures 19.7, 19.8)

- The Human Genome Project undertook the DNA sequencing of the entire human genome and developed computational tools and technology to analyze the huge dataset. The genome project was completed by an international consortium in 2003.

19.3 Proteomes

- A proteome is the collection of proteins that a given cell makes.

- Proteins are often placed into broad categories based on their functions. These include metabolic enzymes, structural proteins, motor proteins, cell-signalling proteins, transport proteins, proteins involved with gene expression and regulation, and those involved with protection and defence. (Table 19.3)

- Protein abundance can refer to their relative abundance in terms of the number of genes in the genome or as direct measurements of protein levels in the cell. (Figure 19.9)

- Protein diversity can increase via alternative splicing and post-translational covalent modifications. (Figure 19.10)

19.4 Bioinformatics

- Bioinformatics involves the use of computers to analyze biological information, particularly genetic data, such as DNA and protein sequences.

- Genetic information is stored in large genetics databases that are analyzed by using computer programs. (Figure 19.11, Table 19.4)

- Homologous genes are derived from the same ancestral genes and have accumulated random mutations that make their sequences slightly different. (Figure 19.12)

- A simple dot matrix illustrates the approach of identifying regions of similarity between two sequences. (Figure 19.13)

- Computer programs, such as BLAST, can identify homologous genes that are found in a database. (Table 19.5)

- Computer algorithms and datasets can provide rapid analysis and links to raw data, other databases, or other methods of analysis. (Figure 19.14)

Test to Assess Your Learning

1. The entire collection of proteins produced by a cell or organism is
   a. a genome.
   b. bioinformatics.
   c. a proteome.
   d. a gene family.
   e. a protein family.

2. Which of the following is not an important reason for studying the genomes of bacteria and archaea?
   a. They may provide information that helps us understand how bacteria infect other organisms.
   b. They may provide a basic understanding of cellular processes that allow us to determine eukaryotic cellular function.
   c. They may provide the means to understand evolutionary processes.
   d. They will reveal the approximate number of genes that an organism has in its genome.
   e. All of the above are important reasons.

3. The enzyme that allows short segments of DNA to move within a cell from one location in the genome to another is
   a. transposase.
   b. DNA polymerase.
   c. protease.
   d. restriction endonuclease.
   e. DNA ligase.

4. A gene family includes
   a. a specific gene found in several different species that has a similar DNA sequence.
   b. all the genes on the same chromosome.
   c. two or more homologous genes found within a single species.
   d. genes that code for structural proteins.
   e. both (a) and (c).

5. Which of the following is *not* a goal of the Human Genome Project?
   a. to identify all human genes.
   b. to sequence the entire human genome.
   c. to address the legal and ethical implications resulting from the project.
   d. to develop programs to manage the information gathered from the project.
   e. to clone a human.

6. Bioinformatics is
   a. the analysis of DNA by molecular techniques.
   b. the use of computers to analyze and store biological information.
   c. a collection of gene sequences from a single individual.
   d. cloning.
   e. all of the above.

7. Through the use of bioinformatics, evolutionary relationships between species can be characterized by identifying and analyzing
   a. phenotypes of selected organisms.
   b. homologous DNA sequences.
   c. fossils of ancestral species.
   d. all of the above.
   e. (a) and (b) only.

8. The BLAST program is a tool for
   a. inserting many DNA fragments into a cell at the same time.
   b. translating a DNA sequence into an amino acid sequence.
   c. identifying homology between a selected sequence and genetic sequences in large databases.
   d. all of the above.
   e. both (b) and (c).

9. Repetitive sequences
   a. are short DNA sequences that are found many times throughout the genome.
   b. may be multiple copies of the same gene found in the genome.
   c. are more common in eukaryotes.
   d. all of the above.
   e. (a) and (c) only.

10. Suppose you used the BLAST program, beginning with a DNA sequence from a *Drosophila* hexokinase gene. (Hexokinase is an enzyme involved with glucose metabolism.) Which of the following choices would you expect to be the closest match?
    a. a *Drosophila* globin gene
    b. a human hexokinase gene
    c. a housefly hexokinase gene
    d. an *Arabidopsis* hexokinase gene
    e. an amoeba hexokinase gene

Articulate to Assess Your Learning

1. Briefly describe whether or not each of the following could be appropriately described as a genome.
    a. the *E. coli* chromosome
    b. human chromosome 11
    c. a complete set of 10 chromosomes in corn
    d. a copy of the single-stranded RNA packaged into human immunodeficiency virus (HIV)

2. Explain how homologous genes may have arisen.

3. Describe two main reasons that the proteomes of eukaryotes species are usually much larger than their genomes.

Collaborate to Assess and Extend Your Learning

1. Compare and contrast the genomes of bacteria, archaea, and eukaryotes.
2. Discuss the concept and importance of transposable elements.

3. Below is a DNA sequence from one strand of a gene. Go to the NCBI Website (www.ncbi.nlm.nih.gov/Tools) and run the BLAST program to determine which gene it is and in which species it is found.

```
GTGAAGGCTCTCAGGGTGAGGAAGGGGATACAGGATCGTTTTTTTTTTCT
AACCTCAAGGCATGTCATAGGTGGAAGTCTCTTGCTTTCTTCACCTGGAC
CCTGAGAACTTTGCATCAGTTTGTTTAATTATGGCCTGGCGCACGTGGAT
TGGTTAAGTTTTGTTTTCTTGCCTTTAGTGGTGACAAGCTTTCTTTTCTA
AGACGAATGAAGTGCTCGGTGAGCTGCACTTTCTTTCCCCAATGGGAAAC
TTCATAACAACACACTGAGTGCTTGATGTTTACAGTTTAGTTATTTGCTG
ATGGCAAGAATCTATGGGACAGTAACAGGGTTAGTTTCTTTCTCCGCAAT
GCACCTTTGC
```

4. Metagenomics is a branch of genomics in which DNA sequencing of samples collected from specific environments is conducted. Obviously, such samples might contain more than one type of organism's DNA. Can you think of applications for this type of approach?

5. A principle of biology is that the genetic material, DNA, provides a dynamic plan for sustaining life. Explain the roles of the genome and proteome with regard to this principle.

Visit McGraw-Hill Ryerson Connect™ for additional study resources.

WHAT'S NEW?

An interview with Professor Mark Bayfield from York University, by Zaib Rahim, a second-year student at the University of Toronto—Scarborough.

Dr. Mark Bayfield is an Assistant Professor at York University, where he teaches and does research in molecular biology and biochemistry.

> **When and how did you get into research?**

My first research experience was for an honours thesis at McGill University during my undergraduate degree. I ended up liking the research and decided that I wanted to pursue it in the future. I feel it is a very worthwhile investment of a student's time to see if they really like research before committing to it in a graduate degree.

> **Undergraduate students trying to get into research find it a little intimidating. What advice do you have for students who are beginning their research careers?**

The best advice I can give to anyone, in general, is try to be proactive. Don't wait for someone to suggest a certain opportunity for you; go find it on your own. The reality is that there are always more people that want to enter research than there are positions available. Students who are more proactive tend to find out about opportunities earlier than students who simply wait. Professors want to take people into their labs who they have already had a good experience with in the past. Students interested in working with a professor should obviously do well in the course, but they should also use the office hours set by professors to meet them. This gives students an advantage as the professors who already know them will be more apt to take them into their lab. The positive relationship makes it easier for the professors to trust those students and easier for the students to get that opportunity. This is no different from applying for a job or any position, in general. Being proactive can really open up opportunities. You don't necessarily have to have an outstanding transcript to get good positions; you need to have good interpersonal skills and be proactive.

In my own experience, by the end of my undergraduate education, the only professors I felt I knew reasonably well were my honours thesis supervisors and the chair of the department, with whom I took a specific course consisting of 12 to 13 students. However, looking back, I could have been more proactive and made connections earlier.

> **What is the focus of your research now, and how do you want your research to affect the world?**

We are interested in the role the La protein plays in cellular processes. La has evolved as a basic cellular RNA processing factor, and to do that it has acquired certain activities. It also has the ability to act as an RNA chaperone. We know that the basic primary function of La is to help the maturation of RNA polymerase 3 precursor transcripts, such as pre-tRNAs, but we think that that has been adapted for other processes. One of the things we are testing is what happens when viruses become dependent on a very abundant and important protein, like La. We want to focus specifically on hepatitis C in the future.

> **Why did you choose the La protein as the main focus of your research?**

When I was doing my doctorate in the United States, I did a series of four-month rotations that allowed me to see what kind of lab I would like to continue my doctorate in. I decided I wanted to work in a lab that was studying ribosomes and translation in *E. coli*. After my doctorate, I realized I did not want to work with *E. coli* but wanted to work with RNA and continue in microorganisms. By choosing a eukaryotic microorganism, such as yeast, I knew my work could be more readily applied to humans. I ended up doing my postdoctorate in a lab that was working on the La protein. I didn't know from the beginning that I wanted to research the La protein, but I did know that I had an interest in that research and wanted to learn more. La interested me because it is a protein that is so essential and conserved but still relatively uncharacterized.

> **What specific aspects of the La protein would you like to further research?**

We want to continue to study basic La functions but also pursue directions that have relevance to human health, specifically how viruses rely on La proteins. We also are interested in La-related stress responses.

UNIT IV
Evolution

Evolution is a heritable change in one or more characteristics of a population from one generation to the next. This process not only alters the characteristics of populations but also leads to the formation of new species.

We will begin Unit IV with a discussion of the hypotheses that have been proposed to explain the origin of life on Earth, and then we'll examine a timeline for the evolution of species from 4 billion years ago to the present. In Chapter 21 you will be introduced to the fundamental concepts of evolution, with an emphasis on natural selection. We will examine observations of evolutionary change, which include the fossil record, a comparison of the characteristics of modern species, and an analysis of molecular data. Chapter 22 continues our discussion of evolution at the molecular level and focuses on how changes in allele and genotype frequencies from one generation to the next are driven by a variety of factors. Chapter 23 shifts the emphasis of evolution to the level of species. We will examine how species are identified and discuss the evolutionary mechanisms by which new species arise. Finally, in Chapter 24 we will examine how biologists determine the evolutionary relationships among different species and produce phylogenic trees that describe those relationships.

 ## Several biological principles will be emphasized in this unit:

- *Populations of organisms evolve from one generation to the next.* This concept is important to the discussion in all chapters.

- *Living organisms interact with their environment.* As we discuss in Chapters 21 and 22, natural selection results in certain individuals having greater reproductive success than others in a given environment.

- *Structure determines function.* Chapters 21 and 22 also consider how structural features change during the evolution of new species. Such changes are related to changes in function.

- *All life is related by an evolutionary history.* Chapter 24 is devoted to examining how biologists determine evolutionary relationships among organisms.

Origin and History of Life

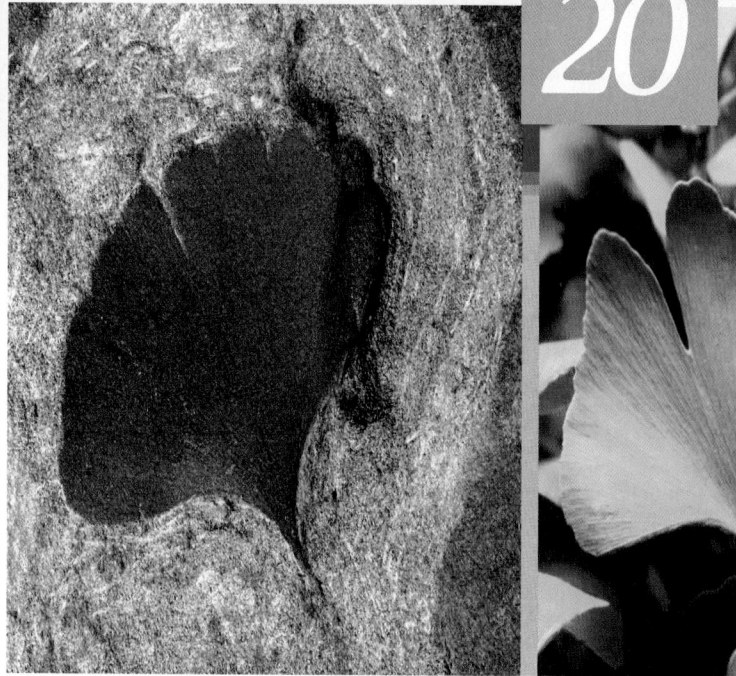

A fossil tree. This fossilized Ginkgo (left) found in British Columbia is a relative of present-day Ginkgo (right), whose genetic line spans the Mesozoic era back to the Triassic and whose lineage has existed for more than 200 million years.

Chapter Outline

Astronomers believe that the universe began about 13.7 billion years ago with an explosion called the Big Bang, when the first clouds of the elements hydrogen and helium were formed. Gravitational forces collapsed these clouds to create stars that converted hydrogen and helium into heavier elements, including carbon, nitrogen, and oxygen, which are the building blocks of life on Earth. These elements were returned to interstellar space by exploding stars called supernovas, forming clouds in which simple molecules, such as water, carbon monoxide, and hydrocarbons, were formed. The clouds then collapsed to make a new generation of stars and solar systems.

Our solar system began about 4.6 billion years ago, after one or more local supernova explosions. According to one widely accepted scenario, about 500 planetesimals (asteroids and comets) occupied the region where Venus, Earth, and Mars are now found. Earth, which is estimated to be 4.55 billion years old, grew from the accumulation of planetesimals over 100 million to 200 million years. For the first half-billion years or so after its formation, Earth was too hot to allow water to accumulate on its surface. By 4 billion years ago, Earth had cooled enough for the outer layers of the planet to solidify and for oceans to form.

The period between 4 billion and 3.5 billion years ago marked the emergence of life on our planet. Though scientists can never be certain how the first ancestral life forms arose, plausible hypotheses have emerged from our understanding of modern life. The first forms of life that we know about produced well-preserved microscopic fossils that were found in western Australia. These fossils, which are 3.5 billion years old, resemble photosynthetic bacteria called cyanobacteria that live today (**Figure 20.1**).

The first section of this chapter will survey a variety of hypotheses regarding the potential origins of biological molecules and living cells. Keep in mind that many of these hypotheses are speculative and are being changed as new information becomes known. Starting 3.5 billion years ago the formation of fossils (such as the one shown in the chapter opening photo)

has provided biologists with a history of life on Earth from its earliest beginnings to the present day. The last section of this chapter surveys a timeline for the history of life. This chapter emphasizes when particular forms of life arose. Later chapters in this unit examine the mechanisms by which populations of organisms change over the course of many generations. This process, termed **biological evolution**, involves genetic changes that occur over one to many generations. Such genetic modifications often lead to dramatic changes in traits and even the formation of new species.

(a) Fossil prokaryote   **(b) Modern cyanobacteria**

Figure 20.1 Earliest fossils and living cyanobacteria. **(a)** A fossilized prokaryote about 3.5 billion years old that is thought to be an early cyanobacterium. **(b)** A modern cyanobacterium, which has a similar morphology. Cyanobacteria are unicellular, but they aggregate into chains, as shown here.

20.1 / ORIGIN OF LIFE ON EARTH

Learning Outcomes:

1. Outline the four overlapping stages that are hypothesized to have led to the origin of life.
2. List various hypotheses about how complex organic molecules formed.
3. Explain the concept of an RNA world and how it could have evolved into a DNA/RNA/protein world.

As you learned in Units I, II, and III, living cells are complex collections of molecules and macromolecules. DNA stores the information for the amino acid sequence of proteins, RNA acts as an intermediary in the process of protein synthesis, and proteins form the foundation for the structure and activities of living cells. Life as we now know it requires this interplay among DNA, RNA, and proteins for its existence and perpetuation. On modern Earth all living cells are made from pre-existing cells.

But how did life begin? As we described in Chapter 1, living organisms have several characteristics that distinguish them from nonliving materials. Because DNA, RNA, and proteins are the central players in the enterprise of life, scientists who are interested in the origin of life have focused much of their attention on the formation of these macromolecules and their building blocks, namely, nucleotides and amino acids. To understand the origin of life, we can view the process as occurring in four overlapping stages:

Stage 1: Nucleotides and amino acids were produced before cells existed.

Stage 2. Nucleotides and amino acids became polymerized to form DNA, RNA, and proteins.

Stage 3: Polymers became enclosed in membranes.

Stage 4: Polymers enclosed in membranes evolved cellular properties.

Obviously, we cannot take a time machine back 4 billion years and determine with certainty how these events occurred. Instead, scientists study the existence of modern life, as well as geological processes and fossils, and speculate about the conditions that existed on ancestral Earth. This approach has led researchers to a variety of hypotheses regarding the origin of life, none of which can be firmly verified. Nevertheless, certain possibilities are becoming more plausible—and perhaps even compelling. In this section we will consider a few scientific viewpoints that wrestle with the question of how life began.

Stage 1: Several Scientific Hypotheses Have Been Proposed to Explain the Origin of Organic Molecules

Let's begin our inquiry into the first stage of the origin of life by considering how nucleotides and amino acids may have been generated before the existence of living cells. In the 1920s

Russian biochemist Alexander Oparin and Scottish biologist John Haldane independently proposed that organic molecules, such as nucleotides and amino acids, arose spontaneously under the conditions that occurred on ancestral Earth. According to this hypothesis, the spontaneous appearance of organic molecules produced what they called a "primordial soup," which eventually gave rise to living cells.

The conditions on ancestral Earth, which were much different from what they are today, may have been more conducive than modern conditions to the spontaneous formation of organic molecules. In particular, scientists think that little oxygen was present, and the atmosphere instead contained inorganic carbon dioxide, nitrogen gas, and water vapour. Current hypotheses suggest that organic molecules, and eventually macromolecules, formed spontaneously; this is termed prebiotic (before life) or abiotic (without life) synthesis. These slowly forming organic molecules accumulated because there was little free oxygen, so they were not spontaneously oxidized, and there were as yet no living organisms, so they were also not metabolized. The slow accumulation of these molecules in the early oceans over a long period formed what is now called the **prebiotic soup**. The formation of this medium was a key event that preceded the origin of life.

Though most scientists agree that life originated from the assemblage of nonliving matter on ancestral Earth, the mechanism of how and where these molecules originated is widely debated. Many intriguing hypotheses have been proposed. Keep in mind that these hypotheses are not mutually exclusive. Indeed, more than one mechanism may have contributed to the formation of a prebiotic soup. A few of the more widely debated ideas are described next.

Reducing Atmosphere Hypothesis Based largely on geological data, many scientists in the 1950s thought that the atmosphere on ancestral Earth was rich in water vapour (H_2O), hydrogen gas (H_2), methane (CH_4), and ammonia (NH_3). These components, along with a lack of atmospheric oxygen, produce a reducing atmosphere because methane and ammonia readily give up electrons and thereby reduce other molecules. As described in Chapters 7 and 8, such oxidation-reduction reactions are required for the formation of complex organic molecules from simple inorganic molecules.

In 1953 Stanley Miller, a student in the laboratory of Harold Urey, was the first scientist to use experimentation to test whether the prebiotic synthesis of organic molecules is possible. His experimental apparatus was intended to simulate the conditions on ancestral Earth that were postulated in the 1950s (**Figure 20.2**). Water vapour from a flask of boiling water rose into another chamber containing H_2, CH_4, and NH_3. Miller inserted two electrodes that sent electrical discharges into the chamber to simulate lightning bolts. A condenser jacket cooled some of the gases from the chamber, causing droplets to form that dropped into a trap. He then took samples from this trap for chemical analysis. In his first experiments, he observed the formation of hydrogen cyanide (HCN) and formaldehyde (CH_2O). Such molecules are precursors of more complex organic

Figure 20.2 Testing the reducing atmosphere hypothesis for the origin of life—the Miller and Urey experiment.

Concept check: *With regard to the origin of life, why are biologists interested in the abiotic synthesis of organic molecules?*

molecules. These precursors also combined to make larger molecules, such as the amino acid glycine. Later experiments by Miller and others demonstrated the formation of sugars, many types of amino acids, and nitrogenous bases found in nucleic acids (for example, adenine).

The studies by Miller and Urey were particularly important because they were the first attempts to apply scientific experimentation to the quest to understand the origin of life. Their pioneering strategy was to determine if a scientific hypothesis is plausible, although it cannot prove that an event in the past really happened that way. In spite of the importance of these studies, critics of the reducing atmosphere hypothesis have argued that Miller and Urey were wrong about the composition of ancestral Earth's environment.

Since the 1950s ideas about the atmosphere on early Earth have changed. More recently, many scientists have suggested that the atmosphere on ancestral Earth was not reducing and instead was a neutral environment composed mostly of carbon monoxide (CO), carbon dioxide (CO_2), nitrogen gas (N_2), and H_2O. These newer ideas are derived from studies of volcanic gas, which has much more CO_2 and N_2 than CH_4 and NH_3, and from the observation that UV radiation destroys CH_4 and NH_3,

so that these molecules would have been short-lived on ancestral Earth. Nevertheless, since the experiments of Urey, many newer investigations have shown that organic molecules can be made under a variety of conditions. Using different combinations of gases based on these corrected assumptions of atmospheric conditions on ancestral Earth, researchers have still achieved similar results. Namely, organic molecules can be made prebiotically from a neutral environment composed primarily of CO, CO_2, N_2, and H_2O.

Extraterrestrial Hypothesis Many scientists have argued that sufficient organic carbon would have been present in the asteroids and comets that reached the surface of early Earth to make them instrumental in stocking the prebiotic soup. Modern evidence in support of this idea comes from the study of these fallen bodies, called meteorites. A significant proportion of meteorites belong to a class known as carbonaceous chondrites. Such meteorites contain a substantial amount of organic carbon, including amino acids and nucleic acid bases. Based on this observation, scientists have postulated that such meteorites could have transported a significant amount of organic molecules to ancestral Earth.

Deep-Sea Vent Hypothesis In 1988 German organic chemist Günter Wächtershäuser proposed that key organic molecules may have originated in deep-sea vents, which are cracks in Earth's surface where superheated water rich in metal ions and hydrogen sulphide (H_2S) mixes abruptly with cold sea water. These vents release hot gaseous substances from the interior of Earth at temperatures in excess of 300°C. Supporters of this hypothesis propose that biologically important molecules may have been formed in the temperature gradient between the extremely hot vent water and the cold water that surrounds the vent at the bottom of the ocean (**Figure 20.3a**).

Experimentally, the temperatures within this gradient are known to be suitable for the synthesis of molecules that form components of biological molecules. For example, the reaction between iron and H_2S yields pyrites and H_2, and it has been shown to provide the energy necessary for the reduction of N_2 to NH_3. Nitrogen is an essential ingredient of the molecular building blocks of life: amino acids and nucleic acids. But N_2, which is found abundantly on Earth, is chemically inert, so it is unlikely to have given rise to life. Most scientists believe instead that NH_3 was required to help life start.

Interestingly, complex biological communities are found near modern deep-sea vents. Various types of fish, worms, crabs, clams, shrimps, and bacteria are found in abundance in those areas (**Figure 20.3b**). Unlike most other forms of life on our planet, these organisms receive their energy from chemicals in the vent and not from the sun. These organisms have evolved unique physiologies that allow them to occupy these novel environments. Dr. Verena Tunnicliffe of the University of Victoria studies the ecology and evolution of hot-vent animals and has discovered more than 75 species new to science over the past 25 years.

(a) Deep-sea vent hypothesis

(b) A deep-sea vent community

Figure 20.3 The deep-sea vent hypothesis for the origin of life. **(a)** Deep-sea vents are cracks in Earth's surface that release hot gases, such as hydrogen sulphide (H_2S). This heats the water near the vent and creates a gradient between the very hot water adjacent to the vent and the cold water that is farther away from the vent. The synthesis of organic molecules can occur in this gradient. **(b)** Photograph of a biological community near a deep-sea vent consisting of giant tubeworms, clams, and crabs.

Concept check: *What properties of deep-sea vents made them suitable for the abiotic synthesis of molecules?*

Stage 2: Organic Polymers May Have Formed on the Surface of Clay

Many scientists have speculated that the synthesis of polymers did not occur in a prebiotic soup but instead took place on a solid surface or in evaporating tidal pools. Experimentally, many research groups have demonstrated the formation of nucleic acid polymers and polypeptides on the surface of clay, given the presence of monomer building blocks.

During the prebiotic synthesis of RNA, the purine bases of the nucleotides interact with the silicate surfaces of the clay. Divalent cations, such as Mg^{2+}, bind the nucleotides to the negative surfaces of the clay, thereby positioning the nucleotides in a way that promotes bond formation between the phosphate of one nucleotide and the ribose sugar of an adjacent nucleotide. In this way polymers, such as RNA, may have been formed.

Structurally, clay is a crystalline hydrous aluminosilicate that also contains other cations. The chemical nature of clay has been used for various industrial organic reactions, including organic rearrangements and addition, elimination, substitution, and oxidation-reduction reactions. As an example, additions to enol ethers take place smoothly in clay catalysts.

Stage 3: Cell-Like Structures May Have Originated When Polymers Were Enclosed by a Boundary

The third stage in the origin of living cells is believed to be the formation of a boundary that separated the environment from internal polymers, such as RNA. The term **protobiont** (or prebiont) is used to describe the first nonliving structures that evolved into living cells. Protobionts had four characteristics that put them on the path to living cells:

1. A boundary, such as a membrane, separated the external environment from the internal contents of the protobiont.
2. Polymers inside the protobiont contained information.
3. Polymers inside the protobiont had enzymatic functions.
4. The protobionts were capable of self-replication.

Scientists envision protobionts as aggregates of prebiotically produced molecules and macromolecules that acquired a boundary, such as lipid bilayer, that allowed them to maintain an internal chemical environment distinct from that of their surroundings. Protobionts were not capable of precise self-reproduction like living cells but probably could divide to increase in number.

Different scenarios have been proposed to explain the formation of protobionts. Russian biologist Aleksandr Oparin hypothesized in 1924 that living cells evolved from **coacervates**, droplets that form spontaneously from the association of charged polymers, such as proteins, carbohydrates, or nucleic acids. Their name derives from the Latin *coacervare*, meaning "to assemble together or cluster." Coacervates measure 1 to 100 μm (micrometres) across, possess osmotic properties, and are surrounded by a tight skin of water molecules (**Figure 20.4a**). This boundary allows the selective absorption of simple molecules from the surrounding medium.

If enzymes are trapped within coacervates, they can perform ancestral metabolic functions (**Figure 20.4b**). For example, researchers have made coacervates containing the enzyme glycogen phosphorylase. When glucose-1-phosphate was made available to the coacervates, it was taken up into them and starch was produced. The starch merged with the wall of the coacervates, which increased in size and eventually divided into two. When the enzyme amylase was

Figure 20.4 **Protobionts and their lifelike functions.** Ancestral cell-like structures like these could have given rise to living cells. **(a)** This micrograph shows coacervates made by Oparin from a mixture of gelatine (composed primarily of protein) and gum arabic (composed of protein and carbohydrate). **(b)** The illustration shows simple metabolism that can be performed by coacervates. **(c)** Micrograph and illustration of microspheres, which are water-filled spheres of macromolecules, such as protein. **(d)** An electron micrograph and illustration of liposomes. Each liposome is made of a phospholipid bilayer surrounding an aqueous compartment.

Concept check: *Which protobiont seems most similar to real cells? Explain.*

BioConnections: *Look back at Figure 3.12. What is the physical/chemical reason that phospholipids tend to form a bilayer?*

included, the starch was broken down to maltose, which was released from the coacervates.

An alternative pathway to protobionts is the formation of **microspheres**, which are small water-filled vesicles surrounded by a macromolecular boundary (**Figure 20.4c**). If hot solutions of proteins are cooled under the correct conditions, they produce microspheres about 2 μm in diameter that are hollow and have an outer layer of protein.

Similar experiments have been done with lipids. When certain types of lipids are dissolved in water, they spontaneously form **liposomes**, which are vesicles surrounded by a lipid bilayer (**Figure 20.4d**). In 2003 researchers were able to show that clay can catalyze the formation of liposomes that grow and divide, an ancestral form of self-replication. Furthermore, if RNA was on the surface of the clay, the researchers discovered that liposomes were formed that enclosed RNA. These experiments are exciting because they show that the formation of membrane vesicles containing RNA molecules is a plausible route to the first living cells based on simple physical and chemical forces.

Stage 4: Cellular Characteristics May Have Evolved via Chemical Selection, Beginning with an RNA World

The majority of scientists favour RNA as the first macromolecule that was found in protobionts. Unlike other polymers, RNA exhibits three key functions. First, RNA has the ability to store information in its nucleotide sequence. Second, because of base pairing, its nucleotide sequence has the capacity for replication. Third, RNA can perform a variety of enzymatic functions. The results of many experiments have shown that RNA molecules can function as **ribozymes**, acting as enzymes to synthesize the macromolecules found in living cells. By comparison, DNA and proteins are not known to have all three attributes. DNA is not known to have enzymatic activity, and proteins are not known to undergo self-replication. Thus, RNA appears to be the most self-sufficient substance of living matter. RNA can perform functions that are characteristic of proteins, and at the same time can serve as genetic material with replicative and informational functions.

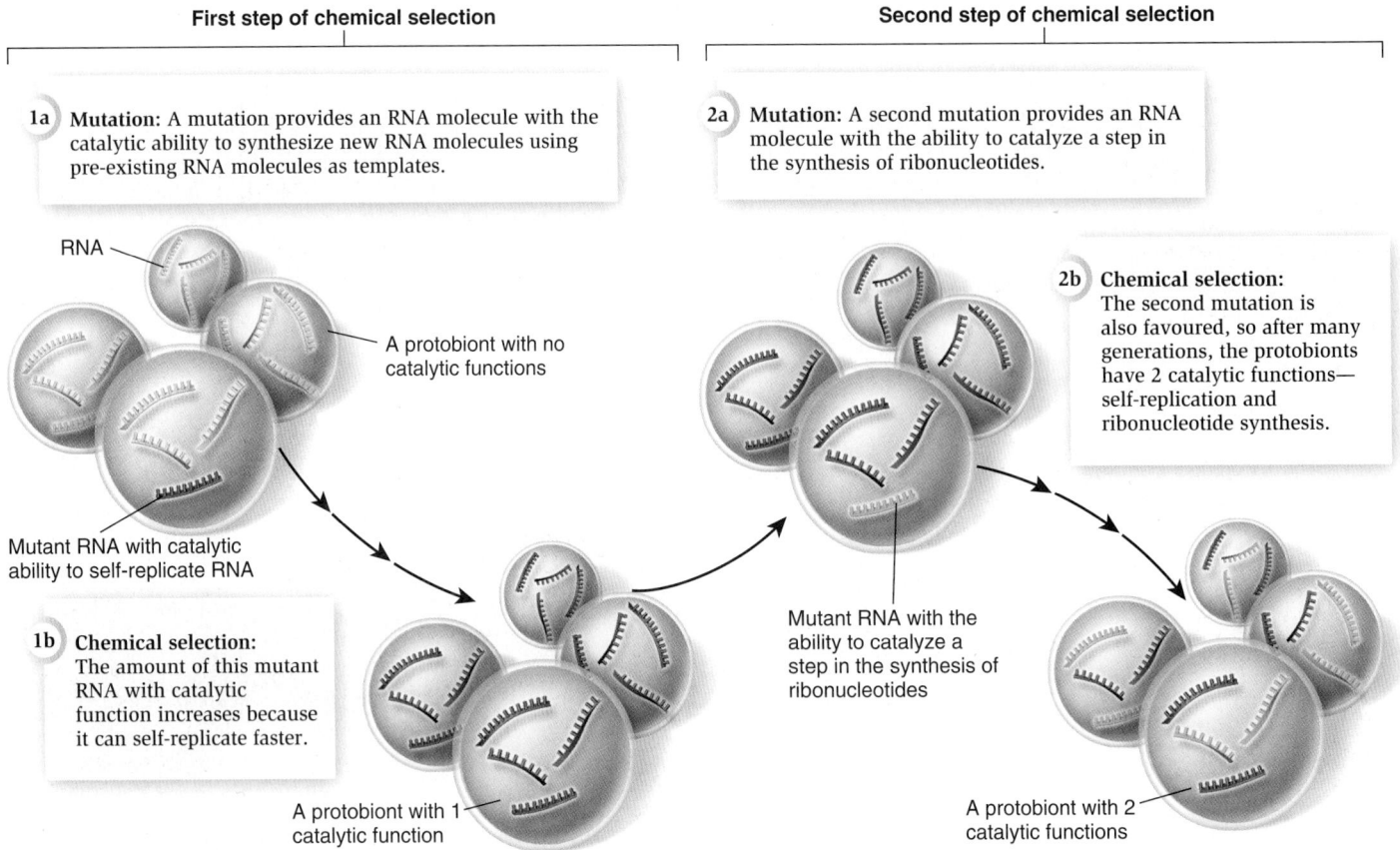

First step of chemical selection

1a **Mutation:** A mutation provides an RNA molecule with the catalytic ability to synthesize new RNA molecules using pre-existing RNA molecules as templates.

RNA

A protobiont with no catalytic functions

Mutant RNA with catalytic ability to self-replicate RNA

1b **Chemical selection:** The amount of this mutant RNA with catalytic function increases because it can self-replicate faster.

A protobiont with 1 catalytic function

Second step of chemical selection

2a **Mutation:** A second mutation provides an RNA molecule with the ability to catalyze a step in the synthesis of ribonucleotides.

2b **Chemical selection:** The second mutation is also favoured, so after many generations, the protobionts have 2 catalytic functions— self-replication and ribonucleotide synthesis.

Mutant RNA with the ability to catalyze a step in the synthesis of ribonucleotides

A protobiont with 2 catalytic functions

Figure 20.5   A hypothetical scenario illustrating the process of chemical selection.   This figure shows a two-step scenario. The first step selects for self-replication and the second step selects for the ability to synthesize ribonucleotides.

Concept check: *What is meant by the term* chemical selection?

But how did the RNA molecules that were first made prebiotically evolve into more complex molecules that produced cell-like characteristics? Researchers propose that a process called chemical selection was responsible for the increased complexity. **Chemical selection** occurs when a chemical within a mixture has special properties or advantages that cause it to increase compared with other chemicals in the mixture. Scientists speculate that, initially, the special properties that enabled certain RNA molecules to undergo chemical selection were its ability to self-replicate and to perform other enzymatic functions.

Because cells are a complex mixture of different macromolecules that carry out many enzymatic functions, researchers cannot establish with certainty the specific sequence of steps that produced modern cells. However, as a way to understand the concept of chemical selection, let's consider a hypothetical scenario showing two steps of chemical selection. **Figure 20.5** shows a group of protobionts that contain RNA molecules that were made prebiotically. RNA molecules inside these protobionts can be used as templates for the prebiotic synthesis of complementary RNA molecules.

A second step of chemical selection is also shown in Figure 20.5 (right side). A second mutation in an RNA molecule could produce the enzymatic function that would promote the synthesis of ribonucleotides, the building blocks of RNA. This

protobiont would have the advantage of not having to rely on the prebiotic synthesis of ribonucleotides, which also is a very slow process. Therefore, the protobiont having the ability to both self-replicate its RNA molecules and synthesize ribonucleotides would have an advantage over a protobiont that could only self-replicate. Over time the faster rate of ribonucleotide synthesis and self-replication would cause an increase in the numbers of the protobionts with both functions.

The **RNA world** is a hypothetical period on ancestral Earth when both the information needed for life and the enzymatic activity of living cells were contained solely in RNA molecules. In this scenario lipid membranes enclosing RNA exhibited the properties of life because of RNA genomes that were copied and maintained through the catalytic function of RNA molecules. Scientists believe that mutations occurred over time in these RNA molecules, occasionally presenting new functional possibilities. Chemical selection for these new functions would have eventually produced an increase in complexity in these cells, with RNA molecules accruing such activities as peptide bond formation and other enzymatic functions.

But is an RNA world a plausible scenario? As described next in the Feature Investigation, chemical selection of RNA molecules can occur experimentally.

FEATURE INVESTIGATION

Bartel and Szostak Demonstrated Chemical Selection in the Laboratory

Remarkably, scientists have been able to perform experiments in the laboratory that can select for RNA molecules with a particular function. The first such study by David Bartel and Jack Szostak was conducted in 1993 (**Figure 20.6**). By using molecular techniques they synthesized a mixture of 10^{15} RNA molecules that we will call the long RNA molecules. Each long RNA in this mixture contained two regions. The first region at the 5′ end was a constant region that formed a stem-loop structure. Its sequence was identical among all 10^{15} molecules. The constant region was next to a second region that was 220 nucleotides long. A key feature of the second region is that its sequence was variable among the 10^{15} molecules. The researchers hypothesized that this variation could occasionally result in a long RNA molecule with the enzymatic ability to catalyze a phosphoester bond, which is a covalent bond between two adjacent nucleotides.

They also made another type of RNA molecule, which we will call the short RNA, which had two important properties. First, the short RNA had a region that was complementary to a site near the constant region of the long RNA molecules. Second, the short RNA had a tag sequence that caused it to bind tightly to column packing material referred to as beads.

To begin this experiment, the researchers incubated a large number of the short and long RNA molecules together. During this incubation period long and short RNA molecules would hydrogen bond to each other because of their complementary regions. Although hydrogen bonding is not permanent, this step allowed the long and short RNAs to recognize each other for a short time. The researchers reasoned that a long RNA with the enzymatic ability to form covalent phosphoester bonds may make this interaction more permanent by catalyzing a phosphoester bond between the long and short RNA molecules. Following this incubation, the mixture of RNAs was passed through a column with beads that specifically bound the short RNA. The aim of this approach was to select for longer RNA molecules that had covalently bonded to the short RNA molecule (see the Conceptual Level of Figure 20.6).

The vast majority of RNAs would not have the enzymatic ability to catalyze a phosphoester bond. These would pass out of the column at step (2), because hydrogen bonding between the long and short RNAs is not sufficient to hold them together for very long. Such long RNAs would be discarded. Long RNAs with the ability to catalyze a phosphoester bond to the short RNA would remain bound to the column beads at step (2). These enzymatic RNAs were then flushed out at step (3) to generate a mixture of RNAs termed pool #1. The researchers expected this pool to contain several different

HYPOTHESIS Among a large pool of RNA molecules, some of them may contain the enzymatic ability to catalyze a covalent bond between nucleotides; these can be selected for in the laboratory.

KEY MATERIALS Many copies of short RNA were synthesized that had a tag sequence that binds tightly to column packing material called beads. Also, a population of 10^{15} long RNA molecules was made that contained a constant region with a stem-loop structure and a 220-nucleotide variable region. Note: The variable regions of the long RNAs were made using a PCR step that caused mutations in this region.

1 Mix together the short RNAs with the 10^{15} different long RNAs. Allow time for covalent connections to form if the long RNA happens to have the enzymatic activity for phosphoester bond formation.

Of the 10^{15} long molecules, the variable region may rarely have the enzymatic ability to covalently connect the 3′ end of the short RNA to the 5′ end of the long RNA.

Figure 20.6 Bartel and Szostak demonstrated chemical selection for RNA molecules that can catalyze phosphoester bond formation.

Figure 20.6 *(Continued)*

2 Pass the mixture through a column of beads that binds the tag sequence found on the short RNA. Add additional liquid to flush out long RNAs that are not covalently attached to short RNAs.

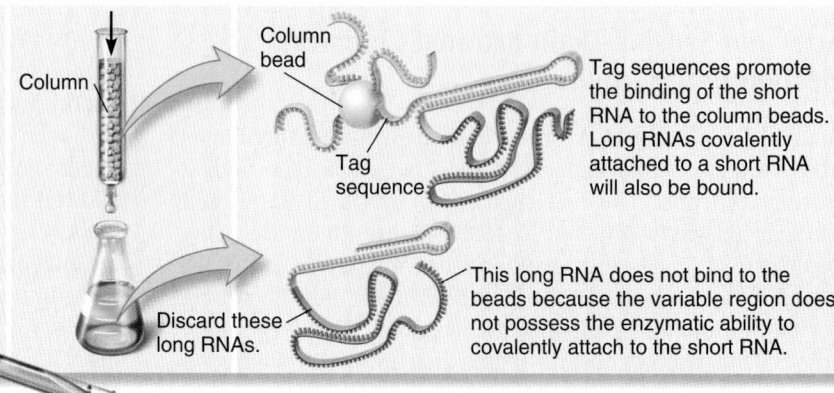

Tag sequences promote the binding of the short RNA to the column beads. Long RNAs covalently attached to a short RNA will also be bound.

This long RNA does not bind to the beads because the variable region does not possess the enzymatic ability to covalently attach to the short RNA.

Discard these long RNAs.

3 Add a low pH solution to prevent the tag sequence from binding to the beads. This causes the tightly bound RNAs to be flushed out of the column.

Low pH wash

4 The flushed-out RNAs are termed pool #1. Use pool #1 to make a second batch of long RNA molecules. This involved a PCR step using reverse transcriptase to make cDNA. The PCR primers recognized the beginning and end of the long RNA sequence and copied only this region. The cDNA was then used as a template to make long RNA via RNA polymerase.

Pool #1

Refer back to Figure 18.8 for a description of PCR.

5 Repeat procedure to generate 10 consecutive pools of RNA molecules.

Pool #1   Pool #2   Pool #3   Pool #4   Pool #5   Pool #6   Pool #7   Pool #8   Pool #9   Pool #10

6 Test a sample of the original population and each of the 10 pools for the enzymatic ability to catalyze a covalent bond between adjacent nucleotides.

Gap

Covalent bond

7 **THE DATA**

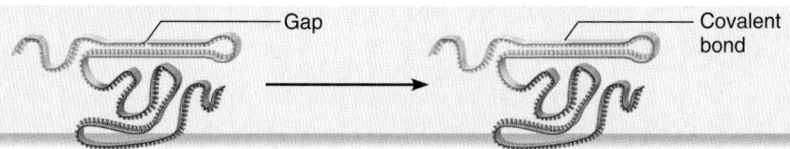

*Original 10^{15} molecules

8 **CONCLUSION** The increase in covalent bond formation from pool 1 to pool 10 indicates that chemical selection can occur.

9 **SOURCE** Bartel, David P., and Szostak, Jack W. 1993. Isolation of new ribozymes from a large pool of random sequences. *Science* 261:1411–1418.

long RNA molecules with varying abilities to catalyze a phosphoester bond.

To further the chemical selection process, the scientists used the first pool of long RNA molecules flushed out at step (3) to make more long RNA molecules. This was accomplished via PCR. This next batch also had the constant and variable regions. However, the variable regions were derived from the variable regions of pool #1 RNA molecules that had enzymatic activity. The researchers reasoned that additional variation might occasionally produce an RNA molecule with improved enzymatic activity. This second batch of long RNA molecules was subjected to the same steps as was the first batch of 10^{15} molecules. In this case the group of long molecules flushed out at step (3) was termed pool #2. This protocol was followed eight more times to generate 10 consecutive pools of RNA molecules. The researchers then analyzed the original random collection of 10^{15} RNA molecules and each of the 10 pools for the enzymatic ability to catalyze a phosphoester bond. As seen in the data, each successive pool became enriched for molecules with higher enzymatic activity. Pool #10 showed enzymatic activity

that was approximately 3 million times as high as the original random pool of molecules!

Much like the work of Miller and Urey, these experiments demonstrated the feasibility of another phase of the prebiotic evolutionary process, in this case evolution via chemical selection. The results showed that chemical selection improves the functional characteristics of a group of RNA molecules over time by increasing the proportions of those molecules with enhanced function.

Experimental Questions

1. What is chemical selection? What was the hypothesis tested by Bartel and Szostak?
2. In the selection experiment among pools of long RNA molecules with various catalytic abilities, what was the purpose of using the short RNA molecules?
3. What were the results of the experiment conducted by Bartel and Szostak? What impact did this study have on our understanding of the evolution of life on Earth?

The RNA World Was Superseded by the Modern DNA/RNA/Protein World

Assuming that an RNA world was the origin of life, researchers have asked the questions of why and how the RNA world evolved into the DNA/RNA/protein world we see today. Many potential pathways to a DNA/RNA/protein world are possible. Some researchers have argued that proteins evolved in parallel with RNA molecules. However, many proponents of the RNA world hypothesis suggest that DNA and proteins evolved later. If so, the RNA world may have been superseded by a DNA/RNA world or an RNA/protein world before the emergence of the modern DNA/RNA/protein world. Let's now consider the advantages of a DNA/RNA/protein world as opposed to the simpler RNA world, and how this modern biological world came into being.

Information Storage   As we discussed previously, RNA can store information in its base sequence. So why did DNA take over that function, as is the case in modern cells? In the RNA world RNA had to perform two roles: informational and catalytic. Scientists have speculated that the incorporation of DNA into cells would have relieved RNA of its informational role and thereby allowed RNA to perform a greater variety of other functions. For example, if DNA stored the information for the synthesis of RNA molecules, such RNA molecules could bind cofactors, have modified bases, or bind peptides that might enhance their catalytic function. Cells with both DNA and RNA would have had an advantage over those with just RNA, and they would have been selected. Another advantage of

DNA is stability. Compared with RNA, DNA is less likely to suffer mutations.

A second issue is how the DNA world came into being. Scientists have proposed that an ancestral RNA molecule had the ability to make DNA by using RNA as a template. This function, known as reverse transcriptase activity, is described in Chapter 16. Interestingly, modern eukaryotic cells can use RNA as a template to make DNA. For example, telomerase, which is described in Chapter 10, copies the ends of chromosomes by using an RNA template.

Metabolism and Other Cellular Functions   Now let's consider the origin of proteins. The emergence of proteins as catalytic entities may have been a great advantage to early cells. Because of the many different chemistries of the 20 amino acids, proteins have vastly greater catalytic potential and efficiency than do RNA molecules, again providing a major advantage to cells that had both proteins and RNA. In modern cells proteins have taken over most but not all catalytic functions. In addition proteins can perform other important tasks. For example, cytoskeletal proteins carry out structural roles, and certain membrane proteins are responsible for the uptake of substances into living cells.

The answer to the question of how proteins came into being after an RNA world seems to be rooted in RNA function. Chemical selection experiments have shown that RNA molecules can catalyze the formation of peptide bonds and even attach amino acids to ancestral tRNA molecules. Modern protein synthesis still includes a central role for RNA. First, mRNA provides the information for a polypeptide sequence.

Second, tRNA molecules act as adaptors for the formation of a polypeptide chain. Finally, ribosomes containing rRNA provide an arena for polypeptide synthesis. Furthermore, RNA within the ribosome acts as a ribozyme to catalyze peptide bond formation. Taken together, the analysis of translation in modern cells is consistent with an evolutionary history in which RNA molecules were instrumental in the emergence and formation of proteins.

20.2 HISTORY OF LIFE ON EARTH

Learning Outcomes:

1. List the types of environmental changes that have affected the history of life on Earth.
2. Describe the cell structure and energy use of the first living organisms that arose during the Archean eon.
3. Explain how the origin of eukaryotic cells might have involved a union between bacterial and archaeal cells.
4. Describe the key features of multicellular organisms, which arose during the Proterozoic eon.
5. Outline the major events and changes in species diversity during the Paleozoic, Mesozoic, and Cenozoic eras.

Thus far we have considered how the first ancestral cells may have come into existence. Recall that the first fossils of single-celled organisms were preserved approximately 3.5 billion years ago (see Figure 20.1). In this section, we will examine some of the major changes in life that have occurred since that time. As you will learn, the period from 3.5 billion years ago to the present has seen dramatic changes in the composition of life on Earth.

We will begin with a brief description of the geological changes that occurred on Earth, which have affected the emergence of new forms of life. Then we will examine how fossils are formed and how they provide a fascinating yet incomplete journey through the history of life.

Many Environmental and Biological Changes Have Occurred Since the Origin of Earth

The **geological timescale** is a timeline of Earth's history from its origin 4.55 billion years ago to the present. This timeline is subdivided into four eons and then further subdivided into many eras. The first three eons are collectively known as the Precambrian. **Figure 20.7** provides the geological timescale and describes some of the major events that occurred during the history of life. Figure 20.7 is not to scale but is distorted to show the periods of life on Earth. The names of several eons and eras end in *zoic* (meaning animal life) because we often recognize these time intervals on the basis of animal life. We will examine these time periods later in this chapter.

The changes that have occurred in living organisms over the past 4 billion years are the result of two interactive processes. First, as discussed in the next several chapters, genetic changes in organisms can affect their characteristics. Such changes often have an important impact on the ability of organisms to survive in their native environment. Second, the environment on Earth has undergone dramatic changes. Such environmental changes have profoundly influenced the types of organisms that have existed during different periods. As we will examine later, environmental influences can be both positive and negative. In some cases, a change can allow new types of organisms to come into being. Alternatively, environmental changes can cause the **extinction** of a species or group of species. A recurring pattern seen in the history of life is the emergence of new species and the extinction of other species (**Figure 20.8**). In some cases biological changes and extinctions are correlated with major environmental changes, which include the following:

- Climate and temperature: During the first 2.5 billion years of its existence, the surface of Earth gradually cooled. However, during the last 2 billion years, Earth has undergone major fluctuations in temperature, producing Ice Ages that alternate with warmer periods. Furthermore, the temperature on Earth is not uniform, which produces many different environments where the temperatures are quite different, such as a tropical rain forest and the Arctic.

- Atmosphere: The chemical composition of the gases surrounding Earth has changed substantially over the past 4 billion years. One notable change involves oxygen. The emergence of organisms that were capable of photosynthesis added oxygen to the atmosphere. Before 2.5 billion years ago, relatively little oxygen was in the atmosphere. Levels of oxygen in the form of O_2 began to rise significantly at about this time. Our current atmosphere contains about 21% O_2.

- Land masses: As Earth cooled, land masses formed that were surrounded by bodies of water. This created two different environments, terrestrial and aquatic. Furthermore, over the course of billions of years, the major land masses, known as the continents, have shifted their positions, changed their shapes, and in some cases become separated from each other. This phenomenon, called **continental drift**, is shown in **Figure 20.9**.

- Floods: Catastrophic floods have periodically had major impacts on the organisms in the flooded regions, sometimes causing extinction.

- Glaciation: On a periodic basis glaciers have moved across continents and altered the composition of species on those land masses. Glaciation also affects the water level of oceans.

- Volcanic eruptions: The eruptions of volcanoes can negatively affect the species near the eruption, sometimes

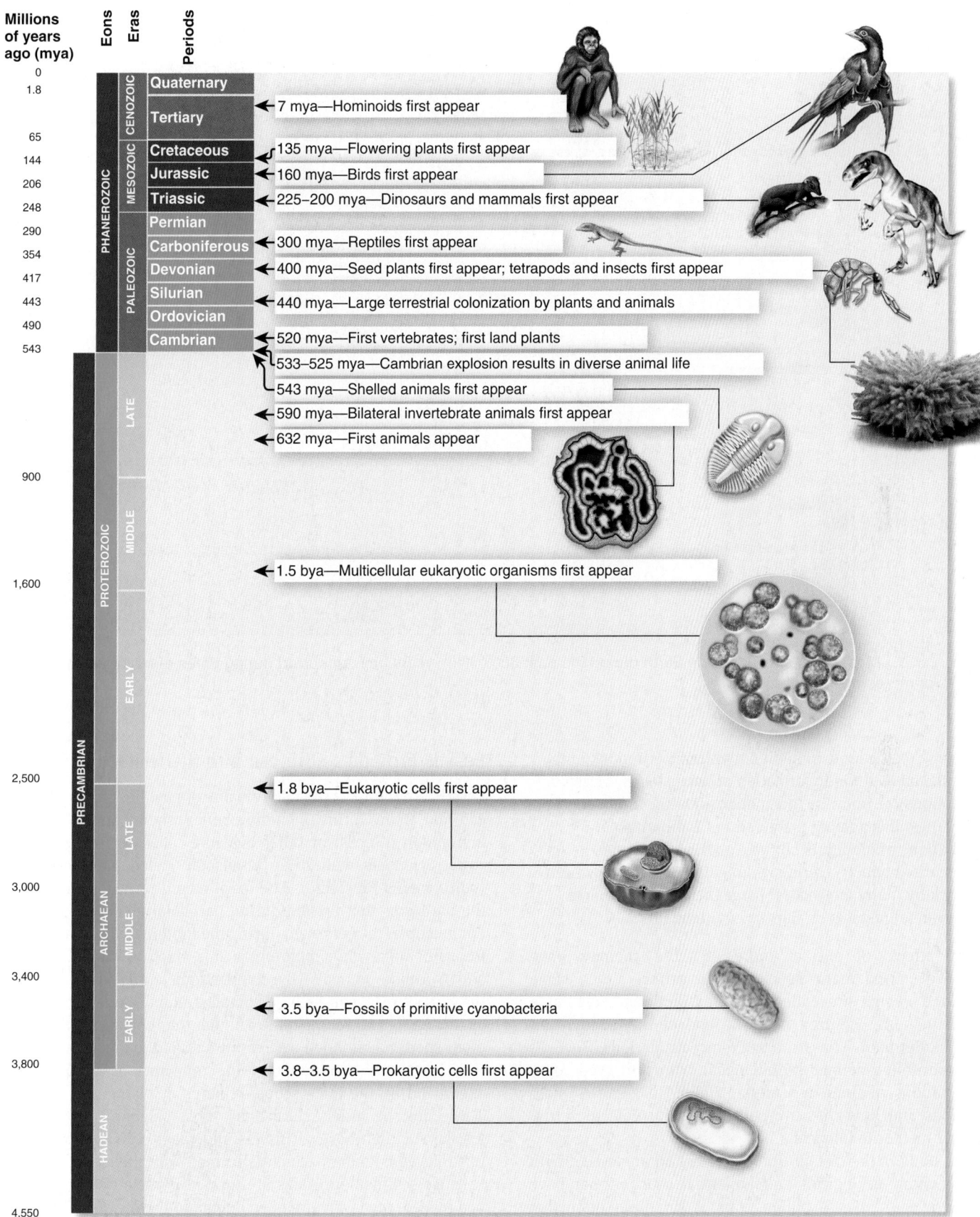

Millions of years ago (mya)

	Eons	Eras	Periods	
0			Quaternary	
1.8			Tertiary	← 7 mya—Hominoids first appear
65			Cretaceous	← 135 mya—Flowering plants first appear
144			Jurassic	← 160 mya—Birds first appear
206			Triassic	← 225–200 mya—Dinosaurs and mammals first appear
248			Permian	
290			Carboniferous	← 300 mya—Reptiles first appear
354			Devonian	← 400 mya—Seed plants first appear; tetrapods and insects first appear
417			Silurian	← 440 mya—Large terrestrial colonization by plants and animals
443			Ordovician	
490			Cambrian	← 520 mya—First vertebrates; first land plants
543				← 533–525 mya—Cambrian explosion results in diverse animal life

Eons column (left to right): PHANEROZOIC, PRECAMBRIAN
Eras: CENOZOIC, MESOZOIC, PALEOZOIC, PROTEROZOIC, ARCHAEAN, HADEAN

← 543 mya—Shelled animals first appear
← 590 mya—Bilateral invertebrate animals first appear
← 632 mya—First animals appear

900

← 1.5 bya—Multicellular eukaryotic organisms first appear

1,600

2,500   ← 1.8 bya—Eukaryotic cells first appear

3,000

3,400   ← 3.5 bya—Fossils of primitive cyanobacteria

3,800   ← 3.8–3.5 bya—Prokaryotic cells first appear

4,550

Figure 20.7 The geological timescale and an overview of the history of life on Earth.

Figure 20.8 Most mass extinctions on Earth during the past 500 million years have occurred during times of major volcanic eruptions or meteorite impacts.

causing extinctions. In addition, volcanic eruptions in the ocean can lead to the formation of new islands. Massive eruptions can spew so much debris into the atmosphere that they affect global temperatures and limit solar radiation, which limits photosynthetic production.

- Meteorite impacts: During its long history Earth has been struck by many meteorites. Large meteorites have had substantial impacts on Earth's environment.

The effects of one or more of these changes have sometimes caused many species to go extinct at the same time. Such events are called **mass extinctions**. Five large mass extinctions occurred near the end of the Ordovician, Devonian, Permian, Triassic, and Cretaceous periods. Geological eras are often defined by biological extinctions and adaptive radiations of flora and fauna. Figure 20.8 shows mass extinctions and how they are correlated with volcanic eruptions and meteorite impacts.

The study of the history of life involves an analysis of both environmental (geological) and biological changes that have occurred over the past 4 billion years. A key observation that provides us with a window into our biological past is the identification and examination of fossils, which are described next.

Fossils Provide a Glimpse into the History of Life

Fossils are the recognizable remains of past life on Earth. They can take many forms, including bones, shells, and leaves; the impression of cells; or other evidence, such as tracks or burrows. Scientists who study fossils are called **paleontologists** (*paleo* means "ancient"). The fossil record provides a record of the life forms that existed during particular geological periods. For example, rocks formed during the Proterozoic eon may have fossils of relatively simple organisms, such as bacteria, algae, and wormlike animals. By comparison, fossils formed during the Phanerozoic eon include complex animals and plants, such as mammals and seed plants. Though the remains of dinosaurs often spark a childhood interest in fossils, the great bulk of the fossil record is dominated by the remnants of animals with shells and by the microscopic remains of plants and animals. These are the fossils studied by most paleontologists. Other fossils, such as those of insects and seeds, can also be found in Cretaceous amber, which is formed from the resin of trees. Because sedimentary rocks are formed particle by particle and bed by bed, the layers are piled one on top of the other in strata. Paleontologists often study changes in life forms over time by studying the fossils in various strata (**Figure 20.10**). The more

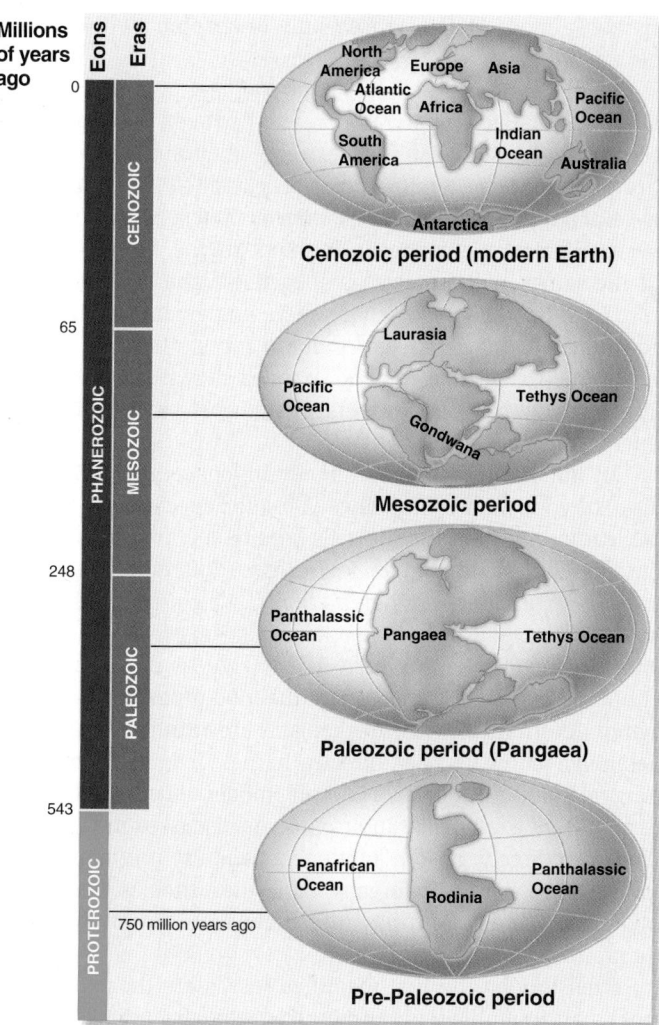

Figure 20.9 Continental drift. The relative locations of the continents on Earth have changed over the past hundreds of millions of years.

Figure 20.10 An example of layers, or strata, of sedimentary rock that contain fossils. This photo shows a site that contains several layers of rock.

Concept check: *Which rock layer is this photo is likely to be the oldest?*

ancient life forms are found in the lower strata, while newer species are found in the upper strata.

A common way to estimate the age of a fossil is by analyzing the elemental isotopes within the accompanying rock, a process called **radioisotope dating**. As discussed in Chapter 2, elements can be found in two or more forms called isotopes. Radioactive isotopes are unstable and decay at a specific rate. The **half-life** of a radioisotope is the length of time required for exactly one-half of the original isotope to decay (**Figure 20.11a**). Each radioactive isotope has its own unique half-life. Within a sample of rock, scientists can measure the amount of a given radioactive isotope, as well as the amount of the isotope that is produced when the original isotope decays. For dating geological materials, several types of isotope decay patterns are particularly useful: carbon to nitrogen, potassium to argon, rubidium to strontium, and uranium to lead (**Figure 20.11b**). Except for recent fossils in which carbon-14 dating can be employed, fossil dating is not usually conducted on the fossil itself or on the

sedimentary rock in which the fossil is found. Most commonly, igneous rock near the sedimentary rock is dated. For example, igneous rock derived from an ancient lava flow initially contains uranium-235 but no lead-207. By comparing the relative proportions of uranium-235 and lead-207, the age of the igneous rock can be accurately determined. Even so, paleontologists expect the fossil record to underestimate the actual date that a species came into existence because they are unlikely to find the first member of a particular species.

We should consider some factors that impart a bias to the fossil record. First, certain organisms are more likely to become fossilized than are others. Such factors as anatomy, size, number, and the environment and time in which they lived play important roles in determining the likelihood that an organism will be preserved in the fossil record. In addition geological processes can create biases because they may favour the fossilization of certain types of organisms. Such processes can also create confusion because they can cause parts of different species to be mixed after death. Finally, unintentional biases arise that are related to the efforts of paleontologists. For example, scientific interests may favour searching for and analyzing certain species over others.

Though the fossil record should not be viewed as a comprehensive, balanced story of the history of life, it has provided a wealth of information regarding the types of life that existed in the distant past. The rest of this chapter will survey the emergence of life forms from 3.5 billion years ago to the present. In addition, the fossil record has provided compelling evidence for the theory of evolution. We will begin to examine this topic in Chapter 21.

(a) Decay of a radioisotope

Radioisotope	Decay product	Half-life (years)	Useful dating range (years)
Carbon-14	Nitrogen-14	5,730	100–30,000
Potassium-40	Argon-40	1.3 billion	100,000–4.5 billion
Rubidium-87	Strontium-87	47 billion	10 million–4.5 billion
Uranium-235	Lead-207	710 million	10 million–4.5 billion
Uranium-238	Lead-206	4.5 billion	10 million–4.5 billion

(b) Radioisotopes that are useful for geological dating

Figure 20.11   Radioisotope dating of fossils.   (a) Rocks can be dated by measuring the relative amounts of a radioisotope and its decay product that they contain. (b) These five isotopes are particularly useful for the dating of fossils.

Concept check: *If you suspected a fossil was 50 million years old, which pair of radioisotopes would you choose to analyze?*

Prokaryotic Cells Arose During the Archean Eon

The Archean (meaning "ancient") eon was a time when diverse microbial life flourished in the primordial oceans. As mentioned earlier in this chapter, the first known fossils of living cells were preserved in rocks that are dated as 3.5 billion years old, though scientists postulate that cells arose many millions of years before this time. Based on the morphology of fossilized remains, these first cells were prokaryotic, lacking a true nucleus. During the more than 1 billion years of the Archean eon, all life forms were prokaryotic. At the time of their emergence, hardly any free oxygen (O_2) was in Earth's atmosphere. Therefore, the single-celled microorganisms of this eon almost certainly used only **anaerobic** (without oxygen) metabolism.

As discussed in Chapter 4, prokaryotes are divided into two domains: Bacteria and Archaea. It has been postulated that the Archaea arose in the early extreme environments found on Earth. Modern-day Archaea can be classified based on their environment as extremophiles (thermophiles, halophiles, and psychrophiles), methanogens, or nonextreme forms (occupying the same environments as eubacteria) and are quite common. Both Bacteria and Archaea share fundamental similarities, indicating that they shared a common ancestor early in the history of life. Extant Bacteria and Archaea show some interesting differences with regard to metabolism, lipid composition, and genetic pathways.

An important factor that greatly influenced the emergence of prokaryotic, and eventually eukaryotic, species is energy. As you learned in Unit II, living cells require energy to survive and reproduce. Organisms may follow two different strategies to obtain energy. Some are **heterotrophs**, which means that their energy is derived from eating other organisms or materials from other organisms. In this case, the energy of chemical bonds within the biological molecules of the food provides a source of energy. Alternatively, many organisms are **autotrophs** and have metabolic pathways that directly harness energy from either inorganic molecules or light. Among modern species, plants are an important example of autotrophs. As discussed in Chapter 8, plants can directly absorb light energy and use it (via metabolic pathways) to synthesize organic molecules, such as glucose. On modern Earth, heterotrophs ultimately rely on autotrophs for the production of food.

Even though the first identified fossils are those of organisms that resembled photosynthetic cyanobacteria, scientists have hypothesized that the first living cells were actually heterotrophs. To be an autotroph, a cell must have the metabolic pathways that are needed to directly use energy to make organic molecules. Instead, evolutionary biologists have speculated that it would have been simpler for the first ancestral cells to use the organic molecules in the prebiotic soup as a source of food. However, because these organic molecules were made by prebiotic processes that were very slow, the proliferation of heterotrophs is postulated to have gradually exhausted this supply of available organic matter. As the organic supply dwindled, cells that evolved the ability to synthesize organic molecules from inorganic sources would have had a growth advantage. For example, cells arose that were capable of photosynthesis. These early photosynthetic cells are proposed to be similar to modern cyanobacteria.

Then why were cyanobacteria preserved in fossils, while their heterotrophic ancestors were not? The most likely answer is related to their manner of growth. Interestingly, certain cyanobacteria promote the formation of a layered structure called a **stromatolite (Figure 20.12)**. The aquatic environment where these cyanobacteria survive is rich in minerals, such as calcium.

(a) Fossil stromatolite

(b) Modern stromatolites

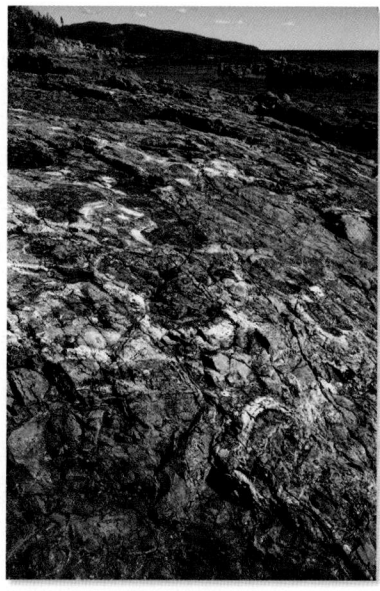

(c) Ancient stromatolites

Figure 20.12   Fossil and modern stromatolites: evidence of autotrophic cyanobacteria.   Each stromatolite is a rocklike structure, typically 1 m in diameter. (a) Section of a fossilized stromatolite. These layers are mats of mineralized cyanobacteria, one layer on top of the other. The existence of fossil stromatolites provides evidence of early autotrophic organisms, which produced organic molecules and oxygen near the beginning of the history of life on Earth. (b) Modern stromatolites that have formed in western Australia. (c) Ancient stromatolites on Lake Superior's north shore, near Schreiber, Ontario.

The cyanobacteria, which grow in large mats, deplete the carbon dioxide in the surrounding water. This causes calcium carbonate to precipitate over the growing mat of bacterial cells, preserving those cells in the lower layers. The bacteria continue to grow upward to produce a new layer. Over time many layers of sediment can be formed.

The emergence and proliferation of ancient cyanobacteria had two critical consequences. First, the autotrophic nature of these bacteria enabled them to produce organic molecules from carbon dioxide. This prevented the depletion of organic foodstuffs that would have been exhausted if only heterotrophs existed. Second, cyanobacteria produce oxygen as a waste product of photosynthesis. During the Archean and Proterozoic eons the activity of cyanobacteria led to the gradual rise in atmospheric oxygen that we discussed earlier. The increase in atmospheric oxygen spelled doom for many prokaryotic groups. Anaerobic species became restricted to a few anoxic (without oxygen) environments, such as deep within the soil. However, oxygen enabled the formation of new **aerobic** (with oxygen) prokaryotic species as well as the emergence and eventual explosion of eukaryotic life forms, which are described next.

GENOMES AND PROTEOMES

The Origin of Eukaryotic Cells During the Proterozoic Eon Involved a Union Between Bacterial and Archaeal Cells

Eukaryotic cells arose during the Proterozoic eon, which began 2.5 billion years ago and ended 543 million years ago (see Figure 20.7). The origin of the first eukaryotic cell is a matter of debate. In modern eukaryotic cells genetic material is found in three distinct organelles. All eukaryotic cells contain DNA in the nucleus and mitochondria, and plant and algal cells also have DNA in their chloroplasts. To address the issue of the origin of eukaryotic species, scientists have paid great attention to the properties of the DNA found in these three organelles and to how that DNA compares with DNA found in modern prokaryotic species. Many eukaryotic and prokaryotic genomes have been completely sequenced, as discussed in greater detail in Chapter 19. These DNA sequences are then compared with each other to determine evolutionary relationships. From such studies the nuclear, mitochondrial, and chloroplast genomes appear to be derived from once-separate cells that came together.

Let's begin with the nuclear genome. From a genome perspective, both bacteria and archaea have contributed substantially to modern eukaryotic genomes. Eukaryotic genes encoding proteins involved in metabolic pathways and lipid biosynthesis appear to be derived from ancient bacteria, while genes involved with transcription and translation are derived from an archaeal ancestor. To account for this observation, several hypotheses have been proposed, the most widely accepted of which involve an association between ancient bacteria and archaea. Such relationships could have been symbiotic or endosymbiotic. A **symbiotic** relationship is one in which two different species live in direct contact with each other. For example, some scientists have postulated an ancient symbiotic relationship in which a bacterium and an archaeon formed a close association. This eventually led to a fusion event that combined the genetic material of the two organisms. Over time selection favoured the retention of bacterial genes involved in metabolism and lipid biosynthesis, and archaeal genes concerned with transcription and translation. A second possible scenario is an **endosymbiotic** relationship, in which one organism lives inside the other. According to this idea, one prokaryotic cell engulfed another, which became an endosymbiont (**Figure 20.13**). For example, an ancient archaeon may have engulfed a bacterium, maintaining the bacterium in its cytoplasm as an endosymbiont. This process may have occurred

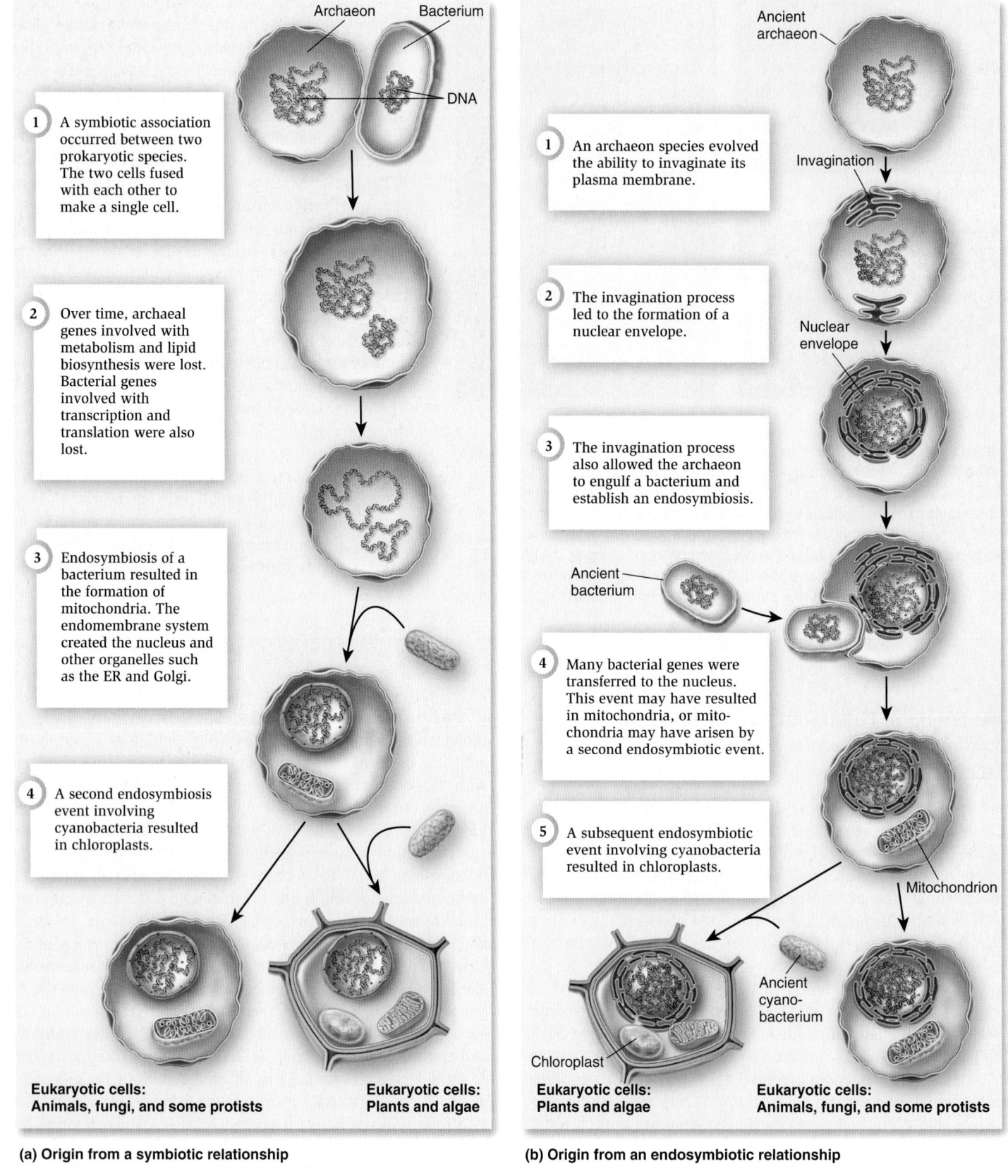

(1) A symbiotic association occurred between two prokaryotic species. The two cells fused with each other to make a single cell.

(2) Over time, archaeal genes involved with metabolism and lipid biosynthesis were lost. Bacterial genes involved with transcription and translation were also lost.

(3) Endosymbiosis of a bacterium resulted in the formation of mitochondria. The endomembrane system created the nucleus and other organelles such as the ER and Golgi.

(4) A second endosymbiosis event involving cyanobacteria resulted in chloroplasts.

Archaeon   Bacterium
DNA

Eukaryotic cells:
Animals, fungi, and some protists

Eukaryotic cells:
Plants and algae

(a) Origin from a symbiotic relationship

(1) An archaeon species evolved the ability to invaginate its plasma membrane.

(2) The invagination process led to the formation of a nuclear envelope.

(3) The invagination process also allowed the archaeon to engulf a bacterium and establish an endosymbiosis.

(4) Many bacterial genes were transferred to the nucleus. This event may have resulted in mitochondria, or mitochondria may have arisen by a second endosymbiotic event.

(5) A subsequent endosymbiotic event involving cyanobacteria resulted in chloroplasts.

Ancient archaeon
Invagination
Nuclear envelope
Ancient bacterium
Mitochondrion
Ancient cyanobacterium
Chloroplast

Eukaryotic cells:
Plants and algae

Eukaryotic cells:
Animals, fungi, and some protists

(b) Origin from an endosymbiotic relationship

Figure 20.13   Possible symbiotic or endosymbiotic relationships that gave rise to the first eukaryotic cells.

BioConnections: *Look back at Figure 4.16. Explain how endocytosis could have played a role in endosymbiosis.*

via endocytosis, which is described in Chapter 6. Over time genes were transferred to the archaeal host cell.

Let's now consider the origin of mitochondrial and chloroplast genomes. In 1905 a Russian botanist named Konstantin Mereschkowsky was the first to suggest that such organelles may have an endosymbiotic origin. However, the question of endosymbiosis was largely ignored until researchers in the 1950s discovered that chloroplasts and mitochondria contain their own genetic material. The issue of endosymbiosis was revived and hotly debated when in 1981 Lynn Margulis published a book presenting evidence in support of this hypothesis entitled *Origin of Eukaryotic Cells*. During the 1970s and 1980s, the advent of molecular genetic techniques allowed researchers to analyze genes from mitochondria, chloroplasts, and prokaryotic species. The data are consistent with the endosymbiotic origin of these organelles.

Mitochondria found in eukaryotic cells are derived from a bacterial species that resembles modern α-proteobacteria, a diverse group of bacteria that can carry out oxidative phosphorylation that is used to make ATP. One possibility is that an endosymbiotic event involving this bacterial species created the first eukaryotic cell, and the mitochondrion is a remnant of that event. Alternatively, symbiosis or endosymbiosis may have produced the first eukaryotic cell, and then a subsequent endosymbiosis resulted in mitochondria (see Figure 20.13). Over the next few years, the sequencing of many prokaryotic and mitochondrial genomes may help to resolve this controversy. DNA sequencing data indicate that chloroplasts were derived from an endosymbiotic relationship between an ancestral eukaryotic cell and a cyanobacterium.

Experimental support for an endosymbiotic origin of eukaryotic cells has also come from the study of proteobacteria. Curiously, an endosymbiotic relationship involving two different proteobacteria was recently reported, which demonstrates the feasibility of an endosymbiotic relationship among prokaryotic species. In mealy bugs, bacteria survive within the cytoplasm of large host cells of a specialized organ called a bacteriome. Recent analyses of these bacteria have shown that the bacteria inside the host cells share their own endosymbiotic relationship. In particular, γ-proteobacteria live inside β-proteobacteria. Such an observation is consistent with the idea that an endosymbiotic relationship could have given rise to the first eukaryotic species more than 2 billion years ago. This is not to say that endosymbiotic relationships do not still exist to this day. For example, dinoflagellates engulf and digest algae and the algal chloroplasts remain both intact and functional. Thus, the dinoflagellate acquires the ability to photosynthesize over a short period.

Multicellular Eukaryotes and the Earliest Animals Arose During the Proterozoic Eon

Multicellular eukaryotes are thought to have first emerged about 1.5 billion years ago, in the middle of the Proterozoic eon, although the oldest fossils are dated at approximately 1.2 billion years old. Simple multicellular organisms could have originated in two different ways. One possibility is that several individual cells found each other and aggregated to form a colony. According to the fossil record, such organisms have remained very simple for hundreds of millions of years. Alternatively, multicellularity can occur in another way: when a single cell divides and the resulting cells stick together. This pattern occurs in many simple multicellular organisms, such as algae and fungi, as well as in species with more complex body plans, such as plants and animals. Biologists cannot be certain whether the first multicellular organisms arose by an aggregation process or by cell division and adhesion. However, the development of complex, multicellular organisms now occurs by cell division and adhesion.

An interesting example that compares unicellular organisms with more complex multicellular organisms is found among species of volvocine green algae that are related evolutionarily. These algae exist as unicellular species, as small clumps of cells of the same cell type, or as larger groups of cells with two distinct cell types. **Figure 20.14** compares four species of volvocine algae. *Chlamydomonas reinhardtii* is a unicellular alga (**Figure 20.14a**). It is called a biflagellate because the cells possess two flagella. *Gonium pectorale* is a multicellular organism composed of 16 cells (**Figure 20.14b**). This simple multicellular organism is formed from a single cell by cell division and adhesion. All the cells in this species are of the same cell type: biflagellate. Other volvocine algae have evolved into larger and more complex organisms. *Pleodorina californica* has 64 to 128 cells (**Figure 20.14c**), while *Volvox aureus* has about 1,000 to 2,000 cells (**Figure 20.14d**). A new feature of these more complex organisms is that they have two cell types—somatic and reproductive cells. The somatic cells are biflagellate cells, while the reproductive cells are not. When comparing *P. californica* and *V. aureus*, *V. aureus* has a higher percentage of somatic cells than does *P. californica*.

Overall, an analysis of these four species of algae illustrates three important principles that are found among complex multicellular species. First, such organisms arise from a single cell that divides to produce daughter cells that adhere to one another. Second, the daughter cells can follow different fates, thereby producing multicellular organisms with different cell types. Third, as organisms get larger, more cells tend to be somatic cells. The somatic cells carry out the activities that are required for the survival of the multicellular organism. The reproductive cells are specialized for the sole purpose of producing offspring.

Toward the end of the Proterozoic eon, multicellular animals emerged. The first animals were **invertebrates**, soft-bodied animals without backbones. The fossil beds of the Burgess Shale deposits show extinct animals exhibiting several different forms

(a) *Chlamydomonas reinhardtii*, a unicellular alga

3 μm

(b) *Gonium pectorale*, composed of sixteen identical cells

10 μm

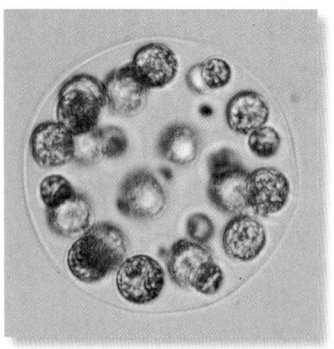

(c) *Pleodorina californica*, composed of 64 to 128 cells, has two cell types, somatic and reproductive

30 μm

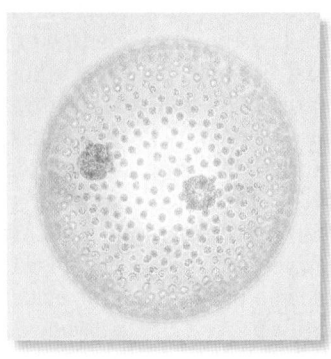

(d) *Volvox aureus*, composed of about 1,000 to 2,000 cells, has two cell types, somatic and reproductive

100 μm

Figure 20.14   Variation in the level of multicellularity among volvocine algae.

Principle: *Living organisms interact with their environment. The formation of different cell types is an emergent property of multicellularity.*

of symmetry, including bilateral symmetry, tripartite symmetry, and radial symmetry. In 2004 Jun-Yuan Chen, David Bottjer, and their colleagues discovered the earliest known ancestor of animals with bilateral symmetry. It was a minute creature shaped like a flattened helmet and barely visible to the unaided eye (**Figure 20.15**). This fossil was found in south China and is approximately 580 million to 600 million years old. Among modern animals, only radially symmetrical and bilaterally

symmetrical organisms are found (see Figure 30.2). Other body forms apparently went extinct after the Cambrian.

The term *Paleozoic* means "ancient animal life." The Paleozoic era covers the time from 543 million years ago (mya) to 248 mya and is subdivided into six periods: the Cambrian, Ordovician, Silurian, Devonian, Carboniferous, and Permian. Periods are usually named after regions where rocks and fossils of that age were first discovered.

Phanerozoic Eon: The Paleozoic Era Saw the Diversification of Invertebrates and the Colonization of Land by Plants and Animals

The proliferation of multicellular eukaryotic life has been extensive during the Phanerozoic eon, which started 543 mya and extends to the present day. Phanerozoic means "well-displayed life," referring to the abundance of fossils of plants and animals that have been identified from this eon. As described earlier in Figure 20.7, the Phanerozoic eon is subdivided into three eras, the Paleozoic, Mesozoic, and Cenozoic. Because they are relatively recent and we have many fossils from these eras, each of them is further subdivided into periods. We will consider separately each era with its associated conditions and prevalent forms of life.

Cambrian Period (543 mya to 490 mya)   The Cambrian climate was generally warm and wet, with no evidence of ice at the poles. During the Cambrian period, an event called the **Cambrian explosion** occurred in which there was an abrupt increase (on a geological scale) in the diversity of animal species. Many fossils telling the story of the Cambrian explosion were found in a rock bed in the Canadian Rockies in Alberta

Figure 20.15   Fossil of an early invertebrate animal showing bilateral symmetry.   This fossil of an early animal, *Vernanimalcula guizouena,* is dated from 580 million to 600 million years ago.

Concept check: *Name three other species that exhibit bilateral symmetry.*

(a) The Burgess Shale

**(b) A fossilized arthropod,
Marrella**

Figure 20.16 The Cambrian explosion and the Burgess Shale. **(a)** This photograph shows the original site in the Canadian Rockies discovered by Charles Walcott. **(b)** A fossil of an extinct arthropod, Marrella, that was collected at this site.

Principle: *Structure determines function. Based on their structure, what might the appendages of* Marrella *been used for? Note that the head shield bears two pairs of large spines and the body has numerous filamentous appendages along its length.*

and British Columbia, called the Burgess Shale, which was discovered by Charles Walcott in 1909. At this site both soft and hard-bodied (shelled) invertebrates were buried in an underwater mudslide and preserved in water that was so deep and oxygen-free that decomposition was minimal (**Figure 20.16a**). The excellent preservation of these softer tissues is what makes this deposit unique (**Figure 20.16b**).

In the middle of the Cambrian period all the existing major types of marine invertebrates arose, plus many others that no longer exist. The Cambrian explosion generated more than 100 major animal groups with significantly different body plans, but only about 30 of these occur in modern species. Examples of those that still exist include echinoderms (sea urchins and starfish), arthropods (insects, spiders, crustaceans), molluscs (clams and snails), and **chordates** (organisms with a spinal cord). Interestingly, although many new species of animals have arisen since this time, these later species have not shown a major reorganization of body plan, but instead exhibit variations on themes that were established during the Cambrian explosion. Approximately 520 million years ago, the first **vertebrates** (animals with backbones) appeared.

The cause of the Cambrian explosion is not understood. Because it occurred shortly after marine animals evolved shells, some scientists have speculated that the changes observed in animal species may have allowed them to exploit new environments and thereby evolve adaptations that would be beneficial in those environments. Alternatively, others have suggested that the increase in diversity may be related to atmospheric oxygen levels. During this period, oxygen levels were increasing, and perhaps more complex body plans became possible only after the atmospheric oxygen surpassed a certain threshold. In addition as atmospheric oxygen reached its present levels, an ozone (O_3) layer was created that screens out ultraviolet radiation, thereby allowing complex life to live in shallow water and eventually on land.

Ordovician Period (490 mya to 443 mya) Like the Cambrian period, the climate of the early and middle parts of the Ordovician period was warm, and the atmosphere was very moist. This period had a diverse group of marine invertebrates, including trilobites and brachiopods (**Figure 20.17**). Marine communities consisted of invertebrates, algae, ancestral jawless

(a) Trilobite

(b) Brachiopod

Figure 20.17 Shelled invertebrate fossils of the Ordovician period.

fish (a type of early vertebrate), molluscs, and corals. Fossil evidence also suggests that ancestral land plants and arthropods may have first invaded the land during this period.

Toward the end of the Ordovician period, the climate changed rather dramatically. Large glaciers formed, which drained the relatively shallow oceans, causing the water levels to drop. This resulted in a mass extinction—estimates suggest that more than 60% of the existing marine invertebrates became extinct during this period.

Silurian Period (443 mya to 417 mya)

In contrast to the dramatic climate changes observed during the Ordovician period, the climate during the Silurian was relatively stable. The glaciers largely melted, which caused the ocean levels to rise.

No new major types of invertebrate animals appeared during this period, but significant changes were observed in existing vertebrate and plant species. Many new types of fish appear in the fossil record. In addition, the coral reefs made their first appearance during this period.

The Silurian marked a large colonization by terrestrial plants and animals. For this to occur, organisms evolved adaptations that prevented them from drying out, such as external cuticles. Ancestral relatives of spiders and centipedes became prevalent. Also, the earliest fossils of **vascular plants**, which can transport water, sugar, and salts throughout the plant body, began in this period.

Devonian Period (417 mya to 354 mya)

In the Devonian, generally dry conditions occurred across much of the northern land masses. However, the southern hemisphere was mostly covered by cool, temperate oceans.

The Devonian saw a major increase in the number of terrestrial species. At first the vegetation consisted primarily of small plants, only a metre tall or less. Later, ferns, horsetails, and **seed plants**, such as gymnosperms, also emerged. By the end of the Devonian the first trees and forests were formed. A major expansion of terrestrial animals also occurred. Insects emerged and other invertebrates became plentiful. In addition **tetrapods**, which are vertebrates with four legs, came into existence. These first tetrapods were amphibians, living on land but requiring water to reproduce because of their jelly-coated eggs.

In the oceans many types of invertebrates flourished, including brachiopods, echinoderms, and corals. This period is sometimes called the Age of Fishes, as many new types of fish emerged to share the oceans with older lineages of fish. During a period of approximately 20 million years near the end of the Devonian period, a prolonged series of extinctions eliminated many marine species. The cause of this mass extinction is not well understood.

Carboniferous Period (354 mya to 290 mya)

The term *Carboniferous* refers to the rich coal deposits that were the result of the vegetation and climate of this period. The Carboniferous had the ideal conditions for the beginnings of coal. It was a cooler period and much of the land was covered by forest swamps. Coal was formed over many millions of years from compressed layers of rotting vegetation.

Plants and animals further diversified during the Carboniferous period. Very large treelike plants (e.g., lycopods; see ahead to Figure 28.9) became prevalent. At Joggins Fossil Cliffs in Nova Scotia, fossil remains of the first reptiles from the Carboniferous have been found (**Figure 20.18**). The first flying insects emerged. For example, giant dragonflies with a wingspan of just less than a metre inhabited the forest swamps. Terrestrial vertebrates also became more diverse. Amphibians were very prevalent. One innovation that seemed particularly

(a)

(b)

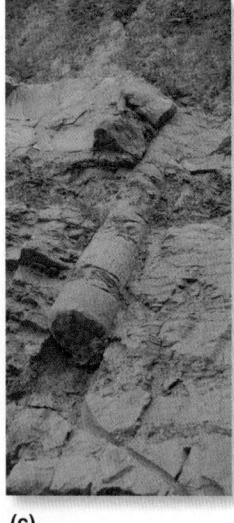
(c)

Figure 20.18 Fossil from the Carboniferous period. (a) The Joggins Fossil Cliffs, Nova Scotia, was designated as a UNESCO World Heritage site in 2008 because of the wealth of fossils from the Carboniferous period, including (b) the earliest known reptiles (*Hylonomus lyelli*) preserved within (c) the intact trunks of ancient lycopod trees.

beneficial was the amniotic egg, which is covered with a leathery or hard shell. This prevented the desiccation of the embryo inside. This innovation was probably critical for the emergence of reptiles, which occurred during this period.

Permian Period (290 mya to 248 mya) At the beginning of the Permian, continental drift had brought much of the total land together, fused into a supercontinent known as Pangaea (see Figure 20.9). The interior regions of Pangaea were probably dry, with great seasonal fluctuations. The forests of fernlike plants shifted to gymnosperms. Species resembling modern conifers first appeared in the fossil record. During this period amphibians were prevalent, but reptiles became the dominant vertebrate species. The first mammal-like reptiles also appeared.

At the end of the Permian period the largest known mass extinction in the history of Earth occurred. As a result of this event, 90%–95% of marine species were eliminated. Similarly, a large proportion of terrestrial species became extinct. The cause of this extinction is the subject of much research and controversy. One possibility is that glaciation destroyed the habitats of terrestrial species and lowered ocean levels, which would have created greater competition among marine species. Another hypothesis is that enormous volcanic eruptions in Siberia produced large ash clouds that abruptly changed the climate on Earth.

Phanerozoic Eon: The Mesozoic Era Saw the Rise and Fall of the Dinosaurs

The Permian extinction marks the division between the Paleozoic and Mesozoic eras. *Mesozoic* means "middle animals." It was a period that saw great changes in animal and plant species. This era is sometimes called the Age of Dinosaurs, as dinosaurs flourished during this time. The climate during the Mesozoic era was consistently hot, and terrestrial environments were relatively dry. Little, if any, ice was found at either pole. The Mesozoic is divided into three periods: the Triassic, Jurassic, and Cretaceous, which we will consider separately.

Triassic Period (248 mya to 206 mya) Reptiles were plentiful in this period, including new groups, such as crocodiles and turtles. Some mammal-like reptiles continued to survive from the Permian period. The first dinosaurs emerged during the middle of the Triassic, as did the first true **mammals**, such as the small *Megazostrodon* (**Figure 20.19**). Gymnosperms were the dominant land plant. Volcanic eruptions near the end of the Triassic are thought to have led to global warming, resulting in mass extinctions that eliminated many marine and terrestrial species.

Jurassic Period (206 mya to 144 mya) Gymnosperms, such as conifers, continued to be the dominant vegetation in this period. Dinosaurs became the dominant land vertebrate. Some dinosaurs attained enormous sizes, such as the massive

Figure 20.19 *Megazostrodon,* the first known mammal of the Triassic period. The illustration is based on fossilized skeletons. *Megazostrodon* was 10 to 12 cm long.

BioConnections: *Look ahead to Table 32.1. What are the common characteristics of mammals?*

Brachiosaurus that reached a length of 25 m and weighed up to 100 metric tons! Bird-like animals (e.g., *Archaeopteryx*, as seen in **Figure 20.20**), emerged in the Jurassic period, and mammals continued to exist, although they were not prevalent.

Cretaceous Period (144 mya to 65 mya) On land, dinosaurs continued to be the dominant animals in this period. The earliest **flowering plants**, called angiosperms, which form seeds within a protective chamber, emerged and began to diversify.

The end of the Cretaceous also witnessed another mass extinction, which brought an end to many previously successful groups of organisms, such as dinosaurs. The dinosaurs and many other species abruptly died out. As with the

Figure 20.20 A fossil of a bird-like vertebrate, *Archaeopteryx,* which emerged in the Jurassic period. *Archaeopteryx* has a combination of both bird and reptile features.

Permian extinction the cause of this mass extinction is also still debated. One plausible hypothesis suggests that a large meteorite or asteroid hit the Yucatán Peninsula of Mexico, lifting massive amounts of debris into the air and thereby blocking the sunlight from reaching Earth's surface. Such a dense haze could have cooled Earth's surface by 11°C–15°C. Evidence is also relatively strong that volcanic eruptions were the primary culprit for this mass extinction. Currently, both the volcanic and the meteorite impact scenarios are reasonable hypotheses to explain the Cretaceous mass extinction, and both may have been contributing factors.

Phanerozoic Eon: Mammals and Flowering Plants Diversified During the Cenozoic Era

The Cenozoic era spans the most recent 65 million years. The Cenozoic is divided into two periods: the Tertiary and Quaternary. In many parts of the world, tropical conditions were replaced by a colder, drier climate. The Cenozoic is sometimes called the Age of Mammals, because during this time mammals became the largest terrestrial animals. However, this phrase is perhaps misleading, because the Cenozoic era has also seen an amazing diversification of many types of organisms, including birds, fish, insects, and flowering plants.

Tertiary Period (65 mya to 1.8 mya)   On land the mammals that had survived from the Cretaceous period began to diversify rapidly. The diversification of mammals occurred during the early part of the Tertiary period. Whales emerged during this period. Likewise, birds and terrestrial insects also diversified. Angiosperms became the dominant land plant, and insects became important for their pollination. In the seas, fish also diversified, and sharks became abundant.

Toward the end of Tertiary period, about 7 million years ago, hominids came into existence. The evolution of **hominids** (which include modern humans, chimpanzees, gorillas, and orangutans, plus all their recent ancestors) is presented in Chapter 32.

Quaternary Period (1.8 mya to Present)   Periodic Ice Ages have occurred during the past 1.8 million years, covering much of Europe and North America. This period has witnessed the widespread extinction of many species of mammals, particularly larger species.

Summary of Key Concepts

- Life began on Earth from nonliving material between 3.5 billion and 4.0 billion years ago. (Figure 20.1)

20.1 Origin of Life on Earth

- The first stage in the formation of life involved the synthesis of organic molecules to form a prebiotic soup. Possible scenarios of how this occurred are the reducing atmosphere, extraterrestrial, and deep-sea vent hypotheses. (Figures 20.2, 20.3)

- The second stage was the bonding of organic molecules to form polymers. This is thought to have occurred on the surface of clay.

- The third stage in the evolution of the first living cells occurred when polymers became enclosed in a structure that separated them from the external environment. Such structures, called protobionts, may have initially been coacervates, microspheres, or liposomes. (Figure 20.4)

- The fourth and final stage that led to the first living cells was chemical selection in which molecules with useful functional properties, such as self-replication and other enzymatic functions, increased in number. (Figure 20.5)

- The precursors of living cells, as well as the first living cells themselves, are thought to have used RNA for information storage and for carrying out enzymatic functions. This earliest phase of life is termed *the RNA world*.

- Bartel and Szostak demonstrated that chemical selection for RNA molecules that can catalyze phosphoester bond formation is possible experimentally. (Figure 20.6)

- The RNA world was later superseded by a DNA/RNA/protein world.

20.2 History of Life on Earth

- The geological timescale, which is divided into four eons and many eras and periods, charts the major events that occurred during the history of life. (Figure 20.7)

- The formation and extinction of new species, as well as mass extinctions, are often correlated with changes in temperature, atmosphere, and land mass locations, as well as floods, glaciation, volcanic eruptions, and meteorite impacts. (Figures 20.8, 20.9)

- Fossils, which are preserved remnants of past life forms, are formed in sedimentary rock. Radioisotope dating is one way to estimate the age of a fossil. The fossil record is incomplete and has several biases. (Figures 20.10, 20.11)

- During the Archean eon the two domains of prokaryotes, Bacteria and Archaea, arose. The first prokaryotes were anaerobic heterotrophs. Later organisms, such as cyanobacteria, became phototrophs and produced oxygen. Cyanobacteria become preserved in structures called stromatolites. (Figure 20.12)

- Eukaryotic cells arose during the Proterozoic eon. This origin involved a union between bacterial and archaeal cells. The origin of mitochondria and chloroplasts was an endosymbiotic relationship. (Figure 20.13)

- Multicellular eukaryotes evolved during the Proterozoic eon and first emerged about 1.5 billion years ago. Multicellularity now occurs via cell division and the adherence of the resulting cells to each other. A multicellular organism can produce multiple cell types. (Figure 20.14)

- The first bilateral animal emerged toward the end of the Proterozoic eon, approximately 580 million to 600 million years ago. (Figure 20.15)

- The Phanerozoic eon is subdivided into the Paleozoic, Mesozoic, and Cenozoic eras. During the Paleozoic era invertebrates greatly diversified, particularly during the Cambrian explosion, and the land became colonized by plants. Terrestrial vertebrates, including tetrapods, also became more diverse. (Figures 20.16, 20.17, 20.18)

- Dinosaurs were prevalent during the Mesozoic era, particularly during the Jurassic period. Mammals and birds also emerged. (Figures 20.19, 20.20)

- During the Cenozoic era, mammals diversified and flowering plants became the dominant species. The first hominids emerged approximately 7 million years ago.

Test to Assess Your Learning

1. The prebiotic soup was
   a. the assemblage of unicellular prokaryotes and eukaryotes that existed in the oceans of ancestral Earth.
   b. the accumulation of organic molecules in the oceans of ancestral Earth.
   c. the mixture of organic molecules that was found in the cytoplasm of the earliest cells on Earth.
   d. a pool of nucleic acids that contained the genetic information for the earliest organisms.
   e. none of the above.

2. Which of the following is not a characteristic of protobionts that was necessary for the evolution of living cells?
   a. a membrane-like boundary separating the external environment from an internal environment
   b. polymers capable of functioning in information storage
   c. polymers capable of enzymatic activity
   d. self-replication
   e. compartmentalization of metabolic activity

3. What are layered structures of calcium carbonate formed by cyanobacteria growing in large mats called?
   a. stromatolites
   b. anaerobicae
   c. bacterial columns
   d. trilobites
   e. brachiopods

4. The movement of land masses that have changed their positions, shapes, and association with other land masses is called
   a. glaciation.
   b. Pangaea.
   c. continental drift.
   d. biogeography.
   e. geological scale.

5. Paleontologists estimate the dates of fossils by
   a. the layer of rock in which the fossils are found.
   b. analysis of radioactive isotopes found in nearby rock.
   c. the complexity of the body plan of the organism.
   d. all of the above.
   e. (a) and (b) only.

6. The fossil record does not give us a complete picture of the history of life because
   a. not all past organisms have become fossilized.
   b. only organisms with hard skeletons can become fossilized.
   c. fossils of very small organisms have not been found.
   d. fossils of early organisms are located too deep in the crust of Earth to be found.
   e. all of the above.

7. The endosymbiosis hypothesis explaining the evolution of eukaryotic cells is supported by
   a. DNA-sequencing analysis comparing bacterial genomes, mitochondrial genomes, and eukaryotic nuclear genomes.
   b. naturally occurring examples of endosymbiotic relationships between bacterial cells and eukaryotic cells.
   c. the presence of DNA in mitochondria and chloroplasts.
   d. all of the above.
   e. (a) and (b) only.

8. Which of the following explanations of the evolution of multicellularity in eukaryotes is seen in the development of complex, multicellular organisms today?
   a. endosymbiosis
   b. aggregation of cells to form a colony
   c. division of cells with the resulting cells sticking together
   d. multiple cell types aggregating to form a complex organism
   e. none of the above

9. What major climate change occurred at the end of the Ordovician period, leading to a mass extinction?
   a. widespread global warming
   b. flooding across many low-lying land masses
   c. glaciers formed, dropping the ocean level
   d. extensive volcanic eruptions spread dust into the atmosphere
   e. (a) and (b) are both correct

10. Which radioisotope would you use to date human remains from early civilizations?
   a. carbon-14
   b. nitrogen-14
   c. potassium-40
   d. rubidium-87
   e. uranium-235

Articulate to Assess Your Learning

1. What changes in Earth's atmosphere facilitated the evolutionary adaptive radiation of animals?
2. How could recent human-caused effects on the atmosphere alter the range and diversity of species on Earth?
3. Why is radioisotope analysis a useful tool? Why not just look at the stratification of fossil samples?
4. What are protobionts and how would they have been suited for the transition to becoming living cells?
5. What forces could have driven the extreme diversity of life forms observed during the Cambrian explosion?

Collaborate to Assess and Extend Your Learning

1. What genetic evidence suggests that endosymbiosis occurred?
2. Discuss processes involved in mass extinctions.
3. What evidence exists for the emergence of life between 4 billion and 3.5 billion years ago? How strong is that evidence?
4. Discuss how multicellular life forms differ from unicellular forms that evolved earlier.
5. Two principles of biology are that (1) living organisms interact with their environment, and (2) populations of organisms evolve from one generation to the next. Describe two examples in which changes in the global climate had an impact on the evolution of species.

Visit McGraw-Hill Ryerson Connect™ for additional study resources.

An Introduction to Evolution

Chapter Outline

Organic life beneath the shoreless waves
Was born and nurs'd in Ocean's pearly caves
First forms minute, unseen by spheric glass,
Move on the mud, or pierce the watery mass;
These, as successive generations bloom,
New powers acquire, and larger limbs assume;
Whence countless groups of vegetation spring,
And breathing realms of fin, and feet, and wing.

From *The Temple of Nature* by Erasmus Darwin (1731–1802), grandfather of Charles Darwin. Published posthumously in 1803.

Teosinte   Modern Corn

Selective breeding. Thousands of years of selective breeding have produced vastly more productive corn.

T he word *evolution* is often associated with a process that involves change. **Biological evolution** is a heritable change in one or more characteristics of a population or species across many generations. Evolution can be viewed on a small scale (**microevolution**) as it relates to changes in one or a few genes in a population over time, or it can be viewed on a larger scale (**macroevolution**) as it relates to the formation of new species or groups of related species. It might be helpful to begin the discussion of evolution with a definition of a species; unfortunately, as we will examine in Chapter 23, giving a precise definition of species is not always possible. As a working definition, biologists define **species** as a group of related organisms that share a distinctive form. Among species that reproduce sexually, such as plants and animals, members of the same species are capable of interbreeding to produce viable and fertile offspring. The term **population** refers to members of the same species that are likely to encounter one another and so have the opportunity to interbreed. Some of the emphasis in the study of evolution is on understanding how populations change over many generations to produce new species.

In the first part of this chapter we will examine the history of evolutionary thought and some of the basic tenets of evolution, particularly those that were proposed by Charles Darwin in the mid-nineteenth century. Although evolutionary thought has been refined over the past 150 years or so, the fundamental principle of evolution has remained unchanged, and it has provided a cornerstone for our understanding of biology. Theodosius Dobzhansky, an influential evolutionary biologist of the early twentieth century, once said, "Nothing in biology makes sense except in the light of evolution." The extraordinarily diverse and seemingly bizarre array of species on our planet can be explained within the context of evolution. The fact that species evolve over time is supported by a substantial body of evidence and a wide range of observations. In fact, evolution provides answers to many questions related to the diversity of life.

In the second part of this chapter we will survey the extensive data that show the results of evolution. These data not only support the existence of evolutionary change over time but also allow us to understand the interrelatedness of different species, whose similarities are often related to descent from a common ancestor. Much of the early evidence supporting evolution came from visual observations and comparisons of modern and extinct species.

More recently, advances in molecular genetics, particularly those related to DNA sequencing and genomics, have revolutionized the study of evolution. Scientists now have information that allows them to understand how evolution involves changes in the DNA of a given species. These changes affect both a species' genes and the proteins they encode. The term **molecular evolution** refers to the molecular changes in genetic material that underlie the phenotypic changes associated with evolution. A theme of this textbook, namely, genomes and proteomes, is rooted in an understanding of these changes. In the last section of this chapter we consider some of the exciting new information that helps us to appreciate evolutionary change at the molecular level. In the other chapters of this unit we will examine how such changes are acted on by evolutionary forces in ways that alter the traits of a species and may eventually lead to the formation of new species.

21.1 HISTORICAL VIEWS ON EVOLUTIONARY CHANGE

Learning Outcomes:

1. Define biological evolution.
2. Describe the factors that led Darwin to his theory of evolution by natural selection.
3. Explain the process of natural selection.

In the mid- to late seventeenth century an early classification system for plants and animals based on overall morphology was developed by an Englishman named John Ray. He established the modern concept of a species, noting that organisms of one species do not interbreed with members of another, and he used the species as the basic unit of his classification system. Ray then used his classification system to address questions in physiology, function, and behaviour, documenting the ways living things are adapted to their environments. For him, this was evidence of God's design and not evidence of evolutionary change. After extensive study, however, Ray came to believe that fossils were once living organisms, contrary to what other thinkers of the day believed.

Ray's ideas on classification were later extended by Swedish naturalist Carolus Linnaeus, who placed special emphasis on reproductive structures to group organisms. Linnaeus is often called the father of taxonomy. Although the term **genus** (plural: genera) was already in use to group similar organisms, it was Linnaeus who grouped genera into orders, orders into classes, and classes into kingdoms. (Other taxonomic ranks were added later.) The systematic classification of plants and animals helped scholars of this period perceive the similarities and differences among living organisms. Neither Ray nor Linnaeus believed that evolutionary change promotes the formation of new species; however, in his later years, Linnaeus accepted that sometimes hybridization could produce a new species of plant (or rarely, animal).

French zoologist and vertebrate paleontologist Baron Georges Cuvier argued against evolutionary change because he viewed organisms as integrated wholes. According to Cuvier, a change in any one structure would upset the functional integration of the whole and the organism would fail to survive.

In the late eighteenth century a small number of European scientists began to quietly suggest that life forms are not fixed. French zoologist George Buffon actually said that living things do change through time. However, Buffon was careful to hide his views in a 44-volume natural history book series. Although he was a quiet pioneer in asserting that species can change over generations, he publicly rejected the idea that one species could evolve into another species.

Shortly thereafter a French naturalist named Jean-Baptiste Lamarck (who was a colleague of Cuvier's but had been mentored by Buffon) suggested an intimate relationship between variation and evolution. By examining fossils, he came to realize that some species had remained the same over the millennia and others had changed. Lamarck hypothesized that species change over many generations by adapting to new environments. He believed that living things evolved in a continually upward direction, from dead matter, through simple to more complex forms, toward human "perfection." According to Lamarck, organisms altered their behaviour in response to environmental change. He thought behavioural changes modified traits in such a way that continued use of a structure would cause it to increase in size, whereas continued disuse of a structure would cause it to decrease in size. Furthermore, he hypothesized that such modified traits were inherited by offspring. He called this idea the **inheritance of acquired characteristics**. However, subsequent research has rejected Lamarck's idea that acquired traits can be inherited.

Interestingly, Erasmus Darwin, the grandfather of Charles Darwin, who was a contemporary of Buffon and Lamarck, was an early advocate of evolutionary change. He was a physician, a plant biologist, and a poet. He was aware that modern species were different from many fossil types and also saw how plant and animal breeders used breeding practices to change the traits of domesticated species (see the chapter-opening photo). He knew that offspring inherited features from their parents and suggested that evolutionary change might occur as a result of competition. He went so far as to say that life on Earth could be descended from a common ancestor.

Overall, Charles Darwin's many scientific predecessors set the stage for the theory of evolution by natural selection. With this historical introduction we will now consider Darwin's observations and the tenets that provide the foundation for his theory of evolution by natural selection.

Darwin Suggested That Species Are Derived from Pre-existing Species

Charles Darwin, a British naturalist born in 1809, played a key role in developing the theory that existing species have evolved from pre-existing species. Darwin's unique perspective and his ability to formulate evolutionary theory were shaped by several different fields of study, including ideas of his time about physical and biological processes.

Two main geological hypotheses predominated in the early nineteenth century. Catastrophism was first proposed by anti-evolutionist Baron Georges Cuvier to explain the age of Earth. Cuvier suggested that Earth was just 6,000 years old and that only catastrophic events had changed its geological structure. This idea fit well with religious teachings. Alternatively, uniformitarianism, proposed by James Hutton and promoted by Sir Charles Lyell, suggested that changes in Earth are directly caused by recurring events. For example, they suggested that geological processes, such as erosion, had existed in the past and that they had happened then at the same gradual rate as they do now. For such slow geological processes to eventually lead to substantial changes in the Earth's characteristics, a great deal of time was required, and so Hutton and Lyell were the first to propose that the age of Earth was well beyond 6,000 years. The ideas of Hutton and Lyell helped to shape Darwin's view of the world.

Darwin's thinking was also influenced by a publication in 1798 called *Essay on the Principle of Population* by Thomas Malthus, an English economist. Malthus asserted that the population size of humans can, at best, increase linearly because of increased land usage and improvements in agriculture, while our reproductive potential is exponential (for example, doubling with each generation). He argued that famine, war, and disease will limit population growth, especially among the poor. An important message from Malthus's work was that only a fraction of any population will survive and reproduce.

Darwin's evolutionary ideas were most influenced by his own experiences and observations. His famous voyage on the *Beagle,* which lasted from 1831 to 1836 (**Figure 21.1**), involved a careful examination of many different species. The main mission of the *Beagle* was to map the coastline of southern South America and take oceanographic measurements. Darwin's job was to record the weather, geological features, plants, animals, fossils, rocks, minerals, and indigenous people. He also collected many specimens of plants and animals, which had to be carefully packed and labelled.

After his expedition Darwin attended the Hunterian lectures given by Sir Richard Owen, a well-known comparative anatomist in Victorian England. One of Owen's lasting contributions was to give us many of the anatomical terms still used today in evolutionary biology, including the concept of homologous structures (look ahead to the definition of homology in Table 21.1).

Though Darwin made many interesting observations on his journey, he was particularly struck by the distinctive traits of island species that provided them with ways to better exploit their native environment. For example, Darwin observed several species of finches found on the Galápagos Islands. We now know that these finches all evolved from a single species similar to the dull-coloured grassquit finch (*Tiaris obscura*), commonly found along the Pacific Coast of South America. Once on the Galápagos Islands, the finches' ability to survive in their new habitat depended, in part, on changes in the size and shape of their bills over many generations. These specializations enabled succeeding generations to better obtain food. For example, the ground and vegetarian finches have sturdy, crushing bills that they use to crush various sizes of seeds or buds. The tree finches have grasping bills that they use to pick insects from trees. The mangrove, woodpecker, warbler, and cactus finches have pointed, probing bills. The first three of these use their probing bills to search for insects in crevices; the cactus finches use their probing bills to open cactus fruits and eat the seeds. One species, the woodpecker finch, even uses twigs or cactus spines to extract insect larvae from holes in dead tree branches. Darwin clearly saw the similarities among these species, yet he noted the differences that provided them with specialized feeding strategies.

With an understanding of geology and population growth, and his observations from his voyage on the *Beagle,* Darwin had formulated his theory of evolution by natural selection by the mid-1840s. He had also catalogued and described all the species he had collected on his *Beagle* voyage, except for one type of barnacle. Some have speculated that Darwin may have felt that he should establish himself as an expert on one species before making generalizations about all of them. Therefore, he spent several additional years studying barnacles. During this time, geologist Charles Lyell, who had greatly influenced Darwin's thinking, strongly encouraged Darwin to publish his theory of

Figure 21.1 **Charles Darwin and the voyage of the *Beagle*, 1831–1836.** (a) A portrait of Charles Darwin (1809–1882) while in Ecuador. (b) Darwin's voyage on the *Beagle,* which took almost five years to circumnavigate the world.

(a) Charles Darwin

(b) The voyage of the *Beagle*

evolution by natural selection. In 1856 Darwin began to write a long book to explain his ideas. In 1858, however, Alfred Wallace, a naturalist working in the East Indies, sent Darwin an unpublished manuscript to read before its publication. In it, Wallace proposed the same ideas concerning evolution. Darwin therefore quickly excerpted some of his own writings on this subject, and two papers, one by Darwin and one by Wallace, were published in the Proceedings of the Linnaean Society of London. These papers were not widely recognized. A short time later, however, Darwin finished his book, *The Origin of Species*, which described his ideas in greater detail and included observational support. This book, which received high praise from many scientists and scorn from others, started a great debate concerning evolution. Although some of his ideas were incomplete because of the fact that the genetic basis of traits was not understood at that time, Darwin's work remains one of the most important contributions to our understanding of biology.

Everyone reading this textbook is fully aware that evolution is fraught with controversy, particularly opposition from faith-based groups. There is little conflict over the findings in other branches of biology, such as cell biology, neurobiology, and molecular biology. Evolution challenges our worldview. Evolution is the biggest idea in biology and probably in all of science. It is a major part of a huge expansion of knowledge about our place in the universe. Two-hundred years ago we didn't know about deep space, that our sun is one of a 100,000 million suns in the galaxy, or that there are 100,000 million galaxies. We didn't know that our planet was 4.5 billion years old. And we didn't know, until Darwin, that we are not a separate creation but a life form that evolved from others. These big ideas, of which evolution is one of the biggest, are controversial because they reduce the status of humans in the universe. We are a product of evolution, and this fact may change the essence of what we think about our existence.

Natural Selection Acting on Genetic Variation Can Change Populations over Generations

The fundamental principle that underlies evolution is that biological species do not have a fixed, static existence but instead exhibit changing characteristics over the course of generations. Darwin hypothesized that existing life forms on our planet are the product of the modification of pre-existing life forms. He expressed this concept of biological evolution as "the theory of descent with modification through variation and natural selection." As its name suggests, evolution is based on two factors: (1) variation within a given species and (2) forces of nature, which are termed natural selection. During the process of **natural selection**, certain individuals are less likely to survive and reproduce in a particular environment, while other individuals with traits that make them better suited to their native environment tend to flourish and reproduce. As Darwin noted from Malthus, there is differential survival of individuals in a population. Thus individuals who are better suited to the current environment are being naturally selected to survive longer. This is not to say that particular traits (alleles) are being selected

for. Individuals survive, not traits. In fact, traits are passed on (from the survivors) to successive generations because they were not selected against. The difference between "selected for" and "failure to be selected against" may seem trivial, but it is very important for several reasons. First, it demonstrates that evolution is not goal directed but is reactive. Second, it allows for variations of traits to stay in a population. Note that a trait is advantageous only under particular environmental conditions (selection pressure). If conditions change over time, what was once an advantageous trait may be become deleterious; and what was once a neutral variant may become advantageous and so forth. Over long periods this process of natural selection eventually leads to **adaptation**, which is a form of evolutionary change in which a population's characteristics change to make its members better suited to their native environment. Note that natural selection affects the survival and reproduction of individuals, which over time affects the evolution of populations and ultimately species. However, evolution by natural selection is not goal oriented.

The genetic basis for variation within a species was not understood at the time Darwin proposed his theory of evolution by natural selection. In fact, Darwin's theory preceded, by a few years, Mendel's pioneering work in genetics. Even so, Darwin and many other people before him observed that offspring resemble their parents more than they do unrelated individuals. Therefore, he assumed that some traits are passed from parent to offspring.

Since Darwin the study of genetics has allowed scientists to understand the relationship between traits and inheritance. Genetic variation is a consistent feature of natural populations. Such variation may involve differences in genes, changes in chromosome structure, and alterations in chromosome number. In contrast to Lamarck's ideas, we now know that these genetic differences are not produced by an individual's behaviour or other response to its environment. Rather, genetic variation is caused by random mutations during gamete formation that alter the genetic composition of individuals. In Chapter 22 we will consider how these random mutations are acted on by evolutionary forces to change the genetic composition of populations over time. In addition you will see that other mechanisms of evolutionary change exist and that natural selection is only one of these.

Based on Darwin's ideas regarding natural selection and a more modern understanding of genetics, biologists in the 1920s to 1940s were able to frame evolutionary theories in a modern perspective termed neo-Darwinism or the **modern synthesis of evolution**. Within a given population of interbreeding organisms, natural variation exists that is caused by random changes in the genetic material. Such genetic changes can affect the phenotype of an individual in a positive, negative, or neutral way depending on the environmental conditions. If a genetic change promotes an individual's survival or ability to successfully reproduce, natural selection can increase the prevalence of that trait in future generations.

For example, let's consider a population of finches that migrates from the South American mainland to a Galápagos island. The seeds produced on this island are larger than those produced on the mainland. Birds with larger beaks would be better able to feed on these seeds and so would be more likely to survive and pass on that trait to their offspring. Therefore, in succeeding generations, the population will tend to have a greater proportion of finches with larger beaks (**Figure 21.2**). Alternatively, if a genetic change happens to be detrimental to an individual's survival or reproduction, natural selection is likely to eliminate this type of variation. For example, if a mutation occurred that causes a finch in the same environment to have a slightly smaller beak, this bird would be less likely to survive and pass on this change to its offspring. Natural selection, which acts on variation involving many different genes, may ultimately produce a new species with a combination of traits that are quite different from those of the original species, such as finches with larger beaks. In other words the newer species has evolved from a pre-existing species. Now let's look at some other examples of change in organisms over time.

21.2 OBSERVATIONS OF EVOLUTIONARY CHANGE

Learning Outcomes:

1. Summarize the different types of evidence for evolutionary change, including the fossil record, biogeography, convergent traits, selective breeding, and homologies.
2. Provide examples of three types of homologies.

Over the past 150 years the research community has learned that no known concept other than descent with modification from a common ancestor can scientifically account for the diversity and unity of life on our planet. Observations regarding biological evolution come from many sources (**Table 21.1**). Historically, the first descriptions of biological evolution came from studies of the fossil record, the distribution of living organisms on the planet, selective breeding experiments, and the comparison of similar anatomical features in different species. More recently, by comparing DNA sequences from many different species, evolutionary biologists have gained great insight into the relationship between the evolution of species and the associated changes in the genetic material. In this section we will survey a variety of observations that show the process of evolutionary change.

Fossils Show Successive Evolutionary Change

As discussed in Chapter 20, the fossil record reveals a history of life from its earliest beginnings some 3.5 billion to 4 billion years ago. Today, scientists have access to a far more extensive fossil record than was available to Darwin or other scientists of his time. Even though the fossil record is still incomplete, the many fossils that have been discovered often provide detailed information regarding evolutionary change in a series of related organisms. When fossils are compared according to their age, from oldest

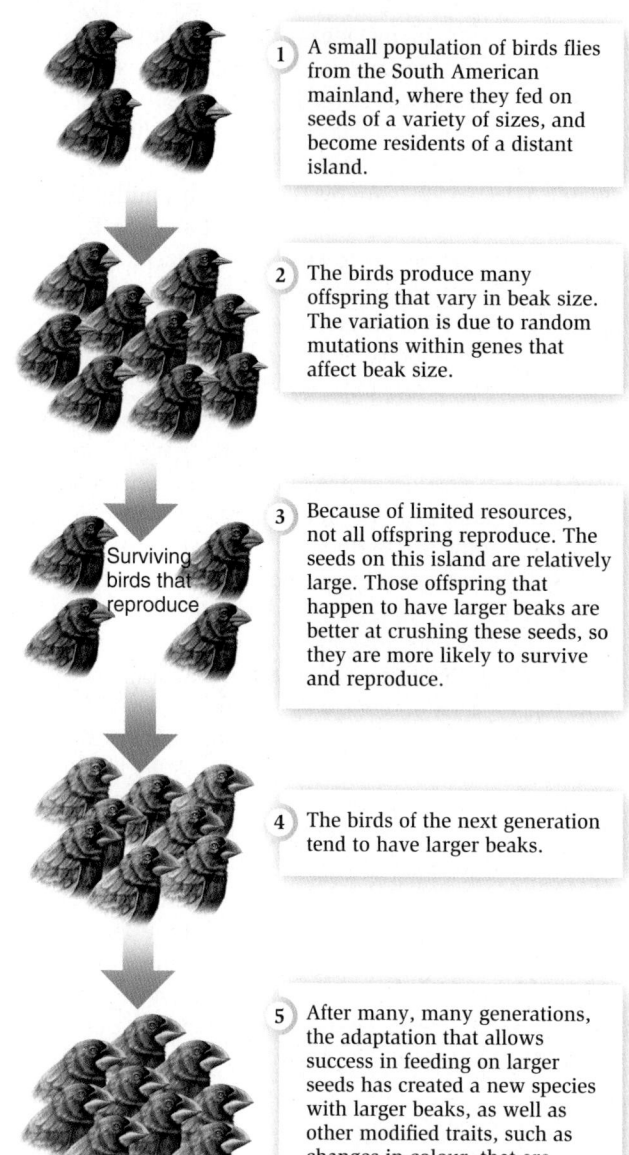

1. A small population of birds flies from the South American mainland, where they fed on seeds of a variety of sizes, and become residents of a distant island.

2. The birds produce many offspring that vary in beak size. The variation is due to random mutations within genes that affect beak size.

3. Because of limited resources, not all offspring reproduce. The seeds on this island are relatively large. Those offspring that happen to have larger beaks are better at crushing these seeds, so they are more likely to survive and reproduce.

Surviving birds that reproduce

4. The birds of the next generation tend to have larger beaks.

5. After many, many generations, the adaptation that allows success in feeding on larger seeds has created a new species with larger beaks, as well as other modified traits, such as changes in colour, that are suited to the new environment.

Figure 21.2 **Evolutionary adaptation to a new environment via natural selection.** The example shown here involves a species of finch adapting to a new environment on one of the Galápagos Islands. The plants on this island produce larger seeds than do the plants on the mainland from which the birds had originated. According to Darwin's theory of evolution by natural selection, the process of adaptation eventually led to the formation of a new species with larger beaks that were better suited to crushing the large seeds in its new environment.

Concept check: *The phrase "an organism evolves" is incorrect. Explain what is wrong with this statement.*

BioConnections: *Look back at Figure 20.5. How is natural selection similar to chemical selection? How are they different?*

Table 21.1   Observations of Biological Evolution

Type of observation	Description
Fossil record	When fossils are compared according to their age, from oldest to youngest, successive evolutionary change becomes apparent.
Biogeography	Unique species found on islands and other remote areas have arisen because the species in these locations have evolved in isolation from the rest of the world.
Convergent evolution	Two different species from different lineages sometimes become anatomically similar because they occupy similar environments. This indicates that natural selection promotes adaptation to a given environment.
Selective breeding	The traits in domesticated species have been profoundly modified by artificial selection practices.
Homologous traits	Homology, a term coined by Sir Richard Owen, refers to fundamental similarities that occur because of descent from a common ancestor.
Anatomical	Evolutionarily related species may possess homologous structures that have been modified in ways that allowed them to be used differently by each species. In some cases, homologous structures are no longer needed and degenerate to nonfunctional vestigial structures in certain species.
Developmental	An analysis of embryonic development often reveals similar anatomical features that point to past evolutionary relationships.
Molecular	At the molecular level, certain characteristics are found in all living cells, suggesting that all living species are derived from a common ancestor. In addition, species that are closely related evolutionarily tend to have DNA sequences that are more similar to each other than they are to those in distantly related organisms.

to youngest, successive evolutionary change becomes apparent. Thus evolution is a cumulative process by which organisms adapt and change over long periods. Many thousands of species have become extinct through evolution.

Let's consider a few examples in which paleontologists have observed evolutionary change. In 2005 fossils of *Tiktaalik roseae*, nicknamed fishapod, were discovered by Edward Daeschler, Neil Shubin, and Farish Jenkins. The fossils illuminate the steps that led to the evolution of tetrapods, which are animals with four legs. *T. roseae* is called a **transitional form** because it provides a link between earlier species and many later species (**Figure 21.3**). In this case the fishapod is a transitional form between fish, which are aquatic animals, and tetrapods, which are usually terrestrial animals. Unlike a true fish, *T. roseae* had a broad skull, a flexible neck, and eyes mounted on the top of its head. Its interlocking rib cage suggests it had lungs. Perhaps the most surprising discovery was that its pectoral fins (those on the side of the body) revealed the beginnings of a primitive wrist and five finger-like bones. These appendages would have been adequate for *T. roseae* to peek its head above the water from shallow river bottoms and look for prey. During the Devonian period, 417 million to 354 million years ago, this could have been an important advantage in the marshy floodplains of large rivers.

As a second example, certain oysters began to undergo a change in shell structure about 200 million years ago. Oysters with smaller, curved shells were superseded by oysters with larger, flatter shells (**Figure 21.4**). This change was observed over 12 million years during the early Jurassic period, when water currents became stronger. Scientists have hypothesized that larger, flatter shells are more stable in disruptive water currents, so these shells were better adapted to the environmental change.

One of the best-studied examples of evolutionary change is our third example, that of the horse family. Modern members include horses, zebras, and donkeys. These species, which are

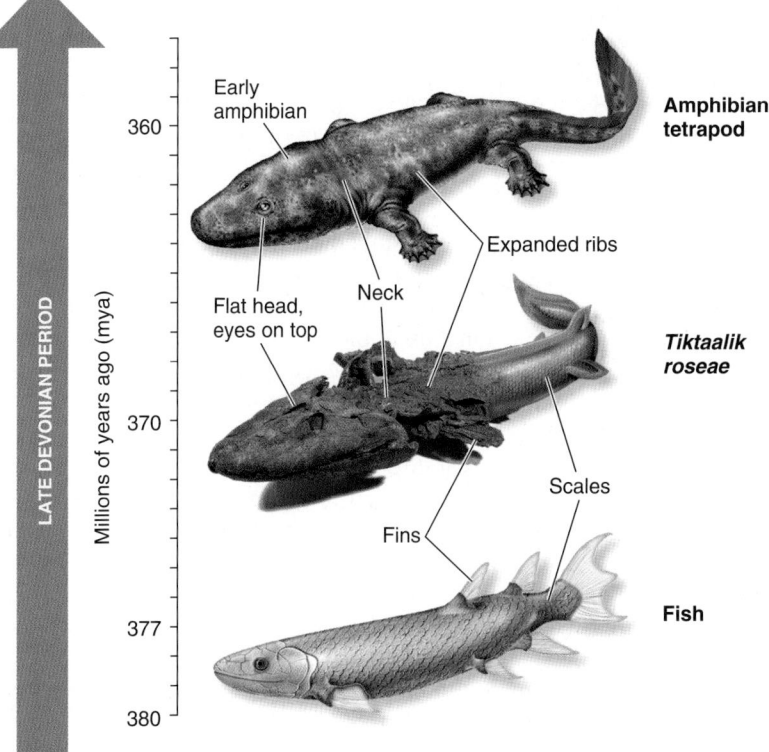

Figure 21.3 Evolutionary change in the tetrapod lineage, showing a transitional form. This figure shows two early tetrapod ancestors: a Devonian fish and the transitional form *Tiktaalik roseae,* as well as one of their descendants, an early amphibian. An analysis of the fossils shows that *T. roseae,* also known as a fishapod, had both fish and amphibian characteristics, so it probably was able to survive brief periods out of the water. The fishapod fossils were found on Ellesmere Island in the Canadian Arctic.

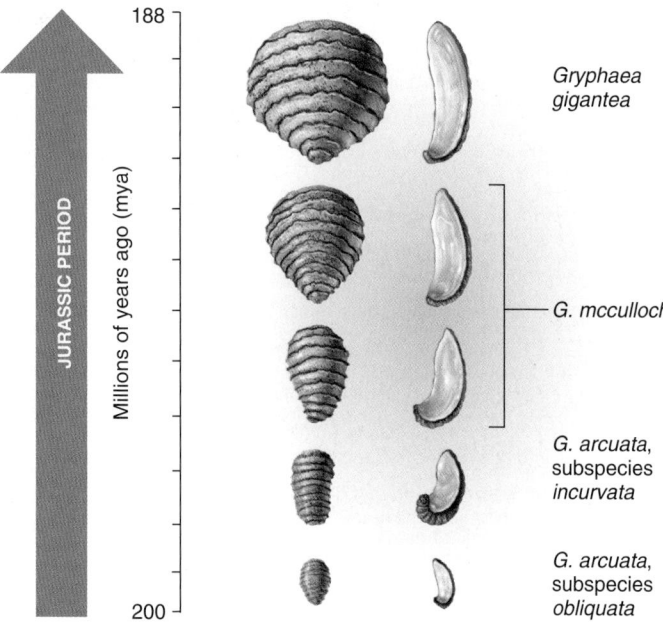

JURASSIC PERIOD

Millions of years ago (mya)

188

200

Gryphaea gigantea

G. mccullochi

G. arcuata, subspecies *incurvata*

G. arcuata, subspecies *obliquata*

Figure 21.4   Evolutionary changes in the shape of oyster shells.   During a 12-million-year period in the early Jurassic, the shells of oysters of the extinct genus *Gryphaea* became larger and flatter. Scientists have hypothesized that such a change was an adaptation to disruptive water currents.

Concept check: *If a population of oysters was transferred to a shallow bay with calm water currents, how might the population change over many generations?*

large, long-legged animals adapted to living in open grasslands, are the remaining descendants of a long lineage that produced many species that are now extinct since its origin approximately 55 million years ago. Examination of the horse lineage provides a particularly interesting case of how evolution involves adaptation to changing environments.

The earliest known fossils of the horse family (termed *Hyracotherium*) revealed that the animals were small with short legs and broad feet (look ahead to Figure 24.10). Such early horses lived in wooded habitats and are thought to have eaten leaves and herbs. Between the time of these first members of the horse family and modern horses, the fossil record has revealed adaptive changes in size, foot anatomy, and tooth morphology. The first horses were the size of dogs (about 20 kg), while modern horses typically weigh about 400 kg. *Hyracotherium* had four toes on its front feet and three on its hind feet. Instead of hooves, these toes were encased in fleshy pads. By comparison the feet of modern horses have a single toe, enclosed in a tough, bony hoof. The fossil record shows an increase in the length of the central toe, the development of a bony hoof, and the loss of the other toes. Finally, the teeth of *Hyracotherium* were relatively small compared with those of modern horses. Over millions of years, horses' teeth have increased in size and developed a complex pattern of ridges on their molars.

These changes in horse characteristics can be attributed to natural selection producing adaptations to changing global climates. Over North America, where much of horse evolution occurred, large areas changed from dense forests to grasslands. Horses' increase in size and changes in their foot structure allowed them to escape predators and travel great distances in search of food. The changes seen in horses' teeth are consistent with a dietary shift from eating more tender leaves to eating grasses and other vegetation that are more abrasive and require more chewing.

Evolutionary processes have not stopped. There is a common misconception that evolution is only the study of what has happened in the past. There are several examples in which evolution in process is being recorded. For example, the North American apple maggot, *Rhagoletis pomonella*, originally laid its eggs on hawthorn on which the developing larvae fed. However, when apples were introduced (ca. 1850) a variant emerged that laid eggs on apples. Now there are two races, one on hawthorns and the other on apples. Thus there is little gene flow between flies that lay eggs on different food sources.

Biogeography Indicates That Species in a Given Area Have Evolved from Pre-existing Species

Biogeography is the study of the geographical distribution of extinct and modern species. Patterns of past evolution are often found in the natural geographical distribution of related species. From such studies scientists have discovered that isolated continents and island groups have evolved their own distinct plant and animal communities. As mentioned earlier in this chapter, Darwin observed several species of finches found on the Galápagos Islands that had unique characteristics, such as beak shapes, when compared with similar finches found on the mainland. As we discussed, scientists now think that these island species evolved from mainland birds that had migrated to the islands and then became adapted to a variety of feeding habits. One example of this was shown in Figure 21.2.

Around the world, islands, which are often isolated from other land masses, provide numerous examples in which geography has played a key role in the evolution of new species. Islands often have many species of plants and animals that are **endemic**, which means they are naturally found only in a particular location. Most endemic island species have closely related relatives on nearby islands or the mainland. For example, consider the island fox (*Urocyon littoralis*), which lives on the Channel Islands located off the coast of southern California between Los Angeles and Santa Barbara (**Figure 21.5**). This type of fox is found nowhere else in the world. It weighs about 1.5 to 3 kg and feeds largely on insects, mice, and fruits. The island fox evolved from the mainland grey fox (*Urocyon cinereoargenteus*), which is much larger, usually 3 to 5 kg. During the last Ice Age, about 16,000 to 18,000 years ago, the Santa Barbara channel was frozen and narrow enough for ancestors of the mainland grey fox to cross over to the Channel Islands. When the Ice Age ended, the ice melted and sea levels rose, cutting the foxes off from the mainland. Over the past 16,000 to 20,000 years, these foxes evolved into the smaller island fox. The smaller size of the

Figure 21.5 The evolution of an endemic island species from a mainland species. (a) The smaller island fox found on the Channel Islands evolved from (b) the grey fox found on the California mainland.

(a) Island fox
   (*Urocyon littoralis*)

(b) Grey fox (*Urocyon cinereoargenteus*)

Concept check: *Explain how geography played a key role in the evolution of the island fox.*

island fox is an example of island dwarfing, the phenomenon in which the size of large animals isolated on an island shrinks dramatically over many generations. It is a form of natural selection in which smaller size provides a survival advantage, probably because of limited food and fewer predators.

The evolution of major animal groups is also correlated with known changes in the distribution of land masses on Earth. The first mammals arose approximately 225 million years ago. The fossils of the first placental mammals, which are those that have long internal gestation and give birth to offspring that are well developed, are only 80 million years old. The first mammals arose when the area that is now Australia was still connected to the other continents. However, the first placental mammals evolved after continental drift had separated Australia from the other continents (refer back to Figure 20.9). Except for a few species of bats and rodents that have migrated to Australia more recently, Australia lacks any of the larger, terrestrial placental mammals. This observation is consistent with the idea that placental mammals first arose somewhere other than Australia and that the barrier of a large ocean prevented most terrestrial placental mammals from migrating there. Instead, Australia has more than 100 species of kangaroos, koalas, and other marsupials. Marsupials are a group of mammal species in which young are born in a very immature condition and then develop further in the mother's abdominal pouch, which covers the mammary glands. Most species of Australian marsupials are not found on other continents. Evolutionary theory is consistent with the idea that the existence of these unique Australian species is due to their having evolved in isolation from the rest of the world for millions of years.

Convergent Evolution Suggests Adaptation to the Environment Occurs

The process of natural selection is also evident in the study of plants and animals that have similar characteristics, even though they are not closely related evolutionarily. This similarity is due to **convergent evolution**, in which two different species from different lineages show similar characteristics because they occupy similar environments. For example, the long snout and tongue of both the giant anteater (*Myrmecophaga*

tridactyla), found in South America, and the echidna (*Tachyglossus aculeatus*), found in Australia, are similar yet independently evolved adaptations that enable these animals to feed on ants (**Figure 21.6a**). The giant anteater is a placental mammal, while the echidna is an egg-laying mammal, so they are not closely related evolutionarily. Another example involves aerial rootlets found in vines, such as English ivy (*Hedera helix*) and wintercreeper (*Euonymus fortunei*) (**Figure 21.6b**). Based on differences in their structures, these aerial rootlets appear to have developed independently as an effective means to cling to the support on which a vine attaches itself.

A third example of convergent evolution is revealed by the molecular analysis of fish that live in very cold water. Antifreeze proteins allow certain species of fish to survive the subfreezing temperatures of Arctic and Antarctic waters by preventing the formation of ice crystals in their blood. By studying these fish, researchers have determined that they are an interesting case of convergent evolution (**Figure 21.6c**). Among different species of fish, one of five different genes has independently evolved to produce antifreeze proteins. For example, in the sea raven (*Hemitripterus americanus*), the antifreeze protein is rich in the amino acid cysteine, and the secondary structure of the protein is in a β sheet conformation. In contrast, the antifreeze protein in the longhorn sculpin (*Trematomus nicolai*) evolved from an entirely different gene. The antifreeze protein in this species is rich in the amino acid glutamine, and the secondary structure of the protein is largely composed of α helices.

The similar characteristics in the examples shown in Figure 21.6, which are the result of convergent evolution, are called **analogous structures** or **convergent traits**. They represent cases in which structures have arisen independently, twice or more, because species have occupied similar types of environments on Earth. By comparison, homologous structures have a single evolutionary origin.

Selective Breeding Is a Human-Driven Form of Natural Selection

The term **selective breeding** refers to programs and procedures designed to modify traits in domesticated species. This practice, also called **artificial selection**, is related to natural

(a) The long snouts and tongues of the giant anteater (left) and the echidna (right) allow them to feed on ants.

 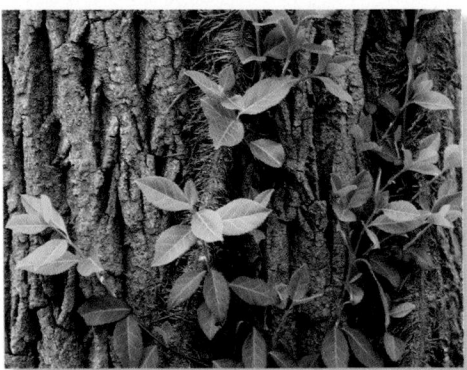

(b) The aerial rootlets of English ivy (left) and wintercreeper (right) allow them to climb up supports.

(c) The sea raven (left) and the longhorn sculpin (right) have antifreeze proteins that enable them to survive in frigid waters.

Figure 21.6 **Examples of convergent evolution.**   For each pair shown in this figure, the organisms are not closely related evolutionarily, but they do occupy similar environments, suggesting that natural selection promotes the formation of similar adaptations that are well suited to a particular environment.

Concept check: *Can you think of another example in which two species that are not closely related have a similar adaptation?*

selection. In forming his theory of natural selection, Charles Darwin was influenced by his observations of selective breeding by pigeon breeders. He was also a pigeon breeder himself. The primary difference between natural and artificial selection

is how the parents are chosen. Natural selection is due to natural variation in reproductive success. Organisms that are able to survive and reproduce are more likely to pass their genes on to future generations. Nature determines or "chooses" which individuals will be successful parents. In artificial selection the breeder chooses as parents those individuals that possess traits desirable to humans.

The underlying phenomenon that makes selective breeding possible is genetic variation. Within a group of individuals of the same species, variation may exist in a trait of interest. For selective breeding to be successful, the underlying cause of the phenotypic variation must be related to differences in the **alleles**, different forms of a particular gene, that determine the trait. The breeder will choose parents with desirable phenotypic characteristics. For centuries, humans have been practising selective breeding to obtain domesticated species with interesting or agriculturally useful characteristics. For example, many breeds of dog are the result of selective breeding strategies (**Figure 21.7**). All dogs are members of the same species, *Canis familiaris,* so they can be interbred to produce offspring. Selective breeding can dramatically modify the traits in a species. When you compare certain breeds of dogs (for example, a greyhound and a dachshund), they hardly look like members of the same species!

Likewise, most of the food we eat is obtained from species that have been profoundly modified by selective breeding strategies. This includes products such as grains, fruits, vegetables, meat, milk, and juices. For example, **Figure 21.8** illustrates how certain characteristics in the wild mustard plant (*Brassica oleracea*) have been modified by selective breeding to create several varieties of domesticated crops, including broccoli, Brussels sprouts, and cauliflower. The wild mustard plant is native to Europe and

(a) French bulldog

(b) Greyhound

(c) Dachshund

Figure 21.7 **Some breeds of dogs that have been obtained by selective breeding.** By selecting parents carrying the alleles that influence traits desirable to humans, dog breeders have produced breeds with distinctive features. For example, the French bulldog has alleles that give it short legs and a flat face. All the dogs shown in this figure carry the same kinds of genes (for example, genes that affect their size, shape, and fur colour). However, the alleles for many of these genes are different among these dogs, thereby allowing humans to select for or against them and produce breeds with strikingly different phenotypes.

Asia, and plant breeders began to modify its traits approximately 4,000 years ago. As seen here, certain traits in the domestic strains differ considerably from those of the original wild species. These varieties are all members of the same species. They can interbreed to produce viable offspring. For example, in the grocery store you may have seen brocciflower, which is produced from a cross between broccoli and cauliflower.

As a final example **Figure 21.9** shows the results of an artificial selection experiment on corn begun at the Illinois Experiment Station in 1896, even before the rediscovery of Mendel's laws. This study began with 163 ears of corn with an oil content ranging from 4% to 6%. In each of 80 succeeding generations, corn plants were divided into two separate groups. In one group members with the highest oil content in the kernels were chosen as parents of the next generation.

Wild mustard plant
(*Brassica oleracea*)

Strain	Kohlrabi	Kale	Broccoli	Brussels sprouts	Cabbage	Cauliflower
Modified trait	Stem	Leaves	Flower buds and stem	Lateral leaf buds	Terminal leaf bud	Flower buds

Figure 21.8 **Crop plants developed by selective breeding of the wild mustard plant.** Although these six agricultural plants look quite different from one another, they carry many of the same alleles as the wild mustard plant. However, they differ in alleles that affect the formation of flowers, buds, stems, and leaves.

Figure 21.9 **Results of selective breeding for oil content in corn plants.** In this example corn plants were selected for breeding based on the high or low oil content of the kernels. Over many generations this had a major impact on the amount of corn oil—an agriculturally important product—that is made by the two groups of plants.

Concept check: *When comparing Figures 21.7, 21.8, and 21.9, what general effects of artificial selection do you observe?*

Principle: *Populations of organisms evolve from one generation to the next. This study illustrates how a trait in corn, namely, oil content, may change over time through human intervention.*

In the other group members with the lowest oil content were chosen. After many generations the oil content in the first group rose to more than 18%. In the other group it dropped to less than 1%. These results show that selective breeding can modify a trait in a very directed manner.

FEATURE INVESTIGATION

The Grants Have Observed Natural Selection in Galápagos Finches

Since 1973 Peter Grant, Rosemary Grant, and their colleagues have studied the process of natural selection in finches found on the Galápagos Islands. For more than 30 years the Grants have focused much of their work on one of the Galápagos Islands known as Daphne Major (**Figure 21.10a**). This small island (0.34 km²) has a moderate degree of isolation (it is 8 km from the nearest island), an undisturbed habitat, and a resident population of the finch *Geospiza fortis,* the medium ground finch (**Figure 21.10b**).

To study natural selection, the Grants have observed various traits in finches over many years. One example is beak size. The medium ground finch has a relatively small crushing beak, allowing it to more easily feed on small, tender seeds. The Grants quantified beak size among the medium ground finches of Daphne Major by carefully measuring beak depth (a measurement of the beak from top to bottom, at its base) on individual birds. During their studies they compared the beak sizes of parents and offspring by examining many broods over several years. The depth of the beak was transmitted from parents to offspring, regardless of environmental conditions, indicating that differences in beak sizes are due to genetic differences in the population. In other words the Grants found that beak depth was a heritable trait.

By measuring many birds every year, the Grants were able to assemble a detailed portrait of natural selection in action. In the study shown in **Figure 21.11**, they measured beak depth from 1976 to 1978. In the wet year of 1976 the plants of Daphne Major produced an abundance of the small seeds that

these finches could easily eat. However, a drought occurred in 1977. During this year the plants on Daphne Major tended to produce few of the smaller seeds, which the finches rapidly consumed. To survive, the finches resorted to eating larger, drier seeds, which are harder to crush. As a result, birds with larger beaks were more likely to survive because they were better at breaking open these large seeds. In the year after the drought the average beak depth of birds in the population increased, because the surviving birds with larger beaks passed this trait on to their offspring. Overall, these results illustrate the power of natural selection to alter the nature of a trait, in this case beak depth, in a given population.

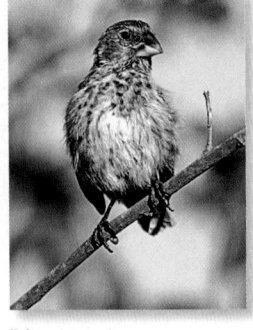

(a)   (b)

Figure 21.10 **The Grants' investigation of natural selection in finches.** (a) Daphne Major, one of the Galápagos Islands. (b) One of the medium ground finches (*Geospiza fortis*) that populates this island.

HYPOTHESIS Dry conditions produce larger seeds and may result in larger beaks in succeeding generations of *Geospiza fortis* because of natural selection.

KEY MATERIALS A population of *G. fortis* on the Galápagos Island called Daphne Major.

	Experimental level	Conceptual level
1 In 1976, measure beak depth in parents and offspring of the species *G. fortis*.	Capture birds and measure beak depth.	This is a way to measure a trait that may be subject to natural selection.
2 Repeat the procedure on offspring that were born in 1978 and had reached mature size. A drought had occurred in 1977 that caused plants on the island to produce mostly large dry seeds and relatively few small seeds.	Capture birds and measure beak depth.	This is a way to measure a trait that may be subject to natural selection.

3 **THE DATA**

4 **CONCLUSION** Because a drought produced larger seeds, birds with larger beaks were more likely to survive and reproduce. The process of natural selection produced postdrought offspring that had larger beaks compared with predrought offspring.

5 **SOURCE** Grant, B. Rosemary, and Grant, Peter R. 2003. What Darwin's finches can teach us about the evolutionary origin and regulation of biodiversity. *Bioscience* 53:965–975.

Figure 21.11 **The Grants and natural selection of beak size among the medium ground finch.** The results are those recorded from 1976 and 1978.

Principle: *Populations of organisms evolve from one generation to the next. This study was aimed at analyzing how beak size may change from one generation to the next.*

Experimental Questions

1. What features of Daphne Major made it a suitable field site for studying the effects of natural selection?
2. Why is beak depth in finches a good trait for a study of natural selection? What environmental conditions were important to allow the Grants to collect information concerning natural selection?
3. What were the results of the Grants' study following the drought in 1977? What impact did these results have on evolutionary theory?

A Comparison of Anatomical, Developmental, and Molecular Homologies Shows Evolution of Related Species from a Common Ancestor

Let's now consider other widespread observations of the process of evolution among living organisms. In biology the term **homology** refers to a fundamental similarity that occurs because of descent from a common ancestor; it is similarity beyond functional necessity. As a result of evolution, homology is often observed between different species. Two species may have a similar trait because the trait was originally found in a common ancestor. As described next, such homologies can involve anatomical, developmental, or molecular features.

Anatomical Homologies   Many observations regarding anatomical features of plants and animals simply cannot be understood in any meaningful scientific way except as a result of evolution. A comparison of vertebrate anatomy is a case in point. An examination of the limbs of modern vertebrate species reveals similarities that indicate that the same set of bones has undergone evolutionary changes to become the bones used today for many different purposes. As seen in **Figure 21.12**, the forelimbs of vertebrates have a strikingly similar pattern of bone arrangements. These are termed **homologous structures** because they are derived from a common ancestor. The forearm has developed different uses among various vertebrates, including grasping, walking, flying, swimming, and climbing. The theory of evolution by natural selection explains how these animals have descended from a common ancestor and how natural selection has modified the same initial pattern of bones in ways that ultimately allowed them to be used for several different purposes.

Another observation of evolution is the phenomenon of **vestigial structures**, which are anatomical features that have no apparent function but resemble structures of the organism's presumed ancestors. **Table 21.2** describes several examples. An interesting case is found in humans. People have a complete set of muscles for moving their ears, even though most people are unable to do so. By comparison, many modern mammals can move their ears, and presumably this was an important trait in a distant human ancestor. Within the context of evolution vestigial structures are evolutionary relics. Organisms having vestigial structures share a common ancestry with organisms in which the structure is functional. Natural selection maintains functional structures in a population of individuals. However, if a species changes its lifestyle so that the structure loses its purpose, the selection forces that would normally keep the structure in a functional condition are no longer present. When this occurs, the structure may degenerate over many generations because of the accumulation of mutations that limit its size and shape. Natural selection may eventually eliminate such traits because of the inefficiency of producing unused structures.

Developmental Homologies   Another example of homology caused by evolution is the way that animals undergo embryonic development. Species that differ substantially at the adult stage

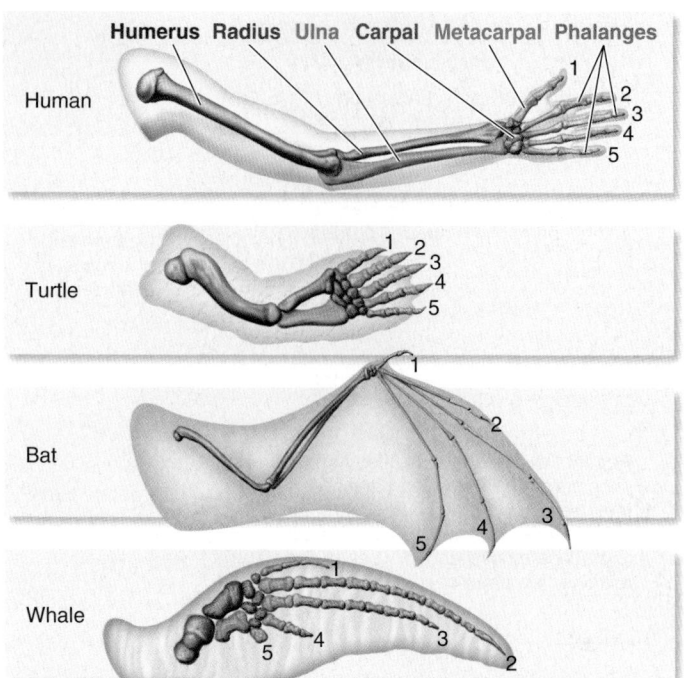

Figure 21.12 An example of anatomical homology: homologous structures found in vertebrates.   The same set of bones is found in the human forearm, turtle forearm, bat wing, and whale flipper, although these bones have been modified in ways that allow them to perform different functions. This homology suggests that all these animals evolved from a common ancestor.

 Principle: *Structure determines function. These homologous sets of bones have evolved into somewhat different structures because of differences in their functions in humans, turtles, bats, and whales.*

often bear striking similarities during early stages of embryonic development. These temporary similarities are called developmental homologies. In addition, evolutionary history is revealed during development in certain organisms, such as vertebrates. For example, if we consider human development,

Table 21.2	Examples of Vestigial Structures
Organism	**Vestigial structures**
Humans	Tail bone and muscles to wiggle ears in adult
Boa constrictors	Skeletal remnants of hip bones and hind legs
Whales	Skeletal remnants of a pelvis
Manatees	Fingernails on the flippers
Dandelion	An asexually reproducing plant (*Taraxicum officinale*) that still makes flowers, even though it does not produce fertile seeds
Hornbills and cuckoos	In certain families of birds, both common carotid arteries are nonfunctional fibrous cords (vascular function of arteries has been assumed by other vessels)

several features are seen in the embryo that are not present at birth. Human embryos possess rudimentary gill ridges like a fish embryo, even though human embryos receive oxygen via the umbilical cord. The presence of gill ridges indicates that humans evolved from an aquatic animal with gill slits. A second observation is that every human embryo has a long bony tail. It is difficult to see the advantage of such a structure in utero, but easy to understand its presence assuming that an ancestor to the human lineage possessed a long tail. These observations, and many others, illustrate that development has evolved over time. Developmental homologies can also be considered anatomical homologies that are seen in embryos or other developmental stages, but they are not obvious when looking at the mature organism's anatomy.

Molecular Homologies Our last example of homology caused by evolution involves molecular studies. When scientists examine the features of cells at the molecular level, similarities called **molecular homologies** are found, which indicate that living species evolved from a common ancestor or interrelated group of common ancestors. For example, all living species use DNA to store information. RNA molecules, such as mRNA, tRNA, and rRNA, are used to access that information, and proteins are the functional products of

most genes. Furthermore, certain biochemical pathways are found in all or nearly all species, although minor changes in the structure and function of proteins involved in these pathways have occurred. For example, all species that use oxygen, which constitutes the great majority of species on our planet, have similar proteins that together make up an electron transport chain and an ATP synthase. In addition, nearly all living organisms can metabolize glucose via a glycolytic pathway that is described in Chapter 7. Taken together, these types of observations indicate that such molecular phenomena arose very early in the origin of life and have been passed to all or nearly all modern forms.

The most compelling observation at the molecular level indicating that modern life forms are derived from a common ancestor is revealed by analyzing genetic sequences and finding genetic homologies, or similar genes. The same type of gene is often found in diverse organisms. Furthermore, the degree to which a genetic sequence from different species is similar reflects the evolutionary relatedness of those species. As an example, let's consider a gene that encodes the p53 protein that plays a role in preventing cancer (see Chapter 13). **Figure 21.13** shows a short amino acid sequence that makes up part of the p53 protein from a variety of species, including five mammals, one bird, and three fish. The top sequence is the human p53

	Short amino acid sequence within the p53 protein	Percentages of amino acids in the whole p53 protein that are identical to human p53
Human (*Homo sapiens*)	Val Pro Ser Gln Lys Thr Tyr Gln Gly Ser Tyr Gly Phe Arg Leu Gly Phe Leu His Ser Gly Thr	100
Rhesus monkey (*Macaca mulatta*)	Val Pro Ser Gln Lys Thr Tyr **His** Gly Ser Tyr Gly Phe Arg Leu Gly Phe Leu His Ser Gly Thr	95
Green monkey (*Cercopithecus aethiops*)	Val Pro Ser Gln Lys Thr Tyr **His** Gly Ser Tyr Gly Phe Arg Leu Gly Phe Leu His Ser Gly Thr	95
Rabbit (*Oryctolagus cuniculus*)	Val Pro Ser Gln Lys Thr Tyr **His** Gly **Asn** Tyr Gly Phe Arg Leu Gly Phe Leu His Ser Gly Thr	86
Dog (*Canis lupus familiaris*)	Val Pro Ser **Pro** Lys Thr Tyr **Pro** Gly **Thr** Tyr Gly Phe Arg Leu Gly Phe Leu His Ser Gly Thr	80
Chicken (*Gallus gallus*)	Val Pro Ser **Thr Glu Asp** Tyr Gly Gly **Asp Phe Asp** Phe Arg **Val** Gly Phe **Val Glu Ala** Gly Thr	53
Channel catfish (*Ictalurus punctatus*)	Val Pro **Val Thr Ser Asp** Tyr **Pro** Gly **Leu Leu Asn** Phe **Thr** Leu His Phe **Gln Glu** Ser **Ser** Gly	48
European flounder (*Platichthys flesus*)	Val Pro **Val Val Thr Asp** Tyr **Pro** Gly **Glu** Tyr Gly Phe **Gln** Leu **Arg** Phe **Gln Lys** Ser Gly Thr	46
Congo puffer fish (*Tetraodon miurus*)	Val Pro **Val Thr Thr Asp** Tyr **Pro** Gly **Glu** Tyr Gly Phe **Lys** Leu **Arg** Phe **Gln Lys** Ser Gly Thr	41

Figure 21.13 An example of genetic homology: a comparison of a short amino acid sequence within the p53 protein from nine different animals.   This figure compares a short region of the p53 protein, which plays a role in preventing cancer. Amino acids are represented by three-letter abbreviations. The orange-coloured amino acids in the sequences are identical to those in the human sequence. The numbers in the right column indicate the percentages of amino acids in the whole p53 protein that are identical to the human p53 protein, which is 393 amino acids in length. For example, 95% of the amino acids, or 373 of 393, are identical between the p53 sequence found in humans and that in Rhesus monkeys.

Concept check: *In the sequence shown in this figure, how many amino acid differences are there between the following pairs: Rhesus and green monkeys, Congo puffer fish and European flounder, and Rhesus monkey and Congo puffer fish? What do these differences tell you about the evolutionary relationships among these four species?*

BioConnections: *Look back at Table 19.5. How are genetic sequences that are retrieved from a database using the BLAST program correlated with the evolutionary relatedness of the species?*

sequence, and the right column describes the percentages of amino acids within the entire sequence that are identical to the entire human sequence. Amino acids in the other species that are identical to humans are highlighted in orange. The sequences from the two monkeys are closest to humans, followed by the other two mammalian species (rabbit and dog). The three fish sequences are the least similar to the human sequence, but you may notice that the fish sequences are similar to each other. Taken together, the data shown in Figure 21.13 illustrate two critical points regarding gene evolution. First, certain genes are found in a diverse array of species, such as mammals, birds, and fish. Second, the sequences of closely related species tend to be more similar to each other than they are to distantly related species. The mechanism for this second observation is described in the next section.

21.3 THE MOLECULAR PROCESSES THAT UNDERLIE EVOLUTION

Learning Outcomes:
1. Explain how paralogs and orthologs are produced.
2. Describe how new types of genes arise via exon shuffling.
3. Distinguish between vertical evolution and horizontal gene transfer.

Historically, the study of evolution was based on comparing the anatomies of extinct and modern species to identify similarities between related species. However, the advent of molecular approaches for analyzing DNA sequences has revolutionized the field of evolutionary biology. Now we can analyze how changes in the genetic material are associated with changes in phenotype and how those changes have led to the formation of new species. In this section we will examine some of the molecular changes in the genetic material that are associated with evolution.

Homologous Genes Are Derived from a Common Ancestral Gene

When two genes are derived from the same ancestral gene, they are called **homologous genes**. The analysis of homologous genes reveals the molecular details of evolutionary change. As an example let's consider a gene in two different species of bacteria that encodes a transport protein involved in the uptake of metal ions into bacterial cells. Such genes, which are homologous but from different species, are said to be **orthologs**. Millions of years ago, these two species had a common ancestor (**Figure 21.14**). Over time the common ancestor diverged into additional species, eventually evolving into *Escherichia coli*,

TTGGTTATATCGATCCCGGTAACTTTGCGACCAA *E. coli*
TAGCCTACATTGATCCTGGTAATTTTGCTACAAA *C. acetylbutylicum*

Figure 21.14   The evolution of orthologs: homologous genes from different species.   After two species diverged the genes accumulated random mutations that created similar but not identical gene sequences called orthologs. These orthologs in *E. coli* and *C. acetylbutylicum* encode metal transporters. Only one of the two DNA strands is shown from each gene. Bases that are identical between the two genes are shown in orange.

Concept check: *Why do these orthologs have similar gene sequences? Why are they not identical?*

Clostridium acetylbutylicum, and many other species. Since this divergence, the metal transporter gene has accumulated mutations that alter its sequence, though the similarity between the *E. coli* and the *C. acetylbutylicum* genes remains striking. In this case the two sequences are similar because they were derived from the same ancestral gene, but they are not identical because of the independent accumulation of different random mutations.

Gene Duplications Create Gene Families

Orthologs are examples of evolutionary change occurring in separate species. Demonstrations of evolutionary change can also be found within a single species. Two or more homologous

GENOMES AND PROTEOMES

New Genes in Eukaryotes Have Evolved via Exon Shuffling

Thus far we have considered how evolutionary change results in the formation of related genes, which are described as orthologs and paralogs. Evolutionary mechanisms are also revealed when the parts of genes that encode protein domains are compared within a single species. Many proteins, particularly those found in eukaryotic species, have a modular structure comprising two or more domains with different functions. For example, certain transcription factors have discrete domains involved with hormone binding, dimerization, and DNA binding. As described in Chapter 12, the glucocorticoid receptor has a domain that binds the hormone, a second domain that facilitates protein dimerization, and a third domain that allows the glucocorticoid receptor to bind to glucocorticoid response elements (GREs) next to genes. By comparing the modular structure of eukaryotic proteins with the genes that encode them, geneticists have discovered that each domain tends to be encoded by one exon or by a

series of two or more adjacent exons. As you learned in Chapter 11, exons contain the coding sequences of a gene, which are separated by noncoding introns.

During the evolution of eukaryotic species, many new genes have been created by a type of mutation known as **exon shuffling**. During this process an exon and the flanking introns are inserted into a gene, thereby producing a new gene that encodes a protein with an additional domain (**Figure 21.15**). This process may also involve the duplication and rearrangement of exons. Exon shuffling results in novel genes that express proteins with diverse functional modules. Such proteins can then alter traits in the organism that can be acted upon by natural selection.

Exon shuffling can occur by more than one mechanism. One possibility is that a double crossover could promote the insertion of an exon into another gene (see Figure 21.15). This is called nonhomologous or illegitimate recombination because the two regions involved in the crossover are not homologous. Alternatively, transposable elements that are described in Chapter 19 may promote the movement of exons into other genes.

Figure 21.15   **The process of exon shuffling.**   In this example a segment of one gene containing an exon and the flanking introns has been inserted into another gene. A rare, abnormal crossing-over event called nonhomologous recombination can cause this to happen. This results in proteins that have new combinations of domains and possibly new combinations of functions.

Concept check: *What is the evolutionary advantage of exon shuffling?*

genes found within a single species are termed **paralogs**. Rare gene duplication events can produce multiple copies of a gene and ultimately lead to the formation of a gene family. **Gene**

families consist of two or more copies of paralogous genes within the genome of a single organism. A well-studied example of a gene family is the globin gene family found in humans and many other animal species. The globin genes encode polypeptides that are subunits of proteins that function in oxygen binding. One such protein is hemoglobin, which is found in red blood cells and carries oxygen throughout the body. The globin gene family comprises 14 genes that were originally derived from a single ancestral globin gene. According to an evolutionary analysis, the ancestral globin gene first duplicated between 500 million and 600 million years ago. Since that time additional duplication events and chromosomal rearrangements have produced the current number of 14 genes on three different human chromosomes (refer back to Figure 19.8).

Gene families have been important in the evolution of traits. Even though all the globin polypeptides are subunits of proteins that play a role in oxygen binding, the accumulation of changes in the various family members has created globins that are more specialized in their function. For example, myoglobin is better at binding and storing oxygen in muscle cells, whereas the hemoglobins are better at binding and transporting oxygen via the red blood cells. Also, different globin genes are expressed during different stages of human development. The (epsilon) ε-globin and (zeta) ζ-globin genes are expressed very early in embryonic life, while the (gamma) γ-globin genes exhibit maximal expression during the second and third trimesters of gestation. Following birth, the γ-globin gene is turned off and the β-globin gene is turned on. These differences in the expression of the globin genes reflect the differences in the oxygen transport needs of humans during the embryonic, fetal, and postpartum stages of life.

What is the evolutionary significance of the globin gene family regarding adaptation? Internal gestation is one way that animals have adapted to a terrestrial environment. On land egg cells and small embryos are very susceptible to drying out if they are not protected in some way. Such species as birds and reptiles lay eggs that have a protective shell. Most mammals, however, have adjusted to a terrestrial environment by evolving the adaptation of internal gestation. The ability to develop young internally has been an important factor in the survival and proliferation of mammals. The embryonic and fetal forms of hemoglobin allow the embryo and fetus to capture oxygen from the bloodstream of the mother.

Horizontal Gene Transfer Also Contributes to the Evolution of Species

At the molecular level the type of evolutionary change depicted in Figures 21.13 through 21.15 is called **vertical evolution**. In these cases species evolve from pre-existing species by the accumulation of gene mutations, gene duplications, and exon shuffling. Vertical evolution involves genetic changes in a series of ancestors that form a lineage. In addition to vertical evolution, species accumulate genetic changes by another process called **horizontal gene transfer,** which involves the exchange of genetic material among different contemporary species.

One possible mechanism for horizontal gene transfer occurs when a eukaryotic cell has engulfed a bacterial cell by endocytosis. During degradation of the bacterium in an endocytotic vesicle, a bacterial gene happens to escape degradation and ends up in the nucleus of the cell, where it is inserted into one of the chromosomes. In this way a gene has been transferred from a bacterial species to a eukaryotic species. By analyzing gene sequences among many different species, researchers have discovered that horizontal gene transfer is a common phenomenon. This process can occur from prokaryotes to eukaryotes, from eukaryotes to prokaryotes, between different species of prokaryotes, and between different species of eukaryotes. Therefore, when we view evolution, it is not simply a matter of one species evolving into one or more new species via the accumulation of random mutations. It also involves the horizontal transfer of genes among different species, enabling those species to acquire new traits that foster the evolutionary process.

Gene transfer among bacterial species is relatively widespread. As discussed in Chapter 16, bacterial species can carry out three natural mechanisms of gene transfer known as conjugation, transformation, and transduction. By analyzing the genomes of bacterial species, scientists have determined that many genes within a given bacterial genome are derived from horizontal gene transfer. Genome studies have suggested that as much as 20% to 30% of the variation in the genetic composition of modern prokaryotic species can be attributed to this process. For example, in *E. coli* and *Salmonella typhimurium*, roughly 17% of their genes have been acquired via horizontal gene transfer during the past 100 million years. The roles of these acquired genes are quite varied, though they commonly involve functions that are readily acted on by natural selection. These include genes that confer antibiotic resistance, the ability to degrade toxic compounds, and pathogenicity (the ability to cause disease).

Evolution at the Genomic Level Involves Changes in Chromosome Structure and Number

Thus far we have considered several ways that a species might acquire new genes: random mutations within existing genes, gene duplications to create gene families, exon shuffling, and horizontal gene transfer. Evolution also occurs at the genomic level, involving changes in chromosome structure and number. When comparing the chromosomes of closely related species, changes in chromosome structure and number are common.

As an example, **Figure 21.16** compares the banding patterns of the three largest chromosomes in humans and the corresponding chromosomes in chimpanzees, gorillas, and orangutans. (See Chapter 14 for a description of chromosome banding.) The banding patterns are strikingly similar because these species are closely related evolutionarily. Even so, you can see some interesting differences. Humans have one large chromosome 2, but this chromosome is divided into two separate

Figure 21.16   An example of genomic evolution.
This figure is a comparison of banding patterns among the three largest human chromosomes and the corresponding chromosomes in apes. It is a schematic drawing of Giemsa-stained chromosomes. The differences between these chromosomes illustrate the changes that have occurred during the evolution of these related species.

Concept check: *Describe two changes in chromosome structure that have occurred among these chromosomes.*

conditions. According to the modern synthesis, natural selection acts on existing genetic variation over many generations to produce populations of organisms with traits that promote greater reproductive success (adaptations). Remember that evolution is not goal oriented and that other mechanisms of evolutionary change will be addressed in Chapter 22. (Figure 21.2)

21.2 Observations of Evolutionary Change

- Observations of evolution include the fossil record, biogeography, convergent evolution, selective breeding, and homologies. (Table 21.1)
- Fossils show successive evolutionary change over long periods. The fossil record often reveals transitional forms that link past ancestors to modern species. (Figures 21.3, 21.4)
- The geographical distribution of species, called biogeography, provides information on how certain species are evolutionarily related. Often, when populations become isolated, they evolve into a new species. (Figure 21.5)
- Continental drift can explain the distribution of many plants and animals.
- Convergent evolution involves independent adaptations resulting in analogous structures that are similar because the organisms have evolved in similar environments. (Figure 21.6)
- Selective breeding, also known as artificial selection, illustrates how changes in genetic variation over many generations can dramatically change the traits of organisms. (Figures 21.7, 21.8, 21.9)
- The Grants showed that natural selection can promote changes in beak size in the medium ground finch. (Figures 21.10, 21.11)
- Homologous structures are fundamentally similar because they are derived from the same ancestral structure. The set of bones in the forelimbs of vertebrates is one example. (Figure 21.12)
- Vestigial structures are found in species because they are derived from structures that were once functional but have degenerated because they no longer have use in a modern species. (Table 21.2)
- Homology also occurs during development and at the molecular level of gene and protein sequences. (Figure 21.13)

chromosomes in the other three species. This explains why human cells have 23 pairs of chromosomes but ape cells have 24. The fusion of the two smaller chromosomes during the development of the human lineage may have caused this difference in chromosome pair numbers. Another interesting change in chromosome structure is seen in chromosome 3. The banding patterns among humans, chimpanzees, and gorillas are very similar, but the orangutan has a large inversion that flips the arrangement of bands in the centromeric region. As discussed in Chapter 23, changes in chromosome structure and number may affect the ability of two organisms to breed with one another. In this way such changes have been important in the establishment of new species.

Summary of Key Concepts

- Biological evolution is a heritable change in one or more characteristics of a population or species across many generations.

21.1 Historical Views on Evolutionary Change

- Charles Darwin proposed the theory of evolution by natural selection based on his understanding of geology and population growth and his observations of species in their natural settings. His voyage on the *Beagle,* during which he studied many species on the Galápagos Islands, was particularly influential. (Figure 21.1)
- Darwin's theory of evolution by natural selection involves descent with modification that leads to better adaptation to environmental

21.3 The Molecular Processes That Underlie Evolution

- Molecular evolution refers to the molecular changes in genetic material that underlie the phenotypic changes associated with evolution.
- Homologous genes are derived from the same ancestral gene. They accumulate random mutations that make their sequences similar but somewhat different. Orthologs are homologous genes in different species. (Figure 21.14)

- Paralogs are homologous genes in the same species, produced by gene duplication events. Paralogs constitute a gene family. An example is the globin gene family that promoted the evolutionary adaptation of internal gestation.

- Exon shuffling is a form of mutation in which exons are inserted into genes and thereby create proteins with additional functional domains. (Figure 21.15)

- Another mechanism that creates genetic variation is horizontal gene transfer, in which genetic material is transferred between different species.

- Evolution is also associated with changes in chromosome structure and chromosome number. (Figure 21.16)

Test to Assess Your Learning

1. An allele is
   a. the full complement of genetic data in an organism.
   b. different forms of a gene.
   c. multiple copies of a gene.
   d. genes that regulate flight.
   e. inbreeding coefficient in animals.

2. Lamarck's vision of evolution differed from Darwin's in that Lamarck believed
   a. living things evolved in an upward direction.
   b. behavioural changes modified heritable traits.
   c. genetic differences among individuals in the population allowed for evolution.
   d. (a) and (b) only.
   e. none of the above.

3. Which of the following scientists influenced Darwin's views on the nature of population growth?
   a. Cuvier
   b. Malthus
   c. Lyell
   d. Hutton
   e. Wallace

4. An evolutionary change in which an organism's characteristics change in ways that make it better suited to its environment is
   a. natural selection.
   b. an adaptation.
   c. an acquired characteristic.
   d. evolution.
   e. both (a) and (c).

5. Vestigial structures are anatomical structures
   a. that have more than one function.
   b. that have no function.
   c. that look similar in different species but have different functions.
   d. that have the same function in different species but have very different appearances.
   e. of the body wall.

6. Which of the following is an example of developmental homologies seen in human embryonic development?
   a. gill ridges
   b. umbilical cord
   c. tail
   d. both (a) and (c)
   e. all of the above

7. Two or more homologous genes found within a particular species are called
   a. homozygous.
   b. orthologs.

   c. paralogs.
   d. heterologs.
   e. duplicates.

8. The phenomenon of exon shuffling
   a. creates new gene products by changing the pattern of intron removal in a particular gene.
   b. creates new genes by inserting exons and flanking introns into a different gene sequence, thereby introducing a new domain in the gene product.
   c. rearranges the sequence of exons in a single gene.
   d. rearranges the introns in a particular gene, creating new gene products.
   e. both (a) and (d).

9. Horizontal gene transfer is
   a. the transmission of genetic information from parent to offspring.
   b. the exchange of genetic material among individuals of the same species.
   c. the exchange of genetic material between mates.
   d. the exchange of genetic material among individuals of different species.
   e. none of the above.

10. The term *endemic* refers to
    a. organisms that evolve in the same ecological zone.
    b. organisms that have adapted to low-light environments.
    c. organisms that have adapted to mountainous environments.
    d. organisms that are naturally found only in a particular location.
    e. organisms that have widespread natural occurrence.

Articulate to Assess Your Learning

1. Briefly describe the various empirical observations in support of the fact that biological evolution has occurred.

2. Explain how homologous forelimbs of vertebrates support the idea of biological evolution.

3. Could the rudimentary gill arches found in human embryos be considered both vestigial structures and developmental homologies? Explain.

4. Explain how exon shuffling works and what it can lead to in offspring at the genetic and organism level.

5. What are the challenges that an endemic, island-dwelling bird would face if transported to the mainland?

Collaborate to Assess Extend and Your Learning

1. Design a biogeographic study of Spix's macaw in the Amazon.
2. Why did so many species of marsupials evolve in Australia?
3. Attempt to provide both a Lamarkian explanation and a Darwinian explanation for the loss of eyes in blind cave-dwelling salamanders.

4. A principle of biology is that populations of organisms evolve from one generation to the next. Explain how the change in beak sizes in Galápagos Finches between 1976 and 1978 indicates that populations evolve from one generation to the next.

Visit McGraw-Hill Ryerson Connect™ for additional study resources.

Population Genetics

Chapter Outline

The white-throated sparrow (*Zonotrichia albicollis*) is recognized by Canadians who have spent time in northern forests by its unique song that sounds like Oh-Canada-Canada-Canada. There is a polymorphism in their plumage, and their heads have either white stripes or tan stripes. The genetic basis of this polymorphism is a chromosomal inversion.

Population genetics is the study of genes and genotypes in a population. The central issue in population genetics is genetic variation. Population geneticists want to know the extent of genetic variation within populations, why it exists, and how it changes over one to many generations. Population genetics helps scientists to understand how underlying genetic variation is related to phenotypic variation and other issues, such as feeding ecology (see the chapter-opening photo).

Population genetics emerged as a branch of genetics in the 1920s and 1930s. Its mathematical foundations were developed by theoreticians who extended the principles given by Mendel and Darwin by deriving equations to explain the occurrence of genotypes within populations. These foundations can be largely attributed to British evolutionary biologists J. B. S. Haldane and Ronald Fisher, and American geneticist Sewall Wright. As you will see, several researchers who analyzed the genetic composition of natural and experimental populations provided support for their mathematical theories. More recently, population geneticists have used techniques to probe genetic variation at the molecular level. In addition the improvements in computer technology have aided population geneticists in the analysis of their genetic theories and data.

In this chapter we will explore the extent of genetic variation that occurs in populations. We will also examine the various ways in which gene and genotype frequencies can change, even over short periods. Population genetics generally looks at microevolutionary processes that can occur over several generations.

3. Use the Hardy-Weinberg equation to calculate allele and genotype frequencies of a given population.
4. List the conditions that must be met for a population to be in Hardy-Weinberg equilibrium.

Population genetics is an extension of our understanding of Darwin's theory of natural selection, Mendel's laws of inheritance, and newer studies in molecular genetics. All the genes in a population make up its **gene pool**. Each member of the population receives its genes from its parents, which, in turn, are members of the gene pool. All individuals that reproduce contribute to the gene pool of the next generation. Population geneticists study the genetic variation within the gene pool and how such variation changes from one generation to the next. The emphasis is often on an understanding of variation in alleles among members of a population. As discussed in Chapter 15, alleles are different forms of the same gene. In this section we will examine some of the general features of populations and gene pools.

A Population Is a Group of Interbreeding Individuals

A **population** is a group of individuals of the same species that can interbreed with one another. Certain species occupy a wide geographic range and are divided into discrete populations. For example, distinct populations of a given species can be located on different continents. (A more detailed

22.1 / GENES IN POPULATIONS

Learning Outcomes:

1. Define a gene pool.
2. Distinguish between allele frequency and genotype frequency.

description of populations and their native environments is given in Chapter 53.) A large mountain or some other type of geographic barrier may separate two or more populations on the same continent.

Populations are dynamic units that change from one generation to the next. They can change in number, geographic location, and genetic composition. Natural populations can go through cycles of gaining or losing individuals. In addition, natural predators or disease can periodically decrease the size of a population significantly, and then later the population may rebound to its original size. Populations or individuals within populations may migrate to a new site and establish a distinct population at a new location that differs in environment from the original site.

As population sizes and locations change, their genetic composition generally changes as well. Some of the genetic changes involve adaptive evolution, which means that a species is better adapted to its environment, making it more likely to survive and reproduce. We will explore how gene frequencies can change through migration or by chance in a process called random drift.

Population Genetics Is Concerned with Allele and Genotype Frequencies

To analyze genetic variation in populations, one approach is to consider the frequency of alleles in a quantitative way. To show the relationship between allele frequencies and genotypes in

GENOMES AND PROTEOMES

Genes in Natural Populations Are Usually Polymorphic

The term **polymorphism** (meaning "many forms") refers to the phenomenon that many traits display variation within a population. Historically, polymorphism first referred to variation in phenotypes. Polymorphisms in colour and pattern have long attracted the attention of population geneticists. **Figure 22.1** illustrates a striking example of polymorphism in the elder-flowered orchid (*Dactylorhiza sambucina*). Throughout the range of this species in Europe, both yellow- and red-flowered individuals are prevalent.

Phenotypic polymorphism is caused by two or more alleles that influence the phenotype of the individual that inherits them. In other words it is due to genetic variation. Geneticists also use the term *polymorphism* to describe the variation in genes; this is sometimes called genetic polymorphism. A gene that commonly exists as two or more alleles in a population is described as a **polymorphic gene**. By comparison a **monomorphic gene** exists predominantly as a single allele in a population. By convention, when 99% or more of the alleles of a given gene are identical, the gene is considered to be monomorphic. Said another way, a polymorphic gene must have one or more additional alleles that make up more than 1% of the alleles in the population.

At the molecular level of a particular gene, a polymorphism can involve various types of changes, such as the deletion of a significant region of the gene, a duplication of a region, or a change in a single nucleotide. This last phenomenon is called a single-nucleotide polymorphism (SNP). SNPs ("snips") are the smallest type of genetic change that can occur within a given gene, and they are also the most common. In human populations, for example, SNPs represent

Figure 22.1   An example of polymorphism: the two colour variations found in the orchid *Dactylorhiza sambucina*.

90% of all the variation in human DNA sequences that occurs among different people. Current estimates indicate that SNPs with a frequency of 1% or more are found very frequently in genes. In humans, a gene that is 2,000 to 3,000 bp long will, on average, contain 10 different SNPs in the human population. The high frequency of SNPs indicates that polymorphism is the norm for most human genes. Likewise, relatively large, healthy populations of nearly all species exhibit a high level of genetic variation, as evidenced by the occurrence of SNPs within most genes. As discussed later in this chapter, genetic variation provides the raw material for populations to evolve over many generations.

a population, **Figure 22.2** considers the relationship between allele frequencies and the way that gametes combine to produce genotypes.

Two fundamental calculations are central to population genetics: **allele frequencies** and **genotype frequencies**. Allele and genotype frequencies are defined as

$$\text{allele frequency} = \frac{\text{number of copies of a specific allele at a particular locus in a population}}{\text{total number of all alleles for that gene in a population}}$$

$$\text{genotype frequency} = \frac{\text{number of individuals with a particular genotype in a population}}{\text{total number of individuals in a population}}$$

Although these two frequencies are related, keep in mind the clear distinction between them. As an example let's consider a population of 100 four o'clock plants with the following genotypes:

49 red-flowered plants with the genotype *RR*
42 pink-flowered plants with the genotype *Rr*
9 white-flowered plants with the genotype *rr*

When calculating an allele frequency for diploid species, remember that homozygous individuals have two copies of an allele, whereas heterozygotes have only one. For example, in tallying the *r* allele, each of the 42 heterozygotes has one copy of the *r* allele, and each white-flowered plant has two copies. Therefore, the allele frequency for *r* is as follows:

$$\text{frequency of } r = \frac{(Rr) + 2(rr)}{2(RR) + 2(Rr) + 2(rr)}$$

$$\text{frequency of } r = \frac{42 + (2)(9)}{(2)(49) + (2)(42) + (2)(9)}$$

$$= \frac{60}{200} = 0.3, \text{ or } 30\%$$

This result tells us that the allele frequency of *r* is 0.3. In other words, 30% of the alleles for this gene in the population are the *r* allele.

Let's now calculate the genotype frequency of *rr* (white-flowered) plants.

$$\text{frequency of } rr = \frac{9}{49 + 42 + 9}$$

$$= \frac{9}{100} = 0.09, \text{ or } 9\%$$

We see that 9% of the individuals in this population have white flowers.

Allele and genotype frequencies are always less than or equal to one (that is, less than or equal to 100%). If a gene is monomorphic, the allele frequency for the single allele will equal or be close to a value of 1.0. For polymorphic genes if we add the frequencies for all the alleles in the population, we should obtain a value of 1.0. In our four o'clock example, the allele frequency of *r* equals 0.3. Therefore, we can calculate

Figure 22.2 Comparing allele and genotype frequencies in a population with the Hardy-Weinberg equation and a Punnett square. A population of four o'clock plants has allele and gamete frequencies of 0.7 for the *R* allele and 0.3 for the *r* allele. Knowing the allele frequencies allows us to calculate the genotype frequencies in the population.

Concept check: *What would be the frequency of pink flowers in a population in which the allele frequency of R is 0.4 and the population is in Hardy-Weinberg equilibrium? Assume that there are only two alleles.*

the frequency of the other allele, *R*, as equal to $1.0 - 0.3 = 0.7$, because they must add to 1.0.

The Hardy-Weinberg Equation Relates Allele and Genotype Frequencies in a Population

In 1908 Godfrey Harold Hardy, an English mathematician, and Wilhelm Weinberg, a German physician, independently derived a simple mathematical expression called the **Hardy-Weinberg equation** that relates allele and genotype frequencies when they are not changing. Let's examine the Hardy-Weinberg equation using the population of four o'clock plants that we have just considered. If the allele frequency of *R* is denoted by the variable *p*, and the allele frequency of *r* by *q*, then

$$p + q = 1$$

For example, if $p = 0.7$, then q must be 0.3. In other words, if the allele frequency of R equals 70%, the remaining 30% of alleles must be r, because together they equal 100%.

For a gene that exists in two alleles, the Hardy-Weinberg equation states that

$$(p + q)^2 = 1$$

(Note: the number 2 in this equation reflects the fact that the genotype is due to the inheritance of two alleles, one from each parent.)
Therefore

$$p^2 + 2pq + q^2 = 1 \text{ (the Hardy-Weinberg equation)}$$

If we apply this equation to our flower colour gene, then

p^2	equals the genotype frequency of RR
$2pq$	equals the genotype frequency of Rr
q^2	equals the genotype frequency of rr

If $p = 0.7$ and $q = 0.3$, then

frequency of $RR = p^2 = (0.7)^2 = 0.49$
frequency of $Rr = 2pq = 2(0.7)(0.3) = 0.42$
frequency of $rr = q^2 = (0.3)^2 = 0.09$

In other words, if the allele frequency of R is 70% and the allele frequency of r is 30%, the expected genotype frequency of RR is 49%, Rr is 42%, and rr is 9%.

The Hardy-Weinberg equation reflects the way gametes combine randomly to produce offspring. In a population the frequency of a gamete carrying a particular allele is equal to the allele frequency in that population. For example, if the allele frequency of R equals 0.7, the frequency of a gamete carrying the R allele also equals 0.7. The frequency of producing an RR homozygote, which produces red flowers, is $0.7 \times 0.7 = 0.49$, or 49%. The probability of inheriting both r alleles, which produces white flowers, is $0.3 \times 0.3 = 0.09$, or 9%. In our Punnett square two different gamete combinations can produce heterozygotes with pink flowers (Figure 22.2). An offspring could inherit the R allele from pollen and r from the egg, or R from the egg and r from pollen. Therefore, the frequency of heterozygotes is $pq + pq$, which equals $2pq$. In our example this is $2(0.7)(0.3) = 0.42$, or 42%.

In this example the R allele and the r allele are codominant. They are both expressed, resulting in an intermediate colour. In other cases one allele may be dominant while the other is recessive. Recessive alleles may represent nonfunctional mutants or an expression pattern that is masked by the dominant allele. Thus, the heterozygote would be phenotypically indistinguishable from the homozygous dominant.

The Hardy-Weinberg equation predicts an **equilibrium** of unchanging allele and genotype frequencies in a population. If a population is in equilibrium, it is not adapting and evolution is not occurring. However, this prediction is valid only if certain conditions are met in a population. These conditions require that evolutionary mechanisms, those forces that can change allele and genotype frequencies, are not acting on a population. For any gene of interest, these conditions are as follows:

- The population is so large that allele frequencies do not change through random sampling error.
- The members of the population mate with one another without regard to their phenotypes and genotypes.
- No migration occurs between different populations.
- No survival or reproductive advantage exists for any of the genotypes—in other words, no natural selection occurs.
- No new mutations occur.

In reality no population satisfies the Hardy-Weinberg equilibrium completely. Nevertheless, in large natural populations with little migration and negligible natural selection, the Hardy-Weinberg equilibrium may be nearly approximated for certain genes. However, researchers often discover instead that allele and genotype frequencies for one or more genes in a given species are not in Hardy-Weinberg equilibrium. In such cases we would say that the population is in disequilibrium—in other words evolutionary mechanisms are affecting the population. When this occurs, population geneticists may want to identify the reasons that disequilibrium has occurred because this may affect the survival of the population.

22.2 EVOLUTIONARY MECHANISMS AND THEIR EFFECTS ON POPULATIONS

Learning Outcomes:

1. Describe the factors that cause microevolutionary changes to occur.
2. Explain how natural selection can result in a population that is better adapted to its environment and more successful at reproduction.
3. Calculate the relative fitness values of given genotypes.
4. List and distinguish among four different types of natural selection.
5. Explain what is meant by sexual selection.
6. Describe the effects that genetic drift, small population size, inbreeding, and migration can have on allele frequencies.

The genetic variation in all natural populations changes over many generations. The term **microevolution** is used to describe changes in a population's gene pool from generation to generation. Such change is rooted in two related phenomena (**Table 22.1**). First, the introduction of new genetic variation into a population is one essential aspect of microevolution. As discussed in Chapter 21, genetic variation can originate by a variety of molecular mechanisms. New alleles of pre-existing genes can arise by random mutation, and new genes can be introduced into a population by gene duplication, exon shuffling, and horizontal gene transfer. Such mutations, albeit rare, provide a continual source of new variation to populations. In 1926 Russian geneticist Sergei

Table 22.1	Factors That Govern Microevolution
Sources of new genetic variation*	
New alleles	• Random mutations introduce new alleles into populations but at a very low rate. • Generally deleterious, but they can be neutral or even beneficial.
Gene duplication	• Abnormal crossover events and transposable elements may increase the number of copies of a gene. • It can create a gene family.
Exon shuffling	• Abnormal crossover events and transposable elements may promote gene rearrangements.
Horizontal gene transfer	• Genes from one species may be introduced into another species.
Random mating	• Generation of new allelic combinations occurs through meiosis and fertilization.
Evolutionary mechanisms that alter existing genetic variation	
Natural selection	• Natural selection is the differential reproductive success of individuals in a population. • It includes not only the survival of an individual but also its ability to reproduce.
Random genetic drift	• Change in genetic variation from generation to generation is caused by random sampling error. • Allele frequencies may change as a matter of chance. • Small populations are more prone to changes through genetic drift.
Migration (gene flow)	• Genes flow between populations that have different allele frequencies.
Nonrandom mating	• Mate choice is based on phenotype.

Described in Chapter 21.

Tshetverikov was the first to suggest that random mutations are the raw material for evolution but do not constitute evolution itself. Mutations clearly supply new genetic variation to a population; however, because of their low rate of occurrence, mutations do not act as a major force in promoting widespread changes in a population. If mutations were the only type of change occurring in a population, that population would not evolve because mutations are so rare. However, the evolution of a population can involve changes in the frequency of existing alleles.

In this section we will discuss the second phenomenon that is required for microevolution: the action of evolutionary mechanisms that alter the prevalence of a given allele or genotype in a population. These mechanisms are natural selection, random genetic drift, migration, and nonrandom mating (Table 22.1). The collective contributions of these evolutionary mechanisms over many generations have the potential to promote widespread genetic changes in a population.

To consider the effects of these evolutionary mechanisms, we will examine how they can affect the type of genetic variation that occurs when a gene exists in two alleles in a population. As you will learn, these mechanisms can cause one allele or the other allele to be favoured, or they may create a balance in which both alleles are maintained in a population. Although we will discuss the effects of these mechanisms on genetic variation involving alleles of a single gene caused by mutation, keep in mind that these same evolutionary mechanisms can also affect the frequencies of new genes that arise in a population by gene duplication, exon shuffling, and horizontal gene transfer.

Natural Selection in Differential Reproductive Success of Individuals in a Population

As we discussed in Chapter 21, Charles Darwin and Alfred Wallace independently proposed the theory of evolution by natural selection. According to this theory, only a certain percentage of the offspring that a species produces will survive. This "struggle for existence" results in the selective survival of individuals that have inherited certain genotypes. Such genotypes confer greater **reproductive success**. In this regard, natural selection usually acts on two aspects of reproductive success. First, certain characteristics make organisms better adapted to their environment and more likely to survive to reproductive age; such organisms have a greater chance to reproduce and contribute offspring to the next generation. Therefore, natural selection favours individuals with adaptations that provide a survival advantage. Second, natural selection favours individuals that produce viable offspring. As discussed later in this chapter, traits that enhance the ability of individuals to reproduce are often subject to natural selection. An important point to keep in mind is that genetic variation is the fuel for natural selection. Population genetics is involved in studying changes in gene frequency. But also note that natural selection is not the only way that gene frequencies can change in a population. Later in this chapter you will also see that gene frequencies can change by random events in a population such as genetic drift and genetic bottlenecks.

Let's consider how natural selection can operate when a gene exists as two alleles in a population. Remember that natural selection acts on individuals, while evolution occurs at the population level. A modern description of natural selection can relate our knowledge of molecular genetics to the phenotypes of individuals.

1. Within a population, allelic variation arises from random mutations that cause differences in DNA sequences. A mutation that creates a new allele may alter the amino acid sequence of the encoded protein. This in turn may alter the function of the protein. Another source of genetic variation is through genetic recombination and random mating. During meiosis, followed by fertilization, new combinations of alleles are produced that can affect multigenic traits.

2. Some alleles, or allelic combinations, may encode proteins that enhance an individual's survival or reproductive

capability compared with that of other members of the population. For example, an allele may produce a protein that is more efficient at a higher temperature, conferring on the individual a greater probability of survival in a hot climate.

3. Individuals with beneficial alleles, or combinations of alleles, are more likely to survive and contribute their alleles to the gene pool of the next generation.

4. Over many generations allele frequencies of numerous different genes may change through natural selection, thereby significantly altering the characteristics of a population. The net result of natural selection is a population that is better adapted to its environment and more successful at reproduction.

As mentioned earlier, Haldane, Fisher, and Wright developed mathematical relationships to explain the phenomenon of natural selection. To begin our quantitative discussion of natural selection, we need to consider the concept of **Darwinian fitness**, which is the relative likelihood that a genotype will contribute to the gene pool of the next generation as compared with other genotypes. Darwinian fitness is a measure of reproductive success.

To examine Darwinian fitness, let's consider an example of a hypothetical gene existing in *A* and *a* alleles. We can assign fitness values to each of the three possible genotypes according to their relative reproductive success. For example, let's suppose that the average reproductive successes of the three genotypes are

AA produces five offspring
Aa produces four offspring
aa produces one offspring

By convention the genotype with the highest reproductive success is given a fitness value of 1.0. Fitness values are denoted by the variable *W*. The fitness values of the other genotypes are assigned values relative to this 1.0 value:

fitness of *AA*: $W_{AA} = 1.0$
fitness of *Aa*: $W_{Aa} = 4/5 = 0.8$
fitness of *aa*: $W_{aa} = 1/5 = 0.2$

Variation in fitness occurs because individuals with certain genotypes have greater reproductive success in a given environment. Such genotypes exhibit a higher fitness compared with others. Natural selection acts on phenotypes that are derived from an individual's genotype.

Likewise, the effects of natural selection can be viewed at the level of a population. The average reproductive success of members of a population is called the **mean fitness of the population**. Over many generations as individuals with higher fitness values become more prevalent, natural selection also increases the mean fitness of the population. In this way the process of natural selection results in a population of organisms that is well adapted to its native environment and likely to be successful at reproduction.

Natural Selection Can Follow Different Patterns

By studying species in their native environments, population geneticists have discovered that natural selection can occur in several ways. In most of the examples described next, natural selection leads to adaptation so that a species is better able to survive to reproductive age.

Directional Selection **Directional selection** favours individuals consistently above or below the mean or median of a phenotypic distribution that have greater reproductive success in a particular environment. Different phenomena can initiate the process of directional selection. One way that directional selection can arise is that a new allele is introduced into a population by mutation, and the new allele confers a higher fitness in individuals that carry it (**Figure 22.3**). If the homozygote carrying the favoured allele has the highest fitness value, directional selection can cause this favoured allele to eventually become predominant in the population, perhaps even becoming a monomorphic allele. An excellent example of directional selection occurs in "oldfield" mice (*Peromyscus polionotus*) in Florida: mice on the beach sand dunes have pale coats, while mice found inland have brown coats. The coat colours have been shown effective in camouflaging the mice from predators, such as hawks, in each environment.

Other examples of directional selection may be due to a population being exposed to a prolonged change in its living environment. Under the new environmental conditions the relative fitness values can change to favour one genotype, and this will promote the elimination of other genotypes. As an example let's suppose a population of finches on a mainland already has genetic variation that affects beak size (refer back to Figure 21.2). A small number of birds migrate to an island where the seeds are generally larger than they are on the mainland. In this new environment birds with larger beaks would have a higher fitness because they would be better able to crack open the larger seeds and thereby survive to reproductive age. Over many generations directional selection would produce a population of birds carrying alleles that promote larger beak size.

Stabilizing Selection **Stabilizing selection** favours the survival of individuals with intermediate phenotypes. The extreme values of a trait are selected against. Stabilizing selection tends to decrease genetic diversity. An example of stabilizing selection involves clutch size (the number of eggs laid) in birds, which was first proposed by British biologist David Lack in 1947. Under stabilizing selection birds that lay too many or too few eggs per nest have lower fitness values than do those that lay an intermediate number of eggs (**Figure 22.4**). Laying too many eggs has the disadvantage that many offspring will die because of inadequate parental care and food. In addition the strain on the parents may decrease their likelihood of survival and therefore their ability to produce more offspring. Having too few offspring, however,

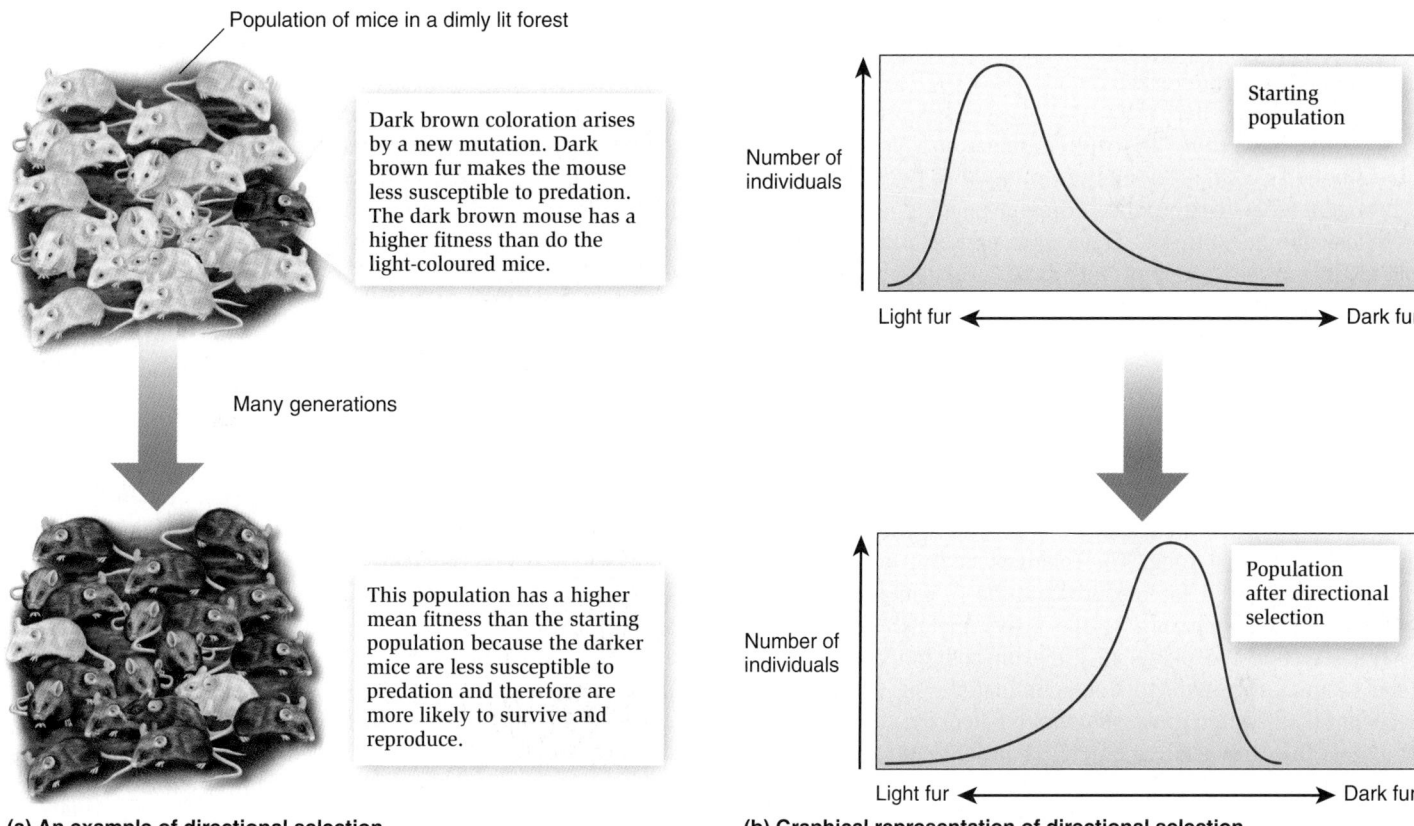

(a) An example of directional selection

(b) Graphical representation of directional selection

Figure 22.3   Directional selection.   This pattern of natural selection selects for a phenotype at one end of the spectrum that confers the highest fitness in the population's environment. **(a)** In this example a mutation for darker fur arises in a population of mice. This new genotype confers higher Darwinian fitness, because mice with dark fur can evade predators and are more likely to survive and reproduce. Over many generations, directional selection will favour the prevalence of darker individuals. **(b)** These graphs show the change in fur colour phenotypes in this mouse population before and after directional selection.

Concept check: *Suppose the climate on an island abruptly changed so that the average temperature was 10°C higher. The climate change is permanent. How would directional selection affect the genetic diversity in a population of mice on the island (1) over the short run and (2) over the long run?*

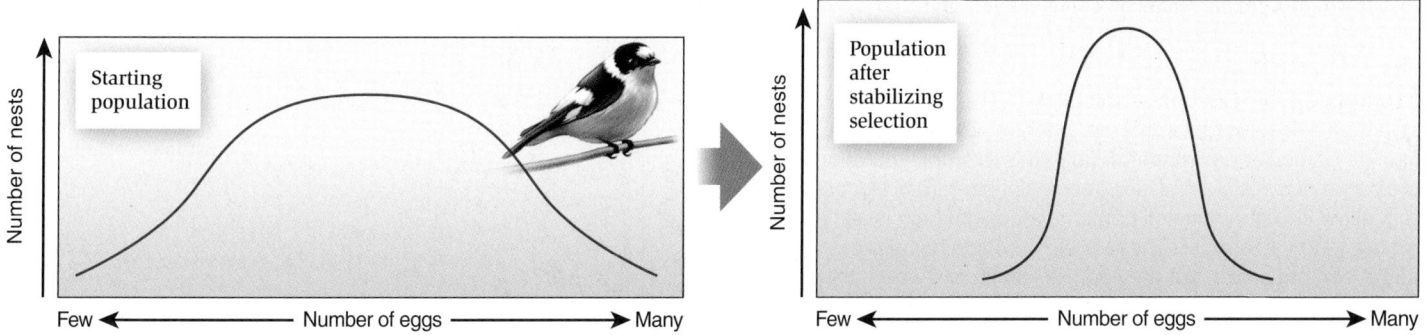

Figure 22.4   Stabilizing selection.   In this pattern of natural selection, the extremes of a phenotypic distribution are selected against. Those individuals with intermediate traits have the highest fitness. These graphs show the results of stabilizing selection on clutch size in a population of collared flycatchers (*Ficedula albicollis*). This process results in a population with less diversity and more uniform traits.

Concept check: *Why does stabilizing selection decrease genetic diversity?*

does not contribute many individuals to the next generation. Therefore, the most successful parents are those that produce an intermediate clutch size.

Disruptive Selection Disruptive selection (also known as diversifying selection) favours the survival of two or more different genotypes that produce different phenotypes. In disruptive selection the fitness values of a particular genotype are higher in one environment and lower in a different environment, while the fitness values of the other genotype vary in an opposite manner. Disruptive selection is likely to occur in populations that occupy diverse environments so that some members of the species will survive in each type of environmental condition. An example involves colonial bentgrass (*Agrostis tenuis*). In certain locations where this grass is found, such as South Wales, the soil in isolated places is contaminated with high levels of heavy metals, such as copper, because of human activities such as mining. The relatively recent metal contamination has selected for the proliferation of mutant strains of grass that show tolerance to the heavy metals. Such genetic changes enable the plants to grow on contaminated soil but tend to inhibit growth on uncontaminated soil. These metal-resistant plants often grow on contaminated sites that are close to plants that grow on uncontaminated land and do not show metal tolerance (**Figure 22.5**).

In the case of metal-resistant and metal-sensitive grasses, the members of a population occupy heterogeneous environments that are geographically continuous; members of the populations can freely interbreed. In other cases members of a single species may occupy two or more different environments that are geographically isolated from each other. Given enough time, disruptive selection caused by heterogeneous environments can eventually lead to the evolution of two or more different species, a process that will be described in Chapter 23.

Balancing Selection Contrary to a popular misconception, natural selection does not always eliminate the less fit alleles. **Balancing selection** is a type of natural selection that maintains genetic diversity in a population. Over many generations balancing selection can create a situation known as a **balanced polymorphism**, or a stable polymorphism, in which two or more alleles are kept in balance and therefore are maintained in a population over many generations.

Balancing selection does not favour one particular allele in the population. Population geneticists have identified two common ways that this pattern of selection can occur. First, for genetic variation involving a single gene, balancing selection favours the heterozygote rather than either corresponding homozygote. This situation is called **heterozygote advantage**. Balanced polymorphisms can sometimes explain the high

(a) Growth of *Agrostis tenuis* on contaminated soil

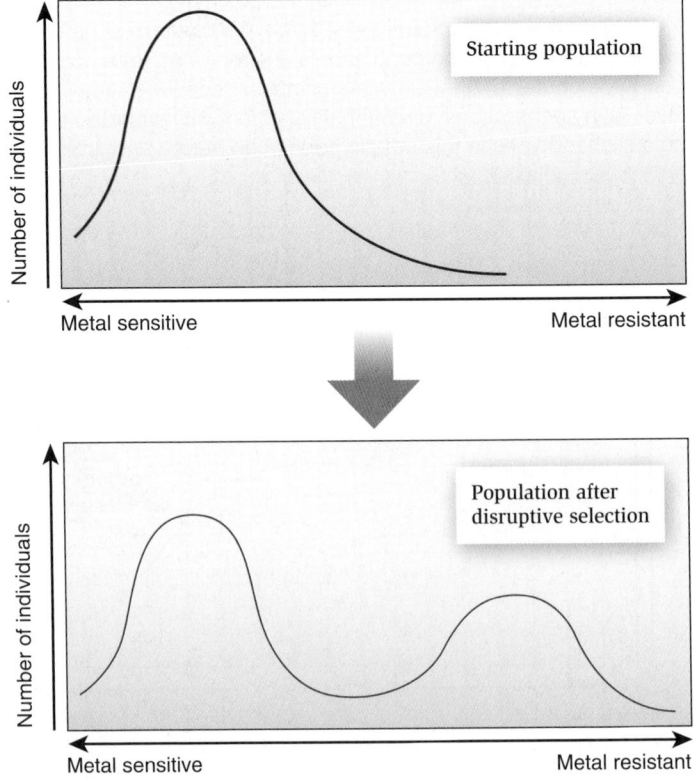

(b) Graphical representation of disruptive selection

Figure 22.5 Disruptive selection. This pattern of natural selection selects for two different phenotypes, each of which is most fit in its particular environment. **(a)** In this example mutations have created metal-resistant alleles in colonial bentgrass (*Agrostis tenuis*) that allow it to grow on soil contaminated with high levels of heavy metals, such as copper. These alleles provide high fitness where the soil is contaminated, but they confer low fitness where the soil is not contaminated. Because both metal-resistant and metal-sensitive alleles are maintained in the population, this situation is an example of disruptive selection caused by heterogeneous environments. **(b)** These graphs show the change in phenotypes in this bentgrass population before and after disruptive selection.

 Principle: *Populations of organisms evolve from one generation to the next. In this example the frequencies of metal-resistant alleles become more prevalent when populations of* A. capillaris *are exposed to toxic metals in the soil.*

frequency of alleles that are deleterious in a homozygous condition. A classic example is the H^S allele of the human β-globin gene, which was described in Chapter 13. A homozygous H^SH^S individual has sickle-cell anemia, a disease that leads to the sickling of the red blood cells. The H^SH^S homozygote has a lower fitness than a homozygote with two copies of the more common β-globin allele, H^AH^A. However, the heterozygote, H^AH^S, has the highest level of fitness in areas where malaria is endemic. Compared with H^AH^A homozygotes, heterozygotes have a 10% to 15% better chance of survival if infected by the malarial parasite *Plasmodium falciparum*. Therefore, the H^S allele is maintained in populations living in areas where malaria is prevalent, even though the allele is detrimental in the homozygous state (**Figure 22.6**). The balanced polymorphism results in a higher mean fitness of the population. In areas where malaria is endemic, a population composed of all H^AH^A individuals would have a lower mean fitness.

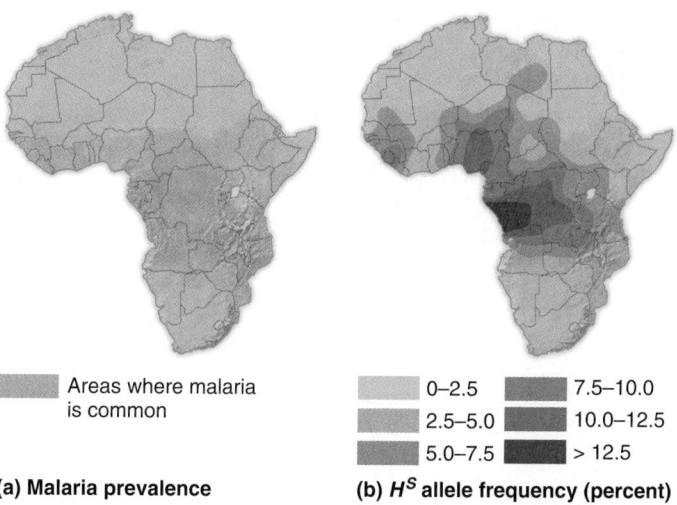

Areas where malaria is common

0–2.5   7.5–10.0
2.5–5.0   10.0–12.5
5.0–7.5   > 12.5

(a) Malaria prevalence   **(b) H^S allele frequency (percent)**

Figure 22.6   **Balancing selection and heterozygote advantage.**   In this pattern of natural selection genetic diversity is maintained in a population. This example shows balancing selection maintaining two alleles of the β-globin gene, designated H^A and H^S, in human populations in Africa. This situation occurs through heterozygote advantage, because the heterozygous condition confers resistance to malaria. (a) The geographic prevalence of malaria in Africa. (b) The frequency of the H^S allele of the β-globin gene in the same area. In the homozygous condition, the H^S allele causes the disease sickle-cell anemia. However, this sickle-cell allele is maintained in human populations as a balanced polymorphism, because in areas where malaria is prevalent, the heterozygote carrying one copy of the H^S allele has a higher fitness than either of the corresponding homozygotes (H^AH^A and H^SH^S).

Concept check: *If malaria were eradicated, what would you expect to happen to the frequencies of the H^A and H^S alleles over time?*

Negative frequency-dependent selection is a second way that natural selection can produce a balanced polymorphism. In this pattern of natural selection the fitness of a genotype decreases when its frequency becomes higher. In other words rare individuals have a higher fitness and common individuals have a lower fitness. Therefore, rare individuals are more likely to reproduce while common individuals are less likely, thereby producing a balanced polymorphism in which no genotype becomes too rare or too common.

An interesting example of negative frequency-dependent selection involves the elder-flowered orchid (*D. sambucina*), which was shown earlier in Figure 22.1. Throughout its range, both yellow- and purple-flowered individuals are prevalent. The explanation for this polymorphism is related to its pollinators, which are mainly bumblebees, such as *Bombus lapidarius* and *Bombus terrestris*. The pollinators increase their preference for the flower colour of *D. sambucina* as it becomes less common in a given area. One reason that this may occur is because *D. sambucina* is a rewardless flower—it does not provide its pollinators with any reward, such as sweet nectar. Pollinators are more likely to learn that the more common colour of *D. sambucina* in a given area does not offer a reward, and this may explain their preference for the flower colour that is less common. For example, in an area where the yellow-coloured flowers are common, the current generation of bumblebees may have learned that this colour does not offer a reward, and so they are more likely to visit purple-flowered plants.

Sexual Selection Is a Type of Natural Selection That Directly Promotes Reproductive Success

Thus far we have focused mainly on examples of natural selection that favour traits that promote the survival of individuals to reproductive age. This form of natural selection often produces adaptations for survival in particular environments. Now let's turn our attention to a form of natural selection, called **sexual selection**, that is directed at certain traits of sexually reproducing species that make it more likely for individuals to find or choose a mate and engage in successful mating. Darwin originally described sexual selection as "the advantage that certain individuals have over others of the same sex and species solely with respect to reproduction." Within a species, members of the same sex (typically males) compete for the opportunity to mate with members of the opposite sex. Such competition results in sexual selection.

In many species of animals sexual selection affects male characteristics more intensely than it does female. Unlike females, which tend to be fairly uniform in their reproductive success, male success tends to be more variable, with some males mating with many females and others not mating at all. (See Chapter 52 for a discussion of different mating strategies between the sexes.) Sexual selection results in the evolution of traits, called secondary sexual characteristics, that favour reproductive success. The result of this process is sometimes a significant difference between the appearances of the sexes in the same species, a situation called sexual dimorphism.

Sexual selection can be categorized as either **intrasexual selection**, between members of the same sex, or **intersexual selection**, between members of the opposite sex. Let's begin with intrasexual selection. Examples of traits that result from intrasexual selection in animals include horns in male sheep, antlers in male moose, and the enlarged claw of male fiddler crabs (**Figure 22.7a**). In many animal species males directly compete for the opportunity to mate with females or for a particular territory. Male fiddler crabs (*Uca paradussumieri*) enter the burrows of females that are ready to mate. If another male attempts to enter the burrow, the male already inside the burrow stands in the burrow shaft and blocks the entrance with his enlarged claw.

Now let's consider an example of intersexual selection, namely, female choice. This type of sexual selection often results in showy characteristics in males. **Figure 22.7b** shows a classic example that involves the Indian peacock (*Pavo cristatus*), the national bird of India. Male peacocks have long and brightly coloured tail feathers, which they fan out as a mating behaviour. Females select among males based on feather colour and pattern and the physical prowess of the display.

A less obvious type of intersexual selection is cryptic female choice, in which the female reproductive system can influence the relative success of sperm. As an example of cryptic female choice, the female genital tract of certain animals selects for sperm that tend to be genetically unrelated to the female. Sperm from males closely related to the female, such as brothers or cousins, are less successful than are sperm from genetically unrelated males. The selection for sperm can occur anywhere on the journey through the reproductive tract. The egg itself may even have mechanisms to prevent fertilization by genetically related sperm. Cryptic female choice occurs in species in which females may mate with more than one male, such as many species of reptiles and ducks. A similar mechanism is found in many plant species in which pollen from genetically related plants, perhaps from the same flower, is unsuccessful at fertilization, while pollen from unrelated plants is successful. One possible advantage of cryptic female choice is that it inhibits inbreeding, which is described later in this chapter. At the population level cryptic female choice can promote genetic diversity by favouring interbreeding among genetically unrelated individuals.

Sexual selection is sometimes a combination of both intrasexual and intersexual selection. During breeding season, male elk (*Cervus elaphus*) become aggressive and bugle loudly to challenge other male elk. Males spar by using their antlers, which usually turns into a pushing match to determine which elk is stronger. Female elk then choose the strongest bulls as their mates.

Sexual selection can explain traits that decrease an individual's chances of survival but increase their chances of reproducing. For example, the male guppy (*Poecilia reticulata*) is brightly coloured compared with the female. In nature, females prefer brightly coloured males. Therefore, in places with few predators, the males tend to be brightly coloured. However, in places where predators are abundant, brightly coloured males are less plentiful because they are subject to predation. In this

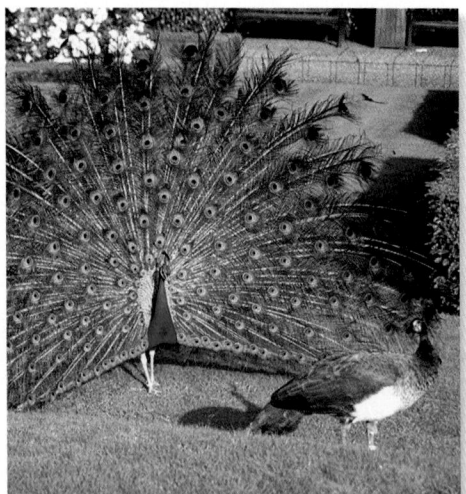

(a) Intrasexual selection   **(b) Intersexual selection**

Figure 22.7 Examples of the results of sexual selection, a type of natural selection.   (a) An example of intrasexual selection. The enlarged claw of the male fiddler crab is used in direct male-to-male competition. In this photograph, a male inside a burrow is extending its claw out of the burrow to prevent another male from entering. (b) An example of intersexual selection. Female peacocks choose males based on the males' colourful long tail feathers and the robustness of their display.

Concept check: *Male birds of many species have loud and elaborate courtship songs. Is this likely to be the result of intersexual or intrasexual selection? Explain.*

case, the relative abundance of brightly and dully coloured males depends on the balance between sexual selection, which favours bright colouring, and escape from predation, which favours dull colouring.

Many animals have secondary sexual characteristics, and evolutionary biologists generally agree that sexual selection is responsible for such traits. But why should males compete, and why should females be choosy? Researchers have proposed various hypotheses to explain the underlying mechanisms. One possible reason is related to the different roles that males and females play in the nurturing of offspring. In some species the female is the primary caregiver, while the male plays a minor role. In such species the Darwinian fitness of males and females may be influenced by their mating behaviour. Males increase their fitness by mating with multiple females. This increases their likelihood of passing their genes on to the next generation. By comparison females may produce relatively few offspring and their reproductive success may not be limited by the number of available males. Females will have higher fitness if they choose males that are good defenders of their territory and have

alleles that confer a survival advantage to their offspring. One measure of alleles that confer higher fitness is age. Males that live to an older age are more likely to carry beneficial alleles. Many research studies involving female choice have shown that females tend to select traits that are more likely to be well developed in older males than they are in immature males. In certain species of birds, for example, females tend to choose males with a larger repertoire of songs, which is more likely to occur in older males.

Overall, sexual selection is a form of natural selection in which the evolution of certain traits occurs differently between the two sexes. Sexual selection is not some extra force in opposition to natural selection; it is governed by the same processes involved in the evolution of traits that are not directly related to sex. Sexual selection can be directional, stabilizing, disruptive, or balancing. For example, directional selection probably played an important role in the evolution of the large and brightly coloured tail of the male peacock. As described next, sexual selection can be diversifying if females select for males with different traits.

FEATURE INVESTIGATION

Seehausen and van Alphen Found That Male Coloration in African Cichlids Is Subject to Female Choice

Cichlids are tropical freshwater fish that are popular among aquarium enthusiasts. This family of fish (Cichlidae) has more different species than any other vertebrate family. The more than 3,000 species vary with regard to body shape, coloration, behaviour, and feeding habits. By far the greatest diversity of these fish is found in Lake Victoria, Lake Malawi, and Lake Tanganyika in East Africa, where, collectively, more than 1,800 species are found. Lake Victoria, for example, has 500 species.

Cichlids have complex mating behaviour and brood care. Females play an important role in choosing males with particular characteristics. To study the importance of female choice, population geneticists Ole Seehausen and Jacques van Alphen investigated the effect of male coloration of *Pundamilia pundamilia* and *Pundamilia nyererei*. In some locations *P. pundamilia* and *P. nyererei* do not readily interbreed and behave like two distinct biological species, while in other places they behave like a single interbreeding species with two colour morphs. They can interbreed to produce viable offspring, and both inhabit Lake Victoria. Males of both species have blackish underparts and blackish vertical bars on their sides (**Figure 22.8a**). *P. pundamilia* males are greyish white on top and on the sides, and they have a metallic blue and red dorsal fin, which is the uppermost fin. By comparison, *P. nyererei* males are orange on top and yellow on their sides.

Seehausen and van Alphen hypothesized that females choose males for mates based on the males' coloration. The researchers took advantage of the observation that colours are obscured under orange monochromatic light. As seen in **Figure 22.8b**, males of both species look similar under these conditions. As shown in **Figure 22.9**, a female of one species

(a) Males of two species in normal light

(b) Males of two species in artificial light

Figure 22.8 Male coloration in African cichlids. **(a)** Two males (*Pundamilia pundamilia*, top, and *Pundamilia nyererei*, bottom) under normal illumination. **(b)** The same species under orange monochromatic light, which obscures their colour differences.

HYPOTHESIS Female African cichlids choose mates based on the males' coloration.

KEY MATERIALS Two species of cichlid, *Pundamilia pundamilia* and *Pundamilia nyererei*, were chosen. The males differ with regard to their coloration. A total of eight males and eight females (four males and four females from each species) were tested.

| | Experimental level | Conceptual level |

1 Place one female and two males in an aquarium. Each male is within a separate glass enclosure. The enclosures contain two males from each species.

This is a method to evaluate sexual selection via female choice in two species of cichlid.

2 Observe potential courtship behaviour for one hour. If a male exhibited lateral display (a courtship invitation) and then the female approached the enclosure that contained the male, this was scored as a positive encounter. This protocol was performed under normal light and under orange monochromatic light.

3 **THE DATA**

Female	Male	Light condition	Percentage of positive encounters*
P. pundamilia	*P. pundamilia*	Normal	16
P. pundamilia	*P. nyererei*	Normal	2
P. nyererei	*P. nyererei*	Normal	16
P. nyererei	*P. pundamilia*	Normal	5
P. pundamilia	*P. pundamilia*	Monochromatic	20
P. pundamilia	*P. nyererei*	Monochromatic	18
P. nyererei	*P. nyererei*	Monochromatic	13
P. nyererei	*P. pundamilia*	Monochromatic	18

*A positive encounter occurred when a male's lateral display was followed by the female approaching the male.

4 **CONCLUSION** Under normal light, where colours can be distinguished, *P. pundamilia* females prefer *P. pundamilia* males, and *P. nyererei* females prefer *P. nyererei* males.

5 **SOURCE** Seehausen, O., and van Alphen, J.J.M. 1998. The effect of male coloration on female mate choice in closely related Lake Victoria cichlids (*Haplochromis nyererei* complex). *Behav. Ecol. Sociobiol.* 42:1–8.

Figure 22.9   A study by Seehausen and van Alphen involving the effects of male coloration on female choice in African cichlids.

was placed in an aquarium that contained one male of each species within an enclosure. The males were within glass enclosures to avoid direct competition with each other, which would have likely affected female choice. The goal of the experiment was to determine which of the two males a female would prefer. Courtship between a male and female begins when a male swims toward a female and exhibits a lateral display (that is,

he shows the side of his body to the female). If the female is interested, she will approach the male, and then the male will quiver. Such courtship behaviour was examined under normal light and under orange monochromatic light.

As seen in the data, Seehausen and van Alphen found that the females' preference for males was dramatically different depending on the illumination conditions. Under normal light, *P. pundamilia* females preferred *P. pundamilia* males, and *P. nyererei* females preferred *P. nyererei* males. However, such mating preference was lost under orange monochromatic light. If the light conditions in their native habitats are similar to the normal light used in this experiment, female choice would be expected to separate cichlids into two populations: *P. pundamilia* females mating with *P. pundamilia* males and *P. nyererei* females mating with *P. nyererei* males. In this case sexual selection appears to have followed a diversifying mechanism in which certain females prefer males with one colour pattern while other females prefer males with a different colour pattern. When this occurs, a possible outcome of such sexual selection is that it can separate one large population into smaller populations that selectively breed with each other and eventually become distinct species. It is interesting

to note that the authors used orange light treatment to simulate the recent environmental effects of eutrophication in Lake Victoria. Thus with increasing eutrophication of Lake Victoria cichlid mate recognition is obscured, which could lead to widespread cichlid hybridization. The topic of species formation is discussed in greater depth in Chapter 25.

Experimental Questions

1. What hypothesis was tested in the Seehausen and van Alphen experiment?
2. Describe the experimental design for this study, illustrated in Figure 22.9. What was the purpose of conducting the experiment under the two different light conditions?
3. What were the results of the experiment in Figure 22.9?

In Small Populations, Allele Frequencies Can Be Altered by Random Genetic Drift

Thus far we have focused on natural selection as an evolutionary mechanism that fosters genetic change. Evolution is simply the change in gene frequency, and in this chapter you will see that natural selection may not be the only force to change gene frequencies. Let's now turn our attention to other ways that the gene pool of a population can change. In the 1930s Sewall Wright played a large role in developing the concept of **random genetic drift**, which refers to changes in allele frequencies caused by random sampling error. The term *genetic drift* is derived from the observation that allele frequencies can "drift" randomly from generation to generation as a matter of chance. Thus random changes in gene frequency can arise through random events that are unrelated to fitness. Not all the gametes from one generation are equally represented in the next generation and relatively few gametes participate in fertilization to form zygotes of the next generation. Small populations are more affected by these random sampling events than are larger populations. These random events can change the allele frequency from one generation to another. Changes in allele frequencies caused by genetic drift happen regardless of the fitness of individuals that carry those alleles. Likewise, random sampling error can influence which alleles happen to be found in the gametes that fuse with each other in a successful fertilization.

What are the effects of genetic drift? Over the long run genetic drift favours either the loss or the fixation of an allele—when its frequency reaches 0% or 100% in a population, respectively. The rate at which an allele is either lost or fixed depends on the population size. **Figure 22.10** illustrates the potential consequences of genetic drift in large (*N* = 200) and small (*N* = 20) populations. This simulation involves the frequency of hypothetical *B* and *b* alleles of a gene for fur colour in a population of mice—*B* is the black allele and *b* is the white allele. At the beginning of this hypothetical simulation, which runs for 50 generations, all these populations had

Figure 22.10 Genetic drift and population size. The effects of random drift happen much more quickly in small populations than in large ones. Each line represents the change in allele frequency for a single population from random genetic drift on small (*N* = 20) and large populations (*N* = 200). In all cases, the starting allele frequencies are 0.5. Note that random drift causes either the elimination or the fixation of alleles more quickly in a small population.

 Principle: *Populations of organisms evolve from one generation to the next. Genetic drift randomly changes allele frequencies and (in the long run) can lead to the loss or fixation of an allele.*

identical allele frequencies: *B* = 0.5 and *b* = 0.5. In the small populations, the allele frequencies fluctuated substantially from generation to generation. Eventually, in one simulation the

B allele was eliminated, while in the other it was fixed at 100%. These small populations would then consist of only white mice or black mice, respectively. At this point the allele has become monomorphic and cannot fluctuate any further. By comparison the frequencies of *B* and *b* in the large population fluctuated much less. As discussed in Chapter 15, the relative effects of random sampling error are much less when the sample size is large. Genetic drift will eventually lead to allele loss or fixation even in large populations, but it will take many more generations to occur than it does in small populations.

In nature genetic drift can rapidly alter allele frequencies when population sizes are small. One example is called the **bottleneck effect**. A population size can be reduced dramatically by events such as earthquakes, floods, drought, and human destruction of habitat. Such occurrences can randomly eliminate most members of the population without regard to genetic composition. The period of the bottleneck, when the population size is very small, may be influenced by genetic drift. This happens primarily for two reasons. First, the surviving members may have allele frequencies that differ from those of the original population. Second, allele frequencies are expected to drift substantially during the generations when the population size is small. In extreme cases alleles can even be eliminated. Eventually, the bottlenecked population may regain its original size, but the new population is likely to have less genetic variation than the original one. A hypothetical example of this process is shown in **Figure 22.11**. In this example a starting population of frogs is found in three phenotypes: yellow, dark green, and striped. Because of a bottleneck caused by a drought, the dark-green variety is lost from the population.

As another example, the whooping crane (*Grus americana*) is an endangered species that suffered a severe population bottleneck; only 14 individuals were alive in 1938. Through conservation efforts the wild population has increased to more than 200 birds. These birds breed in Wood Buffalo National Park in Alberta and migrate to Aransas National Wildlife Refuge in Texas each year. However, it is estimated that only 33% of the pre-bottleneck genetic diversity remains in the population; with this low level of genetic diversity and small population size, a catastrophic event could eliminate the population.

Another common phenomenon in which genetic drift can have a rapid impact is the **founder effect**. This occurs when a small group of individuals separates from a larger population and establishes a colony in a new location. For example, a few individuals may migrate from a large continental population and become the founders of an island population. The founder effect differs from a bottleneck in that it occurs in a new location, although both effects reduce the size of a population. The founder effect has two important consequences. First, the founding population, which is relatively small, is expected to have less genetic variation than the larger original population from which it was derived. Second, as a matter of chance the allele frequencies in the founding population may differ markedly from those of the original population.

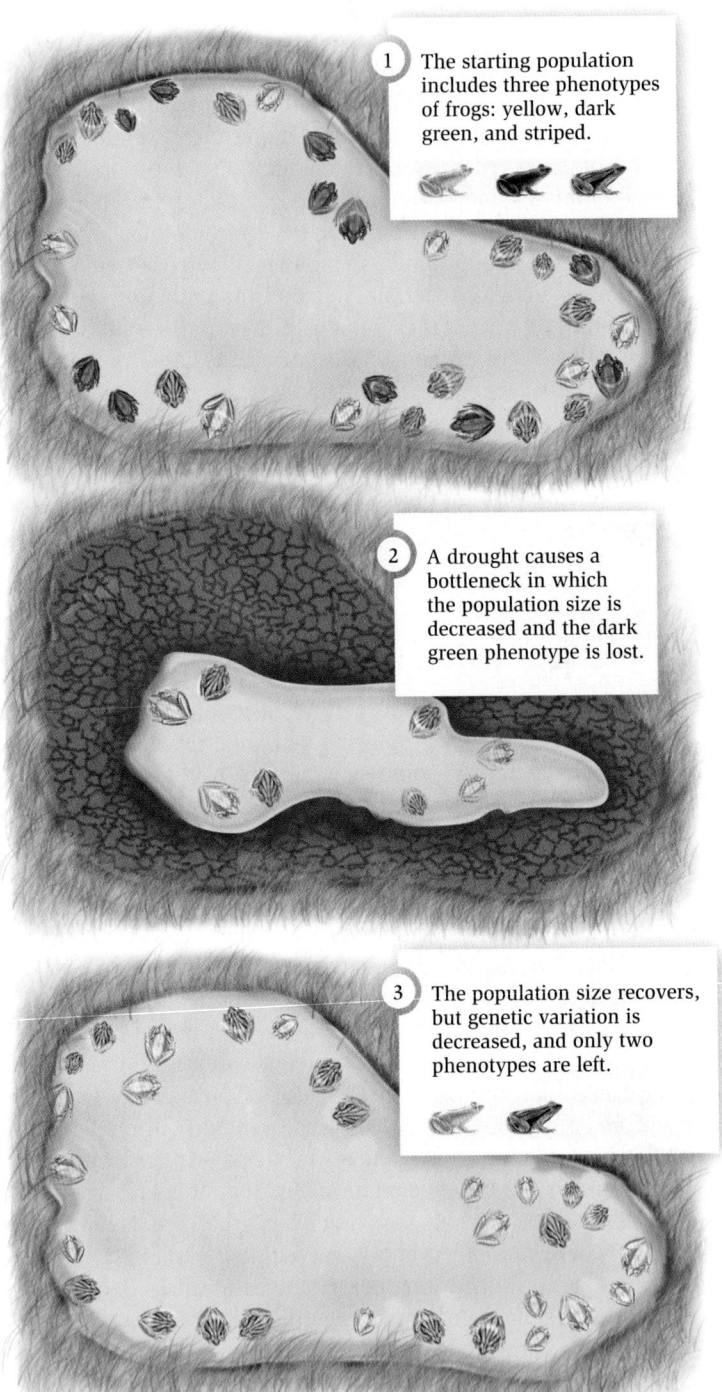

1 The starting population includes three phenotypes of frogs: yellow, dark green, and striped.

2 A drought causes a bottleneck in which the population size is decreased and the dark green phenotype is lost.

3 The population size recovers, but genetic variation is decreased, and only two phenotypes are left.

Figure 22.11   A hypothetical example of the bottleneck effect.   This example involves a population of frogs in which a drought dramatically reduced population size, resulting in a bottleneck. The bottleneck reduced the genetic diversity in the population.

Concept check: *How does the bottleneck effect undermine the efforts of conservation biologists who are trying to save species nearing extinction?*

Population geneticists have studied many examples in which isolated populations were founded via colonization by members of another population. Examples include the Old Order Amish of Lancaster County, Pennsylvania; the Hutterites from South Dakota; the Finnish subpopulation from Koilliskaira; and the Icelandic population. Many of these isolated populations have genetic disorders that occur in higher frequencies than in other human populations. For example, early-onset hypertension (high blood pressure) and dyslipidemia (abnormal cholesterol metabolism) are found more frequently in the French Canadian population from the Saguenay–Lac St-Jean region of Quebec. This population is relatively isolated, and its genealogical records date to the seventeenth century from approximately 2,600 French founders with minimal dilution from intermarriage. These populations have become very important in the identification of the genetic basis of disease since high levels of genetic homogeneity make it possible to detect the presence of specific disease genes in a large subsample of the population.

The Neutral Theory of Evolution Proposes That Genetic Drift Plays an Important Role in Promoting Genetic Change

In 1968 Japanese evolutionary biologist Motoo Kimura proposed that much of the variation seen in natural populations is caused by genetic drift. Because it is a random process, genetic drift does not preferentially eliminate any particular allele—it can eliminate both beneficial and deleterious alleles. Much of the time, genetic drift promotes **neutral variation**, which does not favour any particular genotype. According to Kimura's **neutral theory of evolution**, most genetic variation is due to the accumulation of neutral mutations that have attained high frequencies in a population via genetic drift.

Neutral mutations involve changes in genotypes that do not affect the phenotype of the organism, so they are not acted on by natural selection. For example, a mutation within a structural gene that changes a glycine codon from GGG to GGC would not affect the amino acid sequence of the encoded protein because of the redundancy of the genetic code. The resulting genotypes are theoretically equal in fitness. Because neutral mutations do not affect phenotype, they can spread throughout a population through genetic drift. This theory has been called **non-Darwinian evolution** and "survival of the luckiest" to contrast it with Darwin's "survival of the fittest" theory. Kimura agreed with Darwin that natural selection is responsible for adaptive changes in a species during evolution. His main idea is that much of the modern variation in gene sequences is explained by neutral variation rather than adaptive variation.

The sequencing of genomes from many species supports the neutral theory of evolution. When we examine changes of the coding sequence within structural genes, we find that nucleotide substitutions are more prevalent in the third base of a codon than they are in the first or second base. Mutations in the third base are often neutral because they do not change the amino acid sequence of the protein (refer back to Table 11.1). In contrast, random mutations at the first or second base are more likely to be harmful than beneficial and tend to be eliminated from a population. In addition, when mutations do change the coding sequence, they are more likely to involve conservative substitutions. For example, the difference between two alleles of a given gene may be the replacement of a nonpolar amino acid with another nonpolar amino acid. This change is conservative in the sense that it is less likely to affect protein function.

Migration Between Two Populations Tends to Increase Genetic Variation

Earlier in this chapter we considered how migration to a new location by a relatively small group can result in a founding population with an altered genetic composition caused by genetic drift. In addition, migration between two different established populations can alter genetic variation. As a hypothetical example, let's consider two populations of a particular species of deer that are separated by a mountain range running north and south (**Figure 22.12**). On rare occasions a few deer from the western population travel through a narrow pass between the mountains and become members of the eastern population. If the two populations are different with regard to genetic variation, this migration will alter the frequencies of certain alleles in the eastern population. Of course, this migration could occur in the opposite direction as well and would then affect the western population. This phenomenon, called **gene flow**, occurs whenever individuals migrate between populations having different allele frequencies.

In nature individuals commonly migrate in both directions. Such bidirectional migration has two important consequences. First, migration tends to reduce differences in allele frequencies between neighbouring populations. In fact population geneticists can evaluate the extent of migration between two populations by analyzing the similarities and differences between their allele frequencies. Populations that frequently mix their gene pools via migration tend to have similar allele frequencies, whereas isolated populations are more disparate because of the effects of natural selection and genetic drift. Second, migration tends to enhance genetic diversity within a population. As discussed earlier in this chapter, new mutations are relatively rare events. Therefore, a new mutation may arise in only one population. Migration may then introduce this new allele into a neighbouring population.

Nonrandom Mating Affects the Relative Proportion of Homozygotes and Heterozygotes in a Population

As mentioned earlier in this chapter, one of the conditions required to establish the Hardy-Weinberg equilibrium is random mating. This means that individuals choose their mates

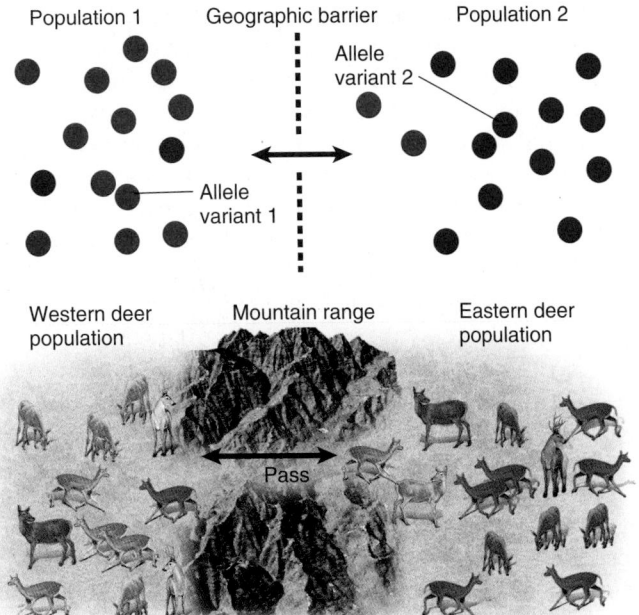

Figure 22.12   **Migration and gene flow.**   In this example two populations of a deer species are separated by a mountain range. On rare occasions a few deer from the western population travel through a narrow pass and become members of the eastern population, thereby changing some of the allele frequencies in the population and promoting gene flow.

Concept check: *What do you expect to happen to genetic differences between two populations in which there is considerable gene flow? What about two populations that have become isolated from each other?*

irrespective of their genotypes. In many cases, particularly in human populations, this condition is frequently violated. Such **nonrandom mating** takes different forms. In positive assortative mating, individuals with similar phenotypes are more likely to mate. If the similar phenotypes are due to similar genotypes, positive assortative mating tends to increase the proportion of homozygotes and decrease the proportion of heterozygotes in the population. The opposite situation, when dissimilar phenotypes mate preferentially, is called negative assortative mating. This type of mating favours heterozygosity. Nonrandom mating differs from sexual selection in that sexual selection results in a sexually dimorphic species: males and females differ in size, shape, or colour.

Another form of nonrandom mating involves the choice of mates based on their genetic history rather than their phenotypes. Individuals choose a mate who is part of the same genetic lineage. The mating of two genetically related individuals, such as cousins, is called **inbreeding**. This sometimes occurs in human societies and is more likely to take place in nature when population size becomes very small.

In the absence of other evolutionary forces, nonrandom mating does not affect allele frequencies in a population.

However, it will disrupt the balance of genotypes that is predicted by the Hardy-Weinberg equilibrium. As an example, let's consider inbreeding in a family pedigree. **Figure 22.13** illustrates a human pedigree involving a mating between cousins. Individuals III-2 and III-3 are cousins and have produced the daughter labelled IV-1. She is said to be inbred, because her parents are genetically related. The parents of an inbred individual have one or more common ancestors. In the pedigree of Figure 22.13, I-2 is the grandfather of both III-2 and III-3.

Inbreeding increases the relative proportions of homozygotes and decreases the likelihood of heterozygotes in a population. This happens because an inbred individual has a higher chance of being homozygous for any given gene than does a noninbred individual, because the same allele for that gene could be inherited twice from a common ancestor. For example, let's suppose that individual I-2 is a heterozygote, *Cc* (see the red lines in Figure 22.13). The *c* allele could pass from I-2 to

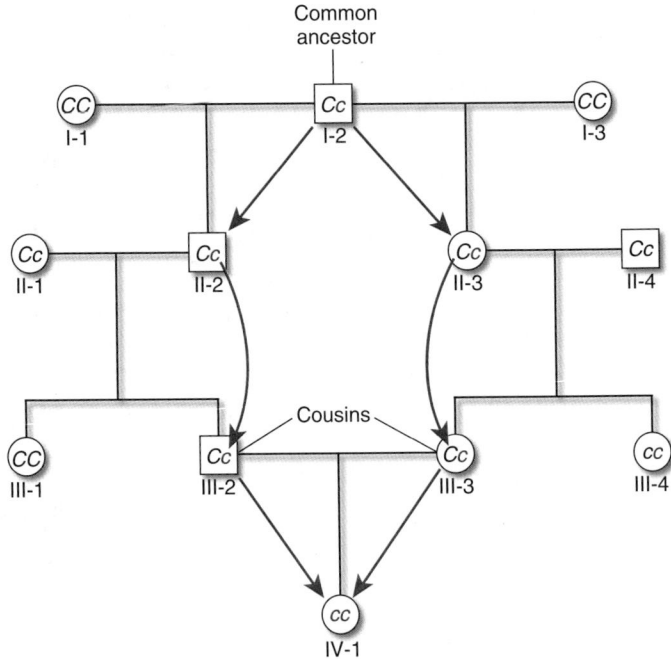

Figure 22.13   **A human pedigree containing inbreeding.**   The parents of individual IV-1 are genetically related. Therefore, individual IV-1 has a higher probability of being homozygous for genes than do members of a noninbred population.

Concept check: *Although inbreeding by itself does not affect allele frequencies, how might inbreeding indirectly affect allele frequencies over the course of many generations if natural selection was also occurring?*

BioConnections: *Many inherited human diseases show a recessive pattern of inheritance (see Table 15.2). Would inbreeding increase or decrease the likelihood of such diseases?*

II-2 to III-2, and finally to IV-1. Likewise, the *c* allele could pass from I-2 to II-3 to III-3, and then to IV-1. Therefore, IV-1 has a chance of being homozygous because she inherited both copies of the *c* allele from a common ancestor of both of her parents. Inbreeding does not favour any particular allele—it does not favour *c* over *C*—but it does increase the likelihood that an individual will be homozygous for any given gene.

Although inbreeding by itself does not affect allele frequencies, it may have negative consequences caused by recessive alleles. Rare recessive alleles that are harmful in the homozygous condition are found in all populations. Such alleles do not usually pose a problem because heterozygotes carrying a rare recessive allele are also rare, making it very unlikely that two heterozygotes will mate with each other. However, when inbreeding is practised, homozygous offspring are more likely to be produced. For example, rare recessive diseases in humans are more frequent when inbreeding occurs.

In natural populations inbreeding will lower the mean fitness of the population if homozygous offspring have a lower fitness value. This can be a serious problem as natural populations become smaller because of human habitat destruction. As the population shrinks, inbreeding becomes more likely because individuals have fewer potential mates from which to choose. The inbreeding, in turn, produces homozygotes that are less fit, thereby decreasing the reproductive success of the population. This phenomenon is called **inbreeding depression**. Conservation biologists sometimes try to circumvent this problem by introducing individuals from one population into another. For example, the endangered Florida panther (*Felis concolor coryi*) suffers from inbreeding-related defects, which include morphological abnormalities and poor sperm quality and quantity. To alleviate these effects, individuals from Texas have been introduced into the Florida population of panthers.

Summary of Key Concepts

- Population genetics is the study of genes and genotypes in a population. The focus is on understanding genetic variation.

22.1 Genes in Populations

- All the genes in a population constitute a gene pool.
- In population genetics a population is defined as a group of individuals of the same species that can interbreed with one another.
- Polymorphism refers to a genotype or phenotype that is found in two or more forms in a population. A monomorphic gene exists predominantly (>99%) as a single allele in a population. (Figure 22.1)
- An allele frequency is the number of copies of an allele divided by the total number of alleles in a population, while a genotype frequency is the number of individuals with a given genotype divided by the total number of individuals.

- The Hardy-Weinberg equation ($p^2 + 2pq + q^2 = 1$) relates allele and genotype frequencies. (Figure 22.2)
- The Hardy-Weinberg equation predicts an equilibrium if the population size is very large, mating is random, the populations do not migrate, no natural selection occurs, and no new mutations are formed.

22.2 Evolutionary Mechanisms and Their Effects on Populations

- Microevolution involves changes in a population's gene pool from one generation to the next.
- Sources of new genetic variation are random gene mutations, gene duplications, exon shuffling, and horizontal gene transfer. This variation is acted on by natural selection, genetic drift, migration, and nonrandom mating to alter allele and genotype frequencies and, ultimately, cause a population to evolve over many generations. (Table 22.1)
- Natural selection favours individuals with the greatest reproductive success. Darwinian fitness is a measure of reproductive success. The mean fitness of a population is its average reproductive success.
- Directional selection is a form of natural selection that favours one extreme of a phenotypic distribution. (Figure 22.3)
- Stabilizing selection is a second form of natural selection that favours an intermediate phenotype. (Figure 22.4)
- Disruptive selection is a third pattern of natural selection that favours two or more genotypes. An example occurs when a population occupies a diverse environment. (Figure 22.5)
- Balancing selection maintains a balanced polymorphism in a population. Examples include heterozygote advantage and negative frequency-dependent selection. (Figure 22.6)
- Sexual selection is a form of natural selection in which individuals with certain traits are more likely than others to engage in successful mating. This can lead to traits described as secondary sexual characteristics. (Figure 22.7)
- Seehausen and van Alphen discovered that female choice of mates in cichlids is influenced by male coloration. This is an example of sexual selection. (Figures 22.8, 22.9)
- Genetic drift involves changes in allele frequencies caused by random sampling error. It occurs more rapidly in small populations and leads to either the elimination or the fixation of alleles. (Figure 22.10)
- The bottleneck effect is a form of genetic drift in which a population size is dramatically reduced and then rebounds. During the bottleneck genetic variation may be lost from a population. (Figure 22.11)
- The neutral theory of evolution by Kimura indicates that much of the genetic variation observed in populations is due to the accumulation of neutral genetic changes.
- Gene flow occurs when individuals migrate between different populations and cause changes in the genetic composition of the resulting populations. (Figure 22.12)
- Inbreeding is a type of nonrandom mating in which genetically related individuals mate with each other. This tends to increase the proportion of homozygotes relative to heterozygotes. Inbreeding depression occurs when homozygotes have lower fitness. (Figure 22.13)

Test to Assess Your Learning

1. Population geneticists are interested in the genetic variation in populations. The most common type of genetic change that can cause polymorphism in a population is
   a. a deletion of a gene sequence.
   b. a duplication of a region of a gene.
   c. a rearrangement of a gene sequence.
   d. a single-nucleotide substitution.
   e. an inversion of a segment of a chromosome.

2. The Hardy-Weinberg equation characterizes the genotype frequencies and allele frequencies
   a. of a population that is experiencing selection for mating success.
   b. of a population that is extremely small.
   c. of a population that is very large and not evolving.
   d. of a community of species that is not evolving.
   e. of a community of species that is experiencing selection.

3. Considering the Hardy-Weinberg equation, what portion of the equation would be used to calculate the frequency of individuals that do not exhibit a disease but are carriers of a recessive genetic disorder?
   a. q
   b. p^2
   c. $2pq$
   d. q^2
   e. both (b) and (d)

4. Which of the following does not alter allele frequencies?
   a. selection
   b. immigration
   c. mutation
   d. inbreeding
   e. emigration

5. Which of the following statements is correct regarding mutations?
   a. Mutations are not important in evolution.
   b. Mutations provide the source for genetic variation that other evolutionary forces may act on.
   c. Mutations occur at such a high rate that they promote major changes in the gene pool from one generation to the next.
   d. Mutations are insignificant when considering evolution of a large population.
   e. Mutations are of greater importance in larger populations than in smaller populations.

6. In a population of fish, body coloration varies from a light shade, almost white, to a very dark shade of green. If changes in the environment resulted in decreased predation of individuals with the lightest coloration, this would be an example of _____ selection.
   a. disruptive
   b. stabilizing
   c. directional
   d. sexual
   e. artificial

7. Considering the same population of fish described in question 6, if the stream environment included several sandy, light-coloured bottom areas and lots of dark-coloured vegetation, both the light- and dark-coloured fish would have selective advantage and increased survival. This type of scenario could explain the occurrence of
   a. genetic drift.
   b. disruptive selection.
   c. mutation.
   d. stabilizing selection.
   e. sexual selection.

8. The microevolutionary force most sensitive to population size is
   a. mutation.
   b. migration.
   c. selection.
   d. genetic drift.
   e. all of the above.

9. The neutral theory of evolution differs primarily from Darwinian evolution in that
   a. neutral theory states natural selection does not exist.
   b. neutral theory states that most of the genetic variation in a population is due to neutral mutations, which do not alter phenotypes.
   c. neutral variation alters survival and reproductive success.
   d. neutral mutations are not affected by population size.
   e. both (b) and (c).

10. Populations that experience inbreeding may also experience
   a. a decrease in fitness caused by an increased frequency of recessive genetic diseases.
   b. an increase in fitness caused by increases in heterozygosity.
   c. very little genetic drift.
   d. no apparent change.
   e. increased mutation rates.

Articulate to Assess Your Learning

1. Explain the five conditions that are required for Hardy-Weinberg equilibrium.

2. List and define the four types of selection.

3. Define the founder effect.

4. Draw a graph to explain stabilizing selection, with labelled axes.

5. In sexual selection what conditions would favour the development of female choice? Male choice?

Collaborate to Assess and Extend Your Learning

1. Discuss four sources of new genetic variation in a population.
2. Could a nearly neutral mutation (e.g., a nonpolar amino acid substitution) become adaptive in a different environment?
3. Discuss why conservation biology uses population genetics concepts.
4. Discuss why human inbreeding may have become taboo in many societies.
5. List the short- and long-term effects of genetic drift on a small population of wildcats.
6. A principle of biology is that populations of organisms evolve from one generation to the next. Explain how genetic drift results in evolution.

Visit McGraw-Hill Ryerson Connect™ for additional study resources.

Origin of Species and Macroevolution

Chapter Outline

Different species of mosquitoes found in Canada. There are more than 80 different species of mosquitoes in Canada. This chapter will examine how different species come into existence.

The origin of living organisms has long been contemplated by philosophers, theologians, and scientists. At the time of Aristotle (fourth century BCE) most people believed that some living organisms could come into being by spontaneous generation, that nonliving materials could give rise to living organisms. For example, it was commonly believed that worms and frogs could arise from mud. By comparison, many religious teachings contended that species were divinely made and have remained the same since their creation. In contrast to these ideas the work of Charles Darwin provided the scientific theory of evolution by descent with modification. His theory helps us to understand the diversity of life, and, in particular, it presents a logical explanation for how pre-existing species can evolve into new species.

This chapter provides an exciting way to build on the information that we have considered in previous chapters. In Chapter 20 we examined how the first primitive cells in an RNA world evolved into prokaryotic cells and eventually eukaryotes. Chapter 21 surveyed the tenets on which the theory of evolution is built, and in Chapter 22 we viewed evolution on a small scale as it relates to populations. In this chapter we will consider evolution on a larger scale, as it relates to the formation of new species.

To biologists the concept of a **species** has come to mean a group of organisms that maintains a distinctive set of attributes in nature. You may already have an intuitive sense of this concept: It is obvious that giraffes and mice are different species. However, as you will learn in the first section of this chapter, the distinction between different, closely related species is often blurred in natural environments, so that it may not be easy to definitively distinguish two species (see the chapter-opening photo). Among other uses, species identification is important because it allows biologists to plan for the preservation and conservation of those species.

In this chapter we will also focus on the mechanisms that promote the formation of new species, a phenomenon called **speciation**. The term **macroevolution** refers to evolutionary changes that create new species and groups of species. It concerns the diversity of organisms established over long periods through the evolution and extinction of many species. Macroevolution occurs by the accumulation of microevolutionary changes, those that occur in a single gene (see Chapter 22). Natural selection results in the evolution of traits that promote environmental adaptation and reproductive success. In this chapter you will learn how the same evolutionary mechanisms that account for microevolution also play a role in the formation of new species.

23.1   SPECIES CONCEPTS

Learning Outcomes:

1. Outline the characteristics that biologists use to distinguish different species.
2. Describe different species concepts.
3. Compare and contrast prezygotic and postzygotic isolating mechanisms.

The number of species on Earth is astounding. In 1991 biologists P. R. Ehrlich and E. O. Wilson reported that approximately 1.4 million species of plants, animals, and microorganisms had been given scientific names, but they speculated that the true number of species on Earth is between 10 million and 100 million. Many species, especially prokaryotic organisms, have yet to be identified.

The difficulty of identifying whether certain groups constitute unique species is often rooted in the phenomenon that a single species can exist in two distinct populations that are in the slow process of evolving into two or more different species.

The amount of time that two populations are separated will have an important impact. If the time is short, the two populations are likely to be very similar and would be considered the same species. If the time is long, sufficient changes may have occurred so that the two populations would show unequivocal differences that allow them to maintain their distinctive set of features in nature. When studying natural populations, evolutionary biologists are often confronted with situations in which some differences between two populations are apparent, but it is difficult to decide whether the two populations truly represent separate species. When two or more groups within the same species display one or more traits that are somewhat different but not enough to warrant their placement into different species, biologists sometimes classify these groups as subspecies.

In this section we will begin by considering different attributes that biologists examine when deciding whether two groups of organisms constitute different species. In later sections we will consider mechanisms that explain how new species arise in nature.

The Members of a Species Have a Common Set of Characteristics That Distinguish Them from Other Species

Biologists adopt methods of species identification that are based on their own experience with the organisms they study. The characteristics that a biologist uses to identify a species depend, in large part, on the species in question. For example, the traits used to distinguish insect species are quite different from those used to identify different bacterial species. To identify most species, biologists rely on some or all of the following: morphological traits, the ability to interbreed, molecular features, ecological factors, and evolutionary relationships. To establish what a species represents, more than 20 different species concepts have been proposed by evolutionary biologists since 1942. A **species concept** is a way to define species and provide an approach to distinguishing one species from another. The two most commonly applied species concepts are the morphological species concept and the biological species concept.

Morphological Species Concept   According to the **morphological species concept**, species can be categorized based on their physical characteristics. Organisms are classified as the same species if their anatomical traits appear to be very similar. Likewise, microorganisms can be classified according to morphological traits at the cellular level. In addition, molecular features, such as DNA sequences, can now be used to compare organisms.

Although this concept is a common way for taxonomists to categorize species, it has a few drawbacks. First, it may be difficult to decide how many traits to consider when characterizing individuals. In addition, it is difficult to analyze quantitative traits that vary in a continuous way among members of the same species. Second, the degree of dissimilarity that separates different species may not be easy to decide on. Researchers often disagree about how much morphological difference is necessary to separate different species. Third, members of the same species sometimes look very different, and, conversely, members of different species sometimes look remarkably similar. For example,

Figure 23.1a shows two different females of the dragonfly species *Aeshna interrupta*, commonly called the Variable Darner. This species exists in several different-coloured morphs, which are individuals of the same species that have noticeably dissimilar appearances. **Figure 23.1b** shows two different species of damselflies, Hagen's bluet (*Enellagma hageni*) and the Marsh bluet (*Enellagma ebrium*), which look very similar.

Biological Species Concept   Why would biologists describe two species, such as Hagen's bluet and the Marsh bluet, as being different if they are morphologically similar? One reason is that they are unable to breed with each other in nature. Therefore, a second way to define a species is by the ability to interbreed. In the late 1920s geneticist Theodosius Dobzhansky proposed that each species is reproductively isolated from other species. Such **reproductive isolation** prevents one species from successfully interbreeding with other species. In 1942 evolutionary biologist Ernst Mayr expanded on Dobzhansky's ideas and formulated the **biological species concept**. According to the biological species concept, a species is a group of individuals whose members have the potential to interbreed with one another in nature to produce viable, fertile offspring but cannot successfully interbreed with members of other species. As discussed later in this section, reproductive isolation among species of plants and animals can occur by an amazing variety of different mechanisms.

The biological species concept has been used to distinguish many plant and animal species, especially those that look alike

(a)

(b)

Figure 23.1   Difficulties in applying the morphological species concept.   In some cases, members of the same species can appear quite different. (a) Two morphs of a single species, the Variable Darner (*Aeshna interrupta*), which is found across Canada. (b) Two different species of damselfly found in Canada, Hagen's bluet (*Enellagma hageni,* left) and the Marsh bluet (*Enellagma ebrium,* right), which look similar.

Concept check: *Can you think of another example of two different species that look very similar?*

but are reproductively isolated. Even so, it suffers from three main problems. First, in nature it may be difficult to determine if two populations are reproductively isolated, particularly if they are large populations with overlapping geographical ranges. Second, taxonomists have noted many cases in which two different species can interbreed in nature yet consistently maintain themselves as separate species. For example, different species of Yucca plants, such as *Yucca pallida* and *Yucca constricta*, do interbreed in nature yet typically maintain populations with distinct characteristics. For this reason they are viewed as distinct species based on the morphological species concept. Third, the biological species concept cannot be applied to asexual species, such as bacteria, nor can it be applied to extinct species. Likewise, some species of plants and fungi are known to reproduce only asexually. Therefore, the biological species concept has been primarily used to distinguish closely related species of animals and plants that reproduce sexually.

Other Species Concepts The **evolutionary lineage concept** was proposed by George Gaylord Simpson in 1961. A **lineage** is a series of species that forms a line of descent, with each new species the direct result of speciation from an immediate ancestral species. According to Gaylord, species should be defined based on the separate evolution of lineages. The **ecological species concept** was described by Leigh Van Valen in 1976. According to this viewpoint, each species occupies an ecological niche, which is the unique set of habitat resources that a species requires, as well as its influence on the environment and other species.

Most evolutionary biologists would agree that different methods are needed to distinguish the vast array of species on Earth. Even so, some evolutionary biologists have questioned whether it is valid to have many different species concepts. In 1998 Kevin de Queiroz suggested that there is only a single general species concept, which concurs with Simpson's evolutionary lineage concept and includes all previous concepts. According to de Queiroz's **general lineage concept**, each species is a population of an independently evolving lineage. Each species has evolved from a specific series of ancestors and, as a consequence, forms a group of organisms with a particular set of characteristics. Multiple criteria are used to determine if a population is part of an independent evolutionary lineage, and thus a species, which is distinct from others. Typically, researchers will use analyses of morphology, reproductive isolation, DNA sequences, and ecology to determine if a population or group of populations is distinct from others. Because of its generality, the general lineage concept has received significant support.

Reproductive Isolating Mechanisms Help to Maintain the Distinctiveness of Each Species

The identification of a species is not always a simple matter. For plants and animals the biological species concept proposed by Mayr has played a major role in the way that biologists study plant and animal species, partly because it identifies a possible mechanism for the process of forming new species—reproductive isolation. For this reason much research has been done to try to understand the mechanisms that prevent interbreeding between

different species, which are called **reproductive isolating mechanisms**. Keep in mind that populations do not intentionally erect these reproductive barriers. Rather, reproductive isolating mechanisms are merely a consequence of genetic changes that occur usually because a species becomes adapted to its own particular environment. The view of evolutionary biologists is that reproductive isolation typically evolves as a by-product of genetic divergence. Over time as a species evolves its own unique characteristics, some of those traits are likely to prevent breeding with other species.

Biologists have discovered many mechanisms that prevent closely related species from interbreeding. These mechanisms fall into two categories: prezygotic and postzygotic. **Prezygotic isolating mechanisms** prevent the formation of a zygote, while **postzygotic isolating mechanisms** block the development of a viable and fertile individual after fertilization has taken place. **Figure 23.2** summarizes some of the more common ways that reproductive isolating mechanisms prevent reproduction between different species. When two species do produce offspring, such an offspring is called an **interspecies hybrid**.

Prezygotic Reproductive Isolating Mechanisms We will consider five types of prezygotic mechanisms. The first is geographic isolation, which occurs when two different species live in geographically separate areas and do not have the opportunity to come together for mating. This is the case for Bicknell's and Gray-Cheeked thrushes in Canada. The second prezygotic isolating mechanism is temporal isolation, in which species reproduce at different times of the day or year. In the northeastern United States, for example, the two most abundant field crickets, *Gryllus veletis* and *Gryllus pennsylvanicus* (spring and fall field crickets, respectively), do not differ in song or habitat and are morphologically very similar (**Figure 23.3**). However, *G. veletis* matures in the spring, whereas *G. pennsylvanicus* matures in the fall. This minimizes interbreeding between the two species.

In the case of animals, mating behaviour and anatomy often play key roles in promoting reproductive isolation. An example of the third type of isolation, behavioural isolation, is found between the eastern meadowlark (*Sturnella magna*) and western meadowlark (*Sturnella neglecta*), both of which are found in Canada. The two species are nearly identical in shape, coloration, and habitat, and their ranges overlap in central North America. (**Figure 23.4**). For many years, they were thought to be the same species. When biologists discovered that the western meadowlark is a separate species, it was given the species name *neglecta* to reflect the long delay in its recognition. In the zone of overlap very little interspecies mating takes place between eastern and western meadowlarks, largely because of differences in their songs. The eastern meadowlark's song is a simple series of whistles, typically about four or five notes. By comparison, the song of the western meadowlark is a longer series of flutelike gurgling notes that go down the scale. These behavioural song differences enable meadowlarks to recognize potential mates as members of their own species.

A fourth type of isolation, called mechanical isolation, occurs when morphological features, such as size or incompatible genitalia, prevent two species from interbreeding. For example, male

Prezygotic isolating mechanisms

Species 1   Species 2

Habitat isolation: Species occupy different habitats, so they never come in contact with each other.

Temporal isolation: Species have different mating or flowering seasons or times of day or become sexually mature at different times of the year.

Behavioural isolation: Sexual attraction between males and females of different animal species is limited because of differences in behaviour or physiology.

Attempted mating

Mechanical isolation: Morphological features, such as size or incompatible genitalia, prevent two members of different species from interbreeding.

Gametic isolation: Gametic transfer takes place, but the gametes fail to unite with each other. This can occur because the male and female gametes fail to attract, because they are unable to fuse, or because the male gametes are inviable in the female reproductive tract of another species. In plants, the pollen of one species usually cannot generate a pollen tube to fertilize the egg cells of another species.

Fertilization

Postzygotic isolating mechanisms

Hybrid inviability: The egg of one species is fertilized by the sperm from another species, but the fertilized egg fails to develop past the early embryonic stages.

Hybrid sterility: An interspecies hybrid survives, but it is sterile. For example, the mule, which is sterile, is produced from a cross between a male donkey (*Equus asinus*) and a female horse (*Equus caballus*).

Hybrid breakdown: The F_1 interspecies hybrid is viable and fertile, but succeeding generations (F_2, and so on) become increasingly inviable. This is usually due to the formation of less-fit genotypes by genetic recombination.

Interspecies hybrid

Figure 23.2 Reproductive isolating mechanisms. These mechanisms prevent successful breeding between different species. They can occur before fertilization (prezygotic) or after fertilization (postzygotic).

BioConnections: *Look back at Figure 22.9. Is female choice an example of a prezygotic or postzygotic isolating mechanism?*

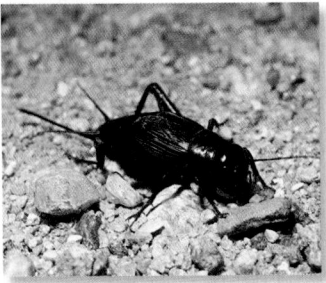

(a) Spring field cricket (*Gryllus veletis*)

(b) Fall field cricket (*Gryllus pennsylvanicus*)

Figure 23.3 An example of temporal isolation. Interbreeding between these two species of crickets does not usually occur because *Gryllus veletis* matures in the spring and *Gryllus pennsylvanicus* matures in the fall.

Concept check: *Is this an example of a prezygotic or a postzygotic isolating mechanism?*

North America

(a) **Eastern meadowlark** (*Sturnella magna*)

Eastern meadowlark
Western meadowlark
Zone of overlap

(b) **Western meadowlark** (*Sturnella neglecta*)

Figure 23.4 An example of behavioural isolation.
(a) The eastern meadowlark (*Sturnella magna*) and (b) western meadowlark (*Sturnella neglecta*) are very similar in appearance. The red region in this map shows where the two species' ranges overlap. However, very little interspecies mating takes place because of differences in their songs. Meadowlarks use their songs to recognize potential mates of their own species.

 Principle: *Populations of organisms evolve from one generation to the next. For these two species of meadowlarks, one evolutionary change that took place is that their mating songs became different.*

dragonflies use a pair of special appendages to grasp females during copulation. When a male tries to mate with a female of a different species, his grasping appendages do not fit her body shape.

A fifth type of prezygotic isolating mechanism can occur when two species attempt to interbreed, but the gametes fail to unite in a successful fertilization event. This phenomenon, called gametic isolation, is widespread among plant and animal species. In aquatic animals that release sperm and egg cells into the water, gametic isolation often serves to prevent interspecies hybrids. For example, closely related species of sea urchins may release sperm and eggs into the water at the same time. Researchers have discovered that sea urchin sperm have a protein on their surface called bindin that mediates sperm-egg attachment and membrane fusion. The structure of bindin is significantly different among different sea urchin species and thereby ensures that fertilization occurs between sperm and egg cells of the same species.

In flowering plants gametic isolation is a particularly vital mechanism to achieve reproductive isolation. As discussed in Chapter 37, plant fertilization is initiated when a pollen grain lands on the stigma of a flower and sprouts a pollen tube that ultimately reaches an egg cell (look ahead to Figure 37.15). When pollen is released from a plant, it could be transferred to the stigma of many different plant species. In most cases when a pollen grain lands on the stigma of a different species, either it fails to generate a pollen tube or the tube does not grow properly and reach the egg cell. The mechanism that controls pollen tube growth in plants has not been widely studied. The process is best understood in members of the mustard genus (*Brassica*), which includes turnips and cabbage. In these species pollen tube growth is known to involve molecules released by pollen grains that activate receptors found in the cell wall of the stigma. If a similar mechanism is used to achieve gametic isolation between different species, the receptors that recognize molecules released by the pollen grain must be very specific for the molecules of their own species and must fail to recognize those molecules released by pollen grains of other species.

Postzygotic Reproductive Isolating Mechanisms Let's now turn to postzygotic mechanisms of reproductive isolation, of which we will discuss three types. These mechanisms tend to be less common in nature, because they are more costly in terms of energy and resources used. The first such mechanism is **hybrid inviability**, in which an egg of one species is fertilized by a sperm from another species, but the fertilized egg cannot develop past the early embryonic stages. A second mechanism is **hybrid sterility**, in which an interspecies hybrid is viable but sterile. A classic example of hybrid sterility is the mule, which is produced by a mating between a male donkey (*Equus asinus*) and a female horse (*Equus caballus*) (**Figure 23.5**). Because a horse has 32 chromosomes per set and a donkey has 31, a mule inherits 63 chromosomes (32 + 31). When a mule tries to produce offspring, not all of its chromosomes have pairs, so it is sterile. Note that the mule has no species name because it is not considered a species because of this sterility. Finally, in the third mechanism, called **hybrid breakdown**, interspecies hybrids are viable and fertile, but subsequent generations harbour genetic abnormalities that are detrimental. These abnormalities can be caused by changes in chromosome structure, such as inversions. In hybrids a crossover may occur in the region that is inverted in one species but not the other. This will produce gametes with too little or too much genetic material. For this reason such hybrids often have offspring with developmental abnormalities.

23.2 | MECHANISMS OF SPECIATION

Learning Outcomes:

1. Describe how allopatric speciation can occur and how it can lead to adaptive radiation.
2. Outline three different mechanisms of sympatric speciation.

The formation of a new species, or speciation, is caused by genetic changes in a particular group that make it different from the species from which it was derived. As discussed in Chapter 22, random mutations in genes can be acted on by natural selection and other evolutionary mechanisms to alter the genetic composition of a population. New species commonly evolve in this manner. In addition interspecies matings changes in chromosome number, and horizontal gene transfer can also cause new species to arise. In all these cases the underlying cause of speciation is the accumulation of genetic changes that ultimately promote enough differences so that we judge a population to constitute a unique species.

Male donkey (*Equus asinus*) × Female horse (*Equus caballus*)

Mule

Figure 23.5 **An example of hybrid sterility.** When a male donkey (*Equus asinus*) mates with a female horse (*Equus caballus*), their offspring is a mule, which is sterile.

Concept check: *Is this an example of a prezygotic or a postzygotic isolating mechanism?*

Even though genetic changes account for the phenotypic differences we observe among living organisms, such changes do not fully explain the existence of many distinct species on our planet. Why does life diversify into the more or less discrete populations that we recognize as species? Two main explanations have been proposed:

1. Species are a consequence of adaptation to different ecological niches.
2. Species of sexually reproducing organisms arise via reproductive isolation.

Depending on the species involved, one or both factors can play a dominant role in the formation of new species. In this section we will begin by considering two different patterns of speciation that occur over many generations. We will then consider several examples of speciation occurring in nature. As you will learn, adaptation and reproductive isolating mechanisms are critical aspects of the speciation process.

Speciation Can Occur as a Linear or a Branching Process

Before we consider mechanisms of speciation, let's first examine the patterns of speciation that are commonly observed. By studying the fossil record and the diversity of modern species, evolutionary biologists have found two different patterns of speciation. During **anagenesis** (from the Greek, *ana,* meaning "up," and *genesis,* meaning "origin") a single species is transformed into a different species over many generations (**Figure 23.6a**). In this process evolutionary mechanisms cause the characteristics of the species to change. For example, a single species of fish in an isolated lake may evolve into a different species because of changes in available food sources.

By comparison, **cladogenesis** (from the Greek *clados,* meaning "branch," and *genesis,* meaning "origin") involves the division of a species into two or more species. In the case of the birds shown in **Figure 23.6b**, the original mainland species has remained relatively unchanged, while populations on neighbouring islands have evolved substantially different traits by natural selection. Such cladogenesis is a more common form of speciation. One reason is related to geographic isolation. If one or more individuals move to a new location that is geographically isolated from the original population, evolutionary mechanisms will operate independently on the two populations. This mechanism of speciation is described next.

Geographic Isolation Can Promote Allopatric Speciation

Although sexual reproduction is not a barrier to anagenesis, it is a barrier to cladogenesis. A population will evolve as a single unit if the members can successfully breed with one another, thereby preventing its divergence into two or more discrete species. The process of cladogenesis begins only when gene flow becomes limited between two or more populations. **Allopatric speciation** (from the Greek *allos,* meaning "other," and the

(a) Anagenesis   **(b) Cladogenesis**

Figure 23.6 A comparison between anagenesis and cladogenesis: two patterns of speciation. (a) Anagenesis is the change of one species into another, whereas (b) cladogenesis occurs when one population diverges into two or more different species.

Concept check: *Explain why cladogenesis requires reproductive isolation and anagenesis does not.*

Latin *patria,* meaning "homeland") is thought to be the most prevalent way for cladogenesis to occur. This form of speciation occurs when some members of a species become geographically separated from the other members. In some cases the separation may be caused by slow geological events that eventually produce quite large geographic barriers. For example, a mountain range may emerge and split a species that occupies the lowland regions. Or a creeping glacier may divide a population. **Figure 23.7** shows an interesting example in which geological separation promoted speciation. A fish called the porkfish (*Anisotremus virginicus*) is found in the Caribbean Sea, whereas the Panamic porkfish (*Anisotremus taeniatus*) is found in the Pacific Ocean. These two species were derived from an ancestral species that was split by the formation of the Isthmus of Panama about 3.5 million years ago. Since this event the two populations have been geographically isolated and have evolved into distinct species via natural selection and other evolutionary mechanisms.

Allopatric speciation can also occur via a second mechanism related to the founder effect that was described in Chapter 22. This occurs when a small population moves to a new location that is geographically separated from the main population. For example, a storm may force a small group of birds from a mainland to a distant island. In this case migration between the island and the mainland population is an infrequent event. In a relatively short time the founding population on the island may evolve into a new species. Different evolutionary forces may contribute to this rapid evolution. First, as discussed in Chapter 22 genetic drift can quickly lead to the random fixation of certain alleles and the elimination of other alleles from the small population. Another factor is natural selection, because the environment on the island may differ significantly from the mainland environment.

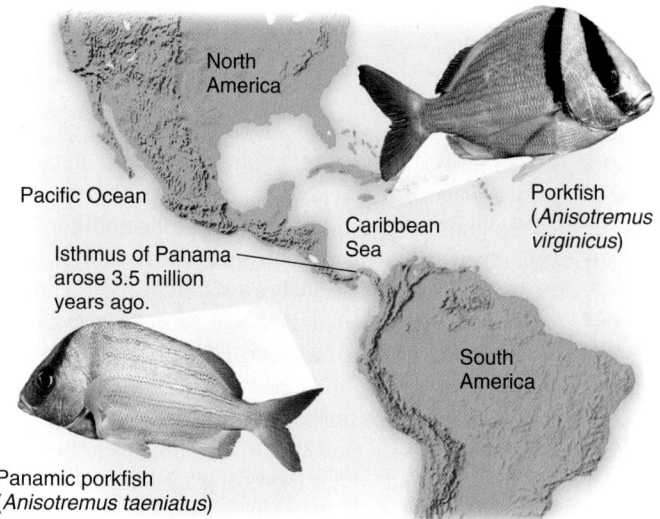

Figure 23.7 **An example of allopatric speciation.** An ancestral fish population was split into two by the formation of the Isthmus of Panama about 3.5 million years ago. Since that time different genetic changes have occurred in the two populations because of their geographic isolation; these changes eventually led to the formation of different species. The porkfish (*Anisotremus virginicus*) is found in the Caribbean Sea, and the Panamic porkfish (*Anisotremus taeniatus*) is found in the Pacific Ocean.

Principle: *All life is related by an evolutionary history. These two species of fish look similar because they share a common ancestor that existed in the fairly recent past.*

Biologists have investigated several examples of **adaptive radiation**, in which a single ancestral species has evolved into a wide array of descendant species that differ greatly in their habitat, form, or behaviour. For example, approximately 1,000 species of *Drosophila* are found dispersed throughout the islands. Evolutionary studies suggest that these were derived from a single colonization by one species of fruit fly. Another striking example is seen with a family of birds called honeycreepers (*Drepanidinae*) (**Figure 23.8**). Researchers estimate

The Hawaiian Islands are a showcase of the founder effect. The islands' extreme isolation, coupled with their phenomenal array of ecological niches, has enabled a small number of founding species to evolve into a vast assortment of different species.

(a) Migration of ancestor to the Hawaiian Islands

Figure 23.8 **An example of the founder effect with subsequent adaptive radiation.** The honeycreepers' ancestor is believed to be related to a Eurasian rosefinch that arrived on the Hawaiian Islands 3 million to 7 million years ago. Since that time at least 54 different species of honeycreepers (*Drepanidinae*) have evolved on the islands. A few selected examples are shown here. Adaptations to feeding have produced species with notable differences in beak morphology.

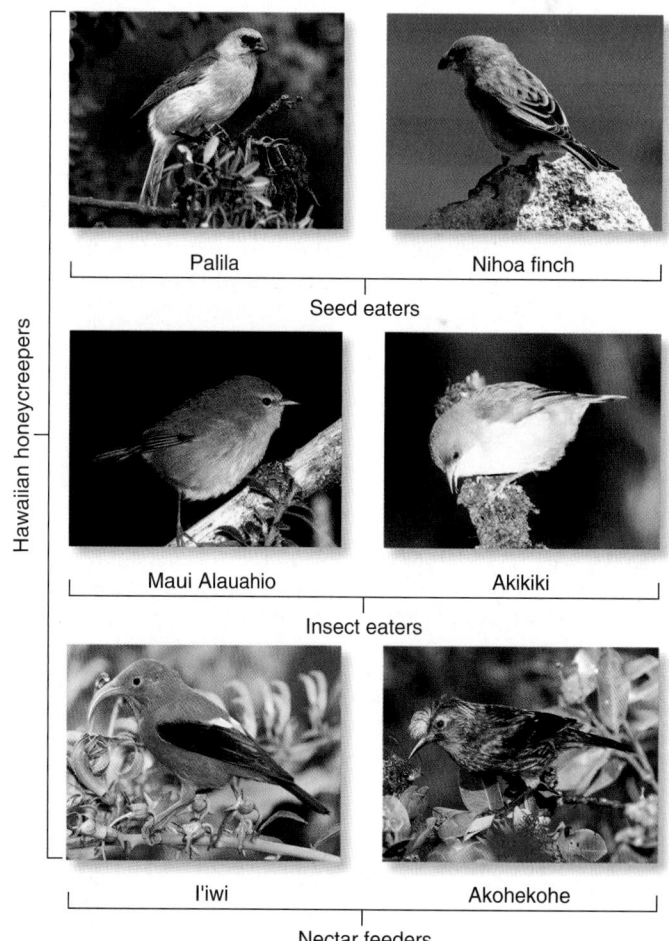

(b) Examples of Hawaiian honeycreepers

BioConnections: *Look back at Figure 22.5b. Discuss how disruptive selection played a role in the diversity of honeycreepers on the Hawaiian Islands.*

FEATURE INVESTIGATION

Podos Found That an Adaptation to Feeding Also May Have Promoted Reproductive Isolation in Finches

To investigate how environmental adaptation may contribute to reproductive isolation, in 2001 American evolutionary biologist Jeffrey Podos analyzed the songs of Darwin's finches on the Galápagos Islands. As in the honeycreepers, the differences in beak sizes and shapes among the various species of finches are adaptations to different feeding strategies. Podos hypothesized that changes in beak morphology could also affect the songs that the birds produce, thereby potentially affecting mate choice. The components of the vocal tract of birds, including the trachea, syrinx, and beak, work collectively to produce a bird's song. Birds actively modify the shape of their vocal tracts during singing. Beak movements are normally very rapid and precise.

Podos focused on two aspects of a bird's song. The first feature is the frequency range, which is a measure of the minimum and maximum frequencies in a bird's song. The second feature is the trill rate. A trill is a series of notes or group of notes repeated in succession. **Figure 23.9** shows a graphic depiction of the songs of Darwin's finches. As you can see, the song patterns of these finches are quite different from one another.

To quantitatively study the relationship between beak size and song, Podos first captured male finches on one of the Galápagos Islands (Santa Cruz) and measured their beak sizes (**Figure 23.10**). The birds were banded and then released into the wild; the banding provided a way to identify the birds whose beaks had already been measured. After release the songs of the banded birds were recorded on a tape recorder, and then their range of frequencies and trill rate were analyzed. Podos then compared the data for the Galápagos finches with a large body of data that had been collected on many other bird species. This comparison was used to evaluate whether beak size, in this case, beak depth—the measurement of the beak from top to bottom, at its base—constrained either the frequency range or the trill rate of the finches.

The results of this comparison are shown in the data of Figure 23.10. As seen here, the relative constraint on vocal

Figure 23.9 **Differences in the songs of Galápagos finches.** These spectrograms depict the frequency of each bird's song over time, measured in kilohertz (kHz). The songs are produced in a series of trills that have a particular pattern and occur at regular intervals. Notice the differences in frequency and trill rate among different species of birds.

HYPOTHESIS Changes in beak morphology that are an adaptation to feeding may also affect the songs of Galápagos finches and thereby lead to reproductive isolation between species.

KEY MATERIALS This study was conducted on finch populations of the Galápagos Island of Santa Cruz.

	Experimental level	Conceptual level
1 Capture male finches and measure their beak depth. Beak depth is measured at the base of beak, from top to bottom.		This is a measurement of phenotypic variation in beak size.

Figure 23.10 The effects of beak depth on song among different species of Galápagos finches.

2 Band the birds and release them back into the wild.

Band

Banding allows identification of birds with known beak depths.

3 Record the bird's songs on a tape recorder.

This is a measurement of phenotypic variation in song.

4 Analyze the songs with regard to frequency range and trill rate.

kHz

Time

The frequency range is the value between high and low frequencies. The trill rate is the number of repeats per unit time.

5 **THE DATA**

The data for the Galápagos finches were compared with a large body of data that had been collected on many other bird species. The relative constraint on vocal performance is higher if a bird has a narrower frequency range or a slower trill rate. These constraints were analyzed with regard to each bird's beak depth.

G. magnirostris

C. pallidus G. scandens

G. fortis

G. fuliginosa

C. psittacula

C. parvulus

C. olivacea

Relative vocal constraint

Beak depth (mm)

6 **CONCLUSION** Larger beak size, which is an adaptation to cracking open large, hard seeds, constrains vocal performance. This may affect mating song patterns and thereby promote reproductive isolation and, in turn, speciation.

7 **SOURCE** Podos, Jeffrey. 2001. Correlated evolution of morphology and vocal signal structure in Darwin's finches. *Nature* 409:185–188.

performance became higher as the beak depth became larger. This means that birds with larger beaks had a more narrow frequency range or a slower trill rate. Podos proposed that as jaws and beaks become adapted for strength to crack open larger seeds, they will be less able to perform the rapid movements associated with certain types of songs. In contrast the finches whose beaks were adapted to probe for insects or eat smaller seeds had less constraint on their vocal performance. From the perspective of evolution, the changes observed in song patterns for the Galápagos finches could have played an important role in promoting reproductive isolation, because song pattern is one factor involved in mate selection in birds. Therefore, a by-product of beak adaptation for feeding is that it also appears to have an effect on song pattern, possibly promoting reproductive

isolation. In this way populations of finches would have evolved into their own distinct species.

Experimental Questions

1. What did Podos hypothesize regarding the effects of beak size on a bird's song? How could changes in beak size and shape lead to reproductive isolation among the finches?
2. How did Podos test the hypothesis that beak morphology caused changes in the birds' songs?
3. Did the results of Podos's study support his original hypothesis? Explain. What is meant by the phrase "by-product of beak adaptation" and how does it apply to this particular study?

that the honeycreepers' ancestor arrived in Hawaii 3 million to 7 million years ago. This ancestor was a single species of finch, possibly a Eurasian rosefinch (*Carpodacus* sp.) or, less likely, the North American house finch (*Carpodacus mexicanus*). At least 54 different species of honeycreepers, many of which are now extinct, have evolved from this founding event to fill available niches in the islands' habitats. Chance mutations in the founder population produced bills with different morphologies. Individuals with stouter, stronger bills were able to crack tough seed husks. Thin, warbler-like bills were then adapted for picking insects from foliage and strong, hooked bills to root out wood-boring insects. And nectar-feeding honeycreepers evolved curved bills for extracting nectar from the flowers of Hawaii's endemic plants.

Hybridization Can Occur When Reproductive Isolation Between Two Populations Is Incomplete

Speciation sometimes occurs when members of a species are only partially separated or when a species lives in one small area or moves about very little. In these cases the geographic separation is not complete. For example, a mountain range may divide a species into two populations, but there may be breaks in the range where the two groups are connected physically. In these zones of contact the members of two populations can interbreed, although this tends to occur infrequently. Likewise, speciation may occur among species that live in one small area even though no large geographic isolation exists. Certain organisms move about so little that 100 to 1,000 metres may be sufficient to limit interbreeding between neighbouring groups. Plants, terrestrial snails, rodents, grasshoppers, lizards, and many flightless insects speciate in this manner.

Before complete reproductive isolation, the zones where two populations can interbreed are known as **hybrid zones**. **Figure 23.11** shows a hybrid zone along a mountain pass that connects two deer populations. For speciation to occur, the amount of gene flow within hybrid zones must become very limited (refer back to Figure 22.12). But how does this happen? As the two populations accumulate different genetic changes, this may decrease the ability of individuals from different populations to mate with each other in the hybrid zone. For example, natural selection in the western deer population may favour an increase in body size that is not favoured in the eastern population. Over time as this size difference between members of the two populations becomes greater, breeding in the hybrid zone may decrease. Larger individuals may not interbreed easily with smaller individuals because of mechanical isolation. Alternatively, larger individuals may prefer larger individuals as mates, while smaller individuals may also prefer each other. Once gene flow through the hybrid zone is greatly diminished, the two populations are reproductively isolated. Over many generations such populations may evolve into distinct species.

Lodgepole pine (*Pinus contorta*) and jack pine (*Pinus banksiana*) are two closely related species that readily create hybrids in zones where their ranges overlap, through northern Alberta and the Northwest Territories (**Figure 23.12**). While

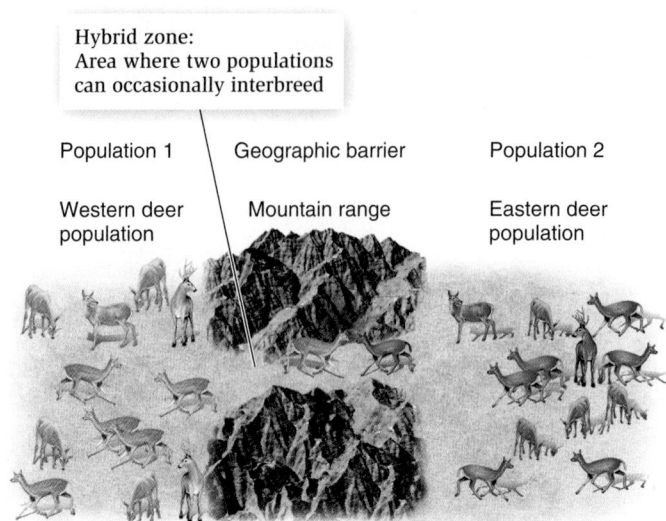

Figure 23.11 **A hypothetical hybrid zone.** A narrow mountain pass allows members of two deer populations to occasionally interbreed, creating hybrids between the two populations. Note the difference between Figure 22.12 of the previous chapter where migration allowed for gene flow between two populations. Here two closely related individuals from separate populations interbreed to form a hybrid zone. Sometimes these hybrid zones are geographically stable over a long period.

it's difficult to distinguish the hybrids from the original species based on morphology, an attempt to delineate the hybrid zone had been based on molecular markers, growth rates, climatic variations, and elevation. Additionally, unlike jack pine, lodgepole pine occupied several smaller climatic refugia during the last Ice Age, leading to the existence of several taxonomic races, further complicating attempts at biogeographic study. (Climatic

■ Distribution in Canada of lodgepole pine
■ Distribution in Canada of jack pine
■ Distribution in Canada of hybrid zone

Figure 23.12 Distribution in Canada of lodgepole pine (dark green), jack pine (light green), and hybrid zone (red).

refugia are places in which plants and animals can shelter during widespread climate change.)

Sympatric Speciation Occurs When Populations in Direct Contact Become Reproductively Isolated from Each Other

Thus far we have considered how geographic isolation can result in allopatric speciation. In the early stages of this process, reproductive isolation occurs because geographic separation prevents interbreeding. After long separation periods reproductive isolation can also involve the accumulation of genetic changes that directly affect reproduction, such as changes in breeding season or mating behaviour. By comparison **sympatric speciation** (from the Greek *sym*, meaning "together," and the Latin *patria*, meaning "homeland") occurs when members of a species that initially occupy the same habitat within the same range diverge into two or more different species. Sympatric speciation tends to involve abrupt genetic changes that quickly lead to the reproductive isolation of a group of individuals. Let's consider a few examples in which such sudden changes can quickly lead to the formation of a new species within the same geographic area as the original species.

One abrupt genetic change that can occur is a change in chromosome number. Plants tend to be more tolerant of changes in chromosome number than are animals, as discussed in Chapter 14. In particular, alterations in the number of sets of chromosomes, such as polyploidy, often produce healthy plants; self-fertilization and asexual reproduction help to promote this method of speciation in plants. Changes in the number of sets of chromosomes are relatively common in plants on an evolutionary timescale and can result in sympatric speciation. Polyploidy is so frequent in plants that it is a major mechanism of their speciation. In ferns and flowering plants about 30% to 50% of the species are polyploid. By comparison polyploidy is much less common in animals, but it can occur. For example, roughly 30 species of reptiles and amphibians have been identified that are polyploids derived from diploid ancestors.

As described in Chapter 14, complete nondisjunction of chromosomes during gamete formation can increase the number of chromosome sets in the same species (autopolyploidy) or in hybrids of different species (allopolyploidy). The formation of a polyploid can abruptly lead to reproductive isolation. As an example, let's consider the origin of a natural species of a plant called the common hemp nettle, *Galeopsis tetrahit*. Although originally Eurasian in distribution, this species became established in Canada by 1884 and is considered an agricultural weed. This species is thought to be an allotetraploid derived from two diploid species: *Galeopsis pubescens* and *Galeopsis speciosa* (**Figure 23.13**). These two diploid species contain 16 chromosomes each ($2n = 16$), while *G. tetrahit* contains 32. Its origin is not known, but one possibility is that an interspecies mating between *G. pubescens* and *G. speciosa* produced an allodiploid with 16 chromosomes (one set from each species) and then the allodiploid underwent complete nondisjunction to become an allotetraploid carrying four sets of chromosomes—two from each species.

The allotetraploid is fertile, because all its chromosomes occur in homologous pairs that can segregate evenly during meiosis. However, a cross between an allotetraploid and a diploid produces an offspring that is monoploid for one chromosome set and diploid for the other set. The chromosomes of the monoploid set cannot be evenly segregated during meiosis. These offspring are expected to be sterile, because they will produce gametes that have incomplete sets of chromosomes. This hybrid sterility, which is an example of a postzygotic isolating mechanism, causes the allotetraploid to be reproductively isolated from both diploid species. Therefore, this process could have led to the formation of a new species, *G. tetrahit*, by sympatric speciation.

Ploidy is often used in agronomy to combine useful traits of two separate species or to produce sterile variants of a single species. For example, Triticale is a sterile hybrid of wheat (*Triticum turgidum*) and rye (*Secale cereale*). In some situations autopolyploid fruits are preferred because they are seedless, such as varieties of watermelon, grape, and banana. These plants can be propogated through only cloning.

Sympatric speciation can also occur when genetic changes enable members of a species to occupy a new niche within the same geographic range as the original species. An example in which this process may be occurring involves colonial bentgrass (*Agrostis tenuis*), which was discussed in Chapter 22. In certain locations, such as South Wales, the soil in isolated patches is contaminated with high levels of heavy metals, such as copper. On these sites natural selection has promoted the proliferation of plants carrying alleles that confer resistance to the heavy metals. These alleles enable *A. tenuis* to grow on contaminated soil but tend to inhibit growth on normal, noncontaminated soil. Metal-resistant populations are continuous with populations that grow on uncontaminated land and do not show metal tolerance (refer back to Figure 22.5). Recently, the metal-tolerant plants have been starting to show a change in their flowering season. Over time if this process continues, the metal-tolerant population may evolve into a new species that cannot interbreed with the original (metal-sensitive) species.

23.3 THE PACE OF SPECIATION

Learning Outcome:

1. Compare and contrast the concepts of gradualism and punctuated equilibrium.

Throughout the history of life on Earth, the rate of evolutionary change and speciation has not been constant, although the degree of inconstancy has been debated since the time of Darwin. Even Darwin himself suggested that evolution can be fast or slow. **Figure 23.14** illustrates contrasting views concerning the rate of evolutionary change. These ideas are not mutually exclusive but represent two different ways to consider the tempo of evolution. The concept of **gradualism** suggests that each new species evolves continuously over long spans of time

(a) Possible formation of *G. tetrahit*

(b) Outcome of breeding among *G. tetrahit*, *G. pubescens*, and *G. speciosa*

Figure 23.13   **Polyploidy and sympatric speciation.**   This example shows how polyploidy may have caused reproductive isolation between three natural species of hemp nettle. The cross-fertilization of diploid species *Galeopsis pubescens* and *Galeopsis speciosa* produced an allotetraploid, *Galeopsis tetrahit;* middle panel). If *G. tetrahit* is mated with either of the other two species, the resulting offspring would be monoploid for one chromosome set and diploid for the other set, making them sterile (bottom panel). Therefore, *G. tetrahit* is reproductively isolated from the diploid species, making it a new species.

Concept check: *Suppose that* G. pubescens *was crossed to* G. tetrahit *to produce an interspecies hybrid as shown at the bottom of this figure. If this interspecies hybrid was crossed to* G. tetrahit, *how many chromosomes do you think an offspring would have? The answer you give should be a range, not a single number.*

(**Figure 23.14a**). The principal idea is that large phenotypic differences that produce new species are due to the accumulation of many small genetic changes. By comparison the concept of **punctuated equilibrium**, advocated in the 1970s by American paleontologists and evolutionary biologists Niles Eldredge and Stephen Jay Gould, suggests that the tempo of evolution is more sporadic (**Figure 23.14b**). According to this idea, species exist relatively unchanged for many generations. During this period, the species is in equilibrium with its environment. These long periods of equilibrium are punctuated by relatively

short periods (that is, on a geological timescale) during which evolution occurs far more rapidly, perhaps because of environmental changes via the founder effect or new mutations that are quickly acted on by natural selection.

In reality neither of the views presented in Figure 23.14 fully accounts for evolutionary change. The occurrence of punctuated equilibrium is often supported by the fossil record. Paleontologists rarely find a gradual transition of fossil forms. Instead, new species seem to arise rather suddenly in a layer of rocks, persist relatively unchanged for a very long time, and

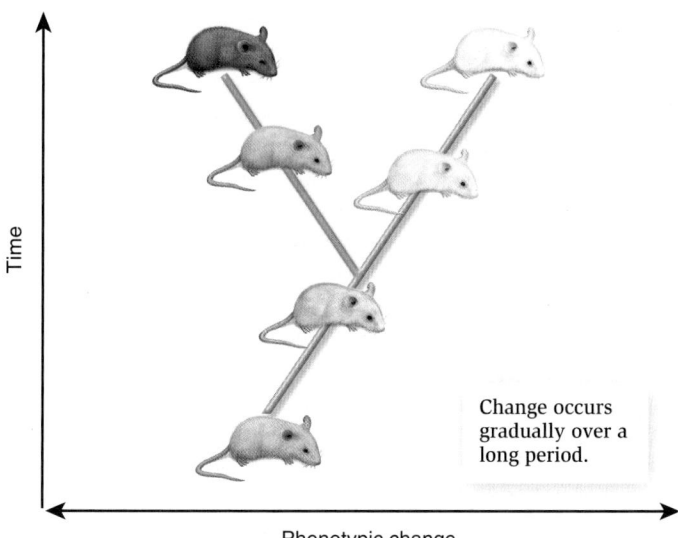

(a) Gradualism

Change occurs gradually over a long period.

Time

Phenotypic change

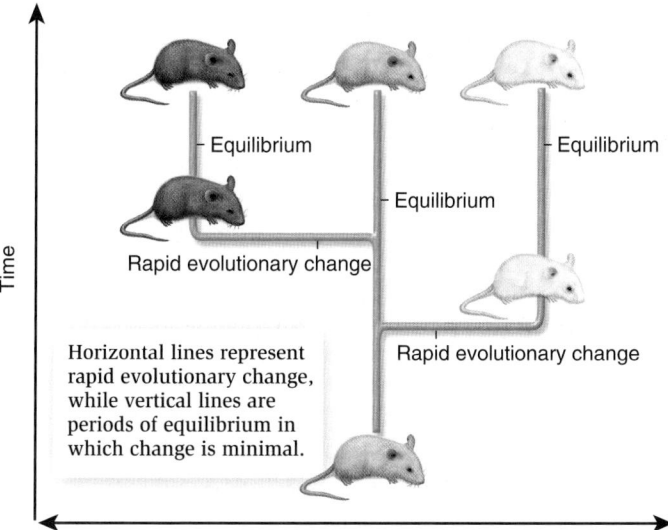

Equilibrium

Equilibrium

Equilibrium

Rapid evolutionary change

Horizontal lines represent rapid evolutionary change, while vertical lines are periods of equilibrium in which change is minimal.

Rapid evolutionary change

Time

Phenotypic change

(b) Punctuated equilibrium

Figure 23.14 A comparison of gradualism and punctuated equilibrium.   (a) During gradualism, the phenotypic characteristics of a species gradually change because of the accumulation of small genetic changes. (b) During punctuated equilibrium, species exist essentially unchanged for long periods, during which they are in equilibrium with their environment. These equilibrium periods are punctuated by relatively short periods of evolutionary change, during which phenotypic characteristics may change rapidly.

 Principle: *Populations of organisms evolve from one generation to the next. Gradualism and punctuated equilibrium are two different views regarding the pace of evolution.*

then become extinct. Scientists think that the transition period during which a previous species evolved into a new species was so short that few, if any, of the transitional members were preserved as fossils. Even so, these rapid periods of change were

probably followed by long periods of equilibrium that likely involved the additional accumulation of many small genetic changes, consistent with gradualism. As discussed earlier, rapid evolutionary change can be explained by genetic phenomena. Single gene mutations can have dramatic effects on phenotypic characteristics. Therefore, only a small number of new mutations are required to alter phenotypic characteristics, eventually producing a group of individuals that makes up a new species. Likewise, events such as changes in chromosome number and alloploidy can abruptly create individuals with new phenotypic traits. On an evolutionary timescale, these types of events can be rather rapid, because one or only a few genetic changes can have a major impact on the phenotype of the organism.

In conjunction with genetic changes, species may also be subjected to sudden environmental shifts that quickly drive the gene pool in a particular direction via natural selection. For example, a small group may migrate to a new environment in which different alleles provide better adaptation to the surroundings. Alternatively, a species may be subjected to a relatively sudden environmental event that has a major impact on survival. For example, the climate may change or a new predator may infiltrate the geographic range of the species. Natural selection can lead to a rapid evolution of the gene pool by favouring those genetic changes that allow members of the population to survive the climatic change or to have phenotypic characteristics that allow them to avoid the predator.

Finally, another issue associated with the speed of evolution is generation time. Species of large animals with long generation times tend to evolve much more slowly than do microbes with short generations. Many new species of bacteria will come into existence during our lifetime, while new species of large animals tend to arise on a much longer timescale. This is an important consideration for people because bacteria have great environmental impact; they are decomposers of both organic materials and pollutants in the environment, and they also play a role in many diseases of plants, animals, and humans.

23.4 EVO-DEVO: EVOLUTIONARY DEVELOPMENTAL BIOLOGY AND THE FORM OF NEW SPECIES

Learning Outcomes:

1. Describe how the spatial expression of genes, such as *BMP4* and *gremlin,* affects pattern formation.
2. Explain the relationship between the number of *Hox* genes and the body plan of an animal species.
3. Outline how differences in the growth rates of body parts can change the characteristics of species.
4. Describe how the study of the *Pax6* gene suggests that the eyes of different animal species evolved from a common ancestor.

As you have learned in this chapter, the origin of new species involves genetic changes that lead to adaptations to environmental niches or to reproductive isolating mechanisms that prevent closely related species from interbreeding. These genetic changes result in morphological and physiological differences that distinguish one species from another. In recent years many evolutionary biologists have begun to investigate how genetic variation produces species and groups of species with novel shapes and forms. The underlying reasons for such changes are often rooted in the developmental pathways that control an organism's morphology. **Evolutionary developmental biology** (referred to as **evo-devo**) is an exciting and relatively new field of biology that compares the development of different organisms in an attempt to understand ancestral relationships between organisms and the developmental mechanisms that bring about evolutionary change. In the past few decades developmental geneticists have gained a better understanding of biological development at the molecular level. Much of this work has involved the discovery of genes that control development in experimental organisms. As more and more organisms have been analyzed, researchers have become interested in the similarities and differences that occur between closely related and distantly related species. Evolutionary developmental biology has arisen in response to this trend.

A central question in evo-devo studies is how new morphological forms come into being. For example, how does a nonwebbed foot evolve into a webbed foot? Or how does a new organ, such as an eye, come into existence? As you will learn, such novelty arises through genetic changes, also called genetic innovations. Certain types of genetic innovation have been so advantageous that they have resulted in groups of many new species. For example, the innovation of feathered wings resulted in the evolution of many different species of birds. In this section you will learn that proteins that control developmental changes, such as cell-signalling proteins and transcription factors, often play a key role in promoting the morphological changes that occur during evolution.

The Spatial Expression of Genes That Affect Development Can Have a Dramatic Effect on Phenotype

In Chapter 17 we considered the role of genetics in the development of multicellular organisms. As you learned, genes that play a role in development may influence cell division and growth, cell differentiation, cell migration, and cell death. The interplay among these four processes creates an organism with a specific body form and function. As you might imagine, developmental genes are very important to the phenotypes of individuals. They affect traits, such as the shape of a bird's beak, the length of a giraffe's neck, and the size of a plant's flower. In recent years the study of development has indicated that developmental genes are key players in the evolution of many types of traits. Changes in such genes affect traits that can be acted on by natural selection. Furthermore, variation in the expression of such genes may be commonly involved in the acquisition of new traits that promote speciation.

You have seen that beak morphology was a key factor in the adaptive radiation of Darwin's finches. Analysis of expression patterns of two regulatory genes, *BMP4* and *CaM*, which are involved in beak development, showed differences in expression that was correlated with beak morphology. Thus small changes in genes that regulate development of body parts can results in large morphological changes. Some of these changes, such as those found in Darwin's finches, could allow for adaptation that allows exploitation of food resources.

As an example, let's compare the formation of a chicken's foot with that of a duck's. Developmental biologists have discovered that the morphological differences between a webbed and a nonwebbed foot are due to the differential expression of two different cell-signalling proteins called bone morphogenetic protein 4 (BMP4) and gremlin. The *BMP4* gene is homologous to that involved in beak morphology in Darwin's finches. The *BMP4* gene is expressed throughout the developing limb; this is shown in **Figure 23.15a**, in which the BMP4 protein is stained blue. The BMP4 protein causes cells to undergo apoptosis and die. The gremlin protein, which is stained brown in **Figure 23.15b**, inhibits the function of BMP4 and thereby allows cells to survive. In the developing chicken limb, the *gremlin* gene is expressed throughout the limb, except in the regions between each digit. Therefore, these cells die, and a chicken develops a nonwebbed foot (**Figure 23.15c**). By comparison, in the duck, *gremlin* is expressed throughout the entire limb, including the interdigit regions, which results in a webbed foot. Interestingly, researchers have been able to introduce gremlin protein into the interdigit regions of developing chicken limbs. This produces a chicken with webbed feet.

During the evolution of birds variation in the expression of these genes determined whether or not their feet were webbed. Mutations occurred that provided variation in the expression of the *BMP4* and *gremlin* genes. In terrestrial settings, having nonwebbed feet is an advantage because these are more effective at holding onto perches, running along the ground, and snatching prey. Therefore, natural selection would maintain nonwebbed feet in terrestrial environments. This process explains the occurrence of nonwebbed feet in chickens, hawks, crows, and many other terrestrial birds. In aquatic environments webbed feet are an advantage because they act as paddles for swimming, so genetic variation that produced webbed feet would have been promoted by natural selection. Over many generations this gave rise to the webbed feet that are now found in loons, ducks, geese, penguins, and other aquatic birds.

But how does having webbed or nonwebbed feet influence speciation? Perhaps this trait does not directly affect the ability of two individuals to mate. However, because of natural selection, birds with webbed feet become more prevalent in aquatic environments, while birds with nonwebbed feet are found in terrestrial locations. Therefore, reproductive isolation occurs because the populations occupy different environments.

The *Hox* Genes Have Been Important in the Evolution of a Variety of Body Plans Found in Different Species of Animals

The study of developmental genes has revealed interesting trends among large groups of species. *Hox* genes, which are discussed

Chicken   Duck

(a) BMP4 protein levels

Future interdigit regions

(b) Gremlin protein levels

(c) Comparison of a chicken foot and a duck foot

Figure 23.15 The role of cell-signalling proteins in the morphology of birds' feet. This figure shows how changes in developmental gene expression can produce new traits.
(a) Expression of the *BMP4* gene in the developing limbs. BMP4 protein is stained blue here. **(b)** Expression of the *gremlin* gene in the developing limbs. Gremlin protein is stained brown here. Note that *gremlin* is expressed in the interdigit region only in the duck. Gremlin inhibits BMP4, which causes programmed cell death. **(c)** Because BMP4 is not inhibited in the interdigit regions in the chicken, the cells in this region die, and the foot is not webbed. By comparison, inhibition of BMP4 in the interdigit regions in the duck results in a webbed foot.

Concept check: *What would you expect to happen to the morphology of the feet of ducks if the* gremlin *gene were underexpressed?*

in Chapter 17, are found in all animals. Developmental biologists have speculated that genetic variation in the *Hox* genes may have been a critical event that spawned the formation of many new body types, yielding many different species. As shown in **Figure 23.16**, the number and arrangement of *Hox* genes varies

considerably among different types of animals. Sponges, the simplest of animals, have at least one *Hox* gene, whereas insects typically have nine or more. In most cases multiple *Hox* genes occur in a cluster in which the genes are close to each other along a chromosome. In mammals such *Hox* gene clusters have been duplicated twice during the course of evolution to form four clusters, all slightly different, with a total of 38 genes.

Researchers propose that increases in the number of *Hox* genes have been instrumental in the evolution of many animal species with greater complexity in body structure. To understand how, let's first consider *Hox* gene function. All *Hox* genes encode transcription factors that act as master control proteins to direct the formation of particular regions of the body. Each *Hox* gene controls a hierarchy of many genes that includes other control genes, which regulate the expression of target genes, as well as structural genes, which encode proteins that ultimately affect the morphology of the organism. The evolution of complex body plans is associated with an increase not only in the number of regulatory genes—as evidenced by the increase in *Hox* gene complexity during evolution—but also in structural genes, which ultimately affect an organism's form and function.

But how would an increase in *Hox* genes enable more complex body forms to evolve? Part of the answer lies in the spatial expression of the *Hox* genes. In fruit flies, for example, different *Hox* genes are expressed in different segments of the body along the anteroposterior axis (refer back to Figure 17.14). Therefore, an increase in the number of *Hox* genes allows each of these master control genes to become more specialized in the region that it controls. One segment in the middle of the fruit fly body can be controlled by a particular *Hox* gene and form wings and legs, while a segment in the head region can be controlled by a different *Hox* gene and develop antennae. Therefore, research suggests that one way for new, more complex body forms to evolve is by increasing the number of *Hox* genes, thereby making it possible to form many specialized parts of the body that are organized along a body axis.

Three lines of evidence support the idea that *Hox* gene complexity has been instrumental in the evolution and speciation of animals with different body patterns. First, as discussed in Chapter 17, *Hox* genes are known to control body development. Second, as described in Figure 23.16, a general trend is observed in which animals with a simpler body structure tend to have fewer *Hox* genes and fewer *Hox* clusters in their genomes than do the genomes of more complex animals. Third, a comparison of *Hox* gene evolution and animal evolution bear striking parallels. Researchers can analyze *Hox* gene sequences among modern species and make estimates regarding the timing of past events. If the DNA sequences of homologous genes in two different species are fairly different, the modern genes evolved from an ancestral gene in the very distant past. In contrast, if two homologous genes are very similar, they arose from an ancestral gene that was more recent. Using this type of approach, geneticists can estimate when the first *Hox* gene arose by gene innovation; the date is difficult to pinpoint but is more than 600 million years ago. The single *Hox* gene found in the sponge has descended from this primordial *Hox* gene. In addition, gene duplications of

Figure 23.16   Relationship between *Hox* gene number and body complexity in different types of animals.   Researchers speculate that the duplication of *Hox* genes and *Hox* gene clusters played a key role in the evolution of more complex body plans in animals. A correlation seems to exist between increasing numbers of *Hox* genes and increasing complexity of body structure. The *Hox* genes are divided into four groups, called anterior, group 3, central, and posterior, based on their relative similarities. Each *Hox* gene family is represented by a different colour in this figure, and the duplication of *Hox* genes are shown as variants with the same colour. The pink portion is the chromosome on which the genes are shown.

Concept check: *What is the relationship between the total number of* Hox *genes in an animal species and its morphological complexity?*

BioConnections: *Look back at Figure 17.14. How is the expression of* Hox *genes related to segmentation and the anteroposterior axis?*

this primordial gene produced clusters of *Hox* genes in other species. Clusters, such as those found in modern insects, were likely to be present approximately 600 million years ago. A duplication of that cluster is estimated to have occurred around 520 million years ago. Remarkably, these estimates of *Hox* gene origins correlate with major speciation events in the history of animals. As described in Chapter 20, the Cambrian explosion, which occurred from 533 million to 525 million years ago, saw a phenomenal diversification in the body plan of invertebrate species. This diversification occurred after the *Hox* cluster was formed and was possibly undergoing its first duplication to create two *Hox* clusters. Also, approximately 420 million years ago, a second duplication produced species with four *Hox* clusters. This

event precedes the proliferation of tetrapods—vertebrates with four limbs—that occurred during the Devonian period, approximately 417 million to 354 million years ago. Modern tetrapods, such as mammals, have four *Hox* clusters. This second duplication may have been a critical event that led to the evolution of complex terrestrial vertebrates with four limbs.

Developmental Genes That Affect Growth Rates Can Also Have a Dramatic Effect on Phenotype and Can Lead to the Formation of New Species

In our example in Figure 23.15 a difference in the spatial expression of the *gremlin* gene affected whether a bird has nonwebbed or webbed feet. In this case, the expression determined if apoptosis would occur in a defined region. Another way that genetic variation can influence morphology is by influencing the relative growth rates of different parts of the body. The pattern whereby different parts of the body grow at different rates with respect to each other is called **allometric growth**. As an example, **Figure 23.17a** compares the progressive growth of the head between a human and chimpanzee. At the fetal stage, the size and shape of the heads look fairly similar. However, after this stage, the relative growth rates of certain regions become markedly different, thereby affecting the shape and size of the head in the adult. In the chimpanzee the jaw region grows faster, giving the chimpanzee a much larger and longer jaw. In the human the jaw grows more slowly and the region of the skull that surrounds the brain grows slightly faster. Therefore, humans have smaller jaws but larger skulls.

Changes in growth rates can also affect the developmental stage at which one species reproduces compared with that of another species. This can occur in two ways. One possibility is that the parts of the body associated with reproduction could grow and mature faster than the rest of the body. Alternatively, reproduction could happen at the same absolute age, but the development of nonreproductive body parts could be slowed down in one species, causing it to reproduce at an earlier stage. In either case the morphological result is the same—reproduction in the adult is observed at an earlier stage in one species than it is in another. The retention of juvenile traits in an adult organism is called **paedomorphosis** (from the Greek *paedo,* meaning "young" or "juvenile," and *morph,* relating to the form of an organism). It is particularly common among salamanders. Even though paedomorphic species have certain juvenile traits as adults, they still have the ability to reproduce successfully. For example, mudpuppies (*Necturus maculosus*) become mature and reproduce in the aquatic form, without changing into a terrestrial adult as do other salamander species (**Figure 23.17b**). The adult form of the common mudpuppy has gills and a large paddle-shaped tail, features that resemble those of the larval stage of other salamander species. These animals are found from southern Manitoba to southern Quebec (**Figure 23.17c**).

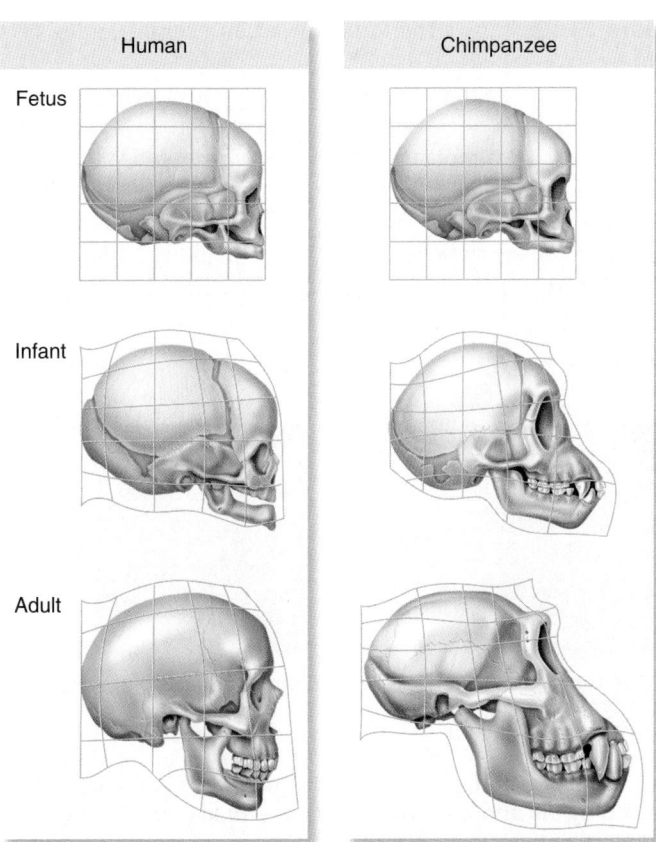

(a) The effects of allometric growth on head morphology in the human and chimpanzee

(b) Distribution of *Necturus maculosus* in Canada

(c) Paedomorphosis in the common mudpuppy

Figure 23.17 Effects of growth rate on development. (a) Allometric growth refers to the phenomenon in which one region of the body grows faster than another. Allometric growth explains why the heads of adult chimpanzees and humans have different shapes even though their fetal shapes are quite similar. (b) Distribution of the common mudpuppy in Canada. (c) Paedomorphosis occurs when an adult species retains characteristics that are juvenile traits in another related species. The common mudpuppy, *Necturus maculosus,* is permanently aquatic. It is the largest species of salamander in Canada and reproduces at the larval stage.

GENOMES AND PROTEOMES

The Study of the *Pax6* Gene Indicates That Different Types of Eyes Evolved from a Simpler Form

Thus far in this section we have focused on the roles of particular genes as they influence the development of the body. Explaining how a complex organ comes into existence is another major challenge for evolutionary biologists. Although it is relatively easy to understand how a limb could undergo evolutionary modifications to become a wing, flipper, or arm, it is more difficult to understand how a body structure comes into being in the first place. In his book *The Origin of Species* Charles Darwin addressed this question and admitted that the existence of complex organs was difficult to understand. As noted by Darwin, the eyes of vertebrate species are exceedingly complex, being able to adjust focus, let in different amounts of light, and detect a spectrum of colours. Darwin speculated that such complex eyes must have evolved from a simpler structure through the process of descent with modification. With amazing insight, he suggested that a very simple eye would be composed of two cell types, a photoreceptor cell and an adjacent pigment cell. The photoreceptor cell, which is a type of nerve cell, is able to absorb light and respond to it. The function of the pigment cell is to stop the light from reaching one side of the photoreceptor cell. This ancestral, two-cell arrangement would allow an organism to sense both light and the direction from which the light comes.

An ancestral eye would provide an additional way for an organism to sense its environment, possibly allowing it to avoid predators or locate food. Vision is nearly universal among animals, which indicates that there must be a strong selective advantage to better eyesight. Over time eyes could become more complex by enhancing the ability to absorb different amounts and wavelengths of light and also by refinements in structures, such as the addition of lenses that focus the incoming light.

Since the time of Darwin many evolutionary biologists have wrestled with the question of eye evolution. From an anatomical point of view, researchers have discovered many different types of eyes. For example, the eyes of fruit flies, squid, and humans are quite different. Furthermore, species that are closely related evolutionarily sometimes have different types of eyes. This observation led evolutionary biologists, such as Luitfried von Salvini-Plawen and Ernst Mayr, to propose that eyes may have independently arisen many different times during evolution. Based solely on morphology, such a hypothesis seemed reasonable and for many years was accepted by the scientific community.

The situation took a dramatic turn when geneticists began to study eye development. Researchers identified a master control gene, *Pax6*, that controls the expression of many other genes and thereby influences eye development in both rodents and humans. (Pax is an acronym for paired box. The protein encoded by this gene contains a domain called a paired box.) In mice and rats a mutation in this gene results in small eyes. A mutation in the human *Pax6* gene causes an eye disorder called aniridia, in which most of the eye is underdeveloped. Similarly, *Drosophila* has a homologous gene named *eyeless* that also causes a defect in eye development when mutant. The *eyeless* and *Pax6* genes are homologous; they were derived from the same ancestral gene.

In 1995 Swiss geneticist Walter Gehring and his colleagues were able to show experimentally that the abnormal expression of the *eyeless* gene in other parts of the fruit fly body could promote the formation of additional eyes. For example, by using genetic engineering techniques, they were able to express the *eyeless* gene in the region where antennae should form. As seen in **Figure 23.18a**, this resulted in the formation of fruit fly eyes where antennae are normally found! Remarkably, the expression of the mouse *Pax6* gene in *Drosophila* can also cause the formation of eyes in unusual places. For example, **Figure 23.18b** shows the formation of an eye on the leg of a fruit fly.

Note that the mouse *Pax6* master control gene switches on eye formation in *Drosophila*, but the eye produced is a *Drosophila* eye, not a mouse eye. This happens because the genes that are activated by the *Pax6* master control gene are all from the *Drosophila* genome. In fact, in *Drosophila*, the *Pax6* homolog called *eyeless* switches on a cascade involving 2,500 different genes required for eye morphogenesis. In more ancestral

(a) **Abnormal expression of *Drosophila eyeless* gene** — Normal eye; Eye where an antenna is normally found

(b) **Abnormal expression of mouse *Pax6* gene in a fruit fly leg** — Eye on the side of a leg

Figure 23.18 Formation of additional eyes in *Drosophila* caused by the abnormal expression of a master control gene for eye morphogenesis. (a) When the *Drosophila eyeless* gene is expressed in the antenna region, eyes are formed where antennae should be located. (b) When the mouse *Pax6* gene is expressed in the leg region of *Drosophila*, a small eye is formed there.

Concept check: *What do you think would happen if a researcher used genetic engineering techniques to express the* Drosophila eyeless *gene at the tip of a mouse's tail?*

eyes the *Pax6* gene would be expected to control a cascade of fewer genes.

Taken together, these results are consistent with two ideas. First, the *Pax6* gene and its *Drosophila* homolog are master control genes that promote the formation of an eye. The second idea is that the eyes of *Drosophila* and mammals are evolutionarily derived from the modification of an eye that arose once during evolution. If *Drosophila* and mammalian eyes had arisen independently, the *Pax6* gene from mice would not be expected to induce the formation of eyes in *Drosophila*.

Since the discovery of the *Pax6* and *eyeless* genes, homologs of this gene have been discovered in many different species. In all cases where it has been tested, this gene directs eye development. The *Pax6* gene and its homologs encode a transcription factor protein that controls the expression of many different genes. Gehring and colleagues have hypothesized that the eyes from many different species all evolved from a common ancestral form consisting of, as proposed by Darwin, one photoreceptor cell and one pigment cell (**Figure 23.19**). As mentioned, such a very simple eye can accomplish some rudimentary form of vision by detecting light and its direction. Eyes such as these are still found in modern species, such as the larvae of certain types of molluscs. Through evolution simple eyes were transformed into more complex types of eyes by modifications that resulted in the addition of more types of cells, such as lens cells and muscle cells.

Figure 23.19 **Genetic control of eye evolution.** In this diagram, genetic changes, under control of the ancestral *Pax6* gene, led to the evolution of different types of eyes.

1. The ancestral *Pax6* gene controlled other genes that produced a primitive two-celled eye.

Ancestral *Pax6* gene

Photoreceptor cell Pigment cell

Simple eye

2. During evolution, species diverged from each other, but each species retained a *Pax6* homolog.

Drosophila eyeless gene   Mammal *Pax6* gene

3. Over time, gene duplications and other genetic changes produced many more genes that added to eye complexity. These additional genes remained under the control of the *Pax6* gene and its homologs.

Ommatidia   Retina   Cornea
Lens
Optic nerve   Iris

***Drosophila* eye**   **Mammal eye**

Summary of Key Concepts

- A species is a group of organisms that maintains a distinctive set of attributes in nature. Speciation is the process whereby new species are formed. Macroevolution refers to the evolutionary changes that create new species and groups of species.

23.1 Species Concepts

- Different characteristics are used to identify species, including morphological traits, reproductive isolation, molecular features, ecological factors, and evolutionary relationships. (Figure 23.1)

- By studying the biological species concept, researchers have identified many reproductive isolating mechanisms, both prezygotic and postzygotic, that prevent two different species from breeding with each other. (Figures 23.2, 23.3, 23.4, 23.5)

23.2 Mechanisms of Speciation

- Anagenesis is the evolution of one species into another species, while cladogenesis is the divergence of one species into two or more different species. (Figure 23.6)

- Allopatric speciation occurs when a population becomes geographically isolated from other populations and evolves into one or more new species. When speciation occurs multiple times through the migration of populations into new environments, the evolutionary process is called adaptive radiation. (Figures 23.7, 23.8)

- Podos discovered that changes in beak depth associated with evolutionary changes involved with feeding may also promote reproductive isolation by altering the song pattern of finches. (Figures 23.9, 23.10)

- As allopatric speciation is occurring, limited reproduction between adjacent populations may take place in a hybrid zone, so that few interspecific hybrids are produced. (Figure 23.11, 23.12)

- Sympatric speciation occurs in the absence of geographic isolation. (Figure 23.13)

23.3 The Pace of Speciation

- Gradualism refers to a pace of speciation that involves many small genetic changes, while punctuated equilibrium is a pattern of evolution in which new species arise rapidly, on an evolutionary timescale, and then remain unchanged for long periods. (Figure 23.14)

23.4 Evo-Devo: Evolutionary Developmental Biology and the Form of New Species

- Evolutionary developmental biology is concerned with changes in developmental patterns that have given rise to new species and groups of species. These changes often involve variation in the expression of transcription factors and cell-signalling proteins.
- The spatial expression of genes that affect development can change phenotypes dramatically, as shown by the expression of the *gremlin* and *BMP4* genes to form webbed or nonwebbed feet in birds. (Figure 23.15)
- The evolution and duplication of *Hox* genes played an important role in producing groups of animals with specific body plans that are organized along an anteroposterior axis. (Figure 23.16)
- Patterns that affect the relative growth rates of body parts are called allometric growth. Paedomorphosis occurs when an adult form of one species retains characteristics that are juvenile traits in another related species. (Figure 23.17)
- The *Pax6* gene of mammals and its homolog in other species are master control genes that control eye development in animals. This result suggests that eyes arose only once during evolution. (Figures 23.18, 23.19)

Test to Assess Your Learning

1. Macroevolution refers to the evolutionary changes that
   a. occur in multicellular organisms.
   b. create new species and groups of species.
   c. occur over long periods.
   d. cause changes in allele frequencies.
   e. occur in large mammals.
2. The biological species concept classifies a species based on
   a. morphological characteristics.
   b. reproductive isolation.
   c. the niche the organism occupies in the environment.
   d. genetic relationships between an organism and its ancestor.
   e. both (a) and (b).
3. Which of the following would be considered an example of a postzygotic isolating mechanism?
   a. incompatible genitalia
   b. different mating seasons
   c. incompatible gametes
   d. mountain range separating two populations
   e. fertilized egg fails to develop normally
4. Hybrid breakdown occurs when species hybrids
   a. do not develop past the early embryonic stages.
   b. have a reduced lifespan.
   c. are infertile.
   d. are fertile but produce offspring with reduced viability and fertility.
   e. produce offspring that express the traits of only one of the original species.
5. The evolution of one species into a single new species is
   a. hybridization.
   b. anagenesis.
   c. cladogenesis.
   d. adaptive radiation.
   e. microevolution.
6. Founder events can lead to rapid speciation because of
   a. differences in natural selection on the new population versus the original population.
   b. genetic differences caused by genetic drift.
   c. enhanced gene flow between the new population and the original population.

   d. all of the above.
   e. (a) and (b) only.
7. A major mechanism of speciation in plants but not animals is
   a. anagenesis.
   b. polyploidy.
   c. hybrid breakdown.
   d. genetic changes that alter the organism's niche.
   e. both (a) and (d).
8. The concept of punctuated equilibrium suggests that
   a. the rate of evolution is constant, with short time periods of no evolutionary change.
   b. evolution occurs gradually over time.
   c. small genetic changes accumulate over time to allow for phenotypic change and speciation.
   d. long periods of little evolutionary change are interrupted by short periods of major evolutionary change.
   e. both (b) and (c).
9. Researchers suggest that an increase in the number of *Hox* genes
   a. would lead to reproductive isolation in all cases.
   b. could explain the evolution of colour vision.
   c. allows for the evolution of more complex body forms.
   d. results in the decrease in the number of body segments in insects.
   e. all of the above.
10. The observation that the mammalian *Pax6* gene and the *Drosophila eyeless* gene are homologous genes that promote the formation of different types of eyes suggests that
    a. *Drosophila* eyes are more complex.
    b. mammalian eyes are more complex.
    c. eyes arose once during evolution.
    d. eyes arose at least twice during evolution.
    e. eye development is a simple process.

Articulate to Assess Your Learning

1. Distinguish, with examples, among the terms *phenotype, genotype,* and *allele.* How do these relate to one another?
2. Distinguish between prezygotic isolating mechanisms and postzygotic isolating mechanisms. Give an example of each.
3. Define punctuated equilibrium.
4. What is polyploidy, and how can it lead to speciation?

Collaborate to Assess and Extend Your Learning

1. Discuss how geographic isolation can lead to speciation.
2. Evolution can proceed at different rates. Discuss the two models that address the speed at which evolution occurs.
3. Discuss the problems that exist with the morphological species concept, and give alternatives. What would be best applied to distinguish among species of beetles? algae? bacteria?
4. What is a sterile hybrid and how do they persist?

5. A principle of biology is that populations of organisms evolve from one generation to the next. Describe one example in which genes that control development played an important role in the evolution of different species.

Visit McGraw-Hill Ryerson Connect™ for additional study resources.

Taxonomy and Systematics

Chapter Outline

I n Chapter 23 we considered the formation of new species and learned that species diversity is enormous. Biologists estimate that between 10 million and 100 million species currently exist on our planet. To make some sense out of such amazing variation, and to be able to communicate with one another about it, biologists have categorized living organisms into groups of related species. **Taxonomy** (from the Greek *taxis*, meaning "order," and *nomos*, meaning "law") is the field of biology that is concerned with the theory, practice, and rules of classifying living and extinct organisms and viruses. Taxonomy results in the ordered division of species into groups based on similarities and dissimilarities in their characteristics. This task has been ongoing for more than 300 years. As we discussed in Chapter 21, John Ray attempted to classify all known forms of life based on anatomy and physiology and therefore was a pioneer in the field of modern taxonomy. Later, Ray's ideas were extended by Carolus Linnaeus.

Systematics is the study of biological diversity and the evolutionary relationships among organisms, both extinct and modern. In 1950 the German entomologist Willi Hennig began classifying organisms in a new way. Hennig proposed that evolutionary relationships should be inferred from new features shared by descendants of a common ancestor. Since that time biologists have applied systematics to the field of taxonomy. In other words taxonomic groups are now based on hypotheses regarding evolutionary relationships that are derived from systematics.

As scientists obtain additional information regarding genetic variation and evolutionary trends, taxonomic groupings have changed to accommodate the new and more accurate data. For example, until recently biologists thought there were two species of elephant in the world: the African savannah elephant (*Loxodonta africana*) and the Asian elephant (*Elephas maximus*). However, by analyzing the DNA of African elephants, a third species, now called the African forest elephant (*Loxodonta cyclotis*), was discovered (see the chapter-opening photo). This surprising finding was made somewhat by accident in 2001. A DNA identification system was set up to trace ivory poachers. By studying the DNA, researchers discovered that Africa has two different *Loxodonta* elephant species. The African forest elephant is found in the forests of central and western Africa. The African savannah elephant, which is larger and has longer tusks, lives on large, dry grasslands.

A new species: the African forest elephant. In 2001 biologists discovered that this is a unique species of elephant, now named *Loxodonta cyclotis*. This is one example of how scientists have changed taxonomic groupings in response to recent discoveries in molecular systematics.

In this chapter we will begin with a discussion of taxonomy from a traditional point of view. However, because recent information has dramatically changed our view of taxonomy, we will also consider newer ways to group organisms that are more logically based on evolutionary relationships. We will then examine how the analyses of morphological and molecular genetic data are used to place species into such groups.

24.1 TAXONOMY

Learning Outcomes:

1. Understand the hierarchy of groupings in taxonomy.
2. Identify the three domains of life.
3. Explain how species are named by using binomial nomenclature.

A hierarchy is a system of organization that involves successive levels. In biology every species is placed into several different groups. Some groups are very large and encompass many species that have fundamental similarities and, at the same time, many differences. For example, a leopard and a fruit fly are both classified as animals, though they differ in many traits. Leopards and lions are placed into a smaller family called felines (more formally named Felidae), which are predatory cats. The felines are a subset of the animal group, which has species that share many similar traits. Different species that are found in small taxonomic groups are likely to share many of the same characteristics.

In this section we will consider how biologists use a hierarchy to group similar species. We also survey the major groups of organisms and some of their common features. As you will learn later in this chapter, a few of our traditional ideas about taxonomy have been challenged as biologists have gathered new information regarding the genetic composition of modern species. For example, taxonomists now believe that fungi and animals are much more closely related than they once thought.

Taxonomy Provides a Hierarchy of Groups of Organisms

Modern taxonomy places species into progressively smaller hierarchical groups. Each group is called a **taxon** (plural: taxa). All forms of life are grouped within three domains: **Bacteria**, **Archaea**, and **Eukarya** (**Figure 24.1**). The terms *Bacteria* and *Archaea* are capitalized when referring to the domains. Alternatively, these terms can also refer to prokaryotic cells and species, in which case they are not capitalized. A single bacterial cell is called a bacterium, while a single archaeal cell is an archaeon. The domain Eukarya is now divided into seven supergroups, three of which correspond to the eukaryotic kingdoms: **Fungi**, **Plantae**, and **Animalia**. Scientists used to refer to a fourth kingdom, the so-called Protista. However, the Protista is no longer considered a natural grouping of related eukaryotes and the species that used to belong to it have been distributed among five supergroups as shown in Figure 24.1.

The three domains of life contain millions of different species. Subdividing them into progressively smaller groups makes it easier for biologists to appreciate the relationships among living species. Proceeding down the hierarchical tree, kingdoms are in turn subdivided into **phyla** (singular: phylum), each of which is divided into **classes**, then **orders**, **families**, and **genera** (singular: genus). Each of these taxa contains fewer species that are more similar to one another than they are to the members of the taxon above it in the hierarchy. For example, the taxon Animalia, which is at the kingdom level, has a larger number of fairly diverse species than does the class Mammalia, which contains species that are relatively similar to one another.

To further understand taxonomy, let's consider the classification of a species, such as the grey wolf (*Canis lupus*) (**Figure 24.2**). The original range of *C. lupus* covered the majority of the northern hemisphere. Primarily because of habitat destruction but also because of persecution by humans, grey wolf populations are much less prevalent now, though they are still found in a few areas in North America and Eurasia. The grey wolf is placed in the domain Eukarya and then within the kingdom Animalia, which includes approximately 2 million species. Next, the grey wolf is classified in the phylum Chordata. The 50,000 species of animals in this group all have four common features at some stage of their development: a notochord (a cartilaginous rod that runs along the back of all chordates at some point in their life cycle), a tubular nerve or spinal cord located above the notochord, gill slits or arches, and a postanal tail. Examples of animals in the Chordata phylum include fishes, reptiles, and mammals.

The grey wolf is in the class Mammalia, which includes all 5,000 species of mammals. Two common features of animals in this group are hair and mammary glands. The mammary glands produce milk, which nourishes the young, and hair helps insulate the body to maintain a warm, constant body temperature. There are 26 orders of mammals; the order that includes the

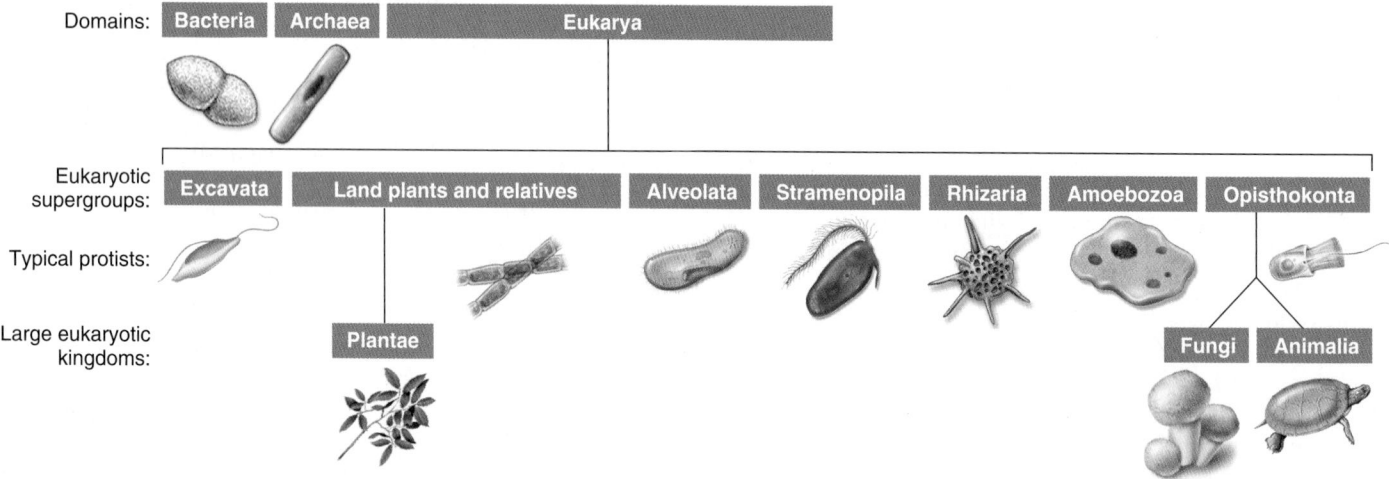

Figure 24.1 **A classification system for living and extinct organisms.** All organisms can be grouped into three large domains: Bacteria, Archaea, and Eukarya. Eukaryotes have been traditionally divided into the four kingdoms: Protista (protists), Fungi (fungi), Plantae (plants), and Animalia (animals). This traditional system has been revised so that only Fungi, Plantae, and Animalia are retained as kingdoms.

BioConnections: *Look back at Figure 4.6. Which of the three domains contains organisms with prokaryotic cells?*

Taxonomic group	Grey wolf found in	Number of species
Domain	Eukarya	~4,000,000– 10,000,000
Supergroup	Ophistrokonta	~2,000,000
Kingdom	Animalia	~2,000,000
Phylum	Chordata	~50,000
Class	Mammalia	~5,000
Order	Carnivora	~270
Family	Canidae	34
Genus	*Canis*	7
Species	*lupus*	1

Figure 24.2 A taxonomic classification of the grey wolf (*Canis lupus*).

Principle: *All life is related by an evolutionary history. A goal of taxonomy is to relate the diversity of species according to their evolutionary relationships.*

Concept check: *Which group is broader, a phylum or a family?*

grey wolf is called Carnivora and has about 270 species. The grey wolf is next categorized in the family known as Canidae. This is a relatively small family of 34 species including different types of wolves, jackals, foxes, wild dogs, coyotes, and domestic dogs. All species in the family Canidae are doglike animals. The smallest grouping that contains the grey wolf is its genus, *Canis,* which includes only two types of wolves, four types of jackals, and the coyote.

As originally advocated by Linnaeus, **binomial nomenclature** is the standard method for naming species. (Binomial refers to the fact that each species has two names, and nomenclature is the naming of species.) The scientific name of every species has two Latinized names, which are its genus name and its species epithet. Sometimes, several species can have the same species epithet, as, for example, *Branta canadensis* (Canada goose), *Castor canadensis* (beaver), *Cornus canadensis* (bunchberry), and *Solidago canadensis* (goldenrod). The species epithet *canadensis* simply means "of Canada," indicating that the species are all found in Canada. The genus name is always capitalized, and the species epithet is not. Both names are italicized or underlined. After the first mention, the genus name is abbreviated to a single letter with a period. For example,

we would write that *Canis lupus* is the grey wolf, and in subsequent sentences, we would write *C. lupus.*

The rules for naming animal species, such as *C. lupus,* have been established by the International Commission on Zoological Nomenclature (ICZN). The ICZN provides and regulates a uniform system of nomenclature to ensure that every animal has a unique and universally accepted scientific name. ICZN publishes the International Code of Zoological Nomenclature containing the rules accepted as governing the application of scientific names to all animals. The ICZN also provides rulings on individual nomenclatural problems brought to its attention. As long as ICZN rules are followed, new species can be named by anyone, not only by scientists. When someone believes he or she has identified a new species, that person generally does research through various publications (journals, books, etc.) to determine whether it is a new species. In addition the person needs to provide specimens to a museum where they will be preserved so someone else can verify the description or do research by using the original specimens. When naming a new species, genus names are always nouns or treated as nouns, while species epithets can be either nouns or adjectives. The names often have a Latin or Greek origin and refer to characteristics of the species or to features of its habitat. For example, the genus name of the newly discovered African forest elephant, *Loxodonta*, is from Greek *loxo*, meaning "slanting," and *odonta*, meaning "tooth." The species epithet *cyclotis* refers to the observation that the ears of this species are rounder compared with those of *L. africana*. International organizations are also involved in the nomenclature of species other than animals. The rules for naming plants and fungi are governed by the International Association for Plant Taxonomy, and the naming of prokaryotes is overseen by the International Committee on Systematics of Prokaryotes.

Organisms of the Three Domains Have Basic Similarities Yet Distinctive Differences.

As discussed in Chapter 20, scientists think that all life originated from primordial prokaryotic cells, sometime between 4.0 billion and 3.5 billion years ago. Soon after the two prokaryotic domains, Bacteria and Archaea, diverged. Between 2.5 billion and 2.0 billion years ago, the first unicellular eukaryotic species came into being via an endosymbiotic or symbiotic relationship between archaea and bacteria. Eventually, multicellular eukaryotic species arose approximately 1.5 billion years ago.

Because of the evolutionary relatedness of Bacteria, Archaea, and Eukarya, the three domains of life share striking similarities:

- DNA is used as the genetic material.
- All species use the same genetic code (with only a few rare codon exceptions).
- Messenger RNA encodes the information to produce proteins.
- Transfer RNA and ribosomes are needed to synthesize proteins, using mRNA as a source of genetic information.
- All living cells are surrounded by a plasma membrane.
- Certain metabolic pathways, such as glycolysis, are found in all three domains.

Biologists believe that these traits are universal because all three domains evolved from a common prokaryotic ancestor. However, when we compare the domains of life in detail, we find that some characteristics are not shared by all three. For example, the cytoplasm of eukaryotic cells is compartmentalized into various types of organelles, while those of bacterial and archaeal cells are not. Such dissimilarities exist because major evolutionary changes have occurred since the time that the three domains diverged from each other. **Table 24.1** compares a variety of molecular and cellular characteristics among Bacteria, Archaea, and Eukarya.

On modern Earth, the domain Bacteria is a diverse collection of many species that can live almost anywhere (**Figure 24.3a**). Bacteria are so widespread that we can make only general statements about their ecology. They are found on the tops of mountains, at the bottoms of oceans, in the guts of animals, and even in the frozen rocks of Antarctica. More bacteria live in a person's digestive tract than the number of people in the world!

Table 24.1	Distinguishing Cellular and Molecular Features of Domains Bacteria, Archaea, and Eukarya*		
Characteristic	**Bacteria**	**Archaea**	**Eukarya**
Chromosomes	Usually circular	Circular	Usually linear
Nucleosome structure	No	No	Yes
Chromosome segregation	Fission	Fission	Mitosis/meiosis
Introns in genes	Rarely	Rarely	Commonly
Ribosomes	70S	70S	80S
Initiator tRNA	Formylmethionine	Methionine	Methionine
Operons	Yes	Yes	No
Capping of mRNA	No	No	Yes
RNA polymerases	One	Several	Three
Promoters of structural genes	−35 and −10 sequences	TATA box	TATA box
Cell compartmentalization	No	No	Yes
Membrane lipids	Ester-linked	Ether-linked	Ester-linked

*The descriptions in this table are meant to represent the general features of most species in each domain. Some exceptions are observed. For example, certain bacterial species have linear chromosomes.

The human mouth is home to more than 500 different species of bacteria. A key reason that bacteria have been so successful in occupying various habitats is their metabolic diversity. Different bacterial species have evolved an amazing variety of ways to obtain energy and organic molecules from their environment. Most species of bacteria decompose existing organic materials, though some can carry out photosynthesis or break down inorganic molecules to create their own organic molecules. Bacterial species can survive on many different sources of energy. Many bacteria metabolize common organic molecules, such as sugars and amino acids. However, some species can use organic molecules that are less common and are not usually broken down by archaea or eukaryotes. These include compounds found in gasoline, crude oil, pesticides, and industrial solvents.

Bacterial species come in myriad shapes and sizes, but individual bacterial cells are usually quite small, around 1 to 5 microns long. Under the microscope, bacterial cells and archaeal cells do not possess morphological differences that would allow them to be distinguished. This is one reason it took so long for researchers to realize that bacteria and archaea should be placed in different domains. Nevertheless, as described in Table 24.1, certain of their molecular features are different.

The domain Archaea is less diverse than Bacteria. However, this domain was discovered relatively recently, in the 1970s, and the list of archaeal species continues to expand. Thus far many archaeal species have been found to live in extreme environments (**Figure 24.3b**). The name *archaea*,

Bacillus thuringiensis, a soil bacterium (SEM)

Escherichia coli, an intestinal bacterium (SEM)

Anabaena torulosa, a freshwater bacterium (LM)

Methanobrevibacter smithii, an intestinal archaeon

(a)

Hot springs

(b)

Thermus aquaticus, an archaeon found in hot springs (SEM)

Figure 24.3 **A comparison of selected species of bacteria and archaea.** **(a)** Bacteria are found in nearly all environments, such as lakes (*Anabaena torulosa*), soil (*Bacillus thuringiensis*), and even within the digestive tracts of animals (*Escherichia coli*). Archaea are also found within the digestive tracts of animals (*Methanobrevibacter smithii*) and **(b)** often occupy extreme environments, such as hot springs (*Thermus aquaticus*).

meaning "ancient," refers to the observation that archaea tend to occupy environments that are thought to be similar to those found on the ancient Earth. Most archaea can be placed into one of three categories: extreme halophiles, methanogens, or hyperthermophiles. Extreme halophiles live in salty environments. Some species can live in water with

salt concentrations above 15% (seawater averages 3.5% salinity). Methanogens release methane as a waste product of cellular metabolism. These species live at the bottom of lakes and swamps and in the intestinal tracts of animals. Methanogens living in your digestive tract cause intestinal gas. Hyperthermophiles live in extremely hot water, even temperatures of more than 100°C. Examples include archaea that live in hot springs and around deep-sea thermal vents. More recently biologists have come to realize that archaea are not entirely restricted to extreme environments. For example, newer research has shown they are abundant in the open sea. Though less diverse than Bacteria, Archaea is nevertheless a diverse domain of successful species.

The third domain, Eukarya, is so diverse that it has been traditionally divided into four kingdoms, based on a set of characteristics that is unique to each kingdom. We will consider these kingdoms next.

The Organisms of Each Traditional Eukaryotic Kingdom Have a Distinctive Set of Characteristics

The four traditional kingdoms of the Eukarya domain, Protista, Fungi, Plantae, and Animalia, provide a broad basis for biologists to appreciate the diversity of eukaryotic species. The members of each kingdom possess certain characteristics that tend to set them apart from the other kingdoms. **Table 24.2** compares some of the common features that are found among species of these four kingdoms.

Protists are species within the traditional kingdom Protista, which contains members that are considered to be the simplest eukaryotes (**Figure 24.4**). Most species are unicellular, but some are colonial, and others are simple multicellular organisms closely related to unicellular protist species. Certain

Table 24.2	A Comparison of the Four Traditional Kingdoms of Domain Eukarya			
Characteristic	**Protista**	**Fungi**	**Plantae**	**Animalia**
Multicellular	A few species	Most species	All species	All species
Cell wall	Some species, various types	Yes, chitin	Yes, cellulose	No
Multiple cell and tissue types	Some species	Some species	Yes	Yes
Capable of photosynthesis	Some species	No	Nearly all species	No
Use of organic molecules in the environment	Some species	All species, digestion begins externally	Rarely	All species, digestion is usually within a digestive tract

protists, such as algae, are capable of photosynthesis, while the remaining species feed on bacterial or other protistan cells, or organic material suspended in water. Protists live in aquatic habitats, and they represent a critical step in the early evolution of eukaryotes. They evolved from prokaryotes and eventually gave rise to the other three kingdoms of eukaryotes.

From the perspective of taxonomy, protists are an unusually diverse group of organisms that were put together because they did not seem to belong to any other group. In some ways the kingdom Protista was a place for leftover eukaryotic species that could not be classified into any of the other three eukaryotic kingdoms. More than 250,000 species of protists are estimated to currently exist. Many biologists are studying the evolutionary relationships among the protists, and the categorization of protists into a single kingdom has been revised. Current models are discussed later in this chapter and in Chapter 26.

The kingdom Fungi contains mushroom-forming fungi, moulds, and yeasts (**Figure 24.5**). Species of fungi are present all over the world, in aquatic and terrestrial environments. Scientists estimate their diversity at more than 100,000 species. Many fungi have symbiotic relationships with plants. These organisms typically secrete digestive enzymes into their environment and then transport the smaller broken down products into their cytoplasm. Along with bacteria, fungi play an important role in the decomposition and recycling of organic materials on our planet. A distinguishing cellular feature is that fungal cells are surrounded by a cell wall that is made of the polysaccharide chitin. Though a few species, such as yeast, are unicellular, most fungi are multicellular, consisting of a mass of threadlike filaments called hyphae that combine to make up the fungal body called the mycelium. The mycelium usually grows underground. For many fungal species the familiar mushrooms that we can see aboveground are actually the reproductive structures of the fungus. Fungi are discussed in more detail in Chapter 27.

The kingdom Plantae is composed of multicellular species that are nearly all capable of photosynthesis. These include mosses, ferns, conifers, and flowering plants (**Figure 24.6**). Approximately 300,000 species are thought to currently exist. Though many species are found in aquatic environments, plants are the foundation of all terrestrial habitats. Rather than using organic molecules from their environment, nearly all plants produce their own organic molecules via photosynthesis. They are therefore Earth's primary producers of the organic molecules that sustain both them and most other living species. (Certain species of bacteria and algae are also capable of photosynthesis.) At the cellular level a distinguishing feature of plant cells is a cell wall that is made primarily of the carbohydrate cellulose. Chapters 28 and 29 provide an introduction to plants, which are covered in more detail in Unit VI.

All species of the kingdom Animalia are multicellular and rely on other organisms for their nourishment. It is a particularly diverse kingdom composed of more than 1 million species. These include sponges, worms, insects, molluscs, fish, amphibians, reptiles (including birds), and mammals (**Figure 24.7**). Most ingest food and digest it in an internal cavity. Except for sponges, the bodies of animals are composed of cells organized into several types of tissues; each tissue is composed of cells that are specialized to perform a particular function. Most animals are capable of complex and relatively rapid movement compared with other organisms. A nervous system enables animals to receive environmental stimuli and respond with specialized movements. At the cellular level a distinguishing feature is that animal cells lack a rigid cell wall, such as that surrounding plant, fungal, and bacterial cells. Animal diversity is discussed in Chapters 30 to 32, and animal form and function are described in more detail in Unit VII.

Our traditional view of four eukaryotic kingdoms has recently changed based on a clearer understanding of the evolutionary relationships among the organisms involved. For example, protists are no longer considered to make up a single kingdom. Later in this chapter we will examine the newer groupings of eukaryotic phyla. In the next section you will see how the information generated by the study of systematics has been instrumental in reshaping the classification of organisms.

(a) An amoeba (_Entamoeba histolytica_)

154 μm

(b) A paramecium (_Paramecium caudatum_) (SEM)

25 μm

(c) A green alga (_Acrosiphonia coalita_)

Figure 24.4 Examples of protists.

(a) A species that forms mushrooms, golden chanterelle (*Cantharellus*

(b) A common bread mould (*Neurospora crassa*)

(c) Baker's yeast (*Saccharomyces cerevisiae*) (SEM)

Figure 24.5   Examples of fungi.

(a) Juniper moss (*Polytrichum juniperinum*)

(b) Royal fern (*Osmunda regalis*)

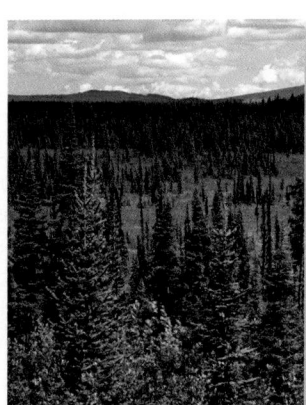

(c) A conifer, the black spruce (*Picea mariana*)

(d) A flowering plant, the common sunflower (*Helianthus annuus*)

Figure 24.6   Examples of plants.

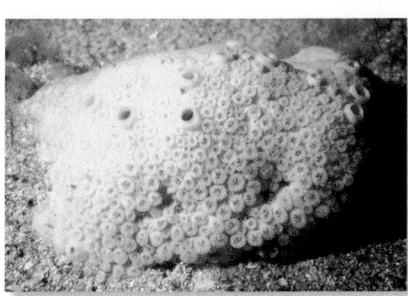

(a) Yellow sponge (*Cleona celata*)

(b) Firefly (*Photinus granulatus*)

(c) Zebra mussel (*Dreissena polymorpha*)

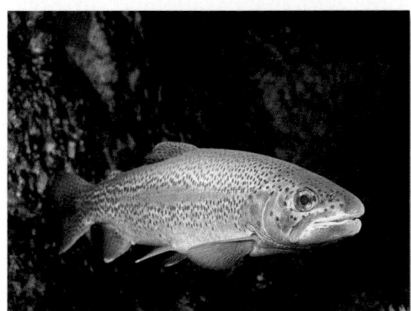

(d) Rainbow trout (*Oncorhynchus mykiss*)

(e) The whooping crane (*Grus americana*)

(f) Red squirrel (*Tamiasciurus hudsonicus*)

Figure 24.7   Examples of animals.

24.2 / SYSTEMATICS

Learning Outcomes:

1. Understand what a phylogenetic tree represents and how it is reconstructed.
2. Identify the different types of data that can be used in phylogenetic reconstruction.
3. Outline the steps of using a cladistics approach in phylogenetic reconstruction, and explain how the principle of parsimony is used to choose among phylogenetic trees.
4. Explain why monophyletic groupings (as opposed to paraphyletic or polyphyletic groupings) are used for modern taxonomic classifications.

Systematics is the study of biological diversity and evolutionary relationships. Biologists use systematics to develop the methods to construct taxonomic groups. For example, the classification of the grey wolf described earlier in Figure 24.2 is based on systematics. Therefore, taxonomy is one part of systematics. By studying the similarities and differences among species, biologists can gain information about **phylogeny**, which is the evolutionary history of a species or group of species. As you will learn, phylogeny helps us understand the relationships among ancestors and their descendants.

In this section we will first consider how evolutionary biologists make diagrams or trees that describe the evolutionary relationships among various species, both living and extinct. Biologists typically gather morphological or molecular genetic data, and then they use different mathematical strategies to analyze those data and reconstruct evolutionary trees. Other data sets that can also be used include behavioural data (especially fixed action patterns), biochemical pathways, and physiology. Newer approaches that use molecular genetic data have revolutionized our understanding of evolutionary relationships, causing biologists to revise the broad taxonomic groupings that have existed for the past few decades.

A Phylogenetic Tree Depicts the Evolutionary Relationships Among Past and Present Species

A systematic approach is followed to produce a **phylogenetic tree**—a diagram that describes a phylogeny. Such a tree is a hypothesis of the evolutionary relationships among various species, based on the information available to and gathered by systematists. Let's look at what information a phylogenetic tree contains and the form in which it is presented.

Figure 24.8 shows a hypothetical phylogenetic tree of the relationships among various plant species, in which the species are labelled A through K. The vertical axis represents time, with the oldest species at the bottom. As discussed in Chapter 23 (refer back to Figure 23.6), new species can be formed by anagenesis, in which a single species evolves into a different species, or more commonly by cladogenesis, in which a species diverges into two or more species. The nodes or branch points in a phylogenetic tree illustrate times when cladogenesis has occurred. For example, approximately 12 million years ago, species A diverged into species A and species B. Figure 24.8 also shows anagenesis. After species B split into species B and D, species D then evolved into species G by anagenesis. The tips of branches represent species that became extinct in the past, such as species B, C, and E, or modern species, such as F, I, G, J, H, and K, which are at the top of the tree. Species A and D are also extinct but gave rise to modern species.

By studying the branch points of a phylogenetic tree, researchers can group species according to common ancestry. A **monophyletic group**, also known as a **clade**, is a group of species, a taxon, consisting of the most recent common ancestor and all of its descendants. For example, the group highlighted in light green in Figure 24.8 is a clade derived from the common ancestor labelled D. The present-day descendants of a common ancestor can also be called a clade. In this case, species G, J, H, and K would form a modern clade. Likewise, the entire tree forms a clade, with species A as a common ancestor. Thus, smaller and more recent clades are subsets of larger clades.

The relationship between a clade and taxonomy depends on how far back we go to choose a common ancestor. For broader taxa, such as a kingdom, the common ancestor existed a very long time ago—hundreds of millions or even billions of years ago. For smaller taxa, such as a family or genus, the common ancestor occurred much more recently, maybe millions or tens of millions of years ago. This idea is shown schematically in **Figure 24.9**. This small, hypothetical kingdom is a monophyletic group that contains 64 species. (Actual kingdoms are obviously larger and more complex.) The diagram emphasizes the taxa that contain the species designated number 43. The common ancestor that gave rise to this kingdom of organisms existed approximately 1 billion years ago. Over time, more recent species arose that became the common ancestors to the phylum, class, order, family, and genus that contain species number 43.

A goal of modern systematics is to create taxa according to evolutionary relationships. Systematics attempts to organize species into monophyletic groups, which means that each group includes an ancestral species and all its descendants. Ideally, every taxon, whether it is a kingdom, phylum, class, order, family, or genus, should be a monophyletic group. However, as biologists gather more information about evolutionary relationships among extinct and modern species, we sometimes discover that previously established taxonomic groups are not monophyletic. When this occurs, efforts are made to revise taxonomy so it is consistent with evolutionary relationships.

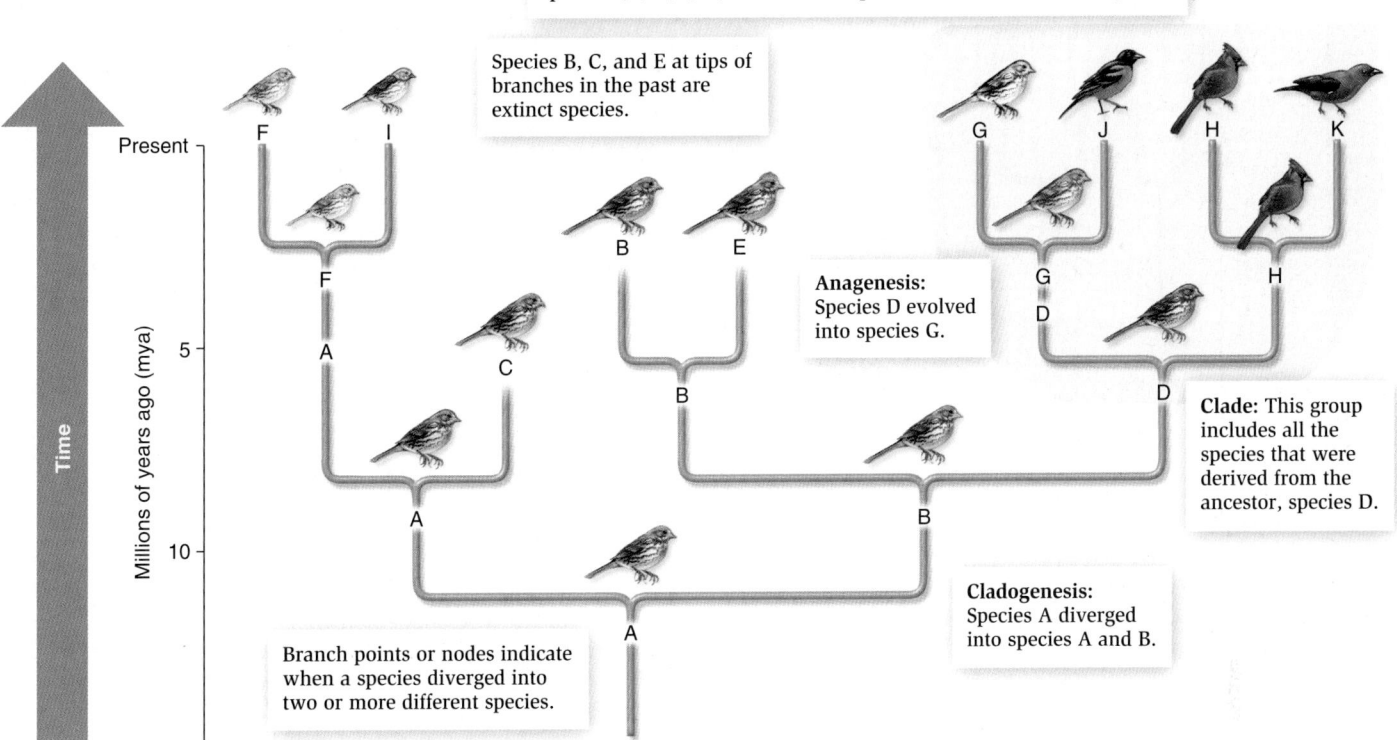

Figure 24.8 **How to read a phylogenetic tree.** This hypothetical tree shows the proposed relationships among various plant species. Species are grouped into clades derived from a common ancestor.

Concept check: *Can two different species have more than one common ancestor?*

The Study of Systematics Is Usually Based on Morphological or Genetic Homology

Systematics assumes that species that have diverged from each other in the very distant past have had a large amount of time to accumulate many genetic differences. Ultimately, such genetic changes are likely to cause differences in morphology and other attributes. By comparison, systematics also assumes that species that have diverged from each other more recently tend to be much more similar both genetically and morphologically.

As we discussed in Chapter 21, the term **homology** refers to similarities among various species that occur because the species are derived from a common ancestor. Attributes that are the result of homology are said to be homologous. For example, the wing of a bat, the arm of a human, and the front leg of a cat are homologous structures (refer back to Figure 21.12). Similarly, genes found in different species are homologous if they have been derived from the same ancestral gene (refer back to Figure 21.14).

In systematics, researchers identify homologous features that are shared by some species but not by others. This allows them to group species based on their similarities. Researchers usually study homology at the level of morphological traits or at the level of genes. In addition the data they gather are viewed

in light of geographic data. Because most organisms do not migrate extremely long distances, species that are closely related evolutionarily are likely to inhabit neighbouring or overlapping geographic regions. Let's now consider how researchers would analyze morphological and genetic homology to reconstruct phylogenetic trees.

Morphological Analysis Traditionally, the first studies in systematics, which occurred before the advent of molecular genetic techniques, focused on morphological features of extinct and modern species. To establish evolutionary relationships based on morphological homology, many traits have to be analyzed to identify similarities and differences as a way to obtain a comprehensive picture of species' relatedness. Researchers use a variety of methods to combine information about different traits. At times, the data can be complex because traits can change more than once during evolution, and the same trait can arise independently in different species. As described in Chapter 21, convergent evolution sometimes leads to convergent or analogous traits—those that arise independently in different species through adaptation to similar environments. For example, the giant anteater (*Myrmecophaga tridactyla*), in South America, and the echidna (*Tachyglossus aculeatus*), found in Australia,

Figure 24.9   Schematic relationship between a phylogenetic tree and taxonomy.   The shaded areas highlight the kingdom, phylum, class, order, family, and genus for species number 43. All the taxa are monophyletic groups or clades. Broader taxa, such as phyla and classes, are derived from more ancient common ancestors. Smaller taxa, such as families and genera, are derived from more recent common ancestors. These smaller taxa are subsets of the broader taxa.

Concept check: *Which taxon would have a more recently living common ancestor: a phylum or an order?*

have similar adaptations, such as long snouts and tongues, that enable these animals to feed on ants (refer back to Figure 21.7). These are convergent traits because they were not derived from a common ancestor. Rather, they arose twice during evolution because of adaptation to similar environments. In systematics, convergent evolution can cause errors if a researcher assumes that a particular trait arose only once and that all species having the trait are derived from a common ancestor.

By studying morphological features of extinct species in the fossil record, paleontologists have reconstructed many phylogenetic trees that chart a series of organisms that led to the existence of modern species. In this approach the tree is based on morphological features that change over many generations. As an example, **Figure 24.10** depicts a current hypothesis of the evolutionary changes that led to the development of the modern horse. This figure shows genera, not individual species. Many morphological features were used to reconstruct this tree. Because hard parts of the body are preserved in the fossil record, this tree is largely based on the analysis of changes in hoof structure, lengths and shapes of various leg bones, skull shape and size, and jaw and tooth morphology. Over an evolutionary timescale, the accumulation of many genetic changes has had a dramatic impact on species' characteristics. In the genera that are shown in this figure, a variety of morphological changes have occurred, such as larger size, fewer toes, and a modified jaw structure suitable for grazing on fibrous grasses.

Molecular Systematics and Molecular Clocks   The field of **molecular systematics** involves the analysis of genetic data, such as DNA sequences, to identify and study genetic homology and reconstruct phylogenetic trees. In 1963 Austrian biologist Emile Zuckerkandl and American chemist and Nobel laureate Linus Pauling were the first to suggest that molecular data should be used to establish evolutionary relationships. Nucleotide base sequences in DNA and amino acid sequences of proteins are particularly well suited to studying relationships, because genetic sequences change over many generations because of the accumulation of mutations. Therefore, when comparing homologous genes in different organisms, DNA sequences from closely related organisms are more similar to each other than they are to sequences from distantly related species.

As discussed in Chapter 22, researchers have speculated that most genetic variation that exists in populations is neutral, meaning that it is not acted on by natural selection. The reasoning behind this concept is that favourable mutations are likely to be very rare, and detrimental mutations are likely to be eliminated from a population by natural selection. A large body of evidence supports the idea that much of the genetic variation observed in modern species is due to the accumulation of neutral mutations. From an evolutionary point of view if neutral mutations occur at a relatively constant rate, they can act as a **molecular clock** on which to measure evolutionary time.

Figure 24.11 illustrates the concept of a molecular clock. The graph's *y*-axis is a measure of the number of nucleotide

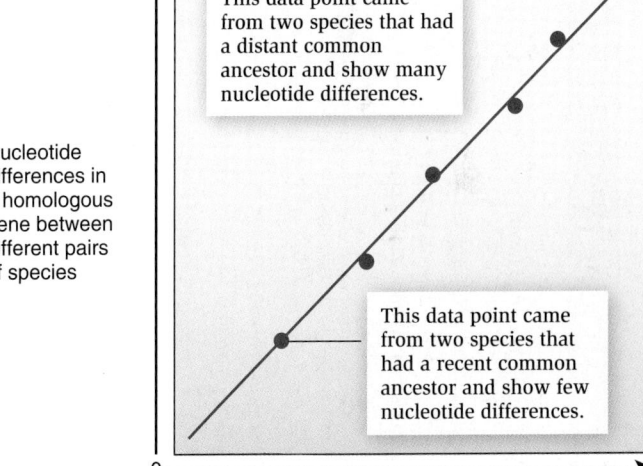

Figure 24.10 **Horse evolution.** An analysis of morphological traits was used to produce this phylogenetic tree showing the evolutionary changes that led to the modern horse. Three important morphological changes that occurred in these genera were larger size, fewer toes, and a shift toward a jaw structure suited for grazing.

Principle: *Structure determines function. The changes in structural features during horse evolution are related to changes in their functional needs. During this time horse populations shifted from feeding on leaves in forested regions to feeding on abrasive grasses in more wide-open spaces.*

An analysis of fossilized bones provided the phylogenetic tree described here.

Nucleotide differences in a homologous gene between different pairs of species

This data point came from two species that had a distant common ancestor and show many nucleotide differences.

This data point came from two species that had a recent common ancestor and show few nucleotide differences.

Evolutionary time since divergence of pairs of species (millions of years)

Figure 24.11 **A molecular clock.** According to the concept of a molecular clock, neutral mutations accumulate over evolutionary time. When comparing homologous genes among species, those species that diverged more recently tend to have fewer differences than do those whose common ancestor occurred in the very distant past.

BioConnections: *Look back at Table 11.1, which shows the genetic code. Propose three changes to a codon sequence that you think would be a neutral mutation.*

sequence differences between pairs of species. The *x*-axis plots the amount of time that has elapsed since a pair of species shared a common ancestor. As seen in this diagram, the number of sequence differences is higher when two species shared a common ancestor in the very distant past than it is in pairs that shared a more recent common ancestor. The explanation for this phenomenon is that the gene sequences of the species accumulate independent mutations after they have diverged; a longer period since their divergence allows for a greater accumulation of mutations, which makes their sequences more different.

Researchers must calibrate their molecular clocks. How much time does it take to accumulate a certain percentage of nucleotide changes? To perform such a calibration, researchers must have information regarding the date when two species shared a common ancestor. Such information could come from the fossil record, for instance. The genetic differences between those species are then divided by the amount of time since their last common ancestor to calculate a rate of change. For example, research suggests that humans and chimpanzees shared a common ancestor that lived approximately 6 million years ago. The percentage of nucleotide differences between mitochondrial DNA of humans and chimpanzees is 12%. From these data the molecular clock for changes in mitochondrial DNA sequences of primates is calibrated at roughly 2% nucleotide changes per million years.

To understand the concept of a molecular clock, let's consider the evolution of some species of primates. **Figure 24.12** illustrates a simplified diagram of evolutionary relationships among several species that was derived by comparing DNA sequences in a mitochondrial gene. This gene encodes a protein called cytochrome oxidase subunit II, which is involved with cellular respiration. The vertical scale represents time, and the branch points that are labelled with letters represent common ancestors. Let's take a look at three branch points (labelled A, D, and E) and relate them to the concept of a

molecular clock. The common ancestor labelled A diverged into two species that ultimately gave rise to siamangs and the other five species. Since this divergence there has been a long time (approximately 23 million years) for the siamang genome to accumulate random neutral changes that would be different from the random changes that have occurred in the genomes of the other five species (see the yellow bar in Figure 24.12). Therefore, the gene in the siamangs is more different than are the genes in the other five species. Now let's compare humans and chimpanzees. The common ancestor that gave rise to these species is labelled D. This species diverged into two species that eventually gave rise to humans and chimpanzees. This divergence occurred a moderate time ago, approximately 6 million years ago, as illustrated by the pink bar. Compared with humans and chimpanzees, humans and siamangs have more differences in their gene sequences because there has been more time for them to accumulate random neutral mutations. Finally, let's consider the two species of chimpanzees, whose common ancestor is labelled E. Since the divergence of species E into two species, approximately 3 million years ago, the time for the molecular clock to tick (that is, accumulate random mutations) is relatively short, as depicted by the green bar in Figure 24.12. Therefore, the two modern species of chimpanzee have very similar gene sequences.

Figure 24.12   Primate evolution.   This phylogenetic tree, which shows relationships among closely related species of primates, is based on a comparison of mitochondrial gene sequences encoding the protein cytochrome oxidase subunit II.

Concept check: *Which pair of species would be expected to have fewer genetic differences: orangutans and gorillas or gorillas and humans?*

Genetic sequence information is primarily used for studying relationships among modern organisms. However, as discussed later in our Feature Investigation, sometimes DNA can be obtained from extinct organisms as well. For evolutionary comparisons the DNA sequences of many genes have been obtained from a wide range of sources. Several genes have been used to reconstruct phylogenetic trees. For example, the gene that encodes an RNA of the small subunit of the ribosome (SSU rRNA) is commonly analyzed to compare higher taxa, such as phyla. Because rRNA is universal in all living organisms, its function must have been established at an early stage in the evolution of life on this planet, and its sequence has changed fairly slowly. The molecular clock for SSU rRNA has been calibrated at approximately 1% sequence change per 50 million years. Furthermore, SSU rRNA is a rather large molecule, so it contains a large amount of sequence information. This gene has been sequenced from thousands of different species.

Slowly changing genes, such as the gene that encodes SSU rRNA, are useful for evaluating distant evolutionary relationships, such as comparing plants and animals. More rapidly changing DNA sequences have been used to study recent evolutionary relationships, particularly among eukaryotic species, such as large animals that have long generation times and tend to evolve more slowly. In these cases slowly evolving genes may not be very useful for establishing evolutionary relationships because two closely related species are likely to have identical or nearly identical DNA sequences for such genes. Instead, sequence differences are more easily found among closely related species when the DNA sequences are more rapidly changing. Our example in Figure 24.12 of closely related species of primates uses sequence changes in the mitochondrial gene for cytochrome oxidase subunit II because this gene tends to change fairly rapidly on an evolutionary timescale.

A Cladistic Approach Is the Most Common Way to Make a Phylogenetic Tree

A **cladistic approach** reconstructs a phylogenetic tree by considering the various possible pathways of evolution and then choosing the most plausible tree. Cladistics is generally accepted as the best method available for the reconstruction of phylogenetic trees, which are known as **cladograms**. A cladistic approach compares traits that are either shared or not shared by different species. A trait shared with a distant ancestor is called a **shared ancestral character**. Such traits are viewed as being older traits—ones that occurred earlier in evolution. In contrast, a **shared derived character** is a trait that is shared by a group of organisms but not by a distant common ancestor. Compared with ancestral characters, derived characters are more recent traits on an evolutionary timescale. For example, among mammals, only some species have flippers, such as whales and dolphins. In this case flippers were derived from the two front limbs of an ancestral species (**Figure 24.13**). The word *derived* refers

With regard to species D and E, having two eyes is a shared primitive character, whereas having two front flippers is a shared derived character.

Two eyes, two front flippers

Two eyes, two front legs

Two eyes, two front legs

Figure 24.13 A comparison of shared derived characters and shared primitive characters.

to the phenomenon that evolution involves the modification of traits in pre-existing species. In other words newer populations of organisms are derived from changes in pre-existing populations. The basis of the cladistic approach is to analyze many shared derived characters among groups of species to deduce the pathway that gave rise to the species.

To understand the concept of ancestral and shared derived characters, **Figure 24.14** shows a cladogram that compares several traits among five species of animals. Shared derived characters are used to establish a cladogram. The various colours in this tree emphasize when particular traits arose during the evolution of these species. A branch point, or node, is the place at which two species differ in shared derived characters. The oldest common ancestor, which would now be extinct, had a notochord and gave rise to all five species. Vertebrae are a shared derived character of the lamprey, salmon, lizard, and rabbit but not the lancelet. By comparison, a hinged jaw is a shared derived character of the salmon, lizard, and rabbit but not of the lamprey or the lancelet. The table shown in **Figure 24.14b** compares the characters that are found in these five species.

In a cladogram an **ingroup** is a monophyletic group in which we are interested. By comparison an **outgroup** is a species or group of species that is most closely related to an ingroup. For example, let's suppose that the salmon,

	Lancelet	Lamprey	Salmon	Lizard	Rabbit
Notochord	Yes	Yes	Yes	Yes	Yes
Vertebrae	No	Yes	Yes	Yes	Yes
Hinged jaw	No	No	Yes	Yes	Yes
Tetrapod	No	No	No	Yes	Yes
Mammary glands	No	No	No	No	Yes

(a) Characteristics among species

(b) Cladogram based on morphological traits

Figure 24.14 **Ancestral versus shared derived characters involving morphological traits.** **(a)** This phylogenetic tree illustrates both ancestral and shared derived characters in a cladogram of relationships among five animal species. **(b)** A comparison of characteristics among these species.

Concept check: *What shared derived character is common to the salmon, lizard, and rabbit but not the lamprey?*

lizard, and rabbit are an ingroup. The outgroup would be the lamprey, because this species is the most closely related to the ingroup but lacks one of the shared derived characters, namely a hinged jaw. The assumption is that all traits that are shared by the outgroup and the ingroup must have arisen in a common ancestor that predates the divergence of the two groups.

Now that you have an understanding of ancestral and shared derived characters, let's suppose you are a researcher and consider the steps you would follow to reconstruct a cladogram by using a cladistics approach. Although morphological and molecular datasets are used extensively to reconstruct phylogenies, it is important to note that other types of data can

also be used, such as comparative physiological, biochemical, behavioural and/or parasitological data.

1. Choose the species in whose evolutionary relationships you are interested. In a simple cladogram, such as those described in this chapter, individual species are compared with each other. In more complex cladograms, species may be grouped into larger taxa (for example, families) and compared with each other. If such grouping is done, the groups must be clades for the results to be reliable.
2. Choose characters for comparing different species. A character is a general feature of an organism. Characters may come in different versions called character states. For example, hair colour is a character, while brown hair and red hair are character states.
3. Determine the order of character states. In other words determine whether a character state is ancestral or derived. This information may be available by examining the fossil record, for example, but is usually done by comparing the ingroup with the outgroup. An assumption is made that the outgroup has the ancestral state(s).
4. Group species (or higher taxa) based on shared derived characters.
5. Build a cladogram based on the following principles:
   - All species (or higher taxa) are placed on tips in the phylogenetic tree, not at branch points.
   - Each cladogram branch point should have a list of one or more shared derived characters that are common to all species above the branch point unless the character is later modified.
   - All shared derived characters appear together only once in a cladogram unless they arose independently during evolution more than once.
6. Choose the most likely cladogram among possible options. When grouping species or higher taxa, more than one cladogram may be possible. Therefore, analyzing the data and producing the most likely cladogram is a key aspect of this process. As described next, different theoretical approaches can be followed to achieve this goal.

Different Strategies Can Be Followed to Produce the Most Likely Cladogram

The challenge in a cladistic approach is to determine the correct order of events. It may not always be obvious which traits are ancestral and came earlier, and which are derived and came later in evolution. Different approaches can be used to deduce the correct order. First, for morphological traits, a common way to deduce the order of events is to analyze fossils and determine the relative dates that certain traits arose. A second strategy that can be used to deduce the correct order is to assume that the best hypothesis is the one that requires the fewest number of evolutionary changes. This concept, called the **principle of**

parsimony, states that the preferred hypothesis is the one that is the simplest. For example, if two species possess a tail, we would initially assume that a tail arose once during evolution and that both species have descended from a common ancestor with a tail. Such a hypothesis is simpler, and more likely to be correct, than assuming that tails arose twice during evolution and that the tails in the two species are not due to descent from a common ancestor.

The principle of parsimony can also be applied to gene sequence data. In a method called maximum likelihood, a model for the most likely changes during gene evolution is applied to the data. Various types of factors are taken into account in the model, such as whether mutations would affect the first, second, or third nucleotide in a codon (mutations affecting the third codon are often neutral) and whether the data conform to a molecular clock. When reconstructing their trees, researchers often have preferences about the kinds of strategies they employ. More than one strategy may be used to reconstruct a cladogram.

In the following example we will use molecular data for four hypothetical taxa (A–D), where A is presumed to be the outgroup and has all of the ancestral states.

```
    1 2 3 4 5
A: GTACA (outgroup)
B: GACAG
C: GTCAA
D: GACCG
```

Given this information, three potential trees are shown in **Figure 24.15**. In these examples, tree 1 requires seven mutations, and tree 2 requires six, while tree 3 requires only five. Therefore, tree 3 requires the fewest number of mutations and is considered the most parsimonious. Based on the principle of parsimony, it would be the most likely choice.

Figure 24.15   The cladistic approach from molecular genetic data.   Three possible evolutionary trees for the evolution of a short DNA sequence are shown. Changes in nucleotide sequence are shown along each tree. According to the principle of parsimony, tree number 3 is the most likely choice because it requires only five mutations. When reconstructing cladograms based on long genetic sequences, researchers use computers to generate trees with the fewest possible genetic changes.

FEATURE INVESTIGATION

Cooper and Colleagues Extracted DNA from Extinct Flightless Birds and Then Compared It with DNA from Modern Species to Reconstruct Their Phylogeny

Starting with small tissue samples from extinct species, scientists have discovered that it is occasionally possible to obtain DNA sequence information. This is called ancient DNA analysis or molecular paleontology. Since the mid-1980s, some researchers have become excited about the information derived from sequencing DNA of extinct specimens. Debate has centred on how long DNA can remain intact after an organism has died. Over time the structure of DNA is degraded by hydrolysis and the loss of purines. Nevertheless, under certain conditions (cold temperature, low oxygen, etc.) DNA samples may be stable as long as 50,000 to 100,000 years. In most studies involving extinct specimens, the ancient DNA is extracted from bone, dried muscle, or preserved skin. These samples are often from museum specimens that have been gathered by paleontologists. In recent years this approach has been used to study evolutionary relationships among modern and extinct species.

In the Feature Investigation shown in **Figure 24.16**, Alan Cooper, Cécile Mourer-Chauviré, Geoffrey Chambers, Arndt von Haeseler, Allan Wilson, and Svante Pääbo investigated the evolutionary relationships among some extinct and modern species of flightless birds. The researchers wanted to gather data to propose a hypothesis regarding the evolutionary relationships among certain species. The kiwis and moas existed in New Zealand during the Pleistocene. Species of

GOAL To gather molecular information to hypothesize about the evolutionary relationships among these species.

KEY MATERIALS Tissue samples from four extinct species of moas were obtained from museum specimens. Tissue samples were also obtained from three species of kiwis, one emu, one cassowary, one ostrich, and two species of rheas.

Experimental level   Conceptual level

1 Treat the cells so that the DNA is released.
   Tissue sample
   Isolate and purify the DNA released from the tissue.
   Cells in tissue
   Mitochondrial DNA

2 Individually, mix the DNA samples with a pair of PCR primers that are complementary to the SSU rRNA gene.
   Add PCR primers.
   DNA
   Mitochondrial DNA
   Primers

3 Subject the samples to PCR, as described in Chapter 18, which makes many copies of the SSU rRNA gene.
   PCR technique
   Many copies of the SSU rRNA gene are made.

4 Subject the amplified DNA fragments to DNA sequencing, as described in Chapter 18.
   Sequence the amplified DNA.
   The amplification of the SSU rRNA gene allows it to be subjected to DNA sequencing.

5 Align the DNA sequences to each other, using computer techniques described in Chapter 19.
   Align sequences, using computer programs.
   Align sequences to compare the degree of similarity.

Figure 24.16 DNA analysis of relationships among modern and extinct flightless birds by Cooper and colleagues.

6　THE DATA

```
Moa 1     GCTTAGCCCTAAATCCAGATACTTACCCTACACAAGTATCCGCCCGAGAACTACGAGCACAAACGCTTAAAACTCTAAGGACTTGGCGGTGCCCCAAACCCA
Kiwi 1    · · · · · · · · · · · ·T·G· · · · · ·GT· ·CT· · · ·C· · · · · · · · · · · · · · · · · · · · · · · · · · · · · · · · · · · · · · · · · · · · · · ·T· · · · · ·
Emu       · · · · · · · · · · · ·TT· · · · ·C· · ·T· · ·CAG· ·C· · · · · · ·T· · · · · · · · · · · · · · · · · · · · · · · · · · · · · · · · · · ·T· · · · · ·
Cassowary · · · · · · · · · · · ·TT· · · · · ·CG·TA· ·CTG· · · · · · · · · · · · · · · · · · · · · · · · · · · · · · · · · · · · · · · · · ·T· · · · · ·
Ostrich   · · · · · · ·T· · · · ·AT· · · · · · · · · ·C· ·CT· · · · · · · · · · · · · · · · · · · · · · · · · · · · · · · · · · · · · · · · · ·T· · · · · ·
Rhea 1    · · · · · · · · ·T· · · · · · · · · · · · ·C· ·CT· · · · · · · · · · · · · · · · · · · · · · · · · · · · · · · · · · · · · · · · · ·T· · · · · ·

Moa 1     CCTAGAGGAGCCTGTTCTATAATCGATAATCCACGATACACCCGACCATCCCTCGCCCGT-GCAGCCTACATACCGCCGTCCCCAGCCCGCCT--AATGAAA
Kiwi 1    · · · · · · · · · · · · · · · · · · · · · ·C· · · · · · · · ·A· · · · ·T· ·T· · ·AAC-A· · · · · ·T· · · · · · · ·G· · · ·T· · · ·AA· · · · ·G·
Emu       · · · · · · · · · · · · · · · · · · · · · ·C· · · · · · · · ·A· · · · ·T· ·T· · ·AA--A· · · · · · · · · · · ·G· · · · · · · · · · · ·--· · · ·
Cassowary · · · · · · · · · · · · · · · · · · · · · ·C· · · · · · · · ·AG· · · ·T· ·T· · ·AA·TA· · · · · · · · · · · ·G· · · · · · · · · · --·G· ·G·
Ostrich   · · · · · · · · · · · · · · · · ·T· · · ·A· ·C· · · ·T· · ·A--T· · · · · · · · · · · · · · · · · ·G· · · · · · · · · ·C--· · ·G·
Rhea 1    · · · · · · · · · · · · · · · · · · · · · · · · · · · · ·T· ·T· · ·A· ·-· · · · · · · · · · · · · · · · · · · · · · · · ·TA·G· · · · ·

Moa 1     G-AACAATAGCGAGCACAACAGCCCTCCCCCGCTAACAAGACAGGTCAAGGTATAGCATATGAGATGGAAGAAATGGGCTACATTTTCTAACATAGAACACC
Kiwi 1    ·-· · · ·C· · · ·A· · · ·TA· ·-· ·A· · · · · · · · · · · · · · · · · · ·C· · · · · · · · · · · · · · · · · · · ·A· · · · · · ·T· ·T
Emu       ·-· · · · · · · ·T· · ·AC--TT· · · · · · · · · · · · · · · · · · · · · ·G· · · · · · · · · · · · · · · · · · · · · · · · · · ·T·T·
Cassowary ·-· · · · · · · ·T· · ·AC--T· · · · · · · · · · · · · · · · · · · · · ·G· · · · · · · · · · · · · · · · · · · · · · · · · · ·T· · ·
Ostrich   ·-· · · · · · · ·T· · · ·A--· · · · · · · · · · · · · · · · · · · · · ·GAG· · · · · · · · · · · · · · · · · · · · · · · ·T· ·A
Rhea 1    ·-· · · ·C· · ·AG· · ·T· ·T· · ·TA---· · · · · · · · · · · · · · · ·G· · · · · · · · · · · · · · · · ·TC· · · · · ·A·

Moa 1     C-------------ACGAAAGAGAAGGTGAAACCCTCCTCAAAAGGCGGATTTAGCAGTAAAATAGAACAAGAATGCCTATTTTAAGCCCGGCCCTGGGGC
Kiwi 1    -· · · · · · · · · · · · ·A· ·GGT· · · · ·T· ·-C· · ·T·G· · · · · · · · · · · · · · · ·C· · ·T· · · ·GA·T· · · · · · · · · · ·--·T· · · · ·A· · · ·
Emu       -· · · · · · · · · · · · ·AG·T· · · · ·T·AC·T· · ·G· · · · · · · · · · · · · · · ·C· · ·T· · · ·GA·T· · · · · · · ·A--·T· · ·T·A· · · ·
Cassowary -· · · · · · · · · · · · ·A· ·G·T· · · · · ·T·A· · · ·T·G· · · · · · · · · · · · · · · ·C· · · · · ·GA·T· · · · · · · ·A---· · · · · ·A· · · ·
Ostrich   -· · · · · · · · · · · · · · · ·G·TA· · · ·T·A· · · · · ·G· · · · · · · · · · · · · · · · · · ·T· · ·GA·T· · · · · · · · ·--T· · · ·T· ·A· · · ·
Rhea 1    -· · · · · · · · · ·G· · · ·GGCA· · · · · ·-AC· · · ·CG· · · · · · · · · · · · ·G· · ·G·TC· · · ·A· · ·C·C· · · · · · · · · ·A· · · ·
```

7　CONCLUSION This discovery-based investigation led to a hypothesis regarding the evolutionary relationships among these bird species.

8　SOURCE Cooper, Alan, et al. 1992. Independent origins of New Zealand moas and kiwis. *Proceedings of the National Academy of Sciences* 89:8741–8744.

---

modern kiwis still exist, but the moas are now extinct. Eleven known species of moas formerly existed. In this study, the researchers investigated the phylogenetic relationships of four extinct species of moas, which were available as museum samples, kiwis of New Zealand, and several other living species of flightless birds. These included the emu and the cassowary (both found in Australia and New Guinea), the ostrich (found in Africa and formerly in Asia), and two rheas (found in South America).

Samples from the various species were subjected to polymerase chain reaction (PCR) to amplify a region of the SSU rRNA gene. This provided enough DNA for DNA sequencing. The data in Figure 24.16 illustrate a comparison of the sequences of a continuous region of the SSU rRNA gene from these species. The first line shows the DNA sequence for one of the four extinct moa species. Below it are the sequences of several of the other species the researchers analyzed. When the other sequences are identical to the first sequence, a dot is placed in the corresponding position. When the sequences are different, the changed nucleotide base (A, T, G, or C) is placed

there. In a few regions the genes are different lengths. In these cases a dash is placed at the corresponding position.

As you can see from the large number of dots, the gene sequences among these flightless birds are very similar, though some differences occur. If you look carefully at the data, you will notice that the sequence from the kiwi (a New Zealand species) is actually more similar to the sequence from the ostrich (an African species) than it is to that of the moa, which was once found in New Zealand. Likewise, the kiwi is more similar to the emu and cassowary (found in Australia and New Guinea) than to the moa. Contrary to their original expectations, the researchers concluded that the kiwis are more closely related to Australian and African flightless birds than they are to the moas. From these results they proposed that New Zealand was colonized twice by ancestors of flightless birds. First, New Zealand was colonized by the ancestor of moas, and then at a later date by an ancestor of the kiwis, which evolved independently of the moas in Australia and New Guinea. As shown in **Figure 24.17**, the researchers reconstructed a new evolutionary tree that illustrates the revised relationships among these modern and extinct species.

Experimental Questions

1. What is molecular paleontology? What was the purpose of the study conducted by Cooper and colleagues?
2. What birds were examined in the Cooper study and what are their geographic distributions? Why were the different species selected for this study?
3. What results did Cooper and colleagues obtain by comparing these DNA sequences? How did the results of this study affect the proposed phylogeny of flightless birds?

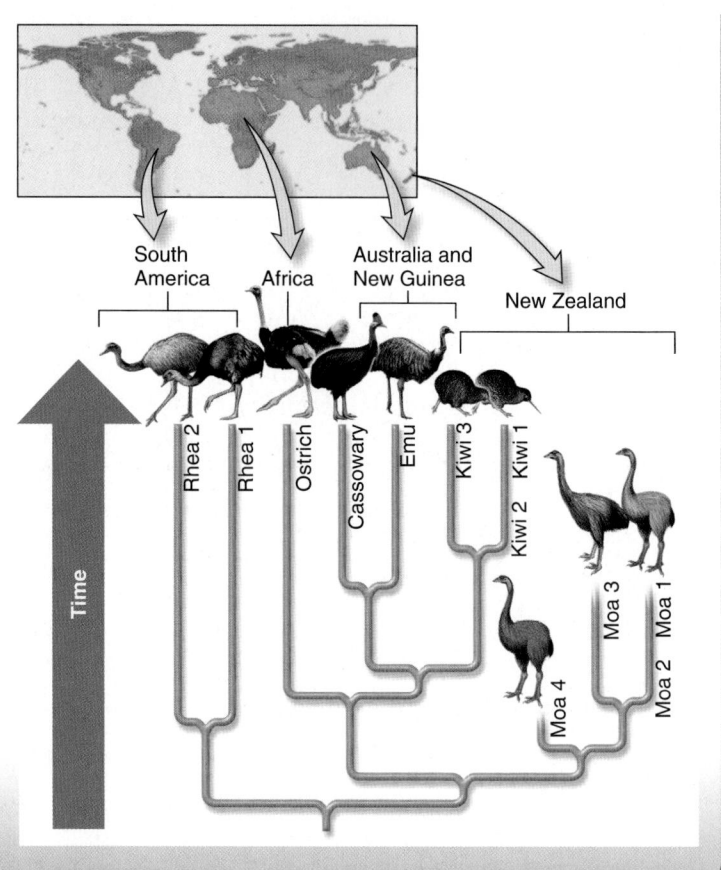

Figure 24.17   **A revised phylogenetic tree of flightless birds.**   This phylogenetic tree was based on a comparison of DNA sequences from extinct and modern birds. The species included are moas, kiwis, emus, cassowaries, ostriches, and rheas. Moas are now extinct, but all other species still exist.

Concept check: *With regard to geography, why are the results in this figure surprising?*

Molecular Systematics Is Changing Our View of Taxonomy

Taxonomy is a work in progress. As researchers gather new information, they sometimes discover that some of the current taxonomic groups are not monophyletic. **Figure 24.18** compares a monophyletic taxon with those that are not. As mentioned earlier, a monophyletic taxon contains a common ancestor and all the species that are derived from that ancestor (**Figure 24.18a**). The ideal goal of taxonomy is to place organisms into monophyletic groups. A **paraphyletic taxon** is a group that contains a common ancestor and some, but not all, of its descendants (**Figure 24.18b**). In contrast a **polyphyletic taxon** consists of members of several evolutionary lines and does not

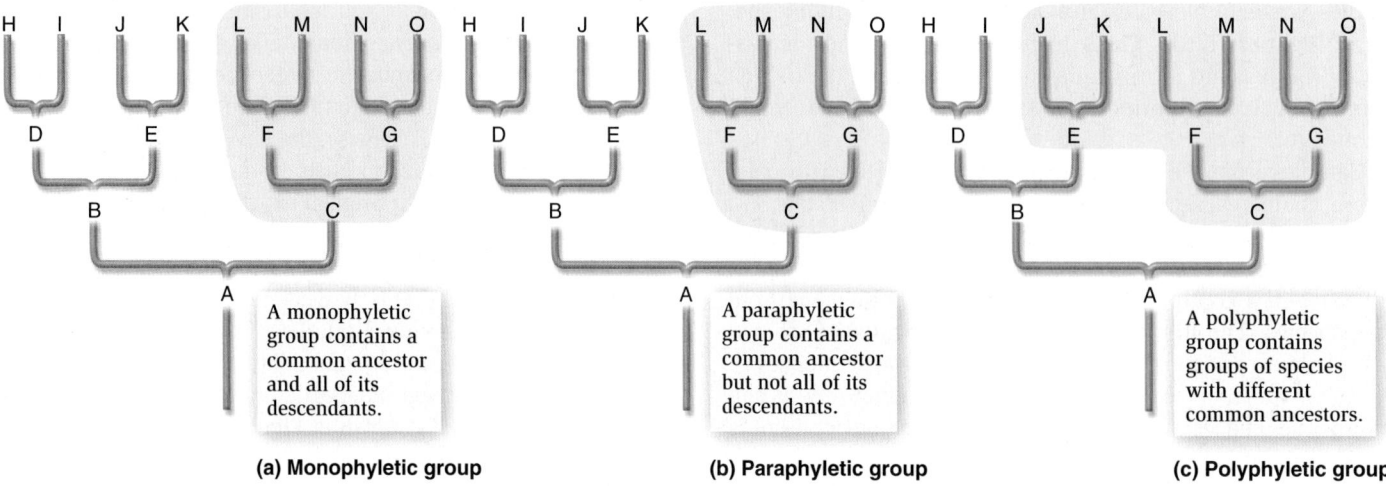

(a) **Monophyletic group**

A monophyletic group contains a common ancestor and all of its descendants.

(b) **Paraphyletic group**

A paraphyletic group contains a common ancestor but not all of its descendants.

(c) **Polyphyletic group**

A polyphyletic group contains groups of species with different common ancestors.

Figure 24.18   A comparison of monophyletic, paraphyletic, and polyphyletic taxonomic groups.

include the most recent common ancestor of the included lineages (**Figure 24.18c**). Over time as we learn more about evolutionary relationships, taxonomic groups are being reorganized in an attempt to recognize monophyletic groups in biological classifications.

In 2003 Paul Hebert and colleagues at the University of Guelph in Ontario proposed **DNA barcoding** as a reliable, inexpensive, and rapid way to identify species. DNA barcoding involves sequencing a short standardized gene region (such as a 648–base pair region from the 5′ region of the mitochondrial cytochrome oxidase 1 [CO1] gene) and including such species-specific molecular tags (i.e., barcodes) in a DNA sequence library or database. For each taxonomically verified specimen, its DNA barcode is a species-specific sequence of the four nucleotides: C, G, A, and T (**Figure 24.19**). In theory DNA barcodes for members of the same species should vary far less than for those of different species. Hebert and collaborators have successfully used CO1 to barcode a wide variety of taxa collected from Canada, including birds, mosquitoes, and freshwater fish. Researchers are still determining which barcode gene is most suitable for plants. The Canadian Barcode of Life Network, made up of nearly 50 researchers from across Canada, is the first national network dedicated to large-scale high-throughput DNA barcoding.

Figure 24.19 **DNA barcoding.** This figure demonstrates how different species have different sequences of the nucleotides C (blue), G (black), A (green), and T (red).

Hermit Thrush   American Robin   Bumblebee   Honey Bee

GENOMES AND PROTEOMES

Because of Horizontal Gene Transfer, the Tree of Life Is Really a Web of Life

Thus far we have considered various ways to reconstruct phylogenetic trees, which describe the relationships among ancestors and their descendants. The type of evolution that is depicted in previous figures is vertical evolution, which involves changes in groups of species because of descent from a common ancestor. Since the time of Darwin vertical evolution has been the traditional way that biologists view the evolutionary process. However, over the past few decades researchers have come to realize that evolution is not that simple. In addition to vertical evolution, horizontal gene transfer has also played a significant role in the phylogeny of all living species.

As discussed in Chapter 21, horizontal gene transfer is the transfer of genes among different species. An analysis of many bacterial genomes has shown that horizontal gene transfer has been a major force in the evolution of prokaryotes. Horizontal gene transfer continued after the divergence of the three major domains of life, including transfer between prokaryotic and eukaryotic species and among eukaryotic species. In modern organisms, horizontal gene transfer is still prevalent among prokaryotic species. By comparison this process is less common among modern eukaryotes, though it does occur. Researchers have speculated that multicellularity and sexual reproduction have presented barriers to horizontal gene transfer in most eukaryotes. For a gene to be transmitted to eukaryotic offspring, it would have to be transferred into a eukaryotic cell that is a gamete or a cell that gives rise to gametes.

Recently, scientists have debated the role of horizontal gene transfer in the earliest stages of evolution, before the emergence of the two prokaryotic domains. The traditional viewpoint was that the three domains of life arose from a single type of prokaryotic (or preprokaryotic) cell called the universal ancestor. However, genomic research has suggested that horizontal gene transfer may have been particularly common during the early

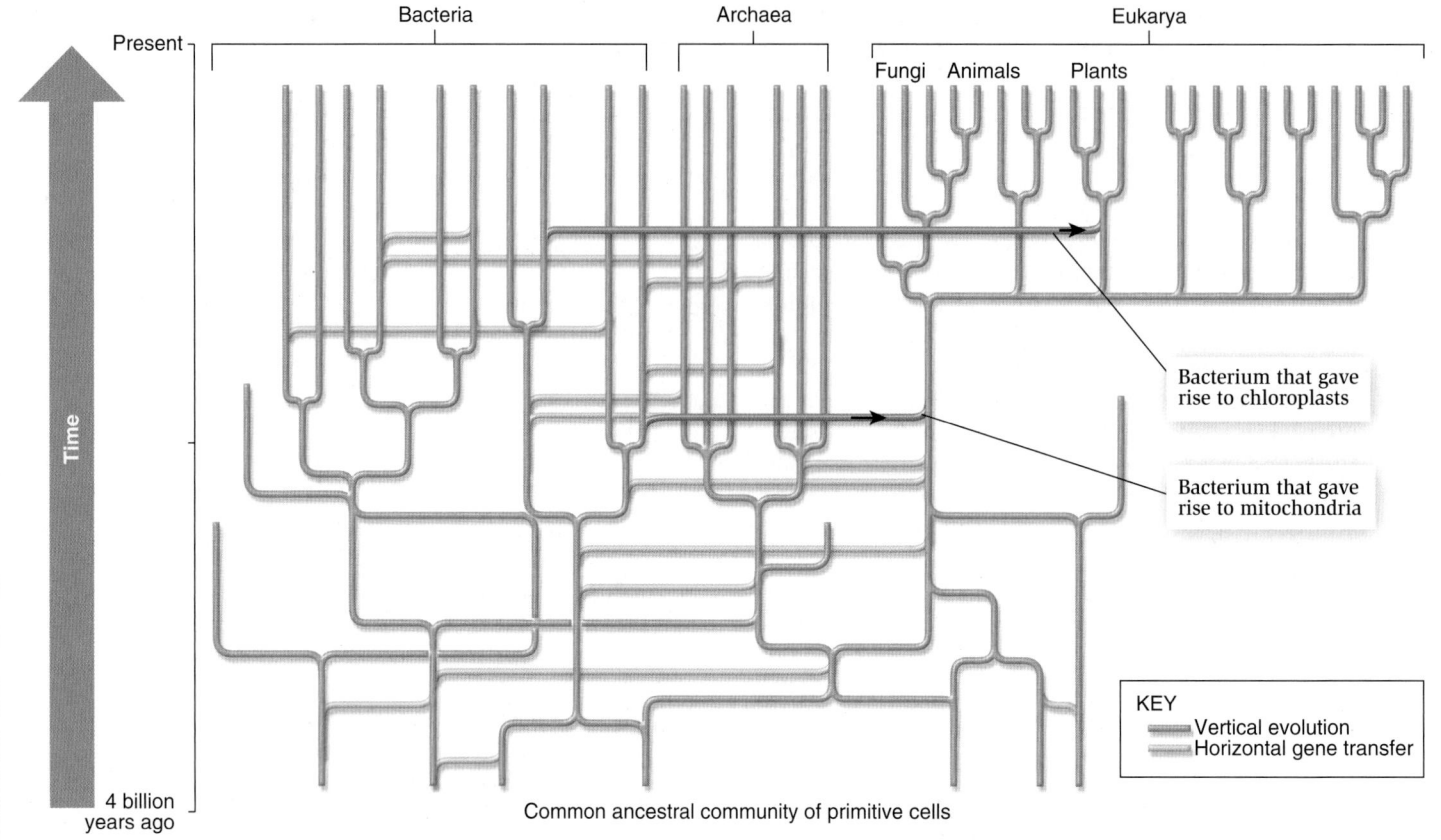

Figure 24.20   **A web of life.**   This phylogenetic tree not only shows the modern classification of all life on Earth but also includes the contribution of horizontal gene transfer in the evolution of species. This phenomenon was prevalent during the early stages of evolution, when all organisms were unicellular. Horizontal gene transfer continues to be a prominent factor in the speciation of Bacteria and Archaea. Note: This tree is meant to be schematic.

Concept check: *How does the phenomenon of horizontal gene transfer muddle the concept of monophyletic groups?*

stages of evolution on Earth, when all species were unicellular. Rather than proposing that all life arose from a single type of prokaryotic cell, horizontal gene transfer may have been so prevalent that the universal ancestor may have actually been an ancestral community of cell lineages that evolved as a whole. If that is the case, the tree of life cannot be traced back to a single universal ancestor.

Figure 24.20 illustrates a schematic scenario for the evolution of life on Earth that includes the roles of both vertical evolution and horizontal gene transfer. This has been described as a "web of life" rather than a "tree of life."

Instead of a universal ancestor, a web of life began with a community of ancestral cells that transferred genetic material in a horizontal fashion. Horizontal gene transfer was also prevalent during the early evolution of bacteria and archaea, and when eukaryotes first emerged as unicellular species. In modern Bacteria and Archaea, it remains a prominent way to foster evolutionary change. By comparison the region of the diagram that contains most eukaryotic species has a more treelike structure, because horizontal gene transfer has become less common in these species, though it does occur occasionally.

Summary of Key Concepts

24.1 Taxonomy

- Taxonomy is the field of biology that is concerned with the theory, practice, and rules of classifying living and extinct organisms and viruses.
- Taxonomy places all living organisms into groups called taxa. The broadest groups are the three domains called Bacteria, Archaea, and Eukarya. (Figure 24.1, Table 24.1)

- Domains are divided into a hierarchy composed of kingdoms, phyla, classes, orders, families, genera, and species. (Figure 24.2)
- Binomial nomenclature provides each species with a scientific name that refers to its genus and species epithet.
- The two prokaryotic domains, Bacteria and Archaea, possess distinctive characteristics at the molecular level and occupy particular environments. (Figure 24.3)
- Eukaryotes were traditionally divided into four kingdoms called Protista, Fungi, Plantae, and Animalia. (Figures 24.4, 24.5, 24.6, 24.7, Table 24.2)

24.2 Systematics

- Systematics is the study of biological diversity and evolutionary relationships. The evolutionary history of a species is its phylogeny.
- A phylogenetic tree is a hypothesis that describes the phylogeny of particular species. A monophyletic group or clade includes all the species that are derived from a common ancestor. (Figure 24.8)
- The hierarchy of taxonomy is related to the timing of common ancestors. Smaller taxa, such as families and genera, are derived from more recent common ancestors than are broader taxa, such as kingdoms and phyla. (Figure 24.9)
- Morphological and genetic data are used to reconstruct phylogenetic trees. (Figure 24.10)
- Assuming that the rate of neutral mutation is relatively constant, genetic data provide a molecular clock on which to measure evolutionary time. (Figures 24.11, 24.12)
- A cladistic approach reconstructs a phylogenetic tree, also called a cladogram, by considering the various possible pathways of evolution. Species are grouped together according to shared derived characters that come from ancestral characters. An ingroup is a clade of interest, while an outgroup is closely related but lacks one or more shared derived characters. (Figures 24.13, 24.14)
- The cladistic approach can produce many possible cladograms. The most likely cladogram is chosen by a variety of methods, such as the principle of parsimony or maximum likelihood. (Figure 24.15)
- Cooper and colleagues analyzed DNA sequences from extinct and modern flightless birds and hypothesized a phylogeny in which New Zealand was colonized twice, once by moas and later by kiwis. (Figures 24.16, 24.17)
- Molecular systematics, which involves the analysis of genetic sequences, has led to major revisions in taxonomy. Ideally, all taxa should be monophyletic, though previously established taxa sometimes turn out to be paraphyletic or polyphyletic. (Figure 24.18)
- DNA barcoding is being developed to assist biologists in the rapid identification of species. (Figure 24.19)
- Because of horizontal gene transfer, the tree of life should really be described as a web of life. (Figure 24.20)

Test to Assess Your Learning

1. The study of biological diversity based on evolutionary relationships is
   a. paleontology.
   b. evolution.
   c. systematics.
   d. ontogeny.
   e. both (a) and (b).
2. Which of the following is the correct order of the taxa used to classify organisms?
   a. kingdom, domain, phylum, class, order, family, genus, species
   b. domain, kingdom, class, phylum, order, family, genus, species
   c. domain, kingdom, phylum, class, family, order, genus, species
   d. domain, kingdom, phylum, class, order, family, genus, species
   e. kingdom, domain, phylum, order, class, family, species, genus
3. When considering organisms within the same taxon, which level includes organisms with the greatest similarity?
   a. kingdom
   b. class
   c. order
   d. family
   e. genus
4. Which of the following characteristics is not shared by prokaryotes and eukaryotes?
   a. DNA is the genetic material.
   b. Messenger RNA encodes the information to produce proteins.
   c. All cells are surrounded by a plasma membrane.
   d. The cytoplasm is compartmentalized into organelles.
   e. Both (a) and (d).

5. The characteristics that define organisms in the kingdom Plantae include
   a. unicellular.
   b. photosynthetic.
   c. multicellular.
   d. (a) and (b) only.
   e. (b) and (c) only.
6. The evolutionary history of a species is
   a. ontogeny.
   b. taxonomy.
   c. evolution.
   d. phylogeny.
   e. embryology.
7. A group composed of all species derived from a common ancestor is referred to as
   a. a phylum.
   b. a monophyletic group or clade.
   c. a phenogram.
   d. an outgroup.
   e. a taxon.
8. The goal of modern taxonomy is to
   a. classify all organisms based on morphological similarities.
   b. classify all organisms in monophyletic groups.
   c. classify all organisms based solely on genetic similarities.
   d. determine the evolutionary relationships among similar species.
   e. none of the above.
9. The concept that the preferred hypothesis is the one that is the simplest is
   a. phenetics.
   b. cladistics.
   c. the principle of parsimony.
   d. maximum likelihood.
   e. both (b) and (d).
10. Researchers believe that horizontal gene transfer is less prevalent in eukaryotes because of
   a. the presence of organelles.
   b. multicellularity.
   c. sexual reproduction.
   d. all of the above.
   e. (b) and (c) only.

Articulate to Assess Your Learning

1. Explain binomial nomenclature and give an example.
2. Explain both the usefulness and the potential pitfalls of morphological analysis.
3. Explain the value of a molecular clock.

Collaborate to Assess and Extend Your Learning

1. Discuss taxonomy and its hierarchical organization.
2. Use the morphological data found in Table 29.1 reconstruct a phylogenetic tree for the gymnosperms.
3. Some researchers are opposed to DNA barcoding. What do you think their objections might be?
4. A principle of biology is that populations of organisms evolve from one generation to the next. What are the advantages and disadvantages of using changes in morphology to reconstruct phylogenetic trees?

Visit McGraw-Hill Ryerson Connect™ For additional study resources

WHAT'S NEW?

An interview with Dr. Steve Marshall from University of Guelph by Adam Jewiss-Gaines, a postgraduate student at Brock University.

Dr. Marshall is a professor and collection director, School of Environmental Sciences, at University of Guelph.

▶ As an entomologist, what kind of research do you do and what are some of your current goals?

I want to know the identities of the species of insect I find, what they do, how they are related to one another, and how they came to their current distributions and biologies. And once I have worked this out, often including the discovery and naming of new taxa, I put a priority on making the information widely accessible.

▶ Are there any specific families or genera of insects that you think are especially important for current study?

Every taxon offers its own set of challenges and rewards. Even well-known pest taxa will still yield secrets to the patient specialist, and poorly studied taxa (like most of the fly groups I work on) offer a steady flow of new discoveries.

▶ How do you define the words *taxonomy* and *systematics,* and how do they relate to one another?

I think of systematics as the study of taxa and any and all relationships between them, and I think of taxonomy as more focused on classification and description than on phylogeny or zoogeography. The terms *taxonomy* and *systematics* have become confounded in recent decades, and are now used interchangeably to refer to the study of biodiversity including classification, identification, phylogeny, and biogeography. I see no problem in following Ross's influential text (*Biological Systematics*) by treating *taxonomy* and *systematics* as synonyms but I still think that that they imply slightly different emphases.

▶ Why do you think the study of taxonomy is an important field of practice for biologists?

It is obviously fundamental to our understanding of the world around us. If you don't know the parts, your understanding of the whole is flawed.

▶ With the onset of technology and methods such as DNA barcoding, do you believe that the study of taxonomy and systematics will continue to remain of importance?

The "onset of technology" was long before I was born, and throughout my lifetime technological advances have influenced every discipline, including systematics. Better optics, computers, critical-point driers, ever-improving cameras, and, most importantly, digital photography and the Web have steadily increased the scope, quality, and quantity of any good taxonomist's work. The downside of "new" technologies is the perception that they are more than just tools to be adopted as practical and useful. This perception can be to the detriment of the discipline as a whole.

Your example of DNA barcoding is a case in point, since it is an application of a technology already widely adopted by the taxonomic community, before it was cleverly branded and vigorously promoted as something totally new and superior to "traditional taxonomy." This led to a huge amount of publicity, and a widespread public perception that "barcoding" is the new taxonomy and that it is on the cusp of providing a system of instantly, cheaply, and reliably naming all life, or at least providing access to the names that taxonomists have assigned to described species of living things. Barcoding is not taxonomy, but instead it is one approach to harvesting and delivering the products of taxonomy. It is thus entirely dependent on good taxonomy. Increasing accessibility of sequence data should have the same effect as other newly available technologies— to increase the scope, quality, and quantity of the taxonomist's work, not to undermine or devalue it.

▶ Do you have any projects that you plan on releasing or starting in the near future?

Of course, there are always ongoing revisions, reviews, and books. My latest book, reviewing the order Diptera on a world basis, will be published this September. [Note from Editor: This interview took place prior to September 2012, when Dr. Marshall's book was published.]

Can you provide any advice for students who wish to specialize and start a career in entomology?

Do it for the pleasure and satisfaction of discovery. And stay broad, while at the same time developing your own unique area of expertise. Be a world expert on some small group, but at the same time be comfortable with the whole world of insects.

In what direction do you think entomological study will shift in the future? Are there any specific areas or divisions of entomology that are likely to become a concern based on current trends?

The continued movement and impact of invasive species will help drive home the need for a good taxonomic baseline for the world fauna. The globalization of taxonomy will be helped by the emergence of strong taxonomic communities around the world, notably in China and Brazil, but it will continue to be hindered by unnecessary restrictions on insect collecting in megadiverse countries. The Web will continue to make taxonomy more international and transparent, and will allow for more contribution by "amateurs" and citizen scientists. Taxonomy will remain a critical foundation for all of entomology. And, I suppose, it will probably continue to be underfunded.

UNIT V
Diversity

Biological diversity encompasses the variety of living things that exist now and all the life forms that lived in the past. Knowing about species that lived in the past and how they are related to modern microorganisms, plants, and animals aids our comprehension of evolutionary process, which is the source of organismal variation. Knowing about the many different kinds of modern organisms also helps us to understand how life forms are structured in ways that allow them to function differently in nature (described in Units VI and VII), and how species interact with each other and with their environments (described in Unit VIII).

Unit V begins with Bacteria and Archaea, the oldest, simplest, and most numerous of Earth's life forms, which have prominent ecological roles described in Chapter 25. In Chapter 26 we survey the surprisingly diverse Protists, which affect humans and other organisms in many important ways. Chapter 27 explores the evolutionary origin of the first plants, a process that explains the features and functions of the seed plants that are vital sources of human food, fibre, and medicine, as described in Chapter 28. The mysteries of the fungi, essential to the brewing and baking industries, as well as to ecological stability, are revealed in Chapter 29. An overview of the diversity and evolutionary history of the animals, provided in Chapter 30, provides the basis for exploring the invertebrates in Chapter 31 and the vertebrates in Chapter 32.

Several biological principles will be emphasized in this unit:

- *Cells are the simplest units of life.* Many of Earth's present and past species have bodies consisting of only one or a few cells, while other species display more complex bodies composed of many cells.

- *Living organisms interact with their environment.* Chapters 25 and 27, for example, explain how ancient microorganisms and plants dramatically changed the composition of Earth's atmosphere and how their modern descendants continue to influence today's atmosphere and climate.

- *All life is related by an evolutionary history.* This concept is emphasized throughout the unit.

- *Structure determines function.* The chapters in this unit provide many examples of ways in which evolutionary change in molecular, cellular, or body structure has allowed organisms to achieve new and diverse functions.

The Bacteria and Archaea

Chapter Outline

Staphylothermus marinus is an archaea. It is an extremophile found in deep ocean hydrothermal vents, thriving on volcanic sulphur and surviving in water temperatures of up to 98°C.

Among Earth's life forms, bacteria and archaea are unique in several ways. These organisms have the simplest cell structure and include the smallest known cells. Bacteria and archaea are also the most abundant organisms on Earth. About half of Earth's total biomass consists of an estimated 10^{30} individuals; just a pinch of garden soil can contain 2 billion, and about 1 million occur in 1 mL of seawater. Bacteria and archaea live in nearly every conceivable habitat, including extremely hot or salty waters that support no other life, and they are also Earth's most ancient organisms, having originated more than 3.5 billion years ago. Their great age and varied habitats have fostered very high diversity. Today, many millions of species of bacteria and archaea collectively display more diverse metabolic processes than occur in any other group of organisms. Many of these metabolic processes are important on a global scale, influencing Earth's climate, atmosphere, soils, water quality, and human health and technology. In this chapter we will survey the diversity, structure, reproduction, metabolism, and ecology of bacteria and archaea. This survey will illustrate major principles of diversity, including descent with modification and horizontal gene transfer.

25.1 DIVERSITY AND EVOLUTION

Learning Outcomes:

1. Make a drawing that shows the evolutionary relationship between the domains of Archaea, Bacteria, and Eukarya.
2. Describe how many species of archaea are able to grow in extreme habitats.
3. Understand the medical, environmental, and evolutionary importance of cyanobacteria and proteobacteria.
4. List common mechanisms for horizontal gene transfer.

As we have noted, one prominent feature of bacteria and archaea is their astounding diversity. In the past microbiologists studied diversity by isolating these organisms from nature

and growing cultures in the laboratory. Such cultures allowed microbiologists to observe variation in structure and metabolism, major features used to classify bacteria and archaea. Today, microbiologists also use molecular techniques to detect diverse bacteria and archaea in nature. By using these new techniques, they have discovered that bacteria and archaea are vastly more diverse than previously realized, and many new species have been discovered. For example, in 2004 Craig Venter, and expert in gene sequencing, and his associates found 148 new bacteria and archaea by sequencing DNA extracted from microbial organisms from the Sargasso Sea. Similar studies of other habitats have also revealed much new diversity, though only 1% of the newly discovered species have been cultured in the laboratory. Many species of bacteria and archaea are known only as a distinctive molecular sequence.

Life on Earth is classified into three domains. Members of the domain Eukarya—animals, plants, fungi, and protists—have cells with a eukaryotic structure. In contrast the **Archaea** (informally, archaea) and **Bacteria** (informally, bacteria) are domains of microorganisms whose cells have a prokaryotic structure. Archaeal and bacterial cells lack nuclei with porous envelopes and other cellular features typical of eukaryotes (see Chapter 4).

Although archaea and bacteria are sometimes collectively termed "prokaryotes," such an aggregation is not a monophyletic group but a paraphyletic group—one that does not include all the descendants of a single common ancestor. That's because the domain Archaea is more closely related to the domain Eukarya than either is to the domain Bacteria (**Figure 25.1**). Even so, archaea and bacteria display some common features in addition to a prokaryotic cell structure.

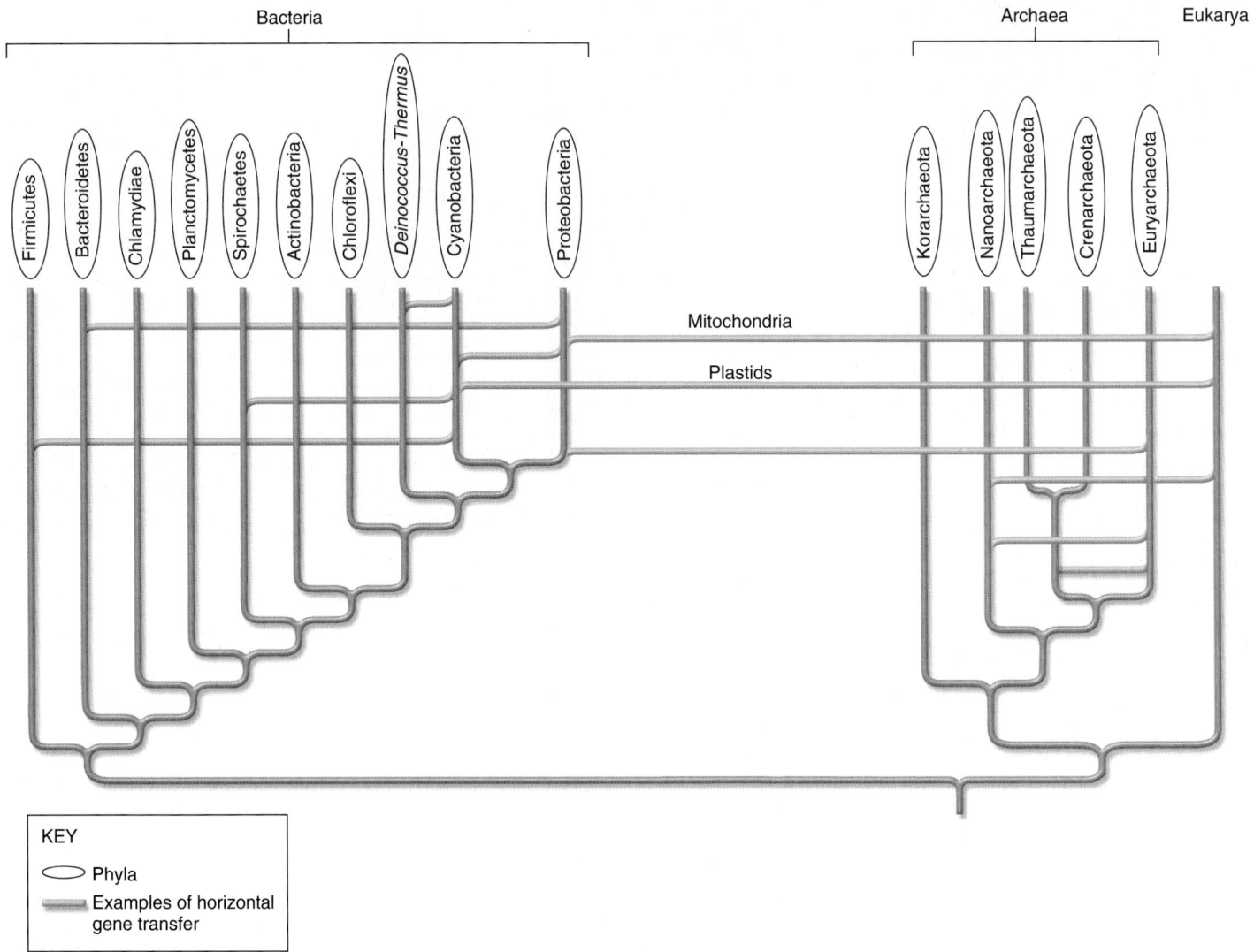

Figure 25.1 **Relationships and diversification of the Bacteria and Archaea.** Bacteria and Archaea are the two domains featuring prokaryotic cells. Eukarya is the domain of organisms composed of eukaryotic cells. Each domain has diversified into multiple kingdoms and phyla. Many cases of horizontal gene transfer among phyla, kingdoms, and domains are known. These cases include the acquisition of mitochondria and chloroplasts by eukaryotes. Note: The domain Bacteria includes about 50 phyla, but for simplicity, only 10 are shown in this figure.

Domain Archaea Includes Inhabitants of Extremely Harsh Environments

Organisms classified in the domain Archaea display some unique characteristics that distinguish this group from the Bacteria. First, archaea possess a number of features in common with the eukaryotic nucleus and cytoplasm, suggesting common ancestry. For example, histone proteins are typically associated with the DNA of both archaea and eukaryotes, but they are absent from most bacteria. Another distinctive feature of archaea is their membrane lipids, which are formed with ether bonds (in contrast, ester bonds characterize the membrane lipids of bacteria and eukaryotes) (**Figure 25.2**). Ether-bonded membranes are more resistant to damage by heat and other extreme conditions, which helps explain why many archaea are able to grow in extremely harsh environments. Archaea aslo use isoprene chains instead of fatty acid chains in making membranes.

Though many archaea occur in soils and surface ocean waters of moderate conditions, diverse archaea occupy habitats of very high salt content, acidity, methane levels, or temperatures that would kill most bacteria and eukaryotes. Organisms that occur primarily in extreme habitats are known as **extremophiles**. One example is the methane producer *Methanopyrus,* which grows best at deep-sea thermal vent sites where the temperature is 98°C. In fact, *Methanopyrus* is so closely adapted to its extremely hot environment that it will not grow when the temperature is less than 84°C. Such archaea are known as hyperthermophiles. Some archaea prefer habitats having both high temperatures and extremely low pH. For example, microbiologist Thomas Brock discovered the archaeal genus *Sulfolobus* in samples taken from sulphur hot springs having a pH of 3 or lower.

Extreme halophiles ("salt-lovers") occupy evaporation ponds used to produce salt from seawater, often growing so abundantly that they colour the ponds red. Halophiles are often red because

Figure 25.2 Bacteria and Archaea. (a) Bacteria and (b) archaea both have prokaryotic cell structure, but (c) bacterial membrane lipids are formed with ester linkages, while (d) archaeal membrane lipids feature ether linkages, which are thought to be more stable under extreme environmental conditions. As shown in transmission electron microscopic (TEM) images (a) and (b), most bacteria feature cell walls made of a material known as peptidoglycan that is often enclosed by an outer envelope, whereas archaea lack these features. Most archaea have outer coverings made of protein.

their plasma membranes contain large amounts of rhodopsins, proteins combined with the red light–sensitive pigment known as retinal. (Similar rhodopsins play important roles in eukaryote light sensing, and they are essential for animals' vision.) In bacteria and archaea, rhodopsin functions as a proton pump, a protein that can move protons and other ions across the plasma membrane.

The domain Archaea includes five phyla: Korarchaeota, Nanoarchaeota, Thaumarchaeota, Crenarchaeota, and Euryarchaeota (see Figure 25.1). Early diverging Korarchaeota are primarily known from DNA sequences found in samples from hot springs. Nanoarchaeota includes the hyperthermophile *Nanoarchaeum equitans,* which appears to be a parasite of the thermal vent crenarchaeote *Ignicoccus.* Thaumarchaeota species that oxidize ammonia are important in global nitrogen cycling. Crenarchaeota includes organisms that live in extremely hot or cold habitats and also some that are widespread in aquatic and terrestrial habitats. The Euryarchaeota includes some hyperthermophiles, diverse methane producers, and extreme halophiles.

Domain Bacteria Includes Proteobacteria, Cyanobacteria, and Many Other Phyla

Molecular studies suggest the existence of 50 or so bacterial phyla (considered kingdoms by some). However, the structural and metabolic features of about half of these are unknown. Though some members of the domain Bacteria live in extreme environments, many more favour moderate conditions. Some bacteria are plant and animal pathogens, while others are essential plant and animal symbionts. Many of these bacteria are

sources of antibiotics themselves, while others are used in the food industry. Others are sources of enzymes and other metabolites. For example, the genus *Thermus* inhabits hot springs. *Thermus aquaticus* has been used in commercial production of a heat stable Taq polymerase enzyme used in the polymerase chain reaction (PCR), an important procedure in molecular biology laboratories. The characteristics of 14 prominent bacterial phyla are summarized in **Table 25.1**. Among these, the Proteobacteria and the Cyanobacteria are particularly diverse and relevant to eukaryotic cell evolution, global ecology, and human affairs. The following phyla are only two examples of the diversity of bacteria.

Proteobacteria Though Proteobacteria share molecular and cell-wall features, this phylum displays amazing diversity of form and metabolism. Based on comparisons of 16S rRNA sequences, genera of this phylum are classified into five major subgroups: alpha (α), beta (β), gamma (γ), delta (δ), and epsilon (ε). As you saw in Chapter 20, the ancestry of mitochondria can be traced to the α-proteobacteria, which also include several genera noted for symbiotic relationships with animals and plants. For example, *Rhizobium* and related genera of α-proteobacteria form nutritionally beneficial associations with the roots of legume plants and are thus agriculturally important (see Chapter 35). Another α-proteobacterium, *Agrobacterium tumifaciens,* causes destructive, cancerlike galls to develop on susceptible plants, including grapes and ornamental crops (**Figure 25.3**). *A. tumifaciens* induces gall formation by injecting DNA into plant cells, a property that has led to the use of the bacterium in the production of transgenic plants (see Chapter 18).

Table 25.1   Some Representative Bacterial Phyla

Phyla	Characteristics
Proteobacteria	• largest group of Gram-negative bacteria • large metabolic diversity • many species important in medicine, agriculture, and industry
Bacteroidetes	• some common in the human intestinal tract, and others are primarily aquatic
Chlamydiae	• obligate intracellular parasites; some cause eye disease in newborns or cause sexually transmitted infections
Spirochaetes	• have distinctive corkscrew shapes, with flagella held close to the body. • *Treponema pallidum* (syphilis) and *Borrelia burgdorferi* (Lyme disease)
Actinobacteria	• spore-forming bacteria • *Mycobacterium tuberculosis* (tuberculosis) • more than 500 different antibiotics known from this group (e.g., streptomycin from *Streptomyces*)
Thermotogae	• hyperthermophiles
Chloroflexi	• green nonsulphur bacteria • photosynthetic without releasing oxygen (anoxygenic photosynthesis)
Deinococcus-Thermus	• extremophiles • *Deinococcus* has high resistance to ionizing radiation • *Thermus* inhabits hot springs
Cyanobacteria	• oxygen-producing photosynthetic bacteria (some also capable of anoxygenic photosynthesis) • cyanobacteria produce blooms and may release toxins harmful to health of humans and wild and domesticated animals

The genus *Nitrosomonas,* a soil inhabitant important in the global nitrogen cycle, represents the β-proteobacteria. *Neisseria gonorrhoeae,* the agent of the sexually transmitted infection gonorrhea, is another member of the β-proteobacteria. *Vibrio cholerae,* a γ-proteobacterium, causes cholera epidemics when drinking water becomes contaminated with animal waste during floods and other natural disasters. The γ-proteobacteria *Salmonella enterica* and *Escherichia coli* strain O157:H7 also cause human disease, and food and water are widely tested for their presence. The δ-proteobacteria include the colony-forming myxobacteria and predatory bdellovibrios, which drill their way through the cell walls of other bacteria to consume them. *Helicobacter pylori*, which causes stomach ulcers, belongs to the ε-proteobacteria.

Cyanobacteria The phylum Cyanobacteria contains photosynthetic bacteria that are abundant in fresh waters, oceans, and wetlands, and on the surfaces of arid soils. Cyanobacteria are named for the typical blue-green (cyan) coloration of their cells (**Figure 25.4**). Blue-green pigmentation results from the presence of accessory phycobilin pigments that help chlorophyll absorb light energy. Cyanobacteria are the only prokaryotes that generate oxygen as a product of photosynthesis. Ancient cyanobacteria produced Earth's first oxygen-rich atmosphere, which allowed for the rise of eukaryotes. The plastids of eukaryotic algae and plants arose from cyanobacteria.

Cyanobacteria display the greatest structural diversity found among bacterial phyla. Some occur as single cells, while others form colonies of cells held together by a thick, gluey substance called mucilage (**Figure 25.4a, b**). Many cyanobacteria form filaments of cells that are attached end to end (**Figure 25.4c**). Some of the filamentous cyanobacteria produce specialized cells and display intercellular chemical communication, the

Figure 25.3 *Agrobacterium tumifaciens* **infection.** This bacterium causes cancerlike tumours to grow on plants.

(a) Unicells   0.1 mm

(b) Colony of cells   60 μm

(c) Unbranched filaments   0.2 mm

(d) Branched filaments   50 μm

Figure 25.4 Major types of microbial cell aggregations found in phylum Cyanobacteria.   (a) The genus *Chroococcus* occurs as unicells. (b) The genus *Merismopedia* is a flat colony of cells held together by mucilage. (c) The genus *Oscillatoria* is an unbranched filament. (d) The genus *Stigonema* is a branched filament that has a mucilage sheath; sunscreen compounds that protect the cells from damage by ultraviolet (UV) radiation cause the sheath to be brown.

> **BioConnections:**   *Look ahead to Figure 26.4d. What eukaryotic microbes also display branched filamentous bodies?*

hallmarks of multicellular organisms. Many cyanobacteria that grow in conditions of high light intensity produce protective brown sunscreen compounds at their surfaces (**Figure 25.4d**).

Cyanobacteria play essential ecological roles by producing organic carbon and fixed nitrogen (see section 25.4). However, several kinds of cyanobacteria, notably the genera *Microcystis,* *Anabaena,* and *Cylindrospermopsis,* form nuisance growths in freshwater lakes during the warm season. Such growths, known as blooms, give the water a pea-soup appearance. Blooms develop when natural waters receive excess fertilizer from sewage discharges or agricultural runoff. Such blooms are becoming more common and are of serious concern because they can produce toxins in amounts sufficient to harm the health of humans and other animals. Consequently, it is inadvisable for people or pets to swim in or consume water that has a visible cyanobacterial bloom. Cyanobacterial blooms have become

problematic in many parts of the world. In Canada cyanobacterial blooms occur in Lake Winnipeg and Lake Erie. In July and August in approximately 50 Quebec lakes, mostly in the Eastern Townships, cyanobacterial blooms create the need for an unprecedented number of bans on drinking water.

Now that you have learned something about the diversity of Archaea and Bacteria, let's consider the effects of gene exchanges within and between these domains.

Horizontal Gene Transfer Influences Diversity of Bacteria and Archaea

Horizontal gene transfer, also known as lateral gene transfer, is the movement of one or more genes from one species to another. This process contrasts with vertical gene transfer from parent to progeny. Horizontal gene transfer increases genetic diversity and influences the methods used to infer the phylogeny of bacteria and archaea. Dr. Doolittle at Dalhousie University has investigated lateral gene transfer in prokaryotes. His research has shown that prokaryotes have generally not evolved by classical Darwinian natural selection over time in a linear fashion. He suggests that lateral gene transfer may have a more important role in the evolution of prokaryotes.

Horizontal gene transfer is common among bacteria and archaea, and it can result in large genetic changes. For example, at least 17% of the genes present in the common human gut inhabitant *E. coli* came from other bacteria. In addition, genes move among the bacterial, archaeal, and eukaryotic domains. For example, about a third of the genes present in the archaeon *Methanosarcina mazei* originally came from bacteria, and there is genetic evidence for transfer of genes from Nanoarchaeota to protists. Viruses are probably important gene transfer vectors. This is illustrated by the fact that photosynthetic genes typical of oceanic cyanobacteria widely occur in marine viruses that infect these prokaryotes.

Horizontal gene transfer has the potential to interfere with human efforts to deduce evolutionary relationships. For example, if a gene that had been inherited by horizontal gene transfer from proteobacteria to euryarcheota were used to deduce evolutionary relationships then one might have falsely concluded that proteobacteria and euryarchaeota were closely related, because both groups possess this distinctive gene. To understand prokaryote relationships, molecular systematists analyze ribosomal RNA (rRNA) genes and other sequences thought to move infrequently in a horizontal manner. Such analyses may more accurately reflect patterns of vertical inheritance. However, even ribosomal genes can be vulnerable to horizontal transfer.

Phylogenetic trees displaying current understanding of relationships (see Figure 25.1) reveal several important concepts. Bacteria and archaea probably evolved from a common ancestor, and the eukaryotic nucleus and cytoplasm likely arose in an ancient archaeal organism. In addition, mitochondria and plastids originated from proteobacteria and cyanobacteria by endosymbiosis (see Chapter 20). In these cases, endosymbiosis resulted in the transfer of many genes from bacteria to eukaryotes. Finally, bacteria and archaea are amazingly diverse, but many phyla and species lack scientific names because microbiologists know so little about them. The next section surveys ways in which the better-known bacteria and archaea vary in structure and locomotion.

25.2 STRUCTURE AND MOTILITY

Learning Outcomes:

1. Discuss the cellular structural adaptations that have increased the complexity of prokaryotic cells.
2. Explain how mucilage influences the behaviour of bacterial cells.
3. Describe the structural differences between Gram positive and Gram negative bacterial cells.
4. List the different means by which prokaryotic cells move.

Bacteria and archaea have several features in common, including small size, rapid growth, and simple cellular structure. With few exceptions bacteria and archaea are 1 to 5 μm in diameter and are thus known as microorganisms or microbes. (By contrast, most plant and animal cells are between 10 and 100 μm in diameter.) Small cell size limits the amount of materials that can be stored within cells but allows faster cell division. When nutrients are sufficient, many microorganisms can divide several times within a single day. This explains how bacteria can spoil food rapidly and why infections can spread quickly within the human body. Despite these common features, prokaryotes differ in many ways. In this section we explore variation in cell structure and shape, in surface and cell wall features, and in movement. We will also learn how these characteristics influence the roles of bacteria and archaea in nature and human affairs.

Bacteria and Archaea Vary in Cellular Structure

Prokaryotic cells are much simpler than eukaryotic cells. Even so, many prokaryotes display surprising complexity of cellular structure resulting from adaptive evolution. For example, cyanobacteria and other photosynthetic bacteria are able to use light energy to produce organic compounds and typically contain large numbers of intracellular tubules known as thylakoids (**Figure 25.5**). The extensive membrane surface of the thylakoids has large amounts of chlorophyll and other components of the photosynthetic apparatus. Thylakoids thus enable photosynthetic bacteria to take maximum advantage of light energy in their environments.

Thylakoids develop by ingrowth of the plasma membrane; in some bacteria, plasma membrane ingrowth has generated additional intriguing adaptations—magnetosomes and nucleus-like bodies—that are sometimes described as bacterial organelles. Magnetosomes are tiny crystals of an iron mineral known as magnetite, each surrounded by a membrane. These structures occur in the bacterium *Magnetospirillum* and related genera (**Figure 25.6**). In each cell about 15 to 20 magnetosomes occur in a row, together acting as a compass needle to orient the bacteria within Earth's magnetic field. This helps the bacteria to locate the low-oxygen habitats they prefer. Microbiologists

Thylakoids provide a greater surface area for chlorophyll and other molecules involved in photosynthesis.

Thylakoids

Food storage particle

Gas vesicles (cross-sections)

Gas vesicles (long sections)

0.6 μm

The gas vesicles buoy this photosynthetic organism to the lighted water surface, where it often forms conspicuous scums.

Figure 25.5 Photosynthetic thylakoid membranes and numerous gas vesicles found in a cell of the cyanobacterial genus *Microcystis*.

 Principle: *Structure determines function. Thylakoids, which contain chlorophyll and other components of the photosynthetic apparatus, are the locations of the light harvesting reactions.*

Concept check: *Do you think this cell would sink or float?*

BioConnections: *Look back to Figure 4.27 to see thylakoids within plant chloroplasts. What similarities to Figure 25.5 help to demonstrate that plastids evolved from endosymbiotic cyanobacteria?*

Arash Komeili, Grant Jensen, and their colleagues used rapid freezing techniques and a special type of transmission electron microscope to observe the development of magnetosomes. They found that the process begins with ingrowth of the plasma membrane that forms a row of spherical vesicles. If *Magnetospirillum* cells are grown in media having low iron levels, the vesicles remain empty. But if iron is available, a magnetite crystal forms within each vesicle. The investigators also observed that fibrils of an actin-like protein keep the magnetosomes aligned in a row. (Recall from Chapter 4 that actin is a major cytoskeletal protein of eukaryotes.) Mutant bacteria lacking a functional form of this protein produce magnetosomes, but they do not remain aligned in a row. Instead, magnetosomes scatter around mutant cells, disrupting their ability to detect a magnetic field.

Archaea and Bacteria Vary in Cell Shape and Arrangement

Microbial cells occur in five major shapes (**Figure 25.7**): spheres (**cocci**) (**Figure 25.7a**), rods (**bacilli**) (**Figure 25.7b**), comma-shaped cells (**vibrios**) (**Figure 25.7c**), and spiral-shaped cells

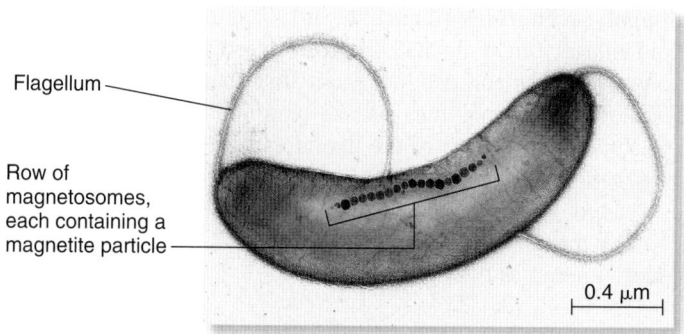

Flagellum

Row of magnetosomes, each containing a magnetite particle

0.4 μm

Figure 25.6   Magnetosomes found in the spirillum *Magnetospirillum magnetotacticum.*   An internal row of iron-rich magnetite crystals, each enclosed by a membrane, functions like a compass needle, allowing this bacterium to detect Earth's magnetic field. This feature allows *M. magnetotacticum* to locate its preferred habitat, low-oxygen sediment, since it is hypothesized that the magnetosome guides the bacterium downward, where the direction of Earth's magnetic fields point downward. These and other bacterial cells use flagella to move from less favourable to more attractive locations.

BioConnections: *Look ahead to Section 42.6, which describes electromagnetic sensing by animals. What animals are like M.* magnetotacticum *in being able to sense and respond to magnetic fields?*

that are either flexible (**spirochaetes**) (**Figure 25.7d**) or rigid (**spirilli**; see Figure 25.6). In addition, such cells can occur in several types of arrangements. Some microorganisms occur only as single cells or pairs of cells resulting from recent division (Figure 25.7a). Others occur as cell aggregates or are attached end to end to form filaments.

The shapes of bacterial cells and the degree of their arrangement in groups can be important diagnostic features in water and medical testing. For example, the presence of abundant rod-shaped cells in samples suggests possible contamination by

E. coli or other proteobacteria that normally occur in the human gut. The proteobacterial genus *Neisseria* occurs as paired cocci, a feature that aids rapid detection of this organism when disease is suspected. Microorganisms may also produce surface mucilage, which plays important roles in disease and ecology.

Slimy Mucilage Often Coats Microbial Surfaces

Many microorganisms produce a coat of slimy mucilage that varies in consistency and extent. Mucilage is composed of polysaccharides, protein, or both, which are secreted from cells, and it serves a variety of functions. One example is the mucilage coat (known as a capsule) that helps some disease bacteria to evade their host's defence system. You may recall that Frederick Griffith discovered the transfer of genetic material while experimenting with capsule-producing pathogenic forms and capsuleless nonpathogenic strains of the bacterium *Streptococcus pneumoniae* (refer back to Figure 10.1). The immune system cells of mice are able to destroy this bacterium only if it lacks a capsule.

Mucilage also holds together the cells of colonial microorganisms (see Figure 25.4b), helps aquatic species to float in water, binds mineral nutrients, and repels predators. Slime sheaths (see Figure 25.4d) often coat bacterial filaments, where they may help to prevent drying. Mucilage is also critical to the formation of biofilms, which are environmentally and medically important. **Biofilms** are aggregations of microorganisms that secrete adhesive mucilage, thereby gluing themselves to surfaces (**Figure 25.8**). They help microbes to remain in favourable locations for growth; otherwise body or environmental fluids would wash them away. A process known as **quorum sensing** fosters biofilm formation. During quorum sensing, individual microbes secrete small molecules (such as homoserine lactones) that have the potential to influence the behaviour of nearby microbes. If enough individuals are present (a quorum), the concentration of signalling molecules builds to a level that causes collective behaviour. In the case of biofilms, populations

1 μm

(a) Sphere-shaped cocci
(*Lactococcus lactis*)

11.4 μm

(b) Rod-shaped bacilli
(*Lactobacillus plantarum*)

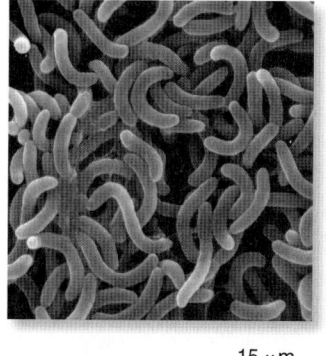

15 μm

(c) Comma-shaped vibrios
(*Vibrio cholerae*)

7.5 μm

(d) Spiral-shaped spirochaetes
(*Leptospira sp.*)

Figure 25.7   Major types of microbial cell shapes.   Scanning electron microscopic views.

Principle: *Cells are the simplest units of life. In unicellular bacteria and archaea, a single cell represents an entire organism.*

Figure 25.8 A biofilm composed of a community of microorganisms glued by mucilage to a surface.   This SEM shows dental plaque, consisting of several types of bacteria artificially tinted purple, green, and blue, attached to a tooth surface by mucilage.

of microbes respond to chemical signals by moving to a common location and producing mucilage.

From a human standpoint, biofilms have both beneficial and harmful consequences. In aquatic and terrestrial environments they help to stabilize and enrich sand and soil surfaces. In contrast, biofilms that form on the surfaces of animal tissues can be harmful. Dental plaque is an example of a harmful biofilm (Figure 25.8); if allowed to remain, the bacterial community secretes acids that can damage tooth enamel. Biofilms can also develop in industrial pipelines, where the attached microbes can contribute to corrosion by secreting enzymes that chemically degrade metal surfaces.

Archaea and Bacteria Differ in Cell-Wall Structure

Whether coated with mucilage or not, most prokaryotes possess a rigid cell wall outside the plasma membrane. Cell walls maintain cell shape and help protect against attack by viruses or predatory bacteria. Cell walls also help microbes avoid lysing in hypotonic conditions, when the solute concentration is higher inside the cell than outside. The structure and composition of cell walls vary in ways that can be important in medical and other contexts.

The cell walls of most archaea and certain bacteria are composed of protein or glycoprotein. In contrast, the polymer known as **peptidoglycan** is lacking in archaea but is an important component of most bacterial cell walls. Peptidoglycan is composed of carbohydrates that are cross-linked by peptides. Bacterial cell walls occur in two major forms that differ in their amount of peptidoglycan, staining properties, and response to antibiotics. The first type of bacterial cell wall features a relatively thick peptidoglycan layer (**Figure 25.9a**). The second bacterial cell-wall type has relatively less wall peptidoglycan and is enclosed by a thin outer envelope whose outer leaflet is rich in

lipopolysaccharides (**Figure 25.9b**). This outer envelope is a lipid bilayer but is distinct from the plasma membrane. Lipopolysaccharides and peptidoglycan affect bacterial responses to antibiotics and sometimes disease symptoms.

For example, part of the peptidoglycan covering of *Bordetella pertussis* is responsible for the extensive tissue damage associated with whooping cough. To identify the two major types of bacterial cell walls, microbiologists use a staining procedure known as the Gram stain.

The Gram Stain   In the late nineteenth century, Danish physician Hans Christian Gram developed the **Gram stain** procedure

Acidic polysaccharides

Thick peptidoglycan layer

Plasma membrane

(a) Gram-positive: thick cell wall, no outer envelope

Lipopolysaccharide-rich outer envelope

Thin peptidoglycan layer

Plasma membrane

(b) Gram-negative: thinner cell wall, with outer envelope

Figure 25.9 Cell-wall structure of Gram-positive and Gram-negative bacteria.   (a) The structure of the cell wall of Gram-positive bacteria. (b) The structure of the cell wall and lipopolysaccharide envelope typical of Gram-negative bacteria.

to more easily detect and distinguish bacteria. The Gram stain remains a useful tool for identifying bacteria and predicting their responses to antibiotics. To perform a Gram stain a microbiologist starts by smearing bacteria onto a glass slide and heating it briefly to aid cell attachment. The microbiologist then floods the slide with crystal violet, a purple dye, followed by an iodine solution. The iodine binds the purple dye, forming an insoluble complex. Next, the microbiologist adds alcohol. The alcohol dehydrates peptidoglycan, thereby trapping the purple crystal violet–iodine complex. The alcohol is able to remove purple dye from thin peptidoglycan walls but not dye bound in cell walls with thick peptidoglycan layers. Finally, safranin, a pink stain, is applied as a counterstain. At the end of the procedure, some bacteria will remain purple; these are known as Gram-positive bacteria (**Figure 25.10a**). Other types of bacteria will lose the purple stain at the alcohol step but retain the final pink stain; these are known as Gram-negative bacteria (**Figure 25.10b**). If a fluorescence microscope is available, a single-step fluorescent stain can be used to distinguish Gram-positive from Gram-negative bacteria (**Figure 25.11**). A closer look at Gram-positive and Gram-negative bacteria will reveal how these staining differences are useful.

Gram-Positive Bacteria Gram-positive bacteria occur in the phyla Firmicutes and Actinobacteria (see Figure 25.1, Table 25.1). Gram-positive bacteria typically have thick peptidoglycan cell walls that lack a lipopolysaccharide envelope. When treated by the Gram stain process, Gram-positive bacteria appear purple because their more abundant peptidoglycan traps a large amount of the crystal violet–iodine dye complex. Such bacteria are typically vulnerable to penicillin and related antibiotics, because these antibiotics interfere with peptidoglycan synthesis. An example of a Gram-positive bacterium is *S. pneumoniae* (see Figure 25.10a). Strains of this organism cause strep throat, streptococcal pneumonia, streptococcal meningitis (an infection of the spinal fluid), and eye infections. Streptococci also include the infamous flesh-eating bacteria (*S. pyogenes*) that cause necrotizing fasciitis, a

Figure 25.11 A commercial fluorescent stain used to distinguish Gram-positive and Gram-negative bacteria. This preparation shows green-fluorescent cells of the Gram-negative bacterium *E. coli* mixed with yellow-fluorescent cells of the Gram-positive bacterium *Staphylococcus aureus.*

Concept check: *For ecological studies what would be the advantages and disadvantages of this fluorescence-staining procedure as compared with the classical Gram stain process?*

disease whose progression is notoriously difficult to control. The entire DNA sequence of *S. pneumoniae* has been determined, revealing the presence of many genes conferring the ability to break down several types of molecules in human tissues for use as food. The presence of these genes explains why *S. pneumoniae* can cause such varying disease symptoms. *Staphylococcus aureus* is another medically important Gram-positive bacterium, which is commonly found on human skin.

Gram-Negative Bacteria Gram-negative bacteria have thin peptidoglycan cell walls enclosed by a lipopolysaccharide envelope. Diverse phyla of bacteria display Gram-negative staining. The outer lipopolysaccharide envelope and lower amount of cell-wall peptidoglycan enable some Gram-negative bacteria to be less sensitive to the effects of penicillin and chemically similar antibiotics. (Gram-negative bacteria are treated with different antibiotics.) *E. coli* is an example of a Gram-negative bacterium that lives in the human lower intestine (see Figure 25.10b). A particularly virulent strain, *E. coli* O157:H7, is a significant cause of food-borne illness.

Distinguishing Gram-positive from Gram-negative bacteria is an important factor in choosing antibiotics for treating infectious diseases. For example, Gram-positive bacteria are typically more susceptible than Gram-negative bacteria to penicillin and related antibiotics because these antibiotics interfere with synthesis of peptidoglycan, which Gram-positive bacteria require in larger amounts. For this reason penicillin or related antibiotics, such as methicillin, are widely used to treat infections caused by Gram-positive bacteria. However, it is of societal concern that some strains of Gram-positive bacteria have become resistant to some antibiotics, an example being methicillin-resistant *Staphylococcus aureus*, or MRSA.

(a) **Gram-positive bacteria**

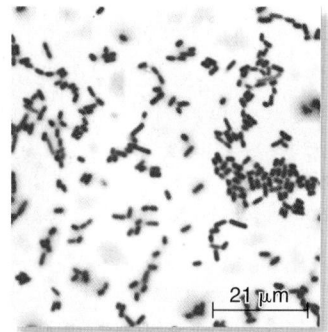

(b) **Gram-negative bacteria**

Figure 25.10 Gram-positive and Gram-negative bacteria. (a) *Streptococcus pneumonia,* a member of the Firmicutes, stains positive (purple) with the Gram stain. (b) *Escherichia coli,* a member of the Proteobacteria, stains negative (pink) when the Gram stain procedure is applied.

Microbes Display Diverse Types of Motility Structures

Many microorganisms have structures at the cell surface or within cells that enable them to change position in their environment. Motility allows microbes to move to favourable conditions within gradients of light, gases, or nutrients. In addition, motility structures allow them to respond to chemical signals emitted from other microbes during quorum sensing and mating. Microbes move by swimming, twitching or gliding, adjusting their flotation in water, or pirating cytoskeletal proteins of invaded eukaryotic cells.

Structures known as **flagella** enable swimming behaviour. Prokaryotic flagella differ from eukaryotic flagella in several ways. Prokaryotic flagella lack an internal cytoskeleton of microtubules, the motor protein dynein, and a plasma membrane covering, all features that characterize eukaryotic flagella (see Chapter 4). Unlike eukaryotic flagella, prokaryotic flagella do not repeatedly bend and straighten. Instead, prokaryotic flagella are propelled by molecular machines composed of a filament, hook, and motor that work together somewhat like a boat's outboard motor (**Figure 25.12**). Lying outside the cell, the long, stiff, curved filament acts as a propeller. The hook links the filament with the motor: a set of protein rings at the cell surface. Hydrogen ions (protons), which have been pumped out of the cytoplasm, usually via the electron transport system, diffuse back into the cell through channel proteins. This proton movement powers the turning of the hook and filament. The bacterial flagellum is the only known example, in any organism, of a structure that experiences complete rotation without a fixed point.

Prokaryotic species differ in the number and location of flagella, which may occur singly, in clumps at one pole of a bacterial cell, or emerging from around the cell (**Figure 25.13**). Differences in flagellar number and location cause microorganisms to exhibit different modes of swimming. For example, spirochaete flagella are located outside the peptidoglycan cell wall but within the confines of an outer membrane that holds them close to the cell. Rotation of these flagella causes spirochaetes to display characteristic bending, flexing, and twirling motions.

Some prokaryotes twitch or glide across surfaces, using threadlike cell surface structures known as **pili** (**Figure 25.14**). *Myxococcus xanthus* cells, for example, move by alternately extending and retracting pili from one pole or the other. This process allows directional movement toward food materials. If nutrients are low, cells of these bacteria glide together to form tiny treelike colonies, which are part of a reproductive process. As you will see, pili can also play important roles in bacterial reproduction and disease processes.

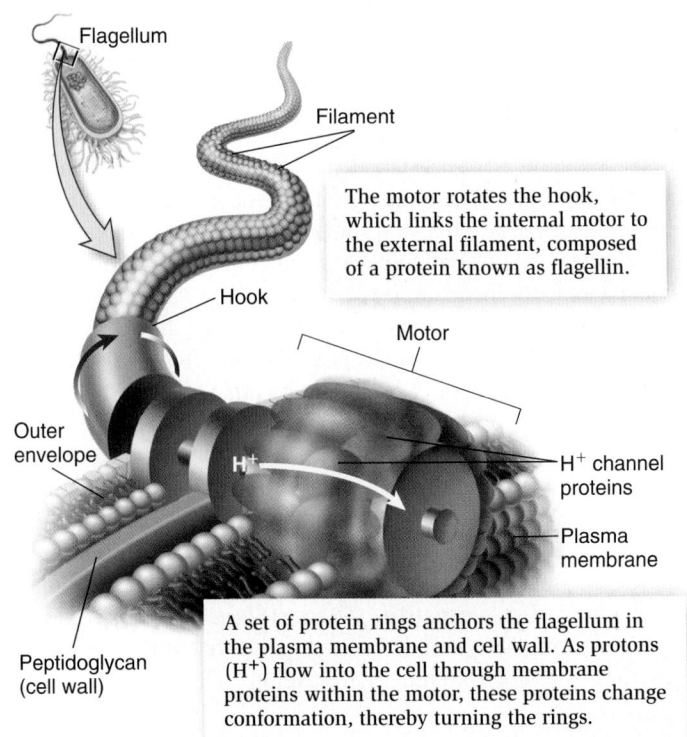

The motor rotates the hook, which links the internal motor to the external filament, composed of a protein known as flagellin.

A set of protein rings anchors the flagellum in the plasma membrane and cell wall. As protons (H^+) flow into the cell through membrane proteins within the motor, these proteins change conformation, thereby turning the rings.

Figure 25.12 Diagram of a prokaryotic flagellum, showing filament, hook, and motor.

Concept check: *Does the filament move more like the arms of a human swimmer or the shaft of a boat propeller?*

(a) Bacteria with a single short flagellum

(b) Bacterium with multiple long flagella

Figure 25.13 Differences in the number and location of flagella. Depending on the species, microbial cells can produce one or more flagella at the poles or numerous flagella around the periphery. **(a)** *Vibrio parahaemolyticus,* a bacterium that causes seafood poisoning, has a single short flagellum. **(b)** *Salmonella enterica,* another bacterium that causes food poisoning, has many flagella distributed around the cell periphery.

BioConnections: *Look ahead to Figure 26.7b. What heterotrophic eukaryote (like V. parahaemoliticus and S. enterica) moves to its food source in the human gut by means of flagella?*

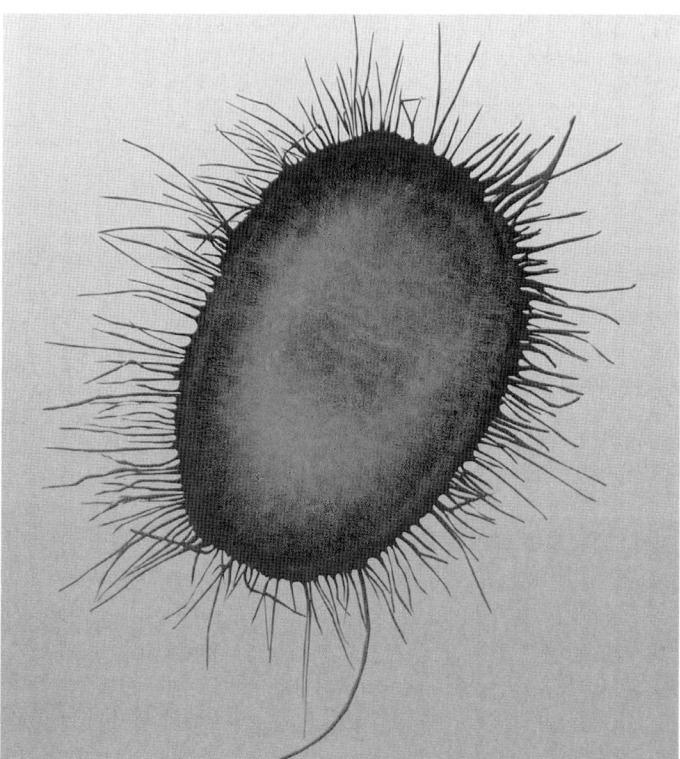

Figure 25.14 Pili extending from the surface of *Proteus mirabilis.*

Concept check: *What type of motion does this cell likely use?*

Cyanobacteria and some other bacteria that live in aquatic habitats use cytoplasmic structures known as **gas vesicles** to adjust their buoyancy. This process allows them to move up or down in the water column, an advantage in finding nutrients and avoiding harmful conditions. Gas vesicles are hollow cylinders whose watertight walls are made of protein. The presence of gas vesicles explains why cyanobacteria often form buoyant scums at the surfaces of ponds and lakes.

25.3 / REPRODUCTION

Learning Outcomes:

1. Understand how populations of prokaryotic organisms increase and how some bacteria survive under stressful conditions.
2. Describe how bacteria can be counted in medical and environmental samples.

Bacteria and archaea enlarge their populations by means of a process known as binary fission. In addition, some microbes produce tough cells that can withstand deleterious conditions for long periods in a dormant condition. Finally, although bacteria and archaea lack meiosis and other features typical of

eukaryotic sexual reproduction, they are able to obtain additional genes by a variety of methods. Each of these aspects of reproduction helps to explain how microbes function in nature and human affairs.

Populations of Bacteria and Archaea Increase by Binary Fission

The cells of bacteria and archaea divide by splitting in two, a process known as **binary fission** (**Figure 25.15a**; also refer back to Figure 16.13) and is an asexual process that is fundamentally different from mitosis. If sufficient nutrients are available, an entire population of identical cells can be produced from a single parental cell by repeated binary fission. This growth process allows microbes to become very numerous in water, food, or animal tissues, potentially causing harm. Bacteria do not engage in sexual reproduction but, as you will see later in this section, they have methods, such as conjugation, transformation, and transduction, that allow for genetic exchange.

Binary fission is the basis for a widely used method for detecting and counting bacteria in patient fluids, food, or water samples. Microbiologists who study the spread of disease need to quantify bacterial cells in samples taken from the environment. Medical technicians often need to count bacteria in body fluid samples to assess the likelihood of infection. But because bacterial cells are small and often unpigmented, they are difficult to count directly. One way that microbiologists count bacteria is to place a measured volume of sample into plastic dishes called Petri dishes filled with a semisolid nutrient medium that is agar based. Bacteria in the sample undergo repeated binary fission to form colonies of cells that are visible to the unaided eye (**Figure 25.15b**). Since each colony represents a single cell that was present in the original sample, the assumption is that the number of colonies in the Petri dish reflects the number of living bacteria in the original sample.

Another way to detect and count bacteria is to treat samples with a stain that binds bacterial DNA, causing cells to glow brightly when illuminated with ultraviolet light. The glowing bacteria can be viewed and counted by the use of a fluorescence microscope (**Figure 25.15c**). The fluorescence method must be used when the microbes of interest cannot be cultured in the laboratory. Microorganisms can also be stained with fluorescent reagents that bind to specific DNA sequences, allowing microbiologists to detect and count bacteria and archaea of precise genetic types. This procedure, known as fluorescence in situ hybridization (FISH), is a powerful technique for finding particular types of microorganisms in mixed populations.

It has been estimated that the vast majority (>95%) of all microorganisms cannot be cultured; they cannot be visualized on Petri dishes containing agar. However, PCR techniques using primers that are complimentary to conserved regions of DNA for most bacteria allow the researcher to amplify sections of DNA, which can then be sequenced. These sequences reveal astonishing prokaryotic diversity samples of water or soil. This PCR technique has also been used to reveal an astonishing

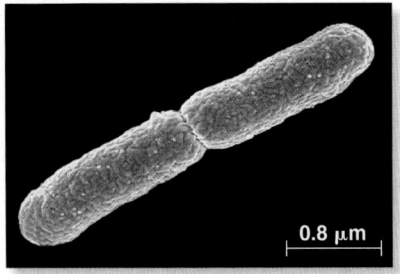

(a) Bacterium undergoing binary fission

(b) Colonies developed from single cells

(c) Bacteria stained with fluorescent DNA-binding dye

Figure 25.15   Binary fission and counting microbes.   (a) Division of a bacterial cell as viewed by scanning electron microscopy. (b) When samples are spread onto the surfaces of Petri dishes that contain nutrients, single cells of bacteria or archaea may divide repeatedly to form visible colonies, which can be counted. The number of colonies is an estimate of the number of culturable cells in the original sample. (c) If a fluorescence microscope is available, cells can be counted directly by applying a fluorescent stain that binds to cell DNA. Each cell glows brightly when illuminated with ultraviolet light.

Concept check: *Which procedure would you choose to count bacteria in a sample that is known to include many species that have not as yet been cultured?*

BioConnections: *Look back to Figure 16.13. How many cells result from the binary fission of a single mother cell?*

diversity of microorganisms that inhabit a human mouth that could not have otherwise been observed by using standard Petri dish plating techniques.

Some Bacteria Survive Harsh Conditions as Akinetes or Endospores

Some bacteria produce thick-walled cells known as akinetes or endospores that are able to survive unfavourable conditions in a dormant state. Akinetes and endospores develop when bacteria have experienced stress, such as low nutrients or unfavourable temperatures. Such cells are able to germinate into metabolically active cells when conditions improve again. For example, aquatic filamentous cyanobacteria often produce large, food-filled **akinetes** when winter approaches (**Figure 25.16a**). Akinetes are able to survive winter at the bottoms of lakes, and they produce new filaments in spring when they are carried by water currents to the brightly lit surface.

Endospores (**Figure 25.16b**) are cells with tough protein coats that are produced inside bacterial cells and then released when the enclosing cell dies and breaks down. Endospores can remain alive, though in a dormant state, for hundreds of years. Some studies suggest they have even longer lifetimes. For example, Raúl Cano and Monica Borucki cultured bacterial cells from viable *Bacillus sphaericus* endospores that were carefully isolated from the gut of a bee that had been trapped in amber (hardened tree resin) for more than 25 million years.

The ability to produce endospores allows some Gram-positive bacteria to cause serious diseases. For example, *Bacillus anthracis* causes the disease anthrax, a potential agent in bioterrorism and germ warfare. Most cases of human anthrax result when endospores of *B. anthracis* enter wounds, causing skin infections that are relatively easily cured by antibiotic treatment. But sometimes

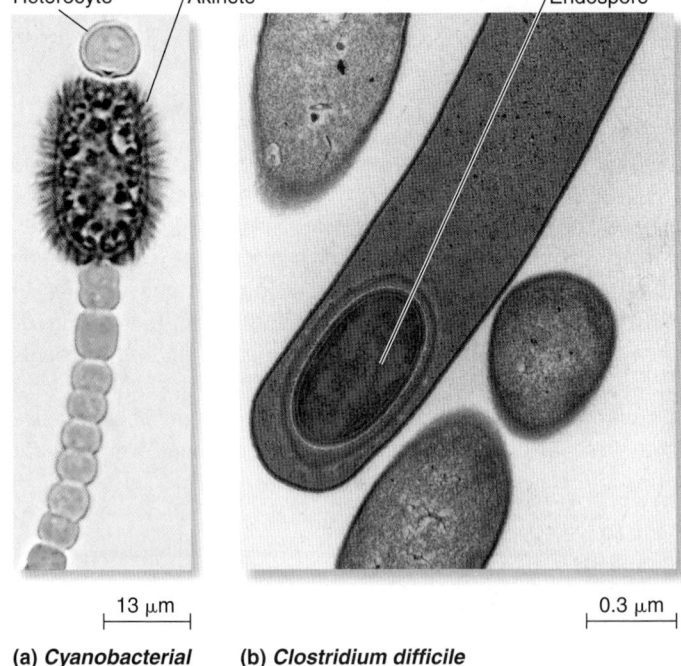

(a) *Cyanobacterial akinete*   **(b) *Clostridium difficile***

Figure 25.16   Specialized cells capable of dormancy. **(a)** Akinetes are thick-walled, food-filled cells produced by some cyanobacteria. They are able to resist stressful conditions and generate new populations when conditions improve. As discussed later, the heterocyte is a specialized cell in which nitrogen fixation occurs. **(b)** An endospore with a resistant wall develops within the cytoplasm of the bacterium *Clostridium difficile*.

Concept check: *How do endospores influence the ability of some bacteria to cause disease?*

the endospores are inhaled or consumed in undercooked, contaminated meat, potentially causing more serious illness or death. *Clostridium botulinum* can contaminate canned food that has not been heated to temperatures high enough to destroy its tough endospores during the canning process. When the endospores germinate and bacterial cells grow in the food, they produce a deadly neurotoxin, as well as NH_3 and CO_2 gas, which causes can lids to bulge. If humans consume the food, the toxin causes botulism, a severe type of food poisoning that can lead to respiratory and muscular paralysis. The botulism toxin has been recently marketed commercially as Botox, which is injected in small doses into the skin, where it paralyzes facial muscles, thereby reducing the appearance of wrinkles. *Clostridium tetani* produces a neurotoxin that causes lockjaw, also known as tetanus, when bacterial cells or endospores enter wounds from soil. The ability of the genera *Bacillus* and *Clostridium* to produce resistant endospores helps to explain their widespread presence in nature and their potential danger to humans.

Bacteria and Archaea Obtain Genetic Material by Transduction, Transformation, and Conjugation

In Chapter 16 you were introduced to the varied ways in which microorganisms can acquire genetic material from other cells. In this chapter we have noted the ecological and evolutionary impacts of horizontal gene exchange. DNA can enter cells by means of viral vectors in a process known as **transduction**. Microbes are able to take up DNA directly from their environments in a process known as **transformation**. Some bacteria transmit DNA during a mating process known as **conjugation**. Pili (see Figure 25.14) help mating cells attach to each other, allowing conjugation to proceed in Gram-negative bacteria. Such gene exchange processes have contributed to the diversity of microbial nutrition and metabolism, our next topic.

25.4 / NUTRITION AND METABOLISM

Learning Outcomes:

1. List the major modes of nutrition used by prokaryotic species.
2. Compare and contrast the effects of oxygen on the metabolism of different types of prokaryotic species.
3. Describe in basic terms the process of biological nitrogen fixation, why it is important, and how oxygen interferes with this process.

Bacteria and archaea use a wide variety of materials and chemical transformations to obtain carbon and energy for growth (**Table 25.2**). These materials and transformations explain the nutritional diversity of microorganisms. Bacteria and archaea together display more diverse types of metabolism than other groups of organisms. Microbes can be classified according to type of nutrition, response to oxygen, and presence of specialized metabolic processes.

Bacteria and Archaea Display Diverse Types of Nutrition and Responses to Oxygen

Cyanobacteria and some other prokaryotes are **autotrophs** (meaning "self-feeders"), organisms that are able to produce all or most of their own organic compounds. Autotrophic microorganisms fall into two categories: photoautotrophs and chemoautotrophs. **Photoautotrophs** are able to use light as a source of energy for oxygenic photosynthesis to produce organic compounds from CO_2 and H_2O. Purple sulphur bacteria can anoxygenically use H_2S as an electron donor to produce organic compounds from CO_2. Photoautotrophs related to cyanobacteria are speculated to have been the organisms involved in initially oxygenating Earth. **Chemoautotrophs** are able to use energy obtained by chemical modifications of inorganic compounds to synthesize organic compounds. Such chemical modifications include nitrification (the conversion of ammonia to nitrate) and the oxidation of sulphur, iron, or hydrogen. The presence of oxygen on Earth, as a by-product of oxygenic photosynthesis, allowed a rapid expansion in the diversity of microorganisms and their ability to gain energy from the oxidation of reduced compounds, such as sulphur, iron, or hydrogen.

Heterotrophs (meaning "other feeders") are organisms that require at least one organic compound, and often more. Some microorganisms are **photoheterotrophs**, meaning that they are able to use light energy to generate ATP, but they must take in organic compounds from their environment. **Chemoheterotrophs** must obtain organic molecules for both energy and as a carbon source. Among the many types of bacterial chemoheterotrophs is *Propionibacterium acnes,* which causes acne, affecting up to 80% of adolescents in Canada. The genome sequence of *P. acnes* has revealed numerous genes that allow it to break down skin cells and consume the products.

Microorganisms differ in their need for oxygen. **Obligate aerobes** require O_2. **Facultative aerobes** are more adaptable than obligate aerobes. They can use O_2 in aerobic respiration, obtain energy via anaerobic fermentation, or use inorganic chemical reactions to obtain energy. One fascinating example of a facultative aerobe is *Thiomargarita namibiensis,* a large

Table 25.2	Major Nutritional Types of Bacteria and Archaea		
Nutrition type	**Energy source**	**Carbon source**	**Example**
Autotroph			
Photoautotroph	Light	CO_2	Cyanobacteria
Chemoautotroph	Inorganic compounds	CO_2	*Sulfolobus*
Heterotroph			
Photoheterotroph	Light	Organic compounds	Chloroflexi
Chemoheterotroph	Organic compounds	Organic compounds	Many

bacterium that can be seen with the naked eye, that lives in marine waters off the Namibian coast of Africa. This heterotroph obtains its energy in two ways: by oxidizing sulphide with oxygen as the terminal electron acceptor or, when oxygen is low or unavailable, by oxidizing sulphide with nitrate as the electron acceptor. In either case the cells convert sulphide to elemental sulphur, which is stored within the cells as large globules.

In contrast to obligate aerobes, **obligate anaerobes**, such as the bacterial genus *Clostridium*, are poisoned by O_2. People suffering from gas gangrene (caused by *Clostridium perfringens* and related species) are usually treated by entering a chamber having a high oxygen content (called a hyperbaric chamber), which kills the organisms and deactivates the toxins. **Aerotolerant anaerobes** do not use O_2, but they are not poisoned by it either. These organisms obtain their energy by anaerobic respiration,

GENOMES AND PROTEOMES

Gene Expression Studies Revealed How Cyanobacteria Fix Nitrogen in Hot Springs

The microbial communities of hot springs in Yellowstone National Park and other thermal areas around the world have long fascinated microbiologists interested in the occurrence of life at high temperatures. Thermal pools characteristically display beautiful, multicoloured microbial mats (**Figure 25.17**). Such mats are composed of diverse photoheterotrophs, chemoautotrophs, chemoheterotrophs, and photoautotrophs, including many types of cyanobacteria. However, in Yellowstone thermal pools, where temperatures range from 50°C to 70°C, single-celled cyanobacteria of the genus *Synechococcus* are the only photoautotrophic organisms present. Heterocyte-producing cyanobacteria are absent from such hot waters, and few heterotrophic diazotrophs tolerate such temperatures, yet nitrogen fixation occurs in these pools. It was not clear which organisms could fix nitrogen until genomic information provided an essential clue.

Anne-Soisig Steunou, Arthur Grossman, and their associates sequenced the genomes of *Synechococcus* cultures obtained from these hot springs and discovered that *nif* (nitrogen fixation)

genes were present. They also determined that *Synechococcus nif* genes were expressed in parts of the microbial mat that had temperatures near 60°C. These results indicated that *Synechococcus* conducts nitrogen fixation in the mats, producing fixed nitrogen and other compounds used by other community members. But the investigators wondered how this single-celled bacterium managed to fix nitrogen without the oxygen arising from photosynthesis disabling the functioning of nitrogenase. They tracked the expression of *Synechococcus* genes over 24 hours and found that after nightfall the expression of a photosynthesis gene (*psaB*) fell dramatically, while expression of nitrogen fixation genes (*nifH*, *nifD*, and *nifK*) increased (**Figure 25.18**). They concluded that *Synechococcus* turns on nitrogen fixation at dusk, when oxygen production from photosynthesis drops. But nitrogen fixation is an energy-intensive process, so how does *Synechococcus* fuel it? Steunou and her colleagues used differential gene expression analyses to establish that *Synechococcus* uses fermentation, an anaerobic metabolic pathway, to supply the ATP needed for nitrogen fixation. This study illustrates not only important features of microbial metabolism but also the essential ecological roles played by bacteria and archaea, a topic that we will explore in more detail next.

Figure 25.18 Daily changes in photosynthesis and nitrogen fixation gene expression in *Synechococcus* cultures isolated from thermal pools.

Concept check: *At what time of the day does the photosynthesis gene psaB reach its lowest level of expression, and when does the nitrogen-fixation gene nifK reach its highest expression level?*

Figure 25.17 A thermal pool in Yellowstone National Park. Brightly coloured mats at the pool edge are microbial communities that include thermophilic cyanobacteria.

which uses electron acceptors other than oxygen in electron transport processes. Anaerobic metabolic processes include denitrification (the conversion of nitrate into N_2 gas) and the reduction of manganese, iron, and sulphate, which are all important in Earth's mineral cycles.

Note the diversity of nutritional modes in bacteria and archaea compared with the eukaryotes, which exhibit only photoautotrophism (most plants) and chemoheterotrophism.

Bacteria Play Important Roles as Nitrogen Fixers

Many cyanobacteria and some other microbes are known as **diazotrophs** ("dinitrogen consumers") because they conduct a specialized metabolic process called **nitrogen fixation**. The removal of nitrogen from the gaseous phase is called fixation. Nitrogen fixation is a process restricted to certain bacteria since no other life forms can perform it. During nitrogen fixation the enzyme nitrogenase converts inert atmospheric gas (N_2) into ammonia (NH_3). Plants and eukaryotic algae can use ammonia (though not N_2) to produce proteins and other essential nitrogen-containing molecules. As a result, many plants have developed symbiotic relationships with diazotrophs, which provide ammonia to the plant partner. For example, nitrogen-fixing cyanobacteria typically live in leaf cavities of water ferns that float in rice paddies. The fern partner and the rice crop both take up ammonia produced by the diazotrophs. This natural fertilizer allows the rice plants to produce more protein. Many types of heterotrophic soil bacteria also fix nitrogen. Examples include *Rhizobium* and its relatives, which form close associations with the roots of legumes (see Chapter 35).

Oxygen binds to nitrogenase, irreversibly disabling it. Thus, most diazotrophs are able to conduct nitrogen fixation only in low-oxygen habitats. Many cyanobacteria accomplish nitrogen fixation in specialized cells known as **heterocytes** (see Figure 25.16a). Heterocytes display many adaptations that reduce nitrogenase exposure to oxygen. These adaptations include thick walls, which reduce inward oxygen diffusion; absence of oxygen-producing photosystems; and increased respiration, which consumes oxygen.

25.5 ECOLOGICAL ROLES AND BIOTECHNOLOGY APPLICATIONS

Learning Outcomes:

1. Discuss the role of bacteria and archaea in the carbon cycle.
2. List examples of bacterial/eukaryote symbiosis and of pathogenic microbes.
3. List ways in which bacteria contribute to industrial and biotechnology applications.

Bacteria and archaea play several key ecological roles, including the production and cycling of carbon. Earth's carbon cycle depends on microorganisms that produce and degrade organic compounds, including methane. Bacteria also play fascinating roles as symbionts living in close associations with eukaryotes. In this section we focus on these diverse ecological roles and also provide examples of ways that humans use the metabolic capabilities of bacteria and archaea in biotechnology.

Bacteria and Archaea Play Important Roles in Earth's Carbon Cycle

Earth's carbon cycle is the sum of all the transformations that occur among compounds that contain carbon. (See Chapter 56 for a detailed discussion of the carbon cycle.) Bacteria and archaea are important in producing and degrading organic compounds. For example, cyanobacteria and other autotrophic bacteria are important **producers**. These bacteria, together with algae and plants, synthesize the organic compounds that are used by other organisms for food. **Decomposers**, also known as saprobes, include heterotrophic microorganisms (as well as fungi and animals). These organisms break down dead organisms and organic matter, releasing minerals for uptake by living things. Microbial decomposers can consume diverse materials, including oil, explosives, and pesticides, making them useful in cleaning up toxic spills and dumps.

Archaea and bacteria also influence Earth's carbon cycle by producing and consuming methane (CH_4). Methane—the major component of natural gas—is a powerful greenhouse gas, as are CO_2 and H_2O vapour. Atmospheric methane thus has the potential to alter Earth's climate. Several groups of anaerobic archaea, known as the **methanogens**, convert CO_2, methyl groups, or acetate to methane and release it from their cells. Methanogens live in swampy wetlands, in deep-sea habitats, or in the digestive systems of ungulate animals, such as cattle. Marsh gas produced in wetlands is largely composed of methane, and large quantities of methane produced long ago are trapped in deep-sea and subsurface Arctic deposits.

Microbes also play a role in limiting atmospheric methane. The balance of methane in Earth's atmosphere is maintained by the activities of aerobic bacteria known as **methanotrophs**, which consume methane. Some methanotrophs live in symbiotic association with marine invertebrates in deep-sea thermal vents or hydrocarbon seep communities. Methane-consuming bacteria also live in close association with wetland plants, which release the oxygen needed by these bacteria to metabolize methane. In the absence of methanotrophs, Earth's atmosphere would be much richer in the greenhouse gas methane, which would substantially increase global temperatures.

The expanding field of microbial ecology has shown that archaea are not primitive outliers of life on Earth but rather occupy niches that were thought not to have been able to support life. Many of the archaea are extreme halophiles, living in the Dead Sea. Others are thermophiles and live near deep-sea vents. The ability of these microorganisms to live in extremely salty or hot environments has biotechnologists isolating commercially useful salt- and heat-resistant proteins and enzymes from archaea.

Many Bacteria Live in Symbiotic Associations with Eukaryotes

As you have seen, many bacteria live in close associations with eukaryotic organisms, a relationship called **symbiosis**. If symbiotic associations are beneficial to both partners, the association is known as a **mutualism**. If one partner benefits at the expense of the other, the association is known as a **parasitism**, and the partner that benefits is termed a parasite or a pathogen. There are numerous examples of mutualistic and parasitic bacteria.

Mutualistic Microbes   Bacteria are involved in many mutually beneficial partnerships in aquatic and terrestrial habitats. Many aquatic protists depend on bacterial partners for vitamins or other essential compounds. For example, the common green seaweed *Ulva* does not display its typical lettuce-leaf-like structure unless bacterial partners belonging to the phylum Bacteroidetes are present. The bacteria produce a compound that induces normal seaweed development. Bioluminescent bacteria form symbiotic relationships with squid and other marine animals. In deep-sea thermal vent communities, sulphur-oxidizing bacteria live within the tissues of tubeworms and mussels, supplying these animals with carbon compounds used as food. Microbial ecologist Cameron Currie, who completed his PhD at the University of Toronto, and his associates have documented a complex land association involving four partners: fungus-growing ants, the fungi that the ants cultivate for food, parasitic fungi that attack the food fungi, and mutualistic Actinobacteria, which produce antibiotics. These antibiotics control the growth of the fungal parasite, preventing it from destroying the ants' fungal food supply. The ants grow the useful bacteria in cavities on their body surfaces; glands near these cavities supply the bacteria with nutrients.

Parasitic and Pathogenic Microbes   **Parasites** are organisms that obtain organic compounds from living hosts. If parasitic microbes cause disease symptoms in their hosts, the microorganisms are known as **pathogens**. Cholera, leprosy, tetanus, pneumonia, whooping cough, diphtheria, Lyme disease, scarlet fever, rheumatic fever, typhoid fever, bacterial dysentery, and tooth decay are among the many examples of human diseases caused by bacterial pathogens. Bacteria also cause many plant diseases of importance in agriculture, including blights, soft rots, and wilts. How do microbiologists determine which bacteria cause these diseases? The pioneering research of the Nobel Prize–winning German physician Robert Koch provides the answer.

In the mid- to late nineteenth century, Koch established a series of steps to determine whether a particular organism causes a specific disease. First, the presence of the suspected pathogen must correlate with the occurrence of symptoms. Next, the pathogen must be isolated from an infected host and grown in pure culture if possible, and cells from the pure culture should cause disease when inoculated into a healthy host. Finally, a researcher should be able to isolate the same pathogen from the second infected host. By using these steps, known as **Koch's postulates**, Koch discovered the bacterial causes of anthrax, cholera, and tuberculosis. Subsequent investigators have used Koch's postulates to establish the causes of many other infectious diseases. As recently as the 1980s bacteriologists used Koch's postulates to establish that Legionnaires' disease is caused by a bacterial pathogen, *Legionella pneumophila.*

How Pathogenic Bacteria Attack Cells   Modern research is providing new information about how bacteria attack cells. Such knowledge aids in developing strategies for disease prevention and treatment. Many pathogenic bacteria attack cells by binding to the target cell surfaces and injecting substances that help them use cell components. During their evolution some pathogenic bacteria have transformed flagella into needle-like systems for injecting proteins into animal or plant cells as part of the infection process. Such modified flagella are known as type III secretion systems called injectisomes (**Figure 25.19a**). *Yersinia pestis* (the agent of bubonic plague) and *Salmonella enterica* (which causes salmonellosis) are examples of bacteria whose type III secretion systems allow them to attack human cells. These bacteria also induce the host cell to form a plasma membrane pocket that encloses the bacterial cell, bringing it into the target cell. Once within a host's cell, pathogenic bacteria use the cell's resources to reproduce and spread to nearby tissues.

Some other bacterial pathogens use a type IV secretion system to deliver toxins or transforming DNA into cells (**Figure 25.19b**). Examples of such bacteria that cause human disease include *Helicobacter pylori, Legionella pneumophila,* and *Bordetella pertussis.* The plant pathogen *Agrobacterium tumifaciens* uses a type IV secretion system to transfer DNA (T DNA) into plant cells. The bacterial T DNA encodes an enzyme that affects normal plant growth, with the result that cancerlike tumours develop (see Figure 25.3). Type IV systems evolved from pili and other components of bacterial mating. Thus, types III and IV attack systems are examples of descent with modification, the evolutionary process by which organisms acquire new features. Some experts propose that type III and IV systems may be useful in human gene therapy, to deliver DNA to target cells.

Antibiotic-Resistant Pathogens   Antibiotic compounds are widely used to treat diseases caused by bacterial pathogens, but overuse of antibiotics can lead to production of resistant bacteria, a serious health problem. For example, some strains of *Staphylococcus aureus,* which causes staph infections, have developed resistance to penicillin and similar antibiotics. To increase the production profit margin, livestock are often fed antibiotics to reduce the effects of minor bacterial infections or to prevent infections from spreading. Unfortunately, this activity promotes the evolution of antibiotic-resistant bacterial strains. Initially, antibiotic-resistant bacteria appear through spontaneous mutation at very low levels in the bacterial population, and in the absence of antibiotics remain at very low levels.

Outer envelope — Plasma membrane

Pathogenic bacterium

Flagellum-like injectisome

Animal cell

Nucleus

Infection proteins

(a) Type III secretion system

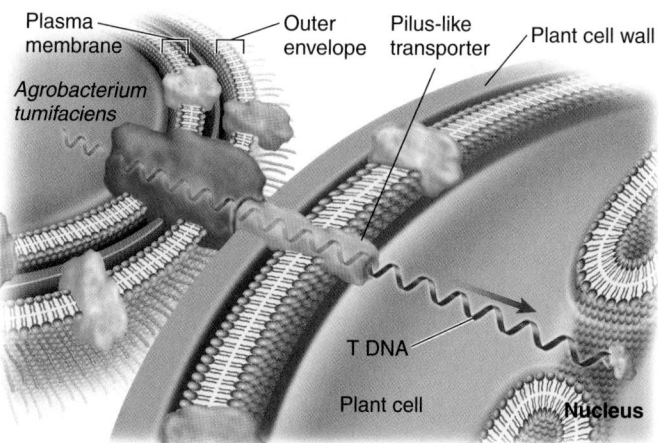

Plasma membrane — Outer envelope — Pilus-like transporter — Plant cell wall

Agrobacterium tumifaciens

T DNA

Plant cell

Nucleus

(b) Type IV secretion system

Figure 25.19 **Attack systems of pathogenic bacteria.**
(a) The type III secretion system functions as a syringe to inject proteins into host cells, in this case an animal cell, thereby initiating the disease process. **(b)** The type IV secretion system forms a channel through which DNA can be transmitted from a pathogen to a host cell, in this case from the bacterium *Agrobacterium tumifaciens* into a plant cell.

Concept check: *How does the type IV secretion system illustrate the evolutionary concept of descent with modification?*

However, if antibiotics are present, the antibiotic-resistant bacteria have a selective advantage, and they then proliferate. When humans become infected by such strains, antibiotic treatments are not effective, and cases have occurred in which patients' infections were resistant to all known antibiotics. At any time, from 20% to 30% of the general population carry *Staphylococcus aureus* on their hands and inside their noses but are not ill. MRSA (methicillin-resistant *Staphylococcus aureus*)

outbreaks have occurred in Canadian hospitals (called nosocomial infections). These *Staphylococcus aureus* are resistant to one of the most modern antibiotics, methicillin.

Some Bacteria Are Useful in Industrial and Other Applications

Several industries have harnessed the metabolic capabilities of microbes obtained from nature. The food industry uses bacteria to produce chemical changes in food that improve consistency or flavour—to make dairy products, including cheese and yogourt, for example. Cheese makers add pure cultures of certain bacteria to milk. The bacteria consume milk sugar (lactose) and produce lactic acid, which aids in curdling the milk.

Many bacteria are beneficial to human health and act as probiotics. These bacteria are added into, or naturally occur in, certain food products, such as yogourt. One of the theories of probiotics is that these beneficial microorganisms occupy the intestine and exclude pathogenic bacteria.

The chemical industry produces materials, such as vinegar, amino acids, enzymes, vitamins, insulin, vaccines, antibiotics, and other useful pharmaceuticals, by growing particular bacteria in giant vats. For example, bacteria produce the antibiotics streptomycin, tetracycline, kanamycin, gentamycin, bacitracin, polymyxin-B, and neomycin.

The ability of microorganisms to live in harsh environments and break down organic compounds makes them very useful in treating wastewater, industrial discharges, and harmful substances, such as explosives, pesticides, and oil spills. This process is known as bioremediation. *Geobacter sulfurreducens,* for example, is used to precipitate metals, such as uranium, from contaminated water, thereby purifying it. This bacterium uses metal ions and elemental sulphur in an electron transport process to oxidize acetate to CO_2, in the process producing ATP needed for growth and reproduction. Taking advantage of this fact, engineers drip acetate into the groundwater, thereby enriching the population of *G. sulfurreducens* to 85% of the microbial community at contaminated sites, which more efficiently precipitates uranium.

In addition to food production and waste treatment, bacteria are also used in agriculture. Several species of *Bacillus,* particularly *B. thuringiensis,* produce crystalline proteins known as Bt-toxins, which kill insects that ingest them. *B. thuringiensis* is an endospore-producing bacterium that also produces a crystal made up of a protein that is toxic to insects. When certain insects ingest this crystal, it is dissolved by the alkaline pH of the insect midgut. The toxin protein molecules then bind to the insect midgut and cause perforations that eventually kill the insect. Tent caterpillars, potato beetles, gypsy moths, mosquitoes, and black flies are among the pests that can be controlled by Bt-toxin. For this reason genes involved in Bt-toxin production have been engineered into some crop plants, such as corn, to limit pests and thereby increase crop yields. *Deinococcus radiodurans* is another example of a bacterial species whose unusual ecological properties may prove useful to humans, as described next.

FEATURE INVESTIGATION

Dantas and Colleagues Found that Many Bacteria Can Break Down and Consume Antibiotics as a Sole Carbon Source

Many microorganisms naturally secrete antibiotics, chemicals that inhibit the growth of other microorganisms. Antibiotic compounds are evolutionary adaptations that allow bacteria and other microbes to avoid attack or reduce competition for resources. People have taken advantage of high antibiotic production by certain bacteria, particularly species of the phylum Actinomycetes, to make commercial antibiotics in industrial processes.

In nature many chemoheterotrophic bacteria have taken advantage of widespread natural antibiotic production by using these organic compounds as a source of carbon. In 2008, Gautam Dantas, George Church, and their colleagues reported this conclusion after experimentally testing their hypothesis that soil bacteria might be able to metabolize antibiotics (**Figure 25.20**). The investigators first cultivated bacteria from 11 different soils in the laboratory, finding diverse phylogenetic types. Almost 90% of the cultured bacteria were Gram-negative Proteobacteria, some closely related to human pathogens, while 7% of the cultures were Gram-positive Actinomycetes. These researchers then tested the ability of the bacteria cultured from different soils (isolates) to use various antibiotics as a sole carbon source. The 18 antibiotics tested included penicillin and related compounds, as well as widely prescribed ciprofloxacin (Cipro). Every antibiotic tested supported the growth of bacteria from soil. Importantly, each antibiotic-eating isolate was resistant to several antibiotics at concentrations used in medical treatment of infections.

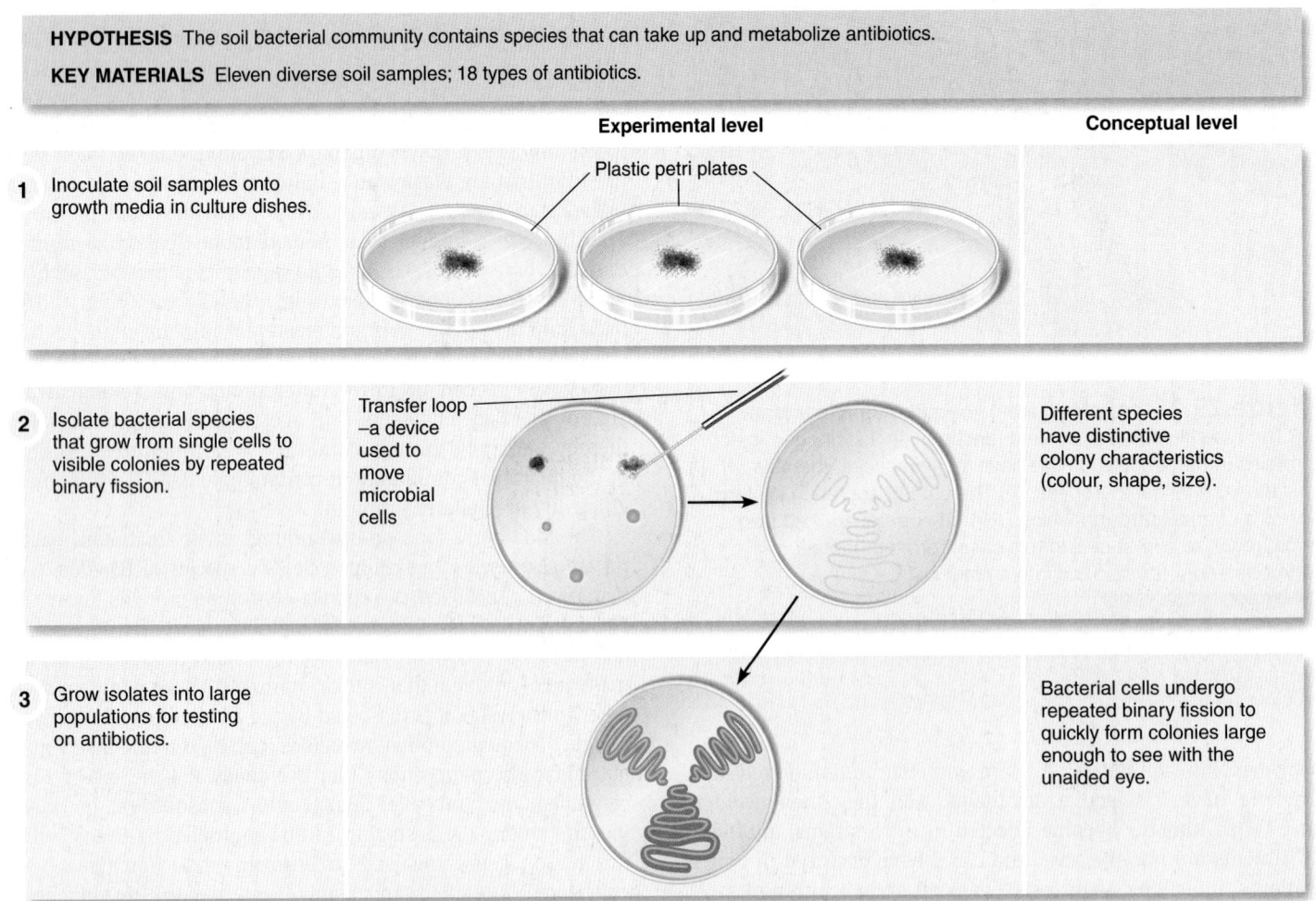

HYPOTHESIS The soil bacterial community contains species that can take up and metabolize antibiotics.

KEY MATERIALS Eleven diverse soil samples; 18 types of antibiotics.

Experimental level | Conceptual level

1 Inoculate soil samples onto growth media in culture dishes.

Plastic petri plates

2 Isolate bacterial species that grow from single cells to visible colonies by repeated binary fission.

Transfer loop –a device used to move microbial cells

Different species have distinctive colony characteristics (colour, shape, size).

3 Grow isolates into large populations for testing on antibiotics.

Bacterial cells undergo repeated binary fission to quickly form colonies large enough to see with the unaided eye.

Figure 25.20 Diverse bacteria from different soils are able to grow on many types of antibiotics.

BioConnections: *Look back at the Genomes and Proteomes section in Chapter 16. How is antibiotic resistance spread?*

4 Inoculate each bacterial isolate onto replicate dishes containing a different antibiotic as the only food source.

Penicillin G (or one of 17 other antibiotics)

Test the ability of each isolate to grow on a range of antibiotics.

5 Allow time for bacterial population growth; compare growth among dishes.

Strong growth of forest soil #1 bacterial isolate on penicillin G food.

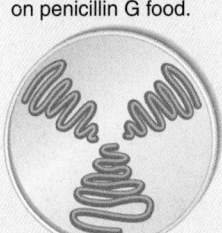

Poor growth of urban soil #3 bacterial isolate on dicloxacillin food.

Compare isolate ability to grow on different antibiotics.

6 **THE DATA**

Most soils tested contained bacterial species that were able to use antibiotics of many types for food and thus were resistant to those antibiotics.

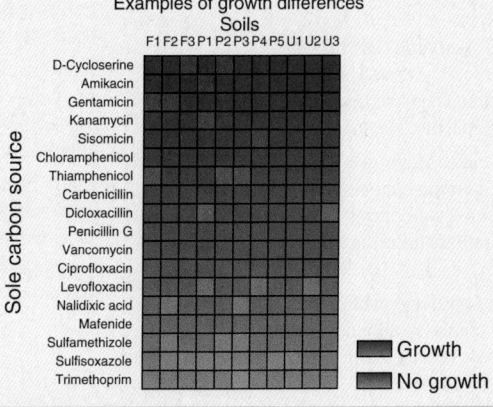

Examples of growth differences

Soils

F1 F2 F3 P1 P2 P3 P4 P5 U1 U2 U3

Sole carbon source:
D-Cycloserine
Amikacin
Gentamicin
Kanamycin
Sisomicin
Chloramphenicol
Thiamphenicol
Carbenicillin
Dicloxacillin
Penicillin G
Vancomycin
Ciprofloxacin
Levofloxacin
Nalidixic acid
Mafenide
Sulfamethizole
Sulfisoxazole
Trimethoprim

■ Growth
■ No growth

7 **CONCLUSION** Natural soils contain bacteria that are able to utilize antibiotics produced naturally by other species as food. Soil bacteria are a previously unrecognized source of antibiotic resistance genes that can be transferred to other species.

8 **SOURCE** Dantas, G., Sommer, M. O. A., Oluwasegun, R. D., and Church, G. M. 2008. Bacteria subsisting on antibiotics. *Science* 320:100–103.

In today's society the widespread use of antibiotics in medicine and agriculture is of concern because it is thought to foster increases in antibiotic resistance. The experiment by Dantas and associates revealed that natural evolutionary processes—the widespread development by diverse soil bacteria of metabolic processes to use many types of antibiotics as food—represent a previously unrecognized source of antibiotic resistance. The study also indicated that natural bacteria are a potential source of antibiotic-resistance genes that could be transferred to disease-causing bacteria.

Experimental Questions

1. What features of soil bacteria attracted the attention of researchers?
2. What processes did the researchers use to test their hypothesis that soil bacteria might use antibiotics as a food source?
3. Why was it important to researchers to test the ability of soil bacteria to resist antibiotics in the same concentrations that physicians use to treat infections?

Summary of Key Concepts

25.1 Diversity and Evolution

- The domains of life are Eukarya, Bacteria, and Archaea (known informally as eukaryotes, bacteria, and archaea). The domain Archaea is more closely related to the domain Eukarya than either is to the domain Bacteria. (Figure 25.1)

- Many representatives of the Archaea occur in extremely hot, salty, or acidic habitats. Ether-linked membrane lipids are among the features of archaea that enable their survival in extreme habitats. (Figure 25.2)

- The domain Bacteria includes 50 or more phyla, including Proteobacteria and Cyanobacteria, which are particularly diverse and of great evolutionary and ecological importance. (Table 25.1)

- Mitochondria arose from a proteobacterial ancestor, and many modern proteobacteria occur in symbiotic relationships with animals or plants. (Figure 25.3)

- Algal and plant chloroplasts arose from a cyanobacterial ancestor. Modern cyanobacteria play important ecological roles, including the production of harmful blooms in overfertilized waters. (Figure 25.4)

- Widespread horizontal DNA transfer has occurred among bacteria and archaea. Horizontal DNA transfer is particularly common among close relatives and inhabitants of the same environment, and it allows microorganisms to evolve rapidly.

25.2 Structure and Motility

- Bacteria and archaea are composed of prokaryotic cells that are smaller and simpler than those of eukaryotes. Even so, structures such as thylakoids, magnetosomes, and nucleus-like bodies are examples of surprising cell structure complexity. (Figures 25.5, 25.6)

- Cells of bacteria and archaea vary in shape. Major cell shape types are spherical cocci, rod-shaped bacilli, comma-shaped vibrios, and coiled spirilli and spirochaetes. Some cyanobacteria display specialized cells and intercellular communication, the hallmarks of multicellular organisms. (Figure 25.7)

- Many microbes secrete a coating of slimy mucilage, which plays a role in diseases and in the development of biofilms. Biofilm development is influenced by quorum sensing, a process in which group activity is coordinated by chemical communication. (Figure 25.8)

- Most prokaryotic cells possess a protective cell wall. Archaea and some bacteria have walls composed of proteins, but most bacterial cell walls contain peptidoglycan, which is composed of carbohydrates cross-linked by peptides. (Figure 25.9)

- Gram-positive bacterial cells have walls rich in peptidoglycan, while Gram-negative cells have less peptidoglycan in their walls and are enclosed by a lipopolysaccharide envelope. Gram-positive bacteria can be distinguished from Gram-negative bacteria by use of the Gram stain and other staining procedures. (Figures 25.10, 25.11)

- Motility enables microbes to change positions within their environment, which aids in locating favourable conditions for growth. Some microorganisms swim by means of flagella; others twitch or glide by the use of threadlike pili, or adjust their buoyancy in water by means of intracellular vesicles. (Figures 25.12, 25.13, 25.14)

25.3 Reproduction

- Populations of bacteria and archaea enlarge by binary fission, a simple type of cell division that provides a means by which culturable microbes can be counted. (Figure 25.15)

- Some bacteria are able to survive harsh conditions as dormant akinetes or endospores. (Figure 25.16)

- Many microorganisms obtain new DNA sequences directly from their environment (transformation), by means of viral vectors (transduction), or by a mating process (conjugation).

25.4 Nutrition and Metabolism

- Bacteria and archaea can be grouped according to nutritional type, response to oxygen, or presence of distinctive metabolic features. Major nutritional types are photoautotrophs, chemoautotrophs, photoheterotrophs, and chemoheterotrophs. (Table 25.2)

- Obligate aerobes require oxygen, whereas obligate anaerobes are poisoned by oxygen. Aerotolerant anaerobes do not use oxygen but are not poisoned by it. Both obligate and aerotolerant anaerobes obtain their energy by anaerobic respiration. Facultative aerobes are able to live with or without oxygen by using different processes for obtaining energy.

- Nitrogen fixation is an example of distinctive metabolism displayed only by certain microorganisms. (Figures 25.17, 25.18)

25.5 Ecological Roles and Biotechnology Applications

- Bacteria and archaea play key roles in Earth's carbon cycle as producers, decomposers, symbionts, or pathogens.

- Methane-producing methanogens and methane-using methanotrophs are important in the carbon cycle, and they influence Earth's climate.

- Parasitic bacteria obtain organic compounds from living hosts, and if disease symptoms result, such bacteria are known as pathogens.

- Bacteria attack eukaryotic cells by means of modified flagella, known as type III secretion systems, or type IV secretion systems, which evolved from pili and other mating components. (Figure 25.19)

- Many bacteria and archaea are useful in industrial and other applications; others are used to make food products or antibiotics or to clean up polluted environments.

- Some bacteria are able to consume antibiotics, a process linked to the evolution and spread of antibiotic resistance. (Figure 25.20)

Test to Assess Your Learning

1. Which of the following features is common to prokaryotic cells?
   a. a nucleus, featuring a nuclear envelope with pores
   b. mitochondria
   c. plasma membranes
   d. mitotic spindle
   e. none of the above

2. The bacterial phylum that produces oxygen gas as the result of photosynthesis is
   a. the proteobacteria.
   b. the cyanobacteria.
   c. the Gram-positive bacteria.
   d. all of the above.
   e. none of the above.

3. The Gram stain is a procedure that microbiologists use to
   a. determine if a bacterial strain is a pathogen.
   b. determine if a bacterial sample can break down oil.
   c. infer the structure of a bacterial cell wall and bacterial response to antibiotics.
   d. count bacteria in medical or environmental samples.
   e. all of the above.

4. Place the following steps in the correct order, according to Koch's postulates:
   I. Determine if pure cultures of bacteria cause disease symptoms when introduced to a healthy host.
   II. Determine if disease symptoms correlate with presence of a suspected pathogen.
   III. Isolate the suspected pathogen and grow it in pure culture, free of other possible pathogens.
   IV. Attempt to isolate pathogen from second-infected hosts.
      a. II, III, IV, I
      b. II, IV, III, I
      c. III, II, I, IV
      d. II, III, I, IV
      e. I, II, III, IV

5. Cyanobacteria play what ecological role?
   a. producers
   b. consumers
   c. decomposers
   d. parasites
   e. none of the above

6. Bacterial structures that are produced by pathogenic bacteria for use in attacking host cells include
   a. type III and IV secretion systems.
   b. magnetosomes.
   c. gas vesicles.
   d. thylakoids.
   e. none of the above.

7. The structures that enable some Gram-positive bacteria to remain dormant for extremely long periods of time are known as
   a. akinetes.
   b. endospores.
   c. biofilms.
   d. lipopolysaccharide envelopes.
   e. pili.

8. By means of what process do populations of bacteria or archaea increase their size?
   a. mitosis
   b. meiosis
   c. conjugation
   d. transduction
   e. none of the above

9. By what means do bacterial cells acquire new DNA?
   a. by conjugation, the mating of two cells of the same bacterial species
   b. by transduction, the injection of viral DNA into bacterial cells
   c. by transformation, the uptake of DNA from the environment
   d. all of the above
   e. none of the above

10. How do various types of bacteria move?
   a. by the use of flagella composed of motor, hook, and filament
   b. by means of pili, which help cells twitch or glide along a surface
   c. by using gas vesicles to regulate buoyancy in water bodies
   d. all of the above
   e. none of the above

Articulate to Assess Your Learning

1. Explain why many microbial populations grow more rapidly than do eukaryotes and how bacterial population growth influences the rate of food spoilage or infection.

2. What processes contribute to antibiotic resistance?

Collaborate to Assess and Extend Your Learning

1. How would you catalogue the phyla of bacteria and archaea that occur in a particular place?
2. How would you develop a bacterial product that could be sold for remediation of a site contaminated with materials that are harmful to humans?
3. Why is agar used as a base to grow bacteria in Petri dishes?

4. A principle of biology is that living organisms interact with their environment. What organisms are responsible for the blue-green blooms that often occur in warm weather on lake surfaces? Think carefully; the answer is not just "cyanobacteria," as you might first guess.

Visit McGraw-Hill Ryerson Connect™ for additional study resources.

Protists

26

Chapter Outline

SEM of a diatom cell wall, showing elaborate ornamentation of the silicate structure.

A **protist** is a eukaryote that lives in moist habitats; most are microscopic. Despite their small size, protists have a greater impact on global ecology and human affairs than most people realize. For example, the photosynthetic protists known as algae generate at least half the oxygen in Earth's atmosphere and produce organic compounds that feed marine and freshwater animals. The oil that fuels our cars and industry derives from pressure-cooked algae that accumulated on the ocean floor over millions of years. Today, algae are being engineered into systems for producing biofuels and cleaning pollutants from water.

Protists also include some parasites that cause serious human illnesses. For example, in 2001 an estimated 5,800 to 7,100 people in the Battlefords area of Saskatchewan, along with hundreds of visitors from other parts of Saskatchewan, Alberta, Manitoba, and British Columbia, became ill from the waterborne protist *Cryptosporidium parvum*. The related protist *Plasmodium falciparum*, which is carried by mosquitoes in many warm regions of the world, causes the disease malaria. Every year, nearly 500 million people become ill with malaria and more than 2 million die of this disease. As you will see in this chapter, sequencing the genomes of these and other protist species has suggested new ways of battling such deadly pathogens.

In this chapter we will survey protist diversity, including structural, nutritional, and ecological variations. We begin by exploring ways of informally classifying protists, by ecological roles, habitat, and motility. We then will focus on the defining features and evolutionary importance of the major protist phyla. Next, we discuss the nutritional modes and defensive adaptations of protists, and we conclude by looking at the reproductive adaptations that allow protists to exploit and thrive in a variety of environments. During the discussion you will also see the enormous role that protists play in ecosystem functioning and in human health. Our study of protists also illustrates important principles of diversity, particularly ways in which organisms modify their environments and provide essential biological services.

26.1 / AN INTRODUCTION TO PROTISTS

Learning Outcomes:

1. List three features that define protists.
2. Classify protists informally by ecological role, habitat, and type of motility.

Protists are eukaryotes that are not classified in the plant, animal, or fungal kingdoms, though some protists are closely related to plants or animals or fungi (**Figure 26.1**). However, the phylogenetic relationships between protists are still not very well defined and the term *protist* is, at this time, a taxonomic term that is used for convenience. The word protist comes from the Greek word *protos,* meaning "first," reflecting the fact that protists were Earth's first eukaryotes. Modern phylogenetic analyses based on comparative analysis of DNA sequences and cellular features reveal that protists do not form a monophyletic group. Instead, protist phyla are classified into several eukaryotic **supergroups** that each display distinctive features (**Table 26.1**). In general a supergroup is a phylogenetic term used to unite organisms based on phylogenetic inference. For protists one supergroup contains several phyla of protists in addition to the plant kingdom, while another supergroup links certain protists to the animal and fungal kingdoms (see Figure 26.1). Such classifications reveal the great importance of protists in our understanding of eukaryotic evolution. Canadian researchers, led by Alistair Simpson at Dalhousie University, are conducting the first phylogenetically broad investigation on protists. They are addressing various issues relating to eukaryotic diversity and classification, and the origin of the eukaryotic cell.

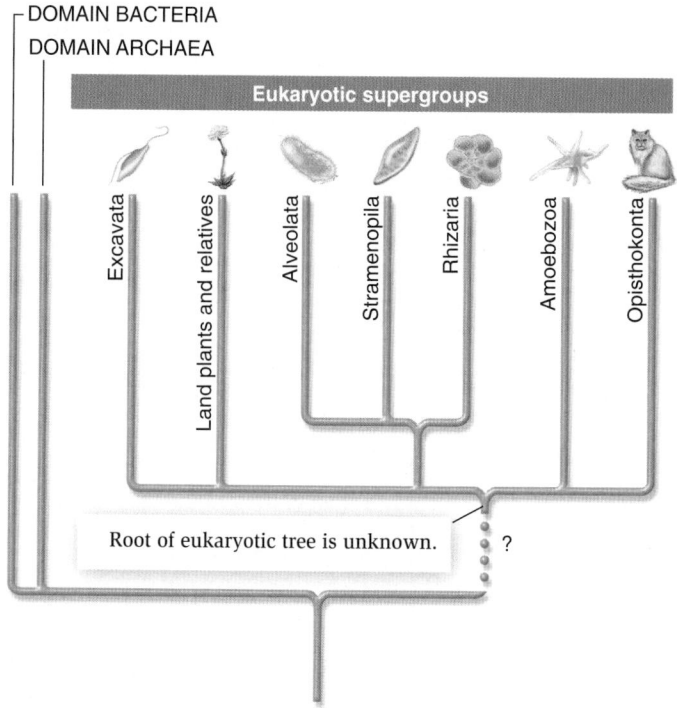

Figure 26.1 **A phylogenetic tree showing the major eukaryotic supergroups.** All the supergroups shown include some protists. The position of the eukaryotic root is uncertain, as are the branching patterns of many supergroups and phyla.

 Principle: *All life is related by an evolutionary history. Many more eukaryotic branches exist than are shown in this streamlined diagram.*

In addition to classification based on evolutionary relationships, protists are often informally classified according to diverse ecological roles, habitats, or type of motility. In this section, we will examine these informal classifications as a way of introducing protist diversity.

Protists Can Be Informally Classified According to Diverse Ecological Roles

Protists are often classified according to ecological roles into three major groups: algae, protozoa, and fungus-like protists. The term **algae** (Latin for "seaweeds") applies to about 10 phyla of protists that include both photosynthetic and nonphotosynthetic species (see Table 26.1). Photosynthetic algae produce organic compounds and oxygen, thereby providing substances used by heterotrophic organisms. For example, the single-celled algae known as diatoms often serve as food for heterotrophic protists (**Figure 26.2**). Despite the common feature of photosynthesis, algae do not form a monophyletic group descended from a single common ancestor (Figure 26.1).

Similarly, the term **protozoa** (Greek for "first life") is commonly used to describe diverse heterotrophic protists. Many protozoa are mobile and use flagella or other specialized motility structures. Protozoa feed by absorbing small organic molecules or ingesting prey. For example, the protozoa known as ciliates move by means

of many short motility structures called cilia, and they consume smaller cells, such as diatoms (Figure 26.2). Like algae, protozoa do not form a monophyletic group. Instead, they are widely distributed among the major protist supergroups (Figure 26.1).

The heterotrophic **fungus-like protists** often resemble true fungi in having threadlike, filamentous bodies and absorbing nutrients from their environments (**Figure 26.3a**). Although the structure and reproduction of fungus-like protists resemble those of a true fungus (**Figure 26.3b**), they are actually more closely related to diatoms than they are to fungi. These examples illustrate that the terms *algae, protozoa,* and *fungus-like protists,* while useful in describing ecological roles, lack taxonomic or evolutionary meaning. Protists can have single-celled forms or multicellular forms. Next we will survey ways in which protists have been informally classified according to diverse habitats.

Protists Can Be Informally Classified According to Diverse Habitats

Although protists occupy nearly every type of moist habitat, they are particularly common and diverse in oceans, lakes, wetlands, and rivers. Even extreme aquatic environments, such as

Figure 26.2 **A heterotrophic protozoan feeding on photosynthetic algae.** The large heterotrophic ciliate protozoan shown here has consumed several oil-rich, golden-pigmented, glass-walled algal cells known as diatoms. The algal cells were ingested by the process of phagocytosis and will be digested as food. Diatom cells that have avoided capture glide nearby.

 Principle: *Living organisms use energy. The diatoms were ingested by the process of phagocytosis, and their organic components will be digested as food.*

Concept check: *Why are diatoms good food for these protozoans?*

Table 26.1	Eukaryotic Supergroups and Examples of Constituent Kingdoms, Phyla, Classes, or Species	

Supergroup	KINGDOMS, Phyla, classes, or *species*	Distinguishing features
EXCAVATA	**Jakobida** *Giardia lamblia* *Trichomonas vaginalis*	Unicellular flagellates, often with feeding groove; mitochondria highly modified in specialized parasites
EUGLENOZOA	**Kinetoplastea** (kinetoplastids) *Trypanosoma brucei* **Euglenida** (euglenoids)	Unicellular flagellates; disk-shaped mitochondrial cristae; secondary plastids (when present) derived from endosymbiotic green algae
ARCHAEPLASTIDA	**Glaucophyta** (glaucophytes) **Rhodophyta** (red algae) **Chlorophyta** (green algae) Charophyceae (charophyceans) **KINGDOM PLANTAE** (land plants)	Primary plastids having only two envelope membranes
ALVEOLATA	**Dinozoa** (dinoflagellates) *Pfiesteria shumwayae* **Ciliophora** (ciliates) **Apicomplexa** (apicomplexans) *Cryptosporidium parvum* *Plasmodium falciparum*	Peripheral membrane sacs (alveoli); some Dinozoa have secondary plastids derived from red algae, some have secondary plastids derived from green algae, and some have tertiary plastids derived from diatoms or cryptomonads; Apicomplexa sometimes have secondary plastids derived from red or green algae
STRAMENOPILA	**Bacillariophyta** (diatoms) Phaeophyceae (brown algae) *Phytophthora infestans* (fungus-like)	Strawlike flagellar hairs; fucoxanthin accessory pigment common in autotrophic forms
RHIZARIA	**Chlorarachniophyta** **Radiolaria** **Foraminifera**	Thin, cytoplasmic projections; secondary plastids (when present) derived from endosymbiotic green algae
AMOEBOZOA	*Entamoeba histolytica* **Dictyostelia** (a slime mould phylum) *Dictyostelium discoideum*	Amoeboid movement by pseudopodia
OPISTHOKONTA	**Choanomonada** (choanoflagellates) **KINGDOM ANIMALIA** **KINGDOM FUNGI** *Nuclearia* spp.	Swimming cells possess a single posterior flagellum

Protist phyla listed in this chapter whose supergroup affiliations are controversial or unknown

	Haptophyta (haptophytes)	Haptonema, derived from a flagellum that aids food-gathering and attachment; many produce calcium carbonate cell coverings; secondary plastids derived from red algae
	Cryptophyta (cryptomonads)	Flagellates; most have secondary plastids derived from red algae

Antarctic ice and acidic hot springs, are habitats for some protists. In these places protists may swim or float in open water or live attached to surfaces, such as rocks or beach sand. These different habitats influence protists' structure and size.

Protists that swim or float in fresh or salt water are members of an informal aggregate of organisms known as plankton, which also includes bacteria, viruses, and small animals. The photosynthetic protists in plankton are called **phytoplankton** ("plantlike" plankton), while heterotrophic protists in plankton are described as protozoan plankton. Planktonic protists are necessarily quite small in size; otherwise they would sink to the bottom. Staying afloat is particularly important for phytoplankton, which need light for photosynthesis. For this reason, planktonic protists occur primarily as single cells, colonies of cells held together with mucilage, or short filaments of cells linked end to end (**Figure 26.4a–c**).

Many protists live within **periphyton**, communities of microorganisms that are attached by mucilage to underwater surfaces, such as rocks, sand, and plants. Because sinking is not a problem for attached protists, these often produce multicellular bodies, such as branched filaments (**Figure 26.4d**). Although some **seaweeds** are very large single cells, most are multicellular algae, which often produce large and complex bodies (**Figure 26.4e**). Seaweeds usually grow attached to underwater surfaces, such as rocks, sand, or offshore oil platforms. Seaweeds require sunlight and carbon dioxide for photosynthesis and growth, so most grow along coastal shorelines, fairly near the water surface. Even so, some seaweeds occur at amazing depths. By using a submersible vehicle, algal ecologists Mark Littler, Diane Littler, and their associates found seaweeds growing 210 m beneath the surface of ocean waters near San Salvador in the Bahama Islands, the deepest known occurrence of photosynthetic eukaryotes.

Protists Can Be Informally Classified According to Type of Motility

Microscopic protists have evolved diverse ways to propel themselves in moist environments. Swimming by means of eukaryotic flagella or cilia, using amoeboid movement, and gliding are major types of protist movements.

(a) Protist attacking a leaf

(b) True fungus

Figure 26.3 **A fungus-like protist and a true fungus.** **(a)** A fungus-like protist, *Phytophthora infestans,* has absorbed enough nutrients from the plant to produce reproductive structures that emerge from pores on the lower leaf surface. The reproductive structures will eventually break off and be dispersed to other host leaves. **(b)** A true fungus (*Phragmidium* spp.) produces threadlike filaments that likewise grow through leaf tissues, absorbing nutrients. These nutrients will be used to produce reproductive structures that perpetuate the parasite.

Concept check: *How could a microbiologist determine whether unknown filaments growing in diseased plant leaves were fungus-like protists or true fungi?*

Planktonic protists

Attached protists

(a) Single-celled Chlamydomonas with flagella

(b) The colonial genus Monactinus

(c) The filamentous genus Desmidium

(d) The branched filamentous genus Cladophora

(e) The seaweed genus Acetabularia

Figure 26.4 **The diversity of algal body types reflects their habitats.** The algae shown in parts (a) to (c) are planktonic protists. **(a)** The single-celled flagellate genus *Chlamydomonas* occurs in the phytoplankton of lakes. **(b)** The colonial genus *Pediastrum* is composed of several cells arranged in a lacy star shape. This arrangement aids in keeping this alga afloat in water. **(c)** The filamentous genus *Desmidium* occurs as a twisted row of cells. The algae shown in parts **(d)** and **(e)** are attached protists that are part of the periphyton. **(d)** The branched filamentous genus *Cladophora* is large enough to see with the unaided eye. **(e)** The relatively large seaweed genus *Acetabularia* grows on rocks and coral rubble in shallow tropical oceans.

Many types of photosynthetic and heterotrophic protists are able to swim because they produce one or more eukaryotic flagella, cellular extensions whose movement is based on interactions between microtubules and the motor protein dynein (eukaryotic flagella are described in Chapter 4). Eukaryotic flagella rapidly bend and straighten, thereby pulling or pushing cells through water. Protists that use flagella to move in water are commonly known as **flagellates** (see Figure 26.4a).

Flagellates are typically composed of one or only a few cells and are small—usually 2 to 20 μm long—because flagellar motion is not powerful enough to keep larger bodies from sinking. Some flagellate protists are sedentary, living attached to underwater surfaces. These protists use flagella to collect bacteria and other small particles for consumption as food. Seaweeds and other immobile protists often produce small, flagellate reproductive cells that have a greater capacity for mobility. Flagellate reproductive cells allow these protists to mate and disperse to new habitats.

Another type of protist motility relies on cilia, tiny hairlike extensions on the outsides of cells. Cilia are structurally similar to eukaryotic flagella but are shorter and more abundant on cells (see Figure 26.2). Protists that move by means of cilia are known as **ciliates** and are classified in the phylum Ciliophora (see Table 26.1). The presence of many cilia allows ciliates to achieve larger sizes than flagellates yet still remain buoyant in water. The coordinated movement of cilia enables some ciliates to scamper across underwater surfaces rich in food materials and other ciliates to generate vortices of water that concentrate food particles.

A third type of motility is amoeboid movement. This kind of motion involves extending protist cytoplasm into lobes, known as pseudopodia ("false feet"). Once these pseudopodia move toward a food source or other stimulus, the rest of the cytoplasm flows after them, thereby changing the shape of the entire organism as it creeps along. Protist cells that move by pseudopodia are described as **amoebae** (**Figure 26.5**). Finally, many diatoms, the malarial parasite *Plasmodium falciparum,* and some other protists glide along surfaces in a snail-like fashion by secreting protein or carbohydrate slime. With the exception of ciliates, motility classification does not correspond with the phylogenetic classification of protists, our next topic.

Pseudopod

88 μm

Figure 26.5   A member of the amoebozoan genus *Pelomyxa,* showing pseudopodia.

BioConnections: *Look ahead to Figure 31.2. What kind of mobile, amoeba-shaped cells carry materials within the bodies of the early-diverging opisthokont animals known as sponges?*

26.2 | EVOLUTION AND RELATIONSHIPS

Learning Outcomes:

1. Describe a distinctive structural characteristic for each of seven eukaryotic supergroups.
2. List at least one species of each eukaryotic supergroup that is important to human life.
3. Draw a diagram showing how the process of endosymbiosis has affected eukaryotic diversity.

Modern biologists study protist diversity and infer their phylogenetic relationships by comparing their cellular structure and gene sequences. Because the relationships of some protists are uncertain or disputed and new protist species are continually being discovered, concepts of protist evolution and relationships are constantly changing. It is important to understand that, as we outlined in Chapter 24, protists are eukaryotes. However, the evolutionary relationships, and thus the phylogeny, of protists is still an ongoing process. Even so, molecular and cellular data reveal that many protists can be classified into diverse eukaryotic supergroups (see Figure 26.1). In this section we survey these supergroups, focusing on the defining features and evolutionary importance of the major protist phyla. We will also examine ways in which protists are important ecologically and in human affairs.

Supergroup Excavata Members Are Unicellular Flagellates with a Characteristic Feeding Groove

The protist supergroup known as the Excavata originated very early among eukaryotes and is important in understanding the early evolution of eukaryotes. The Excavata is named for a feeding groove "excavated" into the cells of many representatives, such as the genus *Jakoba* (phylum Jakobida) (**Figure 26.6**). The feeding groove is an important adaptation that allows these organisms to ingest small particles of food in their aquatic habitats. Once collected within the feeding groove, food particles are taken into cells by a type of endocytosis known as **phagocytosis** or phagotrophy. During phagocytosis a vesicle of plasma membrane surrounds each food particle and pinches off within the cytoplasm. Enzymes within these food vesicles break down the food particles into small molecules that, on their release into the cytoplasm, can be respired for energy.

Phagocytosis is also the evolutionary basis for the process of **endosymbiosis**, because particle ingestion provides a way for host cells to take in endosymbionts. Early in protist history, endosymbiotic proteobacterial cells gave rise to mitochondria, the organelle that is the major site of ATP synthesis. Consequently, most protists possess mitochondria, though these may be highly modified in parasitic species.

Some modern protists that are members of Excavata have become parasitic within animals, including humans. Instead of eating particles via feeding grooves, parasitic species attack host cells and absorb food molecules released from them. *Trichomonas*

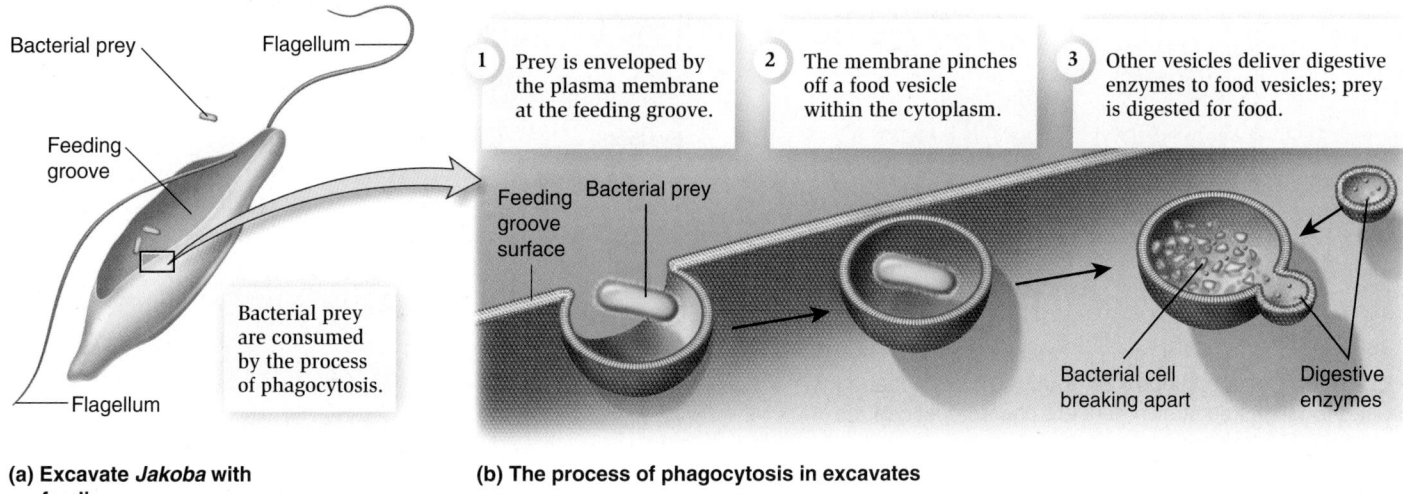

(a) Excavate *Jakoba* with feeding groove

(b) The process of phagocytosis in excavates

Figure 26.6 Feeding groove and phagocytosis displayed by many species of supergroup Excavata. **(a)** Diagram of *Jakoba libera,* phylum Jakobida, showing flagella emerging from the feeding groove. **(b)** Diagram of phagocytosis, the process by which food particles are consumed at a feeding groove.

Concept check: *What happens to ingested particles after they enter feeding cells?*

vaginalis, for example, causes a sexually transmitted infection of the human genitourinary tract. It has an undulating membrane and flagella that allow it to move over mucus-coated skin. *Giardia intestinalis* (also referred to as *G. lamblia)* causes giardiasis (also known as "beaver fever"), an intestinal infection that can result from drinking contaminated water, from contact with infected feces of wild or domesticated animals, or from unsanitary conditions in day care centres (**Figure 26.7**). *T. vaginalis* and *G. intestinalis* were once thought to lack mitochondria but are now known to possess structures that are highly modified mitochondria. In *T. vaginalis* the modified mitochondria are called hydrogenosomes because they produce hydrogen gas. In *G. intestinalis* reduced mitochondria known as mitosomes do not themselves produce ATP, but they do generate iron-sulphur cofactors essential for ATP production in the cytosol by anaerobic processes.

Supergroup Euglenozoa Members Are Unicellular Flagellates with Disk-Shaped Mitochondrial Cristae and Sometimes Secondary Plastids

The Euglenozoa is a supergroup of flagellates whose name originates from that of a common representative genus, *Euglena.* Members of the Euglenozoa feature unique mitochondrial cristae that are paddle-shaped or disk-shaped (**Figure 26.8**).

Euglenoids possess unique, interlocking ribbon-like protein strips just beneath their plasma membranes (**Figure 26.9a**). These strips make the surface of some euglenoids so flexible that they can crawl through mud. This unique type of motility is known as euglenoid movement or metaboly. Many euglenoids are heterotrophic, but some possess green plastids and thus are photosynthetic. Plastids are organelles found in plant and algal cells that are distinguished by their synthetic abilities.

(a) *Trichomonas vaginalis*

(b) *Giardia intestinalis*

Figure 26.7 Parasitic members of the supergroup Excavata. **(a)** The parabasalid protist *Trichomonas vaginalis.* **(b)** *Giardia intestinalis,* a diplomonad protist. These specialized, parasitic flagellates absorb nutrients from living cells of their hosts.

Concept check: *How do these two parasitic protists differ in their transmission from one human host to another?*

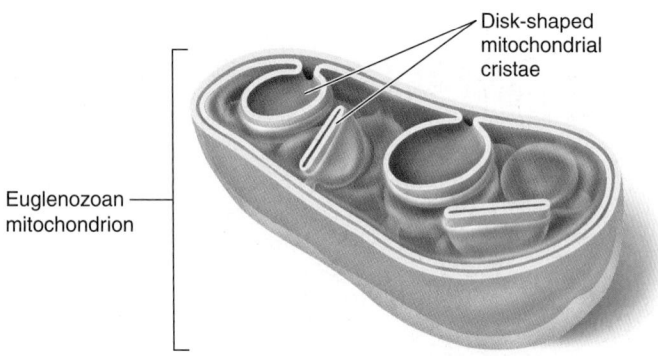

Figure 26.8 A euglenozoan trait. The disk-shaped mitochondrial cristae shown here are characteristic of the supergroup Euglenozoa.

(a) *Euglena*

(b) *Leishmania*   **(c) *Trypanosoma***

Figure 26.9 Representatives of the supergroup Euglenozoa. (a) Euglena has helical protein ribbons near its surface, internal green plastids, white storage carbohydrate granules, and a red eyespot. (b) LM showing the kinetoplast DNA mass typical of kinetoplastid mitochondria. (c) In this SEM, several undulating kinetoplastids appear near disk-shaped red blood cells.

Many euglenoids possess a light-sensing system that includes a conspicuous red structure known as an eyespot or stigma and light-sensing molecules located in a swollen region at the base of a flagellum. Most euglenoids produce storage carbohydrate particles known as paramylon. Euglenoids are particularly abundant and ecologically significant as photosynthesizers and phagotrophs in wetlands.

Kinetoplastids are named for an unusually large mass of DNA (known as a kinetoplast) that occurs in their single large mitochondrion (**Figure 26.9b**). These protists also feature an unusual modified peroxisome that contains glycolytic enzymes; in most eukaryotes, glycolysis occurs in the cytosol. Some kinetoplastids, such as *Trypanosoma brucei,* the causative agent of sleeping sickness, are serious pathogens of humans and other mammals (**Figure 26.9c**).

Supergroup Archaeplastida Members Have Primary Plastids with Two Envelope Membranes

The ancestors of the supergroup Archaeplastida ("ancient plastids") most likely obtained plastids by the process of **primary endosymbiosis**. Such plastids are known as **primary plastids**; these can be identified by the presence of an envelope composed of two membranes (**Figure 26.10a**). Primary plastids arose when heterotrophic host cells captured cyanobacterial cells, thereby acquiring photosynthetic ability. These cyanobacterial endosymbionts evolved into plastids, in the process losing their cell walls and ability to live independently. Most species classified in Archaeplastida possess plastids, though some are heterotrophic because photosynthetic pigments have been lost. Archaeplastida encompasses some very diverse and ecologically important groups of organisms, including (1) the phylum Rhodophyta, informally known as the red algae; (2) the phylum Chlorophyta, informally known as the green algae; (3) the kingdom Plantae, the land plants, which evolved from green algal ancestors; and (4) a small phylum of algae having blue-green plastids, the Glaucophyta, informally called glaucophytes (see Table 26.1).

Grouping the red algae, green algae, land plants, and glaucophytes together within the supergroup Archaeplastida is based on the assumption that all primary plastids originated with a single endosymbiotic event, a notion that remains somewhat controversial. Evolutionary biologist John Stiller and several other experts have used molecular evidence to frame an alternative hypothesis that green and red primary plastids might have evolved independently as the result of separate endosymbiotic events. Further, his research team sequenced the largest subunit of RNA polymerase II from two red algae, a green alga and a relatively derived amoeboid protist. Phylogenetic analyses provided strong evidence for an early evolutionary emergence of the Rhodophyta that preceded the origin of the line that led to plants, animals, and fungi.

Red algae characteristically lack flagella, and most species are multicellular marine seaweeds (**Figure 26.10b, 26.10c**). Some red algae are cultivated in ocean waters for production of industrial and scientific materials or food. Sushi wrappers are composed of the sheetlike red algal genus *Porphyra*. Carrageenan is a complex red algal cell-wall polysaccharide that has numerous applications in the food industry, such as keeping chocolate particles suspended evenly in ice cream or milk. Agar is a material extracted from red seaweeds that is widely used in research laboratories to solidify growth media used for

(a) A primary plastid

(b) *Calliarthron*

(c) *Chondrus crispus*

Figure 26.10 **Red algae and primary plastid of the supergroup Archaeplastida.** (a) A primary plastid, showing the two membranes of the primary plastid envelope. (b) The red algal genus *Calliarthron* has cell walls that are impregnated with calcium carbonate. This stony, white material makes the red alga appear pink. (c) *Chondrus crispus* is an edible red seaweed.

cultivating microorganisms. Molecular biologists commonly use agarose, likewise obtained from red algae, to separate DNA molecules by gel electrophoresis.

Green algae of diverse structural types occur in fresh waters, in the ocean, and on land (see Figure 26.4). A class of modern green algae informally known as charophyceans is closely related to the ancestor of land plants. Charophycean green algae resemble land plants in many aspects of cell structure, reproduction, and molecular biology (see Chapter 28). Thus, charophycean green algae are useful in deciphering the early evolutionary history of land plants.

Supergroup Alveolata Members Have Membrane Sacs (Alveoli) at the Cell Periphery and Sometimes Secondary or Tertiary Plastids

The supergroup Alveolata includes three important phyla: (1) the Ciliophora, informally known as ciliates (see Figure 26.2); (2) the Dinozoa, informally known as dinoflagellates; and (3) the Apicomplexa, a medically important group of parasites. This supergroup is named for saclike membranous vesicles known as alveoli that are present at the cell periphery in all these phyla (**Figure 26.11a**). The alveoli in some dinoflagellates seem empty, so that the cell surface appears smooth (**Figure 26.11b**). By contrast, the alveoli of many dinoflagellates contain plates of cellulose, which taken together form an armourlike enclosure (**Figure 26.11c**). These plates are often modified in ways that provide adaptive advantage, such as protection from predators or increased ability to float.

About half of dinoflagellate species possess photosynthetic plastids of diverse types (see Table 26.1), and half lack plastids and are thus heterotrophic. Dinoflagellates play particularly

(a)

(b)

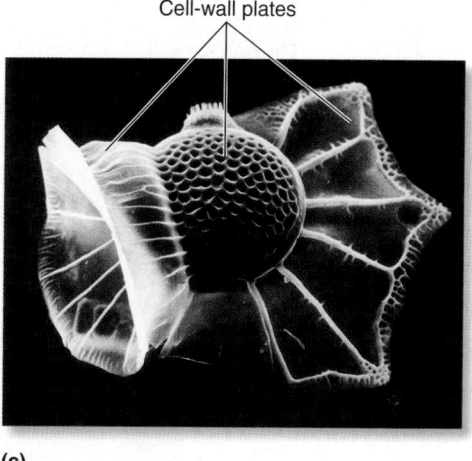

(c)

Figure 26.11 **Dinoflagellates of the supergroup Alveolata and their characteristic alveoli.** (a) Sac-shaped membranous vesicles known as alveoli lie beneath the plasma membrane of a dinoflagellate, along with trichocysts ready for discharge. (b) The surface of *Peridiniopsis berolinensis* appears smooth because the alveoli seem empty. Two types of flagella are seen on this freshwater dinoflagellate. One flagellum coils around a cellular groove; as it moves, this flagellum causes the cell to spin. By contrast, a straight flagellum extends from the cell, acting as a rudder to determine the direction of backward or forward movement. (c) The alveoli of the marine dinoflagellate genus *Ornithocercus* contain cellulose cell-wall plates.

Concept check: *Why do parts of the cell wall of Ornithocercus resemble sails?*

important roles in coastal oceans as the result of their nutrition and defences. Apicomplexans include the malarial agent *Plasmodium falciparum,* the related protist *Cryptosporidium parvum,* and other serious pathogens of humans and other animals.

Supergroup Stramenopila Members Have Strawlike Flagellar Hairs

The supergroup Stramenopila (informally known as the stramenopiles) encompasses a wide range of algae, protozoa, and fungus-like protists that usually produce flagellate cells at some point in their lives. The Stramenopila (from the Greek *stramen,* meaning "straw," and *pila,* meaning "hair") is named for distinctive straw-like hairs composed of glycoprotein that occur on the surfaces of flagella (**Figure 26.12**). These flagellar hairs function something like oars to greatly increase swimming efficiency. Biologists discovered this by using antibodies to clump the flagellar hairs together, which caused hairs to detach without otherwise harming the cells. As a result of this treatment, the flagellate cells could no longer swim as fast. Stramenopiles are also informally known as heterokonts (a term meaning "different flagella") because the two flagella often present on swimming cells have slightly different structures.

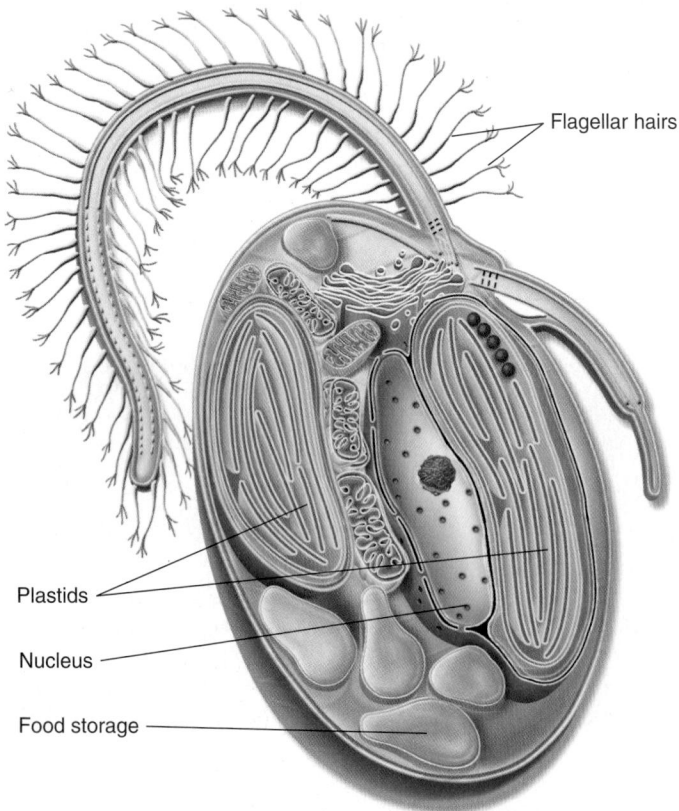

Flagellar hairs

Plastids

Nucleus

Food storage

Figure 26.12   Diagram of a flagellate stramenopile cell, showing characteristic flagellar hairs.

Concept check: *How do the flagellar hairs aid cell motion?*

Fungus-like stramenopiles cause serious diseases of seaweeds, molluscs, fish, and terrestrial crop plants. For example, the fungus-like protist *Phytophthora infestans* (see Figure 26.3a) caused the historic Irish potato crop failure that dramatically influenced immigration to Canada and the United States in the mid-nineteenth century and remains a serious crop pest today. A related species, *Phytophthora ramorum,* causes sudden oak death, and *Phytophthora sojae* is a serious pest of soybeans. These fungus-like protists produce flagellate reproductive cells that enable them to spread on and between plants in films of water. The genomes of these crop parasites are currently being analyzed with the goal of finding better ways to diagnose the presence of the organisms and control their spread in the environment.

Stramenopiles also include many phyla or classes of algae having golden- or brown-coloured plastids. Examples include diverse glass-enclosed diatoms (Bacillariophyta) (see Figure 26.2) and giant brown seaweeds (Phaeophyceae) that form extensive kelp forests in cold and temperate coastal oceans. Kelp forests are essential nurseries for fish and shellfish.

Molecular and biochemical evidence indicates that the plastids of stramenopile algae arose by the process of **secondary endosymbiosis** from ingested red algal cells (**Figure 26.13**). Secondary endosymbiosis occurs when the endosymbiont is a eukaryote having a primary plastid. Recall that red algal cells possess primary plastids. **Secondary plastids** originate with the endosymbiotic incorporation of a eukaryotic cell having a primary plastid. The host cell digests most of the endosymbiont but retains its plastid. Secondary plastids possess envelopes composed of more than two membranes.

Molecular evidence indicates that the plastids of most photosynthetic dinoflagellates also arose by secondary endosymbiosis from red algal cells, as did plastids of the algal phyla Cryptophyta (flagellates commonly known as cryptomonads) and Haptophyta (flagellate haptophytes) (see Table 26.1). Evolutionary protistologist Patrick Keeling at the University of British Columbia and his colleagues hypothesize that alveolates, cryptomonads, haptophytes, and stramenopiles originated from a single common ancestor that had acquired a secondary plastid from a red algal endosymbiont. These scientists explain the occurrence of heterotrophic species in these phyla as the result of multiple plastid loss events, and they have proposed that these phyla should be classified into a supergroup named Chromalveolata.

By contrast, biogeochemist Paul Falkowski and others argue that red algal cells possess molecular features that favoured their incorporation into diverse types of host cells on multiple occasions. In other words the similar plastids of photosynthetic stramenopiles, alveolates, cryptomonads, and haptophytes could have arisen by parallel evolution. If this explanation is correct, grouping these distinctive organisms into a single supergroup would not appropriately reflect phylogenetic relationships.

Relevant to this controversy is the fact that some dinoflagellates possess **tertiary plastids** acquired by engulfing diatoms or cryptomonads. Such plastids were obtained by independent

(a) Primary endosymbiosis

(b) Secondary endosymbiosis

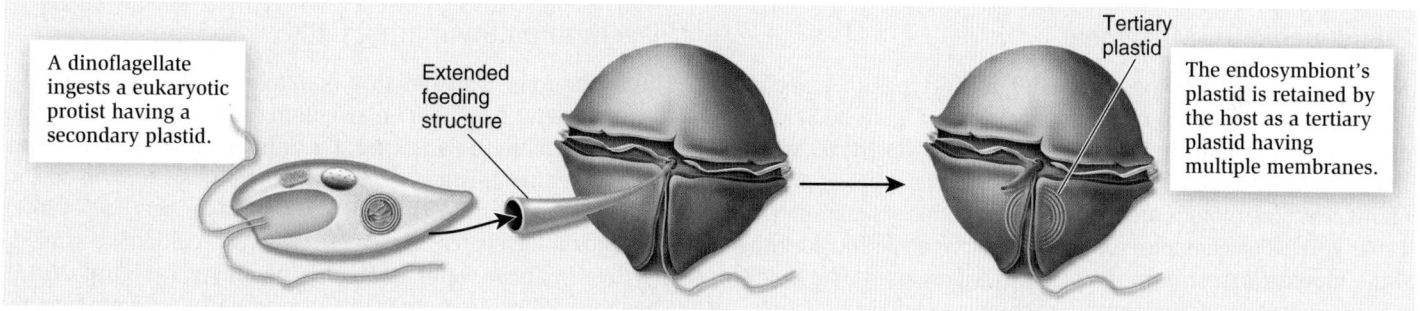

(c) Tertiary endosymbiosis

Figure 26.13   **Primary, secondary, and tertiary endosymbiosis.**   (a) In primary endosymbiosis a host cell without a plastid gains one from a cyanobacterial endosymbiont. During the evolution of a primary plastid, the bacterial cell wall is lost and most endosymbiont genes are transferred to the host nucleus. (b) In secondary endosymbiosis a host cell gains a plastid from a eukaryotic endosymbiont that contains one or more primary plastids. During the evolution of a secondary plastid, most components of the endosymbiont cell are lost, but the plastid is retained within an envelope of endoplasmic reticulum. (c) In tertiary endosymbiosis a host cell gains a plastid from a eukaryotic endosymbiont that has secondary plastids. Tertiary endosymbiosis occurs among dinoflagellates.

occurrences of **tertiary endosymbiosis**—the acquisition by hosts of plastids from cells that already possessed secondary plastids (see Figure 26.13). In addition, many heterotrophic protists and aquatic animals have independently acquired diverse types of algal or plastid endosymbionts, because this adaptation is nutritionally valuable. The acquisition of plastids by endosymbiosis is an example of horizontal gene transfer. It is clear that endosymbiosis has been a powerful force in the evolution of protists.

Supergroup Rhizaria Members Have Thin Cytoplasmic Extensions

Several groups of flagellates and amoebae that have thin, hairlike extensions of their cytoplasm, known as filose pseudopodia,

are classified into the supergroup Rhizaria (from the Greek *rhiza*, root). Rhizaria includes the phylum Chlorarachniophyta, whose spider-shaped cells possess secondary plastids obtained from endosymbiotic green algae (see Table 26.1). The Radiolaria (**Figure 26.14a**) and Foraminifera (**Figure 26.14b**) are two phyla of ocean plankton that produce exquisite mineral shells and frequently have symbiotic algal partners. The accumulated calcium carbonate shells of ancient foraminifera (and haptophyte algae) produced huge chalk deposits about 100 million years ago. Examples include notable geological formations, such as the white cliffs of Dover, England (**Figure 26.14c**). Together, abundant ancient populations of foraminifera and haptophytes also produced the famous North Sea oil deposits.

Filose pseudopodia   Filose pseudopodia

(a) Radiolarian   **(b) Foraminiferan**   **(c) Fossil deposit containing rhizarians**

Figure 26.14 **Living representatives of supergroup Rhizaria and fossil deposits.** **(a)** A radiolarian, *Acanthoplegma spp.,* showing long filose pseudopodia. **(b)** A foraminiferan, showing calcium carbonate shell with long filose pseudopodia extending from pores in the shell. **(c)** Fossil carbonate remains of foraminifera and haptophyte algae deposited over millions of years form the White Cliffs of Dover in Britain.

Supergroup Amoebozoa Members Have Pseudopodia for Movement

The supergroup Amoebozoa includes many types of amoebae that move by extension of pseudopodia (see Figure 26.5). One example is the human parasite *Entamoeba histolytica,* which causes a severe form of intestinal illness. Several types of protists known as slime moulds are also classified in this supergroup (see Table 26.1). For example, the phylum Dictyostelia includes the slime mould *Dictyostelium discoideum,* widely used as a model laboratory system for understanding communication among cells. These slime moulds produce amoebae that feed on small particles. Under starvation conditions, these amoebae aggregate and form reproductive structures known as "fruiting bodies" because they resemble the spore-producing structures of fungi.

Supergroup Opisthokonta Members Have a Single Flagellum on Swimming Cells

The supergroup Opisthokonta is named for the presence of a single posterior flagellum on swimming cells. Because their flagellate cells exhibit this feature, the animal and fungal kingdoms are included in Opisthokonta, as are the protists known as choanoflagellates (formally, the Choanomonada; see Table 26.1). The choanoflagellates are single-celled or colonial organisms that live in fresh water or marine periphyton (**Figure 26.15**). Choanoflagellates feature a distinctive collar surrounding the single flagellum. The collar is made of cytoplasmic extensions known as tentacles, which filter bacterial food from water currents generated by flagellar motion. Molecular evidence suggests that choanoflagellates are the modern protists most closely

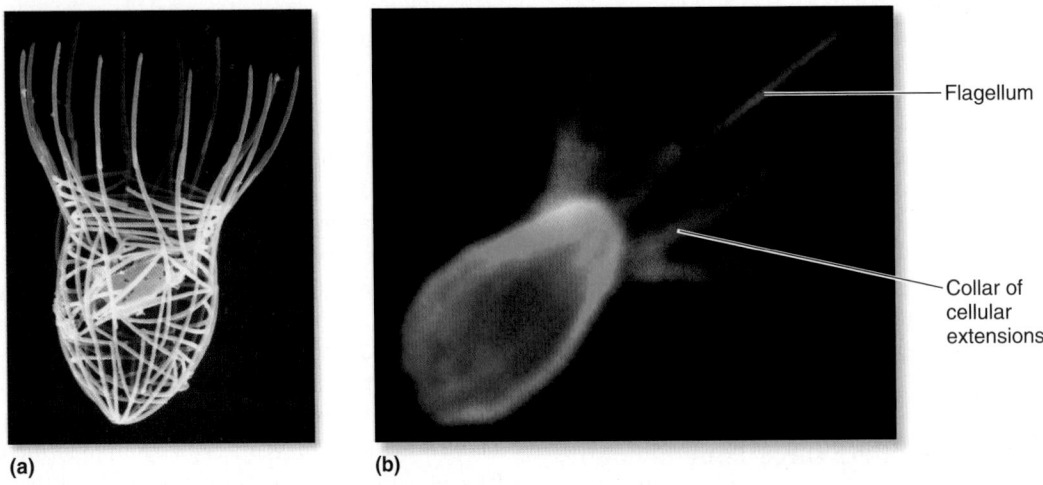

Flagellum

Collar of cellular extensions

(a)   **(b)**

Figure 26.15 Choanoflagellates of the supergroup Opisthokonta.

Concept check: *What features of the ancient choanoflagellate ancestors of animals were important in the evolution of multicellularity? What function do such features serve in modern choanoflagellates?*

related to the common ancestor of animals. Thus, evolutionary biologists interested in the origin of animals study choanoflagellates for molecular clues to this important event in our evolutionary history.

The preceding surveys of protist diversity and evolutionary relationships provide the foundation for a closer look at protist functions in nature. A focus on protist nutritional, defensive, and reproductive adaptations will help explain these roles, which often influence human affairs.

26.3 / NUTRITIONAL AND DEFENSIVE ADAPTATIONS

Learning Outcomes:

1. List four types of protist nutrition.
2. Give examples of major types of protist defensive adaptations.

Wherever you look in moist places, you will find protists playing diverse and important ecological roles. In this section we will survey protist nutritional and defensive adaptations, which help to explain their ecological functions.

Protists Display Four Basic Types of Nutrition

Protists gain nutrition through four different methods: phagotrophy, osmotrophy, autotrophy, and mixotrophy. All these are important in ecological food webs that connect organisms of many types. Heterotrophic protists that specialize in phagotrophy (particle feeding) are known as **phagotrophs**, whereas those relying on osmotrophy (uptake of small organic molecules) are **osmotrophs**. Photosynthetic protists are **autotrophs**, organisms that can make their own organic nutrients. **Mixotrophs** are protists that are able to use autotrophy as well as phagotrophy or osmotrophy to obtain organic nutrients. Note here that the means by which protists gain nutrition, compared with bacteria and archaea, really represent only two general methods, that is, photoautotrophy and chemoheterotrophy (see Table 25.2). The genus *Dinobryon* (**Figure 26.16**), a photosynthetic stramenopile, also consumes enormous numbers of bacteria and is an example of a mixotroph. Mixotrophic protists can switch back and forth between autotrophy and heterotrophy, depending on conditions in their environment. If sufficient light, carbon dioxide, and other minerals are available, mixotrophs produce their own organic food. If any of these resources limits photosynthesis, or organic food is especially abundant, mixotrophs can function as heterotrophs. Mixotrophs thus have remarkable nutritional flexibility.

Heterotrophic protists that feed on nonliving organic material function as decomposers, also known as saprobes. Decomposers, which also include many prokaryotes and fungi, are essential in breaking down wastes and releasing minerals for use by other organisms. Heterotrophic protists that feed on the living cells of other organisms are parasites. Some parasites are

Figure 26.16
A mixotrophic protist. The genus *Dinobryon* is a colonial flagellate that occurs in the phytoplankton of freshwater lakes. The photosynthetic cells have golden plastids and capture and consume bacterial cells.

pathogens, which cause disease in other organisms. *Trichomonas vaginalis, Giardia lamblia, Entamoeba histolytica,* and *Phytophthora infestans* are examples of pathogenic protists that have been described in this chapter. Humans view such protists as pests when they harm us or our agricultural animals and crops, but these protists also play important roles in nature by controlling the population growth of other organisms. Their roles illustrate the principle that organisms modify their environments and provide essential biological services. The diversity of photosynthetic protists and their storage molecules further illustrate these principles.

Algal Protists Vary in Photosynthetic Pigments and Food Storage Molecules

As we noted earlier, algae display a surprising diversity of coloration, from gold to brown, red, and green. Why do so many pigmentation types occur? The answer is related to light availability in these protists' watery environment.

If you dive more than a few metres into lakes or the ocean, the aquatic world will appear intensely blue-green. This occurs because water absorbs the longer red to yellow wavelengths of light to a greater degree than shorter blue and green wavelengths. Little red light penetrates far into natural waters, depriving chlorophyll *a*, the photosynthetic pigment universally present in photosynthetic eukaryotes, of much of the light it would ordinarily absorb. Photosynthetic protists living in water have coped with this filtering effect by adapting their photosynthetic systems so that they capture more of the available blue-green light. Seaweeds, for example, may be red, gold, or brown, in addition to green, because they produce diverse accessory pigments that are able to absorb more of the light that is available underwater and transfer the energy to chlorophyll *a* for photosynthesis. The red accessory pigment phycoerythrin is abundant in plastids of red algae, and golden fucoxanthin enriches the colour of golden and brown algae. Carotene and lutein have similar accessory pigment functions in green algae and were inherited by their land plant descendants, thus playing important roles in human nutrition. These and other accessory pigment adaptations explain why algae occur in so many different colours.

Photosynthetic protists also vary in the types of molecules that serve as food storage. Starch stored in the plastids of green algae and oil droplets in diatom cells are two common examples. Algae use food storage cells for energy when light or minerals are too low to allow photosynthesis; such cells are also desirable food sources for heterotrophs. As a consequence of photosynthesis and food storage, autotrophic and mixotrophic protists play essential roles in aquatic food webs as primary producers. Such protists generate the organic food and atmospheric oxygen consumed by many other organisms.

Protists Defend Themselves in Diverse Ways

Protists use a wide variety of defensive adaptations to ward off attack. Major types of defences are slimy, tough, or spiny cell coverings; sharp projectiles that can be explosively shot from cells; light flashes; and toxic compounds.

Many protists have cell coverings, such as slimy mucilages or cell walls that provide protection from attack by herbivores or pathogens. Cell walls can also aid in preventing osmotic damage and enhancing flotation in water. Rigid cellulose walls are common in brown and green algae, while slimy polysaccharide polymers form a protective matrix around red algal cells. Calcium carbonate forms a stony coat for many protist cells, including foraminifera, haptophytes, and some marine seaweeds. Ornate glassy coatings of silica protect diatoms, while metallic iron and manganese crystals armour other protists.

Several types of protist cells contain compressed protein structures known as trichocysts (see Figure 26.11a). On attack, trichocysts rapidly elongate into spear-shaped projectiles that are shot from protist cells, thereby discouraging herbivores from feeding. Some species of ocean dinoflagellates emit flashes of blue light when disturbed, explaining why ocean waters teeming with these protists display bioluminescence. The light flashes may deter herbivores by startling them, but when ingested, the dinoflagellates make the herbivores glow, revealing them to hungry fish. Light flashes benefit dinoflagellates by helping to reduce populations of herbivores that consume the algae.

Various protist species produce toxins. Toxins probably originated as a means of protection from relatively small herbivores that might otherwise eat protists. Dinoflagellates are probably the most important protist toxin producers; they synthesize several types of toxins that affect humans and other animals. Why does this happen? Under natural conditions, small populations of dinoflagellates produce low amounts of toxin that do not harm large organisms. When people contaminate natural waters with excess mineral nutrients, such as nitrogen and phosphorus from untreated sewage, industrial discharges, or fertilizer that washes from agricultural fields, the excess nutrients foster explosive growth of algal populations called blooms. These large populations produce sufficient toxin to affect birds, aquatic mammals, fish, and humans. Toxins can concentrate in organisms, and humans who ingest shellfish that have accumulated dinoflagellate toxins can suffer paralytic shellfish poisoning (PSP). During blooms, filter-feeding shellfish, such as clams and mussels, accumulate the poisons from the dinoflagellates they eat. PSP is caused by a group of related toxins, the best known of which is saxitoxin (SXT). The relative abundance of each poison varies with the species and strain of dinoflagellate. Gonyautoxin predominates in the Bay of Fundy, and SXT is higher in the Gaspé region of Quebec. SXT is the dominant toxin in some British Columbia species. PSP toxins are relatively heat stable, and normal cooking or canning processes cannot be relied on to make a contaminated product safe to eat.

FEATURE INVESTIGATION

Burkholder and Colleagues Demonstrated That Strains of the Dinoflagellate Genus *Pfiesteria* Are Toxic to Mammalian Cells

A team of investigators led by JoAnn Burkholder performed an experiment to determine whether or not two strains of *Pfiesteria shumwayae* were toxic to mammalian cells (**Figure 26.17**). Although one of these strains (CCMP 1024C) was thought to be toxic to fish and people, other work suggested that a different strain (CCMP 2089) did not produce toxin, a difference that might have resulted from variation in growth conditions. Neither strain had been tested for its impact on mammalian cells. The experiment was conducted in a biohazard containment facility, for the safety of the investigators.

In the first step of the experiment, the team provided both *Pfiesteria* strains with two forms of food—cryptomonad algal cells or juvenile fish—because the impact of food type on toxicity was unclear. In a second step, the dinoflagellates grown in step 1 were transferred to tanks with fish to elicit maximal toxin production. Dinoflagellates were not added to a control tank of fish. Toxin was detected, and fish deaths occurred in all of the tanks except the control. In a third step, dinoflagellate samples from the step (2) treatments were added to mammalian cell cultures, and investigators determined the relative levels of toxicity to the mammalian cells. They found that both strains of *P. shumwayae* were toxic to mammalian cells and that both types of food supported the growth of toxin-producing dinoflagellates.

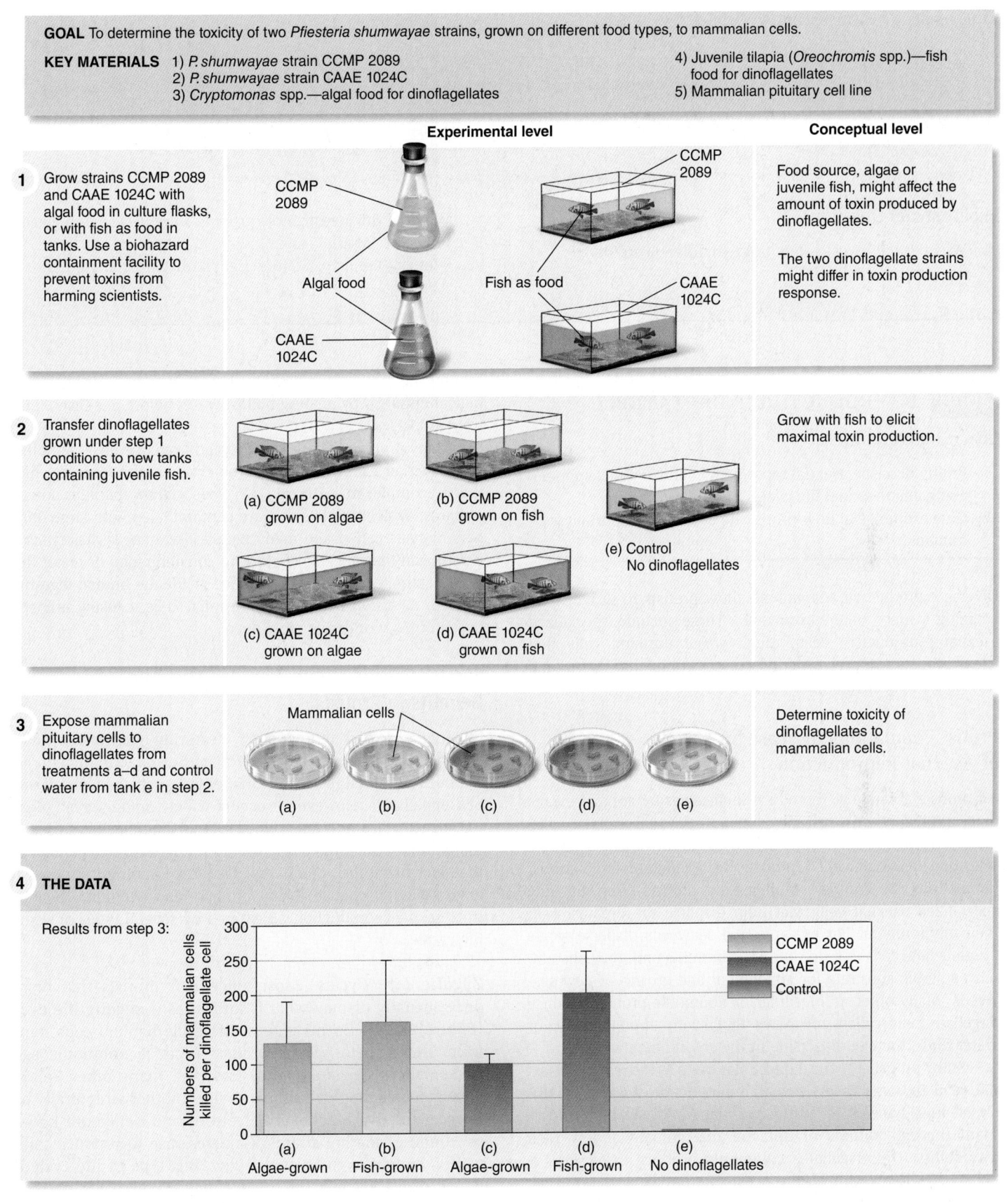

GOAL To determine the toxicity of two *Pfiesteria shumwayae* strains, grown on different food types, to mammalian cells.

KEY MATERIALS
1) *P. shumwayae* strain CCMP 2089
2) *P. shumwayae* strain CAAE 1024C
3) *Cryptomonas* spp.—algal food for dinoflagellates
4) Juvenile tilapia (*Oreochromis* spp.)—fish food for dinoflagellates
5) Mammalian pituitary cell line

Experimental level | Conceptual level

1 Grow strains CCMP 2089 and CAAE 1024C with algal food in culture flasks, or with fish as food in tanks. Use a biohazard containment facility to prevent toxins from harming scientists.

CCMP 2089
Algal food
CAAE 1024C
CCMP 2089
Fish as food
CAAE 1024C

Food source, algae or juvenile fish, might affect the amount of toxin produced by dinoflagellates.

The two dinoflagellate strains might differ in toxin production response.

2 Transfer dinoflagellates grown under step 1 conditions to new tanks containing juvenile fish.

(a) CCMP 2089 grown on algae
(b) CCMP 2089 grown on fish
(c) CAAE 1024C grown on algae
(d) CAAE 1024C grown on fish
(e) Control No dinoflagellates

Grow with fish to elicit maximal toxin production.

3 Expose mammalian pituitary cells to dinoflagellates from treatments a–d and control water from tank e in step 2.

Mammalian cells

(a) (b) (c) (d) (e)

Determine toxicity of dinoflagellates to mammalian cells.

4 **THE DATA**

Results from step 3:

Numbers of mammalian cells killed per dinoflagellate cell

CCMP 2089
CAAE 1024C
Control

(a) Algae-grown
(b) Fish-grown
(c) Algae-grown
(d) Fish-grown
(e) No dinoflagellates

Figure 26.17 Burkholder and colleagues demonstrated that some strains of *Pfiesteria shumwayae* are toxic to fish and mammalian cells.

Figure 26.17 *(Continued)*

5   CONCLUSION Both strains of *P. shumwayae* were toxic to mammalian cells, and both types of food supported the growth of toxic dinoflagellates.

6   SOURCE Burkholder, J.M., et al. 2005. Demonstration of toxicity to fish and to mammalian cells by *Pfiesteria* species: Comparison of assay methods and strains. *Proceedings of the National Academy of Sciences of the United States of America* 102:3471–3476.

Experimental Questions

1. Why did the investigators test two different strains of *Pfiesteria shumwayae*?

2. Why did the investigators grow *P. shumwayae* with algae or fish as food?

3. Why did the investigators use a biohazard containment system?

26.4   REPRODUCTIVE ADAPTATIONS

Learning Outcomes:

1. Briefly describe asexual reproduction and zygotic, sporic, and gametic sexual life cycles in protists.
2. Give examples of how protist life cycles are important to humans.

Diverse reproductive adaptations allow protists to thrive in an amazing variety of environments. These include specialized asexual reproductive cells, tough-walled dormant cells that allow protists to survive periods of environmental stress, and several types of sexual life cycles.

Protist Populations Increase by Means of Asexual Reproduction

All protists are able to reproduce themselves by asexual means that involve mitotic cell divisions of parental cells to produce progeny. When resources are plentiful, repeated mitotic divisions of single-celled protists will generate large protist populations. By contrast, multicellular protists often generate specialized asexual cells that help disperse the organisms in their environment. For example, red seaweeds disperse single nonflagellate cells that drift with the currents until they encounter a suitable substrate for attachment and growth of new seaweeds. Many other multicellular or nonmotile protists produce flagellate cells called zoospores that swim through water or water films, thereby dispersing in the environment.

Many protists produce unicellular **cysts** as the result of asexual (and in some cases, sexual) reproduction (**Figure 26.18**). Cysts often have thick, protective walls and can remain dormant through periods of unfavourable climate or low food availability. Dinoflagellates commonly produce cysts. *Pfiesteria* species lie in wait on the ocean bottom as cysts until fish prey are present. Dinoflagellate cysts in ship ballast water can be transported from one port to another, a problem that has caused harmful dinoflagellate blooms to appear in harbours

around the world. Ship captains can help to prevent such ecological disasters by heating ballast water before it is discharged from ships.

Many protozoan pathogens spread from one host to another via cysts. For example, waterborne cysts are the form in which the apicomplexan pathogen *Cryptosporidium parvum* infects humans. Water supplies that are contaminated with large numbers of cysts can sicken many people. *Entamoeba histolytica* is a pathogen that infects people who consume food or water that is contaminated with its cysts. Once inside the human digestive system, *E. histolytica* attacks intestinal cells, causing amoebic dysentery, a worldwide problem.

Sexual Reproduction Provides Multiple Benefits to Protists

Eukaryotic sexual reproduction, featuring gametes, zygotes, and meiosis, first arose among protists. Sexual reproduction has not been observed in some protist phyla, such as kinetoplastids and euglenoids. However, it occurs widely among green algae, red algae, apicomplexans, ciliates, and dinoflagellates. Sexual reproduction is adaptive because it produces diverse genotypes, thus increasing the potential for faster evolutionary response to environmental change. Many protists reap additional benefits from sexual reproduction, illustrated by several types of sexual life cycles.

Zygotic Life Cycles Most unicellular protists that reproduce sexually display what is known as a **zygotic life cycle** (**Figure 26.19**). In this type of life cycle haploid cells transform into gametes. Some protists produce nonmotile eggs and smaller flagellate sperm. However, many other protists have gametes that look similar to one another structurally but have distinctive biochemical features and hence are known as + and − mating strains. Gametes fuse to produce thick-walled diploid zygotes, which give this type of life cycle its name. Such zygotes often have tough cell walls and can survive stressful conditions, much like cysts. Some of the earliest fossils regarded as ancient protists are probably tough-walled zygotes.

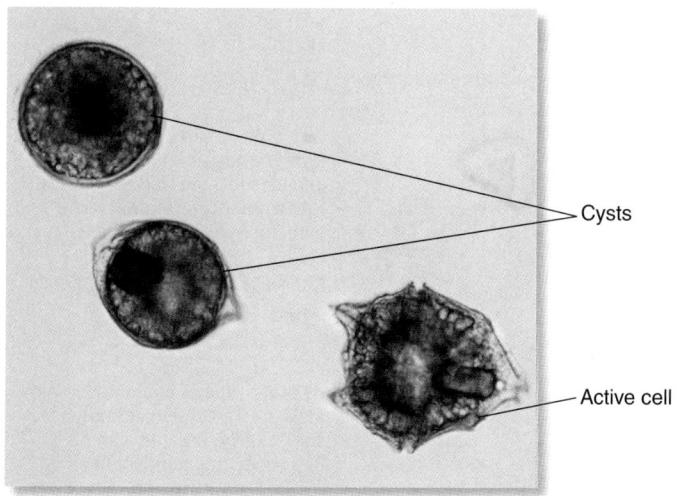

Figure 26.18 **Protistan cysts.** The round cells are dormant, tough-walled cysts of the dinoflagellate *Peridinium limbatum*. The pointed cell is an actively growing cell of the same species. As cysts develop, the outer cellulose plates present on actively growing cells are cast off.

Sporic Life Cycles   Many multicellular green and brown seaweeds display a **sporic life cycle**, also known as alternation of generations (**Figure 26.20a**). Organisms having sporic life cycles produce two types of multicellular organisms: a haploid gametophyte generation that produces gametes (sperm or eggs) by the process of mitosis, and a diploid sporophyte generation that produces spores by the process of meiosis. This type of life cycle takes its name from the characteristic production of spores as the result of meiosis. Each of the two types of multicellular organisms can adapt to distinct habitats or seasonal conditions, thus allowing protists to occupy more types of environments and for longer periods.

Many red seaweeds display a variation of the sporic life cycle that involves alternation of three distinct multicellular generations (**Figure 26.20b**). Their unique type of sexual life cycle is an adaptation that allows red algae to cope with the lack of flagella on sperm. Because red algal sperm are unable to swim to eggs, fertilization occurs only when sperm carried by ocean currents happen to drift close to eggs. Fertilization can thus be rare. Many red algae compensate by making millions of spores that are produced by two distinct sporophyte generations.

Figure 26.19   **Zygotic life cycle, illustrated by the unicellular flagellate genus *Chlamydomonas*.**   In *Chlamydomonas,* most cells are haploid; only the zygote is diploid.

BioConnections: *Look back to Figure 17.1. This figure shows organisms that serve as model systems for the study of plant and animal development. Chlamydomonas is likewise a model system for molecular analysis of flagellar and chloroplast development. What aspects of its life cycle foster such genetic studies?*

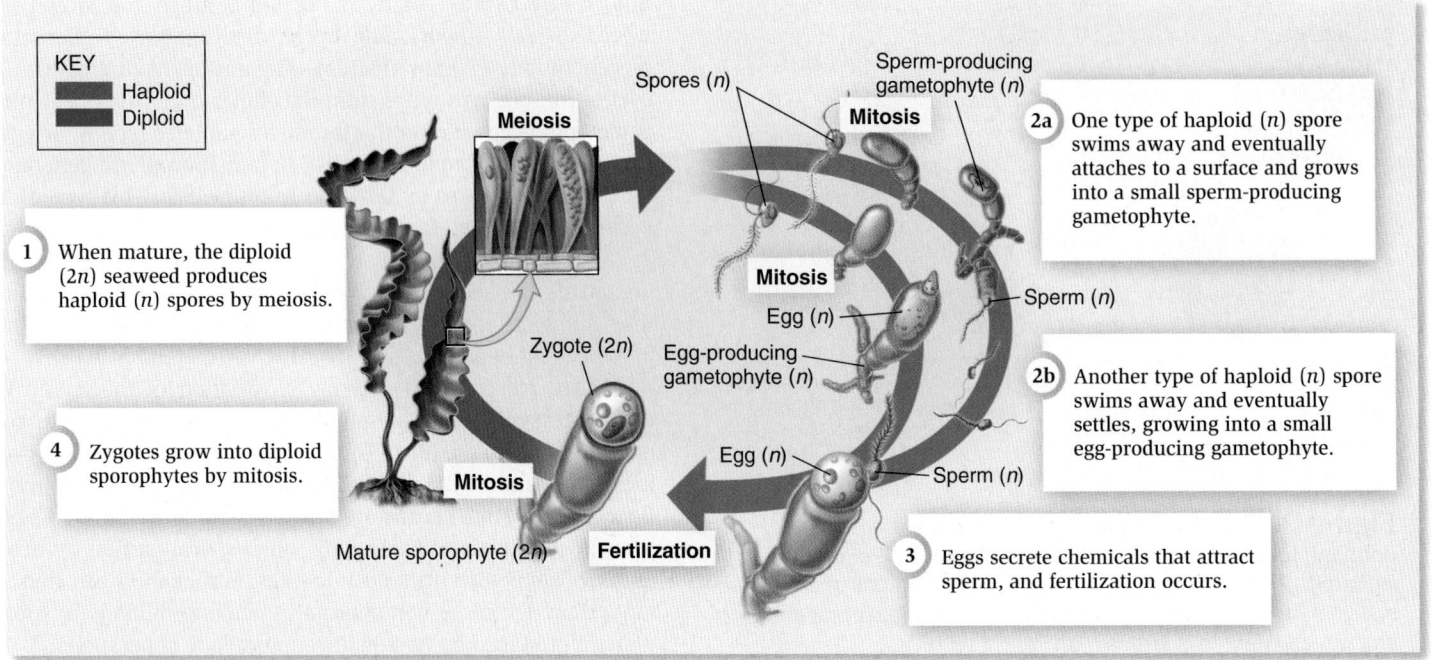

KEY
Haploid
Diploid

Meiosis

1   When mature, the diploid (2*n*) seaweed produces haploid (*n*) spores by meiosis.

4   Zygotes grow into diploid sporophytes by mitosis.

Mitosis

Mature sporophyte (2*n*)   **Fertilization**

Zygote (2*n*)

Spores (*n*)   Sperm-producing gametophyte (*n*)

Mitosis

2a   One type of haploid (*n*) spore swims away and eventually attaches to a surface and grows into a small sperm-producing gametophyte.

Mitosis

Egg (*n*)   Sperm (*n*)

Egg-producing gametophyte (*n*)

2b   Another type of haploid (*n*) spore swims away and eventually settles, growing into a small egg-producing gametophyte.

Egg (*n*)   Sperm (*n*)

3   Eggs secrete chemicals that attract sperm, and fertilization occurs.

(a) *Laminaria* life cycle—alternation of two generations

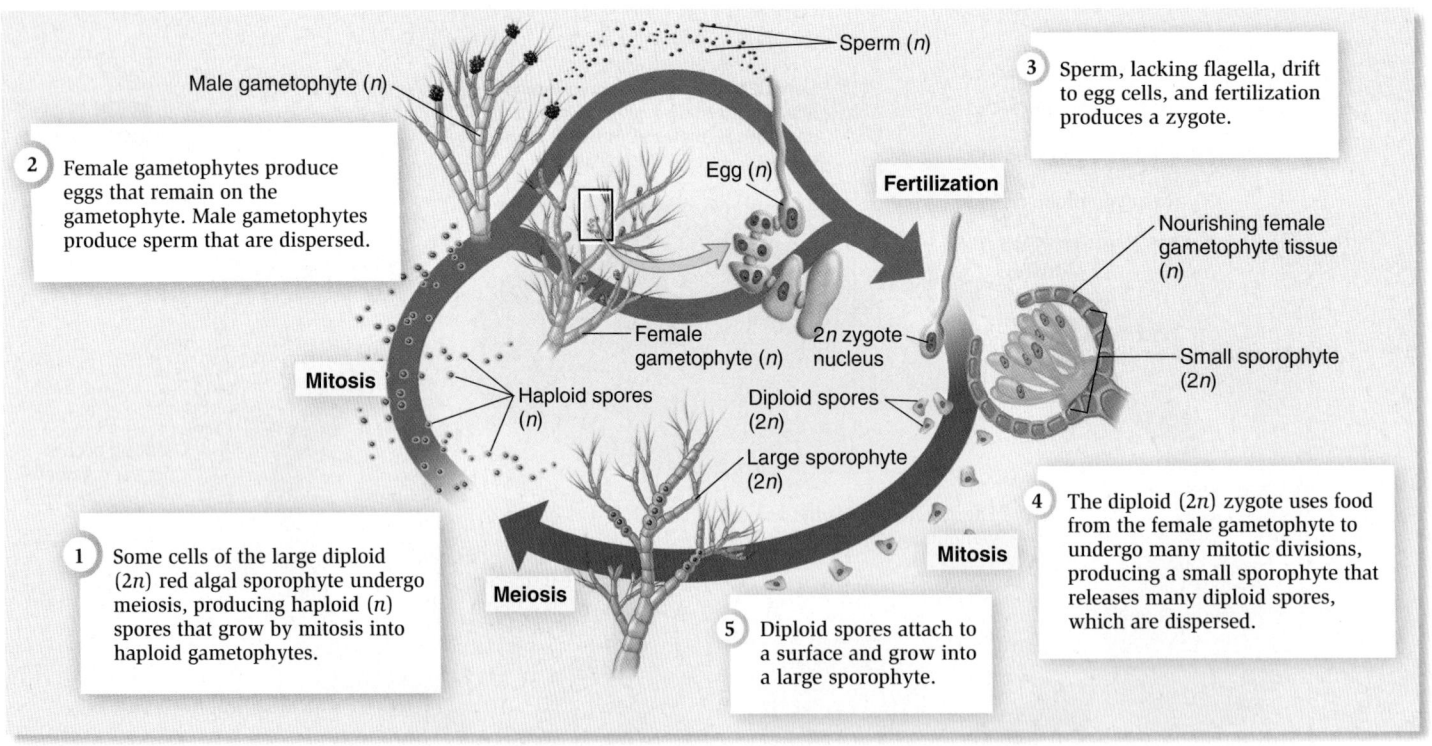

Male gametophyte (*n*)

Sperm (*n*)

3   Sperm, lacking flagella, drift to egg cells, and fertilization produces a zygote.

2   Female gametophytes produce eggs that remain on the gametophyte. Male gametophytes produce sperm that are dispersed.

Egg (*n*)

Fertilization

Nourishing female gametophyte tissue (*n*)

Female gametophyte (*n*)   2*n* zygote nucleus

Small sporophyte (2*n*)

Mitosis

Haploid spores (*n*)   Diploid spores (2*n*)

Large sporophyte (2*n*)

1   Some cells of the large diploid (2*n*) red algal sporophyte undergo meiosis, producing haploid (*n*) spores that grow by mitosis into haploid gametophytes.

Meiosis

5   Diploid spores attach to a surface and grow into a large sporophyte.

Mitosis

4   The diploid (2*n*) zygote uses food from the female gametophyte to undergo many mitotic divisions, producing a small sporophyte that releases many diploid spores, which are dispersed.

(b) *Polysiphonia* life cycle—alternation of three generations

Figure 26.20   Sporic life cycles.   **(a)** Sporic life cycle as illustrated by the brown seaweed *Laminaria*. **(b)** Sporic life cycle involving three alternating generations, illustrated by the red seaweed *Polysiphonia*.

Gametic Life Cycle and the Problem of Diatom Size   Diatoms are examples of a relatively few protists known to display a **gametic life cycle** (**Figure 26.21**). In gametic life cycles, all cells except the gametes are diploid, and gametes are produced by meiosis. Diatoms use sexual reproduction not only to increase genetic variability but also to regenerate maximal cell size characteristic

of a species. Many diatoms must do this as the result of a unique problem that develops during asexual reproduction by mitosis.

In many diatoms one daughter cell arising from mitosis is smaller than the other, and it is also smaller than the parent cell. This happens because diatom cell walls are composed of two overlapping halves, much like two-part round glass laboratory

Figure 26.21 Gametic life cycle, as illustrated by diatoms. **(a)** Diatom asexual reproduction involves repeated mitotic division. Because a new lower-cell-wall piece is always synthesized, asexual reproduction can eventually cause the mean cell size to decline in a diatom population. **(b)** Small cell size may trigger sexual reproduction, which regenerates maximal cell size.

BioConnections: *Look back to Figure 14.16, which illustrates the life cycles of animals, fungi, and plants. Which of these life cycles is most similar to that of diatoms?*

After many cell divisions, some progeny cells are very small.

(a) Asexual reproduction in diatoms

2 Blanketed by mucilage, each cell produces one or more haploid gametes by meiosis. The gametes may look alike or take the form of sperm and eggs.

Meiosis

Haploid (*n*) gametes

3 The gametes fuse to form a diploid zygote that is larger and rounder than a typical diatom cell.

Fertilization

Diploid (2*n*) zygote

KEY
Haploid
Diploid

Mucilage

Mitosis

Lipid food storage

Plastids

1 When diatom cells reach a critical small size or are stimulated by environmental factors, they may begin the process of reproduction.

4 The 2*n* zygote undergoes mitotic divisions to produce diploid cells that have the normal shape and maximum size for that species.

(b) Sexual reproduction in diatoms

dishes having lids that overlap bottoms. After each mitotic division, each daughter cell receives one-half of the parent cell wall. The daughter cell that inherits a larger, overlapping parental "lid" then produces a new "bottom" that fits inside. This daughter cell will be the same size as its parent. However, the daughter cell that inherits the parental "bottom" uses this wall half as its lid and produces a new, even smaller "bottom." This cell will be smaller than its sibling and parent. Consequently, after many such mitotic divisions, the average cell size of diatom populations often declines. If diatom cells become too small, they lose the ability to survive. Sexual reproduction helps to solve this problem.

Sexual reproduction allows diatom species to recover maximal cell size, thereby preventing extinction of populations. Diatom cells mate within a blanket of mucilage, each partner undergoing meiotic divisions to produce gametes. The large, spherical diatom zygotes that result from fertilization later undergo a series of mitotic divisions to produce new diatom cells that have the maximal size for the species.

Ciliate Sexual Reproduction Among protists, ciliates have one of the most complex sexual processes known. Ciliates are unusual in having two types of nuclei, a single large macronucleus, and one or more smaller micronuclei. Macronuclei, which develop from micronuclei, serve as the source of information for cell function, and they divide when ciliates reproduce asexually by mitosis (**Figure 26.22a**). Sexual reproduction in ciliates begins when two cells pair and fuse longitudinally—a process known as **conjugation** (**Figure 26.22b**). In *Paramecium caudatum*, the single micronucleus undergoes meiosis early in conjugation. Of the four haploid micronuclei produced, all disintegrate except one, which divides by mitosis. Then the paired ciliates exchange one of each pair of micronuclei, after which

Macronucleus

Micronucleus

Cyst

Swimming ciliate

Mitotic divison

(a) Asexual reproduction by mitosis and cysts

KEY
Haploid
Diploid

1 Two compatible cells conjugate—line up side by side and partially fuse together.

2 In each cell, the micronucleus undergoes meiosis, producing four haploid products, but three disintegrate.

3 In each cell, the remaining haploid micronucleus undergoes mitosis.

Micronucleus

Macronucleus

Haploid (*n*) micronuclei

Meiosis

Mitosis

7 The cell with eight nuclei undergoes two rounds of cytokinesis to produce four mature cells that have one micronucleus and one macronucleus.

Diploid (2*n*) nuclei

Mitosis

6 The diploid nucleus undergoes three rounds of mitosis, producing four macronuclei and four micronuclei. Note: The diagram shows only one of the two cells from step (5).

5 The paired cells separate. In each cell, the genetically different micronuclei fuse to form a diploid nucleus.

4 The two cells exchange a haploid micronucleus, and each cell's macronucleus disintegrates.

(b) Sexual reproduction by conjugation

Figure 26.22   Ciliate reproduction.   (a) The asexual reproduction process in ciliates. **(b)** The sexual reproduction process in the ciliate *Paramecium caudatum,* which involves conjugation.

the paired cells separate and the macronuclei disintegrate. The two genetically different micronuclei in each cell then fuse, and the new diploid nuclei divide mitotically to produce four macronuclei and multiple micronuclei. Subsequent mitotic divisions occur, distributing one macronucleus plus one or more micronuclei (depending on the species) to each cell. Conjugation seems to be essential for continued existence of ciliate species.

Parasitic Protists May Use Alternative Hosts for Different Life Stages

Parasitic protists are notable for often using more than one host organism, in which different life stages occur. The malarial parasite genus *Plasmodium* is a prominent example. About 40% of humans live in tropical regions of the world where malaria occurs, and, as noted earlier, millions of infections and human deaths result each year. Malaria is particularly deadly for children. The malarial parasite's alternative hosts are mosquitoes classified in the genus *Anopheles*. Though insecticides can be used to control mosquito populations and antimalarial drugs exist, malarial parasites can develop drug resistance. Experts are concerned that the number of cases may double in the next 20 years.

Plasmodium enters the human bloodstream via a mosquito bite in a life stage known as a sporozoite (**Figure 26.23**). These sporozoites eventually reach the victim's liver and enter the liver cells. Following several cycles of cell division in the

6 In mosquitoes, gametocytes produce gametes that fuse to form a diploid zygote. In the gut, zygotes divide by meiosis to produce haploid sporozoites, which move to the salivary glands of the mosquito.

5 Some merozoites produce sexual structures called gametocytes, which can be taken up by a biting mosquito.

Gametes

Fertilization

Mitosis

Gametocytes (*n*)

Zygote (2*n*)

Meiosis

Inside mosquito

Inside human

Sporozoites (*n*) in salivary glands

4 Merozoites continue to infect more red blood cells, causing cycles of chills and fever in the infected person.

1 μm

Liver cell producing merozoites

Sporozoite

1 *Plasmodium* sporozoites enter human blood by a mosquito bite.

Red blood cell

Merozoites (*n*)

Mitosis

2 Sporozoites enter liver cells, where the merozoite stages of *Plasmodium* form.

KEY
Haploid
Diploid

3 Merozoites are released from liver cells, enter red blood cells, and reproduce, causing red blood cells to burst.

Figure 26.23 Diagram of the life cycle of *Plasmodium falciparum,* the causative agent of malaria. This life cycle requires two hosts: humans and *Anopheles* mosquitoes.

Concept check: *In which of the hosts does sexual mating of* P. falciparum *gametes occur?*

exoerythrocytic cycle, life stages known as merozoites develop. Hundreds of merozoites are produced within liver cells (see inset Figure 26.23), which then release into the bloodstream packages of merozoites enclosed by a host-derived cell membrane (see inset Figure 26.23). This membrane protects merozoites from destruction by host immune cells, which would otherwise engulf merozoites by phagocytosis and destroy the invaders. In the bloodstream the protective host membranes disintegrate, releasing merozoites. The merozoites have protein complexes at their front ends, or apices, that allow them to invade human red blood cells. (The presence of these apical complexes gives rise to the phylum name Apicomplexa.) The merozoites consume the hemoglobin in red blood cells. While living within red blood cells (**erythrocytic cycle**), they form ring stages, which can be seen through a microscope after staining and is how malaria is diagnosed. Merozoites reproduce asexually, generating large numbers of new merozoites that synchronously break out of red blood cells at intervals of 48 or 72 hours. These merozoite reproduction cycles correspond to cycles of chills and fever experienced by the infected person. Some merozoites produce sexual structures—gametocytes—which, along with blood, are transmitted to a female mosquito as she bites an infected person.

Within the mosquito's body, the gametocytes produce gametes and fertilization occurs, yielding a zygote, the only diploid cell in *Plasmodium*'s life cycle. Within the mosquito gut, the zygote undergoes meiosis, generating structures filled with many sporozoites, the stage that can be transmitted to a new human host. Sporozoites move to the mosquito's salivary glands, where they remain until injected into a human host when the mosquito feeds. Genomic information about life stages is now helping medical scientists to develop new ways to prevent or treat malaria and other diseases caused by protists.

Plasmodium That Infects Humans Is Related to Gorilla *Plasmodium*

What is the ancestry of *Plasmodium falciparum*, the human malarial parasite? Recent studies by Dr. Liu and colleagues revealed that African primates carry a large diversity of *Plasmodium* species. The researchers collected fecal samples from

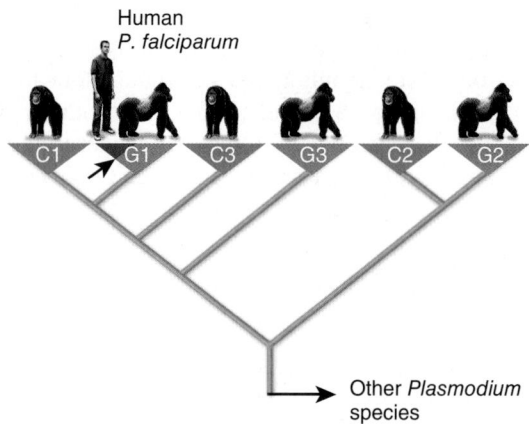

Figure 26.24 **Evolutionary patterns in *Plasmodium* strains.** This tree describes evolutionary patterns in *Plasmodium* strains isolated from chimpanzees (*Plasmodium* lineages C1–C3; green) and western gorillas (*Plasmodium* lineages G1–G3; orange) in central Africa. The point of cross-species transmission from gorillas to humans is marked by an arrow.

nearly 3,000 primate specimens throughout central Africa to use to isolate DNA sequences (which can identify *Plasmodium* species and lineages by using PCR).

As shown in **Figure 26.24**, the researchers found *Plasmodium* infections in chimpanzees (*Pan troglodytes*) and western gorillas (*Gorilla gorilla*) but not in eastern gorillas (*Gorilla beringei*) or bonobos (*Pan paniscus*). A large percentage (about 40%) of chimpanzees and western gorillas sampled carried *Plasmodium* parasites, with mixed infections being commonplace. While the *Plasmodium* lineages that infected gorillas (G1–3) and chimpanzees (C1–3) are variant, the human *P. falciparum* lineage (shown in red) is homogeneous. The *Plasmodium* lineage G1, found in western gorillas, contains the closest relatives of human *P. falciparum*.

The transmission of *Plasmodium* lineage G1 to humans was considered a rare event because this cross-species transmission was predicted to occur only once. Still unknown is when gorilla *P. falciparum* entered the human population and whether present-day ape populations represent a reservoir for recurring human infection.

GENOMES AND PROTEOMES

Genomic Information Aids in Combating Protistan Parasites

Genome sequences have been determined for several protists that cause human disease. This has been done as a way to find new cellular targets for drug treatments that will kill the parasites without harming the human host. The goal is to identify metabolic processes that are present in the parasite but not the host. With such information, medical scientists can look for drugs that affect only the distinctive parasite process.

Genomic data are now available for the malarial parasite *Plasmodium falciparum* and three pathogenic kinetoplastids: *Trypanosoma brucei* (the agent of sleeping sickness), *Trypanosoma cruzi* (Chagas disease), and *Leishmania major* (leishmaniasis). Sleeping sickness is transmitted to humans and livestock by tsetse flies in equatorial Africa and in parts of South America and Asia. Nearly half a million people become infected with sleeping sickness each year, and the disease is fatal if untreated. Chagas disease is a hazard primarily in South America and can be transmitted via blood and organ donations. Leishmaniasis is a risk for anyone who travels to or lives in any of the 88 countries in South and Central America, the Mediterranean region, and Asia, where the disease is endemic; about 2 million cases occur each year.

In the case of *P. falciparum*, genomic data have already highlighted potential new pharmaceutical approaches. The organism's nuclear genome consists of 14 chromosomes and about 5,300 genes. A large proportion of *P. falciparum*'s genes are related to evasion of the host's immune system and interactions between the host and parasite. Two-thirds of the predicted 5,268 proteins appear to be unique to this organism, an unusual situation among eukaryotes. About 550 (about 10%) of the nuclear-encoded proteins are likely imported into a modified plastid, known as an apicoplast, where they are needed for fatty acid metabolism and other processes. Because plastids are not present in the cells of mammals, enzymes in apicoplast pathways are possible targets for the development of drug therapy. Mammals also lack calcium-dependent protein kinases, enzymes that are essential to *P. falciparum*'s sexual development, offering another potential drug target. By contrast, genomic data reveal that kinetoplastids lack plastids, so drug strategies focused on this organelle will not affect these parasites. However, comparative study of their genomes reveals that *T. brucei*, *T. cruzi*, and *L. major* share some distinctive DNA transcription features that might prove useful in developing drug treatments.

Summary of Key Concepts

26.1 An Introduction to Protists

- Protists are eukaryotes that are abundant in moist habitats, and most are microscopic. Modern phylogenetic analysis has revealed that protists do not form a monophyletic group; instead, they are classified into several eukaryotic supergroups. (Figure 26.1, Table 26.1)

- Protists are often classified into three major groups according to ecological roles. The term *algae* is used informally for protist phyla that include photosynthetic protists. The term *protozoa* describes diverse heterotrophic protists that are often mobile. The term *fungus-like protists* describes protists having a structure and nutrition that resemble those of true fungi. (Figures 26.2, 26.3)

- Protists are particularly diverse in aquatic environments. The floating or swimming plankton are relatively small and simple in structure; the phytoplankton are adapted to life in well-illuminated near-surface waters; and the periphyton are attached to underwater surfaces. The multicellular protists known as seaweeds often display complex structure. (Figure 26.4)

- Microscopic protists propel themselves in several ways. Diverse small protists that swim by means of eukaryotic flagella are known as flagellates. The ciliates are a phylum of protists that move by means of many short cilia on their surfaces. Amoebae are diverse protists that move by means of pseudopodia. Other protists are able to glide across surfaces by secreting slime. (Figure 26.5)

26.2 Evolution and Relationships

- New discoveries are constantly changing concepts of protist evolution and relationships, and the relationships of some protists are unknown or controversial. Current phylogenetic analyses reveal that protists do not form a monophyletic group; instead, many can be classified into one of seven major eukaryotic supergroups.

- The supergroup Excavata includes flagellate protists characterized by a feeding groove (such as the genus *Jakoba*) and the specialized parasites *Trichomonas vaginalis* and *Giardia lamblia*, which have modified mitochondria. (Figures 26.6, 26.7)

- The supergroup Euglenozoa consists of flagellates that have disk-shaped mitochondrial cristae. Phyla include the kinetoplastids, which include some human parasites, and euglenoids, some of which are photosynthetic. (Figures 26.8, 26.9)

- The supergroup Archaeplastida includes three algal phyla (green algae, red algae, and glaucophytes) and the plant kingdom, all of which display primary plastids with two envelope membranes. (Figure 26.10)

- The supergroup Alveolata includes the ciliates, dinoflagellates, and apicomplexans, all known for the presence of saclike membranous vesicles called alveoli. (Figure 26.11)

- The supergroup Stramenopila includes a diverse group of protists that produce flagella with strawlike hairs that aid swimming. Stramenopiles include the fungus-like plant parasite Phytophthora, diatoms, and diverse algal classes whose secondary plastids originated from a red alga by secondary endosymbiosis. Such plastids also occur in species of three other algal phyla: Haptophyta, Cryptophyta, and Dinozoa. (Figure 26.12)

- Tertiary plastids arose in protists on more than one occasion, and many heterotrophic protists and aquatic animals contain endosymbiotic algal cells. (Figure 26.13)

- The supergroup Rhizaria consists of flagellates and amoebae that have thin cellular processes known as filose pseudopodia. Three prominent phyla are Chlorarachniophyta, which have secondary green plastids; mineral-shelled Radiolaria; and Foraminifera, which have shells composed of calcium carbonate. (Figure 26.14)

- The supergroup Amoebozoa is composed of many types of amoebae that move by means of pseudopodia and includes the parasite *Entamoeba histolytica* and slime moulds, such as *Dictyostelium discoideum*.

- The supergroup Opisthokonta includes organisms that produce swimming cells that bear a single posterior flagellum. It includes the fungal and animal kingdoms. The protists known as choanoflagellates are considered the modern protists most closely related to the common ancestor of animals. (Figure 26.15)

26.3 Nutritional and Defensive Adaptations

- Protists display four basic types of nutrition. Heterotroph protists called phagotrophs rely on particle feeding, whereas heterotroph protists called osmotrophs absorb small organic molecules. Autotroph protists make their own organic food, and protists that use both autotrophic and heterotrophic means to obtain nutrients are known as mixotrophs. (Figure 26.16)

- Protists that break down wastes and dead organisms are called decomposers, whereas those that feed on living cells are termed parasites.

- Protists defend themselves from attackers by means of defensive adaptations that include protective cell coverings, sharp projectiles, light flashes, and toxic compounds. Dinoflagellates are particularly important as toxin producers. Aquatic ecologists have established that populations of the unicellular dinoflagellate genus Pfiesteria kill fish by means of a toxin that can also harm human cells. (Figure 26.17)

26.4 Reproductive Adaptations

- Protist populations grow by means of asexual reproduction involving mitosis, and many are able to persist through unfavourable conditions in the form of tough-walled cysts. (Figure 26.18)
- Protists that have zygotic life cycles often use tough-walled zygotes to persist through unfavourable conditions. (Figure 26.19)
- Protists displaying sporic life cycles are able to occupy more types of habitats because they produce two or more life stages with differing environmental preferences. (Figure 26.20)
- Diatoms, which have a gametic life cycle, use sexual reproduction to solve a cell size problem that originates from their unique mode of asexual cell division. (Figure 26.21)
- Ciliates display a unique type of sexual reproduction (conjugation) that involves the exchange of genetic material between a mating pair of cells. (Figure 26.22)
- Parasitic protists may have life cycles involving alternative hosts. One example is *Plasmodium,* the malarial agent, whose alternative hosts are humans and mosquitoes. Genomic sequence data have been obtained for several parasitic protists, with the goal of developing new treatments that will kill the parasites without harming hosts. (Figure 26.23)
- The *Plasmodium* that infects humans is related to gorilla *Plasmodium.* (Figure 26.24)

Test to Assess Your Learning

1. Which protist phylum is most closely related to the animal kingdom?
   a. Rhodophyta
   b. Euglenida
   c. Choanomonada
   d. Radiolaria
   e. None of the above

2. Which protist phylum is most closely related to the plant kingdom?
   a. Chlorophyta
   b. Chlorarachniophyta
   c. Choanomonada
   d. Bacillariophyta
   e. Radiolaria

3. Which informal ecological group of protists includes autotrophs?
   a. protozoa
   b. algae
   c. fungus-like protists
   d. all of the above
   e. none of the above

4. How would you recognize a secondary plastid?
   a. It would have one envelope membrane.
   b. It would have two envelope membranes.
   c. It would have more than two envelope membranes.
   d. It would have pigments characteristic of primary plastids of red or green algal cells.
   e. Both (c) and (d) are correct.

5. What organisms have tertiary plastids?
   a. certain stramenopiles
   b. certain euglenoids
   c. certain cryptomonads
   d. certain opisthokonts
   e. none of the above

6. What is unusual about mixotrophs?
   a. They have no plastids, but they occur mixed in communities with autotrophs.
   b. They have mixed heterotrophic and autotrophic nutrition.
   c. Their cells contain a mixture of red and green plastids.
   d. Their cells contain a mixture of mitochondria having differently shaped cristae.
   e. They consume a mixed diet of algae.

7. What advantages do diatoms obtain from sexual reproduction?
   a. increased genetic variability
   b. increased ability of populations to respond to environmental change
   c. evolutionary potential
   d. regeneration of maximal cell size for the species
   e. all of the above

8. What are trichocysts?
   a. hairs that occur on flagella
   b. membrane sacs that occur beneath the cell surface
   c. tough-walled asexual cells that are able to withstand unfavourable conditions
   d. spearlike defensive structures that are shot from cells under attack
   e. none of the above

9. How do autotrophic protists use accessory pigments?
   a. Accessory pigments provide camouflage, so herbivores cannot see algae.
   b. Accessory pigments are able to absorb underwater light and transfer the energy to chlorophyll *a* for use in photosynthesis.
   c. Accessory pigments attract aquatic animals that carry gametes from one seaweed to another.
   d. All of the above.
   e. None of the above.

10. What are the two alternative hosts of the malarial parasite *Plasmodium falciparum*?
    a. humans and ticks
    b. ticks and mosquitoes
    c. humans and *Anopheles* mosquitoes
    d. humans and all types of mosquitoes
    e. none of the above

Articulate to Assess Your Learning

1. Why are protists classified into multiple supergroups, rather than into a single kingdom or phylum?

2. Why have molecular biologists sequenced the genomes of several parasitic protists?

3. Why are protistan cysts important to epidemiologists—biologists who study the spread of disease?

4. Why do all human *Plasmodium* constitute a single lineage while gorilla and chimpanzee have multiple lineages?

Collaborate to Assess and Extend Your Learning

1. Imagine that you are studying an insect species, and you discover that the insects are dying of a disease that results in the production of cysts of the type that protists often generate. You think that the cysts might have been produced by a parasitic protist that could be used as an insect control agent. How would you identify the disease agent?

2. Imagine that you are part of a marine biology team seeking to catalogue the organisms inhabiting a threatened coral reef. The team has found two new seaweeds, each of which occurs during a particular time of the year when the water temperature differs. You suspect that the two seaweeds might be different generations of the same species that have differing optimal temperature conditions. How would you test your hypothesis?

3. A principle of biology is that living organisms use energy. Describe all the different nutritional adaptations that Protists are known to display.

Visit McGraw-Hill Ryerson Connect™ for additional study resources.

The Kingdom Fungi

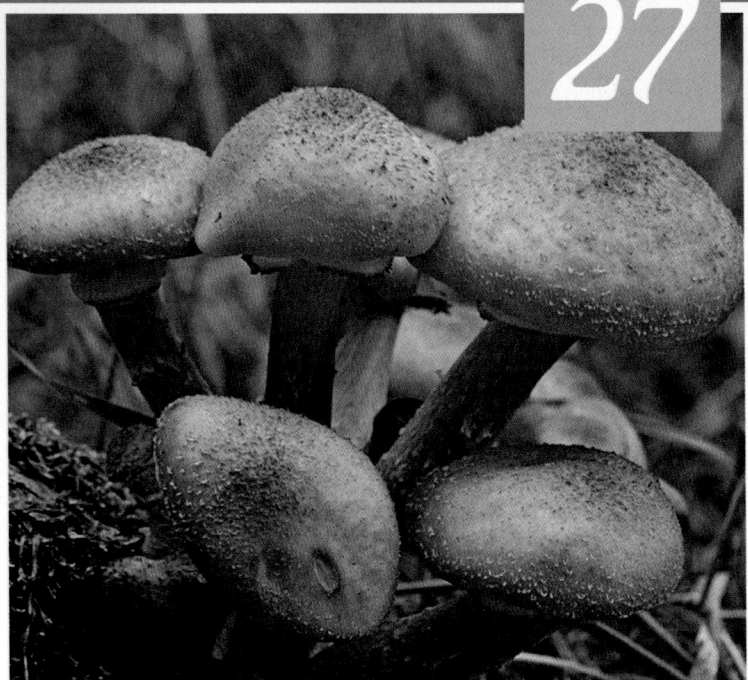

Basidiomycete mushrooms of a fungus in the genus *Armillaria*. This type of fungus might be the largest organism in the world.

Chapter Outline

You might think that the largest organism in the world is a whale or perhaps a giant redwood tree. Amazingly, giant fungi would also be good candidates. For example, an individual fungus in the genus *Armillaria* weighs 10,000 kg, is more than 1,500 years old, and spreads over 15 hectares of Oregon forest soil! Myron Smith, now at Carleton University, and Johann Bruhn and Jim Anderson from the University of Toronto discovered the extent of this enormous fungus when they found identical DNA sequences in samples taken over this wide area. Other examples of such huge fungi have been found, and mycologists—scientists who study fungi—suspect that they may be fairly common underfoot yet largely unseen.

Regardless of their size, fungi typically occur in soil or other materials, becoming conspicuous only when reproductive portions, such as mushrooms, extend above the surface. Even though fungi can be inconspicuous, they play essential roles in Earth's environment, are associated in diverse ways with other organisms, and have many technological applications. In this chapter we will explore the distinctive features of fungal structure, growth, nutrition, reproduction, and diversity. In the process you will learn how fungi are connected to forest growth, food production and food toxins, sick building syndrome, and other topics of importance to humans.

27.1   DISTINCTIVE FEATURES OF FUNGI

Learning Outcomes:

1. Outline the distinctive features of fungi, including how they obtain food.
2. Discuss how fungal feeding is related to fungal growth.

The eukaryotes known as fungi are so distinct from other organisms that they are placed in their own kingdom, the kingdom Fungi (**Figure 27.1**). The monophyletic kingdom Fungi has five major groups: the early diverging fungi: phylachytrids, zygomycetes, and AM fungi; and the later diverging fungi: ascomycetes and basidiomycetes. Because fungi are closely related to the animal kingdom, fungi and animals display some common features. For example, both are **heterotrophic**, meaning that they cannot produce their own food but must obtain it from the environment. Fungi use an amazing array of organic compounds as food, which is termed their **substrate**. The substrate includes soil, a rotting log, a piece of bread, a living tissue, and many other materials. Fungi are also like animals in that they are ingestive heterotrophs. Both fungi and animals secrete enzymes that digest organic materials and absorb the resulting small organic food molecules, as well as minerals and water, into their cells. In addition, both fungi and animals store surplus food in their cells as the carbohydrate glycogen. Despite these nutritional commonalities, fungal structure is quite distinctive. Unlike most animals, fungi do not ingest nutrients; rather, the nutrients diffuse passively or actively into the fungal hyphae. Fungi have a very high surface-area-to-volume ratio that allows for efficient diffusion of nutrients; however, it also makes many fungi vulnerable to desiccation. Several fungi have adaptations that prevent desiccation.

Fungi Have a Unique Cell-Wall Chemistry and Body Form

Unlike animal cells, which lack rigid cell walls, fungal cells are enclosed by tough cell walls composed of **chitin**, a polysaccharide that contains nitrogen. Chitin, which also forms part of the exoskeletons of arthropods, such as insects, resists bacterial attack, thereby helping to protect fungal cells. Fungal cell walls influence two other features that distinguish fungal cells from animal cells: nutrition and motility. Because they have cell walls, fungal cells cannot engulf food particles by phagotrophy. In contrast, some animal cells are capable of phagotrophy, a feature inherited from ancestral protists (see Chapter 26). Additionally, the rigid walls of fungal cells, like those of plant cells, restrict the mobility of nonflagellate cells.

Most fungi have distinctive bodies known as **mycelia** (singular: mycelium) that are composed of microscopic branched

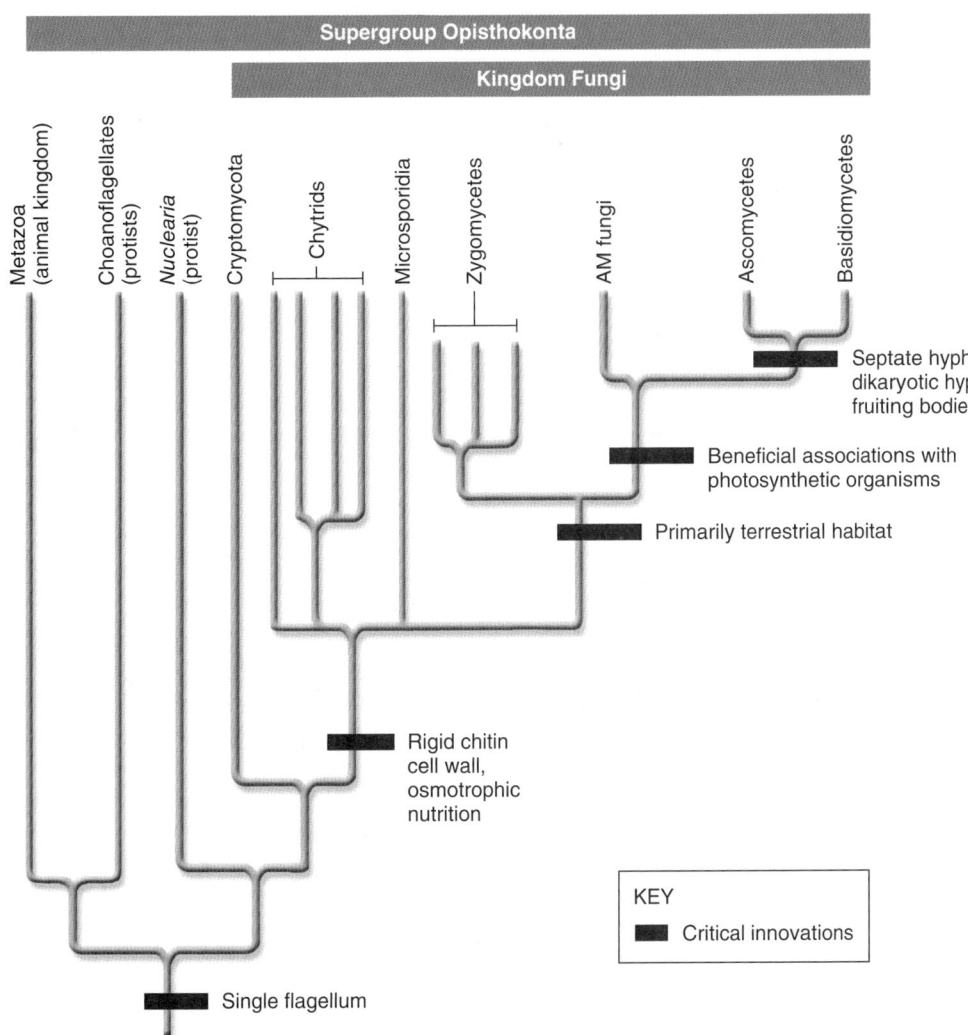

Supergroup Opisthokonta

Kingdom Fungi

Metazoa (animal kingdom)

Choanoflagellates (protists)

Nuclearia (protist)

Cryptomycota

Chytrids

Microsporidia

Zygomycetes

AM fungi

Ascomycetes

Basidiomycetes

Septate hyphae, dikaryotic hyphae, fruiting bodies

Beneficial associations with photosynthetic organisms

Primarily terrestrial habitat

Rigid chitin cell wall, osmotrophic nutrition

Single flagellum

KEY

█ Critical innovations

(a)

Figure 27.1 Evolutionary relationships of the fungi. **(a)** The kingdom Fungi arose from a protist ancestor. Five fungal phyla are described in this chapter: the early diverging Chytridiomycota, Zygomycota, and Glomeromycota, and the later diverging fungi known as Ascomycota and Basidiomycota. **(b)** Representatives of the five major groups of fungi: (i) Basidiomycota. *Amanita muscaria* is often referred to as a toadstool. (ii) Chytridiomycota. A chitrid fungus, *Batrachochytrium dendrobatidis,* is implicated in decimating amphibian populations. (iii) Zygomycota. *Rhizopus stolanifer* is frequently encountered in the home. It infects softening fruit and stale bread. (iv) Glomeromycota. *Geosiphon pyriformis* lives on the roots of plants in the forest. (v) Ascomycota. This is a very diverse group. Most are filamentous. However, yeast, *Saccharomyces cerevisiae* (shown here), is a budding form.

(b)

filaments called **hyphae** (singular: hypha) (**Figure 27.2**). As discussed later, hyphae may be septate or aseptate (a septum is a crosswall in the hyphae observed by light microscopy), and cells may contain one nucleus or multiple nuclei. Most of the fungal mycelium is diffuse, or spread out, within food substrates and thus inconspicuous. In contrast, **fruiting bodies** are the visible fungal reproductive structures, which are composed of more densely packed hyphae that typically grow out of the substrate (**Figure 27.3**). Fruiting bodies are thus the only parts of fungal bodies that most people see. Mushrooms are one type of fungal fruiting body. Fungal fruiting bodies are specialized to produce the walled reproductive cells known as **spores**. Fungal fruiting bodies are amazingly diverse in form, colour, and odour because they are adapted in ways that foster spore dispersal by wind, water, or animals. When spores settle in places where conditions are favourable for growth, they produce new mycelia. When the new mycelia undergo sexual reproduction, they produce new fruiting bodies.

(a) Hyphae on hair

Hyphae
Human hair

(b) Septate hypha

Pores Cell wall
Septa Nuclei

(c) Aseptate hypha

Nuclei Cell wall

Figure 27.2 **Fungal hyphae.** Fungal bodies are composed of delicate filaments known as hyphae. **(a)** Hyphae of *Trichophyton mentagrophites* are shown on human hair. This fungus produces enzymes that break down keratin, a protein that occurs abundantly in skin, nails, and hair. **(b)** A septate hypha before mating. Each cell contains only one nucleus. **(c)** An aseptate hypha before mating lacks septa and contains only one genetic type of nuclei.

 Principle: *Cells are the simplest units of life.*

Fungi Have Distinctive Growth Processes

If you have ever watched food become increasingly mouldy over several days, you have observed fungal growth. When a food source is plentiful, fungal mycelia can grow rapidly, adding as much as a kilometre of new hyphae per day. The mycelia grow at their edges as the fungal hyphae extend their tips through the undigested substrate. The narrow dimensions and extensive branching of hyphae provide a very large surface area for absorption of organic molecules, water, and minerals.

Hyphal Tip Growth How do hyphae grow? Cytoplasmic streaming and osmosis are important cellular processes in hyphal growth. Osmosis (see Chapter 6) is the diffusion of water through a membrane from an area with a low solute concentration into an area with a high solute concentration. Water enters fungal hyphae by means of osmosis because their cytoplasm is rich in sugars, ions, and other solutes. Water entry swells the hyphal tip, producing the force necessary for tip extension. Masses of tiny vesicles carrying enzymes and cell-wall materials made in the Golgi apparatus collect in the hyphal tip (**Figure 27.4**). The vesicles then fuse with the plasma membrane. Some vesicles deliver cell-wall materials to the hyphal tip, allowing it to extend. Other vesicles release enzymes that digest materials in the environment, releasing small organic molecules that are absorbed as food.

3 In appropriate environmental conditions, dikaryotic hyphae form a fruiting body, such as a mushroom.

2 If compatible hyphae occur together, cells of different hyphal branches function as gametes and fuse, producing dikaryotic hyphae.

1 Fungal hyphae grow through substrate.

4 Nuclear fusion in certain dikaryotic cells produces diploid zygotes that undergo meiosis to produce haploid spores that are dispersed by wind, water, or animals.

5 Spores of genetically different types produce new mycelia within substrate.

Dikaryotic mycelium
Cell division
Hyphal branches of compatible mating types
Spores

Figure 27.3 **The reproductive fungal body.** Most of a fungus consists of hyphae that grow and branch from a central point to form a diffuse mycelium within a food substrate, such as soil. After mating, fungal hyphae may aggregate to form fleshy masses known as fruiting bodies that extend above the substrate surface. Fruiting bodies produce spores that are dispersed by wind, water, or animals. In suitable sites, spores may germinate, producing new mycelia.

Hyphal Structure   The hyphae of most fungi are divided into many small cells by a cross wall known as a **septum** (see Figure 27.2b). Each of these cells has one or two nuclei. In such fungi, known as septate fungi, each round of nuclear division is followed by cross-wall formation. A central pore, which may be simple or more complex, perforates hyphal septa (**Figure 27.5**). Complex pores may have caps of modified endoplasmic reticulum. Septal pores are large enough to allow cytoplasmic structures and materials to pass through the hyphae. The hyphae of some fungi are not partitioned into smaller cells; rather, these hyphae are **aseptate** and multinucleate (see Figure 27.2c), a condition that results when nuclei repeatedly divide without intervening cytokinesis.

Fungal Nuclear Division   When the nuclei of fungi divide, in most cases a spindle forms within the nuclear envelope, which does not break down. This **intranuclear spindle** distinguishes nuclear division of fungi from that of animals and plants. (By contrast, in land plants and animals, the nuclear envelope vesiculates during prometaphase and then re-forms at telophase.)

Variations in Mycelium Growth Form   Fungal hyphae grow rapidly through a substrate from areas where the food has become depleted to food-rich areas. In nature, mycelia may take an irregular shape, depending on the availability of food. A fungal mycelium can extend into food-rich areas for great distances, even spreading over thousands of hectares, like the giant fungus *A. ostoyae* noted at the beginning of the chapter. In liquid laboratory media, fungi will grow as a spherical mycelium that resembles a cotton ball floating in water (**Figure 27.6a**). When grown in flat laboratory dishes, the mycelium assumes a more two-dimensional growth form (**Figure 27.6b**).

If you remove the bark from rotting logs or look under dead, wet leaves in a forest, you may find what look like white or coloured strings. The strings are **rhizomorphs**, fungal mycelia that have the shape of roots (**Figure 27.7**). Rhizomorphs transport water to other parts of the same mycelium living in low-moisture habitats.

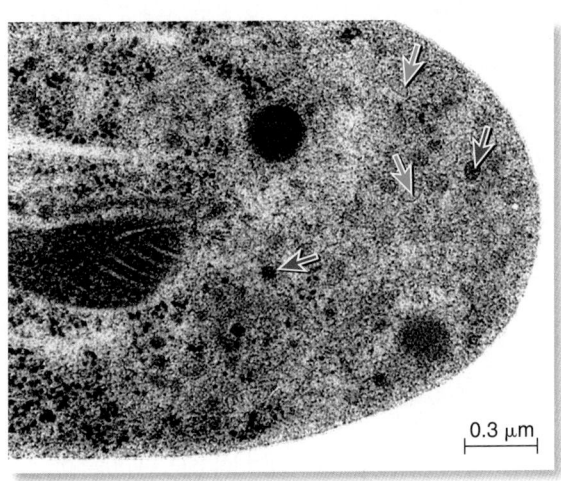

(a) Electron micrograph of a hyphal tip with numerous vesicles

0.3 μm

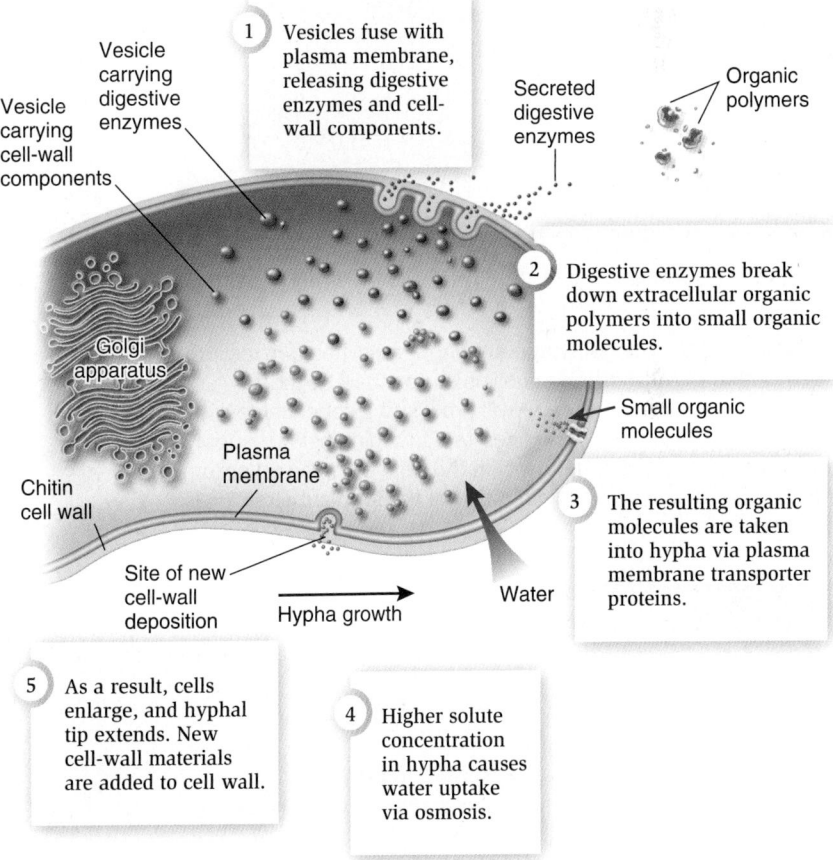

Vesicle carrying digestive enzymes

Vesicle carrying cell-wall components

1 Vesicles fuse with plasma membrane, releasing digestive enzymes and cell-wall components.

Secreted digestive enzymes

Organic polymers

2 Digestive enzymes break down extracellular organic polymers into small organic molecules.

Golgi apparatus

Plasma membrane

Chitin cell wall

Small organic molecules

3 The resulting organic molecules are taken into hypha via plasma membrane transporter proteins.

Site of new cell-wall deposition

Hypha growth

Water

5 As a result, cells enlarge, and hyphal tip extends. New cell-wall materials are added to cell wall.

4 Higher solute concentration in hypha causes water uptake via osmosis.

(b) Mechanism of hyphal tip growth

Figure 27.4 **Hyphal tip growth and absorptive nutrition.**   **(a)** TEM (transmission electron micrograph) showing the hyphal tip of *Aspergillus nidulans,* a fungus commonly used as a genetic model system.
(b) Diagram of a hyphal tip, showing vesicles of two types: those containing cell-wall materials, and those bearing digestive enzymes. On fusion of these vesicles with the plasma membrane, both types of vesicle contents are released to the cell exterior. Digestive enzymes degrade extracellular organic polymers into smaller components that can be taken into hyphae by means of plasma membrane transporter proteins. The uptake of minerals and organic molecules causes osmotic water uptake, with the result that cells enlarge and hyphal tips extend. New cell-wall materials are added to the hyphal tip as it extends.

Concept check: *What do you think would happen to fungal hyphae that begin to grow into a substrate having higher solute concentration? How might your answer be related to food preservation techniques, such as drying or salting?*

(a) Simple pore—ascomycetes

(b) Complex pore—basidiomycetes

Figure 27.5 **Septa divide hyphae of higher fungi into compartments.** **(a)** The septa of ascomycetes have simple pores at the centres. **(b)** More complex pores distinguish the septa of most types of basidiomycetes.

(a) Mycelium growing in liquid medium

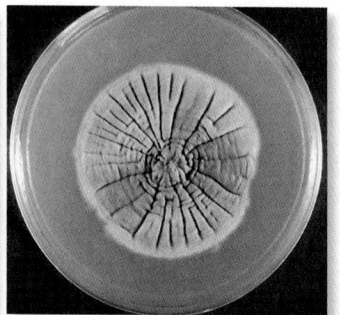

(b) Mycelium growing on flat, solid medium

Figure 27.6 **Fungal shape shifting.** **(a)** When a mycelium, such as that of *Rhizoctonia solani,* is surrounded by food substrate in a liquid medium, it will grow into a spherical form. **(b)** When the food supply is limited to a two-dimensional supply, as shown by *Neotestudina rosatii* in the Petri dish, the mycelium will form a disk. Likewise, distribution of the food substrate determines the mycelium shape in nature.

Figure 27.7 **Rhizomorphs.** In moist forests, hyphae of fungi, such as the honey fungus (*Armillaria mellea*), clump to form conspicuous string-shaped rhizomorphs.

27.2 FUNGAL SEXUAL AND ASEXUAL REPRODUCTION

Learning Outcomes:

1. Give examples of fungal asexual reproduction.
2. Identify some of the distinctive sexual reproductive processes in fungi.
3. Understand that although people may safely consume some fungal fruiting bodies, other fungi fruiting bodies produce substances that are toxic to humans.

Many fungi are able to reproduce both sexually and asexually by means of microscopic spores, each of which can grow into a new adult (**Figure 27.8**). Sexual reproduction generates new allele combinations that allow fungi to colonize new types of habitats. Note that fungi have no sexes. Some fungi have compatible mating types but neither is considered to be male or female. Asexual reproduction is a natural cloning process: it produces genetically identical organisms. Production of asexual spores allows fungi that are well adapted to a particular environment to disperse to similar favourable places.

Fungi Have Distinctive Sexual Reproductive Processes

As is typical of eukaryotes, the fungal sexual reproductive cycle involves the union of gametes, the formation of zygotes, and the process of meiosis. However, many aspects of fungal

(a)   **(b)**

Figure 27.8   Sexual and asexual reproductive cells of fungi.   **(a)** SEM (scanning electron micrograph) showing spores produced after a sexual mating, zygote formation, and subsequent meiosis in the forest mushroom *Coprinus disseminatus.* When mature, these genetically variable spores detach and are dispersed into the environment, where they may find suitable conditions for growth. **(b)** SEM of the asexual conidia of *Aspergillus versicolor,* which causes skin infections in burn victims and lung infections in people with AIDS. Each of these small cells can detach and grow into an individual that is genetically identical to the parent fungus and able to grow in similar conditions.

sexual reproduction are unique, including the function of hyphal branches in reproduction and the development of fruiting bodies (see Figure 27.3).

Fungal Gametes and Mating   The gametes of most fungi are inconspicuous hyphal branches. During sexual reproduction, these hyphal branches fuse with those of a different mycelium of compatible mating type. Particular genes control mating compatibility.

The actual mating process in fungi is also remarkable. In most sexual organisms, gametes undergo fusion of their cytoplasms—a process known as **plasmogamy**—and then the nuclei fuse in a process called **karyogamy**. In contrast, the gamete nuclei of many fungi behave differently. After plasmogamy occurs, the haploid gamete nuclei may remain separate for a long time. During this time the gamete nuclei both divide at each cell division, producing a **dikaryotic** (meaning "two nuclei") mycelium. Each cell of a dikaryotic mycelium possesses two unfused gamete nuclei (see Figure 27.2c). Dikaryotic mycelia are also known as **heterokaryons** (meaning "different nuclei"), reflecting the fact that the two nuclei of each cell are genetically distinct. Some fungi normally persist as heterokaryons, producing clones that can live for hundreds of years. Although the nuclei of dikaryotic mycelia remain haploid, copies of many alleles occur in the separate nuclei. Thus, dikaryotic mycelia are functionally diploid. Eventually, dikaryotic mycelia produce fruiting bodies, the next stage of reproduction.

Fruiting Bodies   Under appropriate environmental conditions, such as seasonal change, a heterokaryotic mycelium will produce a fleshy fruiting body that emerges from the substrate

(see Figure 27.3). All the cells of the fruiting body are dikaryotic. When the fruiting body is mature, the two nuclei in cells at the surface undergo nuclear fusion (karyogamy). This process produces many zygotes, which are the only cells in the fungal life cycle that have a diploid nucleus. In most cases, the fungal zygotes soon undergo meiosis to produce haploid spores. Each spore acquires a tough wall that protects it from drying and other stresses. Wind, rain, or animals disperse the mature spores, which grow into haploid mycelia. If a haploid mycelium encounters hyphae of an appropriate mating type, hyphal branches will fuse and start the sexual cycle over again.

By now it should be clear why fruiting bodies usually emerge from the substrate, while most of the fungal mycelium lies inconspicuously within it. Mycelium growth requires organic molecules, minerals, and water provided by the substrate, but spores are more easily dispersed if released outside the substrate. The structure of fruiting bodies varies in ways that reflect different adaptations that foster spore dispersal by wind, rain, or animals. For example, mature puffballs have delicate surfaces on which just a slight pressure causes the spores to puff out into wind currents (**Figure 27.9a**). Birds' nest fungi form characteristic egg-shaped spore clusters. Raindrops splash on these clusters and disperse the spores. The fruiting bodies of stinkhorn fungi smell and look like rotting meat, which attracts carrion flies (**Figure 27.9b**). The flies land on the fungi to investigate the potential meal and then fly away, in the process dispersing spores that stick to their bodies. The fruiting bodies of fungal truffles are also specialized for spore dispersal by animals. However, they are unusual in being produced underground. Mature truffles emit odours that attract wild pigs and dogs, which break up the fruiting structures while digging for them, thereby dispersing the spores. When collectors seek

 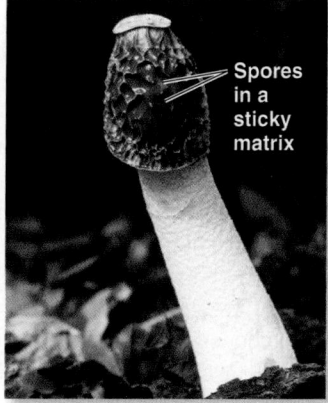

(a) Fruiting bodies adapted for dispersal of spores by wind   **(b) Fruiting body adapted for dispersal of spores by insects**

Figure 27.9   Fruiting body adaptations that foster spore dispersal.   **(a)** When touched by wind gusts or animal movements, spores puff from fruiting bodies of the puffball fungus (*Lycoperdon perlatum*). **(b)** Insects visit fruiting bodies of stinkhorn fungi, such as *Phallus impudicus,* attracted by foul odours and colours like those of dung or rotting meat. Spores, produced in a sticky matrix, attach to the insects and are carried away.

Figure 27.10 Toxic fruiting body of *Amanita muscaria.* Common in conifer forests, *A. muscaria* is both toxic and hallucinogenic. People in ancient times used this fungus to induce spiritual visions and to reduce fear during raids. This fungus produces a toxin, amanitin, that specifically inhibits RNA polymerase II of eukaryotes (but not prokaryotes).

BioConnections: *Look back at Figure 12.14, which illustrates the cellular role of RNA polymerase II in eukaryotes. What effect would the amanitin toxin have on human cells?*

Figure 27.11 Many types of edible fungi are grown for the market.

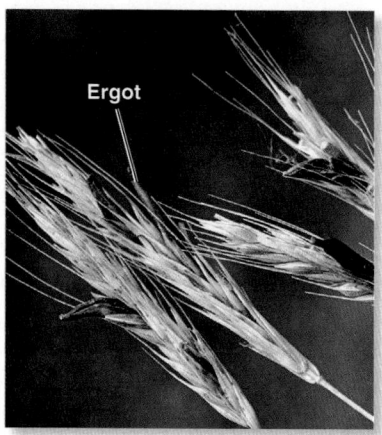

Figure 27.12 Ergot of rye. The fungus *Claviceps purpurea* infects rye and other grasses, producing hard masses of mycelia known as ergots in place of some of the grains (fruits). Ergots produce alkaloids related to LSD and thus cause psychotic delusions in humans and animals that consume products made with infected rye. Ergots were used in folk medicine to treat migraine or hasten childbirth.

to harvest valuable truffles from forests for the market, they use trained pigs or dogs on leashes to locate these fungi.

Though fungi, such as truffles, are edible, the fruiting bodies of many fungi produce toxic substances that may deter animals from consuming them (**Figure 27.10**). When people consume the forest mushroom *Amanita virosa,* known as the "destroying angel," they are also ingesting a powerful toxin that can cause liver failure severe enough to require a liver transplant. Each year, thousands of people in North America alone are poisoned when they consume similarly toxic mushrooms gathered in the wild. There is no reliable way for nonexperts to distinguish poisonous from nontoxic fungi; it is essential to receive instruction from an expert before foraging for mushrooms in the woods. Because several species of edible fungi are cultivated for market sale, many experts recommend that it is better to forage for mushrooms in the grocery store than in the wild (**Figure 27.11**).

Several types of fungal fruiting structures produce hallucinogenic or psychoactive substances. As in the case of fungal toxins, fungal hallucinogens may have evolved as antiherbivore adaptations. Humans have inadvertently experienced their effects. For example, *Claviceps purpurea,* which causes a disease of rye crops and other grasses known as ergot, produces a psychogenic compound related to LSD (lysergic acid diethylamide), a controlled substance (**Figure 27.12**). Some experts speculate that cases of hysteria, convulsions, infertility, and a burning sensation of the skin that occurred in Europe during the Middle Ages resulted from ergot-contaminated rye used in foods. Ergot poisoning may also have caused the behavioural changes that were at the heart of the Salem witch trials in the late seventeenth century. Another example of a hallucinogenic fungus is the "magic mushroom" (*Psilocybe*), which is used in traditional rituals in some cultures. Like ergot, the magic mushroom produces a compound similar to LSD. Consuming hallucinogenic fungi is risky because the amount used to achieve psychoactive effects is dangerously close to a poisonous dose.

Benefits of Asexual Reproduction in Fungi

Asexual reproduction is particularly important to fungi, allowing them to spread rapidly through favourable environments by means of asexual spores. To reproduce asexually, fungi do not need to find compatible mates or expend resources on fruiting-body formation and meiosis. DNA-sequencing studies have revealed that many types of fungi that previously have been shown to reproduce asexually have a sexually reproducing counterpart.

Most fungi reproduce asexually by generating chains of tiny spores from the tips of hyphae. Many fungi produce asexual spores known as **conidia** (from the Greek word for "dust") (see Figure 27.8b). When they land on a favourable substrate, conidia germinate into a new mycelium that produces many more conidia. The green moulds that form on citrus fruits are familiar examples of conidial fungi. A single fungus can produce as many as 40 million conidia per hour.

Figure 27.13
An indoor mould fungus. The black mould *Stachybotrys chartarum* is one of several types of conidial fungi that grow indoors on paper and wood that have been wet for an extended period.

Because they can spread so rapidly, asexual fungi are responsible for costly fungal food spoilage and allergies. *Aspergillus fumigatus* is a common conidial mould that causes a potentially fatal lung disease. *Aspergillus flavus* grows rapidly on stored grains, peanuts, fruits, and spices and produces **aflatoxins**; these cause liver cancer and are a major health concern worldwide. Harmful conidia-producing moulds growing in poorly ventilated, moist places may be the cause of "sick building syndrome," a term used to describe buildings in which occupants or workers experience acute health effects that appear to be linked to time spent inside but where no specific cause can be identified. Some black moulds that also grow in moist building materials are blamed for human illness, even though there is little evidence that they are harmful to adults (**Figure 27.13**). Medically important fungi that reproduce primarily by asexual means include the athlete's foot fungus (*Epidermophyton floccosum*) and infectious yeast (*Candida albicans*).

27.3 FUNGAL ECOLOGY AND BIOTECHNOLOGY

Learning Outcomes:

1. Identify the ecological roles of decomposer and disease fungi.
2. Give examples of fungal diseases of plants and animals, including humans.
3. Explain how mycorrhizae, endophytes, and lichens form beneficial associations with other organisms.
4. List several uses of fungi in biochemistry, biological studies, and industrial processes.

The ability of fungi to degrade diverse materials is important in ecology, medicine, and human biotechnology applications. Fungal decomposers, also known as saprobes, are able to decompose nonliving organic materials. Recycling of materials in ecosystems depends on the activities of fungal decomposers. Fungal hyphae can grow into an animal corpse or plant tissue, digest it with hydrolytic enzymes, and absorb the nutrients. Fungi that attack living animal or plant tissues are pathogens. As hyphae of pathogenic fungi grow through the tissues of plants and animals, food and minerals are absorbed from the host, causing disease symptoms. Mutualistic fungi have formed partnerships with photosynthetic organisms that provide the fungi with organic food. In return, fungi contribute mineral nutrients and water to their photosynthetic partners. In this section we focus more closely on the ecological roles of decomposer, predatory, and mutualistic fungi. Fungi are particularly important as plant and animal decomposers.

Decomposer and Predatory Fungi Play Important Ecological Roles

Decomposer fungi are essential components of Earth's ecosystems. Together with bacteria they decompose dead organisms and organic wastes, preventing litter buildup. For example, only certain bacteria and fungi can break down cellulose, and a few fungi are the major decomposers of lignin, the decay-resistant component of wood. Without decomposers ecosystems would become clogged with organic debris. Decomposers are needed to break down organic compounds into carbon dioxide, which is used by algae and plants for photosynthesis. Decomposer fungi and bacteria are also Earth's recycling engineers. They release minerals to the soil and water, where plants and algae take up the minerals for growth. In the absence of fungi and bacteria, such minerals would remain forever bound up in dead organisms, unavailable for the growth of forests, coral reefs, and other biotic communities.

Some soil fungi are predators—they trap tiny soil animals, such as nematodes, in nooselike hyphae and then proceed to digest their bodies (**Figure 27.14**). Such fungi help control populations of nematodes, some of which attack plant roots. Some fungi attack and kill insects, and certain of these species are used as biological control agents to kill black field crickets (*Teleogryllus commodus*), red-legged earth mites (*Halotydeus destructor*), and other pests. A Canadian International Development Agency project developed a fungus to control locusts in Africa.

Some Fungal Species Cause Plant and Human Diseases

Five thousand fungal species cause serious crop diseases and recent results show that new diseases can arise by horizontal gene transfer. Wheat rust is an example of a common crop disease

Nematode

Hyphal loop

Figure 27.14 **A predatory fungus.** The fungus *Arthrobotrys anchonia* traps nematode worms in hyphal loops that suddenly swell in response to the animal's presence. Fungal hyphae then grow into the worm's body and digest it.

caused by fungi (**Figure 27.15**). Rusts are named for the reddish spores that emerge from the surfaces of infected plants. Many types of plants can be attacked by rust fungi, but rusts are of particular concern when new strains attack crops. For example, in late 2004 agricultural scientists discovered that a devastating rust, *Phakopsora pachyrhizi,* had begun to spread in the U.S. soybean crop. This rust kills soybean plants by attacking the leaves, causing complete leaf drop in less than two weeks. The disease had apparently spread to U.S. farms by means of spores blown on hurricane winds from South America. To control the spread of fungal diseases, agricultural experts work to identify effective fungicidal chemicals and develop resistant crop varieties.

In addition to being spread by wind, the spores of crop-disease fungi can also be introduced on travellers' clothing and other belongings. To reduce the entry of new crop disease fungi—as well as crop viruses and insect pests—agricultural customs inspectors closely monitor the entry of plants, soil, foods, and other materials that might harbour these organisms.

Fungi cause several types of disease in humans. For example, athlete's foot and ringworm are common skin diseases caused by fungi that are known as dermatophytes because they colonize the human epidermis (see Figure 27.2a). *Pneumocystis carinii* is a fungal pathogen that infects individuals with weakened immune systems, such as people with AIDS, sometimes causing death by pneumonia. *Coccidioides immitis, Cryptococcus neoformans,* and *Histoplasma capsulatum* are examples of fungi that cause lung and other diseases. These diseases are of special concern when they occur in people with cancer whose immune systems are weakened by therapy.

Though fungal diseases that attack humans are of medical concern, in nature fungal pathogens often help to control populations of other organisms, which is an important ecological role. Some fungi play important ecological roles as beneficial partners in symbiotic associations with other organisms.

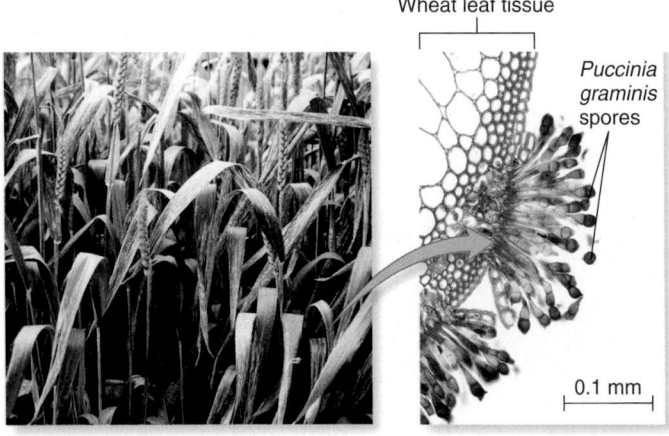

Figure 27.15 Wheat rust. The plant pathogenic fungus *Puccinia graminis* grows within the tissues of wheat plants, using plant nutrients to produce rusty streaks of red spores that erupt at the stem and leaf surface, where spores can be dispersed. Red spore production is one stage of a complex life cycle involving several types of spores. Rusts infect many other crops, causing immense economic damage.

Fungi Form Mutually Beneficial Ecological Associations

Fungi form several types of associations that appear to benefit both partners; these are known as mutualistic interactions (see Chapter 54). For example, leaf-cutting ants, certain termites and beetles, and the salt marsh snail (*Littoraria irrorata*) cultivate particular fungi for food, much as do human mushroom growers. Other fungi obtain organic food molecules from photosynthetic organisms: plants, green algae, or cyanobacteria. We focus next on three types of fungi—mycorrhizal fungi, endophytes, and lichen fungi—that are beneficially associated with other organisms.

Mycorrhizae Associations between the hyphae of certain fungi and the roots of most seed plants are known as **mycorrhizae** (literally, "fungus roots") (see Chapter 35). Mycorrhizal associations are very important in ecology and agriculture; more than 80% of terrestrial plants form mycorrhizae. Plants that have mycorrhizal partners receive an increased supply of water and mineral nutrients, primarily phosphate, copper, and zinc. They do so because an extensive fungal mycelium is able to absorb minerals from a much larger volume of soil than can plant roots lacking fungal associates.

By binding soils, fungal hyphae also reduce water loss and erosion, and they help protect plants against pathogens and toxic wastes. Fungi thereby help plants adapt to and thrive in new sites, thus playing an important role in plant succession (see Chapter 55). For this reason, ecologists increasingly incorporate mycorrhizal fungi into plant-community restoration projects. Some species of oak, beech, pine, and spruce trees will not grow unless their ectomycorrhizal partners are also present (**Figure 27.16**).

Dr. John Klironomos (now at University of British Columbia-Okanagan) has worked extensively on **ectomycorrhizal fungi**. He has found an interesting tritrophic relationship among an ectomycorrhizal fungus, *Laccaria bicolor,* pine trees, and springtails: tiny and numerous soil-dwelling insects. *L. bicolor,* which associates with pine tree roots, can kill springtails in the soil surrounding pine trees. Thus, *L. bicolor* can improve plant nutrition specifically by providing insect-derived nitrogen; in exchange, the fungus receives plant-derived carbohydrate.

Endomycorrhizae (from the Greek *endo,* meaning "inside") are partnerships between plants and fungi in which the fungal hyphae penetrate the spaces between root cell walls and plasma membranes and grow along the surfaces of these membranes (**Figure 27.17**). In such spaces endomycorrhizal fungi often form highly branched, bushy arbuscules (from the word *arbour,* referring to tree shape). As the arbuscules develop, the root plasma membrane also expands. Consequently, the arbuscules and the root plasma membranes surrounding them have very high surface areas that facilitate rapid and efficient exchange of materials: minerals flow from fungal hyphae to root cells, and organic food molecules move from root cells to hyphae. These fungus-root associations are known as **arbuscular mycorrhizae**, abbreviated to AM. AM fungi are associated with apple trees, peach trees, coffee shrubs, and many herbaceous plants, including legumes, grasses, tomatoes, and strawberries.

(a) Ectomycorrhizal fruiting body

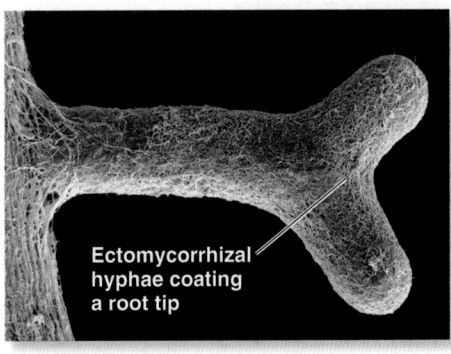

(b) SEM of ectomycorrhizal hyphae

(c) Hyphae invading intercellular spaces

Figure 27.16 **Ectomycorrhizae.** **(a)** The fruiting body of the common forest fungus *Boletus.* This is an ectomycorrhizal fungus that is associated with tree roots. **(b)** Ectomycorrhizal fungal hyphae of *Laccaria bicolor* cover the surfaces of young *Pinus resinosa* root tips. **(c)** Diagram showing that the hyphae of ectomycorrhizal fungi do not penetrate root cell walls but grow within intercellular spaces. In this location, fungal hyphae are able to obtain organic food molecules produced by plant photosynthesis.

Concept check: *What benefits do plants obtain from this association?*

(a) Micrograph of arbuscular mycorrhizae

(b) Hyphae growing between cell walls and plasma membranes

Figure 27.17 **Endomycorrhizae.** **(a)** Light micrograph showing black-stained AM fungi within the roots of the forest herb *Asarum canadensis.* Endomycorrhizal fungal hyphae enter plant roots via root hair cells, and branches then grow in the spaces between plant cell walls and plasma membranes. **(b)** Diagram showing the position of highly branched arbuscules. Hyphal branches of arbuscules are coated with plant plasma membrane, with the result that both hyphae and plant membrane have very high surface areas.

Fungal Endophytes Other mutualistic fungi, known as **endophytes**, live compatibly within the roots, leaves, or stem tissues of various types of plants. The endophytes obtain organic food molecules from plants and in turn contribute toxins or antibiotics that deter foraging animals, insect pests, and microbial pathogens. Endophytic fungi also help some plants to tolerate higher temperatures. As a result, plants with endophytes often grow better than plants of the same species without endophytic fungi. For example, fungal endophytes grow throughout the leaves and stems of many cool-season grasses, such as tall fescue (*Festuca arundinacea*). When such grasses reproduce, fungal hyphae transmitted in seeds will grow in the progeny plants. Grasses with endophytic fungi are larger, more toxic to herbivores, and more drought resistant than those without. These advantages allow tall fescue to invade plant communities and displace other plant species, with deleterious effects on wildlife. Fungal endophytes also occur in many tropical plants, producing compounds that help their hosts to

repel attacks by herbivores and disease microbes. These compounds offer promise for the development of new antibiotics and anticancer drugs for use in human medicine.

Lichens Lichens are partnerships of particular fungi and certain photosynthetic green algae or cyanobacteria, and sometimes both. There are at least 25,000 lichen species, but these did not all descend from a common ancestor. DNA-sequencing studies suggest that lichens evolved independently in at least five separate fungal lineages. Molecular studies also show that some fungi have lost their ancestral ability to form lichen associations.

Lichen bodies take one of three major forms: (1) crustose: flat bodies that are tightly adhered to an underlying surface (**Figure 27.18a**); (2) foliose: flat, leaflike bodies (**Figure 27.18b**); or (3) fruticose: bodies that grow upright (**Figure 27.18c**) or hang down from tree branches. Photosynthetic green algae or cyanobacteria typically occur in a distinct layer close to the lichen's surface (**Figure 27.18d**). Lichen structure differs dramatically from

(a) Crustose lichen

(b) Foliose lichen

(c) Fruticose lichen

(d) Microscopic view of a cross-section of a lichen

Figure 27.18   Lichen structure.   (a) An orange-coloured crustose lichen grows tightly pressed to the substrate. (b) The flattened leaf-shaped genus *Umbilicaria* is a common foliose lichen. (c) The highly branched genus *Cladonia* is a common fruticose lichen. (d) A handmade thin slice of *Umbilicaria* viewed with a compound microscope reveals that the photosynthetic algae occur in a thin upper layer. Fungal hyphae make up the rest of the lichen.

that of the fungal components grown separately, demonstrating that the photosynthetic components influence lichen form.

The photosynthetic partner provides lichen fungi with organic food molecules and oxygen, and in turn it receives carbon dioxide, water, and minerals from the fungal partner. Lichen fungi also

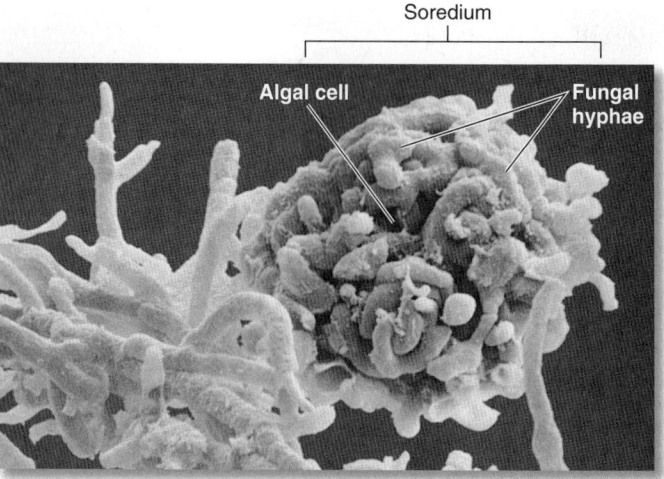

Soredium

Algal cell

Fungal hyphae

Figure 27.19   Lichen asexual reproduction.   Soredia are examples of lichen asexual structures that contain algal or cyanobacterial cells wrapped by fungal hyphae. SEM of a soredium of the lichen *Cladonia coniocraea* that will break off from the parent lichen for dispersal in the environment.

protect their photosynthetic partners from environmental stress. For example, lichens that occupy exposed habitats of high light intensity often produce bright yellow, orange, or red compounds that help prevent damage to the photosynthetic apparatus (see Figure 27.18a). Lichen fungi also produce distinctive organic acids and other compounds that deter animal and microbial attacks.

The fungi associated with about one-third of lichen species can reproduce only asexually. Asexual reproductive structures include **soredia**, small clumps of hyphae surrounding a few algal cells that can disperse in wind currents (**Figure 27.19**). Soredia are lichen clones. By forming soredia, lichen fungi can disperse along with their appropriate photosynthetic partners.

Lichens often grow on rocks, buildings, tombstones, tree bark, soil, or other surfaces that easily become dry. When water is not available, the lichens are dormant until moisture returns. Thus, lichens can spend much of their time in an inactive state; for this reason they often grow very slowly. However, because

FEATURE INVESTIGATION

Piercey-Normore and DePriest Discovered That Some Lichens Readily Change Partners

One of the most interesting issues regarding symbiotic relationships is the extent to which partners have influenced each other's evolution and diversification; when they have, they are said to have cospeciated (coevolved). In the past it was unclear whether or not lichen fungi and their photosynthetic partners coevolved. The fairly recent development of molecular techniques and computer software for analyzing relationships among microorganisms has allowed researchers to attempt to answer this and many other fundamental questions about lichen biology.

Researchers Michelle Piercey-Normore and Paula DePriest devised a way to look for evidence of cospeciation of the fungal and algal partners in a large and diverse lichen group known as the Cladoniaceae (**Figure 27.20**). This group of lichens includes the common "reindeer lichen" (*Cladonia cristatella*). The investigators wanted to know if the pattern of speciation for the fungal partners matched that for the algal partner. The investigators first extracted DNA from the fungal and algal partners in 33 lichens, including diverse species of the genus *Cladonia*. Next, they amplified a region of the rRNA gene for all samples and determined the sequences of these DNAs. Finally, Piercey-Normore and DePriest used the DNA sequences to produce separate phylogenetic trees for the algal and fungal

GOAL To determine whether lichen fungal and algal phylogenies are consistent, as evidence for or against cospeciation.

KEY MATERIALS Fungal and algal components of 33 lichen species in the family Cladoniaceae.

Experimental level   **Conceptual level**

1 Isolate DNA from fungal and algal partners of 33 lichens.

Lichen — Fungal component — Algal component — Fungal DNA — Algal DNA

2 Amplify a region of the rRNA gene using the technique of polymerase chain reaction (PCR) (described in Chapter 18). Use DNA-sequencing techniques (described in Chapter 18) to determine DNA sequences of the rRNA gene region from the algal and fungal partners of 33 lichens.

Use PCR primers specific for fungal rRNA genes and green algal rRNA genes.

PCR — Thermocycler — rDNA Fungal DNA — rDNA Algal DNA

Collect DNA sequences from lichen fungi and lichen algae.

Fungal sequences — **Amplified sequences** — Algal sequences

3 Use DNA-sequence information and computer programs to infer the phylogenies of the algae and the fungi from 33 lichens.

4 **THE DATA**

Connect lines between partners from the same lichen. Look for cases of cospeciation—when phylogenies of the algal and fungal partners match.

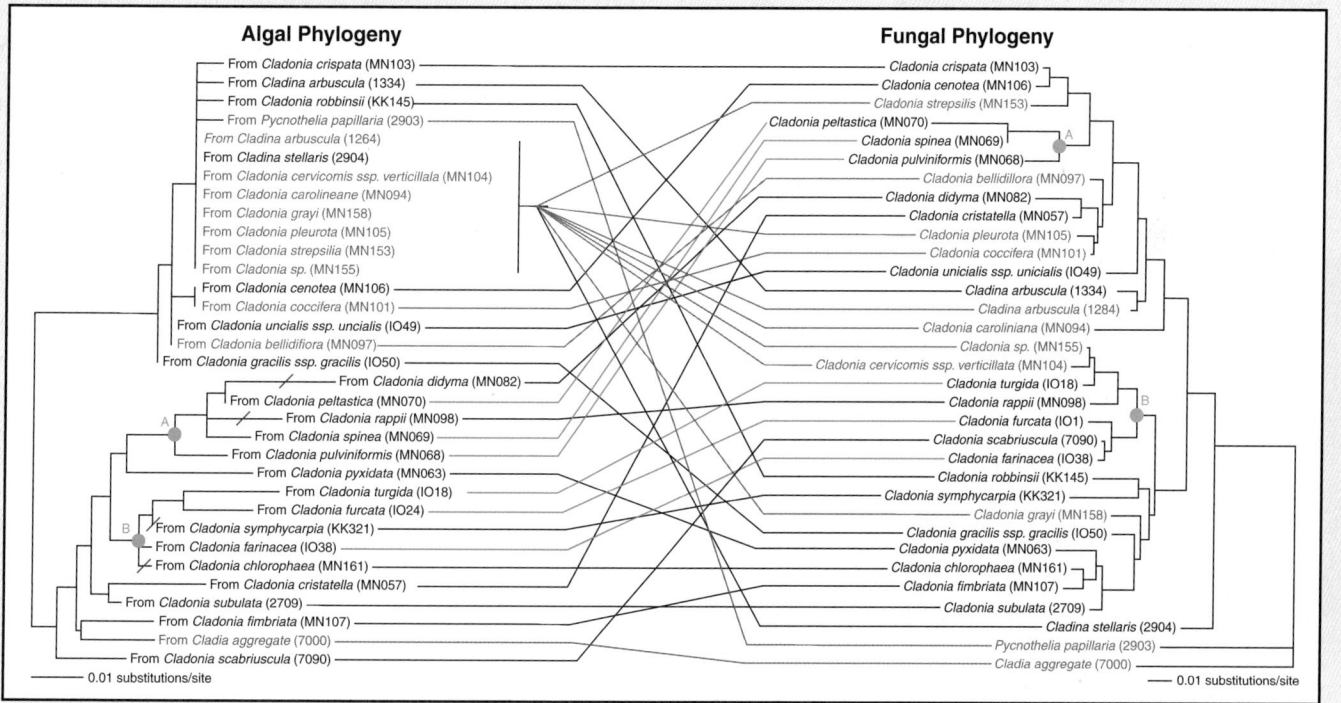

Results from step (4): The green dots marked A and B indicate lichen lineages showing some cospeciation. The partners of these lichens are connected by green lines. Other lineages show little evidence of cospeciation, shown by extensive crossed lines. These results imply a high degree of partner switching in this group of lichens. Partner switching even occurred in lineages A and B (marked with red slashes). These data show that in the lichen family Cladoniaceae, partner switching has been a more frequent occurrence than cospeciation.

Figure 27.20 Piercey-Normore and DePriest discovered that some lichens readily change partners.

partners, and they used statistical procedures to test the possibility that the evolutionary divergence patterns of the fungi and algae were linked.

The results revealed that the fungal and algal phylogenies did not match, indicating that the patterns of their diversification were not congruent. These data indicated that lichen fungi and algae had not generally influenced each other's speciation patterns. If the lichen fungi and algae had undergone species diversification in tandem, their phylogenies should match, that is, be congruent. Instead, the phylogenetic evidence suggested

that lichens often switch algal partners, "trading up" for better algae. The results of this study, published in 2001, revealed that the lichen symbiosis is more complex than previously thought.

Experimental Questions

1. What is meant by the term *cospeciation*?
2. How did Piercey-Normore and DePriest determine whether or not cospeciation had occurred in the Cladoniaceae?
3. What results did Piercey-Normore and DePriest obtain?

they can persist for long periods, lichens can be very old; some are estimated to be more than 4,500 years old.

Lichens are useful as air-quality monitors because they are particularly sensitive to air pollutants, such as sulphur dioxide. Air pollutants severely injure the photosynthetic components, causing death of the lichens. The disappearance of lichens serves as an early warning system of air-pollution levels that are also likely to affect humans. Lichens can also be used to monitor atmospheric radiation levels because they accumulate radioactive substances from the air. After the Chernobyl nuclear power plant accident, lichens in nearby countries became so radioactive that reindeer, which consume lichens as a major food source, became unfit for use as human food or in milk production.

Fungi Have Many Applications in Biotechnology

The ability of fungi to grow on many types of substrates and produce many types of organic compounds represents their diverse ecological adaptations. Humans have harnessed fungal

Hyphae of *Phanerochaete chrysosporium*

Woody tissue; cell walls impregnated with lignin

25 μm

Figure 27.21 Ecological features of fungi can be harnessed in biotechnology.   The forest fungus *Phanerochaete chrysosporium* produces a cobweb-like mycelium on the surfaces of rotting wood. This fungus releases enzymes that break down lignin, thereby making plant cell-wall carbohydrates, such as cellulose, more accessible.

biochemistry in many biotechnology applications. Fungal biochemistry is a valuable asset to the chemical, food processing, and waste-treatment industries. A variety of industrial processes use fungi to convert inexpensive organic compounds into valuable materials, such as citric acid used in the soft drink industry, glycerol, antibiotics such as penicillin, and cyclosporine, a drug widely used to prevent rejection of organ transplants. In the food industry, fungi are used to produce the distinctive flavours of blue cheese and other cheeses. Other fungi secrete enzymes that are used in the manufacture of protein-rich tempeh and other food products from soybeans. The baking industry depends on the yeast *Saccharomyces cerevisiae* for bread production, and yeasts are essential to the brewing and winemaking industries.

Fungi are increasingly being used in industrial processes to replace chemical procedures that generate harmful waste materials. For example, during the production of paper, wood pulp is chemically bleached to remove lignin, but this bleaching process generates harmful compounds, including dioxin, a carcinogenic compound. The forest fungus *Phanerochaete chrysosporium* produces several enzymes that allow it to break down lignin in wood (**Figure 27.21**). Removal of lignin allows the fungi to gain access to cell-wall polysaccharides, which they break down, thereby releasing sugars that the fungus absorbs as food. Fungal lignolytic ("lignin-breaking") enzymes, such as those produced by *P. chrysosporium,* can be used to bleach paper without producing dioxin, thereby reducing a harmful by-product of paper production. In addition, Khadar Valli, Hiroyuki Wariishi, and Michael Gold demonstrated that *P. chrysosporium* is able to decompose dioxin into nontoxic products, suggesting additional potential uses of the fungus in preventing pollution.

27.4 EVOLUTION AND DIVERSITY OF FUNGI

Learning Outcome:

1. Know the distinguishing features of five commonly recognized fungal phyla.

The kingdom Fungi arose from a protist ancestor (see Figure 27.1). The modern fungi have been classified into five phyla, listed in **Table 27.1** by both their common and formal

Table 27.1 Distinguishing Features of Fungal Phyla

Common name (formal name)	Habitat	Ecological role	Reproduction	Examples cited in this chapter
Chytrids (Chytridiomycota)	Water and soil	Mostly decomposers; some pathogens	Flagellate spores	*Batrachochytrium dendrobatidis*
Zygomycetes (Zygomycota)	Mostly terrestrial	Decomposers and pathogens	Nonflagellate asexual spores produced in sporangia; resistant sexual zygospores	*Rhizopus stolonifer*
AM Fungi (Glomeromycota)	Terrestrial	Form mutually beneficial mycorrhizal associations with plants	Distinctively large, nonflagellate, multinucleate asexual spores	The genus *Glomus*
Ascomycetes (Ascomycota)	Mostly terrestrial	Many form lichens; some are mycorrhizal	Nonflagellate sexual spores (ascospores) in sacs (asci) on fruiting bodies (ascocarps); asexual conidia	*Venturia inaequalis, Saccharomyces cerevisiae*
Basidiomycetes (Basidiomycota)	Terrestrial	Less commonly form lichens; many are mycorrhizal; decomposers	Nonflagellate sexual spores (basidiospores) on club-shaped basidia on fruiting bodies (basidiocarps); several types of asexual spores	*Coprinus disseminatus, Rhizoctonia solani, Armillaria mellea, Puccinia graminis, Ustilago maydis, Phanerochaete chrysosporium, Laccaria bicolor, Amanita muscaria, Phallus impudicus, Lycoperdon perlatum*

names: chytrids (Chytridiomycota), zygomycetes (Zygomycota), AM fungi (Glomeromycota), ascomycetes (Ascomycota), and basidiomycetes (Basidiomycota). (The suffixes *mycota* and *mycetes* derive from a Greek word meaning "fungus.") DNA and other data strongly indicate that these phyla all descended from a single common ancestor. Several types of slime moulds and fungus-like protists—though often studied with fungi—are classified with protists rather than true fungi (see Chapter 26). In this section we will survey the characteristics of five phyla of true fungi and examine their distinctive reproductive cycles.

Chytrids Primarily Live in Aquatic Environments

Chytrids are the simplest fungi, and molecular evidence indicates that chytrids were among the earliest fungi to appear. Some chytrids occur as single, spherical cells that may produce hyphae (Figure 27.22), while others exist mainly as branched, aseptate hyphae. Chytrids are the only fungi that produce flagellate cells; these are used for spore or gamete dispersal. The presence of a single, posterior flagellum on chytrid spores or gametes links fungi with the ancestry of choanoflagellates and animals (see Chapter 26). Since species within the phylum Chytridiomycota do not have just one common ancestor, this phylum is not a monophyletic group. By using molecular data, systematists are now assigning some chytrids into new phyla.

Chytrids live in aquatic habitats or in moist soil. Most chytrids are decomposers, but some are parasites of protists (**Figure 27.22**), plants, or animals. For example, the chytrid *Batrachochytrium dendrobatidis* has been associated with declining harlequin frog populations (look ahead to Figure 51.1). Frog populations in Canada, such as western toads (*Anaxyrus boreas*) in southwestern British Columbia, are also showing significant levels of infection.

Zygomycetes Produce Distinctive Zygospores

The **zygomycetes** feature a mycelium that is composed mostly of aseptate hyphae (those lacking cross walls) and distinctive reproductive structures. For example, like most zygomycetes, the black bread mould *Rhizopus stolonifer* produces asexual spores in enclosures known as **sporangia** (singular: sporangium) (**Figure 27.23a**). Bread mould sporangia form at hyphal tips in such large numbers that they make mouldy bread appear black. Zygomycete sporangia can each release up to 100,000 spores into the air! The great abundance of such spores means that bread easily moulds unless retardant chemicals are added.

Zygomycetes are named for the **zygospore**, a distinctive feature of sexual reproduction (**Figure 27.23b**). Zygospore

Algal cell wall

Hyphae

Chytrid

20 μm

Figure 27.22 Chytrids growing on a freshwater protist. The colourless chytrids produce hyphae that penetrate the cellulose cell walls of the dinoflagellate *Ceratium hirundinella,* absorbing organic materials from the alga. Chytrids use these materials to produce spherical flagellate spores that swim away to attack other algal cells.

1 Hyphae produce sporangia that contain asexual spores.

Asexual sporangia

Aseptate hyphae

Bread loaf

3 The hyphae use bread as food to produce more hyphae and new sporangia.

Spores

2 Sporangia open, and spores disperse in air. If spores land in a suitable place such as bread, they germinate into hyphae.

(a) Asexual reproduction

2 If hyphae of compatible mating strains are present, gametangia fuse.

3 The resulting cell develops into a multinucleate heterokaryotic zygosporangium.

KEY
Haploid
Diploid
Heterokaryotic

Fertilization

1 When food supplies run low, hyphae produce multinucleate gametangia.

Gametangium

Cross wall

Hypha

Zygospore within zygosporangium

Parental hyphae

4 Zygosporangial nuclei fuse in pairs to produce many diploid nuclei and a dark, thick-walled zygospore develops within the sporangium.

Aseptate hypha

Spore   **Mitosis**

Meiosis

6 Spores of diverse genetic types are released and dispersed in air. If they land on a suitable site, they germinate, each producing an aseptate hypha.

5 When the environment is suitable, meiosis occurs within the zygospore, producing many haploid spores.

(b) Sexual reproduction

Figure 27.23   The life cycle of a zygomycete, the black bread mould *Rhizopus stolonifer.*

production begins with the development of **gametangia** ("gamete bearers"). In the zygomycete fungi, gametangia are hyphal branches whose cytoplasm is isolated from the rest of the mycelium by cross walls. These gametangia enclose gametes that are basically a mass of cytoplasm containing several haploid nuclei. When food supplies run low, and if compatible mating strains are present, the gametangia of compatible mating types fuse, as do the gamete cytoplasms. The resulting cell, known as a zygosporangium, contains many haploid parental nuclei that fuse, producing many diploid nuclei. Eventually, a dark-pigmented, thick-walled spore known as a zygospore matures within the zygosporangium. Each zygospore contains many diploid nuclei and is capable of surviving stressful conditions. When the environment is suitable, the zygospore can undergo meiosis and germinate, dispersing many haploid spores. If the spores land in a suitable place, they germinate to form aseptate hyphae containing many haploid nuclei produced by mitosis.

Most zygomycetes are saprobes in soil, living on decaying materials, but some are parasites of plants, animals, and insects. The phylum Zygomycetes is not a monophyletic group and thus is likely to be split as more information becomes available.

AM Fungi Live with Plant Partners

The phylum Glomeromycota—commonly known as the AM (for arbuscular mycorrhizal) fungi—has only recently been defined as a distinct group. AM fungi were previously classified with the Zygomycota. Glomeromycota have aseptate hyphae and reproduce only asexually by means of unusually large spores with many nuclei (**Figure 27.24**). Many vascular plants depend on AM fungi, and these fungi are not known to grow separately from plants or cyanobacterial partners.

Molecular evidence suggests that Glomeromycota originated around 600 million years ago. Fossils having aseptate hyphae and large spores similar to those of modern Glomeromycota are known from the time when land plants first became common and widespread, about 460 million years ago (see Chapter 28). This and other fossil evidence suggests that the ability of early plants to live successfully on land may have depended on help from fungal associates, as is common today.

Ascomycetes Produce Sexual Spores in Saclike Asci

The **ascomycetes** and basidiomycetes, when compared with other fungal phyla, have evolved more recently. DNA evidence indicates that the ascomycetes originated more recently than the earliest chytrids, zygomycetes, and AM fungi.

The name *ascomycetes* derives from unique sporangia known as **asci** (from the Greek *asco*, meaning "bags or sacs"), which produce sexual spores called **ascospores** (**Figure 27.25**). The asci are produced on fruiting bodies known as **ascocarps**. Although

Hyphae produce asexual conidia. Conidia grow into new hyphae that are genetically identical to parents.

(a) Asexual reproduction

Figure 27.24   The genus *Glomus* is an example of the Glomeromycota.   The hyphae of these endomycorrhizal (arbuscular mycorrhizal) fungi are found in the roots of many types of plants, helping them to acquire water and nutrients. AM fungi produce large, multinucleate spores, primarily by asexual processes.

Figure 27.25   The life cycles of ascomycete fungi.

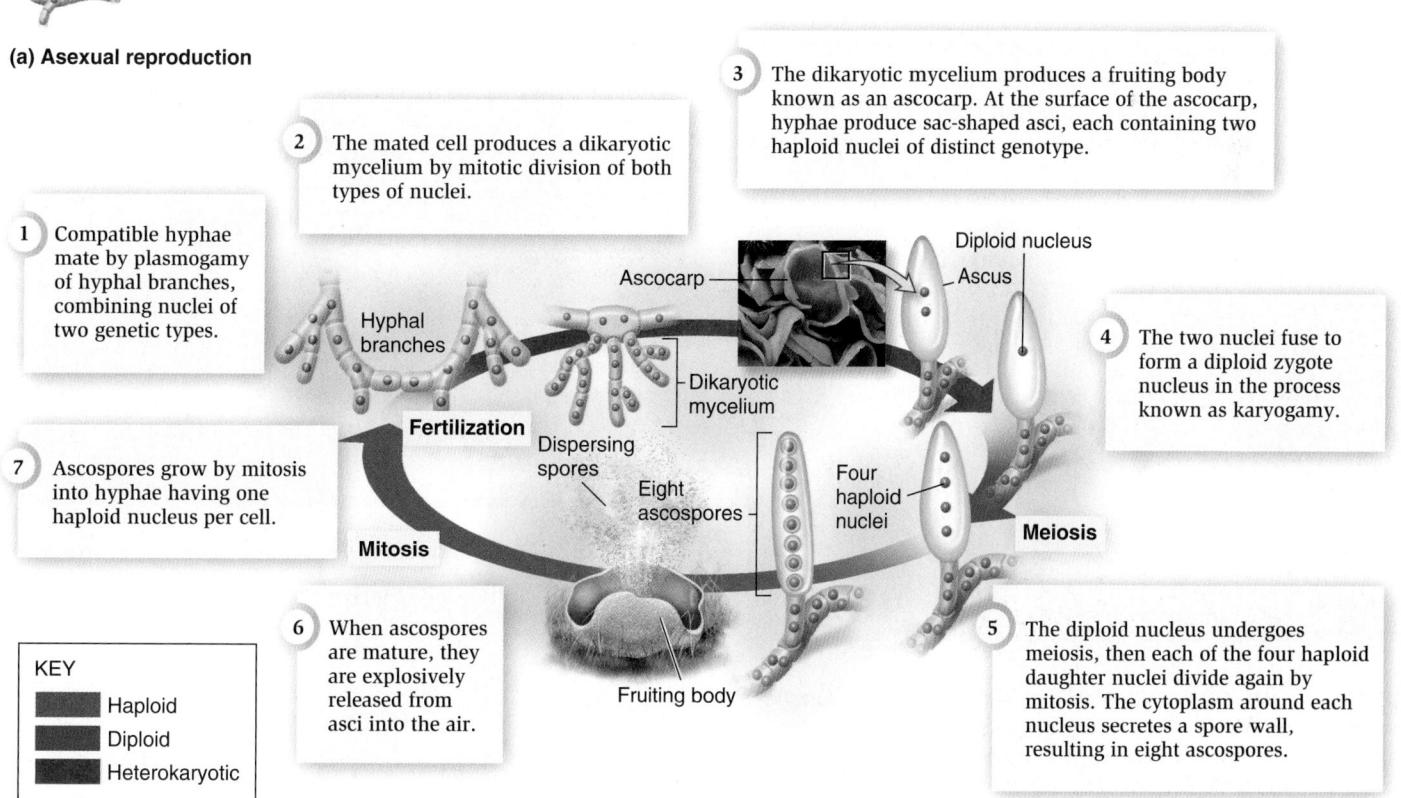

1 Compatible hyphae mate by plasmogamy of hyphal branches, combining nuclei of two genetic types.

2 The mated cell produces a dikaryotic mycelium by mitotic division of both types of nuclei.

3 The dikaryotic mycelium produces a fruiting body known as an ascocarp. At the surface of the ascocarp, hyphae produce sac-shaped asci, each containing two haploid nuclei of distinct genotype.

4 The two nuclei fuse to form a diploid zygote nucleus in the process known as karyogamy.

5 The diploid nucleus undergoes meiosis, then each of the four haploid daughter nuclei divide again by mitosis. The cytoplasm around each nucleus secretes a spore wall, resulting in eight ascospores.

6 When ascospores are mature, they are explosively released from asci into the air.

7 Ascospores grow by mitosis into hyphae having one haploid nucleus per cell.

KEY
- Haploid
- Diploid
- Heterokaryotic

(b) Sexual reproduction of the ascomycete *Aleuria aurantia*

GENOMES AND PROTEOMES

Yeast Is Used as a Model System in Genomics, Proteomics, and Metabolomics

Ascomycete yeasts, such as *Saccharomyces cerevisiae* (**Figure 27.27**) have long served as model systems for cellular, biochemical, genetic, and molecular research. Because of *S. cerevisiae*'s scientific importance, this organism's genome was completely sequenced by an international coalition of more than 600 scientists in more than 100 laboratories, led by molecular biologist André Goffeau. This team found that *S. cerevisiae* has about 6,000 genes on 16 chromosomes and exhibits many cases of gene duplication and divergence of these duplicated genes.

Genome sequences have recently been obtained for two of *S. cerevisiae*'s close relatives, the yeast *Schizosaccharomyces pombe* and *Ashbya gossypii*, a filamentous fungus used in industry for producing vitamin B2. These data allow biologists to perform comparative studies that shed light on the evolution of entire genomes. Fred Dietrich, Peter Philippsen, and colleagues found that compared with other eukaryotes, *A. gossypii* has a comparatively small genome of only 9.2 million base pairs, which includes around 4,700 protein-coding genes on seven chromosomes. The genome of *A. gossypii* has no transposons, relatively few introns, and only a few gene duplications. A similarly stripped-down genome is present in *S. pombe*, with fewer than 5,000 protein-coding genes. These two fungi may illustrate the minimum genome size possible for free-living (nonparasitic) fungi and reveal the genetic mechanisms that result in small genome size.

many ascomycetes have lost the ability to reproduce sexually, hyphal septa with simple pores (see Figure 27.5a) and DNA data can be used to identify them as members of this phylum.

Ascomycetes occur in terrestrial and aquatic environments, and they include many decomposers, as well as parasites. Important ascomycete plant pathogens include powdery mildews, chestnut blight (*Cryphonectria parasitica*), Dutch elm disease (the genus *Ophiostoma*), and apple scab (*Venturia inaequalis*) (**Figure 27.26**). Cup fungi are common examples of ascomycetes. Edible truffles and morels are the fruiting bodies of particular ascomycetes whose mycelia form mycorrhizal partnerships with plants. Ascomycetes are the most common fungal components of lichens. Members of the ascomycetes include most **yeasts**, fungi that can occur as unicells and that reproduce by budding (Figure 27.27). (Some yeasts are classified in the Zygomycota or the Basidiomycota.) Ascomycete yeasts are important to the baking and brewing industries, and some are medically significant as agents of disease. For example, the ascomycete yeast *Candida albicans* causes yeast infections and thrush (oral candidiasis). Yeasts are also widely used for fundamental biological studies.

Basidiomycetes Produce Diverse Fruiting Bodies

DNA-sequencing comparisons indicate that **basidiomycetes** are the most recently evolved group of fungi. Even so, they have a long fossil history, extending back nearly 300 million years.

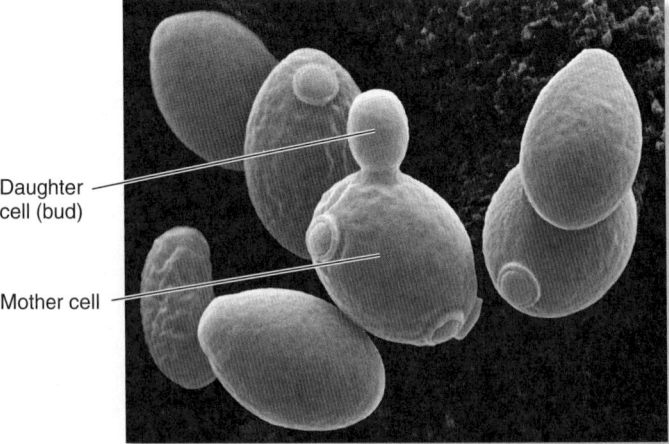

Figure 27.27   The budding yeast *Saccharomyces cerevisiae*.

Daughter cell (bud)

Mother cell

Concept check: *Are all yeasts classified in the ascomycetes?*

BioConnections: *Look back at Table 12.1, which shows the genome characteristics of some model organisms. How does the genome of* S. cerevisiae *compare to genomes of other model organisms?*

Figure 27.26   Apple infected with the ascomycete fungus *Venturia inaequalis,* which causes apple scab disease.   This fungus grows on leaves, flowers, and fruits, leaving harmless but unsightly scabs on their surfaces. Growers usually try to control apple scab by spraying trees with fungicides.

Today, basidiomycetes are very important as decomposers and mycorrhizal partners in forests, producing diverse fruiting bodies commonly known as mushrooms, puffballs, stinkhorns, shelf fungi, rusts, and smuts (**Figure 27.28**; see also Figures 27.9, 27.10, and 27.16a).

The name given to the basidiomycetes derives from **basidia**, the club-shaped cells that produce sexual spores known as **basidiospores** on their surfaces (**Figure 27.29**).

Basidia are typically located on the undersides of fruiting bodies, which are generally known as **basidiocarps**. Though some basidiomycetes have lost sexual reproduction, they can be identified as members of this phylum by unique hyphal structures called clamp connections that help distribute nuclei during cell division. It is a type of connection found within a single hyphal strand of Basidiomycete fungi and functions to ensure that each cell has two different nuclei from mating

(a) Corn smut

(b) Shelf fungi

Figure 27.28 **Basidiomycetes produce diverse fruiting bodies.** **(a)** Corn smut (*Ustilago maydis*) produces dikaryotic mycelial masses within the kernels (fruits) of infected corn plants. These mycelia produce many dark spores in which karyogamy and meiosis occur. Masses of these dark spores cause the smutty appearance. When the spores germinate, they produce basidiospores that can infect other corn plants. **(b)** Shelf fungi, such as this sulphur shelf fungus, are the fruiting bodies of basidiomycete fungi that have infected trees.

KEY
- Haploid
- Diploid
- Heterokaryotic

1 Compatible hyphae mate by plasmogamy of hyphal branches, combining nuclei of two genetic types.

2 The dikaryotic cell divides by mitosis to produce a dikaryotic mycelium, which can be very long lived.

3 Hyphal branches known as clamp connections bridge recently divided cells, ensuring that one of each nuclear type is regularly distributed to each daughter cell.

Mitosis and cell growth in tip cell

Hyphal branch carries one nucleus

Clamp connection forms

New septum forms

Nuclear distribution complete

4 Under appropriate conditions, dikaryotic mycelium can form a fruiting body or basidiocarp.

Gill of mushroom

8 Basidiospores grow into mycelia, the cells of which each possess one haploid nucleus.

Basidium with haploid nuclei

Diploid nucleus

Basidiospore

Basidiospores

Basidium

7 Basidia undergo meiosis to produce four haploid nuclei, which are incorporated into basidiospores that are dispersed.

6 Nuclei in basidia fuse to form diploid nuclei.

5 Dikaryotic basidia occur at the surfaces of gills (or pores of some mushrooms).

Figure 27.29 The sexual cycle of the basidiomycete fungus *Coprinus disseminatus.*

with hyphae of another sexual type. Basidiomycetes can also be identified by distinctive septa having complex pores (see Figure 27.5b) and by DNA methods. Basidiomycetes reproduce

asexually by various types of spores. Rust fungi, for example, can produce up to four different types of asexual spores during their life cycle.

Summary of Key Concepts

27.1 Distinctive Features of Fungi

- Fungi form a monophyletic kingdom of heterotrophs that, like animals, display absorptive nutrition. Fungi secrete enzymes into food substrates, breaking down complex organic molecules into small organic molecules that are absorbed as food. (Figure 27.1)

- Fungal cells possess cell walls composed of chitin, a polysaccharide resistant to microbial attack. Fungal bodies, known as mycelia, are composed of microscopic branched filaments called hyphae. (Figure 27.2)

- During sexual reproduction fungi produce fruiting bodies, formed by aggregated hyphae, that usually extend out of the substrate. Fruiting bodies produce sexual spores and aid their dispersal by means of wind, water, or animals. (Figure 27.3)

- In most cases the fungal body is inconspicuously dispersed within the substrate, but sometimes fungal hyphae aggregate to form stringlike rhizomorphs that aid fungal water transport. (Figure 27.4)

- Fungal mycelia grow at their edges, by tip growth of hyphae. Septate hyphae are divided into cells by cross walls, or septa, perforated by simple or complex pores. Some fungi have aseptate hyphae that are not subdivided into cells. (Figures 27.5, 27.6)

- Mycelial shape depends on the location of nutrients in the environment, which determines the direction in which cell division and hyphal growth will occur. (Figure 27.7)

27.2 Fungal Sexual and Asexual Reproduction

- Fungi disperse in their environments by means of spores produced by asexual or sexual reproduction. (Figure 27.8)

- The gametes of most fungi are relatively unspecialized hyphal branches. During sexual reproduction hyphal branches fuse with those of a different mycelium of compatible mating type. In many fungi dikaryotic hyphae (having two nuclei per cell) that result from mating often persist for long periods before nuclear fusion occurs. Nuclear fusion generates zygotes. Fungal zygotes are the only cells in the life cycle that possess a diploid nucleus.

- Zygotes undergo meiosis to produce haploid spores, which disperse from fruiting bodies. Spores germinate to produce haploid fungal mycelia. Fungi produce diverse types of fruiting bodies that foster spore dispersal by wind, water, or animals. Many fungal fruiting bodies produce defensive toxins or hallucinogens. (Figures 27.9, 27.10, 27.11, 27.12)

- Asexual reproduction does not involve mating or meiosis, and it occurs by means of asexual spores, such as conidia. Many common and destructive moulds spread by means of conidia. (Figure 27.13)

27.3 Fungal Ecology and Biotechnology

- Fungi play important roles in nature as decomposers, predators, and pathogens. Several types of fungi cause disease. (Figures 27.14, 27.15)

- Fungi form important mutualistic symbioses with other organisms. Mycorrhizae are common associations between fungi and plant roots. Ectomycorrhizae coat root surfaces, extending into root

intercellular spaces. Endomycorrhizae commonly form highly branched arbuscules in the spaces between root cell walls and plasma membranes. (Figures 27.16, 27.17)

- Lichens are partnerships between fungi and photosynthetic green algae or cyanobacteria (or both). Lichens can reproduce asexually by means of structures such as soredia, which consist of fungal hyphae wrapped around a few algal cells. When lichen fungi reproduce sexually, the hyphae arising from spore germination must find new algal partners. (Figures 27.18, 27.19)

- Lichens occur in diverse habitats, including harsh environments, and often grow slowly and to great age. Lichens are useful air-quality monitors.

- In at least one lichen family, the Cladoniaceae, the fungal partners have not evolved in tandem with symbiotic algae, and data suggest that such lichen fungi commonly switch algal partners. (Figure 27.20)

- Fungal biochemistry is useful in chemical, food processing, and waste-treatment industries, and fungi are increasingly used to replace chemical procedures that generate harmful waste materials. (Figure 27.21)

27.4 Evolution and Diversity of Fungi

- Currently, fungi are classified into five phyla commonly known as chytrids, zygomycetes, AM fungi, ascomycetes, and basidiomycetes. (Table 27.1)

- Chytrids are among the simplest and earliest divergent fungi. They commonly occur in aquatic habitats and moist soil, where they produce flagellate reproductive cells. (Figure 27.22)

- Zygomycetes are named for their distinctive, large zygospores, the result of sexual reproduction. Common black bread mould and other zygomycetes reproduce asexually by means of many small spores. (Figure 27.23)

- The AM fungi produce distinctive, large, multinucleate spores, and they form mutualistic arbuscular mycorrhizal relationships with many types of plants. (Figure 27.24)

- Ascomycetes produce sexual ascospores in saclike asci located at the surfaces of fruiting bodies called ascocarps. Many are lichen symbionts. The ascomycete yeast *Saccharomyces cerevisiae* is widely used as a laboratory model system for genomic, proteomic, and metabolomic studies. (Figures 27.25, 27.26, 27.27)

- Basidiomycetes produce sexual basidiospores on club-shaped basidia located on the surfaces of fruiting bodies known as basidiocarps. Such fruiting bodies take a wide variety of forms, including mushrooms, puffballs, stinkhorns, shelf fungi, rust, and smuts. The hyphae of basidiomycete fungi are characterized by clamp connections, structures that aid in distributing nuclei of two types after cell division occurs in dikaryotic hyphae. Many basidiomycetes (and some ascomycetes) form intimate mycorrhizal relationships with plant roots. (Figures 27.28, 27.29)

Test to Assess Your Learning

1. Fungal cells differ from animal cells in that fungal cells
   a. lack ribosomes, though these are present in animal cells.
   b. lack mitochondria, though these occur in animal cells.

c. have cell walls, whereas animal cells lack rigid walls.

d. lack cell walls, whereas animal cells possess walls.

e. none of the above.

2. Conidia are

   a. cells produced by some fungi as the result of sexual reproduction.

   b. fungal asexual reproductive cells produced by the process of mitosis.

   c. structures that occur in septal pores.

   d. the unspecialized gametes of fungi.

   e. none of the above.

3. What are mycorrhizae?

   a. the bodies of fungi, composed of hyphae

   b. fungi that attack plant roots, causing disease

   c. fungal hyphae that are massed together into stringlike structures

   d. fungi that have symbiotic partnerships with algae or cyanobacteria

   e. mutually beneficial associations of particular fungi and plant roots

4. Where could you find diploid nuclei in an ascomycete or basidiomycete fungus?

   a. in spores

   b. in cells at the surfaces of fruiting bodies

   c. in conidia

   d. in soredia

   e. all of the above

5. Which fungi are examples of hallucinogens?

   a. *Claviceps* and *Psilocybe*

   b. *Epidermophyton* and *Candida*

   c. *Pneumocystis carinii* and *Histoplasma capsulatum*

   d. *Saccharomyces cerevisiae* and *Phanerochaete chrysosporium*

   e. *Cryphoenectria parasitica* and *Ventura inaequalis*

6. What role do fungal endophytes play in nature?

   a. They are decomposers.

   b. They are human parasites that cause skin diseases.

   c. They are plant parasites that cause serious crop diseases.

   d. They live within the tissues of grasses and other plants, helping to protect plants from herbivores and pathogens.

   e. All of the above.

7. What forms do lichens take?

   a. crustose, flat bodies

   b. foliose, leaf-shaped bodies

   c. fruticose, erect or dangling bodies

   d. single cells

   e. a, b, and c

8. Lichens consist of a partnership between fungi and what other organisms?

   a. red algae and green algae

   b. green algae and cyanobacteria

   c. heterotrophic bacteria and archaea

   d. choanoflagellates and *Nuclearia*

   e. none of the above

9. How can ascomycetes be distinguished from basidiomycetes?

   a. Ascomycete hyphae have simple pores in their septa and lack clamp connections, whereas basidiomycete hyphae display complex septal pores and clamp connections.

   b. Ascomycetes produce sexual spores in sacs, whereas basidiomycetes produce sexual spores on the surfaces of club-shaped structures.

   c. Ascomycetes are commonly found in lichens, whereas basidiomycetes are less commonly partners in lichen associations.

   d. Ascomycetes are not commonly mycorrhizal partners, but basidiomycetes are commonly present in mycorrhizal associations.

   e. All of the above are correct.

10. Which group of organisms listed is most closely related to the kingdom Fungi?

   a. the animal kingdom

   b. the green algae

   c. the land plants

   d. the bacteria

   e. the archaea

Articulate to Assess Your Learning

1. Explain three ways that fungi are like animals and two ways in which fungi resemble plants.

2. Explain why some fungi produce toxic or hallucinogenic compounds.

3. Explain three ways in which fungi function as mutualistic symbionts and what benefit the fungi receive from the partnerships.

Collaborate to Assess and Extend Your Learning

1. Why are there such vast fossil fuel deposits associated with the Carboniferous? Why didn't fungal decomposers do their job?

2. Imagine that you are helping to restore the natural vegetation on a piece of land that had long been used to grow crops. You are placed in charge of planting pine seedlings (*Pinus resinosa*) and fostering their growth. In what way could you consider using fungi?

3. Why are fungal diseases so much more prevalent in plants compared with animals?

4. A principle of biology is that living organisms interact with their environment. Explain three ways in which fungi function as beneficial partners with autotrophs and what benefit the fungi receive from the partnerships.

Visit McGraw-Hill Ryerson Connect™ for additional study resources.

Plants and the Conquest of Land

Chapter Outline

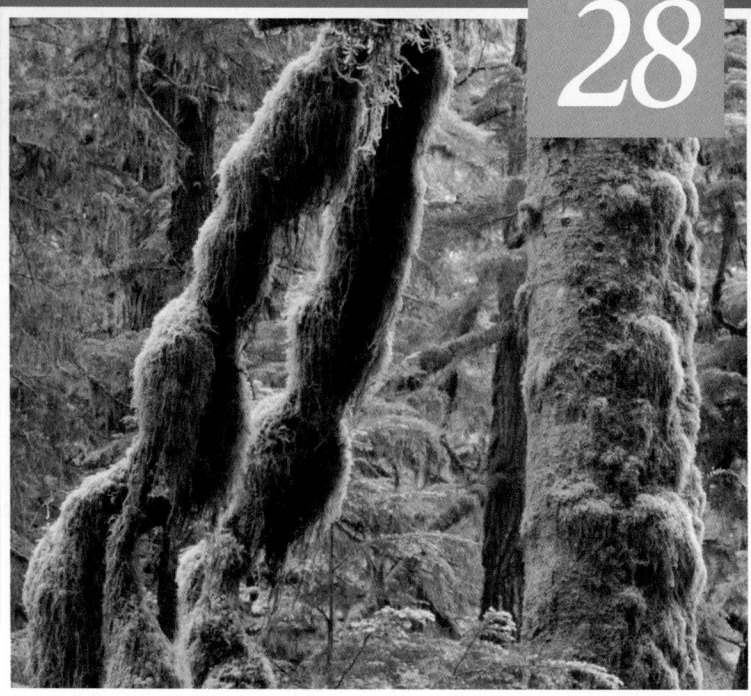

A coastal temperate rain forest in British Columbia, containing diverse plant phyla.

W hen thinking about plants, people envision lush green lawns, shady street trees, garden flowers, or leafy fields of valuable crops. On a broader scale they might imagine dense jungles, vast grassy plains, or tough desert vegetation. Shopping in the produce section of the local grocery store may remind us that plant photosynthesis is the basic source of our food. Just breathing crisp, fresh air might bring to mind the role of plants as oxygen producers—the ultimate air fresheners. Do you start your day with a cup of coffee, tea, or hot chocolate? Then you may appreciate the plants that produce these and many other materials we use in daily life: medicines, cotton, linen, wood, bamboo, cork, and even the paper on which this textbook has been printed.

In addition to their importance to humans and modern ecosystems, plants have played dramatic roles in Earth's past. Throughout their evolutionary history, diverse plants have influenced Earth's atmospheric chemistry, climate, and soils and the evolution of many other groups of organisms. In this chapter we will survey the diversity of modern plant phyla and their distinctive features. This chapter also explains how early plants adapted to land and how plants have continued to adapt to changing terrestrial environments. During this process you will continue to gain insight into principles of diversity and evolution, such as descent with modification, and the biological principle that all life is related by an evolutionary history.

28.1 ANCESTRY AND DIVERSITY OF MODERN PLANTS

Learning Outcomes:

1. List key derived features that land plants share with their closest algal relatives.
2. Name several characteristics unique to land plants.
3. Compare and contrast the features of vascular and nonvascular plants.
4. List adaptations that enable vascular plants to maintain stable water content.

Several hundred thousand modern species are formally classified into the kingdom Plantae, informally known as the plants or land plants (**Figure 28.1**). **Plants** are multicellular eukaryotic organisms composed of cells having plastids, and plants primarily live on land. Molecular and other evidence indicate that the plant kingdom evolved from green algal ancestors that lived in aquatic habitats, such as lakes or ponds.

Together, plants and modern green algal relatives are known as **streptophytes**. Plants are distinguished from their modern algal relatives by the presence of traits that foster survival in terrestrial conditions, which are drier, sunnier, hotter, colder, and

Figure 28.1 **Evolutionary relationships of the modern plant phyla.** For simplicity, only two of the known branches of streptophyte algae are shown. Land plants gradually acquired diverse structural, biochemical, and reproductive adaptations allowing them to better survive in terrestrial habitats.

Principle: *All life is related by an evolutionary history. This diagram shows maximal evolutionary divergence times indicated by molecular clock and some fossil evidence suggesting when clades may first have arisen. Other fossil evidence provides minimal divergence times that indicate when clades had become well established; in this case, more numerous and more easily identified fossils were formed.*

less physically supportive than aquatic habitats. In this section we will examine the modern algae that are most closely related to plants and survey the diverse phyla of living land plants. This process reveals how plants gradually acquired diverse structural, biochemical, and reproductive adaptations that fostered survival on land.

Modern Green Algae Are Closely Related to the Ancestry of Land Plants

Molecular, biochemical, and structural data indicate that the plant kingdom is monophyletic and originated from a photosynthetic protist ancestor that if present today would be classified among the **streptophyte algae**. All streptophyte algae have features in common with land plants, but the later-diverging streptophyte algae display several **critical innovations**—derived features shared with land plants that fostered plant success on land. Examples of these shared features are a distinctive type of cytokinesis, intercellular connections known as plasmodesmata (see Chapter 5), and sexual reproduction by means of flagellate sperm and nonmotile eggs. For this reason, streptophyte algae, including the modern green algal genera Chara and Coleochaete, are good sources of information about the ancestors of land plants (**Figure 28.2**).

1 cm

(a) Chara zeylanica

52 μm

(b) Gametangia on stalk

37 μm

(c) Oogonium

10 μm

(d) Antheridia

Figure 28.2 Streptophyte algae. **(a)** Chara zeylanica. **(b)** Laterally positioned gametangia on Chara sp. In the antheridium, shield cells surround antheridial filaments, each cell of which produces a single sperm cell. Inside the oogonium is a single large egg cell. **(c)** Oogonium of Chara sp. **(d)** Antheridium of Chara sp.

Streptophytes and green algae known as chlorophytes (see Figure 28.1) share distinctive characteristics, such as cellulose-rich cell walls and green, starch-bearing chloroplasts that contain the accessory pigments chlorophyll b and ß-carotene. Even so, the land plants display several common features that distinguish them from green algae, even their closest charophycean relatives.

Distinctive Features of the Land Plants

The features that distinguish land plants represent early adaptations to the land habitat. For example, the bodies of all land plants are primarily composed of three-dimensional tissues, defined as close associations of cells of the same type. Tissues provide land plants with an increased ability to avoid water loss at their surfaces. That's because bodies composed of tissues have lower surface area/volume ratios than do branched filaments. Land plant tissues arise from one or more actively dividing cells that occur at growing tips. Such localized regions of cell division are known as **apical meristems**. The tissue-producing apical meristems of land plants are able to produce relatively thick, robust bodies able to withstand drought and mechanical stress, and produce tissues and organs that have specialized functions.

The land plants also have distinctive reproductive features. These include a sporic life cycle involving alternation between two types of bodies; embryos that depend on maternal tissues during early development; reproductive cells whose tough walls allow dispersal through dry air; and specialized structures that generate, protect, and disperse reproductive cells. The following survey of modern plant phyla and their distinctive features illustrates how these and other fundamental plant features evolved.

Modern Land Plants Can Be Classified into Ten Phyla

Plant systematists use molecular and structural information from living and fossil plants to classify plants into phyla. However, many controversies exist regarding the time of first appearance and species composition of some phyla, and the relationships among plant phyla are not completely clear. As a result, biologists have classified modern plants in different ways, and classifications continue to change as new information becomes available.

In this textbook, 10 phyla of living land plants are described: (1) the plants informally known as **liverworts** (formally called Hepatophyta), (2) **hornworts** (Anthocerophyta), (3) **mosses** (Bryophyta), (4) **lycophytes** (Lycopodiophyta), (5) **pteridophytes** (Pteridophyta), (6) **cycads** (Cycadophyta), (7) **ginkgos** (Ginkgophyta), (8) **conifers** (Coniferophyta), (9) **gnetophytes** (Gnetophyta), and (10) **angiosperms** (Anthophyta), also known as the **flowering plants**. Fossils reveal that additional plant phyla once lived but are now extinct.

Phylogenetic information suggests that the modern plant phyla arose in a particular sequence. Liverworts, mosses, and hornworts originated relatively early; lycophytes and pteridophytes arose later; cycads, ginkgos, conifers, and gnetophytes came next; and flowering plants appeared most recently (see Figure 28.1). Each of these modern plant phyla displays features that reveal how plants became increasingly better adapted to life on land.

Liverworts, Mosses, and Hornworts Are the Simplest Land Plants

Liverworts, mosses, and hornworts are Earth's simplest land plants (**Figures 28.3, 28.4,** and **28.5**) and each forms a distinct monophyletic group. There are about 6,500 species of modern liverworts, 12,000 or more species of mosses, and about 100 species of hornworts. Collectively, liverworts, mosses, and hornworts are known informally as **bryophytes** (from the Greek *bryon,* meaning "moss," and *phyton,* meaning "plant"). Although the term *bryophyte* does not reflect a clade, it is useful for expressing common structural, reproductive, and ecological features of liverworts, mosses, and hornworts. For example, the bryophytes are all relatively small in stature and are most common and diverse in moist habitats, because they lack traits allowing them to grow tall or reproduce in dry places.

Because bryophytes diverged early in the evolutionary history of land plants (see Figure 28.1), they serve as models of the earliest terrestrial plants. They display several features that are absent from charophycean algae but are present in all other land plants. Such bryophyte features are thus likely reflect early adaptations to life on land. The bryophyte life cycle, shared

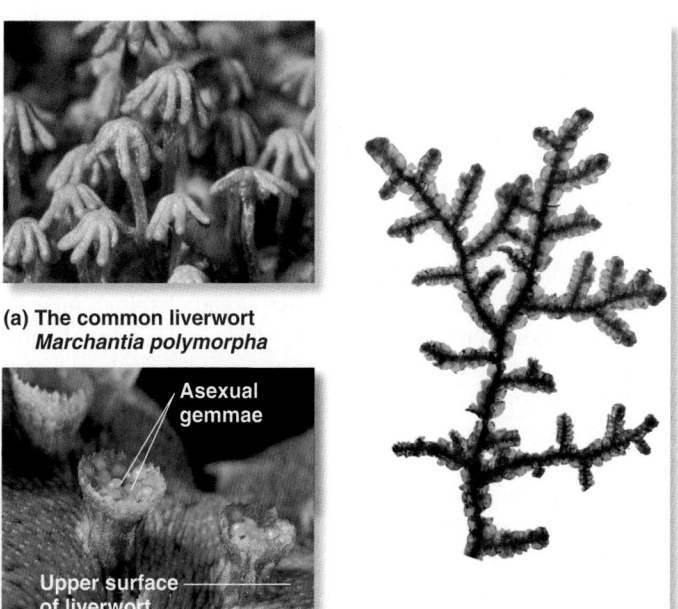

(a) The common liverwort
Marchantia polymorpha

Asexual gemmae

Upper surface of liverwort

(b) Close-up of common
liverwort structures

(c) A species of leafy liverwort

Figure 28.3 Liverworts.   (a) The common liverwort *Marchantia polymorpha,* with raised, umbrella-shaped structures that bear sexually produced sporophytes on the undersides. Mature sporophytes generate and then release spores. (b) A close-up of *M. polymorpha* showing surface cups that contain multicellular, concave, disk-shaped asexual structures known as gemmae that are dispersed by wind and grow into new liverworts. (c) A species of liverwort having leaflike structures, known as a leafy liverwort.

Concept check: *Why do you think liverworts produce their spores on raised structures?*

Sporangium

Sporophyte

Gametophyte

Figure 28.4 Moss.   The common moss genus *Mnium* has leafy green gametophytes (an asexually produced structure that generates gametes) and unbranched, dependent sporophytes, each bearing a spore-producing sporangium at its tip. When mature, these sporangia release spores. Close-up: this SEM shows that the tips of moss sporangia are often specialized so that spores are sprinkled into the wind and dispersed over time, rather than all at once.

Concept check: *Why might it be advantageous for a moss sporophyte to release spores gradually?*

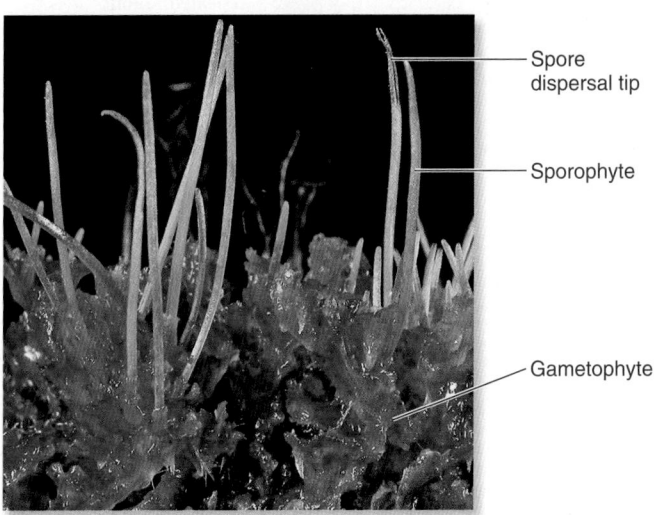

Spore dispersal tip

Sporophyte

Gametophyte

Figure 28.5 Hornworts.   Sporophytes of hornworts generally grow up into the air, whereas the gametophytes grow close to the ground. Hornwort sporophytes become mature and open at the top, dispersing spores.

with other plants, is a good example. A comparison between the life cycle of aquatic charophyceans and that of bryophytes reveals the bryophyte life cycle's adaptive value on land.

The streptophyte algae (e.g., the charophyceans) display a **zygotic life cycle** in which the diploid generation consists of only one cell, the zygote (**Figure 28.6a**). Zygotic life cycles take their name from the observation that the zygote is the only cell that undergoes meiosis. By contrast, sexual reproduction in bryophytes and all other plants involves a **sporic life cycle,** in which there is an alternation of generations (**Figure 28.6b**). A sporic life cycle originated independently in early plants and several other eukaryotic lineages that are not related to land plants (see Chapter 26). In the sporic life cycle meiosis results in the formation of spores, reproductive cells that allow organisms to disperse in the environment. **Alternation of generations** means that land plants produce two types of multicellular bodies that alternate in time. These two types of bodies are known as the diploid (2*n*), spore-producing **sporophytes** in one generation and the haploid (*n*), gamete-producing **gametophytes** in the next generation. Biologists think the plant life cycle originated by a delay in zygotic meiosis, with the result that the diploid generation became multicellular before undergoing meiosis. For the earliest land plants this multicellular diploid generation provided advantages in coping with terrestrial conditions. A closer look at the process of sexual reproduction in bryophytes reveals these advantages and also highlights ways in which bryophytes differ from other plants.

Bryophyte Reproduction Illustrates Early Plant Adaptations to Life on Land

As noted, bryophytes and other land plants display an alternation of generations (**Figure 28.7**). On land a multicellular, diploid, sporophyte generation is advantageous because it allows a single plant to disperse widely by using meiosis to produce numerous, genetically variable haploid spores. Each spore has the potential to grow into a gametophyte. In bryophytes the gametophyte generation is generally green and photosynthetic, and thus its major function is organic food production. The more spores that sporophytes produce, the greater the numbers of gametophytes, helping bryophytes to spread in their environments and thereby increase in fitness. We next discuss how gametophytes and sporophytes function together during the life cycle of a bryophyte, starting with gamete production.

Gametophytes   From an evolutionary and reproductive viewpoint, the role of plant gametophytes is to produce haploid gametes. Because the gametophyte cells are already haploid, meiosis is not involved in producing plant gametes. Instead, plant gametes are produced by mitosis, and so all gametes produced from a single gametophyte are genetically identical.

The gametophytes of bryophytes and many other land plants produce gametes in specialized structures known as **gametangia** (from the Greek, meaning "gamete containers"), in which developing gametes are protected by a jacket of tissue. The gametangial jacket protects delicate gametes from drying and microbial attack while they develop. Round or elongate gametangia that produce sperm are known as **antheridia** (singular, antheridium), whereas flask-shaped gametangia that enclose an egg cell are known as **archegonia** (singular, archegonium), (Figure 28.7). When mature, if moist conditions exist, plant sperm are released from antheridia into films of water. Under the influence of sex-attractant molecules secreted from archegonia, sperm swim toward eggs, twisting their way down the tubular archegonial necks. Sperm then fuse with egg cells to form diploid zygotes, which grow into new sporophytes. However, fertilization cannot occur in bryophytes unless water is present. Conditions of uncertain moisture, common in the land habitat, can thus limit plant reproductive fitness. The plant life cycle, featuring several reproductive advantages, is an adaptive response to this environmental challenge.

(a) Zygotic life cycle of charophyceans

(b) Sporic life cycle of early plants

Figure 28.6   Origin of the plant life cycle.

Figure 28.7 The life cycle of the early diverging moss genus, *Sphagnum*, illustrating reproductive adaptations that likely helped early plants to reproduce on land.

Sporophytes   One reproductive advantage of the plant life cycle is that zygotes remain enclosed within gametophyte tissues, where they are sheltered and fed (a process described in more detail in section 28.3). This critical innovation gives a zygote a good start as it begins to grow into a young sporophyte, which is known as an **embryo**. For this reason, all land plants are known as **embryophytes**. Sheltering and feeding embryos is particularly important when embryo production is limited by water availability, as is the case for bryophytes. Another reproductive advantage is that, when mature, the multicellular sporophytes produce many **spores** in protective enclosures known as **sporangia** (from the Greek, meaning "spore containers"). Bryophyte sporangia open in specialized ways that foster

dispersal of spores into the air, allowing spore transport by wind. A third reproductive advantage is that plant spores have cell walls containing a tough material known as **sporopollenin** that helps to prevent cellular damage during transport in air. If spores reach habitats favourable for growth, their walls crack open, and new gametophytes develop by mitotic divisions, completing the life cycle.

Spore production is a measure of plant fitness, because plants can better disperse progeny throughout the environment when they produce more spores. The larger the diploid generation, the more spores a plant can produce. As a result, during plant evolution, the plant sporophyte has become larger and more complex (**Figure 28.8**).

Figure 28.8 Relative sizes of the sporophyte and gametophyte generations of bryophytes, ferns, and seed plants.

Concept check: *What is the advantage to ferns and seed plants of having larger sporophytes than those of bryophytes?*

Bryophytes Display Several Distinguishing Features

As you have seen, bryophytes share several fundamental adaptive traits: alternation of generations, tissue-producing apical meristems, protective gametangia and sporangia, and sporopollenin-walled spores. These same traits are shared with other land plants. Even so, several features distinguish bryophytes from other land plants. First, bryophyte gametophytes are more common in nature, larger, and longer lived than bryophyte sporophytes. Patches of green moss in the woods are primarily gametophytes. To see bryophyte sporophytes, you would have to look very closely, because organisms in this life stage are quite small and attached to female gametophytes throughout their short lifetime (see Figures 28.5 and 28.7). Plant biologists say that bryophyte gametophytes are the dominant generation in their life cycle. By contrast, in other plants the sporophyte generation is dominant (see Figure 28.8).

Bryophyte sporophytes are small because they remain attached to parental gametophytes, are unable to branch, and have short lifespans. At their tips bryophyte sporophytes produce only a single sporangium containing a limited number of spores. By contrast, the sporophytes of other land plants become independent, produce branches with many sporangia, and are often able to produce spores for many years (see Figure 28.8). In all land plants except bryophytes, the sporophyte generation is the larger, more complex, and longer-lived generation.

Yet another distinguishing feature of bryophytes is that they lack tissues that are specialized for both structural support and conduction. Plant tissues that provide both structural support and conduction of water, minerals, and organic compounds are known as **vascular tissues**. Although the gametophytes of some bryophytes display simple conducting tissues, these do not provide structural support. Thus, bryophytes are informally known as **nonvascular plants**. Other modern plant phyla are known as **vascular plants** because they produce vascular tissues that function in both conduction and support.

Lycophytes and Pteridophytes Are Vascular Plants That Do Not Produce Seeds

If you look outside, most of the plants in view are probably vascular plants. The presence of vascular tissue allows most vascular plants to grow much taller than bryophytes and to reproduce more effectively. As a result, vascular plants are more prominent than bryophytes in most modern plant communities. Vascular plants have been important to Earth's ecology for a long time. Fossils tell us that the first vascular plants appeared later than the earliest bryophytes (see section 28.2) and that several early vascular plant lineages, such as the trimerophytes and psilophytes, once existed but became extinct. Molecular data indicate that the lycophytes are the oldest phylum of living vascular plants and that pteridophytes are the next oldest living plant phylum (see Figure 28.1). In the past, lycophytes were very diverse and included tall trees, but the tree lycophytes became extinct, and now about 1,000 relatively small species exist (**Figure 28.9**). Pteridophytes have diversified more recently, and about 12,000 species of modern pteridophytes exist, including horsetails, whisk ferns, and other ferns (**Figure 28.10**).

In pteridophytes the diploid sporophyte is the dominant generation with clusters of sporangia found on the underside of the mature fern sporophyte leaves. The gametophyte generation is represented by a small, often heart-shaped structure that is anchored in the ground by cells called rhizoids (**Figure 28.11**).

Because the lycophytes and pteridophytes diverged before the origin of seeds, they are informally known as seedless vascular plants. Together, lycophytes, pteridophytes, and seed-producing plants are known as **tracheophytes**. The term takes its name from

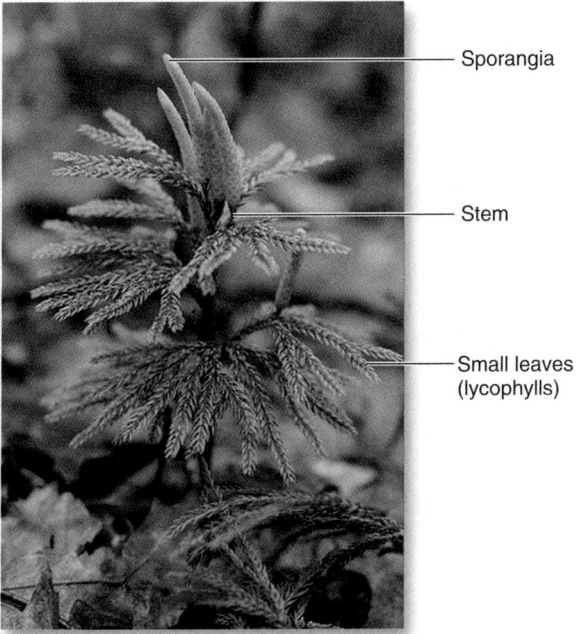

Figure 28.9 *Lycopodium obscurum* **growing on the forest floor.** This species is sometimes called ground fir or princess pine, but it is actually a lycophyte. The stem bears many tiny leaves, and sporangia generally occur in club-shaped clusters. For this reason lycophytes are sometimes called club mosses, another misnomer, because they are not true mosses. The gametophytes (not shown) are small structures that often occur underground.

tracheids, a type of specialized vascular cell that conducts water and minerals and provides structural support. Vascular tissues occur in the major plant organs: stems, roots, and leaves.

Stems, Roots, and Leaves Stems are branching structures that contain vascular tissue and produce leaves and sporangia. At their centres stems contain the specialized conducting tissues known as **phloem** and **xylem,** the latter of which contain tracheids. Such conducting tissues enable vascular plants to conduct organic compounds, water, and minerals throughout the plant body. The xylem also provides structural support, allowing vascular plants to grow taller than nonvascular plants. This support function arises from the presence of a compression and decay-resistant, waterproof phenolic compounds known as **lignins** that occur in the cell walls of tracheids and some other types of plant cells. Most vascular plants also produce **roots**—organs specialized for uptake of water and minerals from the soil—and **leaves,** flattened plant organs that emerge from stems and generally have a photosynthetic function.

Lycophyte roots and leaves differ from those of pteridophytes. For example, lycophyte roots fork at their tips, whereas roots of pteridophytes branch from the inside like the roots of seed plants (see Chapter 35). Lycophyte leaves are relatively small and possess only one unbranched vein, whereas pteridophyte leaves are larger and have branched veins, as do those of seed plants (compare Figures 28.9 and 28.10d). The evolutionary origin of pteridophyte leaves will be discussed in section 28.4.

Adaptations That Foster Stable Internal Water Content In relatively dry habitats, lycophytes, pteridophytes, and other vascular plants are able to grow to larger sizes and remain metabolically active for longer periods than can bryophytes. Vascular plants have this advantage because they are better able to maintain stable internal water content by means of several adaptations. For example, a protective **waxy cuticle** is present

(a) A whisk fern   **(b) The giant horsetail**   **(c) An early-diverging fern**   **(d) A later-diverging fern**

Figure 28.10 **Pteridophyte diversity.** **(a)** The leafless, rootless green stems of the whisk fern (*Psilotum nudum*) branch by forking and bear many clusters of yellow sporangia that disperse spores via the wind. The gametophyte of this plant is a tiny, white structure that lives underground in a partnership with fungi. **(b)** The giant horsetail (*Equisetum telmateia*) displays branches in whorls around the green stems. The leaves of this plant are tiny, light-brown structures that encircle branches at intervals. This plant produces spores in cone-shaped structures, and the wind-dispersed spores grow into small green gametophytes. **(c)** The early diverging fern *Botrychium lunaria*, showing a green photosynthetic leaf with leaflets and a modified leaf that bears many round sporangia. **(d)** The later-diverging fern *Blechnum capense,* viewed from above, showing a whorl of young leaves that are in the process of unrolling from the bases to the tips. The surrounding older leaves have many leaflets. The stem of this fern grows parallel to the ground and is thus not shown. Most ferns produce spores in sporangia on the undersides of leaves.

1 The diploid sporophyte is the dominant generation in the life of ferns and other vascular plants.

2 Sporangia are multicellular structures that develop on the undersides of the mature fern sporophyte leaves. Sporangia occur in clusters known as sori (singular, sorus).

3 Meiosis occurs in cells within sporangia to produce haploid spores, which are dispersed by the wind.

8 The embryo matures into a sporophyte. After developing a root and leaf, fern sporophytes become independent of their gametophyte parent, which eventually rots away.

4 Under favourable conditions, spores undergo mitosis to produce gametophytes. These are often thumbnail-sized and heart-shaped, anchored by cells known as rhizoids.

7 The resulting diploid zygote is retained on the gametophyte, undergoes mitosis, and grows into a multicellular embryo that receives essential nutrients from the gametophyte.

6 When water is present, the male gametangia release the flagellate sperm, which swim to the female gametangia and fertilize the eggs.

5 Mature gametophytes produce eggs in female gametangia and sperm in male gametangia.

Figure 28.11   The life cycle of a typical fern.

on most surfaces of vascular plant sporophytes (**Figure 28.12**). The plant cuticle contains a polyester polymer known as **cutin**, which helps to prevent attack by pathogens, and wax, which helps to prevent desiccation. The surface tissue of vascular plant stems and leaves contains **stomata** (singular: stomate), pores that are able to open and close (see Figure 28.12). Stomata allow plants to take in carbon dioxide needed for photosynthesis and release oxygen to the air, while conserving water. When the soil is very dry, stomata close, which reduces water loss from plants. When the soil is moist, stomata open, allowing photosynthetic gas exchange to occur. These water-conserving features have allowed vascular plants to exploit a wide spectrum of land habitats. Although cuticle and stomata occur in bryophytes, they are not as common as in vascular plants, and bryophytes easily become dry.

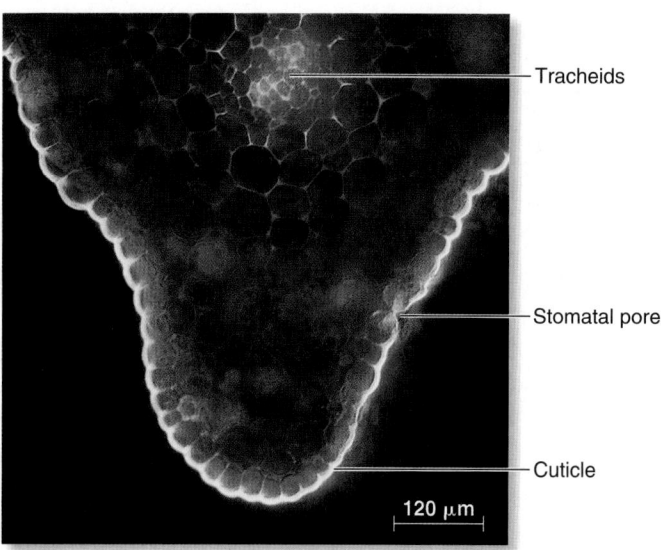

(a) **Stem showing tracheophyte adaptations**

Figure 28.12   **A pteridophyte stem with tracheophyte adaptations for transporting and conserving water.**   **(a)** A cross-section through a stem of the pteridophyte *Psilotum nudum*. When viewed with fluorescence microscopy and illuminated with violet light, an internal core of xylem tracheids glows yellow, as does the surface cuticle. **(b)** Surface pores associated with specialized cells—the complexes known as stomata—allow for gas exchange between plant and atmosphere. This photo naturally lacks colour because it was made with a scanning electron microscope (SEM), which uses electrons rather than visible light to form magnified images.

 Principle: *Living organisms have mechanisms that maintain homeostasis. The structures illustrated in this figure explain how vascular land plants maintain homeostasis in water content.*

(b) **Close-up of stomata**

GENOMES AND PROTEOMES

Comparison of Plant Genomes Reveals Genetic Changes that Occurred During Plant Evolution

The first complete genome sequence for seedless vascular plants was reported for the lycophyte *Selaginella moellendorffii* by Banks and co-workers in 2011. This advance has allowed plant evolutionary biologists to compare the new sequence with previously sequenced plant genomes, with the goal of identifying genes associated with major evolutionary transitions in plants.

Such genome comparisons revealed that 6,820 gene families representing a basic set of embryophyte genes are present in all land plants. The majority of gene families that are involved in flowering plant development were also observed in the lycophyte *Selaginella* and the bryophyte *Physcomitrella*, a moss (see **Figure 28.13**). A comparison of the genomes of *Selaginella* and *Physcomitrella* indicated that 516 genes were gained and 89 genes

were lost during the transition from nonvascular, gametophyte-dominant plants (bryophytes) to vascular, sporophyte-dominant plants (lycophytes). By contrast, 1350 more genes were gained in the evolution of traits specific to angiosperms. These data indicate that the transition from bryophyte to lycophyte was less genetically complex than was the transition from lycophyte to angiosperm.

Comparison of plant genomes has also revealed the great importance of secondary metabolites to all land plants. Secondary metabolites are organic compounds that are not essential for cell structure and growth, but are advantageous to the organism that synthesizes them. An example of a secondary metabolite is caffeine, the stimulatory component of coffee and tea. Caffeine plays a role in plant defence, a common function of secondary metabolites. The data indicate that a small number of secondary metabolite genes present in a common ancestral vascular plant radiated extensively and independently in the lycophytes and angiosperms. In terms of the complexity of their secondary

Figure 28.13   Comparison of (a) lycophyte *Selaginella* and (b) bryophyte *Physcomitrella.*

metabolite genetic repertoire, lycophytes appear to rival the angiosperms, with each group displaying unique compounds. Because many angiosperm secondary metabolites are important to humans and some have medicinal applications, plant biologists suspect that lycophyte secondary metabolites may be potential sources of new pharmaceuticals.

Gymnosperms and Angiosperms Are the Modern Seed Plants

Among the vascular plants, the seed plant phyla dominate most modern landscapes. The modern seed plant phyla, commonly known as cycads, ginkgos, conifers, and gnetophytes, are collectively known as gymnosperms (**Figure 28.14** shows an example). **Gymnosperms** reproduce by using both spores and seeds, as do the flowering plants or angiosperms (**Figure 28.15**). Gymnosperms and angiosperms are thus known informally as the **seed plants**. **Seeds** are complex structures that have specialized tissues that protectively enclose embryos, that is, the young sporophytes. Seeds also contain stores of carbohydrate, lipid, and protein that can be used to provide energy for seed germination and seedling development.

Several additional seed plant phyla once existed and left fossils, but they are now extinct. Collectively, all the living and fossil seed plant phyla are formally known as **spermatophytes** (see Figure 28.1). Modern and fossil seed plants are also formally known as **lignophytes**, a term that reflects the capacity to produce wood. Wood is composed of xylem, the tissue whose cellulose-rich cell walls also contain lignin. Functioning something like superglue, lignin cements the fibrils of cellulose together, making wood exceptionally strong. Wood production enables plants to increase in girth and become tall. Though not all modern seed plants produce wood, many are trees or shrubs that produce considerable amounts of wood.

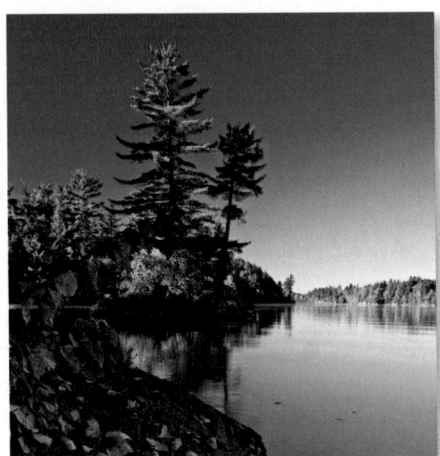

Figure 28.14   This white pine (*Pinus strobus*), towering above the canopy in Algonquin Provincial Park, is an example of a gymnosperm.

Figure 28.15   This sunflower is an example of an angiosperm.

The angiosperms are distinguished by the presence of flowers, fruits, and a specialized seed tissue known as endosperm. **Flowers** are short stems bearing organs that are specialized in ways that enhance seed production. **Fruits** are structures that develop from flower organs, enclose seeds, and foster seed dispersal in the environment. The term *angiosperm* means "enclosed seeds," reflecting the fact that the flowering plants produce seeds within fruits. **Endosperm** is a nutritive seed tissue that increases the efficiency by which food is stored in the seeds of flowering plants (see section 28.4). Flowers, fruits, and endosperm are defining features of the angiosperms, and they are integral components of animal nutrition.

Though gymnosperms produce seeds, and many are woody plants, they lack flowers, fruits, and endosperm. The term *gymnosperm* means "naked seeds," reflecting the fact that gymnosperm seeds are not enclosed within fruits. Despite their lack of flowers, fruits, and seed endosperm, the modern gymnosperms are diverse and abundant in many places. Like the other phyla of plants that we have just surveyed, gymnosperms played significant roles in the past evolutionary history of plants, our next topic.

28.2 | AN EVOLUTIONARY HISTORY OF LAND PLANTS

Learning Outcome:

1. Describe how two major events in plant history affected other life on Earth.

A billion years ago Earth's terrestrial surface was comparatively devoid of life. Some green or brown crusts of cyanobacteria likely grew in moist places, but there was very little soil, no plants, and no animal life. The origin of the first land plants was essential to development of the first substantial soils, the evolution of modern plants, and the ability of animals to colonize land. It is safe to say that if land plants had not appeared hundreds of millions of years ago, and become so marvellously well adapted to life on land, modern ecosystems would not have evolved in their present form.

How can we know about events such as the origin and diversification of land plants? One line of information comes from comparing molecular and structural features of modern plants. For example, the genome sequence of the moss *Physcomitrella patens,* first reported in 2007, reveals the presence of genes that aid heat and drought tolerance, which are especially useful in the terrestrial habitat. Plant fossils provide another line of information.

Modern and Fossil Plants Are Helpful in Inferring Evolutionary History

The distinctive features of living plant phyla reveal the order in which they first appeared—bryophytes earliest, lycophytes and pteridophytes later, gymnosperms next, and angiosperms most recently (see Figure 28.1). Molecular and fossil data support and provide additional information for this inference.

Molecular Approaches to Plant Evolutionary History   Plant evolutionary biologists often use computers and special software to compare gene sequences from diverse plants. Such analyses aid in understanding relationships among plants and the time when different clades originated. Hypotheses of organism relationships are represented as diagrams known as phylogenetic trees (see Figure 28.1). The arrangement of branches on phylogenetic trees can change as new data become available.

Sequence data often reveal past changes in genome structure, such as chromosomal rearrangements and the addition of introns to genes. You may recall that many eukaryotic genes possess noncoding regions known as introns and that transcribed intron sequences are removed during mRNA processing before translation occurs. Introns can be inserted into genes, but such events are relatively rare. As a result, introns can reveal ancient phylogenetic divergences. For example, liverworts lack introns generally present in the genes of other living plant phyla. Plant evolutionary biologists suspect that these introns first appeared within plant genes after liverworts had diverged from the mainstream of plant evolution. Further analysis of sequence data for several genes supports the view that liverworts are the most ancient modern plant phylum.

Sequence data has also been used to show that pteridophytes are monophyletic and are the closest modern relatives of seed plants.

The Use of Fossils to Infer Plant Evolutionary History   Fossils are the remains of dead organisms that have survived decay and other destructive processes long enough to become buried in materials that harden into rocks. The enclosed organic remains become stacked in layers, with the oldest at the bottom and the most recent fossils closer to the rock surface. This layering, together with chemical features, allows biologists to infer the relative ages of fossil remains (refer back to Figure 20.10).

The tough plant compounds lignin, cutin, and sporopollenin help to preserve the structure of plants as they fossilize (**Figure 28.16**). Such preservation allows plant scientists to deduce how fossil plants looked when alive. Plant biologists compare fossils with other fossils and with living plants to deduce the kinds of evolutionary changes that occurred during plant history.

The study of fossils, as well as molecular and other features of modern plants, has revealed an amazing story: how plants conquered the land. This story can be conceptualized as three dramatic episodes: (1) aquatic charophycean algae gave rise to the first land-adapted plants; (2) seedless plants transformed Earth's ecology; and (3) an ancient cataclysm marked the rise of angiosperms.

Aquatic Charophycean Algae Gave Rise to the First Land-Adapted Plants

Land plants inherited some traits from charophycean algae, as we have noted, but also acquired novel features in response to stresses present on land but not in the water. For example, plant biologists Zoe Popper and Stephen Fry discovered that the

Figure 28.16 Plant fossils. Fossil of *Pseudosalix handleyi,* an angiosperm.

cell walls of all land plants possess xyloglucan carbohydrates that cross-link cellulose microfibrils, but charophycean algae lack this feature. Cell-wall xyloglucans are among the new features that appeared as early plants began to adapt to land, possibly aiding in the development of more complex bodies. As previously mentioned, tissue-producing meristems, a sporic life cycle, tough-walled spores, and the sporophyte generation also appeared very early in plant history.

Seedless Plants Transformed Earth's Ecology

In addition to tough spores, other types of decay-resistant tissues evolved in early seedless plants, likely in response to attack by soil bacteria and fungi. When the plants died, some of their organic constituents were not completely degraded to carbon dioxide and instead were buried in sediments that were eventually transformed into rock. Such fossil organic carbon can accumulate and remain buried for very long periods, with the consequence that the amount of carbon dioxide in the atmosphere declined. Carbon dioxide is a greenhouse gas, meaning that an increase in its concentration warms the atmosphere, thereby influencing climate. Very early bryophyte-like land plants and later vascular plants influenced Earth's past climate by reducing the concentration of atmospheric carbon dioxide, and plants continue to do so today.

Ecological Effects of Ancient and Modern Bryophytes Later-diverging modern liverworts and mosses typify a later phase of plant evolution. In addition to possessing tough spores and sporangia, these plants produce decay-resistant body tissues similar to fossils left by ancient land plants. Such tissues help modern bryophytes to avoid attack by decay, bacteria, and fungi. Plant evolutionary biologists Linda Graham and David Hanson and their colleagues determined the amount of decay-resistant mass produced by several modern bryophytes and used these data to estimate the ecological impact of early nonvascular plants. The results suggested that nonvascular plants likely contributed organic substances to early soils, thereby helping to enrich them. The results also indicated that ancient nonvascular plants could have begun a process by which atmospheric carbon dioxide (CO_2) was converted to organic carbon that was buried and thus not respired back to carbon dioxide. Burial of organic carbon is a process that helps to reduce the amount of the greenhouse gas CO_2 in Earth's atmosphere, thereby influencing temperature and precipitation. The investigators calculated that such effects on soil, atmospheric chemistry, and climate might have been significant because they could have occurred over large geographic areas and for millions of years before vascular plants became dominant.

Modern bryophytes likewise play important roles by storing CO_2 as decay-resistant organic compounds. The abundant modern moss genus *Sphagnum* contains so much decay-resistant mass that dead moss has accumulated over thousands of years into deep peat deposits. By storing organic carbon for long periods, *Sphagnum* moss functions as a giant global thermostat that helps to keep Earth's climate steady, to the benefit of humans and other life forms. How does this biological thermostat work? Under cooler than normal conditions *Sphagnum* grows more slowly and thus absorbs less CO_2, allowing atmospheric CO_2 to rise a bit. Since atmospheric CO_2 helps to warm Earth's climate, increasing CO_2 warms the climate a little. When the climate warms sufficiently, *Sphagnum* grows faster, thereby sponging up more CO_2 as peat deposits. Reducing atmospheric CO_2 returns the climate to slightly cooler conditions. The world's peat deposits currently store an estimated 400 gigatons (billion metric tons) of organic carbon. Ecologists have expressed concern that modern global warming could increase the rate at which decay organism populations increase and break down organic peat into CO_2. Such processes have the potential to increase global temperatures sufficiently to harm human and other life.

Ecological Effects of Ancient Vascular Plants Vascular plants originated from extinct plants called protracheophytes, such as the fossil *Aglaophyton major*. Protracheophytes had branched sporophytes and produced numerous sporangia, but their water-conducting cells lacked lignin and thus did not provide structural support, as does the xylem of vascular plants. Vascular plant fossils first appear in rocks deposited 430 million to 420 million years ago and rapidly became diverse and abundant. These fossils reveal that the earliest vascular plants had no leaves or roots, but they did have stems with a central core of lignin-coated water-conducting cells, a tough outer cuticle, and stomata, much like modern pteridophytes (see Figure 28.10). These features suggest that early vascular plants had achieved the ability to maintain a stable internal water level. The presence of lignin and cutin also fostered the ability of vascular plant bodies to resist decaying long enough to fossilize, explaining why vascular plants have left a more extensive fossil record than did the earliest plants.

Fossils tell us that extensive forests dominated by tree-sized lycophytes, pteridophytes, and early lignophytes occurred in widespread swampy regions during the warm, moist Carboniferous period (354 million to 290 million years ago) (**Figure 28.17**). Much of today's coal derives from the abundant remains of these ancient plants, explaining why the Carboniferous is commonly known as the Coal Age. Carboniferous plants converted huge amounts of atmospheric CO_2 into decay-resistant organic materials, such as lignin. Long-term burial of these materials, compressed into coal, together with chemical interactions between soil and the roots of vascular plants, dramatically changed Earth's atmosphere and climate.

Mathematical models of ancient atmospheric chemistry, supported by measurements of natural carbon isotopes, led paleoclimatologist Robert Berner to propose that the Carboniferous proliferation of vascular plants was correlated with a dramatic decrease in atmospheric carbon dioxide, which reached a historic low about 300 million years ago (**Figure 28.18**). During this period of very low CO_2, atmospheric oxygen levels rose to historic high levels, because less O_2 was being used to break down organic carbon into CO_2. High atmospheric oxygen content has been used to explain the occurrence of giant Carboniferous dragonflies and other huge insects, which obtain their air by diffusion. Because atmospheric CO_2 is a greenhouse gas—which allows Earth's atmosphere to retain heat—the great Carboniferous decline in

CO_2 level caused cool, dry conditions to prevail in the late Carboniferous and early Permian periods. As a result of this relatively abrupt global climate change, many of the giant seedless lycophytes and pteridophytes that had dominated Carboniferous forests became extinct, as did organisms such as the giant dragonflies. Cooler, drier Permian conditions favoured extensive diversification of the first seed plants, the gymnosperms. Seed plants were better able than nonseed plants to reproduce in cooler, drier habitats (as you will see in section 28.4). As a result, seed plants came to dominate Earth's terrestrial communities, and they continue to do.

An Ancient Cataclysm Marked the Rise of Angiosperms

Diverse phyla of gymnosperms dominated Earth's vegetation through the Mesozoic era (248 million to 65 million years ago), what is sometimes called the Age of Dinosaurs. In addition, fossils provide evidence that early flowering plants were present in the early Mesozoic and perhaps before that. Likewise, fossils indicate that early mammals existed in the Mesozoic. Gymnosperms and early angiosperms were probably major sources of food for such early mammals and for herbivorous dinosaurs. For example, Dr. Ruth Stockey from the University of Alberta and her colleagues found many fossils of an aquatic angiosperm named *Cobbania* along with bones of the dinosaur *Ornithomimus* in Dinosaur Park, Alberta. This dinosaur may have fed on the plant when alive (**Figure 28.19**). In fact, gymnosperms were probably a major source of food for terrestrial herbivorous dinosaurs, some of which grew to enormous sizes.

Giant lycophyte   Giant dragonfly   Giant horsetail (pteridophyte)

Figure 28.17   **Reconstruction of a Carboniferous (Coal Age) forest.**   This ancient forest was dominated by tree-sized lycophytes and pteridophytes, which later contributed to the formation of coal deposits.

Concept check: *Why did giant dragonflies occur during this time, but not now?*

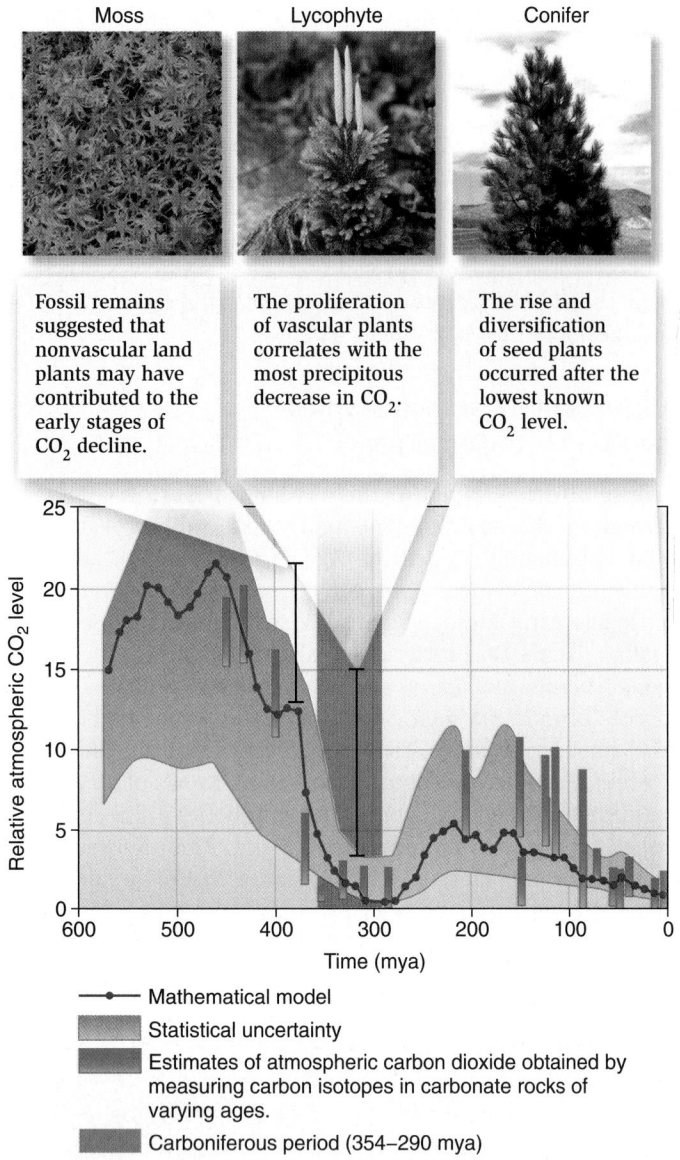

Moss   Lycophyte   Conifer

Fossil remains suggested that nonvascular land plants may have contributed to the early stages of CO_2 decline.

The proliferation of vascular plants correlates with the most precipitous decrease in CO_2.

The rise and diversification of seed plants occurred after the lowest known CO_2 level.

—●— Mathematical model

Statistical uncertainty

Estimates of atmospheric carbon dioxide obtained by measuring carbon isotopes in carbonate rocks of varying ages.

Carboniferous period (354–290 mya)

Figure 28.18 Changes in Earth's atmospheric carbon dioxide levels over geological time.   Geological evidence indicates that carbon dioxide levels in Earth's atmosphere were once higher than they are now, but the rise of land plants caused CO_2 to reach the lowest known level about 300 million years ago.

About 65 million years ago, disaster struck. That day, at least one large meteorite or comet crashed into Earth near the present-day Yucatan Peninsula in Mexico. This episode is known as the **K/T event** because it marks the end of the Cretaceous (sometimes spelled with a K) period and the beginning of the Tertiary (T) period. The impact, together with substantial volcanic activity that also occurred at this time, is thought to have produced huge amounts of ash, smoke, and haze that dimmed the sun's light long enough to kill many of the world's plants. Many groups of plants were forever lost, though some survived and persist today. With a severely reduced food supply, the dinosaurs were also doomed, the only exceptions being their descendants: the birds.

After the K/T event, weedy ferns dominated long enough to leave huge numbers of fossil spores, and then surviving groups of flowering plants began to diversify into the space left by the demise of previous plants. Along with flowering plant diversification, many new types of animals appeared, replacing the dinosaurs that had previously ruled. These new animals were the ancestors of many groups of terrestrial animals that exist today, including the primate ancestors of humans. If the K/T catastrophe had not occurred, mammal evolution might have been quite different.

Our brief survey of plant evolutionary history reveals some important diversity principles. Although environment certainly influenced the diversification of plants, plant diversification has also changed Earth's environment in ways that affected the evolution of other organisms. Plant evolutionary history also serves as essential background for a closer focus on the evolution of critical innovations: new features that foster the diversification of phyla. Among the critical innovations that appeared during plant evolutionary history, embryos, leaves, and seeds were particularly important, as we will discuss next.

Though both early flowering plants and early mammals were present, they primarily existed in the shadows of gymnosperms and dinosaurs.

(a)   (b)   (c)

Figure 28.19   Early angiosperms and gymnosperms, sources of food for the large herbivorous dinosaurs of the Mesozoic era. **(a)** In this artist's habitat reconstruction from fossils, the extinct angiosperm *Cobbania corrugata* is shown growing in wetlands that were also inhabited by large dinosaurs, such as *Ornithomimus,* whose head is illustrated here. **(b)** Single floating plant as seen from top view. **(c)** Side view of two floating plants.

28.3 THE ORIGIN AND EVOLUTIONARY IMPORTANCE OF THE PLANT EMBRYO

Learning Outcomes:

1. Outline how plant embryos might have evolved and why.
2. Discuss the role of placental transfer tissues in the movement of nutrients from mother plant to embryo.

The embryo, absent from charophyceans, was probably one of the first distinctive traits acquired by land plants. Recall that plant embryos are young sporophytes that develop from zygotes, enclosed by maternal tissues that provide sustenance. This feature is critical to plant reproduction in terrestrial environments. Drought, heat, ultraviolet light, and microbial attack could kill delicate plant egg cells, zygotes, and embryos if these were not protected and nourished by enclosing parental tissues. For land plants, the evolutionary origin of a dependent plant embryo was a critical innovation. The first embryo-producing plants diversified into hundreds of thousands of diverse modern species, as well as many species that have become extinct. The embryo is such a defining feature of plants that plant biologists often use the term *embryophytes* as a synonym for plants (see Figure 28.1). A closer look at embryos reveals why their origin and evolution is so important to all land plants.

A plant embryo has several characteristic features. First, as we have previously noted, plant embryos are multicellular and diploid (see section 28.1). Plant embryos develop by repeated mitosis from a single-celled zygote resulting from fertilization (see Figure 28.6b). In addition, we have also learned that plant eggs are fertilized while still attached to the maternal plant body, with the result that embryos begin their development within the protective confines of maternal tissues (see Figure 28.7). Plant biologists say that plants retain their zygotes and embryos. Third, plant embryo development depends on organic and mineral materials supplied by the mother plant. Nutritive tissues composed of specialized **placental transfer tissues** aid in the transfer of nutrients from parent to embryo. Let's take a closer look at the valuable role played by placental transfer tissues.

Placental transfer tissues function similarly to the placenta of mammals, which fosters nutrient movement from the mother's bloodstream to the developing fetus. Plant placental transfer tissues often occur in haploid gametophyte tissues that lie closest to

Parental gametophyte cell

Embryonic sporophyte cell

Cell-wall ingrowths

3 μm

Figure 28.20 TEM of placental transfer tissue in the liverwort genus *Monoclea*.

 Principle: *Structure determines function. This TEM shows that placental transfer tissues contain specialized cells having extensive finger-shaped cell-wall ingrowths. Similar cells occur in all plants and help nutrients to move rapidly from parental gametophytes to embryonic sporophytes, a process that fosters plant reproductive success.*

BioConnections: *Look ahead to Figure 39.9 and 48.12b. How do similar finger-like projections of animal intestine and placenta likewise foster rapid movement of nutrients?*

embryos and in the diploid tissues of young embryos themselves. Such transfer tissues contain cells that are specialized in ways that promote the movement of solutes from gametophyte to embryo. For example, the cells of placental transport tissues display complex arrays of finger-like cell-wall ingrowths (**Figure 28.20**). Because the plant plasma membrane lines this elaborate plant cell wall, the ingrowths vastly increase the surface area and create an intercellular space between the parent tissues and embryo. Minerals move from maternal cells into the intercellular space. Then, abundant membrane transport proteins move solutes into and out of cells. With more transport proteins present, materials are more efficiently imported into the embryo. Classic experiments have revealed the adaptive value of this process in land plant reproduction.

FEATURE INVESTIGATION

Browning and Gunning Demonstrated That Placental Transfer Tissues Increase the Rate at Which Organic Molecules Move from Gametophytes to Sporophytes

In the 1970s plant cell biologists Adrian Browning and Brian Gunning explored placental transfer tissue function. By using a simple

moss experimental system, they determined that placental transfer tissues increase the rate at which radioactively labelled carbon moves through placental transfer tissues from green gametophytes into young sporophytes. This process is expected to increase the ability of mature sporophytes to produce progeny spores, thereby increasing reproductive success. Recall that embryos are very young, few-celled sporophytes and that in mosses and other bryophytes all stages of sporophyte development are nutritionally dependent on gametophyte tissues. Browning and Gunning investigated nutrient flow into young sporophytes because these slightly older and larger developmental stages were easier to manipulate in the laboratory than were tiny embryos.

In the first step the investigators grew many gametophytes of the moss *Funaria hygrometrica* in a greenhouse until young sporophytes developed as the result of sexual reproduction (**Figure 28.21**). In the second step they placed black glass tubing over young sporophytes as a shade to prevent photosynthesis,

---

HYPOTHESES   1. Placental transfer tissues allow organic nutrients to flow from plant gametophytes to sporophytes faster than such nutrients move through plant tissues lacking transfer cells.
2. The rate of organic nutrient transfer into larger sporophytes is faster than into smaller sporophytes.

KEY MATERIALS   Moss *Funaria hygrometrica*, $^{14}CO_2$ (radiolabelled carbon dioxide)

| | **Experimental level** | **Conceptual level** |

1 Grow moss gametophytes until young sporophytes develop from embryos, and measure sporophyte size.

Young sporophytes receive organic nutrients in the same way as embryos but are easier to handle.

2 Shade young sporophytes from light with blackened glass tubing, and enclose whole plant in clear glass jar. Expose plants to $^{14}CO_2$ for 15 minutes. This is called a pulse.

Sporophyte
Dark tubing
Gametophyte
$^{14}CO_2$

Photosynthesis, which requires light, will convert $^{14}CO_2$ into ^{14}C-sugar in gametophytes but not sporophytes.

Light
$^{14}CO_2$
$^{14}CO_2$
Labeled sugar

3 Expose plants to a large amount of nonradioactive CO_2. This is called a chase. Incubate up to 8 hours.

Nonradiolabelled CO_2

Addition of excess nonlabelled CO_2 is known as a chase because it chases away the ability of the cells to make any more radioactive sugars.

Light
Nonradiolabelled CO_2
$^{14}CO_2$ no longer taken up by plant.

4 Pluck young sporophytes of differing sizes from gametophytes. Assay ^{14}C in both sporophytes and gametophytes using a scintillation counter. This was done immediately following the chase, or two or eight hours after the chase.

Scintillation counter

Determine how much organic carbon flowed into sporophytes during each chase time.

5 **THE DATA I**

Organic carbon transfer from gametophyte to sporophyte:

Mean ^{14}C content of 5 gametophytes at 0 chase time	Mean ^{14}C lost from gametophytes after 8-hour chase	Mean ^{14}C gained by sporophytes after 8-hour chase
228 units	145 units	51 units

6 **THE DATA II**

Sporophyte size effect:

Sporophyte size	Mean ^{14}C content of 8 sporophytes after 2-hour chase
5–7 mm	8.47 ± 4.29 units
11–13 mm	9.93 ± 3.94 units
23–25 mm	24.97 ± 5.30 units

Figure 28.21   Browning and Gunning demonstrated that placental transfer tissues increase plant reproductive success.

7 CONCLUSION Organic carbon moves from photosynthetic gametophytes into developing sporophytes, facilitated by transfer cell-wall ingrowths. Larger sporophytes absorb more organic carbon than smaller ones.

8 SOURCES Browning, A.J., and Gunning, B.E.S. 1979. Structure and function of transfer cells in the sporophyte haustorium of *Funaria hygrometrica*. Hedw. II. Kinetics of uptake of labelled sugars and localization of absorbed products by freeze-substitution. *Journal of Experimental Botany* 30:1247–1264.

Browning, A.J., and Gunning, B.E.S. 1979. Structure and function of transfer cells in the sporophyte haustorium of *Funaria hygrometrica*. III. Translocation of assimilate into the attached sporophyte and along the seta of attached and excised sporophytes. *Journal of Experimental Botany* 30:1265–1273.

enclosed the whole plants—gametophytes and their attached sporophytes—within transparent jars, and supplied the plants with radioactively labelled carbon dioxide ($^{14}CO_2$) for measured times known as pulses. Because the moss gametophytes were not shaded, their photosynthetic cells were able to convert the radioactively labelled carbon dioxide into labelled organic compounds, such as sugars and amino acids. Shading prevented the young sporophytes, which possess some photosynthetic tissue, from using the $^{14}CO_2$ to produce organic compounds.

In the third step the researchers added an excess amount of nonradioactive CO_2 to prevent the further uptake of the $^{14}CO_2$ from their experimental system, a process known as a chase. This process stopped the radiolabelling of photosynthetic products. (Experiments such as these are known as pulse-chase experiments.) In the final step Browning and Gunning plucked young sporophytes of different sizes (ages) from the gametophytes and measured the amount of radioactive organic carbon present in the separated gametophyte and sporophyte tissues at various times following the chase.

From these data the researchers were able to calculate the relative amount of organic carbon that had moved from the photosynthetic moss gametophytes to sporophytes. Browning and Gunning discovered that about 22% of the organic carbon produced by gametophyte photosynthesis was transferred to the young sporophytes during an eight-hour chase period (see Data I). They also calculated the rate of nutrient transfer between generations and compared this rate with the rate at which organic carbon moves in several other plant tissues that lack specialized transfer cells

(determined in other studies). By so doing, Browning and Gunning discovered that organic carbon moved from moss gametophytes to young sporophytes nine times as fast as organic carbon moves within other plant tissues (see Data II). These investigators inferred that the increased rate of nutrient movement could be attributed to placental transfer cell structure, namely, the fact that cell-wall ingrowths enhanced plasma membrane surface area. By comparing the amount of radioactive carbon accumulated by young sporophytes of differing ages, they also learned that larger sporophytes absorbed labelled carbon about three times as fast as smaller ones.

These data are consistent with the hypothesis that placental transfer tissues increase plant reproductive success by providing embryos and older sporophytes with more nutrients than they would otherwise receive. Supplied with these greater amounts of nutrients, sporophytes are better able to grow larger than they otherwise would, and eventually they produce more progeny spores.

Experimental Questions

1. What were the goals of the Browning and Gunning investigation?
2. How did Browning and Gunning prevent photosynthesis from occurring in moss sporophytes during the experiment? Why did they do this?
3. How did the measurements Browning and Gunning made after adding an excess amount of unlabelled CO_2 lead them to their conclusions?

28.4 THE ORIGIN AND EVOLUTIONARY IMPORTANCE OF LEAVES AND SEEDS

Learning Outcomes:

1. Describe how the leaves of ferns and seed plants likely evolved from branched stem systems.
2. Discuss how seeds develop from fertilized ovules.
3. Name several advantages that seeds provide.
4. List hypothetical steps in the evolution of seeds.

Like plant embryos, leaves and seeds are critical innovations that allowed plant phyla to diversify extensively. However, unlike the plant embryo, which likely originated just once at the birth of the plant kingdom, leaves and seeds probably evolved several times during plant evolutionary history. Comparative studies of diverse types of leaves and seeds in fossil and living plants suggest how these critical innovations might have originated.

The Leaves of Ferns Evolved from Branched Stem Systems

Leaves are the solar panels of the plant world. Their flat structure enables leaves to effectively capture sunlight for use in photosynthesis. This explains why leaflike structures evolved even on the gametophytes of leafy liverworts and mosses (see Figures 28.3 and 28.5), and also why they occur on the sporophytes of most vascular plants. Among the vascular plants, lycophytes produce the simplest and most ancient leaves. Modern lycophytes have tiny leaves called **lycophylls**, also known as microphylls, that typically have only a single unbranched vein (**Figure 28.22a**). Some experts think that these small leaves may have evolved from sporangia.

In contrast, the leaves of other vascular plant phyla have extensively branched veins. Leaves with branched veins are known as **euphylls** (meaning "true leaves") (**Figure 28.22b**). This explains why the clade that includes pteridophytes and seed plants is known as the **euphyllophytes** (see Figure 28.1). The branched veins of euphylls are able to supply relatively large areas of photosynthetic tissue with water and minerals. Thus, euphylls are typically much larger than lycophylls. Euphylls provide considerable photosynthetic advantage to ferns and seed plants, because they provide more surface for solar energy capture than do small leaves. Hence, the evolution of relatively large leaves allowed plants to more effectively accomplish photosynthesis, enabling them to grow larger and produce more progeny.

Study of fern fossils indicates that euphylls likely arose from leafless, branched stem systems by a series of steps (**Figure 28.22c**). First, one branch assumed the role of the main axis, then the whole branch system became flattened, and finally the spaces between the branches of this flattened system became filled with photosynthetic tissue. This hypothetical process explains why euphylls

have branched vascular systems; these apparently originated from the vascular system of an ancestral branched stem. Plant evolutionary biologists suspect that euphylls arose several times, and it is unclear whether or not the leaves of seed plants originated in the same way as those of ferns. Next, we'll consider what adaptive advantages seeds provide and how seeds might have evolved, beginning with a consideration of seed development.

Seeds Develop from the Interaction of Ovules and Pollen

The seed plants dominate modern ecosystems, suggesting that seeds offer reproductive advantages. Seed plants are also the plants with the greatest importance to humans. For these reasons plant biologists are interested in understanding why seeds are so advantageous and how they evolved. To consider these questions, we must first take a closer look at seed structure and development.

We have earlier noted that all plants produce spores by meiosis within sporangia, and seed plants are no exception. However, seed plants produce two distinct types of spores in two types of sporangia, a trait known as **heterospory**, meaning different spores. Microsporangia produce small **microspores** that give rise to male gametophytes, which develop into pollen grains. Megasporangia produce larger **megaspores** that give rise to female gametophytes

(a) Lycophyll (small leaf)   Single unbranched leaf vein

(b) Euphyll (large leaf)   Branched vascular system

1 Fern ancestors initially had a branched stem system.

2 One branch began to dominate the stem system.

3 The branch system flattened into a single plane.

4 Photosynthetic tissue filled in the spaces between the branches of a system.

Euphyll

(c) Euphyll evolution process in pteridophytes

Figure 28.22   Lycophylls and euphylls.   (a) Most lycophylls possess only a single unbranched leaf vein having limited conduction capacity, explaining why lycophylls are generally quite small. (b) Euphylls possess branched vascular systems having greater conduction capacity, explaining why many euphylls are relatively large. (c) Fossil evidence suggests how pteridophyte euphylls might have evolved from branched stem systems.

Concept check: *Imagine that the leaves of some other plant group evolved from stem systems that were more highly branched (that is, there were more branches per unit length of stem) than those of ferns. How do you think the leaves of such plants might differ from those of ferns?*

that develop and produce eggs while enclosed by protective mega-spore walls. The female gametophytes are not photosynthetic, so they need help in feeding the embryos that develop from fertilized eggs. Female gametophytes get this help by remaining attached to the previous sporophyte generation, which provides gameto-phytes with the nutrients needed for embryo development.

Plants produce seeds by means of reproductive struc-tures known as ovules and pollen, which are structures unique to seed plants. An **ovule** is a sporangium that contained only a single spore that developed into a very small egg-producing gametophyte, the whole enclosed by modified leaves known as **integuments (Figure 28.23a)**. You can think of an ovule as being like a nesting doll with four progressively smaller dolls inside. The smallest doll corresponds to an egg cell; intermediate-sized dolls stand for the gametophyte, spore wall, and megasporangium; and the largest doll represents the integuments. Fertilization converts such layered ovules into seeds. In seed plants, the sperm needed for fertilization are supplied by **pollen,** tiny male gametophytes enclosed by protective sporopollenin walls. A closer look at pol-len and ovules will help in understanding how seeds develop.

Embryos develop as the result of fertilization, which can-not occur until after **pollination,** the process by which pollen of the same species reaches ovules. Pollination typically occurs by means of wind or animal transport (see Chapter 29). Fertiliza-tion occurs when a male gametophyte extends a slender pollen tube that carries two sperm toward an egg. After a pollen tube enters the micropyle and releases the sperm, fertilization may occur. The fertilized egg becomes an embryo, and the ovule's integument develops into a protective, often hard and tough, **seed coat (Figure 28.23b, 28.23c)**.

Gymnosperm seeds contain female gametophyte tissue that has accumulated large amounts of protein, lipids, and carbohydrates before fertilization. These nutrients are used during seed germination to help support growth of the seedling. Angiosperm seeds also contain this useful food supply, but angiosperm ovules do not store food materials before fertiliza-tion. Instead, angiosperm seeds store food only after fertiliza-tion occurs, ensuring that the food is not wasted if an embryo does not form. How is this accomplished? The answer is a process known as **double fertilization**. This process produces both a zygote and a food storage tissue known as endosperm, which is a tissue unique to angiosperms. One of the two sperm delivered by each pollen tube fuses with the egg, producing a diploid zygote, as you might expect. The other sperm nucleus fuses with different gametophyte nuclei to form an unusual cell that has more than the diploid number of chromosomes; this cell generates the endosperm food tissue (see Chapter 37).

Seeds allow embryos access to food supplied by the older sporophyte generation, an option not available to seedless plants. The layered structure of ovules explains why seeds are also layered like nesting dolls, with a protective seed coat (developed from the ovule integuments) enclosing the embryo and also stored food, in many cases. These seed features improve the chances of embryo and seedling survival, thereby increasing seed plant fitness.

Seeds Confer Important Ecological Advantages

Seeds provide plants with numerous ecological advantages, which explains why seed plants have dominated Earth's ecosys-tems since the end of the Coal Age. First, many seeds are able to remain dormant in the soil for long periods, until conditions become favourable for germination and seedling growth. In con-trast, most single-celled spores are unable to survive for long; if conditions are not suitable for germination, they die. In addition

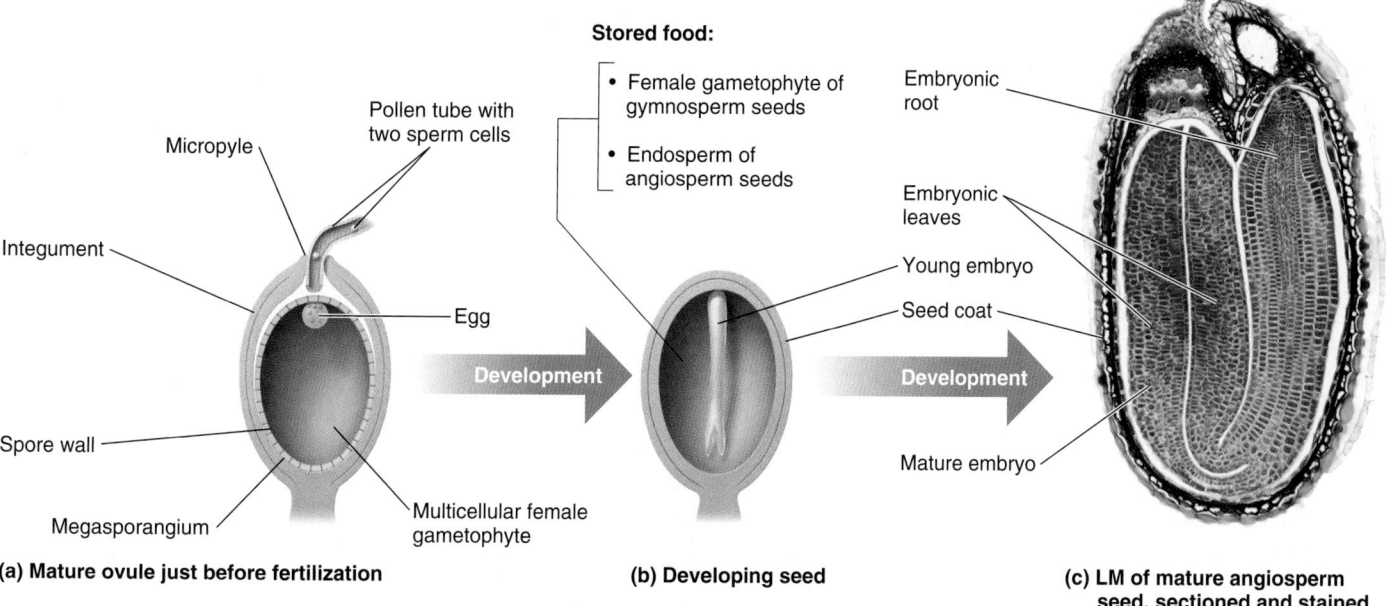

(a) **Mature ovule just before fertilization**

(b) **Developing seed**

(c) **LM of mature angiosperm seed, sectioned and stained**

Figure 28.23   Structure of an ovule developing into a seed.

Concept check: *Can you hypothesize why this angiosperm seed with its mature embryo does not show obvious endosperm tissue?*

seeds are larger and more complex than spores, which improves the ability of seeds to resist mechanical damage and pathogen attack. Further, seed coats have evolutionary adaptations that improve dispersal in diverse habitats. For example, many plants produce winged seeds that are effectively dispersed by wind. Other plants produce seeds with fleshy coverings that attract birds, which consume the seeds, digest their fleshy covering, and eliminate the seeds at some distance from the originating plants.

Another advantage of seeds is that they can store considerable amounts of food, which helps plant seedlings grow large enough to compete for light, water, and minerals. This is especially important for seeds that must germinate in shady forests. Finally, the sperm of seed plants can reach eggs without having to swim through water, because pollen tubes deliver sperm directly to ovules. Consequently, seed plant fertilization is not typically limited by lack of water, in contrast to that of seedless plants. Therefore, seed plants are better able to reproduce in arid and seasonally dry habitats. For these reasons seeds are considered to be a particularly significant plant reproductive adaptation to reproduction in a land habitat.

Ovule and Seed Evolution Illustrate Descent with Modification

As you have seen, seed plants reproduce by using both spores and seeds, and it is important to recognize that seed plants have not replaced spores with seeds. Instead, during seed plant evolution, ovules and seeds were added to an ancestral life history that begins with spores. Ovules and seeds thus originated by a sequence of changes to pre-existing structures and processes. Some clues about ovule and seed evolution arise from comparing reproduction in living lycophytes, pteridophytes, and spermatophytes. Fossils provide additional information.

Let's first consider reproduction of lycophytes and pteridophytes. Most modern lycophytes and pteridophytes release one type of spore and one type of gametophyte, which lives in the open environment and produces both male and female gametangia (see Figure 28.11). However, some lycophytes and pteridophytes produce separate microspores and megaspores, which grow into separate male and female gametophytes in the process known as heterospory. Such gametophytes also grow within the confines of microspore and megaspore walls and thus are known as **endosporic gametophytes**.

An advantage of heterospory is that it mandates cross-fertilization. The eggs and sperm that fuse are derived from different gametophytes and hence from different spores and different meiotic events. This ensures that the gametes are of distinct genotypes. Cross-fertilization increases the potential for genetic variation, which aids evolutionary flexibility. Endosporic gametophytes receive protection from environmental damage by surrounding spore walls. From these observations we can infer that heterospory and endosporic gametophytes were probably also features of seed plant ancestors, and they constitute early steps toward seed evolution (**Figure 28.24**).

1 Sporangium containing spores that are similar in size

2a Microsporangium containing many small microspores

2b Megasporangium containing fewer, larger megaspores

3 Reduction to one megaspore per megasporangium

4 Enclosure of megasporangium within integuments to form ovule; when fertilized, ovule develops into a seed

Early evolution of heterospory

Microsporangium

+

Megasporangium

Megaspore

Integuments

Ovule

Evolution of megasporangium that led to an ovule

Figure 28.24 Hypothetical stages in the evolution of seeds. The parallel evolution of heterospory and endosporic gametophytes in some lycophytes and pteridophytes, as well as the seed plants, suggests that these features were acquired early in the evolution of seeds. Later-occurring events in the origin of seeds were the reduction in the number of megaspores to one per megasporangium and the enclosure of the megasporangium by protective, leaflike integuments.

BioConnections: *Look ahead to Figure 32.16, which illustrates the amniotic egg produced by many terrestrial animals. How is the plant seed like the amniotic egg?*

Fossils and modern plants also illustrate subsequent stages in seed evolution, such as retaining megaspores within sporangia rather than releasing them.

A further step in seed evolution may have been production of only one megaspore per sporangium rather than multiple spores per sporangium, which is common in seedless plants. Reduction of megaspore numbers (from those present in seedless plants) would have allowed plants to channel more nutrients into each megaspore. A final step might have been the retention of megasporangia on parental sporophytes by the development of integuments (Figure 28.24). As we have noted, this adaptation would allow food materials to flow from mature photosynthetic sporophytes to their dependent gametophytes and young embryos.

Fossils provide information about when the process of seed evolution first occurred. Very early fossil seeds, such as *Elkinsia polymorpha* and *Archaeosperma arnoldii,* were present 365 million years ago. Thus, paleobiologists think that the first seeds arose before the Coal Age, during the Devonian period (see Figure 28.1). A newly discovered Devonian fossil known as *Runcaria heinzelinii* is thought to represent a seed precursor (**Figure 28.25**). It had a lacy integument that did not completely enclose the megasporangium.

These hypothesized stages of seed evolution illustrate the stepwise way in which plants probably achieved an increased ability to cope with the stresses of life on land. The evolutionary journey illustrated by the transition from aquatic charophycean algae to bryophytes, to seedless plants, and finally to seed plants reveals how adaptation is related to environmental change, as well as ways in which plants themselves shaped Earth's ecosystems. As a summary of what you learned in this chapter, **Table 28.1** provides a list of the distinguishing features of land plants and their charophycean relatives.

Table 28.1	Distinguishing Features of Modern Charophyceans and Land Plants*
Charophyceans	Primarily aquatic habitat; zygotic life cycle; haploid gametophyte; rosette cellulose synthesizing complexes; sporangia absent; sporophytes absent; cell-wall xyloglucans absent
LAND PLANTS (EMBRYOPHYTES)	Primarily terrestrial habitat; sporic life cycle consisting of alternation of two multicellular generations: diploid sporophyte and haploid gametophyte; multicellular embryos are nutritionally dependent for at least some time during development; spore-producing sporangia; gamete-producing gametangia; sporopollenin spore walls; cell-wall xyloglucans
Nonvascular plants (Bryophytes) (**liverworts, hornworts,** and **mosses**)	Dominant gametophyte generation; supportive, lignin-containing vascular tissue absent; true roots, stems, and leaves absent; sporophytes unbranched and unable to grow independently of gametophytes
VASCULAR PLANTS (TRACHEOPHYTES) (**lycophytes, pteridophytes,** spermatophytes)	Dominant sporophyte generation; lignified water conducting tissue: xylem; specialized organic food conducting tissue: phloem; sporophytes branched; sporophytes eventually become independent of gametophytes
SEEDLESS VASCULAR PLANTS (**lycophytes, pteridophytes**)	
Lycophytes	Leaves generally small with a single unbranched vein (lycophylls); sporangia borne on sides of stems
EUPHYLLOPHYTES (**pteridophytes,** SPERMATOPHYTES)	
Pteridophytes	Leaves relatively large with extensively branched vein system (euphylls or megaphylls); sporangia borne on leaves
SEED PLANTS (SPERMATOPHYTES) Seeds present; leaves are euphylls	
Gymnosperms (**cycads, ginkgos, conifers, gnetophytes**)	Flowers and fruits absent; seed food stored before fertilization in female gametophyte, endosperm absent; "naked seeds"
Angiosperms (flowering plants)	Flowers and fruits present; seed food stored after fertilization in endosperm formed by double fertilization

*Key: Phyla; LARGER MONOPHYLETIC CLADES (synonyms). All other classification terms are not clades.

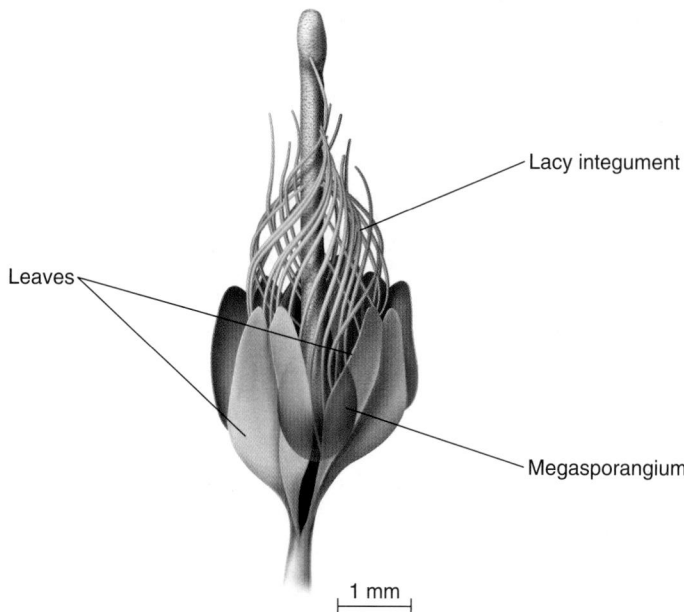

Leaves —
Lacy integument —
Megasporangium —
1 mm

Figure 28.25   The fossil *Runcaria heinzelinii,* a plant with a probable seed precursor.

Concept check: *Based on your knowledge of integument function in modern seed plants, what inference can you make about the function of the lacy integument of Runcaria?*

Summary of Key Concepts

28.1 Ancestry and Diversity of Modern Plants

- Plants are multicellular organisms composed of eukaryotic cells having plastids, which display many adaptations to life on land, and primarily live on land. The modern plant kingdom consists of several hundred thousand species that can be classified into 10 phyla, informally known as the liverworts, mosses, hornworts, lycophytes, pteridophytes, cycads, ginkgos, conifers, gnetophytes, and angiosperms. (Figure 28.1)

- The land plants evolved from ancestors that probably would be classified with modern, complex charophycean algae of freshwater habitats. (Figure 28.2)

- The monophyletic liverwort, hornwort, and moss phyla are together known informally as the bryophytes. Bryophytes illustrate early evolved features of land plants, such as a sporic life cycle involving embryos that develop within protective gametophytic tissues. (Figures 28.3, 28.4, 28.5, 28.6)

- Bryophytes differ from other plants in having a dominant gametophyte generation and a dependent, nonbranching, short-lived sporophyte generation. Bryophytes also lack supportive vascular tissues, in contrast to other modern plant phyla, which are known as the vascular plants or tracheophytes. (Figures 28.7, 28.8)

- Lycophytes, pteridophytes, and other vascular plants generally possess stems, leaves, and roots that have vascular tissues composed of xylem and phloem, but the roots and leaves of these phyla differ in distinctive ways. (Figures 28.9, 28.10, 28.11, 28.13)

- The fern life cycle illustrates the dominant sporophyte characteristic of vascular plants. The fern *Ceratopteris richardii* is used as a model genetic system. (Figures 28.12)

- Cycads, ginkgos, conifers, and gnetophytes are collectively known as gymnosperms. Gymnosperms inherited an ancestral capacity to produce wood. Angiosperms, also known as the flowering plants, produce seeds and many also produce wood. Flowers, fruits, and seed endosperm are distinctive features of the angiosperms. (Figures 28.14, 28.15)

28.2 An Evolutionary History of Land Plants

- Paleobiologists and plant evolutionary biologists infer the history of land plants by analyzing the molecular features of modern plants and by comparing the structural features of fossil and modern plants. (Figures 28.16)

- Seedless plants transformed Earth's ecology by fostering soil buildup and altering atmospheric chemistry and climate. Such plants also influenced the evolutionary history of terrestrial animal life. (Figures 28.17, 28.18, 28.19)

- The K/T meteorite or comet impact event that occurred 65 million years ago helped cause the extinction of previously dominant dinosaurs and many types of gymnosperms, leaving space into which angiosperms, insects, birds, and mammals diversified.

28.3 The Origin and Evolutionary Importance of the Plant Embryo

- Origin of the plant embryo was a critical innovation that fostered diversification of the land plants. Plant embryos are supported by nutrients supplied by female gametophytes with the aid of specialized placental transfer tissues. (Figure 28.20)

- In a classic experiment Browning and Gunning inferred that placental transfer tissues were responsible for an enhanced flow rate of nutrients from parental gametophytes to embryos. (Figure 28.21)

28.4 The Origin and Evolutionary Importance of Leaves and Seeds

- Leaves are specialized photosynthetic organs that evolved more than once during plant evolutionary history. Lycophylls, which occur in lycophytes, are relatively small leaves having a single unbranched vein. Pteridophyte leaves are larger and have an extensively branched vascular system; they are known as euphylls. Fossils indicate that fern euphylls evolved from branched stem systems by dominance by one branch, flattening of the whole branch system, and development of photosynthetic tissue between the branches. (Figure 28.22)

- Seeds develop from ovules: megasporangia enclosed by leaflike integuments. Ovules develop into seeds after fertilization, following pollination. Pollen produces thin cellular tubes that deliver sperm cells to eggs produced by female gametophytes. Mature seeds contain an embryo sporophyte that develops from the zygote. Seeds also contain food stored within female gametophytes of gymnosperms or within endosperm tissues arising from double fertilization in angiosperms. (Figure 28.23)

- Seeds confer many reproductive advantages, including dormancy through unfavourable conditions, greater protection for embryos from mechanical and pathogen damage, seed coat modifications that enhance seed dispersal, and reduction of plant dependence on water for fertilization. Fossil seeds display stages in the evolution of seeds. (Figures 28.24, 28.25)

- The distinctive traits of charophyceans and the different phyla of land plants reveal the occurrence of descent with modification. (Table 28.1)

Test to Assess Your Learning

1. The simplest and most ancient phylum of modern land plants is probably
   a. the pteridophytes.
   b. the cycads.
   c. the liverworts.
   d. the angiosperms.
   e. none of the above.

2. An important feature of land plants that originated during the diversification of charophycean algae is
   a. the sporophyte.
   b. spores, which are dispersed in air and coated with sporopollenin.
   c. tracheids.
   d. plasmodesmata.
   e. fruits.

3. A phylum whose members are also known as bryophytes is commonly known as
   a. liverworts.
   b. hornworts.
   c. mosses.
   d. all of the above.
   e. none of the above.

4. Plants possess a life cycle that involves alternation of two multicellular generations: the gametophyte and
   a. the lycophyte.
   b. the bryophyte.
   c. the pteridophyte.
   d. the lignophyte.
   e. the sporophyte.

5. The seed plants are also known as
   a. bryophytes.
   b. spermatophytes.

   c. pteridophytes.
   d. lycophytes.
   e. euphyllophytes.

6. A waxy cuticle is an adaptation that
   a. helps to prevent water loss from tracheophytes.
   b. helps to prevent water loss from charophyceans.
   c. helps to prevent water loss from bryophytes.
   d. aids in water transport within the bodies of vascular plants.
   e. all of the above.

7. Plant photosynthesis transformed a very large amount of carbon dioxide into decay-resistant organic compounds, thereby causing a historic low in atmospheric carbon dioxide levels during the geological period known as
   a. the Cambrian.
   b. the Ordovician.
   c. the Carboniferous.
   d. the Permian.
   e. none of the above.

8. Which phylum among the plants listed is likely to have the largest leaves?
   a. liverworts
   b. hornworts
   c. mosses
   d. lycophytes
   e. pteridophytes

9. Euphylls probably evolved from
   a. the leaves of mosses.
   b. lycophylls.
   c. branched stem systems.
   d. modified roots.
   e. none of the above.

10. A seed develops from
   a. a spore.
   b. a fertilized ovule.
   c. a microsporangium covered by integuments.
   d. endosperm.
   e. none of the above.

Articulate to Assess Your Learning

1. List several common traits that lead evolutionary biologists to infer that land plants evolved from ancestors related to modern charophycean algae.

2. Why have bryophytes, such as mosses, been able to diversify into so many species even though they have relatively small dependent sporophytes?

Collaborate to Assess and Extend Your Learning

1. Discuss at least one difference in environmental conditions experienced by early land plants and ancestral charophycean-like algae.

2. Discuss as many plant adaptations to land as you can.

3. A principle of biology is that living organisms have mechanisms that maintain homeostasis. Explain how several structural features help vascular plants to maintain stable internal water content.

Visit McGraw-Hill Ryerson Connect™ for additional study resources.

The Evolution and Diversity of Modern Gymnosperms and Angiosperms

Chapter Outline

The Madagascar periwinkle (*Catharanthus roseus*), one of the many seed plants on which humans depend.

The seed plants, gymnosperms and angiosperms, are particularly important in our everyday lives because they are the sources of many products, including wood, paper, beverages, food, cosmetics, and medicines. Leukemia, for example, is effectively treated with vincristine, a drug extracted from the beautiful flowering plant known as the Madagascar periwinkle (*Catharanthus roseus*), shown in the chapter-opening photo. Vinblastine—another extract from *C. roseus*—is used to treat lymphatic cancers. Taxol, a compound used in the treatment of breast and ovarian cancers, was first discovered in extracts of the bark of the Pacific yew tree, a gymnosperm known as *Taxus brevifolia*. Vincristine, vinblastine, taxol, and many other plant-derived medicines are examples of plant secondary metabolites, which are distinct from the products of primary metabolism (carbohydrates, lipids, proteins, and nucleic acids). Secondary metabolites play essential roles in protecting plants from disease, organisms, and plant-eating animals, and they also aid plant growth and reproduction. Though all plants produce secondary metabolites, these natural products are exceptionally diverse in gymnosperms and angiosperms.

In this chapter you will learn how the hundreds of thousands of modern seed plants play many additional important roles in modern ecosystems and the lives of humans. This chapter also illustrates many diversity principles, including descent with modification, horizontal gene transfer, critical innovation, coevolution, biological services, and human impacts on biodiversity.

29.1 THE EVOLUTION AND DIVERSITY OF MODERN GYMNOSPERMS

Learning Outcomes:

1. Describe how gymnosperms evolved from woody but seedless ancestors.
2. Identify four gymnosperm phyla and describe their importance to humans.

Gymnosperms are plants that produce seeds that are exposed rather than enclosed in fruits, as is the case for angiosperms. The word *gymnosperm*, which means "naked seed," comes from the Greek *gymnos*, meaning naked (referring to the unclothed state of ancient athletes), and *sperma*, meaning seed. Gymnosperms inherited many adaptations to life on land from their ancestors (**Figure 29.1**) (see also Chapter 28). In this section we will first consider some fossil plants that help to explain important gymnosperm traits. Then we will survey the structure, reproduction, and ecological roles of modern gymnosperm phyla.

Modern Gymnosperms Arose from Woody Ancestors

Most modern gymnosperms are woody shrubs or trees, such as the famous giant sequoias (*Sequoiadendron giganteum*) native to the Sierra Nevada mountains of the western United States. Giant sequoias are among Earth's largest organisms, weighing

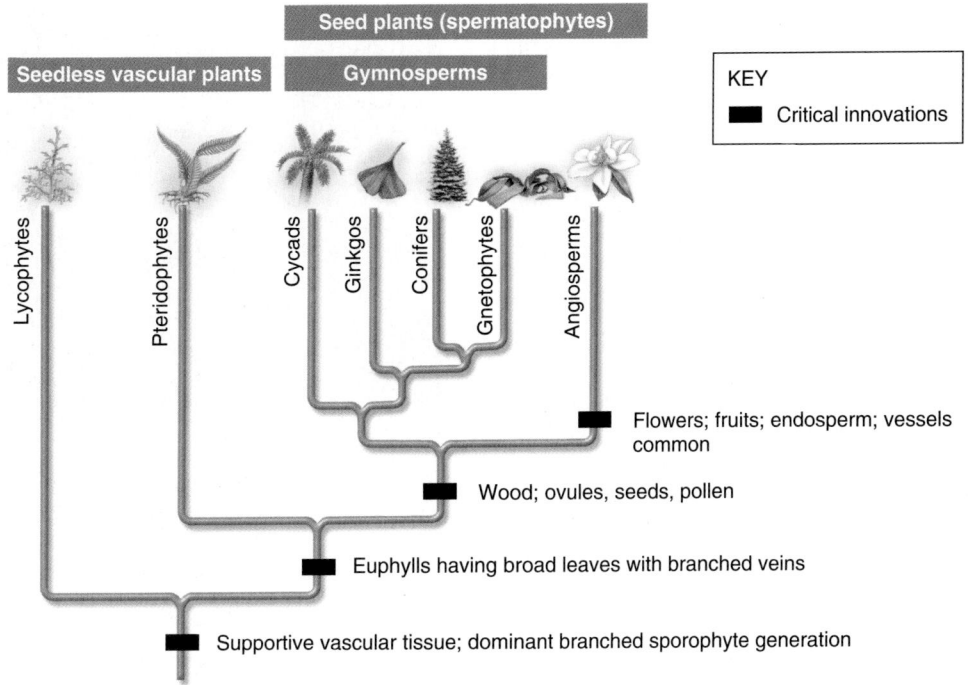

Figure 29.1 Phylogeny of modern seedless and seed plants showing critical innovations.

as much as 5,440 metric tons and reaching an amazing 100 m in height. The large size of sequoias and other trees is based on the presence of **wood**, a tissue composed of numerous pipe-like arrays of empty, water-conducting cells whose walls are strengthened by an exceptionally tough secondary metabolite known as lignin. These properties enable woody tissues to transport water upward for great distances and to provide the structural support needed for trees to grow tall and produce many branches. In modern seed plants a special tissue known as the **vascular cambium** produces both thick layers of wood and thinner layers of inner bark. The inner bark transports watery solutions of organic compounds. (The structure and function of the vascular cambium, wood, and bark are described in more detail in Chapter 33.) Vascular cambium, wood, and inner bark are critical innovations that helped gymnosperms and other seed plants to compete effectively for light and other resources needed for photosynthesis.

Wood first appeared in a group of ancient plants known as the **progymnosperms** (meaning "before gymnosperms"). Woody progymnosperms, such as the fossil plant genus *Archaeopteris*, which lived 370 million years ago, were the first true trees (**Figure 29.2a**). These grew to about 7 m tall and had large fernlike fronds at the top (**Figure 29.2b**). Progymnosperms formed the first extensive forests, found preserved in late Devonian rocks at Escuminac Bay and Gaspé in Quebec, the Ghost River area of Alberta, Hess Mountains in Yukon, and Ellesmere Island in Nunavut. Progymnosperms were able to produce a vascular cambium and wood because their vascular tissue was arranged in a ring around a central pith of nonvascular tissue. (In contrast, the vascular tissue of earlier tracheophytes was arranged differently.) This ring of vascular tissue, known as a **eustele**, contained cells that were able to develop

into the vascular cambium as seedlings grew into saplings. The vascular cambium then produced wood, allowing saplings to grow into tall trees. Modern seed plants inherited the

(a)   (b)

Figure 29.2 Wood first appeared in plants called progymnosperms. (a) The progymnosperm *Archaeopteris* is among the most ancient trees on the planet and was the main constituent of the first forests. Fossils of this tree have been found in Devonian rocks across Canada. (b) A large frond from *Archaeopteris halliana* in the Escuminac Formation from Miguasha Provincial Park, Quebec.

BioConnections: *Look ahead to Figure 51.26a–51.26e. In what way do ancient* Archaeopteris *forests differ from most forests of today?*

eustele, explaining why many gymnosperms and angiosperms are also able to produce vascular cambia and wood. Despite the fact that progymnosperms were woody plants, they did not produce seeds. This fact reveals that wood originated before seeds evolved.

Progymnosperms and diverse early gymnosperms were the major vegetation present during the Mesozoic era, also known as the Age of Dinosaurs. Some groups of gymnosperms became extinct before or as a result of the K/T event at the end of the Cretaceous period 65 million years ago (see Chapter 28). Only a few gymnosperm phyla have survived to modern times: cycads (the Cycadophyta); ginkgos, of which *Ginkgo biloba* is the only surviving member of a once large phylum termed Ginkgophyta; conifers (the Coniferophyta); and gnetophytes (Gnetophyta). These phyla display distinctive reproductive features and play important roles in ecology and human affairs (**Table 29.1**).

Cycads Are Endangered in the Wild but Widely Used as Ornamentals

Cycads are regarded as the earliest diverging modern gymnosperm phylum, originating more than 300 million years ago. Nearly 300 cycad species occur today, primarily in tropical and subtropical regions. However, many species of cycads are rare, and their tropical forest homes are increasingly threatened by human activities. Consequently, all cycads are listed as endangered species, and commercial trade in cycads is regulated by CITES (Convention on International Trade in Endangered Species of Wild Fauna and Flora), a voluntary international agreement between governments.

The structure of cycads is so interesting and attractive that many species are cultivated for use in outdoor plantings or as houseplants. The nonwoody stems of some cycads emerge from the ground much like tree trunks, some reaching 15 m in height, while other cycads produce subterranean stems (**Figure 29.3**). Cycads have spreading, palmlike leaves (*cycad* comes from a Greek word meaning "palm"). Mature leaves of the African cycad *Encephalartos laurentianus* can reach an astounding 8.8 m long!

In addition to underground roots, which provide anchorage and take up water and minerals, many cycads produce coralloid

(a) Emergent cycad stem   **(b) Submergent cycad stem**

Figure 29.3 **Cycads.** Palmlike foliage and conspicuous seed-producing cones are features of most cycads. **(a)** The stems of some cycads emerge from the ground. **(b)** The stems of other cycads are submerged in the ground.

Concept check: *Why should people avoid eating cycad seeds or products made from them?*

roots. Such roots extend aboveground and have branching shapes resembling corals (**Figure 29.4**). Coralloid root tissues harbour a bright blue-green ring of symbiotic cyanobacteria (see Figure 29.4 inset). These cyanobacteria use light to produce

Root surface

Cyanobacteria

(a) Coralloid roots

(b) Coralloid root cross-section

Figure 29.4 **Coralloid roots of cycads.** **(a)** Many cycads produce aboveground branching roots that resemble branched corals. **(b)** This magnified cross-section of a coralloid root shows a ring of symbiotic blue-green cyanobacteria, which provide the plant with a form of nitrogen that can be used to make essential cellular compounds.

Concept check: *Why do the coralloid roots grow aboveground?*

Table 29.1	Distinguishing Characteristics of Modern Seed Plant Phyla			
Seed plant group	Vessels in wood	Flowers, fruit, seed endosperm	Flagellate sperm	Female gametangia
Gymnosperms				
Cycads	No	No	Yes	Yes
Ginkgo biloba	No	No	Yes	Yes
Conifers	No	No	No	Yes
Gnetophytes	Yes	No	No	No
Angiosperms	Yes	Yes	No	No

ATP by cyclic electron flow. The ATP helps to fuel cyanobacterial nitrogen fixation, which produces nitrogen minerals used in host growth (see Chapters 25 and 35).

Recent studies have revealed that the cyanobacteria in *Cycas micronesica* produce an unusual amino acid that is distributed to the host plant's leaves and seeds. The distinctive amino acid, known as BMAA (β-N-methylamino-L-alanine), is harmful to humans who consume flour made from cycad seeds or the meat of bats that have fed on *C. micronesica*. This toxin has been linked to the unusually high occurrence of a dementia resembling Alzheimer's disease among the Chamorro people of Guam in the Mariana Islands chain. BMAA was also found in the brain tissues of people with dementia who had not consumed foods originating from cycads. In an effort to understand these cases, researchers examined many types of cyanobacteria from diverse habitats and discovered that most cyanobacteria produce BMAA in nature, suggesting that the toxic amino acid could be more widely present in the environment than previously thought. Studies of cycad toxicity have thus revealed a potential human health hazard of widespread concern. Because cycads generally produce a variety of toxins that likely deter herbivorous animals, experts recommend that humans should not consume food products made from these plants.

Cycad reproduction is distinctive in several ways. Individual cycad plants produce conspicuous conelike structures that bear either ovules and seeds or pollen (see Figure 29.3). When mature, both types of reproductive structure emit odours that attract beetles. These beetles carry pollen to ovules, where the pollen produces tubes that deliver flagellate sperm to eggs.

Ginkgo biloba Is the Last Survivor of a Once Diverse Group

The beautiful tree *Ginkgo biloba* is the single remaining species of a once diverse phylum that existed during the Age of Dinosaurs (**Figure 29.5a**). *G. biloba* takes its species name from the lobed shape of its leaves, which have unusual forked veins (**Figure 29.5b**). Today, *G. biloba* may be nearly extinct in the wild; widely cultivated modern *Ginkgo* trees are descended

from seeds produced by a tree found in a remote Japanese temple garden and brought to Europe by seventeenth-century explorers.

G. biloba trees are widely planted along city streets because they are ornamental and tolerate cold, heat, and pollution better than most trees. A single tree can live for more than a thousand years and grow to 30 m in height. Individual trees produce either ovules and seeds or pollen, based on a sex chromosome system much like that of humans. Ovule-producing trees have two X chromosomes; pollen-producing trees have one X and one Y chromosome. Wind disperses pollen to ovules, where pollen grains germinate to produce pollen tubes. These tubes grow through ovule tissues for several months, absorbing nutrients that are used for sperm development. Eventually the pollen tubes burst, delivering flagellate sperm to egg cells. After fertilization, zygotes develop into embryos, and the ovule integument develops into a fleshy, bad-smelling outer seed coat and a hard inner seed coat. For street-side or garden plantings, people usually select pollen-producing trees to avoid the stinky seeds (**Figure 29.5c**).

Conifers Are the Most Diverse Modern Gymnosperm Lineage

The conifers are a lineage of trees named for their seed cones, of which pinecones are familiar examples (**Figure 29.6**). Conifers have been important components of terrestrial vegetation since the end of the Carboniferous period some 300 million years ago. Modern conifer families have existed for about 200 million years, survived the K/T event, and today include more than 500 species in 50 genera. Conifers are particularly common in mountain and high-latitude forests and are important sources of wood and paper pulp.

Conifers produce simple pollen cones and more complex ovule-bearing cones (**Figure 29.7**). The pollen cones of conifers bear many leaflike structures, each with a microsporangium in which meiosis occurs and pollen grains develop. By contrast, the ovule cones of conifers are composed of many short branch systems that bear ovules. Ruth Stockey, from the University of

(a) *Ginkgo biloba* tree

(b) *Ginkgo biloba* leaf

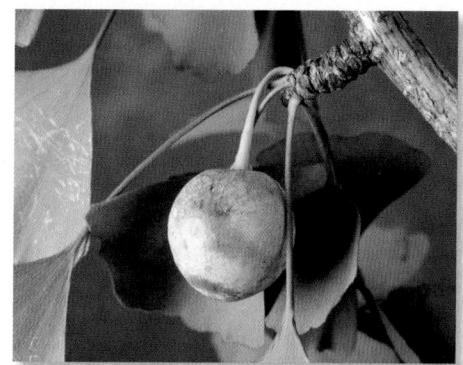

(c) *Ginkgo biloba* seed

Figure 29.5 *Ginkgo biloba.* (a) A *Ginkgo biloba* tree, (b) fan-shaped leaves with forked veins, and (c) seeds with fleshy, foul-smelling seed coats.

(a) Pine (*Pinus ponderosa*)

(b) Dawn redwood (*Metasequoia glyptostroboides*)

Figure 29.6 **Representative conifers.** (a) Many conifers, such as pine, are not deciduous, meaning that they do not lose all their leaves at the same time in the autumn. (b) Some conifers, such as the dawn redwood, are deciduous, meaning that they discard their leaves in the autumn.

2 In ovule cones, megaspores are produced by meiosis within megasporangia. In pollen cones, microspores are produced by meiosis within microsporangia.

3a In ovule cones, megaspores undergo mitosis and produce female gametophytes containing eggs within archegonia. The entire structure, including the outer integuments, is an ovule. Each scale of the cone has two ovules; only one ovule is shown here.

1 Sporophytes produce two types of cones: ovule cones and pollen cones.

Mature sporophyte (2n)

Ovule cone

Cone scale

Megaspore

Scale

Egg (n)

Ovule

Meiosis

Megasporangium

Mitosis

Integument

Female gametophyte (n)

Megasporangium (2n)

Archegonium (n)

Seed coat

Microspores

Pollen grain (n)

Seedling

Pollen cone

Section of cone

Microsporangium

3b In pollen cones, microspores undergo mitosis and develop into pollen grains, which contain young male gametophytes.

KEY

Haploid

Diploid

Ovule

Scale

Seed

4 Pollen grains are dispersed into the wind and encounter ovules.

Male gametophyte (n)

8 Seeds germinate, and embryo sporophytes grow into seedlings.

Sperm

Embryo (2n)

Mitosis

Fertilization

5 The pollen grain's male gametophyte matures, producing sperm cells in a pollen tube.

7 The zygote produces an embryo in a seed. Mature seeds are dispersed.

6 The pollen tube delivers sperm to eggs, where fertilization occurs. Only one egg per ovule is fertilized and develops.

Figure 29.7 The life cycle of the genus *Pinus*.

Principle: *Living organisms grow, develop, and reproduce.* This diagram illustrates the entire seed-to-seed growth and development cycle of conifers.

Alberta, and her colleagues have studied fossil pollen cones from Vancouver Island, British Columbia. The internal structure of these suggests that simple pollen cones probably evolved from more complex cones that were similar to ovulate cones.

When conifer pollen is mature, it is released into the wind, which transports pollen to ovules. All together, it takes more than two years for pine (the genus *Pinus*) to complete the processes of male and female gamete development, fertilization by means of nonflagellate sperm, and seed development (Figure 29.7). The seed coats of pine and some other conifers develop wings that aid in wind dispersal. Other conifers, such as yew and juniper, produce seeds with fleshy coatings that are attractive to birds, which help to disperse the seeds (**Figure 29.8**).

Conifer wood contains water transport cells that are adapted for efficient conduction even in dry conditions. These transport cells, known as tracheids, are devoid of cytoplasm and occur in long columns that function like plumbing pipelines (**Figure 29.9a**). Tracheid side and end walls possess many thin-walled, circular **pits** through which water moves both vertically and laterally from one tracheid to another. Conifer pits have a porous outer region that lets water flow through and

(a) Pine seed

(b) Yew seeds

(c) Juniper cones with seeds

Figure 29.8   **Conifer seeds.**   (a) Winged, wind-dispersed seed of the genus *Pinus*. (b) Fleshy-coated, bird-dispersed seeds of yew (*Taxus baccata*). (c) Fleshy cones of juniper (*Juniperus scopularum*) contain one or more seeds and are dispersed by birds.

BioConnections: *Look ahead to Figure 29.21g. How are wind-dispersed pine seeds similar to wind-dispersed fruits of the angiosperm maple?*

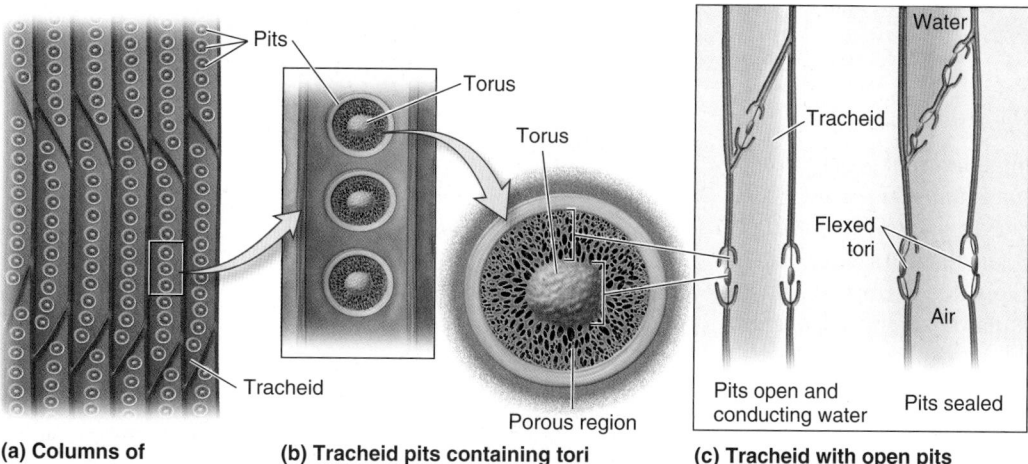

(a) Columns of tracheids showing cell walls

(b) Tracheid pits containing tori

(c) Tracheid with open pits (left side) and tracheid with sealed pits (right side)

(d) Photo of conifer wood (high magnification)

Figure 29.9   **Tracheids in conifer wood.**   (a) The lignin-rich cell walls of the conducting cells called tracheids. (b) Detailed view of a portion of a tracheid that shows the thin-walled areas known as pits, each with a torus. (c) A water-filled tracheid with open pits and an air-filled tracheid with pits sealed by the flexed tori. (d) High magnification of conifer wood.

 Principle: *Structure determines function. This illustration shows how tori in water-conducting cells of conifers aid survival in arid or cold habitats.*

a nonporous, flexible central region—the **torus**—that functions like a valve (**Figure 29.9b**). If tracheids become dry and fill with air, they are no longer able to conduct water. In this case the torus presses against the pit opening, sealing it (**Figure 29.9c**). The torus valve thereby prevents air bubbles from spreading to the next tracheid. This adaptation localizes air bubbles, preventing them from stopping water conduction in other tracheids. These specialized tracheids help to explain why conifers have been so successful for hundreds of millions of years. Conifer wood (and leaves) may also display conspicuous resin ducts, passageways for the flow of syruplike resin that helps to prevent attack by pathogens and herbivores. Resin that exudes from tree surfaces and hardens in the air sometimes forms amber, which traps and preserves insects and other organisms.

Many conifers occur in cold climates and thus display numerous adaptations to such environments. Their conical shapes and flexible branches help conifer trees shed snow, preventing heavy snow accumulations from breaking branches. Conifer leaf shape and structure are adapted to resist damage from drought that occurs in both summer and winter, when liquid water is scarce. Conifer leaves are often scalelike (**Figure 29.10a**) or needle shaped (**Figure 29.10b**); these shapes reduce the area of leaf surface from which water can evaporate. In addition, a thick, waxy cuticle coats conifer leaf surfaces (**Figure 29.10c**), retarding water loss and attack by disease organisms.

Many conifers are evergreen; that is, their leaves live for more than one year before being shed and are not all shed during the same season. Retaining leaves through winter helps conifers start up photosynthesis earlier than deciduous trees, which in spring must replace leaves lost during the previous autumn. Evergreen leaves thus provide an advantage in the short growth season of alpine or high-latitude environments. However, some conifers do lose all their leaves in the autumn. The bald cypress (*Taxodium distichum*) of the southern U.S. floodplains, tamarack (*Larix laricina*) of the northern bogs, and dawn redwood (*Metasequoia glyptostroboides*) are examples of deciduous conifers.

Gnetophytes Are of Evolutionary Interest

The modern gnetophytes consist of three unusual genera: *Gnetum, Ephedra,* and *Welwitschia. Gnetum* is unusual among modern gymnosperms in having broad leaves similar to those of many tropical plants (**Figure 29.11a**). More than 30 species of the genus *Gnetum* occur as vines, shrubs, or trees in tropical Africa or Asia. *Ephedra,* a gnetophyte genus native to arid regions of the southwestern United States, has tiny, brown, scalelike leaves and green, photosynthetic stems (**Figure 29.11b**). *Ephedra* produces secondary metabolites that aid in plant protection but also affect human physiology. Early settlers of the western United States used *Ephedra* to treat colds and other medical conditions. In fact, the modern decongestant drug pseudoephedrine is based on the chemical structure of ephedrine, which was named for and originally obtained from *Ephedra.* Pseudoephedrine sales are now restricted in many places because this compound can be used as a starting point for the synthesis of illegal drugs.

(a) Scale-shaped leaves of Eastern red cedar

(b) Needle-shaped leaves of pine

Thick cuticle

Photosynthetic cells

Tracheids

Stomata

(c) Stained cross-section of pine needle, showing the thick cuticle

Figure 29.10 Conifer leaves. The leaves of conifers are typically shaped as small scales or long needles, with similar internal structure.

Concept check: *In what ways are conifer leaves adapted to resist water loss from their surfaces?*

Ephedrine has also been used to enhance sports performance, a practice that has elicited medical concern.

Welwitschia, the third gnetophyte genus, has only one living representative species. *Welwitschia mirabilis* is a strange-looking plant that grows in the coastal Namib Desert of southwestern Africa, one of the driest places on Earth (**Figure 29.11c**). A long taproot anchors a stubby stem that barely emerges from the ground. Two very long leaves grow from the stem but rapidly

(a) Genus *Gnetum*

(b) *Ephedra californica*

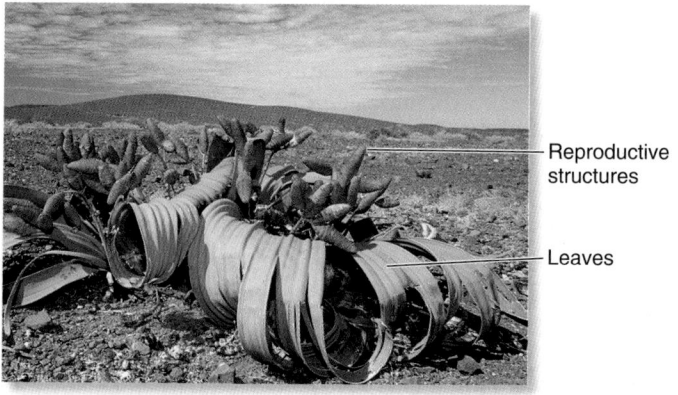

(c) *Welwitschia mirabilis*

Figure 29.11 Gnetophytes. **(a)** A tropical plant of the genus *Gnetum,* displaying broad leaves and reproductive structures. **(b)** *Ephedra californica* growing in deserts of North America, showing minuscule, brown leaves on green, photosynthetic stems and reproductive structures. **(c)** *Welwitschia mirabilis* growing in the Namib Desert of southwestern Africa, showing long, wind-shredded leaves and reproductive structures.

become wind-shredded into many strips. The plant is thought to obtain most of its water from coastal fog that accumulates on the leaves, explaining how *W. mirabilis* can grow and reproduce in such a dry place.

Evolutionary plant biologists are interested in gnetophytes because their relationships to other seed plants are unclear. Some morphological features suggest that gnetophytes might be closely related to the angiosperms. For example, female gametangia (archegonia; refer back to Figure 28.7) are present in the ovules of most gymnosperms but have been lost from gnetophytes and angiosperms. Gnetophytes also possess vessels—a type of large-diameter water-conducting feature—in their vascular tissue, as do most angiosperms but not other gymnosperms (see Table 29.1). However, the vessels of gnetophytes are thought to have evolved independently of angiosperm vessels. In addition, recent molecular evidence links gnetophytes more closely to the conifers or specifically with the conifer genus *Pinus* (pine). The identity of the gymnosperm group from which the angiosperms arose remains unresolved.

29.2 THE EVOLUTION AND DIVERSITY OF MODERN ANGIOSPERMS

Learning Outcomes:

1. List four flower organs and their functions, and explain how each flower part may have first evolved.
2. Describe how diversification of flowers and fruits enhances seed production and dispersal.
3. Name three major types of angiosperm secondary metabolites and how these affect animals.

More than 124 million years ago, one extinct gymnosperm group, although it's unclear which one, gave rise to the **angiosperms**, the flowering plants. Angiosperms retained many structural and reproductive features from ancestral seed plants, but they also evolved several traits not found or seldom found among other land plants.

Flowers and fruits are two of the defining features of angiosperms (**Figure 29.12**), because these features do not occur in other modern plants (see Table 29.1). The term *angiosperm* means "enclosed seed," which reflects the presence of seeds within fruits. Seed endosperm is another defining feature of the flowering plants (see Chapters 28 and 37).

Although humans obtain wood, medicines, and other valuable products from gymnosperms, we depend even more on the angiosperms. Our food, beverages, and spices—flavoured by an amazing variety of secondary metabolites—primarily come from flowering plants. People surround themselves with ornamental flowering plants and decorative items displaying flowers or fruit. We also commonly use flowers and fruit in ceremonies. In this section we focus on how flowers, fruits, and secondary metabolites played key roles in angiosperm diversification. You will also learn that features of flowers, fruits, and secondary metabolites are used to classify and identify angiosperm species.

Figure 29.12 **Angiosperm flowers and fruits.** Citrus plants display the critical innovations of flowering plants: flowers and fruits, shown here, and seed endosperm (not shown).

Diverse Flower Types Are Adaptations That Foster Seed Production

Flowers are complex reproductive structures that are specialized for the efficient production of pollen and seeds. The sexual reproduction process of angiosperms depends on flowers. Thus, as the flowering plants diversified, flowers of varied types evolved as reproductive adaptations to differing environmental conditions. To understand this process, let's start by considering the basic flower parts and their roles in reproduction.

Flower Parts and Their Reproductive Roles Flowers are produced at stem tips and contain four types of organs: sepals, petals, pollen-producing stamens, and ovule-producing carpels (**Figure 29.13**). These flower organs are supported by tissue

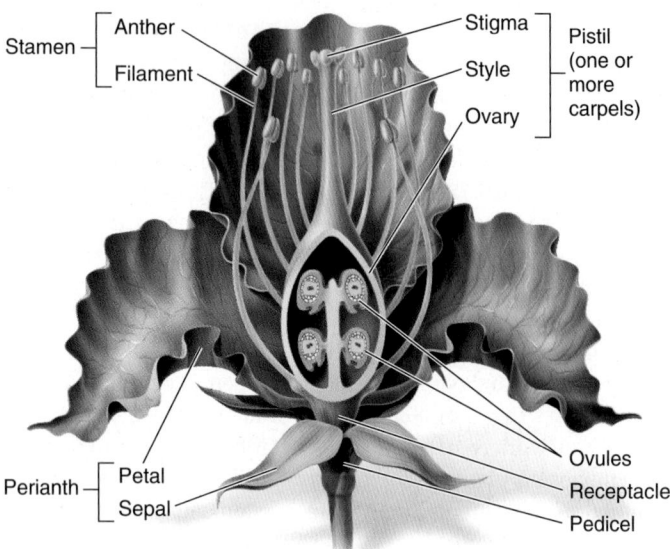

Figure 29.13 **Generalized flower structure.** Although flowers are diverse in size, shape, and colour, they commonly have the parts illustrated here.

known as a receptacle, located at the tip of a flower stalk (also called a pedicel). The functioning of several genes that control flower organ development explains why carpels are the central-most flower organs, why stamens surround carpels, and why petals and sepals are the outermost flower organs (refer back to Figure 17.21).

Many flowers produce attractive petals that play a role in **pollination**: the transfer of pollen among flowers. Sepals of many flowers are green and form the outer, protective layer of flower buds. By contrast, the sepals of other flowers resemble attractive petals. All of a flower's petals and sepals are collectively known as the **perianth**. Most flowers produce one or more stamens, the structures that produce and disperse pollen. Most flowers also contain carpels, structures that produce ovules. Some flowers lack perianths, stamens, or carpels. Flowers that possess all four types of flower organs are known as **complete flowers**, while flowers lacking one or more organ types are known as **incomplete flowers**. Flowers that contain both stamens and carpels are described as **perfect flowers**, while flowers lacking either stamens or carpels are **imperfect flowers**.

Flowers also differ in the numbers of organs they produce. Some flowers produce only a single carpel, others display several separate carpels, and many possess several carpels that are fused together into a compound structure. Both a single carpel and compound carpels are referred to as a **pistil** (from the Latin word *pistillum,* meaning "pestle"), because it resembles the device people use to grind materials to powder in a mortar (see Figure 29.13). Only one pistil is present in flowers that have only one carpel and in flowers with fused carpels. By contrast, flowers possessing several separate carpels display multiple pistils.

Pistils are usually differentiated into three regions having distinct functions. A topmost portion of the pistil, known as the **stigma**, receives and recognizes pollen of the appropriate species or genotype. The stigma allows pollen of appropriate genetic type to germinate, producing a long pollen tube that grows through the elongate **style**. The pollen tube thereby delivers two sperm cells to ovules (**Figure 29.14**). In the distinctive angiosperm process known as **double fertilization**, one sperm fuses with the egg to form a zygote, and the other sperm fuses with other haploid cells of the female gametophyte. The latter is the first step in the development of a characteristic angiosperm nutritive tissue known as endosperm. Fed by the endosperm, the zygote develops into an embryo, and the ovule develops into a seed. Ovaries (and sometimes additional flower parts) develop into fruits.

Early Flowers Fossils of whole plants with recognizable flowers and fruits are known from geological deposits about 124 million years old, though molecular clock data and fossil pollen grains suggest that angiosperms may have originated earlier. Flowers were a critical innovation that led to extensive angiosperm diversification. Evolutionary botanist Peter Endress has studied flower evolution by comparing the structures of modern and fossil flowers. His studies suggest that the earliest flowers were quite small—only about 1 mm

Figure 29.14 The life cycle of a flowering plant, illustrated by the genus *Polygonum.* Flowering plant life cycles differ in the length of the cycle and the number of cells and nuclei occurring in the female gametophyte, the seven-celled, eight-nuclei of *Polygonum* being common.

in diameter—and had few parts, though both stamens and carpels were present. Comparative studies also suggest how modern stamens and carpels might have arisen. Early fossil flowers and some modern flowers have broad stamens that are leaf-shaped, with elongated, pollen-producing microsporangia on the stamen surface (**Figure 29.15a**). In contrast, the stamens of most modern plants have become narrowed to form filaments, or stalks, that elevate anthers, clusters of microsporangia that produce pollen and then open to release it (see Figure 29.13). Filaments and anthers are thus adaptations that foster pollen dispersal. Plant biologists hypothesize that carpels evolved from leaflike structures bearing ovules on their surfaces and that such leaves folded over ovules, protecting them. In support of this hypothesis is the fact that the carpels of some early diverging modern plants are leaflike structures that fold over ovules, with the carpel edges stuck together by secretions (**Figure 29.15b**). In contrast, most modern flowers produce carpels whose edges have fused together into a tube whose lower portion (ovary)

encloses ovules. Plant biologists hypothesize that such evolutionary change increased ovule protection, which would improve plant fitness.

Flowering Plants Diversified into Several Lineages, Including Monocots and Eudicots

Amborella trichopoda, a shrub that occurs in cloud forests on the South Pacific island of New Caledonia, is an example of a modern angiosperm whose flowers display hypothesized ancient features. For example, the fairly small flowers display stamens with broad filaments and have several separate carpels (**Figure 29.16**). Gene sequencing studies indicate that *A. trichopoda* is a very early diverging flowering plant, as are water lilies and the star anise plant and its close relatives (**Figure 29.17**). Magnoliids, represented by the genus *Magnolia,* are closely related to two very large and diverse angiosperm lineages: the **monocots** and the **eudicots**. Monocots and eudicots are named for differences in the number of leaves that occur on their embryos, located within

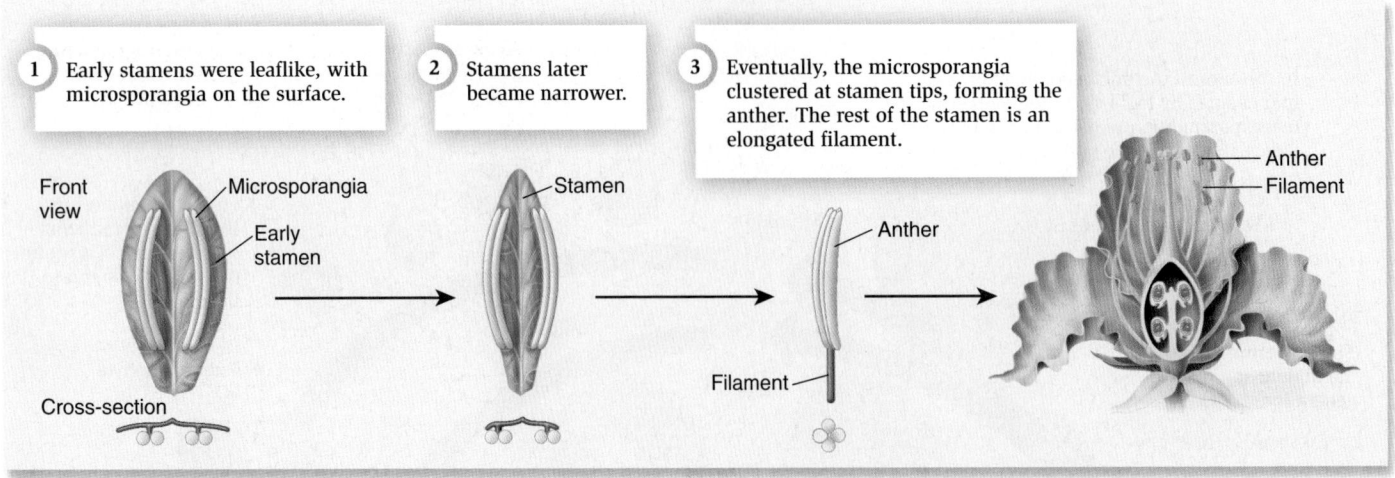

1. Early stamens were leaflike, with microsporangia on the surface.

2. Stamens later became narrower.

3. Eventually, the microsporangia clustered at stamen tips, forming the anther. The rest of the stamen is an elongated filament.

(a) Stamen evolution

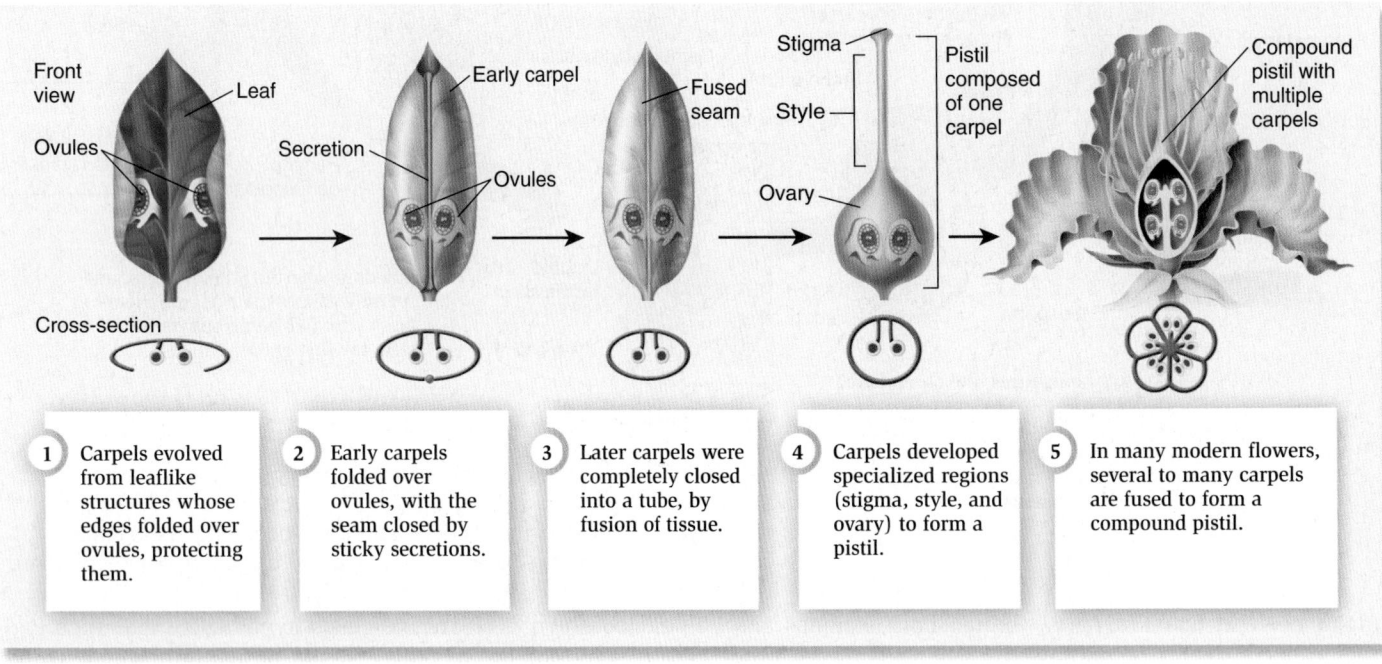

1. Carpels evolved from leaflike structures whose edges folded over ovules, protecting them.

2. Early carpels folded over ovules, with the seam closed by sticky secretions.

3. Later carpels were completely closed into a tube, by fusion of tissue.

4. Carpels developed specialized regions (stigma, style, and ovary) to form a pistil.

5. In many modern flowers, several to many carpels are fused to form a compound pistil.

(b) Carpel evolution

Figure 29.15 Hypothetical evolution of stamens, carpels, and pistil.

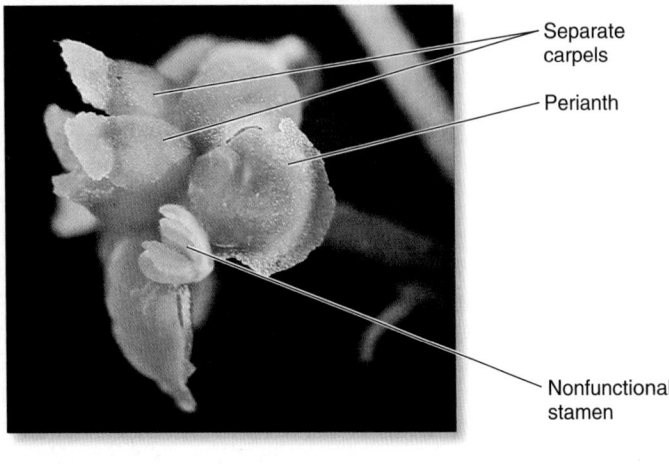

Figure 29.16 *Amborella trichopoda* flower, similar to a hypothesized early flower. This small flower is only about 3 to 4 mm in diameter. It displays several central, greenish carpels; nonfunctional stamens; and a pink perianth. This plant species also produces flowers that lack carpels but have many functional stamens.

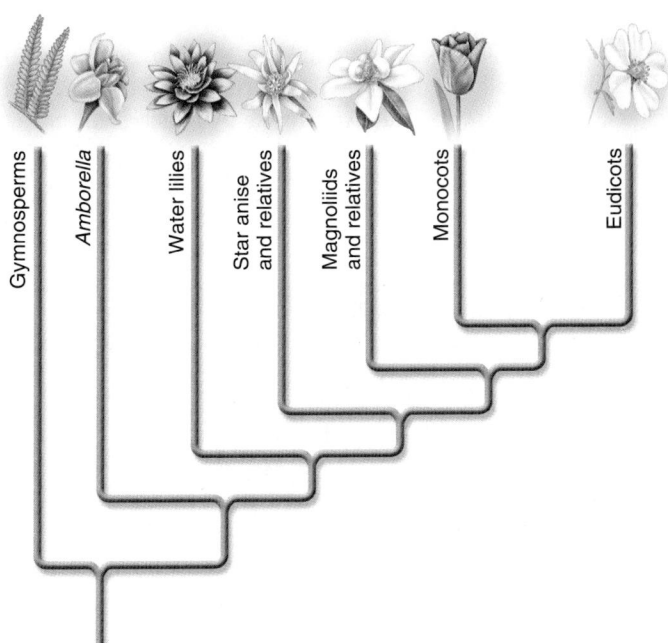

Figure 29.17 A phylogeny showing the major modern angiosperm lineages.

(a) A monocot with six tepals

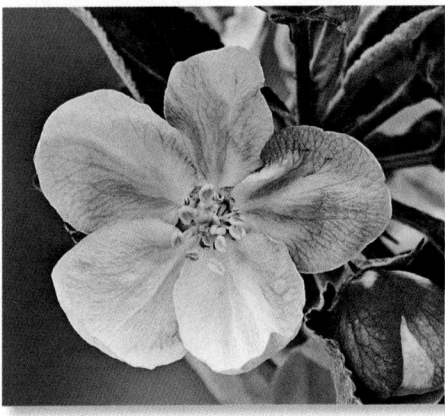

(b) A eudicot with five petals

Figure 29.18 Flower part number is a characteristic difference between monocots and eudicots. **(a)** Flowers and buds of lily (genus *Lilium*), displaying six tepals. **(b)** A flower and buds of apple (genus *Malus*), showing five flower petals. Green sepals are visible around the pink buds.

seeds; monocot embryos have one seed leaf, while eudicots have two embryonic leaves. Monocots differ from eudicots in several additional ways (see Chapter 33). For example, monocots typically have flowers with parts numbering three or some multiple of three (**Figure 29.18a**). In contrast eudicot flower parts often occur in fours, fives, or a multiple of four or five (**Figure 29.18b**). Fossil pollen evidence has shown that monocots and eudicots diverged more than 120 million years ago.

GENOMES AND PROTEOMES

Whole Genome Duplications Influenced the Evolution of Flowering Plants

Genome doubling, also known as polyploidy, occurs in a wide variety of eukaryotes and has happened frequently during the evolutionary history of plants. An estimated 40% to 70% of all plants are polyploid, meaning that the entire diploid genome has been duplicated at least once. Genomic analyses indicate that different patterns of whole genome duplication occurred in monocots and eudicots after their divergence. Whole genome duplication has the potential to affect species' evolutionary pathways because it offers the opportunity for many genes to diverge, forming gene families. For example, whole genome duplications increased the diversity of an important class of plant transcription factors, the MADS-Box proteins, in seed plants.

Two major types of polyploidy occur in plants. Autopolyploid plants can arise when homologous chromosome pairs do not separate during meiosis, a process known as nondisjunction. As a result, plants produce diploid spores, gametophytes, and gametes when these life stages would otherwise be haploid. The mating of two diploid gametes will produce a tetraploid plant: one having four sets of chromosomes.

A second major type of whole genome duplication in plants involves an initial hybridization between two species having different chromosome numbers. Such a hybrid would not be able to produce viable spores because chromosomes could not pair properly at meiosis. However, if such a hybrid plant then undergoes a whole genome duplication process, producing an allopolyploid, homologous chromosomes are available for pairing during meiosis, and viable spores, gametophytes, and gametes can form. Many common crops, including wheat and cotton, are allopolyploids.

In addition to allopolyploidy, plants are known to obtain mitochondrial genes from other plant species by means of horizontal gene transfer. Genes have moved from one angiosperm species to another and between angiosperms and nonflowering plants, probably by mitochondrial fusion. For example, of the 31 genes present in the mitochondrial genome of the early diverging flowering plant *Amborella trichopoda*, at least 20 were obtained from other angiosperms or mosses that grow on *A. trichopoda*'s surfaces. Because plant nuclear genomes commonly take up genes from organelles in the same cell, such foreign mitochondrial genes could end up in the nucleus. Hybridization and mitochondrial transfer are mechanisms by which plant lineages undergo reticulate (network-like) and treelike evolution.

Flower Diversification Has Fostered Efficient Seed Production

During the diversification of flowering plants, flower evolution involved several types of changes that fostered the transfer of pollen from one plant to another. Fusion of flower organs, clustering of flowers into groups, and reducing the perianth are some examples. Orchids are one example of ways in which flower parts have become fused: stamens and carpels are fused into a single reproductive column that is surrounded by attractive tepals (**Figure 29.19a**). This arrangement of flower organs fosters orchid pollination by particular insects and is a distinctive feature of the orchid family. Many plants produce flowers in clusters known as **inflorescences**, which occur in several types. The sunflower family features a type of inflorescence in which many small flowers are clustered into a head (**Figure 29.19b**). The flowers at the centre of a sunflower head function in reproduction and lack showy petals, while flowers at the rim have showy petals that attract pollinators. Heads allow pollinators to transfer pollen among a large number of flowers at the same time. The grass family features flowers having few or no perianths, explaining why grass flowers are not showy (**Figure 29.19c**). This adaptation fosters pollination by wind, because petals would only get in the way of such pollen transfer.

During the evolution of both eudicots and monocots, the petals of some flowers fused into floral tubes. Such tubes hold sugar-rich **nectar** as a reward for **pollinators**, animals that carry pollen between flowers. The diameters of floral tubes vary among flowers and are evolutionarily tuned to the feeding structures of diverse animals, which range from the narrow tongues of butterflies to the wider bills of nectar-feeding birds (**Figure 29.20**). Nectar-feeding bats stick their heads into even larger tubular flowers to lap up nectar with their tongues. Floral tubes have thus allowed plants to diversify in association with pollinators, a process that we will describe later in this chapter.

Diverse Types of Fruits Function in Seed Dispersal

Fruits are structures that develop from ovary walls in diverse ways that aid the dispersal of enclosed seeds. Seed dispersal helps to prevent seedlings from competing with their larger parents for scarce resources, such as water and light. Dispersal of seeds also allows plants to colonize new habitats. Diverse fruit types illustrate many ways in which plants have become adapted for effective seed dispersal. Like flower types, fruit types are useful in classifying and identifying angiosperms.

Many mature angiosperm fruits, such as cherries, grapes, and citrus, are attractively coloured, soft, juicy, and tasty (**Figure 29.21a–29.21c**). Such fruits are adapted to attract animals that consume the fruits, digest the outer portion as food,

(a) An orchid flower with fused pistil and stamens

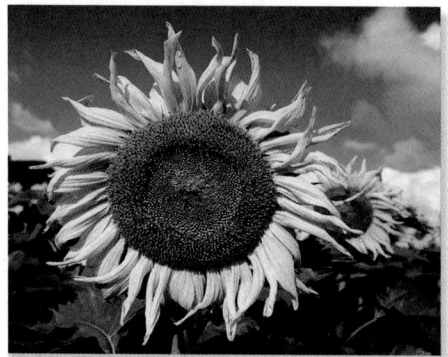

(b) A sunflower plant showing inflorescence

(c) Grass flowers lacking showy perianth

Figure 29.19 Evolutionary changes in flower structure. **(a)** An orchid of the genus *Cattleya* has fused stamens and carpals, and six tepals, one of which is specialized to form a lower lip. **(b)** An inflorescence (head) of sunflower (genus *Helianthus*). This inflorescence includes a rim of flowers with conspicuous petals that attract pollinators and an inner disk of flowers that lack attractive perianths. **(c)** Grass flowers of the genus *Triticum* lack a showy perianth.

Concept check: *What advantage does the nonshowy perianth of grass flowers provide?*

(a) Zinnia flower and butterfly   **(b) Hibiscus flower and hummingbird**   **(c) Saguaro cactus flower and bat**

Figure 29.20 **Floral tubes and coevolved pollinators.** **(a)** This zinnia flower is composed of an outer rim of showy flowers and a central disk of narrow tubular flowers that produce nectar. Butterflies, but not other pollinators, are able to reach the nectar by using their narrow tongues. **(b)** The hibiscus flower produces nectar in a floral tube whose diameter corresponds to the dimensions of a hummingbird bill. **(c)** The saguaro cactus (*Carnegiea gigantea*) flower forms a floral tube that is wide enough for nectar-feeding bats to get their heads inside. The cactus flower has been drawn here as if it were transparent, to illustrate bat pollination.

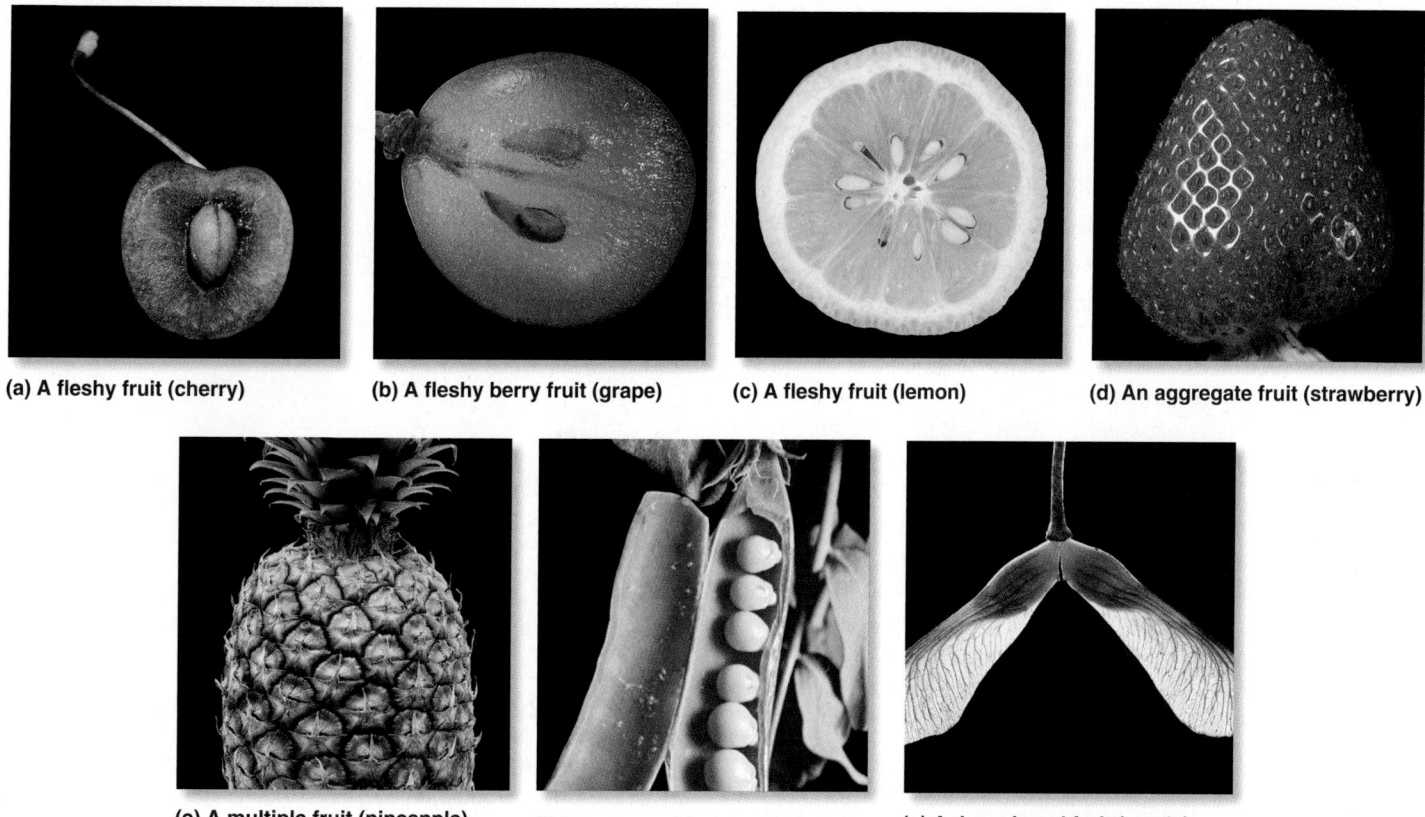

(a) A fleshy fruit (cherry)   **(b) A fleshy berry fruit (grape)**   **(c) A fleshy fruit (lemon)**   **(d) An aggregate fruit (strawberry)**

(e) A multiple fruit (pineapple)   **(f) Legumes with dry pods (peas)**   **(g) A dry, winged fruit (maple)**

Figure 29.21 **Representative fruit types.** **(a–c)** Cherry, grape, and lemon are fleshy, sweet fruits adapted to attract animals that consume the fruits and excrete the seeds. **(d)** Strawberry is an aggregate fruit, consisting of many tiny, single-seeded fruits produced by a single flower. The fruits are embedded in the surface of a fleshy receptacle that is adapted to attract animal seed dispersal agents. **(e)** Pineapple is a large multiple fruit formed by the aggregation of smaller fruits, each produced by one of the flowers in an inflorescence. **(f)** Peas produce legumes, fruits that open on two sides to release seeds. **(g)** Maple trees produce dry fruits with wings adapted for wind dispersal. Tasty fruits often contain extremely hard or poisonous seeds, which discourages consumption of the seeds.

and eliminate the seeds, thereby dispersing them. Hard seed coats prevent the seeds from being destroyed by the animal's digestive system. Strawberries are actually an aggregation of many fruits that all develop from a single flower having multiple pistils (**Figure 29.21d**). The ovaries of these pistils develop into the tiny, single-seeded yellow fruits on a strawberry surface; the fleshy, red, sweet portion of a strawberry develops from the flower receptacle. The strawberry system of aggregate fruits allows a single animal consumer, such as a bird, to disperse many seeds at the same time.

Pineapples (**Figure 29.21e**) are juicy multiple fruits that develop when many ovaries of an inflorescence fuse together. Multiple fruits have the advantage of being larger than individual fruits of the same species. Larger fruits attract relatively large animals that have the ability to disperse seeds for long distances. Mulberries and figs are additional examples of multiple fruits that provide similar benefits.

The plant family informally known as **legumes** is named for its distinctive fruits: dry pods that open down both sides when seeds are mature, thereby releasing them (**Figure 29.21f**). Nuts and grains are additional examples of dry fruits, which have the advantage of rotting less rapidly than juicy fruits. **Grains** are the characteristic single-seeded fruits of cereal grasses, such as rice, corn (maize), barley, and wheat. Maple trees produce dry and thus lightweight fruits with wings, features that foster effective wind dispersal (**Figure 29.21g**). Other plants produce dry fruits with surface burrs that attach to animal fur or produce floating fruits that disperse in water. Thus, flowering plants have diverse mechanisms for dispersing their seeds.

Angiosperms Produce Diverse Secondary Metabolites That Play Important Roles in Structure, Reproduction, and Protection

As we discussed in Chapter 7, secondary metabolism involves the synthesis of organic compounds that are not essential for cell structure and growth but aid in organism survival and reproduction. These molecules, called **secondary metabolites**, are produced by various prokaryotes, fungi, protists, and all plants but are most diverse in the angiosperms. About 100,000 different types of secondary metabolites are known, most of these produced by flowering plants. Because secondary metabolites play essential roles in plant structure, reproduction, and protection, diversification of these compounds has influenced flowering plant evolution. Three major classes of plant secondary metabolites occur: (1) terpenes and terpenoids; (2) phenolics, which include flavonoids and related compounds; and (3) alkaloids (**Figure 29.22**).

About 25,000 types of plant terpenes and terpenoids are derived from units of the hydrocarbon gas isoprene. Taxol, widely used in the treatment of cancer, is a terpene, as are citronella and a variety of other compounds that repel insects. Rubber, turpentine, rosin, and amber are complex terpenoids that likewise serve important roles in plant biology, as well as having useful human applications.

Phenolic compounds are responsible for some flower and fruit colours, as well as the distinctive flavours of cinnamon, nutmeg, ginger, cloves, chilies, and vanilla. Phenolics absorb

Terpene

Natural rubber (complex terpene)

(a) Natural rubber produced by *Hevea brasiliensis* **is an example of a complex terpene.**

Phenolic

Capsaicin

(b) Capsaicin extracted from capsicum pepper is an example of a phenolic compound.

Alkaloid

Caffeine

(c) Caffeine produced by *Coffea arabica* **is an example of an alkaloid.**

Figure 29.22 Major types of plant secondary metabolites. Note that the chemistry of plant secondary metabolites differs from that of the primary compounds produced by all cells. The production by plants of terpenes, phenolics, and alkaloids helps to explain how plants survive and reproduce, and why plants are useful to humans in so many ways.

ultraviolet radiation, thereby preventing damage to cellular DNA. They also help to defend plants against insects and disease microbes. Some phenolic compounds found in tea, red wine, grape juice, and blueberries have antioxidant properties that prevent the formation of damaging free radicals.

Alkaloids are nitrogen-containing secondary metabolites that often have potent effects on the animal nervous system. Plants produce at least 12,000 types of alkaloids, and some plants produce many alkaloids. Caffeine, nicotine, morphine, ephedrine, cocaine, heroin, and codeine are examples of alkaloids that influence the physiology and behaviour of humans. Like flower and fruit structure, secondary metabolites are useful in distinguishing among Earth's hundreds of thousands of flowering plant species.

Plants often produce tissues that seem far more distasteful or poisonous than needed for protection from most organisms that may attempt to eat them; this may be the result of an evolutionary arms race.

FEATURE INVESTIGATION

Hillig and Mahlberg Used Secondary Metabolites to Explore Species Diversification in the Genus *Cannabis*

The genus *Cannabis* has long been a source of hemp fibre used for ropes and fabric. People have also used *Cannabis* (also known as marijuana) in traditional medicine and as a hallucinogenic drug. *Cannabis* produces THC (tetrahydrocannabinol), a secondary metabolite called a cannabinoid. THC mimics compounds known as endocannabinoids, which are naturally produced and act in the brain and elsewhere in the body. THC affects humans by binding to receptor proteins in plasma membranes in the same way as natural endocannabinoids. Today, people undergoing cancer treatment sometimes use *Cannabis* to reduce nausea and stimulate their appetite, which can decline as a side effect. Cannabinoids are produced in glandular hairs that cover most of the *Cannabis* plant's surface but are particularly rich in leaves located near the flowers.

Because humans have subjected cultivated *Cannabis* plants to artificial selection for so long, plant biologists have been uncertain how many species of *Cannabis* existed in cultivation and in the wild. In the past plants cultivated for drug production were often identified as *Cannabis indica,* whereas those grown for hemp were typically known as *Cannabis sativa.* However, these species are difficult to distinguish on the basis of structural features, and the relevance of these names to wild *Cannabis* was unknown. At the same time, species identification has become important for biodiversity studies, agriculture, and law enforcement. For these reasons plant biologists Karl Hillig and Paul Mahlberg investigated the possibility that ratios of THC to another cannabinoid known as CBD (cannabidiol) might aid in defining *Cannabis* species and identifying plant samples to the species level, as shown in **Figure 29.23**. They began by collecting *Cannabis* fruits from nearly a hundred diverse locations around the world and then grew these plants from seed under uniform conditions in a greenhouse. The investigators next extracted cannabinoids, analyzed them by means of gas-liquid chromatography, and determined the ratios of THC to CBD. The results, published in 2004, suggested that the wild and cultivated *Cannabis* samples evaluated in this study could be classified into two species: *C. sativa,* displaying relatively low THC levels, and *C. indica,* having relatively high THC levels. As a result of this work ecologists, agricultural scientists, and forensic scientists can reliably use ratios of THC to CBD to classify samples. Similar studies of plant secondary metabolites offer the benefit of uncovering potential new medicinal compounds or other applications of significance to humans.

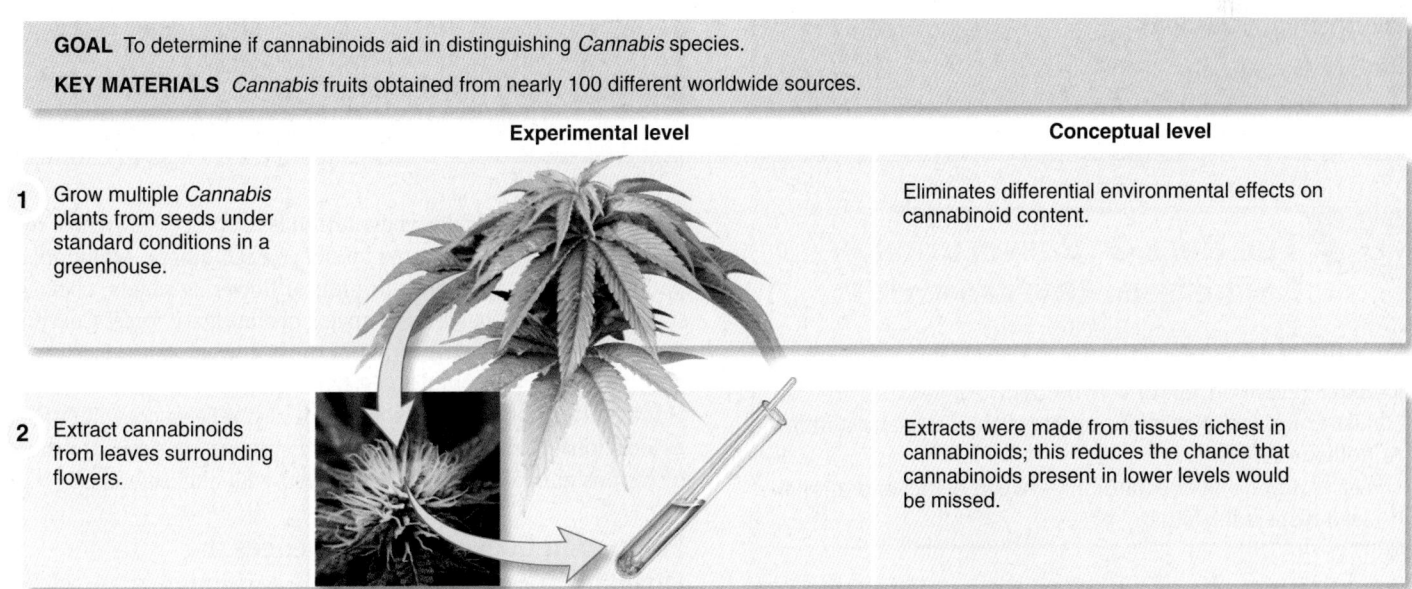

GOAL To determine if cannabinoids aid in distinguishing *Cannabis* species.

KEY MATERIALS *Cannabis* fruits obtained from nearly 100 different worldwide sources.

	Experimental level	Conceptual level
1 Grow multiple *Cannabis* plants from seeds under standard conditions in a greenhouse.		Eliminates differential environmental effects on cannabinoid content.
2 Extract cannabinoids from leaves surrounding flowers.		Extracts were made from tissues richest in cannabinoids; this reduces the chance that cannabinoids present in lower levels would be missed.

Figure 29.23   Hillig and Mahlberg's analysis of secondary metabolites in the genus *Cannabis.*

Figure 29.23   *(Continued)*

3 Analyze cannabinoids by gas-liquid chromatography. Determine ratios of THC (tetrahydrocannabinol) to CBD (cannabidiol) in about 200 *Cannabis* plants.

Previous data suggested that ratios of THC to CBD might be different in separate species.

Cannabidiol (CBD)
$(R = C_5H_{11})$

Tetrahydrocannabinol (THC)
$(R = C_5H_{11}\ \Delta^9)$

4   THE DATA

Cannabis plants isolated from diverse sources worldwide formed two groups—those having relatively high THC to CBD ratios and those having lower THC to CBD ratios.

Plants having low THC to CBD ratios, often used as hemp fibre sources, corresponded to the species *C. sativa*

Plants having high THC to CBD ratios, often used as drug sources, corresponded to the species *C. indica*.

5   CONCLUSION Differing cannabinoid ratios support a concept of two *Cannabis* species.

6   SOURCE Hillig, K.W., and Mahlberg, P.G. 2004. A chemosystematic analysis of cannabinoid variation in *Cannabis* (Cannabaceae). *American Journal of Botany* 91:966–975.

Experimental Questions

1. Why did Hillig and Mahlberg gather nearly a hundred *Cannabis* fruit samples from around the world?

2. Why did the investigators grow plants in a greenhouse before conducting the cannabinoid analysis?

3. Why did they collect samples from the leaves growing nearest the flowers?

29.3   THE ROLE OF COEVOLUTION IN ANGIOSPERM DIVERSIFICATION

Learning Outcomes:

1. Explain the concept of coevolution.
2. List examples of coevolution between plants and animal pollinators.
3. List examples of coevolution between plants and animal seed dispersal agents.

In the previous section you learned that flowering plants are commonly associated with animals in ways that strongly influence plant evolution. As a matter of fact, plants have likewise influenced animal evolution, in a diversity-generating process known as coevolution. Generally, **coevolution** is the process by which two or more species of organisms influence each other's evolutionary pathway. During the diversification of flowering plants, coevolution with animals has been a major evolutionary force. Coevolution explains the diverse forms of most flowers and many fruits, and how plants accomplish effective pollen and seed dispersal. Human attraction to flowers and fruit also reflects coevolutionary associations, because human sensory systems are similar to those of various animals that have coevolved with angiosperms.

Pollination Coevolution Influences the Diversification of Flowers and Animals

Animal pollinators transfer pollen from the anthers of one flower to the stigmas of other flowers of the same species. Pollinators thereby foster genetic variability and plant potential for evolutionary change. Insects, birds, bats, and other pollinators learn the characteristics of particular flowers, visiting them preferentially. This animal behaviour, known as constancy or fidelity, increases the odds that a flower stigma will receive pollen of the appropriate species. Animal pollinators thus offer precision of pollen transfer, which reduces the amount of pollen that plants must produce to achieve pollination. By contrast, wind-pollinated plants must produce much larger amounts of pollen because windblown pollen reaches appropriate flowers by chance.

Flowers attract the most appropriate pollinators by means of attractive colours, odours, shapes, and sizes. Secondary metabolites influence the colours and odours of many flowers. For example, flavonoids colour many blue, purple, or pink flowers. More than 700 types of chemical compounds contribute to floral odours. Most flowers reward pollinators with appropriate food: sugar-rich nectar, lipid- and protein-rich pollen, or both. Thus, flowering plants provide an important biological service, providing food for many types of pollinator animals. But some flowers lure pollinators into visiting or trap pollinators temporarily, thereby achieving pollination without actually rewarding the pollinators. Examples include flowers that look and smell like dead meat to attract flies, which are fooled but carry out pollination anyway.

Although many flowers are pollinated by a variety of animals, others have flowers that have become specialized for particular pollinators, and vice versa. These specializations, which have resulted from coevolution, are known as **pollination syndromes** (**Table 29.2**). For example, odourless red flowers, such as those of hibiscus (see Figure 29.20b), are attractive to birds, which can see the colour red but lack a sense of smell. By contrast, bees are not typically attracted to red flowers because bee vision does not extend to red. Rather, bees are attracted to blue, purple, yellow, and white flowers having sweet odours. If you are allergic to bee stings or just want to reduce the possibility of being stung, do not dress in bee-attracting flower colours or wear fragrant perfumes when in locales frequented by bees. People who work in remote regions where bees occur and where medical care may not be readily available may choose to wear colours that do not attract bees.

Pollination syndromes are also of practical importance in agriculture and in conservation biology. Fruit growers often import bees to pollinate flowers of fruit crops, thus increasing crop yields. Some plants have become so specialized to particular pollinators that if the pollinator becomes extinct, the plant becomes endangered. An example is the Hawaiian cliff-dwelling *Brighamia insignis* (**Figure 29.24**), whose presumed moth pollinator has become extinct. Humans who hand-pollinate *B. insignis* are all that stand between this plant and extinction.

Seed-Dispersal Coevolution Influences the Characteristics of Fruits and Animals

As in the case of pollination, coevolution between plants and their animal seed-dispersal agents has influenced both plant fruit characteristics and those of seed-dispersing animals. In addition, flowering plant fruits provide food for animals, an

Table 29.2	Pollination Syndromes	
Animal features	**Coevolved flower features**
Bees	
Colour vision includes UV	Often blue, purple, yellow, white (not red) colours; flowers often have a landing place
Good sense of smell	Fragrant
Require nectar and pollen	Provide nectar and abundant pollen
Butterflies	
Good colour vision	Blue, purple, deep pink, orange, red colours
Sense odours with feet	Light floral scent
Need landing place	Provide landing place
Feed with long tubular tongue	Nectar in deep, narrow floral tubes
Moths	
Active at night	Open at night; white or bright colours
Good sense of smell	Heavy, musky odours
Feed with long, thin tongue	Nectar in deep, narrow floral tubes
Birds	
Colour vision includes red	Often coloured red
Often require perch (songbirds)	Strong, damage-resistant structure
Poor sense of smell	No fragrance
Feed in daytime	Open in daytime
High nectar requirement	Copious nectar in floral tubes
Hover (hummingbirds)	Pendulous (dangling) flowers
Bats	
Poor colour vision	Light, reflective colours
Good sense of smell	Strong odours that attract bats
Active at night	Open at night
High food requirements	Copious nectar and pollen provided
Navigate by echolocation	Pendulous or borne on tree trunks

important biological service. For example, many of the plants of temperate forests produce fruits that are attractive to resident birds. Such juicy, sweet fruits have small seeds that readily pass through bird guts. Many plants signal fruit ripeness by undergoing colour changes from unripe green fruits to red, orange, yellow, blue, or black (**Figure 29.25**). Because birds have good colour vision, they are able to detect the presence of ripe fruits and consume them before the fruits drop from plants and rot. Apples, strawberries, cherries, blueberries, and blackberries are examples of fruits whose seed dispersal adaptations have made them attractive food for humans as well. By contrast, the lipid-rich fruits of Virginia creeper (*Parthenocissus quinquefolia*) and some other autumn-fruiting plants energize migratory birds but are not tasty to humans. The Virginia creeper's leaves often turn fall colours earlier than surrounding plants, thereby signalling the availability of nutritious, ripe fruit to high-flying birds. It is important to such plants that lipid-rich fruits be consumed as soon as they are ripe because they rot easily, in which case seed dispersal cannot occur.

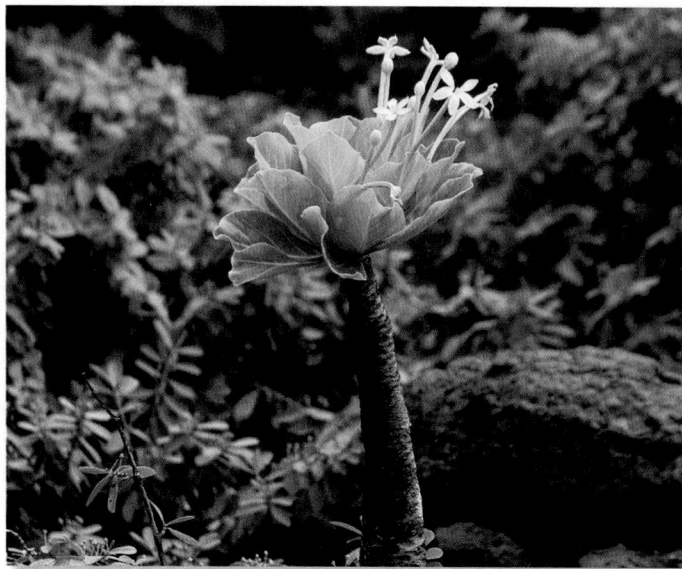

Figure 29.24 *Brighamia insignis,* **an endangered plant.** The pollinator that coevolved with *B. insignis* has become extinct. The plant is unable to produce seed unless artificially pollinated by humans.

Concept check: *What kind of animal likely pollinated B. insignis?*

Figure 29.25 Fruits attractive to animal seed dispersal agents. This cedar waxwing, attracted to the colour and odour of the ripe mountain ash berries, aids in seed dispersal.

Primates of tropical Asia and Africa, but not generally those of Central and South America, have **trichromatic colour vision**—the ability to distinguish blue, green, and red. Trichromatic colour vision in Old World primates is the result of a gene duplication event that occurred early in their evolution but after their divergence from New World primates. Primate specialists have speculated that trichromatic vision may enable Old World tree-dwelling primates to better detect the young, tender leaves of tropical trees, which are often slightly redder than mature leaves. Trichromatic vision also allows primates to more easily detect yellow, red, or orange ripe fruits against a background of leafy green foliage. Since humans evolved from primates native to Africa, we inherited their trichromatic colour vision, helping to explain why humans find brightly coloured flowers and fruits so attractive.

29.4 HUMAN INFLUENCES ON ANGIOSPERM DIVERSIFICATION

Learning Outcome:

1. Understand how humans created the domesticated wheat, corn, and rice grain crops widely planted around the world today.

Through a process known as **domestication**, which involves artificial selection for desirable traits, ancient humans transformed wild plant species into new crop species. More recently, human populations have increased so much that larger areas of natural habitat are being transformed for human use. Deforestation, for example, often results from the conversion of forests to agricultural land. Such habitat destruction is a leading cause of the extinction of plant and other species. In this section we will consider how humans have produced new crop species and influenced the loss of wild species.

Humans Produced New Crop Plants by Domesticating Wild Species

Between 10,000 and 5,000 years ago agriculture originated independently in eight locations around the world. One of the earliest domesticated crops was an African plant commonly known as the bottle gourd (*Lagenaria siceraria*). The bottle gourd was grown for use as containers, musical instruments, and floats for fishing. For planting crops, humans selected seeds from gourds that had thicker rinds because these resisted breakage better than wild gourds. These differences in rind thickness can be detected in fossil remains that are about 10,000 years old. The fossils indicate that bottle gourds were grown as a crop in Asia and from there were transported to the Americas by human colonists.

Cultivated bread wheat (*Triticum aestivum*) was probably among the earliest food crops, having originated more than 8,000 years ago in what is now southeastern Turkey and northern Syria. Bread wheat originated by a series of steps from wild ancestors (*Triticum boeoticum* and *Triticum dicoccoides*). Among the earliest changes that occurred during wheat domestication was the loss of **shattering**, the process by which ears of wild wheat break apart and disperse the single-seeded fruits known as grains. A mutation probably caused the ears of some wheat plants to remain intact, a trait that is disadvantageous in nature but beneficial to humans. Non-shattering ears would have been easier for humans to harvest than normal ears. Early farmers probably selected as seed stock plants that had nonshattering ears and other favourable traits, such as larger grains. These ancient human selection processes, together with modern breeding efforts, explain why cultivated wheat differs from its wild relatives in shattering and other properties. The accumulation of these trait differences explains why cultivated and wild wheat plants are classified as different species.

About 6,500 years ago people living in what is now Mexico domesticated a native grass known as teosinte (*Zea* spp.), producing a new species, *Zea mays,* known as corn or maize. The evidence for this pivotal event includes ancient ears that were larger than wild ones and distinctive fossil pollen. Modern ears of corn are much larger than those of teosinte, corn grains are larger and softer, and modern corn ears do not shatter, as did those of ancestral teosinte (**Figure 29.26**). These and other trait changes reflect artificial selection accomplished by humans. An analysis of the corn genome suggests that human selection has influenced about 1,200 genes.

Molecular analyses indicate that domesticated rice (*Oryza sativa*) originated from ancestral wild species of grasses (*Oryza nivara* and *Oryza rifipogon*). As in the cases of wheat and corn, domestication of rice involved loss of ear shattering. As a result of a mutation causing an amino acid substitution, rice ears remain intact. Ancient humans might have unconsciously selected for this mutation while gathering rice from wild populations, because the mutants would not as easily have shed grains during the harvesting process. Eventually, the nonshattering mutant became a widely planted crop throughout Asia, and today it is the food staple for millions of people.

Nonshattering ear of *Z. mays*

Figure 29.26   **Ears and grains of modern corn and its ancestor, teosinte.**   Domesticated corn ears are much larger than those of the ancestral grass teosinte. In addition, corn fruits are softer and more edible than the grains of teosinte, which are enclosed in a hard casing.

Concept check: *In what other way do corn ears differ from those of teosinte?*

Although humans generated these and other new plant species, in modern times humans have caused the extinction of plants and other species as the result of habitat destruction. Protecting biodiversity will continue to challenge humans as populations and demands on Earth's resources increase. Plant biologists are working to identify one or more molecular sequence tools for use in barcoding plants, a process that is also widely used to identify and catalogue animals (see Chapter 24). The ability to barcode plants is important to those who monitor international trade in endangered plant species.

Summary of Key Concepts

29.1 The Evolution and Diversity of Modern Gymnosperms

- The seed plants (also called spermatophytes) consist of the gymnosperms and the angiosperms. (Figure 29.1, Table 29.1)

- Gymnosperms are plants that produce exposed seeds rather than seeds enclosed in fruits. Many gymnosperms produce wood by means of a special tissue called vascular cambium.

- Several phyla of gymnosperms once existed but have become extinct and are known only from fossils. The diversity of modern gymnosperms includes four modern phyla: cycads, *Ginkgo biloba,* the conifers, and the gnetophytes. (Figure 29.2, Table 29.1)

- Cycads live primarily in tropical and subtropical regions. Features of cycads include palmlike leaves, nonwoody stems, coralloid roots with cyanobacterial endosymbionts, toxins, and large conelike seed-producing structures. (Figures 29.3, 29.4)

- *Ginkgo biloba* is the last surviving species of a phylum that was diverse during the Age of Dinosaurs. Individual trees produce ovules and seeds or pollen, with a sex chromosome system much like that of humans. (Figure 29.5)

- Conifers have been widespread and diverse members of plant communities for the past 300 million years, and they are important sources of wood and paper pulp. Reproduction involves simple pollen cones and complex ovule-producing cones. Conifer wood contains water-conducting tracheids with thin-walled pits that allow water to move from one tracheid to another. Many conifers display additional adaptations that help them to survive in cold climates. (Figures 29.6, 29.7, 29.8, 29.9, 29.10)

- The gnetophytes are of particular interest to plant evolutionary biologists because their relationships to other seed plants are unclear. (Figure 29.11)

29.2 The Evolution and Diversity of Modern Angiosperms

- Angiosperms inherited seeds and other features from ancestors but display distinctive features, such as flowers and fruits. Diversifications of flower structure, fruit structure, and secondary metabolites have played important roles in angiosperm evolution. (Figure 29.12)

- Flowers foster seed production and are adapted in various ways that aid pollination in varying circumstances. The major flower organs are sepals, petals, stamens, and carpels, but some flowers lack one or more of these organs. Pollination is the transfer of pollen from a stamen to a pistil. Pistils display regions of specialized function: the stigma is a receptive surface for pollen, pollen tubes grow through the style, and ovules develop within the ovary. If pollen tubes successfully deposit sperm near eggs in ovules and fertilization occurs, then ovules develop into seeds, and ovaries develop into fruits. (Figures 29.13, 29.14)

- Stamens and carpels may have evolved from leaflike structures bearing sporangia. The two largest lineages of flowering plants, the monocots and eudicots, diverged more than 120 million years ago. (Figures 29.15, 29.16, 29.17, 29.18, 29.19)
- Whole genome duplications, through both autopolyploidy and allopolyploidy, have influenced the diversity of flowering plants. Evidence also exists of horizontal gene transfer between modern monocots and eudicots, and between these plants and earlier diverging lineages.
- Flower diversification involved evolutionary changes, such as fusion of parts, changes in symmetry, loss of parts, and aggregation into inflorescences. (Figure 29.20)
- Fruits are structures that enclose seeds and aid in their dispersal. Fruits occur in many types that foster seed dispersal in varying circumstances. (Figure 29.21)
- Angiosperms produce three main groups of secondary metabolites: (1) terpenes and terpenoids; (2) phenolics, flavonoids, and related compounds; and (3) alkaloids. Secondary metabolites play essential roles in plant structure, reproduction, and defence. (Figure 29.22)
- Hillig and Mahlberg demonstrated the use of particular secondary metabolites in distinguishing species of the genus *Cannabis*. (Figure 29.23)

29.3 The Role of Coevolution in Angiosperm Diversification

- Some flowers form specialized relationships with specific pollinators. These interdependent relationships are known as pollination syndromes. (Table 29.2)
- Coevolutionary interactions with animals that serve as pollen- and seed-dispersal agents played a powerful role in the diversification of both flowering plants and animals. (Figures 29.24, 29.25)
- Human appreciation of flowers and fruits is based on sensory systems similar to those present in the animals with which angiosperms coevolved.

29.4 Human Influences on Angiosperm Diversification

- Humans have produced new crop species by domesticating wild plants. The process of domestication involved artificial selection for traits, such as nonshattering ears of wheat, corn, and rice. (Figure 29.26)
- Large human populations are causing habitat destruction, leading to species extinction. It is hoped that genetic barcodes will allow biologists to identify plants, thus aiding biodiversity conservation and habitat restoration efforts.

Test to Assess Your Learning

1. What feature must be present for a plant to produce wood?
   a. a type of conducting system in which vascular bundles occur in a ring around pith
   b. a eustele
   c. a vascular cambium
   d. all of the above
   e. none of the above
2. What is the correct order of evolution for these critical adaptations?
   a. embryos, vascular tissue, wood, seeds, flowers
   b. vascular tissue, embryos, wood, flowers, seeds
   c. vascular tissue, wood, seeds, embryos, flowers
   d. wood, seeds, embryos, flowers, vascular tissue
   e. seeds, vascular tissue, wood, embryos, flowers
3. How long have ancient and modern groups of gymnosperms been important members of plant communities?
   a. 10,000 years, since the dawn of agriculture
   b. 100,000 years
   c. 300,000 years
   d. 65 million years, since the K/T event
   e. 300 million years, since the Coal Age
4. What similar features do gnetophytes and angiosperms possess that differ from other modern seed plants?
   a. Gnetophytes and angiosperms both produce flagellate sperm.
   b. Gnetophytes and angiosperms both produce flowers.
   c. Gnetophytes and angiosperms both produce tracheids, but not vessels, in their vascular tissues.
   d. Gnetophytes and angiosperms both produce fruits.
   e. None of the above.
5. Which part of a flower receives pollen from the wind or a pollinating animal?
   a. perianth
   b. stigma
   c. filament
   d. peduncle
   e. ovary
6. The primary function of a fruit is to
   a. provide food for the developing seed.
   b. provide food for the developing seedling.
   c. disperse pollen.
   d. disperse seeds.
   e. none of the above.
7. What are some ways in which flowers have diversified?
   a. colour
   b. symmetry
   c. fusion of organs
   d. aggregation into inflorescences
   e. all of the above
8. Flowers of the genus *Fuchsia* produce deep pink to red flowers that dangle from plants, produce nectar in floral tubes, and have no scent. Based on these features, which animal is most likely to be a coevolved pollinator?
   a. bee
   b. bat
   c. hummingbird
   d. butterfly
   e. moth
9. Which type of plant secondary metabolite is best known for antioxidant properties of human foods such as blueberries, tea, and grape juice?
   a. alkaloids
   b. cannabinoids
   c. carotenoids
   d. phenolics
   e. terpenoids
10. What features of domesticated grain crops might differ from those of wild ancestors?
    a. the degree to which ears shatter, allowing for seed dispersal
    b. grain size
    c. number of grains per ear
    d. softness and edibility of grains
    e. all of the above

Articulate to Assess Your Learning

1. Explain why humans should not consume food products made from cycads.
2. Explain why some fruits, such as apples, strawberries, and cherries, are attractive and harmless foods for humans.

Collaborate to Assess and Extend Your Learning

1. Where in the world would you have to travel to find wild plants representing all the gymnosperm phyla, including the three types of gnetophytes?

2. How would you go about trying to solve what Darwin called an "abominable mystery," that is, the identity of the seed plant group that was ancestral to the flowering plants?

3. A principle of biology is that structure determines function. Compare the structures of an apple flower and a sunflower, explaining how they relate to differences in pollination and seed dispersal.

Visit McGraw-Hill Ryerson Connect™ for additional study resources.

An Introduction to Animal Diversity

Chapter Outline

S ince the time of Carl Linnaeus in the eighteenth century, scientists have classified animals based on their morphology, that is, on their physical structure. Researchers have worked hard at determining the unique characteristics of different taxonomic groups and identifying their evolutionary relationships. In the 1990s animal classifications based on similarities in DNA and rRNA became more common. Classifications based on morphology and those based on molecular data were often similar, but some important differences arose. In this chapter we will begin by defining the key characteristics of animals and then look at the major features of the animal body plans that form the basis of the traditional view of animal classification. We will explore how new molecular evidence has made significant alterations to this categorization of the animal kingdom and examine some of the similarities and differences between the morphological and molecular-based phylogenies. As more molecular-based evidence becomes available, systematists will likely continue to redraw the tree of animal life. Thus, as you read this chapter, keep in mind that animal classification is a work in progress.

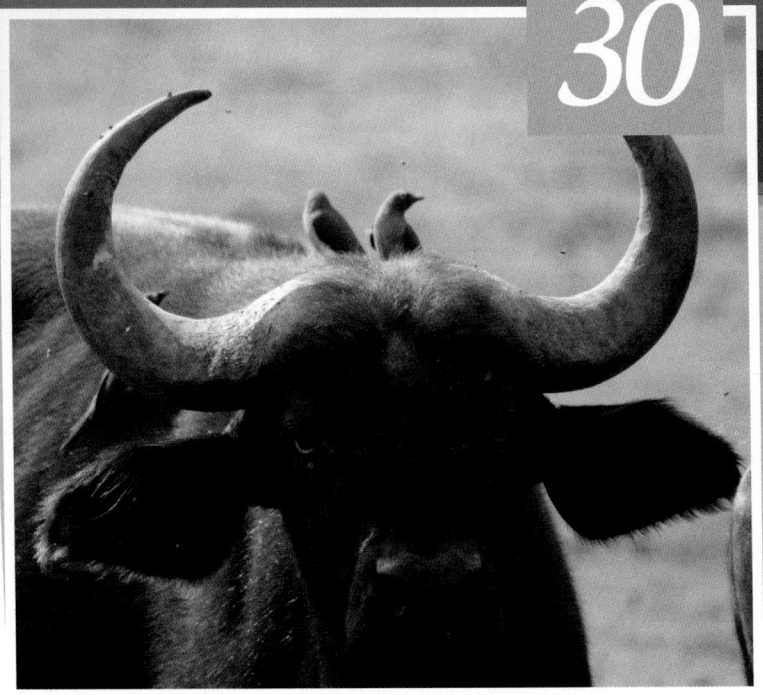

Earth has a staggering variety of animal species. In this photo you can see three interacting species (two vertebrates and one invertebrate).

molecules from inorganic sources and so must feed on other organisms by ingestion. Many, if not most, animals are capable of some type of movement or locomotion to acquire food. This

30.1 / CHARACTERISTICS OF ANIMALS

Learning Outcomes:

1. List the key characteristics of animals that distinguish them from other organisms.

Earth contains more than 1 million known animal species living in environments from the deep sea to the desert and exhibiting an amazing array of characteristics. Most animals move and eat multicellular prey and thus they are loosely differentiated from species in other kingdoms. However, coming up with a firm definition of an animal is tricky: animals are so diverse that biologists can find exceptions to nearly any characteristic. Even so, some key features exist that can help us broadly characterize the group we call animals (**Table 30.1**).

In brief, animals are multicellular heterotrophs whose cells lack cell walls. Most animals have nerves, muscles, the capacity to move at some point in their life cycle, and the ability to reproduce sexually, with sperm fusing directly with eggs. Unlike plants, animals cannot synthesize their essential organic

Table 30.1	Common Characteristics of Animals
Characteristic	**Example**
Multicellularity	Even relatively simple types of animals, such as sponges, are multicellular, in contrast to the single-celled eukaryotic microorganisms called protists (see Chapter 26).
Heterotrophs	Animals obtain their food by eating other organisms or their products. This contrasts with plants and algae, which are autotrophs and essentially make their own food.
No cell walls	Plant, fungal, and bacterial cells are rigid because they possess a cell wall; animal cells lack a cell wall and are quite flexible.
Nervous tissue	The presence of a nervous system in most animals enables them to respond rapidly to environmental stimuli.
Movement	Most animals have a muscle system, which, combined with a nervous system, allows them to move in their environment.
Sexual reproduction	Most animals reproduce sexually, with small, mobile sperm uniting with a much larger egg to form a fertilized egg or zygote.
Extracellular matrix	Proteins, such as collagen, bind cells together to give them added support and strength.
Special clusters of *Hox* genes	All animals possess *Hox* genes, which function in patterning the body axis (see Chapter 17).
Similar rRNA	Animals have very similar genes that encode for RNA of the small subunit (SSU) rRNA.
Characteristic cell junctions	Animals have characteristic cell junctions called anchoring, tight, and gap junctions.

ability has led to the development of specialized systems of sensory structures and a nervous system to coordinate movement and prey capture. Sessile species, such as barnacles, use bristled appendages to obtain food. In many sessile species the adults are immobile, but the larvae can swim. The lack of a rigid cell wall and the existence of nerves and muscles facilitate movement but reduce structural support. Instead, animal cells exist in an extensive extracellular matrix that forms strong fibres outside the cell. Additionally, a group of unique cell junctions, called anchoring, tight, and gap junctions, plays an important role in holding animal cells in place and allowing cell communication.

Although many animals live in aquatic systems, many are terrestrial and therefore face the problem of drying out, or desiccation. When species evolved and moved from water to land, they developed features that enabled them to survive, in much the same way as seeds and other adaptations permitted plants to colonize terrestrial habitats (see Chapter 28). Such features include internal fertilization and the development of a tough, protective shell around the eggs of many species.

30.2 CLASSIFICATION OF ANIMALS

Learning Outcomes:

1. Discuss why choanoflagellates are believed to be the closest living relatives of animals.
2. Describe each of the major morphological and developmental features of animal body plans that form the basis of the classification of animals.

Although animals constitute an extremely diverse kingdom, most biologists agree that the kingdom is monophyletic, meaning that all taxa have evolved from a single common ancestor. We can appreciate this by comparing a portion of the sequence of the small subunit (SSU) rRNA genes of a sponge, flatworm, and seagull (**Figure 30.1**), in much the same way as we did in Chapter 11 (refer back to Figure 11.18). The three animal genomes are very similar, compared with that of a protist, such as a paramecium.

Animals Evolved from a Choanoflagellate-like Ancestor

With the monophyletic nature of the animal kingdom in mind, scientists have attempted to characterize the organism from which animals most likely evolved. According to research, the closest living relative of animals is a flagellated protist known as a choanoflagellate. Choanoflagellates are tiny single-celled organisms, each with a single flagellum surrounded by a collar composed of cytoplasmic tentacles. A number of species are colonial, usually taking the form of a cluster of undifferentiated (morphologically similar) cells on a single stalk. Scientists think that some of these cells may have gradually taken on specialized functions—for example, movement or nutrition—while still maintaining coordination with other cells and cell types. Over time such coordinated groups of cells evolved into a more complex organism that we characterize as an animal. Molecular data also point to choanoflagellates as the closest living relatives of animals.

Today about 35 animal phyla are recognized. At first glance, many of these phyla seem so distantly related to one another (for example, chordates and jellyfish) that making sense of this diversity with a classification scheme seems very challenging. However, over the centuries scientists have come to some basic conclusions about the evolutionary relationships among animals.

Animal Classification Based Mainly on Body Plans

Biologists traditionally classified animal diversity in terms of three main morphological and developmental features of animal body plans:

1. Presence or absence of different tissue types
2. Type of body symmetry
3. Specific features of embryonic development

| KEY | Identical in all four species | Identical in two or three species | Dissimilar in one animal species | Dissimilar in the protist |

Figure 30.1 Comparison of small subunit (SSU) rRNA gene sequences from three animals and a protist. Note the similarities among the animals, even though they are very different species, and the differences when compared with the protist. This and other comparative studies of gene sequences underscore the likelihood that animals share a common ancestor.

We will discuss each of these major features of animal body plans next.

Tissues   Collectively, animals are known as **Metazoa**. Animals can be divided into two subgroups based on whether or not they have specialized types of tissues, that is, stable associations of cells that have a similar structure and function. The **Parazoa** ("alongside animals") are not generally thought to possess specialized tissue types or organs, although they may have several distinct types of cells. Those cells can change their shape and location, making any associations temporary. The Parazoa consist of a single phylum, Porifera (sponges) (**Figure 30.2a**). In contrast, the **Eumetazoa** ("true animals") have more than one type of tissue and, for the most part, have different types of organs.

Symmetry   The Eumetazoa are divided according to their type of symmetry. Symmetry refers to the existence of balanced proportions of the body on both side of a median plane. Radially symmetrical animals, the **Radiata**, can be divided equally by any longitudinal plane passing through the central axis (**Figure 30.2b**). Such animals are often circular or tubular with a mouth at one end and include the animals called cnidarians and ctenophores.

Bilaterally symmetrical animals, the **Bilateria**, can be divided along a vertical plane at the midline to create two halves (**Figure 30.2c**). Thus, a bilateral animal has a left side and a right side that are mirror images, a **dorsal** (upper) and a **ventral** (lower) side that are not identical, and an **anterior** (head) and a **posterior** (tail) end. Note that a radial animal has only an **oral** (top) and an **aboral** (bottom) side. Bilateral symmetry is strongly correlated with both the ability to move through the environment and **cephalization**, the localization of sensory structures at the anterior end of the body. Such abilities permit animals to encounter their environment initially with their head, which is best equipped to detect and consume prey and in turn detect and respond to predators and other dangers.

Another key difference between the Radiata and Bilateria is that radial animals have two layers of embryonic cell layers, called **germ layers**, while bilateral animals have three germ layers. In all animals except the sponges, the growing embryo develops different layers of cells through a process known as **gastrulation** to produce a **gastrula** (**Figure 30.3**). Fertilization of an egg by a sperm creates a diploid zygote. The zygote then undergoes **cleavage**, a succession of rapid cell divisions with no significant growth that produces a hollow sphere of cells called a **blastula**. In gastrulation an area in the blastula invaginates and folds inward, creating in the process the primary germ layers. The inner layer of cells becomes the **endoderm**, which lines the **archenteron**, or primitive digestive tract. The outer layer, or **ectoderm**, covers the surface of the embryo and differentiates into the epidermis and nervous system.

The Bilateria develop a third layer of cells, termed the **mesoderm**, which develops between the ectoderm and endoderm. Mesoderm forms the muscles and most other organs between the digestive tract and the ectoderm. Because the Bilateria have these three distinct germ layers, they are often referred to as **triploblastic**, while the Radiata, which have only ectoderm and endoderm, are termed **diploblastic**.

Embryonic Development   In the developing zygote, cleavage can occur by two mechanisms (**Figure 30.4a**). In **spiral cleavage** the planes of cell cleavage are oblique to the axis of the embryo, resulting in an arrangement in which newly formed upper cells lie centred between the underlying cells. Animals that exhibit spiral cleavage are called **protostomes** and include molluscs, annelid worms, and arthropods. In **radial cleavage** the cleavage planes are either parallel or perpendicular to the vertical axis of the egg. This results in tiers of cells, one directly above the other. Animals exhibiting radial

(a) Parazoa: no tissue types

(b) Eumetazoa: two tissue types
Radiata: radial symmetry

(c) Eumetazoa: three tissue types
Bilateria: bilateral symmetry

Figure 30.2 **Early divisions in the animal phylogeny.**   Animals can be categorized based on **(a)** the absence of different tissue types (Parazoa; the sponges) or **(b, c)** the presence of tissues (Eumetazoa; all other animals). Further categorization is based on the presence of **(b)** radial symmetry (Radiata; the cnidarians and ctenophores) or **(c)** bilateral symmetry (Bilateria; all other animals).

Concept check: *Why are sponges considered animals but simple choanoflagellates are not?*

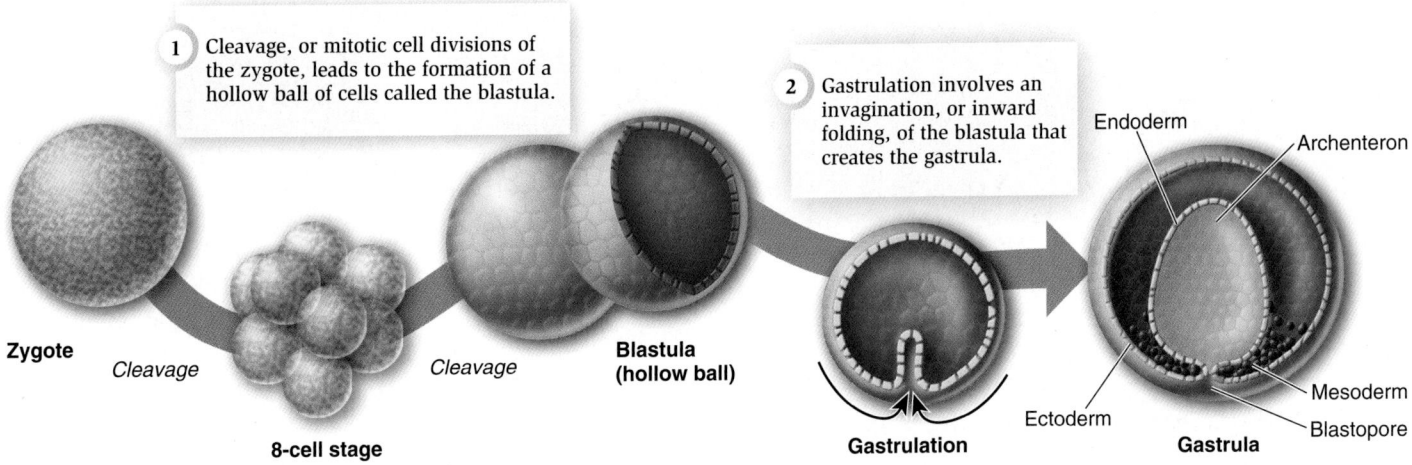

1 Cleavage, or mitotic cell divisions of the zygote, leads to the formation of a hollow ball of cells called the blastula.

2 Gastrulation involves an invagination, or inward folding, of the blastula that creates the gastrula.

Endoderm
Archenteron

Zygote
Cleavage   *Cleavage*
Blastula
(hollow ball)

8-cell stage

Gastrulation   Gastrula

Ectoderm
Mesoderm
Blastopore

3 In the gastrula, the layer of cells lining the archenteron becomes the endoderm. The cells on the outside of the blastula form the ectoderm. In the Bilateria, a middle layer termed the *mesoderm* develops between the ectoderm and endoderm.

Figure 30.3 Formation of germ layers.   Note: radially symmetrical animals do not form mesoderm.

cleavage are called **deuterostomes** and include echinoderms and vertebrates.

Protostome development is also characterized by so-called **determinate cleavage**, in which the fate of each embryonic cell is determined very early (**Figure 30.4b**). If we remove one of the cells from a four-cell mollusc embryo, neither the single cell nor the remaining three-cell mass can form viable embryos, and development is halted. In contrast, deuterostome development is characterized by **indeterminate cleavage**, in which each cell produced by early cleavage retains the ability to develop into a complete embryo. For example, when one cell is excised from a four-cell sea urchin embryo, both the single cell and the remaining three can go on to form viable embryos. Other embryonic cells compensate for the missing cells. In human embryos, if individual embryonic cells separate from one another early in development, identical twins can result. Indeterminate embryonic cells are also known as stem cells and are found not just in the four-cell embryo but also in later embryonic stages. They are called *pluripotent,* because they can develop into almost every cell type of the body.

In addition to differences in cleavage patterns, protostomes and deuterostomes differ in two other embryonic features. The most fundamental of these concerns the development of a mouth and an anus (**Figure 30.4c**). In gastrulation the endoderm forms an indentation, the **blastopore**, which is the opening of the archenteron to the outside. In protostomes (from the Greek *protos,* meaning "first," and *stoma,* meaning "mouth") the blastopore becomes the mouth. If an anus is formed in a protostome, it develops from a secondary opening. In contrast, in the deuterostomes (Greek *deuteros,* meaning "second") the blastopore becomes the anus, and the mouth is formed from the secondary opening.

The last difference between protostomes and deuterostomes concerns coelom formation as described below. In protostomes a solid mass of mesoderm cells splits to form the cavity that becomes the coelom. This pattern is called **schizocoelous** development (from the Greek *schizo,* "to split"). In contrast, in deuterostomes a layer of mesoderm cells form outpockets that bud off from the developing gut to form the coelom. This pattern is known as **enterocoelous** development. The resultant coeloms in both protostomes and deuterostomes are similar; they are just formed in different ways.

Other Morphological Criteria Have Been Used to Classify Animals   In older phylogenetic trees of animal life, classification was also based on morphological features, such as the possession of a fluid-filled body cavity called a **coelom** or the presence of body segmentation. More recent molecular data suggests that although these features are helpful in describing differences in animal structure, they are not as useful in shedding light on the evolutionary history of animals as previously believed.

Body Cavity   In many animals the body cavity is completely lined with mesoderm and is called a true coelom. Animals with a true coelom are termed **coelomates** (**Figure 30.5a**). If the coelom is not completely lined by tissue derived from mesoderm, it is known as a **pseudocoelom** (**Figure 30.5b**). Animals with a pseudocoelom are termed **pseudocoelomates** and include rotifers and roundworms. Some animals, such as flatworms, lack a fluid-filled body cavity and are termed **acoelomates** (**Figure 30.5c**). Instead of fluid, this region contains spongy connective tissue. In some coelomate animals, such as molluscs and arthropods, the coelom is reduced to small pockets around

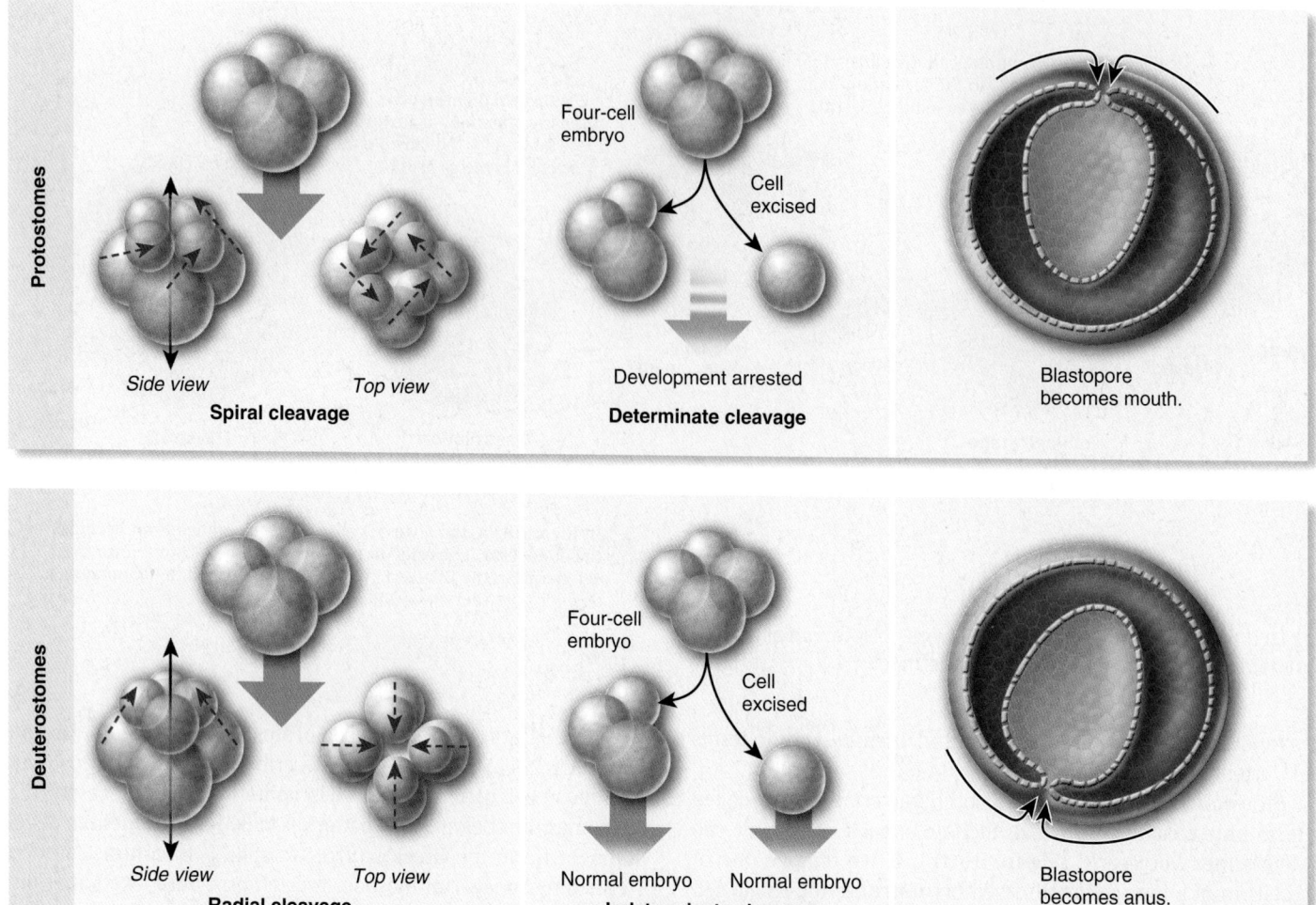

Figure 30.4 **Differences in embryonic development between protostomes and deuterostomes.** **(a)** Many protostomes have spiral cleavage, while most deuterostomes have radial cleavage. The dashed arrows show the direction of cleavage. **(b)** Protostomes have determinate cleavage, whereas deuterostomes have indeterminate cleavage. **(c)** In protostomes the blastopore becomes the mouth. In deuterostomes the blastopore becomes the anus.

the heart and excretory organs, and the main body cavity is known as the hemocoel. In these animals a fluid called hemolymph bathes the tissues directly.

A body cavity has many important functions, perhaps the most important being that its fluid is relatively incompressible and thus cushions internal organs, such as the heart and intestinal tract, helping to prevent injury from external forces. A body cavity also enables internal organs to move and grow independently of the outer body wall. Furthermore, in some soft-bodied invertebrates, such as earthworms, the coelom functions as a **hydrostatic skeleton**, a fluid-filled body cavity surrounded by muscles that gives support and shape to the body of organisms. Because liquid is relatively incompressible, muscle contractions at one part of the body can push fluid

toward another part of the body. This type of movement can best be observed in an earthworm (see Chapter 31). Finally, in some organisms, the fluid in the body cavity also acts as a simple circulatory system.

Segmentation   One other key feature of the animal body plan is the presence or absence of segmentation. In **segmentation** the body is divided into nearly identical subunits called segments. It is most obvious in the annelids, or segmented worms, in which each segment contains the same set of blood vessels, nerves, and muscles, but it is also evident in arthropods and chordates (**Figure 30.6**). Some segments may differ, such as those containing the brain or the sex organs, but most segments are very similar.

Body covering
(from ectoderm)

Muscle layer
(from mesoderm)

Coelom
(fluid-filled
space)

Earthworm

Digestive tract
(from endoderm)

Tissue layer
suspending organs
(from mesoderm)

(a) Coelomate

Body covering
(from ectoderm)

Muscle layer
(from mesoderm)

Pseudocoelom
(fluid-filled
space)

Nematode

Digestive tract (from endoderm)

(b) Pseudocoelomate

Body covering
(from ectoderm)

Muscle layer
(from mesoderm)

Flatworm

Spongy connective tissue
(from mesoderm)

Digestive tract
(from endoderm)

(c) Acoelomate

Figure 30.5   The three basic body plans of bilaterally symmetrical animals.

Concept check: *What advantages does a coelom confer for movement?*

The advantage of segmentation is that it allows specialization of body regions. For example, in arthropods some segments are specialized to form wings for flight. Recent studies have shown that changes in specialization among arthropod body segments can be traced to relatively simple changes in homeotic, or *Hox,* genes. In chordates we can see segmentation in the backbone, muscles, and nervous system.

Annelida

In earthworms, each ring
is a distinct segment.

Arthropoda

Lobsters have developed
specialized appendages
on many segments.

Chordata

Fishes exhibit segmentation
in their muscles and
backbone.

Figure 30.6   Segmentation.   Annelids, arthropods, and chordates all exhibit segmentation.

GENOMES AND PROTEOMES

Changes in *Hox* Gene Expression Control Body Segment Specialization

As you will see in Chapter 31, arthropods exhibit a vast degree of specialization of their segments. For example, many insects have wings and only three pairs of legs, whereas centipedes have no wings and many legs. Crabs, lobsters, and shrimps have highly specialized thoracic appendages called maxillipeds that aid in feeding. In the 1990s Michalis Averof and co-workers elegantly showed how relatively simple changes in the expression patterns of **Hox genes**, genes involved in patterning the body axis, can account for this large variation in appendage types. As described in Chapter 17, animals have several *Hox* genes that are expressed in particular regions of the body. Some are expressed in anterior segments, while others are expressed in posterior segments. The *Hox* genes are designated with numbers 1 through 13.

Shifts in patterns of expression of *Hox* genes in the embryo along the anteroposterior axis are prominent in evolution. In vertebrates the transition from one type of vertebra to another, for example, from cervical (neck) to thoracic (chest) vertebrae, is also controlled by particular *Hox* genes (**Figure 30.7**). The site of the cervical-thoracic boundary appears to be influenced by the *HoxC-6* gene. Differences in its relative position of expression, which occurs before vertebrae development, control the number of vertebrae in the neck. In mice and other mammals the expression of *HoxC-6* begins between vertebrae numbers 7 and 8. In birds, such as chickens and geese, the expression begins further back, between vertebrae 14 and 15, or 17 and 18, respectively. The forelimbs also arise at this boundary in all vertebrates. Interestingly, snakes, which essentially have no neck or forelimbs, do not exhibit this boundary, and *HoxC-6* expression occurs toward their heads. This in effect means that snakes got longer by losing their neck and lengthening their chest.

Evolutionary and development biologist Sean Carroll has remarked that it is very satisfying to find that the evolution of body forms and novel structures in two of the most successful and diverse animal phyla, arthropods and vertebrates, is shaped by the shifting of *Hox* genes. It reminds us of one of the basic tenets of diversity: modern organisms illustrate Darwin's concept of descent with modification. Much of the diversity in animal phyla can be seen as variations on a common theme.

Figure 30.7   Relationship between *HoxC-6* gene expression and neck development.   In vertebrates the transition between neck and trunk vertebrae is controlled by the position of the *HoxC-6* gene. In snakes the expression of this gene is shifted so far forward that a neck does not develop.

30.3 MOLECULAR VIEWS OF ANIMAL DIVERSITY

Learning Outcomes:

1. Discuss the similarities and differences between animal phylogenies based on molecular data and those based on morphological data.

2. List the morphological features of the Ecdysozoa and the Lophotrochozoa.

Although older animal phylogenies were based, to a large extent, on morphological data, biologists are now using new molecular techniques to classify animals by comparing similarities in the DNA and the ribosomal RNA of animals, especially sequences of nucleotides in the gene that encodes RNA of the small ribosomal subunit (SSU rRNA) (see Chapter 24). The DNA sequence contains four easily identified and mutually exclusive character states: A, T, G, and C (RNA has A, U, G, and C). Contrast this with morphological and embryological data in which characters are scored more subjectively, often based on the qualitative assessment of many traits. One of the most influential of the modern studies was the 1997 paper by Anna Marie Aguinaldo and her colleagues, which established evidence for a new monophyletic group (clade) of moulting animals, the Ecdysozoa (see the Featured Investigation).

In addition researchers have also studied the *Hox* genes that control early development and are present in all animals. *Hox* genes

are important because many branches in the traditional phylogeny are based on early developmental differences, such as cleavage, so examination of the genes that regulate these differences should provide insight into the evolution of animal development and to understanding how, when, and why animal body plans diversified.

Although the use of molecular techniques in taxonomy is relatively new, the techniques have had a dramatic impact on traditional classification schemes. Phylogenies based on SSU rRNA and *Hox* genes are similar and, as we will explore, in many cases agree with the structure of the traditional phylogenetic tree. However, some important differences exist.

FEATURE INVESTIGATION

Aguinaldo and Colleagues Used 18S rRNA to Analyze the Taxonomic Relationships of Arthropods to Other Taxa

In 1997 Anna Marie Aguinaldo, James Lake, and their colleagues analyzed the relationships of arthropods to other taxa by sequencing

the complete gene that encodes SSU rRNA from a variety of representative taxa (**Figure 30.8**). Total genomic DNA was isolated by using standard techniques and amplified by the polymerase chain reaction (PCR). PCR fragments were then subjected to DNA sequencing, a technique described in Chapter 18. By using approaches that we described in Chapter 22, the evolutionary relationships among

GOAL To determine the evolutionary relationships among many animal species, especially the arthropods.

KEY MATERIALS Cellular samples from about 50 animals in different taxa.

Experimental level	Conceptual level

1 Isolate DNA from animals and subject the DNA to polymerase chain reaction (PCR) to obtain enough material for DNA sequencing. PCR is described in Chapter 18.

For more detail, refer back to Figure 18.8.

The goal of PCR is to amplify a region in the SSU rRNA gene.

2 Sequence the amplified DNA by dideoxy sequencing, also described in Chapter 18.

For more detail, refer back to Figure 18.8.

CACCGTA

Dideoxy sequencing, in which DNA strands are separated according to their lengths by subjecting them to gel electrophoresis, is used to determine the base sequence of DNA.

3 Compare the DNA sequences and infer phylogenetic relationships using the cladistic approach described in Chapter 24.

Lophotrochozoa   Ecdysozoa

The approach compares traits that are either shared or not shared by different species and creates clades, consisting of a common ancestral species.

Figure 30.8 Approach used to determine the evolutionary relationships among many animal species using molecular data.

Figure 30.8 *(Continued)*

4 **THE DATA**

This process resulted in a large group of DNA sequences that were then analyzed with the use of computer programs.

5 **CONCLUSION** The arthropods are most closely related to the nematodes, and both phyla are placed in the clade Ecdysozoa. All other protostomes belong to a new clade called the Lophotrochozoa.

6 **SOURCE** Aguinaldo, A.M. et al. 1997. Evidence for a clade of nematodes, arthropods, and other moulting animals. *Nature* 387 (6632):489–493.

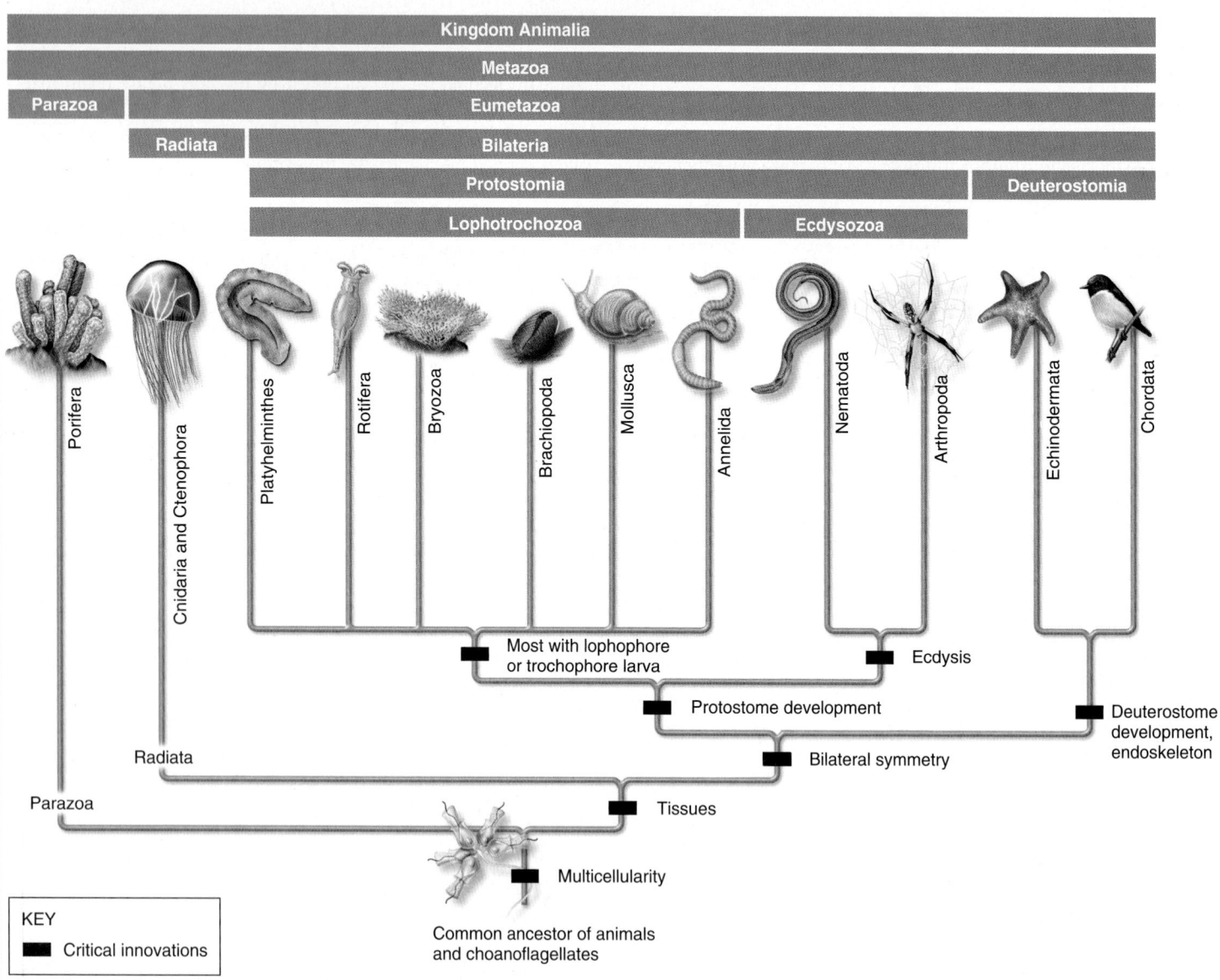

Figure 30.9 Phylogeny of animals based on molecular data of SSU rRNA.

Principle: *All life is related by an evolutionary history.* All animals are believed to be derived from a choanoflagellate ancestor.

Concept check: *What shared derived character is common to the Eumetazoa?*

50 species were determined. The data indicated the existence of a monophyletic clade—the Ecdysozoa—containing the arthropods and nematodes and a number of smaller phyla (see **Figure 30.9**). The name Ecdysozoa means moulting animals, referring to the fact that all organisms in the clade shed their exoskeleton.

The hypothesis that nematodes are more closely related to arthropods than previously thought has important ramifications. In particular it implies that two well-researched model organisms, *Caenorhabditis elegans* (a nematode) and the fruit fly, *Drosophila melanogaster* (an arthropod), are more closely related than had been believed (see their positions in Figure 30.9). Traditional classification assumed that developmental features common to both of these organisms had arisen early in metazoan evolution and thus might be broadly relevant to development in other coelomates, and, in particular, humans. This new classification brings into question the applicability of studies of these organisms to human biology, since commonalities between these organisms might have evolved after the Ecdysozoans diverged. In this case, both nematodes and arthropods would be more closely related to each other than to humans.

Experimental Questions

1. What was the purpose of the study conducted by Aguinaldo and her colleagues?
2. What was the major finding of this study?
3. What impact does the new view of nematode and arthropod phylogeny have on other areas of research?

Molecular Phylogeny Shares Many Similarities with Traditional Phylogeny

The molecular phylogeny is in agreement with the traditional phylogeny with respect to the following features:

1. The clade called Metazoa is monophyletic, meaning all animals came from a single common ancestor.
2. At the earliest stages of evolution, the molecular phylogeny supports the traditional view of the split between Parazoa and Eumetazoa.
3. There is also agreement about an early split between Radiata and Bilateria, with most animal phyla belonging to the Bilateria.
4. The molecular phylogeny also agrees that the echinoderms and chordates belong to a clade called the Deuterostomia.

Molecular Phylogeny Has Some Important Differences from Traditional Phylogeny

Recent molecular analyses have revealed two key differences between models of traditional evolutionary relationships among animals and newer models. The two differences concern (1) the division of the protostomes into two separate clades and (2) the presence or absence of a body cavity.

Protostomes: Lophotrochozoa and Ecdysozoa The most important difference between the molecular and traditional phylogenies involves relationships among the Bilateria. In the traditional view of animal phylogeny, the bilaterally symmetrical animals are split into two clades, the Deuterostomia and the Protostomia, reflecting two basic modes of embryonic development. However, recent molecular studies suggest a different grouping. The deuterostomes are still separate, but the protostomes are divided into two major clades: the **Lophotrochozoa**, which encompasses the annelids, molluscs, and several other phyla, and the **Ecdysozoa**, primarily the arthropods and nematodes (Figure 30.9).

Although the clade was organized primarily through analysis of molecular data, the name Lophotrochozoa stems from two morphological features seen in organisms of this clade. The *lopho-* part is derived from the **lophophore**, a horseshoe-shaped crown of tentacles used for feeding that is present on some members of the group (**Figure 30.10a**). The *trocho-* part refers to the **trochophore larva**, a distinct larval stage of many of the phyla (**Figure 30.10b**).

In traditional phylogeny much debate surrounded the classification of the three minor phyla that possess lophophores: the Bryozoa, Phoronida, and Brachiopoda (collectively called the lophophorates). Although these taxa exhibited some characteristics of protostomes and some of deuterostomes, they were often classified as the Deuterostomia. However, molecular data support their inclusion within the Lophotrochozoa, along with annelids and molluscs.

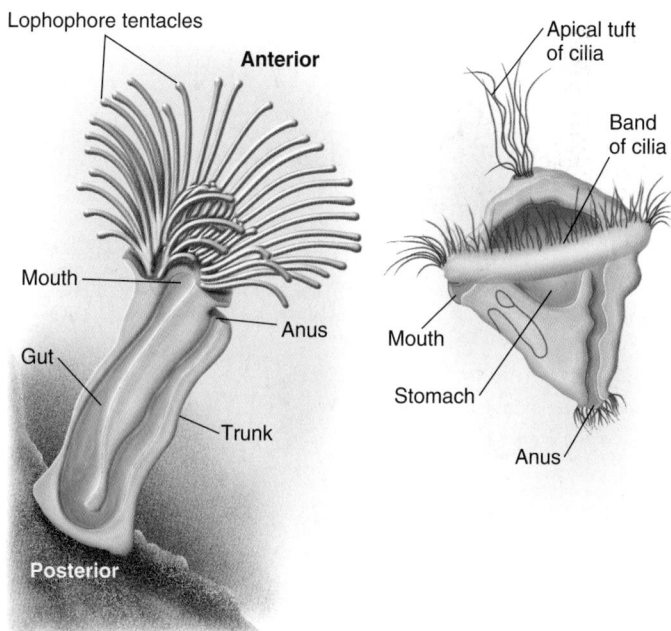

(a) Lophophore of a phoronid worm   **(b) Trochophore larva**

Figure 30.10 Characteristics of the Lophotrochozoa. **(a)** A lophophore, a crown of ciliated tentacles, generates a current to bring food particles into the mouth. **(b)** The trochophore ("wheel-bearer") larval form is found in several animal lineages, such as polychaete worms and molluscs.

The Ecdysozoa are so named because its members secrete a nonliving cuticle, typically an external skeleton (exoskeleton); think of the hard shell of a beetle or that of a crab. As these animals grow, the exoskeleton becomes too small and the animal moults, or breaks out of its old exoskeleton, and secretes a newer, larger one (**Figure 30.11**). This moulting process is called **ecdysis**—hence the name Ecdysozoa.

Figure 30.11 Ecdysis. The Ecdysozoa are a clade of animals exhibiting ecdysis, the periodic shedding (moulting) and re-formation of the exoskeleton.

Principle: *Living organisms grow, develop, and reproduce. For animals with exoskeletons, growth and development require moulting.*

Concept check: *What are the main members of the Ecdysozoa?*

Although named for this morphological characteristic, the clade is strongly supported by molecular evidence, such as similarities in DNA.

Body Cavity The second most important difference between molecular and traditional phylogenies involves the presence or absence of a body cavity. In the traditional view of animal phylogeny the bilaterally symmetrical animals are divided into those lacking a coelom (acoelomates), those with a pseudocoelom (pseudocoelomates), and those possessing a coelom (coelomates) (see Figure 30.5). The Platyhelminthes, or flatworms, are classified as acoelomate and are thus seen as separate from coelomate phyla. Molecular evidence, however, now suggests that the flatworms should be included with the Lophotrochozoa. In this view flatworms are not primitive acoelomate animals. Rather, they evolved from an ancestor that possessed a coelom but lost it during evolutionary modification. Similarly, molecular-based phylogeny places the rotifers and nematodes, the pseudocoelomate phyla, within the Lophotrochozoa and Ecdysozoa, respectively. Thus, molecular data suggest that the presence or absence of a coelom, a distinction traditionally used in the construction of animal phylogenies, may not be a useful way to classify animals.

It is important to stress, however, that more similarities than differences are found between the molecular and traditional phylogenies. Most of the major branch points in the phylogenies are in agreement. As a reference, **Table 30.2** summarizes the characteristics of the major animal phyla.

In the next two chapters the discussion of animal phylogeny is based primarily on findings of molecular data. In Chapter 31 we will concentrate on the invertebrates, and in Chapter 32 we will look at the Chordata, with special emphasis on the vertebrates: fish, amphibians, reptiles, birds, and mammals.

Table 30.2	**Summary of Characteristics of the Major Animal Phyla**											
Feature	*Porifera* Sponges	*Cnidaria* and *Ctenophora* Hydra, anemones, jellyfish	*Platyhelminthes* Flatworms	*Rotifera* Rotifers	*Lophophorates* Bryozoans and others	*Mollusca* Snails, clams, squid	*Annelida* Segmented worms	*Nematoda* Roundworms	*Arthropoda* Insects, arachnids, crustaceans	*Echinodermata* Sea stars, sea urchins	*Chordata* Vertebrates and others
Estimated number of species	8,000	11,000	20,000	2,000	4,000	110,000	15,000	20,000	1,000,000+	6,000+	47,000+
Level of organization	Cellular; lack organs	Tissue; lack organs	Organs	Organs	Organs	Organs	Organs	Organs	Organs	Organs	Organs
Symmetry	Absent	Radial	Bilateral	Bilateral	Bilateral	Bilateral	Bilateral	Bilateral	Bilateral	Bilateral larvae,	Bilateral
Cephalization	Absent	Absent	Present	Present	Reduced	Present	Present	Present	Present	Absent	Present
Germ layers	Absent	Two	Three	Three	Three	Three	Three	Three	Three	Three	Three

(Continued)

Body cavity	Absent	Absent	Absent	Pseudocoelom	Coelom	Reduced coelom	Coelom	Pseudocoelom	Reduced coelom	Coelom	Coelom
Segmentation	Absent	Absent	Absent	Absent	Absent	Absent	Present	Absent	Present	Absent	Present (often reduced)
Digestive system	Absent	Gastro-vascular cavity; Ctenophores have complete gut	Incomplete gut	Complete gut (usually)	Complete gut	Complete gut	Complete gut	Complete gut	Complete gut	Usually complete gut	Complete gut
Circulatory system	Absent	Absent	Absent	Absent	Absent, open, or closed	Open	Closed	Absent	Open	Absent	Closed
Respiratory system	Absent	Absent	Absent	Absent	Absent	Gills, lungs	Absent	Absent	Trachae, gills, or book lungs	Tube feet, gills, respiratory tree	Gills, lungs
Excretory system	Absent	Absent	Protonephridia with flame cells	Protonephridia	Meta-nephridia	Meta-nephridia	Meta-nephridia	Excretory gland cells	Excretory glands resembling metanephridia; Malpighian tubules in insects	Absent	Kidneys
Nervous system	Absent	Nerve net	Brain, nerve net	Brain, nerve cords	No brain, nerve ring	Ganglia, nerve cords	Brain, ventral nerve cord	Brain, nerve cords	Brain, ventral nerve cord	No brain, nerve ring and radial nerves	Well-developed brain; dorsal hollow nerve cord
Reproduction	Sexual; asexual (budding)	Sexual; asexual (budding)	Sexual (most her-maphroditic); asexual (body splits)	Mostly `partheno-genetic; males appear only rarely	Sexual (some her-maphroditic); asexual (budding)	Sexual (some her-maphroditic)	Sexual (some her-maphroditic)	Sexual (some her-maphroditic)	Usually sexual (some her-maphroditic; some partheno-genetic)	Sexual (some her-maphroditic); partheno-genetic; asexual by regeneration (rare)	Sexual, rarely partheno-genetic
Support	Endos-keleton of spicules and collagen	Hydrostatic skeleton	Hydrostatic skeleton	Hydrostatic skeleton	Exoskeleton	Hydrostatic skeleton and shell	Hydrostatic skeleton	Hydrostatic skeleton	Exoskeleton	Endoskeleton of plates beneath outer skin	Endoskeleton of cartilage or bone

Summary of Key Concepts

30.1 Characteristics of Animals

- Animals are a species-rich kingdom. They share a number of key characteristics, including multicellularity, heterotrophic feeding, the possession of nervous and muscle tissues, and sexual reproduction. (Table 30.1)

30.2 Classification of Animals

- The animal kingdom is monophyletic, meaning that all taxa have evolved from a single common ancestor. This can be observed in comparing gene sequences from animals and a protist. (Figure 30.1)

- Animals can be categorized according to the absence of different types of tissues (the Parazoa or sponges) and the presence of tissues (Eumetazoa or all other animals). The Eumetazoa can also be divided according to their type of symmetry, whether radial (Radiata, the cnidarians and ctenophores) or bilateral (Bilateria, all other animals). (Figure 30.2)

- The Radiata have two layers of embryonic cell layers (germ layers) called the *endoderm* and the *ectoderm*. The Bilateria develop a third germ layer termed the *mesoderm*, which develops between the ectoderm and the endoderm. (Figure 30.3)

- Animals are also classified according to patterns of embryonic development. Animals with spiral cleavage are called protostomes, and those exhibiting radial cleavage are considered deuterostomes. In protostomes the blastopore, or opening of the gut to the outside, becomes the mouth; in deuterostomes the blastopore becomes the anus. (Figure 30.4)

- Animals can be classified according to the presence or absence of a coelom, or true body cavity. Animals with a coelom are termed *coelomates*. Animals that possess a pseudocoelom, or coelom that is not completely lined by tissue derived from mesoderm, are called pseudocoelomates. Those animals lacking a fluid-filled body cavity are termed *acoelomates*. (Figure 30.5)

- Metamerism, the division of the body into identical subunits called segments, is another key feature of the animal body plan. (Figure 30.6)

- Shifts in the pattern of expression of *Hox* genes are prominent in evolution. In vertebrates the transition from one type of vertebra to another is controlled by certain *Hox* genes. (Figure 30.7)

- The traditional classification of animals is based on four morphological and developmental features of animal body plans. (Table 30.2)

30.3 Molecular Views of Animal Diversity

- Recent molecular studies propose a division of the protostomes into two major clades: the Lophotrochozoa and the Ecdysozoa. (Figures 30.8, 30.9)

- The Lophotrochozoa are grouped primarily through analysis of molecular data, but they are distinguished by two morphological features—the lophophore, a crown of tentacles used for feeding, and the trochophore larva, a distinct larval stage. The lophophorates were often classified as deuterostomes, but molecular data support their inclusion within the Lophotrochozoa. (Figure 30.10)

- The Ecdysozoa are so named because members secrete a nonliving cuticle, typically an exoskeleton or external skeleton. Ecdysis is the periodic shedding and re-formation of the exoskeleton. (Figure 30.11)

- Molecular evidence suggests that flatworms evolved from a coelomate ancestor and should be considered to be within the Lophotrochozoa and not primitive acoelomate animals.

Test to Assess Your Learning

1. Which of the following is *not* a distinguishing characteristic of animals?
   a. the capacity to move at some point in their life cycle
   b. possession of cell walls
   c. multicellularity
   d. heterotrophy
   e. all of the above are characteristics of animals

2. Terrestrial adaptations seen in animals include
   a. internal fertilization.
   b. tough, protective shells around eggs.
   c. a waxy cuticle covering exposed tissue.
   d. (a) and (b) only.
   e. all of the above.

3. Eumetazoa are animals that have
   a. true tissues.
   b. more than one tissue type.
   c. only one tissue type.
   d. radial symmetry.
   e. spiral cleavage.

4. The localization of sensory structures at the anterior end of the body is
   a. bilateral symmetry.
   b. spiral cleavage.
   c. cephalization.
   d. radial symmetry.
   e. gastrulation.

5. The germ layer that is present in triploblastic animals but is absent in diploblastic animals is
   a. the ectoderm.
   b. the mesoderm.
   c. the endoderm.
   d. the pseudocoelom.
   e. the coelom.

6. Pseudocoelomates
   a. lack a fluid-filled cavity.
   b. have a fluid-filled cavity that is completely lined with mesoderm.
   c. have a fluid-filled cavity that is partially lined with mesoderm.
   d. have a fluid-filled cavity that is not lined with mesoderm.
   e. have an air-filled cavity that is partially lined with mesoderm.

7. Protostomes and deuterostomes can be classified based on
   a. cleavage pattern.
   b. destiny of the blastopore.
   c. whether the fate of the embryonic cells is fixed early during development.
   d. how the coelom is formed.
   e. all of the above.

8. Naturally occurring identical twins are possible only in animals that
   a. have spiral cleavage.
   b. have determinate cleavage.
   c. are protostomes.
   d. have indeterminate cleavage.
   e. (a), (b), and (c).

9. Genes involved in the patterning of the body axis, that is, in determining such characteristics as neck length and appendage formation, are called
   a. small subunit (SSU) rRNA genes.
   b. *Hox* genes.
   c. metameric genes.
   d. determinate genes.
   e. none of the above.

10. A major difference between the molecular phylogeny of animals and the traditional phylogeny of animals is that
    a. the presence or absence of the mesoderm is not important in molecular phylogeny.
    b. molecular phylogeny suggests that all animals do not share a single common ancestor.
    c. body symmetry, whether radial or bilateral, is not an important determinant in molecular phylogeny.
    d. molecular phylogeny does not include the echinoderms in the deuterostome clade.
    e. molecular phylogeny suggests that the presence or absence of a coelom is not important for classification.

Articulate to Assess Your Learning

1. The traditional classification is based on what four features of animal body plans?

2. Distinguish between radial and bilateral symmetry.

3. Define cleavage and gastrulation.

Collaborate to Assess and Extend Your Learning

1. Discuss how animals affect humans both positively and negatively.

2. Construct a traditional morphological phylogeny (as described in the text) and compare it with the molecular phylogeny of Figure 30.9.

3. A principle of biology is that all species (past and present) are related by an evolutionary history. Annelids, arthropods, and chordates all exhibit segmentation. Are these monophyletic, paraphyletic, or polyphyletic groups? Explain your answer. Refer back to Figure 24.18 to remind yourself about these terms.

Visit McGraw-Hill Ryerson Connect™ for additional study resources.

The Invertebrates

Chapter Outline

Coral reefs comprise a diversity of invertebrate organisms, especially sponges and cnidarians.

A s you saw in Chapter 20, the history of animal life on Earth has evolved over hundreds of millions of years. Some scientists suggest that changing environmental conditions, such as a buildup of dissolved oxygen and minerals in the ocean or an increase in atmospheric oxygen, eventually permitted higher metabolic rates and increased the activity of a wide range of animals. Others suggest that with the development of sophisticated locomotor skills, a wide range of predators and prey evolved, leading to an evolutionary arms race in which predators evolved powerful weapons and prey evolved more powerful defences against them. Such adaptations and counteradaptations would have led to a proliferation of different lifestyles and taxa.

Over the next two chapters we will survey the wondrous array of animal life on Earth. In this chapter we examine the **invertebrates**, or animals without a backbone, a category that makes up more than 95% of all animal species (**Figure 31.1**). Although a classification of convenience, it is important to remember that invertebrate is not a monophyletic group. The invertebrates include four types of body plans. First, we begin by exploring the earliest animal lineage, the sponges (Parazoa). The sponges are set apart because they lack true tissues, lack nerve cells, and have no symmetry. The second group are the Radiata, which exhibit radial symmetry. The third group are invertebrates with bilateral symmetry and more complex embryonic development. These include the Lophotrochozoa and Ecdysozoa, the two sister groups of protostomes introduced in Chapter 30. Finally, we turn to the fourth group, the deuterostomes, focusing on the echinoderms and the invertebrate members of the phylum Chordata. The deuterostomes differ from protostomes in developmental differences in mouth and anus formation.

Although the more modern molecular classification outlined in Chapter 30 will serve as the basis of our discussion of animal lineages, we will not ignore the concept of body plans, because it still can provide clues about how different phyla have evolved. The newer molecular phylogeny is still in its infancy, and many refinements will undoubtedly be made as increasing numbers of genes from more species are sequenced and compared. For this reason many biologists are not yet ready to totally set aside the older body plan–based phylogeny.

31.1   PARAZOA: SPONGES, THE FIRST MULTICELLULAR ANIMALS

Learning Outcomes:

1. Outline the body plan and unique characteristics of sponges.
2. Describe how sponges defend themselves against predators.

The Parazoa consist of one phylum, Porifera (from the Latin, "pore bearers"), whose members are commonly referred to as sponges. Sponges are loosely organized and lack true tissues, groups of cells that have a similar structure and function. However, sponges are multicellular and possess several types of cells that perform different functions. Biologists have identified approximately 8,000 species of sponges, the vast majority of which are marine. Sponges range in size from only a few millimetres across to more than 2 m in diameter. The smaller sponges may be radially symmetrical, but most have no apparent symmetry. Some sponges have a low encrusting growth form, while others grow tall and erect (**Figure 31.2a**). Although adult sponges are sessile, that is, anchored in place, the larvae are free-swimming.

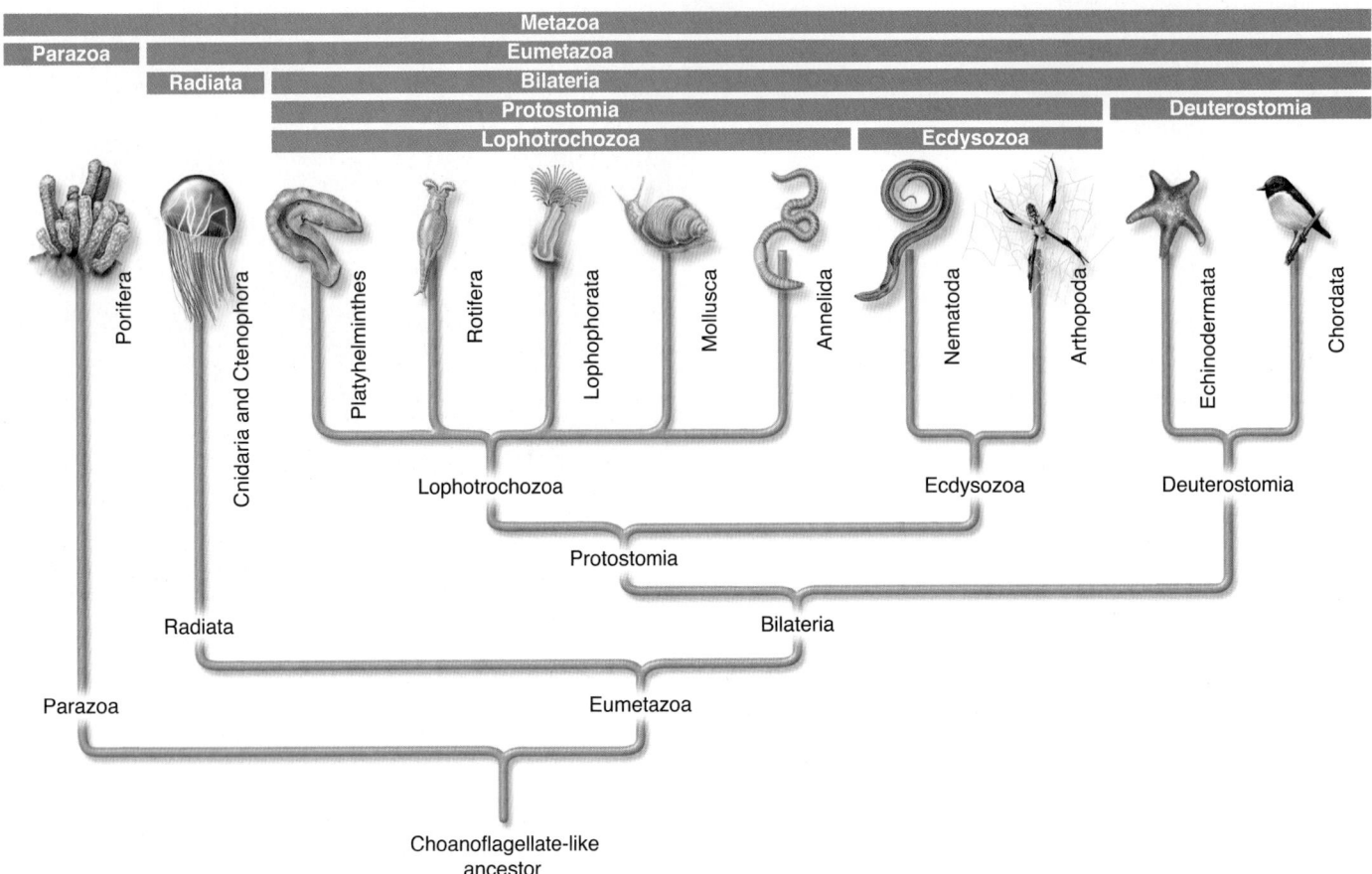

Figure 31.1 Relationships among major invertebrate lineages. Also shown is the vertebrate or Chordata lineage in the Deuterostomia.

The body of a sponge looks similar to a vase pierced with small holes or pores (**Figure 31.2b**). Water is drawn through these pores (ostia, singular: ostium) into a central cavity, the **spongocoel**, and flows out through the large opening at the top called the **osculum**. The water enters the pores by the beating action of the flagella of the **choanocytes**, or collar cells, that line the spongocoel (**Figure 31.2c**). In the process, the choanocytes trap and eat small particulate matter and tiny plankton. As we noted in Chapter 30, because of striking morphological and molecular similarities between choanocytes and choanoflagellates, a group of modern protists having a single flagellum, it is believed that sponges originated from a choanoflagellate-like ancestor. A layer of flattened epithelial cells similar to those making up the outer layer of other phyla protects the sponge body. In between the choanocytes and the epithelial cells lies a gelatinous, protein-rich matrix called the **mesohyl**. Within this matrix are mobile cells called **amoebocytes** that absorb food from choanocytes, digest it, and carry the nutrients to other cells. Thus, considerable cell-to-cell contact and communication exists in sponges.

Some amoebocytes can also form tough skeletal fibres that support the body. In many sponges, this skeleton consists of sharp spicules formed of calcium carbonate or silica. For example, some deep-ocean species, called glass sponges,

are distinguished by needle-like silica **spicules** that form elaborate lattice-like skeletons. The presence of such tough spicules may help explain why there is not much predation of sponges. Sponge spicules come in a diverse array of shapes and sizes, and they are valuable taxonomic tools by which to distinguish different types of sponges. In a small family of carnivorous sponges, the spicules are sticky and capture small crustaceans. In these sponges other cells migrate around the immobilized crustaceans and digest them extracellularly. Not all sponges have spicules, however. Others have fibres of a tough protein called **spongin** that lend skeletal support. Spongin skeletons are still commercially harvested and sold as bath sponges. Many species produce toxic defensive chemicals, some of which are thought to have possible antibiotic and anti-inflammatory effects in humans.

Around the turn of the twentieth century biologist Henry V. Wilson made the incredible discovery that if a sponge is dissociated into its individual cells after being passed through a sieve, its cells can reaggregate into a functional sponge within a short time. Wilson concluded that to do this individual cells recognized and reaggregated with other cells of their own kind. Researchers have since discovered that the cells of other multicellular organisms also recognize cells of their own kind and tend to adhere when mixed with other cells. For example, in

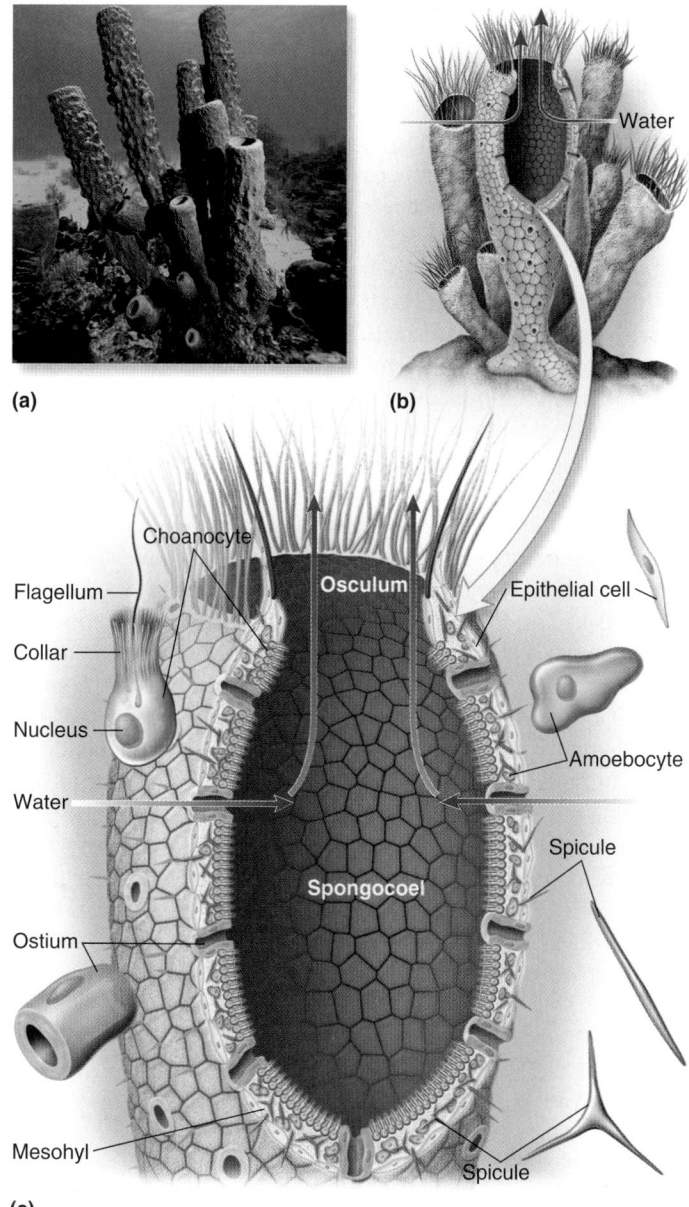

(a)

(b)

(c)

Figure 31.2 Sponge morphology. **(a)** The stovepipe sponge (*Aplysina archeri*) is a common sponge found on Caribbean reefs. **(b)** Many sponges have a vaselike shape. **(c)** A cross-section reveals that sponges are truly multicellular animals, having various cell types but no distinct tissues.

Concept check: *If sponges are soft and sessile, why aren't they eaten by other organisms?*

mammals, liver cells recognize and stick better to other liver cells, and brain cells recognize and adhere to brain cells.

Sponges reproduce through both sexual and asexual means. Most sponges are **hermaphrodites** (from the Greek god Hermes and the goddess Aphrodite), individuals that can produce both sperm and eggs. Gametes are formed in the mesohyl by amoebocytes or choanocytes. While eggs remain in the mesohyl, the sperm are released into the water and carried by water currents

to fertilize the eggs of neighbouring sponges. Zygotes develop into flagellated swimming larvae that eventually settle on a suitable substrate to become sessile adults. In asexual reproduction a small fragment or bud may detach and form a new sponge.

31.2 RADIATA: JELLYFISH, RADIALLY SYMMETRICAL ANIMALS

Learning Outcomes:

1. Compare and contrast the two body forms of cnidarians.
2. Describe how cnidarians defend themselves.
3. Describe the unique features of ctenophores

The Radiata consists of two closely related phyla: the Cnidaria (from the Greek *knide,* meaning "nettle," and *aria,* meaning "related to"; pronounced nid-air-e-ah) and the Ctenophora (from the Greek *ktenos,* meaning "comb," and *phora,* meaning "bearing"; pronounced teen-o-for-ah). Members of the Radiata phyla, or radiates, are mostly found in marine environments, although a few, primarily hydra, are freshwater species. The Cnidaria includes hydra, jellyfish, box jellies, sea anemones, and corals, and the Ctenophora consists of the comb jellies. The Radiata have only two embryonic germ layers: the ectoderm and the endoderm, which give rise to the epidermis and the gastrodermis, respectively. A gelatinous substance called the **mesoglea** connects the two layers. In jellyfish the mesoglea is enlarged and forms the buoyant, transparent jelly, whereas in coral, the mesoglea is very thin.

Both cnidarians and ctenophores possess a **gastrovascular cavity**, where extracellular digestion takes place (**Figure 31.3**).

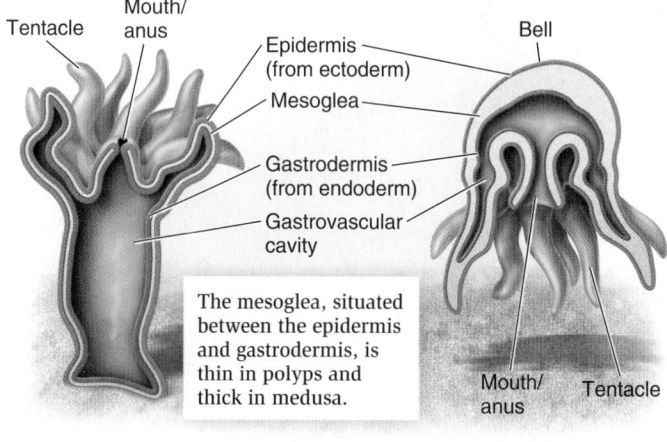

(a) Polyp   **(b) Medusa**

Figure 31.3 Polyp and medusa forms of Cnidarians. Both **(a)** polyp and **(b)** medusa forms have two layers of cells, an outer epidermis (from ectoderm) and an inner layer of gastrodermis (from endoderm). In between is a layer of mesoglea, which is thin in polyps, such as corals, and thick in medusae, such as most jellyfish.

This feature allows the ingestion of larger food particles and represents a major advance over the sponges, which use only intracellular digestion. Most radiates have tentacles around the mouth that aid in food detection and capture. Radiates also have true nerve cells arranged as a **nerve net** consisting of interconnected neurons with no central control organ. In this section we will provide an overview of the biology and diversity of the cnidarians and ctenophores.

The Cnidarians Have Specialized Stinging Cells

Most cnidarians exist as two different body forms and associated lifestyles: the sessile **polyp** or the motile **medusa** (Figure 31.3). For example, jellyfish exist predominantly in the medusa form, and corals exhibit only the polyp form. Many cnidarians, such as *Obelia*, have a life cycle that prominently features both polyp and medusa stages (**Figure 31.4**).

The polyp form has a tubular body with an opening at the oral end that is surrounded by tentacles and functions as both mouth and anus. The aboral end is attached to the substrate. In the eighteenth century Swiss naturalist Abraham Trembley discovered that when a freshwater hydra was cut in two, each part not only survived but could also regenerate the missing half. Polyps exist colonially, as they do in corals, or alone, as in sea anemones. Corals take dissolved calcium and carbonate ions from seawater and precipitate them as limestone underneath their bodies. In some species, this leads to a buildup of limestone deposits. As each successive generation of polyps dies, the limestone remains in place and new polyps grow on top. Thus, huge underwater limestone deposits called coral reefs are formed (look ahead to Figure 51.27b). The largest of these is Australia's

Great Barrier Reef, which stretches more than 2,300 km. Many other extensive coral reefs are known, including the reef system along the Florida Keys, all of which occur in warm water, generally between 18°C and 30°C.

The free-swimming medusa form has an umbrella-shaped body with a mouth on the concave underside that is surrounded by tentacles. More mobile medusae possess simple sense organs near the bell margin, including organs of equilibrium called **statocysts** and photosensitive organs known as **ocelli**. When one side of the bell tips upward, the statocysts on that side are stimulated and muscle contraction is initiated to right the medusa. The ocelli allow medusae to position themselves in particular light levels.

One of the unique and characteristic features of the cnidarians is the existence of stinging cells called **cnidocytes**, which function in defence or the capture of prey (**Figure 31.5a**). Cnidocytes contain **nematocysts**, powerful capsules with an inverted coiled and barbed thread. Although several different types of nematocysts are recognized, they all have the same general structure and function. Each cnidocyte has a hairlike trigger called a **cnidocil** on its surface. When the cnidocil is touched or a chemical stimulus is detected, the nematocyst fires the thread, which penetrates the prey and injects a small amount of toxin. Small prey are immobilized and passed into the mouth by the tentacles. Alternatively, some nematocyst threads can be sticky rather than stinging. After discharge, the cnidocyte is absorbed and a new one grows to replace it. The nematocysts of most cnidarians are not harmful to humans, but those on the tentacles of the larger jellyfish and the Portuguese Man-of-War (**Figure 31.5b**) can be extremely painful and even fatal. Tentacles of the largest jellyfish, *Cyanea arctica*, can be more than 40 m long.

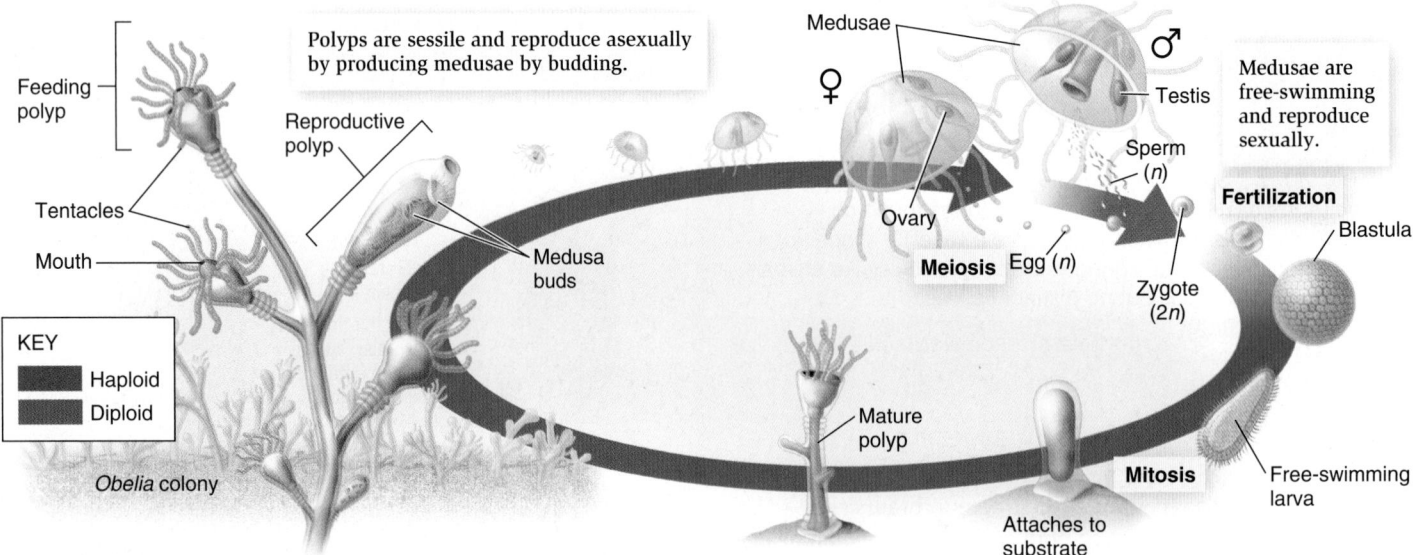

Figure 31.4   Life cycle of *Obelia*, a colonial cnidarian.   This species exhibits both polyp and medusa stages.

Concept check: *What are the dominant life stages of the following types of cnidarians: jellyfish, sea anemone, and Portuguese Man-of-War?*

Gastrodermis Mesoglea Epidermis

Sensory cell

Undischarged nematocyst

Cnidocil

Discharged nematocyst

Filament

Stinging cell (cnidocyte)

When triggered, the cnidocyte discharges the nematocyst, which penetrates the prey.

(a) Cnidocytes

(b) Portuguese Man-of-War (*Physalia physalis*)

Figure 31.5 Cnidarians have specialized stinging cells called cnidocytes. **(a)** Cnidocytes, which contain stinging capsules called nematocysts, are situated in the tentacles. **(b)** The Portuguese Man-of-War (*Physalia physalis*) employs cnidocytes that can be lethal to humans. A gas-filled float allows the animal to stay on the surface of the water.

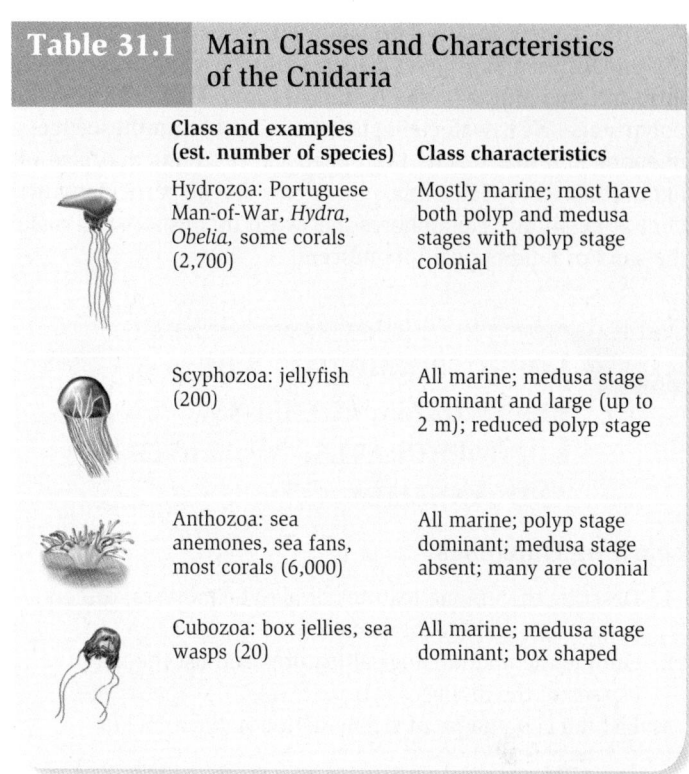

Table 31.1	Main Classes and Characteristics of the Cnidaria

Class and examples (est. number of species)	Class characteristics
Hydrozoa: Portuguese Man-of-War, *Hydra, Obelia,* some corals (2,700)	Mostly marine; most have both polyp and medusa stages with polyp stage colonial
Scyphozoa: jellyfish (200)	All marine; medusa stage dominant and large (up to 2 m); reduced polyp stage
Anthozoa: sea anemones, sea fans, most corals (6,000)	All marine; polyp stage dominant; medusa stage absent; many are colonial
Cubozoa: box jellies, sea wasps (20)	All marine; medusa stage dominant; box shaped

Muscles and nerves exist in their simplest forms in cnidarians. Contractile muscle fibres are found in both the epidermis and the gastrodermis. Although not true muscles, which arise only from the mesoderm and therefore do not appear in diploblastic animals, these muscle fibres can contract to change the shape of the animal. For example, in the presence of a predator, an anemone can expel water very quickly through its open mouth and shrink down to a very small body form. The muscle fibres work against the fluid contained in the body, which thus acts as a hydrostatic skeleton. A nerve net that conducts signals from sensory nerves to muscle cells allows coordination of simple movements and shape changes.

The phylum Cnidaria consists of four classes—Hydrozoa (including *Obelia* and Portuguese Man-of-War), Scyphozoa (jellyfish), Anthozoa (sea anemones and corals), and Cubozoa (box jellies)—whose distinguishing characteristics are shown in **Table 31.1**.

Ctenophores Have a Complete Gut

Ctenophores, also known as comb jellies, are a small phylum of fewer than 100 species, all of which are marine and look very much like jellyfish (**Figure 31.6**). They have eight rows of cilia on their surface that resemble combs. The coordinated beating of the cilia, rather than muscular contractions, propels the ctenophores. Averaging about 1 to 10 cm long, comb jellies are probably the largest animals to use cilia for locomotion. A few ribbonlike species are up to 1 m long.

Comb jellies possess two long tentacles but lack stinging cells. Instead, they have colloblasts, cells that secrete a sticky substance to which small prey adhere. The tentacles are then drawn over the mouth. As with cnidarians digestion occurs in the gastrovascular cavity, but waste and water are eliminated through two anal pores. Thus, the comb jellies possess the first complete gut. Prey are generally small and include tiny crustaceans called copepods and small fish. Comb jellies are often transported around the world in ships' ballast water. *Mnemiopsis leidyi*, a ctenophore species native to the Atlantic coast of North and South America, was accidentally introduced into the Caspian and Black Seas in the 1980s. With a plentiful food supply and a lack of predators, *Mnemiopsis* underwent a population explosion and devastated the local fishing industries.

Figure 31.6 A ctenophore. Cnetophores are commonly called comb jellies because of the eight rows of cilia on their surface that resemble combs. This is *Mnemiopsis leidyi*, the sea walnut, which was accidentally introduced via the ballast water of ships to the Black and Caspian Seas.

All ctenophores are hermaphroditic, possessing both ovaries and testes, and gametes are shed into the water to eventually form free-swimming larvae that grows into adults. There is no polyp stage. Nearly all ctenophores exhibit **bioluminescence**, a phenomenon that results from chemical reactions that give off light rather than heat. Thus, individuals can be particularly evident at night, and ctenophores that wash up onshore can make the sand or mud appear luminescent.

31.3   LOPHOTROCHOZOA: THE FLATWORMS, ROTIFERS, LOPHOPHORATES, MOLLUSCS, AND ANNELIDS

Learning Outcomes:

1. Describe the unique features of platyhelminthes, rotifers, bryozoans, and brachiopods.
2. Outline the main biological features and list the main classes of the molluscs.
3. List the advantages of segmentation in the annelids.

In the traditional view of animal phylogeny (refer back to Figure 30.9), the bilaterally symmetrical animals are split into those with no coelom (the platyhelminthes), those with a pseudocoelom (the nematodes and rotifers), and those with a coelom (the remaining phyla). However, as we explored in Chapter 30, molecular data suggest a different grouping in which the deuterostomes are still separate, but the protostomes are divided into two major lineages: the Lophotrochozoa and the Ecdysozoa (refer back to Figure 31.1). The Lophotrochozoa are a diverse group that generally includes taxa that possess either a lophophore (a crown of ciliated tentacles) or a distinct larval stage called a trochophore. In this grouping are seven major Lophotrochozoa phyla: the Platyhelminthes (flatworms), Rotifera (rotifers), Lophophorata (the lophophorates, a group of three phyla), Mollusca (molluscs), and Annelida (segmented worms). In this section we explore the distinguishing characteristics of these phyla, beginning with some of the simplest lophotrochozoans: the Platyhelminthes.

The Phylum Platyhelminthes Consists of Flatworms with No Coelom

Platyhelminthes (from the Greek *platy*, meaning "flat," and *helminth*, meaning "worm"), or flatworms, lack a specialized respiratory or circulatory system to transport gases. They must obtain oxygen by diffusion, which makes a flat shape necessary, in that no cell can be too far from the surface. Flatworms were among the first animals to develop an active predatory lifestyle. Platyhelminthes, and indeed most animals, are bilaterally symmetrical, with a head bearing sensory appendages.

The flatworms are also believed to be the first animals to develop three embryonic germ layers—ectoderm, endoderm,

and mesoderm—with mesoderm replacing the simpler gelatinous mesoglea of cnidarians. As such, they are said to be triploblastic. The muscles in flatworms, which are derived from mesoderm, are well developed. The development of mesoderm was thus a critical evolutionary innovation in animals, because it also led to the development of more sophisticated organs. Flatworms are sometimes regarded as the first animals to reach the organ-system level of organization. The mesoderm fills the body spaces apart from the gastrovascular cavity; thus, the flatworms are acoelomate, lacking a fluid-filled body cavity in which the gut is suspended (**Figure 31.7**).

The digestive system of flatworms is incomplete, with only one opening, which serves as both mouth and anus, as in cnidarians. Most flatworms possess a muscular pharynx that can be extended through the mouth. The pharynx opens to a gastrovascular cavity, where food is digested. In large flatworms the gastrovascular cavity is branched enough to distribute nutrients to all parts of the body. Any undigested material is egested back through the pharynx. The incomplete digestive system of flatworms thus prevents continuous feeding. Some flatworms are predators, but many species have invaded other animals as parasites.

Flatworms have a distinct excretory system, consisting of **protonephridia**, two lateral canals with branches capped by **flame cells**. The flame cells, which are ciliated and waft water through the lateral canals to the outside (look ahead to Figure 47.7), exist primarily to maintain osmotic balance between the flatworm's body and the surrounding fluids. Simple though this system is, its development was key to permitting the invasion of freshwater habitats and even moist terrestrial areas.

Some free-living flatworms in the class Turbellaria possess light-sensitive eyespots or ocelli at the anterior end and

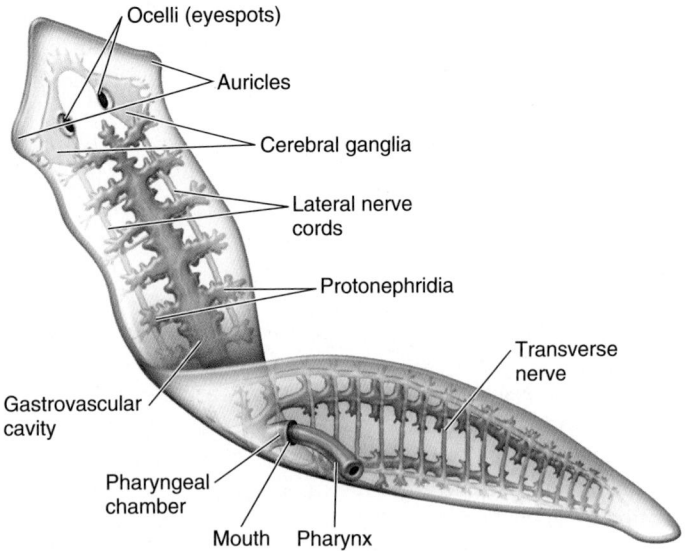

Figure 31.7   Body plan of a flatworm.   Flatworm morphology as represented by a planarian, a member of the class Turbellaria.

Concept check: *How do flatworms breathe?*

chemoreceptive and sensory cells that are concentrated in organs called auricles. A pair of **cerebral ganglia** receives input from photoreceptors in eyespots and sensory cells. From the ganglia, a pair of lateral nerve cords running the length of the body allows rapid movement of information from anterior to posterior. In addition transverse nerves form a nerve net on the ventral surface similar to that of cnidarians. Thus, the flatworms have retained the cnidarian-style nervous system, while possessing the beginnings of a more centralized type of nervous system seen throughout much of the rest of the animal kingdom. In all the Platyhelminthes reproduction is either sexual or asexual. Most species are hermaphroditic but do not fertilize their own eggs. Flatworms can also reproduce asexually by splitting into two parts, with each half regenerating the missing half.

The four classes of flatworms are the Turbellaria, Monogenea, Trematoda (flukes), and Cestoda (tapeworms) (**Table 31.2**). Both cestodes and trematodes are internally parasitic and hence are of great medical and veterinary importance. They possess a variety of organs of attachment, such as hooks and suckers, that enable them to remain embedded within their hosts (**Figure 31.8**). Cestodes often require two separate vertebrate host species, such as pigs or cattle, to begin their life cycle and humans to complete their development. Many tapeworms can live inside humans who consume undercooked, infected meat—hence the value of thoroughly cooking meat to kill any parasites.

The life history of trematodes is even more complex than that of cestodes, involving multiple hosts. The first host, called the intermediate host, is usually a mollusc, and the final host, or definitive host, is usually a vertebrate, but often a second or even a third intermediate host is involved. In the case of the Chinese liver fluke (*Clonorchis sinensis*), the adult parasite lives and reproduces in the definitive host, and the resultant "eggs" (encapsulated miracidia) pass from the host via the feces (**Figure 31.9**). An intermediate host, such as a snail, eats the eggs. The miracidia are released and transform into sporocysts. The sporocysts asexually produce more sporocysts called rediae. The rediae reproduce asexually to produce cercariae. Cercariae bore their way out of the snail and infect their definitive hosts directly by boring into their feet when in water or, for species with a second intermediate host (as in the Chinese liver fluke), by entering fish. Here, the cercariae develop into metacercarial cysts (juvenile flukes) and lodge in fish muscle, which the definitive host will eat. In the definitive host the cyst protects the metacercaria from the host's gastric juices. In the small intestine the metacercariae travel to the liver and grow into adult flukes and the life cycle begins anew. The life cycle of a trematode can thus involve at least seven stages: adult, egg (encapsulated embryo), miracidium, sporocyst, rediae, cercaria, and metacercaria. Because of the low probability of each larva reaching a suitable host, trematodes must produce large numbers of offspring to ensure that some survive.

Blood flukes, *Schistosoma* spp., are the most common parasitic trematodes infecting humans and cause the disease known as schistosomiasis. More than 200 million people worldwide, primarily in tropical Asia, Africa, and South America, are infected with schistosomiasis. The 2.5-cm-long adult flukes can live for years in human hosts, and the release of eggs can cause chronic inflammation and blockage in many organs. Untreated schistosomiasis can lead to severe damage to the liver, intestines, and lungs and can eventually lead to death. Access to clean water can greatly reduce infection rates.

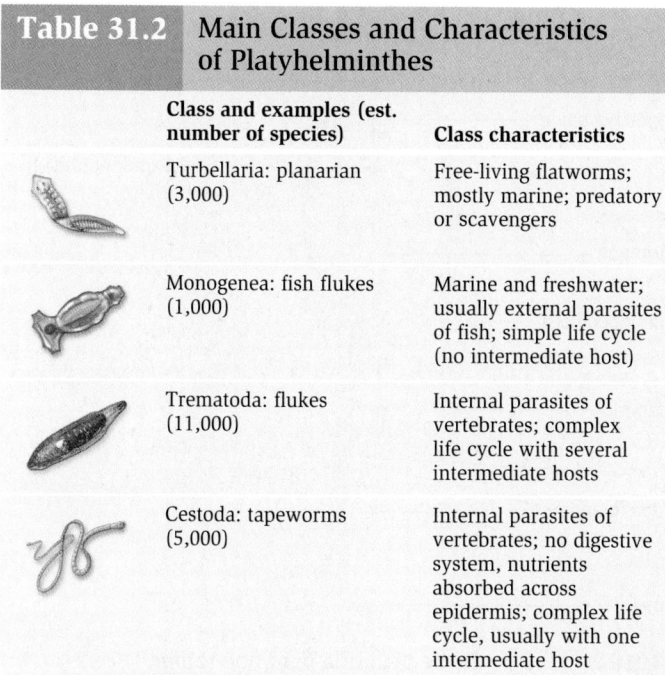

Table 31.2	Main Classes and Characteristics of Platyhelminthes	
	Class and examples (est. number of species)	**Class characteristics**
	Turbellaria: planarian (3,000)	Free-living flatworms; mostly marine; predatory or scavengers
	Monogenea: fish flukes (1,000)	Marine and freshwater; usually external parasites of fish; simple life cycle (no intermediate host)
	Trematoda: flukes (11,000)	Internal parasites of vertebrates; complex life cycle with several intermediate hosts
	Cestoda: tapeworms (5,000)	Internal parasites of vertebrates; no digestive system, nutrients absorbed across epidermis; complex life cycle, usually with one intermediate host

Figure 31.8 A tapeworm, *Taenia pisiformis,* a member of the class Cestoda. Note the scolex, the organ of attachment at the head end, complete with tiny hooks and suckers.

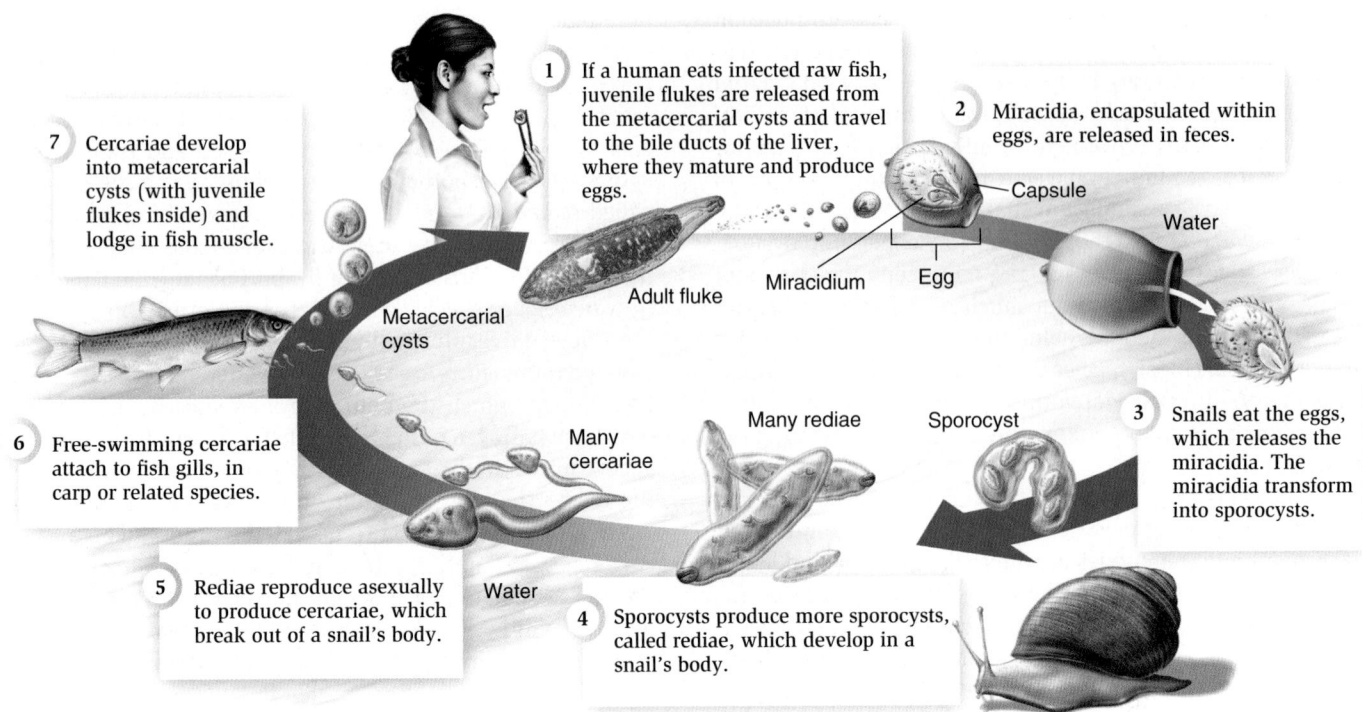

Figure 31.9 **The complete life cycle of a trematode.** As an example, this figure shows the life cycle of the Chinese liver fluke (*Clonorchis sinensis*). This trematode is endemic to South East China, but human cases are frequently documented in Canada as a result of international travel and immigration.

Members of the Phylum Rotifera Have a Pseudocoelom and a Ciliated Crown

Members of the phylum Rotifera (from the Latin *rota*, meaning "wheel," and *fera*, meaning "to bear") get their name from their ciliated crown or **corona**, which, when beating, looks similar to a rotating wheel (**Figure 31.10**). Most rotifers are microscopic animals, usually less than 1 mm long, and some have beautiful colours. There are about 2,000 species of rotifers, most of which inhabit fresh water, with a few marine or terrestrial species. Most often they are bottom-dwelling organisms, living on the pond floor or along lakeside vegetation.

Rotifers have an alimentary canal, a digestive tract with a separate mouth and anus, which means that they can feed continuously. The corona creates water currents that propel the animal through the water and that waft small planktonic organisms or decomposing organic material toward the mouth. The mouth opens into a circular muscular pharynx called a **mastax**, which has jaws for grasping and chewing. The mastax, which in some species can protrude through the mouth to seize small prey, is a structure unique to rotifers. The body of the rotifer bears a jointed foot with one to four toes. **Pedal glands** in the foot secrete a sticky substance that aids in attachment to the substrate. The internal organs lie within a pseudocoelom, a fluid-filled body cavity that is not completely lined with mesoderm. The pseudocoelom serves as a hydrostatic skeleton and as a medium for the internal transport of nutrients and wastes. Rotifers also have a pair of protonephridia with flame bulbs that

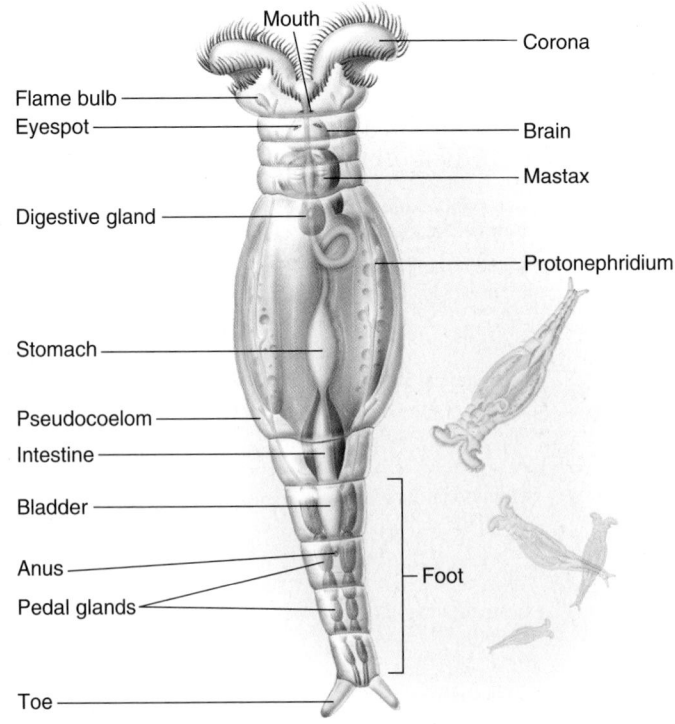

Figure 31.10 Body plan of a common rotifer, *Philodina* genus.

collect excretory and digestive waste and drain into a cloacal bladder, which passes waste to the anus.

The reproductive system in rotifers depends on the species. In some species unfertilized diploid eggs that have not undergone meiotic division, called amictic eggs, develop into females through a process known as **parthenogenesis**. In other species some eggs undergo meiosis and become haploid. These so-called mictic eggs, if unfertilized, develop into degenerate males that cannot feed and only live long enough to produce and release sperm that fertilize other mictic eggs. These fertilized eggs form zygotes, which have a thick shell and can survive for long periods in harsh conditions, such as a water supply that dries up, before developing into new females. Because the tiny zygotes are easily transported, rotifers show up in the smallest of aquatic environments, such as roof gutters and birdbaths.

The Lophophorata Includes Three Closely Related Phyla: Phoronida, Bryozoa, and Brachiopoda

The Lophophorates consist of three distinct phyla: the Phoronida, the Bryozoa, and the Brachiopoda. They all possess a lophophore, a ciliary feeding device (refer back to Figure 30.10a), and a true coelom (refer back to Figure 30.5a). The lophophore is a circular fold of the body wall that bears tentacles that draw water toward the mouth. Because a thin extension of the coelom penetrates each tentacle, the tentacles also serve as a respiratory device. Gases diffuse across the tentacles and into or out of the coelomic fluid and are carried throughout the body. All three phyla have a U-shaped alimentary canal, with the anus located near the mouth but outside the lophophore.

Phylum Phoronida Members of the Phoronida (from the Greek *phoros*, meaning "bearer," and the Latin *nidus*, meaning "nest") are elongated, tube-dwelling marine worms ranging in size from 1 mm to 50 cm long. They live in a tough, leather-like chitinous tube that they secrete and that is often buried in the ground so only the lophophore sticks out (**Figure 31.11a**). The lophophore can be retracted quickly in the presence of danger. Only about 15 species of phoronids are found worldwide.

Phylum Bryozoa The bryozoans (from the Greek *bryon*, meaning "moss," and *zoon*, meaning "animal") are small colonial animals, which means that individuals are incompletely separated and form a collective life form. Most bryozoans are less than 0.5 mm long and can be found encrusted on rocks in shallow aquatic environments. They look very much like plants. There are about 4,000 species, many of which are fouling organisms that encrust boat hulls and have to be scraped off periodically. Within the colony, each animal secretes and lives inside a nonliving case called a **zoecium** (**Figure 31.11b**). The walls of the zoecium may be composed of chitin or calcium carbonate. For this reason bryozoans have been important reef-builders, and since they date back to the Ordovician era, many fossil forms have been discovered and identified.

Phylum Brachiopoda Brachiopods (from the Greek *brachio*, meaning "arm," and *podos*, meaning "foot") are marine organisms with two shell halves, much like modern clams (**Figure 31.11c**). Unlike bivalve molluscs, however, which have a left and right valve (side) of the shell, brachiopods have a dorsal and ventral valve. Brachiopods are bottom-dwelling species that attach to the substrate via a muscular pedicle. Although they are a relatively small group, with about 300 living species, brachiopods flourished in the Paleozoic and Mesozoic eras, and about 30,000 fossil species have been identified. Some of these fossil forms tell of organisms that reached 30 cm in length, although their current relatives are only 0.5 to 8.0 cm long. The species shown in Figure 31.11c is common in the Bay of Fundy.

The Mollusca Is a Large Phylum Containing Snails, Slugs, Oysters, Clams, Octopuses, and Squids

Molluscs (from the Latin *mollis*, meaning "soft") constitute a very large phylum, with more than 100,000 living species, including organisms as diverse as snails, clams and oysters, cephalopods, and chitons. They are an ancient group, as evidenced by the classification of about 35,000 fossil species. Molluscs have a considerable economic, aesthetic, and ecological importance to humans. Many serve as sources of food, including scallops,

(a) A phoronid worm (*Phoronis californica*), buried in the sand with the lophophores extended.

(b) Bryozoans, such as this *Plumatella repens*, are colonial lophophorates that reside in a nonliving case called a zoecium.

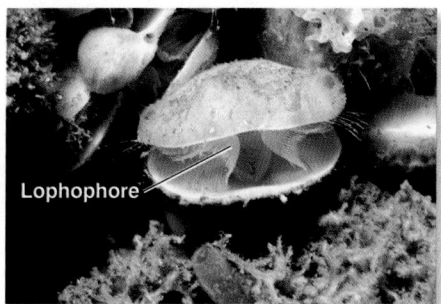

(c) Brachiopods including this northern lamp shell (*Terebratulina septentrionalis*) have a dorsal and ventral shell.

Figure 31.11 Lophophorates.

Concept check: *What are the two main functions of the lophophore?*

oysters, clams, and squid. A significant industry involves the farming of oysters to produce cultured pearls, and rare and beautiful mollusc shells are extremely valuable to collectors. Snails and slugs can damage vegetables and ornamental plants, and boring molluscs can penetrate wooden ships and wharfs. Molluscs are intermediate hosts to many parasites, and several exotic species have become serious pests. For example, populations of the zebra mussel (*Dreissena polymorpha*) were introduced into North America from Asia via ballast water from transoceanic ships. Since their introduction, they have spread rapidly throughout the Great Lakes and an increasing number of inland waterways, significantly affecting native organisms and clogging water intake valves to municipal water treatment plants around the lakes.

One common feature of the molluscs is their soft body, which exists, in many species, under a protective external shell. Most molluscs are marine, although some have colonized fresh water. Many snails and slugs have even moved onto land, but they survive only in humid areas and where the calcium necessary for shell formation is abundant in the soil. The ability to colonize freshwater and terrestrial habitats has led to a diversification of mollusc body plans. Thus, we again see how organismal diversity is related to environmental diversity.

Although great variation in morphology occurs between classes, molluscs have a basic body plan consisting of three parts (**Figure 31.12**). A muscular **foot** is usually used for movement, and a **visceral mass** containing the internal organs rests atop the foot. The **mantle**, a fold of skin draped over the visceral mass, secretes a shell in those species that form shells. The mantle often extends beyond the visceral mass, creating a chamber called the **mantle cavity**, which houses delicate **gills**, specialized filamentous organs that are rich in blood vessels. A continuous current of water, often induced by cilia present on the gills or by muscular pumping, flushes out the wastes from the mantle cavity and brings in new oxygen-rich water.

Molluscs are coelomate organisms, but the coelom is confined to a small area around the heart. Molluscs' organs are served with oxygen and nutrients via a circulatory system. Molluscs have an **open circulatory system** with a heart that pumps body fluid called hemolymph through vessels and into sinuses, which are open, fluid-filled cavities. In comparison, in a closed circulatory system the fluid called blood is always contained within vessels. The organs and tissues are thus continually bathed in hemolymph. From these sinuses the hemolymph drains into vessels that take it to the gills and then back to the heart. The anus and pores from organs called **metanephridia**, which extract nitrogenous and other wastes, discharge into the mantle cavity. The metanephridial ducts can also serve to discharge sperm or eggs from the gonads.

The mollusc's mouth may contain a **radula**, a unique, protrusible, tonguelike organ that has many teeth and is used to eat plants, scrape food particles off rocks, or, if the mollusc is predatory, bore into shells of other species and tear flesh. In the cone shells (*Conus* spp.) the radula is reduced to a few poison-injecting teeth on the end of a long proboscis that is cast about in search of prey, such as a worm or even a fish (**Figure 31.13**). Some Indo-Pacific cone shell species produce a neuromuscular toxin that can kill humans. Other molluscs, particularly bivalves, are suspension feeders that filter water brought in by ciliary currents.

Most shells are complex three-layered structures secreted by the mantle that continue to grow as the mollusc grows. Shell growth is often seasonal, resulting in distinct growth lines on the shell, much the same as tree rings (**Figure 31.14**). Using shell growth patterns, biologists have discovered some bivalves that are more than 100 years old. The innermost layer of the shells of oysters, mussels, abalone, and other molluscs is a smooth, iridescent lining called **nacre**, which is commonly known as mother-of-pearl and is often collected from abalone shells for jewellery. Actual pearl production in molluscs, primarily by oysters, occurs when a foreign object, such as a grain of sand, becomes lodged between the shell and the mantle, and layers of nacre are laid down around it to reduce the irritation.

Most molluscs have separate sexes, although some are hermaphroditic. Gametes are usually released into the water, where they mix and fertilization occurs. In some snails, however, fertilization is internal, with the male inserting sperm directly into the female. Internal fertilization was a key evolutionary development, enabling some snails to colonize land, and can be considered a critical innovation that fostered extensive adaptive radiation. In many species reproduction involves the production of a trochophore larva that develops into a **veliger**, a free-swimming larva that has a rudimentary foot, shell, and mantle (**Figure 31.15**).

Of the eight molluscan classes the four most common are the polyplacophora (chitons), gastropoda (snails and slugs), bivalvia (clams and mussels), and cephalopoda (octopuses, squid, and nautiluses) (**Table 31.3**). The class Gastropoda (from the

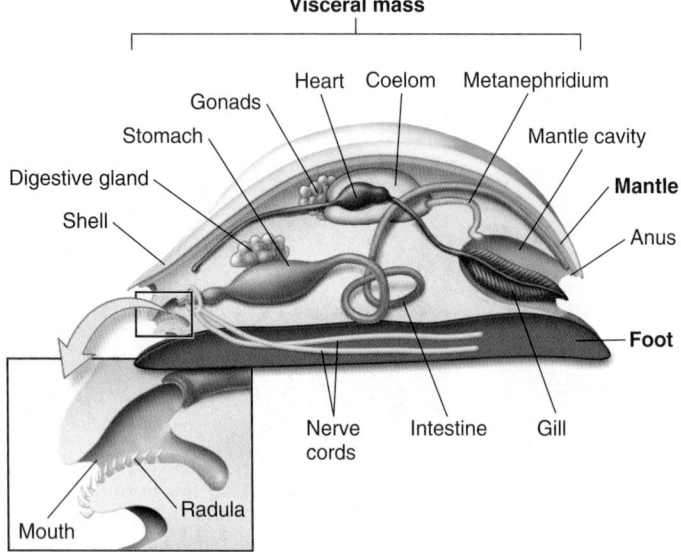

Figure 31.12   The mollusc body plan. The generalized body plan of a mollusc includes the characteristic foot, mantle, and visceral mass.

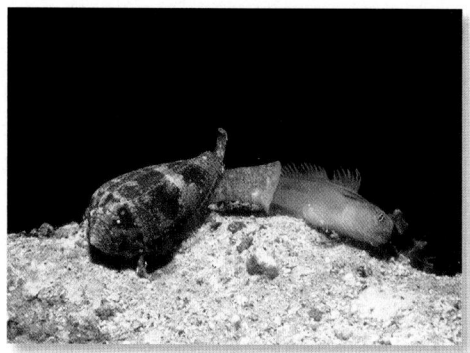

Figure 31.13 **Some gastropods are predators.** The cone shell, *Conus* spp., uses its long proboscis, equipped with poison-injecting teeth, to paralyze its prey—usually a fish.

Figure 31.14 **Bivalve shells have growth rings.** Quahog clams (*Mercenaria mercenaria*), also known as cherrystones or littlenecks (depending on their size), can live for more 20 years. They are an important commercial clam for fisheries in Prince Edward Island, Nova Scotia, and New Brunswick.

Figure 31.15 **A veliger larva.** The immature free-swimming stage of molluscans develops from the trochophore larva.

Greek *gaster,* meaning "stomach," and *podos,* meaning "foot") is the largest group of molluscs and encompasses about 75,000 living species, including snails, periwinkles, limpets, and other shelled members. The class also includes such species as slugs and nudibranchs, whose shells have been greatly reduced or completely lost during their evolution (**Figure 31.16**). Most are marine or freshwater species, but some species, including snails and slugs, have also colonized land. Most gastropods are slow-moving animals that are weighed down by their shell. Unlike bivalves, gastropods have a one-piece shell, into which the animal can withdraw to escape predators.

The 780 species of Cephalopoda (from the Greek *kephale,* meaning "head," and *podos,* meaning "foot") are the most morphologically complex of the molluscs and indeed among the most complex of all invertebrates. They include the octopuses, squids, cuttlefish, and nautiluses. Most are fast-swimming marine predators that range from organisms just a few centimetres in size to the giant squid (*Architeuthis*) which is known to reach more than 17 m in length and weigh 2 metric tons. A cephalopod's mouth is surrounded by many long tentacles commonly armed with suckers. Octopuses have eight arms with suckers, and squids and cuttlefish have ten arms—eight with suckers and two long tentacles with suckers limited to their ends. Nautiluses have between 60 and 90 tentacles around the mouth.

All cephalopods have a beaklike jaw that allows them to bite their prey, and some, such as the blue-ringed octopus

Table 31.3	Main Classes and Characteristics of Molluscs	
	Class and examples (est. number of species)	**Class characteristics**
	Polyplacophora: chitons (860)	Marine; eight-plated shell
	Gastropoda: snails, slugs, nudibranchs (75,000)	Marine, freshwater, or terrestrial; most with coiled shell, but shell absent in slugs and nudibranchs; radula present
	Bivalvia: clams, mussels, oysters (30,000)	Marine or freshwater; shell with two halves or valves; primarily filter feeders with siphons
	Cephalopoda: octopuses, squids, nautiluses (780)	Marine; predatory, with tentacles around mouth, often with suckers; shell often absent or reduced; closed circulatory system; jet propulsion via siphon

Figure 31.16 **A sea slug (*Chromodoris kuniei*).** The sea slugs, or nudibranchs, are a gastropod subclass whose members have lost their shell altogether.

(*Hapalochlaena lunulata*), deliver a deadly poison through their saliva (**Figure 31.17**). Only one group, the nautiluses, has retained an external shell. In octopuses the shell is not present, and in squid and cuttlefish it is greatly reduced and internal. However, the fossil record is full of shelled cephalopods, called ammonites, some of which were as big as truck tires (**Figure 31.18**). Such fossils are common in the Badlands of Alberta. Ammonites became extinct at the end of the Cretaceous period, although the reasons for this are not well understood.

The foot of some cephalopods has become modified into a muscular siphon. Water drawn into the mantle cavity is quickly expelled through the siphon, propelling the organisms forward or backward in a kind of jet propulsion. Such vigorous movement requires powerful muscles and a very efficient circulatory system to deliver oxygen and nutrients to the muscles. Cephalopods are the only molluscs with a **closed circulatory system**, in which blood flows throughout an animal entirely within a series of vessels. One of the advantages of this type of system is that the heart can pump blood through the tissues rapidly. The blood of cephalopods contains the copper-rich protein hemocyanin for transporting oxygen. Less efficient than the iron-rich hemoglobin of vertebrates, hemocyanin gives the blood a blue colour.

The nautiluses are impeded by a coiled, chambered shell and do not move as fast as the jet-propelled squids and octopuses (**Figure 31.19**). As it grows, the nautilus secretes a new chamber and seals off the old one with a **septum**. The older chambers are gas filled and act as buoyancy chambers. A thin strip of living tissue called the siphuncle removes liquid from the old chamber and replaces it with gas. The gas pressure within the chambers is only 1 atmosphere, despite the fact that nautiluses may be swimming at 400-m depths at a pressure of about 40 atmospheres. The shell's structure is strong enough to withstand this pressure differential.

Cephalopods have a well-developed nervous system and brain that support their active lifestyle. Their sense organs, especially their eyes, are also very well developed. Many cephalopods (with the exception of nautiluses) have an ink sac that

Figure 31.18   **A fossil ammonite.**   These shelled cephalopods were abundant in the Cretaceous period.

contains the pigment melanin; the sac can be emptied to provide a "smokescreen" to confuse predators. In many species melanin is also distributed in special pigment cells in the skin that can produce colour changes. Octopuses often change colour when alarmed or during courtship, and they can rapidly change colour to blend in with their background and escape detection. The central nervous system of the octopus is among the most complex in the invertebrate world. Behavioural biologists have demonstrated that octopuses can behave in sophisticated ways, and scientists are currently debating to what degree they are capable of learning by observation.

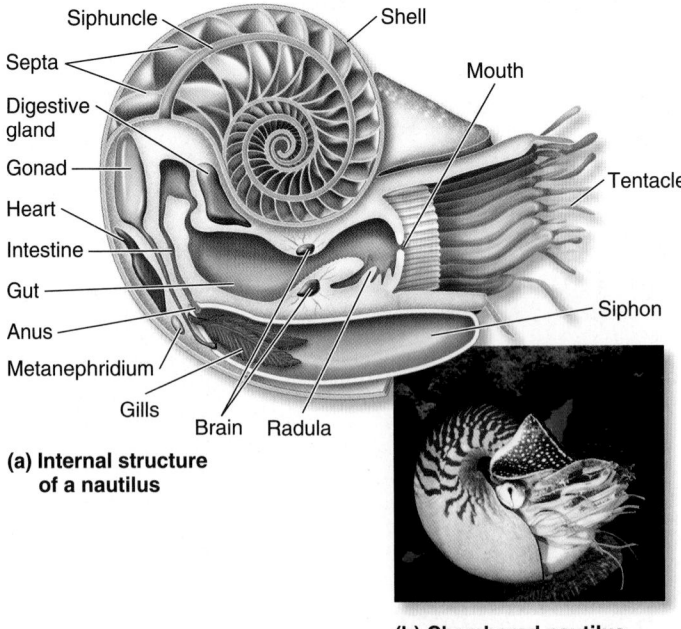

(a) Internal structure of a nautilus

(b) Chambered nautilus

Figure 31.19   **The nautilus.**   (a) A longitudinal section of a nautilus, showing the coiled shell with many chambers. The animal secretes a new chamber each year and lives only in the new one. (b) The chambered nautilus (*Nautilus pompilius*).

Figure 31.17   **The blue-ringed octopus (*Hapalochlaena lunulata*) is highly poisonous.**

FEATURE INVESTIGATION

Fiorito and Scotto's Experiments Showed Invertebrates Can Exhibit Sophisticated Observational Learning Behaviour

We tend to think of the ability to learn from others as a vertebrate phenomenon, especially among species that live in social groups. However, in 1992 Italian researchers Graziano Fiorito and Pietro Scotto demonstrated that octopuses can learn by observing the behaviour of other octopuses (**Figure 31.20**). This was a surprising finding, in part because *Octopus vulgaris,* the species they studied, lives a solitary existence for most of its life

and most animals that exhibit learning from conspecifics are generally social animals.

In the experiments octopuses were trained to attack either a red ball or a white ball by use of a reward (a small piece of fish placed behind the ball that the octopuses could not see) and a punishment (a small electric shock for choosing the wrong ball). This type of learning is called classical conditioning (see Chapter 52). Because octopuses are colour-blind, they must have been distinguishing between the relative brightness of the balls. Octopuses were considered to be trained when they made no mistakes in five trials. Observer octopuses in adjacent tanks were then allowed to

HYPOTHESIS Octopuses can learn by observing another's behaviour.

STUDY LOCATION Laboratory setting with *Octopus vulgaris* collected from the Bay of Naples, Italy.

		Experimental level	Conceptual level

1 Train two groups of octopuses, one to attack white balls, one to attack red. These are called the demonstrator octopuses.

Reward choice of correct ball (with fish) and punish choice of incorrect ball (with electric shock). Training is complete when octopus makes no "mistakes" in five trials.

Conditions a demonstrator octopus to attack a particular colour of ball.

2 In an adjacent tank, allow observer octopus to watch trained demonstrator octopus.

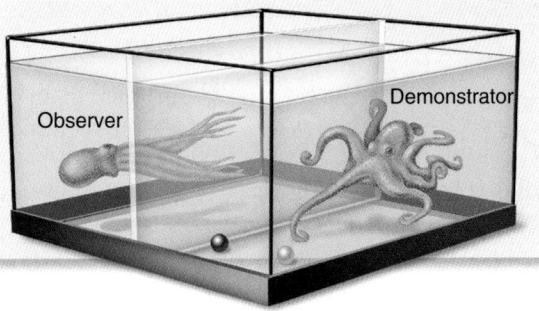

Observer octopus may be learning the correct ball to attack by watching the demonstrator octopus.

3 Drop balls into the tank of the observer octopus. Test the observer octopus to see if it makes the same decisions as the demonstrator octopus.

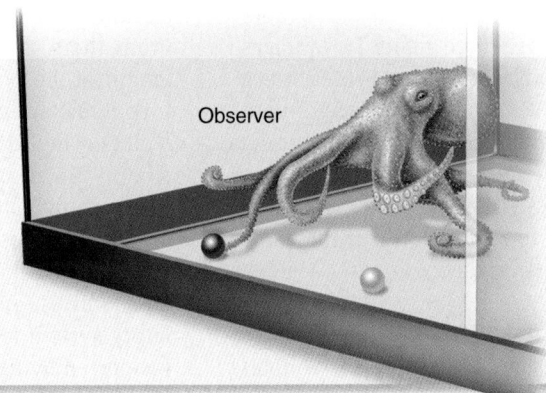

If the observer octopus is learning from the demonstrator octopus, the observer octopus should attack the ball of the same colour as the demonstrator octopus was trained to attack.

Figure 31.20 Observational learning in octopuses.

Figure 31.20 *(Continued)*

4 THE DATA

Participant	Colour of ball chosen in five trials*	
	Red	White
Observers (watched demonstrator attack red)	4.31	0.31
Observers (watched demonstrator attack white)	0.40	4.10
Untrained (did not watch demonstrations)	2.11	1.94

*Average of five trials; data do not always sum to five, because some trials resulted in no balls being chosen.

5 CONCLUSION Invertebrate animals are capable of learning from watching other individuals behave, in much the same way as vertebrate species learn from watching others.

6 SOURCE Fiorito, G., and Scotto, P. 1992. Observational learning in *Octopus vulgaris. Science* 256:545–547.

watch the trained octopuses attacking the balls. In the third part of the experiment, the observer octopuses were themselves tested. The observers nearly always attacked the same colour ball as they had observed the demonstrators attacking. In addition learning by observation was achieved more quickly than the original training. This remarkable behaviour is considered by some as the precursor to more complex forms of learning, including problem solving.

Experimental Questions

1. What was the hypothesis tested by Fiorito and Scotto?
2. What were the results of the experiment? Did these results support the hypothesis?
3. What is the significance of performing the experiment on both observer and untrained octopuses?

The Phylum Annelida Consists of the Segmented Worms

If you look at an earthworm, you will see little rings all down its body. Indeed, the phylum name Annelida is derived from the Latin *annulus,* meaning "little ring." Each ring is a distinct segment of the annelid's body, with each segment separated from the one in front and the one behind by a septum (**Figure 31.21a**). Segmentation, the division of the body into nearly identical subunits, is a critical evolutionary innovation in the annelids and confers at least three major advantages. First, many components of the body are repeated in each segment, including blood vessels, nerves, and excretory and reproductive organs. Excretion is accomplished by metanephridia, paired excretory organs in every segment that extract waste from the blood and coelomic fluid, emptying it to the exterior via pores in the skin (look ahead to Figure 46.8). If the excretory organs in one segment fail, the organs of another segment will still function.

Second, annelids possess a fluid-filled coelom that acts as a hydrostatic skeleton. In unsegmented coelomate animals, muscle contractions can distort the entire body during movement. However, such distortion is minimized in segmented animals, which allows for more effective locomotion over solid

surfaces. In an earthworm when the circular muscles around a segment contract against the hydrostatic skeleton, that segment elongates. When the longitudinal muscles contract, the segment compacts. Waves of muscular contraction ripple down the segments, which elongate or contract independently.

Third, segmentation also permits specialization of some segments, although such specialization is only minimally present at the annelid's anterior end. Annelids have a relatively sophisticated nervous system involving a pair of cerebral ganglia that connect to a subpharyngeal ganglion (**Figure 31.21b**). From there, a large ventral nerve cord runs down the entire length of the body. The ventral nerve cord is unusual because it contains a few very large nerve cells called **giant axons** that facilitate high-speed nerve conduction and rapid responses to stimuli. Such axons are found in other invertebrates, the best known of which is the squid.

Annelids essentially have a double transport system, since both the circulatory system and the coelomic fluid carry nutrients, wastes, and respiratory gases, to some degree. The circulatory system is usually closed, with dorsal and ventral vessels connected by five pairs of pumping vessels that serve as muscular hearts. The blood of most annelid species contains the respiratory pigment hemoglobin, an iron-containing protein involved in oxygen transport in annelids and in vertebrates. Respiration

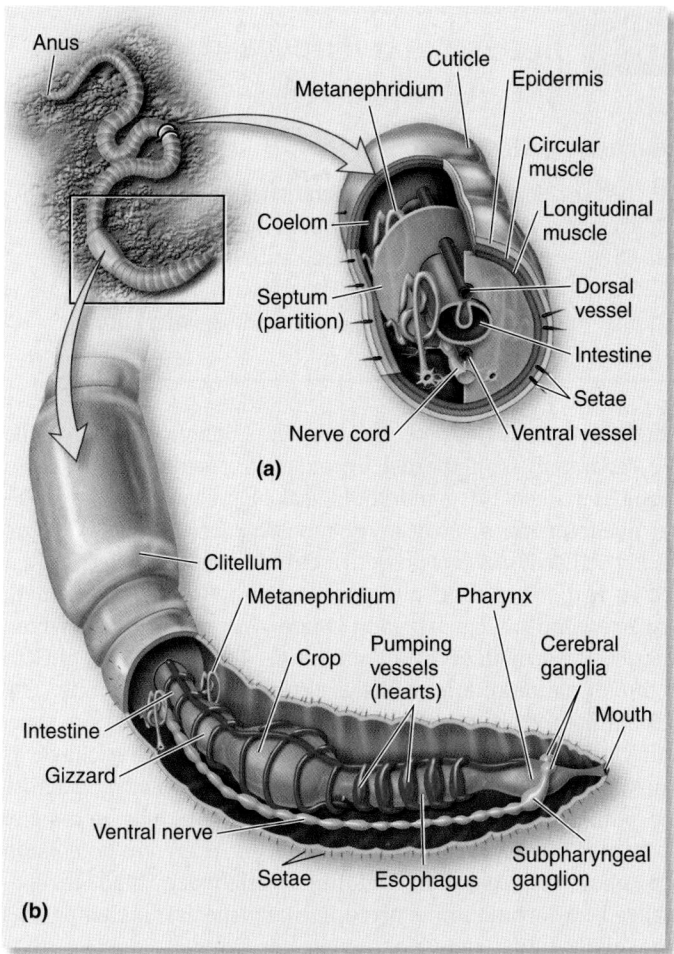

Figure 31.21 The segmented body plan of an annelid, as illustrated by an earthworm. (a) Individual segments are separated by a septum. (b) The segmented nature of the worm is apparent externally and internally.

Concept check: *What are some of the advantages of segmentation?*

occurs directly through the permeable skin surface, which restricts annelids to moist environments. The digestive system is complete and unsegmented, with many specialized regions: mouth, pharynx, esophagus, crop, gizzard, intestine, and anus. Sexual reproduction involves two individuals, often of separate sexes but sometimes hermaphrodites, that exchange sperm via internal fertilization. In some species asexual reproduction by fission occurs, in which the posterior part of the body breaks off and forms a new individual.

Annelids are a large phylum with about 15,000 described species. Its members include the familiar earthworm, marine polychaete worms, and leeches, and they range in size from less than 1 mm to the enormous Australian earthworms, which can reach 3 m. All annelids except the leeches have chitinous bristles called **setae** on each segment. In one class, the polychaetes, these are situated on fleshy, footlike **parapodia** ("almost feet") that are pushed into the substrate to provide traction during

Table 31.4	Main Classes and Characteristics of Annelids

	Class and examples (est. number of species)	Class characteristics
	Polychaeta: Marine worms (10,000)	Well-developed head; usually free living; parapodia present
	Oligochaeta: Terrestrial and freshwater worms such as earthworms (3,500)	Undeveloped head; setae; no parapodia
	Hirudinea: Leeches (630)	Mostly ectoparasites; suckers present at both ends; flattened body; reduced coelom; no setae

movement. Many annelid species burrow into the Earth or into muddy marine sediments and extract nutrients from ingested soil or mud. Some annelids also feed on dead or living vegetation, while others are predatory or parasitic.

The phylum consists of three main classes: the Polychaeta, Oligochaeta, and Hirudinea (**Table 31.4**). Some biologists have recently suggested Oligochaeta and Hirudinea be combined into one larger class called the Clitellata, because they share a common structure called a clitellum, a glandular region of the body that has a role in reproduction. However, this newer taxonomic grouping is still being debated.

Class Polychaeta With more than 10,000 species, the Polychaeta is the most species-rich class of the annelids. Many polychaetes are brightly coloured, and all have many long setae bristling out of their body (*polychaete* means "many bristles"). Most of them are marine organisms, living in burrows in the mud or sand, or in rock crevices, and are often abundant in the intertidal mudflats. They are important prey for predators, such as fish and crustaceans. The polychaete head is well developed and, in predatory species, may exhibit powerful jaws. Some species are filter feeders and have a crown of tentacles that sticks up out of the mud while the bulk of the worm remains hidden.

Class Oligochaeta The Oligochaeta (meaning "few bristles") includes the common earthworms and many species of freshwater worms. Earthworms play a unique and beneficial role in conditioning the soil, primarily through the effects of their burrows and castings. Earthworms ingest soil and leaf tissue to extract nutrients and in the process create burrows in the earth. As plant material and soil passes through the earthworm's digestive system, it is finely ground in the gizzard into smaller fragments. Once excreted, this material—called castings—enriches the soil. Because a worm can eat is own weight in soil every day, worm castings on the soil surface can be extensive. Biologist Charles Darwin was interested in earthworm activity, and his last work, *The Formation of Vegetable Mould, through the Actions of Worms, with Observations on Their Habits,* was the first detailed study of earthworm ecology. In it, he wrote, "All the fertile areas of this planet have at least once passed through the bodies of earthworms."

Class Hirudinea Leeches (class Hirudinea) are primarily found in freshwater environments, but there are also some marine species, as well as terrestrial species that inhabit warm, moist areas, such as tropical forests. Leeches have a fixed number of segments, usually 34, though the septa have disappeared in most species. All leeches feed on other organisms, often as blood-sucking parasites of vertebrates. They have powerful suckers at both ends of the body, and the anterior sucker is equipped with razor-sharp jaws that can bore or slice into the host's tissues. The salivary secretion of leeches (hirudin) acts as an anticoagulant to stop blood clotting. Leeches can suck up to several times their own weight in blood. As such, they were once used in the medical field in the practice of bloodletting, the withdrawal of often considerable quantities of blood from a patient in the belief that this would prevent or cure illness and disease. Even today leeches may be used after surgeries, particularly those involving the reattachment of digits (**Figure 31.22**). In these cases the blood vessels are not fully reconnected and much excess blood accumulates, causing swelling. This excess blood switches off the delivery of new blood and stops the formation of new arteries. If leeches remove the accumulated blood, new capillaries will be more likely to form, and the tissues will become healthy.

Unlike cestode and trematode flatworms, which are internally parasitic and quite host specific, leeches are generally external parasites that feed on a broad range of hosts, including fish, amphibians, and mammals. However, there are always exceptions. *Placobdelloides jaegerskioeldi* is a parasitic leech that lives only in the rectum of hippopotamuses.

Figure 31.22 A leech, a member of the class Hirudinea. This species, *Hirudo medicinalis,* is sucking blood from a hematoma, a swelling of blood that can occur after surgery.

Learning Outcomes:

1. List the distinguishing characteristics of nematodes.
2. Describe the arthropod body plan and its major features.
3. Give examples of the arthropod subphyla Chelicerata, Myriapoda, Hexapoda, and Crustacea.
4. List the features that help account for the diversity of insect species.

The Ecdysozoa is the sister group to the Lophotrochozoa. While the separation is supported by molecular evidence, the Ecdysozoa is named for a morphological characteristic, the physical phenomenon of ecdysis, or moulting (refer back to Figure 30.11). All ecdysozoans possess a **cuticle**, a nonliving cover that serves to both support and protect the animal. Once formed, however, the cuticle typically cannot increase in size, which restricts the growth of the animal inside. The solution for growth is the formation of a new, softer cuticle under the old one. The old one then splits open and is sloughed off, allowing the new, soft cuticle to expand before it hardens. Where the cuticle is thick, as in arthropods, it impedes the diffusion of oxygen across the skin. Such species acquire oxygen by lungs, gills, or a set of branching, air-filled tubes called tracheae. There are no cilia on the cuticle for locomotion, and thus a variety of appendages specialized for locomotion evolved in many species, including legs for walking or swimming and wings for flying.

The ability to shed the cuticle opened developmental options for the ecdysozoans. For example, many species undergo a complete metamorphosis, changing from a wormlike larva into a winged adult. Animals with internal skeletons cannot do this because growth occurs only by adding more minerals to the existing skeleton. Another significant adaptation is the development of internal fertilization, in which the male deposits sperm directly into the female, where fertilization takes place. This trait, which allows animals to breed on dry land, evolved independently in the vertebrates.

Because of these innovations, ecdysozoans are an incredibly successful group. Of the eight ecdysozoan phyla we will consider the most common two: the nematodes and arthropods. The grouping of nematodes and arthropods is a relatively new idea and implies that the process of moulting arose only once in animal evolution. In support of this certain hormones that stimulate moulting have been discovered to exist in nematodes and arthropods.

The Phylum Nematoda Consists of Small Pseudocoelomate Worms Covered by a Tough Cuticle

The nematodes (from the Greek *nematos*, meaning "thread"), also called roundworms, are small, thin worms that range from less than 1 mm to about 5 cm (**Figure 31.23**), although some

Figure 31.23 Scanning electron micrograph of a nematode within a plant leaf.

parasitic species measuring 1 m or more have been found in the placenta of sperm whales. Nematodes are ubiquitous organisms that exist in nearly all habitats, from the poles to the tropics. They are found in the soil, in both freshwater and marine environments, and inside plants and animals as parasites. A shovelful of soil may contain a million nematodes. More than 20,000 species are known, but there are probably at least five times as many undiscovered species.

Nematodes have several distinguishing characteristics. A tough cuticle covers the body. The cuticle is secreted by the epidermis and is made primarily of **collagen**, a structural protein also present in vertebrates. The cuticle is shed periodically as the nematode grows. Beneath the epidermis are longitudinal muscles but no circular muscles, which means that muscle contraction results in more thrashing of the body than smoother wormlike movement. Nematodes possess a pseudocoelom, which acts as a hydrostatic skeleton, and a circulatory system. Diffusion of gases occurs through the cuticle. Roundworms have a complete digestive tract composed of a mouth, pharynx, intestine, and anus. The mouth often contains sharp, piercing organs called **stylets**, and the muscular pharynx functions to suck in food.

Nematode reproduction is usually sexual, with separate males and females, and fertilization takes place internally. Females are generally larger than males and can produce prodigious numbers of eggs, in some cases more than 100,000 per day. Development in nematodes is easily observed because the organism is transparent and the generation time is short. For these reasons the small, free-living nematode *Caenorhabditis elegans* has become a model organism for researchers to study (refer back to Figure 17.1). In fact the 2002 Nobel Prize in Medicine or Physiology was shared by Sydney Brenner, Robert Horvitz, and John Sulston for their studies of the genetic regulation of development and programmed cell death in *C. elegans*. This nematode has 1,090 cells but 131 die, leaving exactly 959 cells. The cells die via a genetically controlled cell death. Many diseases in humans, including acquired immune deficiency

syndrome (AIDS), cause extensive cell death, while others, such as cancer and autoimmune diseases, reduce cell death so that cells that should die do not. Researchers are studying the process of programmed cell death in *C. elegans* in the hope of finding treatments for these and other human diseases.

A large number of nematodes are parasitic in humans and other vertebrates. The large roundworm (*Ascaris lumbricoides*) can reach up to 30 cm in length and is a parasite of the small intestine. More than 1 billion people worldwide carry this parasite. Although infections are most prevalent in tropical or developing countries, the prevalence of *A. lumbricoides* is relatively high in rural areas of the southeastern United States. Eggs pass through in feces and can remain viable in the soil for years. Eggs require ingestion before hatching into an infective stage. Hookworms (*Necator americanus*), so named because their anterior end curves dorsally like a hook, are also parasites of the human intestine. The eggs pass in feces, and recently hatched hookworms can penetrate the skin of a host's foot to establish a new infection. In areas with modern plumbing, these diseases are uncommon.

Pinworms (*Enterobius vermicularis*), while a nuisance, have relatively benign effects on their hosts. In Canada there is a 30% incidence of pinworm infections in children ages seven through ten. Adult pinworms live in the large intestine and migrate to the anal region at night to lay their eggs, which causes intense itching. The resultant scratching spreads the eggs. In the tropics some 250 million people are infected with *Wuchereria bancrofti*, a fairly large (100 mm) worm that lives in the lymphatic system, blocking the flow of lymph, and, in extreme cases, causing elephantiasis or extreme swelling of the legs and other body parts (**Figure 31.24**). Females release tiny, live young called microfilariae, which are transmitted to new hosts via mosquitoes.

Figure 31.24 Elephantiasis in a human leg.   The disease is caused by the nematode parasite *Wuchereria bancrofti*, which lives in the lymphatic system and blocks the flow of lymph.

Concept check: *What other nematodes are parasitic in humans?*

The Phylum Arthropoda Contains the Insects, Crustaceans, and Spiders, All with Jointed Appendages

The arthropods (from the Greek *arthron*, "joint," and *podos*, "foot") constitute perhaps the most successful phylum on Earth. About three-quarters of all described living species are arthropods, and scientists have estimated that they are also numerically common, with an estimated 10^{18}, or 1 billion billion, individual organisms present on Earth. The huge success of the arthropods, in terms of their sheer numbers and diversity, is related to a body plan that permitted conquest of the major biomes on Earth, from the poles to the tropics, and from marine and freshwater habitats to dry land.

The body of a typical arthropod is covered by a hard cuticle, an **exoskeleton** (external skeleton) made of layers of chitin and protein. The cuticle can be extremely tough in some parts, as in the shells of crabs, lobsters, and even beetles, yet be soft and flexible in other parts, between body segments and segments of appendages, to allow for movement. In the class of arthropods called crustaceans, the exoskeleton is reinforced with calcium carbonate to make it extra hard. The exoskeleton provides protection and also a point of attachment for muscles, all of which are internal. It is also relatively impermeable to water, a feature that may have enabled many arthropods to conserve water and colonize land, in much the same way as a tough seed coat allowed plants to colonize land (see Chapter 28). From this point of view the development of a hard cuticle was a critical innovation. It also reminds us that the ability to adapt to diverse environmental conditions can itself lead to increased organismal diversity.

Arthropods are segmented, and many of the segments bear appendages for locomotion, food handling, or reproduction. The evolutionary diversity of jointed appendages may have contributed to the success of the arthropods. In many orders the body segments have become fused into functional units, or **tagmata**, such as the head, thorax, and abdomen of an insect (**Figure 31.25**). Cephalization is extensive, and arthropods have well-developed sensory organs, including organs of sight, touch, smell, hearing, and balance. Arthropods have compound eyes composed of many independent visual units called **ommatidia** (singular: ommatidium) (look ahead to Figure 42.23). Each ommatidium functions as a separate photoreceptor capable of forming an independent image. Together, these lenses render a mosaic-like image of the environment. Some species, particularly some insects, possess additional simple eyes, or ocelli, that are probably only capable of distinguishing light from dark.

The arthropod brain is quite sophisticated, consisting of two or three ganglia connected to several smaller ventral nerve ganglia. Like most molluscs, arthropods have an open circulatory system (look ahead to Figure 44.2), in which hemolymph is pumped from the heart into the aorta or short arteries and then into sinuses, open fluid-filled cavities surrounding the major organs that coalesce to form the hemocoel. From the sinuses, gases and nutrients diffuse into tissues. The hemolymph flows back into the heart via pores, called ostia, that are equipped with valves.

(a) External anatomy

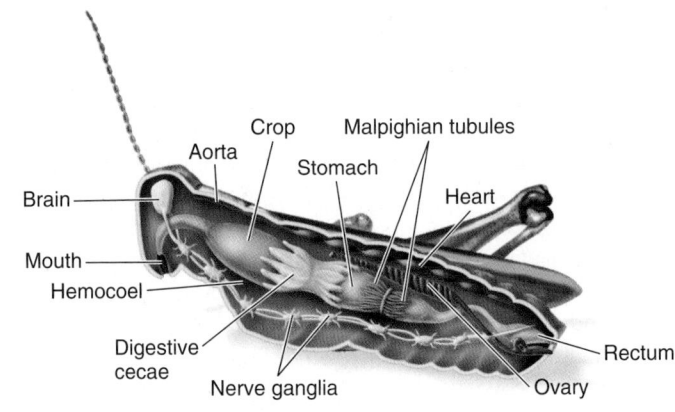

(b) Internal anatomy

Figure 31.25 Body plan of an arthropod, as represented by a grasshopper.

BioConnections: *Look ahead to Figure 46.9. Why did the Malpighian tubule system play a key role in the colonization of land by insects and other arthropods?*

Because the cuticle impedes the diffusion of gases through the body surface, arthropods possess special organs that permit gas exchange. In aquatic arthropods these consist of feathery gills that have an extensive surface area in contact with the surrounding water. Terrestrial species have a highly developed **tracheal system**, a series of finely branched air tubes called tracheae that lead into the body from pores called **spiracles** (look ahead to Figure 45.7). The tracheal system delivers oxygen directly to tissues and cells. Some spiders have book lungs, consisting of a series of sheetlike structures extending into a hemolymph-filled chamber on the underside of the abdomen. Gases also diffuse across thin areas of the cuticle.

The digestive system is complex and often includes a mouth, a crop, a stomach, an intestine, and a rectum. Excretion is accomplished by a specialized metanephridia or, in insects and some other taxa, by **Malpighian tubules**, delicate projections from the digestive tract that protrude into the hemolymph (look ahead to Figure 46.9). Nitrogenous wastes are absorbed by the tubules and emptied into the gut. The intestine and rectum reabsorb water and salts. This excretory system, allowing the retention of water, was another critical innovation that permitted the colonization of land by arthropods.

There are six main classes of arthropods: one now-extinct class—Trilobita (the trilobites)—and five living classes: Arachnida (spiders and scorpions), Diplopoda (millipedes), Chilopoda (centipedes), Insecta (insects), and Crustacea (crabs and relatives) (**Table 31.5**).

Class Trilobita: Extinct Early Arthropods The trilobites were among the earliest arthropods, flourishing in shallow seas of the Paleozoic era, some 500 million years ago, and dying out about 250 million years ago. Most trilobites were bottom feeders and were generally 3 to 10 cm in size, although some reached almost 1 m in length (**Figure 31.26**). Like many arthropods, they had three main tagmata: the head, thorax, and abdomen. Trilobites also had two dorsal grooves that divided the body longitudinally into three lobes—a median lobe and two anterior lobes—a structural characteristic giving the class its name. Most of the body segments showed little specialization. In contrast, as we will explore, more advanced arthropods developed specialized appendages on many segments, including appendages for grasping, walking, and swimming.

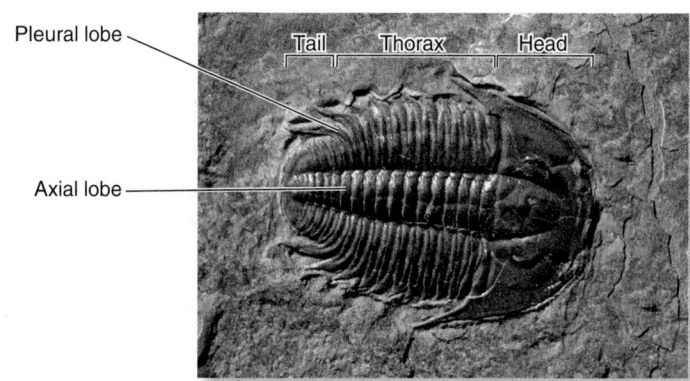

Figure 31.26   A fossil trilobite.   These early arthropods were common in the shallow seas of the Paleozoic era but died out some 250 million years ago. About 4,000 fossil species, including *Huntonia huntonesis* shown here, have been described.

Class Arachnida: The Spiders, Scorpions, Ticks, and Mites The class Arachnida contains predatory spiders and scorpions, as well as the ticks and mites, some of which are blood-sucking parasites that feed on vertebrates. All species have a body consisting of two tagmata: a fused head and thorax called a **cephalothorax**, and an abdomen (**Figure 31.27a**).

In spiders (order Araneae) the two body parts are joined by a **pedicel**, a narrow, waistlike point of attachment. Spiders have six pairs of appendages: the chelicerae, or fangs (**Figure 31.27b**); a pair of **pedipalps**, which have various sensory, predatory, or reproductive functions; and four pairs of walking legs. The fangs are supplied with venom from poison glands. Most spider bites are harmless to humans, although they are very effective in immobilizing or killing their insect prey. Venom from some species, including the black widow (*Latrodectus mactans*) and the brown recluse (*Loxosceles reclusa*), are potentially, although rarely, fatal to humans. The toxin of the black widow is a neurotoxin, which interferes with the functioning of the nervous system, while that of the brown recluse is hemolytic, meaning it destroys tissue around the bite. After the spider has subdued its prey, it pumps digestive fluid into the tissues via the fangs and sucks out the partially digested meal.

Table 31.5	Main Classes and Characteristics of Arthropods

Class and examples (est. number of species)	Class characteristics
Arachnida: spiders, scorpion, ticks, mites (74,000)	Body usually with cephalothorax and abdomen only; six pairs of appendages, including four pairs of legs, one pair of fangs, and one pair of pedipalps; terrestrial; predatory or parasitic
Diplopoda: millipedes (10,000)	Body with head and highly segmented trunk, each segment with two pairs of walking legs; herbivorous
Chilopoda: centipedes (3,000)	Body with head and highly segmented trunk; each segment with one pair of walking legs; predatory, poison jaws
Insecta: beetles, butterflies, flies, fleas, grasshoppers, ants, bees, wasps, termites (>1 million)	Body with head, thorax, and abdomen; mouthparts modified for biting, chewing, sucking, or lapping; usually with two pairs of wings and three pairs of legs; mostly terrestrial, some freshwater; herbivorous, parasitic, or predatory
Crustacea: crabs, lobsters, shrimp (45,000)	Body of two to three parts; three or more pairs of legs; chewing mouthparts; usually marine

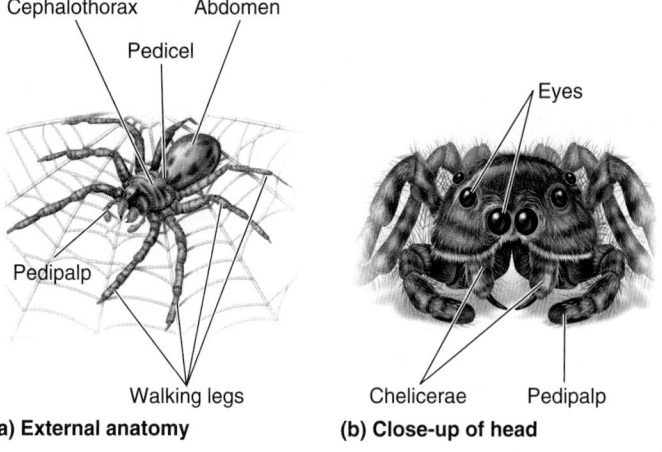

(a) External anatomy

(b) Close-up of head

Figure 31.27   Spider morphology.

Figure 31.28 Spider webs. **(a)** Normal web. **(b)** Web spun by spider fed with prey containing caffeine. **(c)** Web spun by spider fed with prey containing marijuana.

Spiders have abdominal silk glands called **spinnerets**, and many spin webs to catch prey (**Figure 31.28a**). The silk is a protein that stiffens after extrusion from the body because the mechanical shearing changes the organization of the amino acids. Silk is stronger than steel of the same diameter. Each species constructs a characteristic size and style of web and can do it perfectly on its first attempt, indicating that web spinning is an innate (inherited) behaviour (see Chapter 52). Spiders also use silk to wrap up prey and to construct egg sacs. Interestingly, spiders that are fed drugged food (flies) spin their webs differently from undrugged spiders (**Figures 31.28b and 31.28c**). Some scientists have suggested that web-spinning spiders be used to test substances for the presence of drugs or even to indicate environmental contamination. Not all spiders use silk extensively. Other spiders, including the wolf spider (**Figure 31.29a**), actively pursue their prey.

Scorpions (order Scorpionida) are generally tropical or subtropical animals that feed primarily on insects, though they may eat spiders and other arthropods, as well as smaller reptiles and mice. Their pedipalps are modified into large claws, and their abdomen tapers into a stinger, which is used to inject venom. Although the venom of most North American species

is generally not fatal to humans, that of the *Centruroides* genus from deserts in the southwestern United States and Mexico can be deadly. Fatal species are also found in India, Africa, and other countries. Unlike spiders, which lay eggs, scorpions bear live young that the mother subsequently carries around on her back until they have their first moult (**Figure 31.29b**).

In mites and ticks (order Acari) the two main body segments (cephalothorax and abdomen) are fused and appear as one large segment. Many mite species are free-living scavengers that feed on dead plant or animal material. Other mites are serious pests on crops, and some, like chiggers (*Trombicula alfreddugesi*), are parasites of humans that can spread diseases, such as typhus (**Figure 31.29c**). Chiggers are parasites only in their larval stage. It is a myth that chiggers bore into the skin. Rather, it is their bite and salivary secretions that cause skin irritation. *Demodex brevis* is a hair-follicle mite that is common in animals and humans. The mite is estimated to be present in more than 90% of adult humans. Although the mite causes no irritation in most humans, *Demodex canis* causes the skin disease known as mange in domestic animals, particularly dogs.

Ticks are larger organisms than mites, and all are ectoparasitic, feeding on the body surface, on vertebrates. Their life

(a) Wolf spider

(b) Scorpion with young

(c) Chigger mite

(d) Engorged tick

Figure 31.29 Common arachnids. **(a)** This wolf spider (*Lycosa tarantula*) does not spin a web but instead runs after its prey. Note the pedipalps, which look like short legs. **(b)** The Cape thick-tailed scorpion (*Parabuthus capensis*) is highly venomous and carries its white young on its back. **(c)** The chigger mite (*Trombicula alfreddugesi*) can cause irritation to human skin. **(d)** These winter ticks (*Dermacentor albipictus*) are feeding on a moose in northern Ontario.

Concept check: *What is one of the main characteristics distinguishing arachnids from insects?*

cycle includes attachment to a host, sucking blood until they are replete, and dropping off the host to moult (**Figure 31.29d**). Ticks can carry a huge variety of viral and bacterial diseases, including Lyme disease, a bacterial disease so named because it was first found in the town of Lyme, Connecticut, in the 1970s.

Classes Diplopoda and Chilopoda: The Millipedes and Centipedes   The millipedes and centipedes are both wormlike arthropods that are among the earliest terrestrial phyla known. Millipedes (class Diplopoda) have two pairs of legs per segment, as their Latin name denotes (*diplo*, meaning "two," and *podos*, meaning "feet"), not 1,000 legs, as their common name suggests (**Figure 31.30a**). They are slow-moving herbivorous creatures that eat decaying leaves and other plant material. When threatened, the millipede's response is to roll up into a protective coil. Many millipede species also have repugnatorial glands on their underside that can eject a variety of toxic, repellent secretions. Some millipedes are brightly coloured, warning potential predators that they can protect themselves.

Class Chilopoda (from the Latin *chilo*, meaning "lip," and *podos*, meaning "feet"), or centipedes, are fast-moving carnivores that have one pair of walking legs per segment (**Figure 31.30b**). The head has many sensory appendages, including a pair of antennae and three pairs of appendages modified as mouthparts, including powerful claws connected to poison glands. The toxin from venom of some of the larger species, such as *Scolopendra heros*, is powerful enough to cause pain in humans. Most species do not have a waxy

(a)   **(b)**

Figure 31.30   Millipedes and centipedes.   (a) Millipedes have two pairs of legs per segment. (Two millipedes are in the picture.) (b) The venom of the giant centipede (*Scolopendra heros*) is known to produce significant swelling and pain in humans.

waterproofing layer on their cuticle and are restricted to moist environments under leaf litter or in decaying logs, usually coming out at night to actively hunt their prey.

Class Insecta: A Diverse Array of Insects   Insects are in a class by themselves, literally and figuratively. There are more species of insects than all other species of animal life combined. One million species of insects have been described and, according to best estimates, 9 million more species are awaiting description. At least 90,000 species of insects have been identified in North America alone. It is believed that the explosion of diversity in the flowering plants (angiosperms) greatly promoted the huge diversification of insects relative to other classes.

GENOMES AND PROTEOMES

Insect Diversity May Be Explained by the Appearance of the Angiosperms

More species are found in the class Insecta, more than 1 million, than in any other class. Of these, more than half a million are beetles, order Coleoptera. To understand what factors influence biodiversity, we need to understand why there are so many species of insects and beetles. In 1998 biologist Brian Farrell used a genomic study to show that the appearance of angiosperm plants led to an increased richness of insects in general and leaf-eating beetles in particular.

For about the first 50 million years of their order's existence, beetles fed on detritus, dead plant and animal material, and fungi. Plant feeding arose later in beetle history, during the Permian period, but relatively few fossilized beetle genera exist from that time. Jurassic fossils showed the existence of about 150 phytophagous (plant-feeding) beetle genera, which fed on gymnosperm plants: the conifers and cycads. However, many lineages of these ancestral beetles colonized angiosperms independently in the Cretaceous and Tertiary, after the diversification of angiosperms. In each case the lineages that fed on angiosperms have become much more diverse than those that fed on gymnosperms.

In seeking to explain the huge diversity of beetles, Farrell analyzed DNA sequences for the entire 18S ribosomal subunit genes for 115 beetle species, drawn from all beetle subfamilies. In addition, he constructed a data set of 212 morphological characters of the same species. From both sets of data, Farrell constructed a phylogenetic tree. The oldest of the lineages for each of the subfamilies are gymnosperm-affiliated, while the more recently derived lineages are angiosperm-associated species.

Farrell also made five specific phylogenetic comparisons of the species-richness of beetles among subfamilies but that either fed on gymnosperms or angiosperms (**Table 31.6**). In each case, the angiosperm-feeding group speciated frequently and became very diverse. In contrast to the gymnosperm-associated lineages, which generally feed on the pollen-rich reproductive parts of conifers and cycads, the angiosperm-associated subfamilies diversified in feeding habit to chew and mine leaves and feed on seeds and roots as well as reproductive parts. This illustrates how critical innovations can lead to extensive adaptive radiation, one of the principles of diversity noted at the beginning of this unit.

Table 31.6	Five Phylogenetic Comparisons of the Species Richness of Related Beetle Families and Subfamilies			
Comparison*	Gymnosperm-associated family/subfamily	Number of species	Angiosperm-associated family/subfamily	Number of species
1	*Nemonychidae*	85	*Curculionidae*	44,002
2	*Oxycoryninae*	30	*Belinae*	150
3	*Aseminae*	78	*Cerambycinae*	25,000
4	*Palophaginae*	3	*Megalopodinae*	400
5	*Orsodacnidae*	26	*Chrysomelidae*	33,400

*In each comparison, the families and subfamilies are closely related. For example, the Nemonychidae are closely related to the Curculionidae, but the latter has many more species.

Insects are the subject of an entire field of scientific study, **entomology**. They are studied in large part because of their significance as pests of the world's agricultural crops. Insects live in all terrestrial habitats, and virtually all species of plants are fed on by at least one, usually tens, and sometimes, in the case of large trees, hundreds of insect species. Because insects eat approximately one-quarter of the world's crops, we are constantly trying to find ways to reduce insect pest densities. Pest reduction often involves chemical control, the use of pesticides, or biological control, the use of living organisms, to reduce pest populations. Many species of insects are also important pests or parasites of humans and livestock, both by their own actions and as vectors of diseases, such as malaria and sleeping sickness.

Insects do provide many types of essential biological services. We depend on insects, such as honeybees, to pollinate our crops. Bees also produce honey, and silkworms are the source of silk fibre. Despite the revulsion they provoke, fly larvae (maggots) are important in the decomposition process of both dead plants and animals. Insect parasites and predators are used in biological control to reduce densities of pest insects on crops.

Of paramount importance to the success of insects was the development of wings, a feature possessed by no other arthropod and indeed no other living animal except birds and bats. Unlike vertebrate wings, however, insect wings are actually outgrowths of the body wall cuticle and are not true segmental appendages. This means that insects still have all their walking legs. Insects are thus like the mythological horse Pegasus, which sprouted wings out of its back while retaining all four legs. In contrast, birds and bats have one pair of appendages (arms) modified for flight, which leaves them considerably less agile on the ground.

The great diversity of insects is illustrated by the fact that there are 35 different orders, some of which have more than 100,000 species. The most common of the orders are discussed in **Table 31.7**. Different orders of insects have slightly different wing structures, and many of the orders are based on wing type (*pteron* is a Greek word meaning "wing"). Wasps and bees (Hymenoptera) have two pairs of wings hooked together that

move as one wing. Butterflies (Lopidoptera) have wings that are covered in scales (from the Greek, *lepido*, meaning "scale"), while other insects generally have clear, membranous wings. Flies (Diptera) possess only one pair of wings (the front pair); the back pair has been modified to a small pair of balancing organs, called halteres, that act like miniature gyroscopes. In beetles (Coleoptera) only the back pair of wings is functional, as the front wings have been hardened into protective shell-like coverings (elytra), under which the back pair folds when not in use. In ant and termite colonies female individuals called workers have lost their wings, while the queen and the drones (males) have retained theirs. Other species, such as fleas and lice, are wingless.

Insect mouthparts are derived from ancestral appendages and different insect orders have evolved a variety of mouthparts (**Figure 31.31**). Grasshoppers, beetles, dragonflies, and many others have mouthparts adapted for chewing. Mosquitoes and many plant pests have mouthparts adapted for piercing and sucking. Butterflies and moths have a coiled tongue (**proboscis**) that can be uncoiled, enabling them to drink nectar from flowers. Finally, some flies have lapping, spongelike mouthparts that sop up liquid food. Their varied mouthparts allow insects to specialize their feeding on virtually anything: plant matter, decaying organic matter, and other living animals. The biological diversity of insects is thus related to environmental diversity, in this case, the variety of foods that insects eat. Parasitic insects attach themselves to other species, and there are even insect parasites that feed on parasites (called hyperparasites), proving, as eighteenth-century English poet Jonathan Swift noted:

So, naturalists observe, a flea
hath smaller fleas that on him prey;
And these have smaller still to bite 'em,
And so proceed ad infinitum.

All insects have separate sexes, and fertilization is internal. During development, the majority (approximately 85%) of insects undergo a change in body form known as **complete metamorphosis** (from the Greek *meta*, meaning "change," and *morph*, meaning "form") (**Figure 31.32a**). Complete metamorphosis has four stages: egg, larva, pupa, and adult. In these

Table 31.7 Main Orders and Characteristics of Insects

Order and examples (est. number of species)		Order characteristics
Coleoptera: beetles, weevils (500,000)		Two pairs of wings (front pair thick and leathery, acting as wing cases, back pair membranous); armoured exoskeleton; biting and chewing mouthparts; complete metamorphosis; largest order of insects
Hymenoptera: ants, bees, wasps (190,000)		Two pairs of membranous wings; chewing or sucking mouthparts; many have posterior stinging organ on females; complete metamorphosis; many species social; important pollinators
Diptera: flies, mosquitoes (190,000)		One pair of wings with hindwings modified into halteres (balancing organs); sucking, piercing, or lapping mouthparts; complete metamorphosis; larvae are grublike maggots in various food sources; some larvae are aquatic; some adults are disease vectors
Lepidoptera: butterflies, moths (140,000)		Two pairs of colourful wings covered with tiny scales; long tubelike tongue for sucking; complete metamorphosis; larvae are plant-feeding caterpillars
Hemiptera: true bugs; assassin bug, bedbug, chinch bug, cicada (100,000)		Two pairs of membranous wings; piercing or sucking mouthparts; incomplete metamorphosis; many plant feeders; some predatory or blood feeders; vectors of plant diseases
Orthoptera: crickets, roaches, grasshoppers, mantids (30,000)		Two pairs of wings (front pair leathery, back pair membranous); chewing mouthparts; mostly herbivorous; incomplete metamorphosis; powerful hind legs for jumping
Odonata: damselflies, dragonflies (6,000)		Two pairs of long, membranous wings; chewing mouthparts; large eyes; predatory on other insects; incomplete metamorphosis; larvae aquatic; considered ancestral insects
Anoplura: sucking lice (2,400)		Wingless ectoparasites; sucking mouthparts; flattened body; reduced eyes; legs with clawlike tarsi for clinging to skin; incomplete metamorphosis; very host specific; vectors of typhus
Siphonoptera: fleas (2,000)		Wingless, laterally flattened; piercing and sucking mouthparts; adults are bloodsuckers on birds and mammals; jumping legs; complete metamorphosis; vectors of plague
Isoptera: termites (2,000)		Two pairs of membranous wings when present; some stages wingless; chewing mouthparts; social species; incomplete metamorphosis

species the larval stage is often spent in an entirely different habitat from that of the adult, and larval and adult forms use different food sources. They thus do not compete directly for the same resources. The dramatic body transformation from larva to adult occurs in the pupa stage. The remaining insects undergo **incomplete metamorphosis**, in which change is more gradual (**Figure 31.32b**). Incomplete metamorphosis has only three stages: egg, nymph, and adult. Young insects, called nymphs, look like miniature adults when they hatch from their eggs. As they grow and feed, they shed their skin several times, each time entering a new **instar**, or stage of growth.

Finally, some insects, such as bees, wasps, ants, and termites, have developed complex social behaviour and live cooperatively in underground or aboveground nests. Such colonies

(a) Chewing (grasshopper)

(b) Blood sucking (mosquito)

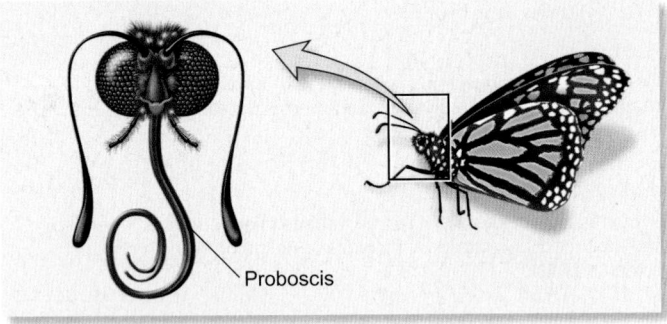

Proboscis

(c) Nectar sucking (butterfly)

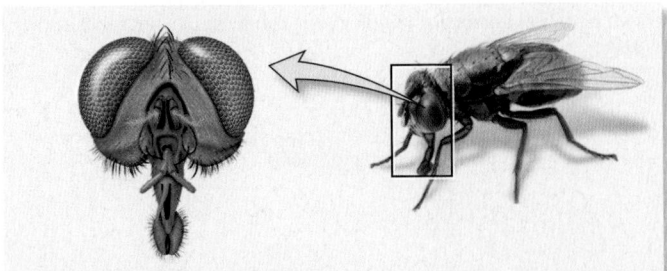

(d) Lapping up liquid (blowfly)

Figure 31.31 A variety of insect mouthparts. Insect mouthparts can be modified to allow insects to feed in a variety of ways, including **(a)** chewing (Orthoptera, Coleoptera, and others), **(b)** blood sucking (Diptera), **(c)** nectar sucking (Lepidoptera), and **(d)** lapping up liquid (Diptera).

BioConnections: *Look forward to Figure 42.32. Some insects do not taste their food with their mouths, so how do they taste?*

exhibit a division of labour, in that some individuals forage for food and care for the brood (workers), others protect the nest (soldiers), and some only reproduce (the queen and one or two males) (**Figure 31.33**).

Class Crustacea: Crabs, Lobsters, Barnacles, and Shrimp

The crustaceans are common inhabitants of marine environments, although some species live in fresh water and a few are terrestrial. Many are economically important food items for humans, including crabs, lobsters, crayfish, and shrimp, and smaller species are important food sources for other predators.

The crustaceans are unique among the arthropods in that they possess two pairs of antennae at the anterior end of the body—the antennule (first pair) and antenna (second pair)

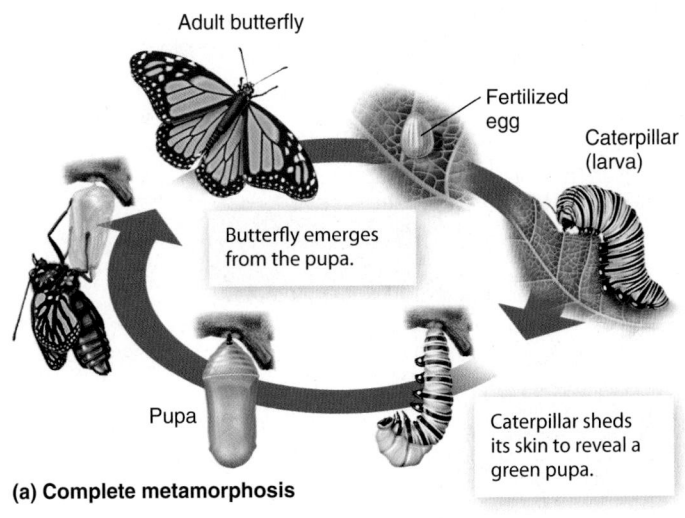

Adult butterfly

Fertilized egg

Caterpillar (larva)

Butterfly emerges from the pupa.

Pupa

Caterpillar sheds its skin to reveal a green pupa.

(a) Complete metamorphosis

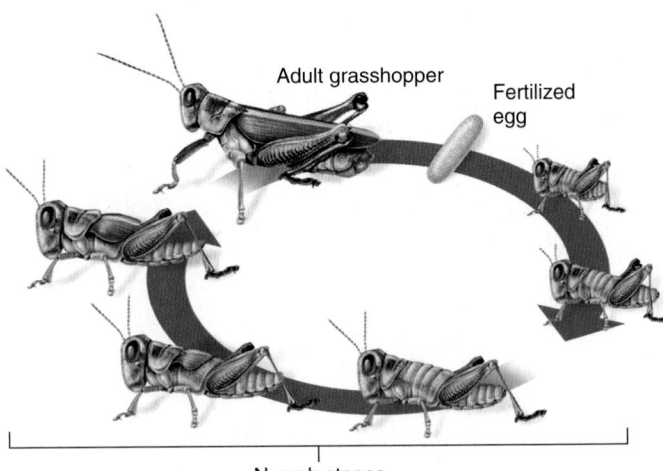

Adult grasshopper

Fertilized egg

Nymph stages

(b) Incomplete metamorphosis

Figure 31.32 Metamorphosis. **(a)** Complete metamorphosis, as illustrated by the life cycle of a monarch butterfly. The adult butterfly has a completely different appearance from the larval caterpillar. **(b)** Incomplete metamorphosis, as illustrated by the life cycle of a grasshopper. The eggs hatch into nymphs, essentially miniature versions of the adult.

(a) Worker and soldier ants   **(b) Queen ant**

Figure 31.33 The division of labour in insect societies.   Individuals from the same insect colony may appear very different. Among these army ants (*Eciton burchelli*) from Paraguay, there are **(a)** workers that forage for the colony and soldiers that protect the colony from predators, and **(b)** the queen, which reproduces and lays eggs.

(**Figure 31.34**). In addition they have three or more sensory and feeding appendages that are modified mouthparts, called mandibles, maxillae, and maxillipeds. These are followed by walking legs and, often, additional abdominal appendages called **swimmerets** and a powerful tail consisting of a telson and uropod. In some orders, the first pair of walking legs, or chelipeds, is modified to form powerful claws. A lost crustacean appendage can regrow. The head and thorax are often fused, forming the cephalothorax. In many species the cuticle covering the head extends over most of the cephalothorax, forming a hard protective fold called the **carapace**. For growth to occur, a crustacean must shed the entire exoskeleton.

Many crustaceans are predatory, but others, such as barnacles, are suspension feeders. Gas exchange typically occurs via gills, and crustaceans, like all other arthropods, have an open circulatory system. Crustaceans possess two excretory organs: antennal glands and maxillary glands, both modified metanephridia, which open at the bases of the antennae and maxillae,

respectively. Reproduction usually involves separate sexes, and fertilization is internal. Most species carry their eggs in brood pouches under the female's body. Eggs of most species produce larvae that must go through many different moults before assuming adult form. The first of these larval stages, called a **nauplius**, is very different in appearance from the adult crustacean (**Figure 31.35**).

Many crustacean orders exist, but most are small and obscure, although many feature prominently in marine food chains, a series of organisms in which each member of the chain feeds on and derives energy from the member below it. These include the Ostracoda, Copepoda, and Euphausiacea. Ostracods are tiny creatures that superficially resemble clams, and copepods are tiny and abundant planktonic crustaceans, both of which are a food source of filter-feeding organisms and small fish. Euphausiids are shrimp-like krill that grow to about 3 cm and provide a large part of the diet of many whales.

The order Cirripedia is composed of the barnacles, crustaceans whose carapace forms calcified plates that cover most of the body (**Figure 31.36a**). Their legs are modified into feathery filter-feeding structures. The order Isopoda (**Figure 31.36b**) contains many small species that are parasitic on marine fish. There are also terrestrial isopods, better known as pill bugs or wood lice, that retain a strong connection to water and need to live in moist environments, such as leaf litter or decaying logs. When threatened, they curl up into a tight ball, making it difficult for predators to get a grip on them.

The most famous order, however, is the Decapoda, which includes the crabs and lobsters, the largest crustacean species (**Figure 31.36c**). As their name suggests, these decapods have 10 walking legs (five pairs), although the first pair is invariably modified to support large claws. Most decapods are marine, but there are many freshwater species, such as crayfish, and in hot, moist tropical countries, even some terrestrial species called land crabs. The larvae of many larger crustaceans are planktonic and grow to about 3 cm. These are abundant in some oceans and are a staple food source for many species.

Cephalothorax (13 segments) Abdomen (6 segments)

Eye
Carapace
Antennule
Antenna
Mandible
Maxillae
Maxillipeds
Telson
Cheliped (first leg)
Claw
Swimmerets
Walking legs
Uropod

Figure 31.34 Body plan of a crustacean, as represented by a shrimp.

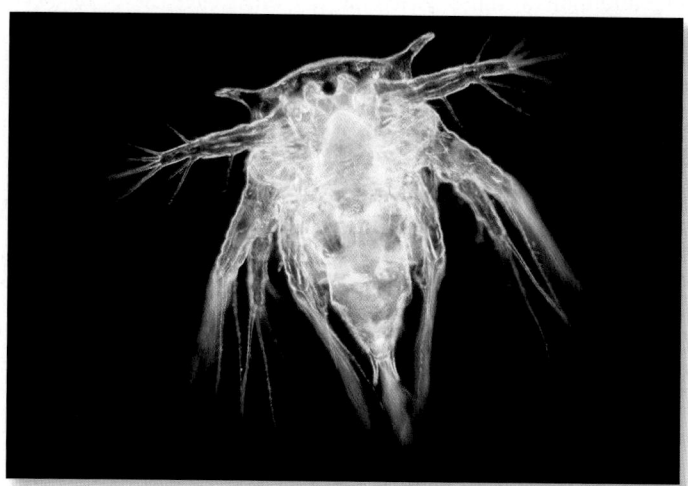

Figure 31.35 Crustacean larva.   The nauplius is a distinct larval type possessed by most crustaceans, which moult several times before reaching maturity.

(a) Barnacles—order Cirripedia   **(b) Pill bug—order Isopoda**   **(c) Fiddler crab: order Decapoda**

Figure 31.36   Common crustaceans.   (a) Barnacles on intertidal rocks. (b) Pill bug or wood louse. (c) Fiddler crab.

31.5   DEUTEROSTOMIA: THE ECHINODERMS AND INVERTEBRATE CHORDATES

Learning Outcomes:

1. Identify the distinguishing characteristics of echinoderms.
2. List the four critical innovations in the body plan of chordates.
3. Describe the two invertebrate subphyla of the phylum Chordata and their relationship to the vertebrates.

As we explored in Chapter 30, the deuterostomes are grouped together because they share similarities in patterns of development (refer back to Figure 30.5). Molecular evidence also supports a deuterostome clade. All animals in the phylum Chordata, which includes the vertebrates, are deuterostomes. Interestingly, so is one invertebrate group, the phylum Echinodermata, which includes the sea stars, sea urchins, and sea cucumbers. Most of the deuterostome clade will be discussed in Chapter 32, but we will conclude our discussion of invertebrate biology by turning our attention to the invertebrate deuterostomes. Refer back to Figure 30.4 for the differences between protostomes and deuterostomes. Based on the embryonic development of the echinoderms, they are more closely related to animals like us than they are to protostome invertebrates.

In this section we will explore the phylum Echinodermata and then introduce the phylum Chordata, looking in particular at its distinguishing characteristics and at its two invertebrate subphyla: the urochordates, also known as the tunicates, and the cephalochordates, commonly referred to as the lancelets.

The Phylum Echinodermata Includes Sea Stars and Sea Urchins, Species with a Water Vascular System

The phylum Echinodermata (from the Greek *echinos*, meaning "spiny," and *derma*, meaning "skin") consists of a unique grouping of deuterostomes. A striking feature of all echinoderms is their modified radial symmetry. The body of most species can be divided into five parts pointing out from the centre. As a consequence cephalization is absent in most classes, and echinoderms move only very slowly. They do not have a brain and have only a simple nervous system. The radial symmetry of echinoderms is secondary, however, because the free-swimming larvae have bilateral symmetry and metamorphose into the radially symmetrical adult form.

Most echinoderms have an endoskeleton (internal skeleton) composed of calcareous plates overlaid by a thin skin. The skeleton is covered with spines and jawlike pincers called **pedicellariae**, the primary purpose of which is to deter settling of such animals as barnacles (**Figure 31.37**). These structures can also possess poison glands.

A portion of the coelom has been adapted to serve as a unique **water vascular system**, a network of canals that branch into tiny **tube feet** that function in movement, gas exchange, and feeding. The water vascular system is powered by hydraulic power, that is, by water pressure generated by the contraction of muscles that enables the extension and contraction of the tube feet, allowing echinoderms to move slowly.

Water enters the water vascular system through the **madreporite**, a sieve-like plate on the animal's surface. From there it flows into a **ring canal** in the central disk, into five radial canals, and into the tube feet. At the base of each tube foot is a muscular sac called an **ampulla**, which stores water. Contractions of the ampullae force water into the tube feet, causing them to straighten and extend. When the foot contacts a solid surface, muscles in the foot contract, forcing water back into the ampulla. Sea stars also use their tube feet in feeding, where they can exert a constant and strong pressure on bivalves, whose adductor muscles eventually tire, allowing the shell to open slightly. At this stage, the sea star everts its stomach and inserts it into the space, and then digests its prey by using juices secreted from extensive digestive glands. Sea stars also feed on sea urchins, brittle stars, and sand dollars, prey that cannot easily escape them.

Echinoderms cannot osmoregulate, so no species have entered freshwater environments. No excretory organs are present, and both respiration and excretion of nitrogenous waste take place by diffusion across the tube feet. Coelomic fluid circulates around the body.

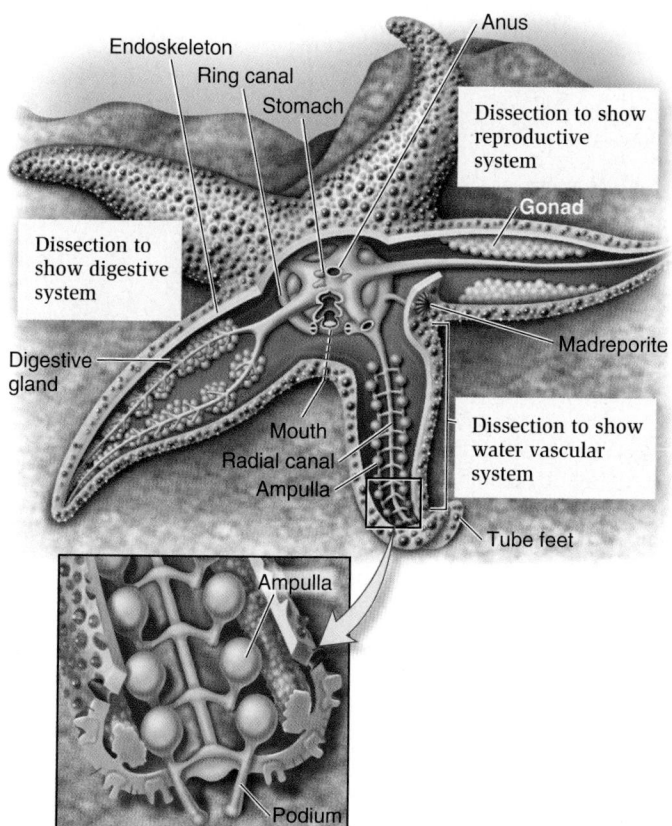

Figure 31.37 Body plan of an echinoderm, as represented by a sea star. The arms of this sea star have been dissected to different degrees to show the echinoderm's various organs.

Concept check: *Echinoderms and chordates are both deuterostomes. What are three defining features of deuterostomes?*

Most echinoderms exhibit **autotomy**, the ability to intentionally detach a body part, such as a limb, that will later regenerate. In some species, a broken limb can even regenerate into a whole animal. Some sea stars regularly reproduce by breaking in two. Most echinoderms reproduce sexually and have separate sexes. Fertilization is usually external, with gametes shed into the water. Fertilized eggs develop into free-swimming bilaterally symmetrical larvae, which undergo metamorphosis into sedentary adults.

Although more than 20 classes of echinoderms have been described from the fossil record, only 5 main classes of echinoderms exist today: the Asteroidea (sea stars), Ophiuroidea (brittle stars), Echinoidea (sea urchins and sand dollars), Crinoidea (sea lilies and feather stars), and Holothuroidea (sea cucumbers). The key features of the echinoderms and their classes are listed in **Table 31.8**.

The most unusual of the echinoderms are members of the class Holothuroidea, the sea cucumbers. These animals really do look like cucumbers, with hard plates of the endoskeleton being less extensive than in sea stars and sea urchins. Sea

Table 31.8	Main Classes and Characteristics of Echinoderms	
	Class and examples (est. number of species)	**Class characteristics**
	Asteroidea: sea stars (1,600)	Five arms; tube feet; predatory on bivalves and other echinoderms; eversible stomach
	Ophiuroidea: brittle stars (2,000)	Five long, slender arms; tube feet not used for locomotion; no pedicellaria; browse on sea bottom or filter feed
	Echinoidea: sea urchins, sand dollars (1,900)	Spherical (sea urchins) or disk shaped (sand dollars); no arms; tube feet and moveable spines; pedicellaria present; many feed on seaweeds
	Crinoidea: sea lilies and feather stars (700)	Often attached to substrate via stalk; arms feathery and used in filter feeding; very abundant in fossil record
	Holothuroidea: sea cucumbers (1,200)	Cucumber-shaped; no arms; spines absent; endoskeleton reduced; tube feet

cucumbers possess specialized respiratory structures called respiratory trees that pump water in and out of the anus. They are typically deposit feeders, ingesting sediment and extracting nutrients. The California sea cucumber is commercially harvested in British Columbia (**Figure 31.38**).

Figure 31.38 Sea cucumbers. The giant red or California sea cucumber, *Parastichopus californicus,* is found along Canada's west coast and is the only sea cucumber that is commercially harvested. However, the fishery is under strict management since stocks have declined. Products from sea cucumber include muscle strips (fresh or frozen) and dried skins or sections, most of which are destined for markets in China and Japan.

When threatened by a predator, a few tropical species of sea cucumber can eject sticky, toxic substances from their anus. If that does not deter the predator, these species can undergo evisceration, ejecting its digestive tract, respiratory structures, and gonads from its anus. If the sea cucumber survives, it can regenerate its organs later.

The Phylum Chordata Includes All the Vertebrates and Some Invertebrates

The deuterostomes consist of two major phyla, the echinoderms and the chordates (from the Greek *chorde*, string). As deuterostomes, both phyla share similar developmental traits. In addition both have an endoskeleton, consisting in the echinoderm of calcareous plates and in chordates, for the most part, of bone. However, the endoskeleton of the echinoderms is usually covered only by a thin layer of skin and functions in much the same way as the arthropod exoskeleton, in that its primary function is providing protection. The chordate endoskeleton serves a very different purpose. In early divergent chordates the endoskeleton is composed of a single flexible rod situated dorsally, deep inside the body. Muscles move this rod, and their contractions cause the back and tail end to move from side to side, permitting a swimming motion in water. The endoskeleton becomes more complex in different lineages that develop limbs, as you will see in Chapter 32, but it is always internal, with muscles attached. This arrangement permits the possibility of complex movements, including the ability to move on land.

Let's take a look at the four critical innovations in the body design of chordates that distinguish them from all other animal life (**Figure 31.39**):

1. *Notochord.* Chordates are named for the **notochord**, a single flexible rod that lies between the digestive tract and the nerve cord. Composed of fibrous tissue encasing fluid-filled cells, the notochord is stiff yet flexible and provides skeletal support for all ancestral chordates. In most chordates, such as vertebrates, a more complex jointed backbone usually replaces the notochord, and only remnants exist as the soft material within the disks of vertebrae.

2. *Dorsal hollow nerve cord.* Many animals have a long nerve cord, but in nonchordate invertebrates, it is a solid tube that lies ventral to the alimentary canal. In contrast the nerve cord in chordates is a hollow tube that develops dorsal to the alimentary canal. In 1822 French naturalist Geoffroy Saint-Hilaire argued that this difference suggested that the ventral side of nonchordate invertebrates (as exemplified by the lobster) was homologous to the dorsal side of vertebrates. Some recent molecular work suggests that, as Hilaire first proposed, there was an inversion of the dorsoventral axis during animal evolution. In vertebrates, the dorsal hollow nerve cord develops into the brain and spinal cord.

3. *Pharyngeal slits.* Chordates, like many animals, have a complete gut, from mouth to anus. However, in chordates, slits develop in the pharyngeal region, close to the

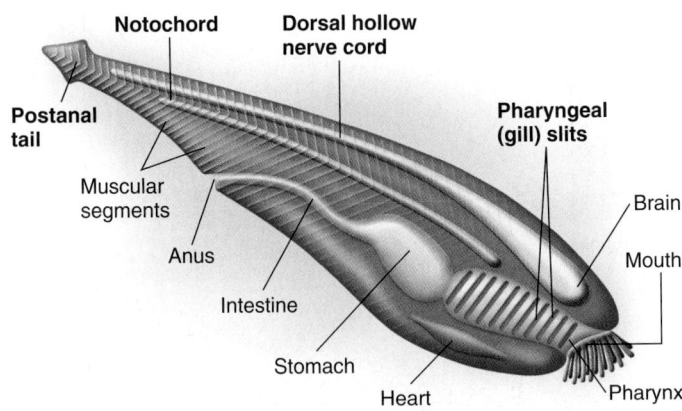

Figure 31.39   Chordate characteristics.   The generalized chordate body plan has four main features: notochord, dorsal hollow nerve cord, pharyngeal slits, and postanal tail.

mouth, that open to the outside. This permits water to enter through the mouth and exit via the slits, without having to go through the digestive tract. In early divergent chordates, **pharyngeal slits** function as a filter-feeding device, while in more advanced chordates, they develop into gills for gas exchange. In terrestrial chordates, the slits do not fully form and become modified for other purposes, such as the auditory (Eustachian) tubes in ears.

4. *Postanal tail.* Chordates possess a postanal tail of variable length that extends posterior to the anal opening. In aquatic chordates, such as fish, the tail is used in locomotion. In terrestrial chordates the tail may be used in a variety of functions or may be absent, as in humans. In virtually all other nonchordate phyla, the anus is terminal.

Although few chordates apart from fishes possess all these characteristics in their adult life, they all exhibit them at some time during development. For example, in adult humans the notochord is replaced by the backbone and the dorsal hollow nerve cord becomes the central nervous system. However, humans exhibit pharyngeal slits and a postanal tail only during early embryonic development. All the pharyngeal slits, except one, which forms the Eustachian tubes in the ear, are eventually lost, and the postanal tail regresses to form the tailbone (the coccyx).

The phylum Chordata consists of the invertebrate chordates—the subphylum Urochordata (tunicates) and the subphylum Cephalochordata (lancelets)—along with the subphylum Vertebrata. Although the Vertebrata is by far the largest of these subphyla, biologists have focused on the Urochordata and Cephalochordata for clues as to how the chordate phylum may have evolved. Comparisons of gene sequences coding for 18S rRNA show that these two subphyla in general, and the cephalochordates in particular, are our closest invertebrate relatives (**Figure 31.40**).

Subphylum Urochordata: The Tunicates   The urochordates (from the Greek *oura*, meaning "tail") are a group of 3,000 marine species also known as tunicates. Looking at an adult tunicate,

CGGCCCCGCCGGGGTCGGCCCACGGCCTTGGCGGAG-GCCT
Human (vertebrate)

CGGCCCCGCCGGGGTCGGCCCACGGCCCTGGCGGAG-CGCT
Lancelet (invertebrate chordate)

TGGTCTCGGCCCGCCTTTCA-CCGGGCGGCGCCGTT-GGTC
Mollusc (invertebrate)

GTGAACATTTGCTAGTCCCTCGGGATTACATTTGAATCGCT
Mosquito (invertebrate)

Figure 31.40 Comparison of small subunit rRNA gene sequences of vertebrate, invertebrate chordate, and invertebrate species. The similarities between the invertebrate chordates (represented by the lancelet) and the vertebrates (represented by a human) suggest they are indeed our closest relatives. Nucleotides are either conserved (yellow), partially conserved (green), variable (red), or insertions or deletions (grey).

you might never guess that it is a relative of modern vertebrates. The only one of the four distinguishing chordate characteristics that it possesses is pharyngeal slits (**Figure 31.41a**). The larval tunicate, in contrast, looks like a tadpole and exhibits all four chordate hallmarks (**Figure 31.41b**). The larval tadpole swims for only a few days, usually without feeding, because the siphons are not functional in the larvae. Larvae settle on and attach to a rock surface via rootlike extensions called stolons. Here they metamorphose into adult tunicates and in the process lose most of their chordate characteristics. In 1928 marine biologist Walter Garstang suggested modern vertebrates arose from a larval tunicate form that had somehow acquired the ability to reproduce. However, both the adult tunicate body plan and the modern molecular data have led Billie Swalla and colleagues to propose that tunicates are so distantly related to other chordates that they should be considered a separate deuterostome phylum called Tunicata.

Adult tunicates are marine animals, some of which are colonial and others solitary, that superficially resemble sponges or cnidarians. Tunicates are filter feeders that draw water through the mouth through an **incurrent siphon**, using a ciliated pharynx, and filter it through extensive pharyngeal slits. The food is trapped on a mucus sheet secreted by what is known as an endostyle; passes via ciliary action to the stomach, intestine, and anus; and exits through the **excurrent siphon**. The whole animal is enclosed in a nonliving **tunic**, which it secretes, made of a protein and a cellulose-like material called tunicin. Tunicates are also known as sea squirts for their ability to squirt out water from the excurrent siphon when disturbed. There is a rudimentary circulatory system with a heart and a simple nervous system of relatively few nerves connected to sensory tentacles around the incurrent siphon. The animals are mostly hermaphroditic.

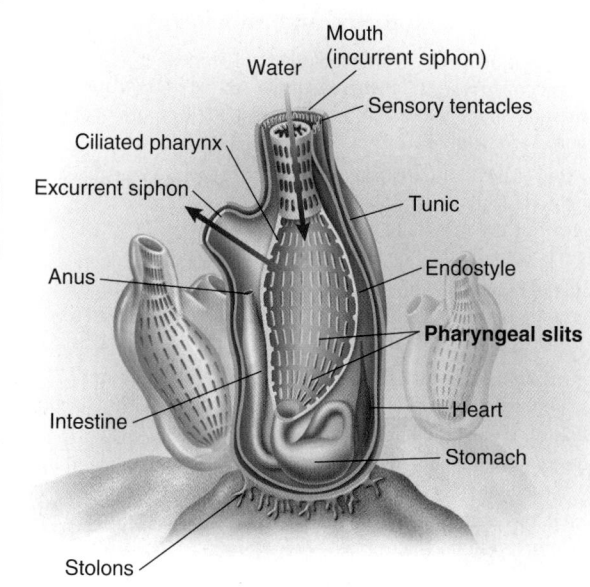

(a) Adult tunicate

Mouth (incurrent siphon)
Water
Sensory tentacles
Ciliated pharynx
Excurrent siphon
Tunic
Anus
Endostyle
Pharyngeal slits
Intestine
Heart
Stomach
Stolons

Excurrent siphon
Dorsal hollow nerve cord
Mouth (incurrent siphon)
Pharyngeal (gill) slits
Postanal tail
Notochord
Stomach
Heart

(b) The larval form of the tunicate

(c) Typical tunicate

Figure 31.41 Tunicates. (a) Body plan of the sessile, filter-feeding adult tunicate. (b) The larval form, which shows the four characteristic chordate features, has been proposed as a possible ancestor of modern vertebrates. (c) Blue tunicate, *Rhopalaea crassa*.

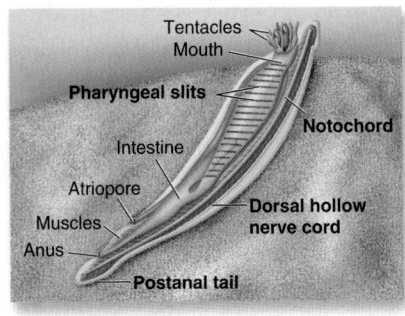

(a) Body plan of the lancelet

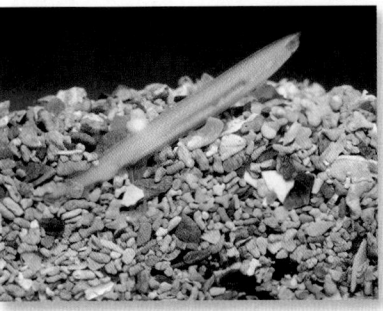

(b) Lancelet in the sand

(c) *Pikaia gracilens*

Figure 31.42 Lancelets. **(a)** The body plan of the lancelet clearly displays the four characteristic chordate features. **(b)** Lancelet in feeding position, showing the segmented body with chevron-shaped muscles in each segment. **(c)** *Pikaia gracilens,* a putative fossil chordate, may have filtered particles from the water as it swam above the sea floor. Well-preserved specimens of this fossil have been recovered from the Burgess Shale deposits near Mount Pika, British Columbia.

Subphylum Cephalochordata: The Lancelets The cephalochordates (from the Greek *cephalo,* meaning "head") look a lot more chordatelike than do tunicates. They are commonly referred to as lancelets, in reference to their bladelike shape and size, about 5 to 7 cm long (**Figure 31.42a**). Lancelets are a small subphylum of 26 species, all marine filter feeders, with four species occurring in North American waters. Most of them belong to the genus *Branchiostoma.*

The lancelets live mostly buried in sand, with only the anterior end protruding into the water so that they can filter feed through the mouth (**Figure 31.42b**). Lancelets have the four distinguishing chordate characteristics: a clearly discernible notochord (extending well into the head), dorsal hollow nerve cord, pharyngeal slits, and postanal tail. In a fashion similar to tunicates, water enters the mouth and moves into the pharynx, where it is filtered through the pharyngeal slits. A mucus net across the pharyngeal slits traps food particles, ciliary action takes the food into the digestive tract, and water exits via the excurrent siphon, here called the atriopore. Gas exchange generally takes place across the body surface. Although the lancelet is usually sessile, it can leave its sandy burrow and swim to a new spot, using a series of serially arranged muscles that appear like chevrons (< < < <) along their sides. These muscles reflect the segmented nature of their body. With a body shape and a swimming motion characteristic of fish, it is not difficult to see how lancelets may have been the precursors to modern fish, especially the more ancient jawless fishes, which we will explore in Chapter 32.

Summary of Key Concepts

- Invertebrates, or animals without a backbone, make up more than 95% of all animal species. (Figure 31.1)

31.1 Parazoa: Sponges, the First Multicellular Animals

- An early lineage—the Parazoa—consists of one phylum, the Porifera, or sponges. Although sponges lack true tissues, they are multicellular animals possessing several types of cells. (Figure 31.2)

31.2 Radiata: Jellyfish, Radially Symmetrical Animals

- The Radiata consists of two phyla: the Cnidaria (hydra, jellyfish, sea anemones, corals, and box jellies) and the Ctenophora (comb jellies). Radiata have only two embryonic germ layers: the ectoderm and endoderm, with a gelatinous substance (mesoglea) connecting the two layers.

- Cnidarians exist as two forms: polyp and medusa. A characteristic feature of cnidarians is their stinging cells or cnidocytes, which function in defence and prey capture. Ctenophores possess the first complete gut and nearly all exhibit bioluminescence. (Figures 31.3, 31.4, 31.5, 31.6, Table 31.1)

31.3 Lophotrochozoa: The Flatworms, Rotifers, Lophophorates, Molluscs, and Annelids

- The Lophotrochozoa include taxa that possess either a lophophore or a trochophore larva. Platyhelminthes, or flatworms, are regarded as the first animals to reach the organ-system level of organization. (Figure 31.7, Table 31.2)

- The four classes of flatworms are the Turbellaria, Monogenea, Trematoda (flukes), and Cestoda (tapeworms). Flukes and tapeworms are internally parasitic, with complex life cycles. (Figures 31.8, 31.9)

- Rotifers are microscopic animals that have a complete digestive tract with separate mouth and anus; the mastax, a muscular pharynx, is a structure unique to the rotifers. (Figure 31.10)

- The Lophophorates consist of the phoronids, bryozoa, and brachiopods, all of which possess a lophophore, a ciliary feeding structure. (Figure 31.11)

- The molluscs, which constitute a large phylum with more than 100,000 diverse living species, have a basic body plan with three parts—a foot, a visceral mass, and a mantle—and an open circulatory system. (Figures 31.12, 31.13, 31.14, 31.15, 31.16)

- The four most common mollusc classes are the polyplacophora (chitons), gastropoda (snails and slugs), bivalvia (clams and mussels), and cephalopoda (octopuses, squid, and nautiluses). (Table 31.3)

- Cephalopods are among the most complex of all invertebrates. They are the only molluscs with a closed circulatory system that have a well-developed nervous system and brain. They are believed to exhibit learning by observation. (Figures 31.17, 31.18, 31.19, 31.20)

- Segmentation, in which the body is divided into nearly identical subunits, is a critical evolutionary innovation in the annelids, although specialization is only minimally present at the anterior end. (Figure 31.21)

- Annelids are a large phylum with three main classes: Polychaeta (the most species-rich class), Oligochaeta (which includes the earthworms), and Hirudinea (leeches). (Figure 31.22, Table 31.4)

31.4 Ecdysozoa: The Nematodes and Arthropods

- The ecdysozoans are so named for their ability to shed their cuticle, a nonliving cover providing support and protection. The two most common ecdysozoan phyla are the nematodes and the arthropods.

- Nematodes, which exist in nearly all habitats, have a cuticle made of collagen, a structural protein. The small, free-living nematode *Caenorhabditis elegans* is a model organism. Many nematodes are parasitic in humans, including *Wuchereria bancrofti,* which causes elephantiasis. (Figures 31.23, 31.24)

- Arthropods are perhaps the most successful phylum on Earth. The arthropod body is covered by a cuticle made of layers of chitin and protein, and it is segmented, with segments fused into functional units called tagmata. (Figure 31.25)

- The six main classes of arthropods are Trilobita (the trilobites; now extinct), Arachnida (spiders and scorpions), Diplopoda (millipedes), Chilopoda (centipedes), Insecta (insects), and Crustacea (crabs and relatives). (Figures 31.26, 31.27, 31.28, 31.29, 31.30, Table 31.5)

- More insect species are known than all other animal species combined. More than half a million insect species are beetles. Researcher Brian Farrell found that the appearance of angiosperm plants led to an increased richness of leaf-eating beetles. (Tables 31.6, 31.7)

- The development of a variety of wing structures and mouthparts was a key to the success of insects. (Figure 31.31)

- Insects undergo a change in body form during development, either complete metamorphosis or incomplete metamorphosis, and have developed complex social behaviours. (Figures 31.32, 31.33)

- Most crustacean orders are small and feature prominently in marine food chains. The most well known order of crustaceans is the Decapoda, which includes the crabs and lobsters. (Figures 31.34, 31.35, 31.36)

31.5 Deuterostomia: The Echinoderms and Invertebrate Chordates

- The Deuterostomia includes the phyla Echinodermata and Chordata. A striking feature of the echinoderms is their radial symmetry, which is secondary; the free-swimming larvae are bilaterally symmetrical. Most echinoderms possess an internal skeleton called an endoskeleton and they have tube feet. (Figure 31.37).

- Five main classes of echinoderms exist today: the Asteroidea (sea stars), Ophiuroidea (brittle stars), Echinoidea (sea urchins and sand dollars), Crinoidea (sea lilies and feather stars), and Holothuroidea (sea cucumbers). (Figure 31.38, Table 31.8)

- The phylum Chordata is distinguished by four critical innovations: the notochord, dorsal hollow nerve chord, pharyngeal slits, and postanal tail. (Figure 31.39)

- The subphylum Urochordata (tunicates) and subphylum Cephalochordata (lancelets) are invertebrate chordates. Genetic studies have shown that cephalochordates are the closest invertebrate relatives of the vertebrate chordates (subphylum Vertebrata). (Figures 31.40, 31.41, 31.42)

Test to Assess Your Learning

1. Choanocytes are
   a. a group of protists that are believed to have given rise to animals.
   b. specialized cells of sponges that function to trap and eat small particles.
   c. cells that make up the gelatinous layer in sponges.
   d. cells of sponges that function to transfer nutrients to other cells.
   e. cells that form spicules in sponges.

2. Which of the following is *not* a characteristic of ctenophores?
   a. complete gut
   b. bioluminescence
   c. stinging cells
   d. ciliary locomotion

3. Which of the following organisms can produce female offspring through parthenogenesis?
   a. cnidarians
   b. flukes
   c. choanocytes
   d. rotifers
   e. annelids

4. A lophophore is
   a. a contractile structure that aids in movement through the water column.
   b. a ciliated structure that aids in movement through the water column.
   c. a ciliated structure that functions primarily in feeding.
   d. a contractile structure that moves food into the coelom.
   e. a contractile structure important for defence.

5. In the annelids, the metanephridia function in
   a. transport of nutrients.
   b. movement.
   c. cellular communication.
   d. waste removal.
   e. reproduction.

6. A defining feature of the Ecdysozoa is
   a. a segmented body.
   b. a closed circulatory system.
   c. a cuticle.
   d. a complete gut.
   e. a lophophore.

7. In arthropods, the tracheal system is
   a. a unique set of structures that function in ingestion and digestion of food.
   b. a series of branching tubes extending into the body that allow for gas exchange.
   c. a series of tubules that allow waste products in the blood to be released into the digestive tract.

    d. the series of ommatidia that form the compound eye.

    e. none of the above.

8. Characteristics of the class Arachnida include

    a. two tagmata.

    b. six walking legs.

    c. an aquatic lifestyle.

    d. a lobed body.

    e. both (b) and (d).

9. Incomplete metamorphosis

    a. is characterized by distinct larval and adult stages that do not compete for resources.

    b. is typically seen in arachnids.

    c. involves gradual changes in life stages where young resemble the adult stage.

    d. is characteristic of the majority of insects.

    e. always includes a pupal stage.

10. In the phylum Echinodermata, the tube feet function in

    a. movement.

    b. gas exchange.

    c. feeding.

    d. excretion.

    e. all of the above.

Articulate to Assess Your Learning

1. Define hermaphrodite.

2. Define nematocyst and explain its function.

3. Explain the difference between complete metamorphosis and incomplete metamorphosis.

Collaborate to Assess and Extend Your Learning

1. Discuss some of the characteristics of the phylum Mollusca.

2. Discuss the four defining characteristics of chordates.

3. A principle of biology is that living organisms grow and develop. Explain the difference between complete metamorphosis and incomplete metamorphosis.

Visit McGraw-Hill Ryerson Connect™ for additional study resources.

The Vertebrates

Chapter Outline

Salmon migration in British Columbia. These salmon are one of Canada's charismatic vertebrate species.

In Chapter 31 we discussed two chordate subphyla, the Urochordates (tunicates) and Cephalochordates (lancelets). The third subphylum of chordates, the Vertebrata, or vertebrates, with about 48,000 species, is by far the largest and most dominant group of chordates. Species range in size from tiny fish weighing 0.1 g to huge whales of more than 100,000 kg. They occupy nearly all Earth's habitats, from the deepest depths of the oceans to mountaintops and the sky beyond. Throughout history humans have depended on many vertebrate species for their welfare and have domesticated species, such as horses, cattle, pigs, sheep, and chickens, and kept countless species, including cats and dogs, as pets. Many other vertebrate species are the subjects of conservation efforts, as you will see in Chapter 57. For example, some vertebrate species require large areas for their survival and as such are considered umbrella species, in that their preservation will help ensure conservation of others.

In this chapter we begin by outlining the characteristics of **craniates**, chordates that have a brain encased in a skull. We will take a brief look at the hagfish, a craniate that has some, but not all, vertebrate characteristics. In the remainder of the chapter we explore the characteristics of vertebrates (**Figure 32.1**), discussing in some depth the evolutionary development of the major vertebrate classes, including fish, amphibians, reptiles, birds, and mammals.

32.1 THE CRANIATES: CHORDATES WITH A SKULL

Learning Outcomes:

1. List the main distinguishing characteristics of craniates.

Although all vertebrates are craniates, not all craniates are vertebrates. One animal, the eel-like hagfish, has characteristics that place it within the craniates but not within the vertebrates.

Hagfish do not have a vertebral column—one of the vertebrate characteristics—but they do have a skull, in this case one made of cartilage and not bone. (Thus, despite its name the hagfish cannot be considered a true fish.) Paleontologists in China have recently discovered similar fishlike fossils that date to around 530 million years ago, the time of the Cambrian explosion. These are believed to be the earliest known craniates. What makes an animal a craniate?

Craniates Are Distinguished by a Cranium and Neural Crest

Craniates have two defining characteristics that distinguish them from other invertebrate chordates:

1. The anterior end of the nerve cord elaborates to form a more developed brain that is encased in a protective bony or cartilaginous housing called the **cranium**. The cranium allows for cephalization—the development of the head end in animals.
2. The **neural crest** is a group of embryonic cells found on either side of the neural tube as it develops. The cells disperse throughout the embryo, where they contribute to the development of the skeleton, especially the cranium and other structures, including nerves, jaws, and teeth.

Although these are the main distinguishing characteristics of craniates, there are others. For example, craniates have at least two clusters of *Hox* genes, compared with the single cluster of *Hox* genes in tunicates and lancelets. This additional gene cluster is believed to have permitted

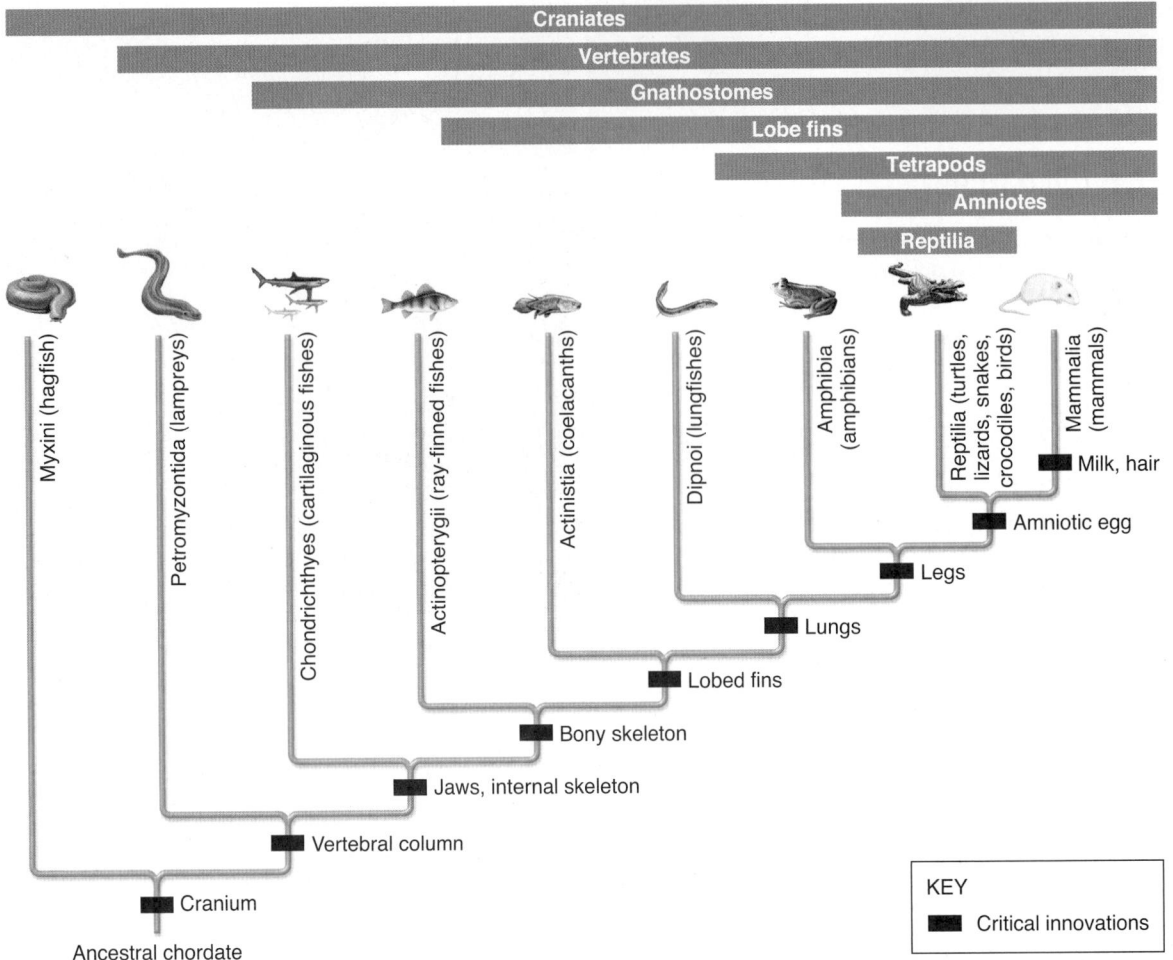

Figure 32.1 **The major classes of vertebrates.** Key characteristics of each group (derived characters) are shown. The nested labels across the top of the figure refer to groupings within the vertebrates.

increasingly complex morphologies than those possessed by other invertebrate chordates.

Hagfish, Class Myxini, Are the Most Ancestral Living Craniates

Although the hagfish, an eel-like, eyeless scavenger, is often called an ancestral fish, its resemblance to a fish is misleading (**Figure 32.2**). The hagfish is not a true vertebrate and thus cannot be considered a true fish. At the same time, it is different from the tunicates and lancelets, the invertebrate chordates we discussed in Chapter 31. Although hagfish do not have a vertebral column—one of the vertebrate characteristics—they do have a skull, one made of cartilage and not bone, in this case. Hagfish are entirely marine, jawless, finless craniates that lack vertebrae. The hagfish skeleton consists largely of a skull that encloses the brain and a cartilaginous notochord. The lack of a vertebral column leads to extensive flexibility. Hagfish live in the cold waters of northern oceans, close to the muddy bottom. Essentially blind, hagfish have a very keen sense of smell and are attracted to dead and dying fish, which they attach

Figure 32.2 **The hagfish: A craniate that is not a vertebrate.** The hagfish possesses craniate characteristics (a skull and neural crest) but is not a true fish or vertebrate.

Concept check: *Why isn't the hagfish a true fish?*

themselves to via toothed plates on the mouth. The powerful tongue then rasps off pieces of tissue. However, most of their diet consists of dead or disabled marine worms and other invertebrates. Though the hagfish cannot see approaching predators, they have special glands that produce copious amounts of slime, which can deter predatory attacks. When provoked, the hagfish's slime production increases dramatically, enough to potentially distract predators or coat their gills and interfere with breathing. Hagfish can sneeze to free their nostrils of their own slime.

32.2 CHARACTERISTICS OF VERTEBRATES

Learning Outcomes:

1. List the main distinguishing characteristics of vertebrates.

The **vertebrates** (from the Latin, *vertebratus,* "back boned") retain all chordate characteristics that we outlined in Chapter 31 and all craniate characteristics noted previously, as well as possessing several additional traits:

1. During development in vertebrates, the notochord is replaced by the vertebral column, a bony or cartilaginous column of interlocking **vertebrae** that provides support and also protects the nerve cord, which lies within its tubelike structure.
2. The cranium and vertebral column are parts of the endoskeleton, the living skeleton of cartilage or bone in vertebrates that forms within the animal's body. Most vertebrates also have two pairs of appendages, whether fins, legs, or arms. The endoskeleton is composed of either bone or cartilage, both of which are very strong materials, yet they are more flexible than the chitin found in insects and other arthropods. The endoskeleton also contains living cells that secrete the skeleton, which grows with the animal, unlike the nonliving exoskeleton of arthropods.
3. Vertebrates possess a great diversity of internal organs, including a liver, kidneys, endocrine glands, and a heart with at least two chambers. The liver is unique to vertebrates, and the vertebrate heart, kidneys, and endocrine system are more complex than analogous structures in other taxa.

Although these features are exhibited in all vertebrate classes, some classes developed innovations that helped them succeed in specific environments, such as on land or in the air. For example, birds developed feathers and wings, structures that enable most species to fly. In fact, each of the vertebrate classes is distinctly different from the others, as outlined in **Table 32.1**. Of the 11 classes of living vertebrates, 5 of them are classes of fish, reflecting the dominance of fish within the vertebrates.

32.3 THE FISH

Learning Outcomes:

1. Describe how jaws evolved.
2. Discuss the distinguishing features of sharks.
3. List the three features that distinguish bony fish from cartilaginous fish.
4. Outline the differences between ray-finned fish and lobe-finned fish.

A critical innovation in vertebrate evolution is the hinged jaw, which first developed in fish. However, not all fish developed hinged jaws. The **ostracoderms**, an umbrella term for several classes of early diverging, heavily armoured fish, now extinct, lacked a hinged jaw (**Figure 32.3**). These fish most likely swam slowly above the substrate, using a strong pharyngeal pump to vacuum up particles. The ostracoderms were common in the Silurian and Devonian periods. A single class of jawless fish— the lampreys—exists today, although these evolved separately from the ostracoderms.

The jawed mouth was a significant evolutionary development. It enabled an animal to grip its prey more firmly, which may have increased its rate of capture, and to attack larger prey species, thus increasing its potential food supply. All vertebrate species that possess jaws are called **gnathostomes** (meaning "jaw mouth") (see Figure 32.1). In contrast the jawless species are termed agnathans (meaning "without jaws"). Accompanying the jawed mouth was the development of more sophisticated head and body structures, including two pairs of appendages called fins. Gnathostomes also possess two additional *Hox* gene clusters (bringing their total to four), which permitted increased morphological complexity.

Biologists have identified about 25,000 species of living fish, more than all other species of vertebrates combined. All are aquatic, gill-breathing ectotherms. There are five separate classes of fish, each of which has distinguishing characteristics (see Table 32.1). We will begin by examining the most ancestral class, the Cephalaspidomorphi (lampreys), which lack jaws and appendages. Most of our attention, however, will focus on the jawed fish: the Chondrichthyes (cartilaginous fish), Actinopterygii (ray-finned fish), Actinistia (coelacanths), and Dipnoi (lungfish).

The Lampreys, Class Cephalaspidomorphi, Are Eel-Like Fish That Lack Jaws

Lampreys are unlike members of other classes of fish because they lack both a hinged jaw and true appendages. However, lampreys do possess a notochord surrounded by a cartilaginous rod that represents a rudimentary vertebral column, and thus they represent one of the earliest diverging groups of vertebrates. Lampreys can be found in both marine and freshwater environments. Sea lampreys are native to the Atlantic Ocean but were accidentally introduced into the Great Lakes in the early

Table 32.1   The Main Classes and Characteristics of Living Vertebrates

Class		Examples (approx. number of species)	Main characteristics
Cephalaspidomorphi		Lampreys (41)	Early diverging fish with no appendages, that is, fins; jawless sucking mouth; parasitic on other fish
Chondrichthyes		Sharks, skates, rays (850)	Fish with cartilaginous skeleton; teeth not fused to jaw; no swim bladder; well-developed fins; internal fertilization; single blood circulation
Actinopterygii		Ray-finned fish, most bony fish (24,600)	Fish with ossified skeleton; single gill opening covered by operculum; fins supported by rays, fin muscles within body; swim bladder often present; mucus glands in skin
Actinistia		Lobe-finned fish, of which coelacanth is the only living member (1)	Fish with ossified skeleton; bony extensions, together with muscles, project into pectoral and pelvic fins; swim bladder filled with oil
Dipnoi		Lungfish (6)	Fish with ossified skeleton; rudimentary lungs allow fish to come to the surface to gulp air; limblike appendages
Amphibia		Frogs, toads, salamanders (4,000)	Tetrapods; adults able to live on land; fresh water needed for reproduction; development usually involving metamorphosis from tadpoles; adults with lungs and double blood circulation; moist skin; shell-less eggs
Mammalia		Mammals (5,500)	Mammary glands, hair, specialized teeth, enlarged skull, external ears, endothermic, highly developed brains, diversity of body forms
Testudines		Turtles (330)	Body encased in hard shell; no teeth; head and neck retractable into shell; eggs laid on land
Lepidosauria		Lizards, snakes (7,800)	Lower jaw not attached to skull; skin covered in scales
Crocodilia		Crocodiles, alligators (23)	Four-chambered heart; large aquatic predators; parental care of young
Aves		Birds (9,600)	Feathers, hollow bones, air sacs, reduced internal organs, endothermic, four-chambered heart

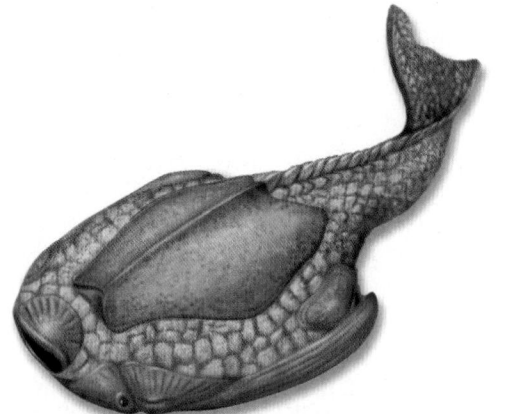

Figure 32.3 Ancient jawless fish. *Cephalaspis* is one of an extinct group of early diverging fish called ostracoderms that were partially armoured and lacked a hinged jaw. Jawless species like this were particularly common in the Silurian and Devonian periods.

twentieth century through shipping canals. Marine lampreys are parasitic as adults. They grasp other fish with their circular mouth (**Figure 32.4a**) and rasp a hole in the fish's side, sucking blood, tissue, and fluids until they are full (**Figure 32.4b**). They can be so destructive that sometimes only 15% of attacked prey fish survive (**Figure 32.4c**). Reproduction of all species is similar, whether they live in marine or freshwater environments. Males and females spawn in freshwater streams, and the resultant larval lampreys burrow into the sand or mud, much like lancelets (refer back to Figure 31.42b), emerging to feed on small invertebrates or detritus at night. This stage can last for three to seven years, at which time the larvae metamorphose into adults. Sometimes, in strictly freshwater species, the adults do not feed at all but quickly mate and die. Marine species migrate from freshwater back to the ocean until they are ready to reproduce; they then return to freshwater to spawn and die.

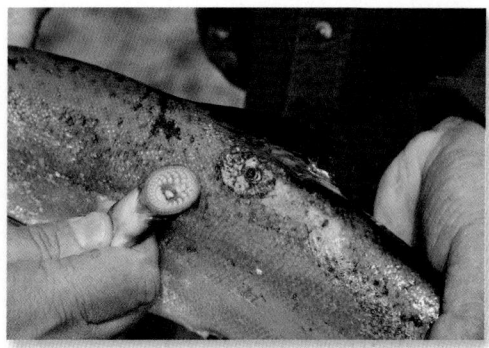

(a) The sea lamprey (*Petromyzon marinus*) has a circular, jawless mouth.

(b) A sea lamprey feeding on a fish.

(c) Wound caused by feeding of sea lamprey.

Figure 32.4   **Modern jawless fish.**   **(a)** The sea lamprey (*Petromyzon marinus*) has a circular, jawless mouth. **(b)** A sea lamprey feeding on a fish. **(c)** A wound caused by a feeding sea lamprey.

Jawed Fish Include the Sharks and Rays and the Bony Fish

As we noted previously, one of the main evolutionary innovations in fish was the development of the hinged jaw. The hinged jaw developed from the cartilaginous pharyngeal arches. Ancestral jawless fish had nine gill arches surrounding the eight gill slits (**Figure 32.5a**). During the late Silurian period, about 417 million years ago, some of these gill arches became modified in jawless fish. The first and second gill arches were lost, while the third and fourth pairs became modified to form the jaws (**Figure 32.5b**, and **32.5c**). This is how evolution usually works; body features do not appear *de novo* but instead become modified to serve other functions.

By the mid-Devonian period, two classes of jawed fish, the Acanthodii (spiny fish) and Placodermi (armoured fish) were common. Some of the placoderms were huge individuals, more than 9 m long. Both classes died out by the end of the Devonian as part of one of several mass extinctions that occurred in Earth's geological and biological history. The reasons for this extinction are not well understood, but other types of jawed fish—the cartilaginous and bony fish—did not go extinct. We will discuss the fish in these classes next.

Chondrichthyans: The Cartilaginous Fish   Members of the class Chondrichthyes (the **chondrichthyans**)—sharks, skates, and rays—are also called cartilaginous fish because their skeleton is composed of flexible cartilage rather than bone. The cartilaginous skeleton is not considered an ancestral character but rather a derived one. This means that the ancestors of the chondrichthyans had bony skeletons but that members of this class subsequently lost this feature. This hypothesis is reinforced by the fact that during development, the skeleton of most vertebrates is cartilaginous, and then it becomes bony (ossified) as a hard calcium-phosphate matrix replaces the softer cartilage. A change in the developmental sequence of the cartilaginous fish is believed to prevent the ossification process.

In the Carboniferous period, 354 million to 290 million years ago, sharks were the great predators of the ocean. Aided by appendages called fins, sharks became fast, extremely efficient swimmers (**Figure 32.6a**). Perhaps the most important fin for propulsion is the large and powerful caudal fin, or tail fin, which, when swept from side to side, thrusts the fish forward at great speed. For example, great white sharks (*Carcharodon carcharias*) can swim at more than 40 km per hour, and Mako sharks (*Isurus oxyrinchus*) have been clocked at nearly 50 km per hour. The paired pelvic fins (at the back) and pectoral fins (at the front) act like flaps on airplane wings, allowing the shark to dive deeper or rise to the surface. They also aid in steering. In addition, the dorsal fin (on the back) acts as a stabilizer to prevent the shark from rolling in the water as the tail fin pushes it forward.

Sharks were among the earliest fish to develop teeth. Their teeth evolved from rough scales on the skin that also contain dentin and enamel. Although shark's teeth are very sharp and hard, they are not set into the jaw, as are human teeth, so they break off easily. To offset this, the teeth are continually replaced, row by row (**Figure 32.6b**). Sharks can have 20 rows of teeth, with the front pair in active use and the ones behind ready to grow as replacements when needed. Tooth replacement time varies from 9 days in the cookie-cutter shark (named for its characteristic of biting round plugs of flesh from its prey) to 242 days in great whites. Some experts estimate that certain sharks can use up to 20,000 teeth in a lifetime.

All chondrichthyans are denser than water, which theoretically means that they would sink if they stopped swimming. Many sharks never stop swimming and maintain buoyancy via the use of their fins and a large oil-filled liver. Another advantage of swimming is that water continually enters the mouth and is forced over the gills, allowing the sharks to extract oxygen and breathe. How then do skates and rays breathe when they rest on the ocean floor? These species, and a few sharks, like the nurse shark, use a muscular pharynx and jaw muscles to pump water over the gills. In these, and indeed all, species of fish, the heart consists of two chambers, an atrium and a ventricle, that contract in sequence. They employ what is known as a single circulation, in which blood is pumped from the heart to capillaries in the gills to collect oxygen, and then it flows

(a) Ancestral jawless fishes

Gill arches one and two were lost; three became modified to form a hinged jaw.

(b) Early jawed fishes (placoderms)

Gill arch four also became modified to form a heavier, more efficient jaw.

(c) Modern jawed fishes (cartilaginous and bony fishes)

Figure 32.5   The evolution of the vertebrate jaw.
(a) Ancestral fish and extant jawless fish, such as lampreys, have nine cartilaginous gill arches that support eight gill slits. **(b)** In early jawed fish, such as the placoderms, the first two pairs of gill arches were lost, and the third pair became modified to form a hinged jaw. This left six gill arches to support the remaining five gill slits, which were still used in breathing. **(c)** In modern jawed fish, the fourth gill arch is also incorporated into the jaw, allowing stronger, more powerful bites to be delivered.

 Principle: Structure determines function. *The development of a jaw increased the predatory capabilities of gnathostomes.*

through arteries to the tissues of the body, before returning to the heart (look ahead to Figure 44.4a).

Many active predators possess a variety of acute senses, and sharks are no exception. They have a powerful sense of smell, facilitated by sense organs in the nostrils (sharks and other fish do not use nostrils for breathing). They can see well but cannot distinguish colours. Sharks have no eardrum, but they can detect pressure waves generated by moving objects. All jawed fish have a row of microscopic organs in the skin, arranged in a line that runs laterally down each side of the body, that can detect movements in the surrounding water. This system of sense organs, known as the **lateral line**, picks up pressure waves and sends nervous signals to the inner ear and then on to the brain.

Fertilization is internal in chondrichthyans, with the male transferring sperm to the female via a pair of **claspers**, extensions of the pelvic fins. Some shark species are **oviparous**, that is, they lay eggs, often inside a protective pouch called a mermaid's purse (**Figure 32.6c**). The eggs, which are not guarded by either parent, then hatch into tiny sharks. In **ovoviparous** species the eggs are retained within the female's body, but there is no placenta to nourish the young. A few species are **viviparous**; the eggs develop within the uterus, receiving nourishment from the mother via a placenta. Both ovoviparous and viviparous sharks give birth to live young.

The sharks have been a very successful vertebrate group, with many species identified in the fossil record. Although many species died out in the mass extinction at the end of the Permian period (ca. 248 million years ago), a further period of speciation of the survivors occurred in the Mesozoic era, when most of the 375 modern-day species appeared. Skates and rays are essentially flattened sharks that cruise along the ocean floor by using hugely expanded pectoral fins. In addition, their thin and whiplike tails are often equipped with a venomous barb that is used in defence (**Figure 32.6d**). Most of the 475 or so species of skates and rays feed on bottom-dwelling crustaceans and molluscs.

The Bony Fish   Bony fish are the most numerous types of fish, with more individuals and more species (about 24,600) than any other. Most authorities now recognize three living classes: the Actinopterygii (ray-finned fish), the Actinistia (coelacanths), and the Dipnoi (lungfish). Fish in all three classes possess a bony skeleton and scale-covered skin. The skin of bony fish, unlike the rough skin of sharks, is slippery and slimy because of glands that produce mucus, an adaptation that reduces drag during swimming. Just as in the cartilaginous fish, water is drawn over the gills for breathing, but in bony fish, a protective flap called an **operculum** covers the gills (**Figure 32.7**). Some early bony fish lived in shallow, oxygen-poor waters and developed lungs as an embryological outpocketing of the pharynx. These fish could rise to the water surface and gulp air. As you will see, modern lungfish operate in much the same fashion. In most bony fish, these lungs evolved into a **swim bladder**, a gas-filled, balloon-like structure that helps the fish remain buoyant in the water, even when it is completely stationary. The swim bladder is connected to the circulatory system, and gases can diffuse in and out of the blood, allowing the fish to change the volume of the swim bladder and to rise and sink. Thus, unlike the sharks, many bony fish can remain motionless and use a "sit-and-wait" ambush tactic when feeding. These three features—bony skeleton, operculum, and swim bladder—distinguish bony fish from cartilaginous fish.

Reproductive strategies of bony fish vary tremendously, but most species reproduce via external fertilization, with the female shedding her eggs and the male depositing sperm on top of them. Although adult bony fish can maintain their buoyancy, their eggs tend to sink. This is why many species spawn in

(b) Rows of shark teeth

(d) Stingray

(a) Silvertip shark

(c) Shark egg pouch

Figure 32.6 **Cartilaginous fish.** **(a)** The silvertip shark (*Carcharhinus albimarginatus*) is one of the ocean's most powerful predators. **(b)** Close-up of the mouth of a sand tiger shark (*Carcharias taurus*), showing rows of teeth. **(c)** This mermaid's purse (egg pouch) of a dogfish shark (*Scyliorhinus canicula*) is entwined in vegetation to keep it stationary. **(d)** Stingrays are essentially flattened sharks with very large pectoral fins.

BioConnections: *Look ahead to Figure 38.5. What types of cells are responsible for forming cartilage?*

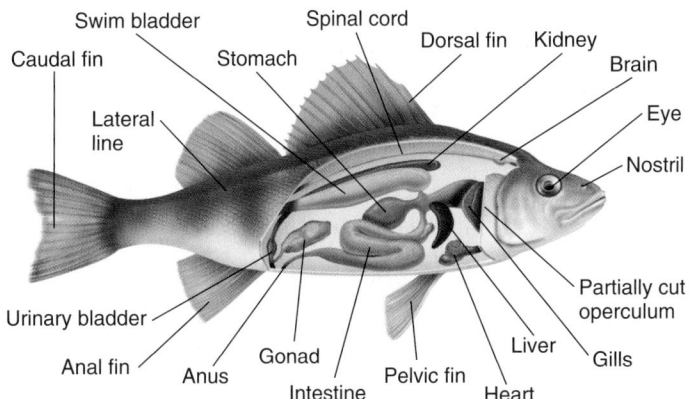

Figure 32.7 **Generalized body plan of a bony fish.**

shallow, oxygen- and food-rich waters, and why coastal areas are such important fish nurseries.

Bony fish have colonized all aquatic habitats. Most cartilaginous fish are marine, but bony fish probably evolved in freshwater habitats and secondarily returned to marine environments. This, of course, required the redevelopment of physiological adaptations to the different osmotic problems seawater presents compared with fresh water (see Chapter 46).

The most species-rich class of bony fish is the Actinopterygii, or **ray-finned fish**. In Actinopterygii the fins are supported by thin, bony, flexible rays and are moved by muscles on the interior of the body. The class has a diversity of forms, from large predatory moray eels to delicate sea dragons (**Figure 32.8**).

(a)

(b)

(c)

Figure 32.8 **The diversity of ray-finned fish.** **(a)** Lionfish (*Pterois volitans*). **(b)** Whitemouth moray eel (*Gymnothorax meleagris*). **(c)** Leafy sea dragon (*Phycodurus eques*).

Figure 32.9 A lobe-finned fish, the coelacanth (*Latimeria chalumnae*).

Figure 32.10 An Australian lungfish (*Neoceratodus forsteri*).

Concept check: *How are lungfish similar to coelacanths?*

Whole fisheries are built around the harvest of species, such as cod, anchovies, and salmon.

The Actinistia (coelacanths) and Dipnoi (lungfish) are both considered Sarcopterygii or **lobe fins**. The name Sarcopterygii used to refer solely to the lobe-finned fish, but since it has become clear that terrestrial vertebrates (tetrapods) evolved from such fish, the definition of the group has been expanded to include both lobe-finned fish and tetrapods (see Figure 32.1). In the **lobe-finned fish** the fins are part of the body, and they are supported by skeletal extensions of the pectoral and pelvic areas that are moved by muscles residing in the fins.

The fossil record revealed that the Actinistia, or coelacanths, were a very successful group in the Devonian period, but all fish of the class were believed to have died off at the end of the Mesozoic era, some 65 million years ago. You can therefore imagine the scientific excitement in 1938, when a modern coelacanth was discovered as part of the catch of a boat fishing near the Chalumna River in South Africa (**Figure 32.9**). Intensive searches in the area revealed that coelacanths were living off the southern African coast and especially off a group of islands near the coast of Madagascar called the Comoros Islands. Another species was more recently found in Indonesian waters.

Early diverging lobe-finned fish probably evolved in fresh water and had lungs, but the coelacanth lost them and returned to the sea. One distinctive feature is a special joint in the skull that allows the jaws to open extremely wide and gives the coelacanth a powerful bite. As further evidence of the coelacanth's unusual body plan, its swim bladder is filled with oil rather than gas, although it serves a similar purpose—to increase buoyancy.

The Dipnoi, or **lungfish**, are not currently a very species-rich class, having just three genera and six species (**Figure 32.10**). Lungfish live in oxygen-poor freshwater swamps and ponds. They have both gills and lungs, the latter of which enable them to come to the surface and gulp air. In fact, lungfish will drown if they are unable to breathe air. When ponds dry out, some species of lungfish can dig a burrow and survive in it until the next rain. Because they also have muscular lobe fins, they are often able to successfully traverse quite long distances over shallow-bottomed lakes that may be drying out.

The morphological features of coelacanths, lungfish, and early diverging land animals, together with the similarity of coelacanth and lungfish nuclear genes to those of ancestral terrestrial vertebrates, suggest to many scientists that lobe-finned ancestors gave rise to three lineages: the coelacanths, the lungfish, and the tetrapods.

32.4 AMPHIBIA: THE FIRST TETRAPODS

Learning Outcomes:

1. List the adaptations required by the transition to life.
2. Describe the amphibian orders and what differentiates them.

During the Devonian period, from about 417 million to 354 million years ago, a diversity of plants colonized the land. The presence of plants served as both a source of oxygen and an extensive food source for animals that ventured out of the aquatic environment. Terrestrial arthropods, especially insects, had evolved to feed on these plants and provided an additional food source for any vertebrate that could colonize the land.

The transition to life on land involved a large number of adaptations. Paramount among these were adaptations preventing desiccation and making locomotion and reproduction on land possible. You have seen that the lungfish evolved the ability to breathe air. In this section we begin by outlining the development of the **tetrapods**, vertebrate animals having four legs or leglike appendages. We will discuss the first terrestrial vertebrates and their immediate descendants, the amphibians. We will then explore the characteristic features and diversity of modern amphibians.

The Origin of Tetrapods Involved the Development of Four Limbs

Over the Devonian period fossils record the evolution of sturdy lobe-finned fish that became fish with four limbs. The abundance of light and nutrients in shallow waters supported a profusion of plant life and the invertebrates that fed on them. The development of lungs enabled lungfish to colonize these productive yet often oxygen-poor waters. Here, the ability to move in shallow water full of plants and debris was more vital than the ability to swim swiftly through open water and may have favoured the progressive development of sturdy limbs. As an animal's weight began to be borne more by the limbs, the vertebral column strengthened, and hip bones were braced against the backbone for added strength. Such modifications, while seemingly dramatic, are believed to be caused by relatively simple changes in the expression of genes, especially *Hox* genes (see the Feature Investigation). In particular, *Hox* genes 9 to 13 work together to specify limb formation from the proximal to the distal direction (**Figure 32.11**).

Some of the transitional taxa between fish and amphibians possessed gills, like fish, but they had four limbs and free digits, characteristics of amphibians. *Acanthostega*, a very early diverging tetrapod, had forelimbs and hindlimbs, and eight digits on each hand, but it also retained many adaptations for aquatic life because it probably only rarely ventured onto land (**Figure 32.12a**). This is an important species, for it may represent a so-called stem species, a common tetrapod ancestor located at the beginning of the tetrapod branch on the tree of life. Eventually, however, species more like modern amphibians evolved, species that were still tied to water for reproduction but increasingly fed on land. In these species the vertebral column, hip bones, and shoulder bones grew even sturdier (**Figure 32.12b**). Such changes were needed as the animal's weight was no longer supported by water but was borne entirely on the limbs. The evolution of a rib cage provided protection for the internal organs, especially the lungs and heart.

By the middle of the Carboniferous period, about 320 million years ago, amphibians had become common in the terrestrial environment. For example, *Cacops* was a large amphibian, as big as a pony (Figure 32.12b). Its skin was heavy and tough, an adaptation that helped prevent water loss; its breathing was accomplished more by lungs than by skin; and it possessed **pentadactyl limbs** (limbs ending in five digits). With a bonanza of terrestrial arthropods to feast on, the amphibians became very numerous and species rich, and the mid-Permian period, some 260 million years ago, is sometimes known as the Age of Amphibians. However, most of the large amphibians became extinct at the end of the Permian period, coincident with the radiation of the reptiles, though whether the rise of reptiles was responsible for the extinction of amphibians is not known. Most surviving amphibians were smaller organisms resembling modern-day species.

(a) *Acanthostega*

(b) *Cacops*

Figure 32.12   The development of ancestral tetrapods. **(a)** *Acanthostega* represents a transitional form between a lobe-finned fish and a true amphibian. It possessed gills and was aquatic but had the tetrapod skeletal structure. **(b)** *Cacops* was a large, early amphibian of the Permian period.

BioConnections: *Refer back to Figure 21.3. What would the relationship be between* Tiktaalik roseae *and the two tetrapods shown here?*

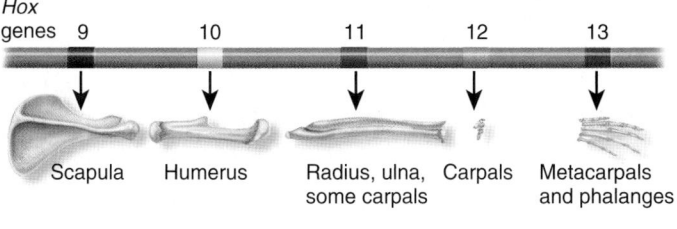

Figure 32.11   The role of *Hox* genes 9 to 13 in specifying limb formation from the proximal to distal direction.   The axis of limb development in mice is shown, together with the associated genes.

FEATURE INVESTIGATION

Davis, Capecchi, and Colleagues Showed a Genetic-Developmental Explanation for Limb Length in Tetrapods

The development of limbs in tetrapods was a vital step in enabling animals to colonize land. The diversity of vertebrate limb types is amazing, from fins in fish and marine mammals to legs and arms in primates to different wing types in bats and birds. In 1995 PhD student A. P. Davis, Professor M. R.

Capecchi, and their colleagues analyzed the effects of mutations in specific *Hox* genes that are responsible for determining limb formation in mice. As described in **Figure 32.13**, they began with strains of mice carrying loss-of-function mutations in *HoxA-11* or *HoxD-11*. They bred the mice to obtain offspring carrying one, two, three, or four mutations.

As seen in the data, the mutations affected the formation of limbs. For example, the wrist contains seven bones: three proximal carpals—called pisiform (P), triangular (T), and navicular

GOAL To determine the role of *Hox* genes in limb development in mice.

KEY MATERIALS Mice with individual mutations in *HoxA-11* and *HoxD-11* genes.

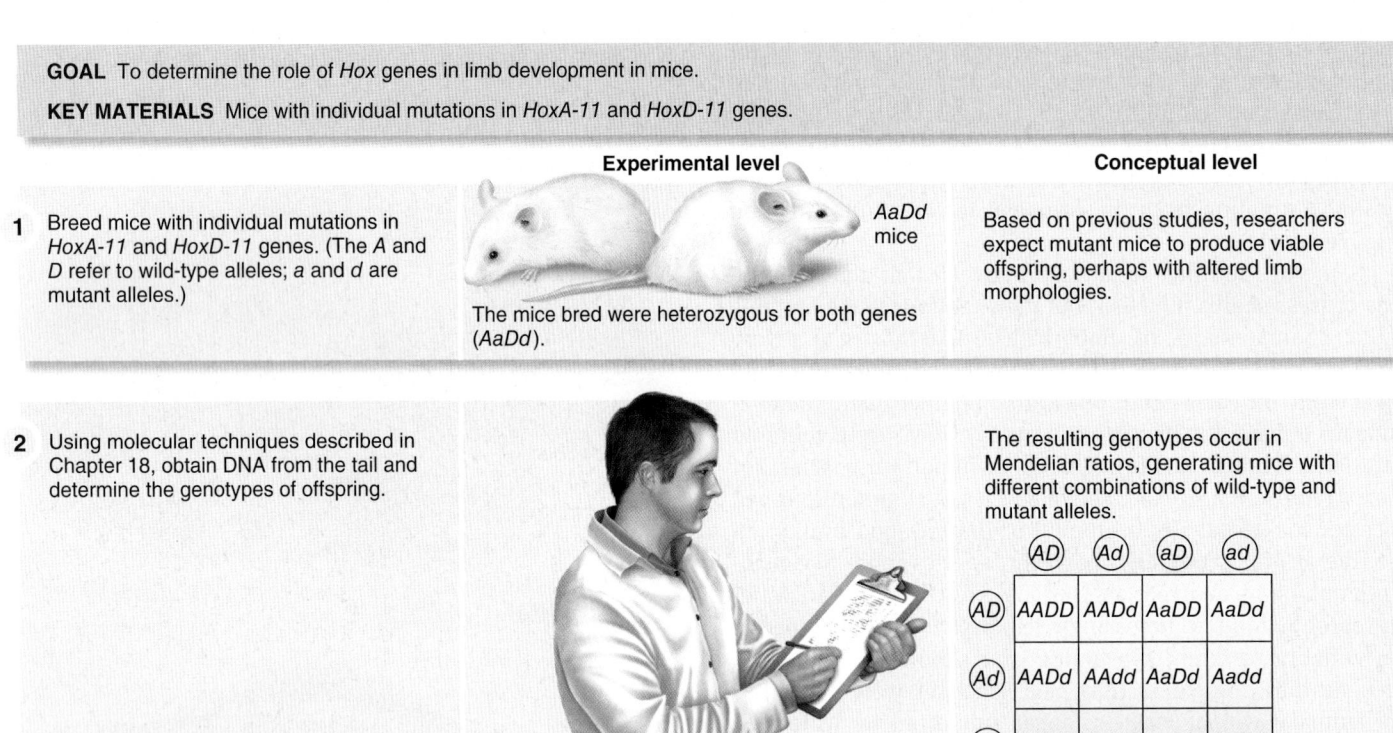

Experimental level

1 Breed mice with individual mutations in *HoxA-11* and *HoxD-11* genes. (The *A* and *D* refer to wild-type alleles; *a* and *d* are mutant alleles.)

AaDd mice

The mice bred were heterozygous for both genes (*AaDd*).

Conceptual level

Based on previous studies, researchers expect mutant mice to produce viable offspring, perhaps with altered limb morphologies.

2 Using molecular techniques described in Chapter 18, obtain DNA from the tail and determine the genotypes of offspring.

The resulting genotypes occur in Mendelian ratios, generating mice with different combinations of wild-type and mutant alleles.

	(AD)	(Ad)	(aD)	(ad)
(AD)	AADD	AADd	AaDD	AaDd
(Ad)	AADd	AAdd	AaDd	Aadd
(aD)	AaDD	AaDd	aaDD	aaDd
(ad)	AaDd	Aadd	aaDd	aadd ← Double mutant

9:3:3:1 phenotypic ratio expected in a dihybrid cross

3 Stain the skeletons and compare the limb characteristics of the wild-type mice (*AADD*) to those of strains carrying mutant alleles in one or both genes.

Mutant mice may have altered bone morphologies.

aadd

AADD

Figure 32.13   Relatively simple changes in *Hox* genes control limb formation in tetrapods.

4   THE DATA

	Carpal bone fusions (% of mice showing the fusion)			
Genotype	Normal (none fused)	NL fused to T	T fused to P	NL fused to T and P
AADD	100	0	0	0
AaDD	100	0	0	0
aaDD	33	17	50	0
AADd	100	0	0	0
AAdd	0	17	17	67
AaDd	17	17	33	33

5   CONCLUSION Relatively simple mutations involving two genes can cause large changes in limb development.

6   SOURCE Davis, A.P. et al. 1995. Absence of radius and ulna in mice lacking *Hoxa-11* and *Hoxd-11*. *Nature* 375:791–795.

lunate (NL)—and four distal carpals (d1 to d4). In mice with the genotypes *aaDD* and *AAdd,* the proximal carpal bones are usually fused together. Individual heterozygotes (*AADd* and *AaDD*) do not show this defect, but compound heterozygotes (*AaDd*) often do. Therefore, any two mutant alleles (either from both *HoxA-11* and *HoxD-11* or one from each locus) will cause carpal fusions. Deformities became even more severe with three mutant alleles (*Aadd* or *aaDd*) or four mutant alleles (*aadd*) (data not shown in the figure). Thus, scientists have shown that relatively simple mutations can control relatively large changes in limb development.

Experimental Questions

1. What was the purpose of the study conducted by A. P. Davis and his colleagues?
2. How were the researchers able to study the effects of individual genes?
3. Explain the results of the experiment shown in Figure 32.13 and how they relate to limb development in vertebrates.

Amphibian Lungs and Limbs Are Adaptations to a Semiterrestrial Lifestyle

Amphibians (from the Greek, meaning "two lives") live in two worlds. They have successfully invaded the land but must return to the water to reproduce. One of the first challenges terrestrial animals had to overcome was breathing air when on land. Amphibians use the same technique as lungfish; they open their mouths to let in air then close and raise the floor of the mouth creating a positive pressure, thus pumping air into the lungs. This method of breathing is called **buccal pumping**. In addition, the skin of amphibians is much thinner than that of fish, and many amphibians can absorb oxygen from the air directly through their moist skin or the skin lining of the inside of the mouth or pharynx.

Amphibians have a three-chambered heart, with two atria and one ventricle. One atrium receives blood from the body, and the other receives blood from the lungs. Both atria pump blood into the single ventricle, which pumps some blood to the lungs and some to the rest of the body (look ahead to Figure 44.4b).

This form of circulation allows the tissues to receive well-oxygenated blood at a higher pressure than is possible via single circulation, because blood returns to the heart to be pumped to the tissues and is not slowed down by passage through the lung capillaries. This development enhances the delivery of nutrients and oxygen to the tissues, but it is still not maximally efficient because some oxygenated and deoxygenated blood are mixed in the ventricle.

Because the skin of amphibians is so thin, the animals face the problem of desiccation or drying out. As a consequence, even amphibian adults are more abundant in damp habitats, such as swamps or rain forests, than in dry areas. Also, amphibians cannot venture too far from water because their larval stages are still aquatic. In frogs and toads fertilization is generally external, with males shedding sperm over the gelatinous egg masses laid in water by the females (**Figure 32.14a**). The fertilized eggs lack a shell and would quickly dry out if exposed to the air. They soon hatch into tadpoles (**Figure 32.14b**), small fishlike herbivores that lack limbs and breathe through gills. As the tadpole nears the adult stage, the tail and gills are resorbed,

(a) Gelatinous mass of amphibian eggs

(b) Tadpole

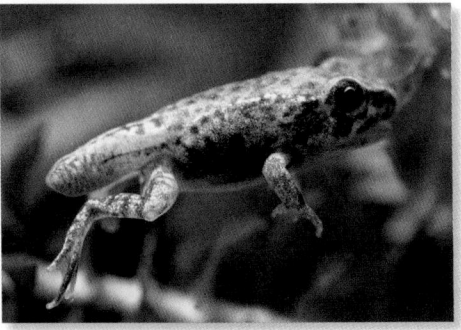

(c) Tadpole undergoing metamorphosis

Figure 32.14 **Amphibian development in the wood frog (*Rana sylvatica*).** Wood frogs are found across Canada. **(a)** Amphibian eggs are laid in gelatinous masses in water. **(b)** The eggs develop into tadpoles, aquatic herbivores that have a fishlike tail and breathe through gills. **(c)** During metamorphosis the tadpole loses its gills and tail and develops limbs and lungs.

BioConnections: *Look ahead to Figure 44.4. Do frogs breathe through their skin while they are underwater?*

and limbs and lungs appear (**Figure 32.14c**). Such a dramatic change in body form is known as metamorphosis, a process regulated by hormones from the thyroid gland. Reproduction is the link that ties amphibians to water, though a few species circumvent this need. Relatively few species are ovoviparous or viviparous.

Modern Amphibians Include a Variety of Frogs, Toads, Salamanders, and Caecilians

Approximately 4,800 living amphibian species are known, and the vast majority of these, nearly 90%, are frogs and toads of the order Anura, meaning tail-less ones (**Figure 32.15a**). The other two orders are the Caudata ("tail visible"), the salamanders, and Gymnophiona ("naked snake"), the wormlike caecilians.

Adult anurans are carnivores, eating a variety of invertebrates by catching them on a long, sticky tongue. In contrast, the aquatic larvae (tadpoles) are primarily herbivores. Frogs generally have smooth, moist skin and long hind legs, making them excellent jumpers and swimmers. In addition to secreting mucus, which keeps their skin moist, some frogs can also secrete poisonous chemicals that deter predators. Some amphibians advertise the poisonous nature of their skin with warning coloration (look ahead to Figure 54.11b). Others use camouflage as a way of avoiding detection by predators. Toads have a drier, bumpier skin and shorter legs than frogs. Although they are less impressive leapers, toads can tolerate drier conditions than can frogs.

Caecilians (order Gymnophiona) are a small order of about 160 species of legless, nearly blind amphibians (**Figure 32.15b**). Most are tropical and burrow in forest soils, while a few live in ponds and streams. They are secondarily legless, which means that they developed from legged ancestors. Caecilians eat worms and other soil invertebrates and have tiny jaws equipped with teeth. In this order fertilization is internal, and females usually bear live young. The young are nourished inside the mother's body by a thick, creamy secretion known as uterine milk. In

most caecilian species, the young grow into adults about 30 cm long, though some species up to 1.3 m long are known.

The salamanders (order Caudata) possess a tail and have a more elongate body than anurans (**Figure 32.15c**). During locomotion, they seem to sway from side to side, perhaps reminiscent of how the earliest tetrapods may have walked. Like frogs, salamanders often have colourful skin patterns that

(a) Red-eyed tree frog

(b) A caecilian

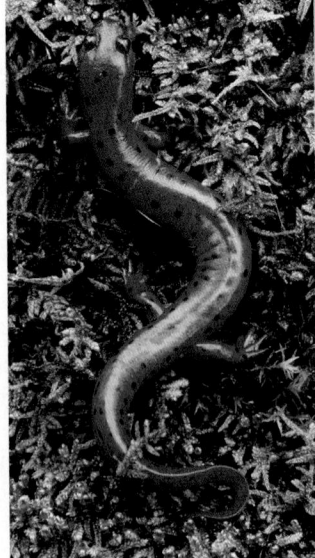

(c) Mud salamander

Figure 32.15 **Amphibians.** **(a)** Most amphibians are frogs and toads of the order Anura, including this red-eyed tree frog (*Agalychnis callidryas*). **(b)** The order Gymnophiona includes wormlike caecilians, such as this species from Colombia, *Caecilia nigricans*. **(c)** The order Caudata includes such species as this mud salamander (*Pseudotriton montanus*).

Concept check: *Do all amphibians produce tadpoles?*

advertise their distastefulness to predators. Salamanders retain their moist skin by living in damp areas under leaves or logs or beneath lush vegetation. They generally range in size from 10 to 30 cm. Fertilization is usually internal, with females using their cloaca to pick up sperm packets deposited by males. A very few salamander species do not undergo metamorphosis, and the newly hatched young resemble tiny adults. Conversely, some species, such as the axolotl, retain the gills and tail fins characteristic of the larval stage into adulthood, a phenomenon known as **paedomorphosis**.

32.5   AMNIOTES: TETRAPODS WITH A DESICCATION-RESISTANT EGG

Learning Outcomes:

1. Diagram the structure of the amniotic egg.
2. Identify the critical innovations of the amniotes.
3. Describe the distinguishing features of the major tetrapod classes.
4. List the features that allow birds to fly.

While successfully living in a terrestrial environment, adult amphibians remain tied to water for reproduction. Amphibians lay their eggs in water or in a very moist place, so the shell-less eggs do not dry out on exposure to air. Thus, a critical innovation in animal evolution was the development of a shelled egg that sheltered the embryo from desiccating conditions on land.

A shelled egg containing fluids was like a personal enclosed pond for each developing individual. Such an egg evolved in the common ancestor of turtles, lizards, snakes, crocodiles, birds, and mammals—a group of tetrapods collectively known as the **amniotes** (refer to Figure 32.1). The amniotic egg permitted animals to lay their eggs in a dry place so that reproduction was no longer tied to water. It was truly a critical innovation. The amniotic egg untethered animals from water in a similar way as the development of seeds liberated plants from water (see Chapter 28).

In time the amniotes came to dominate Earth. Mammals are considered amniotes, too, because even though most of them do not lay eggs, they retain other features of amniotic reproduction. In this section we begin by discussing in detail the morphology of the amniotic egg and other adaptations that permitted species to become fully terrestrial. We then discuss the biology of the reptiles, the first group of vertebrates to fully exploit land.

The Amniotic Egg and Other Innovations Permitted Life on Land

The **amniotic egg** (**Figure 32.16**) contains the developing embryo and the four separate extraembryonic membranes that it produces:

1. The innermost membrane is the **amnion**, which protects the developing embryo in a fluid-filled sac called the amniotic cavity.
2. The **yolk sac** encloses a stockpile of nutrients, in the form of yolk, for the developing embryo.
3. The **allantois** functions as a disposal sac for metabolic wastes.
4. The **chorion**, along with the allantois, provides gas exchange between the embryo and the surrounding air.

Surrounding the chorion is the albumin, or egg white, which also stores nutrients. The **shell** provides a tough, protective covering that is impermeable to water and prevents the embryo from drying out. However, the shell remains permeable to oxygen and carbon dioxide, so the embryo can breathe. In birds this shell is hard and calcareous, while in reptiles and ancestral mammals like the platypus and echidna, it is soft and leathery. Most mammals, however, do not have shelled eggs. Instead, the embryos embed into the wall of the uterus and receive their nutrients directly from the mother.

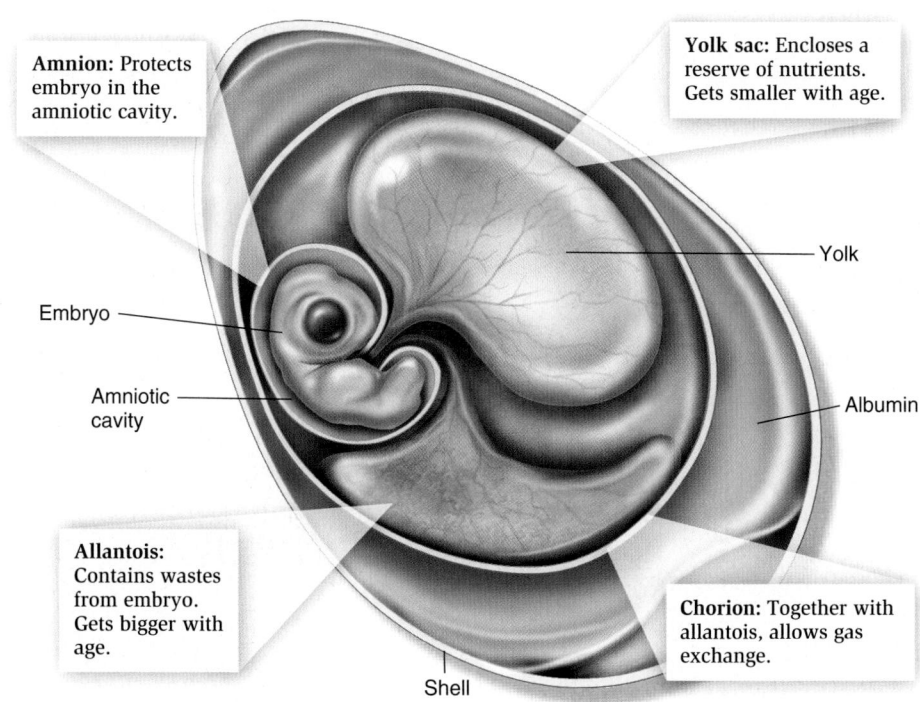

Amnion: Protects embryo in the amniotic cavity.

Yolk sac: Encloses a reserve of nutrients. Gets smaller with age.

Embryo

Amniotic cavity

Allantois: Contains wastes from embryo. Gets bigger with age.

Yolk

Albumin

Chorion: Together with allantois, allows gas exchange.

Shell

Figure 32.16 The amniotic egg.

Along with the amniotic egg, other critical innovations that enabled the conquest of land included the following:

- Desiccation-resistant skin. While the skin of amphibians is moist and aids in respiration, the skin of amniotes is thicker and watertight and contains keratin, a tough protein. This requires that gas exchange take place through the lungs.
- Thoracic breathing. Amphibians breathe by contracting the mouth to force air into the lungs. In contrast, amniotes use **thoracic breathing**, in which coordinated contractions of muscles expand the rib cage, creating a negative pressure to suck air in and then force it out later. This results in a greater volume of air being displaced with each breath.
- Water-conserving kidneys. The ability to concentrate wastes before elimination and thus conserve water is an important role of the amniote kidneys.
- Internal fertilization. Because sperm cannot penetrate a shelled egg, fertilization occurs internally, within the female's body before the shell is secreted. In this process, the male of the species often uses a copulatory organ (penis) to transfer sperm into the female reproductive tract. However, birds transfer sperm from cloaca to cloaca.

The Classification of the Reptiles Has Been Revised

Early amniote ancestors gave rise to all modern amniotes we know today, from lizards and snakes to birds and mammals. The traditional view of amniotes involved three living classes: the reptiles (turtles, lizards, snakes, and crocodilians), birds, and mammals. However, modern systematists argue that enough similarities exist between birds and the classic reptiles that birds should be considered part of the reptilian lineage, as shown in Figure 32.1. The fossil record includes other reptilian classes, all of which are extinct, including two classes of dinosaurs (ornithischian and saurischian dinosaurs), flying reptiles (pterosaurs), and two classes of ancient aquatic reptiles (icthyosaurs and plesiosaurs).

Class Testudines: The Turtles   Turtles is an umbrella term for terrestrial species, also called tortoises, and aquatic species, also known as terrapins. The turtle lineage is ancient and has remained virtually unchanged for 200 million years. The major distinguishing characteristic of the turtle is a hard protective shell into which the animal can withdraw its head and limbs. In most species, the vertebrae and ribs are fused to this shell. All turtles lack teeth but have sharp beaks for biting.

The majority of turtles are aquatic and have webbed feet. The forelimbs of marine species have evolved to become large flippers. All turtles, even the aquatic species, lay their eggs on land, usually in soft sand (**Figure 32.17a**). The gender of hatchlings is temperature dependent, with high temperatures producing more females. Marine species often make long migrations to sandy beaches to lay their eggs. Most land tortoises are quite slow movers, possibly because of a low metabolic rate and a heavy shell. Turtles are a very long-lived species, often surviving for 120 years or more. Many turtle species are in danger of extinction, because of egg hunting, destruction of habitat and nesting sites, and death from entanglement in fishing nets.

Class Lepidosauria: Lizards and Snakes   The class Lepidosauria is the largest class within the traditional reptiles, with about 3,000 species of snakes (order Serpentes) and 4,800 species of lizards (order Sauria). Many species have an elongated body form. One of the defining characteristics of the orders is a **kinetic skull**, in which the joints between various parts of the skull are extremely mobile. The lower jaw does not join directly to the skull but rather is connected by a multijointed hinge, and the upper jaw is hinged and moveable from the rest of the head.

(a)

(b)

(c)

Figure 32.17   **A variety of reptiles.**   (a) A snapping turtle (*Chelydra serpentina*) laying her eggs on the sandy shores of a lake in Algonquin Provincial Park, Ontario. (b) The Florida worm lizard (*Rhineura floridana*) is an amphisbaenian, a type of legless soil-burrowing lizard. (c) The Gila monster (*Heloderma suspectum*), one of only two poisonous lizards, lives in the southwestern United States and Mexico.

Figure 32.18 **The lepidosaur kinetic skull.** In snakes and lizards both the top and the bottom of the jaw are hinged on the skull, thus permitting large prey to be swallowed. This Halloween snake (*Pliocercus euryzonus*) is swallowing a Costa Rican rain frog.

This allows the jaws to open wider than other vertebrate jaws, with the result that lizards, and especially snakes, can swallow large prey (**Figure 32.18**). Nearly all species are carnivores.

A main difference between lizards and snakes is that lizards generally have limbs, whereas snakes do not. Also, snakes may be venomous, whereas lizards are generally not. However, there are exceptions to these general rules. Many legless lizard species exist (see **Figure 32.17b**), and two lizards are poisonous: the Gila monster (*Heloderma suspectum*) of the southwestern United States (see **Figure 32.17c**) and the Mexican

beaded lizard (*Heloderma horridum*). A more reliable distinguishing characteristic is that lizards have moveable eyelids and external ears (at least ear canals), whereas snakes do not.

Class Crocodilia: The Crocodiles and Alligators The Crocodilia is a small class of large aquatic animals that have remained essentially unchanged for nearly 200 million years (**Figure 32.19**). Indeed, these animals existed at the same time as the dinosaurs. Most of the 23 recognized species live in tropical or subtropical regions. There are only two extant species of alligators: one living in the southeastern United States and one found in China.

Although the class is small, it is evolutionarily very important. Crocodiles have a four-chambered heart, a feature they share with birds and mammals (look ahead to Figure 44.4c). In this regard crocodiles are more closely related to birds than any other living reptile class. Their teeth are set in sockets, a feature typical of the dinosaurs and the earliest birds. Similarly, crocodiles care for their young, another trait they have in common with birds. These and other features suggest that crocodiles and birds are more closely related than crocodiles and lizards. As with turtles, nest temperature influences the sex ratio of offspring. With crocodiles, however, when temperatures are warm, more males are produced. Biologists are concerned that a scenario of global warming may reduce the number of breeding females, leading to extinction of some species.

The Dinosaurs: Classes Ornithischia and Saurischia In 1841 English paleontologist Richard Owen coined the term **dinosaur**, meaning terrible lizard, to describe some of the

(a)

(b)

Figure 32.19 **Crocodilians.** The Crocodilia is an ancient class that has existed unchanged for about 200 million years. **(a)** Alligators, such as this American alligator (*Alligator mississippiensis*), have a broad snout, and the lower jaw teeth close on the inside of the upper jaw (and thus are almost completely hidden when the mouth is closed). **(b)** Crocodiles, including this American crocodile (*Crocodylus acutus*), have a longer, thinner snout, and the lower jaw teeth close on the outside of the upper jaw (and thus are visible when the mouth is closed).

BioConnections: *Look ahead to Figure 44.4c. In what ways are crocodilians similar to birds and mammals?*

(a) Ornithischian (*Stegosaurus*)   (b) Saurischian (*Tyrannosaurus*)

Figure 32.20 **Classes of dinosaurs.** **(a)** Herbivorous ornithischians included *Stegosaurus,* and **(b)** carnivorous saurischians included bipedal species, such as *Tyrannosaurus.*

variety of the hundreds of dinosaur species found in fossil form around the world is staggering. However, perhaps not surprisingly for such long-extinct species, the details of their lives are still being hotly debated. For example, an issue still unresolved is whether some dinosaur species were **endothermic**, that is, capable of generating and retaining body heat through their metabolism, just as birds and mammals are. Parental care has been clearly established for some dinosaurs, such as *Maiasaura.* The question remains how widespread such care was among the dinosaurs.

All dinosaurs, and many other animals, went extinct quite abruptly at the end of the Cretaceous period, about 65 million years ago. Although widely attributed to climatic change brought about by the impact of an asteroid, there is ongoing debate over the cause of this mass extinction. It is not known why all the dinosaurs died out, while many other animals, including small mammals, survived.

wondrous fossil animals discovered in the nineteenth century. About 215 million years ago, dinosaurs were the dominant tetrapods on Earth and remained so for 150 million years, far longer than any other vertebrate. The two main classes were the ornithischian or bird-hipped dinosaurs, which were herbivores, such as *Stegosaurus,* and the saurischian or lizard-hipped dinosaurs, which were fast, bipedal carnivores, such as *Tyrannosaurus* (**Figure 32.20**). In contrast to the limbs of lizards, amphibians, and crocodiles, which splay out to the side, the legs of dinosaurs were positioned directly under the body, like pillars, to help support their heavy body. Because less energy was devoted in lifting the body from the ground, some dinosaurs are believed to have been fast runners. Members of different but closely related classes—the pterosaurs (the first vertebrates to fly), and plesiosaurs and ichthyosaurs (marine reptiles)—were also common at this time.

Dinosaurs were the biggest animals ever to walk on the planet, with some animals weighing up to 50 metric tons. The

The Birds: Class Aves The defining characteristics of birds (class Aves, plural of the Latin *avis,* meaning "bird") are that they have feathers and nearly all species can fly. As you will see, the ability to fly has shaped nearly every feature of the bird body. The other vertebrates that have evolved the ability to fly, the bats and the now-extinct pterosaurs, used skin stretched tight over elongated limbs to fly. Such a surface can be irreparably damaged, though some holes may heal remarkably quickly. In contrast, birds use feathers, epidermal outgrowths that can be replaced if damaged. Recent studies in cell signalling show that the developmental changes necessary for animals to grow feathers instead of scales may not be that complex at the molecular level.

In this section we will begin by discussing the evolution of birds from dinosaur ancestors, outline the key characteristics of birds, and provide a brief overview of the various bird orders.

GENOMES AND PROTEOMES

The Differentiation of Scales, Feathers, and Fur May Be Caused by Simple Changes in Developmental Pathways

The skin of reptiles is protected by tough scales containing keratin, a waterproof protein. In birds, the skin is covered in feathers, and in mammals, it is covered by hair or fur. These epithelial appendages look very different but share similarities in initial development. All originate as **epithelial placodes**, regions of slightly thickened epithelial cells. Their spatial distribution on the body is determined by many developmental

signalling pathways, including those controlled by proteins designated Wnt, Notch, and BMP that regulate the properties of the epithelial cells (or epidermis) and the dermis. The timing and level of expression of these regulatory molecules determine the actual appendage that develops in the dermal layer. Wnt and Notch promote cell proliferation, while BMP programs cell death. Scales are formed as an outgrowth of the skin and are turned on by low levels of Wnt and Notch and high levels of BMP, while feathers develop with low levels of BMP and high levels of Wnt and Notch (**Figure 32.21**).

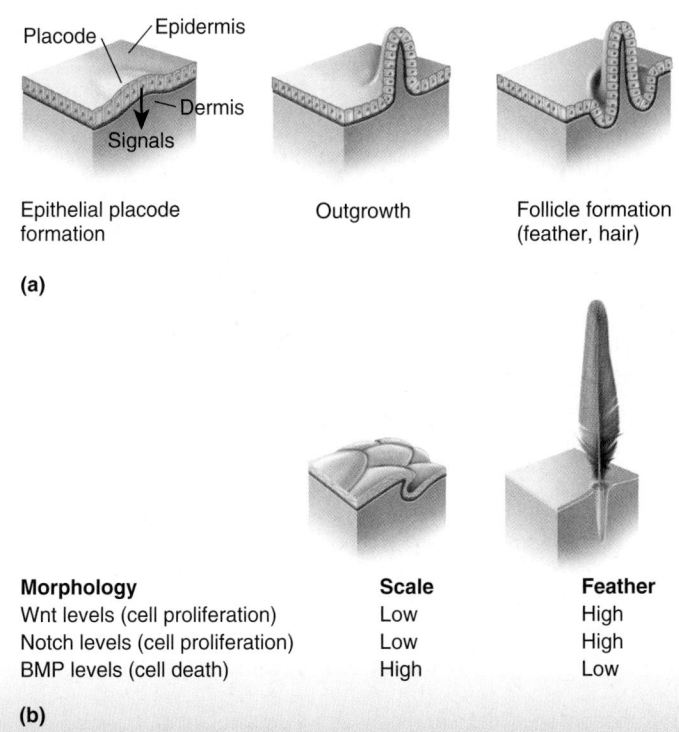

Morphology

	Scale	Feather
Wnt levels (cell proliferation)	Low	High
Notch levels (cell proliferation)	Low	High
BMP levels (cell death)	High	Low

(b)

Different regulatory genes acting in later stages of development can alter the properties of the scales, feathers, or hair. For example, the mouse *HoxC-13* gene is necessary for normal development of mouse hair. Mice with a mutation in this gene have fragile, brittle hair that breaks easily. Other features of the body that are hardened by keratin, the structural component of hair, may also be affected, such as nails and even filiform papillae, which are small projections on the surface of the tongue. The seemingly radical differences in body coverings of different vertebrate classes are actually caused by relatively simple changes in the levels of regulatory molecules.

Figure 32.21   Development of epithelial appendages. **(a)** Epithelial appendages begin as an outgrowth of the epidermis and dermis. In the development of feathers and hair, this outgrowth gives way to the formation of a follicle. **(b)** The difference between the identities of different epithelial appendages, such as scales and feathers, are caused, in part, by the timing and level of early signalling events.

Modern Birds Evolved from Small, Feather-Covered Dinosaurs

To trace the evolution of birds, we must look for the earliest type of animals that had feathers. One of the first known fossils exhibiting the faint impression of feathers was *Archaeopteryx lithographica* (meaning "ancient wings" and "stone picture"), found in a limestone quarry in Germany in 1861. The fossil was dated at 150 million years old. Except for the presence of feathers, *Archaeopteryx* appears to have had features similar to those of dinosaurs (**Figure 32.22a**). First, the fossil had an impression of a long tail with many vertebrae, a dinosaur feature. Some modern birds have long tails, but they are made of feathers, with the actual tailbone being much reduced. Second, the wings had claws halfway down the leading edge, another dinosaur-like character. Among modern birds, only the hoatzin, a South American swamp-inhabiting bird, has claws on its wings, which enable the chicks to climb back into the nest if they fall out. A third dinosaur-like feature is *Archaeopteryx*'s toothed beak. Fourth, the fossils show that *Archaeopteryx* lacked an enlarged breastbone, a feature that modern birds possess to anchor their large flight muscles, so it likely could not fly.

Similarities between the structure of the skull, feet, and hind leg bones have led scientists to conclude that *Archaeopteryx* is closely related to **theropods**, a group of bipedal saurischian dinosaurs. The wings and feathers of *Archaeopteryx*

may have enabled it to glide from tree to tree, to help it keep warm, or to fold over its head when hunting, in much the same way as some herons fold their wings over their heads when they are fishing. Later, the wings and feathers may have taken on functions of flight. We often find that evolution proceeds when previously evolved structures are co-opted into different uses, a diversity principle known as descent with modification.

In 1997 Philip Currie of the Royal Tyrrell Museum of Paleontology, Drumheller, Alberta, and his colleagues studied fossils in China that were of about the same age of *Archaeopteryx*. This discovery strengthened the view that there was a close kinship between dinosaurs and modern birds. The fossil, *Caudipteryx zoui*, was a dinosaurlike animal with feathers on its wings and tail and a toothed beak (**Figure 32.22b**). *Confuciusornis sanctus* was a small, flightless, but completely feathered dinosaur lacking the long bony tail and toothed jaw found in other theropod dinosaurs. Its large tail feathers may have functioned in courtship displays (**Figure 32.22c**).

These three species—*Archaeopteryx*, *Caudipteryx*, and *Confuciusornis*—help trace a lineage from dinosaurs to birds. By the early Cretaceous period, and only a relatively short period after *Archaeopteryx* evolved, the fossil record shows the existence of a huge array of bird types resembling modern species. These were to share the skies with pterosaurs for 70 million years, before eventually having the airways to themselves.

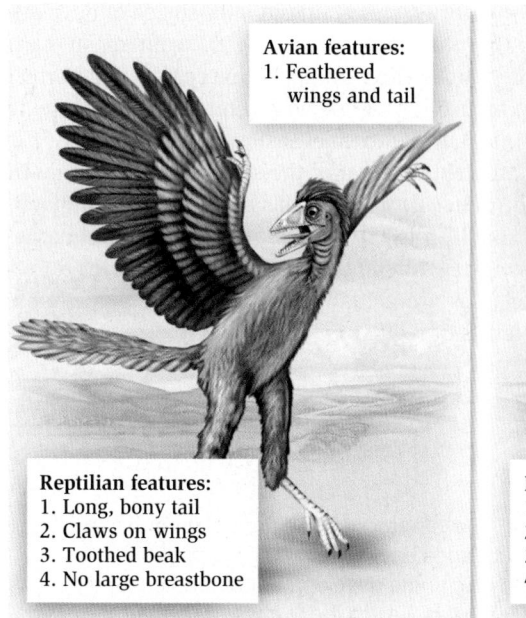

Avian features:
1. Feathered wings and tail

Reptilian features:
1. Long, bony tail
2. Claws on wings
3. Toothed beak
4. No large breastbone

(a) *Archaeopteryx lithographica*

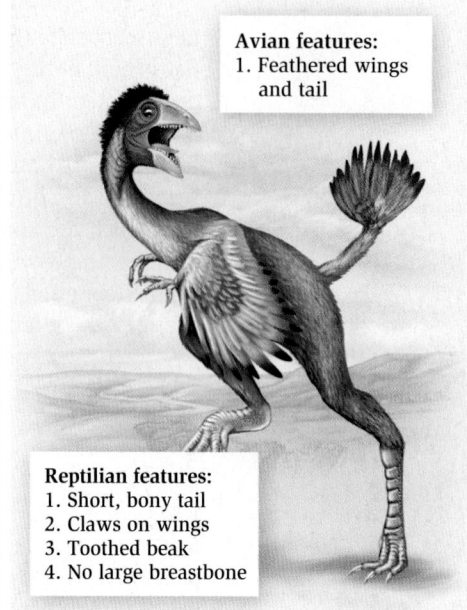

Avian features:
1. Feathered wings and tail

Reptilian features:
1. Short, bony tail
2. Claws on wings
3. Toothed beak
4. No large breastbone

(b) *Caudipteryx zoui*

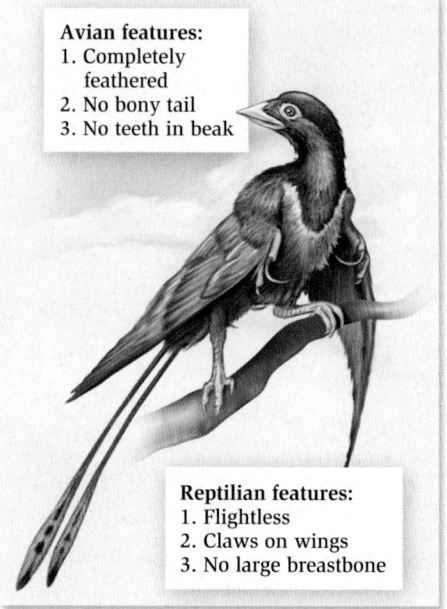

Avian features:
1. Completely feathered
2. No bony tail
3. No teeth in beak

Reptilian features:
1. Flightless
2. Claws on wings
3. No large breastbone

(c) *Confuciusornis sanctus*

Figure 32.22 **Transitional forms between dinosaurs and birds.** (a) *Archaeopteryx lithographica* was a Jurassic animal with dinosaurlike features, as well as wings and feathers. (b) *Caudipteryx zoui* was a dinosaur with feathers on its tail and wings. (c) *Confuciusornis sanctus* was a birdlike animal with a horny, toothless beak.

Birds Display Four Key Characteristics

Modern birds possess many characteristics that reveal their reptilian ancestry. For example, they have scales on their feet and legs, and they lay shelled eggs. In addition, however, among living animals they have four features unique to birds, all of which are associated with flight.

1. Feathers. Feathers are modified scales that keep birds warm, enable flight, and are supported on a modified forelimb (**Figure 32.23a**). Soft, downy feathers maintain heat, while stiffer contour feathers give the wing the airfoil shape it needs to generate lift. Each contour feather develops from a follicle, a tiny pit in the skin. If a feather is lost, a new one can be regrown. The contour feathers consist of many paired barbs, each of which supports barbules that hook together with barbules from neighbouring barbs to give the feather its shape (**Figure 32.23b**).
2. Lightweight skeleton. Most bird bones are thin and hollow and are crisscrossed internally by tiny pieces of bone to give them a honeycomb structure (**Figure 32.23c**). The keeled breastbone, or **sternum**, provides an anchor on which a bird's powerful flight muscles attach. These muscles may contribute up to 30% of the bird's body weight. The bird skull lacks teeth, but the keratin of bird beaks is tough and malleable, and it takes very different shapes in different species (**Figure 32.24**).
3. Air sacs. Flight requires a great deal of energy generated from an active metabolism that requires abundant

oxygen. Birds have nine air sacs—large, hollow sacs that may extend into the bones (look ahead to Figure 45.11). On inhalation air passes into the posterior air sacs. On exhalation half of this air is forced back out through the lungs, where oxygen is extracted, and then goes into the anterior air sacs. On the next inhalation, air is sucked from the posterior air sacs into the anterior air sacs via the lungs. Air is therefore being constantly moved across the lungs during inhalation and exhalation. While making bird breathing very efficient, this process also makes birds especially susceptible to airborne toxins (hence, the use of the canary in the coal mine; the bird's death signalled the presence of harmful carbon dioxide or methane gas that was otherwise unnoticed by miners).

4. Reduction of organs. To decrease the total mass the bird must carry, some organs are reduced in size or are lacking altogether. For example, birds have only one ovary and can carry relatively few eggs. As a result, they lay fewer eggs than most other reptile species. In fact, the gonads of both males and females are reduced, except during the breeding season, when they increase in size. Most birds also lack a urinary bladder.

Birds also have other distinct features, though mammals also possess some of these. For example, birds have a warm body temperature, which ensures rapid metabolism and the quick production of ATP that these active organisms need to fuel flight and other activities. In fact, birds' body temperatures

(a) Wing   **(b) Feather structure**   **(c) Pelican bone**
                                                                                              (*Pelicanus*
                                                                                              occidentalis)

Figure 32.23   **Features of the bird wing and feather.**   **(a)** The wing is supported by an elongated and modified forelimb with extended fingers. **(b)** Each feather has a hollow shaft that supports many barbs, which in turn support barbules that interlock with hooks to give the feather its form. **(c)** The bones of a pelican (*Pelicanus occidentalis*) are hollow but crisscrossed with a honeycomb structure that provides added strength.

Concept check: *What adaptations in birds help reduce their body weight to enable flight?*

BioConnections: *Look ahead to Figure 45.11. How do birds acquire enough oxygen to fuel their metabolism to support flight?*

are generally 40°C to 42°C, considerably warmer than the human body's average of 37°C. Birds have a double circulation and a four-chambered heart to ensure rapid blood circulation. Rapid flight also requires acute vision, and bird vision is among the best in the vertebrate world. Generally, plant material is not energy-rich enough to supply the dietary needs of birds, so most birds are carnivores, eating insects and other invertebrates, though some birds, like parrots, specialize in more nutrient-rich fruits and seeds. Bird eggs also have to be kept warm for successful development, which entails brooding by an adult bird. Often, the males and females take turns brooding so that each parent can feed and maintain its strength. Picking successful partners is therefore an important task, and birds often engage in complex courtship rituals.

Birds Have Many Orders, All with the Same Body Plan

Birds are the most species-rich class of terrestrial vertebrates, with 28 orders, 166 families, and about 9,600 species (**Table 32.2**). Most birds fly and thus most have the same general body shape. The biggest departures from this body shape are the flightless birds, including the kiwis, ostriches, cassowaries, emus, and rheas. These birds have smaller wing bones and the keel on the breastbone is greatly reduced or absent. Penguins are also flightless birds whose upper limbs are modified as flippers for swimming.

32.6   MAMMALS

Learning Outcomes:

1. Identify the four features that separate mammals from other vertebrate classes.
2. List the defining characteristics of primates.
3. Discuss the evolution of modern humans, *Homo sapiens.*

Mammals evolved from amniote ancestors earlier than birds. About 225 million years ago, the first mammals appeared in the mid-Triassic period. They evolved from small mammal-like lizards that went extinct about 170 million years ago. Mammals survived, although most are believed to have been small, insect-eating species that lived in the shadows of dinosaurs. However, in January 2005 two fossils of a 130-million-year-old mammalian species called *Repenomamus* were discovered that challenge the notion of mammals as small insect eaters. One fossil was of an animal estimated to weigh about 13 kg, while the other had the remains of a baby dinosaur in its stomach.

After extinction of the dinosaurs in the Cretaceous period, some 65 million years ago, mammals flourished. Today, biologists have identified about 5,500 species of mammals with a diverse array of lifestyles, from fishlike dolphins to birdlike bats, and from small insectivores, such as shrews, to large herbivores, such as giraffes and elephants. The range of sizes and

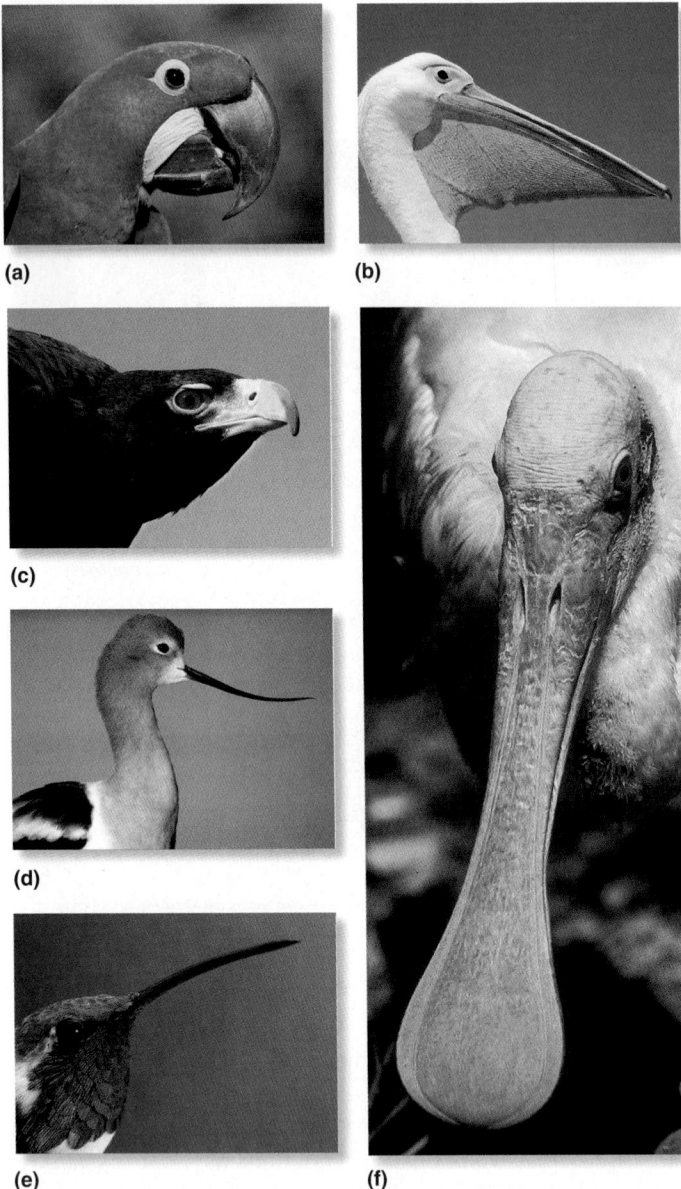

(a)

(b)

(c)

(d)

(e)

(f)

Figure 32.24   A variety of bird beaks.   Birds have evolved a variety of beak shapes for different types of food gathering. **(a)** Hyacinthe macaw (*Anodorhynchus hyacinthinus*): cracking. **(b)** White pelican (*Pelecanus onocrotalus*): scooping. **(c)** Verreaux's eagle (*Aquila verreauxii*): tearing. **(d)** American avocet (*Recurvirostra americana*): probing. **(e)** Lucifer hummingbird (*Calothorax lucifer*): nectar feeding. **(f)** Roseate spoonbill (*Ajaia ajaia*): sieving.

body forms of mammals is unmatched by any other group, and mammals are prime illustrations of the concept that organismal diversity is related to environmental diversity. In this section we will outline the features that distinguish mammals from other taxa. We will also examine the diversity of mammals that exists on Earth and will end by turning our attention to primates and in particular to the evolution of modern humans.

Mammals Have Mammary Glands, Hair, Specialized Teeth, and an Enlarged Skull

The distinguishing characteristics of mammals are the possession of mammary glands, hair, specialized teeth, and an enlarged skull.

- Mammary glands. Mammals, or the class Mammalia (from the Latin, *mamma,* meaning "breast"), are named after the female's distinctive **mammary glands**, which secrete milk. Milk is a fluid rich in fat, sugar, protein, and vital minerals, especially calcium. Newborn mammals suckle this fluid, which helps promote rapid growth.

- Hair. All mammals have hair, although some have more than others. Whales retain only a few hairs on their snout, and humans are relatively hairless. In some animals the hair is dense and referred to as fur. In some aquatic species, such as beavers, the fur is so dense it cannot be thoroughly wetted, so the hair underneath remains dry. Mammals are endothermic, and their fur is an efficient insulator. Hair can also take on functions other than insulation. Many animals, including cats, dogs, walruses, and whales, have sensory hairs called vibrissae (**Figure 32.25a**). Hair can be of many colours, to allow the mammals to blend into their background (**Figure 32.25b**). In some cases as in porcupines and hedgehogs, the hairs become long, stiffened, and sharp (quills) and serve as a defence mechanism (**Figure 32.25c**).

- Specialized teeth. Mammals are the only vertebrates with teeth that are adapted for different types of diets (**Figure 32.26**). Although teeth are generally present in all species, different teeth are larger, smaller, lost, or reduced, depending on diet. Of particular importance to carnivores are the piercing canine teeth, while herbivorous species, like antelopes, depend on their chisel-like incisors to snip off vegetation and on their many molars to grind plant material. Only mammals chew their food in this fashion. Rodent incisors grow continuously throughout life, and species, such as beavers, wear them down by gnawing tough plant material, such as wood.

- Enlarged skull. The mammalian skull, jaw, and head differ from other amniotes in several ways. First, mammals have a single lower jawbone—the dentary—unlike reptiles, whose lower jaw is composed of multiple bones. Second, mammals have three bones in the middle ear, as opposed to reptiles, which have one bone in the middle ear. Third, mammals have pinnae, or external ears. Fourth, the brain is enlarged and is contained within a relatively large skull.

In addition to those uniquely mammalian characteristics, some but not all mammals possess these additional features:

- The ability to digest plants. Apart from tortoises and marine iguanas, certain species of mammals are the only large vertebrates that can exist on a steady diet of grasses or tree leaves; indeed, most large mammals are

Table 32.2 The Main Orders of Birds, in Order of Species Richness

Order		Examples (approx. number of species)	Main characteristics
Passeriformes		Robins, starlings, sparrows, warblers (5,300)	Perching birds with perching feet; songbirds
Apodiformes		Hummingbirds, swifts (430)	Fast fliers with rapidly beating wings; small bodies
Piciformes		Woodpeckers, toucans (380)	Large with specialized bills; two toes pointing forward and two backward
Psittaciformes		Parrots, cockatoos (340)	Large, powerful beaks
Chadradriiformes		Seagulls, wading birds (330)	Shorebirds
Columbiformes		Doves, pigeons (300)	Round bodies; short legs
Falconiformes		Eagles, hawks, kestrels, vultures (290)	Diurnal carnivores; birds of prey; powerful talons and strong beaks
Galliformes		Chickens, pheasants, quail (270)	Often large birds; weak flyers; ground nesters
Coraciiformes		Hornbills, kingfishers (200)	Large bills; cavity nesters
Anseriformes		Ducks, swans, geese (150)	Able to swim; webbed feet; broad bills
Strigiformes		Owls (150)	Nocturnal carnivores; powerful talons and bills
Pelecaniformes		Pelicans, frigate birds, cormorants (55)	Large, colonial fish eaters; often tropical
Sphenisciformes		Penguins (18)	Flightless, wings modified into flippers for swimming; marine; Southern Hemisphere
Casuariformes		Cassowaries, emus (3)	Large, flightless; Australia and New Guinea
Struthioniformes		Ostrich (1)	Large, flightless; only two toes; Africa only

(a)   (b)   (c)

Figure 32.25   Mammalian hair.   (a) The sensory hairs (vibrissae) of the walrus (*Odobenus rosmarus*). **(b)** The camouflaged coat of a bobcat (*Lynx rufus*). **(c)** The defensive quills of the crested porcupine (*Hystrix africaeaustralis*).

(a)   (b)   (c)

(d)   (e)

Figure 32.26   Mammalian teeth.   Mammals have different types of teeth, according to their diet. (a) The wolf has long canine teeth for biting its prey. **(b)** The deer has a long row of front molars for grinding plant material. **(c)** The beaver, a rodent, has long, continually growing incisors used to gnaw wood. **(d)** The elephant's incisors are modified into tusks. **(e)** Dolphins and other fish or plankton feeders have numerous small teeth for filtering prey from seawater.

herbivores. Though mammals cannot digest cellulose, the principal constituent of the cell wall of many plants, some species have a large four-chambered stomach containing cellulose-digesting bacteria. These bacteria can break

down the cellulose and make the plant cell contents available to the animal.

- Horns and antlers. Mammals are the only living class of vertebrates to possess horns or antlers. Many mammals,

(a)　　　　　(b)　　　　　(c)

Figure 32.27 **Horns and antlers in mammals.**   Mammals have a variety of outgrowths that are used for defence or by males as weapons in contests to win females. **(a)** The horns of this male kudu (*Tragelaphus strepsiceros*) are bony outgrowths of the skull covered in a keratin sheath. **(b)** The horns of the black rhinoceros (*Diceros bicornis*) are outgrowths of the epidermis made of tightly matted hair. **(c)** The antlers of the caribou (*Rangifer tarandus*), also known as reindeer, are made entirely of bone and are grown and shed each year.

especially antelopes, cattle, and sheep, have horns, typically consisting of a bony core that is a permanent outgrowth of the skull surrounded by a hairlike keratin sheath (**Figure 32.27a**). Rhinoceros horns are outgrowths of the epidermis consisting of very tightly matted hair (**Figure 32.27b**). In contrast, deer antlers are made entirely out of bone (**Figure 32.27c**). Deer grow a new set of antlers each year and shed them after the mating season. Hooves and claws are also made of keratin and protect an animal's toes from the impact of its feet striking the ground and aid in prey capture, respectively.

Mammals Are the Most Variable Group of Vertebrates Living on Earth

Modern mammals are incredibly variable (**Table 32.3**). They vary in size from tiny insect-eating bats weighing only 2 g, to leviathans, such as the blue whale, the largest animal ever known, which tips the scales at 100 metric tons. The 26 different mammalian orders are divided into three distinct subclasses. The subclass Prototheria contains only the order Monotremata, or **monotremes**, which are found in Australia and New Guinea. There are only three species: the duckbilled platypus (**Figure 32.28a**) and two species of echidna, a spiny animal resembling a hedgehog. Monotremes are considered ancestral mammals because they lay eggs rather than bear live young, lack a placenta, and have mammary glands with poorly developed nipples. The mothers incubate the eggs, and on hatching, the young simply lap up the milk as it oozes onto the fur.

The subclass Metatheria, or the **marsupials**, is a group of seven orders, with about 280 species (**Figure 32.28b**). Once widespread, members of this order are now largely confined to Australia, although some marsupials exist in South America and one species—the opossum—is found in North America. Unlike other mammals, marsupials are extremely small when they are born (often only 1 or 2 cm) and make their way to a ventral pouch called a marsupium for further development. Initially, they are too feeble to suck on the mother's nipple so she simply oozes milk for them to lick up. However, as they grow, marsupial young eventually attach to the nipple, often for a long time.

All the other mammalian orders are members of the subclass Eutheria and considered **eutherians** or placental mammals (**Figure 32.28c**). Even though marsupials have a placenta, it is not as long-lived or complex as that of eutherians. In eutherians fertilization is internal and reproduction is viviparous, as in marsupials, but the developmental period, or gestation, of the young is prolonged, and the mother's placenta provides the fetus with nourishment during development.

Of all the world's animals the diversity of vertebrates, and especially mammals, is the most threatened by human activities. Many species are hunted for food. Others, such as wild cats and whales, are hunted for their products (fur and oil), and still others, like the oryx, have been shot simply for sport.

Table 32.3   The Main Orders of Mammals, in Order of Species Richness

Order		Examples (approx. number of species)	Main characteristics
Rodentia		Mice, rats, squirrels, beaver, porcupine (2,277)	Plant eating, gnawing habit, with two pairs of continually growing incisor teeth
Chiroptera		Bats (1,116)	Insect or fruit eating; small; have ability to fly; navigate by sonar; nocturnal
Soricomorpha		Shrews, moles (428)	Insect eaters; ancestral placental mammals
Primates		Monkeys, apes, humans (404)	Opposable thumb; binocular vision; large brains
Carnivora		Cats, dogs, weasels, bears, seals, sea lions (286)	Flesh-eating mammals; canine teeth
Artiodactyla		Deer, antelopes, cattle, sheep, goats, camels, pigs (240)	Herbivorous hoofed mammals, usually with two toes, hippopotamus and others with four toes; many with horns or antlers
Diprotodontia		Kangaroos, koalas, opossums, wombats (143)	Pouched mammals mainly found in Australia
Lagomorpha		Rabbits, hares (92)	Powerful hind legs; rodent-like teeth
Cetacea		Whales, dolphins (84)	Marine fish or plankton feeders; front limbs modified into flippers; no hind limbs; little hair except on snout
Erinaceomorpha		Hedgehogs, moonrats (24)	Insect eaters; nocturnal; hedgehogs with stiff spines
Perissodactyla		Horses, zebras, tapirs, rhinoceroses (18)	Hoofed herbivorous mammals with odd number of toes, one (horses) or three (rhinoceroses)
Monotremata		Duck-billed platypus, echidna (3)	Egg-laying mammals only found in Australia and New Guinea
Proboscidea		Elephants (3)	Long trunk; large, upper incisors modified as tusks

Primates Are Mammals with Opposable Thumbs and a Large Brain

Of the mammalian orders, the primates, and specifically humans, have had the greatest impact on the world. Primates are primarily tree-dwelling species that are believed to have evolved from a group of small, arboreal insect-eating mammals about 85 million years ago, before dinosaurs went extinct. Primates have several defining characteristics, mostly relating to their tree-dwelling nature:

- Grasping hands. All primates have grasping hands, a characteristic that enables them to hold onto branches. Most primate species also possess an **opposable thumb**, a thumb that can be placed opposite the fingers of the same hand, which gives them a precision grip and enables the manipulation of small objects. All primates, except humans, also have an opposable big toe.
- Large brain. Acute vision and other senses enhancing the ability to move quickly through the trees require the efficient processing of large amounts of information. As a

(a)

(c)

(b)

Figure 32.28 **Variability among mammals.** **(a)** Prototherians, such as this duck-billed platypus (*Ornithorhynchus anatinus*) lay eggs, lack a placenta, and possess mammary glands with poorly developed nipples. **(b)** Metatherians, or marsupials, such as this rock wallaby (*Petrogale assimilis*) feed and carry their developing young, or joeys, in a ventral pouch. **(c)** Gestation lasts longer in eutherians, and their young are more developed at birth, as illustrated by these young cougars (*Felis concolor*).

BioConnections: *Look ahead to Figure 48.12a and 48.12b. The placenta serves as the provisional lungs, intestine, and kidneys of the developing fetus. How much mixing is there of maternal and fetal blood?*

result, the primate brain is large and well developed. In turn, this has facilitated complex social behaviours.

- At least some digits have flat nails instead of claws. This feature is believed to aid in the manipulation of objects.
- Binocular vision. Primates have forward-facing eyes that are positioned close together on a flattened face, though other mammals share this characteristic. Jumping from branch to branch requires accurate judgment of distances. This is facilitated by binocular vision, in which the field of vision for both eyes overlaps, producing a single image.

There are several ways of classifying primates, but many taxonomists divide them into two groups: the prosimians and the anthropoids (**Figure 32.29**). The **prosimians** contain the smaller species, such as bush babies, lemurs, pottos, and tarsiers. These are generally nocturnal and smaller-brained primates (**Figure 32.30a**). The second group consists of the larger-brained and diurnal **anthropoids** including the monkeys (**Figure 32.30b**) and the hominoids (gibbons, orangutans, gorillas, chimpanzees, and humans) (**Figure 32.30c**).

What differentiates monkeys from hominoids? Most monkeys have tails, whereas hominoids do not. In addition, the shoulder bones in the two groups have a different structure; while hominoids can swing from branch to branch, monkeys cannot. Instead, monkeys run along the tops of branches and their movements are more like other four-footed mammals. The 13 species of hominoids are split into two groups: the lesser apes (family Hylobatidae) or the gibbons; and the greater apes (family Hominidae) or the orangutans, gorillas, chimpanzees, and humans. The lesser apes are strictly arboreal, while the greater apes often descend to the ground to feed.

Humans Evolved from Ancestral Primates

Although humans are closely related to chimpanzees and gorillas, they did not evolve directly from them. Rather, all hominoid species shared a common ancestor. Recent molecular studies show that gorillas, chimpanzees, and humans are closer to one another than gibbons and orangutans, so scientists have split the hominoids into groups, including the Ponginae (orangutans) and the Homininae (gorillas, chimpanzees, and humans and their ancestors). In turn the Homininae are split into three tribes: the Gorillini (gorillas), the Panini (chimpanzees), and the Hominini (humans and their ancestors).

About 6 million years ago in Africa, a lineage that led to humans began to separate from other primate lineages. The evolution of humans should not be viewed as a neat, stepwise progression from one species to another. Rather, human evolution, like the evolution of most species, can be visualized more like a tree, with one or two **hominin** species (extinct and modern forms of humans) likely coexisting at the same point in time, with some eventually going extinct and some giving rise to other species (**Figure 32.31**).

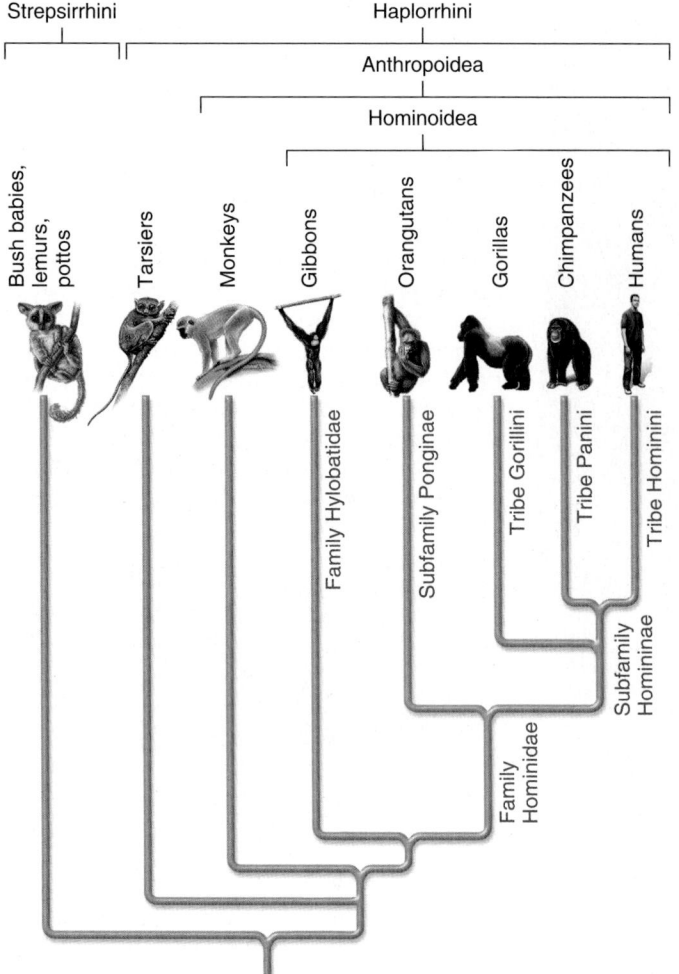

Figure 32.29 Evolutionary tree for the primates.

One of the key characteristics differentiating hominins from other apes is that hominins walked on two feet, that is, they are **bipedal**. At about the time when hominins diverged from other ape lineages, the Earth's climate had cooled and the forests of Africa had given way to grassy savannahs. Now that the hands were not engaged in climbing, bipedalism could have been selected, as it is a more energetically economical form of walking. A bipedal method of locomotion and upright stance may also have been advantageous in allowing hominins to peer over the tall grass of the savannah.

In any event bipedalism resulted in many anatomical changes in hominins. First, the opening of the skull where the spinal cord enters shifted forward, allowing the spine to be more directly underneath the head. Second, the hominin pelvis became broader to support the additional weight, and third, the lower limbs, used for walking, became relatively larger than those in other apes. These are also the types of anatomical changes paleontologists look for in the fossil record to help determine whether fossil remains are hominin. The earliest group of hominins included several species of a smaller-brained genus, *Australopithecus*, one of which gave rise to the genus *Homo,* the humans.

Australopithecines Since 1924, when the first fossil of australo-pithecine ("southern ape") was found in South Africa, hundreds of fossils of this group have been unearthed all over southern and eastern Africa. This was a widespread group, with at least six species. Compared with modern humans, all were relatively small, about 1 to 1.5 m in height, and possessed a facial structure and brain size similar to those of a chimp. Females were much smaller than males, a condition known as sexual dimorphism. In 1974 paleontologist Donald Johanson unearthed the skeleton of a female *Australopithecus afarensis,* dubbed Lucy. More than 40% of the skeleton had been preserved, enough to provide a good idea of the physical appearance of australopithecines. Examination of the bones revealed that *A. afarensis* walked on two legs. Two of the larger species now considered to be a separate genus, *Paranthropus,* weighed about 40 kg and lived contemporaneously with australopithecines and members of *Homo* species. Both *Paranthropus* species died out rather suddenly about 1.5 million years ago.

***Modern Humans and the Genus* Homo** In the 1960s paleontologist Louis Leakey found hominin fossils estimated to be about 2 million years old in Olduvai Gorge, Tanzania. Two particularly interesting facts stand out about these fossils. First, reconstruction of the skull showed an increased brain size, about 680 cubic centimetres (cc) compared with the 500 cc of *Australopithecus.* Second, the fossils were found with a wealth of stone tools. As a result Leakey assigned the fossils to a new species, *Homo habilis,* meaning "handyman." The discovery of several more *Homo* fossils followed, but there have been no extensive finds, as there were with Lucy. This makes it difficult to determine which *Australopithecus* lineage gave rise to the *Homo* lineage (see Figure 32.31), and scientists remain divided on this point.

One of the most important species of *Homo* is believed to be *Homo ergaster,* a hominin with a "human-looking" face and skull, with downward-facing nostrils. *H. ergaster* also evolved in Africa and is thought to have given rise to many species, including *Homo erectus, Homo heidelbergensis, Homo neanderthalensis,* and *Homo sapiens. H. ergaster* is believed to be a direct ancestor of modern humans, with *H. heidelbergensis* viewed as an intermediary step.

H. erectus was a large hominin, as large as a modern human but with heavier bones and a smaller brain capacity of between 750 and 1,225 cc. Fossil evidence shows that *H. erectus* was a social species that used tools, hunted animals, and cooked over fires. *H. erectus* spread out of Africa soon after it appeared, more than a million years ago, and fossils have been found as far away as eastern Asia.

H. heidelbergensis gave rise to two species: *H. neanderthalensis* and *H. sapiens. H. neanderthalensis* was named for the Neander Valley of Germany, where the first fossils of its type were found. Neanderthals were a shorter, stockier species than modern humans, with a more massive skull and large brain size of about 1,450 cc, perhaps associated with their bulk. Males

(a)   **(b)**   **(c)**

Figure 32.30 **Primate classification.** Many authorities divide the primates into two groups: **(a)** the prosimians, smaller, nocturnal species, such as this tarsier (*Tarsius syrichta*), and the anthropoids, larger diurnal species. **(b)** Anthropoids comprise the monkeys, such as this Capuchin monkey (*Cebus capucinus*), and **(c)** the hominoids, such species as this white-handed gibbon (*Hylobates lar*).

Concept check: *What are the defining features of primates?*

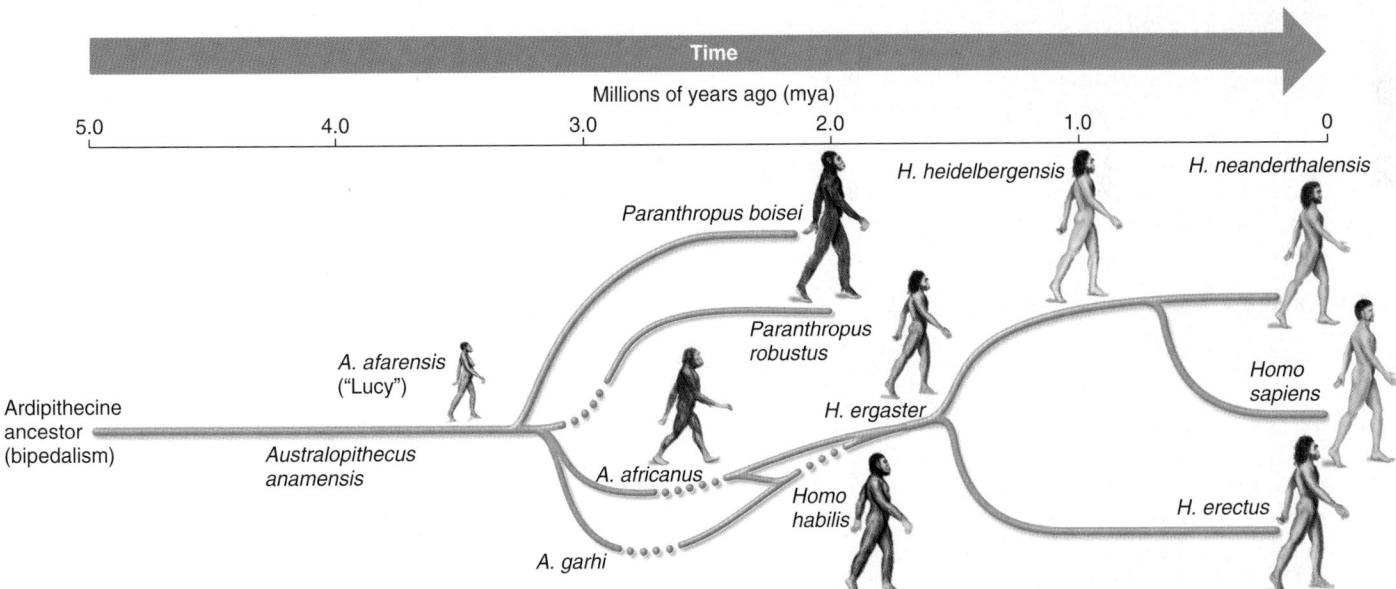

Figure 32.31 **A possible scenario for human evolution.** In this human family tree (based on the ongoing work of Donald Johanson), several hominin species lived contemporaneously with one another, but only one lineage gave rise to modern humans (*Homo sapiens*).

were about 168 cm tall and would have been very strong by modern standards. However, about 30,000 years ago, this species was replaced by another hominin species, *H. sapiens* (meaning "wise man"), our own species. *H. sapiens* was a taller, lighter-weight species with a slightly smaller brain capacity of about 1,350 cc.

Summary of Key Concepts

- The subphylum Vertebrata is the largest group of chordates, occupying nearly all of Earth's major habitats. (Figure 32.1)

32.1 The Craniates: Chordates with a Skull

- Craniates have two defining characteristics that distinguish them from other invertebrate chordates: a cranium and a neural crest. The hagfish (class Myxini) is considered the most ancestral living craniate. (Figure 32.2)

32.2 Characteristics of Vertebrates

- Vertebrates have several characteristic features, including a vertebral column, endoskeleton of cartilage or bone, and internal organs. Of the 11 different vertebrate classes, 5 are classes of fish, reflecting the dominance of fish. (Table 32.1)

32.3 The Fish

- Ostracoderms, a name for several extinct classes of fish, lacked a hinged jaw. (Figure 32.3)

- A single living lineage of jawless fish exists today: the lampreys. (Figure 32.4)

- A critical innovation in vertebrate evolution was the hinged jaw. The hinged jaw evolved from cartilaginous gill arches. (Figure 32.5)

- The chondrichthyans (sharks, skates, and rays) have a skeleton composed of flexible cartilage and powerful appendages called fins. They are active predators with acute senses and were among the earliest fish to develop teeth. (Figure 32.6)

- Bony fish consist of the Actinopterygii (ray-finned fish, the most species-rich class), Actinistia (coelacanths), and the Dipnoi (lungfish). In Actinopterygii, the fins are supported by thin, flexible rays and moved by muscles. (Figures 32.7, 32.8)

- The lobe fins comprise the lobe-finned fish (Actinistia and Dipnoi) and the tetrapods. In the lobe-finned fish, the fins are part of the body. (Figures 32.9, 32.10)

32.4 Amphibia: The First Tetrapods

- Fossils record the evolution of lobe-finned fish to fish with four limbs (*Acanthostega*). Recent research has shown that relatively simple mutations control large changes in limb development. (Figures 32.11, 32.12, 32.13)

- Amphibians live on land but return to the water to reproduce. The larval stage undergoes metamorphosis, losing gills and tail for lungs and limbs. (Figure 32.14)

- The majority of amphibians belong to the order Anura (frogs and toads). Other orders are the Caudata (salamanders) and Gymnophiona (caecilians). (Figure 32.15)

32.5 Amniotes: Tetrapods with a Desiccation-Resistant Egg

- The amniotic egg permitted animals to become fully terrestrial. Other critical innovations included desiccation-resistant skin, thoracic breathing, water-conserving kidneys, and internal fertilization. (Figure 32.16)

- Living reptilian classes include the Testudines (turtles), Lepidosauria (lizards and snakes), Crocodilia (crocodiles), and Aves (birds). Other reptilian classes, all of which are extinct, include two classes of dinosaurs (Ornithischia and Saurischia). (Figures 32.17, 32.18, 32.19, 32.20)

- The differences in body coverings of different vertebrate classes (scales, feathers, hair) are caused by relatively simple changes in the levels of regulatory molecules. (Figure 32.21)

- Three species—*Archaeopteryx*, *Caudipteryx*, and *Confuciusornis*—help trace a lineage from dinosaurs to birds. (Figure 32.22)

- The four key characteristics of birds are feathers, a lightweight skeleton, air sacs, and reduced organs. Birds are the most species-rich class of terrestrial vertebrates. (Figures 32.23, 32.24, Table 32.2)

32.6 Mammals

- The distinguishing characteristics of mammals are the possession of mammary glands, hair, specialized teeth, and an enlarged skull. Other unique characteristics of some mammals are the ability to digest plants and possession of horns or antlers (Figures 32.25, 32.26, 32.27)

- Three subclasses exist: the Prototheria (monotremes), Metatheria (marsupials), and Eutheria (placental mammals). (Figure 32.28, Table 32.3)

- Many defining characteristics of primates relate to their tree-dwelling nature and include grasping hands, a large brain, nails instead of claws, and binocular vision. (Figures 32.29, 32.30)

- About 6 million years ago in Africa, a lineage that led to humans began to separate from other primate lineages. A key characteristic of hominins (extinct and modern humans) is bipedalism.

- Human evolution can be visualized like a tree, with one or two hominin species coexisting at the same point in time, with some eventually going extinct and some giving rise to other species. (Figures 32.31)

Test to Assess Your Learning

1. Which of the following is *not* a defining characteristic of craniates?
   a. cranium
   b. neural crest
   c. two clusters of *Hox* genes
   d. protective housing around the brain
   e. cephalization

2. The hinged jaw is an important adaptation in vertebrates that allowed for
   a. movement onto land.
   b. evolution of more complex body development.
   c. improvement in prey capture.
   d. evolution of speech.
   e. all of the above.

3. The presence of a bony skeleton, an operculum, and a swim bladder are all defining characteristics of
   a. Myxini.
   b. lampreys.
   c. Chondrichthyes.
   d. bony fish.
   e. amphibians.

4. Organisms that lay eggs are said to be
   a. oviparous.
   b. ovoviparous.

   c. viviparous.
   d. placental.
   e. none of the above.

5. Adaptations in animals that allow for life on land include
   a. a waxy cuticle.
   b. strong limbs that provide movement.
   c. internal fertilization.
   d. (b) and (c) only.
   e. all of the above.

6. In some amphibians, the adult retains certain larval characteristics, which is known as
   a. metamorphosis.
   b. parthenogenesis.
   c. cephalization.
   d. paedomorphosis.
   e. hermaphrodism.

7. The membrane of the amniotic egg that serves as a site for waste storage is
   a. the amnion.
   b. the yolk sac.
   c. the allantois.
   d. the chorion.
   e. the albumin.

8. Which of the following is *not* a distinguishing characteristic of birds?
   a. amniotic egg
   b. feathers
   c. air sacs
   d. lack of certain organs
   e. lightweight skeletons

9. Placental mammals that gestate their young for a prolonged time are
   a. monotremes.
   b. marsupials.
   c. eutherians.
   d. therapsids.
   e. all of the above.

10. *Homo sapiens* are believed to have evolved most recently from
   a. *Homo erectus.*
   b. *Homo neanderthalensis.*
   c. *Homo habilis.*
   d. *Homo ergaster.*
   e. *Australopithecus africanus.*

Articulate to Assess Your Learning

1. What are the two defining characteristics that distinguish craniates from other invertebrate chordates?

2. Explain the function of the lateral line and the operculum.

3. List the four extraembryonic membranes in the amniotic egg and explain the function of each.

Collaborate to Assess and Extend Your Learning

1. Discuss the characteristics of the vertebrates.

2. Discuss the three different ways mammals bring their offspring into the world.

3. A principle of biology is that all species (past and present) are related by an evolutionary history. Are birds living dinosaurs?

Visit McGraw-Hill Ryerson Connect™ for additional study resources.

Scott Behie

Dr. Mary Berbee

An interview with Dr. Mary Berbee from the University of British Columbia, by Scott Behie, a postgraduate student at Brock University.

Dr. Berbee is a botany professor at the University of British Columbia.

> ### How did you become interested in fungal diversity and evolution?

I find fungi fascinating. My parents were biologists; my father was a plant pathologist studying fungi that cause disease in forest trees and my mother studied mosses. So, I grew up aware of fungi and enjoyed the inky cap mushrooms in the neighbour's yard. I believe anyone who has ever been fascinated by a giraffe or a *Tyrannosaurus* skeleton could likely become fascinated by fungi too. Fungi have a remarkable variety of colours, odours, forms, and functions, but they remain hidden for most of their lives and they are usually so small that you need a microscope to enjoy the fungal zoo.

> ### What is your current research focus?

Fungi are among the most important decomposers in the planet, breaking down plant and animal remains and helping to recycle the nutrients. I am interested in how they evolved to take on this important ecological role. In partnership with the Joint Genome Institute of the United States Department of Energy, and in collaboration with colleagues, including J. Spatafora, one of my current projects is analyzing sequenced genomes from early diverging fungi. These genomes provide clues about the relationships of fungi and, potentially, what early fungi were able to digest for nutrients. This pure research has potential practical applications because some of the novel digestive enzymes secreted by evolutionarily divergent fungi may have industrial applications, in breaking down wood for ethanol production, for example.

> ### How are you able to determine evolutionary origins of similar species?

My students and I compare the DNA and protein sequences from different fungi. Occasional mutations in DNA sequences are passed on from parent to progeny in fungi, just as they are in other species including humans. Shared DNA substitutions that distinguish one group of fungi from others are evidence that group members are related—group members inherited the same sequence characters from their shared ancestor.

Other kinds of evolutionary events besides substitutions provide insight into how genomes and proteins evolved. Fungal cell walls, for example, are tough and resistant, and they contain chitin as a structural polysaccharide. Comparative analysis of fungal, animal, and protist genomes shows that chitin synthase genes are widespread in eukarya, but that genes for chitin synthesis duplicated repeatedly in the ancestor to fungi. Typical fungi have half a dozen or more different chitin synthases, more than any other eukaryotes. The different kinds of chitin synthases may contribute to making morphologically distinct kinds of walls required for evolution of complex growth forms like mushrooms.

> ### How does fungal diversity compare with the diversity of other microbes?

Like the kingdom Animalia, the kingdom Fungi is just one branch among many in the tree of life. Animalia and Fungi come from a common ancestor, so it is easier to compare them with each other than it is to compare Fungi with other microbes. Estimates of the diversity of Fungi in terms of total number of species (about 1.5 million to 6 million) are comparable to, or at least within an order of magnitude or two of, the diversity of their closest relatives, the animals (about 3 million to 100 million). The reason for the uncertainty in the estimates is that for many animals, including most insects and other arthropods, and for most fungi, the number of species remaining to be discovered is much larger than the total number of known species.

Animals are much more complex and diverse than Fungi in terms of their cell types body plans. However, in terms of metabolic diversity, fungi come out ahead of animals as measured by the complexity of metabolites they produce and the range of chemicals they can use as food.

To return to the original question, microbes other than fungi make up the vast majority of the diversity of life on Earth by any scale of measurement. The combined phylogenetic diversity of bacteria, archaebacteria, and eukaryotic protists is much greater than the phylogenetic diversity of animals or fungi. Species richness of the non-fungal microbes is even more difficult to quantify than in fungi and animals, but it is probably again very high. Keep in mind that fungi and animals represent related twigs in the tree of life. Protistan microbes including ciliates and amoebae represent whole other branches among eukaryotes, whereas bacteria and archaebacteria represent other domains of life.

> ### With respect to mycorrhizal fungi, how can clarifying the specific fungal/tree associations that occur naturally help the forestry industry?

Forest trees associate with dozens of different species of fungi. While by definition, mycorrhizae are mutually beneficial interactions between the root of a plant and a fungus, probably some fungi are more beneficial to the tree than others. Once the specific fungi that associate with the tree can be quickly identified, it will be possible to work out which combinations of fungi improve tree growth and to manipulate the fungal combinations so that trees grow better.

> ### The importance of fungi is likely unknown to most people; how have fungi helped shape the global landscape?

In terms of the human cultural landscape, baker's and brewer's yeast is the unicellular fungus that makes alcohol for wine. Yeast was not coincidentally used for the first research into enzymes that fermented sugars into alcohol, and the word enzyme is derived from a term meaning "in leavening." Much of biochemisty was originally based on the metabolic capacity of this very small fungus. Leland Hartwell, along with two other researchers, was awarded a Nobel Prize in Physiology or Medicine in 2001 for his studies of cell cycle control genes linked to breast cancer in baker's yeast.

Even more importantly, fungi colonized land along with early vascular plants hundreds of millions of years ago. Fossils show that the first plants on land lacked roots, but that they had mycorrhizal fungi. Early fungi may have formed a beneficial relationship with plants that enabled early plants to absorb mineral nutrients. Fungi are able to grow into dead and dying wood and to break it down, helping to form the humus that helps soils hold nutrients, while sending the nutrients trapped in lignin and cellulose back into the environment.

> ### A recent paper of yours deals with the aquatic fungi cryptomycota; how does understanding this fungal lineage challenge existing notions about fungal life cycles?

Almost all fungi get their nutrients by attaching to something larger than themselves, secreting enzymes out across their cell walls and absorbing the dissolved nutrients that diffuse back to them. The aquatic cryptomycota are interesting because they may take up nutrients by phagocytosis, as amoebae do. This could be because they diverged from other fungi before the evolutionary origin of the fungal cell wall. Alternatively, it could be that over the hundreds of millions of years they had to evolve independently from other fungi, cryptomycota lost the cell wall their ancestors once had. Either way, the characters of the cryptomycota are an interesting exception to expectations concerning the fungal way of life.

UNIT VI
Flowering Plants

Flowering plants, also known as the angiosperms, are essential to the lives of humans and most other organisms on Earth. Unit VI reveals molecular, biochemical, structural, evolutionary, and ecological features of the hundreds of thousands of flowering plants that support Earth's life.

Unit VI Chapter 33 provides an overview of flowering plant structure and function, focusing on the seed-to-seed life cycle. Building on this, Chapter 34 explains the genetic and physiological bases of plant behaviour, including examples such as phototropism, photoperiodism, and seed germination. Chapter 35 explains the nutritional requirements of plants, a deep understanding of which is critical to human agriculture and our ability to feed an ever-growing human population. In Chapter 36, we see how plant transport processes influence global climate and how plants import organic food into non-photosynthetic organs and tissues. Chapter 37 focuses on the molecular and cellular bases of plant reproduction, the process that generates seeds and fruits. This final chapter ties together key concepts presented throughout the unit: the seed-to-seed life cycle of plants and their distinctively structured bodies; plant development and growth in response to environmental and hormonal influences; and plant acquisition and transport of materials that support growth and reproduction.

 Certain biology principles will be emphasized in this unit, including the following:

- *Living organisms use energy:* Though sunlight is the major source of energy for photosynthetic plants, hundreds of flowering plant species as well as diverse tissues occurring in all flowering plants are heterotrophic and thus require a supply of organic food as a source of energy.

- *Living organisms interact with their environment:* Some of the ways in which plants detect and respond to light and other environmental factors are similar to those operating in microbes or animals, but others are distinctive.

- *Living organisms have mechanisms that maintain homeostasis:* As is the case for animals, it is essential for flowering plants to maintain water content and energy balance within tolerance limits, or they will die.

- *Living organisms grow, develop, and reproduce:* Some of the cellular and molecular bases of plant growth and development are also features of microbes and animals, but plants display some unique growth and development modes.

- *Structure determines function:* Have you ever wondered why and how trees become so tall? The unique features of plant bodies as well as variations occurring among plants explain how flowering plants function in nature and in human agriculture.

An Introduction to Flowering Plants: Form and Function

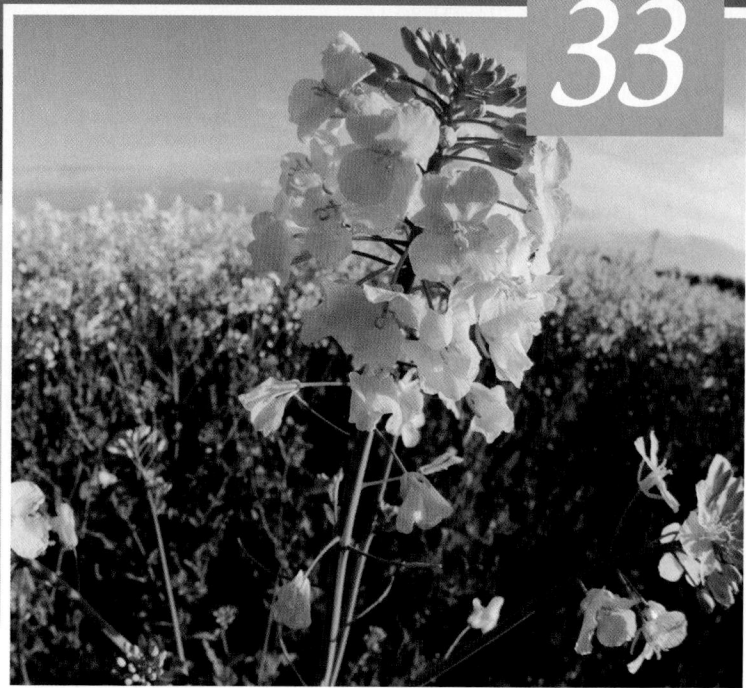

Canola One of the major crop plants in Canada, canola is highly prized for its healthful oil.

Chapter Outline

The diversity of plants in nature is a remarkable accomplishment of evolution. Through many mutation and selection events, primitive plants have adapted to changing environments by coordinated alterations of their biochemistry and anatomy. Directly or indirectly, humans depend on plants for food, fibre, oils, medicines, industrial chemicals, fuel, and the oxygen we breathe. The plants you see every day almost all share some common features—leaves, stems, flowers, roots, and seeds—although they do exhibit differences in these features. By exploiting this diversity, plant scientists and plant breeders have selected for traits that are of agronomic and economic interest. Corn, rice, and wheat are major crop plants used as food sources for both humans and livestock. Other plants, such as cotton, have little or no value as food but produce fibres that are extensively used in the textile industry—you are probably wearing something right now that is made from cotton fibres. One of the greatest Canadian agricultural success stories is that of canola (also featured in Chapter 3). Canadians Baldur Stefansson and Keith Downey and their coworkers developed and utilized biochemical screening and plant breeding techniques to reduce the amount of erucic acid and glucosinolates in the oil and seed meal, generating a nutritious variety that is used world-wide by humans for cooking oil and for lifestock feed.

This chapter provides an introduction to the flowering plants, focusing on fundamental principles of structure and function. These principles are basic to human efforts to use genetic methods to improve crops in ways that enhance human health. Just as medical scientists seek to understand how mutations influence human anatomy and physiology, plant geneticists need to know how genes affect the plant body and its health. The principles of plant form and function are equally important to evolutionary biologists who seek to understand how and why variations in plant body structure arise, as well as ecologists who want to know how plants, animals, and microbes function together in nature.

We will begin by describing the life cycle of a flowering plant, from seed germination to reproductive maturity. Next we will examine how plants grow and develop, revealing fascinating similarities to animals, but also intriguing differences. Finally, centering our attention on the adult plant body reveals how adaptation to different environments has generated diverse species whose form and function vary dramatically. These topics provide essential background for subsequent chapters in this unit, which focus on flowering plant behaviour, nutrition, transport, and reproduction.

33.1 FROM SEED TO SEED: THE LIFE OF A FLOWERING PLANT

Learning Outcomes:

1. List ways in which seed plant reproduction and growth resemble and differ from those of animals.
2. Describe how the two major types of flowering plants–monocots and eudicots–differ in form.
3. Distinguish among annual, biennial, and perennial plants.

Several major events punctuate the lives of flowering plants, also known as the **angiosperms**. When seeds germinate, dormant embryos increase their metabolic activity and begin the process of seedling development. Seedlings grow and develop into mature plants capable of reproduction. Finally, flowers and fruits produce and disperse the next generation of seeds. In this section we will briefly survey the life of flowering plants, focusing on the basic structural features of each life stage.

Seedlings Develop from Embryos in Seeds

Seeds are reproductive structures produced by flowering plants and other seed plants, usually as the result of sexual reproduction. Seeds contain embryos that develop into young

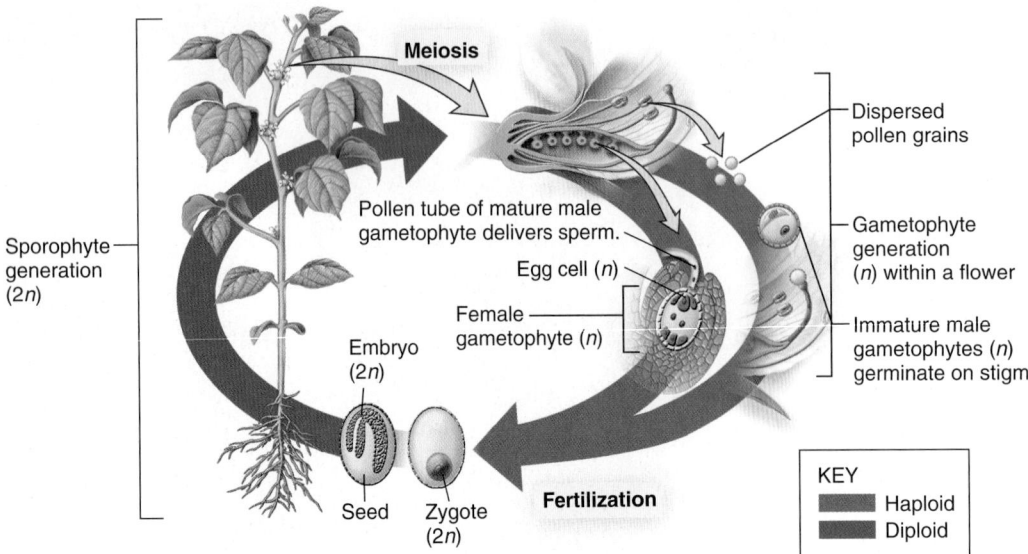

Figure 33.1 **The sexual cycle of flowering plants involves alternation of sporophyte and gametophyte generations.** The sporophyte is the dominant, conspicuous generation, whereas the tiny gametophytes are mostly hidden within flowers. The bean plant shown here produces both male and female gametophytes.

plants—seedlings—when seeds germinate. The embryo is an essential stage in the sexual cycle of a flowering plant. The plant sexual cycle explains how embryos arise.

Unlike animals, sexual reproduction in plants requires two multicellular stages: gamete-producing **gametophytes** and a spore-producing **sporophytes**. In the life cycle of plants, these two life stages alternate with one another, a process called **alternation of generations** (**Figure 33.1**). Flowering plants produce relatively large sporophytes and microscopic gametophytes that grow and develop within flowers. Diploid sporophytes produce haploid spores by the process of meiosis. These spores grow into gametophytes that produce plant gametes—eggs and sperm. Fusion of egg and sperm in the process of fertilization generates a diploid zygote, which undergoes repeated mitotic divisions to form the plant **embryo**.

The plant embryo is a very young sporophyte that lies dormant within seeds, accompanied by a supply of stored food and enclosed by a tough, protective seed coat (**Figure 33.2a**), much like the animal amniotic egg. Like an eggshell, the seed coat protects the delicate embryo during the dispersal of seeds from parent plants into the environment. Dispersed seeds can remain dormant in the soil—sometimes for long periods—and germinate

(a) Embryo in mature seed   **(b) Seedling**   **(c) Reproductively mature plant**

Figure 33.2 **The seed-to-seed life of flowering plants.**   (a) Seed embryos possess embryonic leaves, known as cotyledons, a dormant shoot meristem, and an embryonic root, the radicle, with a dormant root meristem. (b) When seeds germinate, the radicle emerges and produces the seedling root, and the young shoot of the seedling begins to produce leaves. (c) Reproductively mature plants have branched shoot and root systems, and bear flowers and fruits that disperse seeds.

Principle: Living organisms grow and develop. *The plant* Arabidopsis thaliana *is widely used as a model organism for understanding the genetics of plant structure and development.*

when temperature, moisture, and light conditions are favourable. Such conditions activate embryo metabolism, causing embryos to enlarge and break the seed coat. Once free of the seed coat, embryos grow and develop into seedlings (**Figure 33.2b**), and if sufficient resources, such as light, water, and minerals, are available, seedlings develop into mature plants (**Figure 33.2c**)

The angiosperm plant body is simpler in form than most animal bodies and is composed of only three basic types of organs: stems, leaves, and roots. **Stems** produce leaves and branches and bear the reproductive structures of mature plants. **Leaves** are structures that emerge from stems; foliage leaves are specialized in ways that enable photosynthesis to take place. Stems and leaves together make up the plant shoot (see Figure 33.2b). Mature plants often possess multiple stems bearing many leaves, which together form the shoot system. **Roots** provide anchorage in the soil and also foster efficient uptake of water and minerals. The aggregate of a plant's roots make up the **root system** (see Figure 33.2c)

Stems, leaves, and roots are organs so important to plants that they are present even in seed embryos and seedlings. A short, stemlike region of the embryo, known as a hypocotyl, produces embryonic leaves called **cotyledons** or seed leaves. These structures often store food that supplies energy for seedling development. Peas and peanuts are examples of cotyledons that are rich in nutrients, explaining their food value to humans. The embryonic root, known as the **radicle**, is the first organ to emerge from a germinating seed and allows the uptake of the water and minerals needed for seedling growth (see Figure 33.2b).

As in animals, the process of body and organ development involves the differentiation of specialized cells having distinctive structure and function. But unlike animals, plant seedlings and mature plants produce new tissues in areas called meristems. **Meristems** (from the Greek *merizein*, meaning to divide) are regions of undifferentiated cells that produce new tissues by cell division. A dormant meristem occurs at the shoot and root tips of seed embryos, and these meristems become active in seedlings (see Figure 33.2a,b). In mature plants, such meristems are known as shoot and root **apical meristems** because they occur at shoot and root tips, also known as apices.

Mature Sporophytes Develop from Seedlings

As seedlings develop into mature sporophytes, the aboveground shoot typically becomes green and photosynthetic and thus able to produce organic food. Photosynthesis powers the transformation of seedlings into mature plants. The development of mature plants encompasses both **vegetative growth**, a process that increases the size of the shoot and root systems, and reproductive development. Vegetative growth and reproductive development involve an **organ system**, a structure that is that are composed of more than one organ. Branches, buds, flowers, seeds, and fruits are organ systems. The hierarchy of structure in a mature plant, ranging from specialized cells, tissues, organs, and organ systems to root and shoot systems, is shown in **Figure 33.3**.

Figure 33.3   Levels of biological organization in a plant. Flowering plant sporophyte bodies consist of a root system and a shoot system, each composed of organ systems, organs, tissues, and specialized cells.

Vegetative Growth   During their growth, plant shoots produce vegetative **buds**, miniature shoots with a dormant shoot apical meristem. Tough leaflike scales protect bud contents. Under favourable conditions, the bud scales fall off and the vegetative buds open. Newly opened buds display young leaves on a short shoot. The shoot apical meristem then becomes active, producing new stem tissue and leaves. In this way, buds generate leafy branches. Buds are examples of organ systems, because they contain more than one type of organ.

Vegetative shoots often display **indeterminate growth**, meaning that apical meristems continuously produce new stem tissues and leaves as long as conditions remain favourable. This process explains how very large plants, such as trees, can develop from seedlings (**Figure 33.4a**). However, plant size is under genetic control, so some plants remain small even when they are mature. The tiny floating plants of Lemna species, commonly known as duckweeds, which sometimes cover the surfaces of ponds in summer, are examples of plants whose small size is genetically determined (**Figure 33.4b**). Indeterminate growth allows

(a) *Brachychiton*, a tree native to Australia

(b) Lemna (common duckweed)

Figure 33.4   Plants display indeterminate growth, but vary in size.   A large woody angiosperm (a) has the same indeterminate growth pattern as a tiny duckweed plant (b).

plants to adapt their vegetative body structure to environmental conditions. By contrast, animal bodies and flowers display **determinate growth**, which is growth of limited duration.

Reproductive Development   Under favourable conditions, mature plants produce reproductive structures: flowers, seeds, and fruits. Floral buds and **flowers** are reproductive shoots that develop when shoot apical meristems produce flower parts instead of leaves and new stem tissues. Flower development occurs under the control of several genes whose roles are well understood (see Chapter 17). In contrast to shoots (which often show indeterminate growth), flowers are produced by determinate growth. A floral shoot no longer produces new stems or leaves. Thus, vegetative growth and reproductive development are alternative processes. To flower, a plant must give up some of its potential to continue vegetative growth.

Flower tissues enclose and protect tiny male and female gametophytes during their growth and development (see Figure 33.1). Female gametophytes produce eggs within structures known as ovules, produced in the ovary of a flower

pistil. Male gametophytes begin their development within pollen grains produced in the anthers of a flower stamen. Pollen is dispersed to the flower pistil, where pollen grains may germinate, producing a tube that delivers sperm to eggs (refer back to Figure 29.14). Fertilization generates zygotes, which develop into embryos, and also triggers the process by which ovules develop into seeds and flower parts develop into fruits. **Fruits** thus enclose seeds and function in seed dispersal. Together with vegetative buds, flower buds, flowers, fruits, and seeds are organ systems because they consist of more than one organ. For example, flowers typically contain several leafy organs, including sepals and petals, as well as stamens and pistils, that evolved from leaves (refer back to Figure 29.13).

Flowering Plants Vary in the Structure of Organs and Organ Systems

With some exceptions, flowering plants occur in two groups informally known as the **eudicots** and the **monocots**. These groups take their names from the number of seed leaves (cotyledons) that are present on seed embryos. For example, bean plants and relatives, which possess two (*di*) seed leaves, are examples of eudicotyledonous plants (eudicots). Most woody trees, shrubs, and vines are also eudicots. Corn, which has only one seed leaf, is an example of a monocotyledonous plant (monocot) as is the tiny duckweed (Figure 33.4b). Eudicots and monocots also vary in the structure of other organs and organ systems. For example, eudicot flowers typically have petals and other parts numbering four, five, or a multiple of those numbers, whereas monocot flower parts usually occur in threes or a multiple of three. Stems, roots, leaves, and pollen of eudicots and monocots also vary in distinctive ways, as shown in **Table 33.1**.

Flowering Plants Vary in Seed-to-Seed Lifetime

The lifetime of a flowering plant can vary from a few weeks to many years. Plants that die after producing seed during their first year of life are known as **annuals**. Corn and the common bean are examples of annual crops whose nutrient-rich seeds are harvested within a few months after planting and must be replanted at the beginning of each new growing season. Plants that do not reproduce during the first year of life but may reproduce within the following year are known as **biennials**. Such plants often store food in fleshy roots during the first year, and this food fuels reproduction during the second or later year of life. Humans eat some of these fleshy roots, including carrots, parsnips, and sugar beets. Trees are examples of **perennials**, plants that live for more than two years, often producing seeds each year after they reach reproductive maturity. Many flowering plants use environmental signals to time flowering in ways that enhance seed production. Temperature and day length are examples of environmental factors that determine flowering time. Plant seed-to-seed lifetimes are also influenced by the longevity of their seeds. Seeds of some plants are able to germinate after more than a thousand years of dormancy, whereas other plant seeds are unable to remain alive for long periods.

Table 33.1	Distinguishing Features of Eudicots and Monocots, Two Major Groups of Flowering Plants	
Feature	**Eudicots**	**Monocots**
Number of seed leaves (cotyledons)	Two	One
Number of flower parts	Usually four, five, or multiples of these	Usually three or multiple of three
Stem vascular bundles	Arranged in a ring	Scattered
Root system	Branched taproot	Fibrous; adventitious
Leaf venation	Netted or branched	Often parallel
Pollen	Three pores or slits	One pore or slit

33.2 HOW PLANTS GROW AND DEVELOP

Learning Outcomes:

1. Compare and contrast plant body architecture and development with those of animals.
2. Explain how the shoot system differs from the root system.

As plants grow from seedlings, their development depends on four processes that are also essential to animal growth and development: cell division, growth, cell specialization, and apoptosis—programmed cell death. However, cell migration does not occur in plants as it does in animals. Additional and distinctive aspects of plant growth and development include (1) development and maintenance of a distinctive architecture throughout life, (2) an increase in length by the activity of apical meristems, (3) maintenance of a population of youthful stem cells in meristems, and (4) expansion of cells in controlled directions, by water uptake. All these features are under genetic control and can be studied by the use of mutants showing abnormal structure and development, some of which are discussed in this chapter.

Plants Display a Distinctive Architecture

In plant biology, the term *apical* has two distinct meanings. As we have seen, apical refers to the tips of shoots and roots, as in shoot apical meristems or root apical meristems. A second meaning for apical is the part of a plant that projects upward, which is the top of the shoot. By contrast, the bottom of a root is termed the *basal region*. Thus, the shoot apical meristem occurs at the apical pole, and the root apical meristem occurs at the basal pole. This property, known as **apical-basal polarity**, explains why plants produce shoots at their tops and roots at their lower regions. Apical-basal polarity originates during embryo development. As seedlings and maturing plants grow in length by the activity of shoot and root meristems, apical-basal polarity is maintained. In Chapter 17, we discussed groups of genes that determine polarity and segmentation in animals (refer back to Figure 17.11). Similarly plant apical-basal polarity is under the control of a different set of genes. Mutations in such genes result in plant embryos that are cone shaped or spherical and thus lack normal apical-basal architecture.

Plant development is a repeating process in which cells of the meristem are regularly partitioned into new stems, leaves, and floral branches. Cross-sections through tissues, such as the hypocotyl, roots, and stems, show a circular shape, and closer examination reveals that the tissue is **radially symmetrical**. That is, there is no obvious sidedness (slicing a pie, which is also radially symmetrical, illustrates this concept, as does the anatomy of a stem as shown in Table 33.1).

Plants typically produce new stems, leaves, lateral roots and flowers at regular intervals in a specific pattern, which is called **phyllotaxy**. Different species display specific patterns that can be described as alternate, opposite, whorled, or spiral (**Figure 33.5**). The establishment and maintenance of apical-basal polarity, coupled with reiterative patterning, explains why diverse plant species have a fundamentally similar architecture. While radial symmetry also characterizes early-diverging animals, most animals are bilaterally symmetrical (see Chapter 30).

Primary Meristems Drive Growth and Produce New Plant Organs

We have previously noted that plant embryos grow into seedlings by adding new cells from only two growth points: the shoot apical meristem (SAM) and the root apical meristem (RAM). During plant development, the SAM and RAM of the embryo

Alternate   Opposite

Whorled   Spiral

Figure 33.5 Plant architecture is due to reiterative, or repeat, patterning.   In the examples of leaf phyllotaxy given here, new organs are formed in opposite, alternate, whorled, or spiral patterns.

Table 33.2	Example Tissues and Specialized Cells Found in Flowering Plants*

Simple primary tissues (composed of one or two cell types)		Plant cell types found in those tissues
Parenchyma (G)		Parenchyma cells
Collenchyma (G)		Collenchyma cells
Sclerenchyma (G)		Fibres and sclereids
Root endodermis (G)		Endodermal cells
Root pericycle (G)		Pericycle cells
Complex primary tissues (composed of at least two cell types)		**Plant cell types found in those tissues**
Leaf or stem epidermis (D)		Flattened epidermal cells, trichomes, stomatal guard cells
Root epidermis (D)		Flattened epidermal cells, root hairs
Leaf mesophyll (G)		Spongy parenchyma cells, palisade parenchyma cells
Leaf, stem, or root xylem (V)		Tracheids, vessel elements, fibres, parenchyma cells
Leaf, stem, or root phloem (V)		Sieve-tube elements, companion cells, fibres, parenchyma cells
Complex secondary tissues		**Plant cell types found in those tissues**
Secondary xylem (V) (wood)		Tracheids, vessel elements, fibres, parenchyma
Secondary phloem (V) (inner bark)		Sieve-tube elements, companion cells, fibres, parenchyma
Outer bark		Cork cells

*This list does not include all of the tissues and cell types found in flowering plants. Some of these examples will be described later in this chapter

D = dermal, G = ground, V = vascular

give rise to many apical meristems located in the buds of shoots and at the tips of roots. Each apical meristem, in turn, produces additional meristematic tissues that increase plant length and produce new organs. Collectively, such meristems are known as the **primary meristems**, and they ultimately produce **primary tissues** and organs of diverse types (**Table 33.2**). Tissues differ in their cellular complexity. Simple primary tissues are those composed of only one or two cell types, while complex primary tissues are made up of more than one cell type. As described later in this section, the primary meristems of woody plants also give rise to secondary or lateral meristems. In a process known as **secondary growth**, the secondary meristems increase the girth of plant stems and roots by producing secondary tissues (see Table 33.2).

Shoot apical meristems produce three primary tissue meristems called protoderm, procambium, and ground meristem that are present in young stems and leaves (*Figure 33.6*). The **protoderm** generates the outermost **dermal tissue**. The **procambium** produces **vascular tissues**, which make up a vascular system that conducts materials within the plant body and also provide support. The **ground meristem** gives rise to

ground tissues defined by their locations—between dermal and conducting tissues, or at the centre of mature stems, where it is called pith. However, plant biologists have discovered that plant cell specialization and tissue development do not depend much on the lineage (the parentage) of a cell or tissue. Chemical influences are much more important in determining the type of specialized tissue that will be produced by unspecialized plant cells. Examples of such chemical influences are provided in the rest of this chapter.

Primary Stem Structure and Development   New primary stem tissues arise by the cell division activities of primary meristems located near the bases of SAMs. A layer of dermal tissue

Figure 33.6 **Plant apical meristems and the primary tissues they produce.** Shoot and root apical meristems generate three primary meristems: protoderm produces the dermal tissues (shown in tan), ground meristem produces ground tissues (shown in green or brown), and procambium yields vascular tissues (shown in blue). The vascular systems of leaves, stem, and root are connected.

known as the **epidermis** develops at the stem surface. The epidermis produces a waxy surface coating known as the **cuticle**, which helps to reduce water loss from the plant surface, and also helps to protect plants from damage by ultraviolet (UV) light, animals, and disease microorganisms.

Beneath the epidermis lies the stem **cortex**, which is largely composed of a ground tissue known as **parenchyma tissue**. This tissue is composed of only one cell type, thin-walled cells known as **parenchyma cells**. These cells store starch in plastids and thus serve as an organic food reserve. Stem parenchyma also has the ability to undergo cell division (meristematic capacity), which aids wound healing when stems are damaged. The cell division capability of stem parenchyma also explains how people are able to grow new plants from stem cuttings. Stems also contain **collenchyma tissue** composed of flexible **collenchyma cells**, and rigid **sclerenchyma tissue** composed of tough-walled fibres and **sclereids**. Collenchyma tissue and fibres provide support, while sclereids often aid in defence (consider that apple cores and the hard coverings of many seeds and nuts are composed largely of sclereids).

New water- and food-conducting tissues develop at the core of a young shoot. These conducting tissues are known as **primary vascular tissues** because they develop from new cells produced by the SAM. Vascular tissues occur in two forms, **xylem** and **phloem**, which are composed of several types of specialized tissues and cells (see section 33.3 and Table 33.2). Newly formed stem xylem and phloem connect with older conducting tissues that extend throughout the stem system. Stem xylem and phloem link to vascular tissues of the root system, forming a continuous route for conduction of water, minerals, and organic compounds through the plant. However, in contrast to the circulatory system of most animals, the plant conduction system is not closed, but instead is open to the environment (plant transport is described more completely in Chapter 36). Primary vascular tissues are typically arranged in elongate clusters known as **vascular bundles** that appear round or oval when cross-cut (Figure 33.6). In the primary stems of beans and other eudicots, the vascular bundles are arranged in a ring, which is easily seen in thin slices made across a stem (see Table 33.1). By contrast, in the stems of corn and other monocots, the vascular bundles are scattered.

Leaf Structure and Development Young leaves are produced at the sides of a SAM as small bumps known as **leaf primordia** (**Figure 33.7a**). As young leaves develop, they become flattened, a process that expands the area of leaf surface available for light collection during photosynthesis. Leaves also become bilaterally symmetrical, meaning that they can be divided into two equal halves in only one direction, from the leaf tip to its base (**Figure 33.7b**). In addition, upper (adaxial—facing toward the stem) and lower (abaxial—facing away from the stem) leaf tissues develop differently in several ways that foster photosynthesis (**Figure 33.7c**). For example, the more shaded abaxial leaf epidermis displays more pores, known as **stomata**, than the sunnier adaxial leaf surface. When open, stomatal pores allow CO_2 to enter and O_2 to escape leaf tissues; when closed, these pores help to prevent excessive loss of water from plant surfaces. Another example of differentiation between the abaxial and adaxial regions of a leaf is revealed by the positions of different types of photosynthetic ground tissue. The adaxial **palisade parenchyma** consists of closely packed, elongate cells adapted to absorb sunlight efficiently, whereas abaxial **spongy parenchyma** contains rounder cells separated by abundant air spaces. These air spaces, located near stomata, foster CO_2 absorption and O_2 release by leaves. Together the palisade and spongy parenchyma are known as the leaf **mesophyll**.

Leaf veins composed of vascular tissue commonly occur at the junction of palisade and spongy parenchyma, or within the spongy parenchyma (Figure 33.7c). Leaf parenchyma tissues are typically green and active in photosynthesis, a process that requires water, carbon dioxide, and dissolved minerals. Parenchyma cells can take up only carbon dioxide that has first dissolved into water, a feature inherited from ancient aquatic algal ancestors. For this reason, in order to perform photosynthesis,

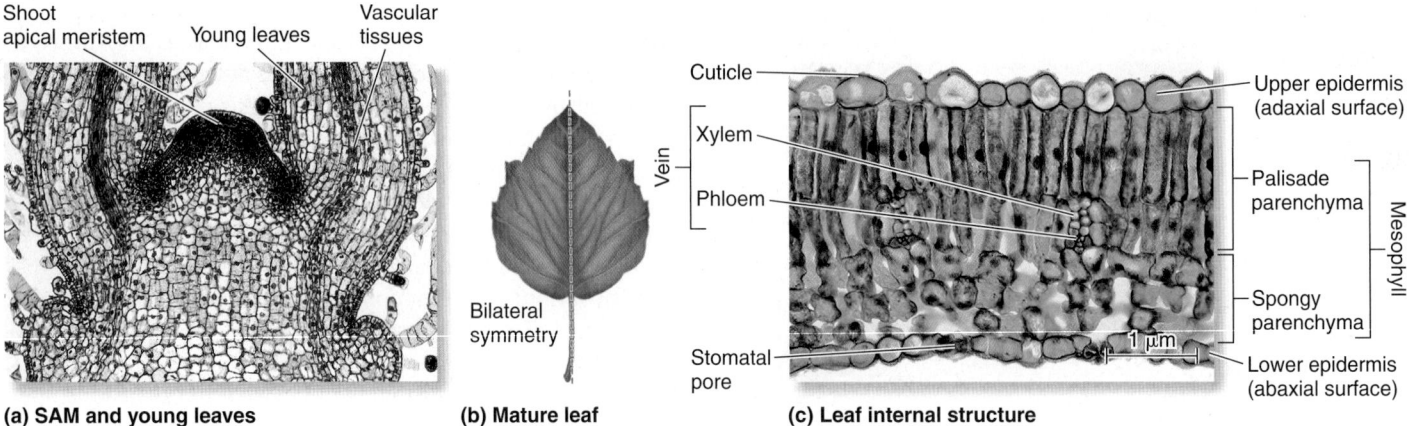

Figure 33.7 Eudicot leaf development and structure.   (a) Leaves develop from primordia produced at the sides of shoot apical meristems, as shown in this thinly sliced, stained shoot tip. (b) Mature leaves are typically thin and flat, and they show bilateral symmetry. (c) An internal view of a thinly sliced and stained leaf reveals top to bottom (adaxial to abaxial) tissue differentiation. A layer of palisade parenchyma lies just beneath the upper epidermis capped with waxy cuticle. Veins of conducting tissue (xylem and phloem) are embedded in the photosynthetic mesophyll. Spongy parenchyma lies above the lower epidermal leaf surface, which displays stomatal pores. These structural features of mature leaves facilitate photosynthesis.

Concept check: *What advantage do plant leaves obtain by having stomata on the lower epidermal surface?*

leaf parenchyma cells must be bathed in water. The xylem tissues of veins conduct water and minerals throughout leaf tissues, fostering photosynthesis. Phloem tissues of leaf veins carry the sugar products of photosynthesis from leaf cells to stem vascular tissues. In this way, sugar produced in leaves can be exported to other parts of the plant. The density of veins in angiosperm leaves is about four times that of other vascular plants. This allows plants to conduct materials more efficiently, which helps to explain why flowering plants are the dominant type of vegetation in most habitats today.

Root System Structure and Development In beans and other eudicots, a main root develops from the embryonic root and then produces branch roots. The root system of eudicots is known as a **taproot system**; this kind of root system has one main root with many branch roots. In contrast, the embryonic root of monocots dies soon after seed germination, and it is replaced by a **fibrous root system** consisting of multiple roots that grow from the stem base (see Table 33.1). Fibrous roots are examples of **adventitious roots**, structures that are produced on the surfaces of stems (and sometimes leaves) of both monocots and eudicots. Roots that develop at the bases of stem cuttings are also adventitious roots.

As noted earlier, the tips of roots and their branches each possess an apical meristem that adds new cells. Expansion of these new cells allows roots to grow into the soil. As they lengthen, roots produce branches, also known as lateral roots. In contrast to stems, roots do not produce buds. As a result, lateral roots develop from meristematic tissues located within the root (see section 33.4). The root system both anchors plants in the soil and plays an essential role in harvesting water and

mineral nutrients. Root tissues are usually not green and photosynthetic. They must rely on organic compounds transported from the shoot. The plant root system and shoot system thus depend on each other.

Plant Meristems Contain Stem Cells

Plant meristems include undifferentiated, forever-youthful cells known as initials or **stem cells**. In the late 19th century biologist Alexander Maximow coined the term *Stammzelle,* which is derived from the German words *Stamm,* meaning "stem," such as a plant stem, or "family," and *Zelle,* meaning "cell." Maximow used the term *stem cell* to describe animal cells that remain undifferentiated but are also able to generate specialized tissues. Animal stem cells are often in the news because of their potential for use in the treatment of human diseases that cause cell or tissue damage. The term *stem cell* is now also widely used for cells of the plant meristems that likewise remain undifferentiated but also can divide and produce the cells that constitute new tissues. In the context of plant development, the term does not mean any cell located in a plant stem, only the undifferentiated cells located within the meristems of the shoot and root

When plant stem cells divide, they produce two cells, one of which remains a slowly dividing stem cell. The second cell may differentiate into various types of specialized cells and typically divides faster than stem cells. As a result of these properties, stem cell numbers influence the size of a meristem, which in turn affects plant growth. Recent molecular studies have shed new light on how stem cell populations and meristem size are controlled.

GENOMES AND PROTEOMES

Plant Shoot Apical Meristem Size Is Genetically Controlled

Much of what is known about the function of stem cells in plant meristems comes from study of the model plant system *Arabidopsis thaliana*. This plant is particularly useful for genetic studies because its entire genome has been sequenced. The normal *Arabidopsis* SAM consists of several hundred stem cells organized into at least three distinct cell regions with different functions: a central zone, a peripheral zone, and an area called the rib meristem (**Figure 33.8**). The central zone consists of stem cells that divide but remain undifferentiated. The peripheral zone is made up of cells that originate from the edges of the central zone and produce leaf and flower primordia at the shoot surface. The rib meristem consists of a group of meristematic cells lying beneath the central zone that generates new ground and vascular tissues. Normal growth depends on a plant's ability to maintain normal sizes of the central zone and SAM. *Arabidopsis* mutants have been used to discover how plants accomplish this process.

Previous studies had established that stem cells in the central zone express and secrete a small peptide known as CLAVATA3. This peptide specifically binds to proteins located in the membranes of underlying meristem cells, causing them to produce substances that control the size of the central zone. In 2005 plant molecular biologists G. Venugopala Reddy and Elliot Meyerowitz reported the results of experiments that added more information about the influence of CLAVATA3 on SAM size. These investigators observed that plants having mutant CLAVATA3 genes produced very large SAMs with enlarged central zones. There were several possible explanations for this result. First, the central zone cells of mutant plants might divide more rapidly than is normal. Alternatively, cells at the edges of the central zone might not develop into peripheral zone cells, as is usual. Finally, peripheral zone cells might abnormally develop into central zone cells.

To determine which of these possibilities was most likely, the investigators disabled the CLAVATA3 gene in experimental plants. They also labelled the central zone with a glowing marker molecule in order to observe changes in its size by microscopic examination. They discovered that loss of CLAVATA3 function caused peripheral zone cells to change their identity to central zone cells. This had the effect of increasing the size of the central zone. In addition, the investigators observed that cell division increased in other parts of the SAM. These results suggest that CLAVATA3 peptide normally prevents peripheral zone cells from differentiating into central zone cells, and it controls the overall cell division rate in the SAM. Together with CLAVATA3 effects that had earlier been observed, these newly discovered processes maintain the central zone at a steady size, which is necessary for normal shoot growth.

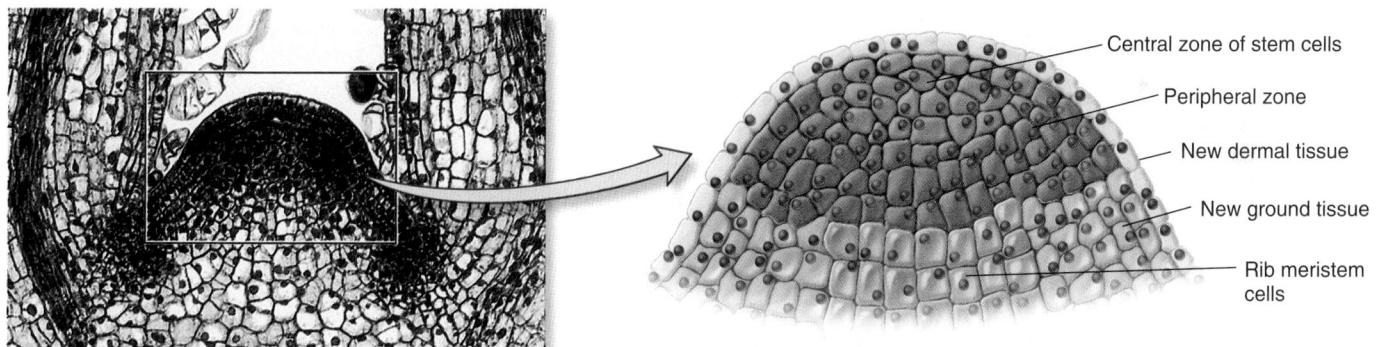

Figure 33.8   **The shoot apical meristem and stem cells.**   In a shoot apical meristem, a central zone of stem cells is surrounded by a peripheral zone of cells in the process of differentiating into dermal tissue. An underlying region of rib meristem cells divides to produce new ground and vascular tissues of the stem.

Plant Cells Expand in a Controlled Way by Absorbing Water

As you have observed, meristem production of new cells is an important component of plant growth. In addition, plant growth involves cell expansion, which is a much less important component of animal growth. The diameters of newly formed stem and root cells are usually equal in all dimensions, but many soon begin to extend lengthwise, thereby helping shoots and roots to grow longer. Recall that plants typically possess a relatively large vacuole (refer back to Figure 4.19).

Cell extension occurs when water enters the central vacuole by osmosis (**Figure 33.9**). As the central vacuole expands, cell volume also increases. By taking up water, plant cells can enlarge quickly, allowing rapid plant growth. Bamboo, for instance, can grow 2 m within a week, and it can grow up to 30 m in less than

Figure 33.9 Plant cells expand by taking up water into their vacuoles.

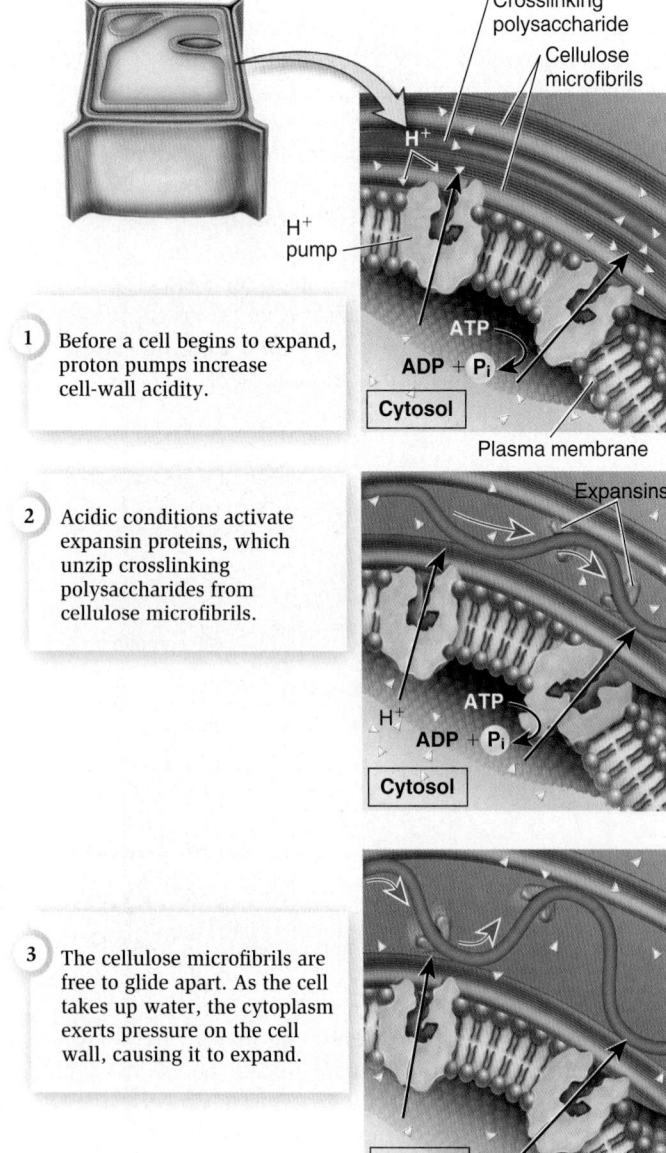

1. Before a cell begins to expand, proton pumps increase cell-wall acidity.

2. Acidic conditions activate expansin proteins, which unzip crosslinking polysaccharides from cellulose microfibrils.

3. The cellulose microfibrils are free to glide apart. As the cell takes up water, the cytoplasm exerts pressure on the cell wall, causing it to expand.

Figure 33.10 A hypothetical model of the process of cell-wall expansion.

three months! The importance of water uptake in cell expansion helps to explain why plant growth is so dependent on water supply.

Plant cell walls contain cellulose microfibrils that are held together by cross-linking polysaccharides. When plant cells and their vacuoles absorb water, pressure builds on cell walls. In response to this pressure and under acidic conditions, proteins unique to plants—known as expansins—are produced. **Expansins** unzip cross-linking cell-wall polysaccharides from cellulose microfibrils, so that the cell wall can stretch (**Figure 33.10**). As a result, cells enlarge, often by elongating in a particular direction, which is important to plant form. Some plant cells are able to elongate up to 20 times their original length.

The direction in which a plant cell expands depends on the arrangement of cellulose microfibrils in its cell wall, which is determined by the orientation of cytoplasmic microtubules. These microtubules are thought to influence the positions of cellulose-synthesizing protein complexes located in the plant plasma membrane. The protein complexes convert sugars into cellulose polymers, spinning cellulose microfibrils onto the cell surface to form the cell wall. As a result, cell-wall cellulose microfibrils encircle cells in the same orientation as underlying cytoplasmic microtubules (**Figure 33.11**). Because cellulose microfibrils do not extend lengthwise, plant cell walls expand

Figure 33.11 The direction of plant cell expansion is controlled by microfibrils and microtubules. Plant cells enlarge in the direction perpendicular to encircling cell-wall cellulose microfibrils, which run parallel to the orientation of underlying cytoplasmic microtubules.

BioConnections: *Look back to Table 4.1 to see images of microtubules. How are plant and animal microtubules different?*

more easily in a direction perpendicular to them. To visualize this process, imagine encircling a spherical balloon with parallel bands of tape before it has been completely inflated. The tape bands, which also do not extend lengthwise, represent encircling cellulose microfibrils. As you add more air, the balloon will tend to extend in the direction perpendicular to the bands of tape.

Microtubules control not only the direction of cell expansion but also the plane of cell division, which is also critical to plant form. The FASS gene mutation in *Arabidopsis* illustrates the importance of microtubule orientation to plant structure. In cells of these mutants, microtubules are randomly arranged, resulting in cell division planes that are abnormal, cells that do not elongate, and mature plants with abnormal, stubby organs.

33.3 | THE SHOOT SYSTEM: STEM AND LEAF ADAPTATIONS

Learning Outcomes:

1. Discuss why plant shoots are said to have a modular structure.
2. Explain why leaves having different shapes and vein patterns exist in nature.
3. Compare the structure and function of the conducting tissues xylem and phloem.
4. Create a drawing showing how bark and wood originate in woody plants.

As you have seen, the shoot system includes all of a plant's stems, branches, leaves, and buds. It also produces flowers and fruits when the plant has reached reproductive maturity. Thus, the shoot system is essential to plant growth, photosynthesis, and reproduction. In this section, we examine stem and leaf structure and development in more detail. We will observe that features of shoot stems and leaves vary among plants in ways that explain plant ecological function and see how these features are very useful in distinguishing plant species.

Shoot Systems Have a Modular Structure

More than 200 years ago German author, politician, and scientist Johann Wolfgang von Goethe realized that plants are modular organisms, composed of repeated units. Shoots are notably modular (**Figure 33.12**). Each shoot module, often known as a **phytomer**, consists of four parts: a stem node, an internode, a leaf, and an axillary meristem or bud. A **node** is the stem region from which one or more leaves emerge. An **internode** is the region of stem between adjacent nodes. Differences in numbers and lengths of internodes help to explain why plants differ in height. The axillary meristem occurs at the upper angle formed where a leaf or branch emerges from the stem. This angle is known as an axil (from the Greek *axilla*, armpit). Axillary meristems generate **axillary buds**, which can produce branches, also known as lateral shoots. Such new

branches bear a SAM at their tips. SAMs located at the apices of both main and lateral shoots produce new leaves. What causes new leaves to arise? The answer involves chemical messengers known as hormones.

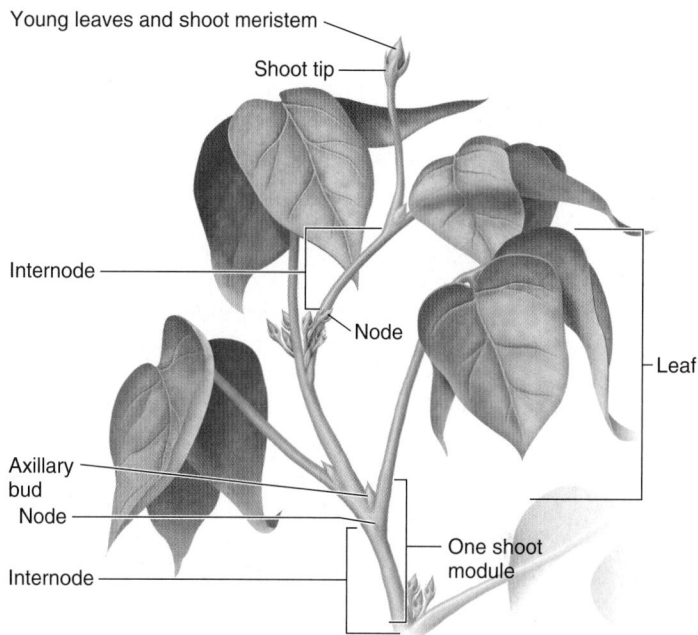

(a) Modular structure of herbaceous shoot

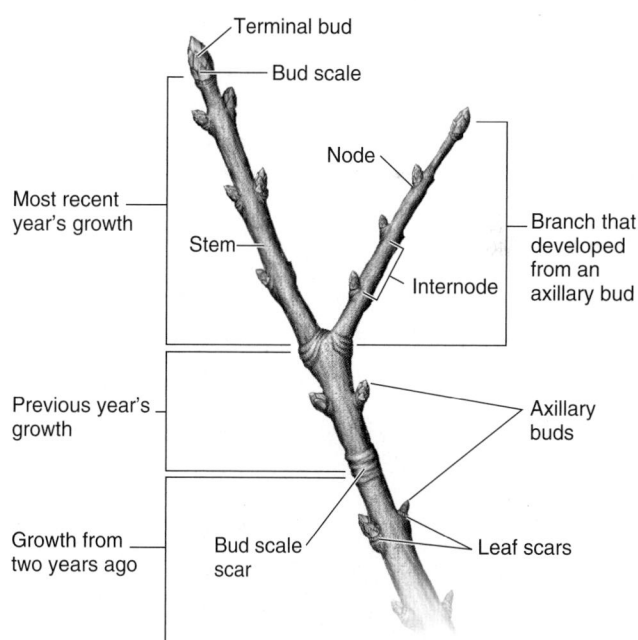

(b) Modular structure of woody shoot in winter

Figure 33.12 **Plant shoots have a modular organization.** (a) The top end of an herbaceous stem showing the shoot modules. Each module consists of a node with its associated leaf and axillary meristem or bud and an internode. (b) The modular organization shown by a woody stem as it appears during winter. Axillary buds lie above the scars left by leaf fall. Regions between successive sets of bud scale scars mark each year's growth.

Hormones and microRNAs Influence Leaf Development

As we have noted, the very youngest leaves, known as leaf primordia, originate as surface bumps at the sides of a shoot apical meristem (see Figure 33.7a). Production of such leaf primordia is under the control of a hormone known as **auxin**. In general, **hormones** are signalling molecules that exert their effects at a site distant from the place where such compounds are produced. Plant hormones are important in coordinating both plant development and plant responses to environmental conditions (see Chapter 34).

The outermost epidermal layer of cells at shoot tips produces auxin, which moves from cell to cell by means of specific membrane transport proteins. Auxin accumulates in particular locations because cells of the shoot apex differ in their ability to import and export auxin. When auxin accumulates in a particular apical region, the hormone causes expansin gene expression to increase. When expansin loosens their cell walls (see Figure 33.9), cells expand by taking up water, thereby forming a tissue bulge—a leaf primordium. The development of leaf primordia depletes auxin from nearby tissue, with the result that the next leaf primordium will develop in a different place on the shoot apex, where the auxin level is higher. Such changes in auxin concentration on the surface of the shoot explain why leaf (and flower) primordia develop in spiral or whorled patterns around the shoot tip. The youngest leaf primordia occur closest to the shoot tip, and successively older leaf primordia occur on the sides of the shoot tip (see Figure 33.7a).

Hormones also influence the transformation of primordia into leaves. KNOX proteins (short for knotted-like homeobox), are normally produced only in the meristem, where they act as transcription factors that repress the biosynthesis of **gibberellic acid** (GA). This contributes to the maintenance of stem cell activity. In leaf primordia, *KNOX* genes are repressed and therefore more GA is produced. These higher levels of GA promote leaf expansion. Other molecules produced by a SAM direct leaf flattening and differentiation of upper adaxial and lower abaxial

leaf tissues (see Figure 33.7c). These signalling effects were first demonstrated in 1955 by plant developmental biologist Ian Sussex, who made surgical cuts around leaf primordia, thereby isolating them from chemical substances produced by the meristem. The isolated primordia retained their initial cylindrical, radially symmetrical structure rather than becoming flat and bilaterally symmetrical—the normal process. Later investigators discovered that a particular set of genes expressed in young primordia causes leaf adaxial tissues to develop and that abaxial development is specified by a different set of genes. What causes this differential gene expression? In 2004 plant biologists Catherine Kidner and Robert Martienssen reported that a specific type of microRNA (miRNA; described in Chapter 12) accumulates in the abaxial regions of a developing leaf. In this location, the miRNA interrupts expression of the set of genes that specify adaxial tissue development, helping to explain why leaf adaxial and abaxial tissues differ. Other types of miRNA molecules influence leaf shape, explaining the diversity of leaf shapes produced by different plant species.

Leaf Shape and Surface Features Reflect Adaptation to Environmental Stress

As we have noted, leaf flatness facilitates solar energy collection, and thinness helps leaves to avoid overheating. Leaf shape and surface features also reflect adaptation to stressful environmental conditions.

Leaf Form   The flattened portion of a leaf is known as the leaf **blade**. In beans and most other eudicots, blades are attached to the stem by means of a stalk known as a **petiole**, and an axillary bud occurs at the junction of a stem and petiole (**Figure 33.13a**). In contrast, corn and other monocots have leaf blades that grow directly from the stem, encircling it to form a leaf sheath (**Figure 33.13b**)

Leaf shape can be simple or compound, each having particular advantages. Simple leaves have only one blade, though the edges may be smooth, toothed, or lobed. Simple leaves

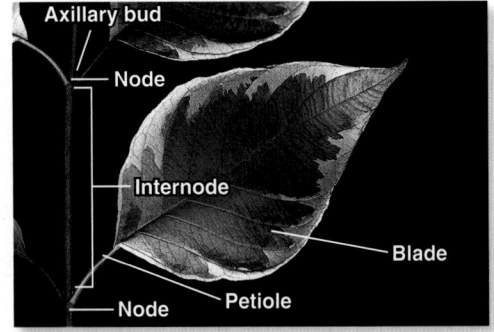

(a) Eudicot stem with simple leaf

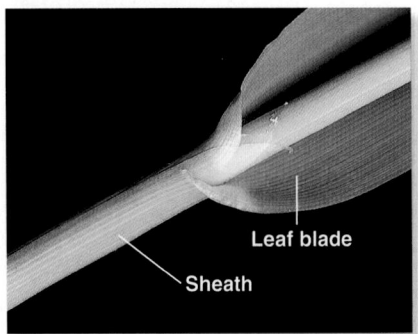

(b) Monocot stem and leaf

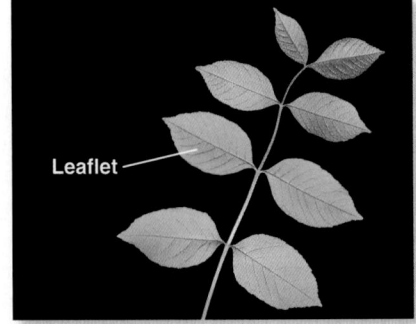

(c) A complex leaf

Figure 33.13   **Examples of variation in leaf form.**   (a) A simple eudicot leaf, showing blade, petiole, and axillary bud. This leaf has a pinnate venation pattern. (b) The leaf of a monocot, showing parallel veins on the blade and how the base of the leaf encircles the stem. (c) A complex (compound) leaf divided into leaflets.

Concept check: *Is the leaf shown in (b) from a eudicot or a monocot plant?*

are advantageous in shady environments because they provide maximal light absorption surface, but they can overheat in sunny environments. As an evolutionary response to heat stress, the blades of some leaves have become highly dissected into leaflets. Such leaves are known as compound leaves (**Figure 33.13c**). Leaflets can be distinguished from leaves in that leaflets lack axillary buds at their bases. Compound leaves are common in hot environments because leaflets foster heat dissipation. During the development of some compound leaves, the transcription factor KNOX becomes active shortly after the leaf primordia form, causing these primordia to produce multiple growth points that generate the leaflets. In contrast, during simple leaf development KNOX is not active, because the expression of other proteins suppresses *KNOX* gene expression

Leaf Vein Patterns   Leaf vein patterns are known as venation. Eudicot leaves have either pinnate (feather-like) or palmate (spreading like the fingers of your hand) venation, with smaller veins connected in a net or branching pattern (see **Figure 33.13a** and Table 33.1). In contrast, monocot leaves, such as those of corn, often have distinctive parallel venation (see Figure 33.13b and Table 33.1). However, evolutionary biologists Thomas Givnish, Chris Pires, and their colleagues discovered that netted veins have evolved among monocots at least 26 different times over the past 90 million years, probably as an adaptation to shady conditions. Plants growing in shady conditions typically have broad leaves, which increase the amount of solar collection surface but require structural support, and netted veins provide more support than parallel veins.

Leaf Surface Features   Leaf surfaces also show adaptive features. As we have previously noted, a layer of epidermal tissue occurs at upper and lower leaf surfaces (see Figure 33.7c). These epidermal cells secrete a cuticle composed of protective wax and polyester compounds (**Figure 33.14**). The cuticle helps plants to avoid drying in the same way that enclosure in waxed paper keeps food moist. Plants that grow in very arid climates often have thick cuticles, whereas plants native to moist habitats typically have thinner cuticles. Cuticles also filter damaging UV radiation, reduce attack by microbes and animals, and

Figure 33.14   **Leaf surface features.**   These features, viewed by SEM, include cuticular wax, stomatal pores with guard cells, and trichomes.

BioConnections: *Look ahead to Figure 36.17 to learn how the control of stomatal pore aperature regulates water and gas exchange.*

foster a self-cleaning process by which water droplets wash debris from the hydrophobic leaf surface.

Some leaf epidermal cells may differentiate into spiky or hairlike projections known as **trichomes** (Figure 33.14). Blankets of trichomes offer protection from excessive light, UV radiation, extreme air temperature, excess water loss, or attack by herbivores—animals that consume plant tissues. Broken trichomes of the stinging nettle, for example, release a caustic substance that irritates animals' skin, causing them to avoid these plants. Leaf epidermal cells include pairs of specialized guard cells located on either side of stomata (Figure 33.14). Each **guard cell** allows stomata to be open during moist conditions and to close when conditions are dry, thereby preventing plants from losing too much water.

FEATURE INVESTIGATION

Elle and Associates Investigated the Cost to *Datura wrightii* of Producing Sticky Leaf Trichomes

The jimsonweed plant (*Datura wrightii*) grows in arid regions of the southwestern United States and Mexico. This plant produces leaves whose epidermal surfaces feature hair-shaped trichomes. Some *D. wrightii* plants produce leaf trichomes that secrete sticky sugar solutions at their surfaces and are thus known as glandular trichomes; such plants are described as "sticky" plants. In contrast, other *D. wrightii* plants produce similarly

shaped, nonglandular leaf trichomes that do not secrete sugars. The leaves of these plants are smooth rather than sticky, and they are described as "velvety." In *D. wrightii*, trichome phenotype is controlled by variation in a single gene, and sticky is dominant over velvety. If the phenotypes were of equal advantage in nature, sticky and velvety plants should occur in a 1:1 proportion. However, the actual frequency of sticky plants in nature ranges from 0% to 93%, depending on the environment. This variation and other data suggest that sticky trichomes deter certain herbivores, thereby providing a growth advantage.

However, sticky trichomes may be excessively costly in terms of resources when those herbivores are not present, because sugar secretion uses up photosynthetic products.

Evolutionary ecologists Elizabeth Elle, Nicole van Dam, and Daniel Hare of Simon Fraser University and the University of California, Riverside, devised an experiment to determine the relative cost of producing sticky trichomes, which is shown in **Figure 33.15**. The team hypothesized that sticky plants might produce fewer viable seeds than velvety plants, because plant photosynthetic products are diverted from reproduction. The investigators grew sticky and velvety *D. wrightii* plants together, protecting some from insect herbivores but not protecting others. Then the investigators compared the numbers of seeds capable of germinating that were produced by sticky and velvety plants. (In this experiment, seed production was a measure of Darwinian fitness.) The team found that velvety plants sustained more insect damage than sticky plants, verifying the protective function of glandular trichomes. When insect herbivores were present, there was no significant fitness difference between sticky and velvety plants. However, when herbivores were absent, though both types of plants flowered similarly, the sticky plants produced 45% fewer viable seeds than did the velvety plants. These data supported the initial hypothesis that sticky trichomes were more costly than smooth trichomes. This and other studies suggest that the investment required to produce sticky trichomes may pay off by reducing the destructive effects of insects.

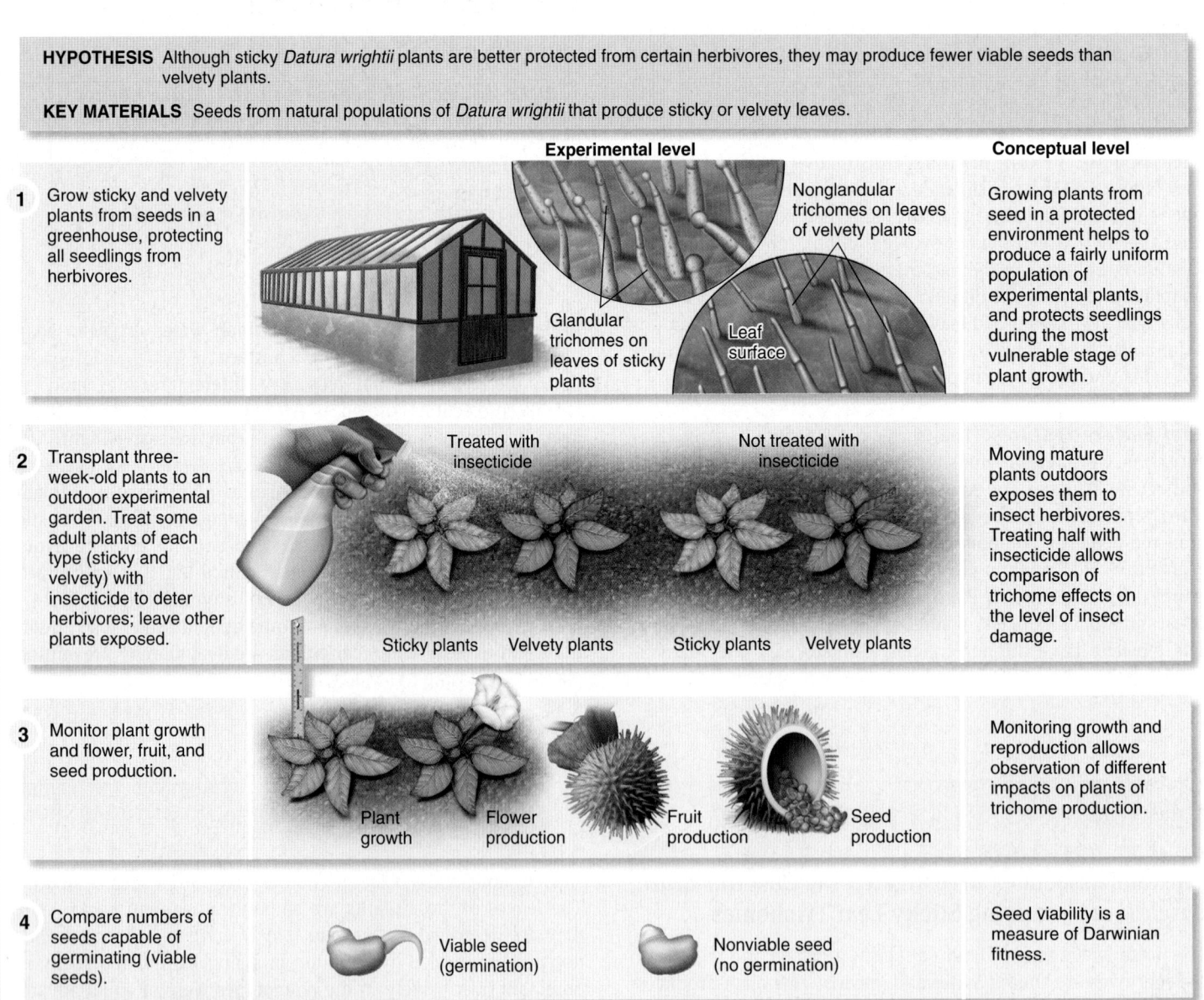

HYPOTHESIS Although sticky *Datura wrightii* plants are better protected from certain herbivores, they may produce fewer viable seeds than velvety plants.

KEY MATERIALS Seeds from natural populations of *Datura wrightii* that produce sticky or velvety leaves.

Experimental level **Conceptual level**

1 Grow sticky and velvety plants from seeds in a greenhouse, protecting all seedlings from herbivores.

Nonglandular trichomes on leaves of velvety plants

Glandular trichomes on leaves of sticky plants

Leaf surface

Growing plants from seed in a protected environment helps to produce a fairly uniform population of experimental plants, and protects seedlings during the most vulnerable stage of plant growth.

2 Transplant three-week-old plants to an outdoor experimental garden. Treat some adult plants of each type (sticky and velvety) with insecticide to deter herbivores; leave other plants exposed.

Treated with insecticide   Not treated with insecticide

Sticky plants   Velvety plants   Sticky plants   Velvety plants

Moving mature plants outdoors exposes them to insect herbivores. Treating half with insecticide allows comparison of trichome effects on the level of insect damage.

3 Monitor plant growth and flower, fruit, and seed production.

Plant growth   Flower production   Fruit production   Seed production

Monitoring growth and reproduction allows observation of different impacts on plants of trichome production.

4 Compare numbers of seeds capable of germinating (viable seeds).

Viable seed (germination)   Nonviable seed (no germination)

Seed viability is a measure of Darwinian fitness.

Figure 33.15   Elle and associates investigated the cost to *Datura wrightii* of producing sticky leaf trichomes.

5 **THE DATA**

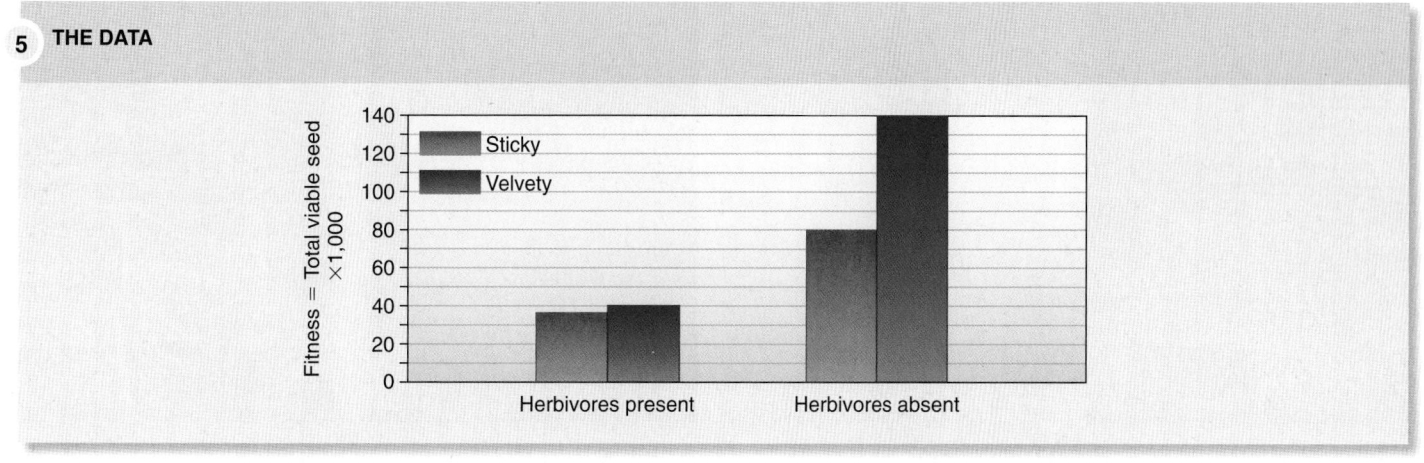

6 **CONCLUSION** Energy expended in producing glandular secretions ensures reproductive fitness in the presence of herbivores, but leads to reduced fitness when herbivores are absent.

7 **SOURCE** Hare, J.D., Elle, E., and van Dam, N.M. 2003. Costs of glandular trichomes in *Datura wrightii*: a three-year study. *Evolution* 57:793–805.

Experimental Questions

1. Why did Elle and colleagues begin their investigation by growing *Datura wrightii* plants from seeds in a greenhouse?

2. Why did Elle and colleagues move the mature plants outdoors but treat only half of them with insecticide?

3. Why did the investigators keep track of plant growth and reproduction during the experiment?

Modified Leaves Perform Diverse Functions

Though most leaves function primarily as photosynthetic organs, some plants produce leaves that are modified in ways that allow them to play other roles. For example, threadlike tendrils that help some plants, such as the American vetch, attach to a supporting structure are modified leaves or leaflets (**Figure 33.16a**). The tough scales that protect buds on plants such as the sycamore from winter damage are modified leaves (**Figure 33.16b**). Poinsettia "petals" are actually modified leaves known as bracts, which are larger and more brightly coloured than the flowers they surround (**Figure 33.16c**). These conspicuous bracts help attract pollinators to the flowers. Cactus spines, such as those on the giant saguaro, are actually modified leaves that have taken on a defensive role, leaving photosynthesis to the cactus stem (**Figure 33.16d**).

Stems May Contain Primary and Secondary Vascular Systems

Stems, leaves, roots, buds, flowers, and fruits all contain vascular systems composed of xylem and phloem tissues that conduct water, minerals, and organic compounds. **Herbaceous plants**, such as corn and bean, produce mostly primary vascular tissues.

In contrast, **woody plants** produce both primary and secondary vascular tissues. A comparison of primary and secondary vascular tissues will aid in understanding their roles.

Primary Vascular Tissues Primary vascular tissues are composed of primary xylem and phloem. Let's begin with primary xylem, a complex tissue containing several cell types (see Table 33.2). These include unspecialized parenchyma cells; stiff fibres that provide structural support; and two types of cells that have differentiated in ways that facilitate water transport: tracheids and vessel elements. Arranged in pipeline-like arrays, **tracheids** and **vessel elements** conduct water, along with dissolved minerals and certain organic compounds. Mature tracheids and vessel elements are no longer living cells and lack cytoplasm, which facilitates water flow. During development, these cells lose their cytoplasm by the process of programmed cell death (apoptosis). However, the cell walls of tracheids and vessel elements do not break down or collapse because they are impregnated with tough polymers known as **lignins** (**Figure 33.17**). The rigid cell walls of tracheids and vessel elements not only foster water conduction but also help support the plant body. Like plastic plumbing pipes, lignin provides the hydrophobic surface needed for water movement, as well as the strength to support trees weighing more than 2,000 metric tons.

(a) Tendrils

(b) Bud scales

(c) Bracts

(d) Spines

Figure 33.16 **Examples of modified leaves.** (a) The tendrils of an American vetch plant are modified leaves that help the plant attach to a trellis. (b) Bud scales, such as those on this sycamore bud, are modified leaves that protect buds from winter damage. (c) The attractive red bracts of poinsettia are modified leaves that function like flower petals to attract pollinator insects to the small flowers. (d) Cactus spines, such as these on this giant saguaro, are modified leaves that have a defensive function.

Concept check: *Since cactus leaves are so highly modified for defence that they cannot effectively accomplish photosynthesis, how do cacti obtain organic compounds?*

 Principle: Structure determines function. *Modified leaves serve a variety of purposes that allow plants to be successful in their native environments.*

In contrast to xylem, living phloem tissues transport organic compounds, such as sugars and certain minerals, in a watery solution. Phloem tissues include **sieve-tube elements**, thin-walled living cells that are arranged end to end to form pipelines (*Figure 33.18*). Pores in the end walls of sieve-tube elements

Tracheid

Vessel element

50 μm

Figure 33.17 **Water-conducting cells of the xylem.** In this thinly sliced portion of a stem, the stained, lignin-impregnated walls of narrow tracheids and wider vessel elements can be distinguished.

Sieve-tube element

50 μm

Figure 33.18 **Food-conducting cells of the phloem.** This thinly sliced portion of a stem shows stained, thin-walled sieve elements, which conduct watery solutions of organic compounds such as sugar and certain minerals.

allow solutions to move from one cell to another. Phloem tissue also includes parenchyma cells, supporting fibres, and companion cells that aid sieve-tube element metabolism (see Table 33.2). Phloem fibres are tough-walled sclerenchyma cells that are surprisingly long, 20–50 mm, and valued for their high strength. The phloem fibres of hemp (*Cannabis sativa*), flax (*Linum usitatissimum*), jute (*Corchorus capsularis*), kenaf (*Hibiscus cannabinus*), and ramie (*Boehmeria nivea*) are commercially important in the production of rope, textiles, and paper.

Secondary Vascular Tissues Woody plants begin life as herbaceous seedlings that possess only primary vascular systems. As these plants mature, they produce secondary vascular tissues and bark (**Figure 33.19**). Secondary vascular tissues are composed of secondary xylem and phloem. **Secondary xylem** is also known as **wood**, a component of plants that plays many important roles in human life. Wood is composed of about 25% lignin, 45% cellulose, and 25% other polysaccharides that are together known as hemicelluloses.

Secondary phloem is the inner bark. **Outer bark** is protective layers of mostly dead cork cells that cover the outside of woody stems and roots. Therefore, bark includes both inner bark (secondary phloem) and outer bark (cork). Woody plants produce secondary vascular tissues, wood and bark, by means of two types of secondary meristems, also known as lateral meristems, which form rings of actively dividing cells that encircle the stem. The two types of secondary meristems are vascular cambium and cork cambium, which are derived from primary meristems.

The meristem known as **vascular cambium** is a ring of dividing cells that produces secondary xylem to its interior and secondary phloem to its exterior. Secondary xylem conducts most of a woody plant's water and minerals. Cell divisions that occur in secondary meristems increase the girth of woody stems. During each new growing season, the vascular cambium produces new cylinders of secondary xylem (wood) and secondary phloem (**Figure 33.20**). Each year's addition of new secondary xylem forms growth rings that can be observed on the cut surfaces of woody stems (**Figure 33.21**). The growth rings of secondary xylem surround the remains of the primary xylem and a central cylinder of parenchyma cells known as the pith. If environmental conditions favour plant growth, the growth rings formed at that time will be wider than those formed during stressful conditions. Climatologists use growth ring widths in samples of old wood to deduce past climatic conditions, and archaeologists use growth ring data to determine the age of wood constructions and artifacts left by ancient cultures.

Secondary xylem can transport water for several years, but usually only the current year's production of secondary phloem is active in food transport. This is because thin-walled sieve elements typically live for only a year, after which they are crushed by the addition of new wood. Thus, only a thin layer of phloem, the **inner bark**, conducts most of the sugar transport

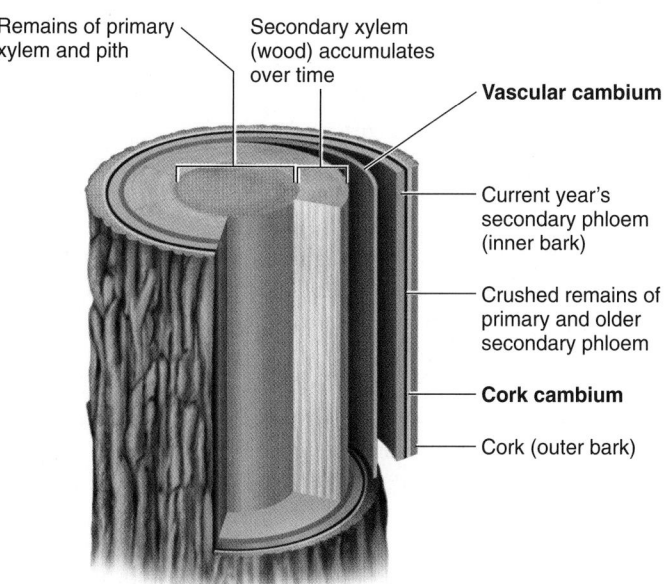

Figure 33.19 Secondary meristems generate wood and bark. The vascular cambium is a thin cylinder of tissue that produces a thick cylinder of wood (secondary xylem) toward the inside of the stem and a thinner cylinder of inner bark (secondary phloem) toward the outside of the stem. The cork cambium forms an outer coating of protective cork (outer bark).

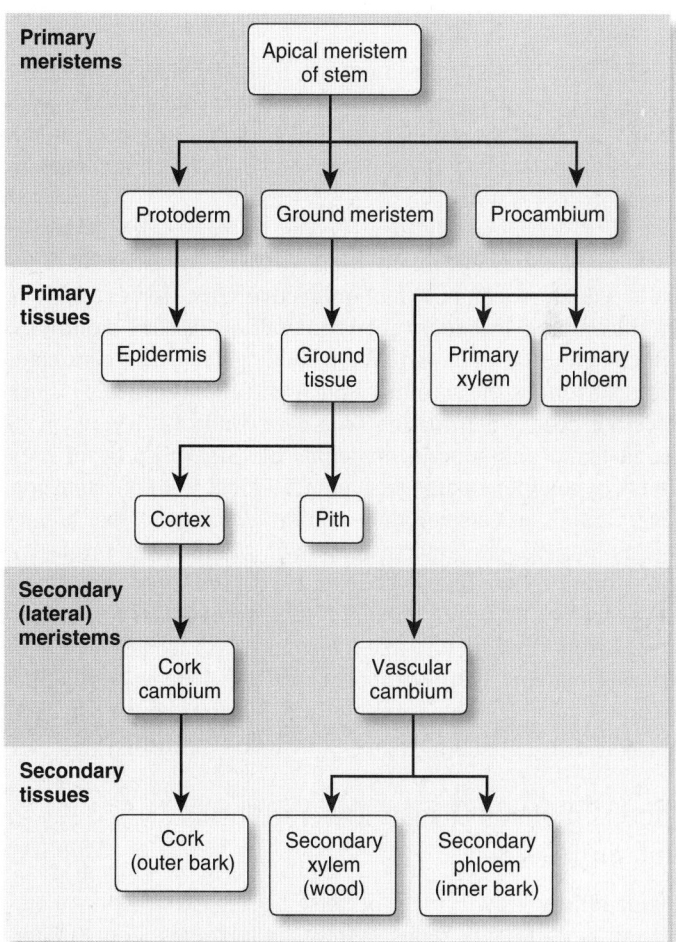

Figure 33.20 An overview of the process of primary and secondary growth in a woody stem.

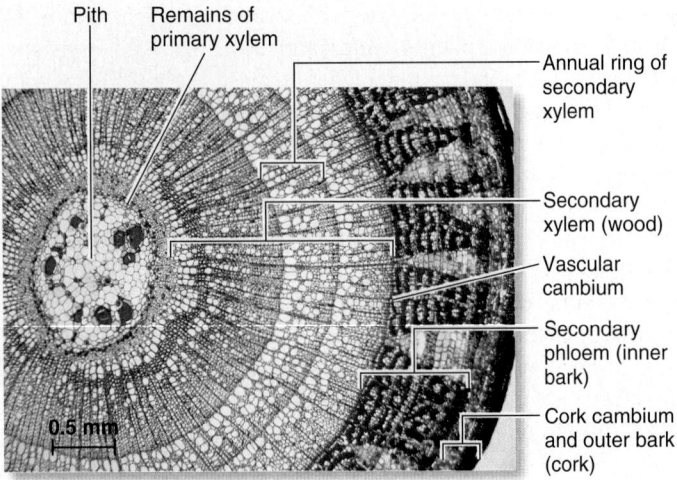

Figure 33.21 **The anatomy of a tree trunk.** Each year a new cylinder of wood is produced; this yearly wood production appears as annual rings on the cut surface of a woody stem.

Concept check: *Why do tree trunks have a thicker layer of wood (secondary xylem) than of inner bark (secondary phloem)?*

in a large tree. Deep abrasion of tree bark may damage this thin phloem layer, disrupting a tree's food transport. In fact, if a groove is cut all the way around a tree trunk—a process known as girdling—the tree will die because all of its functional phloem transport routes will have been interrupted.

As a young woody stem begins to increase in diameter, its thin epidermis eventually ruptures and is replaced by outer bark, which is composed of protective cork tissues. Cork is produced by a secondary meristem called the **cork cambium**, which is another ring of actively dividing cells. The cork cambium surrounds the secondary phloem (see Figure 33.21). Cork cells are dead when mature, and their walls are layered with tough lignin and suberin, materials that help to prevent both attack by microbial pathogens and water loss from the stem surface. Cork tissues also produce tannins, compounds that protect against pathogens by inactivating their proteins, and protective gums and rubbery latexes. The cracked surfaces of tree trunks are dead cork tissues of the outer bark. Commercial cork is harvested from the cork oak tree (*Quercus suber*) for production of flooring material, bottle stoppers, and other items. Additional information about the structure and function of primary and secondary xylem and phloem can be found in Chapter 36.

Modified Stems Display Diverse Forms and Functions

Stems mostly grow upright because light is required for photosynthesis. But some stems, known as rhizomes, occur underground and grow horizontally. For example, potato tubers are the swollen, food-storing tips of rhizomes. Grass stems also grow horizontally, as either rhizomes just beneath the soil surface

or stolons, which grow along the soil surface. The leaves and reproductive shoots of grasses grow upward from the point at which they are attached to these horizontal stems. Grass blades continue to elongate from their bases even if you cut their tips off, explaining why lawns can be mowed repeatedly during the growing season. The horizontal stems of grasses are adaptations that help to protect vulnerable shoot apical meristems against natural hazards, such as fire and grazing animals.

33.4 ROOT SYSTEM ADAPTATIONS

Learning Outcomes:

1. List ways that root structure has been modified in different plants in response to different habitats.
2. Create a drawing that shows how root systems and branch roots develop.
3. Discuss several examples that demonstrate how mobile proteins or miRNAs influence root development.

Roots play the essential roles of absorbing water and minerals, and anchoring plants in soil. The external form of roots varies among flowering plants, reflecting adaptation to particular life spans or habitats. In contrast, root internal structure is more uniform. In this section, we first consider variation in root external structure and then focus on root internal structure and development.

Modified Roots Display Diverse Forms and Functions

As we have observed, the common bean and other eudicots display an underground taproot system, whereas corn and other monocots have a fibrous root system (see Table 33.1). Plants produce several other types of roots that provide adaptive advantages. For example, corn and many other plants produce supportive prop roots from the lower portions of their stems. Many tropical trees grow in such thin soils that the trees are vulnerable to being blown down in windstorms. Such trees often produce dramatic above ground buttress roots that help keep the trees upright (**Figure 33.22a**). Many mangrove trees that grow along tropical coasts produce pneumatophores ("breath bearers"), roots that grow upward into the air (**Figure 33.22b**). Functioning like snorkels, pneumatophores absorb oxygen-rich air, which diffuses to submerged roots growing in oxygen-poor sediments. This is necessary because all roots require a supply of oxygen to produce ATP, which is needed to power the uptake of minerals and nutrients (see Chapter 35).

Root Growth and Tissue Specialization Occur in Distinct Zones

In their study of gene expression in *Arabidopsis* roots, plant molecular biologists Kenneth Birnbaum, Philip Benfey, and associates identified 15 distinct regions of cellular specialization. Such studies reveal that roots are amazingly complex in structure. However, for our purposes, a simpler microscopic

(a) Buttress roots   **(b) Pneumatophores**

Figure 33.22   **Examples of modified above ground roots.** (a) Buttress roots help to keep tropical trees, such as this *Pterocarpus hayesii,* from toppling in windstorms. (b) Pneumatophores produced by mangroves are roots that extend upward into the air. These roots take up air and then transmit it to underwater roots that grow in oxygen-poor sediments.

examination of root internal structure reveals three major zones: (1) a root apical meristem (RAM), (2) a zone of root elongation, and (3) a zone of maturation in which specialized cells can be observed (**Figure 33.23**).

Root Apical Meristem and Root Cap   As you observed earlier, an apical meristem occurs at the tips of roots and their branches. Like the SAM, the RAM contains stem cells, but these are organized differently in root apices. Root stem cells surround a tiny region of cells that rarely divide, known as the

quiescent centre. Signals emanating from the quiescent centre keep nearby stem cells in an undifferentiated state. Root stem cells farther from the quiescent centre produce new cells in multiple directions. Toward the root tip, stem cells produce columella cells that sense gravity and touch, which helps roots extend downward into the soil and around obstacles, such as rocks. At the sides of the quiescent centre, stem cells produce a protective root cap and epidermal cells. Root tip epidermal cells secrete a sticky substance called **mucigel** (Figure 33.23), that lubricates the root as it grows through the soil.

Zones of Elongation and Maturation   Above the RAM lies the **zone of elongation**, in which cells extend by water uptake, thereby dramatically increasing root length (Figure 33.23). Above and overlapping with the zone of elongation is the **zone of maturation**, where most root cell differentiation and tissue specialization occur. Specialized root tissues include mature vascular tissues at the root core, an enclosing cylinder of cells known as the pericycle, another cell cylinder called the endodermis (meaning inside skin), and epidermal cells at the root surface. Relatively unspecialized parenchyma cells form a cortex that lies between the endodermis and the epidermis. Starting with the epidermis and moving inward, we will take a closer look at these root tissues and factors that control their development.

The zone of maturation can be identified by the presence of numerous microscopic hairs that emerge from the root epidermis. **Root hairs** are specialized epidermal cells that can be

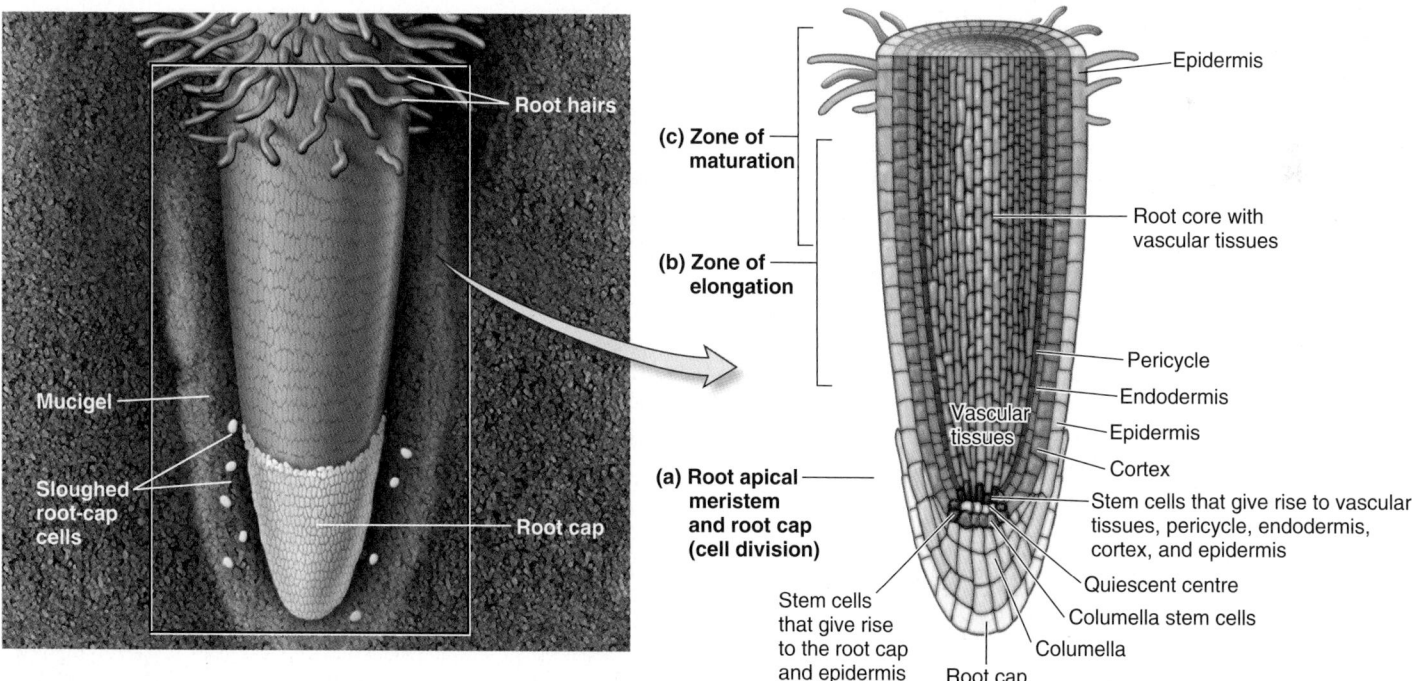

Figure 33.23   **Three zones of root growth.** A longitudinal view of a typical root reveals three major zones: (a) a root apical meristem where cell division occurs protected by a root cap, (b) a zone of elongation, and (c) a zone of maturation, characterized by epidermal root hairs and other specialized cells. Phloem matures sooner than xylem as a way of supplying the energy needs of the growing root tip with organic compounds from the shoot.

BioConnections: *Look ahead to Figure 37.22. What properties of mucigel would be advantageous for seeds?*

as long as 1.3 cm, about the width of your little finger, but are only 10 μm in diameter. Their small diameter allows root hairs to obtain water and minerals from soil pores that are too narrow for even the smallest roots to enter. Root hair plasma membranes are rich in transport proteins that use ATP to selectively absorb materials from the soil (see Chapter 35).

The production of hairs from root epidermal cells is controlled by the activity of transcription factors that move between cells and also by cell position. A root hair will develop from epidermal cells lying over the junction of two cortical cells, whereas no hair will develop if an epidermal cell lies over only one cortical cell. Root hairs are so delicate that they are easily damaged by abrasion as roots grow through the soil, and they live for only four or five days. As a result, root hairs are absent from older regions above the zone of maturation. To compensate, roots must continually produce new root hairs. The average rate of root hair production has been estimated at more than 100 million per day for some plants. One reason that gardeners use care when transplanting seedlings is to prevent extensive damage to the root hair zone.

The epidermis of mature roots encloses a region of ground parenchyma known as the **root cortex** (**Figure 33.24**). Much like the stem cortex, root cortex cells are often rich in starch and thus serve as a food storage site for plants. The root cortex of some plants contains intercellular air spaces that arise from apoptosis and provide routes for oxygen diffusion within the root. Water and dissolved minerals also diffuse from the environment into roots through spaces between cortex cells, stopping only when they reach a specialized tissue known as **endodermis**, an important component of the mechanism by which roots absorb selected minerals (see Chapter 36).

A mobile transcription factor protein that moves outward from the core of root vascular tissue controls the development of the endodermis. In most plants, the endodermis is only one cell thick because the cells that become the endodermis produce a protein known as SCARECROW that binds the mobile transcription factor. Bound in endodermal cells, the transcription factor cannot diffuse outward into other cells. Together, SCARECROW and the bound transcription factor signal the changes that cause endodermal cells to differentiate in a particular way that enables their essential function.

A cylinder of tissue that has cell division (meristematic) capacity, known as the **pericycle**, encloses the root vascular tissue (Figure 33.24). The pericycle produces lateral (branch) roots that force their way through the cortex to the surface.

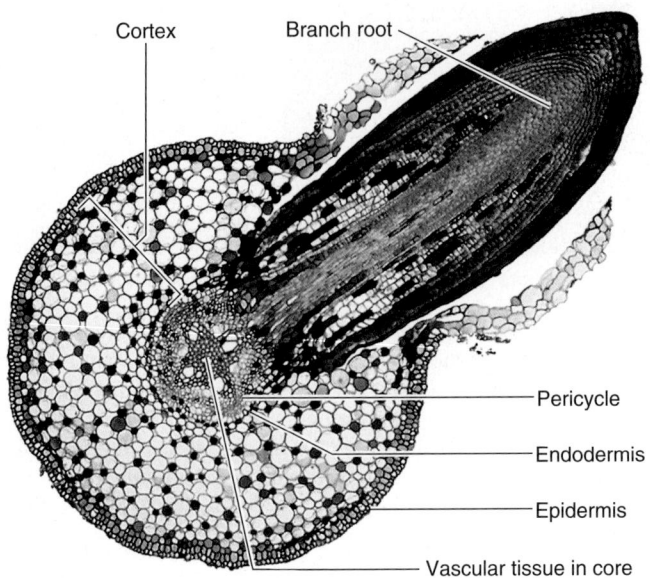

Figure 33.24 Cross-section of a mature root. This stained light micrograph shows the epidermis and cortex of a root surrounding a central core of vascular tissue. An inner cortex layer is the endodermis, which surrounds a cylinder of meristematic tissue called pericycle. The pericycle has produced a young branch (lateral) root that has grown through the cortex and the epidermis.

Concept check: *Why must lateral roots be produced in this way?*

Finally, the primary vascular system in a mature root includes xylem and phloem located at the root core. The xylem exports water and minerals upward to shoots, and the phloem imports a watery solution of organic compounds from the shoots. Root xylem development is regulated by microRNA 165/6, which is produced in and secreted from the endodermis. In newly produced, but as-yet-unspecialized root core cells, these microRNAs act as a signal to repress mRNA levels of a particular transcription factor, causing root core cells to differentiate into xylem. MicroRNA 165/6 and the mobile transcription factors that influence endodermal and root hair development are examples of the strong influence that chemical signalling has on the development of specialized plant tissues.

Summary of Key Concepts

33.1 From Seed to Seed: The Life of a Flowering Plant

- Seed embryos, seedlings, and mature plants are components of the sporophyte generation in the plant sexual cycle; tiny gametophytes develop and grow within flowers. (Figure 33.1)

- Plant organs are composed of two or more tissues that contain specialized cells. The basic plant organs are roots, stems, and leaves. Shoot systems include stems and stem branches, and stems produce leaves, buds, flowers, and fruits. Root systems include one or more main roots with branches. Buds, flowers, fruits, and seeds are organ systems, composed of more than one organ. (Figures 33.2, 33.3)

- The two major groups of flowering plants, eudicots and monocots, differ in the structure of their roots, stems, leaves, flowers, embryos, and pollen. (Table 33.1)

- Many plants exhibit indeterminate growth, meaning that apical meristems continuously generate new lateral organs as long as environmental conditions are favourable. (Figure 33.4)

33.2 How Plants Grow and Develop

- Plants have a fundamental architecture that is generated by reiterative patterning of lateral organs. (Figure 33.5)

- Plants grow by producing new cells at meristems and by controlled cell enlargement involving water uptake.

- Shoot apical meristems produce primary meristems that increase plant length and produce organs. The primary meristems are (1) protoderm, which generates dermal tissues; (2) ground meristem, which produces ground tissues; and (3) procambium, which makes the primary vascular tissues. Thus the primary meristems produce primary tissues as well as lateral meristems that give rise to secondary tissues in many species. (Table 33.2, Figure 33.6)

- Simple plant tissues, containing one or two cell types, include parenchyma, collenchyma, and sclerenchyma. Complex tissues include the vascular tissues known as phloem and xylem, and the primary vascular tissues occur in vascular bundles. (Figure 33.7)

- Leaves develop from primordia produced at shoot apices. Foliage leaves have internal and external structures adapted for photosyntheitic functions.

- Meristems include stem cells, whose numbers influence plant growth and structure and are thus genetically controlled. (Figure 33.8)

- Plant cells are able to expand under conditions that result in loosening of cell-wall components and by water uptake into vacuoles. The direction in which plant cells expand is determined by the arrangement of wall cellulose microfibrils, which is influenced by the orientation of microtubules in the nearby cytoplasm. (Figures 33.9, 33.10, 33.11)

33.3 The Shoot System: Stem and Leaf Adaptations

- Shoots are modular systems; each module includes a node, an internode, a leaf, and an axillary meristem. An axillary bud develops in leaf axils; such buds may grow into new branches. (Figure 33.12)

- Chemical hormones, such as auxin and gibberellic acid, influence leaf development, other aspects of plant development, and environmental responses.

- Variations in leaf structure reflect adaptations that aid photosynthesis or protect against stress. For example, Elle and associates demonstrated the value and cost of sticky, sugar-secreting leaf trichomes when destructive insects were present or absent. (Figures 33.13, 33.14, 33.15)

- Leaves not only function in photosynthesis but also play other roles, including attachment, attraction, and protection. (Figure 33.16)

- Herbaceous plants are those whose stems produce little or no wood, and whose vascular systems are composed of primary xylem and primary phloem. (Figures 33.17, 33.18)

- In addition to primary tissues, woody plants—trees, shrubs, and lianas—possess secondary meristems that produce wood and bark. The vascular cambium produces secondary xylem (wood) and secondary phloem (inner bark). The cork cambium produces cork tissues that form outer bark. (Figures 33.19, 33.20, 33.21)

- Stems occur in diverse forms that reflect adaptation to environmental conditions. Examples include grass rhizomes, which grow horizontally underground and are thereby better protected from fire and grazing animals (as well as lawn mowers).

33.4 Root System Adaptations

- Roots occur in multiple forms that reflect adaptation to environmental conditions. Examples of above ground roots include prop roots, buttress roots, and pneumatophores. (Figure 33.22)

- The internal organization of roots is comparatively uniform, and three major zones can be recognized with the use of a microscope: the root apical meristem and root cap, a zone of cell and root elongation, and a zone of tissue maturation. Features of the mature root include epidermal root hairs that aid nutrient uptake, a food-storing cortex, an endodermis that functions in mineral selection, a pericycle that produces lateral (branch) roots (and vascular cambium in the case of woody roots), and an inner core of vascular tissue. (Figures 33.23, 33.24)

Test to Assess Your Learning

1. Where would you look to find the gametophyte generation of a flowering plant?
   a. at the shoot apical meristem
   b. at the root apical meristem
   c. in seeds
   d. in flower parts
   e. none of the above

2. What is a radicle?
   a. an embryonic leaf
   b. an embryonic stem
   c. an embryonic root
   d. a mature root system of a monocot
   e. a modified leaf that serves a defensive function

3. What is the correct term for a plant that does not reproduce in its first year of life but usually produces flowers and seeds within the following year?
   a. an annual
   b. a biennial
   c. a perennial
   d. a centennial
   e. none of the above

4. Which of the following terms best describes the distinctive architecture of plants?
   a. radial symmetry and apical-basal polarity
   b. bilateral symmetry and apical-basal polarity
   c. radial symmetry and absence of apical-basal polarity
   d. bilateral symmetry and absence of apical-basal polarity
   e. absence of symmetry and absence of apical-basal polarity

5. Which is the most accurate description of how plants grow?
   a. By the addition of new cells at meristems that include stem cells.
   b. By cell enlargement as the result of water uptake.
   c. By both the addition of new cells and cell expansion.
   d. By the addition of fat cells.
   e. none of the above

6. Where would you look for leaf primordia?
   a. at a vegetative shoot tip
   b. at the root apical meristem
   c. at the vascular cambium
   d. at the cork cambium
   e. in a floral bud

7. Which leaf tissues display the greatest amount of air space?
   a. the adaxial epidermis
   b. the abaxial epidermis
   c. the palisade parenchyma
   d. the spongy parenchyma
   e. the vascular tissues

8. What are adventitious roots?
   a. Roots that develop on plant cuttings that have been placed in water.
   b. Buttress roots that grow from tree trunks.
   c. The only kinds of roots produced by monocots, because their embryonic root dies soon after seed germination.
   d. Any root that is produced by stem (or sometimes leaf) tissue, rather than developing directly from the embryonic root.
   e. all of the above

9. During its development, a tracheid will elongate in a direction parallel to the shoot or root axis. Based on this information, what can you say about the orientation of cellulose cell-wall microfibrils and cytoplasmic microtubules in this developing tracheid?
   a. The microfibrils will be oriented perpendicularly (at right angles) to the long axis of the developing tracheid, encircling it, but the cytoplasmic microtubules will be oriented parallel to the direction in which the tracheid is elongating.
   b. Microfibrils and microtubules will both be oriented perpendicularly (at right angles) to the elongating axis of the tracheid.
   c. Microfibrils and microtubules will both be oriented parallel to the direction of tracheid elongation.
   d. Microfibrils will be oriented parallel to the direction of tracheid elongation, but microtubules will be perpendicular (at right angles) to both the microfibrils and the elongating tracheid.
   e. none of the above

10. What are examples of woody plants?
    a. trees
    b. shrubs
    c. woody vines, known as lianas
    d. all of the above
    e. none of the above

Articulate to Assess Your Learning

1. If you saw a particularly beautiful plant in a garden, how could you determine whether it was a monocot or a eudicot?

2. What would be the consequences if leaves were radially symmetrical (shaped like spheres or cylinders)?

3. Why are most tall plants woody rather than herbaceous? Why do many broad-leafed plants exhibit branched venation patterns?

Collaborate to Assess and Extend Your Learning

1. Find a tree stump or a large limb that has recently been cut from a tree (or imagine doing so). Which of the following features could you locate with the unaided eye: the outer bark, the inner bark, the secondary xylem, the vascular cambium, annual rings?

2. Which physical factors would you expect to influence shoot growth most strongly? Which physical factors would you expect to influence underground root growth most strongly?

3. A principle of biology is that structure determines function. Why are most tall plants woody, rather than herbaceous?

Visit McGraw-Hill Ryerson Connect™ for additional study resources.

Flowering Plants: Behaviour

Chapter Outline

The snow buttercup (*Ranunculus adoneus*) grows in deep snow banks in the high Rocky Mountains, with flower stems protruding above the snow surface toward the sun, as shown in the chapter-opening photo. Snow buttercup flowers change their position so that they face the sun throughout the day, a movement process known as sun tracking. Experiments have demonstrated that sun tracking warms snow buttercup flowers, thereby favouring pollen development and pollen tube germination. These processes foster fertilization, which leads to more effective seed production. In this way, sun tracking is an adaptation that increases snow buttercup reproductive fitness. Like sun tracking solar panels, the leaves of alfalfa, lupine, soybean, common bean, cotton, and other wild and agriculturally important plants also track the sun, a process that aids energy storage by photosynthesis.

Sun tracking is but one example of the many ways in which plants display behaviour—that is, responses to stimuli. Plants respond not only to changes in sun position, but also to day length, which is the period of daily illumination. In addition to light, plants respond to gravity, wind, attack by animals and disease-causing microorganisms, and other environmental stimuli. This chapter provides examples of ways in which understanding plant behaviour has been key to increasing agricultural productivity and protecting natural ecosystems.

We begin with a survey of the diverse types of stimuli that induce plant behaviour and review how cells perceive and respond to stimuli by means of signal transduction pathways. Next, we will focus on plant hormones, which are major types of internal mobile molecules that influence plant behaviour. Finally, we consider how responses to environmental stimuli foster plant survival and reproduction.

Behaviour of the snow buttercup The snow buttercup (*Ranunculus adoneus*) holds its flowers above the surface of the snow. The flowers move so that they always face the sun during the day, a behaviour known as sun tracking.

Behaviour is defined as a response of organisms to an internal or external stimulus. Examples of plant behaviour include plant movements, some types of which were described in 1880 by Charles Darwin and his son Francis in their book *The Power of Movement in Plants*. Modern time-lapse photography, which makes behaviour more obvious to humans, reveals that most plants are constantly in motion, bending, twisting, or rotating in dancelike movements known as nutation (**Figure 34.1a**). Some plants display quite rapid movements, illustrated by the sensitive plant *Mimosa pudica*, whose leaves quickly fold when touched (**Figure 34.1b**). Plant shoots typically grow toward light and against the pull of gravity, and roots grow toward water and in the same direction as the gravitational force. Seeds germinate when they detect the presence of sufficient light and moisture for successful seedling growth. Producing flowers, fruits, and seeds only in the season most favourable for reproductive success is a behavioural response to environmental change. Plants also take protective action when they sense attack by disease microbes or hungry animals, thereby preventing excessive damage to their own bodies or those of neighbouring plants. To give you a more complete understanding of plant behaviour, we will begin by surveying the types of stimuli that cause plant responses.

Plant Behaviour Involves Responses to Internal and External Stimuli

Most people are aware that both internal chemical hormones and environmental factors influence animal behaviour. Bird nesting behaviour in spring, for example, involves hormonal changes triggered by seasonal conditions. Plants likewise respond to both internal and environmental influences (**Figure 34.2**).

34.1

34.1 | OVERVIEW OF PLANT BEHAVIOURAL RESPONSES

Learning Outcomes:

1. List examples of plant responses to internal and environmental stimuli.
2. Describe the three stages of cell signalling.

(a) Nutation movements   **(b) Leaf folding**

Figure 34.1   Examples of plant movements.   (a) Sixteen superimposed photographs of a shoot of the honeysuckle vine *Lonicera japonica,* taken over two hours, reveal the circular movement known as nutation. **(b)** Photographs of the sensitive plant (*Mimosa pudica*) made before and shortly after a touch reveal the rapid process of leaf folding. Even if only one leaflet is touched, electrical signals travel throughout the complex leaf, causing the entire organ to fold. The leaves will eventually unfold.

Internal Stimuli   Plants respond to two types of internal stimuli: internal biological clocks and mobile chemical signals. Internal biological clocks, known as **circadian rhythms**, occur not only in plants, but also animals and other organisms. The word *circadian* comes from the Latin words meaning "about" and "day." Circadian rhythms evolved under the influence of Earth's rotation, which causes the regular alternation of night and day. Leaf movements, flower opening, fragrance emission, and many other behaviours result from the operation of circadian rhythms in plants.

Like animals, plants also respond to internal chemical signals that are produced within the body and move from one location to another, acting at very low concentrations. In plants, these chemical signals may move short distances from cell to cell via plasmodesmata, or long distances within the vascular system. Plant chemical signals include transcription factors and microRNAs (see Chapter 33) as well as chemically different compounds known as **hormones**. Some plant hormones are similar to particular animal hormones. One example is the plant hormone jasmonic acid, which is much like prostaglandins produced by animals. The gaseous hormone nitric oxide (NO) functions in both animals and plants. Other hormones are distinctive to plants. Even so, as in the case of animal hormones, plant hormones often interact with each other and with external stimuli to maintain a stable internal environment (homeostasis) and enable progress through life stages.

Environmental Stimuli   Plants sense and respond to many types of physical and biological stimuli (Figure 34.2). Physical stimuli in natural plant environments include light, atmospheric

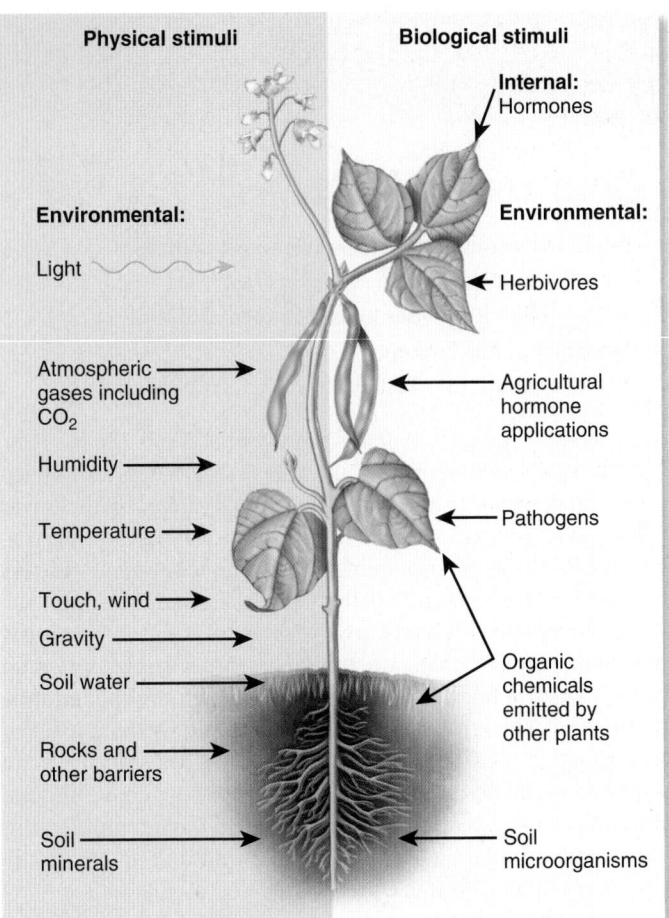

**Figure 34.2   Types of plant stimuli.   Plants respond to both physical and biological stimuli. Stimuli may be generated internally or come from the environment.

gases such as CO_2 and water vapour, temperature, touch, wind, gravity, water, rocks and other barriers to root growth, and soil minerals. Biological stimuli include herbivores (animals that consume plant parts), airborne pathogens (disease-causing microbes), organic chemicals emitted from neighbouring plants, and beneficial or harmful soil organisms. Crop plants also respond to applications of agricultural chemicals, which may include hormones. That plants have evolved such a broad array of sensory capacity is not surprising: all the environmental influences listed here affect plant survival and reproduction.

Plant Responses to Environmental Stimuli   Though plants lack the specialized sense organs typical of animals, receptor molecules located in plant cells sense stimuli and cause responses. When many cells of a tissue receive and respond to the same biological or physical stimulus, whole organs or plant bodies display behaviour. For example, houseplants tend to grow toward a light source, such as a window. This process, known as **phototropism**, involves both a cellular perception of light and a growth response of stem tissue to an internal chemical signal. In general, a **tropism** is a growth response that is dependent on a stimulus that occurs in a particular direction.

How can an environmental signal, such as directional light, cause such stem movements? In the case of phototropism, the plant senses the direction of light and responds by changing the location of a plant hormone known as auxin. The auxin moves into cells where it influences gene expression, causing the stem to bend toward the light. Next we will consider how plant cells receive signals and transmit them intracellularly, a process known as signal transduction (refer back to Chapter 9).

Plant Cell Signalling Involves Receptors, Messengers, and Effectors

Cell signalling is the process by which a cell perceives a physical or chemical signal, thereby switching on an intercellular pathway that leads to a cellular response (**Figure 34.3**). The process of cell signalling often involves three types of molecules: receptors that may become activated, second messengers that transmit signals, and effectors that cause a cellular response (refer back to Figure 9.4).

A **receptor** (also known as a sensor) is a protein that becomes activated when it receives a specific type of signal (Figure 34.3). Receptors occur in diverse cellular locations. Whereas some plant hormone receptors are located within the plasma membrane, light receptors occur in the cytosol, and auxin binds to specific receptors located in the nucleus (see Chapter 9). Some activated receptors directly generate a response, such as increased flow of ions across a membrane. In contrast, many activated receptors first bind to signalling molecules and then initiate an intracellular signalling pathway. For example, the binding of brassinosteroid defence hormones to plasma membrane receptors results in the intracellular production of second messenger molecules that transmit the signal.

Second messengers transmit messages from many types of activated receptors to effector molecules. Cyclic AMP (cAMP), inositol trisphosphate (IP$_3$), and calcium ions (Ca^{2+}) are major types of messengers in animal and plant cells. Calcium ions are particularly common messengers in plant cells. Touch and various other stimuli cause Ca^{2+} to flow from storage sites in the ER lumen into the cytosol. Calmodulin or other calcium-binding proteins then bind the Ca^{2+}. Calcium binding alters the structure of such proteins, causing them to interact with other cell proteins or alter enzymatic function.

Effectors are molecules that directly influence cellular responses. In plants, calcium-dependent protein kinases (CDPKs) are particularly important effector molecules. Cell signalling ends when an effector causes a cellular response, such as opening or closing an ion channel or switching the transcription of particular genes on or off. A single activated receptor can dispatch many second-messenger molecules, which, in turn, can activate scores of effectors, leading to many molecular responses within a single cell.

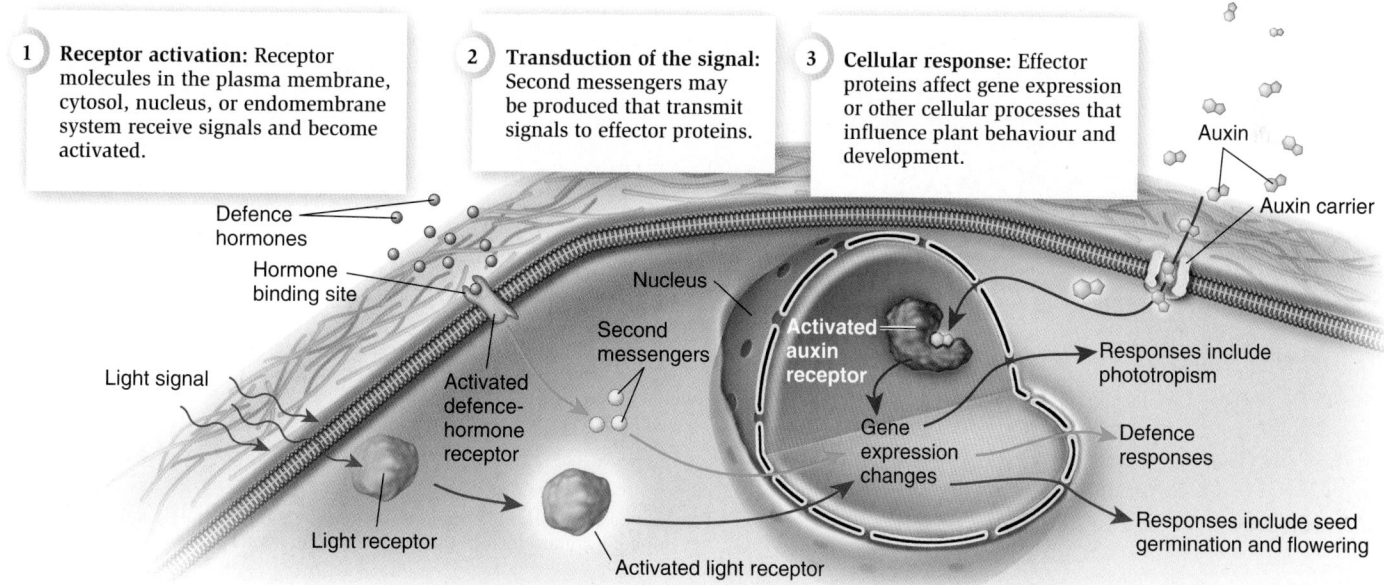

1 **Receptor activation:** Receptor molecules in the plasma membrane, cytosol, nucleus, or endomembrane system receive signals and become activated.

2 **Transduction of the signal:** Second messengers may be produced that transmit signals to effector proteins.

3 **Cellular response:** Effector proteins affect gene expression or other cellular processes that influence plant behaviour and development.

Auxin

Auxin carrier

Defence hormones

Hormone binding site

Nucleus

Second messengers

Activated auxin receptor

Responses include phototropism

Light signal

Activated defence-hormone receptor

Gene expression changes

Defence responses

Light receptor

Activated light receptor

Responses include seed germination and flowering

Figure 34.3 **An overview of plant cell signalling.** Plant cells respond to hormonal signals produced within the plant body, as well as to environmental stimuli. Three different signal transduction processes are shown here: one started by light; a defence hormone that has a plasma membrane receptor; and auxin, which has a receptor located in the nucleus.

 Principle: *Cells are the simplest units of life. Internal and environmental stimuli are received and elicit responses at the cellular level.*

34.2 / PLANT HORMONES

Learning Outcomes:

1. List the major plant hormones.
2. Explain how auxin functions in phototropism.
3. Explain how cytokinins, gibberellins, and ethylene are relevant to agriculture.
4. Discuss how abscisic acid and brassinosteroids help plants cope with environmental stress.

Together with transcription factors and microRNA molecules, plant hormones are chemical signals transported within the plant body; when taken up by target cells, the signals elicit responses. Plant hormones include about a dozen small molecules synthesized in metabolic pathways that also make amino acids, nucleotides, sterols, or secondary metabolites. Of these, auxins, cytokinins, gibberellins, ethylene, abscisic acid, and brassinosteroids are considered to be the major plant hormones (**Table 34.1**). Individual plant hormones often have multiple effects, and different concentrations or combinations of hormones can produce distinct growth or developmental

Table 34.1   The Major Types of Plant Hormones

Type of plant hormone	Chemical structure of an example	Functions
Auxins	Indoleacetic acid (IAA)	Establish apical-basal polarity, mediate phototropism, induce vascular tissue development, promote formation of adventitious roots, inhibit leaf and fruit drop, and stimulate fruit development
Cytokinins	Zeatin	Promote cell division, influence cell specialization and plant aging, activate secondary meristem development, promote adventitious root growth, and promote shoot development on callus
Gibberellins	Gibberellic acid	Stimulate cell division and cell enlargement, promote seed germination, stimulate stem elongation and flowering, and retard leaf and fruit aging
Ethylene	Ethylene $H_2C = CH_2$	Promote seed germination, induce leaf and flower aging and fruit ripening, promote leaf and fruit drop, function in plant responses to flooding, and coordinate plant development and stress responses
Abscisic acid	Abscisic acid	Slow or stop metabolism in stress responses, prevent seed germination in unfavourable conditions, induce bud and seed dormancy, and influence stomatal opening and closing
Brassinosteroids	Brassinolide	Promote cell elongation, stimulate shoot elongation, stimulate xylem development, retard leaf drop, and promote stress responses

responses. Several plant hormones are known to act by causing the removal of gene repressors, thereby allowing gene expression to occur. This general mechanism allows hormones to cause relatively rapid responses. A closer look at the major types of plant hormones reveals their multifaceted roles.

Auxins Are the Master Plant Hormones

Plants produce several types of **auxins** that are considered to be the "master" plant hormones because they influence plant structure, development, and behaviour in many ways, often working with other hormones. Indoleacetic acid (IAA) is one plant auxin (Table 34.1), but other natural and artificial compounds have similar structures and effects. In this section we will refer to this family of related compounds simply as auxin.

Auxin exerts so many effects because it promotes the expression of a diverse set of genes, together known as **auxin-response genes**. Under low auxin conditions, proteins called Aux/IAA repressors prevent plant cells from expressing these genes. The repressor proteins prevent gene expression by binding to activator proteins at gene promoters. When the auxin concentration is high enough, auxin molecules facilitate the binding of the repressors to a protein complex called

TIR1, which causes the breakdown of the repressors (look back to Figure 9.9b). Free of the repressors, the activator proteins enhance the expression of auxin-response genes.

Auxin Transport The way in which auxin is transported into and out of cells is integral to its effects in plants. Auxin is produced in apical shoot tips and young leaves, and it is directionally transported from one living parenchyma cell to another. Auxin in an uncharged form (IAAH) can enter cells by means of diffusion, and the negatively charged form (IAA$^-$) requires the aid of AUX1, a plasma membrane protein known as the **auxin influx carrier**. Several types of PIN proteins transport auxin out of cells and are thus termed **auxin efflux carriers**; they are named for the pin-shaped shoot apices of plants having mutations in *PIN* genes. They are necessary because the auxin found in the cytoplasm is a charged ion that does not readily diffuse out of cells.

In shoots, AUX1 is located at the apical ends of cells, whereas PIN proteins often occur at the basal ends (**Figure 34.4a**). This polar distribution of auxin carriers explains why auxin primarily flows downward in shoots and into roots, a process called **polar transport** (**Figure 34.4b**). However, the locations of auxin carriers can also change within cell plasma membranes, allowing

(a) Cellular mechanism of auxin transport

(b) Auxin transport throughout a plant

Figure 34.4 Auxin transport. **(a)** Polar and lateral auxin transport is controlled by the distribution of auxin efflux carriers located in the plasma membrane. When efflux carriers primarily occur at the basal ends of cells, auxin will flow downward. Auxin may flow laterally when auxin efflux carriers occur at the sides of cells. **(b)** In a whole plant, auxin primarily flows downward from shoot tips to root tips, where it then flows upward for a short distance.

Concept check: *How could auxin carriers be organized to allow auxin to move upward in roots?*

lateral or upward transport of auxin. Differences in the presence and positions of auxin carrier proteins explain variations in auxin concentration within plants. By measuring the local auxin concentration, plant cells determine their position within the plant body and respond by dividing, expanding, or specializing.

Auxin Effects   In nature, auxin influences plants throughout their lifetimes. Auxin establishes the apical-basal polarity of seed embryos, induces vascular tissue to differentiate, mediates phototropism, promotes formation of adventitious roots, and stimulates fruit development. Many of auxin's effects are of practical importance to humans. Auxin is used to produce some types of seedless fruit, retard premature fruit drop in orchards, and stimulate root development on stem cuttings. Auxin produced by intact shoot tips inhibits lateral bud growth, a process known as apical dominance. Gardeners know that if they remove the topmost portion of a plant shoot, nearby lateral buds will begin to grow and produce new branches, allowing plants to become bushier. Such decapitation works by disrupting the flow of auxin from the shoot apex. There is evidence that auxin acts indirectly to inhibit lateral bud outgrowth, but this regulation is complex and not completely understood. However, auxin's role in phototropism has been elucidated by a series of elegant experiments.

The Role of Auxin Phototropism   In the 1880s Charles Darwin and his son Francis were the first to publish results of experiments on plant phototropism. The Darwins performed their experiments on cereal seedlings, whose tips are protected by a sheath of tissue called a coleoptile. In a simple but elegant experiment, they covered either the tips or lower shoot portions of some grass seedlings with shading materials, such as blackened glass tubes, left other seedlings uncovered, and removed the tips of some seedlings. They then compared how those seedlings responded to illumination from the side. The shoots of seedlings whose tips were left uncovered grew toward the light, whereas shoots of seedlings whose tips were covered or removed did not. The Darwins concluded that seedling shoot tips transmit some "influence" to lower shoot portions, causing them to bend toward the light. You can probably guess what this influence was, but technology available at the time did not allow the Darwins to determine this.

Three decades later, in the 1910s, Danish botanist Peter Boysen-Jensen confirmed the Darwins' results and demonstrated that the influence was a chemical substance that diffused from the tips of the seedlings to other parts of the shoots. To do this, Boysen-Jensen cut off the tips of oat seedlings and placed either a porous layer of gelatin or a nonporous material, such as a sheet of the mineral mica, on the cut shoot surface. Then he replaced the shoot tips. Oat seedlings layered with porous gelatin displayed a normal phototropic response, bending toward the light, but those layered with nonporous mica did not. Boysen-Jensen's experiment demonstrated that the phototropic substance was a diffusible chemical, but exactly which one, and how it worked, remained unknown. A series of additional experiments provided some answers.

In the 1920s Dutch plant physiologist Frits Went named the substance discovered by Boysen-Jensen *auxin* (from the Greek word *auxein,* meaning "to increase"). Although the chemical structure of auxin was not determined until 1934, Went performed experiments that helped explain how auxin works. In a first step, Went cut off the shoot tips of oat seedlings and placed these tips onto agar blocks. Agar, a complex polysaccharide derived from red algae, forms a mesh capable of holding considerable water and dissolved compounds. Agar's permeability to auxin is similar to that of the protein gelatin used by Boysen-Jensen, but agar is much more stable to heat and microbial breakdown and thus is easier to use in laboratory experiments. In Went's experiment, the auxin diffused from cut shoot tips into these agar blocks. In the next steps, he treated decapitated shoots in one of four ways: **(a)** he placed auxin-laden agar blocks off-centre on some, **(b)** he placed auxin-laden blocks evenly onto others, **(c)** he placed plain agar blocks off-centre on some, and **(d)** he left some uncapped. All seedlings were then kept in the dark throughout the experiment. Only seedlings that were capped off-centre with agar containing the material later identified as auxin grew in the direction away from the agar block. This experiment demonstrated that auxin application could substitute for the directional light stimulus, and it suggested that asymmetric auxin distribution is the mechanism by which light causes plants to bend.

Subsequently, Went and N. O. Cholodny independently proposed that light causes auxin to move to the unlit side of seedling tips, causing cells on that side to elongate more, which results in bending. But other scientists argued that bending could result if light destroys auxin on the illuminated lit side of a shoot. In the 1950s American plant biologist Winslow Briggs designed two elegant experiments to test these alternative hypotheses.

In his first experiment, which tested the hypothesis that auxin might be destroyed by light, Briggs first grew corn seedlings in the dark. Then he cut off their shoot tips, put the tips on agar blocks, and exposed some to darkness and others to directional light. During this process, auxin from tips diffused evenly into the agar blocks. If auxin were destroyed by light, agar blocks under lighted tips should contain less auxin than blocks under tips kept in the dark. The auxin-destruction hypothesis also predicts that when agar blocks from lighted tips are placed on one side of decapitated shoots, they should cause less bending than would blocks from tips kept in the dark. However, Briggs discovered that both types of agar blocks caused the same amount of shoot bending. This result is not consistent with the hypothesis that light destroys auxin.

Cytokinins Stimulate Cell Division

Like auxins, the plant hormones known as **cytokinins** play varied and important roles in plants. The name of these hormones reflects their major effect: an increase in the rate of plant cytokinesis or cell division. Root tips are the major sites of cytokinin production, but shoots and seeds also make this plant hormone. Cytokinins are transported in the xylem to meristems, seeds,

FEATURE INVESTIGATION

An Experiment Performed by Briggs Revealed the Role of Auxin in Phototropism

In a second experiment, Briggs tested the Cholodny-Went hypothesis that light causes auxin to move to the shaded side of shoots (**Figure 34.5**). Briggs set shoot tips onto agar blocks (step 1) and then used a mica sheet (which is impervious to auxin) to completely divide some tips and blocks into halves (step 2A). In other cases he divided blocks completely but left tips incompletely divided, allowing auxin to diffuse across tips but not the block halves (step 2B). Then Briggs exposed all sets of tips and blocks to directional light. He predicted that

auxin would not be able to move across tips having complete mica barricades but that auxin would be able to move across tips that had been only partially divided. Auxin diffused from tips into blocks, but it could not diffuse evenly across blocks divided by mica sheets. When Briggs later placed the agar block halves on decapitated shoots (step 3), those receiving auxin from completely divided tips were bent by the same amount. By contrast, agar block halves from the unlit side of partially divided tips induced more bending, while halves from the lit sides of partially divided tips caused less bending (see the data in Figure 34.5). These experimental results support the hypothesis that unidirectional light causes auxin to accumulate on the

HYPOTHESIS Directional light causes auxin to move to the shaded side of shoot tips.

KEY MATERIALS Corn seedlings.

		Experimental level	Conceptual level

1 Place shoot tips on agar blocks.

2 Divide some tip/block combinations completely with a mica sheet, which prevents diffusion between the two halves of the tip and agar block. Divide some tip/block combinations only partially with a mica sheet. This allows auxin diffusion across the tip, but not across the agar block. Expose both to directional light.

Mica sheet   A   Mica sheet   B

If directional light causes auxins to move to shaded side of shoot tips, agar block in B will contain more auxin on right side.

3 Remove agar block halves from tips. Place agar halves onto right sides of shoots, which have their tips removed.

If directional light causes auxins to move laterally, the block half beneath the left side of the partially divided tip shown in B should cause the least shoot bending, whereas the block half beneath the right side of B should cause the greatest amount of bending.

4 THE DATA

11°   11°   8°   15°

5 CONCLUSION In A, the mica sheets prevented auxin from moving to the shaded side of tips. In B, auxin was able to move in response to directional light. Agar block pieces from the shaded side of tips contained more auxin and therefore caused greater shoot bending. Hypothesis is correct.

6 SOURCE Briggs, W.R. 1963. Mediation of phototropic responses of corn coleoptiles by lateral transport of auxin. *Plant Physiology* 38(3):237–247.

Figure 34.5 Briggs demonstrated the relationship between light perception and auxin function.

shaded side. Modern plant scientists would explain such auxin movement as the result of lateral transport involving PIN proteins that mediate auxin-dependent phototropism.

How might auxin accumulation cause bending? One widely held hypothesis is that auxin accumulation on the shaded side of a shoot causes plasma membrane proton pumps located there to work at a faster rate. In response, the cell wall becomes more acidic, which activates expansins, proteins that break cross-links between cellulose microfibrils, which fosters plant cell elongation (refer back to Figure 33.9). This process might explain how auxin accumulation in cells located on the shaded side of shoot tips causes them to elongate more than do cells on the sunny side, causing the tip to bend toward the light.

Experimental Questions

1. Use the text discussion to draw a diagram illustrating the experiment that Briggs did in order to determine whether or not light destroys auxin.
2. What is the current hypothesized mechanism by which auxin accumulation causes shoot bending in response to directional light?
3. Figure 34.5 illustrates experiments performed with four seedling tips. Would this number really be enough to allow conclusions to be made about how such seedling tips would generally respond?

leaves, and fruit, where they stimulate cell division. At shoot and root tips, cytokinins influence meristem size, stem cell activity, and vascular tissue development. Cytokinins are also involved in root and shoot growth and branching, the production of flowers and seeds, and leaf senescence (aging).

Plant Tissue Culture   In the laboratory, cytokinin and auxin are essential to cloning plants. This involves a process known as **plant tissue culture**, which is used commercially to produce thousands of identical plants having the same desirable characteristics. Plant tissue culture begins with pieces of stem, leaf, or root that have been removed from a plant. Their surfaces are sterilized to prevent growth of microbes (**Figure 34.6**, step 1), and the cleaned plant pieces are then placed into dishes containing nutrients (minerals, vitamins, and sugar) and various proportions

of auxin and cytokinin. If the proportions of auxin and cytokinin are about the same (1:1), plant cells undergo division, forming a mass of white tissue known as a callus (step 2). If the callus is then transferred to a new dish containing the same nutrients but with auxin-to-cytokinin proportions greater than 10:1, the callus will form roots (step 3). Auxin-to-cytokinin proportions of less than 10:1 cause the callus to develop green shoots (step 4). Thus, by altering the ratios of auxin and cytokinin, entire plants can be regenerated from a callus. A single callus can be divided into many pieces and each piece treated with these hormones, thereby producing many hundreds of identical new plants.

The Discovery of Cytokinin   Plant tissue culture would not be possible without the understanding of cytokinin biochemistry that started with the pioneering work of plant physiologists

| 1 | A block of tissue is removed from a plant, and the surfaces are sterilized. | 2 | Tissue is cultivated in dishes on nutrient media. Treatment with equal proportions of auxin and cytokinin causes formation of an undifferentiated callus. | 3 | Treatment with auxin-to-cytokinin ratios greater than 10:1 causes root development on many replicate plantlets. | 4 | Treatment with auxin-to-cytokinin ratios less than 10:1 induces shoot development on many replicate plantlets. |

Plant tissue   Callus

1 : 1   > 10 : 1   < 10 : 1
auxin : cytokinin   auxin : cytokinin   auxin : cytokinin

Figure 34.6   **The process of plant tissue culture.**   Plant tissue culture illustrates the impact of different proportions of auxin and cytokinin on plant organ development.

Concept check: *How do commercial growers use this process to produce many identical plants?*

Carlos Miller and Folke Skoog in the 1950s. These investigators discovered that the hormones now known as cytokinins are derivatives of adenine, a compound also found in ATP, DNA, and RNA. They made this major discovery during a laborious search for compounds that would foster growth and division of plant cells cultivated in the lab. Miller found that extracts from a particular yeast sample and a particular batch of herring sperm both stimulated plant cultures. Furthermore, the active substance in the yeast and sperm extracts could be precipitated by silver nitrate under lowered pH conditions, suggesting the presence of nucleotides. Suspecting that the active substance was similar to adenine, Miller experimented with autoclaved DNA, purifying from it white crystals that had the expected properties and activity. Collaborating with biochemists, Miller and Skoog determined the chemical structure of these crystals, naming the substance kinetin. Kinetin was the first cytokinin to be discovered. Later, Miller and Skoog purified the cytokinin known as zeatin (see Table 34.1) from corn (*Zea mays*).

Gibberellins Stimulate Cell Division and Elongation

Gibberellins (also known as gibberellic acids or GA; see Table 34.1) are terpenoid-derived hormones that are produced in apical buds, roots, young leaves, and seed embryos. Gibberellins stimulate both cell division and cell elongation, thereby fostering growth. They accomplish this by promoting the destruction of certain nuclear proteins—known as DELLA proteins—which are negative regulators of cell division and expansion. Gibberellins promote stem elongation and flowering, and they retard leaf and fruit aging. They also play roles in seed germination, a topic covered in Chapter 37.

Plant pathologist Eiichi Kurosawa discovered gibberellins when he observed that excessively tall, spindly rice plants were infected with a fungus called *Gibberella*. The fungus produced a substance, later identified chemically and named gibberellin, that caused the rice seedlings to grow taller than normal. Later, it was discovered that plants also produce gibberellins. More than a hundred different forms of gibberellin have been found, though many are not biologically active. Many kinds of dwarf plants are short because they produce less gibberellin than taller varieties of the same species. The dwarf strain of pea plants Mendel used in some of his breeding experiments is an example. When dwarf varieties of plants are sprayed with gibberellin, their stems grow to normal heights. However, dwarf wheat and rice crops are valued in agriculture because they can be more productive and less vulnerable to storm damage than taller varieties. Since the discovery of gibberellin, plant scientists have explained how this plant hormone works at the molecular level and how gibberellin regulation of plant growth evolved, our next topics.

GENOMES AND PROTEOMES

Gibberellin Function Arose in a Series of Stages During Plant Evolution

In flowering plants, gibberellin works by helping to liberate repressed transcription factors. In the absence of gibberellin, DELLA proteins bind particular transcription factors needed for the expression of gibberellin-responsive genes (**Figure 34.7a**). In this way, DELLAs function as brakes that restrain cell division and expansion. But when sufficient gibberellin is present, it binds receptor proteins called GID1 (**Figure 34.7b**). Gibberellin binding increases the ability of GID1 proteins to interact with DELLA proteins, starting a process that leads to the destruction of DELLAs. In the absence of DELLA proteins, transcription factors are able to bind the promoter regions of gibberellin-responsive genes, allowing their expression. As a result, cell division and expansion occur, leading to growth.

In 2007 Yuki Yasumura, Nicholas Harberd, and their colleagues reported that the gibberellin-DELLA mechanism for regulating the growth of flowering plants arose in a stepwise fashion. They discovered this by comparing the DELLA and GID1 proteins of flowering plants with homologous proteins of a bryophyte and a lycophyte. The seedless lycophytes, the oldest living phylum of vascular plants, first appeared millions of years before the first flowering plants, and the seedless, nonvascular bryophytes arose millions of years before the first vascular plants (see Figure 28.1). The investigators studied the interactions of DELLA proteins with GID1 and evaluated the extent to which gibberellin enhanced DELLA-GID1 binding and growth in these different groups of plants.

The results indicated that the bryophyte possesses DELLA and GID1 proteins, but these proteins don't interact, and bryophyte DELLA does not repress growth. In contrast, differences in the protein structure of lycophyte DELLAs enable them to interact with GID1 and gibberellin, but without detectably influencing growth. Neither the bryophyte nor the lycophyte showed detectable growth responses to gibberellin, though their DELLAs were able to repress growth when expressed in a flowering plant. This pattern led the biologists to propose that DELLA-mediated repression of plant growth evolved after the divergence of lycophytes but before the appearance of the first flowering plants (**Figure 34.8**). Though the necessary components (DELLAs and GID1 proteins) were present earlier, they did not assemble into a growth regulation system until later in plant evolutionary history.

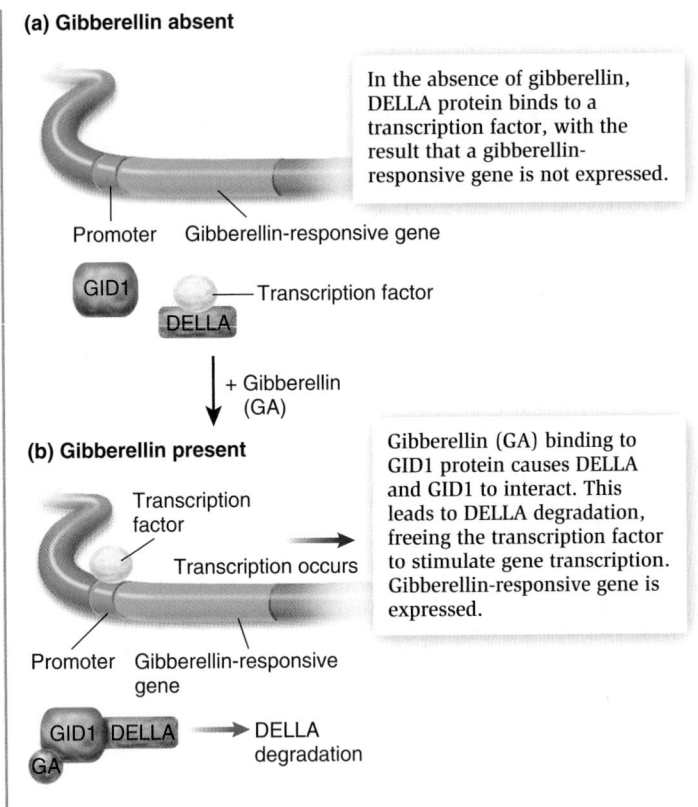

(a) Gibberellin absent

In the absence of gibberellin, DELLA protein binds to a transcription factor, with the result that a gibberellin-responsive gene is not expressed.

Promoter   Gibberellin-responsive gene

GID1

Transcription factor

DELLA

+ Gibberellin (GA)

(b) Gibberellin present

Transcription factor

Transcription occurs

Gibberellin (GA) binding to GID1 protein causes DELLA and GID1 to interact. This leads to DELLA degradation, freeing the transcription factor to stimulate gene transcription. Gibberellin-responsive gene is expressed.

Promoter   Gibberellin-responsive gene

GID1 DELLA
GA

DELLA degradation

Figure 34.7 **Gibberellin works by releasing trapped transcription factors.** **(a)** In the absence of gibberellin, DELLA binds transcription factors and gibberellin-response genes are not expressed. **(b)** When gibberellin binds to the protein GID1, GID1 can bind DELLA proteins, which causes DELLA proteins to be degraded. As a result, transcription factors that had been bound to DELLA proteins are released and can bind to gene promoters, thereby inducing gene expression.

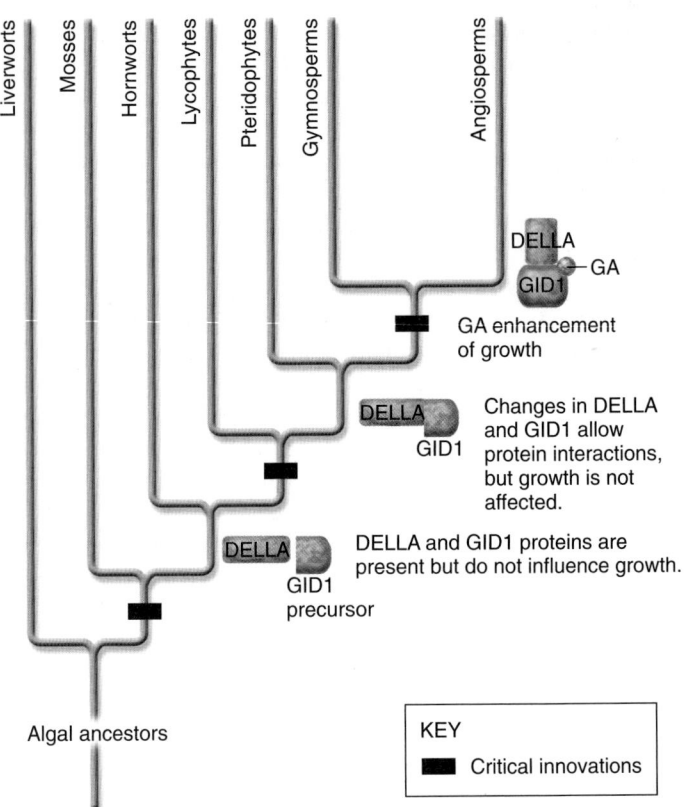

Liverworts   Mosses   Hornworts   Lycophytes   Pteridophytes   Gymnosperms   Angiosperms

DELLA
GA
GID1

GA enhancement of growth

DELLA
GID1

Changes in DELLA and GID1 allow protein interactions, but growth is not affected.

DELLA
GID1

DELLA and GID1 proteins are present but do not influence growth.

GID1 precursor

Algal ancestors

KEY

Critical innovations

Figure 34.8 **Evolution of the gibberellin-DELLA system.** The gibberellin-DELLA system that controls growth of flowering plants evolved step by step. Although DELLA and GID1 proteins are present in a bryophyte, they do not interact, nor does gibberellin bind to GID1. In lycophytes, GID1 interacts with gibberellin and with DELLAs, but the system does not influence growth. The growth responses of gibberellin apparently evolved after the divergence of lycophytes.

 Principle: *All species (past and present) are related by an evolutionary history.* The gibberellin-DELLA system that controls growth of flowering plants evolved in a step-by-step fashion.

Ethylene's Effects Include Cell Expansion

The plant hormone **ethylene** is particularly important in coordinating plant developmental and stress responses. Ethylene is a simple hydrocarbon gas produced during seedling growth, flower development, and fruit ripening. This hormone also plays important roles in leaf and petal aging and drop, and defence against osmotic stress and pathogen attack. As a gas, ethylene is able to diffuse through the plasma membrane and cytosol to ethylene receptors localized in the endoplasmic reticulum. When activated by ethylene binding, these receptors inactivate a protein kinase known as CTR1. This action ultimately enables transcription factors to induce the transcription of various genes.

People first noticed the effects of ethylene gas on plants in the nineteenth century when they observed that street-side trees exposed to leaking street lanterns unexpectedly lost their leaves. A 17-year-old student in St. Petersburg, Dimitry Neljubov, performed the first experiments to explore the effects of illumination gas on plants. He exposed pea seedlings grown in the laboratory to illumination gas and noticed that the pea seedlings grew sideways rather than upward. So he tested the individual chemical components of illumination gas for the same effect. After conducting many experiments, in 1901 Neljubov reported that ethylene was the only component of illumination gas that caused the seedlings to grow horizontally and that ethylene was effective in very low concentrations (as low as 0.06 parts per million in air). Later, scientists established that ethylene influences cell expansion, often in association with auxin. Ethylene does this by increasing the disorder of microtubules within cells, thereby causing random orientation of cell-wall microfibrils. As a result, cells exposed to ethylene tend to expand in all directions rather than elongating.

Ethylene's effects on cell expansion explain this hormone's important role in seedling germination. The tender apical meristems of seedlings could be easily damaged during their growth through crusty soil. Ethylene helps seedlings avoid such damage by inducing what is known as the "triple response" (**Figure 34.9**). First, ethylene prevents the seedling stem and root from elongating. Second, the hormone induces the stem and root to swell radially, thereby increasing in thickness. Together, these responses strengthen the seedling stem and root. Third, ethylene encourages the seedling stem to bend so that embryonic leaves and the delicate meristem grow horizontally rather than vertically, the sideways growth response that Neljubov first observed. The bent portion of the stem, known as a hook, then pushes up through the soil (look ahead to Figure 37.21).

The hook forms as the result of an imbalance of auxin across the stem axis, which causes cells on one side of the stem to elongate faster than cells on the other side. Ethylene drives this auxin imbalance.

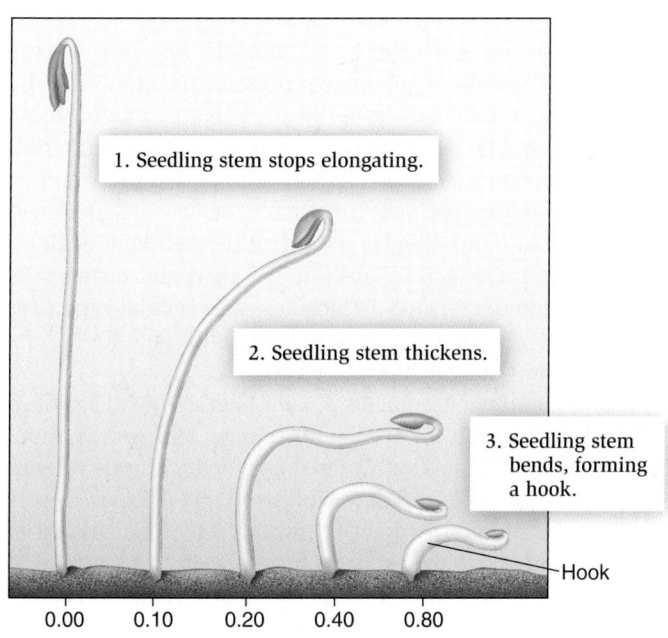

Figure 34.9 **Seedling growth showing the triple response to ethylene.** When applied at levels above a particular concentration (0.80 ppm), ethylene causes seedling stems to cease elongation, swell radially, and bend to form a hook that can push upward through the soil. Ethylene produced naturally within seedlings causes the same response.

Concept check: *What adaptive advantage does this seedling behaviour provide?*

Knowledge of the effects of ethylene on fruits has been very useful commercially. Ripe fruits are easily damaged during transit, but some, such as tomatoes and apples, can be picked before they ripen, allowing them to be transported with minimal damage. At their destination, these fruits can be ripened by treatment with ethylene. However, fruit that becomes overripe may exude ethylene that hastens ripening in nearby, unripe fruit (if you place bananas in a plastic bag, they will ripen quickly as the ethylene they produce cannot escape the bag and thus accumulates).

Several Hormones Help Plants Cope with Environmental Stress

Several plant hormones share the property of helping plants respond to environmental stresses, such as flooding, drought, high salinity, cold, heat, and attack by disease microorganisms and animal herbivores. These protective hormones include the major plant hormones known as **abscisic acid** and **brassinosteroids** (see Table 34.1). Additional protective hormones are salicylic acid (SA), whose chemical structure is similar to that of Aspirin, and a peptide known as systemin. The fragrant compound jasmonic acid, whose structure is similar to that of mammalian prostaglandins, and the gas nitric oxide (NO) are also protective plant hormones.

Abscisic Acid Abscisic acid (ABA), was named at a time when plant biologists thought that it played a role in leaf or fruit drop, also known as abscission. Later they discovered that ethylene actually causes leaf and fruit abscission, whereas abscisic acid slows or stops plant metabolism when growing conditions are poor. For example, ABA may induce bud and seed dormancy. Dormant buds and seeds resume growth only when specific environmental signals reveal the onset of conditions suitable for survival. In preparation for winter, ABA stimulates the formation of tough, protective scales around the buds of perennial plants. Seed coats of apple, cherry, and other plants also accumulate ABA, which prevents seeds from germinating unless temperature and moisture conditions are favourable for seedling growth. Water-stressed roots also produce ABA, which is then transported to shoots, where it helps to prevent water loss from leaf surfaces by inducing leaf pores (stomata) to close (look ahead to Figure 36.17).

Brassinosteroids Brassinosteroids are named after the cruciferous plant genus *Brassica* (which includes cabbage and broccoli), from which they were first identified. However, seeds, fruits, shoots, leaves, and flower buds of all types of plants contain brassinosteroids. These hormones induce vacuole water uptake and influence enzymes that alter cell-wall carbohydrates, thereby fostering cell expansion. Mutations that affect brassinosteroid synthesis cause plants to exhibit dwarfism. Such plants have small, dark green cells because their tissues are unable to expand. Brassinosteroids also impede leaf drop, help grass leaves to unroll, and stimulate xylem development. They can be applied to crops to help protect plants from heat, cold, high salinity, and herbicide injury.

Brassinosteroids are chemically related to animal steroid hormones, such as human sex hormones. However, unlike animal steroid hormones, which bind to receptors in the nucleus or cytosol, brassinosteroids bind to receptors in the plasma membrane. When they bind brassinosteroid, the membrane receptors initiate a signal transduction pathway that activates transcription factors for brassinosteroid-responsive genes.

34.3   PLANT RESPONSES TO ENVIRONMENTAL STIMULI

Learning Outcomes:

1. Describe how photoreceptors allow plants to respond to light, including day length.
2. Discuss how plant roots respond to gravity and touch.
3. Give examples of how plants respond to flood and drought.
4. Outline how plants protect themselves against pathogenic attack.

Plants encounter many types of environmental challenges and behave accordingly. For example, if buried seeds were to germinate beneath soil layers too deep for light to penetrate, or beneath a cover of established plants, seedlings would not be able to obtain sufficient light for photosynthesis and would die. A related reproductive challenge for plants is to flower at times of the year that are most beneficial for achieving pollination or seed dispersal. How do plants determine if there is enough light for seeds to germinate and for seedlings to grow? How do plants determine when to flower?

The answer is that plants possess cellular systems for measuring light and determining the seasonal time of year. Using these systems, plant seeds germinate only when there is sufficient light for seedling growth, and flowering occurs during the most advantageous season. Therefore, plants can sense and respond to their light environments. Plants are also able to respond to other external physical and biological stimuli. In this section, we survey plant responses to these external stimuli, beginning with light.

Plants Detect Light and Measure Day Length

A plant's ability to measure and respond to light amounts and day length, a process called **photoperiodism**, is based on the presence of light receptors within cells. Such light sensors are known as **photoreceptors** and they occur in several types. Some types of plant photoreceptors also occur in animals, whereas others are distinctive to plants. Each type of photoreceptor has a light-absorbing component and other regions that respond to light absorption by switching on signal transduction pathways. Responses by many cells in a tissue or an organ cumulatively result in behaviours such as sun tracking, phototropism, flowering, and seed germination.

Blue-Light Receptors   Cryptochromes and phototropins are two types of blue-light receptors—molecules that absorb and respond to blue light. Experiments suggest that **cryptochromes** help young seedlings determine if their light environment is bright enough to allow photosynthesis. If not, seedlings continue to elongate through the soil, toward the light. How does this process work? In the dark, seedlings produce a nuclear protein known as COP1 (constitutive photomorphogenesis1) that prevents the expression of genes for chlorophyll synthesis and photosynthesis. The result is that seedlings continue to elongate. When seedlings reach the lighted surface, COP1 moves to the cytosol and associates with activated cryptochrome. This prevents COP1 from inhibiting photosynthesis genes. As a result, seedlings are able to produce chlorophyll.

Phototropin is the main blue-light sensor involved in phototropism. This sensor has two components: a protein that has a kinase domain and a flavin pigment molecule that can absorb blue light. In the dark, the flavin is not covalently bound to the protein. However, when the flavin absorbs blue light, it changes conformation and becomes covalently bound to the protein. Flavin binding, in turn, changes the conformation of the phototropin protein, allowing it to phosphorylate itself by means of the protein kinase domain. When a plant organ is exposed to directional blue light, phototropin becomes phosphorylated. In this way, a light signal is converted into a chemical signal that influences auxin movement.

Phytochrome, the Red- and Far-Red-Light Receptor   Many plant growth and developmental processes are influenced by **phytochrome,** a red- and far-red-light receptor. Phytochrome operates much like a light switch, flipping back and forth between two conformations: : P_r that absorbs red light, and P_{fr} that absorbs only far-red light (light having a wavelength longer than that of red light) (**Figure 34.10**). When red light is abundant, as in full sunlight, P_r absorbs red light and changes its conformation to the P_{fr} form, which activates cellular responses such as seed germination. When left in the dark for a long period, P_{fr} slowly transforms into P_r.

The role of phytochrome as a plant "light switch" has been shown experimentally in studies of lettuce seed germination. Researchers have found that water-soaked lettuce seeds will not germinate in darkness, but they will germinate if exposed to as little as one minute of red light (**Figure 34.11**). This amount of light exposure is sufficient to transform a critical amount of P_r to the active P_{fr} form, which stimulates germination. However, if this brief red-light treatment is followed by a few minutes of treatment with far-red light, the lettuce seeds will not germinate. This short period of far-red illumination is enough to convert seed P_{fr} back to the inactive P_r form. The most recent light exposure determines whether the phytochrome occurs in the active or inactive form. In nature, if seeds are close enough to the surface that their phytochrome is switched on by red light, the seeds will germinate. But if seeds are buried too deeply for red light to penetrate, they will not germinate. In this way, seeds can sense if they are close enough to the surface to begin the germination process.

1 P_r, the inactive conformation of phytochrome, occurs in the cytosol and is a receptor for red light.

2 Red light activates phytochrome, converting it to P_{fr}, a receptor for far-red light.

3 Activated P_{fr} moves into the nucleus, where it interacts with specific proteins, thereby regulating genes and causing such responses as seed germination.

Figure 34.10 How phytochrome acts as a molecular light switch.

Concept check: *What kind of light does the active conformation of phytochrome absorb, and what kind of change does such absorption cause?*

DARKNESS

In darkness, seeds do not germinate because phytochrome remains in the inactive P_r conformation.

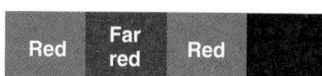

Exposure to red light after far-red light switches phytochrome back to the active P_{fr} conformation, so seeds germinate.

Even a brief exposure to red light generates the active P_{fr} conformation of phytochrome, allowing seeds to germinate.

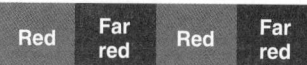

The most recent light exposure determines whether phytochrome occurs in the active P_{fr} or in the inactive P_r conformation. If in the latter, most seeds do not germinate.

Figure 34.11 Phytochrome controls germination by responding to red/far red light signals.

Exposure to far-red light after red-light exposure converts active P_{fr} to inactive P_r, so seeds do not germinate.

Most of our understanding of phytochrome's effect on gene expression comes from the study of the model plant *Arabidopsis*. This plant has five phytochrome genes (*PHYA* to *PHYE*). Each of the five types of phytochrome is composed of two proteins, each having a light-sensitive nonprotein pigment called a chromophore (see Figure 34.10). In the dark, phytochrome molecules in the P_r state reside in the cytosol. After exposure to red light, activated phytochrome (P_{fr}) molecules typically move from the cytosol to the nucleus. Within the nucleus, P_{fr} interacts with a protein known as PIF3 (phytochrome interacting factor 3). PIF3 binds to the regulatory elements of several phytochrome-responsive genes, activating some and repressing others to orchestrate the proper physiological response to specific light conditions.

Photoperiodism   Phytochromes play a critical role in photoperiodism, the response to relative lengths of darkness that influence the timing of dormancy and flowering. Flowering plants can be classified as long-day, short-day, or day-neutral plants. When scientists named these groups they thought that plants measured the amount of daylight. Researchers later discovered that plants actually measure night length.

Lettuce, spinach, radish, beet, clover, gladiolus, and iris are examples of **long-day plants** because they flower in spring or early summer, when the nights are shorter (and thus the days are longer) than a defined period (**Figure 34.12**). In contrast, asters, strawberries, dahlias, poinsettias, potatoes, soybeans, and goldenrods are examples of **short-day plants** because they flower only when the nights are longer than a defined period. Such night lengths occur in late summer, fall, and winter, when days are short. As shown in Figure 34.12, when plants are given an experimental light flash in the middle of a long dark period, the long-day plants flower while the short-day plants do not. These results indicate that both types of plant measure night length. Roses, snapdragons, cotton, carnations, dandelions, sunflowers, tomatoes, and cucumbers flower regardless of the night length, as long as day length meets the minimal requirements for plant growth, and are thus known as **day-neutral plants**.

Ornamental plant growers manipulate night length to produce flowers for market during seasons when they are not naturally available. For example, chrysanthemums are short-day plants that usually flower in the fall, but growers use light-blocking shades to increase night length and produce flowering plants in any season.

Shading Responses   Phytochrome also mediates plant responses to shading. These responses include the extension of leaves from shady portions of a dense tree canopy into the light,

Figure 34.12   Flowering and photoperiodism.   Iris is a long-day plant that flowers in response to the short nights of late spring and early summer, whereas goldenrod is a short-day plant that flowers in response to the longer nights of late summer and early autumn. The length of night is the critical factor, as shown by the effects of light flashes.

Concept check: *What would happen if you gave these plants a brief exposure to darkness in the middle of the daytime?*

and growth that allows plants to avoid being shaded by neighbouring plants. These growth responses occur by the elongation of branch internodes. Leaves detect shade as an increased proportion of far-red light to red light. This means that more of the phytochrome in shaded leaves is in the inactive (P_r) state than is the case for leaves in the sun. Activated phytochrome (P_{fr}) inhibits the growth of shoot internodes, but phytochrome in the inactivated state does not, so branches bearing shaded leaves extend toward sunlight.

Plants Respond to Gravity and Touch

Have you ever wondered what causes plant stems to generally grow upward and roots downward? The upward growth of shoots and the downward growth of roots are behaviours known as **gravitropism**, growth in response to the force of gravity. Shoots are said to be negatively gravitropic because they grow in the direction opposite to the gravitational force. If a potted plant is turned over on its side, the shoot will eventually bend and begin to grow vertically again (**Figure 34.13**). Most roots are said to be positively gravitropic because they grow in the same direction as the gravitational force.

Both roots and shoots detect gravity by means of starch-heavy plastids, known as **statoliths**. Specialized gravity-sensing cells that contain statoliths are known as statocytes. In shoots, statocytes are located in a layer of cells known as the endodermis, which forms a sheath around vascular tissues. In roots, gravity-sensing cells occur in the centre of the root cap. Gravity causes the relatively heavy statoliths to sink, which causes changes in calcium ion messengers that affect the direction of auxin transport. This process induces changes in the direction of shoot or root growth. For example, in a root that becomes oriented horizontally, the statoliths are pulled by gravity to the lower sides of statocytes (**Figure 34.14**). The change in statolith positions causes auxin to move to cells on the lower sides of roots. In roots, auxin inhibits cell elongation (note that auxin has the opposite

Figure 34.13 Negative gravitropism in a shoot. This tomato shoot system has resumed upward growth after being placed on its side. Upward growth started about four hours after the plant was turned sideways; this photo was taken 20 hours later. Shoots sense gravity by means of starchy statoliths present in stem tissue near the central vascular tissue.

effect on shoots in mediating the phototropic response). Thus, root growth slows on the lower side, while cell elongation continues normally on the upper side. This process causes the root to bend, so that it eventually grows downward again.

Recent studies suggest that gravity responses are related to touch responses, known as **thigmotropism** (from the Greek *thigma,* touch). For example, when roots encounter rocks or other barriers to their downward growth in the soil, they display a touch response that temporarily supersedes their response to gravity. Such roots grow horizontally until they get around the barrier, whereupon downward growth in response to gravity resumes. Plant shoots also respond to touch; examples include vines with tendrils that wind around or clasp supporting structures. Wind also induces touch responses. In very windy places,

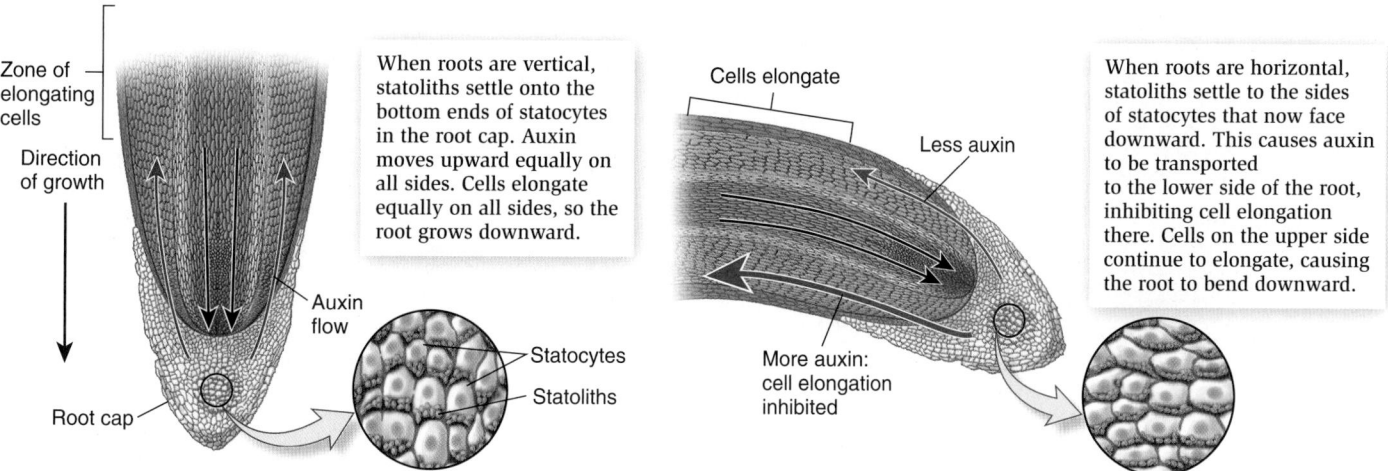

Zone of elongating cells

Direction of growth

Root cap

Auxin flow

Statocytes

Statoliths

When roots are vertical, statoliths settle onto the bottom ends of statocytes in the root cap. Auxin moves upward equally on all sides. Cells elongate equally on all sides, so the root grows downward.

Cells elongate

Less auxin

More auxin: cell elongation inhibited

When roots are horizontal, statoliths settle to the sides of statocytes that now face downward. This causes auxin to be transported to the lower side of the root, inhibiting cell elongation there. Cells on the upper side continue to elongate, causing the root to bend downward.

Figure 34.14 Positive gravitropism in a root. Root-tip cells sense gravity by means of starchy statoliths present in cells at the centre of the root cap.

trees tend to be shorter than normal, giving them the advantage of being less likely to blow over than taller trees. In the laboratory, plant scientists have simulated natural touch responses by rubbing plant stems and found that this treatment can result in shorter plants. Touch causes the release of calcium ion messengers that influence gene expression.

More rapid responses to touch, such as leaf folding by the sensitive plant (see Figure 34.1b), are based on changes in the water content of cells within structures known as pulvini (plural, pulvini), a swelling located at the base of attachment of each pair of leaflets in complex leaves. A pulvinus consists of a thick layer of parenchyma cells that surrounds a core of vascular tissue (**Figure 34.15**). When the leaflet of a sensitive plant is touched, an action potential opens ion channels in parenchyma cells near the top (adaxial) surfaces of the leaflets. These cells expel potassium and chloride ions, causing water to flow out and the cells to become flattened. This bends the leaflets downward and together, starting the leaflet-folding process. The action potential generated at the touch site also flows through the leaf, causing many or all of the leaflets to bend, with the result that the entire leaf folds. Reversal of this process allows the leaf to unfold.

The action of pulvini also explains some plant movements that are unrelated to touch: sleep movements and sun tracking. Sleep movements are changes in leaf position that occur in response to day–night cycles. Sun tracking, as mentioned, is the movement of leaves or flowers in response to the sun's position.

Plants Respond to Flooding, Drought, High Salinity, Heat, and Cold

Plants display many types of adaptations that help them cope with unfavourable growth conditions, such as flooding and drought. These responses are often mediated by hormones.

Flooding   The major harmful effect of flooding is that too much water makes roots unable to obtain sufficient oxygen to fuel respiratory processes. Without oxygen from the air, roots cannot produce the ATP needed to absorb minerals from soil. Many plants can reduce the effects of flooding by producing **aerenchyma**, a tissue containing large, snorkel-like air channels that allow more oxygen to flow from shoots to the submerged roots (**Figure 34.16**).

In some plants, aerenchyma formation is developmentally programmed, and in others, it is a response to change in environmental conditions. For example, aerenchyma develops in the roots of many plants native to wetland habitats even when the soil is not wet. Aerenchyma can also form in the roots of plants such as corn as a response to flooding. Aerenchyma formation is regulated by the action of ethylene, which leads to programmed cell death, followed by cell collapse.

Drought is related to several other environmental stresses—high salinity, heat, and cold—all of which reduce the amount of liquid water present in plant cells. Most plants that lose half or more of their water are unable to recover. Thus, plants possess diverse adaptations that reduce water loss, and the hormone abscisic acid often triggers these responses.

Plants Respond to Biological Stresses Such as Herbivore and Pathogen Attack

Plants are vulnerable to attack by animal herbivores and pathogens: disease-causing viruses, bacteria, and fungi. Structural barriers, such as cuticles, epidermal trichomes, and outer bark, help to reduce infection and herbivore attack (see Chapter 33). Plants also use many types of chemical defences to deter herbivores and respond to pathogens. Such defences explain why remarkably little natural vegetation is lost to herbivore or

Figure 34.15   **Leaf folding in the sensitive plant: how pulvini change the positions of leaflets and leaves.**   The electrical signals known as action potentials result from the rapid flow of ions through membrane ion channels. Electrical signals spread from one cell to another through plasmodesmata. Cells near the lower surface of the pulvinus respond to ion flow by losing water, causing them to flatten.

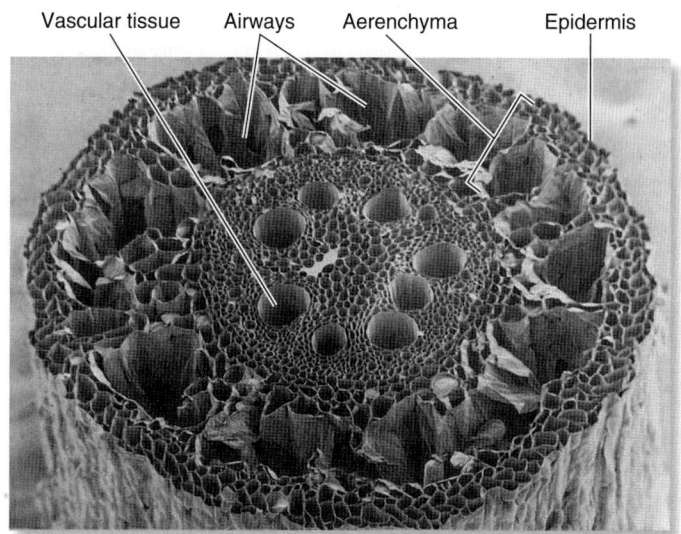

Vascular tissue   Airways   Aerenchyma   Epidermis

Figure 34.16 A plant response to flooding. This illustration of a slice of a root shows air channels within aerenchyma tissue.

 Principle: *Structure determines function. Air channels within aerenchyma tissue allow air to flow from shoots to roots even when the plant is partially submerged.*

pathogen attack. However, agricultural crops can be more vulnerable to attack than their wild counterparts. This is because some protective adaptations have been lost during crop domestication as the result of genetic changes that increase edibility. For this reason, crop scientists are particularly interested in understanding plant defense behaviour, with the goal of being able to breed or genetically engineer crop plants that are better protected from pests.

Plant Responses to Herbivores Plants use a wide variety of chemical defences against herbivores. Defence compounds include the secondary metabolites alkaloids, terpenes and terpenoids, tannins, and phytoalexins. Some of these substances act directly on herbivores, making plants taste bad so that herbivores learn to avoid them. Other chemical compounds function indirectly. For example, when attacked by insect caterpillars, cruciferous plants release terpenoids that attract a bodyguard wasp (*Cotesia rubecula*), which attacks the caterpillars.

Defences against herbivores may involve the action of plant hormones (**Figure 34.17**). For example, when insects wound tomato plants, damaged cells release the peptide hormone systemin. This protective hormone induces undamaged cells to produce the hormone jasmonic acid (JA), which functions as an alarm system. JA travels in the phloem or through the air to

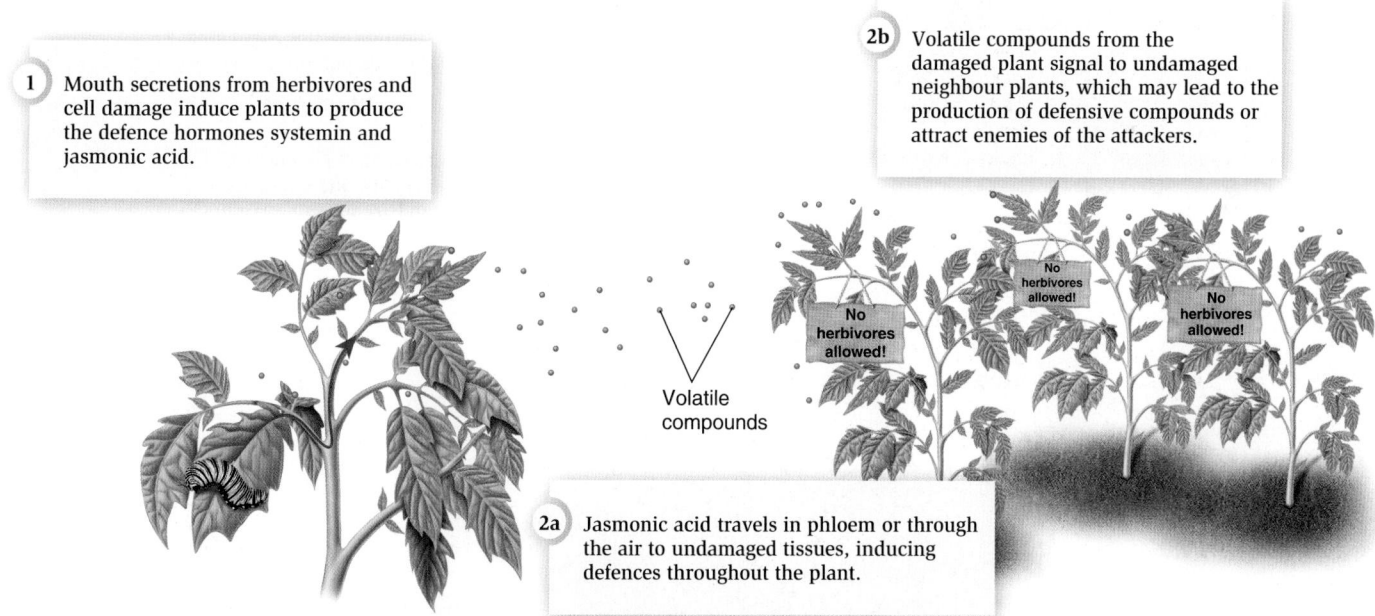

1 Mouth secretions from herbivores and cell damage induce plants to produce the defence hormones systemin and jasmonic acid.

2b Volatile compounds from the damaged plant signal to undamaged neighbour plants, which may lead to the production of defensive compounds or attract enemies of the attackers.

Volatile compounds

No herbivores allowed!

2a Jasmonic acid travels in phloem or through the air to undamaged tissues, inducing defences throughout the plant.

Figure 34.17 Plant responses to herbivore attack. (a) Leaf damage induces local defensive responses, including the production of compounds that travel through the plant and cause defence responses elsewhere. In addition, insect mouth secretions and tissue damage may cause the attacked plant to release volatile compounds. These volatile compounds foster the development of defences in undamaged parts of the same plant. (b) Such volatile compounds may also induce defences in neighbouring plants, which then become less vulnerable to herbivores. Volatile compounds may also attract predators that feed on the herbivore attacker.

Concept check: *What advantage would a predator obtain by responding to the volatile signals emitted from herbivore-damaged plants? What adaptive advantage could a plant obtain by attracting the enemies of its attackers?*

undamaged parts of the plant, inducing widespread preemptive production of defensive compounds (see Figure 34.17, step 2a). Airborne compounds released from herbivore-damaged plants may also attract the enemies of the insect attackers.

In addition, nearby plants may also detect these airborne signals and respond by similarly arming themselves against attack (see Figure 34.17, step 2b). JA functions in plant cells by binding to the protein inhibitors of transcription factors. Such JA binding leads to inhibitor destruction, freeing the transcription factors to start gene expression. In this way, the alarm system is activated only when necessary.

Plant Responses to Pathogen Attack   Every year, about 15% of crop production is lost to disease caused by certain bacteria, fungi, protists, or viruses. During their evolution, plants have evolved mechanisms for detecting and responding to disease microbes, but microbes can rapidly evolve new disease processes. Agricultural scientists aim to understand how pathogenic microbes attack plants and how plants are able to prevent disease, in order to develop disease-resistant crop varieties. Bacterial and fungal pathogens produce many types of compounds known as **elicitors**. Such elicitors promote **virulence**, the infection of plant cells and tissues. A peptide produced by the plant pathogenic bacterium *Pseudomonas syringae* and the fungal cell-wall compound chitin are examples of elicitors. Despite their name, **avirulence genes**—known as *Avr* genes—encode virulence-enhancing elicitors (**Figure 34.18**, step 1). Some bacteria inject elicitors into plant cells by means of syringe-like systems that are also used to attack animal cells. Fungal pathogens often deliver elicitors into plant cells and absorb nutrients from them by means of penetrating structures known as haustoria (whose name derives from a Latin word meaning "to drink").

In response to elicitors, plants have evolved first and second lines of defence. The first line of defence consists of plasma membrane receptors that specifically bind microbe-associated molecules, such as bacterial lipopolysaccharides or the flagellar protein flagellin, or the fungal cell wall compound chitin. These plasma membrane receptors, which are typically protein kinases, allow plant cells to sense disease microbes. Researchers have discovered that animal cells use homologous receptor molecules to sense and respond to pathogens.

A second line of defence occurs in the cytosol. Here, microRNAs help to destroy the nucleic acids of invading viruses, in processes similar to those present in animal cells. In addition, receptors that occur in the cytosol allow plant cells to recognize injected elicitors. The binding of receptors with elicitors triggers the production of chemical defence signals: hydrogen peroxide (H_2O_2), the gas nitrous oxide (NO), and mobile

1. Pathogens produce distinctive elicitor compounds, which are the products of *Avr* genes.

2. Receptors in plant cell membranes or in the cytosol detect and bind elicitors. These receptors are the products of *R* genes.

3. The binding of elicitors causes the production of H_2O_2 and NO. H_2O_2 kills pathogens and stimulates cell-wall strengthening.

4. Together, H_2O_2 and NO stimulate production of defence compounds and alarm signals and induce cell death. Visible necrotic areas of dead cells appear where pathogen growth has been stopped.

Figure 34.18   Pathogen/plant interactions and the hypersensitive response to pathogen attack.

BioConnections: *Look back to Figures 25.9b and 25.19b. What component of the Gram-negative bacterial pathogen* Agrobacterium tumefaciens *might be recognizable by a host plant?*

hormones. Defence responses include deposition of polymers that strengthen plant cell walls at the site of attack, programmed death of infected cells as a way of limiting the spread of infection, and production of compounds that kill pathogens (Figure 34.18).

Many types of **resistance genes** (**R genes**) encode plant disease receptor proteins (Figure 34.18, step 2). If a plant is genetically unable to produce a receptor that can recognize a pathogen's presence or elicitor, disease may result. By contrast, plants successfully resist disease when the product of a dominant *R* gene (a receptor) recognizes a pathogen's presence by characteristic compounds or its dominant *Avr* gene product (an elicitor). Diverse alleles of *R* genes occur in plant populations, providing plants with a large capacity to cope with different types of pathogens. These receptors, together with plant responses—the hypersensitive response and systemic acquired resistance—represent the plant immune system.

The Hypersensitive Response to Pathogen Attack

The plant **hypersensitive response** (**HR**) is a local reaction to pathogen attack that limits the progression of disease (Figure 34.18, steps 3 and 4). Hydrogen peroxide (H_2O_2) can kill pathogens and also helps strengthen the cell wall by deposition of cross-binding polymers. The gaseous hormone NO works with H_2O_2 to stimulate the synthesis of hydrolytic enzymes, defensive secondary metabolites, the hormone salicylic acid (SA), and tough lignin in the cell walls of nearby tissues. NO also induces programmed cell death, which deprives pathogens of food, helping to limit the spread of disease. Necrotic spots are brown patches on plant organs that reveal where disease pathogens have attacked plants and where plant tissues have battled back. SA or the related compound methyl salicylate sends alarm signals to other parts of the plant, which respond by preparing defenses.

Systemic Acquired Resistance

Whereas the hypersensitive response is a local reaction, **systemic acquired resistance** (**SAR**) is an immune response of the whole plant induced by pathogen attack (**Figure 34.19**). The SAR system uses the same type of long-distance signalling process that is associated with herbivore attack (see Figure 34.17). At or near a wound, the production of systemin induces the production of jasmonic acid in nearby vascular tissues. Jasmonic acid is then transported throughout the plant. In addition, the hormone salicylic acid can be converted to volatile methyl salicylate, which perfumes the air surrounding a plant, inducing resistance in uninfected tissues. In response, plant tissues may produce defensive enzymes, which can break down pathogen cell walls, or they may generate tannins, which

Figure 34.19 Systemic acquired resistance to pathogen attack.

Concept check: *In what way is systemic acquired resistance to pathogens similar to plant responses to herbivore attack?*

are toxic to microorganisms. A key mediator of SAR is the protein NPR1, which interacts with several proteins to coordinate the expression of pathogenesis-related genes. Canadian researchers Charles Després at Brock University and Normand Brisson of the Université de Montréal have been instrumental in elucidating how NPR1 is activated by the oxidative state of the cell, and they have identified several proteins that interact with NPR1 to regulate the expression of genes involved in the response. Infection of *Arabidopsis* leaves with the bacterial pathogen *Pseudomonas syringae* leads to induction of SAR within six hours. Thus, HR and SAR are of great importance to agricultural scientists as they endeavour to find new ways to protect crop plants from attack by herbivores and pathogens, which collectively cause billions of dollars in crop damage every year.

Summary of Key Concepts

34.1 Overview of Plant Behavioural Responses

- Plants sense and respond to diverse external stimuli and internal signals, and thus display behaviour. (Figures 34.1, 34.2)
- During the process of cell signalling, cellular receptors respond to environmental stimuli as well as to internal hormonal signals and mobile RNA molecules. The process involves receptor activation, transduction of the signal by messengers, and cellular responses caused by effectors. (Figure 34.3)
- Cellular responses include changes in gene expression and ion channels that influence plant growth, development, reproduction, chemistry, and movements, such as sun tracking and leaf folding.

34.2 Plant Hormones

- Plant hormones interact with environmental stimuli to control plant development, growth, and behaviour. (Table 34.1)

- Auxin plays an important role in many aspects of plant behaviour, including phototropism—as demonstrated by the classic experiments of the Darwins, Went, Briggs, and others. Auxin can be transported downward or upward (polar transport) and sideways (lateral transport) in the plant. The position of auxin influx (AUX proteins) and efflux (PIN proteins) carriers determines the direction of auxin transport. (Figures 34.4, 34.5) The major effect of cytokinins is to increase the rate of cell division. Auxin and cytokinin are used in laboratory and commercial plant tissue culture. (Figure 34.6)

- Gibberellin function illustrates the general principle that plant hormones often act to release cellular brakes on gene expression. The components of a system by which gibberellin and cell proteins interact to influence plant growth evolved in a step-by-step fashion. (Figures 34.7, 34.8)

- The gaseous hormone ethylene plays an important role in seed germination. (Figure 34.9)

- Abscisic acid and brassinosteroids help plants respond to environmental stress.

34.3 Plant Responses to Environmental Stimuli

- Light-sensitive pigments, such as cryptochrome, phototropin, and phytochrome, allow plants to respond to light stimuli, and influence sun tracking, seed germination, and photoperiodic control of flowering. (Figures 34.10, 34.11, 34.12)

- Plant shoots and roots respond to gravity (in the process of gravitropism) by means of starch-heavy statoliths located within statocytes. Rapid touch responses (thigmotropism), such as leaf folding in the sensitive plant, depend on changes in the water content of cells in motor structures known as pulvini. (Figures 34.13, 34.14, 34.15)

- Many plants cope with physical stresses such as flooding and drought through the production of special tissue (aerenchyma), which is regulated by ethylene. (Figure 34.16)

- Plants cope with biological stresses such as herbivore and pathogen attack by means of structural and chemical adaptations. Injured plant parts produce volatile hormones that signal other parts of the same plant and nearby plants to produce defensive responses. Plant pathogens begin their attack by producing elicitor compounds encoded by avirulence (*Avr*) genes. If an attacked plant can produce a compound that interferes with that elicitor, encoded by an *R* (resistance) gene, then the plant can resist infection by that pathogen. The hypersensitive response (HR) is a local defensive response to pathogen attack, whereas systemic acquired resistance (SAR) is a whole-plant immune response. (Figures 34.17, 34.18, 34.19)

Test to Assess Your Learning

1. The major types of plant hormones include
   a. cyclic AMP, IP$_3$, and calcium ions.
   b. calcium, CDPKs, and DELLA proteins.
   c. auxin, cytokinin, and gibberellin.
   d. cryptochrome, phototropin, and phytochrome.
   e. statoliths, pulvini, and aerenchyma.

2. Phototropism is
   a. the production of flowers in response to a particular day length.
   b. the production of flowers in response to a particular night length.
   c. the growth response of a plant, organ system, or organ to directional light.
   d. the growth response of a plant, organ system, or organ to gravity.
   e. the growth response of a plant, organ system, or organ to touch

3. What is the most accurate order of events during signal transduction?
   a. first, receptor activation, then messenger signalling, and, last, an effector response
   b. first, an effector response, then messenger signalling, and, last, receptor activation
   c. first, messenger signalling, then receptor activation, and, last, an effector response
   d. first, an effector response, then receptor activation, and, last, messenger signalling
   e. none of the above

4. Which of the plant hormones is known as the master hormone, and why?
   a. cytokinin, because many plant functions require cell division
   b. gibberellins, because growth is essential to many plant responses
   c. abscisic acid, because it is necessary for leaf and fruit drop
   d. brassinosteroids, because water uptake is so fundamental to plant growth
   e. auxin, because there are many different auxin-response genes

5. Which of the major plant hormones is a diffusible gas?
   a. auxin
   b. gibberellin
   c. cytokinin
   d. ethylene
   e. abscisic acid

6. Photoreceptor molecules allow plant cells to detect light of particular wavelengths. Which of these molecules is considered to be a plant photoreceptor?
   a. cryptochrome
   b. phototropin
   c. phytochrome
   d. all of the above
   e. none of the above

7. Thigmotropism is a plant response to
   a. light.
   b. cold.
   c. touch.
   d. gravity.
   e. drought.

8. Which response is an adaptation to flooding?
   a. geotropism
   b. stomatal closure
   c. photoperiodism
   d. production of aerenchyma
   e. all of the above

9. What are avirulence genes?
   a. plant genes that encode proteins that prevent infection (virulence)
   b. plant genes that cause infection when the proteins they encode bind to pathogen elicitors
   c. pathogen genes that prevent the pathogens from causing plant disease
   d. pathogen genes that encode elicitors that foster disease in plants
   e. none of the above

10. How do plants defend themselves against pathogens?
    a. Plants produce resistance molecules (usually proteins) that bind pathogen elicitors, thereby preventing disease.

b. Plants display a hypersensitive response that limits the ability of pathogens to survive and spread.

c. Plants display systemic acquired resistance, whereby an infection induces immunity to diverse pathogens in other parts of a plant.

d. All of the above are correct.

e. None of the above is correct.

Articulate to Assess Your Learning

1. Why can plants be said to display behaviour?

2. Why do plants produce so many types of resistance (*R*) genes?

3. What kind of light does the active conformation of phytochrome absorb, and what kind of change does such absorption cause?

Collaborate to Assess and Extend Your Learning

1. Why are most wild plants distasteful, and some even poisonous, to people?

2. How could you increase the resistance of a particular crop plant species to particular types of herbivores?

3. How are the response pathways of the hormones auxin and gibberellin similar?

4. You have likely seen insects captured by the Venus flytrap plant. Discuss a plausible mechanism by which the plant detects its prey and closes the trap.

5. A principle of biology is that living organisms interact with their environment. Because diverse plants exude volatile compounds in response to herbivore or pathogen attack, some experts have written about "talking trees." Is there any such thing?

Visit McGraw-Hill Ryerson Connect™ for additional study resources.

Flowering Plants: Nutrition

Chapter Outline

The Venus flytrap (*Dionaea muscipula*) has an active trap that is
stimulated by the touch of its prey, in this case, a fly.

Many types of fascinating carnivorous ("meat-eating") plants grow abundantly in wetlands around the world, even though the soils in these places are infertile. How is this possible? In common with most plants, carnivorous plants are photosynthetic and thus produce their own organic food from water and carbon dioxide, using sunlight as an energy source. These resources are abundant in wetlands, but wetland soils are low in other minerals, such as nitrogen, that are needed for plant growth. Carnivorous plants, such as the Venus flytrap pictured in the chapter-opening photo, have adapted by obtaining some minerals from trapping and breaking down the bodies of insects and other small animals. Carnivorous plants lure animals with enticing fragrances, brightly coloured leaves, or sugar-rich glistening drops of nectar. The unsuspecting prey fall into deep, water-filled pitchers, become ensnared by gluelike mucilage, or are trapped within the walls of leafy jails whose doors suddenly snap shut. Decomposition of the animal bodies releases minerals that plant leaves quickly absorb. Other wild and cultivated plants face similar nutritional challenges and likewise display adaptations that help them acquire sufficient resources for growth and reproduction.

This chapter focuses on plant nutrition, the processes by which plants obtain essential resources. We will begin by describing plant nutrients, the resources needed by plants for completion of their seed-to-seed life cycle in good health. Next, we will explore the role of soil as an essential resource for plants. Last, we will examine the biological sources of plant nutrients, focusing on nutritional associations between plants and microorganisms, sources of nutrients for carnivorous plants, and how some plants obtain nutrients from other plants. An understanding of these topics is crucial for people looking for ways to grow more plant-derived food for humans without causing harmful mineral pollution of Earth's waters. Plant nutritional information is also useful to people who tend gardens or houseplants, and those who seek to restore degraded habitats.

35.1 / PLANT NUTRITIONAL REQUIREMENTS

Learning Outcomes:

1. List the major nutritional resources that most plants need for healthy growth.
2. Describe how some plants have adapted to light limitation in shady habitats.
3. Distinguish between plant macronutrients and micronutrients.

The case of carnivorous plants illustrates the concept that all plants—like all animals—have nutritional requirements. A **nutrient** is a substance that is metabolized by or incorporated into an organism. Photosynthetic plants require carbon dioxide (CO_2), water, and more than a dozen elements, such as potassium, nitrogen, and calcium to produce organic food by means of photosynthesis. CO_2 is primarily absorbed from air, while water and elements are primarily taken up from soil in the form of dissolved ions (**Figure 35.1**). As is the case for animals, deficiency symptoms develop in plants that receive too little of these substances. The environmental scarcity of nutrients selects for adaptations that help plants to acquire them, illustrated by the existence of carnivorous plants.

Essential elements are chemical elements required by plants that play many roles in plant metabolism, often functioning as enzyme cofactors (**Table 35.1**). Elements that are required in amounts of at least 1 g/kg of plant dry matter are known as **macronutrients**. In contrast, elements that are needed in amounts at or less than 0.1 g/kg of plant dry mass are known as **micronutrients** or trace elements. Because insufficient amounts of light, carbon dioxide, water, and other mineral nutrients can

Figure 35.1 **The major types of plant nutrients and their sources.** Elements that are required in relatively large amounts are known as macronutrients, whereas elements required in smaller amounts are known as micronutrients.

limit the extent of green plant growth, any of these resources are known as a **limiting factor**. If you were in charge of a garden, greenhouse, farm, or forest used to generate products such as wood or paper, or if you were overseeing an environmental restoration project, you would want to understand the conditions that foster or limit plant growth. In this section, we focus on plant nutritional requirements, starting with light.

Light Is an Essential Resource for the Growth of Green Plants

All photosynthetic plants require light energy for the formation of the covalent bonds of organic compounds that make up the plant body. Green plants' use of light energy as an essential resource parallels animals' nutritional requirements for organic food as a source of chemical energy. For the several hundred species of heterotropic plants that have lost their photosynthetic capacity, such as the Indian pipe (*Monotropa uniflora*), essential nutrients include absorbed organic compounds that replace light as a source of energy (**Figure 35.2**).

In nature, plants must adapt to environments with varying amounts of light and shade. For example, in forests, light availability limits the growth of tree seedlings and other small plants that are shaded by the leafy tree canopy overhead. But if a canopy tree dies from disease or is blown over by wind, creating a hole in the canopy called a light gap, the plants growing beneath it receive more sunlight and are able to grow taller. Conversely, plants growing in deserts or on mountains often experience light that is so intense that it can damage the photosynthetic components. Plants have evolved adaptations that help them cope with environments that have too little or too much light.

| Table 35.1 | Plant Essential Elements | | | |

Element (chemical symbol)	Approximate percentage of plant dry mass	Major source	Form taken up by plants	Function(s)
Macronutrients				
Carbon (C)	45	Air	CO_2	Component of all organic molecules
Oxygen (O)	45	Air, soil, water	CO_2, O_2, H_2O	Component of all organic molecules
Hydrogen (H)	6	Water	H_2O	Component of all organic molecules, protons used in chemiosmosis and other transport processes (see Chapter 7)
Nitrogen (N)	1.5	Soil	NO_3^-, NH_4^+	Component of proteins, nucleic acids, chlorophyll, coenzymes, alkaloids
Potassium (K)	1.0	Soil	K^+	Has essential role in cell ion balance
Calcium (Ca)	0.5	Soil	Ca^{2+}	Component of cell walls, messenger in signal transduction
Magnesium (Mg)	0.2	Soil	Mg^{2+}	Component of chlorophyll, activates some enzymes
Phosphorus (P)	0.2	Soil	HPO_4^{2-}	Component of nucleic acids, ATP, phospholipids, some coenzymes
Sulphur (S)	0.1	Soil	SO_4^{2-}	Component of proteins, some coenzymes, defence compounds
Micronutrients				
Chlorine (Cl)	0.01	Soil	Cl^-	Required for water splitting in photosystem II, cell ion balance
Iron (Fe)	0.01	Soil	Fe^{3+}, Fe^{2+}	Enzyme cofactor, component of cytochromes
Manganese (Mn)	0.005	Soil	Mn^{2+}	Enzyme cofactor
Boron (B)	0.002	Soil	$B(OH)_3$	Enzyme cofactor, component of cell walls
Zinc (Zn)	0.002	Soil	Zn^{2+}	Enzyme cofactor
Sodium (Na)	0.001	Soil	Na^+	Required to generate PEP in C_4 and CAM plants
Copper (Cu)	0.0006	Soil	Cu^+, Cu^{2+}	Enzyme cofactor
Molybdenum (Mo)	0.00001	Soil	MoO_4^{2-}	Enzyme cofactor
Nickel (Ni)	0.000005	Soil	Ni^{2+}	Enzyme cofactor

Figure 35.2 The heterotrophic flowering plant, Indian pipe (*Monotropa uniflora*). This plant lacks photosynthetic capacity and thus must absorb organic compounds for use as an energy source. In contrast, nearby autotrophic green plants use sunlight as a source of energy.

 Principle: *Living organisms use energy. This nongreen heterotrophic plant lacks photosynthetic capacity and therefore must absorb organic compounds for use as an energy source. In contrast, nearby autotrophic green plants use sunlight as a source of energy.*

(a) Shade leaf

100 μm

(b) Sun leaf

100 μm

Figure 35.3 Shade and sun leaves. These scanning electron micrographs of cut leaves reveal the thinner mesophyll and greater amount of air spaces in (a) shade leaves as compared with (b) sun leaves.

Adaptations to Shade Plants can adapt to shading by producing thin, translucent leaves that allow some light to pass through to other leaves. In a shady environment, a plant or leaf may also produce more total chlorophyll, thereby maximizing the amount of light absorbed. Finally, many plants produce distinctive shade and sun leaves (**Figure 35.3**). Sun leaves have a thicker layer of chlorophyll-containing mesophyll and therefore are able to harvest more of the bright sunlight that penetrates deeply into the leaf. In contrast, shade leaves have thinner mesophyll layers, with more air spaces than do sun leaves. The thinner shade leaves avoid wasting energy by not producing photosynthetic tissues that dim light cannot reach.

Most epidermal cells at leaf surfaces are transparent, allowing light to penetrate to green mesophyll, and in some plants, these epidermal cells are shaped like lenses that focus more light into the green tissue. The arrangement of leaves on plants and stem branching patterns can also reflect adaptations that reduce shading. For example, many tropical forest trees that must compete for light with closely crowded neighbours are extremely tall, and they produce branches and leaves only at their very tops. Shorter plants native to the shady interiors of tropical rain forests are so well adapted to these moist but dim conditions that they make excellent houseplants (**Figure 35.4**).

Adaptations to Excessive Light Too much light can damage the plant chloroplasts by destroying an essential photosynthetic protein, called D1 protein. As an adaptation to excess light, specific xanthophyll pigments in the chloroplast absorb some of the light

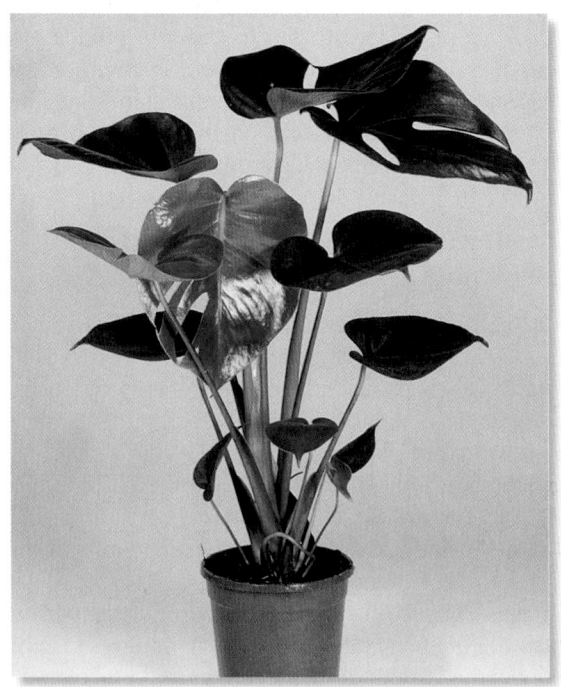

Figure 35.4 The tropical houseplant *Monstera deliciosa*. Houseplants can survive indoors because they have evolved in dimly lit natural habitats. *M. deliciosa* makes an attractive houseplant because its large, deep green leaves are adapted to the moist and shady conditions present in the interiors of tropical forests.

Concept check: *How do the epidermal cells of plants adapted to deep shade sometimes differ from epidermal cells of plants adapted to sunnier habitats?*

energy and dissipate it as harmless heat. These protective pigments can be produced from a precursor xanthophyll within minutes of a plant's exposure to excess light. Other adaptations prevent ultraviolet (UV) damage. Harmful amounts of UV radiation are absorbed by the plant's surface cuticle, as well as by carotenoid and flavonoid compounds located within leaf cells. These protective compounds are often brightly coloured and, when present in large amounts, explain the attractive red or purple colours of some leaves.

Carbon Dioxide Concentration Influences Plant Growth

Although light provides the energy for plant photosynthesis, most plant dry mass originates from carbon dioxide (CO_2). Most plants obtain CO_2 gas from the atmosphere, by absorption through stomata, pores that are found in the plant epidermis. As CO_2 dissolves in water on the surfaces of leaf mesophyll cells, it combines with water to form carbonic acid, which can dissociate into bicarbonate ion and H^+.

$$H_2O + CO_2 \longleftrightarrow H_2CO_3 \longleftrightarrow HCO_3^- + H^+$$

$$\text{carbonic acid} \quad \text{bicarbonate ion}$$

Leaf mesophyll cells then absorb the carbonic acid and bicarbonate ions. Under experimental conditions, plant photosynthetic rates increase with CO_2 concentration until the Calvin cycle enzyme rubisco has become fully supplied; that is, saturated with CO_2. (To review the role of rubisco and the Calvin cycle in photosynthesis, see Chapter 8.)

CO_2 Limitation

In nature, plants are often unable to obtain enough CO_2 for maximal photosynthesis. As a result, CO_2 limits agricultural crop productivity. This is partly because the modern atmospheric concentration of CO_2 is approximately 390 $\mu L/L$ (0.035% of atmospheric content), whereas 1,000 $\mu L/L$ of CO_2 would be required to saturate photosynthesis in most plants. In addition, oxygen can compete with carbon dioxide for the active site in rubisco, causing a reduction in photosynthetic productivity known as photorespiration (see Chapter 8).

Evidence that plant photosynthesis can be limited by CO_2 availability is provided by studies of crops grown in greenhouses where atmospheric gas content can be controlled. When supplied with air enriched with CO_2, tomatoes, cucumbers, leafy vegetables, and some other crops can double their growth rate.

In nature, plants that experience hot, dry conditions are particularly vulnerable to low CO_2 levels when their stomata close to conserve water. When stomata are closed, plants cannot absorb CO_2, which limits photosynthesis. Many plants possess structural and biochemical adaptations that help them cope with CO_2 limitation by improving CO_2 absorption. Such adaptations may be helpful in genetic engineering efforts to improve crop productivity.

Engineering CO_2-Absorption Adaptations into Crop Plants

Many plants that evolved in arid or hot environments display an adaptation known as C_4 photosynthesis, which improves productivity by aiding CO_2 absorption (refer back to Figure 8.18). About 30,000 plant species use C_4 photosynthesis, which is thought to have evolved from ancestral C_3 photosynthesis on more than 40 separate occasions. Today, C_4 plants dominate extensive warm grassland habitats of the world, contributing about 25% of total terrestrial photosynthesis. In addition, 7,500 other plant species possess a variation of C_4 photosynthesis known as CAM (crassulacean acid metabolism; see Chapter 8). However, many other plants that grow in hot environments lack C_4 photosynthesis. Rice, a staple crop for much of the world's population, is a prominent example. Agricultural scientists want to use genetic engineering techniques to endow rice with C_4 photosynthesis, to increase this crop's productivity.

To understand how this valuable crop modification might be accomplished, let's briefly review C_4 photosynthesis. Both C_4 and CAM photosynthesis rely on the leaf mesophyll enzyme phosphoenolpyruvate (PEP) carboxylase. PEP carboxylase binds CO_2 more readily than does rubisco, thereby effectively trapping scarce CO_2 within four-carbon organic acids. Recall that this process is the basis for the term C_4 photosynthesis. In the leaves of most C_4 plants, such as maize (corn), the four-carbon organic acids move through intracellular connections from mesophyll cells into specialized bundle-sheath cells that surround leaf veins. Within the bundle-sheath cells, enzymes release CO_2 from the organic acids, and the CO_2 is bound by rubisco (see Chapter 8).

Molecular biologists have succeeded in transferring maize genes encoding PEP carboxylase and other C_4 enzymes into the rice genome. However, this procedure primarily improved plant stress tolerance, rather than photosynthetic performance, which was the actual goal. Because bundle-sheath cells are often central to C_4 photosynthesis, an alternative strategy is to transform rice with the genes that control development of these specialized cells. Important progress toward this goal was made by plant biologist Jane Langdale and her colleagues, who discovered a family of genes known as the G (for "golden") genes. In maize leaves, which display C_4 photosynthesis, a particular G gene family member is expressed primarily in bundle-sheath cells, whereas a different gene of the same family is expressed in mesophyll cells. These results will help to identify more precisely the genes essential to bundle-sheath cell specialization, which are potentially useful in genetic engineering efforts.

Some other plants accomplish C_4 photosynthesis without specialized bundle-sheath cells, offering additional strategies for crop genetic engineering. For example, PEP carboxylase and rubisco occupy the same mesophyll cells in the aquatic plant *Hydrilla verticillata*. In this case, PEP carboxylase is localized within the cytoplasm, while rubisco occurs within plastids. *Borszczowia aralocaspica*, native to salty, near-desert regions of central Asia, and *Bienertia cycloptera*, native to Iranian deserts, are likewise remarkable for single-cell C_4 photosynthesis. Plant biologists Elena Voznesenskaya, Gerald Edwards, and their colleagues discovered that *B. aralocaspica* and *B. cycloptera* achieve C_4 photosynthesis within the same photosynthetic cells by producing two types of plastids, one type containing PEP carboxylase and the other containing rubisco (**Figure 35.5**). These and other recent discoveries reveal that wild plants have acquired diverse adaptations that improve CO_2 absorption and show that both basic and applied research are essential to efforts to improve food crops.

Figure 35.5 **A CO$_2$-acquisition adaptation.** In contrast to most C$_4$ plants, *Bienertia cycloptera* is able to conduct C$_4$ photosynthesis within the confines of a single cell. In this fluorescence photograph of a *B. cycloptera* cell, the red plastids at the cell periphery function like the mesophyll cells of most C$_4$ plants. In contrast, the red plastids clustered near the green nucleus function much like the bundle-sheath cells of most C$_4$ plants. The plastids appear red because chlorophyll emits red light when it fluoresces.

> **Concept check:** *Which plastids should have more rubisco enzyme in them: plastids at the cell periphery or those clustered near the nucleus?*

Water Is an Essential Plant Resource

Water is essential to plants for several reasons. As a nutrient, water is the source of most of the hydrogen atoms and some of the oxygen atoms in organic compounds (see Table 35.1). You may recall that hydrogen is incorporated during the process of photosynthesis, and oxygen is incorporated during hydrolysis reactions. Water is also the solvent for other mineral nutrients and is the main transport medium in plants, allowing movement of minerals and other solutes throughout the plant body. Cytoplasmic and vacuolar water also help to support plants by maintaining hydrostatic pressure on the cell wall.

Though plants vary in water content, water typically makes up about 90% of the weight of living plants. Most plants die when their water content falls below half of the amount normal for that particular species. Many types of desiccation-resistant plants have adaptations that allow them to survive for extended periods in nearly dry conditions, but all plants require an adequate supply of water for active metabolism and growth.

Soil Provides Additional Plant Nutrients

In addition to light, CO$_2$, and water, plants require additional elements. Macronutrients—the essential elements required in relatively large amounts—include nitrogen, potassium, calcium, magnesium, phosphorus, and sulphur (see Table 35.1). Nitrogen and phosphorus play many important roles in plants, and potassium helps to maintain or alter plant cell water content. Calcium is used in the construction of cell walls and as a cellular signal, while magnesium is an essential component of chlorophyll. Sulphur occurs in the amino acids cysteine and methionine, as well as other cell constituents. In addition, the distinctive flavours of onions, garlic, broccoli, mustard, and horseradish result from plant defence compounds that contain sulphur. Micronutrients—essential elements that plants require in relatively small amounts—include chlorine, iron, manganese, boron, zinc, sodium, copper, molybdenum, and nickel (see Table 35.1). Terrestrial plants obtain these essential elements in the form of ions dissolved in soil water (see Figure 35.1).

Plant biologists have quantitatively analyzed the mineral ion requirements of plants by growing them hydroponically; that is, by bathing plant roots in a water solution to which minerals are added in various combinations and amounts. Hydroponic studies reveal that when plants lack an adequate supply of an essential mineral nutrient, they display characteristic deficiency symptoms. Such symptoms include failure to reproduce, stunted growth, leaf curling, tissue death, and changes in leaf colour (**Figure 35.6**). Yellowing of leaves, known as **chlorosis**, is a

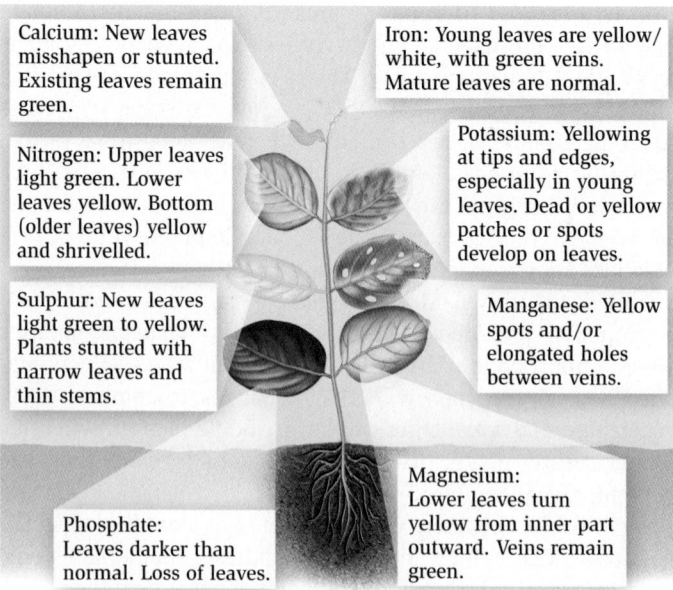

Figure 35.6 **Symptoms of mineral deficiencies.** Limited quantities of a variety of nutrients can result in general chlorosis, stunted growth, death of tissues, and reproductive failures. Although not shown here, most mineral deficiencies also affect root growth.

> **Concept check:** *Why is chlorosis a common symptom of mineral deficiencies?*

common mineral deficiency symptom, because many nutrients are needed for chlorophyll production. Deficiency symptoms are often specific to particular plants. For example, zinc deficiency causes chlorosis in corn, but in fruit trees zinc deficiency causes smaller than normal leaves. Such deficiency symptoms provide clues that crop, garden, or houseplant soils are deficient in one or more essential minerals. Farmers commonly have their soil analyzed for mineral content and, if the soil is deficient, they may amend it with **fertilizers**, soil additions that enhance plant growth by providing essential elements. Fertilizers are also sold for use in enriching garden soil or growing houseplants.

35.2 THE ROLE OF SOIL IN PLANT NUTRITION

Learning Outcomes:

1. List the benefits of soil organic material for plant growth.
2. Explain why plants require a source of fixed nitrogen and how they obtain it.
3. Discuss various plant adaptations that increase the ability to obtain phosphorus.

Soil is an essential resource for most wild and cultivated plants, providing water and other essential nutrients. For this reason, extensive loss of soil by wind and water erosion is of wide concern. Soils vary greatly in fertility; that is, their ability to support plant growth. Thus, plants of many types have had to adapt to the challenges of obtaining nutrients from poor soils. In this section, we explore soil structure and chemistry from the perspective of plant growth and describe how plants take up nutrients from the soil.

The Physical Structure of Soils Affects Their Aeration, Water-Holding Capacity, and Fertility

Natural soils have layers, known as **soil horizons** (**Figure 35.7a**). The remains of dead plants and other organisms form a layer of litter above the **topsoil**, also known as the A horizon. Many of the inorganic minerals and organic materials that enrich high-quality topsoil arise from the activities of microorganisms that decompose the litter. In this way, the minerals contained in living plants are eventually recycled to subsequent generations. Beneath the topsoil lie layers called subsoil and soil base, which are largely composed of mineral materials. Bedrock is the bottom layer that supports the soil horizons. Plant roots play an important role in conveying deep-lying minerals to the surface, thereby helping to enrich the topsoil.

Soil horizons vary in composition and thickness, depending on various factors—including climate, vegetation, bedrock type, and human impact. For example, natural grasslands produce deep, rich topsoil that is used for cropland in many regions of the world (**Figure 35.7b**). In dramatic contrast, tropical rain forests often have only thin layers of topsoil; their low-fertility soils are composed mostly of inorganic materials that are not useful to plants (**Figure 35.7c**). However, certain Amazonian soils, known as *terra preta,* are rich and black with organic materials, because ancient inhabitants fertilized extensive gardens with large amounts of decayed plant material dredged from nearby riverbanks. In other parts of the world, however, human activities have increased topsoil loss by wind or water erosion, a worldwide agricultural concern.

As these examples illustrate, soils are composed of both inorganic minerals and organic materials. The sizes of inorganic particles and the proportions of organic to inorganic materials are used to classify soils into different types. Soils also display variation in amount of aeration, water-holding capacity,

Horizon A topsoil

Horizon B subsoil

Horizon C soil base

Bedrock

(a) Soil structure

(b) Thick layer of topsoil in cropland

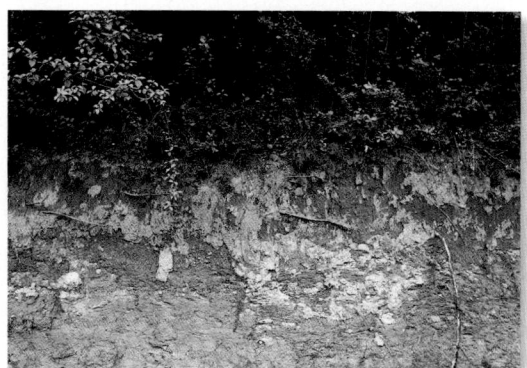

(c) Thin layer of topsoil in rain forest

Figure 35.7 Soil horizons: the structural layers of soil. **(a)** Diagram showing general soil structure. **(b)** A vertical view of an agricultural soil, showing a relatively deep layer of dark topsoil. **(c)** A vertical view of a tropical rain forest soil, showing a thin layer of dark topsoil.

pH, and mineral content. All these soil properties affect plant growth. For this reason, we will take a closer look at the organic and inorganic constituents of soils and the role of fertilizers.

Soil Organic Matter   Soil organic matter, also known as **humus**, is largely derived from plant detritus, the dead and decaying remains of plants, although animal wastes and decayed animal bodies also contribute to the organic content of soils. Organic soil matter provides many benefits. Organic-rich soils, containing more than 8% organic matter, are less likely to erode (wash or blow away with water or wind). Soil organic matter also binds mineral nutrients, thereby fostering soil fertility, and gives soils a soft consistency that fosters plant root growth and farmers' ability to cultivate the soil. Gardeners often produce their own organic matter–rich compost by layering vegetable waste from the kitchen and yard waste with soil, and turning the pile occasionally to introduce the oxygen necessary for decomposition (**Figure 35.8**). Mature compost is then mixed with garden soil to improve its fertility.

Inorganic Soil Constituents   Inorganic materials in soil are derived from the physical and chemical breakdown of rock, a process known as **weathering**. Rock is physically weathered by changes, such as cycles of freezing and thawing. Lichens and plant roots may produce organic acids that contribute to chemical weathering of rocks. During chemical weathering, soluble salts are washed out and minerals are hydrolyzed or oxidized. **Leaching** is the dissolution and removal of inorganic ions as water percolates through materials. Heavy rainfall can reduce the fertility of soils by leaching large amounts of nutrients from them. The leached minerals often end up in natural bodies of water, where they can foster the growth of cyanobacteria, algae, and aquatic plants.

Inorganic soil materials occur as particles that can be categorized according to their size as gravel, coarse sand, fine sand, silt, or clay (**Figure 35.9**). Coarse sand grains range from 2,000

Figure 35.9   The relative sizes of inorganic soil components.

to 200 μm (micrometres) in diameter, whereas fine sand particles can be as small as 20 μm. Particles of silt range from 20 to 2 μm in diameter, and clay particles are less than 2 μm in size. Soils can be classified according to their relative content of coarse and fine materials. For example, soils that contain 45% or more sand and 35% or less clay are classified as sandy soils. The other main types are silty, clay, and loam soils. Loam soil contains a mixture of sand, silt, and clay, and is ideal for the cultivation of plants.

Because of their size differences, sand, silt, and clay particles confer different properties on soils. The relatively large size and irregular shapes of sand particles allow air and water to move rapidly through sandy soils, which are said to be porous (**Figure 35.10**). Sandy soils are well aerated, which is favourable to the growth of plant roots, because they require oxygen for cellular respiration. However, rapid percolation of water through sandy soils reduces the amount of water available to the roots and leaches minerals from the soil.

Silt and clay particles fit closely together, and so soils containing larger amounts of these materials are less porous than sandy soils. Water percolates less easily through silty and clay soils, which therefore retain more ionic mineral nutrients than do sandy soils. Like organic humus, clay particles have negative charges on their surfaces that electrostatically bind positively charged ions (cations) such as NH_4^+, Ca^{2+}, and Fe^{2+} (**Figure 35.11a**). To become available to plants, these cations must be detached from the clay particles. Cations having higher valence numbers (such as Fe^{2+}) are bound more tightly than ions having lower valence numbers (NH_4^+). Hydrogen ions (H^+, protons) are able to replace mineral cations on the surfaces of humus or clay particles, a process known as **cation exchange** (**Figure 35.11b**). Cation exchange releases cations to soil water, making them more available for uptake by plant roots. However, free ions are also more easily washed out of soil. If the H^+ concentration becomes too high, as occurs as a result of prolonged acid rain, large numbers of mineral ions

Figure 35.8   Composting.   Compost can be produced by layering small amounts of soil with vegetable waste from the kitchen or garden and periodically turning the pile to introduce the oxygen needed for decomposition. Compost can be used to increase the humus and mineral content of garden soils.

are released and can be leached from soil by heavy rainfall. The nutrient ions may be lost because of surface runoff, or they may move into deeper subsoil layers where roots do not reach. In addition, metal ions, such as aluminum (Al^{3+}), which are normally bound up as nontoxic aluminum hydroxide, may be released as free Al^{3+}, which can be quite toxic to plants.

Despite their water- and mineral-retention features, silt- and clay-rich soils may be poorly aerated and therefore unfavourable to root growth. Gardeners often mix organic materials and sand into silt or clay-rich soils to improve their aeration properties. Loam is the preferred soil for agriculture because it combines the aeration provided by sand with the mineral- and water-retention capacity of clay and silt.

The Role of Fertilizers Fertilizers are soil additives that enhance plant growth by providing essential elements. The addition of fertilizer to soils can compensate for deficiencies in soil humus or mineral content and thus improve soil fertility. Fertilizers occur in organic and inorganic forms. Organic fertilizers are those in which most of the minerals are bound to organic molecules and are thus released relatively slowly. Organic fertilizers are often produced on the same farm where they will subsequently be used to enrich soils. They play an important role in **organic farming**, a term referring to the production of crops without the use of inorganic fertilizers, growth substances, and pesticides. Manure and compost are examples of organic fertilizers.

In contrast, inorganic fertilizers consist of inorganic minerals, which are immediately useful to plants but are more easily leached from soils by heavy rainfall. Nitrogen (N), phosphorus (P), and potassium (K) are the mineral nutrients that most frequently limit crop growth. For this reason, these minerals are the main components of the most common type of commercial inorganic fertilizers, known as NPK fertilizers. Such fertilizers are available in different ratios of minerals, which are optimal for different types of plants.

Excessive application of fertilizers to farm fields and lawns is undesirable because minerals not taken up by plant roots

Figure 35.10 The movement of air and water in sandy soil.

Concept check: *In which type of soil is nutrient leaching a more common problem, sandy or clay soils?*

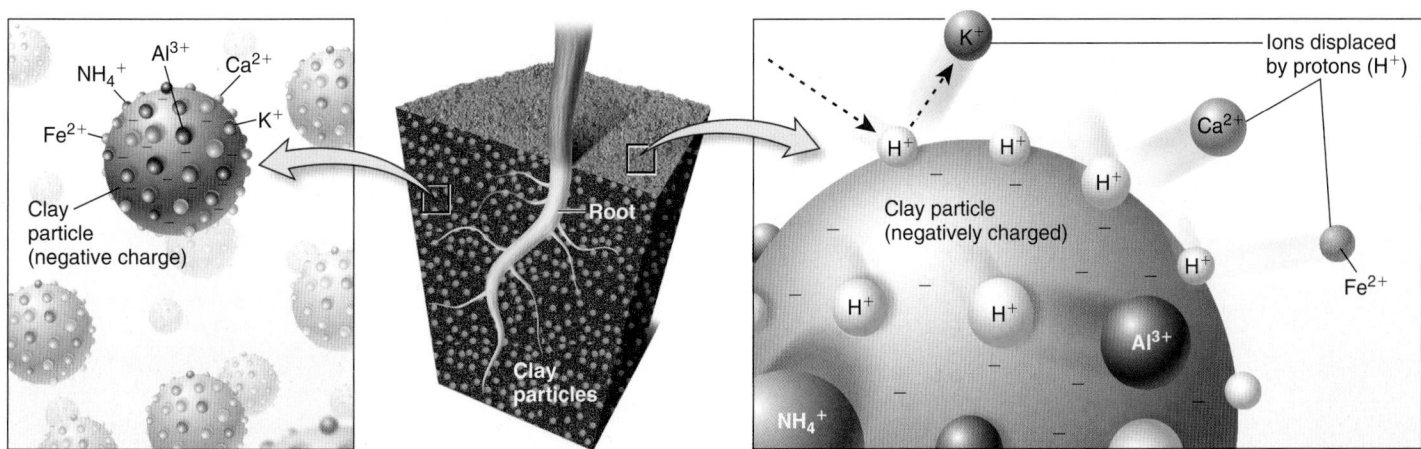

(a) Electrostatic attraction between clay particles and mineral ions

(b) Cation exchange

Figure 35.11 Cation binding and exchange. (a) Clay and humus particles display negative electrostatic surface charges that bind cations. Bound cations include not only plant mineral nutrients, such as NH_4^+, but also cations that are not plant nutrients, such as Al^{3+}. (b) Cation exchange occurs when protons displace cations, releasing them to soil water. This process makes cations more available for uptake by plant roots, but it also increases the potential for cations to leach away during rains or floods. Protons in acid soils or arising from acid rain displace so many cations from soil that its fertility decreases, and toxic ions, such as Al^{3+}, more readily damage plants.

are easily washed by rain into waterways, where they can fuel large growths of cyanobacteria, algae, and aquatic plants that harm other aquatic life forms. For example, large areas of the Gulf of Mexico and other coastal regions are now known as "dead zones" because microbial decomposition of large algal populations has depleted oxygen from the water, suffocating the animal life. These large populations of algae are fostered by fertilizers that wash from farm soils into rivers, such as the Mississippi River, that drain into coastal oceans. More careful application of fertilizers and planting of stream and river edges with vegetation that helps to absorb mineral nutrients are actions that can reduce or prevent dead zones.

Plants Require Fixed Nitrogen

Nitrogen is frequently limiting to plant growth in nature and in crop fields, because large amounts of it are required for plant synthesis of amino acids, nucleotides, and alkaloids, among many other cellular constituents. Nitrogen is the largest component of plants by mass after carbon, oxygen, and hydrogen. Although Earth's atmosphere is 78% nitrogen gas (N_2), plants cannot use nitrogen in this form. To be of use to plants, soil nitrogen must occur in a combined form, such as ammonia

(NH_3), ammonium ion (NH_4^+), or nitrate ion (NO_3^-), also known as **fixed nitrogen**. Ammonia and its dissolved form—ammonium ion—can be used directly for amino acid production by plants, explaining why ammonia is often applied as a fertilizer to farm fields in spring. However, in oxygen-rich soils, microorganisms oxidize much of the ammonium to nitrate, so nitrate may be the form in which fixed nitrogen enters most plants. Plants use ammonium ions and nitrate to make a wide range of essential organic compounds, including amino acids, nucleic acids, and chlorophyll.

Nitrate is imported into root cells by means of plasma membrane transporter proteins (**Figure 35.12**). Once inside the plants, the nitrate can be transported in the xylem for use elsewhere, stored for later use, or assimilated for immediate use. Cells store nitrate by transporting it into vacuoles. To assimilate nitrate, plant cells must reduce it to ammonium ion in a two-step process. First, the cytosolic enzyme nitrate reductase reduces nitrate (NO_3^-) to nitrite (NO_2^-). Second, in plastids, nitrite is reduced to ammonium ion by nitrite reductase. Another plastid enzyme, glutamine synthetase, uses ammonium ion to produce the amino acid glutamine.

Much of the fixed nitrogen in soils has been recycled from compounds previously used by other organisms. Nitrogen flows

1 Uptake: Protons (H^+) pumped from plant cells provide the driving force for the cotransport of protons (H^+) and nitrate (NO_3^-) into the cytosol.

2 Storage: Nitrate can be transported into a vacuole for storage.

OR

3a Assimilation: Cytoplasmic nitrate reductase converts nitrate (NO_3^-) to nitrite (NO_2^-), which enters plastids.

3b In plastids, nitrite reductase converts nitrite to ammonium ion (NH_4^+). Glutamine synthetase uses NH_4^+ to synthesize the amino acid glutamine.

Figure 35.12 How plant cells take up and transform nitrate.

through the environment in a nitrogen cycle, discussed in Chapter 56. New fixed nitrogen can be added to soils by the action of lightning, fire, and air pollution, as well as biological and industrial nitrogen fixation. **Nitrogen fixation** is the process by which atmospheric-nitrogen gas is combined with hydrogen to produce ammonia. Most of the fixed nitrogen in soils is produced by **biological nitrogen fixation**, which is performed in nature only by certain prokaryotes. Nitrogen fertilizers applied to crops are produced by **industrial nitrogen fixation**, a human activity.

Biological Nitrogen Fixation by Bacteria   Nitrogen-fixing prokaryotes include many types of cyanobacteria, which are photosynthetic and occur in oceans, lakes, and other aquatic systems, as well as in surface soil crusts (**Figure 35.13**). Various types of nonphotosynthetic bacteria living in water and soil are also able to fix nitrogen; actinobacteria and the genera *Clostridium, Klebsiella,* and *Azotobacter* are examples. Nitrogen-fixing prokaryotes often excrete a substantial amount of fixed nitrogen, and their death makes still more fixed nitrogen available to plants. Many plants have nitrogen-fixing, prokaryotic symbionts that transfer fixed nitrogen directly to plant cells. Nitrogen-fixation symbioses are so important in nature and in agriculture that they are discussed in more detail in section 35.3.

All nitrogen-fixing prokaryotes use relatively large amounts of ATP and an enzyme known as **nitrogenase** to fix nitrogen (**Figure 35.14**). This process occurs in three steps. In the first step, nitrogenase binds to a molecule of nitrogen gas (N_2). In the second step, the bound nitrogen is reduced by the addition of two hydrogen atoms (2 H), a reaction powered by the breakdown of ATP. Such a reduction occurs three times, with the addition of a total of three hydrogen atoms to each nitrogen

Figure 35.13   A soil surface crust that includes nitrogen-fixing, soil-enriching cyanobacteria.   Such crusts are widespread in grasslands and other arid regions.

Concept check: *How might soil crusts influence the ecology and economy of regions in which grazing is important?*

atom. In a third and final step, two molecules of ammonia (NH_3) are released and dissolve in cell water to form ammonium ions. The nitrogenase enzyme is then free to bind more nitrogen gas.

Because the O_2 molecule resembles N_2, oxygen can bind to the active site of nitrogenase. Oxygen binding disables nitrogenase, thereby stopping nitrogen fixation. Many of the genes involved in prokaryotic nitrogen fixation are known, and crop

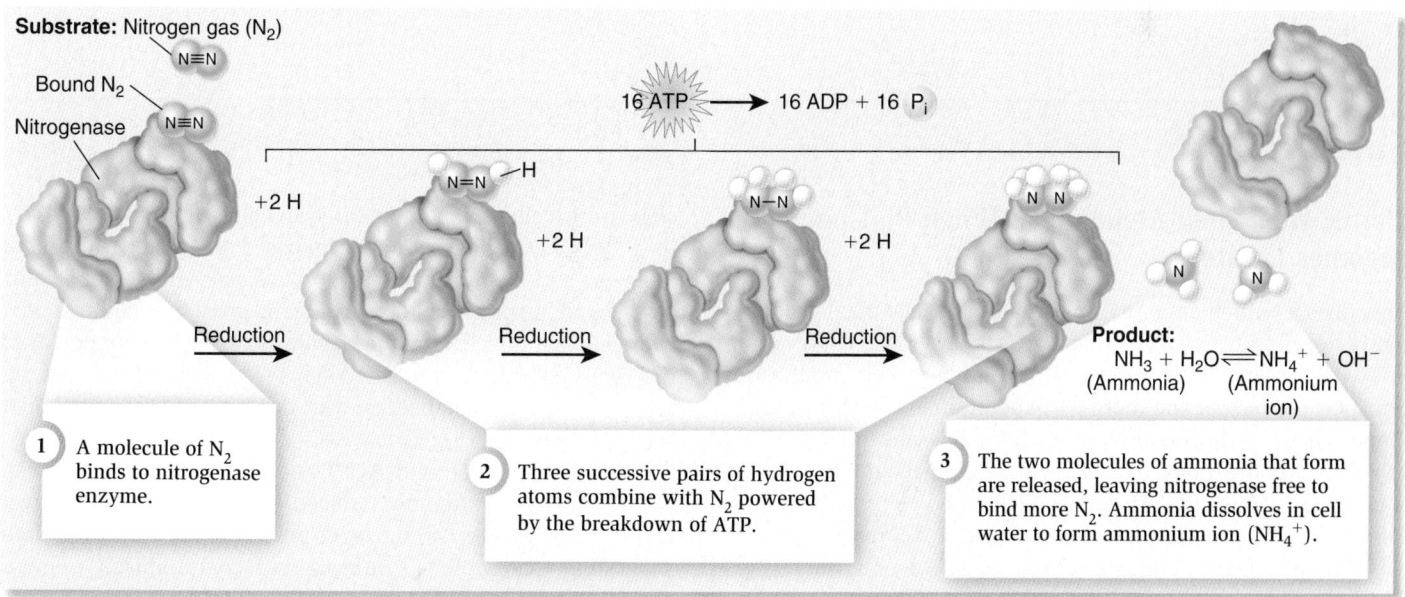

Figure 35.14   The biological process of nitrogen fixation.

Concept check: *What common substance inactivates nitrogenase enzyme by binding to its active site?*

scientists are working to genetically engineer nitrogen fixation capacity into crop plants, such as rice and maize. However, the vulnerability of nitrogenase to oxygen means that this enzyme may need to be altered so that it binds oxygen less readily, or plants must be engineered with some mechanism that protects nitrogenase from oxygen.

Industrial Nitrogen Fixation Worldwide, farmers apply more than 80 million metric tons of nitrogen fertilizer per year. The fixed nitrogen found in fertilizer is produced industrially from nitrogen gas by means of a procedure invented by German chemists Fritz Haber and Carl Bosch in 1909. The reduction of N_2 gas to NH_3 is energetically favourable at room temperature but the activation energy is very high, and so the reaction occurs extremely slowly. By using an iron catalyst, temperatures of 400–650°C, and high pressures (150–400 atmospheres), the Haber-Bosch process generates NH_3 rapidly. However, because of its high energy requirements, industrial nitrogen fixation can be costly for many of the world's farmers. The high cost of fertilizers helps to explain why agricultural scientists are so interested in the possibility of genetically engineering nitrogen fixation into crop plants.

Plants Display Adaptations for Acquiring Phosphorus

Phosphorus (P) is another soil mineral that often limits plant growth. Plants obtain phosphorus from the ion known as phosphate, which occurs in the soil in three dissolved forms: H_3PO_4, $H_2PO_4^-$, and HPO_4^{2-}. The HPO_4^{2-} ion (called hydrogen phosphate ion) is the form most commonly absorbed by plants. Phosphate uptake involves ATP-requiring proton cotransport, as is the case for other anions, such as nitrate and sulphate. The uptake of these nutrients at the root hair surface is discussed further in Chapter 36.

Although phosphorus is abundant in soil, it is often unavailable to plants. One reason is that phosphate forms tightly bound complexes with clay, iron, and aluminum oxides, and with calcium carbonate in soils. In addition, soil microbes convert phosphate ions into organic compounds that are not taken up by plants.

Because plants need copious supplies of phosphate for a variety of cell processes, they have evolved various adaptations that increase their ability to obtain phosphorus from soil. A common adaptation for acquiring phosphorus is the symbiotic association of plant roots with various types of fungi (see section 35.3). In addition, plants that grow in soils with low phosphorus content may produce more highly branched roots and more and longer root hairs. Plant roots also secrete protons and organic acids, such as citrate and malate into the soil; these help release phosphorus from inorganic complexes. For example, the plant *Lupinus alba* releases as much as 25% of its total photosynthetic carbon into the soil as organic acids—a high price to pay, but apparently one that is essential for the plant to obtain sufficient phosphorus. Plants may also secrete phosphatase enzymes from roots; these enzymes release phosphorus from organic compounds in the soil. The general process by which phosphorus, nitrogen, CO_2, and other minerals are released from organic compounds is called **mineralization**.

Farmers and gardeners apply phosphate-rich fertilizers to crop fields and gardens as a way of preventing phosphorus deficiencies, which reduce yields. Phosphorous fertilizers are obtained from phosphate-rich mineral deposits, but experts warn that inexpensive sources of phosphate will be exhausted within the next 90 years. Consequently, there is much interest in devising ways to maximize the efficiency by which plants are able to take up and use phosphorus.

FEATURE INVESTIGATION

Plants Alter Their Metabolism When Phosphorus Becomes Limited

How does a limited amount of phosphorus reduce plant productivity? Recall from Chapter 7 that ATP is the chemical energy that drives many metabolic processes, including protein synthesis, transport processes, and motility. In addition to the many enzymatic reactions that require either inorganic phosphate, ADP, or ATP, carbon fixation in photosynthetic organisms requires a significant amount of ATP and reducing power (mostly in the form of NADPH, a phosphorus-containing compound).

William Plaxton and his colleagues at Queen's University sought to understand how phosphate limitation affects metabolic processes. They generated suspension-cultured cells by employing hormonal treatment of *Brassica* tissues by methods similar to those described in Figure 34.6. These suspension-cultured cells are excellent experimental systems as they can be grown in a defined medium, quickly exposed to altered nutritional regimes, and easily harvested for analyses of metabolic processes and responses. Plaxton's team grew the cultures in a complete medium (containing 10mM Pi) as well as in a medium that was phosphate limited. After seven days in culture, the level of various metabolites was determined by quantitative assays (**Figure 35.15**).

Adenylates (ATP and ADP) and free inorganic phosphate (Pi) levels were extremely reduced in the phosphate deprived plants, and the free amino acid pool was six times as large, suggesting that protein synthesis was compromised (remember that charging tRNAs and some steps of translation require energy from phosphate-rich compounds). Depletion of these metabolites may also limit glycolysis, as it is known that several enzymes require adenylates or Pi to function.

GOAL: To determine how phosphate deprivation alters metabolism.

KEY MATERIAL: Suspension cultured *Brassica* cells.

1 Determine the effect of phosphate deprivation on metabolite levels.

Media with 10 mM Pi

Media without Pi

Seven days in culture

Extract and measure metabolite concentration

2 Metabolite levels of cells in complete media and phosphate deficient media.

Metabolite	Media with 10 mM Pi	Media without Pi
Pi	17,400	400
ATP	138	36
ADP	53	4.7
Free amino acids	13,900	80,200

Values are nanomoles/gram fresh weight

3 Determine how glycolytic enzymes are affected by phosphate deprivation. Grow for seven days, make extracts, and perform enzyme assays to compare enzyme activities.

+0 mM   +5 mM   +10 mM   +15 mM

The enzymatic data

Relative activity

PFP

PFK

0   5   10   15
Media [Pi] mM

Relative activity

3-PGA kinase

P-NAD-G3PDH

NP-NAD-G3PDH

0   5   10   15
Media [Pi] mM

Relative activity

PEP Phosphatase

PK

0   5   10   15
Media [Pi] mM

The biochemical pathway

Fructose 6-P

ATP → ADP   PFK   PFP   PPi → Pi

Fructose 1,6-P

G3P

NAD + Pi → NADH   P-NAD-G3PDH   NADP → NADPH   NP-NADP-G3PDH

1,3 phosphoglycerate

ADP → ATP   3PGA kinase

3-PGA

PEP

ADP → ATP   PK   PEPP   H₂O → Pi

Pyruvate

4 **CONCLUSIONS**

Phosphate limitation quickly alters plant metabolism, increasing the activities of enzymes that allow glycolysis and respiration to continue without ATP or Pi.

5 **SOURCE**: Duff, S.M., Moorhead, G.B.G., Lefebvre, D.D., and Plaxton, W.C. (1989) Phosphate starvation inducible "bypasses" of adenylate and phosphate dependent glycolytic enzymes in *Brassica nigra* suspension cells. *Plant Physiology* 90:1275–1278.

Figure 35.15   The experiment of Plaxton and his colleagues demonstrated that plants can alter their metabolism in response to phosphate deprivation.

Perhaps surprisingly, although the cultures grew slowly, the cells did not die. This result suggested that the cells were able to adjust their metabolism and carry out basic processes, despite the low levels of phosphate. Plaxton's team found that the levels of certain glycolytic bypass enzymes were elevated in cells cultured in the phosphate-free medium. Thus, during periods of prolonged phosphate deprivation, plants can alter their metabolism to generate pyruvate, which can then enter the citric acid cycle and the respiratory chain to provide biosynthetic precursors and energy for the cell. In addition, the bypass enzyme PFP mobilizes

some inorganic phosphate from the pool of pyrophosphate (PPi), and the bypass enzyme PEP phosphatase (PEPP) also liberates Pi when converting phosphoenolpyruvate to pyruvate. These metabolic alterations thus enable respiration to continue and provide a salvage mechanism for inorganic phosphate, but it must be appreciated that this is a short-term solution to phosphate deprivation. Such events can occur after a heavy rainfall, but once environmental conditions become more favourable, mineralization by soil microbes can assist in enriching the soil with phosphate, and plant metabolism can then return to normal.

Experimental Questions

1. What was the primary goal of the work by Plaxton and colleagues?
2. How were the investigators able to manipulate phosphate concentration in their samples?
3. What is the evidence that plants alter their metabolism when phosphate is in limited supply?
4. What are two advantages of inducing the expression of bypass enzymes of glycolysis?

35.3 BIOLOGICAL SOURCES OF PLANT NUTRIENTS

Learning Outcomes:

1. Describe how symbiotic relationships between plants and fungi help plants to obtain nutrients.
2. Explain the similarities between the response of a Venus fly trap to physical stimulation and a human nerve impulse signal.
3. Make drawings that illustrate the interactions that take place between a legume root and rhizobia.

This section focuses on several fascinating ways in which plants use other organisms as sources of nutrients. Biological sources of plant nutrients include symbiotic fungi or bacteria, the animal prey of carnivorous plants, and green plants that serve as hosts for nonphotosynthetic plant parasites.

Mycorrhizal Associations Help Most Plants Obtain Mineral Nutrients

At least 80% of seed plants have symbiotic associations with fungi that live within the tissues of plant roots or that envelop root surfaces (see Chapter 27). These associations are termed **mycorrhizae**; the prefix *myco* refers to fungi, and *rhiza* means "root," and so the term literally means "fungus root."

In mycorrhizal associations, soil fungi obtain organic food from the roots of a photosynthetic plant host, while the fungal partner supplies the plant with water and mineral nutrients. Due to extensive mycelia that fungi produce within the soil, these fungal-root associations provide an exceptionally efficient way for plants to harvest water and minerals, especially phosphate, from a much larger volume of soil than is available to roots by themselves. The presence of lush vegetation on infertile tropical rain forest soils is largely due to the ability of mycorrhizae to rapidly absorb mineral nutrients released by decay and transmit the nutrients directly to plant roots (**Figure 35.16**). In many tropical rain forests, mineral nutrients occur within the bodies of living organisms, rather than accumulating in the soil where they could easily be leached away by heavy, frequent rains.

Various species of ghostly pale plants have lost their photosynthetic pigments (see Figure 35.2) and have thus become dependent on organic compounds supplied by fungi that form mycorrhizal associations with a photosynthetic host, such as a nearby tree. In this process, known as mycoheterotrophy, the fungus serves as an underground conduit for the flow of organic nutrients from a green, photosynthetic plant to a heterotrophic plant. Many plant seedlings that grow in the shade of taller plants also use mycoheterotrophy to survive until they are able to obtain enough light for photosynthesis.

Plant-Prokaryote Symbioses Provide Some Plants with Fixed Nitrogen

Some kinds of plants have symbiotic relationships with bacteria that provide them with fixed nitrogen. Though many nitrogen-fixing bacteria live freely within the soil, some form nitrogen-fixing partnerships with plants, actually living within plant cells or tissues. Such symbioses are advantageous to both partners. The plants provide organic nutrients to the bacteria, while the bacteria supply the plants with a much higher supply of fixed

Figure 35.16 Nutrient acquisition via mycorrhizae. In all forests, but particularly those of tropical regions, mycorrhizal fungi rapidly collect soil minerals released from decaying organisms and transport them directly to plant roots. Such efficient nutrient cycling bypasses the soil, from which mineral ions can be easily leached by heavy rainfall. This process explains how lush forests can grow on thin, infertile soils.

 Principle: *New properties emerge from complex interactions.*

nitrogen than the plants could obtain from most soils. Representatives of three types of prokaryotes—cyanobacteria, actinobacteria, and proteobacteria—are symbiotically associated with specific types of plants. (For more information about the characteristics of these bacterial groups, see Chapter 25.)

Cyanobacterial-Plant Symbioses   Although cyanobacteria are themselves photosynthetic, organic compounds supplied by plant partners subsidize the high energy costs of nitrogen fixation. This allows the cyanobacteria to fix more nitrogen than they require, secreting the excess to plant partners. Nitrogen-fixing cyanobacteria form symbioses with some bryophytes, ferns, and gymnosperms, as well as the flowering plant *Gunnera.* This plant, commonly known as the giant or prickly rhubarb, can produce leaves almost 3 metres wide (**Figure 35.17**). Nitrogen-fixing symbionts are advantageous to *Gunnera* because this large plant grows in nitrogen-poor habitats, such as on volcanic slopes in Hawaii. *Gunnera* harbours cyanobacteria within stems and leaf petioles. In these locations, the cyanobacteria can use cyclic electron flow to transform light energy into the ATP needed to produce fixed nitrogen. The presence of nitrogen-fixing cyanobacteria helps to explain why *Gunnera* can grow to dramatic size on poor soils.

Woody Plant–Actinobacteria Symbioses   In contrast to cyanobacteria, actinobacteria are heterotrophic, nitrogen-fixing bacteria. Actinobacteria known as *Frankia* occur in nodules formed on the underground roots of certain shrubs or trees, such as alder (*Alnus*) and myrtle (*Myrica*). These plants receive fixed nitrogen from their bacterial partners, which in turn obtain organic nutrients. Woody plants, such as *Ceanothus* shrubs, that have *Frankia* symbionts are able to grow abundantly even in places where soil nitrogen is low. This symbiosis helps to explain why *Ceanothus* covers extensive areas in mountainous chaparral regions of the western United States.

Legume–Rhizobia Symbioses   The nitrogen-fixation symbioses most important in nature and to agriculture involve certain proteobacteria that are collectively known as **rhizobia** (from the Greek *rhiza,* "root"). Rhizobia live within root cells of wild and cultivated legumes, forming legume–rhizobia symbioses. In nature, legume plants are important sources of fixed nitrogen for other plants. When legumes die, they generate organic

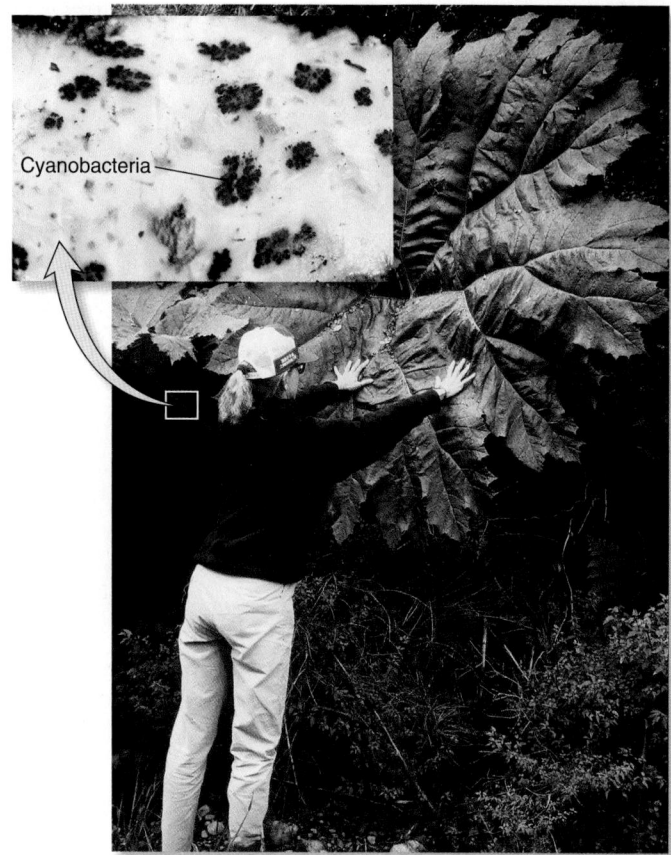

Cyanobacteria

Figure 35.17 *Gunnera* growing on nitrogen-poor soil. Cyanobacteria that live within small cavities in this plant's stems or leaf petioles provide the plant with fixed nitrogen, which explains how such a large plant can grow on infertile soils.

matter that is enriched in fixed nitrogen. Consequently, wild legumes are regarded as particularly valuable members of natural plant communities.

Important legume crops include soybean, pea, beans, peanuts, clover, and alfalfa. Foods produced from soybeans, peas, beans, and peanuts are valued for their high protein content. Clover and alfalfa are used for animal food and to enrich fields with the fixed nitrogen needed by subsequent food crops. The value of these crops arises from their nitrogen-fixation abilities. The amount of ammonia produced by legume–rhizobia symbioses nearly equals the world's entire industrial production.

GENOMES AND PROTEOMES

Development of Legume–Rhizobia Symbioses

Rhizobia can live independently in the soil, but they fix nitrogen only when they occur within lumpy **nodules** that form on legume roots (**Figure 35.18**). Different species of rhizobia preferentially form symbioses with particular plant species. Because of their agricultural importance, these legume–rhizobial symbioses have

been extensively studied, and a great deal is now known about the molecular basis of their development. Now that the technology exists for rapid genome sequencing, several genomics projects have reported complete sequences of many of the important species of rhizobia, and they have shown that the rhizobia often contain very large plasmids (extrachromosomal DNA) that are

Figure 35.18 **Legume root nodules.** The cells of nodules on the roots of this soybean plant (*Glycine max*) and other legumes contain nitrogen-fixing bacteria known as rhizobia.

important in various aspects of infection, nodulation, and nitrogen fixation. Turlough Finan of McMaster University and his collaborators have been instrumental in making these genome analyses and have conducted a number of important studies on the functions of specific symbiont genes involved in diverse processes, such as phosphate uptake, plasmid replication, and coordination of bacterial transcriptional regulation. Such studies provide the critical information necessary to develop strategies for the genetic engineering of nitrogen fixation in nonlegume crops.

Nodule development involves a series of chemical signals sent back and forth between rhizobia and their host plants (**Figure 35.19**). Legumes start this exchange by secreting particular flavonoid compounds from their roots. Recall that flavonoids are phenolic secondary metabolites that play essential roles in plant structure, reproduction, and protection (see Chapter 29). These flavonoids bind to receptors in the plasma membranes of compatible soil rhizobia (Figure 35.19 step 1). In response, the rhizobia secrete **Nod factors** (nodulation factors). Each rhizobial species produces Nod factors with distinctive structural variations that can be recognized by the preferred host species. These Nod factors function something like keys that unlock doors, allowing bacteria to enter roots via root hairs. These factors

Figure 35.19 **Root nodule development.**

1 Plant roots emit flavonoids that bind to receptors in plasma membranes of compatible soil rhizobia.

2 In response to flavonoids, rhizobia secrete Nod factors that bind to receptors in the membranes of host plant root hair cells.

3 Receptor binding causes entry of Ca^{2+} into root hair cells, which causes root hairs to swell at their tips and curl around the rhizobia.

4 Rhizobia inject infection proteins that induce plant roots to develop infection threads; rhizobia penetrate into root cortex cells.

5 Proteins known as nodulins cause root cortex cells to divide, forming nodules. Rhizobia invade nodule cells, inducing further nodule development. Rhizobia divide, then transform into bacteroids.

6 Nodules become pink inside as O_2-regulating leghemoglobin is produced.

7 Nodules develop vascular tissue that transports nitrogen compounds to the shoot, and organic carbon from the shoot to nodule bacteroids.

Rhizobia

Nod factors

Flavonoids

Infected root hair

Infection thread

Root cortex

Root vascular tissue

Nodule vascular tissue

Bacteroids

Developing root nodule

Mature root nodule

bind to receptors in the membranes of root hair cells in the host plant (step 2). Minutes after its membrane receptors bind the Nod factors, the root hair plasma membrane allows an influx of calcium ions, and a few minutes later root hair calcium concentrations start oscillating rapidly. Root hairs respond to these calcium changes by swelling at their tips and curling around the rhizobia (step 3). The rhizobia then inject infection proteins into root hairs. In response, the root hair cell wall degrades and the plasma membrane forms a tubular thread that the rhizobia enter. Rhizobia move through this infection thread into the root cortex and the tip of the infection thread fuses with the plasma membrane of a cortex cell. The rhizobia are then released into the cortex cell cytoplasm, enclosed by the host membrane (step 4).

Meanwhile, plants produce proteins known as **nodulins** that foster nodule development. Within 18–30 hours after the initial infection, root cortex cells start to divide to form root nodules.

Environmental conditions in developing nodules cause rhizobia to undergo changes in their structure and gene-expression patterns. The modified rhizobia present in mature nodules are known as **bacteroids** (step 5). Bacteroid respiration provides the large amounts of ATP that are necessary for nitrogen fixation. Legume nodules typically produce **leghemoglobin** (legume hemoglobin), a pink protein that helps regulate local oxygen concentrations, transporting enough oxygen to bacteroids to support respiration but preventing oxygen from disabling nitrogensase (step 6). Mature nodules also produce vascular tissue that moves nitrogen fixed by bacteroids to the root vascular system for transport throughout the plant. These nodule vascular tissues also supply organic food produced by the legume to their bacteroid partners (step 7). Gene expression studies have revealed that nearly 5,000 gene expression changes are associated with the legume–rhizobia symbiosis.

Carnivorous Plants Are Autotrophs That Obtain Mineral Nutrients from Animals

About 600 species of flowering plants have adapted to low-nitrogen environments by evolving mechanisms for trapping and digesting animals and are thus known as carnivorous plants. Their leaves are modified in ways that allow them to capture animal prey, primarily insects, though larger animals are sometimes snared as well. (Despite the popular play and movie *Little Shop of Horrors,* there are no wild or cultivated carnivorous plants that, like Audrey II, are large enough to consume humans!) Carnivorous plants are photosynthetic autotrophs that supply their own organic compounds; prey animals are primarily sources of nitrogen. The experimental use of radioactively labelled prey insects has revealed that carnivorous plants obtain as much as 87% of their nitrogen from animals.

The trapping mechanisms used by carnivorous plants are classified as passive or active. Plants with passive trapping mechanisms depend on the prey to fall or wander into the trap.

For example, tropical pitcher plants (*Nepenthes* spp.) have leaves that are folded and partially fused to form tubes that collect rainwater (**Figure 35.20a**). The interior walls of these pitchers are slippery and have downward-pointing hairs. Insects and other small animals, such as lizards and frogs, that fall into the pitchers are unable to climb out. Eventually, the trapped animals drown and are digested by microbes living within the pitchers.

Plants with active mechanisms, such as Venus flytraps (see the chapter-opening photo) and sundews, have traps that are stimulated by touch. Charles Darwin, who was fascinated by carnivorous plants, was one of the first to study the trapping mechanisms of Venus flytraps and sundews. The Venus flytrap (*Dionaea muscipula*) has an active trap formed by two-lobed leaves that are edged with lance-shaped teeth. The leaf surface has glands that secrete carbohydrates, which lure prey, as well as glands that secrete digestive enzymes after prey has been trapped. Also present on leaf surfaces are modified hairs, usually three per leaf lobe. If a single hair is touched—perhaps by wind or rain, or debris—and another touch does not occur soon

Figure 35.20 Carnivorous plants.

(a) This pitcher plant (genus *Nepenthes*) passively captures animals that accidentally fall into its water-filled pitcher.

(b) The leaves of the sundew (*Drosera rotundifolia*), shown with a trapped fly, are a plant adaptation for acquisition of nutrients.

thereafter, nothing happens. But when a fly or similar prey lands on the leaf and brushes against the same hair twice, or touches a second hair within 20–40 seconds, the leaf lobes snap shut around it.

Experimental studies indicate that an action potential—much like that occurring during signal transmission in animal nerves—develops in the stimulated hairs. The plant electrical signal travels along plasma membranes, via plasmodesmata, at about 10 centimetres per second. This signal causes leaf cells to take up ions and water so that the leaf enlarges and changes shape, springing the trap. Digestion of the prey is typically finished within 10 days, whereupon the trap reopens. Trap leaves can go through three or four digestive cycles during their lifetime.

Sundews (such as *Drosera votundifolia*) have leaves bearing glandular hairs whose sticky tips glisten in the sunlight. Insects that land on sundew leaves are mired in the sticky mucilage exuded by these hairs (**Figure 35.20b**). As the insects struggle to get away, they become covered with more mucilage and eventually smother as their breathing pores become clogged. Darwin discovered that sundew leaves bend after being touched, and that glandular hairs not originally in contact with the insects also bend, folding over the prey as you would fold your fingers over an object in your palm. Later investigators discovered that this bending involves the plant hormone auxin. In response to touch, auxin accumulates in sundew leaf tips and then flows downward, stimulating the cell expansion that causes the leaf bending. The glandular hairs produce enzymes that digest the prey.

Parasitic Plants Obtain Nutrients from Photosynthetic Plants

More than 4,500 species of plants live as complete or partial **parasites**, obtaining all or much of their water, minerals, and organic compounds from photosynthetic plant hosts. Dodder and witchweed are prominent examples of plants that are completely parasitic.

Dodder (*Cuscuta pentagona*) lacks roots and does not grow from the soil. Instead, all of the 150 species of this parasite live above ground (**Figure 35.21a**). These parasites twine their yellow or orange stems around green plant hosts, into which they sink peg-shaped, absorptive structures known as haustoria. These haustoria tap into the host plant's vascular system, stealing water, minerals, and sugar, which the parasite uses for

Host plant (green)

Dodder (yellow)

(a) Dodder   **(b) Witchweed**

Figure 35.21 Parasitic plants. (a) Dodder (*Cuscuta pentagona*) is an example of a parasitic plant that obtains all its water, minerals, and organic compounds from one or more green plant hosts. (b) Witchweeds (*Striga* spp.) belong to a family of parasitic plants that compromise many African crops.

growth and reproduction. The long, flexible stems of dodder often loop from one plant to another, such that an individual dodder plant can tap into many different plants at the same time. Dodder reproduces very rapidly by means of broken-off stem fragments and seeds. A single dodder plant can produce more than 16,000 seeds. In consequence, dodder is a widespread agricultural pest that attacks citrus, tomatoes, and many other fruit, vegetable, forage, and flower crops.

Another group of parasitic plants, the witchweeds (*Striga* spp.), cause serious agricultural and economic problems, particularly in Africa, as these parasites attack the major cereal crops: corn, sorghum, and millet. Each witchweed plant (**Figure 35.21b**) can produce up to 100,000 seeds, which can remain dormant in the soil for up to 20 years. When crops are planted, exudates from their roots trigger the dormant witchweed seeds to germinate, and the parasitic plant produces haustoria that tap into the host's vascular system to draw off nutrients and water. In Africa, it is estimated that more than 70% of corn, sorghum, and millet crops of subsistence farmers are lost each year, contributing to world hunger and food-security problems. Fortunately, combinations of strategies are being used with positive results; the strigolactones, the growth regulators secreted by the host plants that activate witchweed seed germination, are an area of active research in plant molecular genetics.

Summary of Key Concepts

35.1 Plant Nutritional Requirements

- The nutritional requirements of green plants are light energy, CO_2, water, and several types of minerals absorbed from soil or water. (Figure 35.1, Table 35.1)

- Like animals and fungi, heterotrophic plants obtain chemical energy by metabolizing organic compounds absorbed from their environment. (Figure 35.2)

- Plants display many adaptations that allow them to cope with insufficient or excess amounts of light and inadequate CO_2. Some

of these adaptations may be usefully engineered into crop plants as a way of improving food production. (Figures 35.3, 35.4, 35.5)

- The inability to acquire necessary nutrients causes stunted growth, chlorosis, or other nutrient-deficiency symptoms. (Table 35.1, Figure 35.6)

35.2 The Role of Soil in Plant Nutrition

- Natural soils display layers known as soil horizons. Soils are composed of organic material and inorganic minerals. Soil organic matter is largely derived from plant detritus, animal wastes, and decayed animal bodies. (Figures 35.7, 35.8)

- Inorganic soil components occur as particles that can be categorized according to their size as sand, silt, or clay. Cation exchange releases cations to soil water, making cations available for uptake by plant roots. (Figure 35.9, 35.10, 35.11).
- Plants take up fixed nitrogen in the form of ammonium or nitrate. To use nitrate, plant cells must convert it to an ammonium ion. (Figure 35.12)
- Biological or industrial processes can convert atmospheric nitrogen gas into fixed nitrogen. Biological nitrogen fixation can be performed only by certain prokaryotes. (Figures 35.13, 35.14)
- Plants display several types of adaptations to cope with phosphorus deficiency. Metabolic regulation of key biochemical pathways enables short-term survival and allows phosphate to be scavenged from other phosphorus-containing compounds. (Figure 35.15)

35.3 Biological Sources of Plant Nutrients

- Mycorrhizal fungi, which are associated with the roots of most plants, provide plants with water, phosphorus, and other minerals. (Figure 35.16)
- Nitrogen-fixing prokaryotes living within the tissues of some plants provide them with fixed nitrogen. Legume–rhizobia associations are particularly important in nature and in agriculture. (Figures 35.17, 35.18, 35.19)
- Carnivorous plants obtain mineral nutrients from the digested bodies of trapped animals. (Figure 35.20)
- Parasitic plants obtain water, mineral ions, and organic compounds from green plant hosts. (Figure 35.21)

Test to Assess Your Learning

1. Which of the following substances can limit plant growth in nature?
   a. sunlight
   b. water
   c. carbon dioxide
   d. fixed nitrogen
   e. all of the above
2. In what form do plants take up most soil minerals?
   a. as ions dissolved in water
   b. as neutral salts
   c. as mineral-clay complexes
   d. linked to humus particles
   e. none of the above
3. Why do plants need sulphur?
   a. to construct cell walls
   b. as an essential component of chlorophyll
   c. to produce the amino acids cysteine and methionine
   d. both (b) and (c)
   e. all of the above
4. Soil organic matter provides the benefit of:
   a. allowing water to percolate rapidly through soil.
   b. making soil softer in consistency.
   c. increasing the aluminum content of soil.
   d. causing minerals to be leached more rapidly from soil.
   e. none of the above.
5. Which environments are most conducive to heavy leaching of minerals from soils?
   a. those having soils that are composed primarily of sand particles
   b. those having acidic soils
   c. those impacted by acid rain
   d. regions characterized by heavy rainfall
   e. all of the above

6. Which property is *not* characteristic of clay-rich soils?
   a. high mineral-nutrient retention
   b. high water retention
   c. high aeration
   d. lower amounts of sand than clay
   e. all of the above
7. Which of the plants listed below is most likely to be heterotrophic (to obtain organic food from the environment)?
   a. a green houseplant
   b. a legume plant such as beans
   c. a carnivorous plant such as the sundew
   d. ghostly-white *Monotropa*
   e. none of the above
8. What kinds of organisms occur in nitrogen-fixing symbioses with plants?
   a. cyanobacteria
   b. actinobacteria
   c. rhizobia bacteria
   d. dodder
   e. all of the above
9. How do legume roots attract rhizobia?
   a. They secrete flavonoids.
   b. They secrete carotenoids.
   c. They secrete alkaloids.
   d. They secrete Nod factors.
   e. None of the above.
10. Which plant uses a passive trap to obtain animal prey as a source of mineral nutrients?
    a. the Indian pipe (*Monotropa uniflora*)
    b. the tropical pitcher plant (*Nepenthes* spp.)
    c. the Venus flytrap (*Dionaea muscipula*)
    d. dodder (*Cuscuta* spp.)
    e. all of the above

Articulate to Assess Your Learning

1. Why are agricultural experts and ecologists alike concerned about overfertilization of crop fields?
2. Draw a diagram showing how rhizobia and legume roots communicate chemically during nodule formation.

Collaborate to Assess and Extend Your Learning

1. Imagine that you have bought a farm and want to start growing a crop to sell at a local market. How could you determine whether the soil needs to be fertilized and with what mineral nutrients?
2. Imagine that you own a large farm with a trout stream running through it. How would you protect the water quality of the stream?
3. What are the evolutionary implications of the finding that early steps in the establishment of mycorrhizal and rhizobia symbioses by the legume *Medicago truncatula* involve similar genes, proteins, and signal transduction processes?
4. A principle of biology is that living organisms interact with their environment. Describe ways that plants interact with their environment to obtain nutrients and minerals they require to sustain life.

Visit McGraw-Hill Ryerson Connect™ for additional study resources.

Flowering Plants: Transport

Shade trees. The evaporation of water from plant leaves cools them and us, and even affects local and global climate.

Chapter Outline

O n hot days, people naturally gravitate to the cool shade beneath trees. But most people do not realize that trees are not just sun umbrellas. Plants actually cool the air around them as water evaporates from their surfaces. That's why grass feels cool when you walk barefoot on it, even on a hot day.

Plants benefit from this evaporation process—known as transpiration—because it cools their surfaces and powers the movement of a continuous stream of water from the soil, through roots and stems, to leaves. This evaporation pump not only distributes water throughout the plant body, but also is essential for moving dissolved minerals and organic compounds, such as sugars and hormones, over long distances within plants. Transport is thus crucial for the functions of plant growth, behaviour, and nutrition, which were described in the preceding three chapters.

In addition, plant transport plays a crucial role in Earth's global climate. Worldwide, plant transpiration moves huge amounts of soil water into the atmosphere as water vapour. For example, a single adult oak tree can transpire over 150,000 litres of water per year. Along with water evaporated from the surfaces of oceans and freshwater bodies, plant-produced water vapour is a source of rain. Along with other atmospheric gases (carbon dioxide and methane), water vapour works as a greenhouse gas that helps to warm Earth's climate by absorbing the sun's heat. Plant transport processes are also relevant to agriculture, as humans seek to improve crop productivity and the efficiency of water and nutrient use.

To comprehend plant transport more fully, in this chapter we will first survey the materials that move through plants and the general directions of material movements. Next, we will focus more closely on water and solute uptake by plant cells. We will then examine how these materials are moved within plants over short and long distances, and explore some of the plant adaptations that allow such transport to be as efficient as possible in a variety of environments.

36.1 / AN OVERVIEW OF PLANT TRANSPORT

Learning Outcomes:

1. Describe how plants transport water and minerals from roots to leaves.
2. Describe how plants transport organic molecules from leaves to nonphotosynthetic parts.

Our previous studies of angiosperm plant structure and nutrition described the interdependence of plant root and shoot systems (see Chapters 33 and 35). We have observed that in most plants the root system absorbs water and dissolved minerals from the soil and that the shoot system takes up carbon dioxide (CO_2) from the atmosphere (**Figure 36.1**). Photosynthetic cells use these materials to produce sugar and other organic compounds needed for overall plant growth and reproduction. Nonphotosynthetic plant cells, such as those of roots and flowers, depend on organic food produced by green tissues. Therefore, plants must transport water and minerals upward from roots to shoots and transport organic food from photosynthetic to nonphotosynthetic parts. Since plants can grow very tall, the tallest trees being more than 100 metres tall, transport of materials often occurs over long distances.

The long-distance transport of water, dissolved minerals, and sugar throughout the plant body occurs within a continuous system of conducting tissues. Recall that the complex tissues of vascular plants that primarily conduct water and dissolved minerals are known as the *xylem*, and those that conduct organic substances in a watery sap are termed the *phloem*. These conducting tissues are key to the ability of vascular plants to thrive in terrestrial

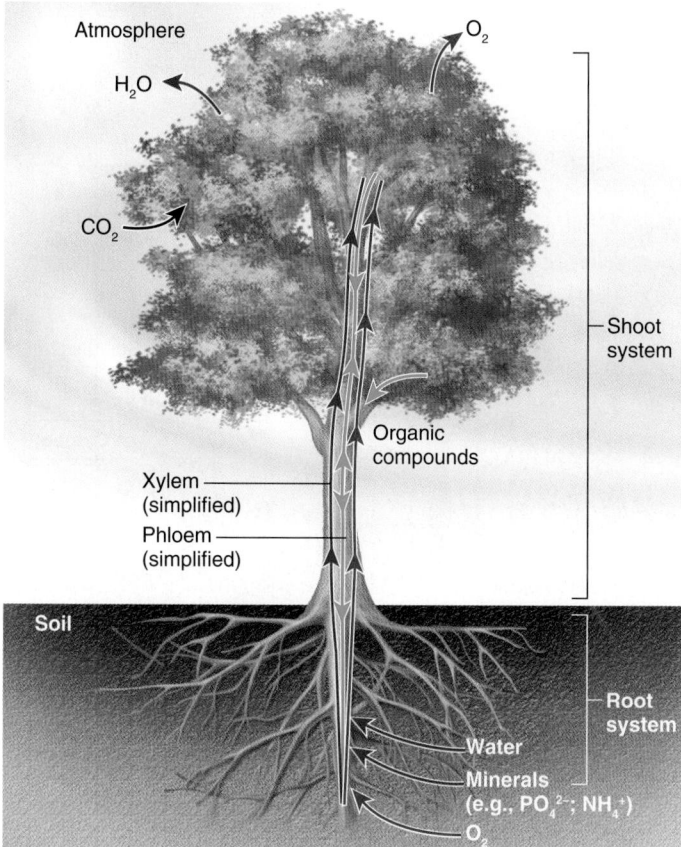

Figure 36.1 Overview of material uptake and long-distance transport processes in plants.

habitats, which can sometimes be quite arid. To fully understand how plants accomplish long-distance transport, we will begin by reviewing the processes by which minerals, organic compounds, and water are taken up and move at the cellular level.

36.2 UPTAKE AND MOVEMENT OF MATERIALS AT THE CELLULAR LEVEL

Learning Outcomes:

1. Describe the differences among turgid, flaccid, and plasmolyzed plant cells.
2. Explain how water potential and relative water content are calculated.
3. List ways in which plants cope with cellular osmotic stress.

Chapter 6 described how cells use both passive and active processes to import or export materials. Here, we briefly review these processes, describing and contrasting them and illustrating how they work in flowering plants.

Passive Transport Does Not Require the Input of Energy

Recall from your earlier studies of plasma membranes that water, gases, and certain other small, uncharged compounds can passively diffuse across membranes in the direction of their concentration gradients. **Passive transport** is the movement of materials into or out of cells down a concentration gradient without the expenditure of energy in the form of ATP. Passive transport across plasma membranes occurs in two ways: by passive diffusion or facilitated diffusion. **Diffusion** into or out of cells is the movement of a solute through a phospholipid bilayer down a concentration gradient. **Facilitated diffusion** is the transport of molecules across plasma membranes down a concentration gradient with the aid of membrane transport proteins (**Figure 36.2a;** see also Chapter 6).

The two main types of membrane transport proteins that function in facilitated diffusion are channels and transporters. **Channels** are membrane pores formed by proteins that allow the movement of ions and molecules across membranes. **Transporters** are proteins that transport molecules by binding them on one side of the membrane and then changing conformation so that the molecule is released to the other side of the membrane (refer back to Figure 6.20). Transporters increase the rate at which specific mineral ions and organic molecules are able to enter plant cells and vacuoles.

Recall that osmosis is the diffusion of water across a selectively permeable membrane in response to differences in solute concentrations. In the case of plants, water moves from a solution that has a lower solute concentration (soil) to one of higher concentration (root cells). Osmotic water uptake into living plant cells is essential to photosynthesis, as well as to cell expansion and structural support. However, the passive diffusion of water does not occur rapidly enough to supply the water needs of rapidly expanding plant cells. In this case, facilitated diffusion of water occurs through channels formed by proteins known as **aquaporins**, which occur widely in living things (refer back to Figure 6.18). Thirty-five distinct aquaporin genes have been identified in the genome of the model plant *Arabidopsis*. Aquaporins increase the rate at which water flows into expanding plant cells and their vacuoles. In the same way, many other types of plasma membrane protein channels and transporters facilitate the diffusion of specific mineral ions and organic molecules into and out of plant cells and vacuoles.

ATP Hydrolysis Powers Active Transport

If a substance must be transported across a plasma membrane against its concentration gradient, however, work must be performed in the process known as active transport. During **active transport**, membrane transporter proteins use energy to move substances against their concentration gradients. An example is the H^+-ATPase proton pump, found in the plasma membranes of plant cells, which uses ATP to pump H^+, which are protons, against a gradient (**Figure 36.2b**). This proton gradient generates an electrical difference, which is known as a **membrane potential**. Energy is released when protons pass back across the

KEY
- Channel
- Proton pump
- Symporter

Vacuole, water, solutes
Vacuole membrane
Cell wall
Plasma membrane

Facilitated diffusion occurs with the concentration gradient. Channels and transporters facilitate the movement of solutes, such as organic molecules and ions, across plasma and vacuolar membranes.

Active transport occurs against the concentration gradient. Proton pumps establish proton gradients across plasma and vacuolar membranes. These gradients are used for symport and to open or close ion channels.

Solutes

Plasma membrane

ADP + P$_i$ ATP

Solutes

Cytosol

Channel

H$^+$-ATPase proton pump

Symporter

Protons

(a) Passive transport: facilitated diffusion

(b) Active transport

Figure 36.2   Passive and active transport.

plasma membrane, in the direction of their electrochemical gradient. This energy can then be used to power other active transport processes. For example, it might be used to open or close ion channels or in proton **cotransport** or **symport** (transport of two substances in the same direction across a membrane) of organic materials, such as sugars, amino acids, and nitrogenous bases.

Active transport proteins are particularly abundant in root cell membranes (**Figure 36.3**), allowing root cells to concentrate dissolved mineral nutrients to more than 75 times their abundance in soil. As a result, soil water flows into root cells by osmosis. We next take a closer look at osmotic water movement into and out of plant cells.

Cellular Water Content Is Influenced by Solute Content and Turgor Pressure

The water content of plant cells depends on osmosis and osmosis depends on two factors: solute content and turgor pressure. **Turgor pressure** is the hydrostatic pressure required to stop the net flow of water across a plasma membrane due to osmosis. Turgor pressure increases as water enters plant cells, because their cell walls restrict the extent to which the cells can swell. Because animal cells lack cell walls, they do not experience turgor pressure.

A plant cell whose cytosol is so full of water that the plasma membrane presses right up against the cell wall is said to be **turgid** (**Figure 36.4a**). The pressure relationship between the cytosol and cell wall recalls the way that a soccer ball's leather skin presses inward on the air within, while at the same time the internal air presses on the ball's cover. If you add more air

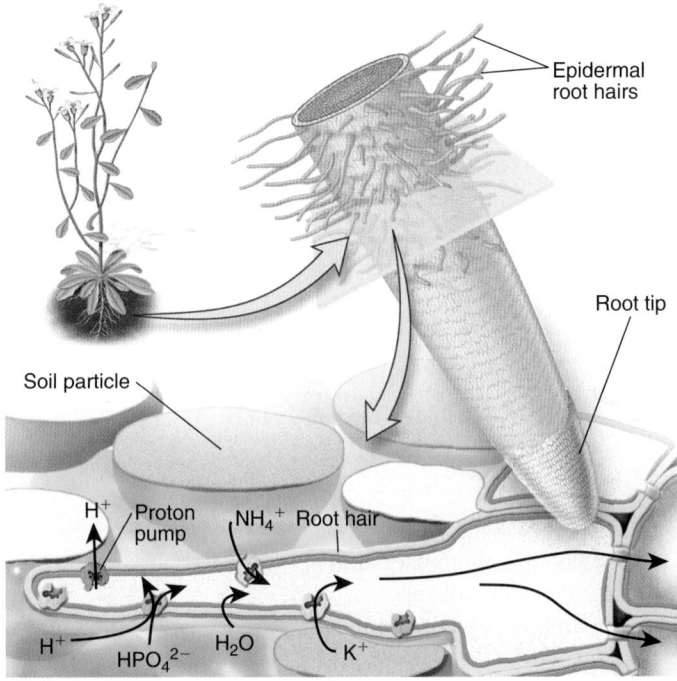

Epidermal root hairs

Root tip

Soil particle

H$^+$ Proton pump   NH$_4$$^+$ Root hair

H$^+$ HPO$_4$$^{2-}$ H$_2$O   K$^+$

Figure 36.3   **Ion uptake at root hair membranes.**   The H$^+$-ATPase proton pump establishes an electrochemical gradient that drives the active uptake of solutes. The resulting increase in intracellular solute concentration also drives the osmotic diffusion of water into the cell.

Principle: *Living organisms use energy. When soil mineral ion concentrations are lower than those within cells, root hair plasma membranes take up nutrient ions by active transport.*

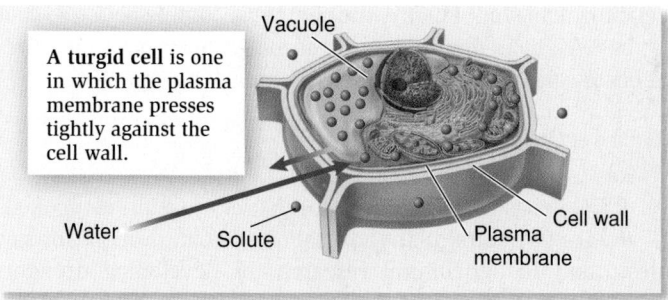

(a) Turgid cell in a hypotonic solution

A turgid cell is one in which the plasma membrane presses tightly against the cell wall.

Vacuole
Water
Solute
Cell wall
Plasma membrane

(b) Plasmolyzed cell in a hypertonic solution

A plasmolyzed cell is one in which so much cell water has been lost by osmosis that the plasma membrane contorts away from the wall.

Plasma membrane

(c) Flaccid cell in an isotonic solution

A flaccid cell is one in which the plasma membrane does not press tightly against the cell wall.

Plasma membrane

Figure 36.4 Turgid, plasmolyzed, and flaccid plant cells. (a) When the concentration of solutes inside a cell is higher than that outside (the cell is surrounded by a hypotonic solution), more water will enter the cell than will leave it. As a result, a plant cell will become swollen or turgid. (b) When the concentration of solutes outside a cell is greater than within it (the cell is surrounded by a hypertonic solution), more water will leave the cell than will enter it. As a result, a plant cell will become plasmolyzed. (c) When the concentration of solutes is the same outside and inside a plant cell (the cell is bathed in an isotonic solution), it will be flaccid.

to a limp ball, the ball will stiffen. In the same way, if a non-turgid cell absorbs more water, it will become more rigid as the water exerts pressure on the cell wall.

By contrast, a plasmolyzed cell is one that has lost so much water by osmosis that turgor pressure has also been lost. **Plasmolysis** is the condition in which the plasma membrane no longer presses on the cell wall (**Figure 36.4b**). The concentration of solutes is the same outside and inside a **flaccid** cell, which will have a water content higher than a plasmolyzed cell but lower than a turgid cell (**Figure 36.4c**).

Together, solute concentration and turgor pressure influence an important plant cell property known as **water potential**, the potential energy of water. A good analogy is a waterfall, which has high gravitational potential energy at its top. Pressure also influences water potential; a waterfall would flow upward if pressure greater than the force of gravity were applied. Solutes and some other factors also affect water potential. Water potential is measured in pressure units known as megapascals (MPa) (a pascal is equal to 1 newton per square metre). One MPa is equal to 10 times the average air pressure at sea level, about the same pressure that occurs within an inflated bicycle tire. As another reference point, 1 MPa is several times the pressure in typical home plumbing pipes, which you experience when turning on a water faucet.

In the study of plants, the concept of water potential is used to understand the movement of water into and out of cells (cellular water potential) and to understand the water status of entire plants or organs (relative water content). Let's first consider the water potential of cells.

Cellular Water Potential A water potential equation can be used to predict the direction of water movement, given information about the solute concentrations inside and outside of plant cells, and a measure of pressure at the cell wall–membrane interface (**Figure 36.5**). In this equation, water potential is symbolized by the Greek letter psi (ψ) with the subscript W for water: ψ_w. In its simplest form, total ψ_w is calculated as the sum of the **solute potential** (ψ_s), also known as the osmotic potential, and the **pressure potential** (ψ_P), also known as the **wall potential**. A simple form of the water potential equation is thus

$$\psi_w = \psi_s + \psi_P$$

Solute potential is the component of water potential caused by the presence of solute molecules. As you might expect, solute potential is proportional to the concentration of solutes in a solution. The solute potential of pure water open to the air, at sea level and room temperature, is defined as zero. When solutes are added, they form bonds with water molecules, dilute the water, and may increase its disorder. As a result, fewer free water molecules are present, which reduces the potential energy of water. Thus, in the absence of a pressure potential, water that contains solutes always has a negative solute potential. The higher the concentration of dissolved solutes, the lower (more negative) the solute potential.

Pressure potential is the component of water potential caused by hydrostatic pressure. In plant cells, the hydrostatic pressure is determined in part by the resistance provided by the cell wall, the turgor pressure. Because of this resistance, the value for pressure potential can be either positive or negative. For example, a turgid cell has a positive pressure potential, which typically measures about 1 MPa. This high pressure inside turgid plant cells is a testimony to the strength of their cellulose-rich plant cell walls. In contrast to turgid cells, both flaccid and plasmolyzed cells will have a pressure potential of zero. Plants or plant organs having many cells with low turgor pressure look wilted. If your houseplants become wilted,

$$\underset{(\psi_W)}{\text{Water}\atop\text{potential}} = \underset{(\psi_S)}{\text{Solute}\atop\text{potential}} + \underset{(\psi_P)}{\text{Pressure}\atop\text{potential}}$$

Solutes

Plasma membrane

Cell wall

Water

Examples of ψ_W calculations:

Turgid cell	Plasmolyzed cell	Flaccid cell
$\psi_S = -0.1$	$\psi_S = -1.0$	$\psi_S = -0.5$
$\psi_P = +1.1$	$\psi_P = 0.0$	$\psi_P = 0.0$
$\psi_W = +1.0$ MPa	$\psi_W = -1.0$ MPa	$\psi_W = -0.5$ MPa

Figure 36.5   Plant cell water potential.   The water potential of a plant cell, which predicts the direction of water movement into or out of a cell, can be simplified as the sum of the solute potential and the pressure potential resulting from pressure exerted by the cell wall–plasma membrane complex. Examples of water potential calculations are shown for a turgid cell, a plasmolyzed cell, and a flaccid cell.

Concept check: *Make a drawing that shows the direction of water movement when a cell of each of these types is placed into a solution of pure water (whose water potential, ψ_w, is defined as 0 MPa). In which direction will water move in each case?*

watering will enable the cells to increase their pressure potential, restoring cell turgor and normal plant appearance. Thus, the water content of an entire organ or plant is influenced by the water potential of its component cells.

Relative Water Content   The property known as **relative water content** (**RWC**) is often used to gauge the water content of a plant organ or an entire plant and is easy to measure with common equipment. RWC integrates the water potential of all cells within an organ or a plant and is thus a measure of relative turgidity. Measurements of RWC can be used to predict a plant's ability to recover from the wilted condition. An RWC of less than 50% spells death for most plants, but some plants can tolerate lower water content for substantial time periods.

A standard method for determining RWC involves three simple weight measurements: fresh weight, turgid weight, and dry weight. Sample tissue taken from a plant is first weighed to obtain the fresh weight, and then it is completely hydrated in water within an enclosed, lighted chamber until constant turgid

weight is achieved. Finally, the sample is completely dried and its dry weight is determined. Researchers use these measurements to calculate RWC by using the following equation:

$$\text{RWC} = \frac{(\text{fresh weight} - \text{dry weight})}{(\text{turgid weight} - \text{dry weight})} \times 100$$

RWC measurements have been very useful in ecological studies of natural plant adaptation to cold, drought, or salt stress, and in agricultural research for developing drought-tolerant crops. Developing new crops that are better able to withstand water stress requires an understanding of not only water potential but also how plant cells cope with cellular osmotic stress, which leads to water stress.

Plant Adaptations to Cellular Osmotic Stress   Plants native to cold, dry, or saline environments have evolved many different adaptations that allow them to cope with low water content. For example, plants often increase the solute concentrations of their cell cytosol, a process known as **osmotic adjustment**. Increased amounts of the amino acid proline; monomeric sugars, such as glucose and fructose; or sugar alcohols, such as mannitol, decrease the cells' water potential, thus drawing water into cells. By increasing the concentration of solutes inside cells, cold-resistant plants prevent water from moving out of their cells when ice crystal formation in intercellular spaces lowers the water potential outside cells. The additional solutes also lower the freezing point of the cytosol. Similar strategies are used by some animals. For example, Kenneth Storey and his colleagues at Carleton University have demonstrated that freezing tolerance in some vertebrates (e.g., frogs) is accomplished by increasing the intracellular sugar concentration.

Plants of arid lands often possess adaptations that help them survive water stress. Many can survive in a nearly dry state for as much as 10 months of the year, growing and reproducing only after the rains come. The cytosol of such desiccation-tolerant plants is typically rich in sugars that bind to phospholipids to form a glasslike structure. This helps to stabilize the cellular membranes, preventing them from becoming damaged during plasmolysis (see Figure 36.4b). As previously noted, plant cells under water stress may also increase the number of plasma membrane aquaporins. These additional protein channels increase the rate of water uptake, allowing cells to recover turgor more quickly when water becomes available.

Halophytes are plants that are able to grow in salty habitats, including coastal salt marshes. Plant cells cannot readily absorb salty water because of its highly negative water potential. Halophytes have thus acquired adaptations to help them cope with osmotic stress. Some halophytes accumulate inorganic salts in their vacuoles and organic solutes in their cytosol, resulting in balancing of solute concentrations inside and outside cells, thus preventing osmotic water loss. Halophytes also display adaptations that help rid their bodies of excess salt. Some halophytes excrete salt from root surfaces, while others transport excess salt to their leaf epidermal cells (look ahead to Figure 51.16). Some halophytes accumulate salt within multicellular surface glands that break off or burst harmlessly. The water potential adaptations of desiccation-tolerant plants and halophytes are of special interest to agricultural scientists seeking to develop crops that are able to grow in arid lands or in places where the soil or water used for irrigation is salty.

36.3 | TISSUE-LEVEL TRANSPORT

Learning Outcomes:

1. Define transmembrane transport, symplastic transport, and apoplastic transport.
2. Explain how the root endodermis functions as a diffusion barrier.

Now that we have reviewed how water, dissolved minerals, and organic compounds enter or leave plant cells, we are prepared to consider short-distance transport within and among nearby tissues. Tissue-level transport occurs in three forms: transmembrane transport, symplastic transport, and apoplastic transport (**Figure 36.6**).

Transmembrane transport involves the export of a material from one cell via membrane proteins, followed by import of the same substance by an adjacent cell (**Figure 36.6a**). One prominent example of transmembrane transport is movement of the plant hormone auxin downward, from shoots to roots. Auxin travels from one phloem parenchyma cell to another in a linear series with the aid of carrier proteins (refer back to Figure 34.4). This process explains how auxin produced in one part of the plant body can influence more distant tissues.

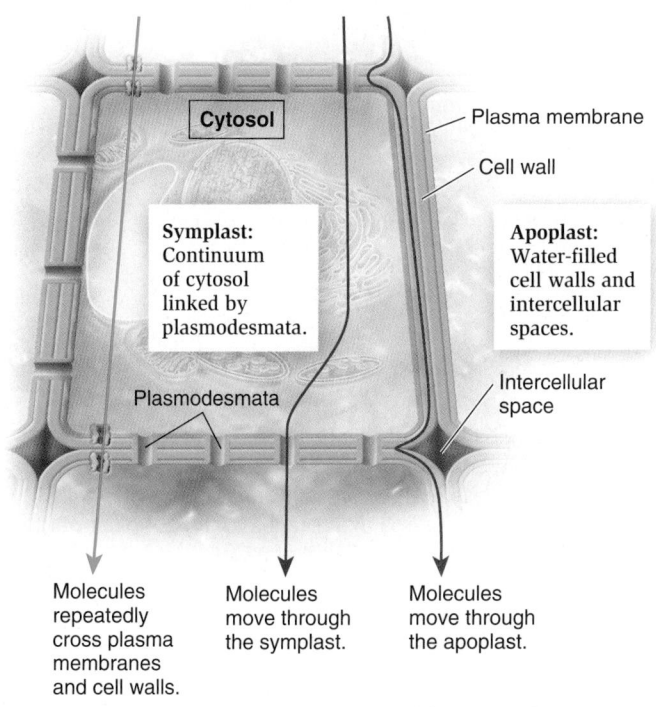

(a) Transmembrane   **(b) Symplastic**   **(c) Apoplastic**

Figure 36.6 Three routes of tissue-level transport in plants: (a) transmembrane, (b) symplastic, and (c) apoplastic.

Symplastic transport is the movement of a substance from the cytosol of one cell to the cytosol of an adjacent cell via membrane-lined channels called plasmodesmata (**Figure 36.6b**). Plasmodesmata are large enough in diameter to allow transport of proteins and nucleic acids, as well as smaller molecules. These molecules primarily move by diffusion, though in some cases special movement proteins facilitate transport through plasmodesmata. Together, all of a plant's protoplast (the cell contents without the cell walls) and plasmodesmata form the **symplast**. Symplastic transport has the potential to move molecules widely among the cells and tissues of the entire plant body. In contrast to the symplast, the **apoplast** refers to the continuum of water-soaked cell walls and intercellular spaces (**Figure 36.6c**). **Apoplastic transport** is thus the movement of solutes along cell walls and the spaces between cells. Water and dissolved minerals often move through plant tissues for short distances by apoplastic transport.

Both symplastic and apoplastic transport play important roles in mineral nutrient transport through the outer tissues of roots (**Figure 36.7**). As we have noted, the plasma membrane of epidermal root hair cells is rich in channels and transporters that selectively absorb essential mineral ions from soil water. Absorbed ions can move symplastically from the cytosol of root hairs, root cortex, and endodermal cells directly to xylem parenchyma cells. Plasmodesmata make such cell-to-cell, tissue-level transport possible.

Apoplastic transport moves soil water and dissolved minerals through root epidermal and cortex tissues. However, apoplastic movement of water and minerals stops at the root **endodermis**, a term meaning "inside skin." In roots, the endodermis is a thin cylinder of root tissue whose close-fitting cells and specialized cell walls form a barrier between the root cortex and the central core of vascular tissue. The plant endodermis is functionally analogous to animal epithelial tissues whose cellular tight junctions likewise form diffusion barriers. Materials in the root apoplast cannot penetrate farther into the root unless endodermal cells transport them into their cytosol, a process that requires specific transporter proteins.

Root endodermal cell walls possess ribbon-like strips of waterproof suberin, composed of wax and phenolic polymers. These suberin ribbons, known as **Casparian strips**, prevent apoplastic transport through endodermal cell walls and into the root vascular tissues (**Figure 36.8**). The endodermal cell walls work like filter paper to prevent small soil particles from entering vascular tissues, where such particles might clog narrow transport pipes. The endodermis also prevents harmful solutes (such as toxic metal ions) from moving through the apoplast to vascular tissues and being transported to the shoot. For example, aluminum ions (Al^{3+}) are commonly dissolved in soil water, but they are not plant nutrients and are highly toxic to plants. Aluminum ions can penetrate the root epidermis and cortex by moving through the apoplast, but they stop at the endodermis because they are unable to enter the cytosol of endodermal cells.

Endodermal plasma membranes possess specific channels and transporters for essential mineral nutrients (such as K^+), which are thereby able to enter the cytosol of endodermal cells.

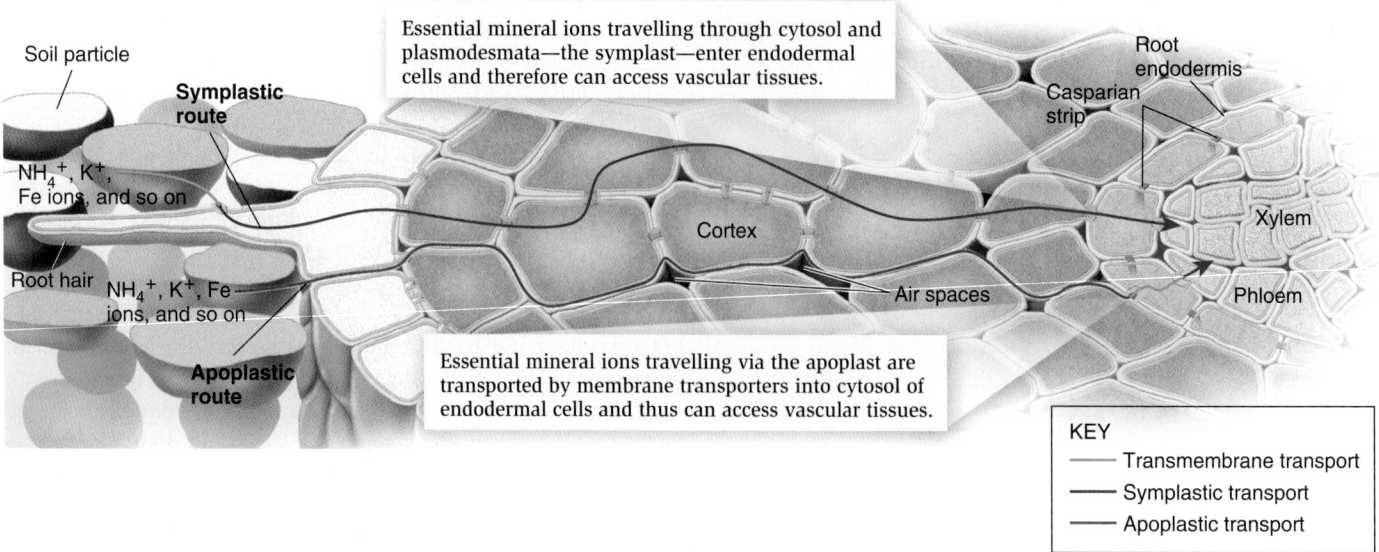

Figure 36.7   Symplastic and apoplastic transport of mineral ions in roots.

Figure 36.8   **Ion transport pathways across the root endodermis.**   Casparian strips in endodermal cell walls prevent apoplastic transport across the root endodermis, limiting entry of harmful soil minerals, such as Al^{3+}, and exit of useful minerals. Mineral nutrients that are transported into the cytosol of endodermal cells are able to pass through the endodermal barrier to xylem parenchyma cells via plasmodesmata. Once past the endodermis, nutrient ions, such as K^+, are moved across plasma membranes to the apoplast of the vascular tissue and are thus able to enter xylem. The inset shows a transmission electron micrograph (TEM) of a Casparian strip in the wall of an endodermal cell.

Concept check: *Where in most plants would you expect to find the highest concentration of Al^{3+}?*

By moving through endodermal cytosol, symplastically transported essential minerals are able to bypass the Casparian strip. Thus, the root endodermis functions as a molecular filter that allows the passage of beneficial solutes that have entered from the symplast or have been specifically transported into endodermal cytosol.

Once solutes have passed the endodermal barrier, they are actively transported out of xylem parenchyma cells and into the apoplast of the vascular system, which includes conducting cells of the xylem (see Figure 36.8). The endodermis prevents solutes from returning to outer root tissues or the soil, so the solute concentrations of vascular tissues rise, decreasing their cellular water potential. As a result, water flows into vascular tissues from outer root tissues and the soil. In the process known as **xylem loading**, large amounts of water and dissolved solutes enter the long-distance conducting cells of the xylem. In the next section we will see how water and solutes are transported for long distances through the plant.

Learning Outcomes:

1. Describe how bulk flow occurs in the xylem and phloem of flowering plants.
2. Explain how vessel elements differ from tracheids, and how both function in the xylem of flowering plants.
3. Describe the cohesion-tension theory as an explanation for long-distance water movement in plants.
4. Explain how stomata and leaf abscission help reduce transpirational water loss.
5. Describe how sieve-tube elements and companion cells work together to form a transport system.
6. Create a diagram showing how and why phloem sap moves from source to sink.

Plants rely on long-distance transport to move water and dissolved materials from roots to shoots and among organs. Tall trees are able to transport water and minerals to astounding heights, more than 100 metres in some cases. This is possible because plants possess an extensive, branched, long-distance vascular system composed of xylem and phloem tissues. Watery solutions move through these tissues by **bulk flow**, the mass movement of liquid caused by pressure, gravity, or both. Plant conducting tissues are specialized in ways that foster bulk flow and aid plants in adapting to water stress. The evaporation of water at plant surfaces, the cohesion of water molecules to each other, the adhesion of water to the walls of conducting cells, and the tension that pulls water through those cells all are important physical forces that influence long-distance water transport. Gravity, though of negligible effect for shorter plants, must also be considered in the case of water transport in tall trees. In this section we will take a closer look at bulk flow and the major factors involved in long-distance transport by this process.

Bulk Flow Is Water Movement Under the Influence of Pressure and Gravity

Bulk flow (also known as mass flow) occurs when molecules of liquid all move together from one place to another as the result of differences in pressure. One example of bulk flow is

leaching, the movement of water and dissolved minerals downward through soil layers as the result of gravity. Bulk flow is one way in which mineral ions can move through soil toward plant roots; diffusion is the other. However, liquids move much faster by bulk flow than by diffusion. Diffusing molecules move only millimetres per day through water, while phloem sap moves by bulk flow up to 1 metre per hour. Bulk flow within xylem moves water from the roots to the uppermost leaves of 100-metre trees in about 10 days. Though diffusion operates effectively in cell- and tissue-level transport, it is far too slow for efficient long-distance transport in plants.

In plants, water and dissolved materials move by bulk flow through xylem tissues as the result of differences in root and shoot cell water potentials (**Figure 36.9**). In the phloem, bulk flow occurs because a high-pressure potential builds up in leaves, which have relatively high solute concentrations. The

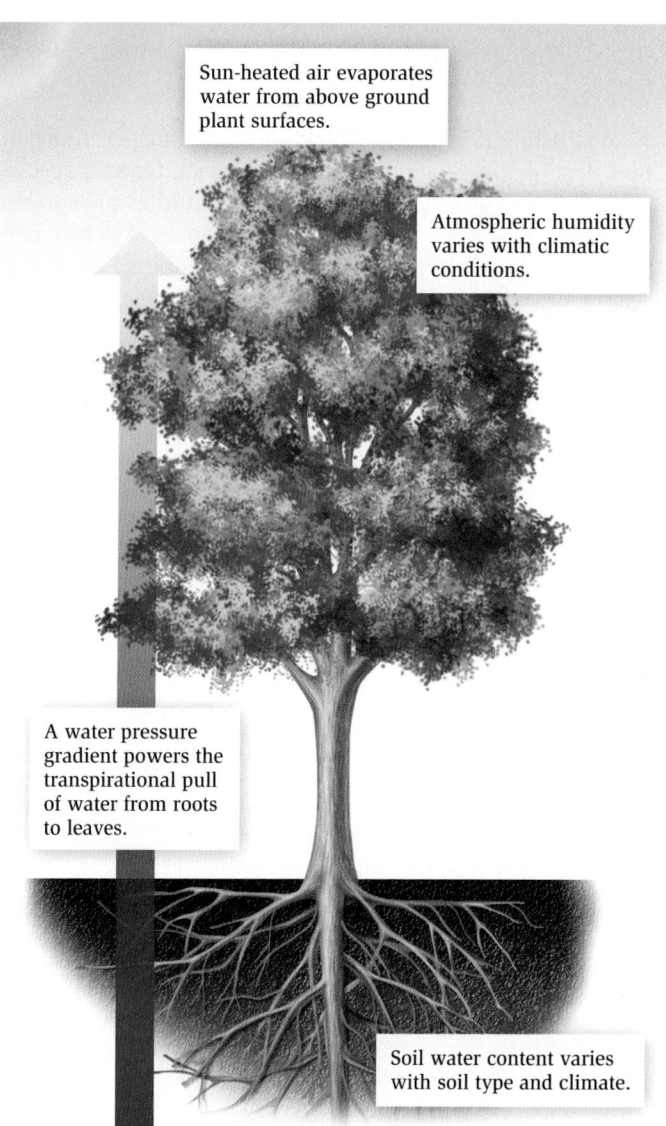

Sun-heated air evaporates water from above ground plant surfaces.

Atmospheric humidity varies with climatic conditions.

A water pressure gradient powers the transpirational pull of water from roots to leaves.

Soil water content varies with soil type and climate.

Figure 36.9 Upward transport of water in xylem. Water potential differences between root and shoot surfaces drive the upward movement of water in plants.

pressure causes the water to flow to other regions having lower solute concentrations, such as developing fruit. Bulk flow is impeded by obstructions, such as cytoplasm. This explains why xylem transport cells are devoid of cytoplasm and why phloem transport cells have reduced amounts of cytoplasm. Xylem and phloem share additional transport features related to bulk flow, which we will discuss later in this chapter.

Although xylem generally serves as the transport system for water and minerals, and phloem for organic compounds dissolved in water, the transport functions of xylem and phloem overlap. For example, xylem can transport organic compounds just as phloem does. In early spring, trees convert starch stored in stem parenchyma cells into sugars, which are transported upward in the xylem sap, supplying the needs of bud expansion and flower development. Maple trees produce a copious flow of sugar-rich xylem sap that people have long tapped to produce maple syrup and sugar (**Figure 36.10**).

Long-Distance Transport of Water and Minerals Occurs in the Xylem

Xylem structure plays an essential role in its transport function. The xylem of flowering plants contains several types of specialized cells, some of which remain alive at maturity, and some of which are dead when they are fully functional. Xylem parenchyma cells are alive, while thick-walled supportive fibres may be alive or dead at maturity. Two types of specialized water-conducting cells are always dead and empty of cytosol when mature: tracheids and vessel elements.

Together, tracheids and vessel elements are known as **tracheary elements**. During the development of tracheary elements, a secondary wall is deposited in patterns on the inside of

Figure 36.10 Maple sugar tapping. In early spring, xylem transports sugar from storage sites to the shoot buds of woody plants, such as this sugar maple (*Acer saccharum*). We use the xylem sap of sugar maples to produce maple syrup.

the primary cell wall. This secondary wall is rich in a plastic-like polymer known as lignin. Because lignin is resistant to compression, microbial decay, and water infiltration, it confers strength, durability, and waterproofing. Like the plumbing pipes of a building, tracheary elements do not readily collapse as water moves through them under tension. These characteristics explain why tracheary elements contribute to structural support of the plant body and to transport.

Tracheids Long and narrow in shape, **tracheids** typically have slanted end walls that fit together to form long tubes (**Figure 36.11a**). The end walls of tracheids are not lignified,

Figure 36.11 Tracheid cells in xylem tissue. (a) Tracheids are long, tubular cells with slanted end walls. Water and ions move from cell to cell through the pits. (b) Light micrograph of extensible tracheids from the xylem of pumpkin.

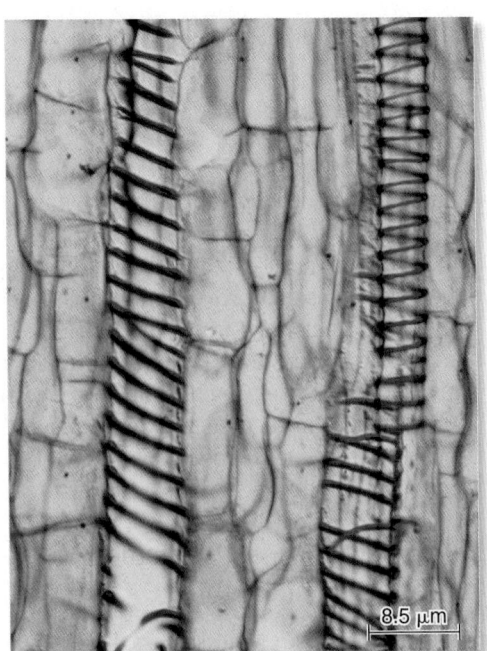

End wall

Pits

8.5 μm

(a) Tracheids

(b) Extensible tracheids

Concept check: *If you applied a stain specific for lignin to tracheids present in a longitudinal slice of a plant stem that is still growing in length, then observed the cells with a light microscope, what portions of the tracheids would be stained and what parts would not be stained?*

nor are large areas of the sidewalls of tracheids that occur in plant tissues that are still growing. Such tracheids are extensible because they have rings or spirals of lignin that allow tracheids to continue elongating (**Figure 36.11b**). In contrast, tracheids that develop in tissues that have already expanded have more lignin, which makes them rigid and unable to elongate any more. Tracheid walls that are extensively lignified display numerous small, lignin-free cell wall regions known as **pits**. At such pits, the thin primary wall of the tracheid remains readily permeable to water. Water moves from one tracheid to another both vertically and laterally through pits.

Vessels and Vessel Elements Mature **vessel elements** are a second type of water-conducting cell present in xylem tissue. Vessel elements are aligned in pipeline-like files known as **vessels** (**Figure 36.12a**). Flowering plants are distinguished from other plant groups by the abundance of vessels; nonflowering plants primarily rely on tracheids for water conduction. Vessel elements are larger in diameter than tracheids, conferring greater capacity for bulk flow, and thus represent one of the many ways in which flowering plants are particularly well adapted to life on land.

Development of vessel elements resembles that of tracheids in some ways. For example, lignified secondary walls are deposited in spirals or sheets on the inside of the primary cell wall. Vessel elements also have numerous pits in their sidewalls. In contrast to tracheids, the end walls and some sidewalls of vessel elements are extensively perforated, meaning that all cell-wall material is removed from some areas (**Figure 36.12b, c**). This

allows water to flow faster from one vessel element to another than it can flow from one tracheid to another.

Because the perforated end walls and large diameter of vessels allow them to transport more water at a faster rate than tracheids, you might wonder why flowering plants possess two types of water-conducting cells. The answer is that vessels are more vulnerable than tracheids to embolism, meaning blockage by air bubbles. Once an embolism forms in a vessel element, it can extend through the large end-wall-perforations into many elements, thereby blocking a vessel. Just as air bubbles can cause disruption of blood circulation in people, sometimes leading to death, such bubbles also disrupt water transport in plants, sometimes severely. An embolism can form within a vessel as the result of physical damage, drought, or repeated cycles of freezing and thawing. Air bubbles form frequently during winter, because air does not dissolve in ice. By the end of a cold winter, the functional vessels of many woody plants have become almost completely blocked by air. Blocked vessels in trees often cease to function in water transport and must be replaced by new growth in the spring. Fortunately, even if vessels become blocked, water conduction can still occur via tracheids. This is because tracheid pits are so small that they do not allow air bubbles to move to other tracheids. Thus, an air bubble is confined to the single tracheid in which it first formed, and water continues to flow through nearby tracheids. Tracheids thus provide a fail-safe conduction route when vessels have become disabled by embolisms.

Some plants are able to refill embolized vessels by means of a process known as **root pressure**. At night, the xylem of

(a) Vessels made up of vessel elements

Large end-wall perforations

Pits

Vessel element

(b) Vessel elements in a walnut tree

43 μm

(c) Perforations in a vessel element end wall

End-wall perforation

Pit

6 μm

Figure 36.12 **Vessels composed of vessel elements in xylem tissue.** (a) This illustration shows the wide diameter of vessel elements with many pits and end-wall perforations. (b) SEM of vessels in the wood of the walnut tree (*Juglans* spp.). (c) SEM of a perforated vessel element end wall from the tulip tree (*Liriodendron tulipifera*).

Concept check: *Which structural features of a vessel element explain the vulnerability of vessels to embolism; that is, blockage by air bubbles?*

Figure 36.13 Guttation, the result of root pressure.

roots may accumulate high concentrations of ions that are not immediately transported upward to shoots. In this case, the root acts much like a cell rich in solutes, with the result that water gushes in so rapidly that it pushes upward to leaves. Evidence of this process can be observed in the early morning as droplets of water at the edges of leaves, a phenomenon known as **guttation** (**Figure 36.13**). As the water rushes upward, it can dislodge air bubbles or dissolve them, thereby reversing embolism. Root pressure refilling has been observed to occur in nonwoody plants, such as corn (*Zea mays*) and in some woody plants, including the sugar maple (*Acer saccharum*).

The Cohesion-Tension Theory Explains the Role of Transpiration in Long-Distance Water Transport

In warm dry air, water evaporates from plant surfaces. This evaporation process is known as **transpiration** (from the French *transpirer*, meaning "to perspire") (**Figure 36.14a**). Transpiration is capable of pulling water by bulk flow up to the tops of the tallest trees and is the primary way in which water is transported for long distances in plants. Plants expend no energy to transport water and minerals by transpiration. Rather, the sun's energy indirectly powers this process by generating a water pressure difference between moist soil and drier air (see Figure 36.9).

How does evaporation at plant surfaces influence long-distance water transport in the xylem? To answer this question, we must consider the unique physical properties of water. Liquid water molecules are linked by hydrogen bonds (see Chapter 2). As a result, liquid water is amazingly cohesive, explaining why water tends to form continuous streams (**Figure 36.14c**). Consequently, when water molecules evaporate from plants, water films present in the intercellular spaces of leaves display high surface tension, causing a curved water surface known as a meniscus to form (**Figure 36.14b**). This force pulls on neighbouring liquid water molecules and eventually on water in the nearest vein, which is connected to the plant's entire water supply. As

(a) Transpiration occurs when leaf water is exposed to drier air.

(b) When water evaporates, the surface tension increases in the intercellular spaces of cells, pulling on the water stream in xylem.

(c) Cohesion in xylem causes water to form a continuous stream.

Figure 36.14 The roles of transpiration, cohesion, adhesion, and tension in long-distance water transport.

the result of water's cohesion, and the tension exerted on water by evaporation at the plant's surface, a continuous stream of water can be pulled by bulk flow through the plant body from the soil, into roots, through stems, and into leaves. This explanation for long-distance water movement in plants is known as the **cohesion-tension theory**.

Plant transpiration moves huge amounts of water from the soil to the atmosphere. About 99% of the water that enters plants through the roots is generally lost as water vapour during transpiration. Each crop season, a single corn plant (*Zea mays*) loses more than 200 litres of water, which is more than 100 times the corn plant's mass. A typical tree loses 400 litres of water per day! On a global basis, plant transpiration has

Figure 36.15 **Plant-transpired water vapour mist rising from a tropical rain forest.** This mist visually illustrates the enormous amount of water that is transpired from the surfaces of plants into the atmosphere. Water vapour derived from plant transpiration is an important source of rainfall, and the process of evaporation cools plant surfaces as well as the local and global climate.

Concept check: *Why does evaporation of water have such a powerful cooling effect?*

enormous climate effects. For example, an estimated one-half to three-quarters of rainfall received by the Amazon tropical rain forest actually originates from plant-transpired water vapour, often visible as mist (**Figure 36.15**). Furthermore, about half of the solar heat received by Amazonian plants is dispersed to the atmosphere during transpiration. This heat dispersal has a cooling effect on regional ground temperature, which would be much higher in the absence of plant transpiration. Such cooling effects result from water's unusually high heat of vaporization, the amount of heat needed to isolate water molecules from the liquid phase and move them to the vapour phase. Most of this energy is needed to break the large numbers of hydrogen bonds that occur in liquid water. The evaporation of large amounts of water from plant surfaces effectively dissipates heat, explaining how plants cool themselves and their environments.

Although evaporation of water from plant surfaces plays an essential role in bulk flow through xylem, if plants lose too much water, they will die. Consequently, plant surfaces, including those of leaves, are typically coated with a cuticle, a wax-containing layer that retards water loss. Only about 5% of water evaporated from plant surfaces emerges through the cuticle. More than 90% of the water that evaporates from plants is lost through **stomata**, surface pores that can be closed to retain water or opened to allow the entry of CO_2 needed for photosynthesis. When the stomata are open, oxygen also exits the plant with water vapour. Stomata are often abundantly located on the lower surfaces of leaves. Tobacco leaves, for example, possess an estimated 12,000 stomata per square centimetre of leaf surface. Plants face a constant dilemma: whether to open their stomata for CO_2 intake and suffer the impact of reduced water content or to close stomata to retain water, thereby preventing CO_2 uptake. For this reason, plants have acquired many adaptations to cope with transpirational water loss, our next topic.

Plant Adaptations Help to Reduce Transpirational Water Loss

Under some conditions, almost all plants experience water stress, which is an inadequate amount of water. Water stress is common for plants of the world's arid regions, and their growth is often limited by water availability. Even plants of moist, forested regions of the world experience water stress during drier or colder seasons or under windy conditions. The leaves at the tops of tall trees are generally under considerable water stress because gravity has a substantial impact on their water potential. Earlier, we considered examples of plant cellular adaptations to deal with water stress, also called osmotic stress. Flowering plants have evolved two additional ways to prevent excessive loss of water by transpiration: regulation of stomatal opening and leaf drop.

Stomatal Opening and Closing Plant stomata close to conserve water under conditions of water stress and open when the stress has been relieved, allowing air exchange with the leaf's spongy mesophyll. Stomata are bordered by a pair of guard cells, which are sausage-shaped chloroplast-containing cells attached at their ends (**Figure 36.16a**). The distinctive structural features of guard cells explain how they are able to open and close a pore. As guard cells become fully turgid, their volume expands by 40%–100%. This expansion does not occur evenly, however, because the innermost cell walls are thicker and less extensible than are other parts of the **guard cell** walls. In addition, the cells expand primarily lengthwise because bands of radially oriented cellulose microfibrils prevent the guard cells from expanding laterally (**Figure 36.16b**). Thus, when guard cells are turgid, a stomatal pore opens between them, allowing air exchange with the leaf's spongy mesophyll. Conversely, when the guard cells lose their turgor, their volume decreases and the stomatal pore closes.

What causes the change in turgor? Stomata often open early in the morning, in response to sunlight. This response makes sense, given that light, water, and carbon dioxide are all required for photosynthesis. Blue light stimulates H^+-ATPase proton pumps, leading to guard cell uptake of ions, especially potassium (K^+), and other solutes. As a result of increases in solute concentrations inside guard cells, osmotic water uptake occurs via plasma membrane aquaporins, resulting in cell expansion and stomatal opening (**Figure 36.17a**).

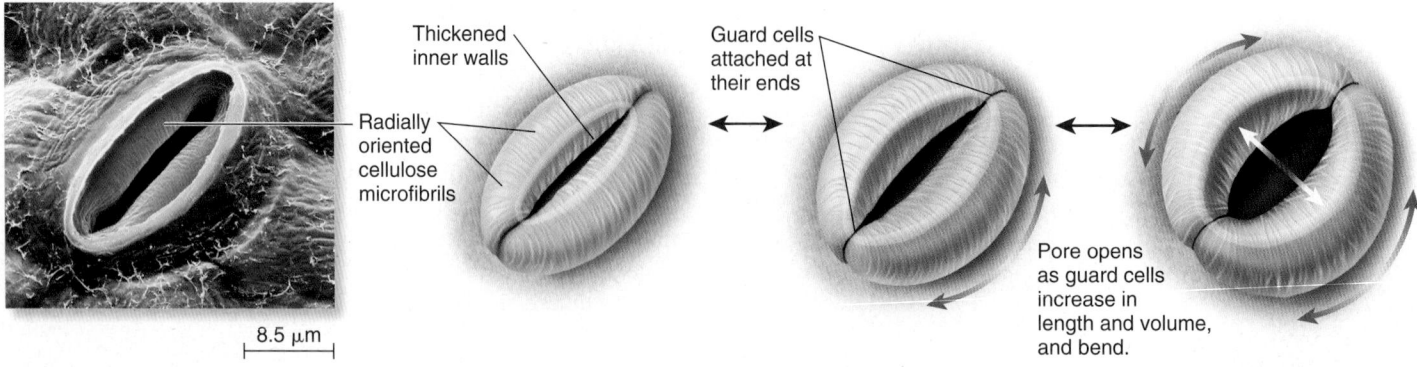

(a) Stomatal guard cells

(b) The roles of radial orientation of cellulose microfibrils and thickened inner walls in opening or closing guard cells

Figure 36.16 **The structure of guard cells affects their function.** When flaccid, guard cells close stomatal pores. Turgid guard cells produce a stomatal opening. (a) An SEM of a stoma in a rose leaf, showing the two guard cells bordering a partly open pore. (b) Thickened inner cell walls and radial orientation of cellulose microfibrils in the guard cell walls explain why they separate when turgid, forming a pore.

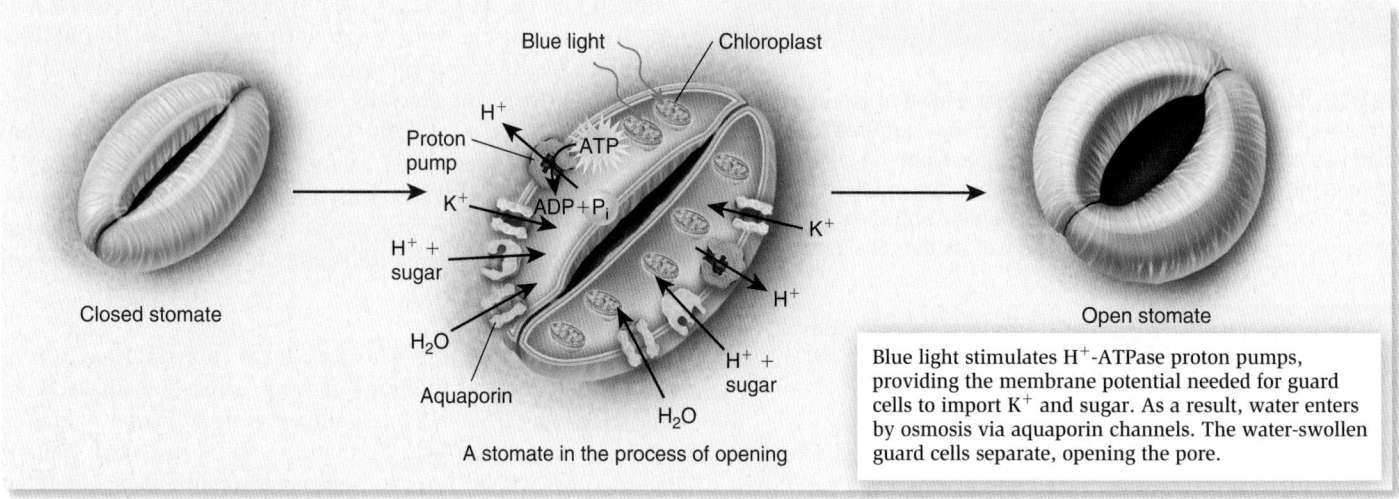

(a) The process of stomate opening

Blue light stimulates H^+-ATPase proton pumps, providing the membrane potential needed for guard cells to import K^+ and sugar. As a result, water enters by osmosis via aquaporin channels. The water-swollen guard cells separate, opening the pore.

(b) The process of stomate closing

At night or under conditions of water stress that stimulate ABA production, K^+ and other solutes exit guard cells. This causes water to leave, deflating guard cells and closing the pore.

Figure 36.17 **How stomatal pores open and close.** (a) Stomata usually open in response to sunlight. (b) Stomata usually close in response to lack of sunlight. They can also close during the day under conditions of water stress, which induces plants to produce more of the hormone abscisic acid (ABA). Stomatal guard cell plasma membranes possess ABA receptors, which receive the drought signal.

At night, the reverse process closes stomata. Potassium and other solutes are pumped out of guard cells, causing water to exit and deflate them, resulting in pore closure. Plants also close stomata during the daytime under conditions of water stress, a process that is mediated by the stress hormone abscisic acid (ABA). Water stress causes a 50-fold increase in ABA, which is transported in the xylem sap to guard cells. ABA then binds to a receptor, which elicits a Ca^{2+} second messenger, causing the guard cells to lose solutes and water and deflate (**Figure 36.17b**). Recently, a negative regulator of ABA signalling was discovered that has created an opportunity to engineer drought-tolerant plants, as will be discussed in the Featured Investigation section.

Some plants in arid habitats keep their stomata closed during the hot daytime hours and open them during the cooler night, allowing carbon dioxide to enter without losing too much water. These plants, known as CAM (Crassulacean acid metabolism) plants, bind the CO_2 taken in at night into an organic acid and release it when the sun rises, thus allowing photosynthesis to occur. Other forms of C_4 photosynthesis are also adaptations that foster plant water retention in hot, dry conditions (see Chapters 8 and 35).

Sometimes stomatal movements are not completely under the plant's control. Certain pathogens cause plant wilt diseases by influencing stomata. For example, the fungal genus *Fusicoccum*, a pathogen of fruit trees, produces a toxin known as fusicoccin that stimulates plant plasma membrane proton pumps. This fungal pathogen thereby causes guard cell turgor to increase. As a result, the stomata open under conditions when they would normally be closed. The subsequent water loss causes leaves of infected trees to wilt.

Leaf Abscission Angiosperm trees and shrubs of seasonally cold habitats experience water stress every winter, when evaporation from plant surfaces occurs, yet soil water is frozen and thus unavailable for uptake by roots. Desert plants experience water stress conditions at less predictable times and for much of the year. Both types of plants are adapted to cope with water stress by dropping their leaves, a process known as **leaf abscission**. Dropping leaves lets these plants avoid very low leaf water potentials and the consequent danger of xylem embolism. Leaf abscission also reduces the amount of root mass that plants must produce to obtain water under arid conditions. The ocotillo (*Fouquieria splendens*) of North American deserts can produce leaves after sporadic rains and then drop all of its leaves as a direct response to drought as many as six times a year (**Figure 36.18**).

The sugar maple (*Acer saccharum*) is an example of the many types of temperate forest trees that drop their leaves each autumn and are known as deciduous plants. Deciduous plants contrast with evergreen conifers, whose needle- or scale-shaped leaves are adaptations that reduce the leaf surface area from which water can evaporate, which helps these gymnosperms cope with water stress during the cold

(a) Ocotillo with leaves   **(b) Ocotillo without leaves**

Figure 36.18 Leaf abscission as a drought adaptation. The ocotillo (*Fouquieria splendens*), a plant native to North American deserts, is known for its ability to respond to intermittent rain and drought by producing and dropping leaves multiple times within a year.

season (Chapter 28). By contrast, the broader, thinner leaves produced by many angiosperms are well adapted for efficient light capture, but more vulnerable to the stresses caused by cold. During their evolution, temperate-zone angiosperm trees and shrubs have acquired the genetic capacity to predict the onset of cold, dry winter conditions and respond with preemptive leaf abscission. In contrast to the case of the ocotillo, autumn leaf drop in temperate angiosperms is not directly induced by drought.

Leaf abscission is a highly coordinated developmental process. The hormone ethylene stimulates an abscission zone to develop at the bases of leaf petioles (**Figure 36.19a**). The abscission zone contains two types of tissues: a separation layer of short, thin-walled cells and an underlying protective layer of suberin-impregnated cork cells (**Figure 36.19b**). Suberin contains both waterproofing wax and phenolic polymers that retard microbial attack. As the abscission layer develops across the vein linking the petiole with the stem, it eventually cuts off the water supply to the leaf. Chlorophyll in the leaf degrades, revealing colourful orange and yellow carotenoid and xanthophyll pigments that were hidden beneath. In addition, some plants synthesize red and reddish-blue pigments in response to changing environmental conditions. The presence of these pigments explains colourful autumn vegetation in temperate zones. Enzymes eventually break down the cell-wall components of the separation layer, causing the petiole to break off the stem. The underlying protective layer forms a leaf scar that seals the wound, helping to protect the plant from water loss and pathogen attack.

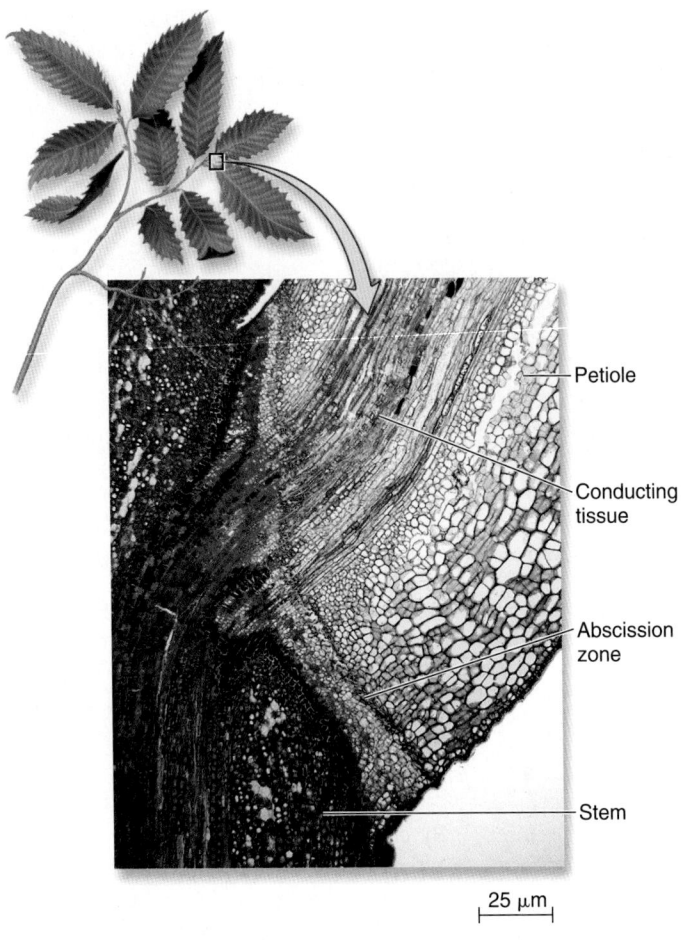

Petiole

Conducting tissue

Abscission zone

Stem

25 μm

(a) LM of leaf abscission zone at the junction of a petiole and stem, stained with dyes

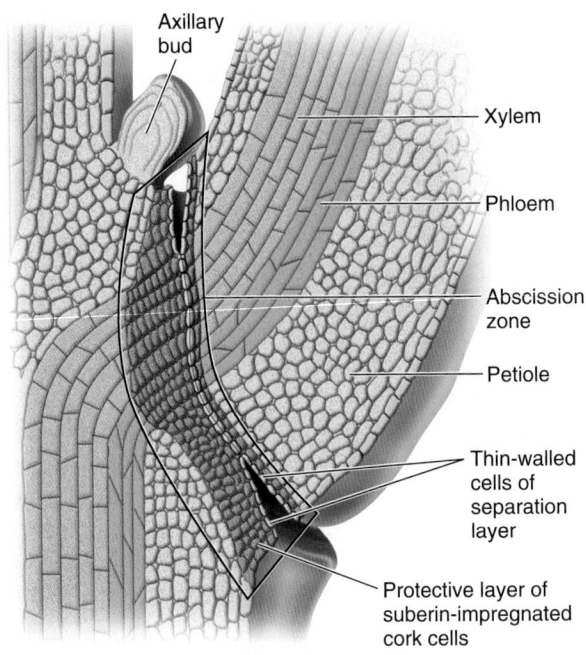

Axillary bud

Xylem

Phloem

Abscission zone

Petiole

Thin-walled cells of separation layer

Protective layer of suberin-impregnated cork cells

(b) Tissues involved in leaf abscission

Figure 36.19 Leaf abscission. Leaf abscission helps maintain plant hydration.

 Principle: *Living organisms maintain homeostasis. This is illustrated by leaf drop in response to, or in anticipation of, arid conditions.*

FEATURE INVESTIGATION

McCourt and Colleagues Engineer Drought Tolerance into Crops

As sessile organisms, plants have evolved many mechanisms to mitigate the potential damage of abiotic stresses, such as drought. In general, plant hormones play roles in either sensing change or participating in molecular signalling events that cause changes in cellular physiology in response to the specific stress. The hormone abscisic acid (ABA) has been implicated as a key mediator of stress responsiveness, slowing metabolism when growth conditions are unfavourable, inducing bud and seed dormancy, and regulating stomatal movements.

When conditions become favourable for seed germination (temperature and water availability are the critical factors), dormancy is broken and the seedling emerges from the seed. This process is mediated by an increase in the level of gibberellic acid, which promotes germination, and a concomitant decrease in the levels of ABA, which maintains the dormant state. Part

of the signalling networks involve perception of the hormone level, and therefore it should be possible, by using genetic approaches, to identify mutants that are either insensitive or supersensitive to a hormone.

Peter McCourt and his colleagues at the University of Toronto embarked on such a mutant hunt, looking for *Arabidopsis* seeds that displayed abnormal responses to ABA. Normally, wild-type seeds will germinate efficiently on a minimal medium containing low concentrations of ABA (0.3 μM), but mutants that exhibit an enhanced response to ABA should not (**Figure 36.20**). From a population of nearly 200,000 mutagenized seeds, seven lines were selected that could not germinate on 0.3 μM ABA but that did germinate when the seeds were transferred onto a minimal medium without added ABA. One of these, designated *era-1*, showed recessive Mendelian inheritance and was selected for further molecular and physiological characterization.

McCourt reasoned that if the mutant was indeed involved in ABA sensing, then other stress responses mediated by ABA would also be altered. In collaboration with Julian Schroeder at the University of California, San Diego, these scientists initiated a series of experiments to examine guard cell behaviour and stomatal movements in response to both ABA and drought stress. They used a technique called **patch clamping**, which allows scientists to determine ion channel activity. A micropipette containing an electrode is placed against the sample cell (in this case a guard cell). Gentle suction is applied to create a tight seal that connects the plasma membrane to the solution inside the electrode. As such, any potential signalling molecule, such as ABA, can be introduced to the cell through the pipette; if this results in a change in ion channel activity, a change in the electrical parameters of the plasma membrane can be recorded by a very sensitive electrode.

Both wild-type and *era-1* cells were analyzed by this method. First, the anion channel current was measured in the absence of ABA, and both kinds of cells exhibited identical electrical recordings, presented in the graph as pico amperes (10^{-12} amperes) per unit time. After the application of ABA, the wild-type cells responded by opening their channels, and a small current was recorded. For *era-1*, ABA application resulted in a more profound increase in current flow that persisted for a longer time, suggesting that *era-1* plants are very sensitive to ABA.

Physiologically, as ion efflux continues, an osmotic gradient is established and water begins to flow out of the cell, resulting in cell shrinkage. As the guard cell pair that surrounds a stomate shrink, the stomatal pore decreases, closing the pore and limiting water loss via transpiration. McCourt and colleagues directly demonstrated that *era-1* plants close their stomata at low ABA concentrations that do not affect wild-type plants. Importantly, these *era-1* plants were also shown to be significantly more drought tolerant than wild-type plants.

The explosion of genomics techniques and the ease with which transgenic plants can be created produced an excellent opportunity put this basic knowledge of ABA signalling to work in a practical application. McCourt collaborated with Performance Plants, an agricultural biotechnology company, with the goal of introducing drought tolerance into agriculturally important plants. Unfortunately, it is not possible to create targeted mutations in specific genes in a large genome, but it is possible to "phenocopy" a mutation by employing RNA interference, which we discussed in Chapter 12. Recall that the basis of RNA interference is the presence of a double-stranded mRNA molecule that serves as a target for the RNA-induced silencing complex (RISC) that degrades the normal

HYPOTHESIS Regulatory mutants of ABA sensing can be identified. Guard cells of *era-1* mutants are responsive to ABA.

KEY MATERIAL Mutagenized *Arabidopsis* seeds.

Experimental level	Conceptual level
1 Sow seeds on minimal medium containing 0.3 μM ABA. Minimal + ABA	Most seeds germinate; a few do not. These represent potential mutants that are super-sensitive to the inhibitory effects of ABA.
2 Transfer seeds that do not germinate on ABA to minimal medium. Minimal only	Seeds that germinate are indeed viable and a dose response experiment can be conducted to show that the progeny seeds have an enhanced response to ABA: these mutants are designated *era* mutants.
3 Use the patch clamp technique as shown. Pipette containing media and electrode Living cell Add ABA	Channels closed, no current flows Application of ABA through the pipette activates ion channels. Opening causes current to flow and is measured by the electrode.

Figure 36.20   McCourt and colleagues engineer drought tolerance into crops.

Figure 36.20 *(Continued)*

---

4   THE DATA

Patch clamp recording data.

WT   – ABA   *era-1*

+ ABA

100 pA ⌐
        10 s

In the absence of ABA, both wild-type (WT) and the *era-1* mutant have negligible anion current flow.

The addition of ABA induces anion channel opening in WT, but this response is more pronounced in the *era-1* mutant.

Physiological effects.

K⁺ —
H₂O
Pore   Ca²⁺
— ABA
— ABA receptor
— Ca²⁺
— Cl⁻
— K⁺
H₂O

ABA induces efflux of ions and water leaves the cell along the osmotic gradient; the cells begin to contract, closing the stomatal pore.

era-1 mutants close their stomata at low ABA concentrations.

Stomatal aperture (μm) vs *[ABA] μM*

WT

era-1

0   .001 .01 .1   1   10

At low ABA concentrations (e.g., 0.05 μM), *era–1* plants close their stomata by more than 50%, whereas the wild-type plants have not responded.

---

5   Genetic engineering: basic science translated into practical applications.

Drought inducible rd29A promoter →

Transgene
Antisense *era-1* gene
5'   3' ——— mRNAs ——— 3'   5'

Wild-type gene
Sense *era-1* gene

RISC complex

5'
3' dsRNA

Transgenic plants expressing an antisense gene produce mRNAs that are complementary to the normal sense mRNA of the *era-1* gene. These double-stranded RNAs (dsRNA) are degraded by the RISC complex to phenocopy the *era-1* mutant.

---

6   Drought stress is well tolerated by the antisense plants.

WT

YPT2

Wild-type and antisense line YPT2 were grown under optimal conditions and then exposed to drought stress. These photos, taken after rewatering, show that YPT2 is much healthier and produced many more seeds.

---

7   CONCLUSION

By manipulating the expression of the *era-1* gene, it is possible to engineer plants for drought resistance.

---

8   **SOURCE**: Pei, Z-M., Ghassimian, M., Kwak, C.M., McCourt, P., and Schroeder, J.I. 1998. Role of farnesyltransferase in ABA regulation of guard cell anion channels and plant water loss. *Science* 282:287–290.

mRNA. If there is no mRNA, no protein is produced; therefore, introducing an antisense *era-1* gene into cells results in the synthesis of a mRNA that is complementary to the endogenous-sense mRNA. Base pairing results in a double-stranded mRNA that triggers its own destruction by the RISC complex. To make this work most efficiently, these investigators used the rd29A promoter to control the antisense gene. Previous studies had shown that this promoter is induced by drought stress, and therefore the engineered gene should be expressed to produce the antisense transcripts during periods of drought.

Canola plants were chosen as the test plant and the engineered gene introduced into them. The resulting transgenic plants displayed normal growth and development, as well as enhanced ABA sensitivity that resulted in accelerated stomatal closure. When challenged by drought stress, these transgenic lines remained healthy and survived, whereas wild-type plants were severely affected. If the drought stress occurs during flowering in an important seed crop such as canola, flower abortion can occur, leading to severe losses in yield. In contrast, such short-term drought conditions are well tolerated by the transgenic lines, protecting the plants and preserving yield.

Experimental Questions

1. How did McCourt and his team screen for mutants that had altered responses to ABA?
2. How is the technique of patch clamping performed? How does it measure changes in the activity of an ion channel?
3. Why would guard cells change their shape when ions are extruded? What structural features allow them to alter their shape in a way that opens the stomatal pore?

Long-Distance Transport of Organic Molecules Occurs in the Phloem

Our examination of xylem structure and function provides the background needed to understand phloem structure and function. As we have noted, phloem plays an essential role in long-distance transport of dissolved organic compounds and ions in the plant body. Phloem often transports sugars from where they are produced to other sites where they are also used. Recall that primary phloem occurs in the vascular bundles of herbaceous plants, and secondary phloem occurs as the inner portion of bark of woody plants. In contrast to xylem, whose transport tissues are dead and empty of cytoplasm at maturity, mature phloem tissues remain alive and retain at least some cytoplasmic components. A closer look at phloem structure and function will help to illuminate these differences.

Phloem Structure   Phloem tissues of flowering plants include supporting fibres, parenchyma cells, sieve-tube elements, and adjacent companion cells. **Sieve-tube elements** are arranged end to end to form transport pipes (**Figure 36.21**), analogous to the way that the xylem's vessel elements are aligned to form longitudinal vessels. Together, the sieve-tube elements and companion cells form a transport system for the soluble organic material made during photosynthesis.

Each sieve-tube element and companion cell pair has a common origin. They are produced by an unequal division of a single precursor cell and are thus linked by plasmodesmata formed at cytokinesis. The smaller of the two cells develops into a companion cell, whose name reflects its life-support function. The larger of the two cells develops into a sieve-tube element, which loses its nucleus and most of its cytoplasm as an adaptation that reduces obstruction to bulk flow. Mature sieve-tube elements retain only a thin film of peripheral cytoplasm that includes some endoplasmic reticulum, plastids, and mitochondria. The end walls of developing sieve-tube elements become perforated by the action of wall-digesting enzymes that enlarge existing plasmodesmata. The perforated end walls of mature sieve-tube elements are known as **sieve plates**, and the numerous perforations are known as **sieve plate pores**. Phloem sap passes through these plates from one sieve-tube element to another.

Mature sieve-tube elements are not dead. However, because they lack a nucleus, they are dependent on their neighbouring companion cells for messenger RNA (mRNA) and proteins, which are supplied via plasmodesmata. For example, when a plant's conducting system is damaged, a short-term wound response occurs that involves production of a protein known as **P protein** (for phloem protein). Masses of this protein congeal along sieve plates, preventing loss of phloem sap (**Figure 36.22**). This mass functions much like a clot that helps reduce blood loss from wounded animals. P protein also binds to the cell walls of pathogens, thereby helping to prevent

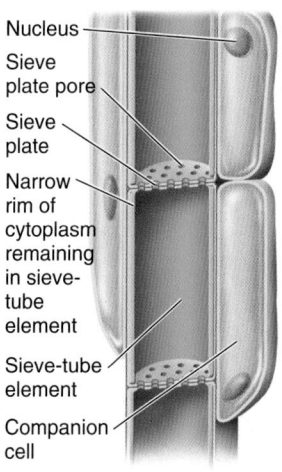

Nucleus
Sieve plate pore
Sieve plate
Narrow rim of cytoplasm remaining in sieve-tube element
Sieve-tube element
Companion cell

(a) Sieve-tube elements and companion cells

20 μm

(b) Light micrograph of phloem stained with blue dye, showing sieve-tube elements

Figure 36.21   Sieve-tube elements and companion cells in phloem tissue.

Figure 36.22 Phloem wound response. When phloem is damaged, the cytoplasm of a sieve-tube element surges toward the sieve plate, depositing P protein, stained red in this light micrograph. In this location, P protein helps to prevent infection and leakage of solutes.

infection at wounds. However, sieve-tube elements cannot produce P protein by themselves. Their companion cells provide either P protein mRNA or the protein itself to sieve-tube elements. In the longer term, plants synthesize and deposit a carbohydrate called callose as a sealant at the wound site.

Phloem Loading Companion cells also play an essential role in conveying sugars to sieve-tube elements for long-distance transport, a process known as **phloem loading**. Although glucose and some other monosaccharides are found in phloem, the disaccharide sucrose is the main form in which most plants transport sugar over long distances. Plant biologists think that sucrose is less vulnerable to metabolic breakdown en route than are monosaccharides.

Two types of phloem loading occur: symplastic and partly apoplastic. Many woody plants transport sucrose from sugar-producing cells of the leaf mesophyll to companion cells and then to sieve-tube elements via plasmodesmata, a process known as symplastic phloem loading (**Figure 36.23a**). The advantage of symplastic loading is that it does not require ATP; by moving through plasmodesmata, sugar does not have to cross plasma membranes.

In contrast, most herbaceous plants, including important crop plants and the model plant *Arabidopsis*, load sugar into sieve-tube elements or companion cells from intercellular spaces, often against a concentration gradient. ATP must be used to move the sugar across a plasma membrane into a companion cell or sieve-tube element (**Figure 36.23b**). Thus, this second type of phloem loading is partly apoplastic and partly a transmembrane process.

The Pressure-Flow Hypothesis Explains Transport in Phloem Tissues We have learned that the sun's energy drives transpirational water movement in plant xylem by a process of cohesion, adhesion, and tension. Once sugar has been loaded into phloem sieve-tube elements, how does it move within the plant? The most common explanation is that phloem transport is driven by differences in turgor pressure that occur between cells of a **sugar source**, where sugar is produced, and those of a **sugar sink**, where sugar is consumed. Photosynthetic leaf mesophyll is the main sugar source. Roots and developing leaves, seeds, and fruits are examples of sugar sinks. In the process known as **translocation**, phloem transports substances from source to sink. The direction of phloem movement can be horizontal or vertical, depending on the relative positions of the sources and sinks.

Because sieve-tube elements near source tissues have higher solute contents than surrounding tissues, water tends to rush into them from nearby xylem, thereby building turgor

(a) Symplastic phloem loading

(b) Partly apoplastic phloem loading

Figure 36.23 Symplastic and partly apoplastic phloem loading.

Figure 36.24 Pressure-flow hypothesis for phloem transport.

pressure. The production of turgor pressure requires an intact plasma membrane. This explains why mature phloem sieve-tube elements must be alive in order to function.

In contrast to sieve-tube elements near source tissues, sieve-tube elements near sink tissues have a lower solute concentration. The resulting water pressure difference drives the bulk flow of phloem sap from source to sink tissues. This explanation for phloem transport is known as the **pressure-flow hypothesis** (**Figure 36.24**). At sink tissues, sugar is typically unloaded through plasmodesmata (Figure 36.24). Because plasmodesmata are very narrow in comparison with sieve-tube elements, they slow the flow of phloem sap from sieve-tube elements into sink tissues. This reduction in flow rate helps to equalize the distribution of phloem sap, preventing delivery of too much sap to any single sink. When the solute concentration of phloem sap has been sufficiently reduced, water flows from the phloem back into the xylem, where upward transport occurs. The reliance of phloem bulk flow on water supplied by the xylem explains the close proximity of phloem and xylem tissues in vascular bundles and woody stems.

GENOMES AND PROTEOMES

Microarray Studies of Gene Transcription Reveal Xylem- and Phloem-Specific Genes

Xylem and phloem tissues have important economic, agricultural, and ecological roles. For example, secondary xylem produced by the vascular cambium and otherwise known as wood forms the basis of our forest products industry. The ability of plants to respond to environmental factors also relies on vascular tissues, which transport hormones. Seeking increased fundamental understanding and enhanced ability to engineer plants, molecular biologists have tried to identify the genes involved in xylem and phloem development. The use of microarrays, also known as gene chips, is providing a genomewide view of gene expression related to xylem and phloem.

Chengsong Zhao, Eric Beers, and their co-workers recently compared gene expression in xylem (X), phloem plus vascular cambium (PC), and nonvascular (NV) tissues dissected from young *Arabidopsis* plants. Recall that the vascular cambium is the meristematic tissue that produces secondary phloem (inner bark) and secondary xylem (wood; see Chapter 33). The investigators used a dissecting microscope to view one-centimetre pieces of tissue and a razor blade to make a longitudinal cut into nonvascular tissues and phloem, isolating the xylem. Then they peeled the nonvascular tissue away from the phloem. They ensured that their tissue samples were pure and authentic by checking for the expression of marker genes already known to be tissue specific. The investigators ascertained that their X and NV tissue samples had very low expression of certain PC genes and that their PC samples had very low expression of certain X and NV genes. They then extracted RNA from the three separate tissues and used it to make labelled nucleic acid for hybridization to gene microarrays containing about 90% of the *Arabidopsis* genome (refer back to Figure 18.12).

Binding of labelled nucleic acid revealed which genes were expressed. By comparing the binding patterns on different chips hybridized with nucleic acid from distinct tissues, the researchers were able to determine the genes that were preferentially expressed in X, PC, and/or NV tissues. These differences are revealed by a triangle plot that reflects the proportions of genes expressed in the three tested tissues (**Figure 36.25**). Genes expressed primarily in only one tissue type cluster at the triangle apices, and genes expressed in two tissues but not the third are plotted at the triangle edges. Genes expressed in all three tissues fall into the centre. The researchers identified 319 X-biased genes, 211 PC-biased genes, and 154 NV-biased genes. Not surprisingly, 17% of the X-expressed genes were related to cell-wall biosynthesis, including lignin production. The investigators then confirmed, via microscopy, that several proteins predicted by microarray data to be located in X, PC, or NV tissue were actually made in these tissues. This study is an essential first step toward determining the function, timing of expression, and cellular locations of xylem- and phloem-specific proteins.

Figure 36.25 Triangle plot showing gene expression related to xylem, phloem, and nonvascular tissue in *Arabidopsis*.

Summary of Key Concepts

36.1 An Overview of Plant Transport

- The plant root system takes up water and minerals, while the shoot system absorbs carbon dioxide from the air. Photosynthetic cells use these materials to produce organic compounds. The vascular system xylem transports water and minerals from roots to shoots, while the phloem transports organic compounds from photosynthetic to non-photosynthetic tissues. (Figure 36.1)

36.2 Uptake and Movement of Materials at the Cellular Level

- Facilitated diffusion is the transport of molecules across plasma membranes down a concentration gradient with the aid of membrane transport proteins, typically channels and transporters. Active transport, the transport of substances across plasma membranes against concentration gradients, usually requires ATP. Plasma membrane proton pumps use the energy released by ATP hydrolysis to move protons from the cytosol into the intercellular space, generating a membrane potential. Potential energy released by the flow of protons back into the cell can be coupled to the transport of ions and solutes. (Figures 36.2, 36.3)

- Turgor pressure increases as water enters plant cells because cell walls restrict the extent to which cells can swell. A cell that is so full of water that the plasma membrane presses closely against the cell wall is turgid. A cell that contains so little water that the plasma membrane pulls away from the cell wall is plasmolyzed. A flaccid cell has a water content between these extremes (Figure 36.4)

- Solute potential and pressure potential arising from the presence of a cell wall are major factors affecting cellular water potential. Water moves from a region of higher water potential to a region of lower water potential. (Figure 36.5)

- Plants display a variety of adaptations that help them cope with cellular osmotic stress.

36.3 Tissue-Level Transport

- Tissue-level transport occurs in three forms. Transmembrane transport involves the movement of materials from one cell to another from intercellular spaces, across plasma membranes, and into the cytosol. The symplast is the continuum of all plant cytosolic compartments linked by plasmodesmata. Symplastic transport allows materials to move from one cell to another through the symplast, the cells' cytosol and plasmodesmata, without crossing plasma membranes. In apoplastic transport, water and solutes move through the apoplast, the water-filled cell walls and intercellular spaces of tissues. (Figures 36.6, 36.7)

- In roots, waxy Casparian strips on cell walls of endodermal tissue act as diffusion barriers that reduce the movement of toxic ions and concentrate useful minerals into the plant vascular system. (Figure 36.8)

36.4 Long-Distance Transport

- Water and solutes move for long distances by bulk flow within the xylem and phloem. Plant vascular tissues are adapted in ways that reduce resistance to bulk flow. Bulk flow of water upward in xylem is powered by the water pressure difference between moist soil and drier air, the latter resulting from solar heating. (Figure 36.9).

- Xylem is the main conduit for water and dissolved mineral nutrients, but it may also transport certain organic compounds (Figures 36.9, 36.10). The water-conducting cells of xylem, tracheids, and vessel elements (together known as tracheary elements), are dead and empty of cytoplasm at maturity. Pits in tracheary element walls allow water entry and exit, and narrow or constrict in response to xylem sap solute content. Vessel elements are wider than tracheids but are more vulnerable to blockage by air bubbles or embolisms. Root pressure, the effects of which include the morning water drops on leaf tips known as guttation, helps some plants to refill embolized vessels. (Figures 36.10, 36.11, 36.12, 36.13).

- Transpiration is the evaporative loss of water from plant surfaces. The cohesion-tension theory proposes that as the result of water's cohesion and the tension exerted on water at the plant's surface by evaporation, a continuous stream of water can be pulled up through the plant body from the soil, into roots, through stems, and into leaves. (Figures 36.14, 36.15, 36.16)

- Regulation of stomata helps plants prevent excessive water loss by transpiration. Expansion of guard cells causes stomata to open, allowing CO_2 intake. Guard cell deflation causes pores to close, limiting water loss. Plants under existing or predicted water stress often drop their leaves in a process known as abscission, an adaptive response that lets plants avoid very low water potentials and the threat of embolism (Figures 36.17, 36.18, 36.19, 36.20)

- Organic solutes and minerals are transported in phloem sap as the result of osmosis. Phloem sap moves within sieve-tube elements that are living when mature but lack a nucleus and are thus dependent on companion cells. Phloem loading, the movement of sugars into sieve-tube elements for long-distance transport, occurs by symplastic or partly apoplastic transport. (Figures 36.21, 36.22, 36.23)

- In the process known as translocation, phloem transports substances from source to sink. The pressure-flow hypothesis helps to explain translocation as a process driven by differences in turgor pressure that occur between a sugar source (e.g., leaves) and a sugar sink (e.g., developing fruit). (Figures 36.24, 36.25)

Test to Assess Your Learning

1. An aquaporin is
   a. a channel protein that allows the influx of K^+ into cells, causing water to also flow in between the phospholipids of a plasma membrane.
   b. a type of blue-coloured pore in the epidermal surfaces of plants.
   c. a protein channel in plasma membranes that facilitates the diffusion of water.
   d. a protein transporter in plasma membranes that uses protons to cotransport water.
   e. none of the above.

2. Why is turgor pressure a property of plant cells?
   a. Plant cells possess the necessary chloroplasts.
   b. Plant cells possess a cell wall, necessary for the formation of turgor.
   c. Plant cells possess mitochondria, which provide the ATP needed for turgor.
   d. Both (b) and (c).
   e. All of the above.

3. How might plant cells avoid losing too much water in very cold, dry, or saline habitats?
   a. They may balance the osmotic condition of their cytosol with that of the environment.
   b. They may drop their leaves.
   c. They may stabilize their membranes with sugars.
   d. They may produce more aquaporin water channels to take maximum advantage of available moisture.
   e. All of the above are possible.

4. What are ways in which plants accomplish tissue-level transport?
   a. transmembrane transport of solutes from one cell to another
   b. symplastic transport of materials from one cell to another via plasmodesmata

   c. apoplastic transport of water and dissolved solutes through cell walls and intercellular spaces
   d. both (a) and (b)
   e. all of the above

5. A root endodermis is
   a. an innermost layer of cortex cells that each display characteristic Casparian strips.
   b. a layer of cells just inside the epidermis of a root.
   c. a layer of cells just above the epidermis of a root.
   d. a group of cells that occur within the root epidermis.
   e. none of the above.

6. Which of the statements listed best explains how water enters root cells from the soil?
   a. Roots accumulate sugars from shoots, thereby increasing root cell ability to absorb water by osmosis.
   b. Roots actively pump water from the soil using the chemical energy of ATP.
   c. Water enters the spongy spaces between cells and within cell walls.
   d. Membrane-level transport of ions from soil into root hair cells increases the osmotic flow of water into them.
   e. Both (c) and (d).

7. What features of water explain how it can be drawn up a tall tree from roots to leaves?
   a. cohesion, the result of extensive hydrogen bonding
   b. adhesion, water's tendency to stick to surfaces, such as the inner walls of tracheid and vessels
   c. high surface tension that develops when water evaporates from intercellular leaf spaces
   d. both (a) and (c)
   e. all of the above

8. What feature of vascular plants contributes to their ability to maintain relatively stable internal water content?
   a. a waxy surface cuticle
   b. an extensive root system that mines water from soil
   c. specialized water-conducting tracheary elements composed of dead cells
   d. epidermal pores that open and close
   e. all of the above

9. What structural features of stomatal guard cells foster their ability to form an open pore in plant epidermal surfaces?
   a. thickened inner cell walls and radially oriented microfibrils
   b. thickened outer cell walls and radially oriented microfibrils
   c. thickened inner cell walls and longitudinal microfibrils
   d. thickened outer cell walls and longitudinal microfibrils
   e. uniform thickness of cell walls and randomly arranged microfibrils

10. What substances plug wounded sieve-tube elements, thereby preventing the leakage of phloem sap?
    a. X protein and callose
    b. C protein and callose
    c. P protein and callose
    d. P protein and sucrose
    e. none of the above

Articulate to Assess Your Learning

1. Why is it a bad idea to overfertilize your houseplants?

2. Why is it a bad idea for subsistence farmers (those barely able to grow enough crops to feed themselves) to allow livestock to graze natural vegetation to the point that it disappears?

Collaborate to Assess and Extend Your Learning

1. Imagine that you are part of a team that is assigned to determine what environmental conditions best suit a new crop, so that the crop can be recommended to farmers in appropriate climate regions. What features of the crop plants might you investigate?

2. Take a look outside or imagine a forest or grassland. What can you deduce about the availability of soil water from the types of plants that occur?

3. How might you go about identifying genes involved in the development and maturation of tracheary elements?

4. A principle of biology is that living organisms interact with their environment. In the desert southwestern United States, the ocotillo plant is often used as a landscaping plant, thanks to its interesting shape and beautiful floral displays. Imagine that you are responsible for property landscaped with ocotillo but find the plants bare of leaves. Can you assume that the plants are dead and need to be replaced?

Visit McGraw-Hill Ryerson Connect™ for additional study resources.

Flowering Plants: Reproduction and Development

37

Chapter Outline

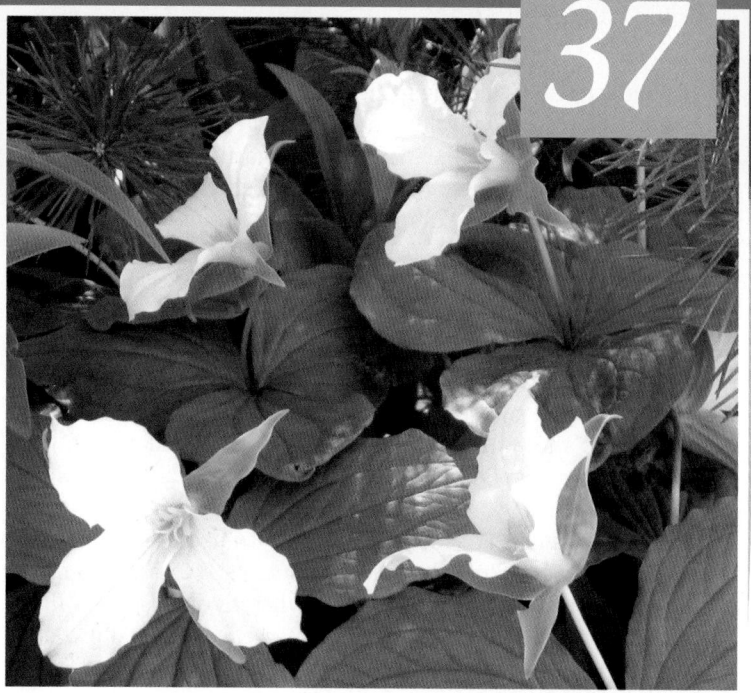

Trillium, flowering in an Ontario woodland.

Terrestrial plants are sessile organisms, meaning that they are anchored by their roots and therefore must endure seasonal environmental changes. In the preceding chapters we discussed how plants perceive their environment and coordinate their biochemical activities. As the days become longer and warmer in the spring, conditions become favourable for seed germination and the reactivation of bulb plants (e.g., tulips, daffodils). Across much of Canada and the United States, spring wildflowers, such as the *Trillium* shown in the chapter-opening photo, bloom profusely, often covering large areas of forest landscapes. *Trillium,* like most flowering plants, produce flowers that contain both male and female reproductive structures, which in turn produce the sperm and eggs needed for fertilization to create the next generation. Typically, the fertilized egg develops into an embryo, which is housed within a seed. In some cases, the seed is surrounded by tissue that we consider a fruit (e.g., tomato, apple).

This chapter begins with an overview of the reproductive cycle of flowering plants that describes how flowers, fruits, and seeds function. This overview provides essential background for a closer look at flower structure and development, and some of the genes that control flower production and appearance. We will also examine the sexual reproductive processes by which plants produce gametes and accomplish fertilization, thereby producing zygotes and embryos. We will explore how seeds, fruits, and seedlings develop. Finally, we will consider ways in which some plants reproduce without using the sexual process. Throughout this chapter you will find examples of ways in which flowering plant reproduction plays an essential role in ecology and agriculture.

37.1   AN OVERVIEW OF FLOWERING PLANT REPRODUCTION

Learning Outcomes:

1. Explain how the sexual life cycle of flowering plants differs from that of earlier-evolved mosses.
2. List the four organs found in many flowers and the functions of each organ.
3. Describe the phenomenon of double fertilization.
4. Know the parts of an angiosperm seed, and how each part is produced and functions.

Most flowering plants display **sexual reproduction**, the process by which new individuals arise by the fusion of gametes (fertilization) to form zygotes that develop into mature adults. Flowering plants, also known as angiosperms, inherited their sexual life cycle, known as alternation of generations, from ancestors extending back to the earliest land plants (see Chapters 28 and 29). Though all plants share the same basic life cycle, flowering plants display unique reproductive features. In this section, we first review the general features of alternation of generations and then consider more specific features of the angiosperm life cycle.

Flowering Plants Display Alternation of Generations

All groups of land plants produce two multicellular life cycle stages—in essence, two distinct plants. These two life cycle stages are the diploid spore-producing sporophyte, and the haploid gamete-producing gametophyte. In all groups of plants, haploid spores are typically produced by diploid **sporophytes** as the result of meiosis. These spores undergo mitotic cell divisions to produce multicellular **gametophytes**. Certain cells within the gametophytes differentiate into gametes. Thus, meiosis does not directly generate the gametes of plants. The processes of meiosis and fertilization form the transitions between the sporophyte and gametophyte life stages and link them in a cycle (**Figure 37.1**). The land plant life cycle is known as **alternation of generations** because it involves the cycling between distinct sporophyte and gametophyte generations.

During the evolutionary diversification of land plants, the sporophyte generation has become larger and more complex. By contrast, the gametophyte generation has become smaller and less complex. To illustrate this, let's compare the life cycle stages of mosses to those of angiosperms. Mosses diverged early in the history of land plants, whereas angiosperms first appeared much later. During the intervening time, the relative sizes and dependence of the sporophyte and gametophyte generations changed dramatically. Moss sporophytes are small structures that always grow attached to larger, photosynthetic gametophytes, because moss sporophytes are incapable of independent life (**Figure 37.2a**). Moss sporophytes are dependent on gametophytes to supply them with essential nutrients.

In contrast, flowering plant sporophytes are notably larger and more complex than gametophytes. A tall oak tree, for example, is a single sporophyte. However, oak gametophytes are few-celled structures that develop and grow within flowers (**Figure 37.2b**).

(a) Gametophyte-dominant bryophyte (moss)

(b) Sporophyte-dominant flowering plant (oak)

Figure 37.2 Evolutionary shift in plant life cycle stage dominance. (a) In mosses, the gametophyte is the dominant life cycle stage, and the sporophyte is dependent on the gametophyte for resources. (b) In flowering plants, such as oak, the sporophyte life cycle stage is dominant. Microscopic flowering plant gametophytes develop and grow within sporophytic flower tissues, and are completely dependent on sporophytes.

Concept check: *What advantages do flowering plants obtain by having such small and dependent gametophytes?*

In addition, photosynthetic oak seedlings and trees grow independently, but nonphotosynthetic oak gametophytes are completely dependent on the sporophyte generation for their nutrition. A closer look at flower structure will help you gain a more complete view of angiosperm gametophyte structure and function.

Flowers Produce and Nurture Male and Female Gametophytes

A **flower** is defined as a reproductive shoot, a stem branch that produces reproductive organs instead of leaves. Flower organs are produced by shoot apical meristems, and are thought to have evolved from leaflike structures by descent with modification (refer back to Figure 29.15).

Most flowers contain four types of organs: sepals, petals, stamens, and carpels (**Figure 37.3**). **Sepals** often function to protect the unopened flower bud. **Petals** often are bright in colour and usually serve to attract insects or other animals for pollen transport (refer back to Figures 29.19 and 29.20).

KEY
Diploid
Haploid

Figure 37.1 Alternation of generations, the plant life cycle.

BioConnections: *Look back to Figure 29.14 to see a more detailed illustration of the flowering plant life cycle. How can one recognize and where can one find the gametophyte generation of a flowering plant?*

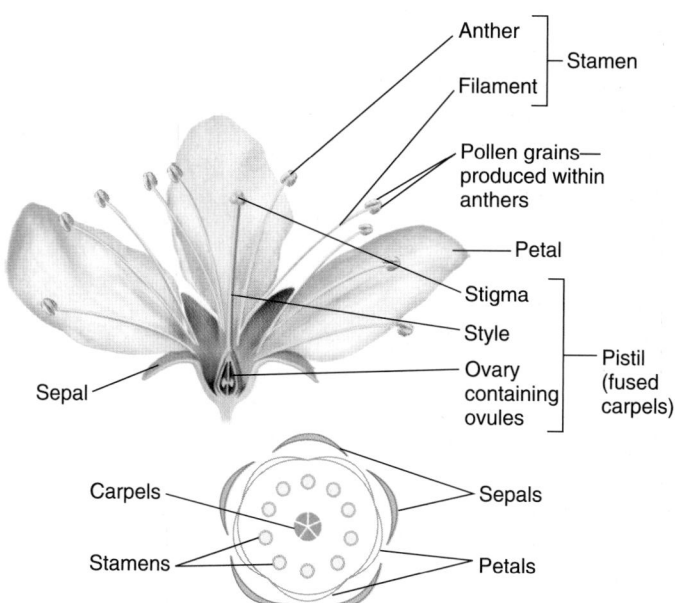

Anther
Filament — Stamen
Pollen grains—
produced within
anthers
Petal
Stigma
Style
Ovary
containing
ovules
Pistil
(fused
carpels)
Sepal

Carpels
Stamens
Sepals
Petals

Figure 37.3 **The structure of a typical flower.**
(a) Generalized schematic of floral structures. The lower figure represents a cross-section through a flower. Note that the number of organs is variable and species specific.

Stamens and **carpels** each produce distinctive types of spores by the process of meiosis. From these spores, tiny multicellular gametophytes develop and certain gametophytic cells become specialized gametes.

Stamens Stamens produce **male gametophytes** and foster their early development. Most stamens display an elongate stalk, known as a **filament**, which is topped by an anther (see Figure 37.3). Filaments contain vascular tissue that delivers nutrients from parental sporophytes to anthers. Each **anther** is a group of four sporangia, structures in which spores are produced. Within the anther's sporangia, many diploid cells undergo meiosis, each producing four tiny haploid spores. Because they are so small, generally 25–50 μm in diameter, the spores produced within anthers are known as **microspores**. Immature male gametophytes, otherwise known as **pollen grains**, develop from microspores. The term *pollen* comes from a Latin word meaning "fine flour," reflecting the small size of pollen grains. Pollen grains are eventually dispersed through pores or slits in the anthers. At the time of dispersal, the pollen grain is a two- or three-celled male gametophyte produced by mitotic division. During a later phase of development, a mature male gametophyte produces **sperm** cells.

Carpels Carpels are flask-shaped structures that produce, enclose, and nurture **female gametophytes**. Carpels contain veins of vascular tissue that deliver nutrients from the parent

sporophyte to the developing gametophytes. The term **pistil** (named for its resemblance to the pestle used to grind materials to a powder) refers to a single carpel or several fused carpels (Figure 37.3), but some flowers have separate pistils that are each composed of a carpel. The topmost portion of a pistil, known as a **stigma**, receives pollen grains. The **style** is the middle portion of the pistil, and an ovary is at the bottom of the pistil. The **ovary** produces and nourishes one or more ovules. An **ovule** consists of a spore-producing structure (a sporangium) and enclosing tissues known as **integuments**. Within an ovule, a diploid cell produces four **megaspores** by meiosis, three of which undergo programmed cell death. The surviving megaspore generates a female gametophyte by mitosis. The female gametophytes of flowering plants typically consist of seven cells, one of which is the female gamete, the **egg** cell. This basic information about male and female gametophytes will help you understand how they function to produce a young sporophyte within a seed.

Fertilization Triggers the Development of Embryonic Sporophytes, Seeds, and Fruits

In flowering plants, fertilization leads to the production of a young sporophyte that lies within a seed, completing the life cycle (**Figure 37.4**). Prior to fertilization, pollen grains released from anthers first find their way to the stigma of a compatible flower, a process known as **pollination**. Many flowers are attractive to insects or other animals that transport pollen, but many angiosperm flowers are adapted for pollen transport by wind, and a few move pollen by means of water currents. Some plants display **self-pollination**, in which pollen from the anthers of a flower is transferred to the stigma of the same flower, or between flowers of the same plant. **Cross-pollination**, which occurs when a stigma receives pollen from a different plant of the same species, is also common.

Pollen Germination When pollen grains land on the stigma, the stigma functions as a gatekeeper, allowing only pollen of appropriate genotype to germinate. During germination, a pollen grain produces a long, thin **pollen tube** that contains two sperm cells. The pollen tube grows through the style toward the ovary. On reaching the ovules, the pollen tube grows through the **micropyle**, an opening in the ovule integuments, and delivers sperm to the female gametophyte (Figure 37.4). These sperm unite with haploid cells of the female gametophyte in the process of **fertilization**. Note that pollination and fertilization are distinct processes in flowering plants.

Double Fertilization Angiosperms display an amazing phenomenon known as **double fertilization**. In this process, two different fertilization events occur. One of the two sperm cells delivered by a pollen tube fertilizes the egg cell, thereby forming a diploid **zygote**. This zygote may develop by mitotic division into a young sporophyte, known as an **embryo**. Fertilization thus begins a new cycle of alternation between sporophyte and gametophyte generations. The other sperm delivered

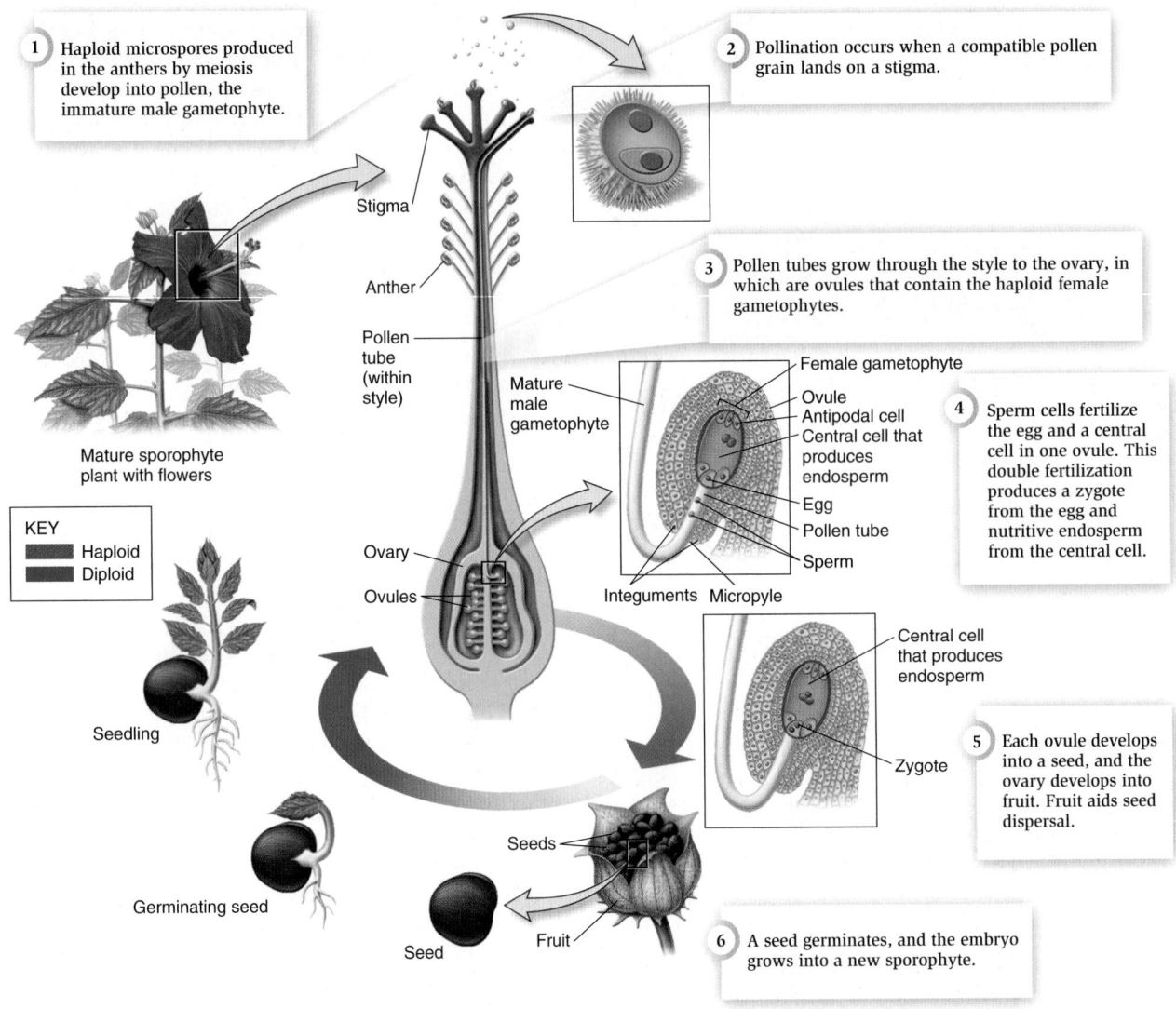

1 Haploid microspores produced in the anthers by meiosis develop into pollen, the immature male gametophyte.

2 Pollination occurs when a compatible pollen grain lands on a stigma.

3 Pollen tubes grow through the style to the ovary, in which are ovules that contain the haploid female gametophytes.

4 Sperm cells fertilize the egg and a central cell in one ovule. This double fertilization produces a zygote from the egg and nutritive endosperm from the central cell.

5 Each ovule develops into a seed, and the ovary develops into fruit. Fruit aids seed dispersal.

6 A seed germinates, and the embryo grows into a new sporophyte.

Stigma

Anther

Pollen tube (within style)

Mature sporophyte plant with flowers

KEY
Haploid
Diploid

Seedling

Ovary

Ovules

Mature male gametophyte

Female gametophyte

Ovule

Antipodal cell

Central cell that produces endosperm

Egg

Pollen tube

Sperm

Integuments Micropyle

Central cell that produces endosperm

Zygote

Seeds

Germinating seed

Seed

Fruit

Figure 37.4 **The life cycle of a flowering plant.** The plant reproductive cycle is illustrated here by hibiscus.

Concept check: *What advantage does the hibiscus flower gain by clustering its stamens around the pistil?*

by the same pollen tube fuses with two nuclei located in a central cell of the female gametophyte. The cell formed by this second fertilization undergoes mitosis, eventually producing a nutritive tissue known as the **endosperm**. The embryo and the endosperm are essential parts of maturing seeds. Fertilization not only starts the development of zygotes into embryos but also triggers the transformation of ovules into seeds and ovaries into fruits. Embryo, seed, and fruit development occur at the same time.

Embryos and Seeds An embryo is a young, multicellular diploid sporophyte that develops from a single-celled zygote by mitosis. Because they are not yet capable of photosynthesis,

embryos depend on organic food and other materials supplied by sporophytes. Thus, embryo development occurs within developing seeds located in a flower ovary. **Seeds** develop from fertilized ovules. Each developing seed contains an embryo and nutritive endosperm tissue, enclosed and protected by a tough **seed coat** that develops from the ovule integuments. When embryos and the seed coat have fully matured, they undergo drying and the seed enters a phase of metabolic slowdown known as **dormancy**. Fully mature, dormant seeds are ready to be dispersed.

Fruit and Seed Dispersal A fruit is a structure that encloses and helps to disperse seeds (Figure 37.4). Seed dispersal

(a) Coconut fruit and seed

Fruit husk (pericarp)
Seed coat
Solid endosperm
Location of liquid endosperm

(b) Apple fruit and seed

Fruit wall (pericarp)
Seed coat

Figure 37.5   The structure of fruits as adaptations for seed dispersal.   (a) The coconut's outer fruit wall, called a husk, allows the fruit to float and thus disperse its seed among tropical shores. (b) The apple is a juicy, sweet fruit that attracts animals to consume it, thereby helping to disperse its seed.

benefits plants by reducing competition for resources among seedlings and parental plants, and it allows plants to colonize new sites.

Fruits develop from the flower's ovary and sometimes include other flower parts. Young fruits bearing immature seeds are typically small and green. During the time that embryos and seeds are developing, the fruit also matures. The ovary wall changes into a fruit wall known as a **pericarp** (from the Greek word meaning "surrounding the fruit"). Mature fruits vary greatly among plant species in size, shape, colour, and water content. These variations represent adaptations for seed dispersal in different ways. For example, single-seeded dandelion fruits are dry, lightweight, and bear a fluffy "parachute" derived from the flower's sepals. These features foster dispersal by wind. In contrast, coconut fruits feature an airy husk (the outer pericarp) that keeps them afloat in ocean currents, allowing coconuts to disperse from one tropical shore to another. Inside the coconut fruit is a single large seed loaded with liquid and solid endosperm, which people use as coconut milk and coconut meat (**Figure 37.5a**). These large amounts of endosperm provide nutrients that sustain coconut seedling growth on infertile, sandy shores. Fruit variation is also extremely important to wild animals and in human agriculture. For example, most fruit crops are juicy and sweet, with relatively small seeds (**Figure 37.5b**). In nature, these features foster dispersal by birds and other animals that feed on such fruits.

Seed Germination and Seedlings   If a dispersed seed encounters favourable conditions, including sufficient sunlight and water, it will undergo seed **germination**. During seed germination, the embryo absorbs water, becomes metabolically active, and grows out of the seed coat, producing a seedling. If the seedling obtains sufficient nutrients from the environment, it grows into a mature sporophyte capable of producing flowers. In the next section, we focus on flower production, structure, and development.

FLOWER PRODUCTION, STRUCTURE, AND DEVELOPMENT

Learning Outcomes:

1. List some examples of particular genes that control flower production or shape.
2. Give an example of how gene expression affects flowering time or flower appearance.
3. Explain recent research findings on how flowers bloom, that is, open up from a closed bud.

Many flowers are essential sources of food for many animal pollinators. As the result of coevolutionary relationships with such animals, flowers occur in a spectacular array of colours and forms that attract particular pollinators (refer back to Table 29.2).

Flowers also attract humans. We give bouquets to show love and appreciation; decorate homes, workplaces, and objects with flowers; display flower arrangements on ceremonial occasions; and make perfume from flowers. Consequently, many types of flowers are grown for the florist and perfume industries. Flowers are necessary for the production of grain and other fruit crops. For these and other reasons, biologists investigate how flower development is controlled by environmental signals and changes in gene expression.

Developmental Genes Control Flower Structure

Organ identity genes specify the four basic flower organs—sepals, petals, stamens, and carpels. Other genes determine flower shape, colour, odour, or grouping into bunches known as inflorescences.

The Genetic Basis of Flower Organ Identity   Sepals, petals, stamens, and carpels occur in four concentric rings known as **whorls**. Sepals (collectively known as the **calyx**) form the outermost whorl, while petals (together known as the **corolla**) occur

GENOMES AND PROTEOMES

Environmental Signals and Developmental Genes Control Flower Production

You've probably noticed that different plants flower at particular times of the year. How do plants determine when to flower, and how do plants transform leaf-producing shoots into flowering shoots? Studies of the genes and proteins of *Arabidopsis*, rice (*Oryza*), and other plants whose genomes have been completely sequenced provide answers to these questions.

Although temperature often influences flowering, day length is the main flowering signal for many plants. For example, crop plants, such as rice and soybean, are known as short-day plants because they flower when day length is decreasing. In contrast, pea and other plants are known as long-day plants because they flower when day length has increased beyond a critical level (refer back to Figure 34.12). The model plant *Arabidopsis* can flower during periods of long days or short days, but flowering occurs much faster in response to long days. How do plants detect the day-length signal?

At sunrise each day, the light-sensing pigment phytochrome in leaves is stimulated by red light and resets a molecular clock that occurs within plant cells. Each day, this clock starts the accumulation of cellular proteins that influence flowering. In short-day plants, such as rice, a protein that represses flowering fails to accumulate to critical levels in short days, so flowering occurs. In long-day plants, including *Arabidopsis*, the cellular clock starts the production of a nuclear protein known as CONSTANS (CO) that accumulates during the day but degrades at night. In long days, the CO protein is stabilized against regulated degradation, and enough CO accumulates to induce flowering in *Arabidopsis* (**Figure 37.6a**).

Let's consider how CO exerts its effects. Experiments performed in the 1970s revealed that leaves transmit a flowering

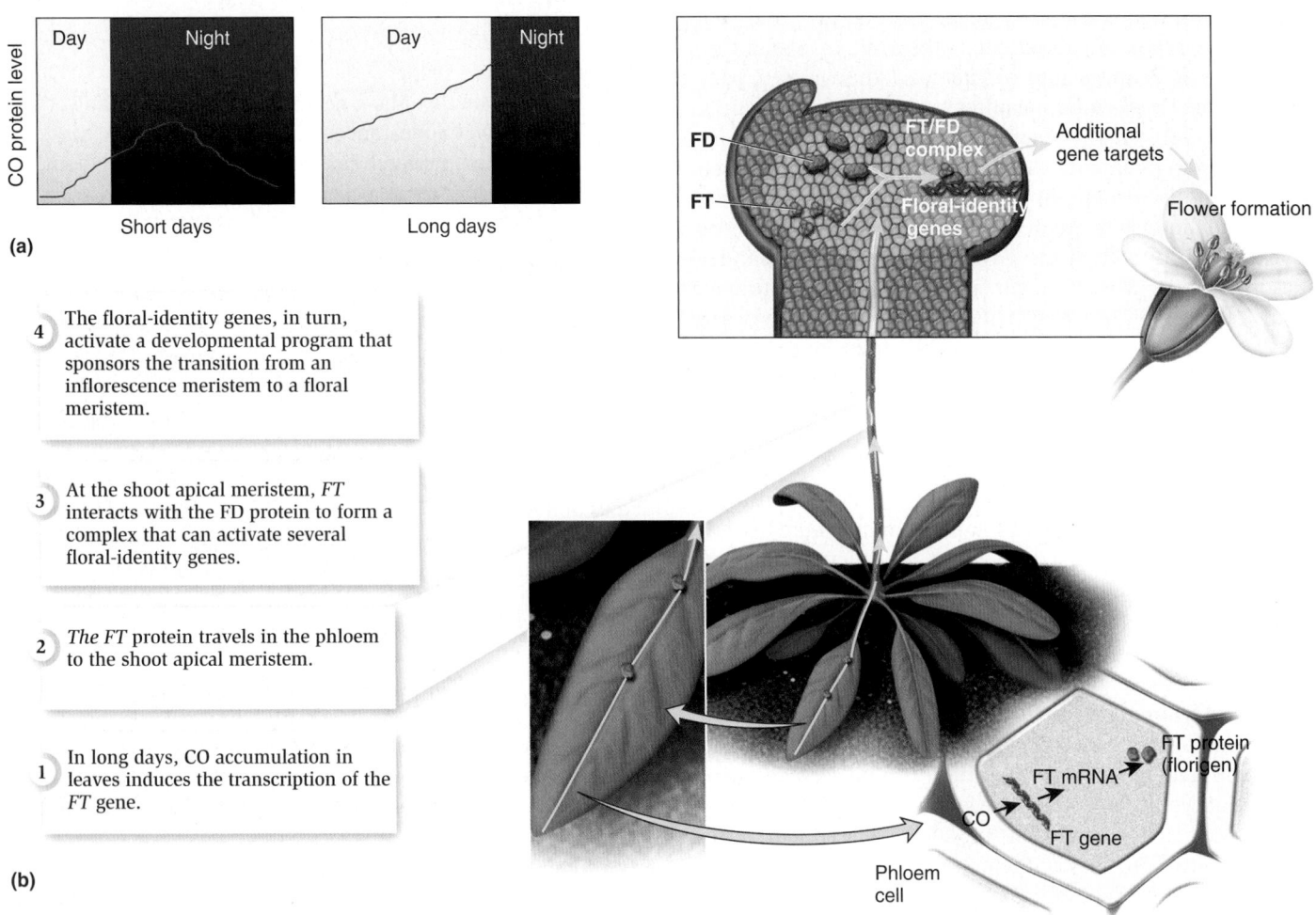

(a)

4 The floral-identity genes, in turn, activate a developmental program that sponsors the transition from an inflorescence meristem to a floral meristem.

3 At the shoot apical meristem, *FT* interacts with the FD protein to form a complex that can activate several floral-identity genes.

2 *The FT* protein travels in the phloem to the shoot apical meristem.

1 In long days, CO accumulation in leaves induces the transcription of the *FT* gene.

(b)

Figure 37.6   Long-day stimulation of flower development in *Arabidopsis.*   (a) During short days, the transcription factor CONSTANS (CO) does not reach threshold levels, in part because of short day length and in part because it is degraded in the dark. In long days, CO accumulates to relatively high levels and triggers flowering. (b) The accumulation of CO activates the *FT* gene, and the FT protein produced travels in the phloem to shoot meristems to induce flower formation.

signal to the shoot apical meristem via phloem. Based on these results, plant scientists hypothesized the existence of a flowering hormone, which they named **florigen**, meaning "flower generator." However, the chemical nature of florigen remained unknown until recently. In 2005 three groups of plant molecular biologists working with *Arabidopsis* made critical discoveries that revealed florigen's identity. In long days, CO accumulation induces the transcription of a flowering time gene (*FT*) in leaf

phloem tissues (**Figure 37.6b**). The FT protein, which is also a transcription factor, moves through the phloem to the shoot apical meristem, where it forms a complex with a transcription factor called FD. Together the FT/FD complex activates floral-identity genes, which in turn stimulate the transformation of a leaf-producing apical meristem into a reproductive meristem. FT is probably the long-sought florigen molecule.

in an adjacent whorl. Stamens (collectively, the **androecium**) create a third type of whorl, and carpels (the **gynoecium**) form the innermost whorl (**Figure 37.7**). The **perianth** is the calyx plus the corolla.

You may recall that *A*, *B*, *C*, and *E* genes encode transcription factors that control the production and arrangement of these whorls (refer back to Figure 17.21). Class A genes control the development of sepals and petals, class B genes specify petal and stamen formation, and class C genes determine the identities of the stamen and carpels. *E* gene expression distinguishes the sepals from the other whorls. However, not all flowers produce all four types of organs.

Variation in Number of Whorls

Flowers that possess all four types of flower whorls—sepals, petals, stamen, and carpels—are known as **complete flowers**. In contrast, flowers that lack one or more flower whorls are described as **incomplete flowers**. Flowers having both stamens and carpels are said to be perfect, whereas flowers lacking stamens or carpels are described as imperfect. An imperfect flower that produces carpels is known as a carpellate flower (or pistillate flower). Imperfect flowers that produce only stamens are described as staminate flowers.

Corn produces both imperfect carpellate and staminate flowers (**Figure 37.8**). The flowers of corn start to develop as perfect flowers, but in carpellate flowers, the stamens stop developing. After pollination and fertilization, each carpellate flower produces one of the kernels on a cob of corn. In contrast, staminate flowers of corn, which are found in corn tassels, produce the pollen. Corn is termed **monoecious** (meaning "one house") because it produces staminate and carpellate flowers on the same plant. Holly and willow also produce staminate and carpellate flowers, though on separate plants, and are examples of plants described as **dioecious** (meaning "two houses").

Variation in Flower Organ Number

In addition to variation in whorls, flowers vary in number of organs. Recall that flowering plants occur in two major groups differing in flower structure and other features: the eudicots and the monocots (see Chapter 33). Eudicot flower organs often occur in fours or fives or a multiple of these numbers. By contrast, monocot flower organs often occur in threes or a multiple of three. Other flowers possess relatively few organs. For example, the minuscule flowers of the tiny aquatic flowering plant *Lemna gibba* produce no perianths and only two stamens.

Many plants sold for use in gardens have been bred so that the flowers produce multiple organs. Garden roses, for example, typically have many more petals than do wild roses. This change results from a mutation that causes organs that would have become stamens to instead develop into additional petals.

Variation in Flower Colour

Different flower parts can vary in colour. The calyx and corolla of monocot flowers, such as tulip, are often similar in appearance and attractive function. In contrast, eudicot flowers tend to have green, leaflike sepals that are quite distinct from petals, which are often colourful and fragrant. For example, the sepals of petunia (*Petunia hybrida*) resemble leaves in having numerous stomata on both epidermal surfaces and internal parenchyma tissue rich in chloroplasts. Petunia petal epidermis lacks stomata, and the parenchyma tissue usually lacks

(a) Staminate flowers of *Zea mays* (corn)   (b) Carpellate flowers of *Zea mays* (corn)

Figure 37.8 Imperfect flowers of corn, a monoecious plant. Staminate flowers lack carpels, and carpellate flowers lack stamens, but both types of flowers occur on a single corn plant. In contrast, dioecious plants produce staminate and carpellate flowers on separate plants.

Concept check: *What inference can you make from the observation that corn flowers lack showy petals?*

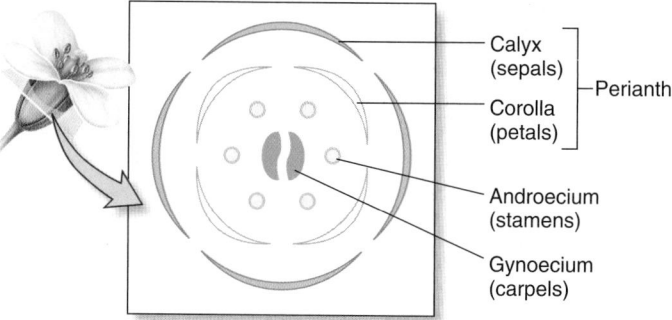

Calyx (sepals)
Corolla (petals)
— Perianth
Androecium (stamens)
Gynoecium (carpels)

Figure 37.7 The occurrence of flower parts in whorls.

chlorophyll. Instead, the cell vacuoles of petals are often coloured by **flavonoids**, a type of secondary metabolite (see Chapter 29). Among the pigments responsible for pink, red, blue, violet, purple, or yellow petals and other flower parts, flavonoids are the most important. Colour variations arise from differences in gene action that influence pigment biosynthesis pathways. Petunia has become an important model system for understanding the evolution of genes and proteins that control petal colour.

Interestingly, research involving flower colour has led to important discoveries in genetics. In 1990 plant molecular biologist Rich Jorgensen and his colleagues reported gene silencing in petunia. In an attempt to produce flowers of deeper colour, the researchers introduced an extra copy of a pigment-producing gene into petunia plants. To their surprise, they sometimes obtained flowers whose petals had white patches or were completely white (**Figure 37.9**). Adding the extra gene caused the plants to produce short interfering RNAs (siRNAs, Chapter 12), that not only silenced the expression of the extra gene but also the natural pigment-producing gene, resulting in white patches on the petals.

Variation in Flower Fragrance   The fragrances of flowers result from secondary metabolites that diffuse into the air from petals and other flower organs. One example is the terpene known as geraniol, that gives roses their distinctive fragrance. Diverse fragrances function to attract particular types of animal pollinators. Because humans possess sensory systems similar to those of many pollinators, we are also attracted to many of these fragrances. Genetic variation in the synthesis of different types of secondary metabolites is responsible for the many types of flower scents.

Flower Shape Variation Resulting from Organ Fusion   During their development, many flowers undergo genetically controlled fusion of the organs within a whorl or fusion between whorls. For example, stamen filaments often partially fuse with the corolla or form a tube surrounding the pistil, a feature

displayed by hibiscus flowers (see Figure 37.4). Each small dandelion flower has five petals that are fused at their sides to form a single strap-shaped structure. Some flowers have petals that are fused together to form a tube that holds nectar consumed by animal pollinators (see Figure 29.20).

Mutants of the *HOTHEAD* (*HTH*) gene of *Arabidopsis* display similar floral organ fusions that likewise arise from epidermal interactions. In 2005 plant molecular biologists Susan Lolle of the University of Waterloo, and Robert Pruitt and his colleagues at Purdue University reported their surprising discovery that about 10% of *HOTHEAD* plants with two copies of a mutant gene could revert to producing normal flowers whose organs are not fused. According to Mendel's laws of inheritance, all such offspring should have displayed the same mutation. These investigators propose that the *HOTHEAD* reversions result from a previously unknown genetic repair mechanism involving a store of nongenomic DNA or perhaps RNA. These results, like Mendel's use of pea crosses to uncover basic laws of inheritance and Jorgensen's discovery of gene silencing in petunia, illustrate the importance of flowering plant systems to basic biological research.

Flower Symmetry Variations   Flower shape variation can also result from changes in symmetry. Flowers that possess radial symmetry are described as regular (actinomorphic) flowers. Flowers having radial symmetry can be divided into two equal parts by more than one plane inserted through the centre of the flower. In contrast, flowers that display bilateral symmetry are known as irregular (zygomorphic) flowers. Flowers having bilateral symmetry can be divided into two equal parts by only a single plane inserted through the centre. The evolution of bilateral symmetry in flowers can often be linked to insect pollination. Symmetry, like other flower features, is under genetic control. For example, snapdragon (*Antirrhinum majus*) flowers are normally bilaterally symmetrical, but mutation in the *CYCLOIDEA* gene causes these flowers to display radial symmetry (**Figure 37.10**). A *CYCLOIDEA* gene also specifies bilateral symmetry in another eudicot, the legume *Lotus japonicus,* which is only distantly related to snapdragon.

Variation in Flower Arrangements   Flowers can occur singly or arranged in clusters of various types known as **inflorescences**. Diverse inflorescence types represent adaptations to particular pollination mechanisms. For example, cereals, such as corn and other grasses, are wind pollinated and thus produce inflorescences whose component flowers lack showy perianth parts (see Figure 37.8). Pollen is readily shed from such flowers into the wind. For example, a single staminate flower of corn disperses more than 10,000 pollen grains. Hairy grass stigmas (e.g., the "silks" of corn) effectively catch pollen from the wind, and clustering flowers into inflorescences also aids in pollen capture.

In corn, an inflorescence of staminate flowers is called a tassel, and an inflorescence of carpellate flowers is the ear (see Figure 37.8). Both types of inflorescence result from branching of the flowering meristem, with the result that a single corn shoot meristem produces many flowers rather than just one. One gene that plays an essential role in corn tassel and ear development is *barren inflorescence2* (*bif2*). In 2001 plant

(a) Normal purple petunia flowers   (b) Petunia flower affected by miRNA

Figure 37.9   **Gene silencing influences flower colour in petunia.**   **(a)** Normal purple petunia (*Petunia hybrida*) flowers produced by the expression of all genes involved in flavonoid synthesis. **(b)** Flower of a genetically engineered plant displays petal tissues in which one of the genes needed for production of purple pigment production has been silenced (suppressed) by microRNA.

(a) Normal snapdragon flower

(b) Snapdragon flower with *CYCLOIDEA* mutation

Figure 37.10 Genetic control of flower symmetry. **(a)** Normal snapdragon flowers, with functioning *CYCLOIDEA* genes, are bilaterally symmetrical. **(b)** Snapdragon plants carrying mutations in the *CYCLOIDEA* gene produce flowers that have radial symmetry.

 Principle: *The genetic material provides a blueprint for sustaining life. This principle is illustrated by a comparison of normal and mutant snapdragon flowers.*

molecular biologists Paula McSteen and Sarah Hake reported that nonfunctional *bif2* mutant corn plants produce few or no inflorescence branches and thus make few or no flowers. Such corn plants are reproductively barren.

Many flowers that are pollinated by animals also occur in inflorescences. Daisies, marigolds, zinnias, thistles, sunflowers, and broccoli are examples of plants that produce flowers in inflorescences known as heads. In the case of broccoli, there are several clustered inflorescence stalks, each bearing many flowers (**Figure 37.11**). Individually, the small flowers would be unlikely to attract pollinators from very far, but inflorescences are visible for much greater distances. Insects can easily walk around on the surfaces of heads, delivering pollen to many flowers during a single visit, thereby increasing pollination efficiency.

Figure 37.11 An inflorescence adaptation for pollination. The clustering of flowers into a type of inflorescence known as a head, displayed here by a broccoli plant, is an adaptation that fosters pollination by insects.

Now that we have surveyed aspects of flower development that influence overall flower structure, let's turn our attention to the development of male and female gametophytes within stamens and carpels.

37.3 MALE AND FEMALE GAMETOPHYTES AND DOUBLE FERTILIZATION

Learning Outcomes:

1. Explain how plant sperm production differs from sperm production in animals.
2. Discuss how the pistil controls pollen germination.
3. Describe the structure of the female gametophyte.
4. Outline the different fates of the two sperm cells transmitted by each pollen tube.

In flowering plants, mature male gametophytes are pollen grains that contain sperm cells, the male gametes. Mature female gametophytes are located within ovules and produce egg cells, the female gametes. In this section, we will focus on the structure and function of male and female gametophytes to learn more about how fertilization occurs.

Pollen Grains Are Immature Male Gametophytes

In animals, the cells that will produce gametes—known as the germ line—are set aside from other body cells during early development, but this is not the case for plants. Instead, plants make gamete-producing cells from body cells each time that stamens form, on an "as needed" basis. Plant sperm arise from male gametophytes. Immature male gametophytes, known as pollen grains, are produced within stamens.

Pollen grains develop within sporangia located in the anthers of stamens (see Figure 37.4). Sporangia are structures produced by all plants, within which meiosis generates spores. (Note that in plants, meiosis generates haploid spores, not haploid gametes as in animals.) Inside protective plant sporangia, diploid cells give rise to a cluster of four haploid microspores, each having a thin cellulose cell wall. The development of microspores into pollen grains involves two processes that occur at the same time. First, the microspore divides within its cell wall, producing a two- or three-celled young male gametophyte. Second, each male gametophyte develops a tough pollen wall that protects the gametophyte during pollen transport. Both of these processes are completed before anthers release mature pollen.

Each microspore nucleus undergoes one or two mitotic divisions to form a young male gametophyte. The first division gives rise to two specialized cells: a tube cell and a generative cell suspended within the tube cell (**Figure 37.12a**). The **generative cell** divides to produce two sperm cells, either before or (more commonly) after pollination. The **tube cell** produces the pollen tube, which delivers sperm to the female gametophyte.

A mature pollen grain has a tough wall, and each plant species produces pollen whose wall has a distinctive sculptural shape (**Figure 37.12b**). The **pollen wall**, which surrounds the plasma membrane, is composed largely of a nearly indestructible polymer known as **sporopollenin**. In fact, sporopollenin is so chemically inert that its biochemical composition is still uncertain. Named for its presence on the surfaces of mature spores and pollen, sporopollenin confers physical strength, chemical inertness, and resistance to microbial attack. Sporopollenin protects spores and pollen from damage.

Development of the pollen wall starts with deposition of a blanket of the carbohydrate **callose** around each cluster of four microspores after they form by meiosis. Callose plays several crucial roles in male gametophyte development. First, the callose blanket seals off microspores from the influences of adjacent sporophyte tissues, thereby aiding pollen differentiation. Callose also provides a surface pattern for sporopollenin deposition and holds microspores together until an anther enzyme degrades the callose, freeing developing pollen grains from each other.

As pollen grains mature, anther cells secrete a **pollen coat**, a layer of material that covers the sporopollenin-rich pollen wall. Coat materials include additional sporopollenin and pigments that give pollen its typically yellow, orange, or brown coloration, and lipids and proteins that aid in pollen attachment to carpels. Certain of these pollen coat compounds are responsible for allergic reactions in people exposed to particular types of air-borne pollen. It is no wonder that pollen allergies are common, because about 10% of flowering plants are wind pollinated, and such plants produce copious amounts of pollen. For example, ragweed plants (*Ambrosia* spp.), which are commonly associated with allergies, each produce an estimated 1 billion pollen grains during a year.

The production and dispersal of pollen grains is just the first phase of male gametophyte development. You will learn more about the second phase of male gametophyte development, the production of a pollen tube, after we look at female gametophyte development.

A Female Gametophyte Develops Within Each Ovule

Each ovule produces a single female gametophyte (**Figure 37.13**). Although flowering plant female gametophytes vary somewhat in size and structure, many possess seven cells and eight nuclei. One of these cells is an egg cell, which lies wedged between two cells known as **synergids**. These synergids have characteristic cell-wall ingrowths that increase the area of the plasma membrane, thereby helping to move nutrients from the larger sporophyte to the nonphotosynthetic female gametophyte. The other four cells of the angiosperm female gametophyte consist of three antipodal cells, whose functions are not well understood, and a large **central cell**. The central cell contains two nuclei, which accounts for the extra nucleus in the female gametophyte.

After Pollination, the Pistil Controls Pollen Germination

Pollen grains adhere to the surfaces of the stigma, which provides a receptive surface. The stigma and the style determine whether or not pollen grains germinate and pollen tubes grow. In some plants, pistils allow pollen from the same plant to

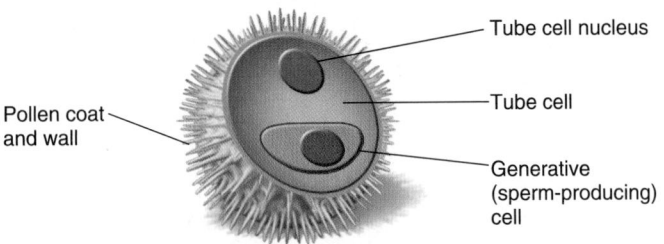

(a) Illustration of a pollen grain showing the immature male gametophyte

Tube cell nucleus
Tube cell
Pollen coat and wall
Generative (sperm-producing) cell

189 μm

(b) SEM of whole pollen grains showing distinctive pollen wall ornamentation

Figure 37.12   Pollen grains.

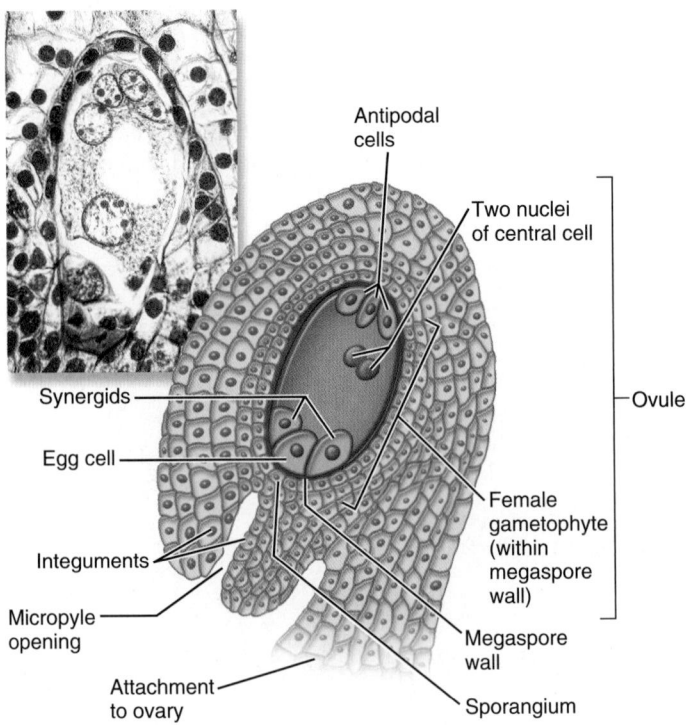

Antipodal cells
Two nuclei of central cell
Synergids
Egg cell
Integuments
Micropyle opening
Attachment to ovary
Ovule
Female gametophyte (within megaspore wall)
Megaspore wall
Sporangium

Figure 37.13   Female gametophyte within an ovule.

Concept check: *How do female gametophytes obtain nutrients?*

germinate, but in many cases pistils prevent the germination of pollen from different species and pollen that is genetically too similar, such as pollen from the same flower.

Rejection of pollen that is genetically too similar to the pistil is a phenomenon known as **self-incompatibility (SI)**. This feature helps to decrease the likelihood of recessive disorders in offspring. In the absence of self-incompatibility, self-fertilization and matings between closely related parent plants are more likely to produce progeny that are homozygous for many deleterious alleles, which would then be expressed. How then do pistils recognize compatible pollen grains of the appropriate species that are genetically distinct? Recognition involves interactions between proteins of pollen and pistil cells. These interactions influence the ability of pollen to take up water, a process known as rehydration. Pollen is nearly dry when it reaches the stigma, and incompatible pollen will not rehydrate and will eventually die. In contrast, compatible pollen rehydrates, a process that activates pollen metabolism and allows it to germinate. Pollen-stigma interactions thus form an important part of a flowering plant's mate recognition and selection system.

Let's look at SI systems a bit more closely. In many plants, SI involves the S gene locus, which encodes S proteins. Each locus contains two genes, one that determines pollen compatibility

traits and another that determines pistil compatibility traits. Multiple S alleles for both genes occur in plant populations. Two major types of SI are known: gametophytic SI and sporophytic SI. Gametophytic SI occurs when an S gene within a pollen grain itself determines compatibility. Because pollen is a haploid gametophyte, the pollen genome contains only one pollen-compatibility allele. This allele encodes a specific S protein that is located in the pollen cytosol. When the gametophyte controls compatibility, tubes may start to grow from incompatible pollen, but an S protein encoded by the same locus in pistil cells enters the tubes and destroys RNA. This halts tube growth. In contrast, S protein within genetically different pollen binds the pistil-produced protein, thereby preventing destruction of pollen tube RNA and allowing tube growth to continue (**Figure 37.14a**).

Sporophytic SI occurs when pollen compatibility is determined by the sporophyte that produces the pollen. This control is exerted when anthers deposit proteins into the pollen coat. Because anther cells belong to the sporophyte generation, they possess two S genes and thus heterozygotes will produce two different pollen coat S proteins. When the sporophyte controls compatibility, pollen cannot germinate when S proteins in the plasma membranes of stigma cells recognize (bind) the S proteins of incompatible pollen. In this case, protein binding leads

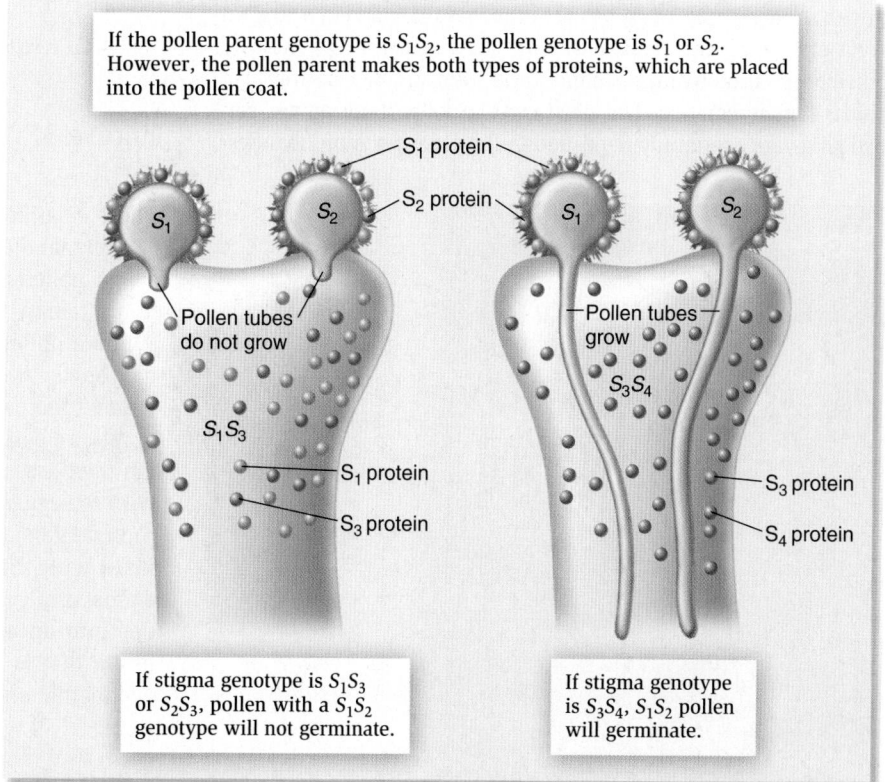

(a) Gametophytic SI: If pollen *S* allele does not match either stigma allele, pollen will germinate.

(b) Sporophytic SI: If pollen coat S proteins do not match either stigma S protein, pollen tubes will grow.

Figure 37.14 Self-incompatibility. Self-incompatibility helps plants to avoid the combination of gametes that are too genetically similar, and it is controlled by interactions between proteins of pollen and the pistil. (a) In gametophytic self-incompatibility, compatibility between pollen and pistil is determined by the haploid genotype of the pollen. In this case, S protein is located in the pollen cytosol. (b) In sporophytic self-incompatibility, compatibility between pollen and pistil is determined by the sporophyte that produced the pollen and contributed S proteins to its coat.

to signal transduction processes that prevent pollen germination. However, pollen can germinate if stigma proteins are unable to bind genetically distinct S proteins in its coat (**Figure 37.14b**).

If the SI system becomes inactivated by mutation, a plant species can become self-pollinating. This has occurred during the evolution of self-pollinating lines of the model plant *Arabidopsis* from an ancestor that possessed SI. An estimated 20% to 50% of all modern plant species, including many crop plants, display self-pollination. The ability to self-pollinate can be advantageous to plants as they colonize new habitats, and it is a common characteristic of weedy and invasive plant species. Self-pollination in plants is also useful when scientists perform genetic experiments with *Arabidopsis*. Pea plants are also self-pollinating, a feature that was useful to Mendel in performing his classic experiments on inheritance (see Chapter 15).

Pollen Tubes Deliver Sperm Cells that Accomplish Double Fertilization

When pollen grains germinate successfully, they take up water, and the tube cell produces a long pollen tube. Within the tube, the generative cell divides by mitosis to produce two sperm cells. To deliver sperm to egg cells, the tube must grow at its tip from the stigma, through the style to reach the ovule (**Figure 37.15**).

Tip growth is controlled by the tube cell nucleus. During tip growth, new cytoplasm and cell-wall material are added to the tip of an elongating cell (**Figure 37.16**). Golgi vesicles continuously deliver the carbohydrate pectin to the tube tip, whose thin cell wall is largely composed of pectin. As a pollen tube grows, callose plugs are commonly deposited in the older parts of the tubes.

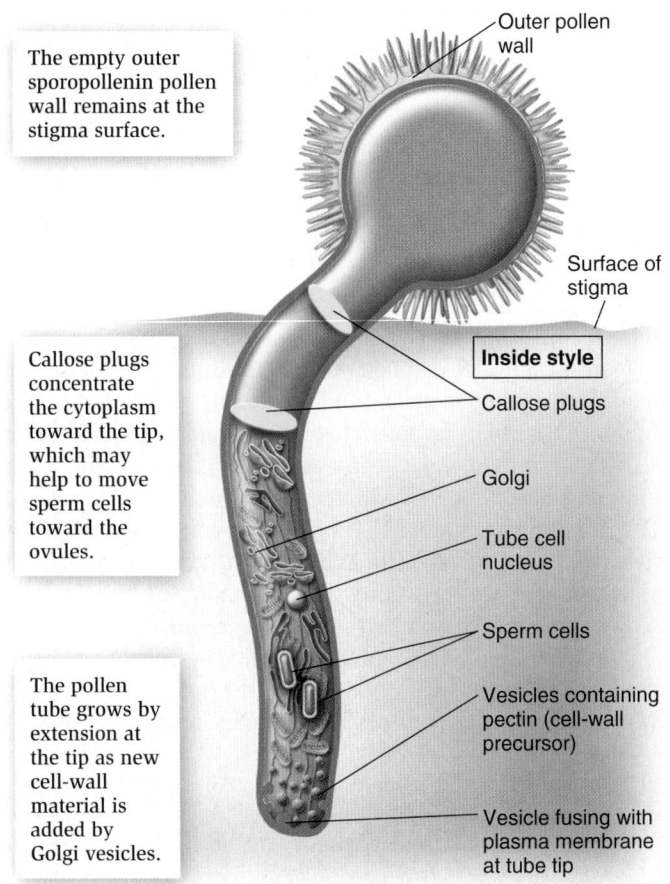

The empty outer sporopollenin pollen wall remains at the stigma surface.

Outer pollen wall

Surface of stigma

Inside style

Callose plugs concentrate the cytoplasm toward the tip, which may help to move sperm cells toward the ovules.

Callose plugs

Golgi

Tube cell nucleus

Sperm cells

The pollen tube grows by extension at the tip as new cell-wall material is added by Golgi vesicles.

Vesicles containing pectin (cell-wall precursor)

Vesicle fusing with plasma membrane at tube tip

Figure 37.16   Tip growth by a pollen tube.

These plugs concentrate the tube cytoplasm at the tip, which helps to maintain the turgor pressure necessary for continued tip growth.

A pollen tube grows toward an ovule at about 0.5 mm per hour, taking from 1 hour to 2 days to reach its destination. When a pollen tube encounters an ovule, it enters through the micropyle. Attracted by secretions from a nearby synergid, the pollen tube penetrates the synergid. The thin tube tip wall then bursts, releasing the sperm into the female gametophyte. During the process of double fertilization, one sperm nucleus fuses with the egg cell to produce a zygote, the first cell of a new sporophyte generation (see step 4 in Figure 37.4). The other sperm fuses with the two nuclei of the central cell to form the first endosperm cell (see step 5 in Figure 37.4). As the zygote develops into an embryo, the endosperm develops into a nutritive tissue that is usually triploid. The cellular and developmental events that ensue are discussed next.

Figure 37.15   Pollen tubes delivering sperm to ovules.   This fluorescence microscopic view shows pollen grains (the light objects) germinating on the stigma surface (SG), and pollen tubes (PT) growing through the style (ST) toward ovules.

SG

Stigma

ST

Style (with many pollen tubes growing through)

PT

Pollen tube entering an ovule

Ovule

150 μm

37.4   EMBRYO, SEED, FRUIT, AND SEEDLING DEVELOPMENT

Learning Outcomes:

1. Discuss the major stages in angiosperm embryo development.

2. List examples of environmental and internal factors that influence seed germination.
3. Explain how seed germination varies among plants.

Seeds and fruits are major components of plant reproduction. Seeds contain dormant plant embryos that develop into seedlings under favourable conditions. As earlier noted, fruits aid seed dispersal, which allows plants to colonize new sites. Embryos, seeds, and fruits mature simultaneously, and their development is coordinated by hormonal signals that were introduced in Chapters 33 and 34. Seedling development is also hormonally regulated.

Endosperm Provides Nutrients for Developing Embryos Within Seeds

Endosperm is a tissue present in developing angiosperm seeds and also occurs in the mature seeds of many plants. Rich in protein, lipid, carbohydrate, vitamins, and minerals, endosperm supplies the nutritional needs of developing embryos and often seedlings. We have already noted how humans use the coconut's liquid and solid endosperm as food (see Figure 37.5a). In fact, a large percentage of human and animal food protein comes from seed endosperm of grain crops. Corn, wheat, rice, and other grain crops generate more than 170 billion kilograms of endosperm per year in the United States alone.

How does this valuable tissue develop? Recall that the first cell of the endosperm tissue arises by the fusion of a sperm nucleus with the two nuclei of the female gametophyte's central cell. The resulting nucleus is typically triploid, combining one set of chromosomes from the male parent with two sets from the female parent. Mitotic division of the triploid cell generates endosperm tissue. The food stored in endosperm comes from the parent sporophyte via apoplastic transport through moist cell walls and intercellular spaces.

As the embryo develops, it uses food stored in the endosperm but food storage differs in eudicots and monocots. By the time that most eudicot seeds are mature, they contain little or no endosperm because such embryos store organic food in two embryonic leaves: the cotyledons. Each species is genetically programmed to produce specific types of reserves (seed storage proteins, lipids, and carbohydrates) in characteristic ratios. Derek Bewley and his colleagues at the University of Guelph have investigated this area of plant biology for more than 40 years. Their work has established that genes encoding seed storage proteins are activated early in seed development, and when mature, more than 50% of the total seed protein consists of only a few types of these proteins. In addition, Bewley's group has shown that during germination, a variety of genes that encode hydrolytic enzymes are activated and these enzymes mobilize stored reserves to provide energy and raw materials to the developing seedling until it can break the surface of the soil and begin to conduct photosynthesis.

The seeds of legumes, such as beans, peas, and peanuts, are valued as food because their cotyledons contain high levels of proteins, carbohydrates, fibre, and iron and are easily harvested.

The dry seeds have a long shelf life. Similarly, many grain crops (e.g., corn, wheat) are monocots whose seeds are highly valued as food sources, but they store their reserves within the endosperm.

Embryos Develop from Zygotes Within Seeds

Mature plant embryos are young sporophytes that possess several types of organs and lie dormant within seeds. Embryos develop from single-celled zygotes by mitotic divisions in a process known as **embryogenesis**. This process begins with an unequal cell division and proceeds through several distinctive stages, as illustrated by the model eudicot plant *Arabidopsis* (**Figure 37.17**).

Some time within days to several weeks following fertilization, a zygote begins to divide. At this point, a zygote is blanketed with a layer of callose, which helps to seal it off from the environment, thereby fostering embryo-specific gene expression. The zygote's first cell division is unequal, producing a smaller cell and a larger cell. This unequal division helps to establish the apical-basal (top-bottom) polarity of the embryo, which persists through the life of the plant. The smaller cell develops into the embryo, whose radial symmetry is established at this point and continues in adult plants. The larger cell develops into a **suspensor**, a short chain of cells anchored near the micropyle at the ovule entrance. The suspensor channels nutrients and hormones from the parent sporophyte into the young embryo, which absorbs them at its surfaces. Researchers have found that the functional loss of a gene called *TWN* (twin) transforms the suspensor into a second, twin embryo. This indicates that when TWN protein is active, it prevents the suspensor from developing into an embryo, thereby maintaining normal suspensor attachment and nutrient transport functions. The suspensor usually disappears by programmed cell death during embryo development. Older embryos rely on nutrients supplied by the endosperm.

Young eudicot embryos are spherical, but they soon become heart shaped as the seedling leaves, called **cotyledons**, start to develop. At this point, the young shoot and root are established at the apical and basal poles, respectively. This process is controlled by the expression of the gene *TOPLESS*, which represses auxin-responsive genes that would otherwise promote root development at the apical pole. (Mutants that have lost normal *TOPLESS* function have roots at both apical and basal poles but no shoots and are thus topless.) Eudicot embryos, such as *Arabidopsis*, then become torpedo shaped, and as the cotyledons grow, they often curl to fit within the developing seed (Figure 37.17, step 4). In contrast, mature monocot embryos are cylindrical, with a single cotyledon and a side notch where the apical meristem forms. Mature embryos then become dormant as seeds mature.

Mature Seeds Contain Dormant Embryos

As seeds mature, they undergo changes leading to dormancy, an adaptation that prevents them from germinating when environmental conditions are not suitable for seedling growth. During this process, embryos become dry and thus able to survive in the absence of water. Seed maturation includes transformation of the ovule's integuments into a tough seed coat (see Figure 37.17, step 5). The seed coat

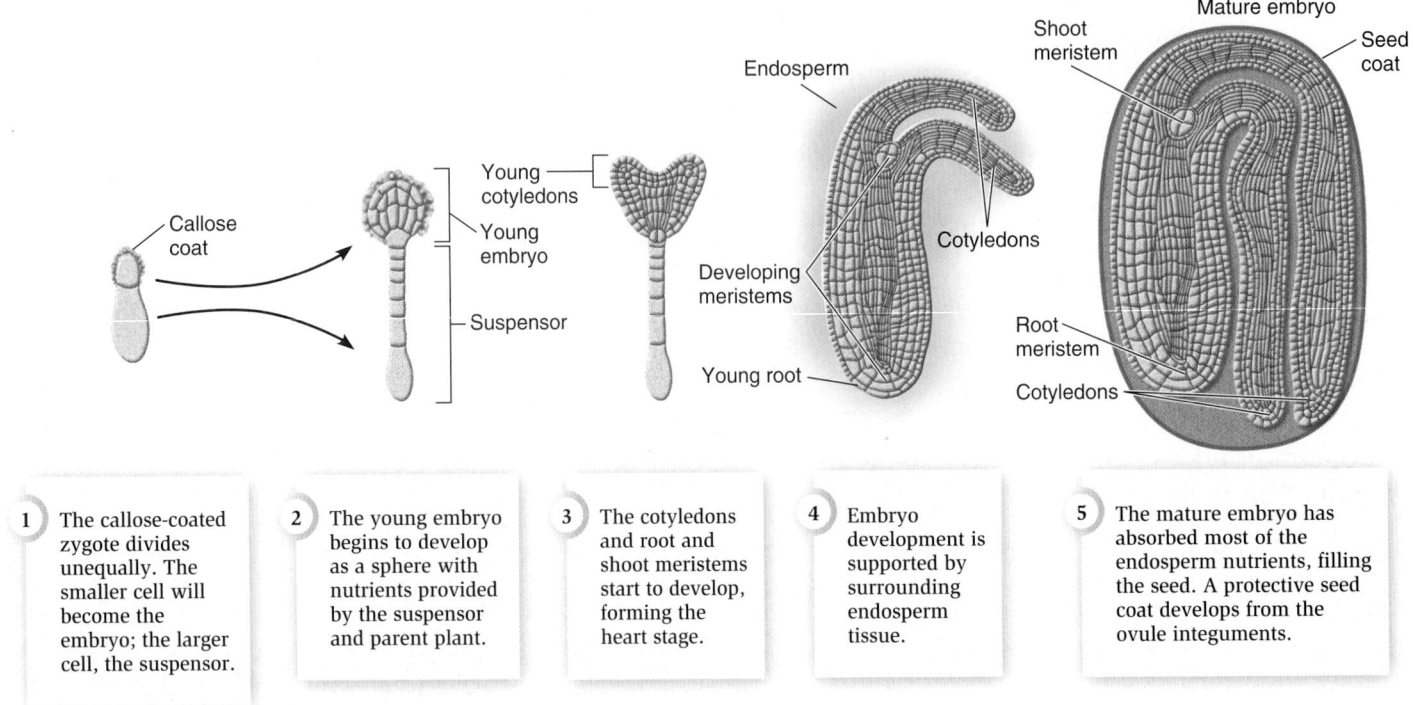

1 The callose-coated zygote divides unequally. The smaller cell will become the embryo; the larger cell, the suspensor.

2 The young embryo begins to develop as a sphere with nutrients provided by the suspensor and parent plant.

3 The cotyledons and root and shoot meristems start to develop, forming the heart stage.

4 Embryo development is supported by surrounding endosperm tissue.

5 The mature embryo has absorbed most of the endosperm nutrients, filling the seed. A protective seed coat develops from the ovule integuments.

Figure 37.17   Embryogenesis in the eudicot *Arabidopsis*.

Concept check: *How would this embryo differ if its* TOPLESS *genes were nonfunctional?*

restrains seedlings from growing and prevents the entry of water and oxygen, which maintains low seed metabolism. In addition, the coats of some seeds are darkly coloured with pigments that may help to prevent damage by UV radiation or microbial attack. Another change leading to seed dormancy is gradual, controlled loss of water from the embryo and other seed tissues. As the result, the water content of dispersed seeds is only 5–15%. Abscisic acid (ABA) is a hormone that induces the activity of genes that help embryo tissues to survive the drying process. Some of these desiccation-tolerance genes encode proteins that form loose coils enclosing cell contents, thereby preventing damage as the cytoplasm becomes almost completely dry.

The structure of mature monocot and eudicot seeds differs. Within eudicot seeds, mature embryos often display an **epicotyl**, the portion of an embryonic stem with two tiny leaves in a first bud that is located above the point of attachment of the cotyledons (**Figure 37.18a**). The **hypocotyl** is the portion of an embryonic stem located below the point of attachment of the cotyledons. An embryonic root, the **radicle**, extends from the hypocotyl. Much of the endosperm has been absorbed into the large cotyledons. In contrast, mature monocot embryos, such as those of corn, feature an epicotyl with a first bud enclosed in a protective sheath known as the **coleoptile**. The young monocot root is enclosed within a protective envelope known as the **coleorhiza** (**Figure 37.18b**). When the seeds of flowering plants are dry and ready for dispersal, they are released from the plant while enclosed in a fruit or released when the fruit breaks open.

Fruits Develop from Ovaries and Other Flower Parts

Though all fruits develop from ovaries (and sometimes other flower parts), fruits occur in diverse forms that aid seed dispersal. Some fruits are dry, whereas others are moist and juicy; some fruits open to release seeds and others do not. Fruits also display a wide variety of sizes, colours, and fragrances. These variations result from differences in the process of fruit development. Plant hormones, including auxin, gibberellic acid, and cytokinin, control this transformation. Abscisic acid stimulates cell expansion, and ethylene influences fruit ripening. For instance, ethylene helps to ripen nuts, a type of dry fruit, by inducing plasma membranes to rupture, causing water loss. Under the influence of plant hormones, the pericarp (ripened ovary wall) of peaches, plums, and related fruits swells and softens, while orange or red chromoplasts replace green chloroplasts. As fruits mature, the outer protective cuticle often becomes very thick, contributing to peel toughness, which helps to prevent microbe attack. In addition, many maturing fruits increase their sugar and acid content, which produces the distinctive tastes of ripe fruit. Many fruits also produce fragrant volatile compounds.

Differences in the fragrance, colour, shape, and moisture content of wild fruits reflect evolutionary adaptation for effective seed dispersal. Though many fruits and seeds are dispersed by wind or water, or by attaching to animal fur, others are consumed by fruit-eating animals that are attracted by fruit colour and fragrance. Blackberries provide a good example of fruits adapted for animal dispersal. Blackberry flowers produce many separate pistils, each containing a single ovule (**Figure 37.19a**). Following

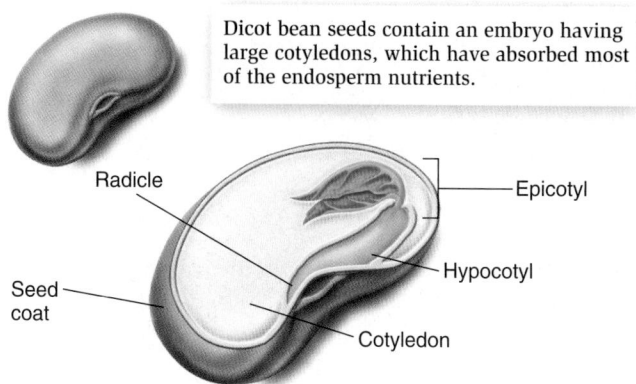

Dicot bean seeds contain an embryo having large cotyledons, which have absorbed most of the endosperm nutrients.

(a) Eudicot bean seed, showing embryo with epicotyl, hypocotyl, and radicle

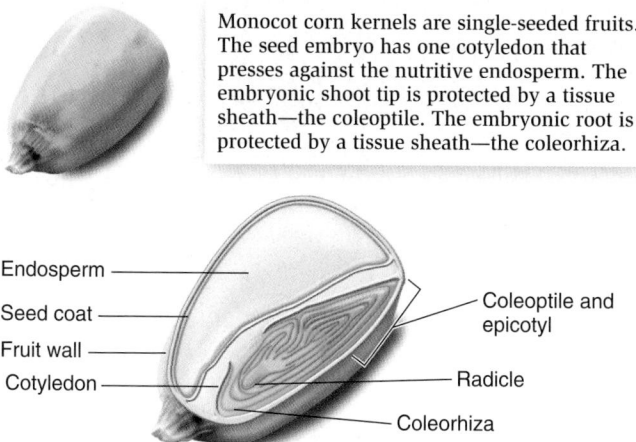

Monocot corn kernels are single-seeded fruits. The seed embryo has one cotyledon that presses against the nutritive endosperm. The embryonic shoot tip is protected by a tissue sheath—the coleoptile. The embryonic root is protected by a tissue sheath—the coleorhiza.

(b) Monocot corn seed, showing an embryo protected by coleoptile and coleorhiza

Figure 37.18 Structure of eudicot and monocot seeds.

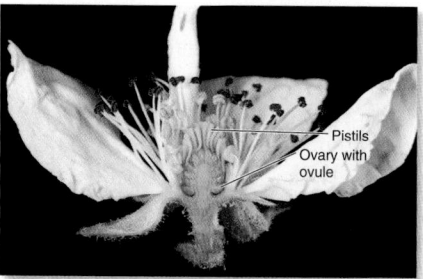

(a) *Rubus allegheniensis* (common blackberry) flower

(b) Blackberry fruit

Figure 37.19 Blackberry flower and fruit. **(a)** Each of the many separate pistils in a blackberry flower is able to produce a single one-seed fruit (called a fruitlet) if fertilization occurs. **(b)** Together, the individual fruitlets of the blackberry compose an aggregate fruit. A shrivelled style with a stigma is attached to each fruitlet.

 Principle: *Living organisms interact with their environment. This principle is illustrated by the dispersal by birds of many blackberry seeds at the same time.*

pollination and fertilization, the ovary of each pistil develops into a sweet, juicy fruitlet containing a single seed. As the individual fruitlets develop, they fuse together at the sides. Consequently, the many fruitlets produced by a single blackberry flower are dispersed together, in a structure known as an aggregate fruit (**Figure 37.19b**). Attracted by the colour, birds consume the whole aggregate and excrete the seeds, thereby dispersing many at a time. Many other types of fruits occur and these likewise represent adaptations that foster seed dispersal (refer back to Figure 29.21).

Although a fruit is usually defined as a mature ovary containing seeds, commercial seedless fruits are produced by genetic modification or treatment with artificial auxin.

Environmental and Internal Factors Influence Seed Germination

Seeds vary greatly in their ability to germinate after dispersal. Small seeds, such as those of dandelions and lettuces, germinate quickly if light is available. Other seeds require a period of dormancy before germination occurs. Some seeds can remain dormant for amazingly long periods. For example, a lotus (*Nelumbo nucifera*) seed collected from a lake bed in China germinated

at the age of 1,300 years, as determined by radiocarbon dating. In 2005 plant scientists germinated a 2,000-year-old date seed found in Israel. Arctic lupine (*Lupinus arcticus*) seeds germinated after having been collected among animal remains in Yukon that were dated at more than 10,000 years of age.

Water is generally required to rehydrate seeds so that embryos can resume their metabolic activity. Water absorption also swells seeds, helping to break the seed coat and allowing embryonic organs to emerge. In some cases, rainfall of sufficient duration to leach germination-inhibiting compounds out of seeds is required. The optimal temperature for germination of most seeds lies between 25°C and 30°C. This explains why gardeners wait until the soil is warm before planting seeds outdoors in spring. However, some seeds need a period of cold treatment or seed coat abrasion before they will germinate.

Such physical stimuli induce the activity of more than 2,000 genes associated with seed germination. In *Arabidopsis*, several phases of cell division occur after dry seeds have been moistened. Cell division in the radicle, the embryonic root, occurs first. As a result, the radicle is the first organ to emerge from a germinating seed, which allows seedlings to take up water even more rapidly. Next, cell division rates rise in the cotyledons and then in the shoot apical meristem, which increases the size of the embryonic shoot.

When grass seeds rehydrate, the young shoot secretes the hormone gibberellic acid from the seed cotyledon into the outermost endosperm layer, known as the aleurone. In response, the aleurone secretes digestive enzymes into the central endosperm layer, releasing sugars from stored starch (**Figure 37.20**). The seedling uses these sugars for growth. This highly coordinated process allows grass seeds to quickly germinate when it rains, an advantage in arid grassland habitats. Humans also use this basic process to make beer. In the process known as malting, beer brewers apply gibberellic acid to barley seeds to induce them to germinate simultaneously. The barley seeds are then baked at a high temperature to stop germination, a process that produces malt. Baking also caramelizes sugars, contributing to the distinctive flavours and colour of beer. To make beer, brewers treat malt with water and heat, add the dried flowers of the hop plant (the genus *Humulus*), and add yeasts to ferment the plant sugars to alcohol.

Once seeds have germinated, plants vary in the process by which the embryonic shoot emerges. When bean and onion seeds germinate, the embryo forms a hook that first breaches the soil surface and then straightens, thereby pulling the rest of the embryo and cotyledons above ground (**Figure 37.21a, b**). In contrast, when pea seeds germinate, the epicotyl forms a hook that pulls the shoot tip out of the ground, leaving the cotyledons beneath the soil surface (**Figure 37.21c**). In such cases, the tough hook cells bear the brunt of passage through hard surface soil crusts, thereby protecting the delicate shoot tips. The

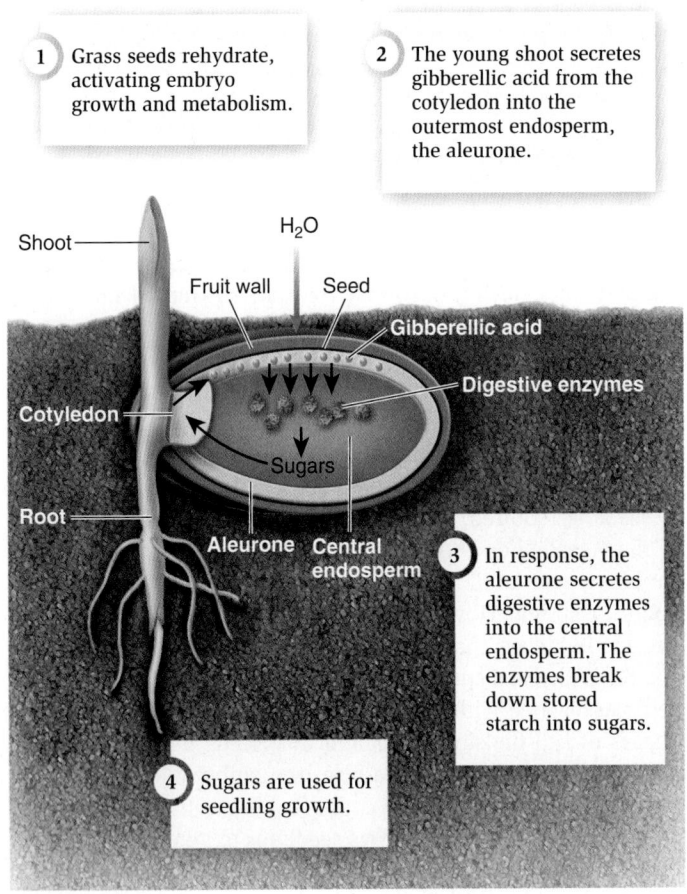

Figure 37.20   Germination of grass seeds involves mobilization of stored reserves.

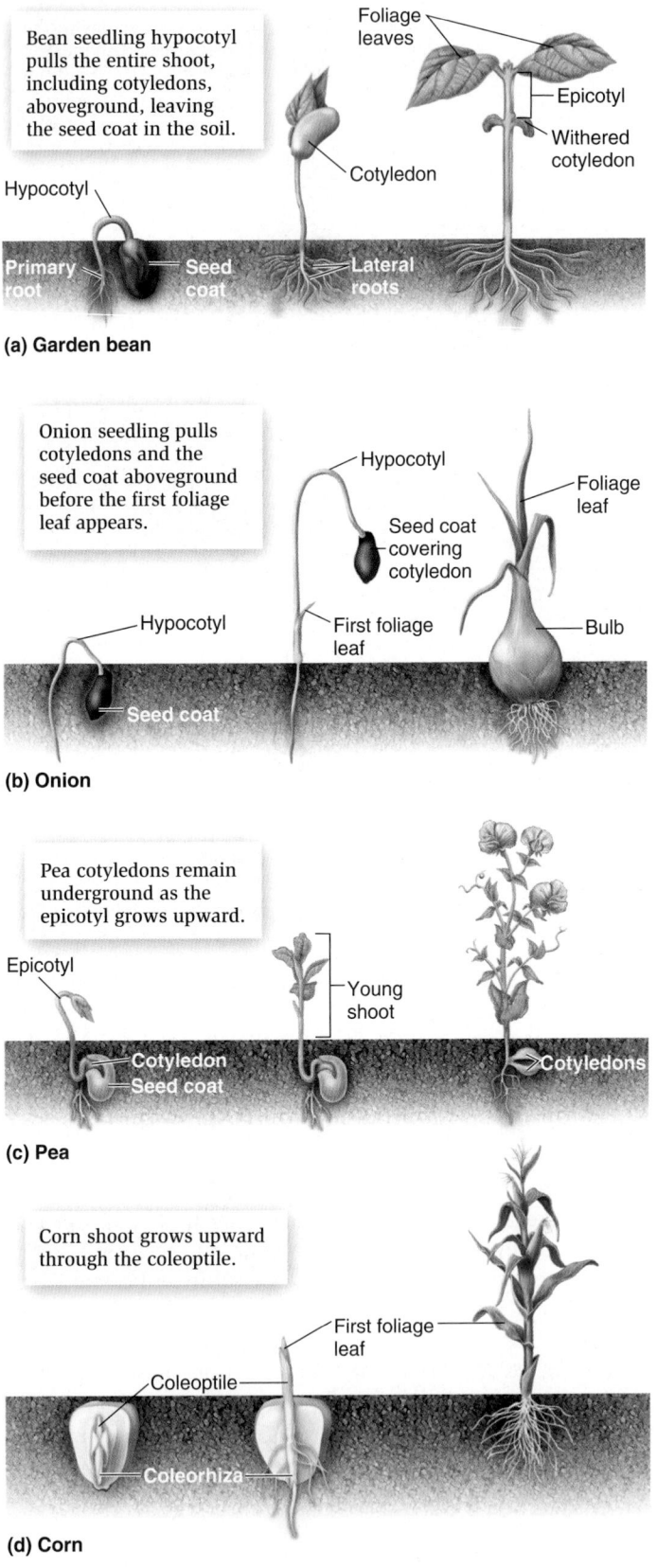

Figure 37.21   Variations in seed germination and seedling growth patterns.

plant hormone ethylene controls seedling hook formation, as described in Chapter 34. However, not all seedlings form hooks. For example, as they grow through the soil, the shoot tips of

corn seedlings and those of other grasses are protected by the coleoptile, which functions as a protective tube for the first foliage leaves (**Figure 37.21d**).

FEATURE INVESTIGATION

Western and Haughn Identify Genes Involved in Seed Coat Mucilage Composition and Properties

As you have learned, angiosperm seeds consist of mature embryos that are surrounded by nutritive tissues and enclosed in a seed coat. Upon fertilization, the ovule integuments begin to differentiate and in some species, the outer integument cells become very active in the synthesis and secretion of complex polysaccharides that are referred to as mucilage. During the late stages of seed development, the epidermal cells of the seed die, and in conjunction with the normal desiccation processes, the mucilage also dehydrates. When seeds are exposed to water, the mucilage expands, rupturing the seed coat and encapsulating the seed in a gel-like matrix.

Pectin (an acidic polysaccharide) is a major component of mucilage in many species, and its presence and concentration can be determined by staining with the dye Ruthenium red. Tamara Western of McGill University, and George Haughn of

the University of British Columbia and their coworkers utilized the model plant *Arabidopsis thaliana* to explore the development of the seed coat mucilage layer and to identify mutants that exhibit alterations in mucilage. Beginning with a large population of mutagenized plants, Western and Haughn conducted a novel genetic screen using Ruthenium red (RR) staining of seeds (**Figure 37.22**). A small proportion of the mutants produced seeds that exhibited little or no RR staining. These mutants were referred to as *mum* mutants (mucilage modified). The *mum* mutants were further characterized for mucilage sugar composition by gas chromatography. Several of the *mum* mutants exhibited distinct differences in the levels of certain sugars, implying that the mutations affect enzymes involved in mucilage biosynthesis and/or extrusion. For example, when investigators extracted mucilage by shaking intact seeds in water, and then measured the most abundant sugars in mucilage (rhamnose and galacturonic acid) they discovered that the amount of mucilage recovered from *mum2* seeds was much less than that found in

Goal: To identify mutants with altered mucilage properties.

KEY MATERIAL: *Arabidopsis* seeds.

Figure 37.22   Western and Haughn discover and characterize *mum* (mucilage modified) mutants.

Figure 37.22   *(Continued)*

| **3** | Sugar analysis in whole seed extracts. | Extract sugars from whole seeds of wildtype and *mum2* and analyze sugar content as described above. | Whole seeds contain similar amounts of each of the sugars, indicating that sugars are not readily extractable from the *mum2* mucilage. 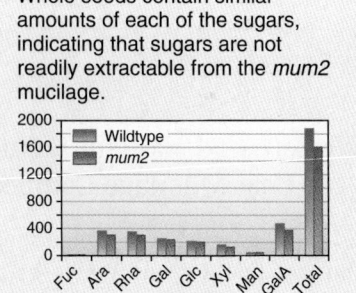 |

| **4** | The *mum*-like mutant, *bxl1*, exhibits a delay in seed germination. | Seeds of wildtype and *bxl1* were grown on agar plates under identical conditions and seed germination was scored. | The *bxl1* mutant exhibits a delay in germination; likely due to a reduced water holding capacity. |

5 **CONCLUSION** A variety of mucilage mutants that act in the synthesis or modification of mucilage can be isolated. Some of these affect seed germination and may provide the basic tools for applied research to enhance seed germination in agriculture and horticulture.

6 **SOURCES:** Gillian H. Dean, Huanquan Zheng, Jagdish Tewari, Jun Huang, Diana S. Young, Yeen Ting Hwang Tamara L. Western, Nicholas C. Carpita, Maureen C. McCann, Shawn D. Mansfield, and George W. Haughn. 2007. The *Arabidopsis MUM2* gene encodes a β-galactosidase required for the production of seed coat mucilage with correct hydration properties. *Plant Cell* 19: 4007–4021.

Andrej A. Arsovski, Theodore M. Popma, George W. Haughn, Nicholas C. Carpita, Maureen C. McCann, and Tamara L. Western. 2009. *AtBXL1* encodes a bifunctional β-D-Xylosidase/a-L- Arabinofuranosidase required for pectic arabinan modification in Arabidopsis mucilage secretory cells. *Plant Physiology* 150:1219–1234

Wildtype seeds. However, when the experiment was repeated with ground up whole seeds, the levels of rhamnose and galacturonic acid in Wildtype and *mum2* were found to be very similar, leading the investigators to conclude that the *mum2* mutant can make as much mucilage as Wildtype but the mucilage is not released from the seed. In addition, there was a higher proportion of the pectin side-chain sugars galactose and arabinose relative to rhamnose and galacturonic acid, suggesting that the pectin composition of mucilage was altered. Map-based cloning of the *MUM2* gene revealed that it encodes a β-galactosidase, an enzyme that removes galactose from carbohydrates. Thus the *MUM2* gene appears to encode a protein that modifies the pectin in mucilage and this modification is likely necessary to allow the expansion of mucilage when the seeds are exposed to water.

What is the function of mucilage and why study it? Remember that seeds can be dormant for prolonged periods, but when environmental conditions are favorable, germination can be induced. The availability of water is the major determinant of germination (although temperature and sometimes light play major roles). When a seed absorbs water, the mucilage greatly expands to form a gel-like coating. In different plant species, this may serve one or more roles. First, the developing seedling is very sensitive to water stress and, as you learned in Chapter 36, water drives cell and tissue expansion. The gel-like layer that surrounds the seed serves to facilitate and maintain seed hydration. You can explore this in your own kitchen. Take some flax, chia, or mustard seeds and place them in water for a few minutes, then try to pick them up with your fingers. You will find that they are very slippery—the expanded mucilage layer creates this sliminess.

The Western and Haughn labs investigated the effect of another *mum*-like mutant on seed germination. The *bxl1* mutant exhibits patchy Ruthenium red staining and the mucilage has an altered sugar composition due to a mutation in gene encoding a xylosidase/arabinase enzyme, that like β-galactosidase, removes side chains from mucilage carbohydrates. Seeds from both Wildtype and the *bxl1* mutant were plated onto minimal media plates and germination was scored over a six-day period. The *bxl1* mutant mucilage released more slowly and germination of the seeds was delayed, presumably due to comparatively poor hydration of the seeds. These experiments have provided a critical link between the composition of mucilage, its physical properties, and its role in maintaining a favorable environment for the seed to germinate and begin photoautotrophic growth.

In addition to a role for mucilage in seed hydration, it is also produced in other tissues, most notably the root (refer back to Figure 33.23). Recall that roots absorb both water and dissolved minerals, which are then transported to distant tissues through the vascular system. Thus, mucilage provides a surface property that aids absorption, but it also serves as a lubricant to enable the root to penetrate through soil layers.

Lastly, in some species mucilage plays a role in seed dispersal. The stickiness of the mucilage allows some seeds to adhere to animals that assist in dispersing the seed, sometimes far from the source.

Experimental Questions

1. How did Western and Haughn identify seeds defective in mucilage production?
2. How might one distinguish between mutants that have altered mucilage composition from those which do not secret mucilage?
3. What type of bioassay might you use to prove that mucilage is important for germination?

37.5 ASEXUAL REPRODUCTION IN FLOWERING PLANTS

Learning Outcomes:

1. Explain the benefits of asexual reproduction in flowering plants.
2. List several examples of ways in which plant asexual reproduction is important to agriculture.

Many plants rely on sexual reproduction. However, a wide variety of angiosperms reproduce primarily by asexual means, and other plants commonly use both sexual and asexual reproduction. **Asexual reproduction** is the production of new individuals from a single parent without the occurrence of fertilization. Although sexual reproduction provides beneficial genetic variation, asexual reproduction can be advantageous in other ways. For example, asexual reproduction maintains favourable gene combinations that allow faster population growth in stable environments. Asexual reproduction is also advantageous in stressful habitats in which pollinators or mates are rare, because it allows a single individual to start a new population. Finally, asexual reproduction allows some plants to persist for very long periods. Among the oldest known plants are creosote bushes that are asexual clones of a parent that grew from a seed about 12,000 years ago. The artificial vegetative propagation of plants from cuttings is a form of asexual reproduction that is widely used commercially and by home gardeners. In this section, we will explore the three main mechanisms of plant asexual reproduction: specialized vegetative structures, somatic embryogenesis, and apomixis.

Vegetative Asexual Reproduction Generates Plant Clones from Organs

Roots, stems, and leaves are vegetative plant organs that can function as asexual reproductive structures. Root sprouts, such as those produced by aspens, can generate entire groves of genetically identical trees.

Sucker shoots, such as those appearing at the bases of banana plants and date palms, and potato plants that develop from the pieces of tuber-bearing "eyes" (which are buds), are examples of vegetative asexual reproduction that have agricultural importance. Attractive horticultural varieties of African violets and other plants can be propagated from leaf cuttings. Such asexual offspring grow into adult plants that have the same valued properties as their parent plant. In contrast, these crops grown from seed would produce diverse progeny, not all of which would have economically prized properties.

Somatic embryogenesis is the production of plant embryos from body (somatic) cells. Embryos can develop from many types of cells, including microspores. Somatic embryos develop normally to the torpedo stage but do not dehydrate and become dormant, as is normal for zygotic embryos. Rather, somatic embryos produce root and shoot systems and develop into mature plants. Somatic embryogenesis occurs naturally in citrus, mango, onion, and tobacco plants, but agricultural scientists have made use of it as well.

In the 1950s plant biologist F. C. Steward and associates were the first researchers to successfully clone a complex organism, carrot plants, by means of somatic embryogenesis. They used differentiated cells from carrot roots, grew the cells in conditions that caused some cells to lose their specialized properties and develop into embryos, and then cultivated each embryo in conditions that favoured development into a mature carrot plant. Many types of plants are now cloned by somatic embryogenesis, which allows commercial growers to produce large numbers of genetically identical individuals. The common houseplant *Kalanchoë* has leaves bearing many tiny plantlets at their edges. When these detach, they are able to take root and grow into new individuals (**Figure 37.23**).

Apomixis Is Seed Production Without Fertilization

Apomixis, which means "away from mixing" (that is, genetic mixing), is a natural asexual reproductive process in which fruits and seeds are produced in the absence of fertilization. More than 300 species of flowering plants, including hawkweeds, dandelions, and some types of citrus, are able to reproduce asexually by apomixis. Dandelions and some other apomictic plants require pollination to stimulate seed development, but others do not. Some weedy plant species are apomictic; this

Figure 37.23 **An example of asexual reproduction.**
The leaves of this *Kalanchoë* plant bear small plantlets around the edges. When mature, these plantlets drop off and, under the right conditions, grow into new plants.

BioConnections: *Look back at Figure 31.4, which illustrates the life cycle of the animal Obelia, a colonial cnidarian related to jellyfish and corals. How is the life cycle of this animal similar to that of the Kalanchoë plant?*

process allows them to reproduce quickly, a characteristic of weeds. In addition to their concern about weeds, agricultural scientists are interested in apomixis as a potential method for producing genetically uniform seeds, propagating hybrids, and removing the need for fertilization in crop plants.

Most studies of apomixis have been carried out with dandelions, because they are widespread and locally abundant. Dandelions are herbaceous perennials that flower in their first year. Although some European dandelion populations contain individuals that reproduce sexually, many dandelion populations are composed mainly of individuals that reproduce by apomixis. In apomictic plants, meiosis produces diploid megaspores because homologous chromosomes do not pair and meiosis II does not occur. These diploid megaspores produce diploid female gametophytes, which generate diploid eggs. These eggs develop into normal embryos without fertilization, a process known as parthenogenesis. In apomictic dandelions, the endosperm develops from diploid central cells. Though such plants produce microspores via meiosis, most pollen grains have abnormal numbers of chromosomes and can produce pollen tubes, but not sperm cells. Hence, fertilization does not occur. However, pollination stimulates dandelions to produce their single-seeded fruits. Fruits that develop in the absence of fertilization are known as parthenocarpic fruit.

Summary of Key Concepts

37.1 An Overview of Flowering Plant Reproduction

- Flowering plants display a sexual life cycle known as alternation of generations. The gamete-producing male and female gametophytes of flowering plants are very small and entirely dependent on nurturing sporophytic tissues. Plant gametes arise by the process of meiosis and mitosis. (Figures 37.1, 37.2)

- Flowers are reproductive shoots that develop from a shoot apical meristem. The role of flowers is to promote seed production. A flower shoot generally produces four types of organs: sepals, petals, carpels, and stamens. Stamens produce pollen, which are immature male gametophytes. Carpels produce, enclose, and nurture female gametophytes. (Figure 37.3)

- Mature male gametophytes each produce two sperm and deliver them to ovules via a pollen tube. Flowering plants display double fertilization: one of the two sperm released from a pollen tube combines with an egg cell to form a zygote, while the other fuses with two nuclei located in a central cell of the female gametophyte, producing the first cell of endosperm tissue. Endosperm is a nutritive tissue that supports development of an embryonic sporophyte. (Figure 37.4)

- Seeds are reproductive structures that contain a dormant embryo enclosed by a protective seed coat that develops from ovule integuments. Fruits are structures that contain seeds and foster seed dispersal. Like flowers and endosperm, fruits are unique features of flowering plants. (Figure 37.5)

37.2 Flower Production, Structure, and Development

- Plants flower in response to environmental stimuli, such as temperature and day length, by the conversion of a leaf-producing shoot into a flowering shoot. In *Arabidopsis*, phytochrome in leaves interacts with clock genes to induce expression of the transcription factor protein CO. The buildup of CO in long days activates the *FT* (flowering time) gene in phloem. The FT protein travels in the phloem to the shoot apical meristem, and forms a complex with a protein known as FD. The resulting FT/FD complex triggers expression of the floral identity genes that induce flower development. (Figure 37.6)

- Flowers vary in the type of whorls present, the number of flower organs, colour, fragrance, organ fusion, symmetry, and arrangement (whether single or in inflorescences). These variations are related to pollination mechanisms and are genetically controlled. Studies of genes controlling flower development led to the discovery of gene silencing and previously unknown genetic repair mechanisms. (Figures 37.7, 37.8, 37.9, 37.10, 37.11)

37.3 Male and Female Gametophytes and Double Fertilization

- Pollen grains are immature male gametophytes protected by a tough sporopollenin wall. Female gametophyte development occurs within an ovule. Mature female gametophytes include an egg cell surrounded by two synergids, a central cell with two nuclei, and three antipodal cells. (Figures 37.12, 37.13)

- After pollination, interactions between proteins of pistil cells and those of pollen regulate pollen germination and self-incompatibility. (Figure 37.14)

- Germinated pollen delivers two sperm to female gametophytes by means of a long pollen tube. The style plays a role in the guidance, nutrition, and fate of the pollen tube. Pollen tubes that enter female gametophytes burst, releasing sperm. One sperm nucleus fuses with the egg to produce a zygote, the first cell of a new sporophyte generation; the other sperm nucleus fuses with the two nuclei of the central cell, generating the first cell of the nutritive endosperm tissue. (Figures 37.15, 37.16)

37.4 Embryo, Seed, Fruit, and Seedling Development

- Unequal division of a zygote leads to development of a nutritive suspensor and an embryo. Young eudicot embryos are heart shaped as two embryonic leaves (cotyledons) develop and assume a torpedo shape as the embryonic root forms. Monocot embryos produce only a single cotyledon; the embryonic shoot tip is protected by the coleoptile, and the embryonic root is protected by the coleorhiza. (Figures 37.17, 37.18, 37.19)

- Seed germination requires the mobilization of nutrient reserves, stored in either the endosperm or the cotyledons. The hormone gibberellic acid is an important regulator of germination. (Figure 37.20)

- Seed germination is influenced by environmental and internal factors. Mucilage expansion upon wetting allows the seed to remain hydrated. The embryonic root (radicle) is the first organ to emerge, an adaptation that allows rapid water uptake, essential for seedling development. (Figures 37.21, 37.22)

37.5 Asexual Reproduction in Flowering Plants

- Asexual reproduction is the production of new individuals from a single parent without the occurrence of fertilization. Vegetative reproduction is the development of whole plants from nonreproductive structures. Apomixis is a mechanism by which some plants produce seeds from flowers without fertilization. Somatic embryogenesis is the production of embryos from body cells. (Figure 37.23)

Test to Assess Your Learning

1. Where do mature male gametophytes of flowering plants primarily develop?
   a. in the anthers of a flower
   b. in the carpels of a flower
   c. while being dispersed in wind, water, or by animals
   d. within ovules
   e. on the surfaces of leaves

2. Where would you find female gametophytes of a flowering plant?
   a. in the anthers of a flower
   b. at the stigma of a pistil
   c. in the style
   d. within ovules in a flower's ovary
   e. none of the above

3. How does double fertilization occur in flowering plants?
   a. The two sperm in a pollen tube fertilize the two egg cells present in each female gametophyte.
   b. One of the two sperm in a pollen tube fertilizes the single egg in a female gametophyte, while the other fuses with the two nuclei present in the central cell.
   c. Two sperm, one contributed by each of two different pollen tubes, fertilize the two egg cells in a single female gametophyte.
   d. Two sperm contributed by separate pollen tubes enter a single female gametophyte; one of the sperm fertilizes the egg cell, while the other fertilizes the central cell.
   e. None of the above.

4. The endosperm is
   a. an embryo produced by the fertilization of an egg and which is protected by a seed coat.
   b. a structure that germinates to form a seedling under the right conditions.
   c. an embryo produced by parthenogenesis that is enclosed by a seed coat.
   d. a nutritive tissue that surrounds and nourishes the developing embryo.
   e. none of the above.

5. What is the likely chemical composition of florigen, the long-sought chemical stimulus of flowering?
   a. the hormone auxin
   b. the CONSTANS protein
   c. the carbohydrate callose
   d. the mineral ion K^+
   e. none of the above

6. How many whorls of organs occur in complete flowers?
   a. two
   b. four
   c. six
   d. eight
   e. none of the above

7. If an ovary contains eight ovules, how many seeds could potentially result if pollen tubes reach all eight ovules?
   a. one
   b. four
   c. eight
   d. more than 20
   e. none of the above

8. Which of the following statements about gametophytic self-incompatibility is correct?
   a. Incompatible pollen grains germinate a pollen tube that grows through the style but then stops.
   b. Both the SI alleles of the pollen parent must match the alleles of the stigma in order for pollen rejection to occur.
   c. If only one of the SI alleles of the pollen parent matches the alleles of the stigma, pollen rejection occurs.
   d. Incompatible pollen grains do not germinate a pollen tube.
   e. Both a and c.

9. What function(s) does the polysaccharide callose have in the reproduction of flowering plants?
   a. Callose forms a coat that isolates young embryos during their early development.
   b. Callose forms a coat that isolates groups of four microspores during their early development into pollen grains.
   c. Callose helps to pattern the sculptured sporopollenin walls of pollen grains.
   d. Callose forms plugs that concentrate pollen tube cytoplasm at the tips, thereby aiding tip growth.
   e. All of the above.

10. From what structure does a fruit pericarp primarily develop?
    a. the style
    b. a stamen filament
    c. the ovary wall
    d. a group of fused sepals
    e. the stigma

Articulate to Assess Your Learning

1. Why are pollen grain walls composed of sporopollenin?
2. Why are seed coats often tough?

Collaborate to Assess and Extend Your Learning

1. Observe or view images of orchid flowers. Are these flowers bilaterally symmetrical or radially symmetrical? Are these flowers more likely to be wind pollinated or pollinated by animals? What gene might be involved in the production of orchid flower shape?
2. Discuss the advantages and disadvantages of asexual reproduction in plants.
3. What advantages do flowering plants obtain by having small and sporophytically dependent gametophytes?
4. Why do mature seeds of eudicots lack extensive amounts of endosperm?
5. A principle of biology is that all species (past and present) are related by an evolutionary history. Modern flowering plants likely possessed a single common ancestor. Why, then, do flowers occur in such a diversity of shapes and colours?

Visit McGraw-Hill Ryerson Connect™ for additional study resources.

WHAT'S NEW?

Valentina Slobodenuic

Dr. Quentin Cronk

An interview with Dr. Quentin Cronk from the University of British Columbia, by Valentina Slobodenuic, fourth-year student at the University of Toronto, 2009.

Dr. Quentin Cronk is a professor in plant science at UBC Biodiversity Research Centre and former director of the University of British Columbia Botanical Garden and Centre for Plant Research, 2002–08.

▶ Dr. Cronk, most of your research was done in the United Kingdom. However, in 2002, you were offered the position of director of the UBC Botanical Garden and Centre for Plant Research. What made you decide to accept the job and move to British Columbia?

British Columbia is home to a high diversity of great plants: from the alpine plants in the mountains to the temperate rainforest plants and those of the temperate grasslands. This, together with being able to develop and guide a botanical garden, was a combination that I could not resist. And I think it is the best decision that I have ever made.

▶ In your article "Aspects of sexual failure in the reproductive processes of a rare bulbiliferous plant, *Titanotrichum oldhamii* (Gesneriaceae), in subtropical Asia" (2004), you focus on *Titanotrichum oldhamii* as your study species. Why did you pick that plant?

I was contacted by a student in Taiwan who wanted to work with me for his PhD degree, and I thought that it would be nice if he worked on a species from the Gesneriaceae family, which I was studying at that time, that came from his home country. I already knew that *Titanotrichum oldhamii* was endemic to Taiwan, with rare populations in mainland China.

It turned out that the wild populations of this plant possess an interesting characteristic: most of them never reproduce by seed. Instead, they reproduce asexually by forming vegetative propagules, called bulbils, which are produced after the flowers. We had to ask why this plant does not reproduce by seed. We found that, among its many problems, there seems to have been some collapse of the normal function of the flowers. A large fraction of pollen tubes fail to find their way to the micropyle. We have attributed this to a genetic defect that resulted from extensive inbreeding of the population.

Actually, in 2009, a paper was published in the journal *Nature* that identified the biochemical signal that guides the pollen tube into the micropyle, which is a very exciting finding. The failure of the pollen tube to penetrate the micropyle is probably due to a loss of a chemical attractant.

▶ Would this loss be on a genetic basis?

Yes, because in small and inbred populations you can easily get mutations that can interfere with the process of pollen tube guidance, particularly if there is an alternative method of reproduction. In *Titanotrichum oldhamii*, this has led to a decay of sexual function and an increasing reliance on asexual means of reproduction.

▶ So, based on that, do you foresee a loss of sexual reproduction along the evolutionary path, with the accumulation of nonlethal mutations that negatively affect this process?

Loss of sexual reproduction has a very negative effect, and it can really be only a short-term solution, because sexual reproduction is the main way by which plants, or any organism, generate new combinations of genes that eventually are needed for adaptation to changing environmental conditions.

I think that in *Titanotrichum oldhamii*, asexual reproduction is also clearly a short-term solution, because even though it has survived by reproducing asexually, it is not doing well in the wild. Furthermore, it is a rare tropical mountain plant, which is potentially threatened significantly by global warming if it fails to adapt.

▶ Because bulbil formation is the main reproductive strategy, why does it increase only in August and September, rather than being dominant throughout the flowering season?

What we found is that bulbil production is day-length sensitive, and it begins at the end of the summer when the day length shortens. The fact that the conversion of a single flower meristem into many different bulbils (essentially meristem branching) was day-length sensitive led us to examine the expression of the gene *LEAFY*. *LEAFY* is a gene required for flower formation that was first found in *Arabidopsis thaliana*, where the mutant, instead of having flowers, had a branched inflorescence and many leaves. This gene is photoperiod sensitive and loss of function causes the meristem to branch, failing to produce flowers. This is analogous to what we see happening in *Titanotrichum oldhamii*, where a single meristem is converted into multiple bulbils rather than into a single flower. We found that as day-length decreased, *LEAFY* expression went down in developing inflorescences, and this was closely correlated with bulbil appearance.

> You have also indicated that one of the causes of lower seed and fruit set is environmental stress, such as resource limitation and drought. Why does this affect the flowers but not the bulbil formation?

It is probably through this gene *LEAFY*, which is a very important environmental integrator. For instance, *LEAFY* responds to the endogenous gibberellin signals (gibberellin hormones influence plant growth and development) and to photoperiod, which makes it very cued in to what is happening in the environment. So, *LEAFY* is required for flower production, and when its expression goes down because of the environmental cues, then you start seeing the production of bulbils instead.

> Based on your findings, you have proposed a conservation strategy that involves the artificial transplantation of individuals from neighbouring populations to stimulate the sexual reproduction success. Do you know if anything has been done in that respect?

I do not know, but I think that this strategy is enormously important, as we have found strong evidence that loss of sexual reproduction is a consequence of inbreeding. The only way to get healthy populations is to put the populations together, do the transplanting experiments, and get the genes mingling again, which will lead to increased seed production.

> Have you or are you planning to pursue further research in this area? What sort of research are you focusing on right now?

I would like to do more research in this area, particularly examining the chemical signals that guide the pollen tubes into the ovules, but this is dependent on finding the right student who is interested in this phenomenon. At the moment, we are pursuing some interesting research examining the genes that are responsible for the control of flower development. We are using the pea family, Leguminosae, for this, but again this work is all part of deciphering the gene control behind the development of flowers.

> On a different note, in your article "Plant evolution and development in a post-genomic context" (2001), you mentioned that when you compared selected features of higher plants and animals, the presence of a thick cell wall stood out as a distinguishing feature because plant cells, unlike animal cells, do not have cell-lineage-controlled development, and their fate is probably controlled by cell-to-cell cues. Would you please explain that in more detail?

In animals, when cells form in an embryo, they do not necessarily stay in the place of their formation. Some cells actually migrate by sliding over other cells and move from one end of the embryo to another. An animal cell has programmed into it, as a result of its history, the fact that it has to become a particular organ in a particular position—it has a determined cell lineage. Plant cells do not move, conversely, because of the rigidity of the cell wall. When a plant cell is formed, it stays among the same neighbours all the time. What determines the fate of a plant cell is not necessarily its innate identity but the cues received as signals from the neighbouring cells. Therefore, positional information, rather than lineage information, is much more important in plants.

> You mentioned the "neo-Goldschmidtian" model of evolution, which contrasts with the "neo-Darwinian" view in that it proposes that a single change in a principal regulatory gene can possibly cause a very big effect on morphology. How do you think it can be caused?

I think the fact that single mutations can cause big changes is not a problem. What neo-Darwinians would say is that none of these offspring would survive because the chance of a major mutation surviving out in the wild is close to zero—there is so much mortality that anything that is not perfectly, or nearly perfectly, adapted to the environment would fail. Therefore, you can have evolution only by tiny little changes that would not affect the phenotype very much. However, what if one of the big mutations finds an environment that was perfectly suited to it? In theory, it is possible to get a big jump, but there is a debate on how frequent it is. This big change could have just been a sum of many little jumps. As we understand more about gene evolution, we would be able to resolve this argument.

UNIT VII
Animals

In Chapters 30 to 32, we considered the amazing diversity and evolutionary history of animal life. Yet despite the obvious differences between a worm and a human, or an insect and a fish, fundamental similarities link the millions of animal species together. We will explore many of these similarities in this unit. The basic features of animal bodies, the relationship between structure and function, and the ability of animals to maintain homeostasis are introduced in Chapter 38 and reiterated throughout the unit. The digestive system is presented in Chapter 39 and homeostatic mechanisms are discussed in-depth in Chapter 40. Chapters 41 and 42 will describe major principles of nervous systems in animals and how they allow an animal to interact with its environment. The ability of animals to move through their environments and the dependence of such locomotion on nervous systems will be covered in Chapter 43. Circulatory, respiratory, excretory, and endocrine systems are then covered in Chapters 44 to 47. The unit concludes with Chapters 48 to 50, which cover animal reproduction, development, and immune systems, respectively.

Several biological principles will be emphasized in this unit, including:

- *Structure determines function.* Animal biology is founded on the relationship between anatomy and physiology. To understand how organs and organ systems function, you need to understand specific anatomical features. The relationship between structure and function is evident at all levels of organization, including cells, tissues, organs, organ systems, and whole bodies.

- *Living organisms have mechanisms that maintain homeostasis.* This is one of the fundamental principles of biology and a key to understanding virtually all aspects of animal biology.

- *Living organisms use energy.* Energy is used to achieve and maintain homeostasis; it takes energy to obtain oxygen, to maintain blood flow, to regulate body temperature, and to maintain a stable concentration of sodium and other salts in an animal's body fluids.

- *Living organisms interact with their environment.* Animal cells constantly interact with the internal environment in the body by means of plasma membrane transporters and ion pumps. Sensory systems of animals can detect changes in the external environment, such as light and dark, odours, vibrations, and so on.

- *Living organisms grow, develop, and reproduce.* Genetic and environmental factors regulate how an embryo develops into a mature animal.

Introduction to Animal Form and Function

Chapter Outline

In this chapter we will look at some of the characteristics common to animals and the link between structure and function. You will see how animals maintain internal conditions within normal limits, despite fluctuations in their external environments. **Anatomy** is the study of animal structure, while **physiology** is the study of how those structures function. Collectively, anatomy and physiology form the foundation of animal biology. We begin, therefore, with an examination of the physical structure and organization of animal bodies.

Head of a male mosquito showing the enormous surface area of the antenna. Males use their antennae to detect conspecific females.

38.1   ORGANIZATION OF ANIMAL BODIES

Learning Outcomes:

1. List the categories of animal tissue, providing general functions and specific examples of each.
2. Name the organ systems found in many animals, list the components of each, and describe their general functions.
3. Describe the movement of solutes and water between compartments.

All animal cells share similarities in the ways in which they exchange materials with their surroundings, obtain energy from organic nutrients, synthesize complex molecules, duplicate themselves, and detect and respond to signals in their immediate environment. Animals usually begin life as a single cell—most commonly a fertilized egg—which divides to create two cells, each of which divides in turn, resulting in four cells, and so on. If cell multiplication were the only event occurring, the end result would be a spherical mass of identical cells. As you will see in Chapter 49, however, cells become specialized during development to perform a particular function (i.e., they differentiate), such as by becoming muscle or nerve cells. Cells also migrate to new locations within the developing organism and form clusters with other cells. In this way the cells of an animal's body are arranged in various combinations to form organized, multicellular structures (**Figure 38.1**). Cells with similar properties group to form tissues (e.g., muscle tissue), which combine with other types of tissues to form organs (e.g., a bladder), which are anatomically or functionally linked together to form organ systems (e.g., the urinary system).

Specialized Cells Are Organized into Tissues

Specialized cells of a given type often cluster together to form **tissues**. The tissues in a typical animal's body can be classified into four categories, according to the types of functions they perform: muscle, nervous, epithelial, and connective tissues. Most structures in an animal's body contain at least two types of tissues and often contain all four. Within each of these functional categories, subtypes of tissues perform variations of that function. For example, as described next, there are three subtypes of muscle tissue, all of which generate force but only one of which produces animal locomotion.

Muscle Tissues   **Muscle tissues** consist of cells that are specialized to contract, generating the mechanical forces that produce body movement, exert pressure on a fluid-filled cavity, or decrease the diameter of a tube. Complex animals have three types of muscle tissue: skeletal, smooth, and cardiac (**Figure 38.2**). **Skeletal muscles** are generally attached to bones in vertebrates and to the exoskeleton of invertebrates. Contraction of these muscles is under voluntary control and can produce the types of movements required for locomotion, such as extending limbs or flapping wings. Skeletal muscles may also attach to skin, such as the muscles producing facial expressions. **Smooth muscles** surround hollow tubes and cavities inside the body's organs, such that their contraction can propel the contents of those organs. For example, the contraction of smooth muscle in the stomach wall propels partially digested food into the small intestine. Smooth muscle also forms part of the small blood vessels and airway tubes (bronchioles). Contraction in those regions reduces blood flow or movement of air, respectively. Contraction of all smooth muscle is involuntary, which means that it occurs automatically without conscious control. In the third type, **cardiac muscle**, physical and electrical connections between individual cells enable many of the cells to

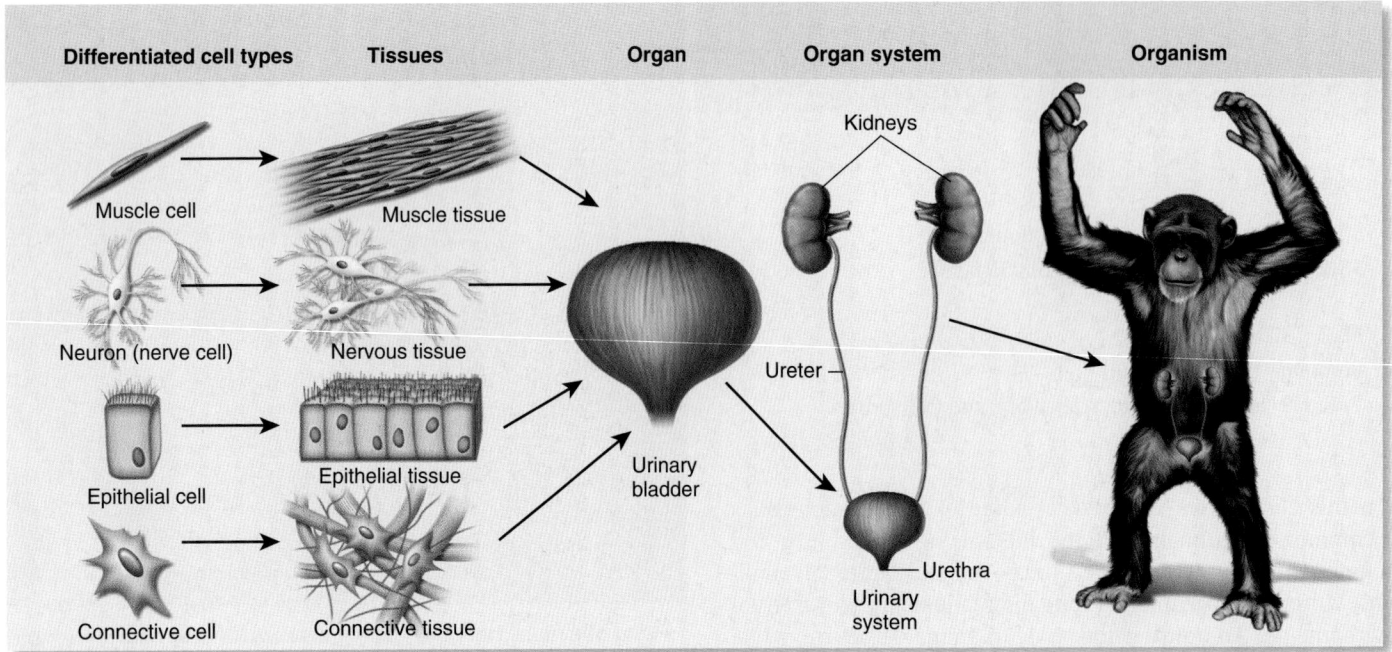

Figure 38.1   **The internal organization of cells, tissues, organs, and organ systems in a mammal.**   Most animals share the same four tissue types.

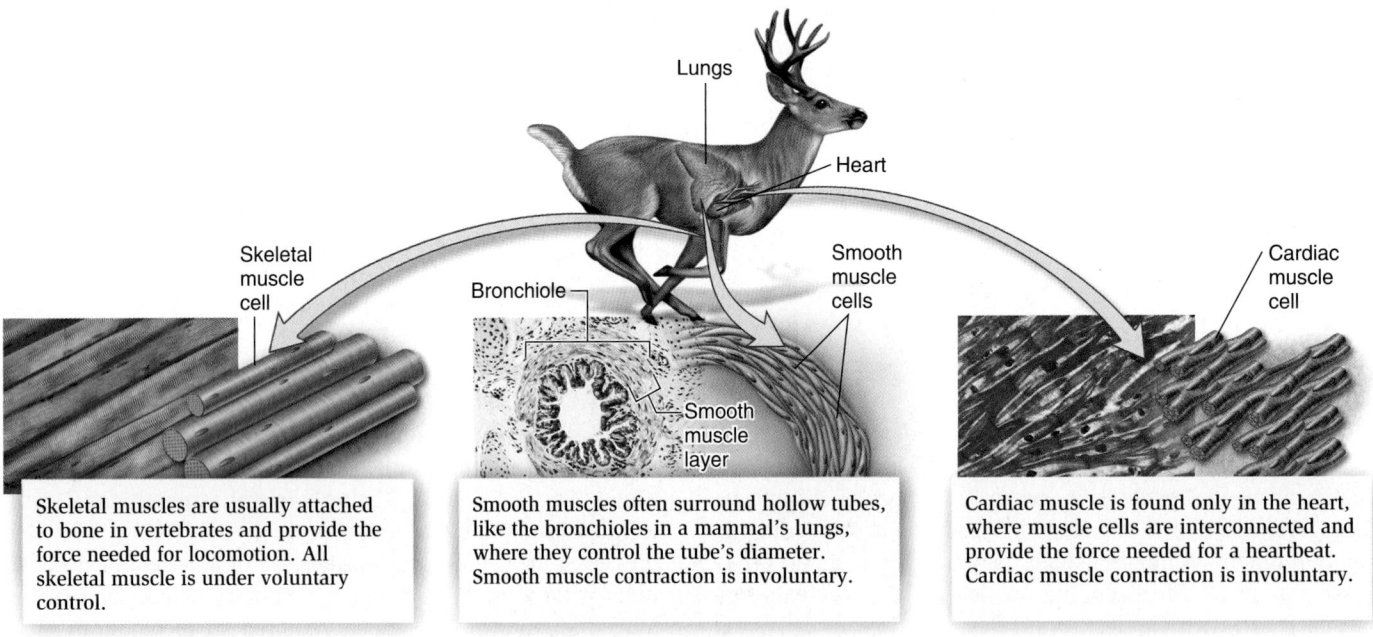

Figure 38.2   **Three types of muscle tissue: skeletal, smooth, and cardiac muscle.**   All three types of muscle produce force, but they differ in their appearance and in their locations within animals' bodies.

Concept check: *All muscles produce movement, but only skeletal muscle produces locomotion. What is meant by this statement?*

contract simultaneously. Like smooth muscle, cardiac muscle is involuntary. It is found only in the heart, however, where it provides the force that generates sufficient pressure to pump blood through an animal's body.

Nervous Tissues   **Nervous tissues** initiate and conduct electrical signals from one part of an animal's body to another part

(**Figure 38.3**). A single nerve cell may connect two or more other nerve cells and be only a few microns long. Such nerve cells are found widely throughout the vertebrate brain, for example. By sharp contrast, a nerve cell leaving the spinal cord of a giraffe and extending to its hoof can extend for 2 m! Depending on where it is located in an animal's body, an electrical signal produced in one nerve cell may stimulate or inhibit other nerve

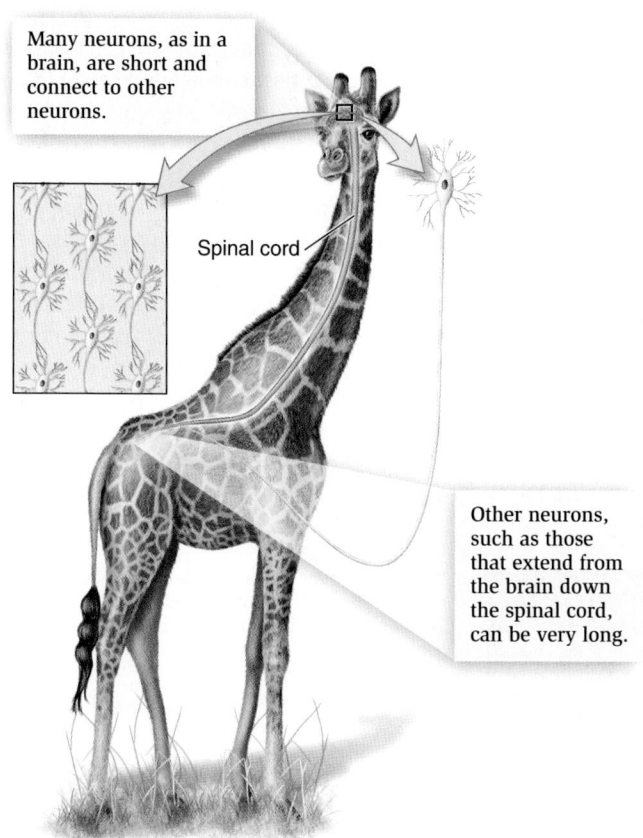

Many neurons, as in a brain, are short and connect to other neurons.

Spinal cord

Other neurons, such as those that extend from the brain down the spinal cord, can be very long.

Figure 38.3 Variation in the shape and length of nerve cells. Most nerve cells in the brain of an animal are only microns long, while others, like those that send signals from the brain to the posterior end of the spinal cord, can have very long axons.

Principle: *Living organisms interact with their environment.* *Animals interact with their environment in many ways. This inter- action largely depends on the use of nervous tissue, which allows animals to sense and respond to changes in the environment.*

cells to initiate new electrical signals, stimulate muscle tissue to contract, or stimulate glandular cells to release chemicals into the animal's blood. Thus, nervous tissue provides a critical means of controlling many diverse activities of body cells.

Epithelial Tissues **Epithelial tissues** are sheets of densely packed cells that cover the body or individual organs or line the walls of various cavities inside the body. Epithelial cells are specialized to protect structures and secrete and absorb ions and organic molecules. For example, epithelial tissue can invag- inate (fold inward) to form sweat glands that secrete water and ions onto the surface of an animal's skin. Epithelial cells come in a variety of shapes, such as cuboidal (cube-shaped), squa- mous (flattened), or columnar (elongated), and are arranged in epithelial tissues as simple (one layer), stratified (multiple layers), or pseudostratified (one layer but with the nuclei stag- gered so the tissue appears to be stratified) (**Figure 38.4**). When epithelial cells are simple and thin, rapid diffusion of

Apical side

Nasal passage: Pseudostratified ciliated columnar

Basil lamina

Basal side

Kidney tubules: Simple cuboidal

Esophagus lining: Stratified squamous

Lungs: Simple squamous

Urinary system: Transitional

Intestines: Simple columnar

Figure 38.4 Examples of epithelial tissue. The types of epithelial tissue are distinguished by their appearance. Epithelial tissue is used to construct body coverings and the protective sheets that line and cover hollow tubes and cavities. The epithelial cells that compose epithelial tissues have an apical and a basal (or basolateral) membrane; the apical side typically faces the exterior of the body or the lumen of a structure, such as the gut.

Principle: *Structure determines function. Note in this illustration how epithelial cells arranged in different ways form tissues with different functions. For example, when arranged as tubules in the kidney, they permit the passage of filtered body fluids. When modified as ciliated columns of cells in the nasal passage, they act as filters of airborne particles and debris.*

gases, nutrients, or liquids is possible. Ciliated epithelial cells are specialized for moving substances: ciliated epithelial cells in the respiratory tract move mucus, containing trapped dust and microbes, to the back of the throat for swallowing. Regardless of their location or function, all epithelial cells are asymmetrical, or polarized. This means that one side of the cell is anchored to an extracellular matrix called the basal lamina or basement membrane. The other side faces the internal or external environment of the animal. Thus, epithelial tissues can function as selective barriers between different body compartments. For example, epithelial tissues in an animal's skin help to form a barrier that prevents most substances in the external environment from entering the body.

Connective Tissues As their name implies, **connective tissues** connect, surround, anchor, and support the structures of an animal's body. Connective tissues include blood, adipose (fat-storing) tissue, bone, cartilage, loose connective tissue, and dense connective tissue (**Figure 38.5**).

An important function of some types of connective tissue is to form the extracellular matrix around cells by secreting a mixture of fibrous proteins and carbohydrates, such as glycosaminoglycans. These carbohydrates may covalently attach to proteins to form proteoglycans. In some cases the extracellular matrix is rich in minerals. The final characteristics of any type of connective tissue are determined in part by the relative proportions and types of proteins, proteoglycans, and minerals secreted into the

Blood is composed of red and white blood cells and cell fragments called platelets, all three of which are suspended in a watery fluid called plasma that is rich in electrolytes, proteins, and other solutes.

Adipose tissue is composed of fat-filled cells, which provide a layer of protection and insulation around internal organs and under the skin. Adipose tissue is also a major energy store.

Dense connective tissue has tightly packed layers of collagen fibres in parallel arrays, giving the tissue great strength but very little flexibility, as in tendons and ligaments.

Bone is composed of bone-forming cells that secrete the protein collagen. The collagen is embedded in a hard casing composed of calcium and phosphorus, which gives bone its inflexible, tough characteristics suitable for support and protection.

Loose connective tissue is abundant throughout animals' bodies, where it holds internal organs in place and provides much of the internal framework of the body. It is composed of loosely arranged collagen fibres mixed with elastin fibres, which allows it to be flexible.

Cartilage is formed by collagen-secreting cells. Cartilage is not mineralized and is therefore softer and more flexible than bone, providing flexibility of movement and cushioning of joints in animals with bony skeletons.

Figure 38.5 **Examples of connective tissue.** Connective tissue connects, surrounds, anchors, and supports other tissues and may exist as isolated cells (blood), clumps of cells (fat), or tough, rigid material like that forming bone and cartilage. The samples have been stained or the micrographs have been computer-colourized to reveal connective tissue.

extracellular matrix. The matrix serves several general functions: (1) providing a scaffold to which cells attach, (2) protecting and cushioning parts of the body, (3) providing mechanical strength, and (4) transmitting information to the cells that helps regulate their activity, migration, growth, and differentiation.

The proteins of the extracellular matrix of a tissue consist of insoluble fibrous proteins, such as **collagen**, and the rubber band-like protein **elastin**; these proteins are often referred to as fibres. A second category is adhesive proteins (fibronectin and laminin) that serve to organize the protein and carbohydrate components of the extracellular matrix.

Different Tissue Types Combine to Form Organs and Organ Systems

An **organ** is composed of two or more kinds of tissues arranged in various proportions and patterns, such as sheets, tubes, layers, bundles, or strips. For example, the vertebrate stomach (**Figure 38.6**) consists of

- an outer covering of epithelial tissue
- a connective tissue layer covering and cementing the organ together
- layers of smooth muscle tissues, in longitudinal, circular, and oblique arrangements, whose contraction propels food through the stomach
- nervous tissue that comes in close contact with the smooth muscle tissues and helps regulate their activity
- an inner lining of epithelial tissue that secretes hormones (long-distance signalling molecules) and enzymes important in the digestive process.

In an **organ system** different organs work together to perform an overall function. In the example just described, the stomach is part of the digestive system, along with other structures such as the intestines, mouth, and anus. In another familiar example the kidneys, the urinary bladder, the tubes leading from the kidneys to the bladder, and the tube leading from the bladder to the exterior of the body constitute the urinary system in mammals, which helps remove waste products from the blood in the form of urine (Figure 38.1). The organ systems found in animals are listed in **Table 38.1**. Some organ systems are rudimentary in some animals (such as the simple nervous systems of worms and other early diverging lineages of animals).

Organ systems frequently work together. For example, signals from the nervous system and endocrine system strongly influence how much water the mammalian kidney retains as it forms urine, an adaptation that can be lifesaving under certain circumstances. Likewise, nerve signals from the bladder relay information to the cells of the brain when the bladder is full and needs to be emptied.

The spatial arrangement of organs into organ systems is part of the overall body plan of animals. Organ systems and other structures, such as an animal's limbs, tentacles, and other appendages, develop at specific times and locations within the body and along the anteroposterior body axis. Remarkably, the body plan of animals appears to be under the control of a highly conserved family of genes with homologues in all animals, as described next.

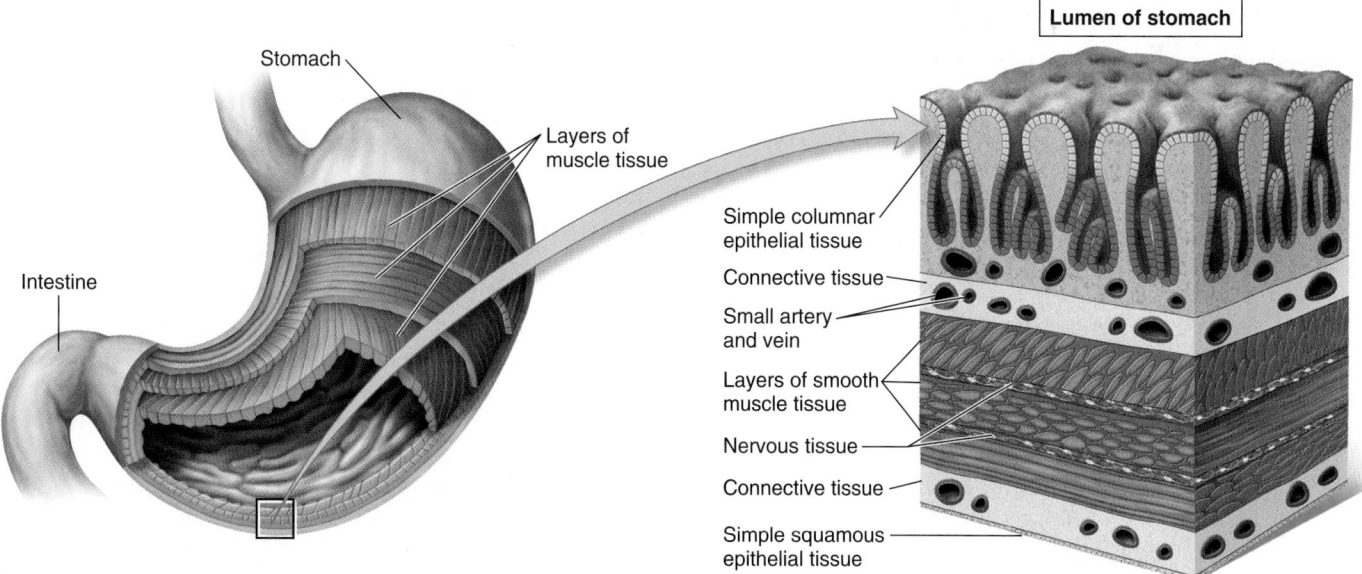

Figure 38.6   The vertebrate stomach as an example of an organ composed of all four tissue types.

Concept check: *Why do some animal organs contain all four tissue types while others do not?*

BioConnections: *Look ahead to Figure 39.9 and compare the structure of the small intestine in that figure to the structure of the stomach shown in this figure. What can you conclude about common functions of the stomach and intestine from this comparison?*

Table 38.1	Organ Systems Found in Animals	
Organ system	**Major components***	**Major functions**
Circulatory	Contractile element (heart or vessel); distribution network (blood vessels); blood or hemolymph	Transport and distribute solutes (nutrients, gases, wastes, etc.) to and from all parts of an animal's body
Digestive	Ingestion structures (mouth or mouthparts); salivary glands; storage structures (crop, stomach); digestive and absorptive structures (intestines); elimination structures (rectum, anus); accessory structures (pancreas, gallbladder)	Break complex foods into smaller, absorbable units; absorb salts and water; eliminate solid wastes
Endocrine	All glands, organs, or tissues that secrete hormones; examples include the brain and the pituitary and thyroid glands	Regulate and coordinate processes such as growth, development, metabolism, mineral balance, and reproduction
Excretory	Kidneys or comparable structures (e.g., Malpighian tubules of insects); storage sites for soluble wastes (bladder); tubes connecting kidneys and bladder, and bladder to external environment	Eliminate soluble metabolic wastes; regulate body fluid volume and solute concentrations
Immune and lymphatic	Circulating white blood cells; lymph vessels and nodes	Defend against pathogens
Integumentary	Body surfaces (skin)	Protect from dehydration and injury; defend against pathogens; regulate body temperature; in some animals gas and fluid transport
Muscular-skeletal	Muscles, bones, cartilage, tendons, ligaments, chitin	Produce locomotion; generate force; propel materials through body organs; support body
Nervous	Brain, spinal cord, peripheral nerves and ganglia, sense organs	Regulate and coordinate many body activities, such as movement, learning, and sensation
Reproductive	Gonads and associated structures	Produce gametes (sperm and egg); in some animals, provide nutritive environment for embryo and fetus, and nourish offspring
Respiratory	Gills, skin, lungs, tracheae (insects)	Exchange oxygen and carbon dioxide with environment; regulate blood pH

Selected examples only; these do not necessarily pertain to all animals.

GENOMES AND PROTEOMES

Organ Development and Function Are Controlled by Homeotic Genes

In previous chapters you learned about a family of ancient, highly conserved genes called homeotic genes that are found in all animals. These genes determine the timing and spatial patterning of the anteroposterior body axis during development. For example, you saw in Chapter 17 how homeotic genes determine the number and position of legs and wings in *Drosophila*. In vertebrates the homeotic genes are known as *Hox* genes, and they play a similar role in determining the spatial patterning of the vertebrate body and appendages. Recently, scientists have begun exploring the role of *Hox* genes in the development and spatial patterning of internal organs that constitute animals' organ systems.

By generating homozygous, null mutant ("knockout") mice that fail to express one or more *Hox* genes, researchers have discovered the important role these genes play in determining where within the vertebrate body particular organs form. For example, *HoxA-3* is important for development of anterior parts of the body, including the neck. When this gene is knocked out, mouse embryos show defects in neck structure, such as

abnormal blood vessels. Also, the organs within the neck—including the thymus, thyroid, and parathyroid glands—do not develop normally. Experimental deletion of *Hox* genes that are associated with other body segments does not affect the development and function of neck glands and organs.

Of particular interest is the discovery that *Hox* genes are important not only for spatial patterning of organs but also for their growth, development, and function. Genes in the *Hox* 1 and 3 groups, for instance, help determine the final branching patterns of the airways of the lungs, the final size of the lungs, and the ability of the lungs to produce secretions that are important for breathing air after birth. Other *Hox* genes have been shown to control cell proliferation and shape changes, apoptosis, cell migration, and cell–cell adhesion within various organs. This is also true in invertebrates, such as the leech, where homeotic genes are first expressed during organ formation, and in *Drosophila*, where the final shape and size of the heart is partly controlled by homeotic genes.

Chapter 49 will describe in greater detail how organs form. It is clear, however, that *Hox* genes in vertebrates and their homologues in invertebrates are important in organ positioning, development, and function. This explains, in part, why the thyroid gland forms in the neck region of vertebrates and not in the legs or tail, for example. Interestingly, *Hox* genes continue to be expressed long after embryonic development has ceased, and it is believed that they play roles in organ function even in adult animals. In fact, expression of abnormal *Hox* genes in a mature organ has been hypothesized to be a contributing factor in organ disease, such as lung disorders and leukemia (cancer of the white blood cells).

Body Fluids Are Distributed into Compartments

In addition to various tissues and organs all animal bodies are composed primarily of water. Indeed, even terrestrial animals can be thought of as "living in water," since all the cells of an animal's body are filled with and surrounded by water.

Most of the water in an animal's body is contained within the **intracellular fluid** inside its cells (from the Latin *intra*, meaning "inside of"). The rest of the water in its body exists outside the cells and is therefore called **extracellular fluid** (Latin *extra*, meaning "outside of"). Extracellular fluid is composed of the fluid part of blood, called **plasma**, and the fluid-filled spaces that surround cells, called **interstitial fluid** (Latin *inter*, meaning "between") (**Figure 38.7**). In vertebrates and some invertebrates plasma and interstitial fluid are kept separate within a closed circulatory system, while in many invertebrates plasma and interstitial fluid are intermingled into a single fluid called hemolymph (see Chapter 44).

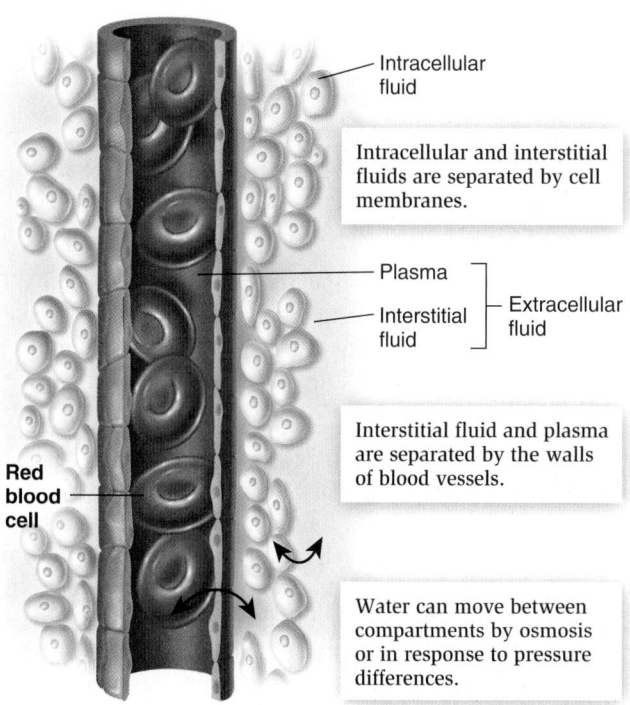

Red blood cell

- Intracellular fluid

Intracellular and interstitial fluids are separated by cell membranes.

- Plasma
- Interstitial fluid

Extracellular fluid

Interstitial fluid and plasma are separated by the walls of blood vessels.

Water can move between compartments by osmosis or in response to pressure differences.

Blood vessel (capillary)

Figure 38.7 Fluid compartments in a typical vertebrate. Most of the fluid within an animal's body exists within cells (intracellular fluid). Extracellular fluid is that portion of the body's fluid that lies outside cells (interstitial fluid) and within blood vessels (plasma). Arrows indicate directions of water movement between adjacent compartments.

The solute composition of the extracellular fluid may be very different from that of the intracellular fluid. Maintaining differences in fluid composition across the plasma membrane is an important way in which animal cells regulate their own activity. For example, many different proteins are confined to intracellular fluid, because they are important in regulating cellular events, such as mitosis, cytokinesis, and metabolism.

The fluids depicted in Figure 38.7 are enclosed in compartments. The sum of the water in the three compartments (intracellular fluid, plasma, and interstitial fluid) accounts for about two-thirds of the body weight of a typical vertebrate. Normally, up to two-thirds of total body water is intracellular, and the remaining one-third is extracellular, the majority of which is located in the interstitial compartment.

Movement of Water Between Compartments Barriers separating adjacent fluid compartments determine which solutes can move between them. Solute movement in turn accounts for the differences in composition of the different compartments. In the case of the body fluid compartments, plasma membranes separate the intracellular fluid from the extracellular fluid. The two components of extracellular fluid in vertebrates and many invertebrates—the interstitial fluid and the plasma—are separated by the walls of the blood vessels (e.g., arteries, capillaries, and veins).

Fluid can readily move between adjacent compartments in an animal's body, because barriers such as plasma membranes tend to be highly permeable to water. This movement depends on osmosis (see Chapter 6), in which water moves from a region of lower solute concentration to a region of higher solute concentration. For cells to function properly, they require a relatively stable internal composition, including ion and protein concentrations, cellular volume, and pH. An increase in solute concentration outside a cell, for example, causes water to move by osmosis from inside the cell to outside. In other words osmosis redistributes fluid from the intracellular to the interstitial compartments. This causes a cell to become deformed as it shrinks because of the loss of fluid. A deformed animal cell rarely operates as well as a normal cell; in fact, it may die if its membrane ruptures. **Figure 38.8** shows examples of mammalian red blood cells in which intracellular fluid levels have been altered. This could occur, for example, if the blood cells were exposed to extracellular fluids that were either more dilute (hypoosmotic) or more concentrated (hyperosmotic) than the fluid inside the blood cell. Such dramatic deformities can rupture blood cells and cause them to release their contents and die.

Pressure differences can also cause fluid to move between compartments in an animal's body. As you will see in Chapter 44, the pressure generated by the beating of the heart can force plasma through tiny openings that are found between the

Red blood cell in a solution of normal osmolarity (an isotonic solution)

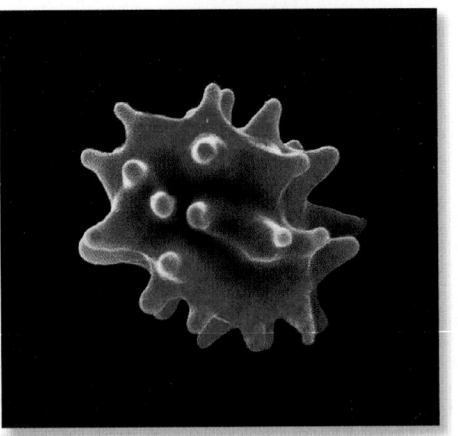
Red blood cell that has lost intracellular fluid when placed in a solution of higher than normal osmolarity (a hypertonic solution)

Red blood cell that has gained intracellular fluid when placed in a solution of lower than normal osmolarity (a hypotonic solution)

Figure 38.8 **Changes in cell shape caused by alterations in intracellular fluid volume.** Alterations in intracellular fluid volume can have drastic effects on cell shape, as shown by these scanning electron micrographs of red blood cells. Each cell is approximately 7 μm in diameter. Dramatic changes in shape like these are usually lethal for cells.

Concept check: *What effect would changes in intracellular fluid volume have on intracellular solute concentration?*

endothelial cells that make up the walls of the smallest blood vessels. This allows water and solutes, such as nutrient molecules, to be transferred from the blood to the interstitial fluid, from which they may gain access to cells.

Movement of Solutes Between Compartments Like water, solutes must also move between body fluid compartments. In this way cells in the body maintain normal levels of ions, nutrients, and gases, such as oxygen. We discussed the mechanisms by which solutes move in Chapter 6. Let's summarize those mechanisms, which apply to all animal cells.

Passive diffusion, a major form of solute transport, is the movement of a solute down its concentration gradient without the aid of a transport protein or hydrolysis of ATP. Passive diffusion is one way in which cells gain and lose solutes. Molecules capable of crossing lipid bilayers are able to passively diffuse into or out of a cell. Examples include nonpolar solutes, such as lipids, and extremely small polar solutes, such as alcohol. Most polar molecules and ions can diffuse through a plasma membrane only if the membrane has pores or channels of some type that permit the ion to pass through the bilayer. The rate of diffusion of any solute can be calculated as follows: rate of diffusion = (permeability of the membrane, a constant) × (the cross-sectional area of the barrier across which diffusion is occurring) × (difference in concentrations of the solute at the two sides of the barrier, such as inside and outside the cell).

The way in which most solutes move between compartments or across plasma membranes is mediated by transport proteins via facilitated diffusion and the various types of active transport (see Chapter 6). Each of these processes is critical to animal regulation of intracellular and extracellular fluid composition. In Chapter 39 we will discuss one example: the

mechanism by which cells obtain glucose, their most important energy source. Because glucose is a relatively large and polar molecule, it cannot diffuse through lipid bilayers. Instead, it is transported from the interstitial fluid into cells by membrane-bound proteins.

38.2 THE RELATIONSHIP BETWEEN STRUCTURE AND FUNCTION

Learning Outcomes:

1. Provide an example of how the structure of an animal's tissues or organs can help predict their function.
2. Describe the importance of the surface area/volume (SA/V) ratio to animal form and function.

One of the principles of biology is that structure determines function. The organization of an animal's body into tissues, organs, organ systems, and fluid compartments can often help us predict the function of each of those structures. For example, the respiratory systems of animals exchange oxygen from the environment and carbon dioxide generated by the body. Let's compare the respiratory systems of an insect and a mammal (**Figure 38.9**). Although many important differences will be covered in Chapter 45, notably the absence of lungs in insects, certain structural similarities suggest that both systems serve similar functions. In both cases, for example, a series of internal branching tubes composed of epithelial and connective tissues arises from one or more openings that connect with the outside environment (the mouth and nose in the mammal, and the spiracles in the insect). These tubes become smaller and smaller

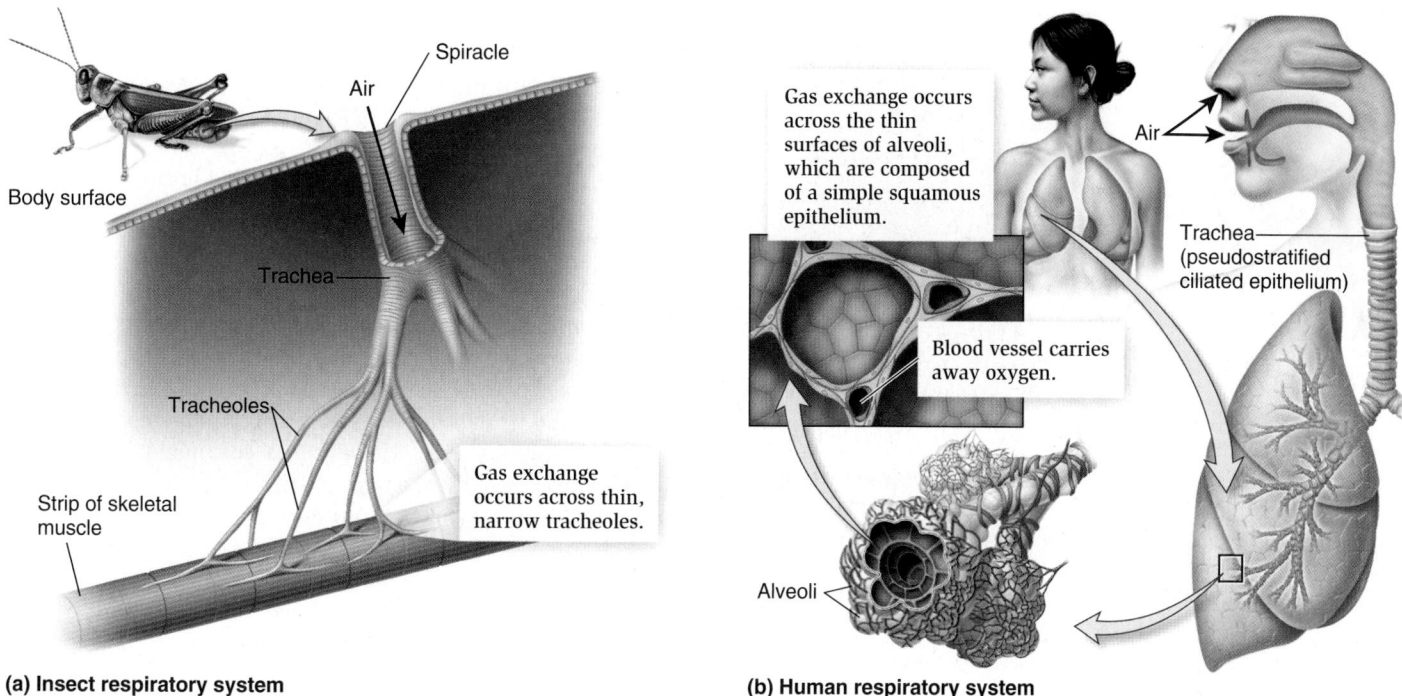

(a) Insect respiratory system

(b) Human respiratory system

Figure 38.9   Comparison of the branching air tubes in (a) an insect and (b) a mammal.   Note the similar features of highly branching, internalized hollow tubules that connect to the outside air, suggesting that these systems perform similar functions.

as they continue to branch, eventually terminating in narrow structures that are only one cell thick.

Without knowing anything else about the respiratory systems of these two animals, we can surmise that in both cases these branching tubes serve as conduits for air to flow back and forth between the environment and the internal spaces of the animal. In the insect the ends of the branching tubes, called tracheoles, are where oxygen diffuses from the air to the fluid around individual cells (and from there to intracellular fluid (**Figure 38.9a**)). In the mammal, the ends of the tubes form saclike structures through which oxygen diffuses into the bloodstream.

If we examine the mammalian lung in greater detail (**Figure 38.9b**), we see that the air sacs are composed of extremely thin, simple squamous epithelial cells. The shape of the cells provides a clue to their function. Their thinness

permits diffusion of gases across the cells as rapidly and efficiently as possible. Imagine the resistance to oxygen diffusion if the cells were thick or scaly, like the cells of the body surface of many animals, for example. Thus, both the gross and microscopic anatomy of the gas-exchange surfaces of respiratory systems facilitates their functions. An additional structural similarity found in essentially all respiratory surfaces, including gills, is an extensive surface area. In fact, we can expand our discussion to include all cells, tissues, and organs that mediate diffusion or absorption of a solute from one compartment to another. Consider, for instance, the fingerlike projections of the small intestine of a human, the skin folds of a frog, the cellular extensions on the surface of nerve cells of a mouse, and the feathery antennae of a moth (**Figure 38.10**). What do these structures have in common? They all display a large surface

(a) Human intestine

(b) Frog skin

(c) Mouse brain neuron stained with a fluorescent marker

(d) Moth antennae

Figure 38.10   Examples of structures in which extensive surface area is important for function.   A large surface area allows **(a)** high rates of transport of digested foods across the intestine of a human, **(b)** rapid diffusion of oxygen across the skin of a frog, **(c)** extensive communication between nerve cells in a mouse's brain, and **(d)** detection of airborne chemicals by moth antennae.

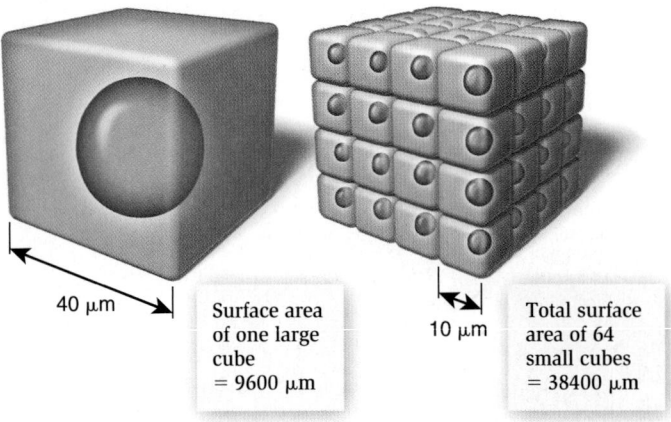

40 μm

Surface area
of one large
cube
= 9600 μm

10 μm

Total surface
area of 64
small cubes
= 38400 μm

Figure 38.11 **Example of the relationship between surface area (SA) and volume (V).** The SA/V ratio of cells is important for determining how rapidly nutrients or waste products can cross the cell membranes. In this example volume remains the same, but the relative SA/V ratio changes. One large cell has less total surface area than the sum of many small cells.

area, which maximizes the ability of a tissue or organ to absorb solutes (intestine), exchange oxygen and carbon dioxide with the environment (frog skin; **Figure 38.10b**), communicate with other cells (nerve cells; **Figure 38.10c**), or sense airborne molecules (moth antennae; **Figure 38.10d**). However, increased surface area could also mean that the structure requires more space inside or outside the body. In some cases this is avoided by changes in shape (see, for example, the way the inner surface of the intestines in **Figure 38.10a** fold inward). The ratio between a structure's surface area and the volume in which the structure is contained is called the **surface area/volume (SA/V) ratio** (**Figure 38.11**). A high SA/V ratio is ideal for exchange of heat, solutes, and water across a surface without contributing greatly to the mass of an animal or body part. This concept will appear throughout this unit as we explore the ways in which animals obtain energy, regulate their body temperature, eliminate wastes, obtain oxygen, and regulate their metabolism.

When all of an animal's organ systems operate normally and body fluid levels and solute composition are maintained within normal limits, the animal is generally considered to be in a healthy condition. In the rest of this chapter, we will examine the process of achieving and maintaining this condition.

38.3 HOMEOSTASIS

Learning Outcomes:

1. Discuss the concept of homeostasis as it applies to the internal environment of animals.
2. Distinguish between conforming and regulating as strategies to maintain homeostasis.

3. List several variables that are regulated within a homeostatic range in vertebrate animals.
4. Describe how negative feedback, positive feedback, and feedforward regulation contribute to the maintenance of homeostasis in animals.
5. Explain the importance of paracrine and hormonal signalling to homeostasis, and provide examples of each.

The environmental conditions in which animals live are rarely, if ever, constant. Animals are exposed to fluctuations in air and water temperatures, nutrient and water supplies, pH, and in some cases oxygen availability. Any one of these environmental changes could be harmful or even fatal if an organism is unable to respond appropriately. However, as you might expect from the incredible diversity of environments in which they exist, animals can adjust in many ways to their surroundings and thrive.

The process of adjusting to the external environment and maintaining a stable internal environment is known as **homeostasis** (from the Greek *homoios,* meaning similar, and *stasis,* meaning standing still). The concept of homeostasis originated in the nineteenth century with French physician and physiologist Claude Bernard, who postulated that a constant *milieu interieur* ("internal environment") was a prerequisite for good health. The ability to maintain homeostasis imparts a clear selection advantage for animals, because many of the fundamental processes of life—for example, enzyme activity—operate most efficiently within narrow limits of variables such as intracellular pH.

Some Animals Conform to External Environments; Others Regulate Their Internal Environments

Generally speaking, animals use two strategies to maintain homeostasis: conforming and regulating. Some animals conform to their environments so that some feature of their internal body composition matches their external surroundings. A marine crab, for example, maintains about the same solute concentration in its body fluids as is found in seawater. Likewise, the body temperatures of many fish and aquatic invertebrates match the temperatures of the surrounding waters. Energetically speaking, conforming is a cheap strategy for survival. It would take a great deal of energy for a small fish to maintain its body temperature at, say, 37°C when swimming in the waters of Antarctica.

Other animals regulate the internal composition of their fluids and solutes at levels that are different from those of the external environment. With respect to internal body composition, most vertebrates are regulators, but exceptions exist. A single animal can be both a conformer and a regulator with respect to different physiological variables. A fish may conform its body temperature to the environment but regulate its internal solute concentrations at levels different from that of fresh or salty water. Regulating the internal environment requires considerable energy in the form of ATP. For this reason, homeostasis for regulators can be metabolically expensive.

Table 38.2	Examples of Homeostatic Variables in Animals	
Variable	**Factors that influence homeostasis**	**Examples of functions**
Minerals	Eating food; excreting wastes	
Na^+ and K^+		Establish electrical differences across plasma membranes (e.g., in muscle, nerve, and heart cells)
Ca^{2+}		Muscle contraction; nerve function; skeleton and shell formation
Fe^{2+}		Bind and transport oxygen in blood or body fluids (some invertebrates use copper instead of iron)
Fuel sources	Eating food; expending energy	
Glucose		Broken down to provide energy for use by all cells, especially brain cells
Fats		Provide an alternative source of energy, particularly for cells not in the nervous system; major component of plasma membranes
ATP		Provides energy to drive most chemical reactions and body functions; modifies function of many proteins by transferring terminal phosphate group to protein
Body temperature	Changing rates of energy expenditure; behavioural mechanisms (see Chapter 40)	Determines the rate of chemical reactions in an animal's body
pH of body fluids	Hydrogen ion pumps in cells; buffers in body fluids; rates of energy expenditure	Affects enzymatic activity in all cells
Other variables		
Oxygen	Movement of air or water across respiratory surfaces (e.g., lungs and gills); rates of energy expenditure	Circulates in body fluids and enters cells, where it is used to make ATP
Water	Drinking, eating, excretion of wastes, perspiration, osmosis across body surface (e.g., skin or gills)	Numerous biological functions (see Chapter 2)

Vertebrates Maintain Most Physiological Variables Within a Narrow Range

The common physiological variables found in healthy organisms—concentrations of blood-borne solutes, like minerals, glucose, and oxygen, for example—are maintained within a certain range despite variable external environmental conditions (**Table 38.2**). In its simplest form homeostasis can be defined as a state of stable balance of physiological variables. This simple definition cannot capture the scope of homeostasis, however. For example, no physiological function is constant for very long, which is why we call them variables. Some variables fluctuate around an average value during a single day and are still considered to be in balance. That is because homeostasis is a dynamic process, not a static one.

Consider an example in your own body. Normally, blood glucose (blood sugar) remains at fairly steady and predictable concentrations in a healthy individual. After a meal, however, the concentration of glucose in your blood can increase quickly, especially if you have just eaten something sweet. Conversely, if you skip a few meals, your blood glucose level may drop slightly (**Figure 38.12**). Such fluctuations above and below the normal value would suggest that blood glucose levels are not homeostatic, but this is incorrect. The important fact is that once blood glucose increases or decreases, homeostatic mechanisms restore glucose concentrations back toward normal. In the case of glucose the endocrine system is primarily responsible for this quick adjustment, but in other examples, a wide variety of control systems can be initiated. In later chapters you will see how every organ and tissue of an animal's body contributes to homeostasis, sometimes in multiple ways and usually in concert with each other.

Thus, homeostasis does not imply that a given physiological function or variable is rigidly constant. Instead, homeostasis means that a variable fluctuates within a certain normal range and that once disturbed from that range, compensatory mechanisms restore the variable toward normal levels.

Homeostatic Control Systems Maintain the Internal Environment

The activities of cells, tissues, and organs must be regulated and integrated so that any change in the extracellular fluid—the internal environment—initiates a reaction to correct the change. These compensating regulatory responses are performed by homeostatic control systems. A homeostatic control system must have several components:

- a set point, the normal value for a controlled variable;
- a sensor, which monitors the level or activity of a particular variable;
- an integrator, which compares signals from the sensor to a baseline set point;
- an effector, which compensates for any deviation between the actual value and the set point.

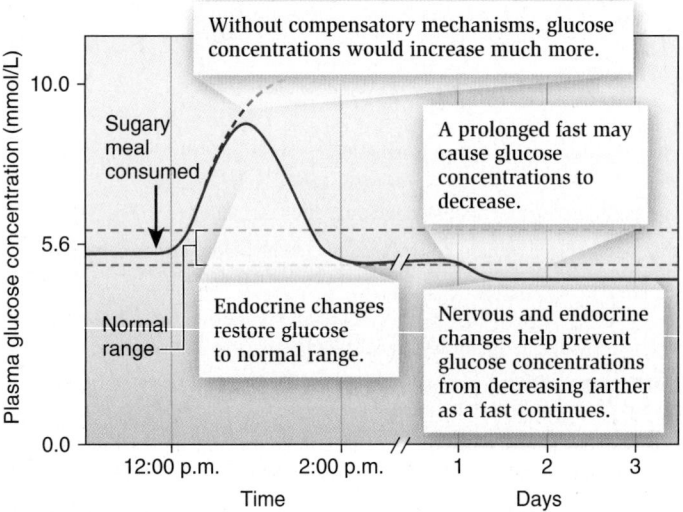

Figure 38.12 An example of a homeostatically controlled variable: blood levels of glucose in a human. Note that glucose levels in the plasma rise or fall depending on whether an animal has recently eaten. However, even after a sugary meal or a prolonged fast, homeostatic mechanisms either return glucose levels to normal (around 5.6 mmol/L) or enable those levels to remain within the range required for survival.

Figure 38.13 shows an example of a homeostatic control system that regulates body temperature in mammals. This system is somewhat analogous to the heating system of a home. In that case a sensor and an integrator within the thermostat compare the actual room temperature to the temperature set by turning the thermostat dial or setting it digitally to a given temperature. If the room temperature becomes cooler than the thermostat setting, the effector (furnace) is activated and adds heat to the room. In a mammal the sensors are temperature-sensitive nerve endings in the skin and elsewhere, while the integrator is within the brain. Signals from the brain are sent along nerves to the effectors, which include skeletal muscles. The muscles contract vigorously in response to these signals, resulting in shivering—a key way in which mammals' bodies generate heat. We will discuss other heat-conserving and heat-generating mechanisms that contribute to this homeostatic control system in Chapter 40.

When a homeostatic control system operates normally, changes in a physiological variable are kept to a minimum. These changes are limited by the process of feedback, as you will now see.

Feedback Is a Key Feature of Homeostasis

Feedback is a fundamental feature of homeostasis and a major way in which disturbances to a physiological variable are minimized. The temperature regulation system just described is an example of a **negative feedback loop**, in which a change in the variable being regulated brings about responses that move the variable in the opposite direction. Thus, a decrease

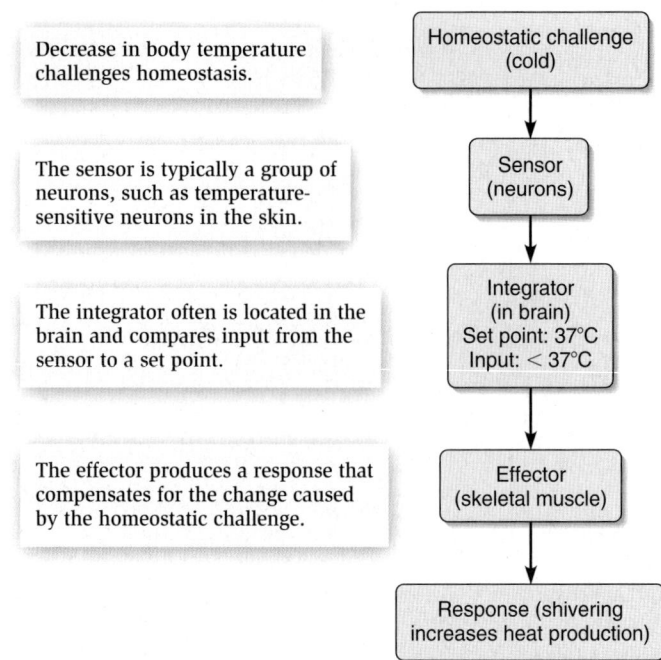

Figure 38.13 An example of a homeostatic control system. The sensor and effector for responding to a decrease in body temperature are shown. Different homeostatic control systems have different sensors and effectors.

BioConnections: *Look back at Figure 7.9 for an example of negative feedback inhibition that occurs at the molecular level. In both examples negative feedback contributes to the maintenance of homeostasis.*

in body temperature leads to responses that increase body temperature—that is, move it back toward its original value.

Negative feedback also prevents homeostatic responses from overcompensating. When the blood pressure of a bleeding animal falls, for example, pressure sensors in certain blood vessels detect the change and send the information to the brain, where the signal is compared with a set point (**Figure 38.14**). The brain stimulates the endocrine system to release hormones whenever blood pressure decreases for any reason. These hormones act in conjunction with the nervous system on the effectors of the compensatory response, such as the heart and blood vessels, to raise blood pressure back toward normal. The increase in pressure removes the stimulus from the sensor (negative feedback). The hormones also feed back to inhibit the brain's ability to continue stimulating the endocrine system. If feedback inhibition did not occur, the blood pressure would not only rebound back to baseline but also might rise to abnormally high and possibly dangerous levels.

Negative feedback can occur at the organ, cellular, or molecular level. For instance, feedback mechanisms regulate many enzymatic processes. In one example, ATP regulates the rate of its own formation in cells by inhibiting certain of the intracellular enzymes that catalyze the breakdown of glucose molecules, a key event in the production of ATP.

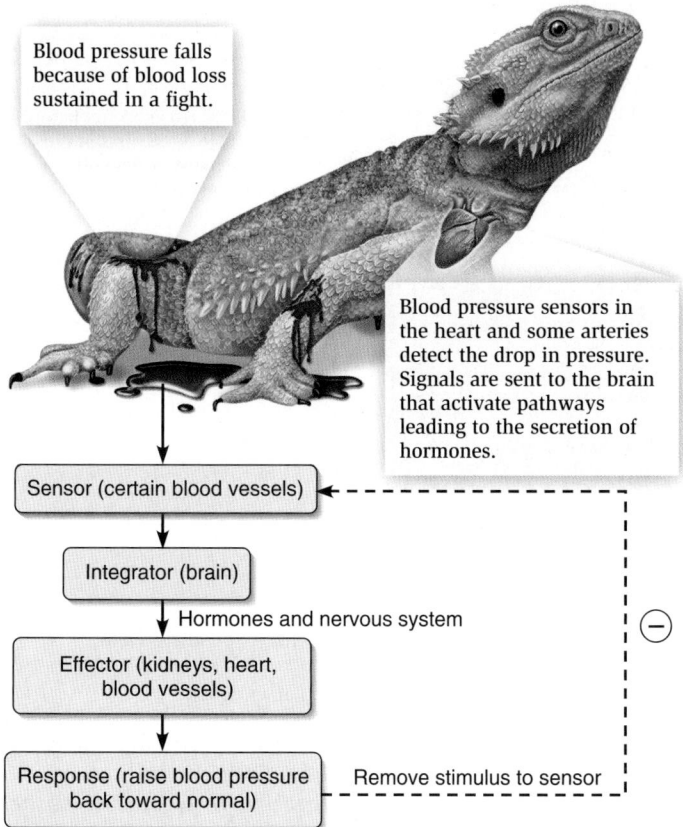

Figure 38.14 Negative feedback as a mechanism by which homeostatic control systems operate. In this example, loss of blood results in a drop in blood pressure, which could be life threatening if not corrected. Effectors, such as the heart and blood vessels, help restore blood pressure toward normal. They do not raise blood pressure above normal, however, because of negative feedback (as denoted by the minus sign).

Not all forms of feedback contribute to homeostasis. In some cases a **positive feedback loop** may accelerate a process, leading to what is sometimes called an explosive system (think of an avalanche that begins with a small snowball rolling down a steep hill). This is contrary to the principle of homeostasis, because positive feedback has no obvious means of being stopped. Not surprisingly, perhaps, positive feedback is far less common in animals than is negative feedback. Nonetheless, examples are found in animal biology in which positive feedback is crucial. One is the process of birth in mammals (**Figure 38.15**), which is triggered by a positive feedback loop between nerve signals arising from smooth muscle cells of the birth canal and the mother's brain and pituitary gland (a component of the endocrine system). As the uterus pushes the baby's head against the birth canal, nerve signals from the canal send information to the brain, which triggers hormone release from the pituitary gland. The hormones stimulate the uterus to contract with more force, which causes additional nerve signals to the brain, and so on. Eventually, the uterus contracts strongly enough that the baby is born.

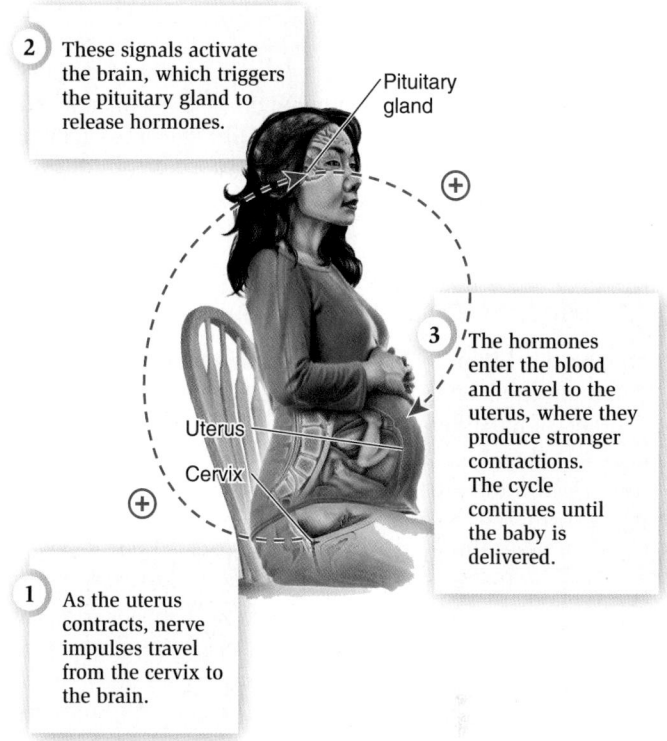

Figure 38.15 The human birth process as an example of positive feedback.

Feedforward Regulation Prepares for an Upcoming Challenge to Homeostasis

Built into the homeostatic mechanisms of many animals, particularly those with well-developed nervous systems, is another important feature that minimizes large swings in physiological variables. In **feedforward regulation** an animal's body begins preparing for a change in some variable (for example, blood glucose levels) before it even occurs. Consider the anticipatory changes that occur when a hungry dog smells or sees food. First, the animal starts to salivate and its stomach begins to churn. Salivation and movements of the stomach wall are important components of the digestive process, yet at this stage the animal has not actually eaten any food. Instead, its digestive system is already preparing for the arrival of food to maximize digestive efficiency, speed the flow of nutrients into the blood, and minimize the time required for active cells to replenish energy stores. Thus, feedforward regulation speeds up the body's homeostatic responses and minimizes fluctuations in the level of the variable being regulated—that is, it reduces the amount of deviation from the set point.

In the preceding example, feedforward control used sensory detectors that recognize odours and sights. Many examples of feedforward control, however, result from or are modified by the phenomenon called learning. The first times they occur, early in life, changes in the external environment might trigger relatively large fluctuations in regulated internal environmental factors. In responding to these changes, the nervous system learns to anticipate and resist them more effectively. Familiar examples are the increased heart rate and breathing rate that occur just before an athletic competition, a phenomenon not unique to human athletes (**Figure 38.16**). The most famous example, however, was first demonstrated in the early twentieth century by Russian physiologist Ivan Pavlov.

Local Homeostatic Responses Fine-Tune the Activities of Tissues and Organs

A common thread that links all homeostatic processes together is communication between cells, whether cells are close to each other or in different parts of an animal's body. Some homeostatic responses may be highly localized, occurring only in the area of a disturbance. For example, damage to an area of skin causes cells in the injured area to release molecules that help contain the injury, prevent infections, and promote tissue repair in the immediate vicinity (see Chapter 50). Local responses provide areas of the body with mechanisms for local self-regulation. It would be of no benefit to an animal to promote tissue repair in regions of the body that are not injured. This type of cellular communication—in which molecules are released into the interstitial fluid and act on nearby cells—is called **paracrine** signalling (see Chapter 9).

Another example of extremely localized paracrine signalling occurs between nerve cells. Most nerve cells communicate through the release of a **neurotransmitter**. Neurotransmitters are small signalling molecules that are synthesized and stored in nerve cells. Neurotransmitters are released from one nerve

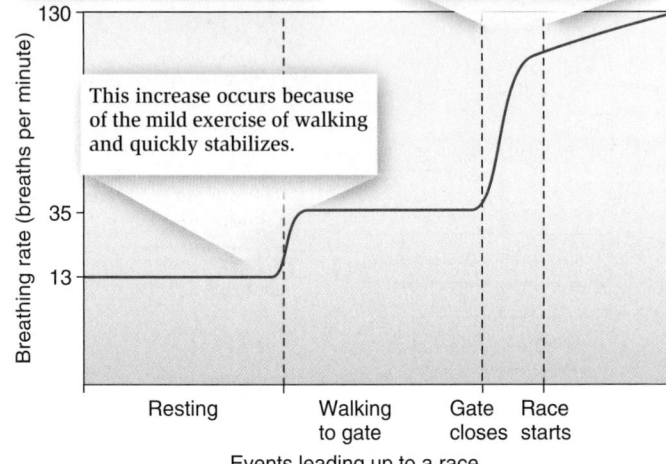

This increase occurs before the race even though the horse is standing still (feedforward).

This increase occurs because of the mild exercise of walking and quickly stabilizes.

Figure 38.16   Feedforward control of breathing rate in an animal trained for athletic exercise.   Feedforward processes prepare the body for an ensuing challenge or event, such as the race shown here.

Concept check: *What kind of similar feedforward response might occur in nature?*

FEATURE INVESTIGATION

Pavlov Demonstrated the Relationship Between Learning and Feedforward Processes

Russian physiologist Ivan Pavlov made numerous contributions to our understanding of the digestive processes in mammals (see Chapter 39), for which he earned a Nobel Prize in Physiology and Medicine in 1904. Today, however, Pavlov is best remembered for work he did later in his career, when he demonstrated that feedforward processes associated with digestion could be conditioned to an irrelevant stimulus.

Pavlov was interested in the factors that increase the production of saliva in a hungry animal. Saliva is an important secretion made by glands in the mouth because it aids in swallowing and contains enzymes that begin the process of digesting certain foods. We are all familiar with the sight of a hungry dog or other animal salivating when it sees or smells food; indeed, the same phenomenon happens in humans. Pavlov

discovered that dogs that were accustomed to being fed by the same researcher each day would begin to salivate when they saw the researcher approaching, even before receiving, seeing, or smelling any food. This did not happen in dogs that were not yet accustomed to the regular feeding schedule of the laboratory. Pavlov questioned whether any stimulus could elicit the feedforward process of salivation, even one that is not normally associated with feeding, so long as that stimulus was somehow paired with feeding.

To test this hypothesis, Pavlov presented two groups of dogs with either food (the control group) or food plus the ticking of a metronome (the experimental group), as shown in **Figure 38.17**. Each dog was isolated in a room so that it could not see, hear, or smell the researcher or any other cues that might interfere with the experiment. In fact, the researcher observed the experiments from behind a wall at the rear of the animal. The stimulus Pavlov used was not the ringing of a bell,

HYPOTHESIS It is possible to condition a feedforward response to an irrelevant stimulus through learning.

KEY MATERIALS Experimental animals (dogs), metronome, collection ports for saliva, food, soundproofed testing rooms

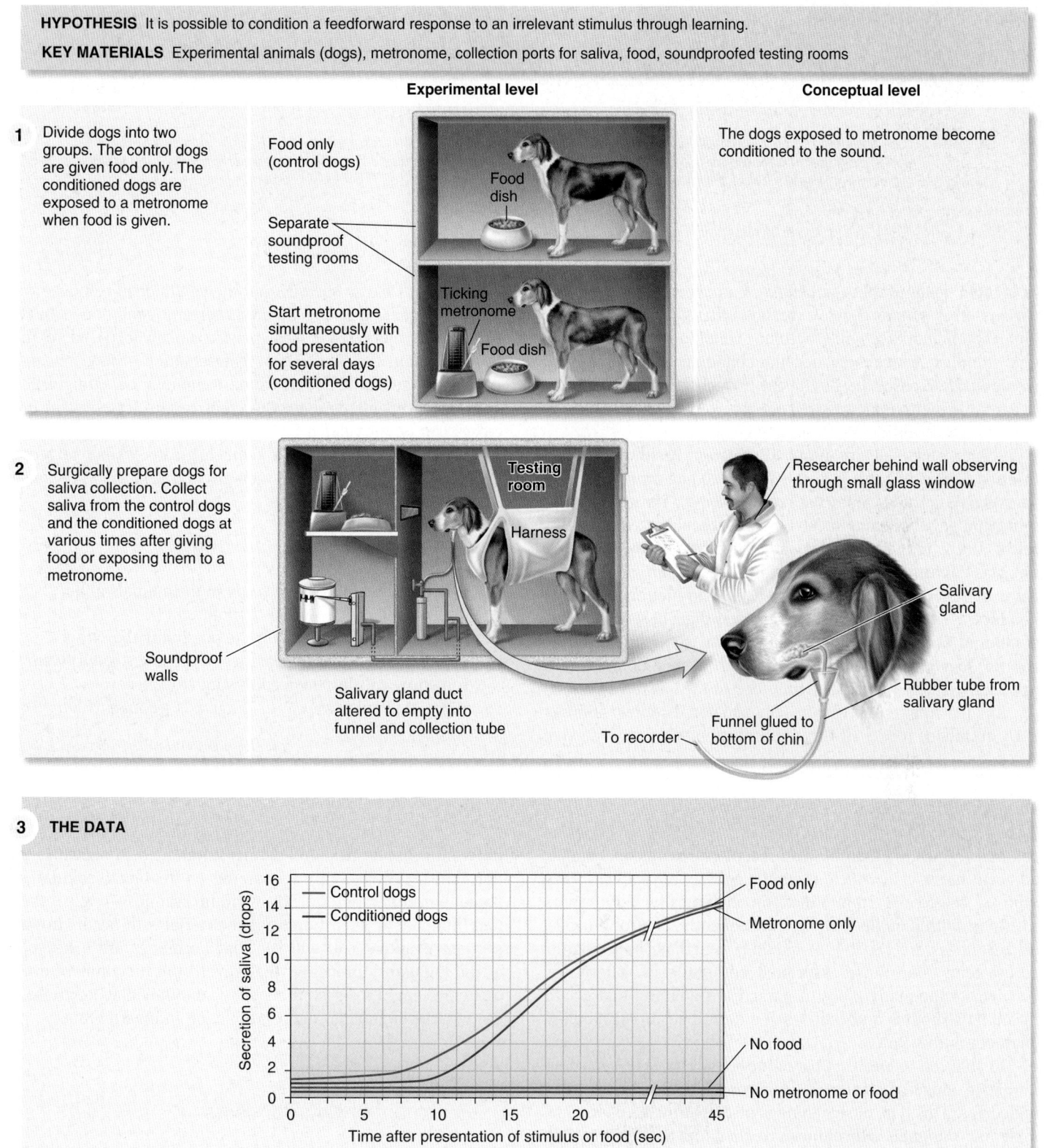

Experimental level | Conceptual level

1   Divide dogs into two groups. The control dogs are given food only. The conditioned dogs are exposed to a metronome when food is given.

Food only (control dogs)

Food dish

Separate soundproof testing rooms

Start metronome simultaneously with food presentation for several days (conditioned dogs)

Ticking metronome

Food dish

The dogs exposed to metronome become conditioned to the sound.

2   Surgically prepare dogs for saliva collection. Collect saliva from the control dogs and the conditioned dogs at various times after giving food or exposing them to a metronome.

Testing room

Harness

Soundproof walls

Salivary gland duct altered to empty into funnel and collection tube

Researcher behind wall observing through small glass window

Salivary gland

Rubber tube from salivary gland

Funnel glued to bottom of chin

To recorder

3   **THE DATA**

Secretion of saliva (drops) — y-axis: 0, 2, 4, 6, 8, 10, 12, 14, 16

— Control dogs
— Conditioned dogs

Food only
Metronome only

No food
No metronome or food

Time after presentation of stimulus or food (sec): 0, 5, 10, 15, 20, 45

Figure 38.17 Feedforward events can be conditioned to external stimuli.

Figure 38.17 (*continued*)

4   **CONCLUSION** The feedforward response of salivation can be modulated by experience and learning, demonstrating the adaptability of animals' physiological responses.

5   **SOURCE** These are idealized data compiled from several of the original published experiments performed by Pavlov and coworkers. The original experiments were reported in Pawlow, J. 1903. Sur la sécrétion psychique des glandes salivares. *Archives Internationales Physiologie* 1:119–135. (Note the alternate spelling of Pavlov's name.)

as is often believed, but the ticking of a metronome, as well as various other sounds. Pavlov reasoned that after some period, the experimental dog would become "conditioned" to the auditory stimulus, which he called the conditioned stimulus, and would learn to associate it with the arrival of food. If this was correct, the metronome by itself should eventually be sufficient to elicit the feedforward process of salivation.

To measure salivary production rates, Pavlov surgically inserted a plastic tube into the ducts leading from the salivary glands located under the dogs' tongues. The tube exited through a small opening created in the cheek and emptied the saliva into a funnel glued beneath the chin. Pavlov's hypothesis was confirmed when, after a conditioning period of several days, the conditioned stimulus by itself (the metronome) elicited increased salivation in the dog in less than 10 seconds. The amount of saliva produced was comparable to that produced in control dogs that had not been exposed to conditioning trials and that were then presented with food in the usual way.

In later experiments Pavlov demonstrated that other stimuli, such as touch, produced the same phenomenon he observed with sound. He also showed that the conditioned response was not permanent. If a dog that was already conditioned to the sound of a metronome was then repeatedly exposed to that sound without the simultaneous presentation of food, the salivary response to the sound would eventually be extinguished. These experiments demonstrated that certain feedforward processes can be modulated by experience and learning, and they suggested that animals have a much greater ability to recognize and adapt to changes in their environment than previously thought.

Experimental Questions

1. What process did Pavlov study in the animals in his experiment? What was his hypothesis?
2. How did Pavlov control for the possibility that other stimuli, such as the appearance of the investigator, were somehow causing the feedforward response?
3. What did Pavlov measure? What was his major finding?

cell and diffuse to combine with receptor proteins on a single adjacent nerve cell, which alters the activity of that cell. This type of cell-to-cell communication is typically very rapid, finishing within milliseconds. Consequently, neurotransmitter responses are capable of making immediate homeostatic adjustments, like those associated with reflexes. These are just two of the many types of paracrine signalling that occur in animals' bodies and that will be described in subsequent chapters in this unit.

In addition to localized paracrine signalling, cells can communicate longer distances by releasing chemical messenger molecules. This type of signalling is mediated by the endocrine systems of animals. **Hormones** are chemical messengers that are produced in a gland or other structure, are secreted into the blood, and act on distant target cells in one or more parts of the body (see Chapter 47). A hormone released in response to a homeostatic disturbance, such as the drop in blood pressure described earlier, can influence the activities of many different cells, tissues, and organs simultaneously because the hormone is carried throughout the entire blood circulation. Some hormones act quickly—within seconds—while others take minutes or even hours for their effects to occur. In subsequent chapters you will see that hormones are a key part of the regulatory processes that govern the functions of every organ system in a vertebrate's body, and they play key roles in growth, development, and reproduction in invertebrates.

Summary of Key Concepts

38.1 Organization of Animal Bodies

- In an animal's body differentiated cells with similar properties group to form tissues, which combine with other types of tissues to form organs. Organs are linked to form organ systems. (Figure 38.1)

- Muscle tissues consist of cells that are specialized to contract, generating the mechanical forces that produce movement, exert pressure on a fluid-filled cavity, or decrease the diameter of a tube. There are three categories of muscle tissue: skeletal, smooth, and cardiac. (Figure 38.2)

- Nervous tissues initiate and conduct electrical signals from one part of an animal's body to another part. (Figure 38.3)

- Epithelial tissues are specialized to protect structures and to secrete and absorb ions and organic molecules. (Figure 38.4)

- Connective tissues connect, surround, anchor, and support the structures of an animal's body. Connective tissues include bone, cartilage, blood, adipose (fat-storing) tissue, loose connective tissue, and dense connective tissue. (Figure 38.5)

- An organ is composed of two or more kinds of tissues. In an organ system different organs work together to perform an overall function. (Figure 38.6, Table 38.1)

- The development, spatial positioning, and function of many body organs are under the control of homeotic genes, such as *Hox* genes in vertebrates.

- An animal's body fluids are distributed into three compartments (plasma, interstitial fluid, and intracellular fluid). The properties of the barriers between the compartments determine which substances can move between them. (Figures 38.7, 38.8)

38.2 The Relationship Between Structure and Function

- The structure of an animal's tissues and organs is related to the function of those structures. (Figure 38.9)

- Extensive surface area maximizes the ability of a tissue or an organ to absorb solutes, exchange oxygen and carbon dioxide with the environment, communicate with other cells, and receive sensory information from the environment. The high surface area/volume (SA/V) ratio principle applies to many structures and across all animal taxa. (Figures 38.10, 38.11)

38.3 Homeostasis

- Homeostasis is the dynamic process of adapting to the external environment and maintaining a relatively stable internal environment. Depending on the physiological variable in question, a single species can be a conformer for one variable and a regulator for another.

- Vertebrates maintain most physiological variables within a certain range despite variations in external environmental conditions. (Table 38.2, Figure 38.12)

- Homeostatic control mechanisms regulate the internal environment. A sensor monitors a variable, an integrator compares signals from the sensor with a set point, and an effector compensates for any deviations from the set point. Negative feedback minimizes changes in a variable and prevents homeostatic responses from overcompensating. (Figures 38.13, 38.14)

- Positive feedback loops accelerate a process and may not contribute to homeostasis. Feedforward regulation prepares the body for an upcoming challenge to homeostasis. (Figures 38.15, 38.16)

- Pavlov's experiments with dogs demonstrated that certain feedforward responses, such as salivation, could be conditioned to irrelevant stimuli, such as the ticking of a metronome. (Figure 38.17)

- Chemical communication between cells is essential to homeostasis. Types of chemical messengers include paracrine signals, such as neurotransmitters, and long-distance signals, such as hormones.

Test to Assess Your Learning

1. Tissue that is specialized to conduct electrical signals from one structure in the body to another structure is _____ tissue.
   a. epithelial
   b. connective
   c. nervous
   d. adipose
   e. muscle

2. Structures that are composed of two or more tissue types arranged in various proportions and patterns are
   a. cells.
   b. tissues.
   c. organs.
   d. organ systems.
   e. organisms.

3. The extracellular matrix of connective tissue
   a. contains different proteins that provide structural support to cells.
   b. provides a scaffolding for the cells of the tissue.
   c. plays a role in cellular communication.
   d. all of the above.
   e. (a) and (b) only.

4. When examining the structure of many animal organs
   a. it is apparent that all organ systems are fully functional in all animals.
   b. the function can be predicted based on the structural adaptations.
   c. the function of the structure is difficult to determine because of the lack of variation among the different structures of the body.
   d. all four tissues are equally represented in all organs.
   e. none of the above.

5. Most of the water in an animal's body
   a. lacks any type of ions or other solutes.
   b. is found in the spaces between cells.
   c. is contained inside the cells.
   d. is located in the extracellular fluid.
   e. is unable to move between body compartments.

6. The folds, convolutions, or extensions found in many structures of animals results in
   a. decreased level of activity in that particular structure.
   b. interruption in the normal functioning of the structure.
   c. increased surface area for absorption, communication, or exchange.
   d. higher susceptibility to infection.
   e. none of the above.

7. Adapting to changes in the external environment and maintaining a relatively stable internal environment is
   a. natural selection.
   b. evolution.
   c. positive feedback.
   d. homeostasis.
   e. both (c) and (d).

8. Which of the following statements regarding negative feedback is **incorrect?**
   a. It helps regulate variables such as body temperature and blood pressure.
   b. It is part of the process by which birth occurs in mammals.
   c. It is a major feature of homeostatic control systems.

d. It prevents homeostatic responses from overcompensating.

e. It may occur at the organ, cellular, or molecular level.

9. The ability of an animal's body to prepare for a change in some variable before the change occurs is called

a. positive feedback.

b. negative feedback.

c. homeostasis.

d. feedforward regulation.

e. autoregulation.

10. A hormone differs from a neurotransmitter in that

a. hormones act extracellularly; neurotransmitters act within the cell that synthesized them.

b. hormones are released only by nerve cells; neurotransmitters are released by many different types of cells.

c. hormones cause fast responses (seconds or less) to stimuli; neurotransmitters cause slow responses (minutes to hours) to stimuli.

d. hormones affect only epithelial cells; neurotransmitters affect only muscle cells.

e. hormones are released into the bloodstream and can activate many cells in many parts of the body; neurotransmitters are released by nerve cells and affect adjacent cells.

Articulate to Assess Your Learning

1. Describe the relationship between structure and function in animals.

2. What would be the effect of a large SA/V ratio as versus a small SA/V ratio when calculating how rapidly a gas can diffuse across a cell membrane?

3. Blood glucose levels are controlled by homeostatic mechanisms in the body. Using what you have learned about this, propose a healthful breakfast that dieters should be eating to lose weight and maintain normal blood glucose levels.

Collaborate to Assess and Extend Your Learning

1. Discuss the terms homeostasis, negative feedback loop, and positive feedback loop.

2. Discuss the organization of animal bodies from the cellular to the organ system level.

3. Two principles of biology are that living organisms use energy and that living organisms maintain homeostasis. How are energy use and the maintenance of homeostasis related?

Visit McGraw-Hill Ryerson Connect™ for additional study resources.

Nutrition, Digestion, and Absorption

Obtaining and using nutrients is a fundamental process in all animals, such as this great blue heron feeding on a frog.

A **nutrient** is any substance consumed by an animal that is needed for survival, growth, development, tissue repair, or reproduction. All animals require nutrients to survive. Because animals cannot use the energy of sunlight to make nutrients, as plants do, they must have ways of obtaining food that contains these vital substances. The process of food use in animals occurs in four phases: ingestion, digestion, absorption, and elimination (**Figure 39.1**). **Ingestion** is the act of taking food into the body, via a structure, such as a mouth. From there, the food moves into a digestive cavity or canal. If the nutrients in food are in a form that cannot be directly used by cells, they must be broken down into smaller molecules, a process known as **digestion**. This is followed by the process of **absorption**, in which ions, water, and small molecules diffuse or are transported from the digestive cavity into an animal's circulatory system. **Elimination** is the process of undigested material passing out of the body. In this chapter, we look at the diverse ways in which animals obtain, digest, and absorb nutrients. We begin by examining the types of nutrients they consume.

39.1 ANIMAL NUTRITION

Learning Outcomes:

1. List the major categories of nutrients consumed by animals and some of their general functions.
2. Identify four groups of essential nutrients, listing several examples of each.

The organic nutrients required by animals fall into five categories: carbohydrates, lipids, proteins, nucleic acids, and vitamins. In addition, animals require inorganic nutrients in the form of water and minerals, such as Ca^{2+}, K^+, and Fe^{3+}. In many cases, the same nutrients serve comparable functions in different animals. For example, we have seen that the plasma membranes of every animal are made of proteins, carbohydrates, and lipids. As another example, all animals that have muscles use amino acids to make the same specialized proteins that allow their muscles to contract. All animal cells require calcium ions to carry out common activities, such as exocytosis and cell division. Similarly, all animal cells require a regular source of energy to replace the high-energy bonds of ATP that are used in phosphorylation and other biochemical reactions.

Despite these basic similarities, however, nutritional demands differ depending on a given animal's physiology. The digestive systems of **herbivores**, animals that eat only plants, contain microbes that assist in the digestion of cellulose, and so these animals are well adapted to subsist on plants and algae. By contrast, **carnivores** are primarily adapted to consume animal flesh or fluids, while **omnivores** have the ability to eat and survive on both plant and animal products. In this section, we will examine the various organic and inorganic nutrients consumed by animals and some of the major functions of these molecules.

Animals Require Nutrients for Macromolecule Synthesis, Energy, and Chemical Reactions

As stated earlier, all animals must obtain nutrients from the environment. Nutrients common to animals include those organic and mineral compounds that provide the substrates for building and replenishing cellular components, such as proteins and nucleic acids (DNA and RNA). The chemical bonds in organic compounds, such as sugars and fats, are also used as a source of energy from which ATP can be formed. Indirectly, therefore, sugars and fats provide the energy needed for most of the chemical reactions that occur in animals' bodies.

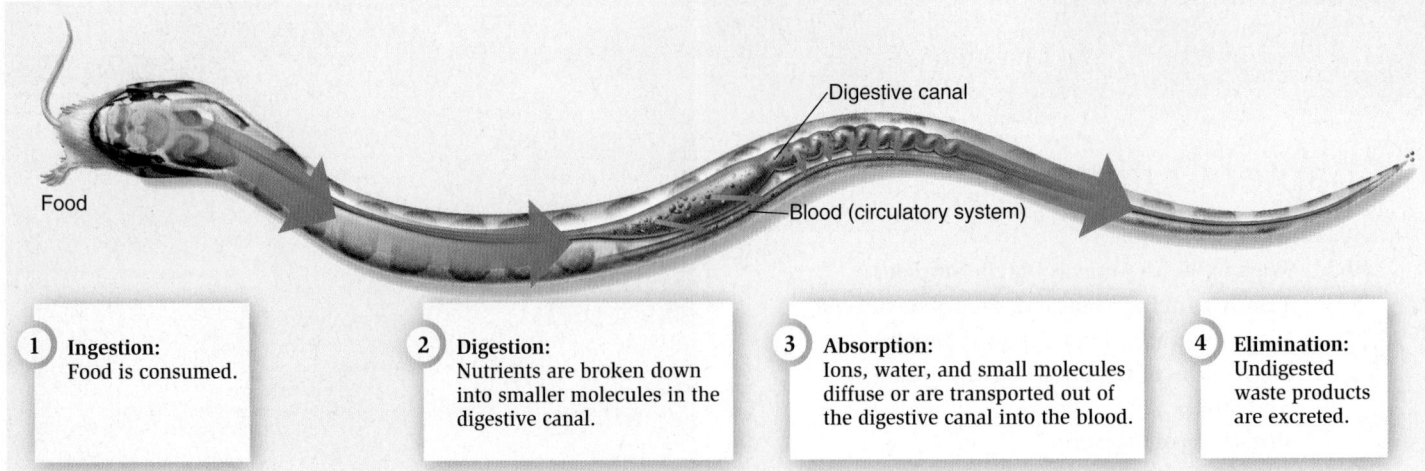

Figure 39.1   An overview of the four phases of food use in animals: ingestion, digestion, absorption, and elimination.

Minerals, such as iron and zinc, are needed as cofactors or constituents of enzymes and other proteins. Other minerals, such as calcium, are needed for bone, muscle, and nerve function, while still others—sodium and potassium—establish ion gradients across plasma membranes and therefore are critical for heart, skeletal muscle, and nerve activity. **Table 39.1** summarizes the major nutrients, their dietary sources, some of their important functions, and some health consequences associated with their deficiencies.

Although different species consume a wide variety of foods, all animals require the same fundamental organic nutrients. These include carbohydrates to supply energy-yielding glucose; lipids to supply fatty acids, cholesterol, and triglycerides for energy and membrane building; and proteins to supply amino acids, which are used to make new proteins and the purines and pyrimidines needed for DNA and RNA synthesis. The amount of each nutrient needed by an animal depends on its activity level, or metabolic rate, which we will discuss in Chapter 40. Generally, highly active and energetic animals, such as most birds and mammals, are endotherms. They require a greater amount of nutrients each day than do relatively inactive or sedentary animals such as nonmotile invertebrates. However, exceptions to this general rule exist. If a normally sedentary animal temporarily expends more energy than usual, it will require additional nutrients to replenish that energy. Conversely, some mammals that are active at one time of year may hibernate for the winter, during which time they use very little energy and exist on nutrients that were previously consumed and stored (e.g., as fat).

When an animal consumes polymers, the polymers are typically too large to be absorbed across the epithelial cells that line the digestive tract. Therefore, these molecules are first broken down by enzymes into monomers and then transported into the blood and cells of the body. Once in the cells, metabolic enzymes can synthesize new polymers from these monomers. In this way, cells can obtain the polysaccharides, proteins, triglycerides, and nucleic acids they require. Thus, even though

organic nutrients may be consumed as polymers, they typically are first broken down into monomers that can more easily exit the digestive tract and enter the blood circulation.

Essential Nutrients Must Be Obtained from the Diet

Certain compounds cannot be synthesized from any ingested or stored precursor molecule. These **essential nutrients** must be obtained in the diet in their complete form. The word *essential* refers to the fact that they must come from food. It does not mean that other nutrients are less important, since many nutrients are essential for an animal's survival. The essential nutrients can be classified into four groups: essential amino acids, essential fatty acids, minerals, and vitamins. Note that different taxa may have different sets of essential nutrients.

Essential Amino Acids   Eight **essential amino acids** are required in the diet of humans and many other animals: isoleucine, leucine, lysine, methionine, phenylalanine, threonine, tryptophan, and valine. These amino acids are required for building proteins but cannot be synthesized or stored by the animal's cells. Without a recurring supply of these eight amino acids, therefore, protein synthesis in each cell in an animal's body would slow down or stop completely. Carnivores and omnivores readily obtain all the essential amino acids, because meat (animal muscle) contains all 20 amino acids. People who follow strict vegetarian diets must find ways to balance the types of plant matter they eat. Unlike animal meat, most plants do not contain every essential amino acid in sufficient quantities to supply a human's nutritive needs. By contrast, some herbivores, such as cows, have evolved the capacity to synthesize the essential amino acids, which allows them to subsist entirely on a plant diet.

Essential Fatty Acids   The **essential fatty acids** are certain polyunsaturated fatty acids, such as linoleic acid, that cannot be

Table 39.1	Major Nutrients in Animals, Their Dietary Sources, and Some of Their Functions in Vertebrates		
Class of nutrient	**Dietary sources**	**Functions in vertebrates**	**Symptoms of deficiency**
Food source			
Carbohydrates	All food sources	Energy source, components of some proteins, source of carbon	Muscle weakness, weight loss, ketone formation (decreases pH of blood)
Lipids	All food sources, especially fatty meats, milk or milk products, plant oils	Major component of cell membranes, energy source, thermal insulator	Hair loss, dry skin, weight loss, hormonal and reproductive disorders
Proteins	All food sources, especially meat, legumes, cereals, roots	Provides amino acids to make new proteins, builds muscle, some amino acids used as energy source	Weight loss, muscle loss, weakness, weakened immune system, increased likelihood of infections
Nucleic acids	All food sources	Provides nucleotides to make DNA, RNA, and ATP	
Minerals			
Calcium (Ca)	Milk or milk products, cereals, legumes, whole grains, green leafy vegetables, bones (eaten by some animals)	Bone and tooth formation, exocytosis of stored secretions in nerves and other cells, muscle contraction, blood clotting	Muscular disorders, loss of bone, reduced growth in children
Chlorine (Cl)	Meats, milk or milk products, blood, natural deposits of salt	Participates in electrical, acid-base, and osmotic balance across cell membranes, notably nerve and heart cells	Muscular and nerve disorders
Chromium (Cr)	Liver, seafood, some nuts, meats, mushrooms, some vegetables	Needed for proper glucose metabolism, possibly by aiding insulin action	Disorders of lipid and glucose balance in blood, hypoglycaemia (short term), obesity (long term)
Copper (Cu)	Fish, shellfish, nuts, legumes, liver, and other organs	Required for hemoglobin production and melanin synthesis, needed for connective tissue formation, serves as oxygen-binding molecule in some invertebrates	Anemia (abnormally low number of red blood cells), bone changes
Iodine (I)	Seaweed, seafood, milk, iodized salt	Required for formation of thyroid hormones	Inability to make thyroid hormones, resulting in enlarged thyroid gland
Iron (Fe)	Liver and other organs, some meats, eggs, legumes, leafy green vegetables	Oxygen-binding component of hemoglobin	Anemia
Magnesium (Mg)	Hay, grasses, whole grains, green leafy vegetables	Cofactor for ATP and many enzymes	Changes in nervous system function
Manganese (Mn) and Molybdenum (Mo)	Nuts, whole grains, legumes, vegetables, liver	Cofactors for many enzymes	Poor growth, abnormal skeletal formation, nervous system disorders (convulsions)
Phosphorus (P)	Milk or milk products, grains, legumes, nuts, meats	Bone and tooth formation, component of DNA, RNA, and ATP	Bone loss, muscle weakness
Potassium (K)	Meats, fruits, vegetables, milk or milk products, grains	See chlorine	Muscle weakness, serious heart irregularities, gastrointestinal symptoms
Selenium (Se)	Seafood, eggs, chicken, soybeans, grains	Antioxidant, cofactor for some enzymes	Keshan disease (damage to and loss of heart muscle)
Sulphur (S)	Proteins from any source	Component of two amino acids (methionine and cysteine)	Inability to synthesize many proteins
Sodium (Na)	Many fruits, vegetables, meats, and natural salt deposits	See chlorine	Muscle cramps, changes in nerve activities
Zinc (Zn)	Widely found in meats, fish, shellfish (oysters), grains	Many functions related to tissue repair, sperm development, cofactor for many metabolic enzymes, needed for certain transcription factors to bind to DNA	Stunted growth, loss of certain sensations such as taste, impaired immune function, skin lesions

synthesized by animal cells. Saturated fatty acids, conversely, can be synthesized from carbon sources, such as glucose. Linoleic acid is vital to an animal's health because it is the building block that is converted in cells to arachidonic acid. This fatty acid is the precursor for production of several compounds

known to be important in many aspects of animal physiology. Some animals—such as felines—cannot synthesize arachidonic acid from linoleic acid, and so arachidonic acid is an essential fatty acid in those species. Unsaturated fats are found primarily in plants, which provide a dietary source for both herbivores and omnivores. Obligate carnivores, such as cats, however, obtain their essential fatty acids from fish or from the adipose tissue of birds and mammals.

Minerals   **Minerals** are inorganic ions required to build skeletons, maintain the balance of salts and water in the body, provide a source of electric current across plasma membranes, and provide a mechanism for exocytosis and muscle contraction, among other functions. Table 39.1 summarizes some of the most important minerals and their functions. Many minerals are required in only trace amounts, far less than 1 mg/day in a relatively large mammal such as humans. Nonetheless, without regular consumption of these small amounts, serious health problems can arise.

Some minerals can be stored in a typical vertebrate animal's body, reducing the risk of deficiency when the mineral is not available in the diet. Iodine, for example, is stored in large amounts in the thyroid gland, where it is required for proper thyroid function. If a vertebrate's diet is deficient in iodine, which is common in areas where iodine periodically leaches from the soil as a result of considerable rainfall, there is usually enough stored iodine to permit normal thyroid gland function for days or even months, depending on the species. As another example, calcium is stored in huge quantities in bone in vertebrates and in the shells of some invertebrates. If the dietary intake of this mineral falls, calcium is released from these storage sites and secreted into the blood.

Not all minerals are used the same way or at the same rate by all animals. For instance, copper helps to bind and transport oxygen in the fluids of some invertebrates, such as horseshoe crabs, while in all vertebrates and in most other invertebrates, iron serves this function. Factors that affect mineral usage are an animal's species, age, weight, overall health status, and the types of food it eats.

Vitamins   **Vitamins** are important organic nutrients that serve as coenzymes for many metabolic and biosynthetic reactions. The two categories of vitamins are fat soluble and water soluble. Fat-soluble vitamins, such as vitamin A, are stored in adipose tissue, whereas water-soluble vitamins, for example, vitamin C, are not stored in the body and must be regularly ingested. Not all animals require the same vitamins in their diet, however. Among vertebrates, for example, only primates and guinea pigs cannot synthesize their own vitamin C and must therefore consume it in the diet.

Inadequate vitamin intake can have serious consequences, as shown by the health problems of British sailors in the eighteenth century. Sailors would often remain at sea for months or even years, subsisting on a poor diet with few fruits or vegetables. Many developed **scurvy**, a potentially fatal vitamin C deficiency characterized by weakness, bleeding gums, tooth loss, and wounds that will not heal. In guinea pigs, vitamin C deficiency also causes poor teeth and bone development, swollen joints, lameness, bleeding gums, and hemorrhages under the skin and into the joints.

39.2   WAYS IN WHICH ANIMALS OBTAIN NUTRIENTS

Learning Outcomes:

1. Discuss some examples of the diversity of animal feeding habits.
2. Identify the three broad categories of strategies that animals use to get food and relate this to specialized adaptations such as teeth.

Several factors determine how and when an animal obtains food, including its energetic demands, the local environment, the structure of its digestive system, and whether or not it is capable of locomotion. In this section, you will see that despite the enormous number of animal species and the highly varied environments in which they live, the major ways in which animals obtain food can be classified into just a few categories.

Animals May Eat Plants, Other Animals, or Both

Unlike plants, which make their own food, all animals are heterotrophs, which means they must consume their food. As stated earlier, most animals can be grouped into one of three dietary categories: herbivores, carnivores, or omnivores.

The gastrointestinal (GI) tracts, or **gut**, of carnivores and omnivores resemble each other much more than either resembles those of herbivores. This reflects differences in the enzymatic processing and the energetic quality of the foods they eat. Generally the nutritive value of meat is much greater than that of plants. Consequently, carnivores usually need to eat less frequently than herbivores, many of whom eat almost continuously to supply sufficient nutrients for energy and growth.

Although useful, the three dietary categories are limited when describing the diversity of animal species. For example, some animals are almost strictly carnivores at one time of year but herbivores at other times. Many nonmigratory birds, for example, feed on insects and worms during the summer but switch to eating whatever vegetation, buds, or seeds they can find during the winter. Similarly, a coyote prefers to eat only meat but will consume plants and fruits if hungry enough. A hungry fruit-eating bat will eat leaves, nectar, or pollen if fruit is not available. Animals like these are said to be **opportunistic**. They have a strong preference for one type of food but can adjust their diet if the need arises.

An animal's life stage may also influence its diet. Mammals begin life as milk drinkers and later switch to consuming plants, animals, or both. Caterpillars eat leaves, but after metamorphosis, most species of moth or butterfly are strictly fluid drinkers, typically the nectar in flowers. Other animals that undergo metamorphosis also change their diet as adults. Tadpoles, for example, are mostly herbivores, while frogs are insect-eating carnivores.

The three major categories also do not indicate what type of plant or animal is consumed. Grasses, cereals, and fruits, for example, each have different energy and nutrient contents. Some herbivores eat primarily fruits, and some carnivores only drink the blood of other animals. To better describe the nutrition of animals, therefore, we need to investigate the strategies by which they obtain food.

Animals Have Evolved Multiple Strategies for Obtaining Food

The ways in which an animal obtains its food are related to its environment. Not surprisingly, a sessile (nonmotile) marine invertebrate and a highly mobile terrestrial vertebrate face different challenges and opportunities.

Aquatic animals that are sedentary or nonmotile may use sticky surfaces or tentacles to trap food that floats or swims their way. Sea squirts trap suspended food particles in mucus-coated branchial baskets, while sea anemones use tentacles to capture and kill prey that swims within reach.

Other aquatic animals, both motile and nonmotile, include **suspension feeders**, which sift water, filtering out the organic matter and expelling the rest (**Figure 39.2**). Shelled molluscs filter seawater and capture floating bits of organic material on mucus-covered cilia located in their gills, which move the material into the animal's mouth. Baleen whales (such as the fin, minke, and humpback whales that are found in the St. Lawrence River) have specialized comblike plates (known as baleen or whalebone), which are made of keratin and are suspended from the roofs of their mouths. The whale draws in a mouthful of seawater and squeezes it back out through the baleen, which acts like a feeding sieve to filter out small animals and protozoa for ingestion.

Carnivores, which inhabit aquatic and terrestrial environments, are generally **predators** (they kill live prey) or **scavengers** (they eat the remains of dead animals). Carnivores' teeth are well developed for biting and tearing. They normally do not chew food to any large degree but rather swallow large chunks

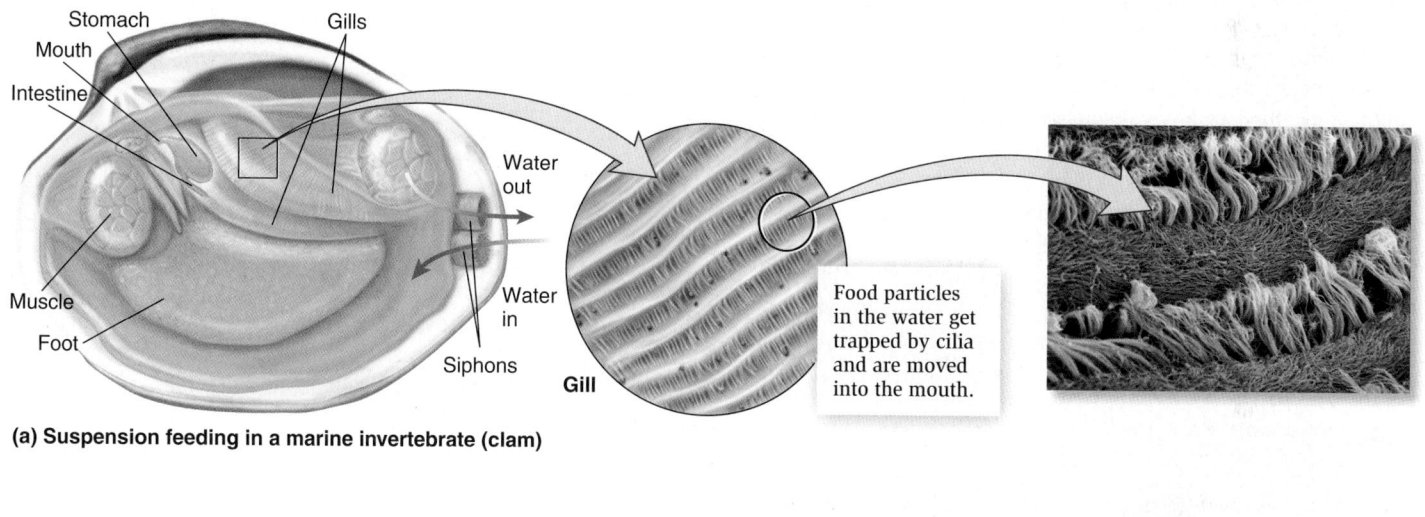

(a) Suspension feeding in a marine invertebrate (clam)

(b) Suspension feeding in a large vertebrate (baleen whale)

Figure 39.2 **Suspension feeding.** Suspension feeders include species of both invertebrates and vertebrates. **(a)** Bivalves, such as the clam shown here, use a siphon mechanism to move water across their gills. Cilia located along the gills trap and move food particles to the mouth. **(b)** Baleen whales draw in water with their mouths and then use their tongue to force the water back out through the comblike baleen. The baleen filters out tiny organisms or bits of organic matter from the water.

Principle: *Living organisms use energy. An implication of this principle is that living organisms must obtain energy in order to use it. Animals obtain energy from food. As you read this chapter, think about the energy required by animals to obtain the food they require. That energy may be used to move cilia, as in the clam, or to sustain muscle activity in animals foraging or hunting over great distances.*

at once. This does not hinder their ability to digest their food, because meat is still fully digested if swallowed whole, although not as quickly as it would be if it were chewed. Swallowing food whole allows a carnivore to quickly get another bite when competing with other hungry animals. The strategy of consuming entire chunks of food without chewing is seen in species from all the vertebrate classes. Birds of prey, for example, use their sharp beaks to tear away pieces of flesh that can be engulfed all at once. Chewing, when or if it occurs in a carnivore, is mostly a means of breaking food into pieces small enough to swallow.

Herbivores have powerful jaw muscles and large, broad teeth that are highly adapted for grinding tough, fibrous plants. **Grazers**—herbivores that feed almost constantly on grasses—must chew to facilitate the digestion of plant material. Some herbivores, such as the ruminants (e.g., sheep, goats, alpacas, cows), will even regurgitate partially digested food and chew it a second time. Other herbivores called **frugivores** are adapted primarily to feed on fruits.

Fluid feeders lick or suck fluid from plants or animals and so do not need teeth except, perhaps, to puncture an animal's skin. Fluid feeding has evolved independently in many types of animals, including insects, worms, birds, and mammals. The sea lamprey, *Petromyzon marinus,* which attaches itself to fish and can be found in the Great Lakes, is also a fluid feeder. Usually fluid feeders have specialized mouthparts, such as the piercing needle-like extension of a mosquito's mouth or the tiny jaws and teeth of a blood-sucking leech (**Figure 39.3a**). Fluid-feeders that consume blood have developed a fascinating set of strategies to ensure a full meal from the host. Leeches, for example, secrete a local anaesthetic at the site of the bite. An enzyme digests the host's connective tissue to allow the leech to firmly embed its mouth into the host's flesh, and a locally acting chemical is secreted to keep the host's blood vessels open.

(a) Blood-sucking animals like this leech use their teeth to prick the skin of their host.

(b) Hummingbirds use their long, thin beaks to consume nectar from flowers.

Figure 39.3 **Strategies of fluid feeders.** Fluid feeders use their specialized mouths to suck (a) the blood of animals or (b) the nutrient-rich nectar of plants.

Concept check: *To obtain sufficient nutrients, blood-sucking animals, like mosquitoes, leeches, and some bats, must consume large amounts of blood at each meal. For mosquitoes and bats, would this hinder their ability to take flight after eating?*

Finally, to ensure that the blood does not clot before the leech has drunk its fill, the saliva of leeches and other blood-sucking animals often contains an anticoagulant.

Not all fluid feeders consume blood. Many birds and bats drink nectar from plants and have specialized beaks, tongues, or mouths that enable them to reach the nectar of a particular flower (**Figure 39.3b**).

Regardless of what an animal eats, the useful parts of the eaten material must be digested into molecules that its cells can absorb. Next, we turn to a discussion of how animals digest their food and absorb the nutrients.

39.3 PRINCIPLES OF DIGESTION AND ABSORPTION OF FOOD

Learning Outcomes:

1. Compare the processes of intracellular and extracellular digestion, and explain why one is far more common than the other.
2. Describe the general structure of an alimentary canal.
3. Distinguish between passive and active absorption of food.

Digestion requires enzymes capable of hydrolyzing the chemical bonds in carbohydrates, lipids, proteins, and nucleic acids. These enzymes are named after their substrates. Thus, we have polysaccharidases, lipases, proteases, and nucleases. Once the enzymes digest the food, the products of digestion must be absorbed by diffusion or by energy-dependent transport across plasma membranes. Not all the food that is eaten, however, is digested. Minerals, vitamins, and monomers of macromolecules do not require digestion and are absorbed intact. Digestion is needed only to convert polymers into smaller units that can be absorbed across plasma membranes. In this section, we will examine some of the major principles of digestion and absorption in animals, beginning with where digestion takes place.

Digestion Can Occur Intracellularly or Extracellularly

Intracellular digestion occurs only in some very simple invertebrates, such as sponges and single-celled organisms. It involves the phagocytosis of food particles directly into a cell, where the food is segregated from the rest of the cytoplasm in food vacuoles. Once inside the vacuoles, hydrolytic enzymes digest the food into monomers, which exit the vacuole and are used directly by that cell. Intracellular digestion cannot support the metabolic demands of an active animal for long, because only tiny bits of food can be phagocytosed at one time; it also does not provide a mechanism for storing large quantities of food so that an animal can digest it slowly while going about its other activities.

Most animals digest food via extracellular digestion in a cavity of some sort. Extracellular digestion protects the interior of the cells from the actions of hydrolytic enzymes and allows animals to consume large prey or large pieces of plants. Food enters the digestive cavity, where it is stored, slowly digested, and absorbed gradually over long periods, ranging from hours (e.g., after a human eats a pizza) to weeks (after a python eats a gazelle).

In the simplest form of extracellular digestion—seen in invertebrates, such as flatworms and cnidarians—the digestive cavity has one opening that serves as both an entry and an exit port (**Figure 39.4**). The digestive cavity of these animals is called a **gastrovascular cavity**, because not only does digestion occur within it but fluid movements in the cavity serve as a circulatory—or vascular—system to distribute digested nutrients throughout the animal's body. Food within a gastrovascular cavity is partially digested by enzymes that are secreted into the cavity by the cells lining the cavity. As the food particles become small enough, they are phagocytosed by the lining cells and further digested intracellularly. Undigested material that remains in the gastrovascular cavity is expelled.

Most Digestive Cavities Are Tubes with Specialized Regions and Openings at Opposite Ends

In contrast to the gastrovascular cavities of simple invertebrates, other animals possess digestive systems that consist of a single

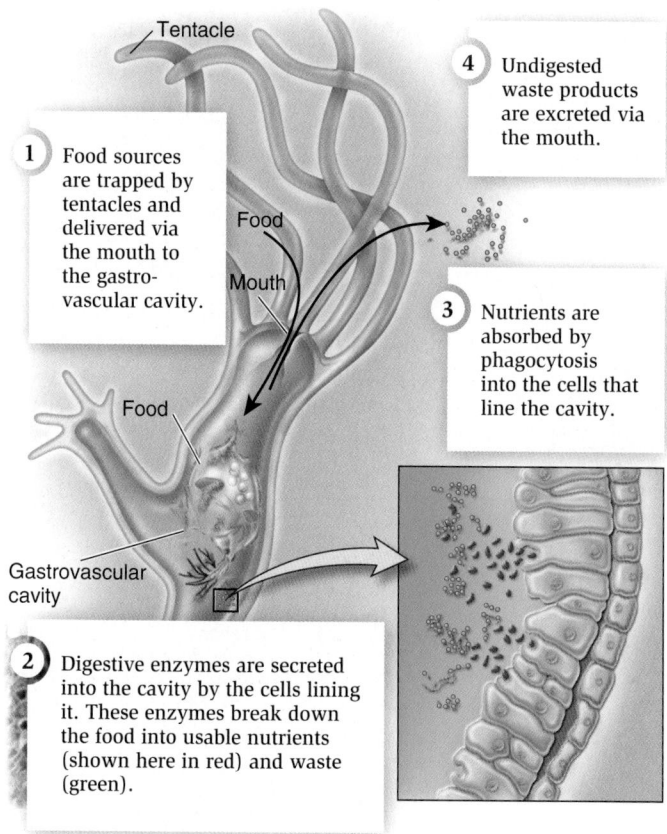

Figure 39.4 **Extracellular digestion in a gastrovascular cavity.** In animals with gastrovascular cavities, such as the cnidarian Hydra illustrated here, digestion occurs extracellularly within the cavity.

elongated tube with an opening at both ends, through which food passes from one end to the other. The digestive tract in arthropods differs from that of most other animals in having anterior and posterior invaginations (stomodeum and proctodeum, respectively); these regions are of ectodermal origin and are chitin lined. Thus, the foregut (stomodeum) and hindgut (proctodeum) are relatively impermeable. The foregut is the site of food ingestion, mechanical processing, and storage, whereas the hindgut is capable of absorbing water and is essential in forming the feces. Between the two regions lies the midgut, which is of endodermal origin, and it is the major site of enzyme production and secretion, as well as digestion and absorption. To facilitate these functions, it often has structures that increase internal surface area, such as pouches or outcroppings. Depending on the species and its diet, a variety of modifications occur along the length of the digestive tract in arthropods to increase the efficiency with which nutrients from food are processed and wastes are excreted.

The vertebrate **alimentary canal**, too, has several specialized regions along its length for storage of undigested food (e.g., stomach), digestion under either low pH (stomach) or higher pH (small intestine) conditions, movement of digested material out of the canal, production of feces, and excretion of wastes from the body. The alimentary canal is lined on its interior surface by a layer of epithelial cells that synthesize and secrete digestive enzymes and other factors into the alimentary canal, and that secrete certain hormones that help regulate digestive processes. Because of these specializations, digestive processes requiring acidic conditions can be segregated from those requiring higher pH, and undigested food can be stored in one region while digestion continues in another area. The ability to store food in the stomach, for example, allows some animals to reduce the number of times they must feed each day.

Absorption of Food Can Be Passive or Active

Once food is digested, the nutrients must be absorbed by the epithelial cells that line specialized portions of the alimentary canal. This occurs in different ways: either by passive or facilitated diffusion or by active transport (see Chapter 6). Small, hydrophobic molecules, such as fats, passively diffuse down concentration gradients across the epithelium, while ions and other molecules are transported by facilitated diffusion or active transport. Minerals are ions and therefore do not readily cross plasma membranes. Instead, they are usually actively transported across the membranes of the epithelial cells of the canal by ATP-driven ion pumps. In other cases, small, hydrophilic organic nutrients are transported by secondary active transport, usually with sodium ions.

After nutrients enter the epithelial cells of the alimentary canal, the cells use some of the nutrients for their own needs. Most of the nutrients, however, are transported out of the cells and into nearby blood vessels, where they enter the blood and circulate to the other cells of the body. Thus, nutrients enter the alimentary canal in food, are digested within the canal into monomers that can be transported into epithelial cells, and from there are released into the blood, where they can reach all of the body's cells. In the special case of water, osmotic gradients established by the transport of ions and other nutrients out of the epithelial cells draw water by osmosis from the canal, across the epithelial cells, and into the blood.

The mechanisms that activate and control the digestive and absorptive functions of the alimentary canal have been extensively studied in vertebrates and have great importance for human health. In the rest of this chapter, we will explore the structure and function of the digestive systems of vertebrates.

39.4 | OVERVIEW OF VERTEBRATE DIGESTIVE SYSTEMS

Learning Outcomes:

1. Describe the general structure of the vertebrate digestive system.
2. Discuss how food moves through regions of the alimentary canal, and how each part contributes to the processes of digestion and absorption.
3. Outline how microorganisms can help digest cellulose in ruminants and other herbivores.

The vertebrate **digestive system** consists of the alimentary canal—also known as the gastrointestinal, or GI, tract—and several associated structures, not all of which are found in all vertebrates: the salivary glands, liver, gallbladder, and pancreas (**Figure 39.5a**). The differences between the digestive systems of various vertebrates reveal much about their respective feeding strategies. In this section, we will look at some of the most important differences as we discuss the form and function of each part of the vertebrate digestive system. We begin with an overview of the form, or anatomy, of a typical vertebrate digestive system.

Alimentary Canals Are Divided into Functional Regions

The alimentary canal is one continuous tube that changes in appearance and function along its length (**Figure 39.5b**). The anterior end, which functions primarily in the ingestion of food, contains the oral cavity, salivary glands, pharynx (throat), and esophagus. The middle portion, which functions in storage and initial digestion of food, contains one or more food storage or digestive organs, including the crop, gizzard, and stomach, depending on the species. Next come the upper part of the small intestine and the accessory structures of the gastrointestinal system that connect with the intestine, including the pancreas, liver, and gallbladder. The posterior part of the canal functions in final digestion and absorption, and the elimination of indigestible wastes. It consists of the remainder of the small intestine, the large intestine, the rectum, and the anus.

Oral cavity
Obtains and processes food

Esophagus
Transports food to stomach

Liver
Produces bile to assist in fat digestion

Gallbladder
Stores bile until needed; secretes bile into small intestine

Large intestine
Absorbs some water and minerals; prepares wastes for defecation

Rectum
Stores wastes (feces)

Salivary glands
Secrete saliva

Pharynx
Pathway to esophagus

Stomach
Stores and mechanically disrupts food; digests some proteins

Pancreas
Secretes digestive enzymes into small intestine

Small intestine
Site of most digestion and absorption

Anus
Eliminates wastes (defecation)

Figure 39.5   **A vertebrate digestive system, as shown in the human.**   This figure shows the organs of the gastrointestinal tract and the accessory structures. Not all vertebrates share identical features of the digestive system; for example, some fish lack a stomach and many birds lack a gallbladder.

From the midesophagus to the anus, the gastrointestinal tract has the same general structure, with a hollow cavity called a lumen that is lined by a layer of epithelial cells. Included in the epithelial layer are secretory cells that release a protective coating of mucus into the lumen of the tract, and other cells that release hormones into the blood in response to the presence of food. Connected to the epithelium are secretory glands that release acid, enzymes, water, and ions into the lumen. From the stomach onward, the epithelial cells are linked together along the edges of their luminal surfaces by tight junctions that prevent digestive enzymes and undigested food from moving across and out of the canal. In some places, such as the small intestine, the luminal surface is highly convoluted, a feature that increases the surface area available for digestion and absorption.

The epithelial cell layer is surrounded by layers of tissue made up of smooth muscles, nerves, and connective tissue. The nerves are activated by the sight and smell of food, and by the presence of food in the gut. Contraction of the muscles mixes the contents of the stomach or intestine. This helps speed up digestion and also brings digested foods into contact with the epithelium to facilitate absorption.

Food Processing and Polysaccharide Digestion Begin in the Mouth

The shape and size of teeth reflect the way in which animals feed (**Figure 39.6**). As stated earlier, herbivores chew their food extensively while many carnivores do not chew at all. Some carnivores consume prey whole (**Figure 39.6a**), while others chew in a vertical motion and usually have jagged molars and sharp incisors and canine teeth (**Figure 39.6b**), all of which are adaptations for slicing and tearing animal flesh. Many herbivores have large, flat molars and well-developed jaw muscles for chewing tough, fibrous plant material. Incisors and canine teeth are poorly developed or absent in many herbivores. When present, they are usually for defence (as in hippos and some primates) or for nipping grass, as in horses (**Figure 39.6c**). Chewing occurs by a rotary motion, which grinds up the tough plant cell walls and releases the digestible intracellular contents. Other herbivores specialize on algae and have cropping teeth (**Figure 39.6d**). Omnivores often have a combination of grinding molars and sharp canines and incisors (**Figure 39.6e**).

Saliva Saliva is a watery fluid containing proteins, mucus, and antibacterial agents. Salivary glands within the mouth produce a constant flow of saliva, which keeps the mouth moist and clean. In response to food, chemical and pressure detectors in the walls of the mouth and tongue increase the secretion of saliva. Saliva production can also be increased simply by the smell or sight of food.

Most herbivores salivate constantly because they eat almost continuously while awake. Increased secretion of saliva can be produced in most animals, however, by a large increase in blood flow to the salivary glands, which occurs in response to signals sent from the nervous system. In mammals, the volume of saliva secreted per gram of tissue is among the largest secretion of any of the glands in the animal. Saliva has several functions:

1. It moistens and lubricates food to facilitate swallowing.
2. It dissolves food particles to facilitate the ability of specialized chemical-sensing structures called taste buds to taste food.
3. It kills ingested bacteria with a variety of antibacterial compounds, including antibodies.
4. It initiates digestion of polysaccharides through the action of a secreted enzyme called **amylase**.

Digestion is the least important of these functions, accounting for only a few percent of total polysaccharide digestion. Nonetheless, it is possible to detect the action of amylase in your own saliva with a simple test. If you chew on a starchy soda cracker and leave it in your mouth for a while, you may notice it begins to taste sweet. That is because some of the polymers in the cracker have been digested to sweet-tasting disaccharides.

The other functions of saliva, however, are very important. For example, imagine trying to swallow a large piece of unchewed food with a perfectly dry mouth. Also, the antibiotic properties of saliva help cleanse the mouth. In people who have had their salivary glands removed due, for example, to cancer of the glands, the teeth and gums often become diseased to the point of losing teeth.

Pharynx, Esophagus, and Crop The next segments of the alimentary canal, the **pharynx** (throat) and **esophagus**, do not contribute to digestion but serve as a pathway to the stomach. The muscles in the walls of these segments control swallowing. In the pharynx, swallowing begins as a voluntary action but continues in the esophagus by the process of **peristalsis**: rhythmic, spontaneous waves of muscle contraction that begin near the mouth and end at the stomach. When most vertebrates eat, the mouth and stomach are roughly horizontal with respect to each other. In fact, the head of a grazing animal is often lower than its stomach when eating. Peristalsis allows propulsion of food toward the stomach without the aid of (or even against) gravity. The wavelike action of peristalsis ensures that food will be pushed toward the stomach and not merely sit in the esophagus or even move backward into the mouth if the head is lowered.

In some animals, food moves directly from the esophagus to a storage organ called the **crop**, which is a dilation of the lower esophagus (**Figure 39.7**). Crops are found in most birds and many invertebrates, including insects and some worms. Food is stored and softened by watery secretions in the crop, but little or no digestion occurs there. Because they need to process large amounts of tough food, birds that eat primarily grains and seeds have larger crops than do birds that eat insects and worms. The material that birds regurgitate to their young comes from the crop. In some species, such as pigeons and doves, the cells that line the crop wall secrete a lipid-rich watery solution called crop or pigeon milk into the material to be regurgitated.

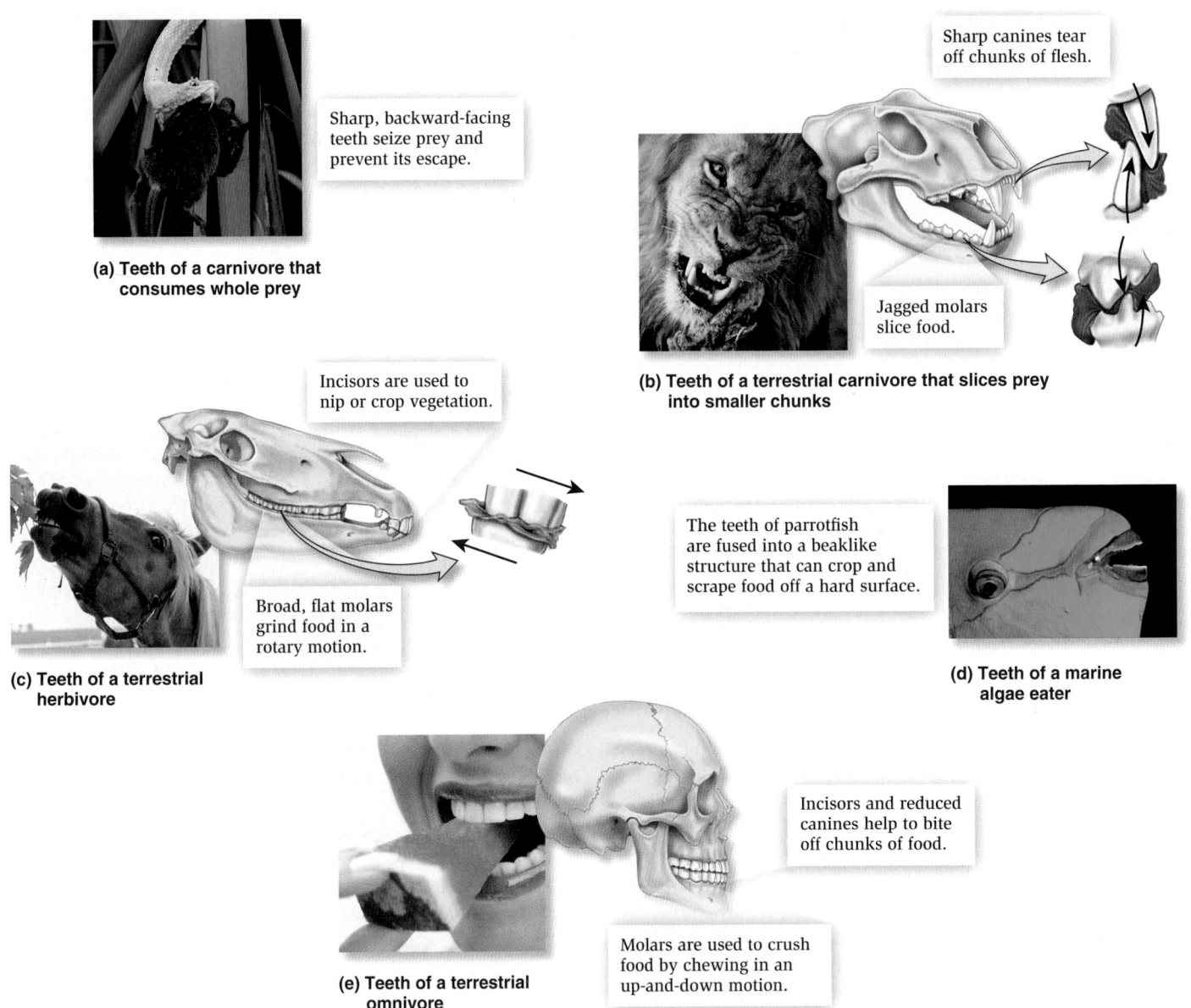

(a) Teeth of a carnivore that consumes whole prey

Sharp, backward-facing teeth seize prey and prevent its escape.

Sharp canines tear off chunks of flesh.

Jagged molars slice food.

(b) Teeth of a terrestrial carnivore that slices prey into smaller chunks

Incisors are used to nip or crop vegetation.

Broad, flat molars grind food in a rotary motion.

(c) Teeth of a terrestrial herbivore

The teeth of parrotfish are fused into a beaklike structure that can crop and scrape food off a hard surface.

(d) Teeth of a marine algae eater

Incisors and reduced canines help to bite off chunks of food.

Molars are used to crush food by chewing in an up-and-down motion.

(e) Teeth of a terrestrial omnivore

Figure 39.6 **Examples of teeth in bulk feeders.** The shape and size of teeth reflects the way in which animals feed and the types of food they consume. In carnivores, teeth may be used for **(a)** seizing prey that will be swallowed whole, or **(b)** slicing food into pieces small enough to be swallowed. The teeth of herbivores and algae eaters may be used for **(c)** nipping and grinding vegetation, and **(d)** scraping or cropping food off coral or other hard surfaces. **(e)** Omnivores typically have a mix of teeth resembling those found in both carnivores and herbivores. The molars may be adapted for crushing hard foods.

Despite the small amount of polysaccharide digestion that occurs in the mouth, no absorption of carbohydrates or any other nutrients into the blood occurs up to this point, except for a small amount of water.

Food Processing Continues and Protein Digestion Begins in the Stomach

The **stomach** is a saclike organ that most likely evolved as a means of storing food. In addition to its storage function, however, the stomach partially digests some of the macromolecules

in food and regulates the rate at which the contents empty into the small intestine. Glands within the stomach wall secrete hydrochloric acid and an inactive molecule called pepsinogen into the stomach lumen. One function of the acid is to convert pepsinogen into the active enzyme **pepsin**, which begins the digestion of protein. Stomach cells secrete pepsinogen, because if the cells produced active pepsin, they would digest their own cellular proteins.

Within the stomach lumen, hydrochloric acid kills many of the microbes that may have been ingested with food. The acid also dissolves the particulate matter in food. The acid

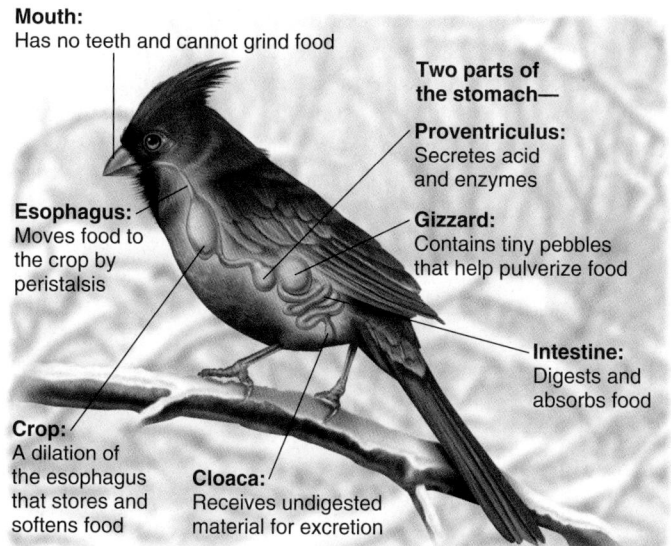

Mouth:
Has no teeth and cannot grind food

Esophagus:
Moves food to
the crop by
peristalsis

Crop:
A dilation of
the esophagus
that stores and
softens food

**Two parts of
the stomach—**

Proventriculus:
Secretes acid
and enzymes

Gizzard:
Contains tiny pebbles
that help pulverize food

Intestine:
Digests and
absorbs food

Cloaca:
Receives undigested
material for excretion

Figure 39.7   **The alimentary canal of birds.**   The avian alimentary canal contains specialized regions for storing and softening food (the crop) and pulverizing food (the gizzard). The gizzard and proventriculus constitute the stomach. Undigested material is excreted through the cloaca.

Concept check: *Smooth, polished stones have been found in the stomach region of fossilized sauropod dinosaurs. What does this suggest about the alimentary canal of such animals?*

environment in the stomach (or gastric) lumen alters the ionization of polar molecules, especially proteins. This disrupts the structural framework of the tissues in food and makes the proteins in food more accessible to pepsin. The proteins released by the dissolving action of hydrochloric acid are partially digested in the stomach by pepsin. By contrast, no significant digestion of carbohydrates or fat occurs in the stomach.

In birds, the stomach is divided into two parts: the proventriculus and the gizzard (Figure 39.7). The **proventriculus** is the glandular portion of the stomach, and it secretes the acid and pepsinogen. Partially digested and acidified food then moves to the **gizzard**, a muscular structure with a rough inner lining capable of grinding food into smaller fragments. The gizzard contains sand or tiny stones swallowed by the bird, which take the place of teeth and help mash and grind ingested food. It is believed that this function of the gizzard evolved partly as an adaptation for flight, since large jaws and associated chewing muscles and teeth would result in a larger, heavier, and less aerodynamic head.

Eventually, the tiny pebbles in the gizzard become smaller as they are worn away, and they are excreted. Thus, birds need to occasionally restock the gizzard with new grinding stones. Grain-eating birds, particularly chickens and other fowl, many passerines, and pigeons and doves, generally have more muscular gizzards than insectivorous birds, because of the difficulty in breaking down plant cell walls. In other birds, such as owls, gizzards help compress the indigestible parts of their meals (bones, teeth, fur, feathers) into a pellet that can be regurgitated.

Gizzards, incidentally, are not unique to birds. Certain reptiles that are closely related to birds, such as crocodiles, also contain muscular gizzards.

Digestive actions of the stomach reduce food particles to **chyme**, a solution that contains water, salts, molecular fragments of proteins, nucleic acids, polysaccharides, droplets of fat, and various other small molecules. Virtually none of these molecules, except water, can cross the epithelium of the stomach wall, and thus little or no absorption of organic nutrients occurs in the stomach.

Some Herbivores Use Microbes to Aid Digestion in the Stomach

Herbivores face a special challenge because they must digest cellulose, but they lack the enzyme cellulase required for the job. Instead, herbivores rely on microbes living within their digestive tracts that do have the capacity to digest cellulose. The microbes break down the cellulose into monosaccharides that can be absorbed along with other by-products of microbial digestion, such as fatty acids and some vitamins. In this way, bacteria and protists predigest the food for the animal.

In animals with simple stomachs, such as horses, the microbes exist in the large intestine, and the region that connects the small intestine to the large intestine is called the cecum. Other herbivores, such as ruminants, have complex stomachs consisting of several chambers, beginning with three outpouchings of the lower esophagus collectively referred to as the forestomach (**Figure 39.8**). The forestomach is composed of the rumen, reticulum, and omasum, in sequence. The rumen and reticulum contain microbes that digest the cellulose, while

Forestomach

Intestines

Rumen

Omasum

Reticulum

Esophagus

Abomasum (stomach)

Figure 39.8   **Digestive tract of a ruminant.**   Ruminants have a complex arrangement of three modified pouches together called the forestomach (the rumen, reticulum, and omasum) arising from the esophagus. The forestomach is connected to the true stomach, or abomasum. The rumen and reticulum act as storage and processing sites, and the omasum absorbs some water and salts. Digestion by acid and pepsin takes place in the abomasum, which connects with the small intestine. In large ruminants, the rumen may store up to 95 litres of undigested food.

the omasum absorbs some of the water and salts released from the chewed and partially digested food. The tough, partially digested food (the cud) is occasionally regurgitated, rechewed, and swallowed again. Eventually the partially digested food, the microbes, and the by-products of microbial digestion reach the true stomach, the abomasum, which contains the acid and proteolytic enzymes typical of other vertebrate stomachs. From the abomasum, the material passes to the intestines, where digestion and absorption are completed. Some microbes remain in the rumen and quickly multiply to replenish their populations.

Most Digestion and Absorption Occurs in the Small Intestine

Nearly all digestion of food and absorption of food and water occur in the first quarter of the **small intestine**, a tube that leads from the stomach to the large intestine. Hydrolytic enzymes break down molecules of organic nutrients into monosaccharides, fatty acids, monoglycerides, nucleotides, and amino acids. Some of these hydrolytic enzymes are on the luminal surface of the intestinal lining cells, while others are secreted by the pancreas and enter the intestinal lumen. The products of digestion are absorbed across the epithelial cells and enter the blood. Vitamins and minerals, which do not require enzymatic digestion, are also absorbed in the small intestine. Water is absorbed by osmosis from the small intestine in response to the movement of nutrients across the intestinal epithelium.

The ability of the small intestine to carry out the bulk of digestion and absorption is aided by infoldings and specializations along its length. Extending from the luminal surface into the lumen of the small intestine are finger-like projections known as

villi (**Figure 39.9**). The surface of each villus is covered with a layer of epithelial cells whose surface membranes form small projections called **microvilli**, known collectively as the **brush border**. The combination of folded mucosa, villi, and microvilli increases the small intestine's surface area about 600-fold over that of a flat-surfaced tube having the same length and diameter. This brings the total surface area of the human small intestine to about 300 m^2—roughly the size of a tennis court! This enormous surface area means that the likelihood of an ingested food particle encountering a digestive enzyme and being absorbed across the epithelium is very high, so digestion and absorption proceed rapidly.

The centre of each intestinal villus is occupied by a special type of vessel called a **lacteal**, and by capillaries, the smallest blood vessels in the body (Figure 39.9). Most of the fat absorbed in the small intestine exists as bulky protein-bound particles that are too large to enter capillaries. Consequently, absorbed fat enters the larger, wider lacteals, which are part of the lymphatic system. Material absorbed by the lacteals eventually empties into the circulatory system. Other nutrients are absorbed directly into the capillaries and from there into veins.

The small intestine has three major sections: duodenum, jejunum and ileum. The relative lengths of each of these sections varies among species. Overall, herbivores tend to have much longer small intestines than do carnivores, allowing added time for plant material to be digested and absorbed (**Figure 39.10**). Even within a single animal, the length of the small intestine can change. In a bird that switches from eating insects and worms in summer to buds and other nutrient-poor vegetation in winter, the small intestine grows and elongates considerably to meet the digestive challenges associated with an herbivorous diet.

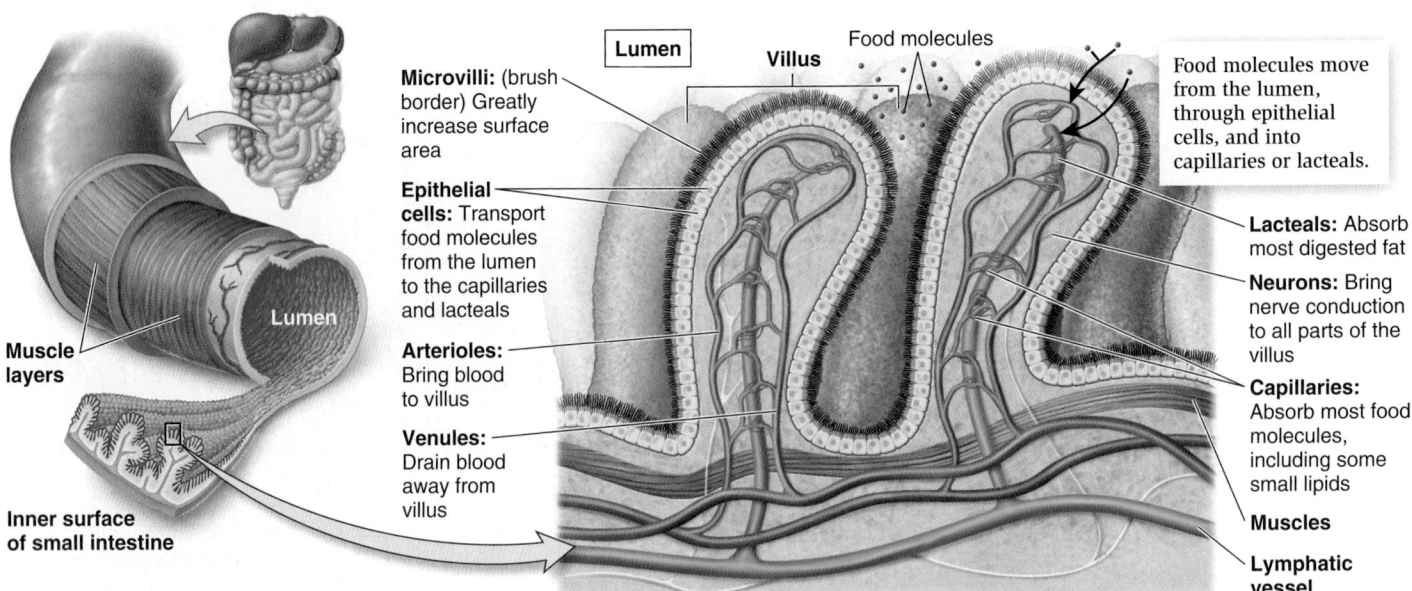

Figure 39.9   The specialized arrangement of tissues in the small intestine.   The small intestine is folded into numerous villi, which increase the surface area for digestion and absorption. Within each villus are capillaries and lymphatic vessels (lacteals) into which absorbed nutrients are transported. The epithelial cells of the villi have extensions from their surface called microvilli that constitute the brush border of the intestine and greatly add to the total surface area.

Figure 39.10 **The alimentary canals of a nonruminant herbivore and a small carnivore.** Note that the small intestine and cecum are considerably longer in the herbivore, adaptations that facilitate the digestion of plant matter.

Red-sided garter snakes (*Thamnophis sirtalis parietalis*), which are fairly common in southern and central Manitoba, are able to tolerate long fasts. During periods without food, the intestinal mucosa becomes thinner and the lengths of the intestinal villi and microvilli become shorter relative to actively feeding snakes. These structural changes are fully reversible when the snakes resume feeding.

The Pancreas and Liver Secrete Substances That Aid Digestion

Two major organs—the pancreas and liver—secrete substances that flow via ducts into the small intestine. The **pancreas**, an elongated gland located behind the stomach, has several functions, but in this chapter we will focus on those that are directly involved in digestion (**Figure 39.11**). The gland secretes digestive enzymes and a fluid rich in bicarbonate ions (HCO_3^-). The bicarbonate neutralizes the acidic chyme coming from the stomach, which would otherwise inactivate the pancreatic enzymes in the small intestine.

The **liver** is the site of bile production. **Bile** contains bicarbonate ions, cholesterol, phospholipids, a number of organic wastes, and a group of substances collectively termed **bile salts**. The bicarbonate ions, like those from the pancreas, help neutralize acid from the stomach, while the bile salts solubilize dietary fat and increase its accessibility to digestive enzymes.

The liver secretes bile into small ducts that join to form the common hepatic duct (from the Greek *hepar*, liver). Between meals, secreted bile is stored in the **gallbladder**, a small sac underneath the liver. During a meal, the smooth muscles in the gallbladder wall contract, injecting the bile solution into a connecting duct called the common bile duct (Figure 39.11). The opening of a sphincter allows entry of the bile into the small intestine. However, many animals that secrete bile do not have a gallbladder. In humans, the gallbladder can be surgically removed without impairing bile secretion by the liver or its flow into the intestinal tract. People without a gallbladder can still digest fat, but they must limit the amount of fat they eat at one time since bile secretion can no longer be timed to a meal.

The Large Intestine Concentrates Undigested Material

The digested nutrients, along with minerals, vitamins, and water, are absorbed across the plasma membranes of the brush border cells. Peristalsis in the walls of the small intestine slowly propels the remaining luminal contents toward the large

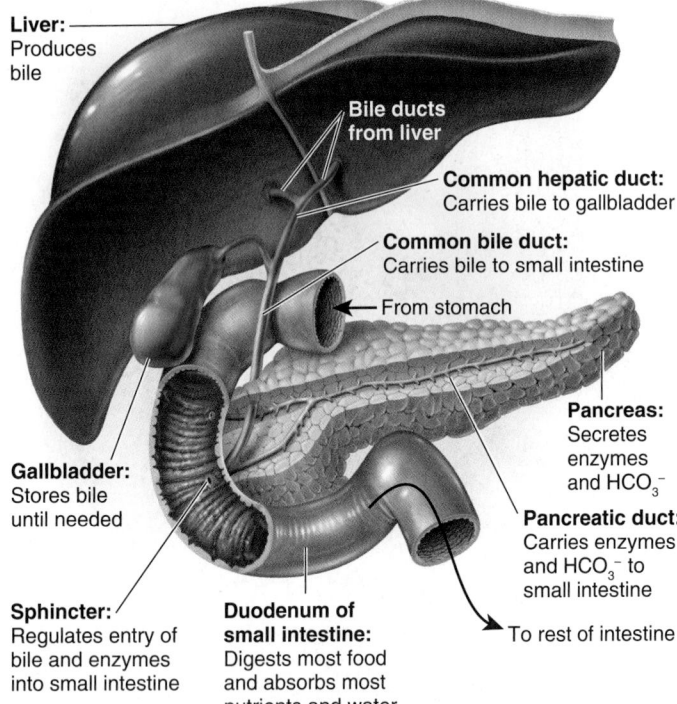

Figure 39.11 The arrangement and functions of the vertebrate liver, gallbladder, pancreas, and small intestine.   Bile drains from the liver into the gallbladder through the common hepatic duct. During a meal, bile is secreted from the gallbladder and enters the small intestine through the common bile duct. Simultaneously, secretions from the pancreas travel through another duct that joins with that from the gallbladder and empties into the small intestine. A muscular sphincter controls the entrance to the small intestine.

Concept check: *What advantage does an animal gain by having a gallbladder?*

intestine. In humans and other similarly sized animals, the large intestine is a tube about 6 centimetres in diameter and a little over a metre long. Its first portion, the **cecum**, forms a small pouch from which extends the **appendix**, a finger-like projection having no known essential function but historically may have been part of the body's defence mechanisms. However, the cecum of many herbivores is much more developed and serves as a storage organ that permits resident microbes sufficient time to further digest cellulose (Figure 39.10). The next part of the large intestine, the **colon**, consists of three relatively straight segments: the ascending, transverse, and descending portions. The terminal portion of the descending colon is S-shaped, forming the sigmoid colon, which empties into the rectum, a short segment of the large intestine that ends at the anus.

Chyme enters the cecum through a sphincter. This sphincter is normally closed, but it periodically relaxes after a meal, allowing chyme to enter. Although the large intestine has a greater diameter than the small intestine, its epithelial surface area is far less—particularly in carnivores and omnivores—because it lacks the convolutions and villi of the small intestine.

Because most substances are absorbed in the small intestine, only a small volume of water, salts, and undigested material is passed on to the large intestine. The large intestine temporarily stores the undigested material and concentrates it by absorbing salts and water. **Defecation** occurs when contractions of the rectum and relaxation of associated sphincter muscles expel the feces through the final portion of the canal: the anus (Figure 39.5).

The large intestine also absorbs some of the products formed by bacteria inhabiting this region, including small amounts of vitamins. Although this source of vitamins generally provides only a small part of the normal daily requirement, it may make a significant contribution when dietary vitamin intake is low. Sometimes people develop a vitamin deficiency if treated with antibiotics that inhibit these species of bacteria. Other bacterial products include gas (**flatus**), which is a mixture of nitrogen and carbon dioxide, with small amounts of hydrogen, methane, and hydrogen sulphide. Bacterial processing of undigested polysaccharides produces these gases, except for nitrogen, which is derived from swallowed air. Certain foods (beans, for example) contain large amounts of carbohydrates that cannot be digested by intestinal enzymes but are readily metabolized by bacteria in the large intestine, producing flatus.

39.5 | MECHANISMS OF DIGESTION AND ABSORPTION IN VERTEBRATES

Learning Outcomes:

1. Describe the mechanisms of digestion and absorption of carbohydrates, proteins, and fats in vertebrates, and the importance of enzymes in some of these processes.
2. Understand how some nutrients do not require digestion prior to being absorbed.

The preceding sections provided an overview of nutrition and the basic features of digestive systems. We turn now to a more detailed description of how each of the three major foodstuffs is processed in the vertebrate digestive system, and how the end products of digestion are absorbed across intestinal cells. In this section, we will focus on how digestion and absorption occur at the cellular and molecular levels.

Carbohydrates Are Digested and Absorbed in the Small Intestine

In a typical omnivore, such as a human, most of the ingested carbohydrates are the polysaccharides starch and cellulose from plants, and glycogen from animals. The remainder consists of simple carbohydrates, such as the monosaccharides fructose and glucose in fruit, and disaccharides, such as lactose in milk. Humans also add the disaccharide sucrose (table sugar) to their diets, although sucrose also occurs naturally, in maple sap and sugarcane, for example, and is consumed by other animals.

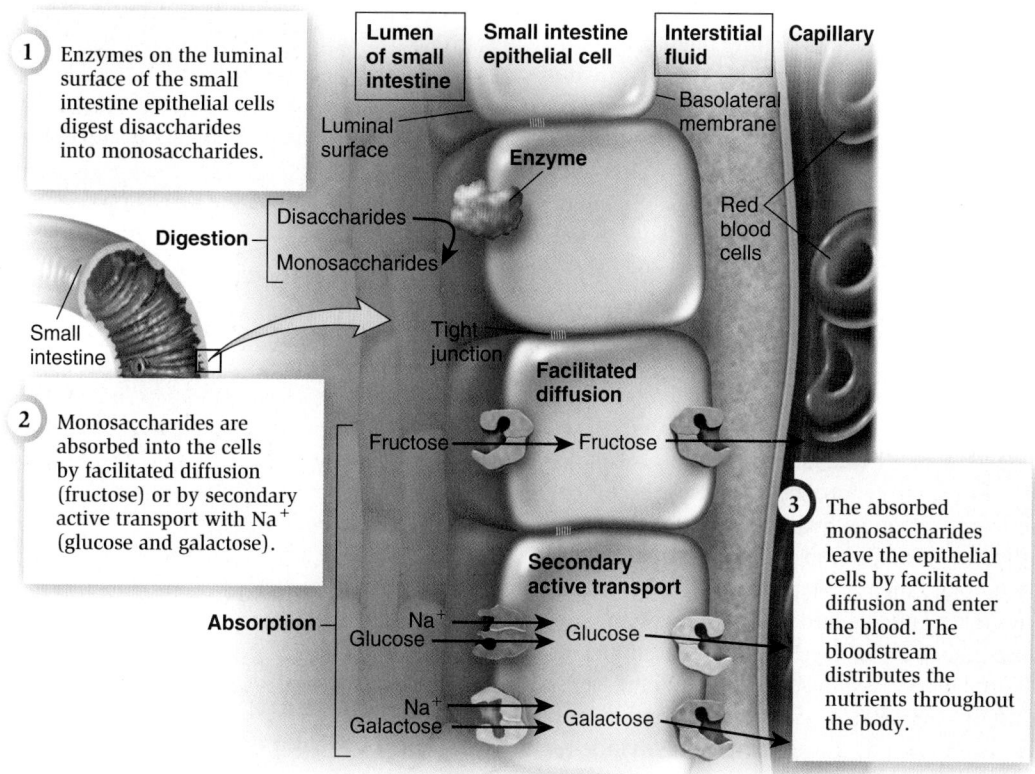

Figure 39.12 **Digestion and absorption of carbohydrates in the small intestine.** Digestion and absorption occur in the same cells but are shown separately here for clarity. For simplicity, the microvilli (brush border) are not shown.

Concept check: *The absorption of many nutrients requires secondary active transport. What can we conclude from that about the energetic cost of absorption?*

BioConnections: *Are the transport processes shown here, including facilitated diffusion and secondary active transport, unique to animal cells? See Figure 6.2 for help if needed.*

Starch digestion by salivary amylase begins in the mouth, but the acid in the stomach destroys the amylase and prevents further starch digestion there. Starch digestion resumes in the small intestine by amylase secreted into the intestine by the pancreas. The products of starch digestion via amylase are molecules of maltose (**Figure 39.12**). Maltose, along with ingested sucrose and lactose, are broken down into monosaccharides—fructose, glucose, and galactose—by enzymes located on the brush border of the small intestine epithelial cells. The monosaccharides are then transported across the intestinal epithelium into the blood. Fructose enters the epithelial cells by facilitated diffusion, while glucose

and galactose undergo secondary active transport coupled to sodium. Monosaccharides then leave the epithelial cells and enter the blood by way of facilitated diffusion transporters located in the basolateral membranes of the epithelial cells. The transport of substances from the lumen to the blood is called **transepithelial transport** because it occurs across a layer of epithelial cells.

Do you feel ill after drinking milk or eating dairy products? If so, you are among the majority of people who cannot digest lactose, the chief disaccharide in milk. A small percentage of humans, however, retain the ability to digest lactose throughout life. Next, we'll examine these phenomena.

GENOMES AND PROTEOMES

Genetics Explains Lactose Intolerance

With rare exceptions, the milk of all mammals contains lactose. A human with lactose intolerance cannot digest lactose because the intestinal enzyme lactase, which cleaves lactose into glucose and galactose, is inactive, absent, or present only in very small amounts. Normally, symptoms of the condition do not appear until a child is several years old.

Milk is the sole food of most mammals shortly after birth and the primary food for various lengths of time thereafter until weaning: the transition from consuming mother's milk to eating a diet of solid foods. Once weaned, mammals never again drink milk, except, of course, for humans. Since the only dietary source for lactose is milk, it is not surprising that older mammals lose the ability to digest this disaccharide. The developmental mechanisms that turn off lactase production and activity are not firmly established, but they are known to involve decreased transcription of the lactase gene.

If an adult mammal were to drink milk, the undigested lactose would remain in the gut. As a result, water that normally would be absorbed by osmosis with the digested monosaccharides formed from lactose would also remain in the gut. Farther down the alimentary canal, however, microbes in the large intestine digest some of the lactose for their own use, and in the process release by-products, such as hydrogen and other gases. The combination of water retention and bacterial action results in gastrointestinal symptoms, such as diarrhea, gas, and cramps. Adult house pets and farm animals suffer the same symptoms and will usually refuse milk if it is offered. The popular notion of cats lapping up milk from a bowl is a misconception. Some visits to the veterinarian are in fact related to gastrointestinal symptoms caused by well-meaning owners who fed milk to their pets.

If the ability to digest lactose is normally lost on weaning, why are some people able to consume dairy products without getting ill? In fact, it is estimated that at least 90% of the world's human population cannot fully digest lactose after early childhood. In other words, lactose intolerance is not a disorder; it is a normal condition for humans, just as it is for all other mammals.

The ability of human adults to digest lactose is clearly linked to genetic background (**Table 39.2**). Lactose intolerance is an example of a human polymorphism, a genetic trait that varies among people. Other than individuals who trace their ancestry to northern Europe and a few isolated regions in western Africa, nearly every population of humans shows a considerable degree of lactose intolerance, reaching essentially 100% in most of South and East Asia. One hypothesis for this phenomenon appears to be a behavioural and cultural change that occurred in Neolithic times, when certain populations domesticated cattle and added cow's milk to their diet. Adults who were able to digest lactose—presumably because of some mutation affecting the expression of the lactase gene—enjoyed a selective advantage and tended to thrive and pass on their genes more frequently than those whose digestive systems could not handle milk. In other words, natural selection resulted in certain populations carrying mutations that caused the lactase gene to be expressed after weaning. Eventually, nearly everyone in those regions of the world retained sufficient intestinal lactase to use milk as a staple food.

Table 39.2	Incidence of Lactose Intolerance in the Human Population
Population	**Percentage of people with lactose intolerance***
South and East Asia	>99%
Sub-Saharan Africa (average)	75%–95%
Fulani tribe (West Africa)	15%–20% (traditional cattle herders)
Yoruba tribe (S.W. Nigeria)	99% (no history of cattle herding)
Greenland Inuit	80%
Southern India	70%–90%
North-central India	15%–50%
Ashkenazi Jews	70%–80%
Israeli Jews	55%–60%
Southern Europe (for example, southern Italy)	70%–75%
Northern Europe (for example, Denmark, United Kingdom)	1%–15%
Canada (average)	6%
First Nations (Williams Lake, B.C.)	63%
United States (average)	25%
African American	70%–77%
Mexican American	50%–55%

*Percentages are estimates obtained from a variety of sources, including the U.S. Department of Health and Human Services. Canadian data are from Shrier, I., Szilagyi, A., and Correa, J. A. 2008. Impact of lactose containing foods and the genetics of lactase on diseases: An analytical review of population data. Nutrition and Cancer 60:292–300; and Leichter, J., and Lee, M. 1971. American Journal of Digestive Diseases 16:809–814.

To understand how this trait was passed on, let's examine the gene that codes for lactase. Surprisingly, the coding regions of the lactase gene and the lactase core promoter are identical whether individuals are lactose intolerant or lactose tolerant. Recently, however, Finnish investigators have uncovered two single nucleotide changes located in presumed regulatory sites that control the expression of the lactase gene. These changes are associated with prolonged lactase expression, allowing it to occur after weaning. People carrying these mutations are lactose tolerant and can consume milk products through adulthood. By comparison, adults who lack these mutations—and are therefore lactose intolerant—can consume dairy products only in small amounts or not at all. However, their ability to do so is greatly improved if the product has been commercially treated with purified lactase to predigest the lactose.

Proteins Are Digested in the Stomach and Small Intestine, and Absorbed in the Small Intestine

Proteins are broken down to peptide fragments in the stomach by pepsin and in the small intestine by the proteases **trypsin** and **chymotrypsin**. The pancreas secretes the latter two enzymes as zymogens, which are inactive precursors of enzymes. This prevents the active enzymes from digesting the pancreas itself. Once the zymogen form of trypsin enters the small intestine, it is enzymatically cleaved into the active molecule by another enzyme, whose active site is located on the luminal membranes of the intestinal cells. Trypsin then activates the zymogen form of chymotrypsin.

The peptide fragments produced by the cleavage of ingested proteins by trypsin and chymotrypsin are further digested into individual amino acids by the actions of specific proteases located on the luminal membranes of the small intestine epithelial cells. These proteases, called aminopeptidases and carboxy-peptidases, cleave off one amino acid at a time from the N-terminus and C-terminus of peptides, respectively. Individual amino acids enter the epithelial cells by secondary active transport coupled to sodium. Amino acids leave the intestinal cell and enter the blood through a facilitated diffusion carrier in the plasma membranes on the opposite side of the intestinal lumen. As with carbohydrates, protein digestion and absorption are largely completed in the upper portion of the small intestine.

Fat Digestion and Absorption Occur in the Small Intestine

Most ingested fat is in the form of triglycerides. Fat digestion occurs entirely in the small intestine. The major digestive enzyme in this process is pancreatic **lipase**, which catalyzes the splitting of bonds linking fatty acids to the first and third carbon atoms of glycerol, producing two free fatty acids and a monoglyceride as products.

$$\text{triglyceride} \xrightarrow{\text{lipase}} \text{2 fatty acids + monoglyceride}$$

Fats are poorly soluble in water and aggregate into large lipid droplets, much like a mixture of oil and vinegar after shaking. Because pancreatic lipase is a water-soluble enzyme, its digestive action in the small intestine can take place only at the surface layer of a lipid droplet. Therefore, if most of the ingested fat remained in large droplets, lipid digestion would be very slow. The rate of digestion is substantially increased by the process of **emulsification**, which disrupts the large lipid droplets into many tiny droplets, each about 1 millimetre in diameter, thereby increasing their total surface area and exposure to lipase action. The resulting suspension of small lipid droplets is called an emulsion.

Emulsification of fat requires mechanical disruption of the large fat droplets into smaller droplets and an emulsifying agent, which prevents them from recombining back into larger droplets. The muscular contractions of the stomach and small intestine provide mechanical disruption to mix the luminal contents. Phospholipids and bile salts, both secreted in the bile, serve as emulsifying agents because they are amphipathic. The nonpolar portions of the phospholipids and bile salts associate with the nonpolar interior of the lipid droplets, and the polar portions remain exposed at the water surface outside the droplet. When two lipid droplets come together, the polar regions of the phospholipids and bile salts coating the droplets repel each other. This prevents the reaggregation of smaller lipid droplets into larger ones.

Although emulsification speeds up digestion, absorption of the poorly soluble products of the lipase reaction is facilitated by a second action of the bile salts, the formation of **micelles**, which are similar in structure to emulsion droplets but much smaller at 4–7 nm in diameter (**Figure 39.13a**). Micelles consist of bile salts, phospholipids, fatty acids, and monoglycerides clustered together, with the polar ends of each molecule oriented toward the micelle's surface and the nonpolar portions forming the micelle's core. Also in the core of the micelle are small amounts of fat-soluble vitamins and cholesterol. Micelles continually break down and re-form near the epithelium of the intestine. When a micelle breaks down, individual molecules are released into the solution and diffuse across the intestinal epithelium. As the lipids diffuse into epithelial cells, micelles release more lipids into the aqueous phase. Thus, the micelles keep most of the insoluble fat digestion products in small soluble aggregates, while gradually releasing very small quantities of lipids to diffuse into the intestinal epithelium. Note that it is not the micelle that is absorbed but rather the individual lipid molecules that are released from the micelle.

Although fatty acids and monoglycerides enter epithelial cells from the intestinal lumen, it is triglycerides that are released on the other side of the cell into the interstitial fluid. In other words, during their passage through the epithelial cells, fatty acids and monoglycerides are resynthesized into triglycerides. This occurs in the smooth endoplasmic reticulum, where the enzymes for triglyceride synthesis are located. This process lowers the concentration of cytosolic free fatty acids and monoglycerides in the epithelial cells and thus maintains a diffusion gradient for these molecules from the lumen into the cell. The resynthesized triglycerides aggregate into **chylomicrons**, large droplets coated with amphipathic proteins that perform an emulsifying function similar to that of bile salts (**Figure 39.13b**). In addition to triglycerides, chylomicrons contain phospholipids, cholesterol, and fat-soluble vitamins that have been absorbed by the same process that led to fatty acid and monoglyceride movement into the epithelial cells of the small intestine.

Chylomicrons are released by exocytosis from the epithelial cells and pass into the lacteals within the intestinal villi. Chylomicrons are too large to diffuse into blood capillaries. However, lacteals have large, slit pores in their walls through which the chylomicrons can pass. The fluid from the lacteals eventually empties into a large vein and from there into the general blood circulation.

Vitamins, Minerals, and Water Are Not Digested and Must Be Absorbed

As stated earlier, vitamins, minerals, and water do not require digestion, and they are absorbed in their complete form. Most water-soluble vitamins are absorbed by diffusion or active transport. The fat-soluble vitamins—A, D, E, and K—follow the pathway for fat absorption described in the previous section. Any interference with the secretion of bile or the action of bile salts in the intestine decreases the absorption of fat-soluble vitamins, a condition known as **malabsorption**. Malabsorption syndromes can lead to vitamin and mineral deficiencies.

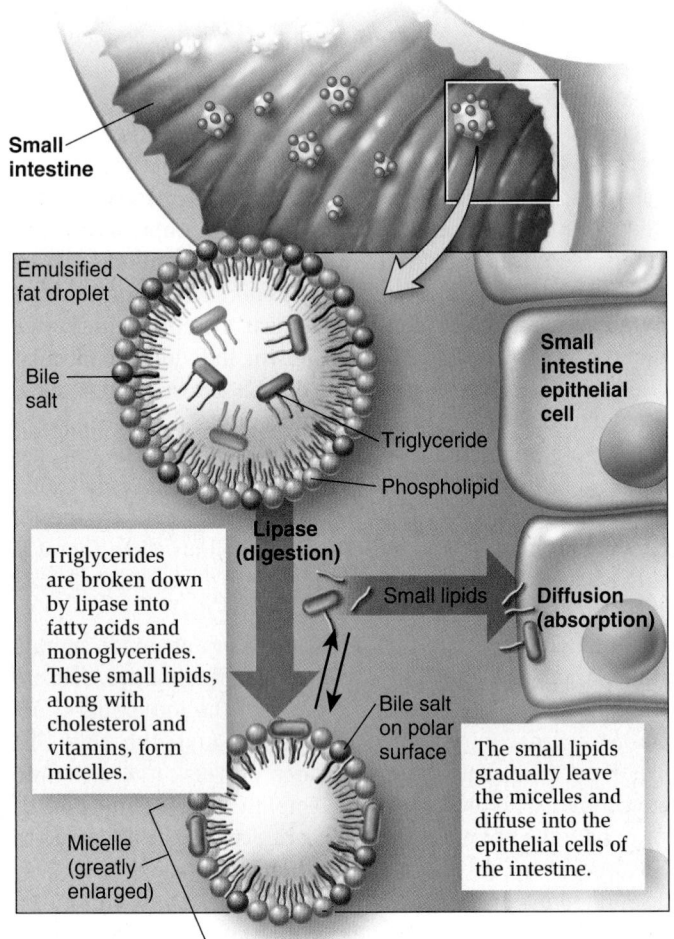

(a) Digestion of emulsified fats into micelles, and absorption into intestinal cells

(b) Synthesis of triglycerides and the formation and release of chylomicrons

Figure 39.13   Digestion and absorption of emulsified fat in the small intestine.

For example, a common genetic disorder in humans called **celiac sprue** results in a loss of intestinal surface area because of sensitivity to the wheat protein gluten. In addition to symptoms such as diarrhea, the decreased absorptive area can reduce absorption of fat-soluble vitamins, such as vitamin D. Because vitamin D promotes calcium absorption from the small intestine, celiac sprue may lead to decreased calcium absorption and imbalances in blood calcium levels.

Water is the most abundant substance in chyme. Small amounts of ingested water are absorbed in the stomach, but the stomach has a much smaller surface area available for diffusion and lacks the solute-absorbing mechanisms that create the osmotic gradients necessary for water absorption. The epithelial membranes of the small intestine are very permeable to water, and water diffusion occurs across the epithelium whenever an osmotic gradient is established by the active absorption of solutes, particularly Na^+, Cl^-, and HCO_3^-. Other minerals present in smaller concentrations, such as potassium, magnesium, and calcium, are also absorbed, as are trace elements, such as zinc and iodine. The mechanisms of absorption of these molecules generally involve transport proteins or ion pumps.

39.6   REGULATION OF DIGESTION

Learning Outcomes:

1. Explain how the nervous system controls different features of the digestive process.
2. Name three major hormones important for the regulation of digestion in vertebrates and describe the role of each.

The digestive systems of animals are under complex control regulated in part by other organ systems, especially the nervous and endocrine systems. Secretions from nerve endings and endocrine glands control the volume of saliva produced, the amount of acid produced in the stomach, the timing and amount of secretions from the gallbladder and pancreas, and the rate and strength of muscle contractions along the walls of the alimentary canal.

In this section, we examine the major mechanisms by which the nervous and endocrine systems control the activity of the digestive system.

The Nervous System Controls Muscle and Secretory Activity

The nervous system can affect the activities of the digestive system in two major ways: (1) control of muscle and glandular activity by the local nerves within the alimentary canal, and (2) long-distance regulation by the brain.

Within the walls along the length of the gastrointestinal tract is a highly branched, interconnected collection of nerve cells. These nerve cells interact with nearby smooth muscles, glands, and epithelial cells located within the tract. Stimulation of nerve activity at one point along the alimentary canal can lead to impulses that are transmitted up and down the canal. When food enters the small intestine, for example, the intestine is stretched. This directly activates the nerve cells in the intestinal wall. Impulses are sent from these nerve cells to the muscles of the stomach, where they decrease the contractions of the stomach. This slows the rate at which chyme moves from the stomach into the small intestine, giving the intestine sufficient time for digestion and absorption. In this way, the alimentary canal can regulate its own function independent of the brain. However, the brain can communicate with nerve cells in the walls of the stomach and intestines, and thereby influence the movement and secretory activity of the gastrointestinal tract. For example, emotional stress, a brain-related event, can affect digestive processes. Likewise, the sight, smell, and taste of food activate digestive functions even before food reaches the stomach. These stimuli act via nerves from the brain to begin the process so that digestion can begin as soon as food is swallowed.

Hormones Regulate the Rate of Digestion

Hormones are chemical messengers secreted by specialized cells into the blood, where they travel to all parts of the body and act on various target cells (see Chapter 47). Hormones that control the digestive system are secreted mainly by cells scattered throughout the epithelium of the stomach and small intestine (**Figure 39.14**). One surface of each hormone-producing cell is exposed to the lumen of the gastrointestinal tract. At this surface, chemical substances in chyme stimulate the cell to release its hormones into the blood, by which they travel to their target cells. These include the cells of the pancreas, which responds to the presence of the hormones by secreting digestive enzymes into the small intestine, and the gallbladder, which responds by secreting bile. One such hormone released by the small intestine is secretin, a polypeptide whose discovery not only initiated the field of endocrinology—the study of hormones—but also

1. The stomach secretes gastrin into the blood in response to a meal.

2. Gastrin returns to the stomach and stimulates muscle contraction and acid production.

3. The partially digested food, which is called chyme, moves into the small intestine and stimulates the secretion of CCK and secretin into the blood.

4. CCK and secretin stimulate the secretion of digestive enzymes and bicarbonate ions from the pancreas into the small intestine.

5. CCK also stimulates contraction of the gallbladder, which then releases bile into the small intestine.

Figure 39.14   Hormonal regulation of digestion rate in the stomach and small intestine.

BioConnections: *In Chapter 38 you learned about the process of negative feedback, which helps maintain homeostasis in animals. Can you make a prediction about the possible feedback effects, if any, of cholecystokinin (CCK) on the stomach? Do you think CCK might stimulate or inhibit smooth muscle activity and acid production in the stomach?*

provided the first clear understanding of how the gut and its accessory structures communicate, as described next.

FEATURE INVESTIGATION

Starling and Bayliss Discovered a Mechanism by Which the Small Intestine Communicates with the Pancreas

The dependence of digestive function on the nervous system and the brain was established by the pioneering work of Ivan Pavlov. Pavlov's work suggested that nerves conveyed signals between the gut and other structures, such as the brain and pancreas, and in this way the gut could communicate with these structures. Such communication is essential for the synchronized release of pancreatic enzymes and bicarbonate ions with the arrival of food in the intestine. Two English scientists, Ernest

Starling and his brother-in-law, William Bayliss, hypothesized that nerves were not the only structures controlling gut activity.

To test this hypothesis, Starling and Bayliss carefully dissected away the nerves in the small intestine of an anaesthetized dog. Next, they directly injected a small quantity of acid into the intestinal lumen, because it was known at the time that the acidic contents arriving from the stomach somehow triggered secretion of digestive enzymes and bicarbonate ions from the pancreas, as shown in **Figure 39.15**. They placed a tube into the duct that carries secretions from the pancreas to the small intestine, so that they could collect the pancreatic secretions. Each drop of secretion was recorded as a hatch mark on a chart recorder. They discovered that even in the absence of intact nerves, simply adding acid into the intestinal lumen resulted in increased pancreatic secretions after a short lag period. Starling and Bayliss postulated that the lag was due to the time required for the intestinal cells to produce and secrete a factor that entered the blood and travelled to the pancreas.

To confirm their results, and to counter the suggestion made by Pavlov and others that their first experiment merely failed to sever all the intestinal nerves, Starling and Bayliss performed a follow-up experiment. First, they removed a section of a dog's small intestine, added acid to it, and then ground it up in the acid. The mashed tissue was then filtered to produce an extract of any secretions that may have been produced by the intestine in response to the acid. Next, they injected the filtered extract into the bloodstream of another anaesthetized dog whose pancreatic duct was opened as in the first experiment.

What they discovered was remarkable: the extract derived from the acid-stimulated intestine of one dog caused the almost immediate secretion of pancreatic enzymes and bicarbonate from the second dog. This demonstrated conclusively that the small intestine secreted some chemical or chemicals in response to the presence of acid and that these secretions could reach the pancreas—presumably through the bloodstream—and stimulate the gland to release its contents. Although it might be considered cruel nowadays to conduct experiments such as these, the discoveries made by Starling and Bayliss at the beginning of the twentieth century were pivotal in establishing that chemical messengers play a vital role in regulating the digestive system. It was Starling and Bayliss who called these chemicals *hormones*, from a Greek verb meaning "to excite or arouse to action," and they named the hormone that activated the pancreas secretin.

Experimental Questions

1. Explain the first experiment conducted by Starling and Bayliss, which indicated that other factors besides signals from nerves may influence digestive gland secretion.
2. What criticism did Starling and Bayliss need to address to provide more conclusive evidence that the secretion was not due to neural regulation. How did they address it?
3. What conclusions did the investigators draw from their second experiment?

In the rest of this chapter, we will examine the impact of digestive system disorders on human health.

HYPOTHESIS The activity of the digestive tract may be regulated independently of signals from the brain.

KEY MATERIALS Anesthetized dogs, surgical tools, HCl

Experimental level   **Conceptual level**

1 Experiment 1:

Anesthetize dog and expose small intestine. Dissect away and cut nerves to and from intestine.

Anesthetic — Dog #1

Small intestine — Cut nerves — Nerves to and from brain and spinal cord

2 Inject solution of HCl (acid) directly into lumen of exposed region of small intestine. Sample duct of pancreas for secretion of drops containing digestive enzymes and HCO_3^-.

HCl — Dog #1 pancreas — Duct of pancreas — Collection tube — Data show drops of enzyme and HCO_3^- counted by recording device.

Outer wall of intestine containing blood vessels into which epithelial cells could secrete molecules — Syringe needle — Blood vessel — Lumen — HCl — Epithelial lining cells of intestine

Figure 39.15 Bayliss and Starling discovered the mechanism by which the small intestine and pancreas work together in digestion.

Figure 39.15   *(Continued)*

3   **THE DATA from Experiment 1:**

Time lag between response
and injection of acid

Each hatch mark made on a recording device is
due to a drop of secretion into the collection tube.

Record of drops

HCl added

Pancreatic secretions increased following
HCl injection directly into small intestine.

0   5   10   15

Time (min)

4   **Experiment 2:**

Cut out a piece of an untreated
region of small intestine from dog
#1. Expose the piece to acid, grind
it up, and filter the ground tissue.
Inject filtrate into bloodstream of
another dog (dog #2).

Stomach

Small
intestine

Filtrate from
ground up tissue

Dog #2

Cut

HCl and
intestine

5   Test for pancreatic secretions into small
intestine of dog #2.

Pancreas of
dog #2

Pancreatic
secretions
present?

If the filtrate from dog #1 contained chemical
signals released upon exposure to acid, those
signals should stimulate the pancreas of dog #2
to secrete enzymes and HCO_3^-.

6   **THE DATA from Experiment 2:**

Prior to the injection of the filtrate into dog #2,
the pancreas did not produce any secretion.

After the injection, pancreatic secretion increased rapidly. Each hatch mark
corresponds to a drop of fluid collected from the duct of the pancreas.

Filtrate from dog #1 injected

0   5   10   15

Time (min)

Figure 39.15   *(Continued)*

7   CONCLUSION The small intestine contains molecules whose secretion into the blood is stimulated by acid. The molecules travel through the blood to the pancreas, causing secretion of pancreatic enzymes and HCO_3^-.

8   SOURCE Bayliss, W.M., and Starling, E.H. 1902. The mechanism of pancreatic secretion. *Journal of Physiology* 28:325–353.

39.7 / HUMAN HEALTH CONNECTION

Learning Outcomes:

1. Describe the impact of heartburn, ulcers, and diarrhea on public health.
2. Identify the primary cause of ulcers.

As we have seen, the functioning of the vertebrate digestive system is extraordinarily fine-tuned by the brain, nerves, and hormones. When people are well nourished, therefore, you might assume that digestive problems would be rare. However, each year in North America, the most common GI problems registered by hospitals and physicians are heartburn, ulcers, and diarrhea.

Excess Stomach Acid Production Can Lead to Heartburn

Approximately one in four people in Canada suffers at some time from **dyspepsia** or indigestion. Symptoms include stomach pain, heartburn, and bloating. The term *heartburn* is actually a misnomer, because the painful burning sensation is caused by stomach acid and arises within the esophagus, not the heart. Dyspepsia is also known as gastroesophageal reflux. Normally, the stomach contents do not move backward into the esophagus, largely because of the muscular sphincter at the esophageal–stomach juncture. However, under some conditions, the sphincter either does not close entirely or is forced open by the pressure of material in the stomach. When this happens, the acid in the stomach lumen enters the esophagus and irritates nerve endings there.

Many circumstances may contribute to dyspepsia, such as overeating, lying down after a big meal, smoking, and consuming alcohol, citrus fruits (which are acidic), chocolate (which contains caffeine, a known inducer of heartburn), or fatty foods (which take longer to digest than other foods and therefore remain in the stomach longer). Another common cause of dyspepsia is pregnancy. Toward the middle of pregnancy, the growing fetus pushes up on the abdominal contents, which tends to force material from the stomach into the esophagus.

Common antacids contain carbonate ions, which buffer the acid in the stomach and esophagus. In severe cases, heartburn can damage the walls of the esophagus enough to cause a chronic cough and pain, or even perforate the esophagus.

Antacids may not be sufficient to treat these patients, who are instead given drugs that inhibit the stomach's ability to produce acid.

Erosion of the Walls of the Alimentary Canal Causes an Ulcer

Although heartburn is usually treated before the acid begins eroding away the lining of the esophagus or stomach, occasionally this does occur. Erosion of any portion of the alimentary canal for any reason is called an ulcer. Most ulcers occur in the stomach, lower esophagus, and the part of the small intestine that connects to the stomach, because these sites have the greatest acid concentrations. Peptic ulcers (found in the stomach or duodenum) are most common in people over 40 years of age, people who take nonsteroidal anti-inflammatory drugs (NSAIDs), those who have a type of bacteria in their stomach mucus called *Helicobacter pylori*, people with a history of peptic ulcer disease, those who smoke, and men. The ulcers are typically less than two centimetres wide, but they may allow luminal contents to leak into the surrounding body cavity, where the enzymes and acids from the stomach can do considerable damage.

In the 1980s two Australian scientists, Barry Marshall and J. Robin Warren, proposed that most stomach ulcers arise from a bacterial infection. This idea did not gain quick acceptance because many scientists believed that bacteria could not survive the acidic conditions in the stomach. However, Marshall and Warren demonstrated the existence of *Helicobacter pylori* in the stomachs of a majority of patients with ulcers, and killing the bacteria with antibiotics proved to be an effective treatment. Once the bacteria are gone, the normal body repair mechanisms heal the wound created by their secretions. Marshall and Warren received the 2005 Nobel Prize in Medicine for their revolutionary discovery, which has improved the quality of life for millions of people. Today, a combined treatment of antibiotics and the same drugs used to neutralize or inhibit stomach acid production in dyspepsia patients is effective in reducing or eliminating the symptoms of ulcers.

Diarrhea Is the Most Common Gastrointestinal Disorder Worldwide

Diarrhea—loose, watery stools occurring at least three times per day—is the most common gastrointestinal disorder worldwide.

In Canada, nearly all episodes of diarrhea stop in a day or two. Typically, they result from viral infections (noroviruses, such as Norwalk virus) or bacterial infections (such as *Salmonella* spp., *Escherichia coli*, *Listeria monocytogenes*). According to the Public Health Agency of Canada (PHAC) about 5%–10% of all patients who enter a health facility will develop a nosocomial (health care or hospital-acquired) infection; one particular nosocomial infection, *Clostridium difficile*, receives considerable public attention in Canadian nursing care facilities. It is also the most common cause of infectious diarrhea in the industrialized world. However, diarrhea can also be caused by food sensitivities (such as gluten or lactose intolerance), reactions to medications, stress-related disorders, or parasites.

One cause of diarrhea stands apart as particularly dangerous. Cholera is a disease caused by infection by the bacterium *Vibrio cholerae*, usually ingested by consuming contaminated food or water. According to the World Health Organization, at least 2,000 people die of cholera each year, with another 100,000 people contracting the disease but surviving. Nearly all cases of cholera occur in Africa, parts of Asia (notably China), and India. *V. cholerae* releases a toxin that alters the permeability of salts and water in the large intestine, resulting in a massive flow of these substances into the intestinal lumen. As in all cases of diarrhea, the chief concern with cholera is the loss of nutrients and water and the dehydration that ensues. In addition to killing the bacteria with antibiotics, therefore, the major treatment of cholera is the same as for any cause of diarrhea, which includes drinking solutions of salts and water to replace those that were lost in the feces.

Summary of Key Concepts

39.1 Animal Nutrition

- The four phases of food use in animals are ingestion, digestion, absorption, and elimination. (Figure 39.1)
- Animals require organic nutrients—carbohydrates, proteins, and lipids—and inorganic nutrients in the form of water and minerals. Differences in nutritional demands reflect an animal's physiology and environment.
- Essential nutrients (essential amino acids, essential fatty acids, vitamins, and minerals) are species specific and must be obtained from the diet. Humans and many other animals require eight essential amino acids for building proteins. The essential fatty acids are polyunsaturated fatty acids, which cannot be synthesized by animal cells. Vitamins are organic nutrients that serve as coenzymes for metabolic and biosynthetic reactions. Minerals are inorganic ions that serve many functions. (Table 39.1)

39.2 Ways in Which Animals Obtain Nutrients

- Herbivores eat only plants, carnivores primarily consume animal flesh or fluids, and omnivores eat both plant and animal products.
- An animal's environment may determine how it obtains food. Suspension feeders sift water to filter out organic matter. Bulk feeders eat food in large pieces, and display a variety of adaptations in the size and shape of teeth. Fluid feeders lick or suck fluid from plants or animals. (Figures 39.2, 39.3)

39.3 Principles of Digestion and Absorption of Food

- Intracellular digestion occurs in simple invertebrates and single-celled organisms.
- Most animals digest food via extracellular digestion. Flatworms and cnidarians have a gastrovascular cavity with one opening that serves as both an entry and an exit port. (Figure 39.4)
- All other animals have an alimentary canal, open at the mouth and anus and segregated into specialized regions, through which food passes from one end to the other. Once food has been digested, the nutrients must be absorbed via simple diffusion, facilitated diffusion, or primary or secondary active transport.

39.4 Overview of Vertebrate Digestive Systems

- The vertebrate digestive system consists of the alimentary canal plus associated glands and organs, not all of which are found in all vertebrates. The anterior portion of the canal contains the oral cavity, salivary glands, pharynx (throat), and esophagus. The middle portion contains food storage or digestive organs (crop, gizzard, or stomach, depending on species), and the upper part of the small intestine (duodenum). The final part of the alimentary canal contains the remainder of the small intestine, the large intestine, the rectum, and the anus. (Figure 39.5)
- Carnivores, which have teeth developed for biting and tearing, are generally predators or scavengers. The teeth and jaw muscles of herbivores are adapted for grinding plants. Omnivores generally have a mix of teeth resembling those found in both carnivores and herbivores. (Figure 39.6)
- Saliva helps animals to lubricate, chew, and swallow food. Peristalsis moves food through the pharynx and esophagus to the stomach. Some animals have a crop in which food is stored and softened. (Figure 39.7)
- The stomach stores food, partially digests proteins, and regulates the rate at which chyme empties into the small intestine. Ruminants have a complex stomach with several chambers. (Figure 39.8)
- Nearly all digestion of food and absorption of food and water occur in the small intestine. The combination of villi and microvilli increases the small intestine's surface area and maximizes the efficiency of digestion and absorption. (Figure 39.9)
- Herbivores generally have longer intestines than carnivores do, which allows added time for plant material to be digested and absorbed. (Figure 39.10)
- The pancreas secretes digestive enzymes and a bicarbonate-rich fluid that neutralizes chyme. The liver secretes bile, which aids in the digestion of fat. (Figure 39.11)

39.5 Mechanisms of Digestion and Absorption in Vertebrates

- Starch digestion begins in the mouth and is completed in the small intestine. Starch is digested by amylases into molecules of the disaccharide maltose. Maltose and other disaccharides are digested into monomers by cells of the brush border. (Figure 39.12)
- Humans with lactose intolerance cannot digest lactose because the intestinal enzyme lactase is inactive or not present, a trait that is linked to genetic background. (Table 39.2)
- Proteins are broken down to peptide fragments in the stomach by pepsin, and they are further broken down into amino acids in the small intestine.
- Lipid digestion and absorption occurs entirely in the small intestine. The major digestive enzyme in this process is pancreatic lipase. (Figure 39.13)

- Most water-soluble vitamins are absorbed by diffusion or active transport. Fat-soluble vitamins follow the pathway for fat absorption.
- The large intestine stores and concentrates fecal material before defecation, and it absorbs some of the remaining salts and water that were not absorbed in the small intestine.

39.6 Regulation of Digestion

- The digestive systems of animals are regulated primarily by the nervous and endocrine systems. The nervous system can affect the digestive system in two major ways: (1) control of muscular and glandular activity by the local nerves in the alimentary canal, and (2) long-distance regulation by the brain. (Figure 39.14)
- Starling and Bayliss demonstrated that hormones play a vital role in gastrointestinal function. (Figure 39.15)

39.7 Human Health Connection

- Common disorders involving the gastrointestinal tract include heartburn, ulcers, and diarrhea.

Test to Assess Your Learning

1. The process of breaking down large molecules into smaller molecules that can be used by the cell is
   a. absorption.
   b. anabolism.
   c. ingestion.
   d. digestion.
   e. secretion.

2. Essential nutrients are
   a. all the carbohydrates, proteins, and lipids ingested by an organism.
   b. nutrients that an animal cannot manufacture.
   c. nutrients that must be obtained from the diet in their complete form.
   d. all of the above.
   e. (b) and (c) only.

3. An animal that has a strong preference for a particular food but can adjust its diet if necessary is said to be
   a. herbivorous.
   b. omnivorous.
   c. carnivorous.
   d. opportunistic.
   e. both (b) and (d).

4. Which of the following statements is *not* correct?
   a. Fluid feeders include animals that consume animal and plant fluids.
   b. Suspension feeding occurs only in invertebrates.
   c. Predators are animals that kill and consume live prey.
   d. Animals that eat primarily fruits are called frugivores.
   e. Blood-sucking animals may have anticoagulants in their saliva.

5. The pancreas connects to which part of the alimentary canal?
   a. esophagus
   b. stomach
   c. small intestine
   d. cecum
   e. large intestine

6. Which of the following statements regarding the vertebrate stomach is *not* correct?
   a. Its cells secrete the protease enzyme pepsin.
   b. It is a saclike organ that evolved to store food.
   c. Its cells secrete hydrochloric acid.
   d. It is the initial site of protein digestion.
   e. Little or no absorption of nutrients occurs there.

7. Absorption in the small intestine is increased by
   a. the many villi that are present on the inner surface of the small intestine.
   b. the brush border formed by microvilli on the cells of the villi.
   c. the presence of numerous transporter molecules on the epithelial cells.
   d. all of the above.
   e. (a) and (b) only.

8. In birds, the portion of the stomach responsible for the secretion of acid and pepsinogen is
   a. the crop.
   b. the gizzard.
   c. the proventriculus.
   d. the vent.
   e. the gallbladder.

9. Bile is secreted by
   a. the liver.
   b. the gallbladder.
   c. the pancreas.
   d. the small intestine.
   e. the cecum.

10. Which of the following is a function of the large intestine?
    a. It participates in cellulose digestion by microbes that exist in the cecum of herbivores.
    b. It stores and concentrates fecal material.
    c. Its cells absorb salts and water that remain in chyme after it leaves the small intestine.
    d. Its cells absorb certain vitamins produced by bacteria.
    e. All of the above.

Articulate to Assess Your Learning

1. Distinguish between digestion and absorption.
2. Explain the functions of the crop and gizzard in birds. Why do mammals lack a crop and gizzard?

Collaborate to Assess and Extend Your Learning

1. What would happen if a ruminant were fed a diet consisting of meat by-products instead of a diet of hay or grass?
2. Specific nutrients can be obtained only from an animal's diet. Why is the list of essential nutrients not the same for all herbivores or for all carnivores?
3. Create a table that summarizes where (along the gastrointestinal tract) each of the following is digested and then absorbed: carbohydrates, lipids, and proteins. Be sure to include the enzymes responsible for the digestion.
4. A principle of biology is that structure determines function. Explain the difference between the alimentary canals of herbivores and carnivores with this biological principle in mind.

Visit McGraw-Hill Ryerson Connect™ for additional study resources.

Control of Energy Balance, Metabolic Rate, and Body Temperature

40

Chapter Outline

A black bear, *Ursus americanus*, hibernates in its den.

I n Chapter 39, we saw that all animals require sources of carbon, nitrogen, and other nutrients to assemble the macromolecules that make up body tissues. Some of the ingested nutrients, such as sugars, lipids, and proteins, also represent a form of fuel, or energy, that can be used to generate ATP within cells.

Many organisms, however, do not have the luxury of a constant supply of nutrients. For example, insects, cephalopods, and vertebrates, for instance, sleep or have periods of greatly reduced activity for part of the day, during which time they do not eat. In addition, environmental changes may reduce the food supply, leading to long fasts. As a consequence of the irregular and sometimes unpredictable flow of nutrients into the body, animals have evolved an array of mechanisms to adequately maintain levels of important fuel molecules even during a fast. In the first part of this chapter, we will explore how ingested nutrients are stored in the body for such times of need and the mechanisms by which these stores are tapped.

Metabolism refers to all the activities and chemical reactions in an organism's body, and **metabolic rate** describes the rate at which an organism uses fuel to supply ATP for these reactions. Different animals have different metabolic rates, which determine the amount of nutrients they require. Indeed, the metabolic rates of vertebrate ectotherms and vertebrate endotherms have a tenfold difference. The greater an animal's metabolic rate, the more heat it generates as a byproduct of breaking down nutrients and using the energy of their chemical bonds to synthesize ATP. Some of this heat escapes to the environment, and some is used to warm an animal's body. Metabolism and body temperature are therefore closely related, and we will examine this relationship in the second part of the chapter.

40.1 NUTRIENT UTILIZATION AND STORAGE

Learning Outcomes:

1. Describe the processes of absorption of glucose, triglycerides, and amino acids during the absorptive state.
2. Discuss the two major ways that vertebrates can increase their blood glucose concentrations during the postabsorptive period.

The utilization of nutrients can be divided into two alternating phases. The **absorptive state** occurs when ingested nutrients enter the blood from the gastrointestinal tract. The **postabsorptive state** occurs when the gastrointestinal tract is empty of nutrients and the body's own stores must supply energy. An average meal in a human requires approximately four hours for complete absorption, and therefore a three-meal-a-day pattern places us in the postabsorptive state during the late morning and afternoon and part of the night.

During the absorptive period, some of the ingested nutrients supply the immediate energy needs of the body. The remaining nutrients are added to the body's energy stores to be called on during the next postabsorptive period. Total body energy stores are adequate for the average human to withstand a fast of several weeks, provided that water is available. By contrast, some animals can barely survive a single skipped meal—particularly if they have low energy reserves—because their metabolic needs are much higher than our own. In this section, we will focus on nutrient absorption, utilization, and storage in vertebrates, with a closer look at mammals.

Absorbed Carbohydrates Are Consumed for Energy or Stored for Future Use

The chief carbohydrate monomers absorbed from the gastrointestinal tract of vertebrates are glucose, galactose, and fructose. In mammals, the latter two sugars either are converted to glucose by the liver or enter the same metabolic pathways as does glucose.

Glucose is one of the body's two major energy sources during the absorptive state, fats being the other. Much of the absorbed glucose enters cells and is enzymatically broken down to carbon dioxide and water, in the process releasing the energy required to form ATP from ADP and inorganic phosphate (**Figure 40.1**). Because skeletal muscle makes up a large fraction of body mass in most vertebrates, it is a major consumer of glucose, particularly when an animal is active. Skeletal muscle also incorporates some of the glucose into the polymer glycogen, which is stored in the muscles to be used later during fasting periods. If more glucose is absorbed than is required for immediate energy, a portion of the excess is incorporated into glycogen in the liver, and the remainder into triglycerides in fat cells. The structures of glycogen and triglycerides are described in Chapter 3.

Most Absorbed Triglycerides Are Stored for Future Use

Triglycerides are too large to diffuse across the plasma membranes of the intestinal epithelial cells. As described in Chapter 39, they are digested into monoglycerides and fatty acids in the lumen of the small intestine and then resynthesized into triglycerides once they diffuse into the intestinal epithelial cells. The triglycerides and other ingested lipids (e.g., cholesterol) are packaged into chylomicrons, which enter the blood circulation. As blood moves through adipose tissue, a blood vessel enzyme called lipoprotein lipase releases the fatty acids in the chylomicrons' triglycerides. The released fatty acids then enter fat cells and combine with glycerol to form triglycerides in adipose cells (Figure 40.1). These triglycerides are stored in fat cells until the body requires additional fuel.

As with glucose, some of the ingested fat is not stored but is used during the absorptive state by most organs to provide energy. The relative amounts of carbohydrate and fat used for energy during the absorptive period depend largely on the composition of a meal.

Absorbed Amino Acids Are Primarily Used to Build Proteins

Amino acids are taken up by all body cells, where they are used to synthesize proteins (Figure 40.1). All cells require a constant supply of amino acids, because proteins are constantly being synthesized and degraded. Any excess amino acids that are ingested are not stored as protein in the sense that glucose is stored as glycogen or that both glucose and fat are stored as triglycerides. Instead, they are converted by liver cells into glucose or triglycerides. Therefore, eating large amounts of protein does not normally increase stores of body protein. An exception would be a young, rapidly growing animal with its continuous increase in body protein.

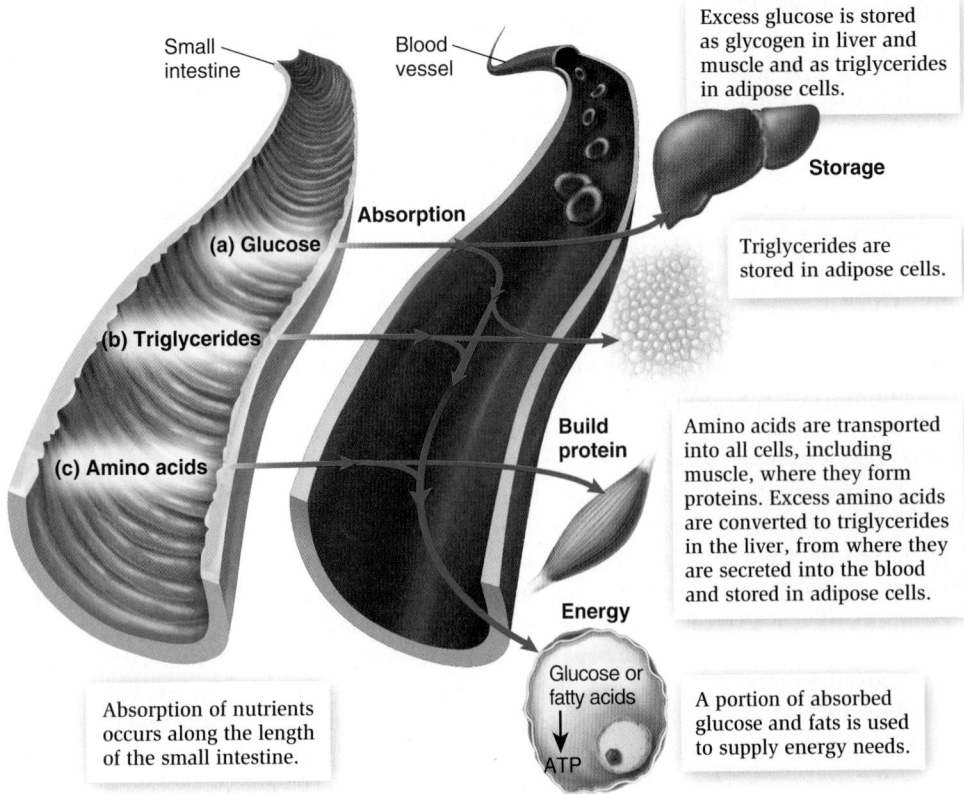

Figure 40.1   Events of the absorptive state. The products of digestion are absorbed into the blood along the length of the small intestine. The nutrients are used for immediate energy needs, or they are deposited in cells as energy stores or as macromolecules important in cell function, such as for building proteins.

Table 40.1	Relative Changes in Fuel Usage and Generation During the Absorptive and Postabsorptive Periods					
	Glucose absorption from gut	**Glucose utilization by cells**	**Synthesis of triglycerides**	**Fat utilization by cells**	**Breakdown of glycogen**	**Blood levels of glucose**
Absorptive period	High	High	High	Low	Low	Normal
Postabsorptive period	Absent	Highest in brain	Low	High	High	Normal

Glycogen and Noncarbohydrate Precursors Provide Glucose

As the absorptive period ends, synthesis of glycogen and fat slows and the breakdown of these substances begins. No glucose is absorbed from the intestinal tract during this time, yet the blood glucose concentration must be maintained because the brain normally uses only glucose for energy. If blood glucose levels fall too low, brain function can be affected, ranging from subtle impairment of mental function to seizures, coma, or even death.

The events that maintain blood glucose concentration fall into two categories: (1) reactions that provide glucose to the blood and (2) cellular utilization of fat for energy, thus sparing glucose for the brain and nervous system.

Vertebrates can increase their blood glucose levels during the postabsorptive period in two major ways. First, the stored glycogen can be broken back down into molecules of glucose by hydrolysis, a process known as **glycogenolysis**. This occurs primarily in the liver, following which the glucose is released into the blood, where it can travel to all cells.

The amount of glycogen available to provide glucose during the postabsorptive period varies among animals, but it is generally not sufficient to maintain blood glucose levels for more than a brief time, such as an overnight fast in a human. Therefore, a second mechanism for maintaining blood glucose levels is required if the postabsorptive period continues longer. In the process of **gluconeogenesis** (creation of new glucose), enzymes in the liver convert noncarbohydrate precursors into glucose, which is then secreted into the blood.

The primary precursor for gluconeogenesis is the sugar-alcohol glycerol, which is released from triglycerides in adipose tissue by the process of **lipolysis**. In lipolysis, enzymes within fat cells hydrolyze triglycerides into fatty acids and glycerol, both of which enter the bloodstream. The fatty acids diffuse into cells, where they are used as an alternative energy source to glucose (except for parts of the nervous system). The glycerol is taken up by the liver, where enzymes convert it into glucose, which is then released back into the bloodstream.

If the postabsorptive period continues for a long time—as when an animal fails to find food—protein becomes an important source of blood glucose. Large quantities of protein in muscle and other tissues can be broken down to amino acids without serious cellular malfunction. The amino acids enter the blood and are taken up by the liver. In the liver, the amino group is removed from each amino acid, and the remaining molecule is converted into glucose by a stepwise series of enzyme-catalyzed reactions. This process, however, has limits. Continued protein loss can result in the death of cells throughout the body because they depend on proteins for vital processes such as plasma membrane function, enzymatic activity, and formation of organelles.

Table 40.1 summarizes what happens during the absorptive and postabsorptive periods.

40.2 REGULATION OF THE ABSORPTIVE AND POSTABSORPTIVE STATES

Learning Outcomes:

1. Explain how insulin acts to control blood glucose concentration.
2. Describe how the human body regulates the use and storage of glucose.
3. Discuss the impact of physical activity on energy demands and the mechanisms that are activated to meet those demands.

Tight control mechanisms are required to maintain homeostatic levels of fuel molecules in the blood. These controls come in the form of several hormones produced by cells of the endocrine system and from nerve signals arising from cells of the nervous system. In this section, you will learn that one common function of the endocrine and nervous systems is to regulate the processes of glycogenolysis and gluconeogenesis so that glucose is made available to cells at all times.

Insulin Is a Key Regulator of Metabolism

The blood concentration of **insulin**, a hormone made by the pancreas, increases during the absorptive state and decreases during the postabsorptive state. Insulin binds to a cell surface receptor and stimulates a signalling pathway that acts in cells to facilitate the diffusion of glucose from blood into the cytosol of cells. This is necessary because as a relatively large and polar molecule, glucose cannot diffuse by itself through plasma membranes. Insulin increases glucose uptake by promoting the movement of glucose transporters (GLUTs) located within intracellular vesicles to the plasma membrane (**Figure 40.2**).

Figure 40.2 Insulin promotes the transport of glucose across plasma membranes. The presence of insulin results in the fusion of intracellular vesicles containing GLUT proteins with the plasma membrane, where they facilitate glucose diffusion into the cell.

Concept check: *What benefit is there to having GLUT proteins premanufactured and stored in intracellular vesicles?*

BioConnections: *In what other contexts have you learned about the fusion of intracellular vesicles with a cell's plasma membrane?*

Thus, insulin assists the glucose in entering cells, which lowers blood glucose levels. Insulin also inhibits glycogenolysis and gluconeogenesis in the liver, because these processes are not required during the absorptive state.

Insulin exerts its effects mainly on muscle cells and adipose tissue cells, because these cells have insulin receptors in their plasma membranes. However, not all GLUTs are identical and not all require insulin for their activity, as we see next.

GENOMES AND PROTEOMES

GLUT Proteins Transport Glucose in Animal Cells

All animal cells use glucose for energy and thus require transporters to move glucose across their plasma membranes. GLUTs in mammals make up a family of at least 14 related proteins that share similar structures but that are expressed in different tissues (**Table 40.2**). All GLUTs have 12 membrane-spanning helical domains that anchor the protein in plasma membranes. The structures of GLUTs are very similar across phyla. Numerous studies have provided evidence that the four different GLUT clusters arose by duplication of a common ancestral gene. At Memorial University of Newfoundland, William Driedzic and his colleagues have sequenced four GLUT genes from Atlantic cod, *Gadus morhua,* and compared them with other taxa. The insulin-sensitive GLUT4 from Atlantic cod shows 84% amino acid identity to GLUT4 from Coho salmon and brown trout, and 65% identity with mammals, such as humans, cows, and mice.

The different GLUTs vary in their ability to bind glucose. For example, some GLUTs have high affinity for glucose and others have low affinity. High affinity means the protein binds glucose even at very low concentrations of the glucose. Muscle and fat express the protein GLUT4, which has a low affinity

for glucose that matches the concentration of glucose normally found in blood. This is also the only GLUT protein whose movement to the plasma membrane requires the cell to be stimulated by insulin. Thus, as glucose levels rise in the blood after a meal, insulin recruits more GLUT4 molecules from the cell cytosol to the plasma membrane of muscle and fat cells.

Table 40.2	Distribution and Affinities of Common GLUTs		
Transporter	**Tissue distribution**	**Affinity for glucose**	**Insulin sensitive**
GLUT1	Cells that make up blood vessels of the brain, red blood cells, embryo cells	Very high	No
GLUT2	Liver, kidney, pancreas, small intestine	Low	No
GLUT3	Brain and nervous system cells, testes, placenta, fibroblasts	Very high	No
GLUT4	Skeletal and cardiac muscle cells, adipose cells	Low	Yes

By comparison, GLUT1 and GLUT3 are found in the brain, where they act in concert to mediate transport of glucose from blood vessels to the interstitial fluid of the brain and from there into brain cells. GLUT1 and GLUT3 have much higher affinity for glucose than do other GLUT proteins and, unlike GLUT4, insulin is not required for their expression. This means that nerve cells of the brain can transport glucose into their cytosol even if the blood level of glucose is very low, and even in the absence of insulin. Thus, if an animal's blood glucose level plummets, perhaps because of disease or starvation, the most important cells in the body—those of the brain and nervous system—would still receive adequate energy for survival.

Expressing multiple types of the same functional class of protein means that different parts of an animal's body can meet their own particular metabolic demands. Moreover, expression may differ among tissue types. For example, GLUT4 expression in starved Atlantic cod decreased in heart muscle but increased in white skeletal muscle. These differences are presumed to be related to insulin responsiveness in heart muscle, whereas in white muscle it is necessary to maintain high levels of glucose transporter protein in the face of starvation-associated proteolysis.

If insulin is the key regulatory molecule that controls blood glucose levels through its actions on GLUT4, what factors regulate the production of insulin? This is described next.

Blood Glucose Levels Control Insulin Secretion

What stimulates the pancreas to secrete insulin into the blood? The answer is the blood glucose concentration. An increase in blood glucose levels, such as after a meal, stimulates the cells of the pancreas to secrete insulin. After glucose is taken up by cells of the body, a decrease in blood glucose levels removes the signal for secretion (**Figure 40.3**). Thus, rising glucose levels stimulate insulin secretion, which lowers blood glucose levels, which in turn removes the signal for insulin secretion. This is an example of negative feedback, as described in Chapter 38.

In addition to blood glucose levels, inputs from nerve cells to the pancreas also play a role in regulation of insulin secretion. During a meal, nerve signals from the brain stimulate the secretion of insulin. Other nerve signals can inhibit insulin, for example, during acutely stressful situations in which an animal's blood glucose increases to supply the active brain.

Blood Glucose Levels Are Maintained Within a Normal Range

Like all homeostatic variables in an animal's body, blood glucose levels are controlled by a system of checks and balances. Several factors act in concert to prevent blood glucose from falling below the normal homeostatic range, even when an animal is fasting. Otherwise, glucose could drop so low that despite the high-affinity GLUT1 and GLUT3 proteins in brain cells, there would not be enough glucose to keep brain cells alive.

If blood glucose levels fall below the normal homeostatic range for an animal, this activates brain cells that are specialized for monitoring glucose concentrations in extracellular fluid. Signals from the brain then stimulate the production of glucose-elevating factors. These include numerous hormones, notably another one secreted by the pancreas called **glucagon**. Glucagon stimulates the processes of glycogenolysis, gluconeogenesis,

and the synthesis of ketones in the liver (**Figure 40.4**). In addition, other factors released by nerve cells and endocrine glands stimulate adipose tissue to release fatty acids into the blood. The fatty acids diffuse across plasma membranes and provide another source of energy for cellular synthesis of ATP. The overall effects are to increase the blood concentrations of glucose, fatty acids, and ketones during the postabsorptive period or during a prolonged fast.

More Fuel Is Required During Physical Activity

Physical activity increases an animal's metabolic rate. Generally, an animal becomes active to seek something, such as food, shelter, or a mate, or to elude something, such as a predator or a storm. The type of physical activity animals engage in, therefore, can be quite varied. When a cheetah sprints after a zebra, for example, the activity of both predator and prey is brief and intense, perhaps lasting only a few seconds. By contrast, a tuna may spend its entire life swimming at a moderate pace, while a migrating bird may fly a hundred kilometres a day for a few weeks.

For any type of physical activity, fuel in the form of nutrients must be available to provide the energy required for skeletal muscle contraction, increased heart and lung activity, and increased activity of the nervous system, which directs the activities of all the other organs in the body. These fuels include glucose, fatty acids, and the muscle's own glycogen.

The liver supplies the blood with the glucose used during physical activity by breaking down its glycogen stores and by gluconeogenesis. This occurs even in the absorptive state, and thus blood glucose levels increase above normal when an animal is active at such times. In addition, an increase in adipose tissue lipolysis releases fatty acids into the blood, which provides a source of energy for the active muscle. These events are mediated by the same hormones and nerves that are responsible for the regulation of the postabsorptive state. Thus, the body taps stored forms of energy in similar ways in response to both fasting and physical activity.

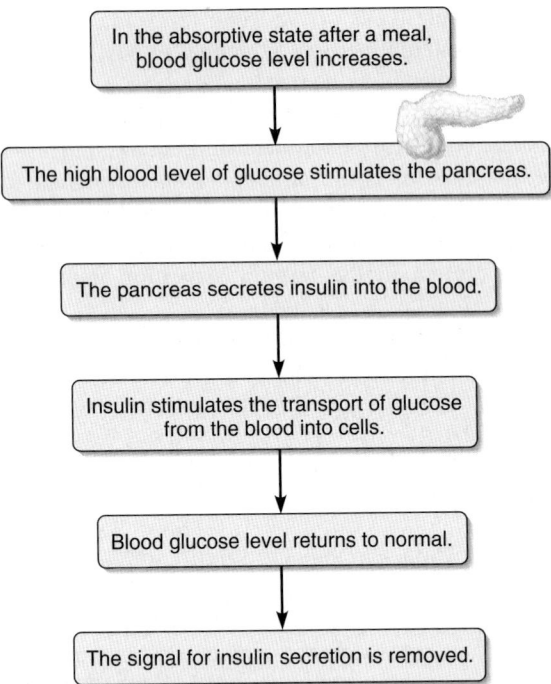

Figure 40.3 **Maintenance of normal blood glucose levels.**   A high glucose level stimulates insulin secretion from the pancreas. Insulin stimulates glucose transport into cells, thus lowering blood glucose levels, which removes the stimulatory signal for the pancreas.

Principle: *Living organisms have mechanisms that maintain homeostasis. Most animals cannot feed constantly and thus the ability to tap into stored reserves of energy sources allows them to maintain the concentration of glucose within a homeostatic range. This, in turn, ensures that homeostasis can be maintained, because cells are supplied with energy even when an animal has not recently ingested nutrients.*

40.3   ENERGY EXPENDITURE

Learning Outcomes:

1. Define the basal metabolic rate (BMR) and how it is measured.
2. List the factors that influence metabolic rate.
3. Understand the role of hormones in regulating metabolic rate, appetite, and body mass.

Animals have a wide range of metabolic needs that depend on numerous factors. Active animals, such as migrating birds, burn fuel more rapidly than inactive animals, such as hibernating mammals. Juveniles typically burn fuel more quickly than older animals. An animal's **energy expenditure** refers to the amount of fuel it uses in a given time to power all of its metabolic requirements.

A fundamental feature of energy is that it can be neither created nor destroyed, but it can be converted from one form

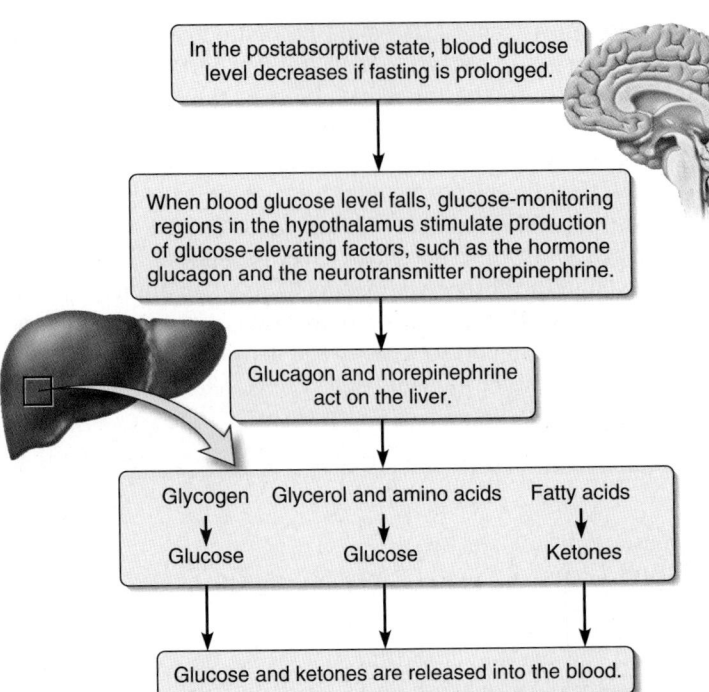

Figure 40.4 **The role of the liver in fuel supply to the blood.**   If glucose levels decrease, glucose-monitoring regions in the brain initiate a series of responses that result in the secretion of hormones, such as glucagon, that stimulate the breakdown of glycogen, glycerol, amino acids, and fatty acids in the liver. The glucose and ketones that form as a result of this breakdown enter the bloodstream, where they travel to all the body's cells and supply energy.

to another. The breakdown of organic molecules liberates the energy locked in their molecular bonds and transfers it to the bonds in ATP. This is the energy that cells use to perform various biological activities, such as muscle contraction, active transport, and molecular synthesis. We refer to these functions as work. Not all the energy is used to do work, however. Some of it appears as heat, which contributes to an animal's body temperature. In this section, we examine how energy expenditure is measured in animals and the factors that control energy consumption and expenditure to achieve a balance between the two.

Energy Expenditure Is Determined by Measuring Metabolic Rate

The standard unit of energy is the joule but, historically, biologists have quantified the energy of metabolism in calories. A **calorie** (equivalent to 4.187 joules) is the amount of heat required to raise the temperature of one gram of water one degree Celsius. Most biological activities, however, require much greater amounts of energy than a calorie, and thus the more common unit of measurement is the kilocalorie (1,000 calories, or **kcal**). (In food labelling, a Calorie with a capital C is also the same as kcal.) The metabolic rate is the total energy expenditure of an animal per unit of time. Biologists often compare the metabolic rates of different animals to learn, for example, how some animals are capable of hibernating, how an animal's body temperature influences its metabolic rate, and how hormones and other factors alter an animal's metabolism.

The most common method for comparing metabolic rates of different species is to obtain the **basal metabolic rate (BMR)**. In the basal condition, the animal is at rest, in the postabsorptive state, and at a standard temperature. For **endotherms**, animals that generate their own internal heat and maintain relatively constant body temperatures, the temperature is within the range that causes the animal to neither generate heat (e.g., by shivering) nor lose heat (e.g., by perspiration). This is called the animal's thermoneutral zone. The BMR of **ectotherms**, animals whose body temperature changes with the environmental temperature, is measured at a standard temperature for each species—one that approximates the average temperature that a species normally encounters. In this case, the term **standard metabolic rate (SMR)** is used instead of BMR, since the basal condition in ectotherms is harder to define than for endotherms. Because BMR and SMR apply only to animals in the postabsorptive state and at a standard temperature, any animal that has recently eaten or been active has a higher metabolic rate than its basal metabolic rate.

The BMR is often called the metabolic cost of living, and most of it can be attributed to the routine functions of the heart, liver, kidneys, and brain. Two methods are used to obtain a good estimate of BMR. **Direct calorimetry** was invented by

Antoine Lavoisier in 1780 (**Figure 40.5**). In Lavoisier's experiment, an animal was placed in an enclosed, insulated chamber that was surrounded by ice. As the animal metabolized fuel, it generated heat, which dissipated into the chamber and melted the ice. The amount of water collected from an opening at the bottom of the chamber could be used to estimate the amount of heat generated by the animal. Today, direct calorimetry is measured by using more sophisticated instrumentation, but the principle remains the same. It provides an ideal measure of metabolism, because metabolic rate and heat production are directly related. However, the method is not very practical, particularly with large animals.

The second and more practical method of measuring BMR, **indirect calorimetry**, is based on the principle that animals require oxygen to metabolize fuel. The more fuel being metabolized—that is, the greater the BMR—the more oxygen that must be consumed by the animal. By measuring the rate at which an animal uses oxygen, therefore, we can obtain a good estimate of BMR. Indirect calorimetry can also be used to compare the metabolic rates of an animal at rest and when active, when oxygen consumption increases (**Figure 40.6**). One limitation to this method is that a small percentage of fuel is metabolized anaerobically—that is, without oxygen and thus indirect calorimetry underestimates actual metabolic rate.

BMR and SMR are indicators of total body metabolic rates. However, not all tissues in the body use oxygen and produce

Figure 40.6 Measuring BMR via oxygen consumption with indirect calorimetry.   Many animals, like this goose, can be trained to walk on a treadmill, which allows scientists to compare metabolism during rest and exercise. Oxygen consumption can be determined by sampling the air exhaled into a tightly fitting mask. One-way valves prevent inhaled and exhaled air from mixing.

Concept check: *If the air had been sampled from the mask just before starting the treadmill while the goose was resting, would this have been a good estimate of BMR?*

Figure 40.5 Lavoisier's pioneering direct calorimetry method of measuring BMR.   Direct calorimetry determines an animal's basal metabolic rate by determining how much the heat given off by its body raises the temperature of a surrounding ice-filled chamber.

Air in

Air out

The guinea pig was placed at rest in a chamber surrounded by ice.

A second ice-filled chamber insulated the inner chamber from the environment.

Outer ice-filled chamber

Inner ice-filled chamber

Collection port from inner chamber

As the animal's body heat is conducted to the ice of the inner chamber, the ice melts, producing water. The volume of water is proportional to the amount of heat produced.

heat at the same rate. Some structures, such as skin, consume very little oxygen under resting conditions, while others, such as the brain, heart, or liver, have high rates of metabolism even when an animal is sleeping. Moreover, metabolism is not always basal, and the metabolic rates of different tissues can vary independently. For example, the metabolism of the gut increases when food is being digested, as does that of skeletal muscle during exercise (**Figure 40.7**).

Metabolic Rate Depends on Many Factors

As just stated, metabolic rate is not always basal. Many factors have an impact on metabolism. These include skeletal muscle activity, whether an animal has recently eaten, body size, and whether or not an animal is hibernating.

The primary factor that increases metabolic rate is altered skeletal muscle activity. Even minimal increases in muscle contraction significantly increase metabolic rate and strenuous activity even more so. For example, the total daily expenditure of kilocalories may vary for a healthy young adult human from approximately 1,350 kcal for a small person at rest to more than 7,000 kcal for a cyclist competing in the Tour de France. Changes in muscle activity also affect metabolic rate during sleep, because of decreased muscle activity, and during exposure to cold temperatures, because of increased muscle activity from shivering.

Eating and digesting food increase the metabolic rate. Particularly in mammals that eat meat, this may raise metabolic rate by 10% to nearly 50% for a few hours after eating. You may have noticed this **food-induced thermogenesis** after consuming a large meal, such as Thanksgiving dinner. Ingested protein—for example, turkey—produces the greatest effect, while carbohydrate and fat produce less. The increased heat production is believed to result at least partly from the processing of the absorbed nutrients by the liver and the energy expended by the gastrointestinal tract in digestion and absorption. Food-induced thermogenesis is observed in nearly all vertebrates, but it is most notable in certain reptiles that eat large and infrequent meals. Because of food-induced thermogenesis, BMR tests must be performed in the postabsorptive state.

A third factor affecting metabolic rate is body size. In general, a large animal uses greater amounts of energy than does a small animal because the large animal has more mass and more cells, all of which consume fuel and generate heat. The metabolic rate and heat generation of an elephant is clearly greater than that of a mouse, for instance. However, when the metabolic rates of an elephant and a mouse are scaled to their respective body masses, we find that the energy expenditure per gram of body mass in a mouse is much higher than the comparable calculation in an elephant. **Mass-specific BMR** is the amount of energy expended per gram of body mass. Mass-specific BMR is a relative term that allows comparisons to be made of metabolic rates among animals of different sizes. Research has shown that the relationship between mass-specific BMR and body mass follows an exponential curve (**Figure 40.8**). One possible explanation for this phenomenon is that because the ratio of an animal's surface area to body mass is greater in smaller animals than in larger animals, smaller animals lose heat more rapidly than do larger ones. According to this hypothesis, smaller animals must generate more heat per gram of body mass than larger animals do to replace their heat loss. However, although this hypothesis appears to provide an explanation for the relationship between metabolism and body size in endotherms, it does not explain the fact that the same relationship exists in almost all animals, including ectotherms.

The smallest endotherms—hummingbirds, shrews, mice and other rodents, and some bats—face the special challenge of fuelling their very high mass-specific BMRs. This becomes difficult and even impossible during cold months, or any time when food is unavailable. Many such animals have evolved a strategy of lowering their internal body temperature to just a few degrees above that of the environment, a process called **torpor**. Torpor may occur on a nightly basis, while the animal continues to be active during the daylight hours, as in hummingbirds, or it can extend for months, in which case it is called **hibernation**.

Liver
Kidney
Stomach
Small intestine
Brain
Heart
Skeletal muscles

Resting after a meal   Exercise

Figure 40.7 **Changes in metabolic rate of selected structures in a mammal's body during different activities.** Red areas are regions of high metabolism; blue areas are regions of low metabolism. Note that during exercise, skeletal muscle becomes more active and areas associated with food digestion and absorption become less active. At all times, however, the heart, liver, and brain are highly active.

Concept check: *Why does metabolism decrease in the gut during exercise?*

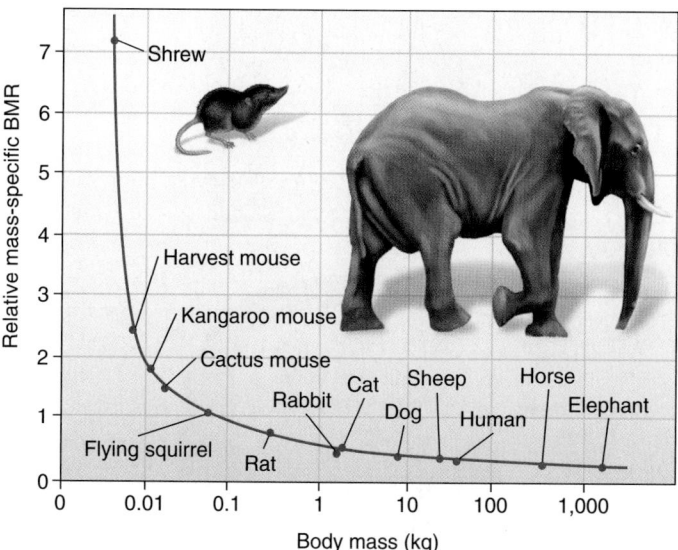

Figure 40.8 **Metabolic rates of animals that differ in size.** Metabolism can be scaled to body mass by measuring oxygen consumption and normalizing it to the animal's body mass (mass-specific BMR). Note that when expressed in this way, the mass-specific BMR of a shrew is higher than that of an elephant, even though the total oxygen consumption and heat output of the elephant would be much greater. The values on the *y*-axis are relative units of metabolism. Sizes of the animals shown are not to scale.

 Principle: *Living organisms use energy. The data shown here illustrate that whereas living organisms use energy, how much energy they use depends in the case of animals upon various factors. These include things such as an animal's life history, age, and, as shown here, its relative body mass.*

Concept check: *Can the relationship between body size and metabolic rate be used to propose hypotheses about metabolic rates of extinct animals?*

A reduction in body temperature reduces the metabolic demands of all body cells. BMR in a small hibernating rodent, for example, may drop to less than 1% of what it would be at the normal body temperature of around 38°C. This allows the animal to conserve energy for remarkably long times. Ground squirrels, for example, may hibernate for up to eight months.

Total Body Energy Stores Are Balanced Between Consumption and Expenditure

When the daily amount of energy consumed is equal to the amount of energy expended, an animal's body weight remains stable. Tipping the balance in either direction causes weight gain or loss; that is, the total body energy content increases or decreases. Normally, energy is stored in the form of fat in adipose tissue.

Body weight in an adult animal usually hovers around a stable set point that differs among species. Body weight is maintained by adjusting caloric intake and energy expenditure in response to changes in body weight. This mechanism usually works very precisely in those animals in which it has been studied. For example, a mammal that eats less one day will eat enough the next day to compensate for the previous day's deficit. Similarly, if an animal is overfed one day, it may eat less the next day, and its metabolic rate will increase to burn off the extra fuel in its body. The hypothesis accepted today by scientists is that appetite and metabolism change when food intake is more or less than the amount needed to maintain the body's set point. This phenomenon explains why some dieters initially lose weight easily and then become stuck at a plateau, because appetite increases and metabolic rate decreases to compensate for the weight loss. Conversely, it also helps explain why some very thin people have difficulty gaining weight.

Short-term control of feeding generally involves a feeling of **satiety**, that is, fullness. As an animal's stomach and small intestine stretch to accommodate food, nerves send inhibitory signals from these structures to the appetite center in the hypothalamus. At the same time, the stomach and small intestine release hormones into the blood that suppress appetite. These **satiety signals** remove the sensation of hunger and set the time period before hunger returns again.

Over the long term, such as weeks, months, or years, total energy consumption tends to remain fairly constant. An animal may go through a period of fasting and then make up for it when food becomes available. In other words, meals may vary from day to day, or during different seasons of the year, but the average amount of food consumed does not change much. Long-term control of food intake is mediated by many different brain molecules, by hormones, and by emotional state, particularly in humans. One molecule that has received considerable attention in recent years for its ability to control appetite and metabolic rate is **leptin** (Greek *leptos,* meaning "thin"). Leptin is produced by adipose cells in proportion to fat mass. As more fat is stored in adipose cells in the body, more leptin is secreted into the blood. Leptin acts on brain centres to reduce appetite and increase metabolic rate. In this way, the brain is made aware of how much fat is stored in the body at all times, and it can adjust appetite and energy expenditure appropriately if fat stores decline or increase.

If an animal fasts, its adipose cells shrink as they release their stored fat into the blood. The decrease in leptin secretion resulting from the decreased fat mass results in a decrease in BMR and an increase in appetite. This may be the true evolutionary significance of leptin, namely that its disappearance from the blood lowers the BMR, thus prolonging life during periods of starvation (**Figure 40.9**). Leptin was not discovered until 1994, but its existence was postulated decades before that by the pioneering work of Douglas Coleman, who investigated the nature of mutations in mice that result in obesity.

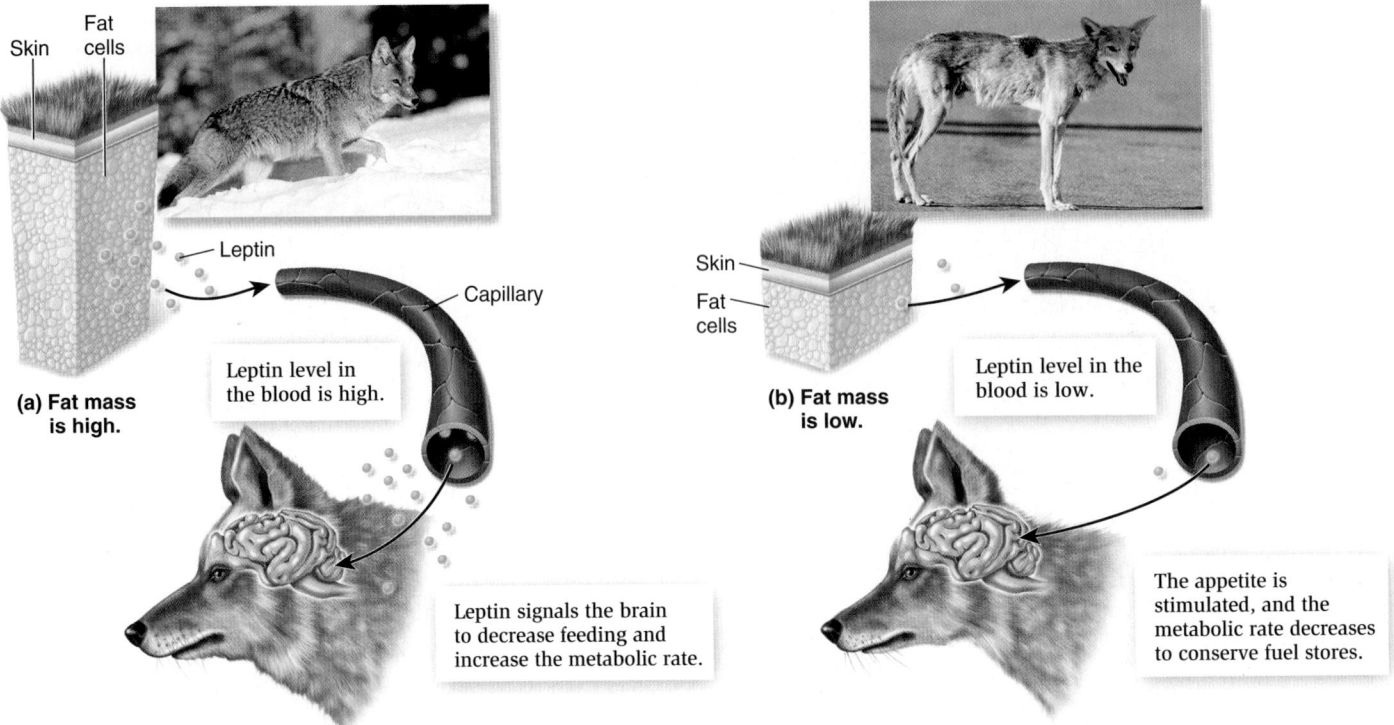

Figure 40.9 The role of leptin in regulating appetite and metabolic rate.   In animals, like this coyote, changes in blood leptin levels result directly from changes in fat mass. Animals with more fat make more leptin.

FEATURE INVESTIGATION

Coleman Revealed a Satiety Factor in Mammals

For many years, scientists wondered how most animals appeared to regulate their body mass around a predetermined set point, despite fluctuations in the food supply. They postulated that other parts of the body somehow communicated with the brain to signal when energy stores were above or below normal. In the 1970s researcher Douglas Coleman tested this hypothesis in an experiment involving parabiosis, the surgical connection of the bloodstreams of two animals, such that the blood from one animal mingles with that of the other.

Coleman used two strains of mice called ob and db mice, carrying different mutations that resulted in inherited forms of obesity. Coleman first connected the bloodstream of a wild-type mouse, one that lacked these mutations, with the bloodstream of either an ob mouse, or a db mouse, as shown in **Figure 40.10**. He discovered that when the circulatory system of the ob mouse was in contact with the circulation of the wild-type mouse, the ob mouse ate less and gained less weight than usual. This suggested that the blood of the wild-type mouse contained a circulating factor that signals the brain when an animal has sufficient fat stored in its body and adjusts appetite accordingly. The ob animal apparently lacked this factor, but when exposed to it via the wild-type mouse's circulation, it responded in the correct way. The wild-type mouse of the parabiosis pair apparently retained a sufficient amount of the factor in its blood, because it maintained its body weight at a normal level.

Coleman noticed, however, that a db mouse continued to gain weight at an abnormally high rate even when parabiosed with a wild-type mouse, while the wild-type animal lost weight. Coleman concluded that the db mouse must produce the same factor as the wild-type mouse, but for some reason it was unable to respond to it. The wild-type mouse that was parabiosed to the db mouse lost weight because it received the factor from the db mouse, in addition to having its own supply of the factor. Thus, whether the factor was absent as in the ob mouse, or present but unable to act as in the db mouse, the resulting phenotype was the same: obesity.

In 1994 Jeffrey Friedman and co-workers at Rockefeller University identified this circulating factor as the protein leptin. The ob mice were found to be homozygous for a mutation in the leptin gene, which produced an inactive leptin molecule, while db mice produced leptin but did not respond to it. In fact, the db mice were found to produce even greater amounts of leptin than wild-type mice, which explained why the wild-type mouse in Coleman's experiments lost weight when parabiosed with a db mouse. Friedman and others later showed that

HYPOTHESIS Body weight is controlled by a factor that circulates in the blood. This factor is absent in strains of mice that have an inherited form of obesity.

KEY MATERIALS Two different strains of genetically obese mice, normal (wild-type) mice.

Experimental level	Conceptual level

1 Surgically connect the abdominal walls of an obese and normal (wt; wild-type) mouse. After a few days, blood vessels from each mouse cross to the other mouse. Monitor changes in body weight. Note: Two different strains of obese mice were tested, called ob and db mice.

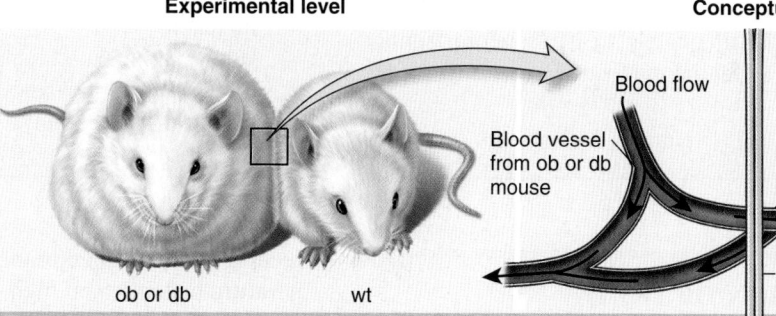

2 Allow mice a normal diet for several weeks, and then visually inspect and weigh each pair.

3 THE DATA

4 CONCLUSION Wild-type mice secrete a blood-borne factor that reduces body weight. The factor is absent from ob mice, but present in db mice. Ob mice retain the ability to respond to the factor, unlike db mice, which cannot respond to it.

5 SOURCE Coleman, D.L. 1973. Effects of parabiosis of obese with diabetes and normal mice. *Diabetologia* 9:294–298.

Figure 40.10 Coleman's parabiosis experiments revealed a satiety factor in wild-type mice that was absent or nonfunctional in genetically obese mice.

adipose cells produce leptin in direct proportion to the total fat mass of an animal. The brain responds to increased amounts of leptin by reducing appetite and increasing metabolic rate, both of which result in weight loss. Conversely, a decrease in blood levels of leptin, which arises when fat stores decline, causes an increase in appetite and a decrease in metabolic rate, which helps prevent further weight loss. It is now known that all classes of vertebrates produce leptin.

At first, the work of Coleman and Friedman generated considerable excitement that leptin might be useful to treat obesity in humans, but this has thus far proven difficult. Why? Recent research has revealed that most obese humans are more like the db mice than the ob mice. That is, they produce leptin but apparently fail to respond adequately to it; therefore, simply increasing blood levels of leptin may not have a significant effect on body weight.

Experimental Questions

1. What observation led to the experiments on satiety conducted by Coleman?
2. What was the hypothesis tested by Coleman, and how did he test it?
3. How did the experimental linking of the bloodstreams of the wild-type mice and the mutant mice affect the body weight of both strains?

40.4 REGULATION OF BODY TEMPERATURE

Learning Outcomes:

1. Provide examples of how changes in temperature affect chemical reactions, other protein functions, and membrane structure.
2. List and define the four terms used to categorize organisms based on their source of heat and ability to maintain body temperature.
3. Identify the four main mechanisms animals use to exchange heat with the environment.
4. Define several mechanisms by which animals can alter the rate of heat gain or loss.
5. Describe the mechanisms and adaptations demonstrated by animals to adjust to temperature extremes.

As we have seen, energy expenditure is linked to body temperature. Next, we discuss why body temperature is important for the health and survival of all animals, and we consider mechanisms by which the body gains or loses heat.

Temperature Affects Chemical Reactions, Plasma Membrane Structure, and Protein Function

For several reasons, most animals can survive only in a relatively narrow range of temperatures. First, chemical reactions depend on temperature. Heat accelerates the motion of molecules, and so as an animal's temperature rises, the rates at which the molecules in its body move and react with one another also increase. In addition, enzymes have an optimal temperature range for their maximal catalytic function. Compared with temperatures below the optimal range, most chemical reactions in an animal's body are observed to double or even triple in rate for every 10°C increase in body temperature. Low temperatures slow down chemical reactions, making it harder for an animal to remain active.

A second effect of temperature is that heat alters the structures of plasma and intracellular membranes. At low temperatures, membranes become less fluid and more rigid, partly due to changes in membrane phospholipids. Rigid membranes are less able to perform biological functions, such as transporting ions and fuels and binding extracellular molecules to receptors on the membrane surface. Alternatively, if the temperature becomes too high, membranes can become leaky.

Likewise, unusually high temperature can also inhibit enzyme function and slow chemical reactions. At very high temperatures many proteins are denatured; that is, they lose the three-dimensional structure that is crucial to their ability to function properly. This occurs because the bonds that form tertiary and quaternary protein structures result from weak interactions, such as hydrogen bonds, and can be disrupted by heat. Denaturation of enzymes is especially serious, because enzymes catalyze many reactions in the body, including those involved in metabolism. Most animals have an upper limit of body temperature at which they can survive. In humans, for example, a body temperature of 41°C causes loss of protein function and breakdown of the nervous system, and a body temperature of 42–43°C is fatal. Birds, which have slightly higher resting body temperatures than mammals (approximately 40–41°C compared with 35–38°C for most mammals), cannot survive at body temperatures above 46–47°C. At environmental temperatures greater than 50°C, nearly all animals die.

At the other end of the temperature spectrum, though, extreme cold is better tolerated. For example, some animals can freeze and survive after thawing. Freezing and thawing is normally dangerous because ice crystals form inside cells and rupture membranes. Also, the ice forms from water in the cells' cytosol, which dehydrates the cells. However, many insects, such as the woolly caterpillar; a few species of amphibia, such as the wood frog (**Figure 40.11**); and a very small number of reptiles, such as the painted turtle, can block crystal formation in their cells. They do this by responding to ice on their skin surfaces with an enormous outpouring of glucose from the liver. The glucose enters the blood and the cells, lowering the freezing point so that the cells do not freeze solid. Other regions of the body that are less critical, such as the lumens of the stomach and bladder, do freeze. These animals can have 65% or more of their bodies completely frozen for long periods, only to thaw during warm periods without harmful effects. The glucose is reabsorbed by the liver at that time.

Ectotherms and Endotherms May Have Fluctuating or Stable Body Temperatures

Biologists classify animals according to both their source of heat and their ability to maintain body temperature. Recall that ectotherms depend on external heat sources to warm their bodies,

Figure 40.11 Adaptation to extreme cold in an ectotherm. Several species of insects, reptiles, and amphibia—like the wood frog shown here—can reduce the risk of freezing by increasing glucose levels, which decreases the freezing point of their body fluids. Furthermore, some species can tolerate being partially frozen because they can prevent ice crystals from forming inside their cells.

Homeotherms maintain a fairly stable body temperature despite swings in the environmental temperature.

Heterotherms have a body temperature similar to that of their surroundings.

Figure 40.12 Body temperature and environmental temperature in homeotherms versus heterotherms. Homeotherms maintain stable body temperatures across a wide range of environmental temperatures. Heterotherms, by contrast, have body temperatures that depend in part on the temperature of their surroundings.

Concept check: *What is the thermoregulatory category to which humans belong?*

while endotherms use their own metabolically generated heat to warm themselves. **Homeotherms** maintain their body temperature within a narrow range, while **heterotherms** have body temperatures that vary with the environment (**Figure 40.12**). Most animals fall into two categories. Birds and mammals are endothermic and homeothermic, while other vertebrates and most invertebrates are ectothermic and heterothermic.

Not all animals, however, can be neatly classified into two categories at all times. Hibernating mammals, such as the black bear shown in the chapter-opening photo, are endotherms. They are homeothermic, but during the winter their body temperature drops dramatically as their metabolism slows to conserve energy for the winter. Hibernators behave like heterotherms during the transition from fall to winter and again from winter to spring. During the winter, however, they are homeothermic except for brief periods of arousal, but at a lower body temperature than at other times of year. Similarly, a fish swimming in deep ocean waters is an ectotherm but also homeothermic because the temperature of the water—and the temperature of its body—is essentially constant. Fish that live in waters with fluctuating temperatures, by contrast, are ectothermic and heterothermic.

Even endothermic homeotherms do not have truly constant body temperatures. They have a narrow range of body temperature that increases or decreases slightly in extreme climates, during exercise, or even during sleep. The important feature is that birds and mammals can quickly adjust the body's mechanisms for retaining or releasing heat such that body temperature remains relatively stable. This provides the advantage that the body's chemical reactions are at optimal levels even when the environment imposes extreme challenges. The metabolic rate of a resting mammal, for example, is roughly six times greater than that of a comparably sized reptile. A suddenly awakened

mammal is instantly capable of intense activity even on a winter day, but an icy-cold reptile could be at the mercy of a predator because of the time required to warm itself and flee.

Endothermy does have two major disadvantages, however. First, to produce sufficient heat through metabolic processes, endotherms must consume larger amounts of food to provide substrates for ATP production. Small endotherms with high BMRs, such as shrews, must eat almost continually and may die if deprived of food for as little as a day. By contrast, many ectotherms, such as snakes, can go for weeks without eating. Second, endotherms run the risk of overheating during periods of intense activity, even in cold weather.

Animals Exchange Heat with the Environment in Four Ways

The surface of an animal's body can lose or gain heat from the external environment via four mechanisms: radiation, conduction, convection, and evaporation (**Figure 40.13**).

Radiation is the emission of electromagnetic waves by the surfaces of objects. The rate of emission is determined by the temperature of the radiating surface. Thus, if the body surface is warmer than the environment, the body loses heat at a rate that depends on the temperature difference. If the outside temperature is warmer than body temperature, the body gains heat, for instance, from sunlight. We can observe radiated heat from an animal's body with imaging devices that detect infrared light (**Figure 40.14**).

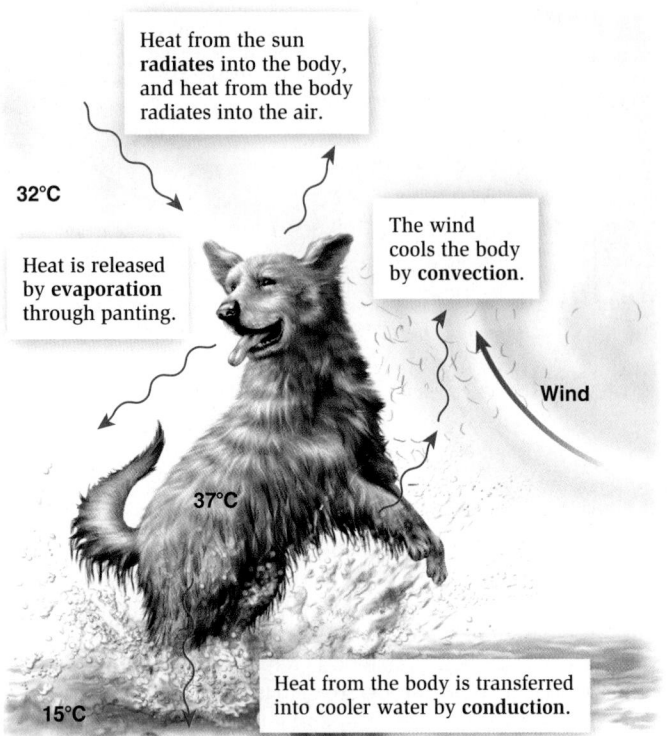

Heat from the sun **radiates** into the body, and heat from the body radiates into the air.

32°C

Heat is released by **evaporation** through panting.

The wind cools the body by **convection**.

Wind

37°C

15°C

Heat from the body is transferred into cooler water by **conduction**.

Figure 40.13   The four ways in which animals exchange heat with the environment are radiation, evaporation, convection, and conduction.

In **conduction**, the body surface loses or gains heat through direct contact with cooler or warmer substances. The greater the temperature difference, the greater the rate of heat transfer. Different materials have different abilities to absorb heat, however. As we saw in Chapter 2, water has a higher heat capacity than air,

| 37.0° C |
| 36.1 |
| 35.2 |
| 34.3 |
| 33.4 |
| 32.5 |
| 31.6 |
| 30.7 |
| 29.8 |
| 28.9 |
| 28.0° C |

Figure 40.14   Visualization of heat exchange in an ectotherm and an endotherm.   Dr. Glenn Tattersall of Brock University took this photograph by using a thermal-imaging camera. Note the cold skin of the snake versus the warm surface of the mouse, although they are both at the same environmental temperature. Note also that the tips of the mouse's ears are cooler than its body.

meaning that at any temperature water will retain greater amounts of heat than will air. Thus, aquatic animals in water that is 10°C lose considerably more heat in a short time than terrestrial animals in air that is 10°C. Indeed, on a hot day, terrestrial animals can lose heat efficiently by immersing themselves in cooler water. An animal's body surface area plays an important role in the rate of heat conduction across its body surface. In some animals, certain body regions are particularly good heat conductors, such as the ears of an elephant or the wings of a bat (**Figure 40.15**).

Convection is the transfer of heat by the movement of air or water next to the body. For example, the air close to an endotherm's body is heated by conduction. Since warm air is less dense than cold air, the warm air near the body rises and carries away heat by convection. Convection is aided by creating currents of air around an animal's body. Humans do this by sitting near fans, but other animals can create cooling air currents by other means, such as when a bat flaps its wings or an elephant waves its ears.

Animals can also lose body heat through **evaporation** of water from the skin and membranes lining the respiratory tract, including the surface of the tongue. A large amount of energy in the form of heat is required to transform water from the liquid to the gaseous state. Thus, whenever water vaporizes from the body's surface, the heat required to drive the process is conducted from the surface, thereby cooling the animal.

The four processes of heat transfer just described can be regulated in animals, such that heat is retained within the body at some times and lost at other times, as we see next.

Several Mechanisms Can Alter Rates of Heat Gain or Loss

For purposes of temperature control, think of the body as a central core surrounded by a shell consisting of skin and subcutaneous (just below the skin) tissue. The temperature of the central core of endotherms is regulated at approximately 37–40°C, but the temperature of the outer surface of the skin varies considerably. If the skin were a perfect insulator, the body would never lose or gain heat by conduction. The skin does not insulate completely,

(a)   (b)

Figure 40.15   Striking examples where high surface area releases heat.   Structures with a large surface area, such as (a) the elephant's ears and (b) the bat's wings, aid the conduction of heat from an animal's body into the surrounding air.

however, so the temperature of its outer surface generally is somewhere between that of the external environment and the core. Only in animals that store large amounts of subcutaneous fat (blubber) does the body surface provide considerable insulation. In endotherms without blubber, the main form of insulation is a covering of hair, fur, or feathers, which traps heat from the body in a layer of warm air near the skin, reducing heat loss.

Changes in Skin Blood Flow Rather than acting as an insulator in most animals, the skin functions as a heat exchanger that can be adjusted to increase or decrease heat loss from the body. As more blood reaches the skin from the core, the skin's temperature approaches that of the core. In effect, blood vessels deliver heat to the skin surface, some of which is lost by conduction to the external environment (**Figure 40.16**). Temperature-sensitive nerves and smooth muscles largely control the opening and closing of these blood vessels. Diving birds and mammals are good examples of this mechanism. Ducks, seals, and walruses dramatically reduce the amount of blood flowing to the skin when they dive in cold waters. This allows them to retain body heat that would otherwise be conducted into the water. In many terrestrial endotherms, certain areas of skin play a more prominent role in heat exchange than others—recall the elephant ears and bat wings mentioned earlier—so skin temperature varies with location.

Countercurrent Heat Exchange Many endotherms and ectotherms regulate heat loss to the environment through **countercurrent heat exchange**, in which heat is transferred between fluids flowing in opposite directions. Countercurrent exchange regulates heat loss to the environment by returning heat to the body's core and keeping the core much warmer than the extremities. In endotherms, countercurrent heat exchange occurs primarily in the extremities—the flippers of dolphins, for example, or the legs of birds and certain other terrestrial animals (**Figure 40.17a**). As warm blood travels through arteries down a bird's leg, heat moves by conduction from the artery to adjacent veins that are carrying cooler blood in the other direction (**Figure 40.17b**). By the time the arterial blood reaches the tip of the leg, its temperature has dropped considerably, reducing the amount of heat lost to the environment and returning the heat to the body's core.

(a) Countercurrent heat exchange in the leg of an endotherm

(b) Cross section and surface view of veins covering an artery

Figure 40.17 Countercurrent heat exchange. **(a)** Countercurrent exchange retains heat in the leg of an endotherm, such as this egret. Arrows in vessels indicate direction of blood flow. **(b)** An SEM of the arrangement of veins surrounding an artery in a bird's leg. The artery is almost completely covered by overlying veins, allowing efficient heat exchange between the vessels.

Figure 40.16 Regulation of heat exchange in the skin. As shown in this schematic illustration, the skin functions as a variable heat exchanger. The arrows in the blood vessels indicate direction of blood flow.

Internet. A lack of exercise is associated with fat accumulation because of a reduction in daily energy expenditure. Children are at risk of becoming overweight or obese because many have fewer opportunities to be physically active at school, and fewer children walk to and from school every day.

The Government of Canada provides a number of web-based resources for healthy living that address the need for healthy eating (www.healthycanadians.ca) and for promoting the health benefits of regular physical activity (www.phac-aspc .gc.ca/pau-uap/fitness/about.html).

Summary of Key Concepts

40.1 Nutrient Utilization and Storage

- From an energetic point of view, an animal's life can be divided into two phases: the absorptive state, during which ingested nutrients are entering the blood from the gastrointestinal tract, and the postabsorptive state, during which the GI tract is empty of nutrients and the body's own stores must supply energy.

- Glucose and fats are the body's two major energy sources during the absorptive state. Much of the absorbed glucose immediately enters cells and is enzymatically broken down to carbon dioxide and water, in the process providing the energy required to synthesize ATP. Most absorbed triglycerides are stored in fat cells until the body requires additional energy. Amino acids are taken up by all body cells, where they are used to synthesize proteins. (Figure 40.1)

- The events that maintain blood glucose concentration fall into two categories: (1) reactions that provide glucose to the blood and (2) cellular use of fat for energy, which spares glucose for use by the nervous system. An animal can increase its blood glucose levels during the postabsorptive period via glycogenolysis or gluconeogenesis. Most organs and tissues reduce their glucose use and increase their fat use during this time. (Table 40.1)

40.2 Regulation of the Absorptive and Postabsorptive States

- Tight control mechanisms, in the form of several hormones and the nervous system, maintain homeostatic levels of fuel in the blood. The hormone insulin acts on cells to facilitate the diffusion of glucose from blood into the cell cytosol. (Figure 40.2)

- All animal cells use glucose transporter proteins (GLUTs) to move glucose across their plasma membranes. In vertebrates, an increase in blood glucose levels stimulates the cells of the pancreas to secrete insulin, and a decrease in glucose removes the signal for secretion. (Table 40.2, Figures 40.3, 40.4)

- Physical activity increases an animal's metabolic rate, thereby increasing its requirement for nutrients to provide energy. The source of these nutrients includes glucose and fatty acids.

40.3 Energy Expenditure

- The most common method for comparing metabolic rates of different species is to compare the basal metabolic rate (BMR), most of which is due to the routine functions of the heart, liver, kidneys, and brain. (Figures 40.5, 40.6)

- Many factors have an impact on metabolism, including skeletal muscle activity, whether an animal has recently eaten, and body size. (Figures 40.7, 40.8)

- Short-term control of feeding generally involves satiety signals that remove the sensation of hunger and set the time before hunger returns again. Experiments by Coleman and Friedman investigated leptin as a satiety factor in mammals. Leptin has since been found in all classes of vertebrates. (Figures 40.9, 40.10)

40.4 Regulation of Body Temperature

- Most animals can survive only in a relatively narrow temperature range that allows molecules in the body to move and react with one another, maintains the structures of membranes, and avoids denaturing proteins. (Figure 40.11)

- Animals can be classified according to their source of heat and their ability to maintain body temperature. Ectotherms depend on external heat sources to warm their bodies, while endotherms use their own metabolically generated heat to warm themselves. Homeotherms maintain their body temperature within a narrow range, while heterotherms have body temperatures that vary with the environment. All animals fall into two of these categories. (Figure 40.12)

- The surface of an animal's body can lose or gain heat from the external environment via four mechanisms: radiation, conduction, convection, and evaporation. (Figures 40.13, 40.14, 40.15)

- Blood vessels deliver heat to the skin surface to be lost by conduction to the external environment. Both endotherms and ectotherms regulate heat loss through countercurrent heat exchange, which conserves heat by returning it to the body's core and keeping it warmer than the extremities. Heat exchange can also be regulated by changing the rate of water evaporation via perspiration. Behavioural mechanisms can alter heat loss by radiation, conduction, and convection. (Figures 40.16, 40.17, 40.18)

40.5 Human Health Connection

- Excess body fat increases the risk of many diseases. A body mass index (BMI) of 25 or more is generally considered overweight, while a BMI of 30 or greater is considered obese.

Test to Assess Your Learning

1. During the absorptive phase, an animal is
   a. fasting.
   b. relying on stored molecules for energy.
   c. absorbing nutrients from a recently ingested meal.
   d. metabolizing lipids stored in adipose tissue to supply ATP to its cells.
   e. both (a) and (b).

2. Gluconeogenesis occurs when
   a. the liver synthesizes glucose from noncarbohydrate precursors.
   b. glycogen is broken down to glucose.
   c. an animal is in the absorptive phase.
   d. triglycerides are being stored in adipose cells.
   e. none of the above.

3. During _____, most tissues of the body increase metabolism of fat to ensure that _____ tissue has an adequate supply of glucose.
   a. gluconeogenesis, muscle
   b. glucose sparing, epithelial
   c. gluconeogenesis, nervous system
   d. glucose sparing, nervous system
   e. gluconeogenesis, epithelial

4. Ketones are compounds derived from
   a. glucose.
   b. glycogen.
   c. fatty acids.
   d. amino acids.
   e. proteins.

5. Insulin primarily regulates blood glucose levels by
   a. stimulating the recruitment of glucose transporter proteins from the cytosol to the plasma membrane for transport of glucose from extracellular to intracellular fluid.
   b. stimulating gluconeogenesis.
   c. suppressing glucose uptake by muscle tissue.
   d. stimulating the release of glucose from glycogen reserves.
   e. none of the above.

6. The rate at which the body uses fuel to synthesize ATP, which is used for all the activities and chemical reactions occurring in an animal's body, is
   a. body mass index.
   b. an animal's energy consumption.
   c. metabolic rate.
   d. an animal's energy expenditure.
   e. both (c) and (d).

7. Which factor may affect metabolic rate?
   a. muscle activity
   b. food-induced thermogenesis
   c. an animal's body size
   d. fasting
   e. all of the above

8. The molecule that has an effect on brain centres in reducing appetite and increasing metabolic rate is
   a. GLUT.
   b. insulin.
   c. leptin.
   d. glycogen.
   e. ketones.

9. Animals that have body temperatures that are maintained within a very narrow range are
   a. endotherms.
   b. ectotherms.
   c. homeotherms.
   d. heterotherms.
   e. both (b) and (d).

10. The rate of heat loss is regulated by
    a. the degree of blood flow at the surface of the skin.
    b. the level of perspiration.
    c. behavioural adaptations.
    d. all of the above.
    e. (a) and (b) only.

Articulate to Assess Your Learning

1. Describe the function of insulin and explain what would happen if the body received too little insulin or too much insulin.

2. Explain how appetite is controlled. Does this explain why extremely obese people are generally unable to lose weight by dieting alone?

Collaborate to Assess and Extend Your Learning

1. Discuss the differences between being ectothermic and endothermic, and being heterothermic and homeothermic.

2. Use the information in Figures 40.3 and 40.4 to construct a homeostatic feedback loop that explains how blood glucose levels are maintained within normal levels.

3. A principle of biology is that structure determines function. How does this principle apply to countercurrent exchange?

Visit McGraw-Hill Ryerson Connect™ for additional study resources.

Cells of the Nervous System

Chapter Outline

A giant neuron from a pond snail, *Lymnaea* sp., positioned on a microchip. Neurons such as these are large in size (diameter: up to ~100 μm).

Can you describe what your body is doing as you read this text? Your eyes are sensing light reflected off this page and your brain is interpreting the meanings of the words you are reading. In fact, even the part of the brain involved in interpreting sounds is active, despite the fact that you are probably not reading aloud. Hundreds of thousands, if not millions, of neurons are involved in your reading of this text. This process and many others are under the control of the **nervous system**, coordinated circuits of cells that sense internal and environmental changes and transmit signals that enable us and other animals to respond in an appropriate way. Nervous systems help us to exert control over our bodies. They also allow animals, including humans, to sense what is going on in the outside world, initiate actions that influence events and respond to demands, and regulate internal processes—all while maintaining homeostasis (see Chapter 40). You are conscious of reading this text or feeling hungry. However, maintaining your body temperature and controlling your heart rate occur without your awareness.

Neuroscience is the scientific study of nervous systems. Neuroscientists are interested in topics such as the structure and function of the brain and the biological basis of consciousness, memory, and learning. Neuroscience is now experiencing rapid growth and an unprecedented number of new discoveries. It interfaces with other disciplines, such as cell biology, psychology, and behavioural biology.

In this chapter, our focus on neuroscience will be at the cellular level. Nervous systems are composed of circuits of **neurons**, highly specialized cells that communicate with each other and with other types of cells by electrical or chemical signals (see chapter-opening photo). In complex animals, neurons become organized into nuclei (singular: **nucleus**), clusters of cells that carry out a particular function. Nuclei typically form in a central processing area of the nervous system called a **brain**. The brain sends commands to various parts of the body through **nerves**: bundles of neuronal cell projections running to various tissues and organs of the body.

We will investigate the special features of neurons that make them suited for rapid communication between cells. The next two chapters will explore how nervous systems are organized, how the brain functions, and how animals use their nervous systems to sense the world around them.

41.1 CELLULAR COMPONENTS OF NERVOUS SYSTEMS

Learning Outcomes:

1. Explain the difference between the central nervous system (CNS) and the peripheral nervous system (PNS).
2. List the cellular components of the nervous system and describe the function of each cell type.
3. Identify the different parts of a typical neuron.
4. Describe the functional relationships among sensory neurons, motor neurons, and interneurons.
5. Explain what a reflex is, and why reflexes are important in animals.

Nervous systems are organized to provide extremely rapid responses to changes in an animal's external or internal environment and to maintain homeostasis. In complex animals, the **central nervous system (CNS)** consists of a brain and a nerve cord, which in vertebrates extends from the brain through the vertebral column and is called the **spinal cord**. The **peripheral nervous system (PNS)** consists of all neurons and projections of their plasma membranes that are outside of and connect with the CNS, such as projections that end on muscle and gland cells. In certain invertebrates with simple nervous systems, the distinction between central and peripheral nervous systems is less clear or not present.

The evolution of nervous systems has allowed animals to receive information about the environment via their PNS, interpret that information in a CNS, and, if necessary, initiate a behavioural response via their PNS (**Figure 41.1**). For example, if a hungry hyena receives a stimulus, such as the smell of food, odour-sensing cells in the nose act as receptors for the stimulus and then send signals to the brain, which interprets them and

1 Peripheral nervous system: Neurons in the nose detect a stimulus (odour) and send a signal to the brain.

2 Central nervous system: Neurons in the brain interpret the odour as food.

Odour

3 Peripheral nervous system: The brain sends a signal to neurons in the PNS that stimulate the salivation response.

Saliva

Figure 41.1 Roles of the central and peripheral nervous systems. In this example, a hungry hyena smells an odour, which the brain interprets as a potential food source. This initiates a biological response (salivation) that prepares the hyena for eating.

Principle: *Living organisms interact with their environment. Throughout this and the following two chapters, you will see many examples of how the nervous system of animals is a key way in which this biological principle is manifest. In this example, a hungry animal uses both divisions of its nervous system to interact with its environment.*

BioConnections: *Look back at Figure 38.17. What type of response is demonstrated by the production of saliva in this figure? Note that saliva is being produced before the animal has begun eating.*

thereby recognizes the smell. The brain then sends a signal to nerves that stimulate gland cells in the mouth, which respond by producing saliva in preparation for the arrival of food. In this section, we will survey the general properties of the cells of the CNS and PNS.

Cells of the Nervous System Are Specialized to Transfer Signals

Nervous systems transfer signals from one part of the body to another and direct the activities of cells, tissues, and organs. Although these are complex tasks, nervous systems have only two unique classes of cells: neurons and glia.

Neurons   Neurons are the cells in the nervous system that send and receive electrical and chemical signals to and from other neurons throughout the body (**Figure 41.2a**). All animals except sponges have neurons. The number of neurons in the nervous systems of different species varies widely, partly as a function of the size of an animal's head and brain, and partly as a function of the complexity of its behaviour. Thus, the tiny, short-lived nematode C. elegans has only 302 neurons in its nervous system, compared with several thousand in a wasp, several hundred thousand in a salamander, 300 million in an octopus, and more than 100 billion in a human.

Regardless of the total number, neurons in one animal species look and act much like neurons from any other species. A neuron is composed of a **cell body** or **soma**, which contains the cell nucleus and other organelles. Two types of extensions or projections that arise from the cell body are the dendrites and the axon. **Dendrites** (from the Greek word *dendron*, meaning "tree") can be single projections of the plasma membrane but more commonly are elaborate treelike structures with numerous branching extensions. Chemical and electrical messages from other neurons are received by the dendrites, and electrical signals move toward the cell body. An **axon** is an extension of the plasma membrane that is involved in sending signals from a neuron to neighbouring cells (**Figure 41.2b**). An axon may be less than a millimetre long in an insect or as long as two metres in a giraffe's neck. A typical neuron has a single axon, which may have branches. The part of the axon closest to the cell body is named the **axon hillock**, which, as we will see later, is important in nerve cell communication. At the other end of the axon are terminal branches or nerve terminals that send electrical or chemical messages to other cells, such as neurons or muscle cells (**Figure 41.2c**).

Within an animal's body, many axons tend to run in parallel bundles to form nerves. Each axon within a nerve is surrounded by glial cells, and the entire bundle is covered by a protective layer of connective tissue. Nerves enter and leave the CNS, and they make contact with structures outside the CNS. Along the way, the terminal branches of axons communicate with particular cells of the body. Nerves transmit signals between the CNS and PNS.

Glia   Surrounding the neurons are cells called the **glia** (from the Greek word meaning "glue"). Glial cells perform various functions and are many times more numerous than neurons, depending on the species. In the human brain, for example, glial cells outnumber neurons by about 50 to 1. In vertebrates, specialized glial cells wrap around the axons to form an insulating layer called a **myelin sheath** (Figure 41.2). In the human brain and spinal cord, these cells are called **oligodendrocytes**, while **Schwann cells** are the glial cells that form myelin on axons that travel outside the brain and spinal cord. As you will see later, myelin increases the speed with which electrical signals pass down the axon.

Glial cells also perform other roles. Astrocytes, which are a type of glial cell, provide metabolic support for neurons and also are involved in forming the blood-brain barrier, which is a physical barrier between blood vessels and most parts of the central nervous system. This barrier protects the CNS by preventing the passage of toxins and other damaging chemicals

(a) Micrograph of a neuron

38 μm

Dendrites — Cell body — Axon hillock — Nucleus

Signal direction

Node of Ranvier — Axon — Myelin sheath

Axon cytoplasm — Node of Ranvier — Axon plasma membrane — Glial cell

A single glial cell wraps itself around an axon to form a segment of the myelin sheath.

500 nm

Axon terminals

(b) A myelinated neuron

Dendrites receive electrical and chemical messages from other neurons.

Cell body processes incoming signals and generates outgoing signals.

Axon sends outgoing signals to axon terminals.

Axon terminals make contact with nearby cells and transmit signals to them.

(c) Information flow through a neuron

Figure 41.2   Structure and basic function of a typical vertebrate neuron and associated glial cells.   (a) A neuron seen at high magnification (confocal microscopy). (b) A diagrammatic representation of a neuron with glial cells, also known as Schwann cells (oligodendrocytes in the CNS). The Schwann cells wrap their membranes around the axon at regular intervals, creating a myelin sheath. (c) The structures involved in the processing of information by a neuron; information flows only in the direction shown.

from the blood into the CNS. Astrocytes also help to maintain a constant concentration of ions in the extracellular fluid. Other glia, called microglia, remove cellular debris produced by damaged or dying cells. In developing embryos, glia form tracks along which neurons migrate to form the nervous system. In addition, some glia function as stem cells to produce more glial cells and neurons.

Sensory, Motor, and Interneurons Form Pathways in a Nervous System

Neurons can be categorized into three main types: sensory neurons, motor neurons, and interneurons. The structures of these types of neurons reflect their specialized functions (**Figure 41.3**).

Sensory Neurons   As their name suggests, the role of **sensory neurons** is to detect or sense information from the outside world, such as light, sound, touch, and heat. In addition,

sensory neurons detect internal body conditions, such as blood pressure and body temperature. Sensory neurons are also called **afferent neurons** because they transmit information to the CNS. They often have a very long axon, which is involved in rapidly communicating signals. Sensory neurons are unusual because the axon bypasses the cell body and goes directly to the CNS (**Figure 41.3a**). This arrangement allows for the rapid transmission of a sensory signal to the CNS.

Motor Neurons   The role of **motor neurons** is to send signals away from the CNS and elicit some type of response. They are so named because one type of response they cause is movement. However, motor neurons may cause other effects, such as the secretion of hormones from endocrine glands. Because they send signals away from the brain, motor neurons are also called **efferent neurons**. Like sensory neurons, motor neurons tend to have long axons (**Figure 41.3b**). However, the axons of motor neurons originate from an axon hillock at the cell body.

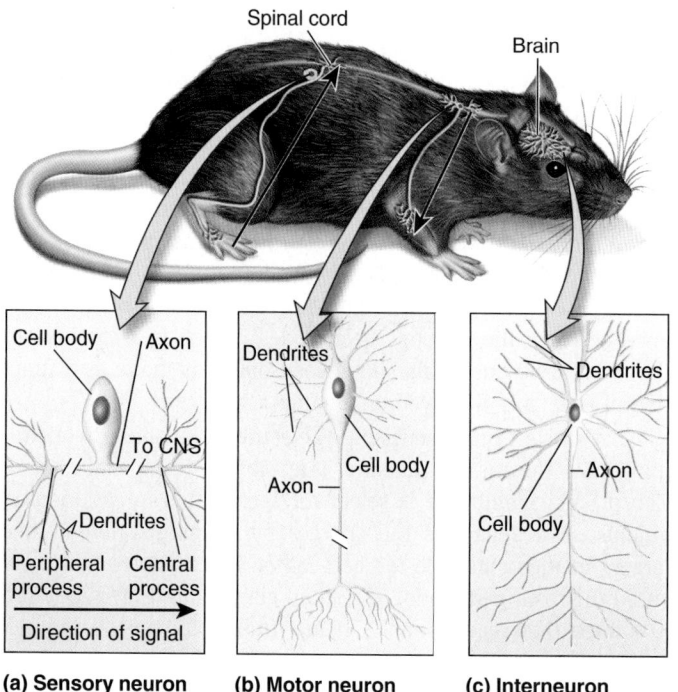

(a) Sensory neuron **(b) Motor neuron** **(c) Interneuron**

Figure 41.3 **Types of neurons.** **(a)** The vertebrate sensory neurons are afferent neurons with an axon that bypasses the cell body and projects to the CNS. **(b)** Motor neurons are efferent neurons that leave the CNS and usually have long axons that enable them to act on distant cells. **(c)** Interneurons are usually short neurons that connect two or more other neurons within the CNS. Although short, the axons and dendrites may have extensive branches, allowing them to receive many inputs and transmit signals to many neurons.

Principle: *Cells are the simplest units of life.* Cells are the simplest units of an organ system, including the nervous system. However, the variety and complexity of cells within an organ system can be great, as seen here.

axons are typically short and highly branched (**Figure 41.3c**). This arrangement allows interneurons to form complex connections with other cells.

Reflex Circuits As a way to understand the interplay among sensory neurons, interneurons, and motor neurons, let's consider a simple example in which of these types of neurons form interconnections. Neurons transmit information to each other through a series of connections that form a circuit. An example of a simple circuit is a **reflex arc**, which allows an organism to respond rapidly to inputs from sensory neurons and consists of only a few neurons (**Figure 41.4**). The stimulus from sensory neurons is sent to the CNS, but there is little or no interpretation of the signal; few, if any, interneurons are involved. The signal is then transmitted to motor neurons, which elicit a response, such as a knee jerk. Such a response is very quick and automatic. Reflexes are among the oldest and most important

Interneurons A third type of neuron, called the **interneuron**, forms interconnections between other neurons in the CNS. The greatest complexity of nervous systems occurs among interneurons, such as those found in the brain. The signals that are sent between interneurons are critical in the interpretation of information that the CNS receives, as well as the response that it may elicit. Interneurons tend to have many dendrites, and their

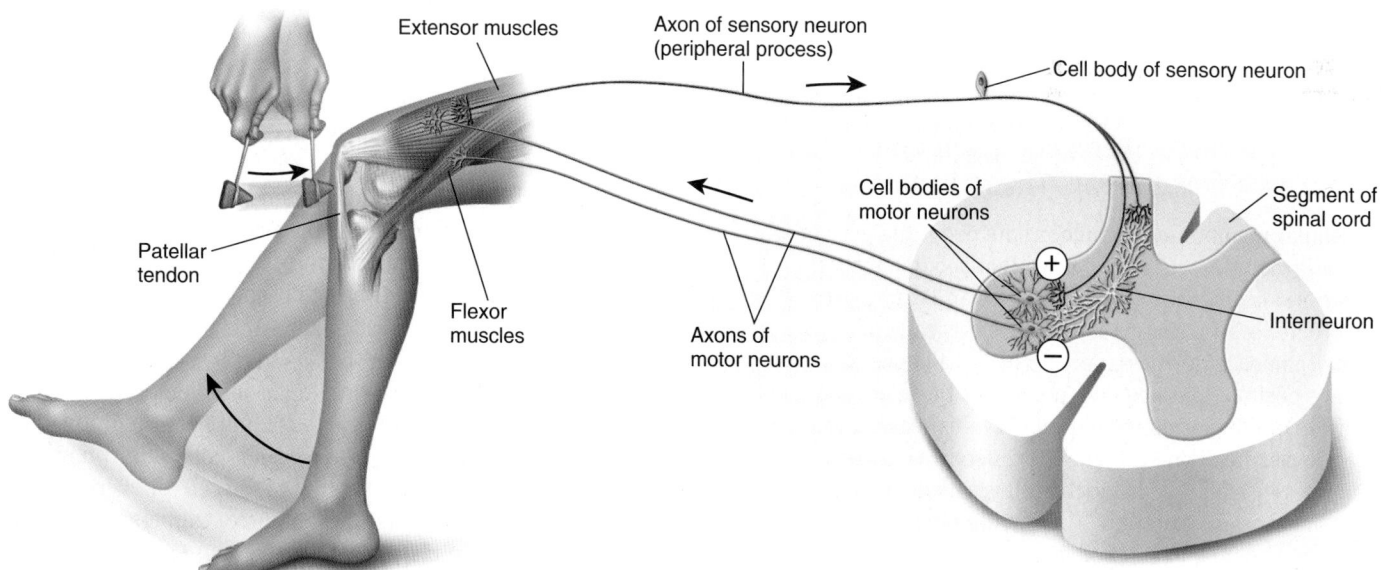

Figure 41.4 **A reflex arc.** The knee-jerk response is an example of a reflex arc. A tap below the kneecap stretches the patellar tendon and acts as a stimulus, initiating a reflex arc that causes the extensor muscle on top of the thigh to contract. At the same time, an interneuron inhibits the motor neuron of the flexor muscle, causing it to relax.

Concept check: *Animals have many types of reflexes. Once initiated, must all reflexes occur to completion, or do you think that in some cases they may be overridden or partially suppressed?*

features of nervous systems, because they allow animals to respond quickly to potentially dangerous events. For instance, many vertebrates will immediately cringe, jump, leap, or take flight in response to a loud noise, which could represent sudden danger. Animals that live in the water will reflexively dive deeper in response to a shadow overhead, which could represent a passing shark or other predator. Infant primates have strong grasping reflexes that help them hold onto their mothers as they move about. Countless examples of useful reflexes are found in animals, and their importance is evident from the observation that they exist in simple animals, such as flatworms, as well as complex mammals, such as humans.

41.2 ELECTRICAL PROPERTIES OF NEURONS

Learning Outcomes:

1. Explain what a membrane potential is.
2. Describe how the resting potential is established and maintained.
3. Describe how an electrochemical gradient determines the direction an ion will move.
4. Define the Nernst equation and how it can be used to make predictions about the ways in which different ions move across a cell membrane.

Neurons use electrical signals to communicate with other neurons, muscles, or glands. These signals, or **nerve impulses**, involve changes in the amount of electric charge across a cell's plasma membrane. In this section, we examine the concept of chemical and electrical gradients across the plasma membrane of neurons. Later in this chapter, we will explore how such gradients provide a way for neurons to conduct signals.

Neurons Establish Differences in Ion Concentration and Electric Charge Across Their Membranes

Like cellular membranes throughout the body, the plasma membrane of a neuron acts as a barrier that separates charges. Ion concentrations differ between the interior and exterior of the cell. Such differences in charge act as an electrical force measured in **volts**, named after Alessandro Volta. Analogous to a battery, there are positive and negative poles, but these are the outside and inside of the plasma membrane. For this reason, a neuron is said to be electrically **polarized**. The difference between the electric charges inside and outside the cell is called a potential difference or **membrane potential**. The **resting potential** refers to the membrane potential of a cell that is not sending nerve impulses.

How do scientists measure electrical changes in a structure as tiny as a neuron? Several invertebrates, such as squid, lobsters, and earthworms, have large neurons that have been used successfully to measure membrane potentials. The squid giant axon, for example, can have a diameter of 1 mm, making it relatively easy to impale with a microelectrode, which is a recording instrument constructed of a glass pipette with an extremely

thin tip of less than 1 μm in diameter. Within the microelectrode is a salt solution that can conduct ions. The squid giant axon has been used extensively since the mid-twentieth century to determine the mechanisms by which nerve cells generate electrical signals (**Figure 41.5**). A neuron is dissected from the squid and placed in a solution that has similar ionic concentrations as normal extracellular fluid. A microelectrode is pushed through the axon membrane to record from inside the cell, and another microelectrode is placed within the solution bathing the neuron outside the cell. A voltmeter records the voltage difference between the two microelectrodes, which is a measure of the membrane potential. This measurement is made as a function of time and displayed on a computer screen.

Let's begin our discussion of electrical signalling by examining how the resting potential is established and maintained. The plasma membrane is selectively permeable to cations and anions, so it separates the charges by keeping different ions largely inside or outside the cell. When investigators first measured the resting potential of a squid giant axon, they registered a voltage that read about −70 mV (millivolts) inside the cell with respect to the outside bathing medium. This means that the interior of the cell had a more negative charge than the exterior, which turns out to be true of all animal cells in their resting state. A resting potential of −70 mV is tiny compared to the voltages used to provide electric current in a home (approximately 120 V) or even that of a small 1.5-V battery. Nonetheless, this tiny difference in charge across the membrane of a neuron is sufficient to generate a nerve impulse that can travel from one end of a neuron to the other, as you will see later in this chapter.

The resting potential is determined by the ions located along the inner and outer surfaces of the plasma membrane (**Figure 41.6a**). Ions of opposite charges align on either side of the membrane because they are drawn to each other through electrical forces. Negative ions within the cell are drawn to the positive ions arrayed on the outer surface of the plasma membrane. The actual number of ions that contribute to the resting membrane potential is extremely small compared with the rest of the ions within and outside the cell. **Table 41.1** lists the ions that are important in maintaining the resting potential and their concentrations inside and outside the cell. The ions that are most critical for establishing the resting potential are Na^+, K^+, and intracellular anions, such as negatively charged proteins and Cl^-.

Three factors are primarily responsible for the resting membrane potential (**Figure 41.6b**). First, the sodium-potassium pump (Na^+/K^+-ATPase) within the plasma membrane continually moves sodium ions out of the cell and potassium ions into the cytosol (see Chapter 6). The sodium-potassium pump utilizes ATP to transport three Na^+ out of the cell for every two K^+ it moves into the cell. Thus, the pump contributes to a charge difference across the plasma membrane and establishes gradients for Na^+ and K^+. Second, the plasma membrane contains ion-specific channels that affect the permeability of ions across the membrane. Channels that are specific for Na^+ or K^+ influence the resting potential by allowing the passive movement of ions. In particular, K^+ channels tend to be open more frequently at the resting potential. Most neurons have about 50 times as many potassium channels as sodium channels, and so the membrane is more permeable to potassium than to sodium. Third, negatively charged molecules, such as proteins, are more abundant inside the cell. These anions do not readily move

(a) Insertion of microelectrode

(b) Measurement of membrane potential

Figure 41.5 Recording the membrane potential of neurons. **(a)** The giant axon from a squid is removed from the animal and placed in a bathing medium. A microelectrode impales the axon. **(b)** The potential difference across the membrane of the axon is recorded by comparing the charge inside and outside the axon. The membrane potential is steady at times and fluctuates at other times, depending on experimental conditions. At first, before the intracellular ("recording") microelectrode is lowered into the axon, the potential difference between it and the extracellular ("reference") microelectrode is zero, because both electrodes are in the same solution. Once the intracellular electrode impales the cell, however, a negative potential is registered, indicating that the interior of the axon is negatively charged with respect to the external solution.

Concept check: *What obvious difference (besides its size) can you see between the giant axon of the squid, as illustrated here, and the illustration of the vertebrate axon depicted in Figure 41.2b?*

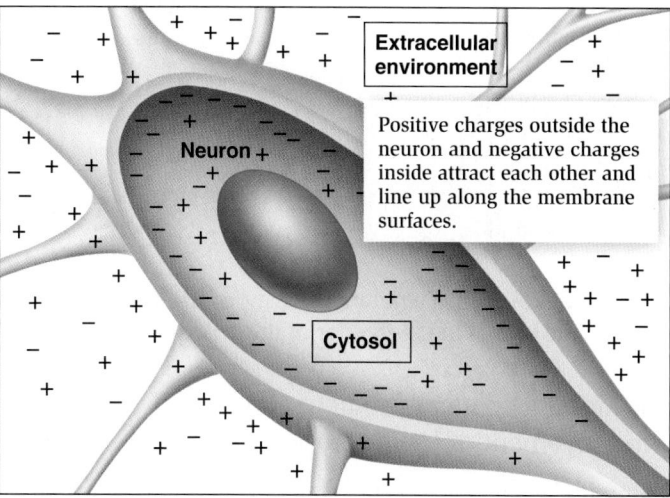

(a) Distribution of charges across the neuronal plasma membrane

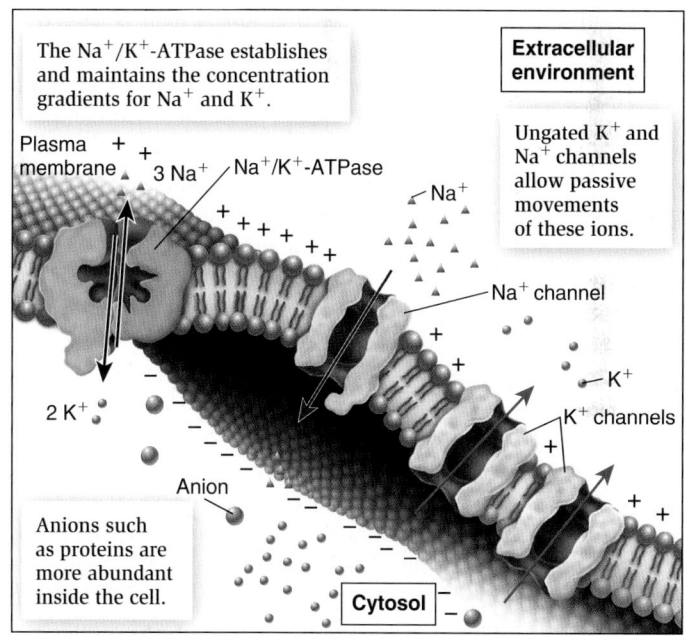

(b) Three factors that influence the resting potential

Figure 41.6 The resting membrane potential. The slight excess of negative charges inside the cell is shown in part **(a)**. In part **(b)**, the three major factors that contribute to this charge distribution are shown: the Na$^+$/K$^+$-ATPase pump that establishes ion concentrations gradients, ungated ion channels that permit diffusion of Na$^+$ and especially K$^+$ across the membrane, and intracellular anions.

 Principle: *Living organisms use energy. The Na$^+$/K$^+$-ATPase pump uses the energy stored in ATP to pump ions across the neuronal plasma membrane. Consequently, establishing and maintaining resting membrane potentials accounts for a significant fraction of the energy consumed per day in an animal like ourselves.*

Table 41.1	Extracellular and Intracellular Concentrations of Ions for a Typical Mammalian Neuron		
	Concentration (mM/L)		
Ion	**Extracellular**	**Intracellular**	
Na$^+$	145	15	
K$^+$	5	150	
Anions found in macromolecules	< 1	65	
Cl$^-$	10	7	

through the plasma membrane so they contribute more negative electric charge to the interior of the cell.

An Electrochemical Gradient Governs the Movement of Ions Across a Membrane

Both the membrane potential and the chemical concentration of ions influence the direction of ion movement across a membrane. The direction that an ion will move depends on the **electrochemical gradient** for that ion, which is the combined effect of both an electrical and a chemical gradient. **Figure 41.7** considers the concept of an electrochemical gradient for K$^+$. This hypothetical drawing illustrates two compartments that are separated by a semipermeable membrane that can permit the flow of K$^+$. **Figure 41.7a** illustrates an electrical gradient. In this case, the chemical concentration of K$^+$ is equal on both sides of the membrane, but the concentrations of other ions, such as Na$^+$ and Cl$^+$ are unequal on both sides of the membrane and thereby produce an electrical gradient. Because K$^+$ is positively charged, it will be attracted to the side of the membrane with more negative charge. **Figure 41.7b** shows a chemical gradient in which K$^+$ concentration is higher on one side. In this scenario, K$^+$ will move from a region of high to low concentration. Finally, **Figure 41.7c** shows a situation in which a chemical gradient is balanced by an electrical gradient. The electrical gradient favours the movement of K$^+$ from left to right, while the chemical gradient favours movement from right to left. These opposing forces can create an equilibrium in which there is no net movement of K$^+$ in either direction.

With two different forces—chemical and electrical gradients—acting on a given ion, is it possible to predict the direction that an ion will move across a membrane at any concentration gradient? In other words, can we compare the relative strengths of the chemical and electrical gradients and predict their net effect? By measuring the membrane potential of isolated neurons in the presence of changing concentrations of extracellular ions, scientists have deduced a mathematical formula that relates chemical and electrical gradients to each other. This formula, named the **Nernst equation** after the Nobel laureate Walther Nernst, gives the **equilibrium potential** for an ion at any given concentration gradient. For monovalent cations, such as Na$^+$ and K$^+$, the Nernst equation can be expressed as

$$E = 60 \text{ mV } \log_{10}([X_{\text{extracellular}}]/[X_{\text{intracellular}}])$$

(a) Electrical gradient, no chemical gradient for K$^+$

(b) Chemical gradient for K$^+$, no electrical gradient

(c) K$^+$ equilibrium, electrical gradient is balanced by the chemical gradient for K$^+$

Figure 41.7 **Electrical and chemical gradients.** This hypothetical example depicts two chambers separated by a membrane that is permeable to K$^+$. **(a)** In this example, the compartments initially contain equal concentrations of K$^+$, but an electrical gradient exists because of an unequal distribution of Na$^+$ and Cl$^-$. Potassium ions are attracted to the more negative charge on the right side of the membrane. **(b)** In this case, there is no electrical gradient across the membrane, and the left compartment contains a lower concentration of KCl compared with the right compartment. In water, the KCl dissociates to K$^+$ and Cl$^-$. Under these conditions, K$^+$ diffuses down its chemical concentration gradient from right to left. **(c)** This example illustrates opposing chemical and electrical gradients. The right compartment contains a higher chemical concentration of K$^+$, while the left side has more positive charge. These gradients balance each other so that no net movement of K$^+$ occurs and a state of electrochemical equilibrium is reached.

Concept check: *In part (b), does the diffusion of K$^+$ down its chemical gradient result in an electrical gradient? What will eventually stop the net diffusion of K$^+$?*

where, E is the equilibrium potential, inside relative to outside; [X] is the concentration of an ion, outside or inside the cell; and 60 mV is a constant that depends on temperature, valence of the ion, and other factors.

The Nernst equation allows neuroscientists to predict when an ion is in equilibrium and when it is not. To understand the usefulness of this equation, let's consider two examples. First, suppose the membrane potential is -88.6 mV and the K^+ concentration is 5 mM outside and 150 mM inside. If we plug these chemical concentrations into the Nernst equation:

$$E = 60 \text{ mV } \log_{10} (5/150) = 60 \text{ mV } (-1.48)$$

$$E = -88.6 \text{ mV}$$

Under these conditions, K^+ is in equilibrium and no net flow of K^+ will occur, even when many K^+ channels are open.

As a second example, let's suppose that the membrane potential is at the typical resting potential of -70 mV and the Na^+ concentration is 100 mM outside and 10 mM inside. If we plug these chemical concentrations into the Nernst equation:

$$E = 60 \text{ mV } \log_{10} (100/10) = 60 \text{ mV } (1)$$

$$E = 60 \text{ mV}$$

At a resting potential of -70 mV, the value of 60mV tells us that Na^+ is not in equilibrium. Na^+ will tend to flow into the cell. Both the chemical and the electrical gradients favour an inward flow. However, at Na^+ concentrations of 100 mM outside and 10 mM inside, Na^+ would not tend to flow—it would be in equilibrium—if the membrane potential was at 60 mV.

By establishing electrochemical gradients and maintaining them with the sodium-potassium pump, neurons have the ability to suddenly allow ions to move across the plasma membrane by opening additional channels that were previously closed. The movement of a charged ion down its gradient results in an electric current. This current is different from the type of current that runs through electrical wires and is much smaller in amplitude. Even so, this small current provides the electrical signal that neurons use to communicate with one another, as you will see next.

41.3 COMMUNICATION BETWEEN NEURONS

Learning Outcomes:

1. Distinguish between ligand-gated and voltage-gated ion channels.
2. Compare and contrast graded potentials and action potentials.
3. Describe the events in the conduction of an action potential.
4. Discuss how myelination influences the speed of an action potential.
5. Describe the structural features of a synapse.
6. Distinguish between two types of potentials produced in postsynaptic cells: excitatory postsynaptic potentials (EPSPs) and inhibitory postsynaptic potentials (IPSP).
7. List the classes of neurotransmitters and provide brief descriptions of their generalized functions.
8. Describe the two general types of postsynaptic membrane receptors.

Communication between neurons begins when one cell receives a stimulus and sends an electrical signal along its plasma membrane via currents generated by ion movements. This signal will then influence the next neuron in a circuit. Each signal is brief (only a few milliseconds), but a neuron can receive and transmit millions of signals in its lifetime. In this section, we will survey the ability of neurons to send brief signals with amazing speed.

Signalling by a Neuron Occurs Through Changes in the Membrane Potential

Recall that a cell is polarized because of the separation of charge across the membrane. The resting potential is more negative inside. Changes in the membrane potential, therefore, are changes in the degree of polarization. **Depolarization** occurs when the cell becomes less polarized; that is, less negative relative to the surrounding fluid. As described later, when a neuron is stimulated by an electrical or chemical stimulus, one or more types of gated channels open and sodium ions move into the cell, bringing with them their positive charge. This increases the membrane potential to a level somewhat more positive than the resting membrane potential. The membrane potential is said to be depolarized. In contrast, **hyperpolarization** occurs when the cell becomes more polarized. For example, increased movement of K^+ out of the cell makes the internal charge of the cell more negative than the resting potential.

Though all cells in an animal's body have a membrane potential, neurons and muscle cells are called **excitable cells** because they have the capacity to generate electrical signals. For a cell to communicate by using electrical signals, it must be able to change its membrane potential very rapidly. This is accomplished by gated ion channels, so called because they open and close like a gate in a fence (**Figure 41.8**). **Voltage-gated channels** open and close in response to changes in voltage across the membrane. **Ligand-gated channels**, also known as chemically gated channels, open or close when ligands, such as small molecules, bind to them. The opening and closing of voltage-gated and ligand-gated channels are responsible for two types of changes in the neuron's membrane potential called graded potentials and action potentials.

Graded Potentials A **graded potential** is a depolarization or hyperpolarization that varies depending on the strength of the stimulus. A large change in membrane potential will occur when a strong stimulus opens many channels, while a small stimulus causes a small change because only a few channels are opened (**Figure 41.9**). Graded potentials occur locally on a particular area of the plasma membrane, such as dendrites and the cell body, where a chemical or an electrical stimulus opens ion channels. From this area, a graded potential spreads a small distance across a region of the plasma membrane. In a short time, the membrane potential returns to the resting potential.

Graded potentials occur on all neurons and are particularly important for the function of sensory neurons, which must distinguish between strong and weak stimuli coming into the organism from the environment. When a graded potential is

(a) Voltage-gated ion channel

(b) Ligand-gated ion channel

Figure 41.8   **Examples of gated ion channels.** **(a)** A voltage-gated ion channel allows ions to diffuse into the cell. These channels open or close depending on changes in charge (voltage) across the membrane. **(b)** A ligand-gated ion channel opens or closes in response to ligand binding. In the example here, the binding of a neurotransmitter opens the channel.

BioConnections: *Are ions the only substances that can move through channels in plasma membranes? Look back at Figure 5.31 for another important molecule that diffuses through membranes via channels.*

sufficiently large, this stimulates the second type of electrical signal, the action potential.

Action Potentials   **Action potentials** are the nerve impulses that carry an electrical signal along an axon. In contrast to a graded potential, an action potential is always a large depolarization, and all action potentials in a given neuron have the same amplitude, which is the degree to which an action potential changes the membrane potential from its resting state. Once an action potential has been triggered, it is expressed in an all-or-none fashion. In other words, it cannot be graded. Unlike a graded potential, an action potential is actively propagated along the axon, renewing itself as it travels. In this sense, an action potential is said to be regenerative. An action potential travels rapidly down the axon to the axon terminal, where it initiates a response at the junction with the next cell.

Figure 41.9   **Graded membrane potentials.** Within a limited range, the change in the membrane potential occurs in proportion to the intensity of the stimulus. If the membrane potential becomes more positive, the resulting change is called a depolarization. Hyperpolarization results from the membrane potential becoming more negative following a stimulus.

Figure 41.10a shows the electrical changes that occur in a localized region of an axon when an action potential is occurring. Voltage-gated sodium channels and potassium channels are present in very high numbers from the axon hillock to the axon terminus. An action potential begins when a graded potential is large enough to spread to the axon hillock and depolarizes the membrane to a value called the threshold potential. The **threshold potential** is the membrane potential that is sufficient to open voltage-gated Na^+ channels and to trigger an action potential, typically around -50 mV.

Sodium channels open rapidly when the membrane potential changes from the resting potential (-70 V) to the threshold potential (-50 mV). The opening of sodium channels involves a change in the conformation of the membrane-spanning region of the channel (**Figure 41.10b**). When the protein changes shape, the central pore opens, and Na^+ rapidly diffuses into the cell down its electrochemical gradient. This further depolarizes the cell, causing even more voltage-gated Na^+ channels to open and resulting in the spike in membrane potential that characterizes the action potential. This process is so rapid that, within 1 msec (millisecond), the membrane potential reaches its peak positive value. In a typical action potential, approximately 7,000 sodium ions move through each voltage-gated Na^+ channel.

When the membrane potential becomes very polarized, a conformational change in the sodium channel blocks the continued flow of Na^+ into the cell. The conformational change involves the **inactivation gate**, a string of amino acids that juts out from the channel protein into the cytosol (Figure 41.10b). The inactivation gate swings into the channel, thereby preventing the movement of Na^+ into the cell. Under these conditions, the Na^+ channel is said to be inactivated. The inactivation gate does not swing out of the channel until the membrane returns to its resting potential.

Figure 41.10 Changes that occur during an action potential. The electrical gradient across the plasma membrane of an axon first depolarizes and then hyperpolarizes. These changes in the membrane potential are caused by the opening and closing of Na⁺ and K⁺ channels.

Concept check: *How would the shape of the action potential be affected if the Na⁺ channels were missing their inactivation gate?*

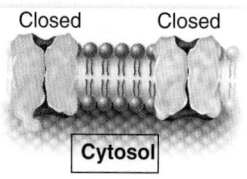

1 **Resting membrane potential:** The membrane is at the resting potential, occasionally generating graded potentials.

2 **Depolarization to threshold:** An action potential is triggered when the threshold potential of about −55 to −50 mV is reached. Voltage-gated Na⁺ channels open. Na⁺ diffuses into the cell and depolarizes the membrane.

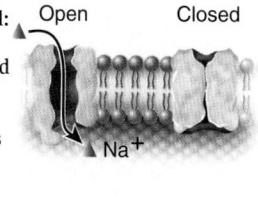

3 **Peak of action potential:** At about +30 mV, voltage-gated Na⁺ channels are inactivated, and voltage-gated K⁺ channels open. K⁺ exits the cell and repolarizes the membrane. At this time, the membrane is in its absolute refractory period.

4 **Repolarization:** Voltage-gated Na⁺ channels change from inactivated to closed. Voltage-gated K⁺ channels remain open, causing a hyperpolarization of the membrane. The membrane is now in its relative refractory period.

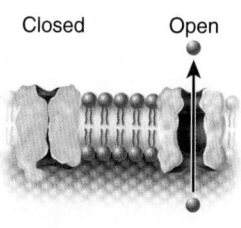

5 **Restoration of resting membrane potential:** Voltage-gated K⁺ channels close, and the resting potential of the membrane is restored by the Na⁺/K⁺-ATPase pump.

Voltage-gated potassium channels are also triggered to open by the change in voltage to the threshold potential, but they open about 1 msec later than Na⁺ channels. When K⁺ channels open, potassium ions leave the cell down their electrochemical gradient and the membrane potential becomes more negative again. The membrane shows a brief period of hyperpolarization because the K⁺ channels remain open and the electrical gradient approaches the equilibrium potential for K⁺, which is slightly more negative than the resting potential. When the voltage-gated K⁺ channels eventually close, the membrane returns to the resting potential. At this stage, both the Na⁺ and K⁺ channels are closed, and they have the ability to reopen if the resting potential rises to the threshold potential.

The evolution of K⁺ channels with a slightly slower opening time than Na⁺ channels was a key event that led to the formation of nervous systems. Imagine what would happen if the voltage-gated Na⁺ and K⁺ channels opened simultaneously: As Na⁺ ions entered the cell down their electrochemical gradient, K⁺ ions would leave the cell down their electrochemical gradient, and they would negate each other's effects on the membrane potential.

While the inactivation gate of the Na⁺ channel is closed, the cell is **refractory**, or unresponsive to another stimulus. A change in voltage will not open the Na⁺ channels while they are inactivated. Therefore, this refractory period places limits on the frequency at which a neuron can generate action potentials. As we will see, this also ensures that the action potential does not "retrace its steps" by moving backward toward the cell body.

Many natural toxins work by blocking the actions of sodium and potassium channels. Some animals use these toxins as defensive mechanisms or for capturing prey, and they can be deadly. For instance, tetrodotoxin, a chemical produced by puffer fish, blocks voltage-gated Na⁺ channels and therefore nerve activity. An animal that eats a puffer fish dies because the poison paralyzes muscles, including those that depend on nerve stimulation to control breathing and movement. Eating even a small amount can paralyze or kill a human. Other toxins from wasps, bees, and scorpions can block the action of voltage-gated K⁺ channels, resulting in abnormal action potentials and loss of normal muscle responses.

Our present understanding of action potentials began with experiments carried out in the 1940s by two British physiologists: Alan Hodgkin and Andrew Huxley. By using the squid giant axon and measuring ion movements into and out of the cell, they showed that the action potential depends on voltage-gated Na⁺ and K⁺ channels. They also showed that the timing with which these channels open and close is responsible for shaping the action potential. They noted that Na$^+$ channels open and close rapidly, while voltage-gated K$^+$ channels open later than Na$^+$ channels and close only toward the end of the action potential. This results in Na$^+$ channels being involved in the initiation and early phase of the action potential, while K$^+$ channels control the duration and termination of the action potential.

Since those early studies, we have learned a great deal about the structure and function of voltage-gated Na$^+$ and K$^+$ channels. These studies have largely involved selectively mutating amino acids within these proteins and observing whether changes occur in the function of the channels. The Na$^+$ channel consists of one long protein that crosses or spans the membrane 24 times, while the K$^+$ channel consists of four separate protein subunits that each span the membrane 6 times. The pores of the Na$^+$ and K$^+$ channels are made of different amino acids and have different diameters, and this results in each ion being able to pass only through its own channel. Researchers have identified 10 different Na$^+$ channel genes in mammals alone and as many as 100 types of K$^+$ channel genes, each encoding channels with slightly different properties, such as how quickly they open or close.

Action Potentials Are Conducted Down the Axon with Great Speed

Thus far, we have considered the electrical changes that happen when an action potential is initiated. We will now consider how this event occurs in the direction from the axon hillock to the axon terminus (**Figure 41.11**). Let's begin at the axon hillock. Because the neuron receives stimuli from other cells, this results in a graded potential at the axon hillock that changes the resting potential to the threshold potential. This triggers the abrupt opening of several voltage-gated Na$^+$ channels just beyond the axon hillock, where many Na$^+$ channels are found. This event triggers the opening of more Na$^+$ channels, which allow Na$^+$ to depolarize a region closer to the axon terminus. In this way, the sequential opening of Na$^+$ channels along the axon membrane conducts a wave of depolarization from the axon hillock to the axon terminus.

But why doesn't the action potential move backward from the terminus to the hillock? The key is the inactivation state of the Na$^+$ channel. Again, let's begin at the hillock. When these Na$^+$ channels open for 1 msec, they allow Na$^+$ to rapidly enter the cell, and then they become inactivated. This inactivation prevents the action potential from moving backwards (Figure 41.11). While they are inactivated, K$^+$ channels open and the resting potential is restored. At the resting potential, the Na$^+$ channels switch from the inactivated to the closed state. The opening of K$^+$ channels also travels from the axon hillock to the axon terminus, but it causes a wave of hyperpolarization that re-establishes the resting potential.

The speed with which the action potential is conducted down the axon can be as fast as 100 m/sec or as slow as a centimetre or two per second. The speed is determined by two factors: the axon diameter and the presence or absence of myelin.

Figure 41.11 Conduction of the action potential along an axon. All Na$^+$ and K$^+$ channels shown refer to voltage-gated channels.

1 Unstimulated neuron; Na$^+$ channels are closed.

Action potential
Na$^+$ channel open

2 Threshold potential is reached at axon hillock. Na$^+$ channels open, and an action potential is generated.

Inactivation gate closed

3 Entry of Na$^+$ depolarizes membrane and opens channels toward the axon terminal, generating new action potentials. Previously opened Na$^+$ channels are inactivated.

4 Continued entry of Na$^+$ depolarizes the membrane and opens channels farther down the axon. Previously opened Na$^+$ channels are inactivated. Previously inactivated Na$^+$ channels switch to a closed state when K$^+$ channels (not shown) open and restore the resting potential.

5 Process continues and action potential moves down axon.

KEY

Closed Na$^+$ channels   Open Na$^+$ channels   Inactivated Na$^+$ channels

The axon diameter influences the rate at which incoming ions can spread along the inner surface of the plasma membrane. In a broad axon, the flow of ions meets less resistance compared to a thin axon, just as water moves more easily through a wide hose than a narrow one. Therefore, in a broad axon the action potential will move faster. The large axons of the squid or lobster conduct action potentials very rapidly, allowing the animals to move quickly when threatened by a predator.

Myelination is the second factor that influences the speed of an action potential. Myelinated axons conduct action potentials at a faster rate than unmyelinated axons. Invertebrate neurons lack myelin, while vertebrate neurons may be myelinated or unmyelinated. Recall that glial cells (oligodendrocytes and Schwann cells) wrap around axons to form an insulating sheath of membrane. However, this myelin sheath is not continuous (**Figure 41.12**). At regular intervals, the axons of myelinated neurons have exposed areas known as the **nodes of Ranvier**, which contain many voltage-gated Na⁺ channels. The nodes of Ranvier are the only areas of myelinated axons that have enough Na⁺ channels to elicit an action potential. When sodium ions move into the cell, the charge moves rapidly through the cytosol to the next node, where the action potential continues. This type of conduction is called **saltatory conduction** (from the Latin, *saltare*, meaning "to leap") because the action potential seems to jump from one node to the next. Saltatory conduction speeds up the conduction process because it takes less time for the action potential to travel from node to node rather than continuously along the length of the axon.

Neurons Communicate Electrically or Chemically at Synapses

Neurons communicate with other cells at a **synapse**, which is a junction where a nerve terminal meets a target neuron, muscle cell, or gland. At a synapse, an electrical or chemical signal passes from the nerve terminal to the next cell. A synapse includes the axon terminal of the neuron that is sending the message, the nearby plasma membrane of the receiving cell, and the **synaptic cleft**, or extracellular space between the two cells. The **presynaptic cell** sends the signal and the **postsynaptic cell** receives it (**Figure 41.13**).

By studying neurons from both invertebrates and vertebrates, researchers have identified two types of synapses. The first type, called an **electrical synapse**, directly passes electric current from the presynaptic to the postsynaptic cell. The electrical signal passes through this type of synapse extremely rapidly, because the plasma membranes of adjacent cells are connected by gap junctions that can move electric charges freely from one cell to the other (see Chapter 5). An example of cells that use electrical synapses are cardiac muscle cells. In some aquatic invertebrates such as leeches, electrical synapses are known to occur where a group of neurons must fire rapidly and synchronously, such as when an animal must coordinate a number of muscles to swim or escape danger. A second type of

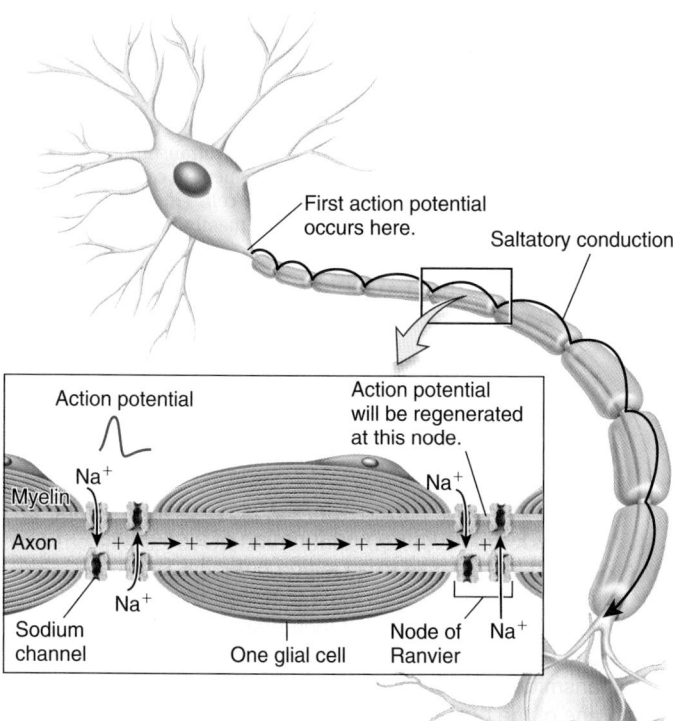

Figure 41.12 **Saltatory conduction along a myelinated axon.** Action potentials are generated only at the nodes of Ranvier, which lack a surrounding sheath of myelin.

Concept check: *What is the main advantage of saltatory conduction?*

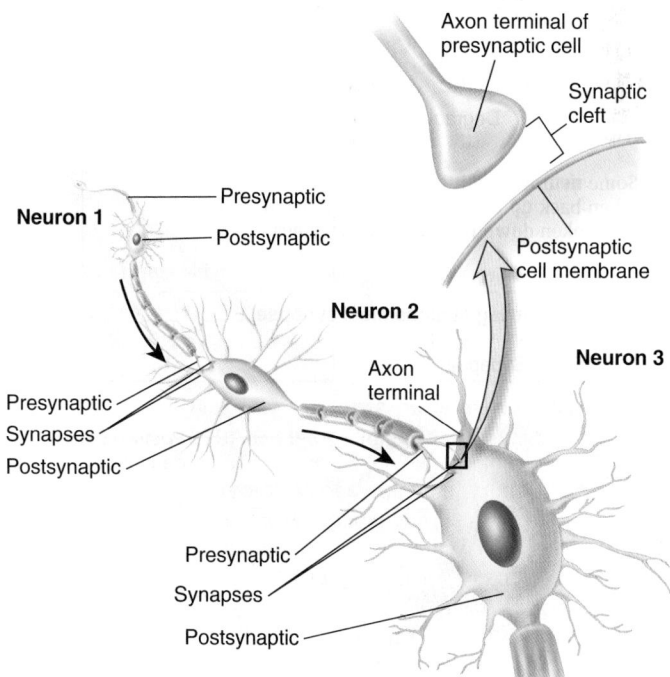

Figure 41.13 **Presynaptic and postsynaptic cells.** The arrows show the direction of signal transmission from one neuron to the next. Note that neuron 2 is postsynaptic with respect to neuron 1, and presynaptic with respect to neuron 3.

will reach the axon hillock, where the high concentration of Na⁺ channels can trigger an action potential. Synapses that occur far from the axon hillock, for instance at the end of a long dendrite, are less effective than synapses on the cell body nearer the axon hillock.

Several Classes of Neurotransmitters Stimulate Responses in Postsynaptic Cells

Neuroscientists have identified more than 100 different neurotransmitters in animals. Generally, neurotransmitters are categorized by size or molecular structure (**Table 41.2**). Both excitatory and inhibitory neurotransmission occurs in nervous systems. The changing balance between excitation and inhibition controls the state of nervous system circuits at any one time. To understand how neurotransmitters work, imagine driving a car with one foot on the accelerator and one foot on the brake. To speed up, you could press down harder on the accelerator, ease up on the brake, or both, and to slow down, you could do the opposite. All nervous systems operate in this way, with combined excitatory and inhibitory actions of neurotransmitters.

Table 41.2	Classes of Neurotransmitters and Their Functions
Transmitter	**Some major functions**
Acetylcholine	CNS: Stimulates the brain; important in memory, motor control, and many other functions
	PNS: Stimulates skeletal muscle at neuromuscular junction, inhibits cardiac muscle, promotes digestion
Biogenic amines	
Catecholamines: dopamine, norepinephrine, epinephrine	CNS: Regulate mood, attention, learning, and many other functions
Serotonin	PNS: Catecholamines stimulate cardiac muscle, improve lung function, help animals respond to stressful situations
Histamine	
Amino acids	
Excitatory amino acids: glutamate, aspartate	Widespread mediators of activity in all areas of CNS; the major on and off signals of the CNS
Inhibitory amino acids: gamma-aminobutyric acid (GABA), glycine	
Neuropeptides	
Opiate peptides: endorphin, enkephalin	CNS: Modulate postsynaptic cell response to neurotransmitters; play a role in mood, behaviour, appetite, pain perception, and many others
Oxytocin	
Gases	
Nitric oxide, carbon monoxide	CNS: Possible role in memory and odour sensation
	PNS: Relaxes smooth muscle, especially in blood vessels

Next, we highlight major features of the different chemical classes of neurotransmitters found in animals, which include acetylcholine, biogenic amines, amino acids, neuropeptides, and gaseous neurotransmitters. With the exception of acetylcholine, all these classes contain several different neurotransmitters that are similar in chemical structure but may have different functions in nervous systems.

Acetylcholine Acetylcholine, one of the most widespread neurotransmitters in animals, is released at the synapses of **neuromuscular junctions** in vertebrates, where a neuron contacts skeletal or cardiac muscle. It is also released at synapses within the brain. Acetylcholine acts as an excitatory neurotransmitter in the brain and skeletal muscle cells, but it is inhibitory to neurons that control cardiac muscle contraction. Therefore, it stimulates skeletal muscle but inhibits cardiac muscle. As you will see later, the same neurotransmitter can exert both excitatory and inhibitory effects depending on the type of receptor to which it binds.

Biogenic Amines The biogenic amines are compounds containing amine groups that are formed from amino acids or their precursors. Catecholamines are formed from tyrosine and include dopamine, norepinephrine, and epinephrine. Dopamine and epinephrine are primarily active in the brain, while norepinephrine acts in the brain and at synapses in the peripheral nervous system. Serotonin is formed from the amino acid tryptophan. In addition to widespread physiological effects such as control of heart and lung function, these neurotransmitters are psychoactive; that is, they affect mood, attention, and learning. In humans, abnormally high or low levels of the biogenic amines have been associated with a variety of disorders, including schizophrenia, Parkinson's disease, and depression. Histamine is formed from the amino acid histidine and plays various roles in the body. As a neurotransmitter, it helps to maintain the awake state.

Amino Acids In addition to their role in the formation of proteins, the amino acids glutamate, aspartate, and glycine function as neurotransmitters. Glutamate is the most widespread excitatory neurotransmitter found in animal nervous systems. Though not involved in protein formation, another amino acid, gamma-aminobutyric acid (GABA), is the most common inhibitory neurotransmitter. GABA hyperpolarizes the postsynaptic membrane by opening chloride channels, allowing chloride ions to move into the cell (Table 41.1) and acting as the major brake on the central nervous system.

Neuropeptides Neuropeptides are short chains of 2 to about 15 amino acids. They remained largely unknown until the 1970s, when it began to be apparent that perhaps 100 or so peptides can act as neurotransmitters. As with the other neurotransmitters discussed, neuropeptides can be excitatory or inhibitory. They are produced within the cell body, packaged in vesicles in the Golgi apparatus, and transported to the axon terminal, where they are released. Neuropeptides are often called **neuromodulators**, because they can alter or modulate the response of the postsynaptic neuron to other neurotransmitters. For example, a cell exposed to a neuropeptide may increase the number of receptors for another neurotransmitter, which makes it more responsive to that neurotransmitter. One group of neuropeptides is called the opiate peptides because opium-like drugs (e.g., morphine) bind to their receptors. Opiate peptides include the endorphins, a group of peptides that decrease pain and cause natural feelings of euphoria, which may be important in helping animals deal with stress. A second example is enkephalin, which acts as a sedative in the body and appears to affect mood and motivation. Oxytocin is a neuropeptide that acts as both a hormone and a neurotransmitter. In the brain, oxytocin seems to play a role in bonding and social recognition, and it might even be involved in the formation of trust between people.

Neurotransmitters Gaseous molecules, such as nitric oxide (NO) and carbon monoxide (CO), act locally in many tissues and sometimes function as neurotransmitters. Unlike other neurotransmitters, they are not sequestered into vesicles and are produced locally as needed. Gaseous neurotransmitters are short acting and influence other cells by diffusion. In humans, NO is responsible for relaxing the smooth muscle surrounding blood vessels, including those in the penis. When a male becomes sexually aroused, NO levels increase in this tissue, dilating the vessels and increasing blood flow into the penis, producing an erection. Several drugs used for male sexual dysfunction enhance erections by increasing or mimicking the action of NO on smooth muscle. The functions of CO are still uncertain, but it is believed to act as a neurotransmitter in the sense of smell in some animals, such as the terrestrial mollusc *Limax maximus.*

FEATURE INVESTIGATION

Otto Loewi Discovered Acetylcholine

German physiologist Otto Loewi was interested in how neurons communicate with muscle. He already knew that the electrical stimulation of a nerve in a frog's leg would result in muscle contraction, so it appeared that neurons communicate with the muscle by electrical signals. In the early 1920s he turned his studies to the heart. If he removed a frog's heart and put it in a bath containing saline, it continued to beat for several hours. As we will see in Chapter 44, all vertebrate hearts receive both stimulatory and inhibitory nerve impulses that regulate the rhythm and intensity of the heartbeat. When dissected from an animal, these nerves remain attached to the heart and their function can be studied in a bath solution.

When Loewi electrically stimulated a certain nerve attached to the frog's heart, the rate at which the heart contracted increased. However, if he stimulated a different nerve, known as the vagus nerve, the heart rate decreased. Loewi wondered how electrical activity in different neurons could have opposite effects. He hypothesized that a stimulated neuron released a chemical substance that could influence muscles and other neurons in different ways, but he did not know how to test the hypothesis. As he described later, the idea for the definitive experiment came to him in the middle of the night: "The night before the Easter Sunday of that year I awoke, turned on the light, and jotted down a few notes on a tiny slip of paper. Then I fell asleep again. It occurred to me at six o'clock in the morning that during the night I had written down something most important, but I was unable to decipher the scrawl. The next night, at three o'clock, the idea returned. . . . I got up immediately, went to the laboratory, and performed a simple experiment on a frog heart according to the nocturnal design."

As shown in **Figure 41.16,** Loewi placed two frog hearts in separate, but connected, chambers containing saline. He used an electrode to stimulate the vagus nerve that was still attached to the first heart and recorded the heart rate. As he expected from an earlier experiment, the heart rate slowed. Within a few minutes, the heart rate of the second heart also slowed even though he had not stimulated the nerve to that heart at all. He concluded that a chemical substance was released from the nerve of the first heart into the surrounding fluid and diffused into the second chamber, where it exerted its effects on the second heart.

Loewi initially named this substance *Vagusstoff* (vagus substance) after the vagus nerve he stimulated, but it was later renamed acetylcholine when its chemical nature (acetic acid bonded to choline) was determined. Acetylcholine was the first neurotransmitter discovered, which was a major achievement in neuroscience. Loewi's research opened the door for what we now know about chemical transmission at synapses, and the enormous pharmaceutical industry, which builds on this knowledge to treat neurological disorders.

Experimental Questions

1. What observations led Loewi to develop his hypothesis of how nerves stimulate muscle contractions?
2. What was Loewi's hypothesis to explain the observations of changes in the rate of contraction of the frog heart muscle? Describe his experimental design to test his hypothesis. Why did he use two hearts?
3. What were the results of Loewi's experiment? Did the results support his hypothesis?

HYPOTHESIS Neurons release chemical substances that influence the activity of the heart.

KEY MATERIALS Two frog hearts, saline solution, and stimulating and recording electrodes.

| Experimental level | Conceptual level |

1 Dissect hearts from two frogs and place in saline solution. Heart 1 still has its vagus nerve attached.

Saline solution

Vagus nerve

Heart 1 with vagus nerve intact

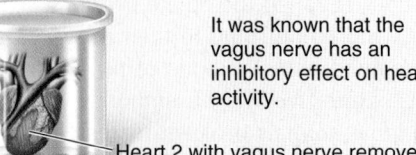

It was known that the vagus nerve has an inhibitory effect on heart activity.

Heart 2 with vagus nerve removed

2 Electrically stimulate vagus nerve of heart 1.

Heart 1

Stimulating electrode

Action potential

Branches of vagus nerve

Action potentials travel along vagus nerve to heart 1.

3 Record strength and number of beats in heart 1 before and after electrical stimulation of vagus nerve. Next, remove a sample of the saline solution in and around heart 1, and transfer to heart 2. Record activity of heart 2. This was done using mercury manometers that were connected to each heart. The manometers measure pressure, which is due to the contractile force of the heart beating.

Heart 1   Heart 2

If stimulation of vagus nerve resulted in the release of chemicals onto heart 1, then these same chemicals (some of which may diffuse into the saline solution) should have an identical effect on heart 2.

4 | **THE DATA**

Stimulation of vagus nerve of heart 1

Contractile force

Time (sec)

Heart 1 response

Addition of saline solution from within and around heart 1

Contractile force

Time (sec)

Heart 2 response

5 | **CONCLUSION** Electrical stimulation causes the vagus nerve to secrete chemicals that decrease heart contractions.

6 | **SOURCE** Loewi, O. 1921. On humoral transmission of the action of heart nerves. Pflügers archives. *European Journal of Physiology* 189:239–242.

Figure 41.16 Loewi's experimental discovery of chemical neurotransmission.

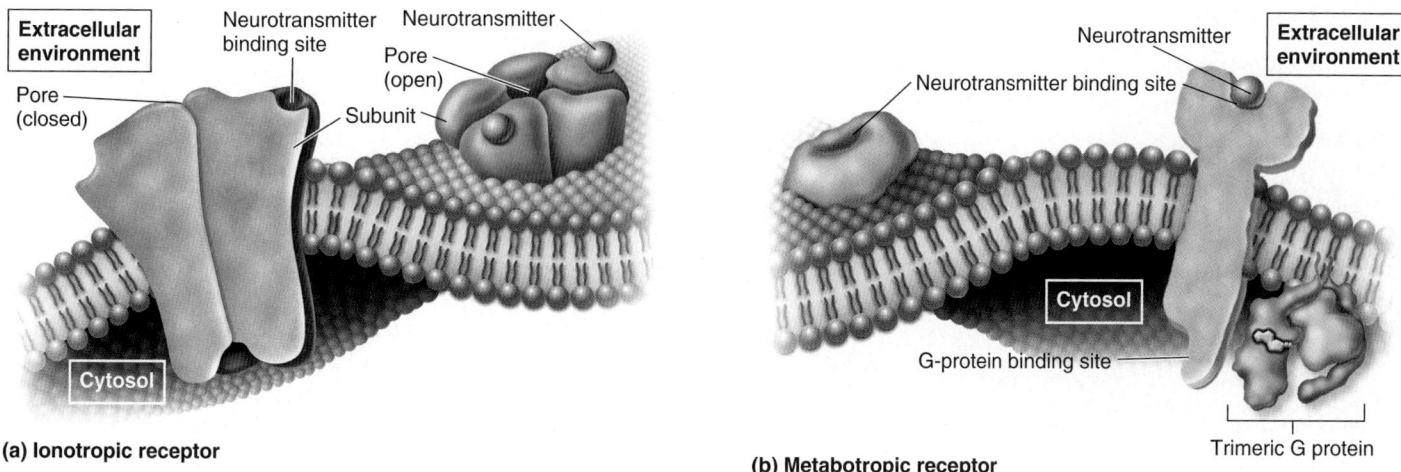

Figure 41.17 The two major categories of postsynaptic receptors. (a) Ionotropic receptors have several subunits. Neurotransmitters bind to ionotropic receptors and directly open ion channels in the membrane. (b) Metabotropic receptors are G-protein-coupled receptors, which are discussed in Chapter 9. Neurotransmitters bind to metabotropic receptors and open ion channels indirectly through G proteins.

Postsynaptic Receptors Determine the Response to Neurotransmitters

As we have seen, the same neurotransmitter can have both excitatory and inhibitory effects. The response of the postsynaptic neuron depends on the type of receptor that is present in the postsynaptic membrane. The two major types of postsynaptic receptors are ionotropic and metabotropic, and many neurotransmitters act on both (**Figure 41.17**). Neurotransmitter molecules bind to the extracellular portion of these receptors.

Ionotropic receptors are ligand-gated ion channels that open in response to binding of a neurotransmitter molecule. When neurotransmitter molecules bind to these receptors, ions flow through the channels to cause an EPSP or IPSP. Acetylcholine, the biogenic amines, and amino acids bind to ionotropic receptors. Ionotropic receptors are composed of multiple subunits. Like K$^+$ channels, the subunits associate in a ring to form the receptor's channel. For instance, the ionotropic acetylcholine receptor has five subunits, named alpha, beta, and so on. The α subunit is the only one that binds acetylcholine.

Metabotropic receptors are G-protein-coupled receptors (GPCRs), which are described in Chapter 9. They do not form a channel but instead are coupled to an intracellular signalling pathway that initiates changes in the postsynaptic cell. Metabotropic cascades produce second messengers as part of signal transduction pathways that produce a postsynaptic response. A common type of response is the phosphorylation of ion channels for sodium, potassium, or calcium ions, which are present in the plasma membrane. Metabotropic receptors are important in activating sensory cells that respond to visual and other stimuli.

GENOMES AND PROTEOMES

Neurotransmitter Receptors Have Varied Subunit Compositions

As mentioned earlier, gamma-aminobutyric acid (GABA) is an inhibitory neurotransmitter that opens Cl$^-$ channels. Though cells can possess different types of GABA receptors, we will focus here on one type that functions as a ligand-gated ion channel. This ionotropic receptor, which we will simply refer to as the GABA-A receptor, binds GABA and thereby opens the channel. This event allows Cl$^-$ to diffuse into the cell, causing a hyperpolarization of the plasma membrane and shifting the membrane toward the equilibrium potential for Cl$^-$ (usually around -90 mV) (**Figure 41.18**). In this way, GABA binding to this receptor decreases the likelihood that a neuron will generate an action potential.

The GABA-A receptor is a good example of how receptor subunits can influence a postsynaptic response to a neurotransmitter. GABA-A receptor proteins are usually composed of five subunits (designated α, β, and so on). The genomes of humans and other mammals have a group of homologous genes that encode at least 19 different GABA-A receptor subunits. In addition, subunit variation can be further increased by alternative splicing, which is described in Chapter 12. This amazing

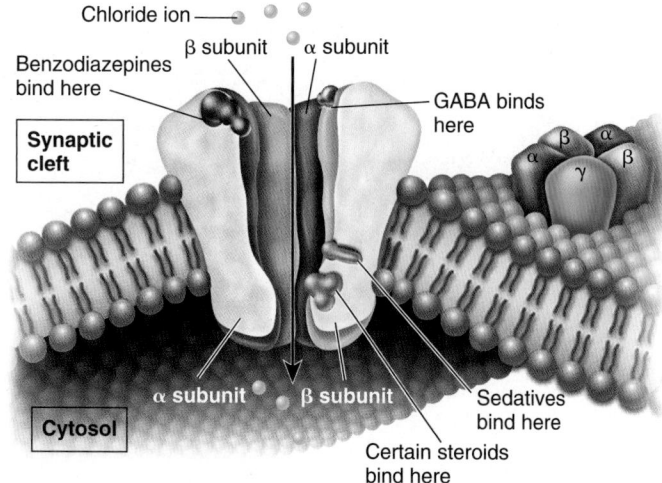

Figure 41.18   The structure and function of the GABA-A receptor.   Each type of GABA-A receptor has five subunits that form an anion channel allowing the passage of Cl⁻ ions. When GABA binds to the receptor, chloride ions move through the open channel and hyperpolarize the cell. Various other molecules bind to different sites on the receptor. These include molecules that naturally occur in animals' bodies, such as certain steroid hormones, and drugs, such as sedatives and benzodiazepines, used to treat anxiety and other disorders.

 Principle: *Structure determines function. Neurotransmitter receptors are excellent examples of this biological principle at the molecular level. The three-dimensional structure of the receptor determines its ability to bind a particular neurotransmitter and, as shown in this figure, various other ligands that can modulate the receptor's activity.*

variety in subunits allows cells to express many different kinds of GABA-A receptors.

What are the benefits of having so many different GABA-A subunits? Though the answer is not entirely understood, each type of subunit has its own unique properties that can fine-tune the function of the GABA-A receptor so that it works optimally in the neuron in which it is expressed. The various subunits may differ in their affinity for GABA and the rate of Cl⁻ movement through the channel. In addition, neuroscientists have been particularly interested in whether the various subunits differ in their ability to recognize molecules other than GABA (Figure 41.18). This work has shown that the subunits of the GABA receptor bind a variety of other molecules, including naturally occurring ones such as certain steroid hormones. Presumably, the binding of these molecules enhances or reduces GABA's effectiveness in activating the receptor. This knowledge has proven beneficial in understanding how certain drugs exert their actions. For example, ethanol—found in alcoholic drinks—binds to one of the GABA-A receptor subunits expressed in brain and motor neurons, and enhances the actions of GABA. This explains why alcohol depresses the activity of the brain and impairs motor coordination, among other effects. Other subunits of the GABA-A receptor bind drugs, such as Valium, that are used to treat certain psychological problems, such as chronic anxiety. Apparently, the inhibitory effects of GABA are part of the mechanism for achieving a balance between alertness, anxiety, and calmness. The ability of the receptor to bind numerous ligands, and the many different combinations of subunits in the receptor, provides an enormous degree of control over precisely how this neurotransmitter system regulates the activity of the brain.

41.4   HUMAN HEALTH CONNECTION

Learning Outcomes:

1. Describe how disorders of neurotransmission can affect human mood.
2. List several "recreational" and illicit drugs and describe the corresponding effects these drugs have on the nervous system.
3. Give examples of disorders of neural conduction and how they arise.

When neurons fail to develop properly or their function is impaired, the consequences can be severe, affecting mood, behaviour, and even the ability to think or move. More than 100 neurological disorders (diseases of the nervous system) have been identified in humans, and drugs to treat them are among the most widely prescribed medicines today (**Table 41.3**). Many recreational drugs also exert their effects by altering neurotransmission. The use of these drugs, therefore, results in symptoms similar to those of neurological disorders.

Disorders of Neurotransmission Can Impact Mood

Several neurological disorders result from disrupted neurotransmission between cells. Genetic processes involved in the production of neurotransmitters or malfunction of synaptic events can increase or decrease activity at synapses, which in turn affects emotions and behaviour. One mood disorder is manic depression, also called bipolar disorder, in which individuals experience shifts between periods of euphoria (extreme happiness) and despair.

The most common mood disorder is major depression (unipolar depression), which results in prolonged periods of sadness and despair without alternating episodes of euphoria. Major depression affects 5%–12% of men and 10%–25% of women at some point in their lifetime. This condition is thought to result from decreased activity of synapses that release biogenic amines, such as serotonin, which changes neuronal activity within specific areas in the brain involved in processing emotion. Only recently has it become accepted that mood disorders can be caused by changes in the balance of neurotransmitters in the brain. Perhaps the best evidence of a physiological basis for depression is that mood

Table 41.3   Effects of Common Drugs on Neurotransmitter Action and Mood

Name of drug	Actions on neurotransmission	Effects on mood	Effects of abuse
Alcohol (ethanol)	Enhances inhibitory GABA transmission, increases dopamine transmission, inhibits glutamate transmission	Relaxation, euphoria, sleepiness	Liver damage, brain damage
Amphetamines *uppers, crystal meth, pep pills*	Stimulate the release of dopamine and norepinephrine; prevents their reuptake from synapse	Euphoria, increased activity	High blood pressure, psychosis
Antidepressants *Tricyclic antidepressants; for example, Elavil, Anafranil*	Block the reuptake of norepinephrine from synapses	Relieve depression and obsessive-compulsive disorder	Drowsiness, confusion
Selective serotonin reuptake inhibitors; for example, Prozac, Zoloft, Paxil, Lexapro	Block the reuptake of serotonin from synapses	Relieve depression and obsessive-compulsive disorder	Insomnia, anxiety, headache
Monoamine oxidase inhibitors; for example, Parnate, Nardil	Block the breakdown of biogenic amine neurotransmitters	Relieve depression	Liver damage, hyperexcitability
Antianxiety drugs *Benzodiazepines; for example, Xanax, Valium, Librium, Rohypnol, (date rape drug, roofies, roach)*	Bind to GABA receptors and increase inhibitory neurotransmission	Sedation, sleepiness, amnesia	Drowsiness
Antipsychotic drugs *Phenothiazines; for example, Thorazine, Mellaril, Stelazine, Abilify, Risperdal*	Block dopamine receptors	Ease schizophrenic symptoms	Decreased movement
Cocaine	Causes release of dopamine and norepinephrine; blocks dopamine reuptake	Intense euphoria followed by depression	Convulsions, hallucinations, death from overdose
LSD (lysergic acid diethylamine)	Binds to serotonin receptors	Hallucinations, sensory distortions	Unpredictable and irrational behaviour
Marijuana (tetrahydrocannibinol)	Binds to receptors for natural cannabinoids	Increased sense of well-being, decreased short-term memory, decreased goal-directed behaviour, increased appetite	Delusions, paranoia, confusion
Narcotics *Heroin, morphine, Demerol, codeine*	Bind to opiate receptors	Pain relief, euphoria, sedation	Slowed breathing, death from overdose
Nicotine	Initially stimulates but then depresses activity in adrenal medulla and neurons in the peripheral nervous system; increases dopamine in brain	Increased attention, decreased irritability	Heart disease and lung disease
PCP (phencyclidine) *Angel dust, ozone*	Blocks channel for excitatory amino acid neurotransmitters; increases dopamine activity	Violent behaviour, feelings of power, numbness, disorganized thoughts	Psychosis, convulsions, coma, death

disorders occur more frequently in certain families, suggesting a genetic component. Drugs can be very effective in treating these disorders (Table 41.3).

Recreational Drugs Disrupt Normal Neurotransmission

Most so-called recreational drugs work at the synapse to either enhance or interfere with the normal mechanisms of neurotransmission (Table 41.3). In the presynaptic terminal, drugs can decrease neurotransmitter release by reducing calcium movement into the cell or preventing the exocytosis of vesicles containing stored neurotransmitters. In the synaptic cleft, drugs can slow the rate at which the neurotransmitter is broken down into an inactive form or taken back up into the presynaptic neuron, thereby prolonging the action of the neurotransmitter in the synaptic cleft. Some substances act on the postsynaptic membrane by either preventing the neurotransmitter from binding to its receptor, or acting as a substitute for the neurotransmitter by stimulating the receptor.

In effect, these drugs produce changes or imbalances in neurotransmission similar to those observed in some neurological disorders. These substances can induce euphoria, increase activity, alter mood, and produce hallucinations. They can also have serious, sometimes life-threatening effects and can be highly addictive.

Some drugs, such as cocaine, block the removal of dopamine from the synaptic cleft by preventing its reuptake into the presynaptic terminal. Morphine and marijuana mimic the actions of biological substances already in the brain, binding to receptors on the postsynaptic membrane. For these drugs, the resulting effects are much stronger than the effects of natural neurotransmitters. It is no surprise that recreational drugs are mind altering. They do, after all, change the ways in which neurons communicate with each other.

Disorders of Conduction May Result in Motor Problems and Abnormal Neuronal Development

Some human diseases are caused by the inability of the axon to properly conduct an action potential. This occurs most commonly because an axon fails to become myelinated or a myelinated axon becomes demyelinated.

In **cretinism**, axons fail to become wrapped with myelin during fetal life, which leads to slow conduction speeds and abnormal connections between brain neurons. This results in profound mental defects that cannot be reversed unless treatment begins immediately after birth. Cretinism is caused by insufficient levels of thyroid hormone in the fetus, usually because the mother's dietary intake of iodine (which is required for synthesis of thyroid hormone) was too low. Cretinism is rare in Canada since the advent of iodized table salt, but it is not uncommon in many parts of the world.

Unlike cretinism, **multiple sclerosis (MS)** begins in adulthood—usually between the ages of 20 and 50—in individuals with apparently healthy nervous systems. With MS, the patient's own body, for reasons that are unknown, attacks and destroys myelin as if it were a foreign substance. Eventually, these repeated attacks leave multiple scarred (sclerotic) areas of tissue in the nervous system and impair the function of myelinated neurons that control movement, speech, memory, and emotion. MS is a serious and unpredictable disease, characterized by flare-ups followed by periods of remission in which symptoms are reduced or absent. No cure is currently available, but certain drugs may slow its progression and reduce the severity of symptoms. MS affects roughly 50,000 Canadians and 2.5 million people worldwide, 60%–75% percent of them women.

Summary of Key Concepts

41.1 Cellular Components of Nervous Systems

- The central nervous system (CNS) is composed of a brain and a nerve cord. The peripheral nervous system (PNS) consists of all neurons and their projections that are outside of and connect with the CNS. (Figure 41.1)
- The two major classes of cells in nervous systems are neurons and glia. (Figure 41.2)

- Types of neurons include sensory neurons, motor neurons, and interneurons. A neuron's structure is a reflection of its function. (Figure 41.3)
- The most basic circuit is a reflex arc, which occurs rapidly in response to inputs from sensory neurons and consists of only one or a few afferent and efferent cells. (Figure 41.4)

41.2 Electrical Properties of Neurons

- Neurons use electrical signals to communicate with other neurons, muscles, or glands. These nerve impulses involve changes in the amount of electric charge across a cell's plasma membrane. (Figures 41.5, 41.6, Table 41.1)
- Diffusion of ions through membrane channels occurs as a result of the relative concentration of an ion on both sides of the membrane and the electric charge across the membrane. Ions move in response to an electrochemical gradient. (Figure 41.7)
- The Nernst equation gives the equilibrium potential for an ion at any given concentration gradient.

41.3 Communication Between Neurons

- Gated ion channels enable a cell to communicate by changing its membrane potential rapidly. The opening and closing of voltage-gated and ligand-gated ion channels cause two types of changes in the neuron's membrane potential: graded potentials and action potentials. (Figures 41.8, 41.9)
- When a graded potential is large enough to spread to the axon hillock and depolarize the membrane to its threshold potential, this causes an action potential that carries an electrical signal from the axon hillock to the axon terminal. (Figures 41.10, 41.11)
- Axon diameter and myelination influence the speed of an action potential. (Figure 41.12)
- Electrical synapses are connected via gap junctions. Most vertebrate neurons communicate via chemical synapses in which a neurotransmitter carries the signal from the presynaptic to the postsynaptic cell. Many EPSPs generated at one time can sum together and bring the membrane potential to the threshold potential for action potential firing. (Figures 41.13, 41.14, 41.15)
- Chemical classes of neurotransmitters found in animals include acetylcholine, biogenic amines, amino acids, neuropeptides, and gaseous neurotransmitters. (Table 41.2, Figure 41.16)
- The response of the postsynaptic neuron determines the types of signals that pass from one neuron to the other. The two major types of postsynaptic receptors are ionotropic and metabotropic. (Figures 41.17, 41.18)

41.4 Human Health Connection

- Most neurological conditions can be classified as disorders of either neurotransmission or conduction. Mood disorders caused by disrupted neurotransmission include major depression (unipolar depression). Drugs used in the treatment of neurological disorders and recreational drugs usually alter neurotransmission. (Table 41.3)
- Some neurological conditions are caused by the inability of the axon to conduct an action potential. This occurs most commonly because axons fail to become myelinated (cretinism), or myelinated axons become demyelinated (multiple sclerosis).

Test to Assess Your Learning

1. In vertebrates, the brain and the spinal cord are parts of
   a. the peripheral nervous system.
   b. the enteric nervous system.
   c. the central nervous system.
   d. the autonomic nervous system.
   e. the endocrine system.

2. The structures of a neuron that function mainly in receiving signals from other neurons are
   a. the myelin sheaths.
   b. the axons.
   c. the nerve termini.
   d. the dendrites.
   e. the K^+ channels.

3. The glial cells that form the myelin sheath in the peripheral nervous system are called
   a. astrocytes.
   b. oligodendrocytes.
   c. microglia.
   d. neurons.
   e. Schwann cells.

4. Neurons that function mainly in connecting other neurons in the central nervous system are
   a. sensory neurons.
   b. efferent neurons.
   c. motor neurons.
   d. afferent neurons.
   e. interneurons.

5. The difference in charges across the plasma membrane of an unstimulated cell is called
   a. the membrane potential.
   b. the resting potential.
   c. homeostasis.
   d. the graded potential.
   e. the action potential.

6. Which of the following influences the resting potential of a membrane?
   a. negatively charged molecules or ions inside the cell
   b. active transport of ions across the membrane
   c. concentration of Na^+ and K^+ inside and outside the cell
   d. all of the above
   e. (b) and (c) only

7. A cell has reached a threshold potential when it has depolarized to the point where voltage-gated
   a. K^+ channels open.
   b. Na^+ channels open.
   c. K^+ channels close.
   d. Na^+ channels close.
   e. both (b) and (d).

8. The speed of transmission of an action potential along an axon is influenced by
   a. the presence of myelin.
   b. an increased concentration of $Ca2^+$.
   c. the diameter of the axon.
   d. all of the above.
   e. (a) and (c) only.

9. Gap junctions are characteristic of
   a. electrical synapses.
   b. chemical synapses.
   c. acetylcholine synapses.
   d. GABA synapses.
   e. (c) and (d) only.

10. The response of the postsynaptic cell is determined by
    a. the type of neurotransmitter released at the synapse.
    b. the type of receptors the postsynaptic cell has.
    c. the number of Na^+ channels in the postsynaptic membrane.
    d. the number of K^+ channels in the postsynaptic membrane.
    e. all of the above.

Articulate to Assess Your Learning

1. Distinguish between neurons and glial cells and give an example of a glial cell.

2. Describe the difference between a graded potential and an action potential.

3. Explain how the transmission of an impulse occurs across a chemical synapse.

Collaborate to Assess and Extend Your Learning

1. Discuss different types of reflexes in animals. Once initiated, must all reflexes occur to completion, or do you think that in some cases they can be overridden?

2. Select three types of drugs that affect neurotransmitter action and discuss what would happen if someone were to take all three at once.

3. 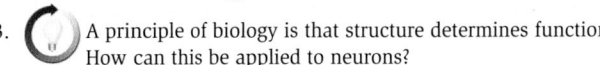 A principle of biology is that structure determines function. How can this be applied to neurons?

Visit McGraw-Hill Ryerson Connect™ for additional study resources.

The Brain, Nervous Systems, and Sensory Reception

Chapter Outline

Three-dimensional reconstruction of the brain of *Drosophila*. The brains of animals are organized into anatomic structures with specialized functions.

The brain of an adult person weighs only about 1.5 kilograms, yet it consumes 20%–30% of the body's energy! This amazing fact emphasizes the enormous level of metabolic activity that goes on continually in the brain, even during sleep. The human brain is incredibly complex and has several thousand kilometres of interconnected neurons, which number around 100 billion. The brain allows us to move, think, and experience sensation and emotion. Groups of neurons also coordinate homeostatic functions, such as breathing, blood circulation, and body temperature. When we examine the way that groups of neurons communicate, we begin to understand the complex mental functions of nervous systems, including learning, memory, and motivation.

The challenge of neuroscience is to transform the overwhelming complexity of nervous systems into manageable proportions. For this reason, most neuroscientists do not study the human nervous system, because of its great complexity and the difficulties inherent in doing research on humans. Many animals, however—including the nematode *Caenorhabditis elegans*, the sea slug *Aplysia californica*, the fruit fly *Drosophila melanogaster* (see the chapter-opening photo), the zebrafish *Danio rerio*, and the mouse *Mus musculus*—provide excellent opportunities to study how neurons work and how groups of neurons cooperate to produce animal behaviour. The genomes of most of these animals have been sequenced, and neuroscientists are identifying genes that are critical for the structure and function of nervous systems. Many of the relevant genes are homologous to human genes, so the study of the molecular control of the nervous system in these model animals has the potential to reveal new treatments for many genetically inherited neurological diseases in humans.

In this chapter, we will first survey a variety of nervous systems, which allow animals to sense and respond to environmental changes. Detailed information about the complex nervous system of humans can be found in the Appendix to this chapter, available on Connect™. However, keep in mind that we still have much to learn about the organization, connectivity, and functions of nervous system structures.

42.1 EVOLUTION OF THE BRAIN AND NERVOUS SYSTEMS

Learning Outcomes:

1. List the different types of nervous systems found in animals.
2. Describe the general anatomical organization of the brain in vertebrates.
3. Discuss the changes in brain complexity that accompanied the evolution of mammals.

The nervous systems of animals are the products of hundreds of millions of years of evolution. They provide advantages to animals that promote reproductive success. For example, nervous systems allow animals to keenly sense their environment and respond to changes in an appropriate way. In addition, nervous systems form connections with muscle systems and facilitate movements, which has allowed animals to travel short and long distances to obtain food. Likewise, nervous systems help animals to avoid predation.

Studying the evolution and development of nervous systems helps us understand how particular nervous systems are adapted to different functions. At the structural level, the organization of nervous systems ranges from a relatively simple network of a few cells to the marvellous complexity of the human brain. The characteristics of an animal's nervous system determine the behaviours that it displays. In this section, we will survey the nervous systems of invertebrates and vertebrates, and examine the brains of vertebrates in greater detail.

Nervous Systems Evolved to Sense and Respond to Changes in the Environment

Except for sponges, all animals have a nervous system. The simplest nervous system is the **nerve net** of the cnidarians (jellyfish, hydras, and anemones) (**Figure 42.1a**). In these organisms, no single group of neurons controls all the others. Instead, the neurons connect to one another in a network that can be activated all at once. This allows the organism to contract and move large areas of its tentacles and body simultaneously. Some cnidarians, such as the jellyfish, have two nerve nets, one for moving tentacles and one for swimming. Sea stars and other echinoderms have a slightly more sophisticated nervous system with a nerve ring around the mouth that is connected to larger radial nerves extending into the arms (**Figure 42.1b**). This arrangement allows the mouth and arms to operate independently.

More complex invertebrate nervous systems usually consist of one or two **nerve cords** that extend from the anterior end of the animal to the tail. In the flatworm (*Planaria*), collections of neurons in the animal's head form **ganglia** (singular: ganglion), which are groups of neuronal cell bodies that perform basic functions of integrating inputs from sense organs, such as the eyes, and controlling motor outputs, such as those involved in swimming (**Figure 42.1c**). Two nerve cords extend along the ventral surface of the animal into the tail and are connected to each other by transverse nerves. In annelids (segmented worms), the basic structure is similar, except that more neurons

are present and the ventral nerve cord has ganglia located in each body segment (**Figure 42.1d**). In the head, a ganglion, known as an integrative centre, functions as a rudimentary brain to control body movements. The other ventral ganglia along the nerve cord receive sensory information from a particular body segment and control local movements. In the simpler forms of molluscs, such as the snail, the nervous system is very similar to that of the annelids. The brain is composed of a pair of anterior ganglia; paired nerve cords extend from these ganglia to the eyes, muscular foot, and gut.

During the evolution of animals, more complex body types have been associated with **cephalization** (from the Greek, *cephalo*, meaning "head"), which is the formation of an increasingly complex **brain** in the head that controls sensory and motor functions of the entire body. Within the brain, neuronal pathways provide integrative functions necessary for an animal to make more sophisticated responses to its environment. Brains are found in all vertebrates and most invertebrates, and they are usually composed of more than one anatomical and functional region. For instance, in *Drosophila* (**Figure 42.1e**), the brain has several subdivisions with separate functions, such as a region devoted to learning and memory. More derived molluscs, such as the squid and octopus, have brains with well-developed subdivisions that allow these animals to coordinate complex visual and motor behaviours necessary for their predatory lifestyle (**Figure 42.1f**). In vertebrates and simpler chordates, the brain is connected to the **spinal cord** and constitutes

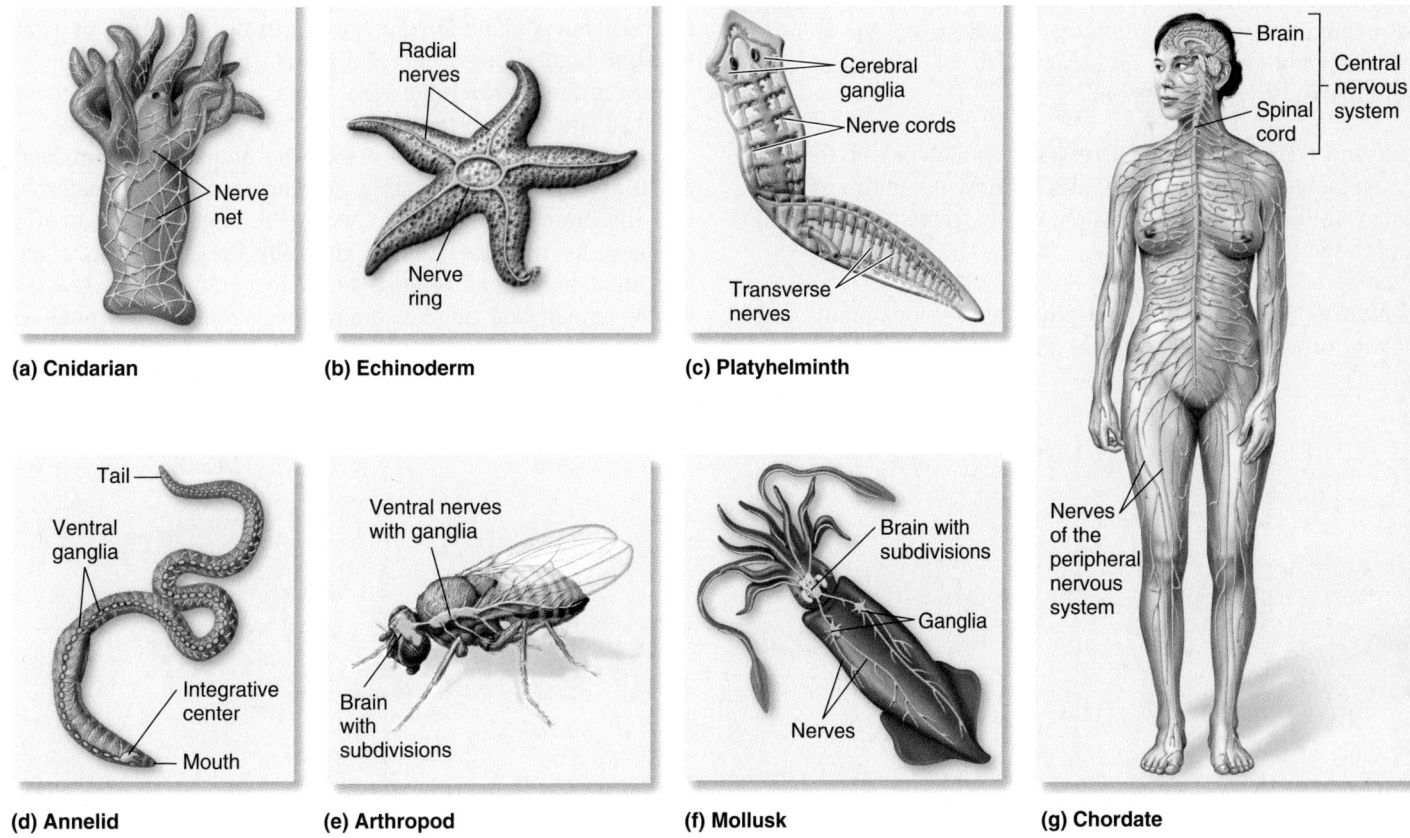

(a) Cnidarian   (b) Echinoderm   (c) Platyhelminth

(d) Annelid   (e) Arthropod   (f) Mollusk   (g) Chordate

Figure 42.1   Representative nervous systems throughout the animal kingdom.

the **central nervous system (CNS)** (**Figure 42.1g**). As discussed later, nerves from the **peripheral nervous system** route information into and out of the central nervous system at separate regions along the spinal cord. The vertebrate spinal cord and the bony vertebrae have an organization that shows similarities to the segmented nervous system of invertebrates.

Brains of Vertebrates Have Three Basic Divisions

Development of the vertebrate brain begins with the formation of a central fold in the embryo called the **neural tube**. This hollow tube is the structure from which the entire nervous system develops. Bending and folding of the neural tube during embryonic development results in bulges that become separate divisions of the nervous system. The anterior end develops into the brain, while the posterior portion becomes the spinal cord.

In vertebrates, the brain has a triad structure—**hindbrain**, **midbrain**, and **forebrain**. In fish, the brain remains a three-part structure. Fossils of jawless fishes that lived 500 million years ago show that their brains were already organized into the three basic divisions that have been retained in all modern vertebrates. In vertebrates with more complex brains, the hindbrain and forebrain each form two separate divisions, but the midbrain does not divide. The development of brain subdivisions (**Figure 42.2**) provides additional specialization and increases the capacity of the brain to perform complex functions.

Hindbrain   The hindbrain includes the medulla oblongata, pons, and cerebellum. The medulla oblongata coordinates many basic reflexes and bodily functions, such as breathing, that maintain the normal homeostatic processes of the animal. The cerebellum and pons are responsible for monitoring and coordinating body movements.

Midbrain   The midbrain processes several types of sensory inputs, including vision, smell, and hearing. It controls sophisticated tasks, such as coordinating eye movement with visual inspection of the environment.

Forebrain   The forebrain also processes sensory inputs and consists of a group of structures that are responsible for the higher functions of conscious thought, planning, and emotion. Many of these functions are attributed to the cerebrum. The surface layer is called the cerebral cortex, which is only a few millimetres thick. Other structures of the forebrain are beneath the cerebrum. These include the thalamus and hypothalamus, which we will discuss later in this chapter.

The relative sizes of the brain divisions vary in different animals (Figure 42.2). Usually, a larger area plays a greater role in an animal's life. In addition, the functions performed by these divisions have changed through evolution. For instance, the midbrain in fishes is relatively large compared with the other two areas, and it plays a key role in vision. By comparison, the forebrain is the largest division in birds and mammals and is largely responsible for vision.

Increased Brain Complexity Involves a Larger, Highly Folded Cerebrum

As vertebrates with more complex nervous systems evolved, the size of the cerebrum also increased, making up a greater proportion of the brain. Many of the important functions of the cerebrum are carried out by neurons along its outer surface called the cortex. Therefore, increased complexity of the brain is also correlated with an increased surface area of the cerebral cortex. During the evolution of more complex mammals, this increase in surface area is thought to have occurred more rapidly than an expansion in the size of the skull. But how could this occur? The answer is that the external surface of the cerebrum may be highly convoluted, forming many folds. Compare the relatively smooth-looking surface of the cerebrum of a rat with the highly folded one of a human in **Figure 42.3**. If the surface of the human brain were spread out, it would be about 2,300 square centimetres!

As body size increases across the animal kingdom, you might expect that brain mass would increase proportionately—that the brain of an elephant would be larger than that of a monkey, for instance. That is generally the case, with a few important exceptions (**Figure 42.4**). In particular, the masses of the human and dolphin brains are greater than would be expected on the basis of body mass.

   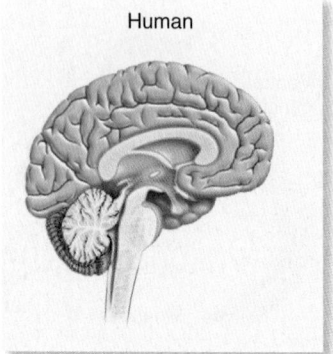

Figure 42.2   **Comparison of vertebrate brains.**   The three major divisions of the brain are shown in a fish, a frog, a bird, and a human.

Figure 42.3 The degree of cerebral cortex folding in different mammalian species. The brains are not shown to scale.

Concept check: *Based on size and cerebral cortex folding, pick two animals capable of more complex behaviours and two that would be less capable.*

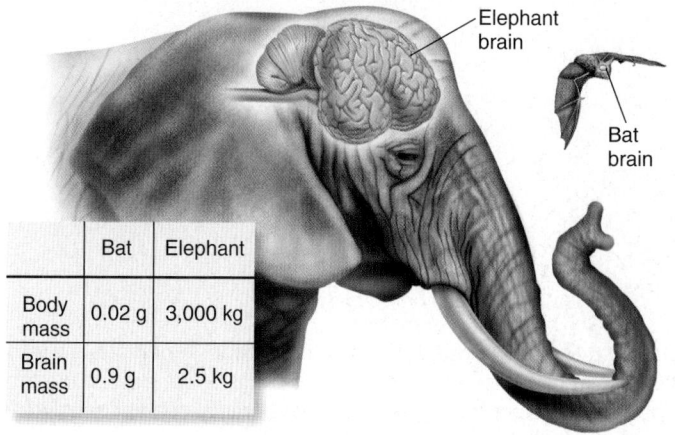

	Bat	Elephant
Body mass	0.02 g	3,000 kg
Brain mass	0.9 g	2.5 kg

Figure 42.4 Brain mass as a function of body mass in mammals. For most mammals, brain weight is in proportion to body mass. However, humans and dolphins have a much higher brain mass relative to their body mass than do other mammals.

Brain mass and the amount of folding are correlated with more complex behaviours. Why is this so? The outer surface of the brain, the cerebral cortex, plays a key role in conscious thought, reasoning, and learning. Greater size and folding provide more surface area, which allows greater processing and interpretation of information. Even so, evidence does not suggest that people with small differences in brain size differ in intelligence. Also, it would be wrong to assume that an animal with a small brain is profoundly limited in its behavioural repertoire. A bat with a 0.9-g brain and an elephant with a 2,500-g brain can both perform a great variety of interesting and complex behaviours, such as navigating across great distances and interacting with conspecifics.

42.2 CENTRAL AND PERIPHERAL NERVOUS SYSTEMS

Learning Outcomes:

1. Outline the anatomical organization of the vertebrate nervous system.
2. Describe the organization of the peripheral nervous system.

3. Distinguish between the somatic and autonomic nervous systems.
4. Briefly describe the major structures and functions of the human hindbrain, midbrain, and forebrain.

The nervous system of the human is wonderfully complex—the brain alone has more than 100 billion neurons and has the highest ratio of glia to neurons of any vertebrate. Complexity is defined by more than just numbers of cells. Within the human brain, for example, are enormous numbers of connections among neurons—a single neuron in the cerebellum may have as many as 10^5 synapses with other cells. In this section, we will examine the human nervous system, with an emphasis on the functions of the major parts of the brain and spinal cord.

The Nervous System Is Composed of the Central and Peripheral Nervous Systems

As mentioned, the brain and spinal cord constitute the central nervous system (CNS) of vertebrates (**Figure 42.5**). The peripheral nervous system (PNS) is composed of neurons and axons of neurons that are outside the CNS and communicate with it. The CNS and PNS are connected anatomically and functionally.

Central nervous system

Brain

Spinal cord

Peripheral nervous system

Cranial nerves

Ganglia

Spinal nerves

Brain

Spinal cord

(a) **The human nervous system**

(b) **The amphibian nervous system**

Figure 42.5 **Organization of the vertebrate nervous system.** The central nervous system is similar in vertebrates as distantly related as **(a)** humans and **(b)** frogs. It consists of the brain and spinal cord, both of which are encased in bone (not shown). The peripheral nervous system includes cranial nerves, ganglia, and spinal nerves, which carry information to and from the CNS, and many other neurons throughout the body.

The CNS receives information about the internal or external environment from the PNS. The CNS interprets that information and may initiate a response that is then carried out by the PNS. For example, suppose you accidentally lean against a newly painted fence. Neuronal endings in your skin, which are part of the PNS, would transmit information about the sense of touch through axons that bring information directly into the spinal cord. From there, the information travels to your brain, where the sensation is analyzed and identified as something wet. Signals are sent from your brain, down your spinal cord, and through the neurons of the PNS to your muscles, causing you to move away.

Within the nervous system, groups of neurons may associate with each other and perform a particular function. In the CNS, the cell bodies of neurons that are involved in a similar function may be grouped into a structure called a **nucleus** (plural: nuclei), which may include thousands of cells. For instance, cell bodies that regulate body temperature and those that recognize visual information are located in separate nuclei in the brain. As mentioned earlier, the term ganglion is also used to refer to a group of neuronal cell bodies but usually in the PNS (Figure 42.5). Within an animal's body, many myelinated axons may run in parallel bundles. (Myelination is described in Chapter 41.) Such a structure is called a **tract** when it is found in the CNS. Tracts convey information within the brain and between the brain and the spinal cord. Bundles of myelinated axons also form **nerves**, which are found in the PNS. Nerves make contact with structures outside the CNS and transmit signals that enter or leave the CNS. Nerve connections between the PNS and the CNS occur at the brain or spinal cord. **Cranial nerves** are directly connected to the brain. They are located in the head and transmit incoming and outgoing information between the PNS and the brain. By comparison, **spinal nerves** are connections between the PNS and spinal cord (Figure 42.5).

One of the most obvious characteristics of the CNS becomes noticeable in nonliving tissue. After death, some parts look white, while others appear grey (**Figure 42.6**). The **white matter** consists of myelinated axons that are bundled together in large numbers to form tracts. The **grey matter** consists of neuronal cell bodies, dendrites, and some unmyelinated axons. The cerebral cortex is composed of grey matter that sits on top of a large collection of white matter pathways. In the spinal cord, the grey matter is located in the centre and forms two dorsal horns and two ventral horns. Each dorsal horn connects to a dorsal root, which is part of a spinal nerve. Dorsal roots receive incoming information from sensory (afferent) nerves of the PNS. The ventral horn connects to the ventral root, which is also part of a spinal nerve that transmits outgoing information to motor (efferent) nerves.

Figure 42.6 **Grey matter and white matter in the CNS.** The grey matter is composed of groups of cell bodies, dendrites, and unmyelinated axons, while the white matter consists of tracks of myelinated axons. **(a)** Cross section of a rat brain, **(b)** Cross-section of a human brain.

Unlike the PNS, the CNS is encased in protective structures including bone (the skull and backbone) and three layers of sheathlike membranes called **meninges**. The outermost membrane, the dura mater (from the Latin, "hard mother"), is a thick protective layer that lies just inside the skull and vertebrae. The middle membrane is called the arachnoid mater (Latin, "spidery mother") because it has numerous weblike tissue connections to the innermost membrane, the pia mater (Latin, "thin mother"). The pia mater is a very thin membrane that lies on the surface of the brain and spinal cord, folding with the brain's surface.

Between the arachnoid mater and pia mater is the subarachnoid space. This space is filled with **cerebrospinal fluid**, which surrounds the exterior of the brain and spinal cord and absorbs physical shocks to the brain resulting from sudden movements or blows to the head. The cerebrospinal fluid contains nutrients, hormones, and other substances that are taken up by cells of the brain, and the fluid is also a reservoir for waste products that are carried away by the circulatory system. In addition to the subarachnoid space, the cerebrospinal fluid also fills a series of connected cavities called the ventricles that lie deep within the brain and run along a central canal that extends the length of the spinal cord. These fluid-filled structures provide a cushion of support and protection for the CNS.

The PNS Carries Information to and from the CNS

The PNS of vertebrates is subdivided into two major functional and anatomical components: the somatic nervous system and the autonomic nervous system. Both divisions have sensory (afferent) nerves and motor (efferent) nerves. The primary function of the **somatic nervous system** is to sense the external environmental conditions and control skeletal muscles. The sensory neurons of the somatic nervous system receive stimuli, such as heat, vision, smell, taste, hearing, and touch, and transmit signals to the CNS. The motor neurons of the somatic nervous system control skeletal muscles. The cell bodies of these motor neurons are actually located within the CNS. The axons from these cells leave the spinal cord and project directly onto skeletal muscle without making any intermediary synapses along the way.

The somatic nervous system is said to be voluntary because the responses can usually be controlled consciously. For example, we use our somatic nervous system to walk and hold a pencil. However, not all responses are voluntary. An example is a reflex arc, such as the knee-jerk response, which is automatic (see Chapter 41).

The **autonomic nervous system** (also called the visceral nervous system) regulates homeostasis and organ function. For example, it is involved in regulating the rate of heart contractions, blood pressure, and the amount of stomach acid secreted. Though the autonomic nervous system is predominantly composed of motor neurons, certain of its sensory neurons detect internal body conditions. For example, baroreceptors are sensory neurons that detect blood pressure. For the most part, the autonomic nervous system is not subject to voluntary control. We usually cannot consciously change our heart rate or blood pressure.

The efferent pathways of the autonomic nervous system involve two motor neurons. The cell body of the first neuron is within the CNS and synapses on a second neuron in a ganglion of the PNS. This second neuron sends its axon to an effector cell, where it alters that cell's function. These neurons control smooth muscles, cardiac muscle, and glands.

The efferent nerves of the autonomic system are subdivided into the sympathetic and parasympathetic divisions (**Figure 42.7**). Both divisions of the autonomic system act on the same organs and usually have opposing actions. The **sympathetic division** is responsible for rapidly activating systems that prepare the body for danger or stress. This is the fight-or-flight response, which is characterized by increased heart rate, stronger pumping action of the heart, faster breathing, additional blood flow to skeletal muscles, and increased secretion of glucose and fats into the blood by the liver and adipose

Sympathetic division

Parasympathetic division

Dilates pupils

Inhibits salivation

Increases heartbeat and force of contraction

Relaxes airways

Inhibits digestion and stomach activity

Stimulates release of glucose into the blood; inhibits insulin release from pancreas

Inhibits activity of small intestines

Stimulates secretion of epinephrine and norepinephrine from adrenal glands

Relaxes urinary bladder

Promotes ejaculation and vaginal contraction

Constricts pupils

Stimulates salivation

Slows heartbeat

Constricts airways

Stimulates digestion and stomach activity

Increases glucose utilization by liver cells; stimulates insulin secretion from pancreas

Increases activity of small intestines to promote absorption of nutrients

Stimulates urinary bladder to contract

Promotes erection of genitals

Cranial nerves

Celiac ganglion

Inferior mesenteric ganglion

Chain of sympathetic ganglia

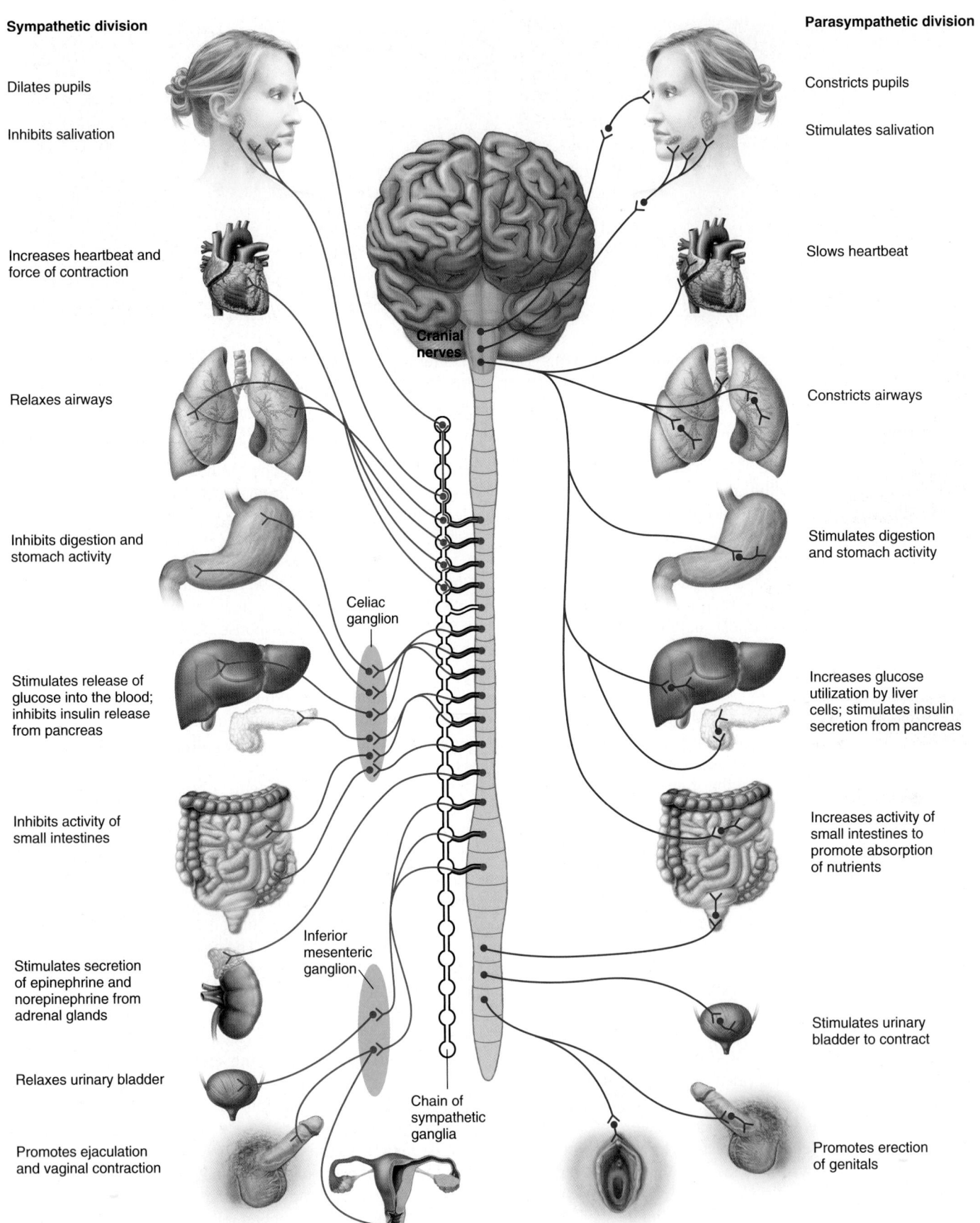

Figure 42.7   Parasympathetic and sympathetic divisions of the autonomic nervous system.   For simplicity, only some of the major functions of each division are shown in this figure. The parasympathetic and sympathetic systems tend to have opposite effects, and most parts of the body receive inputs from both divisions. Nerves from the sympathetic division make connections with ganglia, most of which are alongside the spinal cord, while nerves from the parasympathetic division make connections in ganglia near or in their targets.

tissue. These features prepare us to confront (fight) or avoid (flight) a perceived threat.

The **parasympathetic division** of the autonomic nervous system is involved in maintaining and restoring body functions. It is active during restful periods or after a meal, which is why it is sometimes called the rest-or-digest system. Neurons of the parasympathetic division promote digestion and absorption of food from the gut, slow the heart rate, and decrease the amount of fuel supplied to the blood from the liver and adipose tissue.

The Hindbrain Is Important for Homeostasis and Coordination

Let's now turn our attention to the structure and function of the hindbrain. We will begin with the evolutionarily oldest structures of the brain, some of which are located in the hindbrain and control the basic processes that sustain life.

The **medulla oblongata** coordinates many basic reflexes and bodily functions that maintain the normal homeostatic processes. It is involved in the control of heart rate, breathing, cardiovascular function, digestion, swallowing, and vomiting.

The **cerebellum** and **pons** are responsible for monitoring and coordinating body movements. Major nerve tracts pass through the pons into and out of the cerebellum so that the pons serves as a relay between the cerebellum and other areas of the brain. The cerebellum, a large structure that sits dorsal to the pons and medulla oblongata, receives sensory inputs from the cerebral cortex and the hearing and visual areas of the brain. It also receives inputs from the spinal cord that convey information about the position of joints and the contraction or relaxation of muscles. The overall function of the cerebellum is to maintain balance and coordinate movements.

The Midbrain Processes Sensory Inputs

The midbrain processes several types of sensory inputs, including vision, smell, and hearing. It has tracts that pass this information to other parts of the brain for further processing and interpretation. In vertebrates with less developed brains, such as fish, the midbrain is the only area that interprets vision, but in mammals this function is largely performed by the forebrain, to which we now turn.

The Forebrain Is Responsible for Thought, Learning, and Emotion

The forebrain comprises the thalamus and hypothalamus (diencephalon) and the cerebrum (telencephalon), which consists of the basal nuclei, limbic system, and cerebral cortex.

In vertebrates, the **thalamus** plays a major role in relaying sensory information to appropriate parts of the cerebrum and, in turn, sending outputs from the cerebrum to other parts of the brain. It receives input from all sensory systems. The thalamus is organized according to the type of sensation. For example, certain parts of the thalamus process visual inputs while other parts process sounds. The thalamus also directs outgoing motor instructions that it receives from the cortex, sending directions

to the spinal cord to generate voluntary movements. The thalamus is involved in the perception of pain and the degree of mental arousal in the cortex.

The **hypothalamus**, located below the thalamus at the floor of the forebrain, controls functions of the gastrointestinal and reproductive systems, and it regulates many basic behaviours, such as eating and drinking. This area has great importance for homeostasis of the body and the control of behaviour. Though small, it is composed of many nuclei, each with its own function. A major role of the hypothalamus is the production of hormones, which travel to the pituitary gland located just beneath the brain. The pituitary gland, in turn, regulates hormone secretion from other glands in the body, including the thyroid, gonads, and adrenal glands. In addition to producing hormones, the hypothalamus is sensitive to their actions. For example, certain hormones produced by cells in the stomach, intestine, adipose tissue, gonads, and elsewhere act within the hypothalamus to facilitate the expression of feeding, drinking, sexual, and aggressive behaviours. Finally, a small pair of hypothalamic nuclei called the suprachiasmatic nuclei are the "master clocks" of the CNS, establishing circadian rhythms, which control the expression of behavioural, physiological, and hormonal rhythms over the 24-hour day.

The **basal nuclei** are a group of nuclei that surrounds the thalamus on both sides and lies beneath the cerebral cortex. Like the cerebellum, the basal nuclei are involved in planning and learning movements. They also function via a complex circuitry to initiate or inhibit movements.

The **limbic system** refers to certain areas of the telencephalon and parts of the diencephalon. It is made of evolutionarily older structures that form an inner layer at the base of the forebrain. These include structures such as the **olfactory bulbs** (which process information about smells), amygdala, and hippocampus, as well as parts of the thalamus and hypothalamus. However, not all neuroscientists agree on which brain structures constitute the limbic system. The limbic system is primarily involved in the formation and expression of emotions, and it also plays a role in learning, memory, and the perception of smells.

The **amygdala** is one of the areas known to be critical for understanding and remembering emotional situations. This area also is involved in the ability to recognize emotional expression in others. Emotions are not unique to humans, however, and are clearly present in other primates and mammals. Being able to express and detect emotions imparts a selective advantage by enabling animals to establish and maintain relationships. Emotions, such as fear, help an animal defend itself against danger by avoiding conflict. Likewise, anger is associated with aggression, a key behaviour by which many animals defend their territories.

The **hippocampus** is composed of several layers of cells that are connected in a circuit. Experiments with laboratory animals have demonstrated the importance of the hippocampus for memory and learning in mammals. In a particularly well studied example, rats are placed into a pool of milky water containing a hidden platform. The animals swim until they find the platform, on which they can safely stand. The time it takes to find the platform in subsequent trials is shorter as they learn and remember its whereabouts. This type of spatial learning depends on activity in

GENOMES AND PROTEOMES

Several Genes Have Been Important in the Evolution of the Cerebral Cortex

A number of genes are known to be involved in the development of the cerebral cortex. Some have been identified by examining genetic mutations in people with developmental disabilities, and others by comparing human genes with genes that are known to be involved in brain development in other species, such as *Drosophila*. Researchers have also compared these genes in many species that show notable differences in cerebral structure. This last approach can determine whether a relationship exists between the expression of a particular gene and the organization of the cerebral cortex.

One inherited disorder that involves abnormal development of the cerebral cortex is polymicrogyria (meaning "many small folds"), which results in mental impairment as well as disrupted gait and language production. In people with this disorder, the cortex is characterized by multiple abnormal surface folds and fewer layers of cells. One type of polymicrogyria is a recessively inherited condition for which eight different mutations of a single gene are known. This gene, called GPR56, encodes a G-protein-coupled receptor (described in Chapter 9) that has large extracellular loops. All eight mutations that produce polymicrogyria alter the extracellular loops of the receptor, and it is thought that this alters the ability of the G-protein-coupled receptor to bind its ligand.

Two other genes, called microcephalin (meaning "small head") and ASPM (abnormal spindle-like microcephaly-associated gene), have been shown to be determinants of brain size and thus possibly involved in the evolution of brain size. For example, mutations of these genes in the human population produce individuals with a much smaller frontal cortex. Interestingly, the sequences of these genes in several primates, including humans, and in other mammals, such as dogs and sheep, have shown that the proteins produced by the normal microcephalin and ASPM genes have undergone greater changes in humans and great apes than in other species. Therefore, these genes may have been under greater selective pressure in animals with larger cortices, suggesting that the genes play a key role in cortex development.

---

the hippocampus. Rats with parts of their hippocampus destroyed fail to improve their times with repeated trials. The hippocampus also receives extensive inputs from the olfactory bulbs, which may explain why smells are such potent triggers of memory in humans and why many animals use their sense of smell as a major way to learn and remember aspects of their environments.

As mentioned earlier, the **cerebral cortex** is the surface layer of grey matter that covers the cerebrum (Figure 42.6). The neocortex (literally, new cortex) is the layer that evolved most recently in mammals and has only six layers of cells. Older parts of the cortex, including areas involved in processing the sense of smell, have fewer layers. In humans, the cerebral cortex is only a few millimetres thick but it contains about 10% of all the neurons in the brain.

42.3 ⃫ CELLULAR BASIS OF LEARNING AND MEMORY

Learning Outcomes:

1. Define the terms learning and memory and describe their relationship to one another.
2. Discuss how memory is related to changes in the strength of connections between neurons.
3. Describe the evidence that shows the brain is capable of neurogenesis.

In the past few decades, researchers have begun to understand complex behaviours, such as learning and memory, at the cellular level. Though it is difficult to separate the two concepts, **learning** can be defined as the process by which new information is acquired, while **memory** involves the retention of that information over time. Memory is the glue that connects our experiences throughout life. Our behaviour is largely controlled by what we have learned and remember from past experiences. Neuroscientists want to understand how the brain learns and how it captures memories. In this section, we will examine some ideas about how this may be achieved at the cellular level and consider experimental approaches that neuroscientists follow when trying to investigate such complicated phenomena.

Learning and Memory Occur via Changes Within Neurons and Their Connections

In the 1960s Austrian neuroscientist Eric Kandel took a reductionist approach by studying learning and memory in a simpler organism: the California sea slug (*Aplysia californica*), which he chose for several key reasons. First, it has only about 20,000 nerve cells, making it easier to identify pathways that are involved in specific types of behaviour. Second, some of the neurons are extremely large, allowing the study of action potentials via microelectrodes (as described in Chapter 41). In addition, the large size made it possible to inject substances into the neurons to study their effects. Finally, another major advantage is that Kandel and colleagues could isolate proteins and mRNA from these large neurons, and identify the biochemical and genetic changes that occur when the animal learns about its outside world and retains memory.

Much of Kandel's work focused on one type of learning involving the gill-withdrawal reflex, which is thought to involve fewer than 100 neurons in the CNS. The gill and siphon are organs involved in respiration. When the siphon is gently touched with a fine probe, the sea slug closes the siphon and retracts its gills into the mantle for protection (**Figure 42.8**). Though called a reflex, this behaviour is subject to learning. It can be modified to occur at a faster or slower rate. For example, if the touching of the siphon is accompanied with a shock in the tail, the sea slug can learn to withdraw its gill more quickly. The sea slug can learn that the two events occur at the same time.

Over the years, the work of Kandel and colleagues revealed many clues regarding the cellular basis of learning and memory. As they do in vertebrates, these processes in the sea slug occur in two phases (**Figure 42.9**). Short-term memory lasts for minutes or hours. This type of memory is typically caused by a single stimulus. Kandel found that short-term memory does not require the synthesis of new proteins. Rather, a single stimulus activates intracellular second messenger pathways (described in Chapter 9) that make it easier for the neurons involved in a particular behaviour to communicate. For example, as shown in **Figure 42.9a**, a single stimulus can lead to the activation of protein kinases in the presynaptic (sensory) cell that phosphorylate proteins, such as ion channels and proteins involved with the release of neurotransmitter. These changes enhance the transmission of a signal between the presynaptic and postsynaptic cells.

Kandel and colleagues also discovered that repeated stimuli result in long-term memory, which lasts days or weeks. Such repeated stimuli require the synthesis of new proteins (**Figure 42.9b**). Long-term memory involves the activation of genes in the presynaptic cell, which leads to the synthesis of

(a) Sea slug

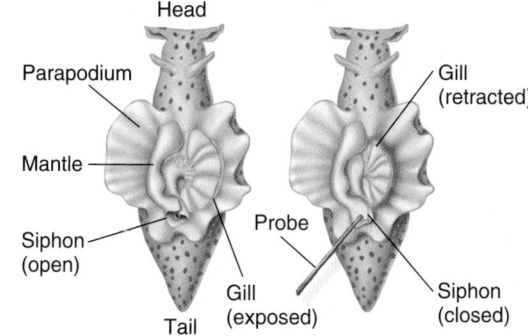

(b) Gill-withdrawal reflex

Figure 42.8 The gill-withdrawal reflex in the sea slug. **(a)** Photo of *Aphysia californica* in its natural habitat. **(b)** When touched with a probe, the siphon closes and the gill retracts. In this drawing, the parapodia are moved apart for a better view of the gill.

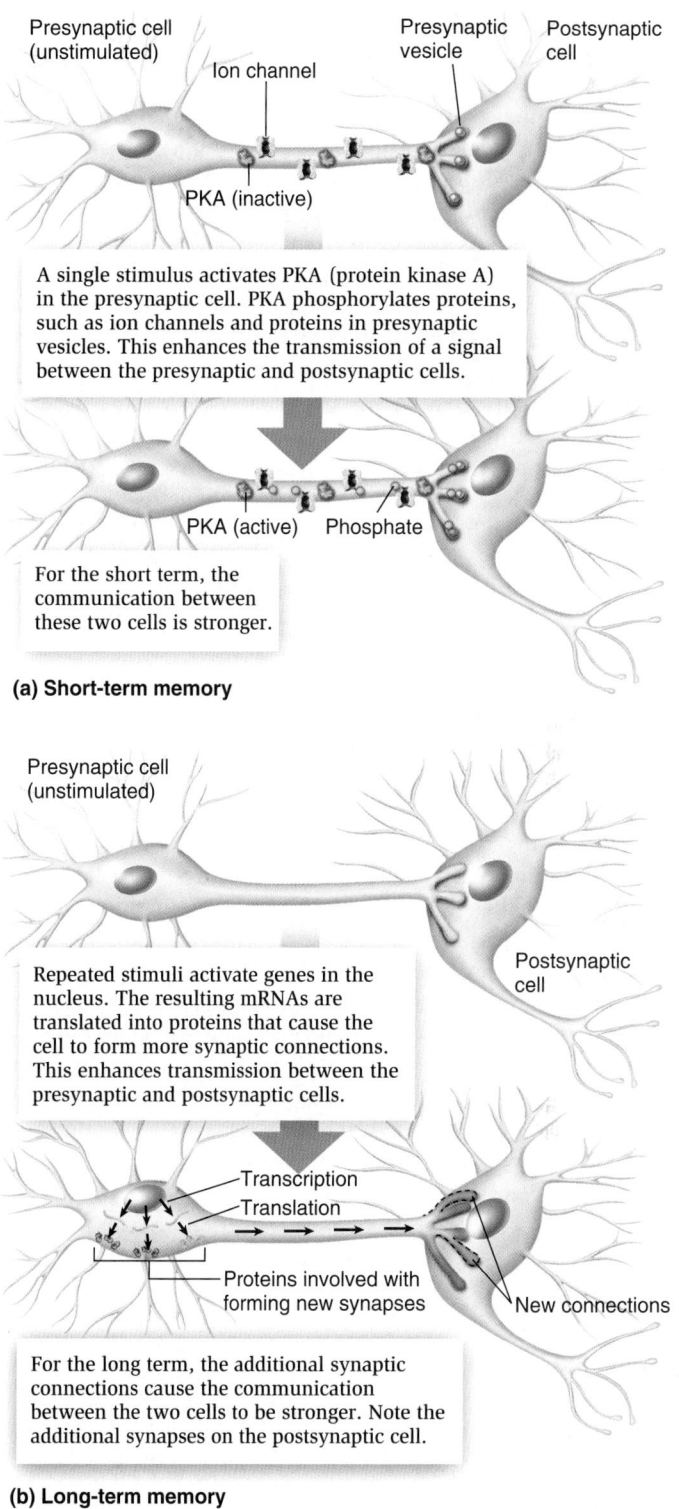

(a) Short-term memory

(b) Long-term memory

Figure 42.9 Cellular changes associated with short-term and long-term memory in the sea slug.

mRNA and the translation of the encoded proteins. Once made, such proteins cause the formation of additional synaptic connections. These connections also allow the presynaptic and postsynaptic cells to communicate with each other more readily. Such a change in synapses, which occurs as a result of learning, is termed **synaptic plasticity**.

The work of Kandel provides a foundation for our ability to understand how learning and memory may occur at the cellular level. Short-term memory may involve changes in existing cellular proteins that make it easier for neurons to communicate, while long-term memory results in protein synthesis that causes physical changes in the synapse itself, also affecting communication. In the case of the sea slug, learning does not change the pathways of neurons but instead changes the strength of the signals along those pathways. When a light touch on the siphon was coupled with an unpleasant shock, the animal became sensitized and could react more strongly to the light touch because the set of connections had strengthened. Kandel also studied how learning can occur in the opposite way. A sea slug can learn to ignore a harmless touch. In that case, the connections between neurons became weaker. Later studies by Kandel and others showed that such changes also occur in vertebrates, such as the mouse. For his work on learning and memory, Kandel was awarded the Nobel Prize in Physiology or Medicine in 2000.

Neurogenesis May Also Contribute to Learning and Memory

In 1983 neuroscientists demonstrated that the adult brain of birds is capable of **neurogenesis**—the production of new neurons by cell division. It was soon realized that the adults of several vertebrate species (including primates and humans) also displayed neurogenesis and that the central nervous systems of primates and humans contain stem cells (see Chapter 17). A key question is whether the neurogenesis observed in adult brains is involved in learning and memory. This question is hotly debated and has not been resolved. However, some evidence suggests that it could play a role. For example, the hippocampus of adult rhesus monkeys grows new neurons when the animals are placed in enriching environments, and the formation of these neurons slows when animals are chronically stressed. Also, studies in the rat suggest that new neurons are retained in the hippocampus in response to training on particular tasks that require hippocampus function.

42.4 / SENSORY RECEPTION

Learning Outcomes:

1. Understand the relationship between sensation and perception.
2. Discuss how sensory receptors pass along the intensity of a stimulus.
3. List the classes of sensory receptors and the stimuli to which they respond.

Senses allow living organisms to perceive their environment. Animals with nervous systems often have acute senses, such as the ability to perceive light, touch, and sound. In neuroscience, a broad definition of a **sense** is a system that consists of sensory cells that respond to a specific type of chemical or physical stimulus and send signals to the central nervous system, where the signals are received and interpreted. The senses allow animals to detect subtle and complex aspects of their environment. Common senses include sight, hearing, touch, taste, smell, balance, and the ability to sense temperature and pain.

Of course, some organisms have a greater ability to detect stimuli than others. Hawks can see mice from 100 metres above ground, while polar bears can smell a seal several kilometres away. Humans do not see ultraviolet light but some bees do, and apes cannot hear extremely high-pitched sounds although rodents can.

In the rest of this chapter, we will examine how nervous systems collect incoming sensory information and how membrane potentials of specialized neurons change in response to sensory inputs. We will learn that other structures of the nervous system can modify or enhance this neural activity before sending it to the brain, where it is interpreted.

Sensory systems convert chemical or physical stimuli from an animal's body and the external environment into a signal that causes a change in the membrane potential of sensory neurons. **Sensory transduction** is the process by which incoming stimuli are converted into neural signals. Sensory transduction involves cellular changes, such as opening of ion channels, which cause either graded potentials or action potentials in neurons.

Perception is an awareness of the sensations that are experienced. For instance, touching a hot stove generates a thermal sensation, which initiates a neuronal response, giving us the perception that this stimulus is hot. Perception requires integration of incoming stimuli by the CNS. Not all sensations are consciously perceived by an organism. Most of the time, for example, we are not aware of the touch of our clothing. The brain also processes sensory information in areas that do not generate conscious thought. For instance, certain neurons constantly monitor blood pressure, blood levels of oxygen and glucose, and heart rate, but we are not aware that this is occurring.

We will begin by examining the specialized cells—called sensory receptors—whose function it is to receive sensory inputs. A **sensory receptor** is either a neuron or a specialized epithelial cell that recognizes an internal or environmental stimulus and initiates signal transduction by creating graded potentials (described in Chapter 41) in the same cell or an adjacent cell (**Figure 42.10**). When a response is strong enough, sensory receptors can initiate electrical responses to stimuli, such as chemicals, light, touch, heat, and sound, which leads to action potentials that are sent to the CNS.

An Intense Stimulus Generates More Frequent Action Potentials

Sensory transduction begins when the specialized endings of a sensory receptor, such as dendrites, respond to a stimulus. In some cases, sensory receptors are depolarized when a stimulus opens ion channels that allow sodium ions into the cell. The amount of depolarization is directly related to the intensity of the stimulus, because a stronger stimulus will open more ion channels. When a stimulus is strong enough,

(a) A neuron as a sensory receptor

(b) A specialized epithelial cell as a sensory receptor

Figure 42.10 **Sensory receptors.** **(a)** Many sensory receptors are neurons that directly sense stimuli. **(b)** Others are specialized epithelial cells that sense stimuli and secrete a neurotransmitter that stimulates nearby sensory neurons. In both cases, when stimulated, the neurons send action potentials to the CNS, where the signals are interpreted.

Concept check: *What is the difference between the sensory receptor described in this chapter and the membrane receptors described in Chapter 9?*

it will depolarize the membrane to the threshold potential at the axon hillock and produce an action potential in a sensory neuron (see Chapter 41).

The first response of a sensory receptor is usually a graded change in the membrane potential that is proportional to the intensity of the stimulus (**Figure 42.11**). This example involves the sense of touch. The membrane potential, known as the **receptor potential** in these cells, becomes more and more positive as the strength of the stimulus increases. A higher membrane potential results in more action potentials being generated by the sensory receptor itself, which is a neuron, as described in Figure 42.10a. These action potentials are transmitted to the CNS, where the stimulus is perceived.

Recall from Chapter 41 that action potentials proceed in an all-or-none fashion, regardless of the nature of the stimulus that elicits them. How can action potentials provide information about the intensity of a stimulus? The answer is that the

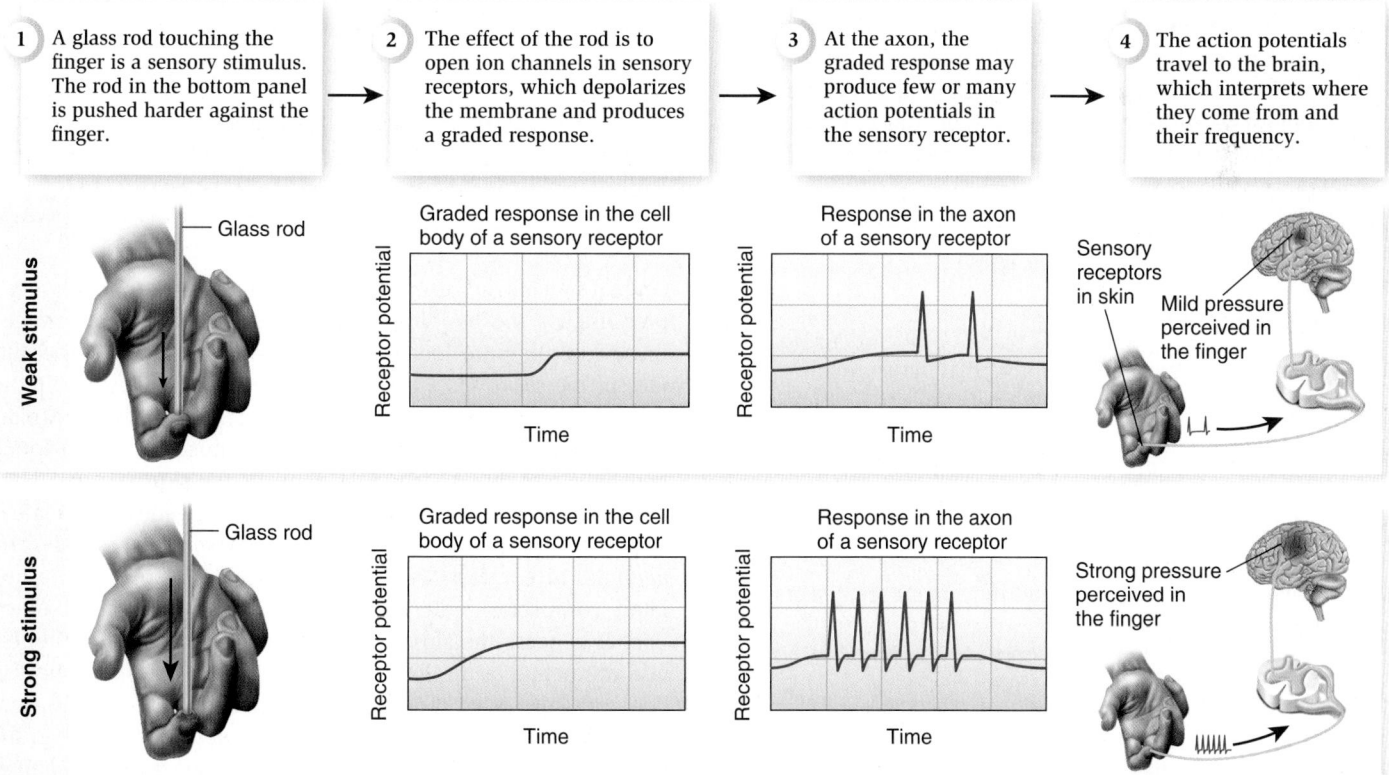

| 1 | A glass rod touching the finger is a sensory stimulus. The rod in the bottom panel is pushed harder against the finger. | 2 | The effect of the rod is to open ion channels in sensory receptors, which depolarizes the membrane and produces a graded response. | 3 | At the axon, the graded response may produce few or many action potentials in the sensory receptor. | 4 | The action potentials travel to the brain, which interprets where they come from and their frequency. |

Figure 42.11 **Transduction of a sensory stimulus of two different intensities.** In this example, the sensory receptor is a neuron.

strength of the stimulus is indicated by the frequency of action potentials generated. A particularly strong stimulus will generate many action potentials in a short time. As a result, the frequency of action potentials is higher when the stimulus is strong than when it is weak. The action potentials are transmitted into the CNS and carried to the brain for interpretation. The brain interprets a higher frequency of action potentials as a more intense stimulus.

The CNS Processes Each Sense Within Its Own Pathway

Different stimuli produce different sensations because they activate specific neural pathways that are dedicated to processing only that type of stimulus. We know that we are seeing light because the signals generated by visual sensory receptors are transmitted along a neural pathway that sends action potentials into areas of the brain that are devoted to processing vision. For this reason, the brain interprets such signals as visual stimuli.

We can classify sensory receptors into general classes, based on the type of stimulus to which they respond. Each type uses a different mechanism to respond to signals and transmits the response to different regions of the CNS. **Mechanoreceptors** transduce mechanical energy such as pressure, touch, stretch, movement, and sound. **Thermoreceptors** respond to cold and heat. **Nociceptors**, or pain receptors, respond to extreme heat, cold, and pressure, as well as to certain molecules, such as acids. **Electromagnetic receptors** detect radiation within a wide range of the electromagnetic spectrum, including visible, ultraviolet, and infrared light, as well as electrical and magnetic fields in some animals. **Photoreceptors** are electromagnetic receptors that respond to visible light energy. **Chemoreceptors** respond to specific chemical compounds. The remaining sections of this chapter will examine the structures and functions of these types of sensory receptors and the organs in which they are found.

42.5 / MECHANORECEPTION

Learning Outcomes:

1. List the types of mechanoreceptors that detect touch, stretch, or movement, and how this relates to hearing and balance.
2. Describe the structure of the mammalian ear and how mechanical forces move through it.
3. Give examples of adaptations for hearing in animals that inhabit different environments.
4. Describe how body position and movement are detected by sense organs.

Mechanoreceptors are cells that detect physical stimuli, such as pressure, touch, stretch, movement, and sound. Physically touching or deforming a mechanoreceptor cell opens ion channels in the plasma membrane. Some mechanoreceptors are neurons that send action potentials to the CNS in response to

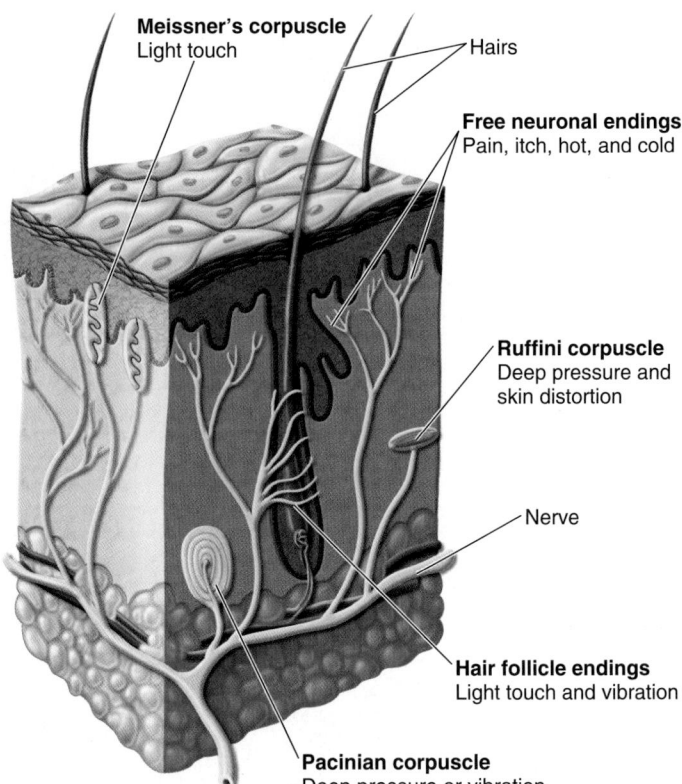

Figure 42.12 Examples of sensory receptors in the skin of mammals.

Concept check: *There are several types of touch receptors in the skin that respond to different stimuli. What different qualities of touch are you aware of?*

physical stimuli, whereas others are specialized epithelial cells with cilia that bend in response to mechanical forces.

Skin Receptors Respond to Touch and Pressure

Several specialized receptors in the skin respond to touch, deep pressure, or the bending of hairs on the skin. In mammals, these receptors are located at different depths below the surface of the skin, which makes them suitable for responding to different types of stimuli (**Figure 42.12**). For example, **Meissner's corpuscles** (also called tactile corpuscles), sense touch and light pressure and lie just beneath the skin surface. They are found throughout the skin but are concentrated in areas sensitive to light touch, such as the fingertips, lips, eyelids, and genitals. In contrast, **Pacinian corpuscles** (also called lamellated corpuscles) and **Ruffini corpuscles** are located much deeper beneath the surface, particularly in the soles of the feet and the palms of the hands. These corpuscles respond best to deep pressure or vibration. All the skin corpuscles contain sensory receptor neurons that generate action potentials when the structure of the corpuscle is deformed. Other skin mechanoreceptors located in the hair follicles respond to movements of hairs and whiskers.

Stretch Receptors Detect Expansion

Stretch receptors, a type of mechanoreceptor found widely in organs and muscle tissues that can be distended, are nerve endings found in muscles and in the walls of organs, like the stomach and bladder. When the mammalian stomach stretches after a meal, its stretch receptors are deformed, causing them to become depolarized and to send action potentials to the brain. The brain interprets the signals as fullness, which reduces appetite. Similarly, the degree to which certain blood vessels are stretched gives the brain information about an animal's blood pressure. Similar stretch receptors are also found in the midgut of biting flies, such as mosquitoes, and indicate to the fly that it is full of blood.

Hair Cells Are Mechanoreceptors with Deformable Stereocilia

Thus far, we have considered skin and stretch receptors, which are neurons that detect physical stimuli. Other mechanoreceptors are specialized epithelial cells, called **hair cells**, which have deformable projections, called **stereocilia**, that resemble hairs when looked at under the microscope. These stereocilia are bent by water currents or other physical stimuli (**Figure 42.13**). Many types of hair cells contain ion channels that open or close when the stereocilia bend and thereby change the membrane potential. When the plasma membrane depolarizes, this opens voltage-gated Ca^{2+} channels and results in the release of neurotransmitter molecules from the hair cells (refer back to Figure 41.14). The neurotransmitter then binds to protein receptors in adjacent sensory neurons and can result in action potentials being sent to the CNS. Even when unstimulated, hair cells usually release a small amount of neurotransmitter onto nearby sensory neurons, resulting in a resting level of action potentials in the sensory neurons. In the example shown in Figure 42.12, bending of the stereocilia in one direction increases the release of neurotransmitter from the hair cell, while bending in the other direction decreases the release of the same neurotransmitter. The result is an increase or a decrease, respectively, in the number of action potentials produced in the sensory neurons.

Hair cells are found in the ear and equilibrium (balance) organs of many invertebrates and vertebrates, where they respond to sound or changes in head position. They are also found along the body surface of fish and some amphibians, where they respond to external water currents, as described next.

Mechanoreceptors in the Lateral Line System Detect Movements in Water

Fish and some toads detect changes in their environment through a **lateral line system** (**Figure 42.14**). This sensory system has hair cells that detect changes in water currents brought about by waves, nearby moving objects, and low-frequency sounds travelling through the water. The lateral line organ runs along both sides and the head of the animal. Small pores let water enter into a lateral line canal. The stereocilia of hair cells protrude into a gelatinous structure called a **cupula** within the lateral line organ. When the cupula is moved by the water, the stereocilia bend, causing the release of neurotransmitter from the hair cell, which stimulates a response in a neuron at the base of the hair cell. The response provides information to the brain about changes in water movement, such as the approach of a predator.

At rest

Stereocilia of sensory receptor cell

Neurotransmitter at synapse
Sensory neuron
To CNS

At rest, a small amount of neurotransmitter is released at all times, resulting in a steady number of action potentials being generated in the sensory neuron.

Excited

Fluid

More neurotransmitter

Fluid moving in one direction causes the release of more neurotransmitter, which results in more action potentials in the sensory neuron.

Inhibited

Fluid

Less neurotransmitter

Fluid moving in the opposite direction inhibits the release of neurotransmitter, which results in fewer action potentials in the sensory neuron.

Figure 42.13 **The response of hair cells to mechanical stimulation.**   The stereocilia inside these hair cells are hairlike projections of the plasma membrane that contain actin filaments. They are structurally different from cilia, which are described in Chapter 4.

BioConnections: *How are stereocilia different from cilia, which are described in Figure 4.21?*

1) A stimulus, such as water motion, enters the pores and travels through the canal.

2) The stimulus bends the cupula and stereocilia within the cupula, which causes hair cells to release neurotransmitter and thereby stimulate sensory neurons.

Figure 42.14   Mechanoreceptors in the lateral line system that detect changes in water movement.

Hearing Involves the Reception of Sound Waves

The sense of hearing, **audition**, is the ability to detect and interpret sound waves. It is a critical sense for the survival of many types of animals. For example, a mother seal locates her pup by hearing its calls, and a male bird sings an elaborate song to attract a mate. Hearing is also important for detecting the approach of danger—a predator, a thunderstorm, an automobile—and locating its source.

Sound travels through air or water in waves. The distance from the peak of one wave to the next is a **wavelength**. The number of complete wavelengths that occur in one second is called the **frequency** of the sound, measured in number of waves per second, or Hertz (Hz), after German physicist and pioneer of radio wave research Heinrich Hertz. The length and frequency of sound waves impart certain characteristics to the stimulus. Short wavelengths have high frequencies that are perceived as a high **pitch** or tone, while long wavelengths have lower frequencies and a lower pitch.

The sense of hearing is present in vertebrates and arthropods, but not in other phyla. Arthropods do not appear to have more than a general sensitivity to sound, although some exceptions exist. For example, some species of moths have sound-sensitive membranes that detect the frequencies emitted by their chief predators, bats. The sense of hearing, however, is especially well developed in vertebrates (notably birds and mammals), and we turn therefore to a detailed discussion of the mammalian ear and the mechanism by which it detects sound.

Structure of the Mammalian Ear   The mammalian ear has three main compartments (**Figure 42.15**). The **outer ear** consists of the external ear, or pinna, and the auditory canal. Mammals have a wide variety of shapes and sizes of the external ear, which reflects their different abilities to capture sound waves. The outer ear is divided from the **middle ear** by the tympanic membrane (eardrum); the middle ear contains three small bones called ossicles that connect the eardrum with the

oval window. These are named the malleus (or hammer), the incus (or anvil), and the stapes (or stirrup). The oval window is another membrane similar to the eardrum that separates the middle ear from the **inner ear**. The inner ear is composed of the bony **cochlea** (from the Latin, meaning "snail")—a coiled structure containing the hair cells and other structures that generate the responses that travel via the auditory nerve to the brain—and the vestibular system, which plays a role in balance, as described later.

Both the tympanic membrane and the oval window must be able to vibrate when sound waves meet the eardrum. For this to occur properly, the air pressure in the outer and middle ear compartments must be equal. The pressure in the outer ear is the atmospheric pressure. The **Eustachian tube**, a connection from the middle ear to the pharynx, maintains the pressure in the middle ear at atmospheric pressure as well. If you change altitude quickly, as during a plane takeoff, the pressure in the outer ear changes because atmospheric pressure decreases with altitude. After a while, the pressures in the outer and middle ear equalize. However, if the outer ear pressure becomes greater than the middle ear pressure, which would occur when the plane descends, the eardrum will be pushed or bowed inward. The eardrum is less able to vibrate in response to sounds when it is deformed under pressure, and thus hearing becomes muffled. Swallowing or yawning will open the Eustachian tube and equalize the pressure in the middle ear with atmospheric pressure. The popping sound you hear when the plane ascends or descends is the sudden return of the eardrum to its normal position.

Generation of Electrical Signals in the Mammalian Ear
To understand how we hear, let's first consider how mechanical forces move through the ear. Sound waves entering the outer ear cause the tympanic membrane to vibrate back and forth. The ossicles transfer the vibration of the tympanic membrane to the oval window, causing it to vibrate against the cochlea (**Figure 42.16**). This sends pressure waves, which also travel

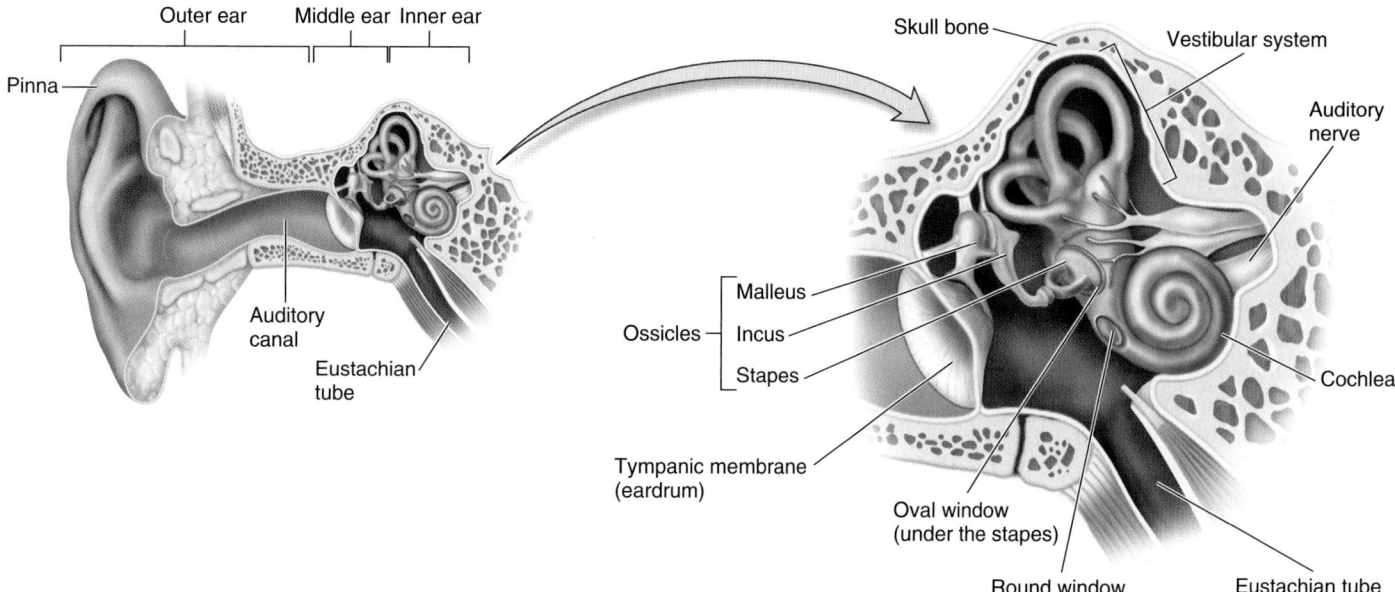

Figure 42.15   **The structure of the human ear.**   The three main compartments are the outer, middle, and inner ear.

in a back-and-forth manner, through a fluid called perilymph, which is found within the vestibular canal and tympanic canal of the cochlea. The waves travel from the vestibular canal to the tympanic canal and eventually strike the round window, where they dissipate. Sounds of very low frequency create pressure waves that take the complete route through the vestibular and tympanic canals (see green arrows in Figure 42.16). We would not be able to hear such sounds. Sound of higher frequency, however, produces pressure waves that take a shortcut. For example, the shortcut shown by the blue arrows in Figure 42.16 represents sound of 8,000 Hz. These waves pass through the cochlear duct, and then through the basilar membrane, before reaching the tympanic canal. As this happens, the basilar membrane vibrates—that is, moves up and down.

Figure 42.16   Movement of sound waves through the human ear.

Mechanical forces are transduced into electrical signals within the organ of Corti (named after Italian anatomist Alfonso Corti), which rests on top of the basilar membrane. To understand how this works, we need to look at a cross-section through the cochlea (**Figure 42.17**). The organ of Corti contains supporting cells and rows of hair cells. The stereocilia of the hair cells are embedded in a gelatinous tectorial membrane. The back-and-forth vibration of the basilar membrane bends the hairs in one direction and then the other. When bent in one direction, the hair cells depolarize and release neurotransmitter, which activates adjacent sensory neurons that then send action potentials to the CNS via the auditory nerve. When bent in the other direction, the hair cells hyperpolarize and shut off the release of neurotransmitter. In this way, the frequency of action potentials by the sensory neurons is determined by the up-and-down vibration of the basilar membrane.

The basilar membrane is lined with protein fibres that span its width. These fibres function much like the strings of a guitar. The fibres near the oval and round windows at the base of the cochlea are short and rigid, and they vibrate in response to high-frequency waves. Longer and more resilient fibres are near the other end of the cochlea and vibrate to lower-frequency waves. For this reason, hair cells closer to the oval and round windows respond to high-pitched sounds, while those at the opposite end are triggered by lower-pitched sounds. When we hear a great number of sound frequencies at once, such as at a musical concert, the sound waves move hair cells all along the basilar membrane in a physical representation of the music! These cells stimulate sensory neurons, which send multiple action potentials to the auditory areas of the brain for processing. The most incredible feature of this process, however, is that—unlike a radio, which can be tuned to only one frequency at a time—the mammalian ear and brain can "tune in" to all these frequencies simultaneously.

Adaptations for Hearing Allow Animals to Live in a Wide Range of Habitats

Different animals are capable of hearing sounds of different pitches. For example, humans can hear between 20 and 20,000 Hz (conversation averages 90–300 Hz, while a human scream is 3,000 Hz). Bats and toothed whales can hear probably the highest-frequency sound waves, while baleen whales and elephants hear the lowest-pitched sounds. These adaptations increase the animals' ability to communicate and survive. For instance, high-pitched sounds are useful for locating small prey, such as flying insects, while low-pitched sounds carry great distances through water or air and are ideal for animals with large territories.

Locating a Sound   A vital feature of hearing is the ability of organisms to be able to locate the origin of a sound. For example, this ability makes the difference between a successful and an unsuccessful hunter. How does an animal locate a sound? Under most circumstances, sound does not arrive at both ears simultaneously. Sound waves coming from the right will excite the sensory receptors in the right ear first and the left ear milliseconds later, and therefore the brain receives action potentials from the auditory nerves of each ear at slightly different times. The brain interprets the time difference to determine the origin of the sound.

Animals, such as owls, that rely on hearing to locate prey tend to be extremely good at localizing the source of a sound. An interesting experiment demonstrated this by outfitting owls in a dark room with small headphones. Just as in a human hearing test, sounds could be sent to either headphone or to both. If the investigator sent a high-pitched noise that mimicked a scurrying mouse first to the left headphone, and then a millisecond later to the right headphone, the owl turned its head to the left, because the owl's brain perceived the sound to come from that direction. If the noises reached both headphones simultaneously, the owl interpreted the signal as coming from in front.

Hearing in Air and Water   Amphibians have the special challenge of hearing both on land and underwater, their two natural environments. Ears of amphibians have several interesting specializations that are adapted to these demands. First, they do not have external ears. The tympanic membrane is located on the outer surface of the head behind the eye (**Figure 42.18**). This arrangement allows them to swim through the water without being impeded by pinnae and to receive sound waves from any direction. Amphibians also have unusually wide Eustachian tubes. When they are on land, sound waves can pass from one

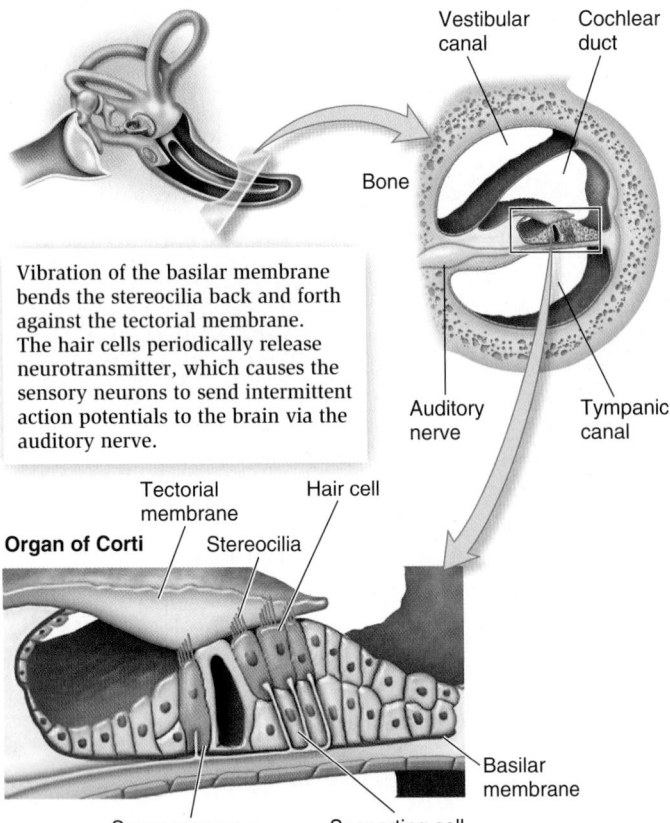

Vibration of the basilar membrane bends the stereocilia back and forth against the tectorial membrane. The hair cells periodically release neurotransmitter, which causes the sensory neurons to send intermittent action potentials to the brain via the auditory nerve.

Vestibular canal

Cochlear duct

Bone

Auditory nerve

Tympanic canal

Tectorial membrane

Organ of Corti

Hair cell

Stereocilia

Basilar membrane

Sensory neuron

Supporting cell

Figure 42.17   Transduction of mechanical vibrations to electric signals in the organ of Corti.

Figure 42.18   The tympanic membrane of a frog.

ear through the Eustachian tube to the pharynx and then travel up the Eustachian tube of the other ear, where they hit the backside of the tympanic membrane. Air from the lungs also can pass into each ear in this manner. When a bullfrog emits its loud call, pressure coming through the Eustachian tubes and from the outside of the head prevents his own eardrum from vibrating and being injured by the loud sound.

Echolocation   Bats in the air, whales and dolphins in the sea, and shrews in underground tunnels generate high-frequency sound waves to determine the distance and location of an object. This phenomenon is called **echolocation**, because the sound waves bounce off a distant object, like an echo, and return to the animal. The time it takes for the sound to return indicates the distance of the object. Echolocation can be useful in situations where vision is limited, such as in the dark.

James Fullard of the University of Toronto has studied the auditory control of defensive behaviours in noctuid moths, which have a pair of tympanic membranes (simple ears) on their thorax. These moths are able to hear the echolocation calls of hunting bats and they respond with evasive flight behaviours. The moths are also able to hear other sounds, such as the clicking songs of cicadas, yet they do not respond with evasive actions. This suggests that they are able to ignore audible but innocuous sounds.

The Sense of Balance Is Mediated by Statocysts in Invertebrates and the Vestibular System in Vertebrates

Let's now turn our attention to the sense of balance, also called equilibrium. Balance is part of a broader sense called proprioception, which is the ability to sense the position, orientation, and movement of the body. Being able to sense body position is vital for the survival of animals. This is how a lobster, for example, rights itself when flipped over by a predator, or a bird maintains its balance while flying rapidly through space. Many aquatic invertebrates have sensory organs called **statocysts** that send information to the brain about the position of the animal in space (**Figure 42.19**). Statocysts are small round structures made of an outer sphere of hair cells and **statoliths**, which are

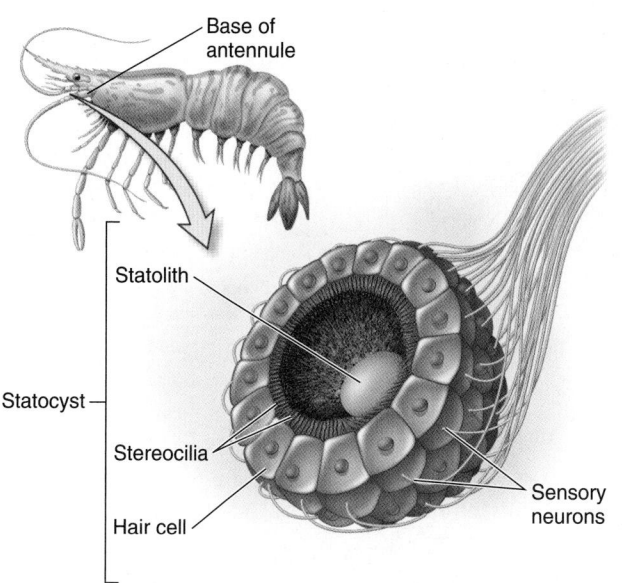

Figure 42.19   Sensing of balance in aquatic invertebrates. Statocysts located near the antennae consist of a sphere of sensory hair cells surrounding a stony statolith. When the animal moves, gravity shifts the statolith and stimulates the hair cells beneath it.

BioConnections: *Is the use of statoliths unique to animals? Look back to Figure 34.14 for a hint.*

tiny granules of sand or other dense objects. When the animal moves, gravity alters the statoliths' position. If the animal turns on its left side, for example, the movement of statoliths stimulates a new set of hair cells to release neurotransmitter, generating action potentials in sensory neurons that inform the brain of the change in body position.

Several experiments have demonstrated the importance of the statoliths. In one particularly dramatic example, researchers replaced the statoliths of crayfish with iron filings. Moving a magnet to different positions around the animal displaced the filings, causing the animal to change its position, and even to swim upside down when the magnet was placed directly above its head.

The organ of balance in vertebrates, known as the **vestibular system**, is located in the inner ear next to the cochlea (**Figure 42.20**). The vestibular system is composed of a series of fluid-filled sacs and tubules. The utricle and saccule, two sacs nearest the cochlea, detect linear movements of the head as an animal runs and jumps. The hair cells within these structures are embedded in a gelatinous substance that contains granules of calcium carbonate called **otoliths** (from the Latin, meaning "ear stones"). When the head moves forward, the heavy otoliths move forward more slowly, and the inertia bends the stereocilia of the hair cells. This changes the membrane potential of the hair cells and alters the electrical responses of nearby sensory neurons.

Three **semicircular canals** open out of the utricle. The function of the semicircular canals is to detect rotational motions of the head. The hair cells in the semicircular canals are embedded

Vestibular system

Ampullae

Semicircular canal

Vestibular nerve

Utricle

Saccule

Fluid flow

Direction of body movement

Otoliths
Gelatinous substance
Stereocilia
Hair cell
Dendrites of sensory neurons

(a) Linear movement
(Hair cells in saccule)

When the head moves forward, the otoliths move forward more slowly, and the inertia bends the stereocilia on the hair cells. Electrical signals are sent to the brain via the vestibular nerve, which interprets the stimulus as linear motion.

Flow of fluid through semicircular canal

Cupula
Stereocilia
Hair cell
Sensory neuron

(b) Rotational movement
(Fluid in ampulla of semicircular canal)

The semicircular canals are at right angles to each other. The fluid in each canal will move more slowly in the direction of motion, bending the stereocilia within the cupula. This sends a signal via the vestibular nerve. The brain interprets the signals from all three canals as various rotational movements of the head.

Figure 42.20 **The vertebrate vestibular system.** In the cupula of the semicircular canals, hair cells move when fluid within the canal shifts. In the utricle and saccule, hair cells are stimulated by otoliths that bend the cilia in response to forward movement.

Concept check: *Note the orientation of the three semicircular canals with respect to one another. Why are the canals oriented in three different planes?*

in a gelatinous cone called the cupula (similar to the cupula of the fish lateral line). When the head moves, the fluid in the canal shifts in the opposite direction because of inertia, pushing on the cupula and bending the stereocilia of the hair cells. The three canals are oriented at right angles to each other, and each canal is maximally sensitive to motion in its own plane. For example, the canal that is oriented horizontally would respond greatest to rotations, such as shaking the head "no." Overall, by comparing the signals from the three canals, the brain can interpret the motion in three dimensions.

The vestibular system of vertebrates provides conscious information about body position and movement. It also supplies subconscious information for reflexes that maintain normal posture, control head and eye movements, and assist in locomotion. Motion sickness in humans results when the vestibular system has not adapted to unfamiliar patterns of movement, such as spinning around or sailing aboard a ship. In these cases, the sense from your vestibular system conflicts with information coming from your vision. Vertigo, an illusion of movement or spinning, can result from malfunction of the vestibular system.

42.6 THERMORECEPTION, NOCICEPTION, AND ELECTROMAGNETIC SENSING

Learning Outcomes:

1. Explain how thermoreception and nociception are vital to the safety and survival of an animal.
2. Identify ways that animals use electromagnetic receptors to sense their environments.

The perception of temperature and pain enables animals to respond effectively to their environments. As described in this section, these sensory stimuli are related in that their receptors are located in some of the same areas (skin), share similar physical features, and under certain conditions result in similar perceptions.

Thermoreceptors Detect Temperature

Sensing the outside temperature is important because body temperature is affected by the external temperature, particularly in ectotherms. Animals can survive at body temperatures only within certain limits, because the proteins in their cells function optimally within a particular temperature range. Thermoreceptors respond to cold or hot temperatures by activating or inhibiting enzymes within their plasma membranes, which alter membrane channels. Two types of thermoreceptors respond to either hot or cold. The endings of cold receptors are located nearer the surface of the skin than are hot receptors. Thermoreceptors are often linked with reflexive behaviours, such as when an animal steps on a hot surface and pulls its foot away.

In addition to skin receptors that sense the outside temperature, thermoreceptors in the brain also detect changes in core body temperature. Activation of skin or brain thermoreceptors triggers physiological and behavioural adjustments that help maintain body temperature. These changes, described in Chapter 40, include changes in blood flow, shivering, and behavioural events, such as seeking shade or sunlight.

Nociceptors Warn of Pain

The sense of pain is one of the most important of all the senses. It tells an animal whether it has been injured, and triggers behavioural responses that protect it from further danger. Although in many cases we cannot know whether or how animals perceive pain, it is thought that all classes of animals have the ability to discern some type of painful sensation.

Nociceptors, the receptors for pain, are nerve endings in the skin and internal organs. They respond to tissue damage or to stimuli that are about to cause tissue damage. Nociceptors are unusual because they can respond not only to external stimuli, such as extreme temperatures, but also to internal stimuli, such as molecules released into the extracellular space from injured cells. Damaged cells release a number of substances, including acids and prostaglandins, that cause inflammation and make nociceptors more sensitive to painful stimuli. Aspirin and ibuprofen reduce pain by preventing the production of prostaglandins.

Signals arising from nociceptors travel to the CNS and reach the cerebrum, where the type or cause of the pain is interpreted. The signals are also sent to the limbic system, which holds memories and emotions associated with pain, and to the reticular formation, which increases alertness and arousal—an important response to a painful stimulus.

Electromagnetic Sensing

As mentioned earlier, electromagnetic receptors detect radiation within a wide range of the electromagnetic spectrum, including those wavelengths that correspond to visible light, ultraviolet light, and infrared light, as well as electrical and magnetic stimuli. Photoreceptors are specialized electromagnetic receptors that respond to light and are covered in a later section. Here, we will examine the ability of some animals to sense electrical and magnetic fields and also heat in the form of infrared radiation.

The more ways in which an animal can detect other animals, either predators or prey, the better it can avoid danger or obtain a meal. Many fish living in dark waters can detect weak electrical signals given off by other fish, and sharks and

rays can even detect the tiny electrical signals generated by the heartbeats of their prey. Similarly, receptors on the skin of the platypus's bill detect very small electrical currents produced by prey that might otherwise be undetectable in the murky waters of streams and ponds.

Homing pigeons use one type of electromagnetic sensing to return to their starting points from as far away as 1,500 km. This navigational feat is made possible by small particles of magnetite (iron oxide) in their beaks that act as a compass to tell direction. The magnetic particles respond to Earth's magnetic field and alter neurotransmission in neurons that project to the brain. In one experiment, pigeons were placed individually in large tubes and trained that food was present in only one end of the tube. When the tube was placed in a changeable magnetic field, pigeons readily learned which end contained food based solely on the magnetic polarity of the tube. In another experiment, the pigeons lost this ability when their beaks were anaesthetised or cooled, procedures that block action potentials from being sent to the brain. This demonstrates that their magnetic sensing ability is located in the beak and communicated by nerves to the brain.

Magnetite has also been found in the heads of migratory fish, such as rainbow trout. It is unlikely, however, that this entirely explains the extraordinary ability of migratory animals to navigate great distances, because other cues, such as smell and visual recognition of landmarks, also play a role.

Venomous snakes known as pit vipers (e.g., rattlesnakes) can localize prey in the dark with detectors that sense the heat emitted from animals as infrared radiation. These detectors are located in pits on each side of the head between the eyes and nostrils (**Figure 42.21**). Within the pit a thin, nerve-rich, temperature-sensitive membrane becomes activated in response to infrared waves emitted by live animals. When the snake detects the heat of the animal, it localizes its prey by moving its head back and forth until both pits detect the same intensity of radiation. This indicates that the prey is centred in front of the snake, and the snake is ready to strike.

Electrical, magnetic, and infrared sensing are adaptations for long-distance migration or low-light environments. When light is available, however, photoreception becomes a dominant sensory ability in many animals, as described next.

Pit—contains heat sensors

Figure 42.21 **Infrared sensing.** Sensory pits enable a white-lipped pit viper to detect the heat given off by its prey.

42.7 | PHOTORECEPTION

Learning Outcomes:

1. Describe the structure of invertebrate visual organs.
2. Describe the structure of the vertebrate (single-lens) eye and how it forms images.
3. Compare and contrast the structure and function of rods and cones.
4. Explain the mechanisms by which photoreceptors respond to light in a single-lens eye.
5. Outline the neural pathway by which visual signals travel to reach the brain.

Although it is a form of electromagnetic reception, photoreception is such an important and widespread sense that we will cover it separately here. Visual systems employ photoreceptors, which detect photons of light arriving from the sun or other light sources, or reflecting off an object. A photon is the fundamental unit of electromagnetic radiation and has the properties of both a particle and a wave. The properties of light are described in Chapter 8. In this section, we will examine the organs found in animals, usually called **eyes**, that detect light and send signals to the brain.

Eyecups and Compound Eyes Are Found in Certain Invertebrates

One of the simplest visual organs is found in the flatworm (*Planaria*); it is a concave **eyecup** containing the endings of photoreceptor cells (**Figure 42.22**). The eyecup, also called an eyespot, has a layer of pigment cells that shields the photoreceptors from one side. The left and right eyecups receive light from different directions. This allows the eyecups to detect the direction as well as the presence or absence of light. The nervous system compares the amount of light detected by each eyecup, and the flatworm moves toward darkness, a behaviour that protects it from predators. This type of photoreceptor can sense only the presence or absence of light, not form visual images of the environment.

In contrast, arthropods and some annelids have image-forming **compound eyes**, consisting of several hundred to several thousand light detectors called ommatidia (**Figure 42.23**). Each ommatidium makes up one facet of the eye. The **lens** and crystalline cone focus light onto a long central structure called a **rhabdom**. The rhabdom is a column of photosensitive microvilli that project from the cell membranes of retinula cells, which are the photoreceptor cells of the ommatidium. Each ommatidium senses the intensity and colour of light. Combined with the different inputs from neighbouring ommatidia, the compound eye forms an image that the brain interprets. Animals, such as bees and fruit flies, with large numbers of ommatidia, presumably have sharper vision than those with fewer sensory cells, such as grasshoppers. The compound eye is extremely sensitive to movement and helps flying insects evade birds and other predators.

Figure 42.22 **The eyecup of the flatworm.** The orientation of the eyecup allows light to stimulate photoreceptors from only one direction. This type of eye senses only the presence or absence of light and does not form visual images.

Behavioural studies have shown, however, that the resolving power of even the best compound eye is considerably less than that of the single-lens eye, which we will consider next.

Vertebrates and Some Invertebrates Have a More Complex Single-Lens Eye

Single-lens eyes are found in vertebrates, and also in some molluscs, such as squid and octopus, and in some snails and annelids. Different patterns of light emitted from images in the animal's field of view are transmitted through a small opening or **pupil**, through the lens, to a sheetlike layer of photoreceptors called the **retina** at the back of the eye (**Figure 42.24a**). Photoreceptors trigger electrical changes in neurons that pass out of the eye through the **optic nerve**, which carries the signals to the brain.

The vertebrate eye has a strong outer sheath called the **sclera** (the white of the eye), which in the front is continuous with a thin, clear layer known as the **cornea**. Within the eye are two chambers filled with liquid. At the front of the eye immediately behind the cornea is the smaller anterior chamber, which contains a thin liquid called the **aqueous humour**. The larger posterior chamber contains the thicker **vitreous humour**, which helps maintain the shape of the eye. Between the anterior and the posterior cavities are the **iris**—the circle of pigmented

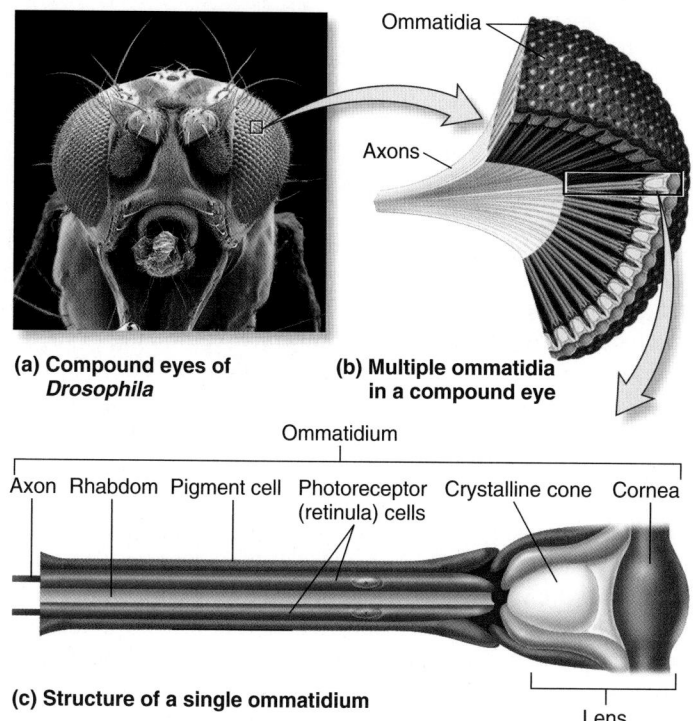

(a) Compound eyes of Drosophila

(b) Multiple ommatidia in a compound eye

(c) Structure of a single ommatidium

Figure 42.23   The compound eye of insects.   (a) Close-up of the eyes of a fruit fly (*Drosophila melanogaster*). **(b)** Each eye has approximately 1,000 ommatidia, which form a sheet on the surface of the eye. **(c)** Each ommatidium has a lens that directs light to the photosensitive rhabdom.

smooth muscle that is responsible for eye colour—and the single lens. The hole in the centre of the iris is the pupil. The size of the pupil changes when the muscles of the iris relax or contract to allow more or less light to enter the eye.

Because light radiates in all directions from a light source, light must be bent inward toward the photoreceptors at the back of the eye. This is accomplished by the cornea and the lens. Whenever light passes from one medium to another medium of a different density, light waves will bend (try looking at a pencil in a glass partly filled with water). The cornea is at the interface between the air and the aqueous humour, and it is the cornea that initially bends the light. The light then passes through the thick lens, where it is focused onto the layer of photoreceptors, the retina, at the back of the posterior cavity. The bending of the incoming light results in an upside-down image on the retina, but the brain adjusts for this and the image is perceived correctly.

(a) Human eye structure

(b) Lens accommodation

Near vision

When ciliary muscles contract, the lens becomes rounder.

Distant vision

When ciliary muscles relax, the lens becomes flatter.

Figure 42.24   The vertebrate single-lens eye.   (a) The structure of the human eye. **(b)** Changes in lens shape during accommodation. When an object is near, the ciliary muscles contract and the lens becomes rounder, causing light to bend more. When the object is far away, the ciliary muscles relax and the lens flattens. **(c)** Demonstration of the blind spot. First, hold the picture up in front of your face. Next, close your left eye and stare at the black spot with your right eye while you move the picture toward and away from your face. At some point, light reflecting off the plus (+) sign will fall directly on your blind spot, and it will seem to disappear.

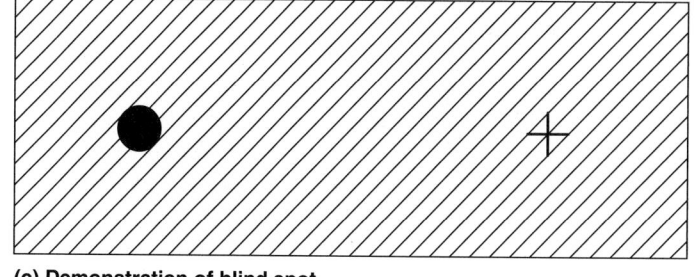

(c) Demonstration of blind spot

The lens is adjusted to focus light that comes from nearby or far away. In fish and amphibians, the lens is moved forward or backward. In the avian and mammalian eye, the lens remains stationary but changes shape to become more or less convex. When the lens is stretched, it flattens, and light passing through it bends less than when it is round. Contraction and relaxation of the ciliary muscles adjust the lens according to the angle at which light enters the eye, a process called **accommodation** (**Figure 42.24b**).

In the eye, the image on the retina sends signals to the brain through neurons that exit the eye in the optic nerve. In vertebrates, the point on the retina where the optic nerve leaves the eye does not have any photoreceptors, forming a *blind spot* where light does not activate a response (**Figure 42.24c**). Invertebrates with single-lens eyes do not have a blind spot, because the optic nerve does not pass through the layer of photoreceptors before leaving the eye.

The **fovea**, a small area on the retina directly behind the lens where the image is focused, has numerous photoreceptors for colour. The fovea is responsible for the sharpness with which we and other animals see in daylight.

Rods and Cones Are Photoreceptor Cells

Two types of photoreceptors have names that are derived from their shape (**Figure 42.25**). **Rods** are very sensitive to low-intensity light and can respond to as little as one photon, but they do not discriminate different colours. Rods are utilized mostly at night, and they send signals to the brain that generate a black-and-white visual image. **Cones** are less sensitive to low levels of light but, unlike rods, can detect colour. Cones are used in daylight by most diurnal vertebrate species and by some insects such as the honeybee, which can detect the yellow colour of pollen. Compared with rods, the human retina has fewer cones, which are clustered in and around the fovea. Cones provide sharp images because of their density at the fovea. Although they are less sensitive to light than rods, this is less critical in daylight because the amount of light reaching the eyes in daytime far exceeds what is needed to stimulate any

photoreceptor cell. Because the two types of photoreceptor are specialized for either night or day vision, neither rods nor cones function at peak efficiency at twilight. This accounts for our relatively poor vision at this time.

Rods and cones have highly convoluted membranes that form the **outer segment** of the cells (**Figure 42.26**). The folds of the membrane form stacks of membranous discs. These disks contain the pigment molecules that absorb light. The **inner segment** of the cell contains the cell nucleus and other cytoplasmic organelles. The cell does not have an axon but has a synaptic terminal with neurotransmitter-containing vesicles, and that synapses with other neurons within the retina.

Nocturnal animals rely predominantly on rod vision, though some have limited colour vision, too. In diurnal animals with both rods and cones, such as humans, the rods are located around the periphery of the retina away from the fovea. Therefore, it is easiest to see low-intensity light if it comes into the eye at an angle. You can test this with a simple experiment. In early evening, before many stars are visible, look at the sky until you notice a star out of the corner of your eye. Now shift your gaze to where you thought you saw the star. You will probably not be able to locate it anymore. When you look away again so that light from the dim star enters your eye at an angle, it will reappear. This demonstrates that under low-light conditions, your vision is better when the light is directed to the part of the retina that contains only rods.

Rods and Cones Contain Visual Pigments That Detect Light

Visual pigments are molecules that span the disc membranes of the outer segment of rods and cones and absorb light. These pigments consist of two components bonded together. The first

Figure 42.25   Rod and cone photoreceptors.   Rods are shown as green and cones as blue in this false-colour image (SEM).

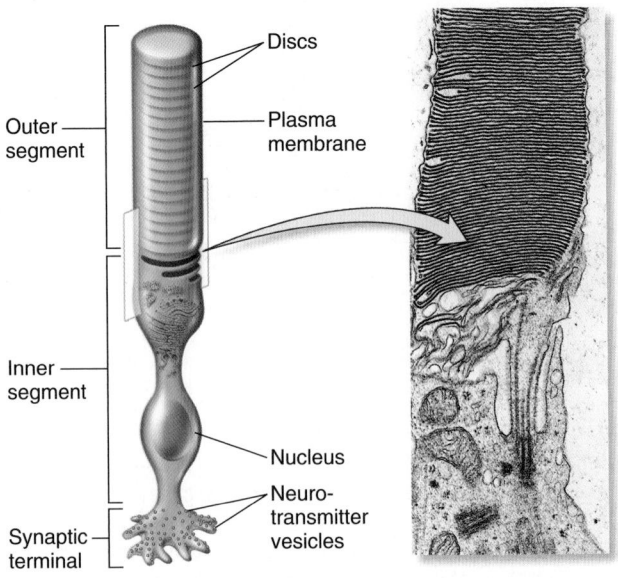

Figure 42.26   Structure of a photoreceptor.   The illustration shows the structure of a rod photoreceptor and its appearance in an electron micrograph. Note the multiple stacks of membranous discs in the outer segment of the cell.

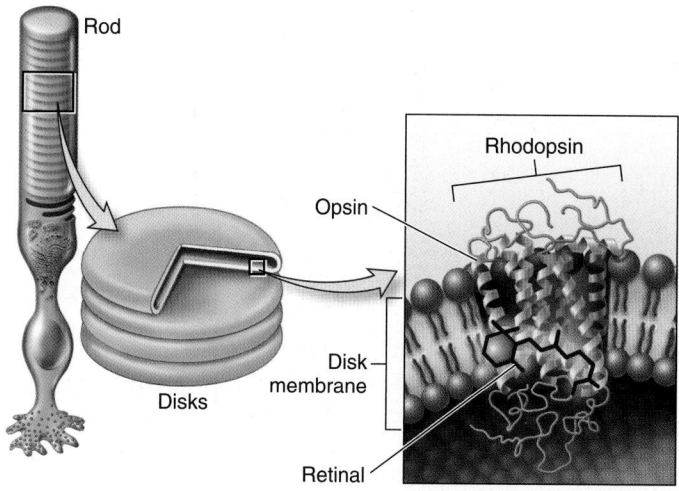

Figure 42.27 **A visual pigment.** Rhodopsin is found within the membrane of the rod photoreceptor discs. It is composed of a transmembrane protein, opsin, that is bonded to a molecule of retinal.

 Principle: *Structure determines function. The stacks of discs in the photoreceptor outer segment are an excellent example of a structural adaptation that increases surface area without significantly increasing volume, thereby allowing for greater light-capturing ability and improving the function of the cell as a sensory cell.*

is **retinal**, a derivative of vitamin A that is capable of absorbing light energy. The discovery of retinal in the visual pigment explains the need for vitamin A in the diet and its importance in vision. The second component of visual pigments is a protein, called **opsin**, of which there are several types.

Rods and cones contain visual pigments that differ with regard to the type of opsin protein they contain. In rods, the visual pigment is named **rhodopsin** (from "rod-opsin") (**Figure 42.27**). Cones contain several types of visual pigments called **cone pigments**. Opsins, found in both rhodopsin and cone pigments, are examples of G-protein-coupled-receptors (see Chapter 9), which trigger a biochemical cascade that changes the permeability of membrane channels to ions.

In humans, cone pigments are composed of retinal plus one of three possible opsin proteins. Each type of opsin protein determines the wavelength of light that retinal can absorb. For this reason, each cone pigment can respond to red, green, or blue light. Any given cone cell makes only one type of cone pigment. Many different shades of these colours can be perceived, however, because the brain uses information about the proportion of each type of cone that was stimulated to generate all other colours. Red, green, and blue opsins are not present in all species, and many species have only one or two opsins. Presumably, the more types of cones an animal has, the more shades of colour it perceives. It is intriguing, therefore, to imagine how birds see the world, because they have up to five cones of overlapping wavelength sensitivity.

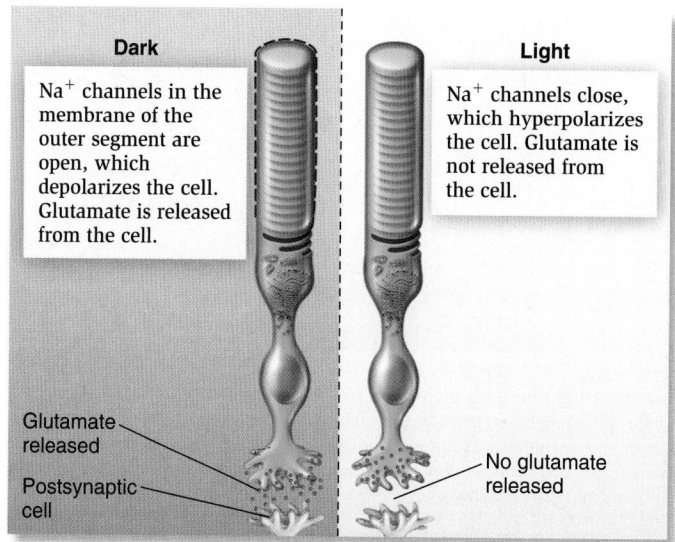

Figure 42.28 Synaptic response of photoreceptors to dark and light.

Photons Change Photoreceptor Activity by Altering the Conformation of Visual Pigments

Photoreceptors differ from other sensory receptor cells because their membrane potential is in a slightly depolarized state when the cell is at rest, and it is hyperpolarized rather than depolarized in response to a stimulus (**Figure 42.28**). The membranes of the resting cell are highly permeable to sodium ions, which depolarizes the membrane potential. Sodium ions flow into the cell through open channels in the membrane of the outer segments and are pumped back out of the cell by Na^+/K^+-ATPase pumps in the membrane of the inner segment. In the dark, sodium channels remain open due to the binding of cGMP. The depolarization that is present when the photoreceptor is unstimulated (no light) results in a continuous release of the neurotransmitter glutamate from the synaptic terminal of the photoreceptor.

When the photoreceptor is exposed to light, the retinal within the visual pigment absorbs a photon. The energy of the photon alters the retinal from *cis*-retinal to *trans*-retinal, an isomer with a slightly different conformational state because of a rotation at one of the molecule's double bonds (**Figure 42.29**). This change results in a brief dissociation of retinal from the opsin protein, causing the opsin to change shape and activate a G protein called transducin. The activated transducin, in turn, activates the enzyme phosphodiesterase. Phosphodiesterase reduces the amount of cGMP by converting it to GMP. GMP molecules cannot hold the sodium channels open, so the channels close, and sodium movement into the cell stops. The membrane potential of the cell becomes less positive than it was in the dark. Therefore, the response of the cell is a hyperpolarization that is proportional to the intensity of the light. The final result is a decrease in glutamate release from the photoreceptor.

Figure 42.29 **Mechanism of photoreception.** Molecular changes in photoreceptor (rod) cell in response to light.

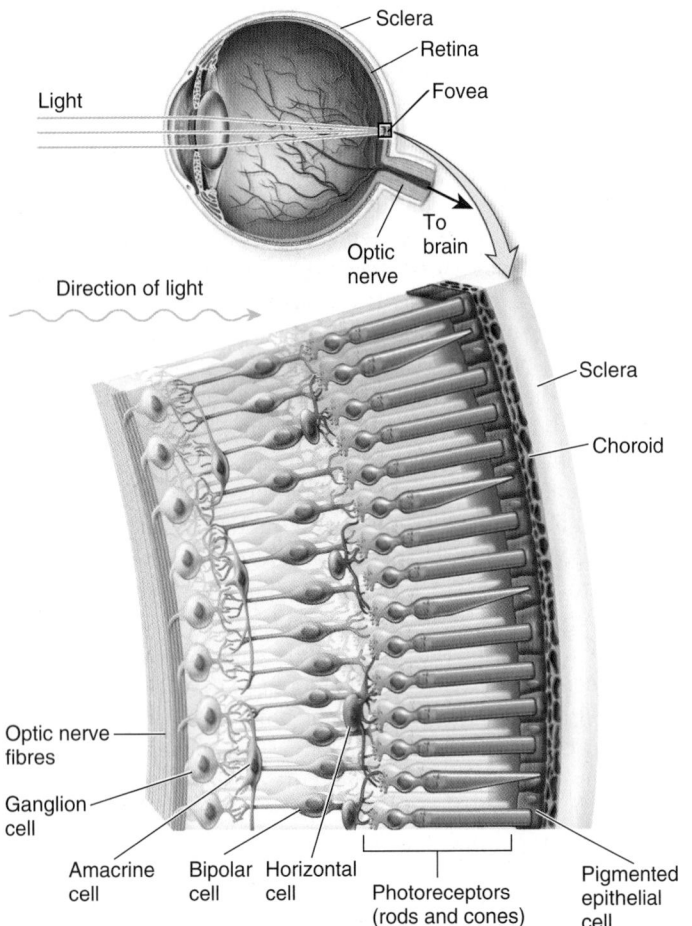

Figure 42.30 **The arrangement of cells in the retina.** Light passes through two layers of cells before it reaches the photoreceptors. Amacrine and horizontal cells integrate the responses of the bipolar and ganglion cells. The ganglion cells generate action potentials to carry the information to the brain.

The Visual Image Is Refined in the Retina

Thus far, we have considered the structure of the eye and how photoreceptors transduce light. We will now turn our attention to the neural pathways through which the visual signal travels to reach the brain. To do so, we must consider the cellular organization of the vertebrate retina, which has three layers of cells (**Figure 42.30**). The rods and cones form the deepest layer, closest to the inside of the sclera along with a layer of pigmented epithelial cells that absorb scattered light. Light must pass through two other layers of cells, which are transparent, before it reaches the photoreceptors. The middle layer contains **bipolar cells**, so named because they make synapses with the photoreceptors and relay responses to the third layer of cells, the **ganglion cells**. The ganglion cells send their axons out of the eye into the optic nerve. In addition to these three layers, two types of cells, horizontal and amacrine cells, are interspersed across the retina.

The pathway for light reception begins at the photoreceptor cells (rods and cones). The photoreceptor cells release neurotransmitter molecules that affect the membrane potential of bipolar cells. The membrane potential of the bipolar cells determines the amount of neurotransmitter that bipolar cells release, which, in turn, controls the membrane potential of ganglion cells. When a threshold potential is reached in ganglion cells, action potentials are sent out of the eye via the optic nerve to the occipital lobe of the cerebral cortex, where visual information is further refined and interpreted. The visual cortex responds to characteristics of the visual scene, such as whether something is moving, how far away it is, how one colour compares to another, and the nature of the image (e.g., a face).

Horizontal and amacrine cells modify electrical signals as they pass from the photoreceptors to the ganglion cells. These cells adjust the signal significantly, enhancing an animal's ability to visualize a scene by emphasizing the differences between images. Horizontal cells make connections between photoreceptors and help to define the boundaries of an image, while amacrine cells are important in light adaptation and motion sensitivity. The ability of the retina to refine the image is especially well developed in birds and reptiles, which have complex retinas that process the image extensively before it is interpreted in the brain.

Vertebrate Eyes Are Adapted to Environmental Conditions and Life Histories

Many vertebrates show unique modifications of their visual systems that are the result of evolutionary adaptations to environmental conditions. Other adaptations have occurred as a result of behavioural requirements for obtaining food or attracting a mate.

Light Intensity   Over a day, wide variation occurs in the amount of light that stimulates the eye. The vertebrate eye can adjust to the differences in illumination in part by adjusting the diameter of the pupil. In addition, the eye can adapt to light differences by changing the relative amounts of *cis*- and

trans-retinal. Such changes can alter the light sensitivity of the eye by as much as a million-fold.

In a dark environment, a large amount of *cis*-retinal is available for light absorption. When light stimulates *cis*-retinal to change into *trans*-retinal, the visual pigment no longer responds to additional light and is said to be bleached. Such bleaching makes the eye less sensitive to low levels of light. When we enter a dark theatre on a bright day, most of our visual pigments have been bleached by the sunlight and are temporarily unavailable for use. For a few minutes, we are unable to detect even low levels of light. This process of adjusting to dim light, called dark adaptation, involves the gradual reconversion of *trans*-retinal to *cis*-retinal.

Conversely, when we move from a dark room into bright sunlight, the large amount of *cis*-retinal makes our eyes extremely sensitive to light and temporarily overwhelms our ability to see colours and shapes. In light adaptation, the bright light stimulates bleaching of the visual pigments, which reduces the response to bright light.

Eye Placement   Animals with both eyes located at the front of the head have **binocular vision**, because the overlapping images coming into both eyes are processed together in the brain to form one perception (**Figure 42.31a**). Binocular vision provides excellent depth perception because the images come into each eye from slightly different angles. The brain processes those tiny differences to determine where an object is relative to other objects in its environment. Predators benefit from binocular vision because it helps them judge distance and determine the location of their prey. In contrast, animals with eyes on the sides of the head have **monocular vision** (**Figure 42.31b**). Monocular vision allows an animal to see a wide area at one

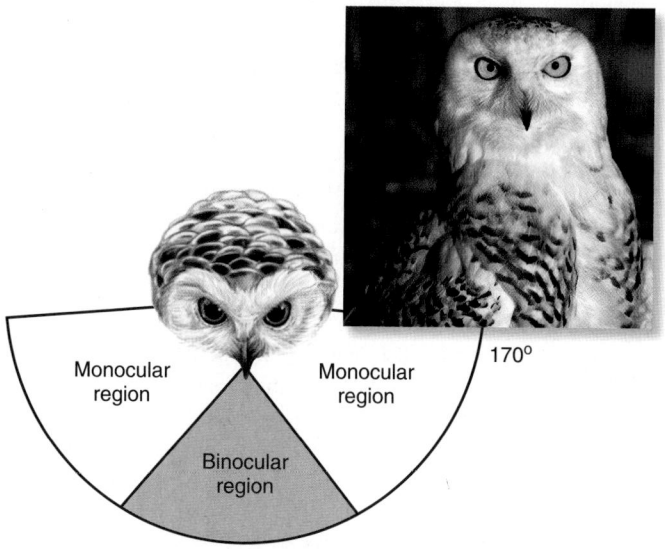

(a) Visual field of the snowy owl

(b) Visual field of the American woodcock

Figure 42.31   **Examples of binocular and monocular fields of vision.**   Visual fields are shown for **(a)** the snowy owl and **(b)** the American woodcock. Monocular regions are white, and binocular regions are shaded.

Principle: *Living organisms interact with their environment. Different animals may interact with their environments in ways that are hard for us to imagine. Not only do different animals have vastly different visual fields, but some see better at night than we do, some see wavelengths of light that we cannot see, and some can resolve images travelling at speeds that would appear blurry to us.*

time, though depth perception is reduced. Many prey species have monocular vision, perhaps because it helps them scan for predators across a wide field of vision.

Vision in the Deep Sea   Fish and other deep-sea vertebrates have colour vision that is limited primarily to the colour blue. Light with longer wavelengths that would be seen as red or orange does not usually penetrate more than 6 m into the water, while the higher-energy short-wavelength light, which is seen as blue, can penetrate to greater depths. Aquatic animals that live in the deep sea are usually capable of seeing only blue, because they generally have only one opsin, which is responsive to blue light. Deep-dwelling fish tend to be drab colours, because most wavelengths of light do not penetrate that far and could not, therefore, reflect off the surface of the fish. In those deep-dwelling fish with more than one type of opsin, the additional visual pigments detect the bioluminescence (self-generated light, like that of a firefly) produced by their own or other species.

By contrast, fish that live near the water's surface sometimes have four or five different opsins, giving them excellent colour vision. Not surprisingly, shallow water and surface-dwelling fish are often very colourful, because light of all wavelengths penetrates shallow water. These fish have adapted by using coloration for protection (camouflage) or for identification.

Vision with Speed   Peregrine falcons, like other raptors, have exceptionally good eyesight. They dive at speeds that can reach 240 to 320 km/h to kill prey, and their visual system is specialized to maintain great sensitivity during the dive. The retina of a falcon has two foveas. A deep fovea has a central pit and provides the highest visual accuracy when objects are far away and to the side. However, when the falcon uses the deep fovea it does not have good depth perception. A shallow fovea provides the best images of nearby objects and good depth perception. When the falcon dives, it first uses the deep fovea to locate the prey and steer toward it. When the falcon gets closer, it switches to the shallow fovea. Some details of the image are sacrificed, but the improved depth perception allows it to gauge when it will reach its prey.

Tapetum Lucidum   Did you ever wonder why cats' eyes seem to glow in photographs? What you see is light being reflected off the **tapetum lucidum**, a reflective layer of tissue located beneath the photoreceptors at the back of the eye. When light enters the retina, some of it passes into the layer containing the photoreceptors, but some light also passes through this layer. Normally, the pigmented epithelium at the back of the eye absorbs this light. However, in animals with a tapetum lucidum, the light reflects off this structure and back to the photoreceptors. This enhances the amount of light that the photoreceptors receive and makes it easier to detect low levels of light. Many nocturnal animals, both vertebrate and invertebrate, have a tapetum lucidum, which increases their ability to see in the dark.

42.8   CHEMORECEPTION: SMELL AND TASTE

Learning Outcomes:

1. Describe olfaction and gustation in insects.
2. Describe how olfactory receptors respond to the binding of odour molecules.
3. Outline how receptor cells within taste buds respond to the binding of food molecules.

Chemoreception includes the senses of smell (**olfaction**) and taste (**gustation**), which involve detecting chemicals in air, water, and food. These chemicals bind to chemoreceptors, which initiate electrical responses in other neurons that pass into the brain. Amazingly, the binding of a single molecule to a receptor cell can sometimes be perceived as an odour. Airborne molecules that bind to olfactory receptors must be small enough to be carried in the air and into the nose. Taste molecules can be heavier because they are conveyed in food and liquid.

A close relationship exists between taste and smell. In fact, the distinction is largely meaningless for aquatic animals, because for them all chemoreception comes through the water. Even in terrestrial animals, about 80% of the perception of taste is actually due to activation of olfactory receptors. This is why food loses its flavour when olfaction is impaired, such as when you have a cold.

Olfaction and Taste in Insects Involve Chemoreceptors in Sensory Hairs

Insects are highly dependent on odour and taste for finding food and mates. Chemoreceptors are located on sensory hairs on the proboscis, legs, feet, and antennae. Each sensory hair on the proboscis and feet has a pore at the tip through which the substance passes (**Figure 42.32a**). The blowfly, which feeds on sugary secretions (nectar or aphid-derived honeydew) and liquids from decomposing corpses, has four separate chemoreceptors within each hair, and each of these neurons responds to different molecules. Dendrites of the chemoreceptor cells inside the pore bind to the molecules and initiate a sensory transduction pathway that opens ion channels in the membrane. This depolarizes the chemoreceptor cell and generates action potentials.

In certain moths, males have elaborate antennae that can sense pheromones, extremely potent signalling molecules given off by a female. The female secretes a sexual-attractant pheromone into the air from an abdominal gland (**Figure 42.32b**), and the chemosensory hairs on the male's antennae (**Figure 42.32c**) can detect extremely low concentrations of it from several kilometres away. This highly sensitive detection system enables the male to locate the female in the dark.

Mammalian Olfactory Receptors Respond to the Binding of Odour Molecules

The olfactory sensitivity of mammals varies widely depending on their supply of olfactory receptor cells, which ranges from

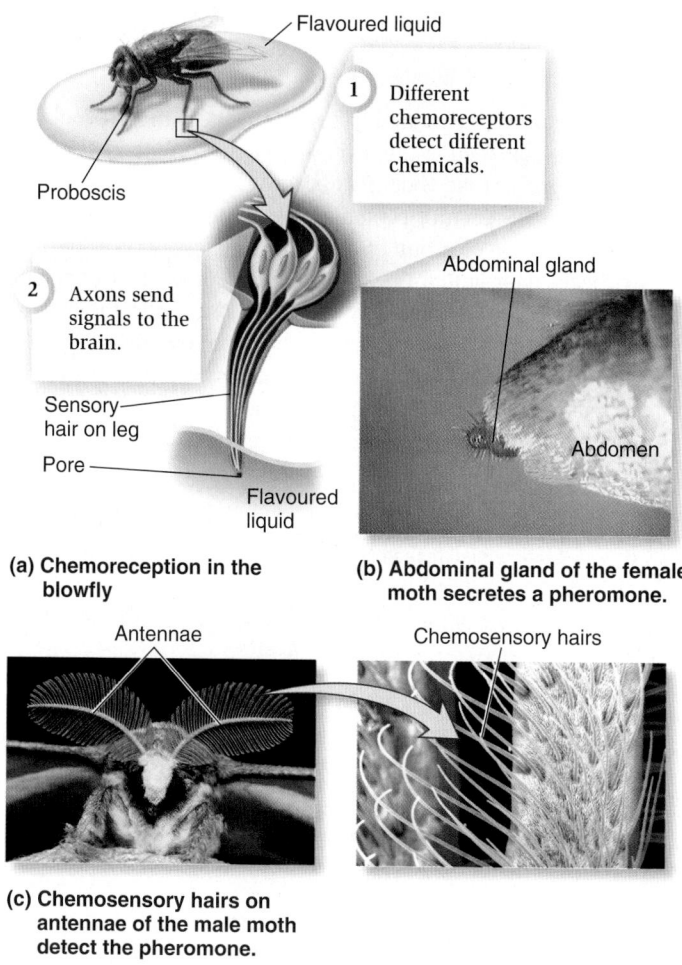

(a) Chemoreception in the blowfly

1 Different chemoreceptors detect different chemicals.

2 Axons send signals to the brain.

(b) Abdominal gland of the female moth secretes a pheromone.

(c) Chemosensory hairs on antennae of the male moth detect the pheromone.

Figure 42.32 **Chemoreception in insects.** **(a)** Chemosensory cells of the blowfly located on the proboscis, legs, and feet sense different chemicals. **(b)** Female moths secrete a pheromone from abdominal glands, which is detected by **(c)** chemosensory hairs on a male's antennae that bind odour molecules.

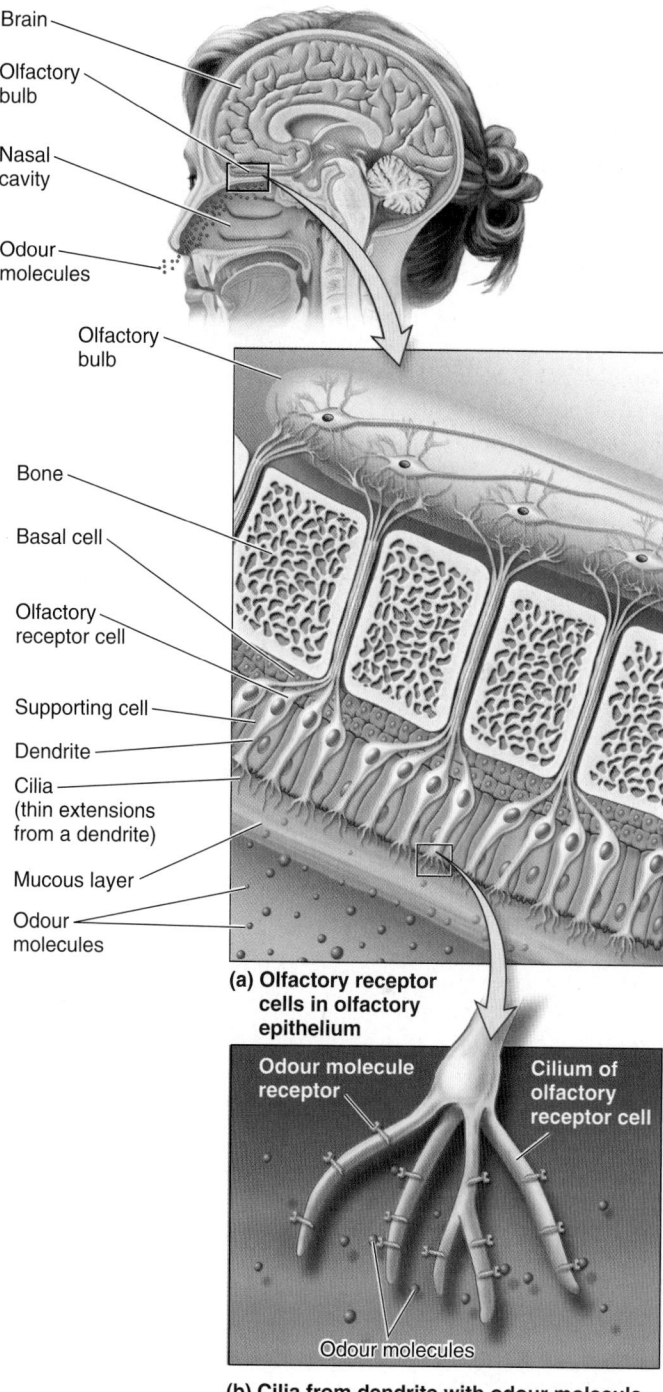

(a) Olfactory receptor cells in olfactory epithelium

(b) Cilia from dendrite with odour molecule receptors

Figure 42.33 **Olfactory structures in the human nose.** Odour molecules dissolve in a layer of mucus that coats the olfactory receptor cells. The molecules bind to protein receptors on the membrane of cilia that extend from the olfactory receptor cells. Action potentials in the olfactory receptor cells are conducted to cells in the olfactory bulb, and from there to the brain for interpretation. Basal cells periodically replace dead or damaged olfactory receptor cells.

5 million or 6 million in humans to 100 million in rabbits and 220 million in dogs. Olfactory receptors are located in the epithelial tissue at the upper part of the nasal cavity in mammals (**Figure 42.33a**). These cells are surrounded by two additional cell types: supporting cells, which are located between the receptor cells and provide physical support for the olfactory receptors, and basal cells. The basal cells differentiate into new olfactory receptors every 30–60 days, replacing those that have died after prolonged exposure of their cell endings.

Olfactory receptors have dendrites from which long, thin extensions called cilia emerge into a mucus layer that covers the epithelium. Despite the similarity in structure, these cells do not function like the mechanoreceptor hair cells of the auditory and vestibular systems; these cilia are different from stereocilia that bend. Instead, olfactory receptor cells have receptor proteins within the plasma membranes of the cilia (**Figure 42.33b**). Airborne molecules dissolve in the mucus and bind to these receptor proteins. When an odour molecule binds to its protein receptor, this initiates a signal transduction pathway that

ultimately opens sodium channels in the plasma membrane. The subsequent depolarization results in action potentials being transmitted to the next series of cells in the olfactory bulbs,

FEATURE INVESTIGATION

Buck and Axel Discovered a Family of Olfactory Receptor Proteins That Bind Specific Odour Molecules

How does the olfactory system discriminate between thousands of different odours? American neuroscientists Linda Buck and Richard Axel set out to study this question. When they began, two hypotheses were proposed to explain this phenomenon. One possibility is that many different types of odour molecules might bind to one or just a few types of receptor proteins, with the brain responding differently depending on the number or distribution of the activated receptors. Alternatively, odours might be distinguished at the level of receptor proteins. The second hypothesis is that olfactory receptor cells can make many different types of receptor proteins, each type binding a particular odour molecule or group of odour molecules.

To begin their study, Buck and Axel assumed that olfactory receptor proteins would be highly expressed in the olfactory receptor cells, but not in other parts of the body. Based on previous work, they also postulated that the receptor proteins would be members of the large family of G-protein-coupled receptors (GPCRs), which are described in Chapter 9. As shown in **Figure 42.34**, they isolated

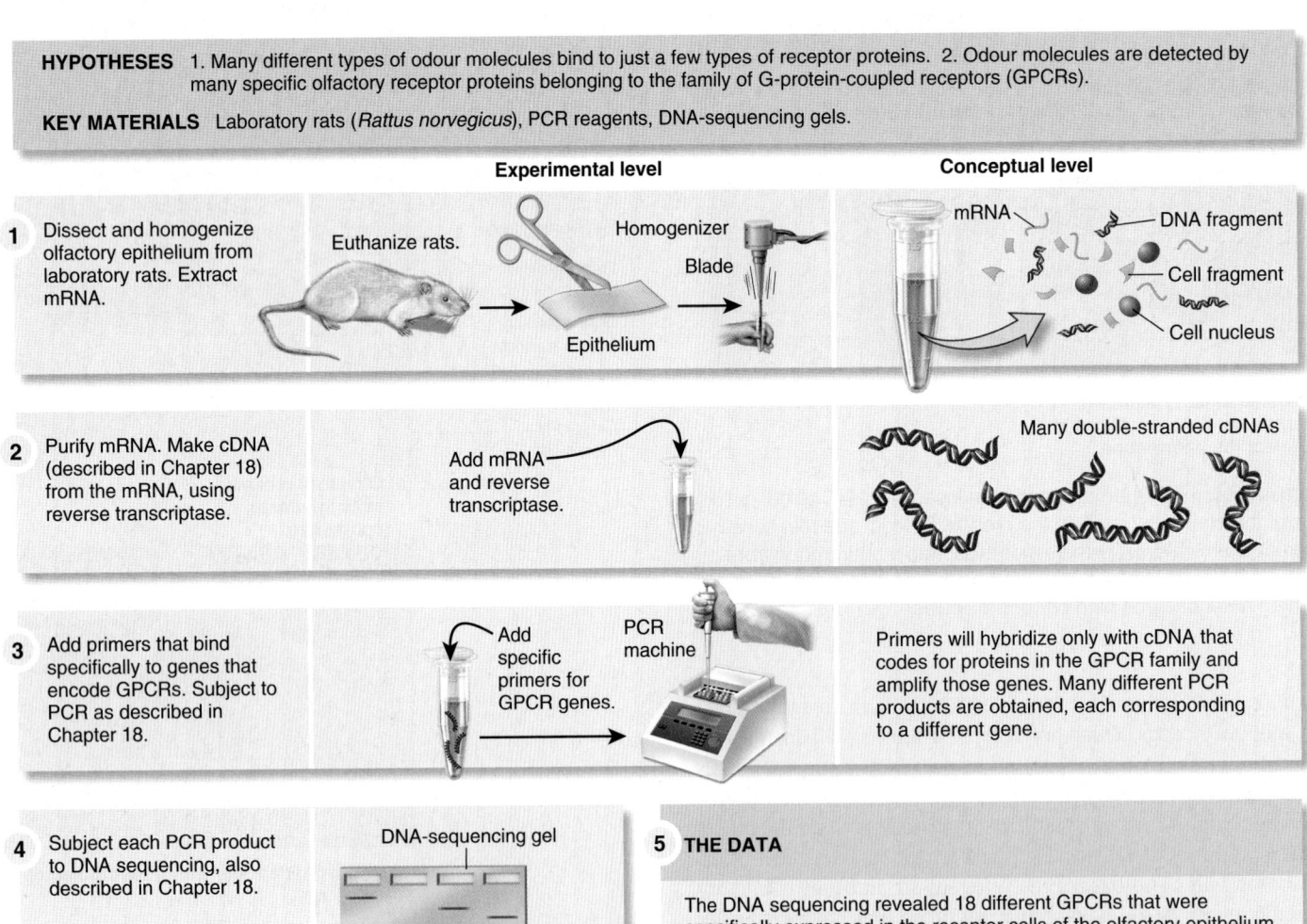

HYPOTHESES 1. Many different types of odour molecules bind to just a few types of receptor proteins. 2. Odour molecules are detected by many specific olfactory receptor proteins belonging to the family of G-protein-coupled receptors (GPCRs).

KEY MATERIALS Laboratory rats (*Rattus norvegicus*), PCR reagents, DNA-sequencing gels.

Experimental level / **Conceptual level**

1 Dissect and homogenize olfactory epithelium from laboratory rats. Extract mRNA.
Euthanize rats. Homogenizer Blade Epithelium
mRNA — DNA fragment — Cell fragment — Cell nucleus

2 Purify mRNA. Make cDNA (described in Chapter 18) from the mRNA, using reverse transcriptase.
Add mRNA and reverse transcriptase.
Many double-stranded cDNAs

3 Add primers that bind specifically to genes that encode GPCRs. Subject to PCR as described in Chapter 18.
Add specific primers for GPCR genes. PCR machine
Primers will hybridize only with cDNA that codes for proteins in the GPCR family and amplify those genes. Many different PCR products are obtained, each corresponding to a different gene.

4 Subject each PCR product to DNA sequencing, also described in Chapter 18.
DNA-sequencing gel
A T G C
Different GPCRs will have slightly different DNA sequences.

5 **THE DATA**
The DNA sequencing revealed 18 different GPCRs that were specifically expressed in the receptor cells of the olfactory epithelium.

6 **CONCLUSION** Olfactory receptor cells express many different receptor proteins that account for an animal's ability to detect a wide variety of odours.

7 **SOURCE** Buck, L., and Axel, R. 1991. A novel multigene family may encode odourant receptors: a molecular basis for odour recognition. *Cell* 65:175–187.

Figure 42.34 Buck and Axel identified olfactory receptor proteins in olfactory receptor cells.

olfactory-receptor cells from rats and then broke open the cells to release the RNA. The purified RNA was then used to make cDNA via reverse transcriptase. This would generate a large pool of cDNAs, which would represent all of the genes that are expressed in olfactory receptor cells. To determine if any of these cDNAs encoded GPCRs, they used primers that recognized regions within previously known GPCR genes that are highly conserved. A highly conserved region is a DNA sequence that rarely changes among different family members. The primers were used in the technique of PCR to amplify cDNAs that encoded GPCRs. This produced many PCR products that were then subjected to DNA sequencing. Buck and Axel identified 18 different genes, each encoding a GPCR with a slightly different amino acid sequence. Further research showed that these 18 genes were expressed in nasal epithelia but not in other parts of the rat's body. These results were consistent with the second hypothesis stated earlier, namely that organisms make a large number of receptor proteins, each type binding a particular odour molecule or group of odour molecules.

Since these studies, researchers have determined that this family of olfactory genes in mammals is surprisingly large. In humans, more than 600 genes that encode olfactory receptor proteins have been identified, though about half of these are pseudogenes that are no longer functional. This value underscores the importance of olfaction even in humans, who have

a relatively poor sense of smell compared with certain animals. Each olfactory receptor cell is thought to express only one type of GPCR that recognizes its own specific odour molecule or group of molecules. Most odours are due to multiple chemicals that activate many different types of odour receptors at the same time. We perceive odours based on the combination of receptors that become activated and then send signals to the brain.

The research of Buck and Axel explained, in part, how animals detect odours. In 2004 they received a Nobel Prize for this pioneering work.

Experimental Questions

1. What were the two major hypotheses to explain how animals discriminate between different odours? How did Buck and Axel test the hypothesis of multiple olfactory receptor proteins?
2. What were the results of Buck and Axel's study?
3. Considering the two hypotheses explaining how animals discriminate among different odours, which one was supported by the results of this experiment? With the evidence presented by Buck and Axel, what is the current hypothesis explaining the discrimination of odours in animals?

---

which are located at the base of the brain. From there, the information is sent to the cerebral cortex and limbic system for processing and interpretation.

The relative size of the olfactory bulbs indicates the importance of olfaction to an animal. In humans, the olfactory bulbs make up only about 5% of the weight of the brain, while in nocturnal animals such as rats and mice they can comprise as much as 20%. Even with their limited olfactory sensitivity, however, humans have the capacity to detect up to 10,000 different odours, and other mammals are believed to respond to many more. Exactly how this is possible remained a mystery until 1991, when two scientists uncovered the molecular basis of olfaction.

Taste Buds Detect Food Molecules

Chemical senses are present in all animal phyla, although not all animals have taste-sensing organs. Many animals use their taste sense to select appropriate foods. Butterflies select nectar based on the sugars found in a particular flower, and carnivorous animals detect the taste of different meats based on the combination of amino acids, fats, and sugars that are present. Some aquatic animals, such as catfish and lobsters, have highly sensitive chemoreceptors for amino acids. Taste can also help an animal seek out necessary nutrients, such as salt, and avoid poisonous chemicals. Toxic substances are often perceived as bitter, which may cause an animal to stop eating immediately.

Taste buds are a group of chemosensory cells that detect particular molecules in food. Humans have about 9,000 taste buds, while other mammals, such as pigs and rabbits, have approximately 15,000 to 18,000. The bumps that you see on your tongue are not the taste buds but the papillae, elevations from the tongue that collect food molecules and direct them to the sensory receptor cells in the taste buds. The sensory receptor cells along with several supporting cells in the taste bud are organized like the segments of an orange (**Figure 42.35**). The tips of the sensory receptor cells have microvilli that extend into a taste pore. Here, molecules in food that have dissolved in saliva bind to receptor proteins. This triggers intracellular signals that alter ion permeability and membrane potentials. The sensory cells release neurotransmitters onto underlying sensory fibres. Action potentials travel from these neurons to the thalamus and other regions of the cerebrum, where the taste is perceived and recognized.

The senses of taste and smell are enhanced when we are hungry, a phenomenon that most likely occurs in other animals as well. Once we have eaten, we are less aware of the smell and taste of food. The importance of this for survival is clear: A hungry animal needs to eat. An improved sense of smell aids in locating food, and a heightened sense of taste encourages an animal to eat. Afterward, these senses become temporarily dampened so as not to distract the animal from its other needs.

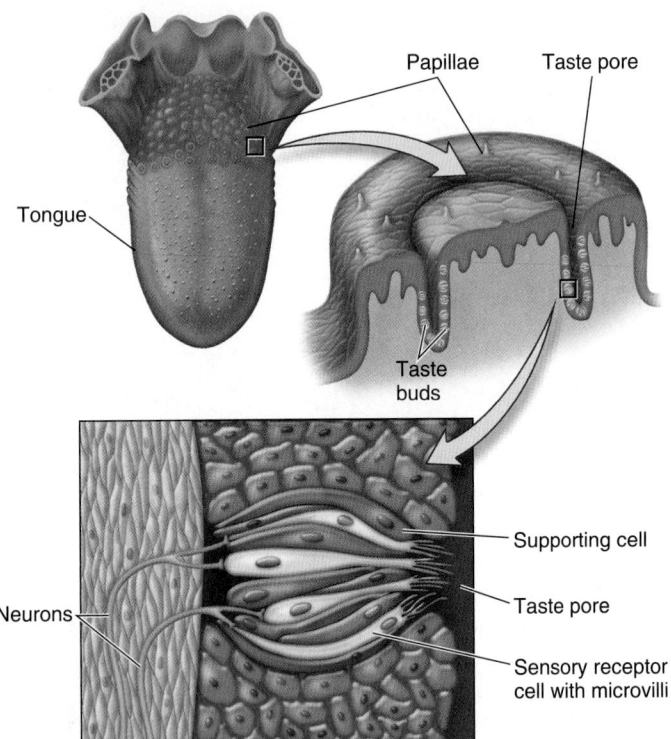

Figure 42.35 Structures involved in the sense of taste. This sense occurs in taste buds, which contain the sensory receptor cells that respond to dissolved food molecules.

Concept check: *Why have many animals, including humans, evolved the ability to sense salty, sweet, sour, bitter, and umami?*

42.9 HUMAN HEALTH CONNECTION

Learning Outcomes:

1. List the broad groups of diseases affecting the human nervous system.
2. Discuss the impact of meningitis and Alzheimer disease on public health.
3. Identify common types of visual and hearing deficits in humans, and the causes of each.

Neurological disorders can be classified in broad categories, including infectious diseases (inflammation of the brain), neurodegenerative disorders, movement disorders, seizure disorders, sleep disorders, tumours, headache disorders, mood disorders, demyelinating disorders, sensory disorders, and injury-related disorders. Next, we will consider three disorders that result from very different causes.

Meningitis Is an Infectious Disease That Attacks the Meninges

Meningitis is caused by a viral or bacterial infection of the meninges. The result is an inflammation in which fluid accumulates in the affected area. The excess fluid in the subarachnoid space raises pressure within the skull, which can lead to severe headaches, fever, seizures, unconsciousness, and even death within hours if untreated. Many patients with meningitis develop a stiff neck because the inflammation proceeds down the spinal cord.

Several different viruses or bacterial species can cause meningitis. It usually results from another infection typically in neighbouring regions, such as the sinuses behind the eyes, nose, or ears, that has gone untreated. Meningitis can be confirmed by using a long needle to sample the cerebrospinal fluid (CSF) in the spinal cord and analyzing the pressure and contents of the CSF. Large numbers of white blood cells, which are the body's chief infection-fighting cells, indicate infection in the CSF and meninges. If the infection is the result of bacterial invasion, meningitis can be treated with bacterial-killing agents such as antibiotics. Antibiotics do not kill viruses, but, fortunately, the viral form of meningitis is usually less serious than the bacterial form and runs its course after several days or weeks.

Between 1,000 and 2,000 people a year in Canada develop meningitis, and mortality rates are about 10%. Despite the existence of several vaccines, meningitis is still a dangerous and prevalent disease. It tends to occur in individuals living in close quarters, such as college dormitories, where infections may spread rapidly, but it can affect people of any age. Occasionally, meningitis can become epidemic. For example, 250,000 people in sub-Saharan Africa were infected and 25,000 died in 1996, and nearly 75,000 people in Southeast Asia died of meningitis in 2004.

Alzheimer's Disease Impairs Memory, Thought, and Language

Alzheimer's disease (AD), the most common type of dementia worldwide, is characterized by a loss of memory and intellectual and emotional function. AD is a progressive disease that begins with small memory lapses, leading in later stages to problems with language and abstract thinking, and finally to loss of normal motor control. The disease usually appears after age 65, though some inherited forms can strike people in their 30s and 40s.

Although psychological testing can help to diagnose AD, a definitive diagnosis can be made only after death when the brain is examined microscopically. Brains of people with AD show two noticeable changes: senile plaques and neurofibrillary tangles (**Figure 42.36**). Senile plaques are extracellular deposits of an abnormal protein, β-amyloid, that forms large, sticky aggregates. These plaques were first noted in 1906 by German physician Alois Alzheimer, after whom the disease was named. Neurofibrillary tangles are intracellular, twisted accumulations of cytoskeletal fibres. It is not clear how these changes influence intellectual function and memory. AD is also associated with the degeneration and death of neurons, particularly in the hippocampus and parietal lobes, which is why it is considered a neurodegenerative disease.

Researchers have identified variations in a few genes whose products are associated with the likelihood of developing AD later in life, but the underlying changes that result in the expression of these and other possible AD-related genes are still the subject of considerable research. Although genetics undoubtedly plays a role in AD, it is not the only possible cause.

Neurofibrillary
tangle

Plaques

46 μm

Figure 42.36 Cellular section from the brain of a person who died from Alzheimer's disease.   Note the senile plaques and neurofibrillary tangles.

For example, when one identical twin develops AD, the other appears to be at increased risk but does not always develop the disease, even if he or she survives to very old age. Moreover, evidence suggests that severe head injuries, metabolic diseases like diabetes, and heart and blood vessel disease may predispose a person to AD in later life.

Currently, AD cannot be prevented or cured. However, three major clinical approaches are currently being tested to prevent or slow its progression. These approaches are designed to (1) induce a person's immune system to destroy β-amyloid as soon as it is formed, (2) prevent the formation of β-amyloid with drugs that block its synthesis, or (3) prevent the accumulation of β-amyloid into large aggregates by using antiaggregation drugs. Each of these approaches holds great promise but is still unproven.

Three times as many women as men in Canada have AD, and until a cure is found, its impact on public health will remain enormous. About 500,000 Canadians have AD, and the total number is expected to increase to approximately 1.3 million by 2035, as members of the baby-boomer generation reach age 65.

Visual Disorders Include Glaucoma, Macular Degeneration, and Cataracts

Sensory disorders are among the most common neurological problems found in humans and range from mild (e.g., needing eyeglasses) to severe (e.g., blindness). Visual disorders affect an enormous part of the world's population. In Canada, more than 820,000 people have some sort of visual limitation, with about 11% of these people considered legally blind. Although vision loss has many causes, three account for more than half of all cases: glaucoma, macular degeneration, and cataracts.

Normally, the fluid that makes up the aqueous humour is produced and reabsorbed (drained) in a circulation that keeps the fluid levels constant. In **glaucoma** (**Figure 42.37a**), drainage of aqueous humour in the eye becomes blocked and the pressure inside the eye increases as the fluid level rises. If untreated, this eventually damages cells in the retina and leads to irreversible loss of vision. The cause of glaucoma is not always known, but in some cases it is due to trauma to the eye, chronic use of certain medicines, and diseases, such as diabetes. Some forms of glaucoma may have a genetic component. Glaucoma can be treated with eye drops that reduce fluid production in the eye, or with laser surgery to reshape the structures in the eye. Incidentally, rubbing your eyes increases the intraocular pressure, and habitual rubbing can also damage vision. It is estimated that about 300,000 Canadians have glaucoma.

In **macular degeneration** (**Figure 42.37b**), photoreceptor cells in and around the fovea of the retina are lost. Because this is the region where cones are densely packed, this condition is associated with loss of sharpness and colour vision. It does

(a) How the world is seen by a person with glaucoma

(b) How the world is seen by a person with macular degeneration

(c) How the world is seen by a person with cataracts

Figure 42.37 The visual field as seen by a person with (a) glaucoma, (b) macular degeneration, and (c) cataracts.

not usually occur before age 60, but some cases are hereditary and can occur at any age. According to the Canadian National Institute for the Blind (CNIB) macular degeneration is the leading cause of blindness in Canada, accounting for roughly 50% of new CNIB clients each year, but its causes remain obscure.

Cataracts (**Figure 42.37c**), the accumulation of protein in the lens, cloud the lens and cause blurring, poor night vision, and difficulty focusing on nearby objects. By age 65, as many as 50% of individuals have one or more cataracts in at least one eye and this jumps to 70% by age 75. Many cataracts are small enough not to affect vision. In fact, many people do not even realize they have cataracts until they undergo an eye exam. The causes of cataracts are not all known but include trauma, medicinal drugs, diabetes, and heredity. The treatment, when needed, is to wear a powerful contact lens to help do the job formerly done by the person's own lens, or to have the affected lens surgically removed and replaced with a plastic lens. Without the lens, which helps protect the retina by absorbing some of the high-energy ultraviolet light from the sun, the retina must be protected during the day by wearing dark sunglasses.

Summary of Key Concepts

42.1 Evolution of the Brain and Nervous System

- All multicellular animals except sponges have a nervous system. Simpler nervous systems include the nerve net of cnidarians and ganglia, which integrate inputs from sense organs. As animal bodies become more complex, the integrative centre in the head becomes a brain that is larger and capable of more functions. (Figure 42.1)

- In all vertebrates, the three major divisions of the brain are the hindbrain, midbrain, and forebrain. (Figure 42.2)

- Additional folding of the brain and increased mass allows for expansion of regions associated with conscious thought, reasoning, and learning. (Figures 42.3, 42.4)

42.2 Central and Peripheral Nervous Systems

- In vertebrates, the brain and spinal cord are the central nervous system (CNS), while the neurons and all axons outside the CNS, including the cranial and spinal nerves, constitute the peripheral nervous system (PNS). The CNS cannot learn anything about the internal or external environment without the PNS, and the PNS relies on commands from the CNS. (Figure 42.5)

- The grey matter of the CNS is composed of dendrites, cell bodies, and unmyelinated axons, while the white matter consists of tracts of myelinated axons. (Figure 42.6)

- The PNS can be subdivided into the somatic and autonomic nervous systems. The somatic nervous system senses external environmental conditions and controls skeletal muscles and skin. The autonomic nervous system senses internal body conditions and controls homeostasis.

- The efferent part of the autonomic nervous system is divided into two components: sympathetic (fight or flight) and parasympathetic (rest or digest). (Figure 42.7)

42.3 Cellular Basis of Learning and Memory

- Learning is the process by which new information is acquired, while memory involves the retention of that information over time.

- Studies of the sea slug indicate that short-term memory is caused by a single stimulus that activates second messenger pathways,

while long-term memory is caused by repeated stimuli that activate genes, which results in more synaptic connections, a phenomenon called synaptic plasticity. (Figures 42.8, 42.9)

42.4 Sensory Reception

- Sensory receptors are either neurons or specialized epithelial cells that respond to stimuli and begin the process of sensory transduction. (Figure 42.10)

- A graded response is proportional to the intensity of the stimulus. (Figure 42.11)

42.5 Mechanoreception

- Mechanoreceptors respond to physical stimuli, such as pressure, touch, stretch, movement, and sound.

- In mammals, several types of mechanoreceptors in the skin detect stimuli such as touch and pressure, including Meissner's corpuscle, Ruffini's corpuscle, and Pacini's corpuscle. (Figure 42.12)

- Hair cells have stereocilia that respond to specific types of stimuli and then release a neurotransmitter that may result in action potentials in an adjacent sensory neuron. (Figure 42.13)

- The lateral line system of fish detects water movements. (Figure 42.14)

- Hearing is the ability to sense sound waves and is well developed in mammals. The human ear has three main compartments called the outer, middle, and inner ear. (Figure 42.15)

- As pressure waves move through the cochlea of the ear, they may cause the basilar membrane to vibrate. This causes the stereocilia of hair cells to bend back and forth, which results in intermittent action potentials being sent to the brain. (Figures 42.16, 42.17)

- Many adaptations for hearing improve an animal's ability to sense sound. (Figure 42.18)

- Statocysts in certain invertebrates allow an animal to sense its body position or equilibrium. (Figure 42.19)

- The vestibular system in vertebrates allows animals to sense linear and circular motions. (Figure 42.20)

42.6 Thermoreception, Nociception, and Electromagnetic Sensing

- Thermoreceptors in the skin and brain allow an animal to sense external and internal temperatures, respectively.

- Nociceptors in the skin and internal organs sense pain.

- Some animals can detect electrical and magnetic stimuli. (Figure 42.21)

42.7 Photoreception

- The eyecup in *Planaria* is a primitive eye that detects light and its direction. (Figure 42.22)

- The compound eye found in many invertebrates consists of many ommatidia that focus light. (Figure 42.23)

- The eye found in vertebrates and certain invertebrates is a single-lens eye. Stretching and flattening of the lens in mammals aids in focusing on objects at different distances away. (Figure 42.24)

- Rods and cones are photoreceptors found in the vertebrate eye. The visual pigment consists of retinal and a protein called opsin. (Figures 42.25, 42.26, 42.27)

- The retina is composed of layers of cells that receive light input and send electrical signals to the brain via the optic nerve. (Figures 42.28, 42.29, 42.30)

- The vertebrate eye has several adaptations that aid in proper vision for particular animals (Figure 42.31).

42.8 Chemoreception: Smell and Taste

- Invertebrates have taste receptors on their proboscis, legs, feet, and antennae. Some insects can detect pheromones. (Figure 42.32)
- Olfactory receptors in vertebrates detect odour. They contain cilia with protein receptors that bind specific odour molecules. Buck and Axel discovered that olfactory receptors have many different types of protein receptors for odour molecules. (Figures 42.33, 42.34)
- Taste buds contain chemoreceptors that sense molecules in food. (Figure 42.35)

42.9 Human Health Connection

- Meningitis is a potentially life-threatening infectious disease in which the meninges become inflamed.
- Alzheimer's disease, the leading cause of dementia worldwide, is a progressive disorder characterized by the formation of senile plaques and neurofibrillary tangles in brain tissue. (Figure 42.36)
- Common visual disorders include glaucoma, macular degeneration, and cataracts. (Figure 42.37)

Test to Assess Your Learning

1. A nerve net consists of
   a. bilateral neurons that extend from the head of the animal to the tail.
   b. a group of neurons that are interconnected and are activated all at once.
   c. a single nerve cord with ganglia in each body segment.
   d. a central nervous system with peripheral nerves associated with different body structures.
   e. none of the above.

2. The division of the vertebrate brain that includes the cerebellum is
   a. the hindbrain.
   b. the telencephalon.
   c. the midbrain.
   d. the forebrain.
   e. the diencephalon.

3. In general, the brains of more complex vertebrates
   a. are larger.
   b. have fewer neurons.
   c. have more folds in the cerebral cortex.
   d. use less oxygen.
   e. both (a) and (c).

4. The white matter of the CNS is composed of
   a. dendrites.
   b. unmyelinated axons.
   c. myelinated axons.
   d. cell bodies.
   e. (a) and (b) only.

5. The division of the nervous system that controls voluntary muscle movement is
   a. the autonomic nervous system.
   b. the sensory division.
   c. the somatic nervous system.
   d. the parasympathetic division.
   e. the sympathetic division.

6. Which of the following is *not* a characteristic response to the activation of the sympathetic division of the autonomic nervous system?
   a. increased breathing rate
   b. decreased heart rate
   c. increased blood flow to the skeletal muscles
   d. increased blood glucose levels
   e. all of the above are characteristic responses

7. The process whereby incoming sensory stimulation is converted to neural signals is
   a. an action potential.
   b. a threshold potential.
   c. perception.
   d. sensory transduction.
   e. reception.

8. Photoreceptors are examples of
   a. nociceptors.
   b. baroreceptors.
   c. mechanoreceptors.
   d. electromagnetic receptors.
   e. thermoreceptors.

9. The sensory receptors for hearing are located in
   a. the organ of Corti.
   b. the Eustachian tube.
   c. the retina.
   d. the tympanic membrane.
   e. (a), (b), and (c).

10. The stimulation for olfaction involves odorant molecules
    a. bending the cilia of olfactory receptor cells.
    b. binding to receptors of olfactory receptor cells.
    c. entering the cytoplasm of olfactory receptor cells.
    d. closing K^+ channels of olfactory receptor cells.
    e. all of the above.

Articulate to Assess Your Learning

1. List the three major divisions of the brain of vertebrates, and briefly describe the function of each.

2. Define sensory transduction and perception.

3. Explain how eye placement affects binocular vision.

Collaborate to Assess and Extend Your Learning

1. Dolphin brains are four to five times as large, and human brains seven times as large, in proportion to heir body sizes, compared with other animals. What implications does this have for the relative intelligence of dolphins and humans?

2. Different mechanoreceptors will adapt (i.e., return to a normal firing rate) either slowly or quickly after being presented with a constant stimulus. What would you expect the rate of adaptation to be in the different mechanoreceptors discussed in the text and why?

3. A principle of biology is that living organisms interact with their environment. This is certainly a fundamental principle of sensory neuroscience. Of the ways in which you use your senses to interact with the environment, which do you think is the least important?

Visit McGraw-Hill Ryerson Connect™ for additional study resources.

The Muscular-Skeletal System and Locomotion

Chapter Outline

Adept at walking and swimming, sometimes a polar bear will leap into open water.

In the previous three chapters, you learned how the nervous system gives animals the ability to respond to external and internal cues. Another key feature of the nervous system of animals is its ability to control muscle function. Muscles are composed of highly specialized cells that have the ability to contract in response to stimuli. The three types of muscle—skeletal, smooth, and cardiac—were introduced in Chapter 38. In this chapter, you will learn about the structure and function of skeletal muscle, and how skeletal muscle controls **locomotion**, the movement of an animal from place to place.

For skeletal muscles to produce locomotion, they must exert their actions on an animal's skeleton. We begin the chapter, therefore, with a description of the types of animal skeletons. Then we examine the structure and function of skeletal muscle. Next, we consider the various modes of locomotion in animals. We conclude with a discussion of two important bone diseases in humans.

43.1 TYPES OF ANIMAL SKELETONS

Learning Outcomes:

1. Distinguish among hydrostatic skeletons, exoskeletons, and endoskeletons.
2. List the advantages and disadvantages of an exoskeleton.

When we think of the word *skeleton,* an image of the vertebrate system of bones usually comes to mind. However, invertebrates possess a skeleton as well, although it is not made of bone. It is better to think of a **skeleton** in a broader sense, therefore, as a structure or structures that serve one or more functions related to support, protection, and locomotion. Using this definition, the three types of skeletons found in animals are hydrostatic skeletons, exoskeletons, and endoskeletons. The first two are found in invertebrates, while endoskeletons are found in some sponges, and in all echinoderms and vertebrates.

Hydrostatic Skeletons Consist of Fluid-Filled Body Compartments

Many soft-bodied invertebrates use hydrostatic pressure to support their bodies and generate movements. The combination of muscles and water in the body constitutes what is known as a **hydrostatic skeleton**. Water is nearly incompressible, which means that if an animal exerts a force on the water that fills its body cavities, it can use the hydrostatic pressure created to move the body, much like a balloon partly filled with water can be deformed by squeezing it along its length. In cnidarians, such as *Hydras,* for example, contractile cells in the body wall can exert a pressure on the water in the gastrovascular cavity. Depending on the direction of the force, a hydra's body and tentacles will either be elongated or shortened by the movement of water into and out of different regions of the cavity. These changes contribute to the animal's ability to capture prey, retain food in its cavity, extend or contract its tentacles, and, even in a limited way, move about.

Segmented worms, such as earthworms, move forward by passing a wave of muscular contractions along the length of their body, segment by segment (**Figure 43.1a**). The muscles are arranged in two orientations: circular and longitudinal. Contraction of circular muscles squeezes and elongates the body, while contraction of the longitudinal muscles shortens and widens it. The worm is squeezed forward by hydrostatic pressures created along its body by the muscles. Bristles along its body surface help the animal grip the ground to prevent backsliding.

Exoskeletons Are on the Outside of an Animal's Body

Arthropods have an **exoskeleton**, an external skeleton that surrounds and protects most of the body surface (**Figure 43.1b**). Exoskeletons provide support for the body, protection from the environment and predators, and protection for internal organs. The skeleton is made of a polysaccharide called chitin, and in crustaceans, such as lobster and shrimp, it is sometimes strengthened with calcium and other minerals. Exoskeletons are often tough, durable, and segmented to allow movement, but to allow growth they must be shed, regrown, and strengthened again, a process known as **ecdysis** or moulting. Consequently, one disadvantage of exoskeletons is that when an animal must shed its exoskeleton to grow, it is temporarily more vulnerable to predators and the environment.

Exoskeletons vary enormously in their complexity, thickness, and durability. The differences in exoskeletons are usually adaptations that enhance an animal's survival. Think, for example, of the difference between the exoskeleton of a fly maggot and the exoskeleton of a lobster. One allows for movement through decaying organic matter, while the other provides

(a) Hydrostatic skeleton in an annelid (earthworm)

(b) Exoskeleton being shed by a moulting arthropod (spiny lobster)

(c) Echinoderm (sea star) and (right) SEM of its endoskeleton

Figure 43.1 Types of skeletons. (a) Hydrostatic skeleton. By alternately contracting and relaxing circular and longitudinal muscles, earthworms use hydrostatic pressure to achieve locomotion. Clinging bristles along the body surface help prevent backsliding. (b) Exoskeleton. An arthropod's skeleton covers and protects its body, but it must be periodically shed and replaced to allow growth. (c) Endoskeleton. Echinoderms, such as the sea star (starfish), have endoskeletons of bony plates made of calcium carbonate (shown in inset).

Concept check: *Endoskeletons do not provide protection for the body surface of animals. How can the lack of an external skeleton also be an advantage for animals?*

 Principle: *Living organisms grow, develop, and reproduce. Part of the growth and development of animals includes their skeletons, as shown in Part (b) of this figure. For animals with exoskeletons, however, this may create a brief period when the animal is vulnerable to predation.*

a very effective defence against predators in the sea. The exoskeletons of adult insects may be soft or hard, depending on the insect's ecological niche. Many muscles attach to the undersurface of the exoskeleton to allow for movement.

Endoskeletons Are Internal Support Structures

Endoskeletons are functionally similar to exoskeletons in that both types of skeletons provide support and protection. Unlike exoskeletons, however, endoskeletons are internal structures and do not protect the body surface, only the internal organs and other structures.

Minerals, such as calcium, magnesium, phosphate, and carbonate, supply the hardening material that gives the endoskeleton its firm structure. The endoskeletons of sponges and echinoderms consist of spiky networks of proteins and minerals or mineralized platelike structures. Beneath the body surface of echinoderms, for example, arrays of mineralized plates made largely of calcium carbonate extend into the spines and arms that radiate from the main body (**Figure 43.1c**). Vertebrate skeletons, by contrast, are composed of either cartilage or bone. Next we consider the structure and function of the vertebrate skeleton in greater detail.

43.2 | THE VERTEBRATE SKELETON

Learning Outcomes:

1. List the major functions of the vertebrate skeleton.
2. Describe the composition of vertebrate bone.

Vertebrate skeletons are composed of either cartilage (see Chapter 38)—as in cartilaginous fish (sharks, rays, and skates)—or both cartilage and bone, as in bony fish, amphibians, reptiles, birds, and mammals. First we consider the skeleton as a whole before examining bones in greater detail.

The Vertebrate Skeleton Performs Several Important Functions

In the vertebrate skeleton, bones are connected in ways that allow for support and movement. The vertebrate endoskeleton is often considered in two parts (**Figure 43.2**). The axial-skeleton is composed of the bones that form the main longitudinal axis of an animal's body, including the skull, vertebrae, sternum, and ribs. The appendicular skeleton consists of the limb bones

Figure 43.2   The vertebrate endoskeleton.   The axial skeleton is shown in beige, and the appendicular skeleton in green. The human skeleton consists of 206 separate bones. Three examples of movable joints (i.e., pivot, hinge, and ball-and-socket) are shown.

Table 43.1	Functions of the Vertebrate Skeleton

- Provide structural framework to support the body
- Protect delicate internal organs such as the heart and lungs
- Provide a leverlike system for muscle attachment, thus enabling locomotion and movement of body parts and external objects
- House and nurture immature blood cells
- Provide a reservoir of calcium and phosphate ions that can be exchanged with the blood to maintain the circulating concentrations of these ions within a narrow, homeostatic range

and the bones that connect the limb bones to the axial skeleton. A **joint** is formed where two or more bones come together. Some joints permit free movement (e.g., the shoulders), while others allow no movement (fixed joints like those of the skull bones) or only limited movement (such as those of the vertebral column). Figure 43.2 illustrates the three types of freely movable joints: pivot, hinge, and ball-and-socket joints. Each of these allows a different type of movement.

The skeleton of vertebrates serves several functions in addition to support and locomotion (**Table 43.1**). For example, blood cells and platelets, the latter of which help blood to clot (see Chapter 45), are formed within the inner part of certain bones, such as the ilea, vertebrae, and the ends of the femurs. In addition, calcium and phosphate homeostasis is achieved in large part through exchanges of these ions between bone and blood. For example, if dietary intake of calcium is low, calcium is removed from bone and added to the blood so that all of the vital cellular activities that depend on calcium, such as nerve and muscle function, can continue to operate normally. When dietary calcium is restored to normal, calcium is redeposited in bone. In fact, about 99% of all the calcium in a typical vertebrate's body exists in bone. This represents a huge reservoir of calcium ions for the blood.

Bone Consists of a Mixture of Organic and Mineral Components

Bone is a living, dynamic tissue with both organic and mineral components. Organic materials include cells that form bone (**osteoblasts**) and cells that break it down (**osteoclasts**), and fibres made from the protein collagen, whose unique triple helical structure gives bone both strength and flexibility. The mineral component is composed of a crystalline mixture of Ca^{2+}, PO_4^{2-}, and other ions that provides bone its rigidity. These ions must be obtained in an animal's diet, absorbed into the blood, and deposited in bone.

A proper ratio of the organic and mineral components is required for normal bone function. Too little mineral, for example, makes bone too easily fractured. Bone is formed at high rates during an animal's growth periods, but even in adulthood bone continues to be continually formed, broken down, and reformed. In fact, the skeleton is continually changing. The one in your body right now is not identical to the one in your body a few years ago, or the one you will have a few years from now.

Bones cannot move by themselves but instead provide the scaffold on which muscles act to cause body movement. We turn now to a discussion of skeletal muscle and the mechanism by which it generates force.

43.3	SKELETAL MUSCLE STRUCTURE AND THE MECHANISM OF FORCE GENERATION

Learning Outcomes:

1. List the three types of muscle found in vertebrates and where they are found in the body.
2. Identify the structural components of a muscle down to the level of the sarcomere.
3. Explain how muscles contract.
4. Describe the anatomic features of a neuromuscular junction, and the role of acetylcholine in mediating skeletal muscle excitation.

As introduced in Chapter 38, vertebrates have three types of muscle that are classified according to their structure, function, and control mechanisms: cardiac muscle, smooth muscle, and skeletal muscle. Skeletal muscle is found throughout the body and is directly involved in locomotion. In vertebrates, skeletal muscle can generate action potentials in response to a stimulus. The muscle action potentials result in increases in cytosolic Ca^{2+}, which triggers force generation. In contrast, invertebrate skeletal muscles have graded membrane potentials but do not have action potentials.

A Skeletal Muscle Is a Contractile Organ That Supports and Moves Bones

A **muscle** is a grouping of cells—called **muscle fibres**—bound together into fascicles by a succession of connective tissue layers (**Figure 43.3**). Vertebrate skeletal muscles are usually linked to bones by bundles of collagen fibres known as tendons.

Some tendons are very long, with the site of tendon attachment to bone far removed from the end of the muscle. For example, some of the muscles that move the fingers are in the forearm. Wiggle your fingers and feel the movement of the muscles in your lower arm. These muscles are connected to the fingers by long tendons.

Skeletal muscle fibres increase in size during growth from infancy to adulthood, but no new fibres are formed during that time. As described later, enlargement of skeletal muscles in adults, as from weight lifting, is also a function of enlarged fibres, not the formation of new fibres.

Muscle Fibres Contain Myofibrils Composed of Arrays of Filaments

The most striking microscopic feature of skeletal muscle is a series of light and dark bands perpendicular to the muscle's long axis. Because of this characteristic striped pattern, skeletal muscle is also known as **striated muscle**. This pattern results from the presence of cylindrical bundles known as **myofibrils** (**Figure 43.4**).

Figure 43.3 **Skeletal muscle structure.** Skeletal muscles attach to bone by tendons, which are bundles of collagen fibres. Each muscle consists of bundles of muscle fibres (cells) bound together by connective tissue. Each fibre consists of numerous myofibrils.

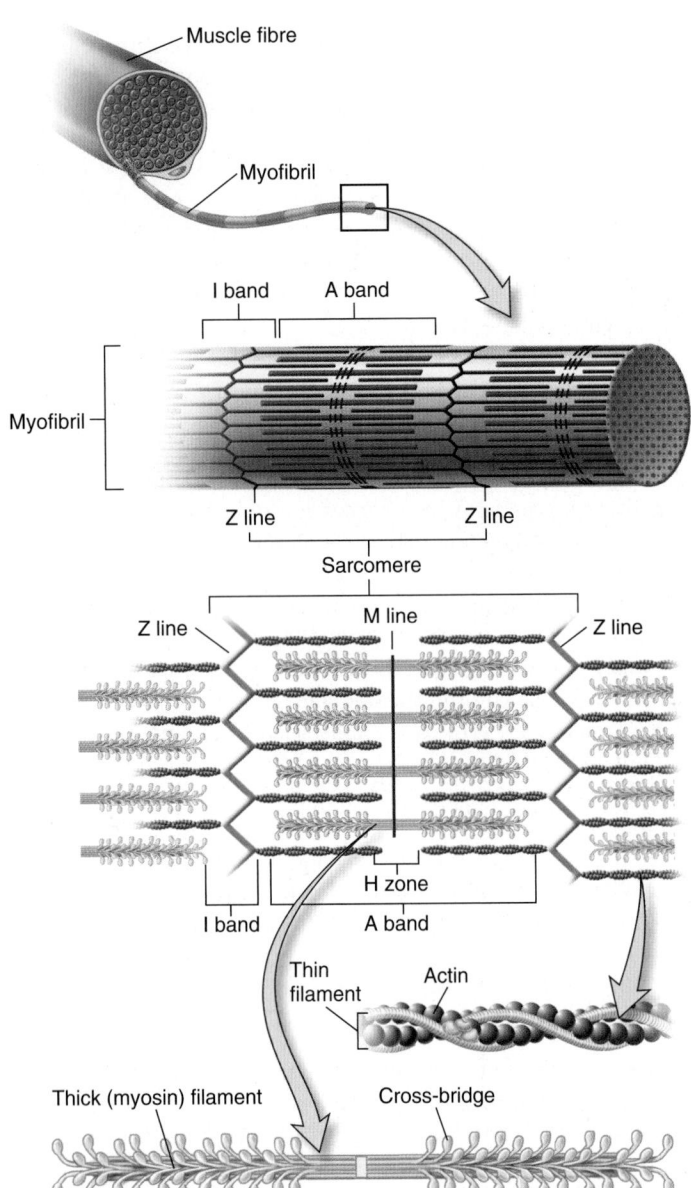

Most of the cytosol of a muscle fibre is filled with myofibrils, each of which extends from one end of the fibre to the other and is linked to the tendons at the ends of the fibre.

Within each myofibril are structures called thick and thin filaments, which are arranged in a repeating pattern running the length of the myofibril. One complete unit of this repeating pattern is known as a **sarcomere** (from the Greek, *sarco*, muscle, and *mer*, part). The **thick filaments** are composed almost entirely of the motor protein **myosin**. The **thin filaments**, which are about half the diameter of the thick filaments, contain the cytoskeletal protein **actin**, as well as two other proteins—troponin and tropomyosin—that play important roles in regulating contraction.

The thick filaments are located in the middle of each sarcomere, where their orderly parallel arrangement produces a wide, dark band known as the **A band** (Figure 43.4). Each sarcomere contains two sets of thin filaments, each set anchored to a network of proteins at the **Z line**. The thin filaments overlap a portion of the thick filaments. Two successive Z lines define the limits of one sarcomere.

A light band known as the **I band** lies between the A bands of two adjacent sarcomeres. Each I band contains those portions of the thin filaments that do not overlap the thick filaments, and each I band is bisected by a Z line.

Figure 43.4 **Myofibril structure.** Each muscle fibre consists of numerous myofibrils containing thick and thin filaments. Their arrangement produces a striated banding pattern seen under the microscope. Each repeating unit of the arrayed filaments constitutes a sarcomere.

Principle: *Cells are the simplest units of life. A muscle consists of many cells called fibres arranged in a very precise way. As the cells change their shape by shortening, the shape of the entire muscle changes, too. This is true for all types of muscle, not just the skeletal muscle shown here and in Figure 43.3.*

Figure 43.5 Sliding filament mechanism of muscle contraction. **(a)** The sliding of thin filaments past the overlapping thick filaments shortens the sarcomere but does not change the lengths of the filaments themselves. **(b)** Transmission electron micrograph of a section of skeletal muscle in the relaxed and shortened states.

Two additional features are present in the A band of each sarcomere. The **H zone** is a narrow, light region in the centre of the A band. It corresponds to the space between the two sets of thin filaments in each sarcomere. A narrow, dark band in the centre of the H zone, known as the **M line**, corresponds to proteins that link together the central regions of adjacent thick filaments.

The spaces between overlapping thick and thin filaments are bridged by projections known as **cross-bridges**, which are regions of myosin molecules that extend from the surface of the thick filaments toward the thin filaments (Figure 43.4). As we see next, during muscle contraction the cross-bridges make contact with the thin filaments and exert force on them.

Skeletal Muscle Shortens When Thin Filaments Slide over Thick Filaments

As used in muscle physiology, the term *contraction* does not necessarily mean shortening. Instead it refers to activation of the cross-bridges within muscle cells. Holding a heavy weight at a constant position, for example, requires muscle contraction, but muscle shortening does not occur. When the mechanisms that initiate force generation are turned off, contractions end, allowing relaxation of the muscle fibre.

The way in which a muscle fibre actually shortens is known as the **sliding filament mechanism** of muscle contraction (**Figure 43.5**). In muscle contraction, the sarcomeres shorten, but there is no change in the lengths of either the thick or the thin filaments themselves. Instead, the thick filament remains stationary while the thin filaments actually slide. This movement is propelled by the cross-bridges.

During shortening, each myosin cross-bridge attaches to a thin filament actin molecule and moves in a motion much like an oar on a boat. This motion of many cross-bridges forces the thin filaments toward the centre of the sarcomere, thereby shortening the sarcomere. One stroke of a cross-bridge produces only a very small movement of a thin filament relative to a thick filament. As long as a muscle fibre is stimulated to contract, however, each cross-bridge repeats its motion many times, resulting in continued sliding of the thin filaments. Thus, the ability of a muscle fibre to generate force and movement depends on the amount of interaction of actin and myosin.

Each actin molecule of a thin filament contains a binding site for myosin. Actin molecules form polymers and are arranged into two intertwined helical chains that are closely associated with molecules of troponin and tropomyosin (**Figure 43.6a**). Myosin, by contrast, is composed of six protein subunits: two large, intertwined heavy chains and four smaller light chains.

These polypeptides combine to form a protein that consists of two heads and a long tail formed by the two intertwined heavy chains. The tail of each myosin molecule lies along the axis of the thick filament, and the two globular heads extend out to the sides, forming the cross-bridges. Each globular head contains two binding sites, one for actin and one for ATP. The hydrolysis of ATP provides the energy for the cross-bridge (that is, the myosin head) to move.

The myosin proteins at the two ends of each thick filament are oriented in opposite directions, such that their tail ends are directed toward the centre of the filament (**Figure 43.6b**). Because of this arrangement, the movements of the cross-bridges bring the attached thin filaments at the two ends of the sarcomere toward the centre of the sarcomere during shortening.

The Cross-Bridge Cycle Requires ATP and Calcium Ions

Let's now turn our attention to how actin and myosin interact to promote contraction. The sequence of events that occurs between the time when a cross-bridge binds to a thin filament

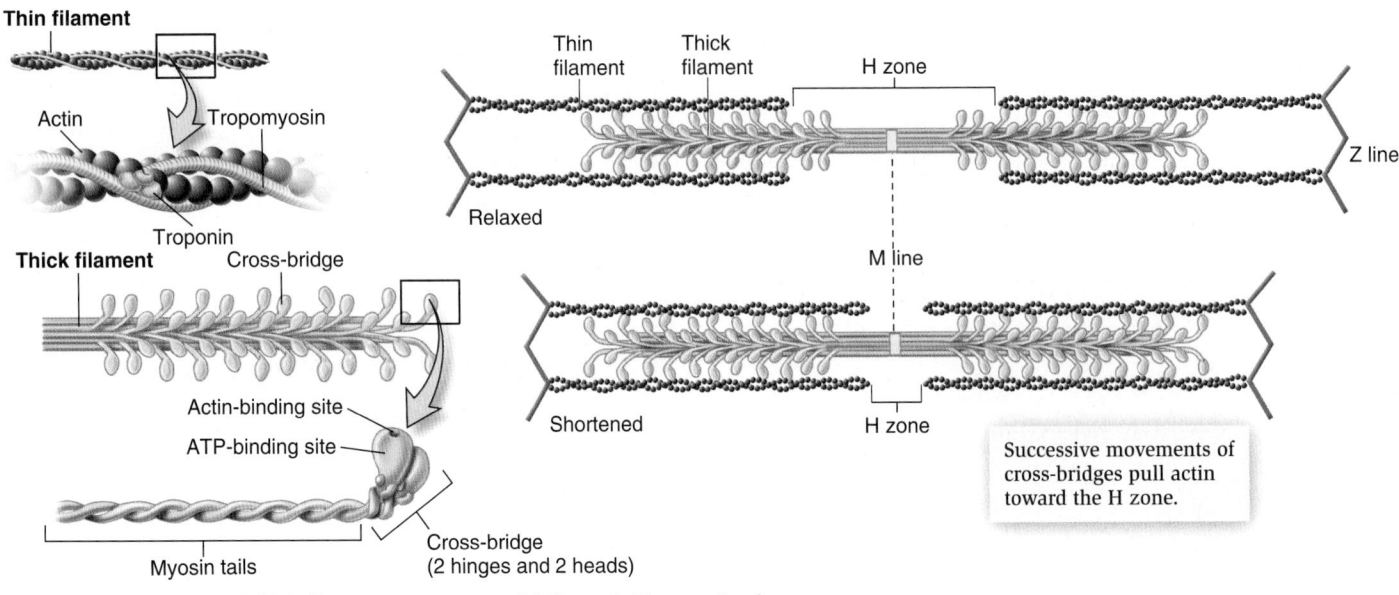

(a) Structure of thin and thick filaments

(b) Cross-bridge mechanism

Figure 43.6   **Structure and function of the thick and thin filaments.**   **(a)** Thin filaments are composed of two intertwined actin molecules and associated proteins tropomyosin and troponin. Thick filaments are made of the protein myosin, which has two intertwined heavy chains, each with two associated light chains, an actin-binding site, and an ATP-binding site. The end of a myosin molecule that contains the actin-binding sites is bent at an angle to form the globular heads. **(b)** When the cross-bridges on myosin molecules bind to actin filaments, the thin filaments are pulled toward each other, shortening the sarcomere.

Principle: *Structure determines function. It is the precise structural arrangement of the proteins that comprise thick and thin filaments that gives them their function. Without this structure, actin and myosin would not produce a coordinated force resulting in skeletal muscle cell shortening.*

and when it is set to repeat the process is known as a **cross-bridge cycle**.

The chemical and physical events during the four steps of the cross-bridge cycle are illustrated in **Figure 43.7**. When ATP is hydrolyzed, the myosin cross-bridges are said to be in an energized state in which the hydrolysis products ADP and inorganic phosphate remain bound to myosin. This storage of energy in myosin is analogous to the storage of potential energy in a stretched spring. In this conformation, the myosin head is cocked backward.

Cross-bridge cycling begins whenever the Ca^{2+} level increases inside the cell, usually when neural input results in the release of calcium from intracellular storage sites (described in detail shortly). The four-step cycle begins with the binding of an energized myosin cross-bridge, with its associated ADP and P_i, to an actin molecule on a thin filament.

Step 1: Cross-bridge binds to actin.

$$actin + energized\ myosin \bullet ADP \bullet P_i$$

$$\longrightarrow actin \bullet myosin \bullet ADP \bullet P_i\ complex$$

Step 2: Cross-bridge moves and the thin filaments move.

The binding of an energized myosin cross-bridge to actin triggers the movement of the bound cross-bridge (sometimes called the **power stroke**) and the release of P_i. The release of

P_i causes the cross-bridge to rotate forward, which moves the actin filament and releases ADP.

$$actin \bullet myosin\ F \bullet ADP \bullet P_i\ complex$$

$$\longrightarrow actin \bullet myosin\ complex + ADP + P_i$$

This sequence of storage and release of energy by myosin is analogous to the operation of a mousetrap: Energy is first stored in the trap by cocking the spring (ATP hydrolysis, step 4) and then released by the springing of the trap (binding to actin and power stroke, steps 1 and 2). During the power stroke, the actin filament moves.

Step 3: ATP binds to myosin, causing the cross-bridge to detach.

During the cross-bridge movement in step 2, myosin is bound very firmly to actin, and this linkage must be broken to allow the cross-bridge to be re-energized and repeat the cycle.

The binding of a new molecule of ATP to myosin breaks the link between actin and myosin.

$$actin \bullet myosin\ complex + ATP \longrightarrow actin + myosin \bullet ATP$$

The dissociation of actin and myosin by ATP is an example of allosteric regulation (see Chapter 7) of protein activity. The binding of ATP at one site on myosin decreases myosin's

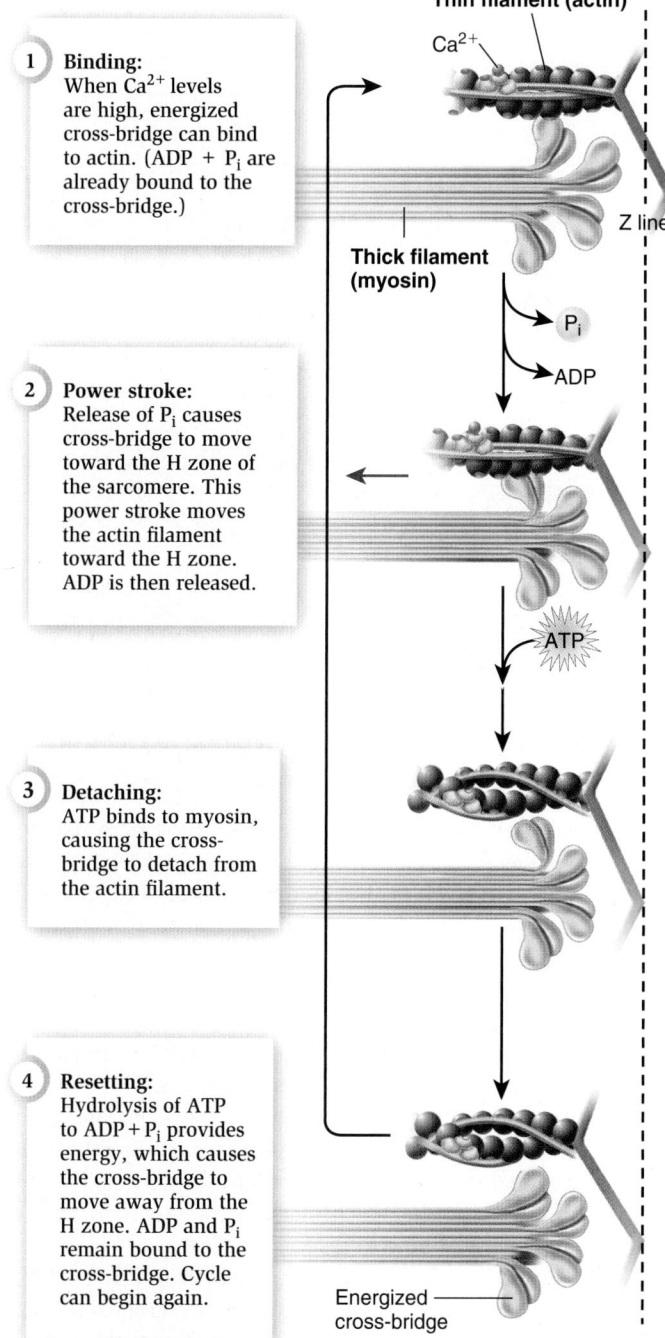

1 Binding:
When Ca^{2+} levels are high, energized cross-bridge can bind to actin. (ADP + P$_i$ are already bound to the cross-bridge.)

2 Power stroke:
Release of P$_i$ causes cross-bridge to move toward the H zone of the sarcomere. This power stroke moves the actin filament toward the H zone. ADP is then released.

3 Detaching:
ATP binds to myosin, causing the cross-bridge to detach from the actin filament.

4 Resetting:
Hydrolysis of ATP to ADP + P$_i$ provides energy, which causes the cross-bridge to move away from the H zone. ADP and P$_i$ remain bound to the cross-bridge. Cycle can begin again.

Thin filament (actin)
Ca^{2+}
Z line
Thick filament (myosin)
P$_i$
ADP
ATP
Energized cross-bridge

Figure 43.7 The four stages of cross-bridge cycling in skeletal muscle.

Concept check: *Rigor mortis is a condition of contracted skeletal muscle that occurs shortly after death. Why would the muscle remain contracted after death, and why does such contraction eventually stop?*

affinity for actin bound at another site. Note that ATP is not hydrolyzed in this step. Instead, ATP acts here only as an allosteric modulator of the myosin head that weakens the binding of myosin to actin.

Step 4: Hydrolysis of ATP re-energizes the cross-bridge.

actin + myosin • ATP $\longrightarrow$ actin + energized myosin • ADP • P$_i$

Following the dissociation of actin and myosin, the ATP bound to myosin is then hydrolyzed (step 4), thereby re-forming the energized state of myosin.

If calcium is still present at this time, the cross-bridge can reattach to a new actin molecule in the thin filament, and the cross-bridge cycle repeats, causing further shortening of the muscle fibre.

As we have seen, ATP performs two different roles in the cross-bridge cycle. The energy released from ATP hydrolysis provides the energy for cross-bridge movement, and ATP binding breaks the link formed between actin and myosin during the cycle, allowing the cycle to be repeated. Although the precise mechanisms may differ slightly between vertebrates and invertebrates, all skeletal muscle is believed to function according to steps similar to those just described, and to require calcium ions, the actions of which we describe next.

The Regulation of Muscle Contraction by Calcium Ions Is Mediated by Tropomyosin and Troponin

How does the presence of calcium in the muscle fibre cytosol regulate the cycling of cross-bridges? The answer requires a closer look at the two additional thin filament proteins mentioned earlier, tropomyosin and troponin.

Tropomyosin is a rod-shaped molecule composed of two intertwined proteins, with a length equal to that of about seven actin molecules (**Figure 43.8a**). Chains of tropomyosin molecules are arranged end to end along the actin thin filament. In the absence of calcium ions, they partially cover the myosin-binding site on each actin molecule, thereby preventing cross-bridges from making contact with actin. Each tropomyosin molecule is held in this blocking position by **troponin**, a smaller, globular-shaped protein that is bound to both tropomyosin and actin. One molecule of troponin binds to each molecule of tropomyosin. In this way, troponin and tropomyosin cooperate to block access to myosin-binding sites on actin molecules in the relaxed muscle fibre.

Troponin is capable of binding calcium ions. The binding of Ca^{2+} produces a change in the shape of troponin, which—through troponin's linkage to tropomyosin—allows tropomyosin to move away from the myosin-binding site on each actin molecule (**Figure 43.8b**). This permits cross-bridge cycling to occur. Conversely, removal of Ca^{2+} from troponin reverses the process, turning off contractile activity.

Thus, the concentration of cytosolic Ca^{2+} determines the number of ions bound to troponin molecules, which in turn determines the number of actin sites available for cross-bridge binding. The cytosolic concentration of Ca^{2+}, however, is very low in resting muscle. How is the Ca^{2+} concentration increased so that contraction can occur? This topic is discussed next.

Figure 43.8 Role of calcium, tropomyosin, and troponin in cross-bridge cycling. (a) When cytosolic Ca^{2+} is low, the cross-bridge myosin-binding sites on actin are blocked by tropomyosin. (b) When cytosolic Ca^{2+} increases, Ca^{2+} binds to troponin, which in turn allows tropomyosin to move away from the myosin-binding sites on actin.

Contraction of Skeletal Muscle Is Coupled with Electrical Excitation

Like neurons, skeletal muscle cells are capable of generating and propagating action potentials in response to an appropriate stimulus. This causes a rise in the concentration of cytosolic Ca^{2+}, which triggers contraction of a muscle fibre. The sequence of events by which an action potential in the plasma membrane of a muscle fibre leads to cross-bridge activity by the mechanisms just described is called **excitation-contraction coupling**. The electrical activity in the plasma membrane does not directly act upon the contractile proteins but instead is the stimulus that increases cytosolic calcium concentration, which continues to activate the contractile apparatus long after electrical activity in the membrane has ceased.

The source of the increased cytosolic Ca^{2+} that occurs following a muscle action potential is the fibre's **sarcoplasmic reticulum**, which acts as a Ca^{2+} reservoir. The sarcoplasmic reticulum, which is a specialized form of the endoplasmic reticulum found in most cells, is composed of interconnected sleevelike compartments around each myofibril (**Figure 43.9**). Separate tubular structures, the **transverse tubules** (**T-tubules**) are invaginations of the plasma membrane that open to the extracellular fluid. The T-tubules run around each myofibril and conduct action potentials from the outer surface of the muscle fibre to inner regions where the myofibrils are found. The action potential causes the opening of calcium channels in the sarcoplasmic reticulum, which allows Ca^{2+} to flow into the cytosol and bind to troponin.

A contraction continues until Ca^{2+} is removed from troponin. This is achieved by ion pumps in the sarcoplasmic reticulum that lower the Ca^{2+} concentration in the cytosol back to its resting level.

Electrical Stimulation of Skeletal Muscle Occurs at the Neuromuscular Junction

We have just seen that an action potential in the plasma membrane of a skeletal muscle fibre is the signal that triggers contraction. How are these action potentials initiated? The only mechanism by which action potentials are initiated in a skeletal muscle involves stimulation by a motor neuron. The junction of a motor neuron's axon and the muscle fibre is known as a **neuromuscular junction** (**Figure 43.10**). Near the surface of the muscle fibre, the axon divides into several short processes, or terminals, containing synaptic vesicles filled with the neurotransmitter acetylcholine (ACh; see Chapter 41). The region of the muscle fibre plasma membrane that lies directly under the axon terminal is called the **motor end plate**; it is folded into so-called junctional folds, which increase the total surface area available for the membrane to respond to ACh.

When an action potential in a motor neuron arrives at the axon terminal, it releases its stored ACh, which crosses the synaptic cleft and binds to receptors in the junctional folds of the muscle fibre. The ACh receptor is a ligand-gated ion channel (see Chapter 6). The result of ACh binding is an influx of Na^+ into the muscle cell through a channel created by the receptor. This Na^+ influx causes depolarization of the muscle cell, resulting in an action potential that spreads over the surface of the muscle fibre. Most neuromuscular junctions are located near the middle of a muscle fibre, and newly generated muscle action potentials propagate from this region in both directions toward the ends of the fibre and throughout the T-tubule network.

Now that we have learned about the structural characteristics of skeletal muscle, and the events that initiate and produce force generation, we turn to a discussion of how skeletal muscle is adapted to meet the varied functional demands of vertebrates.

Figure 43.9 Structure and function of the sarcoplasmic reticulum, transverse tubules, and myofibrils in a skeletal muscle fibre. Action potentials propagate along the plasma membrane and down the transverse tubules. Inset: The depolarization produced by the action potentials opens Ca^{2+} channels in the membranes of the sarcoplasmic reticulum, through which Ca^{2+} diffuses into the cell cytosol. Ca^{2+} then binds to troponin, initiating muscle contraction. Ca^{2+} is then pumped back into the sarcoplasmic reticulum by ATP-dependent ion pumps. This results in muscle relaxation.

BioConnections: *Where else have you learned about voltage-gated Ca^{2+} channels and their role in cell-to-cell communication?*

43.4 | SKELETAL MUSCLE FUNCTION

Learning Outcomes:

1. Outline the general characteristics of the three types of skeletal muscle fibres.
2. Explain how muscles adapt to exercise.
3. Describe how antagonistic muscles work at a joint.

Animals use skeletal muscle for a wide variety of activities, such as locomotion, stretching, chewing, breathing, and maintaining balance, to name a few. Thus it is not surprising that not all skeletal muscle fibres share the same mechanical and metabolic characteristics. In this section, we will consider how different types of fibres can be classified on the basis of their rates of shortening (as either fast or slow), and the way in which they produce the ATP needed for contraction (as oxidative or glycolytic).

Skeletal Muscle Fibres Are Adapted for Different Types of Movement

Different muscle fibres contain forms of myosin that differ in the maximal rates at which they can hydrolyze ATP. This, in turn, determines the maximal rates of cross-bridge cycling and muscle shortening. Fibres containing myosin with high ATPase activity are classified as **fast fibres**. Those containing myosin with lower ATPase activity are considered **slow fibres**. Although the rate of cross-bridge cycling is about four times as

(a) SEM of neuromuscular junction

(b) Structures of, and events at, the neuromuscular junction (only part of the motor neuron is shown)

Figure 43.10 **The neuromuscular junction.** The structure of a neuromuscular junction **(a)** as seen in a scanning electron micrograph, and **(b)** as depicted schematically. Action potentials in the motor neuron cause exocytosis of ACh-containing synaptic vesicles. ACh binds to receptors in the plasma membrane of the junctional folds of the skeletal muscle cell. This initiates an action potential in the muscle cell.

BioConnections: *What is the function of the myelin indicated in this figure? Refer back to Figures 41.2 and 41.12 for help.*

fast in fast fibres as in slow fibres, the maximal force produced by both types of cross-bridges is approximately the same.

The second means of classifying skeletal muscle fibres relates to the type of metabolic pathways available for synthesizing ATP. (See Chapter 7 for a review of the biochemical processes associated with ATP production.) Fibres that contain numerous mitochondria and have a high capacity for oxidative phosphorylation are classified as **oxidative fibres**. Most of the ATP production by such fibres depends on blood flow to deliver oxygen and nutrients to the muscle. Not surprisingly, therefore, these fibres are surrounded by many small blood vessels. They also contain large amounts of the oxygen-binding protein **myoglobin**, which increases the availability of oxygen in the fibre by providing an intracellular reservoir of oxygen. The large amounts of myoglobin present in oxidative fibres give these fibres a dark red colour. Oxidative fibres are often referred to as red muscle fibres.

By contrast, **glycolytic fibres** have few mitochondria but possess both a high concentration of glycolytic enzymes (see Chapter 7 for a discussion of glycolysis) and large stores of glycogen, the storage form of glucose. Corresponding to their limited use of oxygen, these fibres are surrounded by relatively few blood vessels and contain little myoglobin. The lack of myoglobin is responsible for the pale colour of glycolytic fibres and their designation as white muscle fibres.

On the basis of these two characteristics, three major types of skeletal muscle fibres have been distinguished:

1. **Slow-oxidative fibres** have low rates of myosin ATPase activity but have the ability to make large amounts of ATP. These fibres are used for prolonged, regular activity, such as flight, long-distance swimming, or the maintenance of posture. These types of activities require muscles that do not fatigue easily. These muscles, for example, are what give the red colour to the breast meat of ducks, which use the muscles for flight.

2. **Fast-oxidative fibres** have high myosin ATPase activity and can make large amounts of ATP. Like slow-oxidative fibres, these fibres do not fatigue quickly and can be used for long-term activities. They are particularly suited for rapid actions, such as the rapid trilling sounds made by the throat muscles in songbirds or the clicking sounds of a rattlesnake's shaking tail.

3. **Fast-glycolytic fibres** have high myosin ATPase activity but cannot make as much ATP as oxidative fibres, because their source of ATP is glycolysis. These fibres are best suited for rapid, intense actions, such as a short sprint at maximum speed or a cat pouncing on its prey. Fast-glycolytic fibres fatigue more rapidly than oxidative fibres. The breast meat of chickens, for example, appears white because unlike ducks, chickens do not fly except for very short distances, and therefore do not require oxidative pectoral muscles.

Different muscle groups within the body have different proportions of each fibre type interspersed with one another, and many activities require the action of all three types of fibres at once. This is important when you consider the wide range of animal activities related to locomotion alone, including walking, climbing, running, crawling, crouching, jumping, swimming, flying, and maintaining balance and posture. Depending on the needs of an animal at any given moment, the motor nerve inputs can be adjusted to stimulate different ratios of fibre types. When a person lifts a heavy weight for a brief time, the motor units containing fast-glycolytic fibres in the arm muscles are activated in large numbers. When a crab uses its pincers to grab prey, fast-glycolytic muscles snap the claws closed quickly, but then slow-oxidative fibres maintain a tight, relentless grip for as long as needed. The characteristics of the three types of skeletal muscle fibres are summarized in **Table 43.2**.

Muscles Adapt to Exercise

The regularity with which a muscle is used, as well as the duration and intensity of its activity, affects the properties of the muscle. Increased amounts of contractile activity—in other words, exercise—can produce an increase in the size of muscle fibres as well as changes in their capacity for ATP production. Because the number of fibres in a muscle remains essentially constant throughout adult life, the increases in muscle size that occur with exercise do not result from increases in the number of muscle fibres, but instead from increases in the size of each fibre.

Exercise of relatively low intensity but long duration—popularly called aerobic exercise, including running and swimming—produces increases in the number of mitochondria in the fibres that are needed in this type of activity. In addition, the number of blood vessels around these fibres increases to supply the greater energy demands of active muscle. All of these changes increase endurance with a minimum of fatigue.

By contrast, short-duration, high-intensity exercise, such as weight lifting, primarily affects fast-glycolytic fibres, which are used during strong contractions. These fibres undergo an increase in fibre diameter because of the increased synthesis of actin and myosin filaments, which form more myofibrils. In addition, glycolytic activity is enhanced by elevated synthesis of glycolytic enzymes. The results of such high-intensity exercise are the increased strength and bulging muscles of a conditioned weight lifter. Such muscles, although very powerful, have little capacity for endurance and therefore fatigue rapidly.

Table 43.2	Characteristics of the Three Types of Skeletal Muscle Fibres		
	Slow-oxidative	Fast-oxidative	Fast-glycolytic
Primary source of ATP production	Oxidative phosphorylation	Oxidative phosphorylation	Glycolysis
Mitochondria	Many	Many	Few
Blood supply	High	High	Moderate
Myoglobin content	High (red muscle)	High (red muscle)	Low (white muscle)
Rate of fatigue	Slow	Intermediate	Fast
Myosin-ATPase activity	Low	High	High
Rate of contraction	Slow	Fast	Fast

A decline or cessation of muscular activity results in the condition called **atrophy**, a reduction in the size of the muscle. Likewise, if the neurons to a skeletal muscle are destroyed or the neuromuscular junctions become nonfunctional, the denervated muscle fibres will become progressively smaller in diameter. This condition is known as denervation atrophy. Even with an intact nerve supply, a muscle can atrophy if it is not used for a long period, as when a broken limb is immobilized in a cast.

The mechanism by which changes occur in skeletal muscle during exercise is an active area of research in biology, but a recent discovery has provided an intriguing clue, as described next.

FEATURE INVESTIGATION

Evans and Colleagues Activated a Gene to Produce "Marathon Mice"

While investigating possible ways to reverse or prevent obesity in humans and other mammals, Ron Evans and his colleagues at the Salk Institute in California discovered one way in which the ratios of oxidative and glycolytic fibres change in skeletal muscle. Evans was interested in a gene that codes for a transcription factor called PPAR-delta. Activation of this protein results in the expression of genes that enable cells to more efficiently burn fat instead of glucose for energy. Evans hypothesized that mice in which PPAR-delta was chronically activated at high levels would lose weight because of increased fat burning, as shown in **Figure 43.11**.

To test this hypothesis, Evans created transgenic mice (see Chapter 18) in which the **PPAR-delta** gene was introduced in a modified form. The modified gene had a skeletal muscle-specific promoter so that it would be expressed in skeletal muscle cells only. The coding sequence of the gene that encoded PPAR-delta was linked to a viral protein domain called VP16. This domain also facilitates gene activation. The combination of PPAR-delta and VP16 was expected to strongly activate genes that enable cells to more efficiently burn fat instead of glucose for energy. The modified gene was used to make transgenic mice that carried the gene in all of their cells and could therefore transmit the gene to their offspring. Evans then monitored the body weights of the mice after they reached adulthood. Transgenic mice gained significantly less weight compared with wild-type mice when fed high-fat diets (which normally cause mice—like humans—to gain weight), confirming Evans's hypothesis. As is often the case in scientific discovery, an unexpected finding arose from this study when Evans examined several tissues in these mice. Under the microscope, it was observed that the skeletal muscle of the transgenic mice showed a dramatic shift from glycolytic fibres to slow-oxidative fibres. The muscle in transgenic mice appeared redder than it did in wild-type mice. It contained more myoglobin and mitochondria and had higher levels of oxidative enzymes capable of providing the cells with

HYPOTHESES   1. Increased expression of genes that lead to increased fat oxidation in skeletal muscle cells will prevent obesity in mice.
2. Transgenic mice have a greater capacity for prolonged exercise than do wild-type mice.

KEY MATERIALS   Mice, light and electron microscopes, motorized treadmills.

	Experimental level	Conceptual level

1 Prepare a modified gene containing a skeletal muscle-specific promoter and a coding sequence that links *VP16* and *PPAR-δ*. See Chapter 18 for gene cloning methods.

Skeletal muscle-specific promoter

VP16   PPAR-δ

Skeletal muscle-specific promoter ensures gene is turned on only in skeletal muscle.

VP16 domain is a domain that always activates transcription.

PPAR-δ codes for a transcription factor that specifically activates genes that allow cells to efficiently burn fat.

2 Make transgenic mice expressing the *VP16–PPAR-δ* gene.

See Chapter 18 for a discussion of gene addition.

All the cells will carry this gene, but only skeletal muscle cells will express the gene.

3 Perform the following tests:

(a) Feed wild-type control mice and transgenic mice a normal-fat diet (4%) and then switch to a high-fat diet (35%). Weigh mice weekly.
(b) Examine the muscle fibres in the mice.
(c) Test their endurance on a treadmill.

Scale

Microscope

Treadmills

(a) Eating a high-fat diet is known to cause obesity in mice and other mammals.
(b) The appearance of skeletal muscle can be examined by light and electron microscopy.
(c) The treadmills are motorized to keep mice moving until they become exhausted, at which time the treadmills are stopped.

4   THE DATA

(a) **Weight gain**

Body weight increase (g) vs Days after switching to high-fat diet. Wild type curve rising to ~25 g; Transgenic curve rising to ~10 g.

(b) **Difference in skeletal muscle**

Characteristics of skeletal muscle in transgenic mice:

– redder than wild-type
– more myoglobin
– more mitochondria
– more slow-oxidative fibres

(c) **Muscle endurance**

Running time (min): Wild-type ~90, transgenic ~113.

Running distance (m): Wild-type ~900, transgenic ~1800.

Figure 43.11   Activating a gene to produce "marathon mice."

5   **CONCLUSION**   *PPAR-δ* contributes to both weight loss and endurance in mice. The fibre-type switching associated with exercise does not require exercise, because increasing fat oxidation in skeletal muscle cells resulted in more oxidative fibres even without exercise training.

6   **SOURCE**   Wang, Y. X., et al. 2004. Gene targeting turns mice into long-distance runners. *Public Library of Science Biology* 2:322.

sustained levels of ATP. These changes occurred even though the mice had not been subjected to exercise training.

Based on these observations, Evans also tested the hypothesis that the transgenic mice would have a greater capacity for prolonged exercise than wild-type mice. When the transgenic mice were challenged with an endurance exercise test, Evans discovered that they outperformed age- and weight-matched wild-type mice by a factor of nearly twofold. They could sustain a high level of activity on a miniature treadmill for nearly two times longer than wild-type mice (hence the nickname "marathon mice"). This effect occurred in transgenic mice even in the absence of prior exercise training. In other words, simply increasing the ratio of oxidative to glycolytic fibres gave the mice greater ability to sustain aerobic activity.

Elevating the levels of activated PPAR-delta facilitates an oxidative state that somehow signals skeletal muscle to convert fibres to types that are best suited for oxidative metabolism. This study suggested that the switch in fibre type that occurs normally in exercise training does not require exercise per se, and it may be mediated in part by proteins that activate or induce *PPAR-delta* expression. These results may have important implications for exercise endurance in humans, as well as for possible treatments for various muscle diseases.

Experimental Questions

1. What is the normal function of the PPAR-delta protein in mice?
2. What was the hypothesis proposed by Evans in relation to PPAR-delta and obesity?
3. How did Evans and his colleagues test this hypothesis? What did they observe?

Skeletal Muscles and Bones May Cause Limb Flexion and Extension

A contracting muscle exerts a force on bones through its connecting tendons. When the force is great enough, the bone moves as the muscle shortens. A contracting muscle exerts only a pulling force, so that as the muscle shortens, the bones to which it is attached are pulled toward or away from each other. Muscles that bend a limb at a joint are called **flexors**, whereas muscles that straighten a limb are called **extensors**. Groups of muscles that produce oppositely directed movements at a joint are known as **antagonists**. For example, in **Figure 43.12** we can see that contraction of the hamstrings flexes the leg at the knee,

whereas contraction of the antagonistic muscle, the quadriceps, causes the leg to extend. Both antagonistic muscles exert only a pulling force when they contract.

43.5 | ANIMAL LOCOMOTION

Learning Outcomes:

1. Explain the mechanisms of animal locomotion in water, on land, and in air.
2. Compare the relative energy costs of swimming, running, and flying.
3. Explain how evolution has shaped the structures used for locomotion.

Animal locomotion occurs in only a limited number of forms, including swimming, flying, walking or running, crawling or sliding, or jumping or leaping, as in the polar bear shown in the chapter-opening photo. In all cases, animals experience certain constraints to locomotion. For example, all animals must overcome frictional forces (drag) generated by the air, water, or surface of Earth. In addition, all forms of locomotion require energy to provide thrust, defined as the forward motion of an animal in any environment, and lift, which is movement against gravity.

Although the precise mechanism may differ among animals, locomotion always results from muscular contractions that exert force on one of the three types of skeletons discussed at the beginning of this chapter. In this section, we will examine the similarities and differences concerning locomotion in water, on land, or in air.

Figure 43.12   Actions of flexors and extensors.   The figure shows how skeletal muscles cause flexion or extension of a limb in an animal with an endoskeleton. When the flexor muscle contracts, the extensor relaxes, and vice versa.

Labels in figure:
Extensors relaxed (quadriceps)
Flexors contracted (hamstring)
Extensors contracted
Flexors relaxed

GENOMES AND PROTEOMES

Do Different Genes Get Upregulated or Downregulated in Fast-Swimming Versus Slow-Swimming Fish?

Canadian researcher Dr. Louis Bernatchez (Université Laval) has studied the phenotypic environmental-transciptome associations between two different ecotypes of lake whitefish (*Coregonus clupeaformis*), dwarf and normal, that co-exist in Maine and Quebec. Dr. Bernatchez has developed a broad-based approach in his research program that includes studies on the evolution of the whitefish phenotypes and the genetic basis and the differential upregulation of genes in the two whitefish ecotypes.

The whitefish ecotypes probably evolved allopatrically in geographically isolated refugia during the Pleistocene glaciation (ca. 500,000 to 18,000 years ago). Secondary contact between the ecotypes subsequently occurred approximately 15,000 years ago in Maine and Quebec. Sympatric populations maintain a strong bimodal size distribution, and very little gene flow occurs between the two ecotypes. Dwarf whitefish mature in one to two years, are smaller in size and weight, and feed on smaller limnetic prey. The normal whitefish do not mature until year two, are larger in size, and feed on larger, epibenthic prey.

The differences in feeding behaviours also relate to differences in swimming behaviours. The dwarf whitefish display higher swimming activity, such as burst swimming, which is consistent with limnetic foraging species. Bernatchez and his colleagues have been able to correlate swimming behaviour with the upregulation of genes in white muscle of the whitefish ecotypes. By using cDNA gene microarrays the research group found that dwarf whitefish overexpressed genes associated with muscle contraction speed (e.g., actin, myomesin, tropomyosin, and creatine kinase) and upregulation of genes involved in higher metabolic activity (e.g., genes involved in glycolysis and ATP synthesis). Furthermore, mapping of expression quantitative trait loci (eQTL) showed that the genes involved in master regulation of the functional gene groups were tightly linked. The tradeoff for the dwarf whitefish was lower bioenergetic conversion efficiency, resulting in slower growth and a younger age at sexual maturity. This is one of very few studies to investigate gene expression and regulation in the context of ecological interactions and adaptive radiation.

Aquatic Animals Must Overcome the Resistance of Water

The greatest challenge to locomotion in water is the density of water, which is much greater than that of air. This is apparent when you compare waving your hand through the air and underwater. The resistance to movement posed by the density of water increases exponentially as the speed of locomotion increases, which is one reason why many fish swim at relatively slow speeds. Overcoming this resistance requires considerable muscular effort. Most swimming animals, including fish, amphibians, reptiles, and marine mammals, have evolved streamlined bodies that reduce drag and make swimming more efficient (**Figure 43.13**). Other animals that swim only occasionally or spend time on the surface of the water have evolved adaptations, such as the webbed feet of ducks, that assist their muscles in generating greater thrust through the water.

An energetic advantage to swimming is that fish and other swimmers do not need to provide lift to overcome gravity. Because the density of water is similar to that of an animal's body, water provides buoyancy, which helps support the animal's weight.

The mechanism of swimming is similar among many different vertebrates. Most fish, for example, contract posterior skeletal muscles to move the tail end of the animal from side to side. This pushes water backward and propels the fish forward. Other fins provide additional thrust and enable changes in direction. Likewise, amphibians and marine reptiles rely predominantly on their hind legs, their tail, or undulations of the posterior parts of the body for propulsion through the water. Cetaceans use up-and-down thrusts of their tail flukes to provide propulsion. Confining most of the swimming muscles to the rear of an animal's body has its advantages. With the rear end devoted to movement, the front end is free to explore the environment, fight off aggressors, or find food. In contrast, pinnipeds use their flippers to provide thrust and their tails to steer. This allows them to venture onto land as well.

In contrast to swimming vertebrates, many aquatic invertebrates move through water by means other than swimming. Cephalopods such as squids use propulsion provided by the ejection of water to give them brief but rapid bursts of speed, while many other aquatic invertebrates move passively on water currents or crawl along rocks and other underwater surfaces.

Because of streamlining, the relatively slow speed of most swimmers, and the buoyancy of water, swimming is energetically the cheapest form of locomotion. By contrast, terrestrial animals face considerable energetic costs to locomotion, as we examine next.

Walking and Running on Land Are Energetically Costly

In contrast to swimming, locomotion on land is, on average, the most energetically costly means of locomotion (**Figure 43.14**). Flying may seem costlier, but it is not. Many migratory birds can travel hundreds of kilometres daily for many days. No terrestrial animal could possibly match such a feat by walking or running.

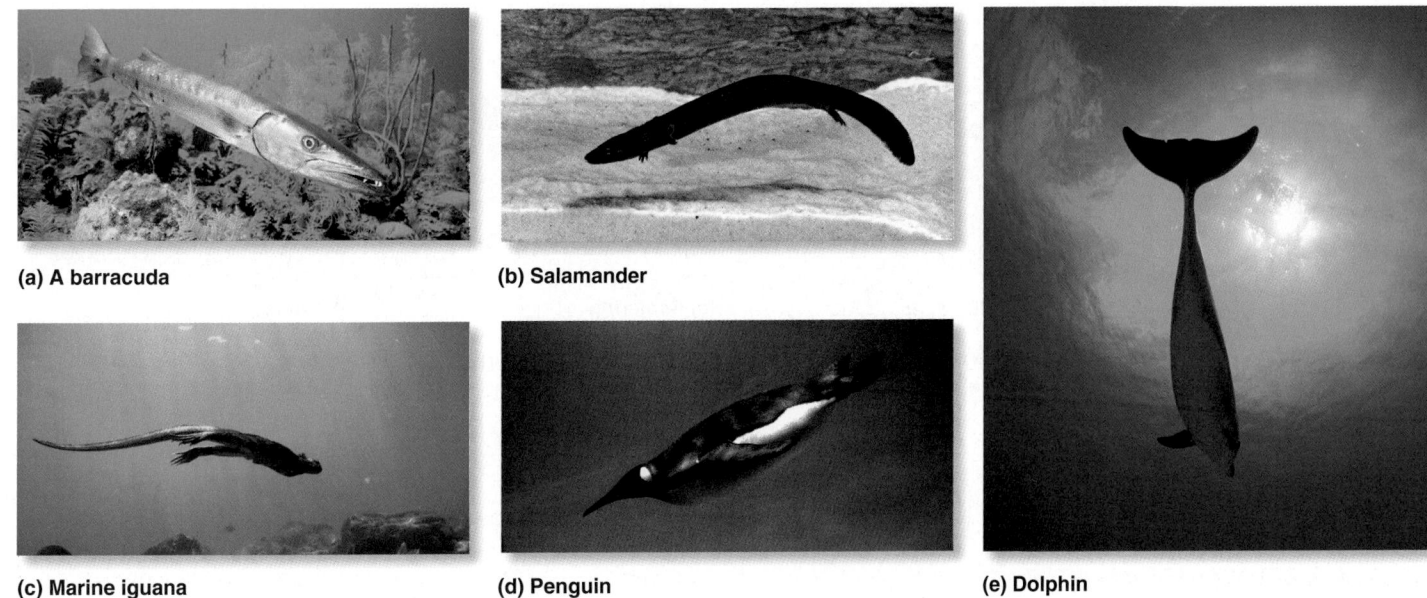

(a) A barracuda (b) Salamander

(c) Marine iguana (d) Penguin (e) Dolphin

Figure 43.13 **Adaptations for swimming.** Streamlined bodies that greatly reduce frictional drag underwater are found in all classes of swimming vertebrates.

Concept check: *Is streamlining unique to animals that swim?*

Figure 43.14 **Energy costs of locomotion.** The energy costs of three different modes of locomotion for animals of different sizes are shown. The *y*-axis gives the relative energy costs, determined by measuring how much oxygen an animal consumes during locomotion. Energy costs are highest for runners compared with similarly sized fliers and swimmers.

Concept check: *Does this graph indicate that smaller animals expend more energy than larger animals when moving a similar distance?*

Whereas gravity is not an important factor for locomotion in swimming animals, terrestrial animals must overcome gravity each time they take a step. Of even greater importance to walking and running animals, though, is the necessity of accelerating and decelerating the limbs with every step. In essence, each step is like starting a movement from scratch, without the luxury of occasionally gliding through water or air as fish and birds do. This challenge is even greater when an animal moves uphill or over rough terrain.

Apart from molluscs, which move along the surface of Earth on a layer of secreted mucus, and snakes, which undulate along the ground on a portion of their ventral body surface, most terrestrial animals limit the amount of contact with the ground while moving, thereby minimizing the amount of friction they encounter. Tetrapods usually have only two feet on the ground at any time when walking, and for brief moments a horse galloping at full speed has all four feet off the ground (**Figure 43.15**).

Having fewer legs on the ground surface at any one time helps increase speed but can compromise stability. Arthropods, for example, have at least six legs. This apparently provides excellent stability but reduces maximal speed. At the other extreme are animals that move by jumping—fleas, certain spiders, click beetles, grasshoppers, and kangaroos.

Flying Has Evolved on Four Separate Occasions

Flying is a highly successful means of locomotion, having evolved on four occasions: in pterosaurs (extinct reptiles), insects, birds, and mammals (bats). The advantages to flying are numerous. Animals can escape land-based predators, scan their surroundings over great distances, and inhabit environments such as high cliffs that may be inaccessible to nonflying animals. The mechanics of flight, however, require animals to overcome gravity and air resistance, which makes flying energetically costlier than swimming but still cheaper than running on land (Figure 43.14). As with swimming, resistance to flight is decreased by streamlined bodies. However, earthbound animals have one advantage over their flying cousins—they can grow to much larger sizes than animals that fly. The vast majority of flying animals have a mass between about 1 milligram and 1 kilogram. Only a

(a) Walking   **(b) Trotting**   **(c) Cantering**   **(d) Galloping**

Figure 43.15 Walking and running in a tetrapod. By minimizing the number of feet in contact with the ground as they accelerate to running speed, many tetrapods reduce the energy cost of locomotion, as shown in this horse **(a)** walking, **(b)** trotting, **(c)** cantering, and **(d)** galloping.

few large birds have masses exceeding 10 kilograms. Although this represents an enormous range, it falls far short of the sizes achieved by earthbound or aquatic animals.

In flying vertebrates, lift and thrust are provided by pectoral and back muscles that move the wings. The pectoral muscles are so powerful and massive that they constitute as much as 15%–20% of a bird's total body mass and up to 30% in hummingbirds, which use their wings not only to fly but also to hover. The requirement for large, strong pectoral muscles is one reason that the remaining body mass of flying vertebrates is limited. The extinct pterosaurs would seem to be an exception because some species were known to have had wingspans of nearly 10 metres. However, it is believed that these large animals glided from trees or cliffs and were unable to provide the force required to lift their massive bodies off the ground.

In birds and bats, the wings are modifications of the forelimbs. In general, bat wings are far more manoeuvrable than bird wings, because unlike birds, bats have fingers at the end of their forelimbs/wings (see Figure 21.12). This allows bats to precisely alter the shape of their wings and provide for rapid, fine-tuned changes in direction, even at high speeds. Bird wings are more similar to those of a fixed-wing aircraft. The largest birds, such as hawks and eagles, are able to glide because of the great surface area of their large wings. By using a bird's momentum to propel it forward, gliding provides a considerable energy savings. Bats and small birds, however, can glide for only very brief moments.

In this chapter, we have seen how skeletal muscles and (in vertebrates) bones work together to provide animals with protection and to enable them to move around in their environments. Next we turn to examples of bone and muscle problems in humans.

43.6 HUMAN HEALTH CONNECTION

Learning Outcomes:

1. Describe the impact of the bone diseases rickets and osteoporosis on human health.

A number of diseases can affect bone structure and function. Bone disease may involve defects in either the mineral or organic components of bone. Poor bone formation and structure may result from inadequate nutrition, hormonal imbalances, aging, or skeletal muscle atrophy, to name just a few of the common causes.

In addition, many diseases or disorders directly affect the contraction of skeletal muscle. Some of them are temporary and not serious, such as muscle cramps, whereas others are chronic and severe, such as the disease muscular dystrophy. Also, some diseases result from defects in parts of the nervous system that control contraction of the muscle fibres rather than from defects in the fibres themselves. One example is poliomyelitis (polio), a viral disease in which the destruction of motor neurons leads to skeletal muscle paralysis that may result in death from respiratory failure. Polio, once thought to be nearly eliminated from the human population, is still a threat in parts of the world.

Rickets and Osteoporosis Affect the Bones of Millions of People

Bone diseases are fairly common, particularly among individuals after age 50. Two major abnormalities can occur in bone (**Figure 43.16**). The first is improper mineral deposition in bone, usually because of inadequate dietary calcium intake or inadequate absorption of calcium from the small intestine. Without adequate minerals, bone becomes soft and easily deformed, as occurs in the weight-bearing bones of the legs of children with rickets (or osteomalacia, as it is called in adults). These disorders are best prevented or treated with vitamin D, because this vitamin is the most important factor in promoting absorption of calcium from the small intestine.

Much more common is a disease called **osteoporosis**, in which both the mineral and the organic portions of bone are reduced. This disease, which affects four times as many women as men, occurs when the normal balance between bone formation and bone breakdown is disrupted.

One way in which osteoporosis occurs is as a result of prolonged disuse of muscles. In ways that are not completely clear, the force produced by active skeletal muscle contractions

(a) X-ray image of leg bones of a child with rickets

(b) Histologic appearance of normal bone (top) and bone from a person with osteoporosis (bottom)

Figure 43.16 Deformation in human bones caused by (a) rickets and (b) osteoporosis. (a) X-ray image of leg bones of a child with rickets, (b) Appearance of normal bone (top) versus osteoporotic bone (bottom).

helps maintain bone mass. When muscles are not or cannot be used—because of paralysis or long-term immobilizing illnesses, or even during prolonged space flight in which the lack of gravity reduces the need for muscles to work hard—bone mass declines.

Osteoporosis may also result from hormonal imbalances. Some hormones—for example, estrogen—stimulate bone formation. When estrogen levels decline after menopause (the time when a woman's reproductive cycles cease), bone density may decline, increasing the risk of bone fractures. By contrast, some hormones act to demineralize bone as part of the way in which the body normally maintains mineral homeostasis in the blood. If such hormones are present in excess, however, they can cause enough demineralization of bone to cause osteoporosis. This may happen in rare cases when the glands that make these hormones malfunction and overproduce the hormones.

Osteoporosis can be minimized with adequate calcium intake, weight-bearing exercise programs, and adequate vitamin D intake. In some cases, postmenopausal women may be given estrogen to replace what their bodies are no longer producing. It is estimated that 2 million Canadians have osteoporosis. It results in annual national expenditures of approximately $1.3 billion in hospital and other costs.

Summary of Key Concepts

- Locomotion is the movement of an animal from place to place.

43.1 Types of Animal Skeletons

- Skeletons are structures that provide support and protection, and also function in locomotion.

- Three types of skeletons are found in animals. In hydrostatic skeletons, found in many soft-bodied invertebrates, muscle contractions acting on fluid-filled body cavities create hydrostatic pressure that supports the body and generates movements. Exoskeletons, which are found in arthropods, are protective external structures that must be shed to accommodate growth of the animal. Endoskeletons are internal structures that grow with the animal but do not protect its body surface; endoskeletons are found in some species of sponges, echinoderms, and all vertebrates. (Figure 43.1)

43.2 The Vertebrate Skeleton

- A joint is formed where two or more bones of a vertebrate endoskeleton come together. (Figure 43.2)

- In addition to the functions of support, protection, and locomotion, the vertebrate skeleton produces blood cells and constitutes a reservoir for ions that are crucial to homeostasis. (Table 43.1)

43.3 Skeletal Muscle Structure and the Mechanism of Force Generation

- A skeletal muscle is a grouping of cells, called muscle fibres, bound together by a succession of connective tissue layers. The striations of skeletal muscle result from the presence within muscle fibres of cylindrical bundles known as myofibrils, each of which contains thick and thin filaments arranged in repeating units called sarcomeres. The arrangements of thick and thin filaments within each sarcomere create various light and dark regions designated the I and A bands, the Z and M lines, and the H zone. Thick filaments are composed almost entirely of the motor protein myosin, whereas thin filaments contain the cytoskeletal protein actin plus two other proteins called troponin and tropomyosin. Portions of the thick filaments are called cross-bridges. (Figures 43.3, 43.4)

- During muscle contraction, the sarcomeres shorten by a process known as the sliding filament mechanism. In muscle contraction, the thick filaments remain stationary while the thin filaments slide past them propelled by action of the cross-bridges. (Figure 43.5)

- Sarcomeres are composed of thick (myosin) and thin (actin) filaments. (Figure 43.6)

- The repeated interaction of cross-bridges on the thick filaments and the protein components of the thin filaments occurs according to a process called the cross-bridge cycle. (Figure 43.7)

- Calcium plays an important role in excitation-contraction coupling, the sequence of events by which an action potential in the plasma membrane of a muscle fibre leads to cross-bridge activity. (Figure 43.8)

- The source of the cytosolic calcium involved in a muscle action potential is the muscle fibre's sarcoplasmic reticulum. Tubular structures called the transverse tubules (T-tubules) conduct action potentials from the outer surface of the muscle fibre to the myofibrils. (Figure 43.9)

- Electrical stimulation of skeletal muscle occurs at a neuromuscular junction, in which a motor neuron's axon and a muscle fibre are in close proximity. (Figure 43.10)

43.4 Skeletal Muscle Function

- On the basis of the rates at which muscle fibres shorten and the way in which they produce the ATP needed for contraction, three major types of skeletal muscle fibres have been distinguished. Slow-oxidative fibres have low rates of myosin ATP hydrolysis; they do not fatigue easily and are used for prolonged, regular activities. Fast-oxidative fibres have high myosin activity, do not fatigue quickly, and are particularly suited for rapid actions. Fast-glycolytic fibres have high myosin activity but cannot make as much ATP as oxidative fibres; they are best suited for rapid, intense actions. (Table 43.2)

- Increased expression of PPAR-delta in mice results in increased slow-oxidative muscle, greater exercise endurance, and weight loss. (Figure 43.11)

- Groups of muscles that produce oppositely directed movements at a joint are known as antagonists. Muscles that bend a limb at a joint are called flexors, whereas muscles that straighten a limb are called extensors. (Figure 43.12)

43.5 Animal Locomotion

- Because of streamlining, the relatively slow speed of most swimmers, and the buoyancy of water, swimming is energetically the most efficient form of locomotion. Locomotion on land is, on average, the energetically costliest means of locomotion; the energy expenditure required for flight is intermediate between those for swimming and land-based locomotion. (Figures 43.13, 43.14, 43.15)

43.6 Human Health Connection

- Rickets and osteoporosis are two important health issues in humans. (Figure 43.16)

Test to Assess Your Learning

1. The hydrostatic skeleton common in soft-bodied invertebrates is composed of
   a. muscle and cartilage.
   b. cartilage and a neural net.
   c. muscle and water.
   d. cartilage and water.
   e. bone and muscle.

2. Which of the following is *not* a function of the vertebrate skeleton?
   a. structural support
   b. protection
   c. calcium reserve
   d. blood cell production
   e. all of the above are functions of the vertebrate skeleton

3. The protein that provides strength and flexibility to bone is
   a. actin.
   b. myosin.
   c. myoglobin.
   d. collagen.
   e. elastin.

4. In a sarcomere, the _____ contains thin filaments and no thick filaments.
   a. A band
   b. M line
   c. I band
   d. H zone
   e. both (a) and (d)

5. The function of ATP during muscle contraction is to
   a. cause an allosteric change in myosin so it detaches from actin.
   b. provide the energy necessary for the movement of the cross-bridge.
   c. expose the myosin-binding sites on the thin filaments.
   d. all of the above.
   e. (a) and (b) only.

6. The function of calcium ions in skeletal muscle contraction is to
   a. cause an allosteric change in myosin so it detaches from actin.
   b. provide the energy necessary for the movement of the cross-bridge.
   c. expose the myosin-binding sites on the thin filaments.
   d. bind to tropomyosin.
   e. (a) and (c) only.

7. Stimulation of a muscle fibre by a motor neuron occurs at
   a. the neuromuscular junction.
   b. the transverse tubules.
   c. the myofibril.
   d. the sarcoplasmic reticulum.
   e. none of the above.

8. Muscle fibres that have a high number of mitochondria, contain large amounts of myoglobin, and exhibit low rates of ATP hydrolysis are called _____ fibres.
   a. slow-glycolytic
   b. fast-glycolytic
   c. intermediate
   d. fast-oxidative
   e. slow-oxidative

9. Which of the following statements about movement and locomotion is incorrect?
   a. Terrestrial animals and flying animals expend energy to provide lift.
   b. Swimming animals expend energy to provide thrust but not lift.
   c. Flexors and extensors are examples of muscles called agonists.
   d. Flexors cause bending at a joint.
   e. Extensors cause straightening of a limb.

10. Swimming is energetically the cheapest type of locomotion because of
    a. streamlined body forms in aquatic organisms.
    b. slow speed of movement.
    c. buoyancy.
    d. (a) and (c) only.
    e. (a), (b), and (c).

Articulate to Assess Your Learning

1. Select three nonhuman animals that you have seen this week, and list the different types of locomotion that each might use in a day.

2. Distinguish between exoskeletons and endoskeletons.

3. Striations are found in cardiac muscle as well as in skeletal muscle. Why do you think this is?

Collaborate to Assess and Extend Your Learning

1. Discuss the structure and function of the three different types of skeletons found in animals.

2. Humans have dark leg muscles and white arm muscles (similar to the dark muscles in chicken drumsticks and the white muscles in chicken breasts). Why do you think this is? What would you expect to find in a fast-running quadruped such as a cheetah?

3. A principle of biology is that living organisms use energy. How is that principle illustrated in this chapter?

Visit McGraw-Hill Ryerson Connect™ for additional study resources.

Circulatory Systems

Chapter Outline

Image from cardiac angiography (dye contrast injection to visualize coronary blood vessels).

In Chapters 39 and 40, we learned how animals obtain and use nutrients. In this chapter, we will examine how nutrients and other substances are transported throughout an animal's body to individual cells. Single-celled organisms are small enough that dissolved substances are able to diffuse into and out of their bodies. In larger animals, however, dissolved substances must move greater distances between cells, as well as between the internal and external environments. Transporting materials over long distances requires a circulatory system.

The primary function of **circulatory systems** is to transport necessary materials to all the cells of an animal's body and to transport waste products away from the cells where they can be released into the environment. Necessary materials include organic and inorganic nutrients and gases, such as oxygen. Waste products that must be eliminated include carbon dioxide and other breakdown products of metabolism. Most circulatory systems are capable of adjusting their activities to an animal's changing metabolic demands. For instance, you will see how exercise increases the ability of the vertebrate heart to pump blood and directs blood to the skeletal muscles where it is most needed.

The three basic types of circulatory systems are gastrovascular cavities, open systems, and closed systems. We begin with the simplest form of circulation, that provided by the water in which certain invertebrates live.

44.1 TYPES OF CIRCULATORY SYSTEMS

Learning Outcomes:

1. Compare and contrast the different types of animal circulatory systems.
2. List the key structural and functional characteristics of open and closed circulatory systems.
3. Describe single, intermediate, and double circulations in vertebrates.

In cnidarians (jellyfish and hydras), the surrounding water not only contains the nutrients and oxygen needed to sustain life but also serves the functions of the animals' circulatory system. These animals rely on water currents to bring a steady supply of water into contact with their body surfaces. Water enters the **gastrovascular cavity**, a body cavity with a single opening to the outside. Food is digested within the cavity and absorbed by body cells, and wastes are excreted into the cavity (see Chapter 39). Digested foods reach all the cells because water circulates throughout the entire cavity. All of the animal's body cells are located near the gastrovascular cavity or slender extensions that branch from it (**Figure 44.1**).

In some cnidarians, cilia that line the opening of the gastrovascular cavity propel water through these extensions. In addition, muscular efforts of the body wall—as a hydra stretches and relaxes, for instance, or a jellyfish propels itself by contracting its bell—help move water throughout the cavity. The harder the muscles work, the more effectively they propel water, thus providing a form of circulation. In this way, the muscles of cnidarians serve some of the same functions as a beating heart.

The muscles of the jellyfish bell are controlled by nerve cells that are scattered throughout the bell. This, too, is comparable to what occurs in animals with hearts, because nerves regulate the beating of a **heart**. Thus, animals that possess a gastrovascular cavity already show several elements of more complex circulatory systems.

Open Circulatory Systems

Arthropods and some molluscs have a true circulatory system with three basic components:

1. **Blood** or **hemolymph**, an internal body fluid containing dissolved solutes;

(a)

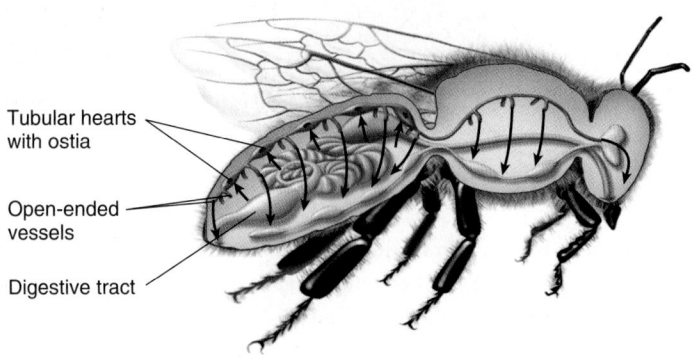

Tubular hearts with ostia

Open-ended vessels

Digestive tract

Figure 44.2   **An open circulatory system.**   In open systems, one or more muscular, tubelike hearts pump hemolymph through open-ended vessels, where it percolates through the body. In arthropods, such as this honeybee, hemolymph re-enters the heart through ostia. The arrows show the movement of hemolymph.

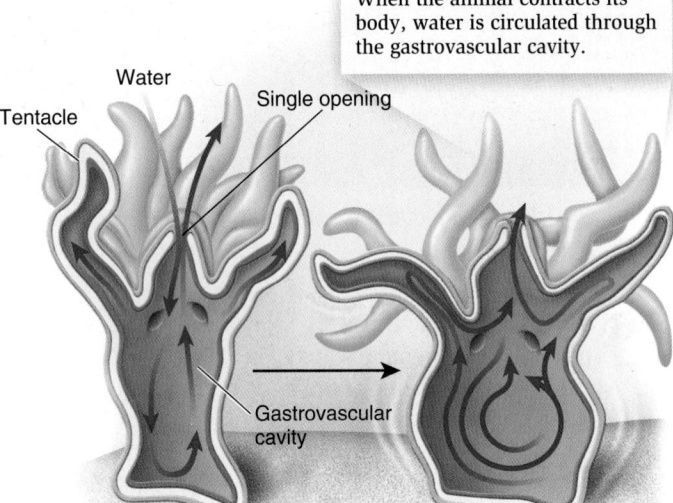

When the animal contracts its body, water is circulated through the gastrovascular cavity.

Water

Tentacle

Single opening

Gastrovascular cavity

(b)

Figure 44.1   **Circulation of water through the gastrovascular cavity of *Hydra*.**   **(a)** Longitudinal section of *Hydra*. **(b)** The animal's movements assist the flow of water throughout the cavity, which extends into the tentacles. The single opening is used as both mouth and anus.

BioConnections: *Look back at Figure 39.4. Can you see how the circulation of water in a gastrovascular cavity is related to the digestive functions of Hydra?*

2. **Blood vessels**, a system of hollow tubes within the body through which blood travels;
3. One or more hearts, muscular structures that pump blood through the blood vessels.

Circulatory systems containing these three components are also known as a **cardiovascular system** (from the Greek *kardia*, heart, and Latin *vas*, vessel). In an **open circulatory system**, the vessels open into the animal's body cavity. Therefore, the fluid in the vessels and the interstitial fluid that surrounds cells mingle in one large, mixed compartment, rather than being located in separate body compartments. The blood and interstitial fluids form one fluid, called hemolymph. One or more muscular hearts pump hemolymph through blood vessels, where it exits into the

animal's body cavity (**Figure 44.2**). Nutrients and wastes are exchanged by diffusion between the hemolymph and the body cells, and the hemolymph is recirculated back to the heart. In molluscs with open circulatory systems, hemolymph re-enters the heart through blood vessels, while in arthropods it returns to the heart through small openings in the heart called **ostia**.

In insects, hemolymph primarily transports nutrients and wastes, while in molluscs it also brings oxygen to body cells. However, components of hemolymph (insect blood) do many of the same things as do vertebrate blood components. For example, cells called hemocytes offer immunity against foreign invaders through such defences as phagocytosis and encapsulation. Insects have a unique oxygen-delivery system that does not involve the circulatory system (see Chapter 45).

Open circulatory systems are energetically inexpensive because they do not require much energy to circulate hemolymph. In addition, open systems can adapt to changes in an animal's metabolic demands. As an insect takes flight, for example, its flight muscles contract more forcefully and rapidly, which acts to expand and compress the animal's thorax. This helps propel hemolymph more rapidly throughout the body cavity and into and out of the heart. In other words, as the animal's activity increases, its circulation becomes more efficient, recharging metabolically active cells with nutrients. As noted earlier, the ability to adjust circulation to meet an animal's needs is one of the most important features of any circulatory system. Open systems, therefore, are highly effective, particularly for smaller animals.

Because the hemolymph empties in bulk into the general body cavity, several insects have evolved accessory pulsatile organs to help deliver the hemolymph to particular body parts. For example, Peter Koladich and Stephen Tobe from the University of Toronto and Jeremy McNeil from Laval University demonstrated in a noctuid moth (*Pseudaletia unipuncta*) that its ventral diaphragm is fused to the dorsal surface of the ventral nerve cord. This unique arrangement allows the ventral nerve cord to oscillate at relatively high speeds; thus, in this insect, the ventral nerve cord itself is physically capable of directing hemolymph flow.

Open circulatory systems are not ideal for larger, more active animals in which higher pressure is required to pump blood to all body cells at a rate sufficient to meet energetic demands. During exercise in vertebrates, larger amounts of blood are delivered to leg muscles and away from less metabolically active structures, an adaptation that results in greater endurance. These animals have evolved a closed circulatory system, which we will examine next.

Closed Circulatory Systems Separate Blood from Interstitial Fluid

In a **closed circulatory system**, blood and interstitial fluid are physically separated by blood vessel walls, and they differ in their components and chemical composition. Closed circulatory systems are found in earthworms, cephalopods (squids and octopi), and all vertebrates (**Figure 44.3**). Despite differences in structure, closed circulatory systems share certain key features:

- Blood remains within tubelike vessels that distribute it throughout the body.
- Blood is pumped under pressure by one or more contractile, muscular hearts.

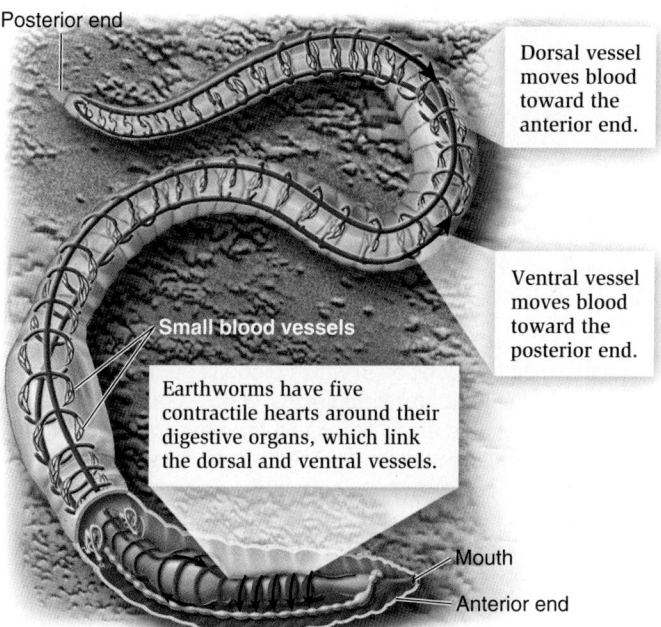

Posterior end

Dorsal vessel moves blood toward the anterior end.

Ventral vessel moves blood toward the posterior end.

Small blood vessels

Earthworms have five contractile hearts around their digestive organs, which link the dorsal and ventral vessels.

Mouth

Anterior end

Figure 44.3   A closed circulatory system.   In closed systems, such as that of the earthworm, blood remains in vessels or hearts and recirculates without emptying into the body cavity. The arrows indicate the direction of blood flow.

Concept check: *Look back at Figure 44.2. Why is it incorrect to think of open circulatory systems as "primitive" compared to closed systems?*

- Blood contains dissolved solutes that are transported throughout the body and can be exchanged with the environment and the body's cells.
- In most cases, blood contains disease-fighting cells and molecules.
- The activity of the circulatory system can be adjusted to match the animal's metabolic demands.
- Closed circulatory systems generally have the capacity to heal themselves when wounded, by forming clots at the site of injury.
- Closed systems grow in size as an animal grows.

A closed circulatory system offers several advantages. First, animals can grow to a larger size, because blood can be directed to every cell of an animal's body, no matter how large. Nearly all body cells are within one or two cell-widths away from a blood vessel. Second, blood flow can be selectively increased or decreased to supply different parts of the body with the precise amount of blood needed at any given moment. After a meal, for example, more blood can be directed to the gut to absorb nutrients, and on a hot day additional blood can be routed to the skin to dissipate heat. Animals with open systems cannot make these adjustments.

The closed circulatory systems of vertebrates can be divided into two major groups: single and double circulations. In a single circulation, blood is pumped under low pressure from the heart to the respiratory surface (e.g., gills), where it picks up oxygen and drops off carbon dioxide. From there, blood circulates to the tissues of the body, where it releases oxygen and picks up carbon dioxide. The blood then circulates back to the heart. In a double circulation, blood is pumped under low pressure from the heart to the lungs and is returned to the heart, to be pumped under high pressure to the tissues and finally returned again to the heart. Single circulations are seen in fish, and double circulations are seen in crocodiles, birds, and mammals. Amphibians and most reptiles have a circulation that combines features of both.

In the single circulation of fish, the heart has a single filling chamber—an **atrium**—to collect blood from the tissues and another chamber—a **ventricle**—to pump blood out of the heart (**Figure 44.4a**). Blood vessels called **arteries** carry blood away from the heart to the gills, where the fish picks up oxygen from the water in which it swims and unloads carbon dioxide into the water. The freshly oxygenated blood then circulates via other arteries to the rest of the body. There, oxygen and nutrients are delivered to cells and carbon dioxide diffuses from cells into the blood. Finally, the deoxygenated blood is returned to the heart via blood vessels called **veins**, where it is pumped back to the gills for another load of oxygen.

An important feature of all respiratory surfaces is that they function best when the blood flowing through them is maintained at a low pressure. Thus, the fish heart does not generate high pressure when it pumps blood to the gills. This means that blood leaving the gills will also be under low pressure, thus limiting the rate at which oxygenated blood can be delivered to the body's cells.

Unlike fish, most adult amphibians, including frogs, rely on lungs and their highly permeable skin to obtain oxygen and

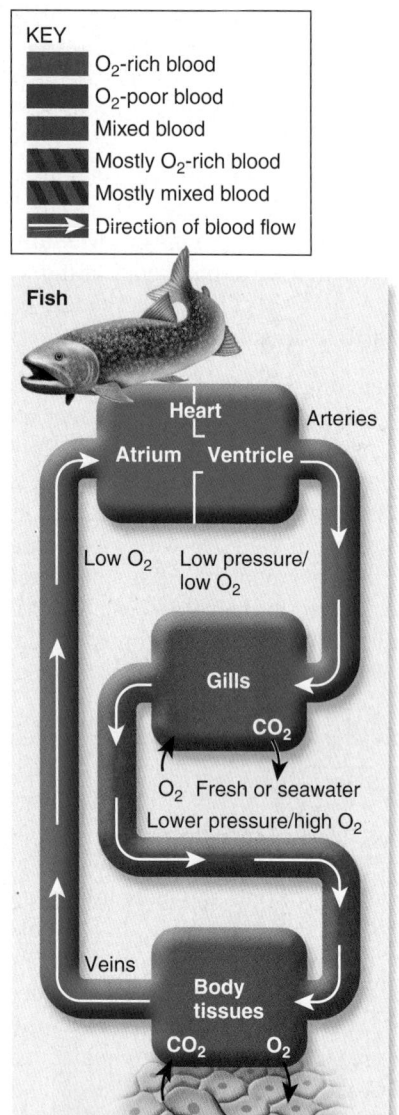

(a) Single circulation in fish

(b) Features of both single and double circulation in most amphibians

(c) Double circulation in birds and mammals

Figure 44.4 **Representative vertebrate circulatory systems.** **(a)** Fish have a single circulation in which blood is pumped from the heart to the gills, from where it circulates to the rest of the body tissues and returns to the heart. **(b)** Amphibians, such as frogs, have a heart with a single ventricle that is able to separate most of the oxygenated and deoxygenated blood entering it from the two atria. Some mixing does occur, however, as represented in this figure by the white dashed line. A significant advantage of this type of circulation is the ability to redirect blood from the lungs to the skin when underwater. Because the skin is somewhat permeable to oxygen, this partly compensates for the lack of air breathing. Note that blood returning from the skin has picked up oxygen but is returned to the right atrium, not the left atrium as is the case with the lungs. **(c)** Birds and mammals have a double circulation, in which oxygenated blood is pumped under high pressure to the body's tissues, and deoxygenated blood is pumped under low pressure to the lungs.

Concept check: *What is the advantage of completely separating oxygenated and deoxygenated blood in a double circulation?*

rid themselves of carbon dioxide. While amphibians are on land, their deoxygenated blood is pumped from the heart to the lungs and, to a lesser extent, the skin. Oxygen diffuses from the air into the blood vessels within the lungs and beneath the skin, and carbon dioxide diffuses in the opposite direction. While amphibians are underwater, deoxygenated blood from the heart bypasses the lungs and is directed almost entirely to

the skin so that oxygen in the water can diffuse across the skin and into the circulation. Oxygenated blood from the lungs and skin does not travel directly to the rest of the body but instead returns to the heart, where it is pumped out to the tissues of the body.

The amphibian heart, therefore, pumps oxygenated and deoxygenated blood to two separate locations. Blood is routed from the heart through different vessels to either the respiratory surfaces (the **pulmocutaneous circulation**) or the body tissues (the **systemic circulation**). This would not be possible if an amphibian's heart and circulation were the same as that of a fish, where blood travels through a single circulation. Instead, the amphibian heart has two separate atria for collecting blood (**Figure 44.4b**). The right atrium receives blood that has passed through all of the body except the lungs and is therefore depleted of much of its oxygen. However, some oxygen-rich blood returning from the skin also enters the right atrium and mixes with the blood returning from the systemic circulation. This is an important adaptation for amphibians when they are underwater, because as stated, the circulation through the lungs is decreased at such times and therefore diffusion across the skin becomes the sole means of obtaining oxygen.

When an amphibian breathes air, oxygen-rich blood from the lungs is delivered to the left atrium. Each atrium of the amphibian heart empties its blood into a single large ventricle. The internal structure of the single ventricle keeps the oxygenated and deoxygenated blood from the two atria mostly separate. Some mixing of the two streams of blood, however, does occur in the ventricle. This would not occur if each atrium emptied into a separate ventricle. Because there is only a single ventricle, however, the blood travelling to the tissues is not fully oxygenated, and this imposes limits on the metabolic activity of amphibians.

Like amphibians, all the noncrocodilian reptiles have hearts with two atria and a single ventricle, although the ventricle is further subdivided into two partially but completely separated chambers. These chambers allow more efficient separation of oxygenated and deoxygenated blood entering the ventricle from the two atria, which contributes in part to the higher activity levels of reptiles compared with amphibians. Despite this, because reptiles and amphibians have only a single ventricle that must pump blood to both the tissues and the respiratory surfaces, blood must

be pumped under low or moderate pressure in these animals to minimize the pressure of blood flowing through the lung tissue.

Crocodiles, Birds, and Mammals Have a Double Circulation with Four-Chambered Hearts

In crocodiles, birds, and mammals, oxygenated and deoxygenated blood are completely separated into two distinct circuits: the systemic circulation and the **pulmonary circulation** (**Figure 44.4c**). This is made possible by a heart that has a second ventricle. The crocodilian circulatory system is somewhat different from that of birds and mammals, because crocodiles spend part of their lives underwater and are considerably less active than birds and mammals. When resting or underwater, crocodiles can divert blood between the two circuits in ways that birds and mammals cannot. Nonetheless, all animals with double circulations have a left and right atrium, and a left and right ventricle. The left ventricle receives oxygenated blood from the left atrium, and the right ventricle receives deoxygenated blood from the right atrium.

A major advantage of a double circulation is that the two ventricles can function as if they were, in effect, two hearts, each with its own ability to pump blood under different pressures. This means that blood from the right ventricle can be pumped under low pressure to the lungs. Once the blood picks up oxygen from the lungs, it can be returned to the left side of the heart. The left ventricle is more muscular than the right ventricle and therefore can generate much higher pressures when pumping blood. Thus, the oxygenated blood leaving the left side of the heart has sufficiently high pressure to reach all the cells of the animal's body and deliver oxygen and nutrients at a high rate, even to regions above the heart that must contend with gravity. This is no small feat considering the distance blood must travel in some large mammals. The left ventricle of a giraffe, for example, is particularly muscular compared with that of other animals.

GENOMES AND PROTEOMES

A Four-Chambered Heart Evolved from Simple Contractile Tubes

The heart is the first vertebrate organ to become functional during embryonic development, and the factors responsible for its development have been extensively studied. Interestingly, at least one of these developmental factors has also recently shed light on how a heart develops four chambers in crocodiles, birds, and mammals.

The first heart-like organ appears to have evolved at least 500 million years ago. Ancestral hearts may have resembled the type observed today in cephalochordates and urochordates, a simple linear tube with wavelike contractile properties but no valves or chambers. A valve-like structure first appears in the tubular hearts of some arthropods, such as *Drosophila*, but such hearts do not have clearly

defined chambers. Analyses of animal genomes have identified numerous genes that are critical for the development of the chambered vertebrate heart, including a core set of five highly conserved genes and their proteins. Interestingly, however, one or more of these five genes are also expressed in linear tube hearts such as those just described, and even in contractile structures in animals without hearts. For example, as described earlier, cnidarians do not have a heart or blood vessels, but have muscle cells in their contractile bell that not only produce locomotion but, in the process, circulate water through the animal's gastrovascular cavity. These muscle cells express at least three of these heart developmental genes. Nematodes also do not have a heart, but have a contractile pharynx that serves part of the same function; the pharyngeal muscles of these animals express four of the five key heart developmental genes that are found in all vertebrates. Thus, the genes required for the formation of a contractile, multi-chambered heart are ancient and conserved. A question that arises, however, is why are some vertebrate hearts four-chambered, while others are not?

In a 2009 study, Benoit Bruneau and colleagues compared the expression of one of the major heart developmental genes, called *Tbx5*, in the hearts of amphibians, reptiles, birds, and mammals. They discovered that the expression of *Tbx5* became increasingly restricted in animals displaying greater separation of the ventricles into two chambers (**Figure 44.5**). In amphibians, which have a single ventricle, *Tbx5* was expressed throughout the developing ventricle. In reptiles in which an incomplete septum partially divides the ventricles, *Tbx5* expression was absent in a portion of the right half of the ventricle. In birds and mammals, *Tbx5* was completely absent

from the developing right ventricle and highly expressed in the left ventricle. This suggests that a gradient of *Tbx5* is required for the ventricle to form two chambers and thereby a complete double circulation. The investigators also showed that if *Tbx5* expression were experimentally induced in the heart of an embryonic mouse in a pattern that mimicked that seen in lizards, the mouse heart developed only three clearly defined chambers—there was no distinction between left and right ventricle!

From these and other studies, it appears that there are a core set of genes whose expression is vital for the formation of a heart or heartlike structure, and a smaller set of genes like *Tbx5* that are critical for the division of the heart into chambers. The most common congenital organ defects in humans are those associated with the heart and its major vessels.

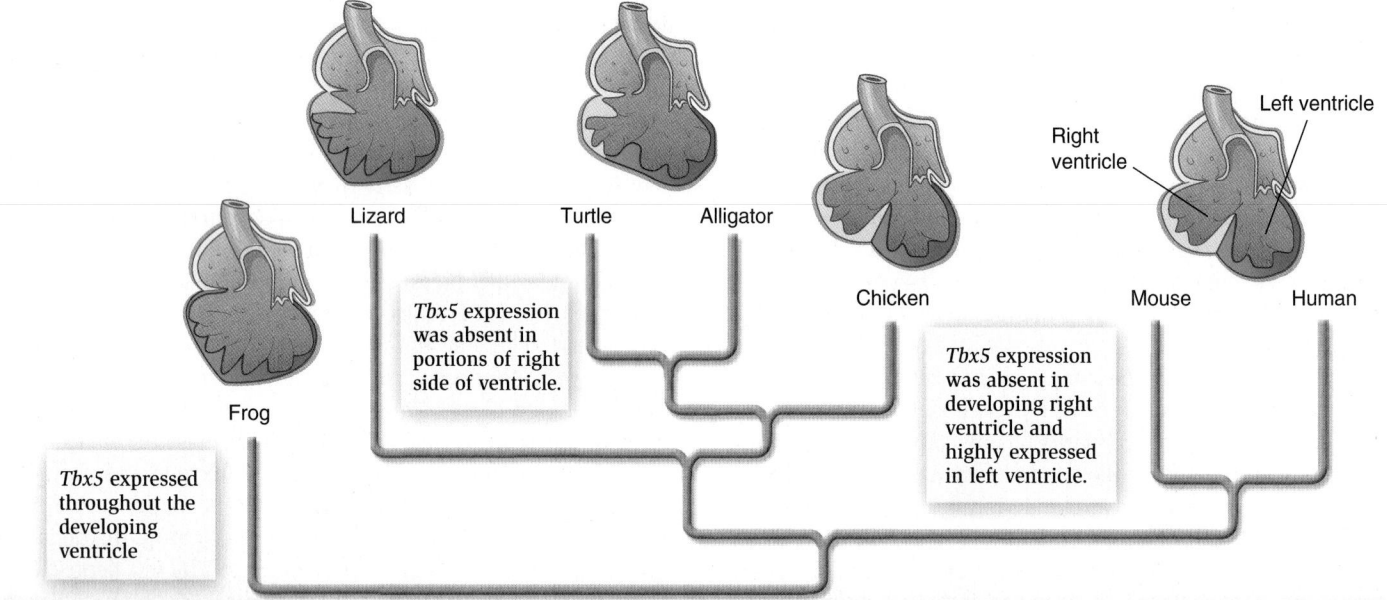

Figure 44.5 Expression of *Tbx5* gene in embryonic vertebrate hearts. The colour indicates where in the developing heart muscle the gene was expressed.

44.2 BLOOD AND BLOOD COMPONENTS

Learning Outcomes:

1. List the four components of blood and the composition and functions of each.
2. Describe the process of blood clotting in mammals.

Blood Is Composed of Cells and Water with Dissolved Solutes

Blood is a fluid connective tissue consisting of cells and, in mammals, cell fragments suspended in a solution of water containing dissolved nutrients, proteins, gases, and other molecules. Blood has four components: plasma, leukocytes, erythrocytes, and platelets or thrombocytes.

Plasma If we collect a blood sample and spin it in a device called a centrifuge, the blood separates into distinct layers (**Figure 44.6a**). The top layer is **plasma**, a yellowish solution that typically makes up about 35%–60% of the total volume of blood in vertebrates. It contains water and the dissolved organic and inorganic nutrients that were absorbed from the digestive tract or secreted from cells. Plasma also contains dissolved oxygen; waste products of metabolism, such as carbon dioxide; and other molecules released by cells, such as hormones. In addition to transporting molecules throughout the body, plasma has other functions. For example, plasma contains buffers that help keep the body's pH within its normal range. It is also important in maintaining the fluid balance of cells. Changes in plasma salt concentrations can affect the movement of water between intracellular and extracellular fluid compartments. Plasma also transports cells of the immune system and cells involved in oxygen transport, as well as proteins that serve several important

(a)   **(b)**

Figure 44.6 Components of blood. (a) When a blood sample is centrifuged, it forms three visible layers. Plasma is composed of water and dissolved solutes, leukocytes are the white blood cells that make up part of the body's immune system, and erythrocytes are red blood cells, which carry oxygen. An additional component of blood, thrombocytes (platelets in mammals), which participate in blood clotting reactions, is not visible under these conditions because of small numbers and size. Note: the leukocyte layer is enlarged and not to scale, for illustrative purposes. (b) The characteristic biconcave shape of mammalian erythrocytes, seen here in a SEM magnified more than 1,600 times, increases their surface area and aids in the diffusion of oxygen from the cell walls to the extracellular fluid.

> **BioConnections:** *Leukocytes are part of the immune system of animals. Are immune defenses unique to animals? (Look back at Figure 34.19 for a hint.)*

functions, such as forming blood clots, which seal off wounds to blood vessels.

Leukocytes Beneath the plasma in our sample is a narrow white layer of **leukocytes**, also known as **white blood cells**. Leukocytes develop from the inner parts (the marrow) of certain bones in vertebrates. Although there are several types—which we describe further in Chapter 50—all leukocytes perform vital functions that defend the body against infection and disease.

Erythrocytes The bottom visible layer of our blood sample consists of **erythrocytes**, also called **red blood cells** because of their colour. **Hematocrit** refers to the volume of blood that is composed of red blood cells, usually between 40%–65% among vertebrates. Erythrocytes serve the critical function of transporting oxygen throughout the body. There are approximately a thousand times as many red blood cells as white blood cells in the circulation. Like leukocytes, red blood cells are derived from cells in the bone marrow. In most vertebrates, mature red blood cells retain their nuclei and other cellular organelles, but in all mammals (and a few species of fish and amphibia) the nuclei are lost on maturation. The lack of a nucleus and many other organelles in the mammalian red blood cell increases the cell's oxygen-carrying capacity and contributes to its characteristic

biconcave shape (**Figure 44.6b**). The shape increases its surface area compared with the flattened disk or oval shape seen in most other vertebrates. This is believed to make gas exchange between the red blood cell and the surrounding body fluids more efficient.

Oxygen is poorly soluble in plasma. Consequently, the amount of oxygen that dissolves in plasma usually cannot support a vertebrate's basal metabolic rate, let alone more strenuous activity. Within the cytosol of red blood cells are large amounts of the protein **hemoglobin**. Each molecule of hemoglobin contains four protein subunits, each with an atom of iron at its core that reversibly binds to a molecule of oxygen (**Figure 44.7**). Thus, each hemoglobin molecule has four iron atoms and can reversibly bind four oxygen molecules. The oxygen attached to hemoglobin greatly increases the reservoir of oxygen in the blood and enables animals to be active. Chapter 45 describes the mechanisms by which hemoglobin binds and releases oxygen.

Anemia refers to lower than normal levels of hemoglobin, which reduces the amount of oxygen that can be stored in the blood. Among possible causes are loss of blood, impaired

Figure 44.7 Hemoglobin. Erythrocytes contain large amounts of the protein hemoglobin. Oxygen binds reversibly to iron atoms at the core of each subunit of hemoglobin.

> **Principle:** *Structure determines function. It is the precise quaternary structure of hemoglobin that permits its association with heme groups, which contain the iron atoms that bind oxygen molecules. Without a correct protein structure, the ability of hemoglobin to bind oxygen would be greatly compromised.*

> **Concept check:** *How many atoms of oxygen can be bound to a single molecule of hemoglobin?*

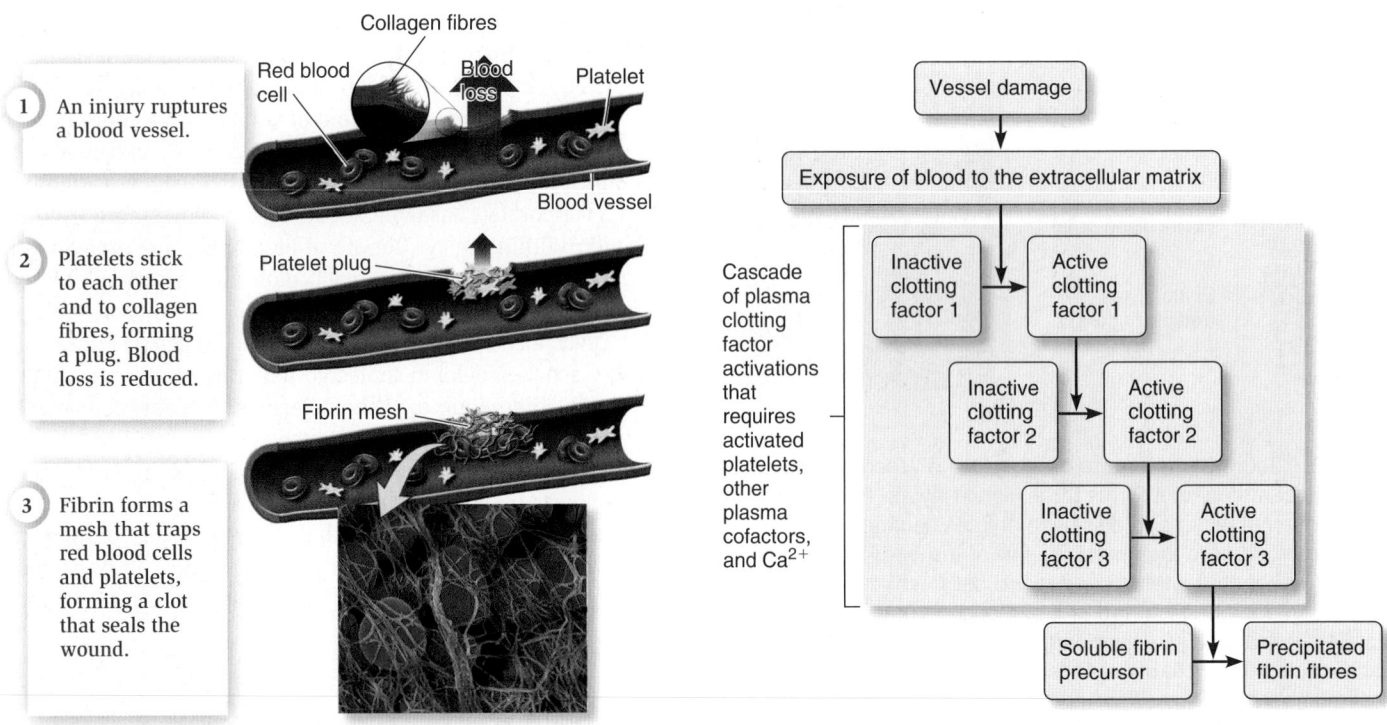

(a) Formation of a blood clot

(b) Role of clotting factors in clot formation

Figure 44.8   Platelets and the process of blood clot formation.   (a) A blood clot forms in two major steps: a platelet plug reduces initial blood loss, and a fibrin clot then seals the wound. (b) Formation of the clot requires several clotting factors to work together. These are enzymes, which catalyze a cascade of reactions that leads to the production of fibrin fibres. Several steps in the process are omitted here for simplicity.

Principle: *Living organisms have mechanisms that maintain homeostasis. Because the blood carries with it the nutrients, hormones, proteins, and waste products that must circulate throughout an animal's body, a loss of blood due to injury can be catastrophic unless the wound is healed and the blood loss is stopped. In this way, blood clotting is a key feature that indirectly contributes to the ability of animals to maintain homeostasis.*

production of erythrocytes, or increased breakdown of erythrocytes, each of which reduces hematocrit. By contrast, **polycythemia** is a condition of increased hemoglobin caused by increased hematocrit. Polycythemia occurs when terrestrial animals living at low altitudes ascend to higher altitudes, where the air pressure is lower and it is harder to bring oxygen into the blood. The decreased blood oxygen levels trigger release from the liver and kidneys of a protein that stimulates the production of red blood cells. Polycythemia can also occur rapidly to increase the blood's oxygen-carrying capacity, such as when a seal dives underwater or a horse sprints. In this case, red blood cells are released from the spleen, which acts as an erythrocyte storehouse.

Platelets   Vertebrate blood has a fourth component—called **platelets** in mammals and **thrombocytes** in other vertebrates—which is not visible in our centrifuge sample because of its low numbers. Thrombocytes are intact cells, and platelets are cell fragments that lack a nucleus. Like leukocytes and erythrocytes, thrombocytes and platelets are formed in the bone marrow. They play a crucial role in the formation of blood clots, which limit blood loss after injury. Although clot formation in mammals is a multistep process, two essential steps involve platelets (**Figure 44.8a**).

First, platelets secrete substances that cause them to stick to each other and to collagen fibres in the surrounding connective tissue at a wound site, forming a plug that stops blood loss. Second, other platelet secretions interact with plasma proteins to cause the precipitation from the solution of the fibrous protein **fibrin**. Fibrin forms a mesh of threadlike fibres that wrap around and between platelets and red blood cells, enlarging and thickening the clot. Blood clotting begins within seconds and helps prevent injured animals from bleeding to death. Eventually, the body absorbs the clot as the injured vessel heals. The importance of clotting is most evident when it fails to occur normally.

The process of blood clotting is not a simple one—at least a dozen different substances must be present in the right amounts for a clot to form. These substances are known as clotting factors and include proteins and ions such as Ca^{2+}. Platelets secrete some of these substances; others circulate in the plasma in an inactive form until activated by platelet and cellular secretions.

The clotting process is a chain reaction that begins when an injury to a blood vessel exposes blood to the surrounding extracellular matrix (**Figure 44.8b**). When one inactive clotting factor in blood interacts with proteins in the matrix, the factor is activated. This initiates a cascade in which clotting factors sequentially activate each other, finally producing fibrin. In the disease **hemophilia**, an inherited deficiency of a specific clotting factor inhibits the clotting process that leads to fibrin formation. Consequently, injured blood vessels take longer to heal and blood loss is excessive. Minor cuts are not necessarily serious, but uncontrolled bleeding in internal tissues and joints can be life threatening.

Table 44.1	Comparative Features of Representative Mammalian Hearts			
Animal	**Body mass* (kg)**	**Heart mass* (kg)**	**Stroke volume* (L)**	**Heart rate* (bpm)†**
Shrew‡	0.0024 (24 g)	0.000035 (35 mg)	0.000008 (8 μL)	835
Rat	0.20	0.001	0.0018	360
Dog	23	0.12	0.025	95
Human	75	0.38	0.075	70
Elephant	4,000	25	4.0	25
Blue whale	100,000	600	100	10

* *Values are based on average body masses and resting conditions. In some cases, stroke volumes are estimates based on heart size. Note that heart rate decreases as animals get larger, but heart mass and stroke volume increase roughly in proportion with body mass. Similar relationships are observed in other vertebrates, notably birds.*
† *bpm = beats per minute.*
‡ *The shrew reported here is the Etruscan shrew, one of the smallest known mammals. Its heart is somewhat larger than would be predicted for its body mass. Note its heart rate, at 835 bpm, the heart beats 14 times per second!*

44.3 THE VERTEBRATE HEART AND ITS FUNCTION

Learning Outcomes:

1. Explain the difference between neurogenic and myogenic hearts.
2. Describe the two phases of the excitation of the vertebrate heart.
3. Outline the events of the cardiac cycle, including the relationship between electrical and contractile events.
4. Understand the significance of the tracings on an electrocardiogram.

The Vertebrate Heart Has Multiple Chambers Separated by Valves

As described earlier, all vertebrate hearts have at least one upper or anterior chamber called an atrium, and at least one lower or posterior chamber called a ventricle. In hearts with more than one atrium or ventricle, like the mammalian heart, which has two of each chamber, the chambers are physically separated by a thick strip of connective tissue called a septum. **Figure 44.9** depicts the route blood takes through the mammalian heart. Blood enters the atria from systemic or pulmonary veins, moves down a pressure gradient through the one-way **atrioventricular (AV) valves** into the ventricles, and is pumped out through the one-way **semilunar valves** into the systemic and pulmonary arteries.

The heart beats (contracts) with a steady rhythm that can increase during exercise. Each beat of the heart pumps out a volume of blood that depends on the size of the animal's heart (**Table 44.1**). Typically, heart size varies in proportion to body mass within a given class of vertebrates, with birds and mammals having larger hearts than similarly sized fish, amphibians, or reptiles. Birds and mammals, being endotherms, tend to be more active for longer periods, and thus they burn more fuel than ectotherms. A more powerful heart delivers oxygen and nutrients throughout the body at a faster rate, thus sustaining higher metabolic activity.

Vertebrates Have Myogenic Hearts Capable of Beating on Their Own

Animals cannot consciously initiate heart contractions. The beating of the heart is initiated either by nerves or by intrinsic activity of the heart muscle cells themselves. Many arthropods and decapod crustaceans have a **neurogenic heart** that will not beat unless it receives regular electrical impulses from the nervous system. All vertebrates, however, have a **myogenic heart**; that is, the signalling mechanism that initiates contraction resides within the cardiac muscle itself.

Myogenic hearts are electrically excitable and generate their own action potentials. The electrical signals produced by the cells of these hearts initiate the cellular events that trigger muscle contraction (see Chapter 43). Although nerves from the nervous system terminate on the vertebrate heart and can regulate the rate of the heartbeat, myogenic hearts will continue to beat on their own if dissected out of an animal and placed in a nutrient bath, even without any nerves present.

Excitation of the Vertebrate Heart Begins in the SA Node

The electrical signals of myogenic hearts are generated either at the junction of the veins and the single atrium in fish, or within the wall of the right atrium in other vertebrates, at the **sinoatrial (SA) node**, or **pacemaker** (**Figure 44.10a**). The SA node is a collection of modified cardiac cells that spontaneously and rhythmically generate action potentials that spread across the entire atria. The spread occurs because cardiac muscle forms a structure called a syncytium—a group of cells, all of which are electrically coupled by gap junctions (see Chapter 5). The action potentials trigger an influx of Ca^{2+} into the muscle cell cytosol, which activates contraction. Because the gap junctions allow electrical charge to flow freely from one cardiac cell to the next, the impulses spread very rapidly across the atria, so that both atria contract almost as if they were one large muscle cell. Atrial contraction pumps blood through the AV valves into the ventricles.

Electrical impulses initiated in the SA node reach another node of specialized cardiac cells, the **atrioventricular (AV) node**.

Figure 44.9 **The mammalian heart and the route blood takes through it.** The figure shows the major blood vessels entering and leaving the heart, the locations of the valves, and the direction of blood flow through the chambers of the heart. Oxygenated blood is shown in red, deoxygenated in blue. Note that the pulmonary veins are red because they return blood from the lungs, while veins from the systemic circulation are blue.

| | Atrial excitation | | Ventricular excitation | |
	Begins	Complete	Begins	Complete
AV valves	OPEN	OPEN	Beginning to close	CLOSED
Semilunar valves	CLOSED	CLOSED	CLOSED	OPEN
Phase of cardiac cycle	Diastole	Diastole	Systole beginning	Systole
Atria	Relaxed	Contracted	Beginning to relax	Relaxed
Ventricles	Relaxed	Relaxed	Beginning to contract	Contracted
Chambers with highest pressure	All are low pressure	Atria (slightly)	Ventricles	Ventricles

Figure 44.10 **Coupling of electrical and mechanical activity in the mammalian heart.** Electrical activity begins in the SA node and quickly spreads through the atria to the AV node. Branches from the AV node transmit electrical activity throughout the ventricles. The atria and ventricles do not contract until they have become electrically excited. Changes in pressure gradients between the atria and ventricles, and between the ventricles and the aorta and pulmonary arteries, cause the four heart valves to open and close.

The AV node sits near the junction of the atria and ventricles and conducts the electrical events from the atria to the ventricles. Like the SA node, the AV node is electrically excitable, but its cells require a longer time to become excited than do the cells of the atria. This allows time for the atria to contract before the ventricles do. Branches from the AV node spread electrical impulses throughout the walls of the ventricles (**Figure 44.10**). Once the ventricles are electrically excited, they contract.

Because the ventricular walls are thicker and stronger than the atrial walls, ventricular contractions generate much greater pressure. The pressure exerted by the ventricles on the blood within their cavities causes the AV valves to shut, preventing blood from flowing backward into the atria. This is why the electrical delay that is built into the AV node is important. If the atria and ventricles were excited and contracted at the same time, the AV valves would close too soon and the ventricles would not receive their normal volume of blood.

The Cardiac Cycle Has Two Phases: Diastole and Systole

Each beat of the vertebrate heart requires the coordinated activities of the atria and ventricles. The events that produce a single heartbeat are known as the **cardiac cycle**, which can be divided into two phases (**Figure 44.10**). In the first phase, **diastole**, the ventricles fill with blood coming from the atria through the open AV valves. In the second phase, **systole**, the ventricles contract and eject the blood through the open semilunar valves.

The valves open and close as a result of pressure gradients established between the atria and ventricles, and the ventricles and arteries. During diastole, pressure in the ventricles is lower than in the atria and the arteries, and therefore the AV valves are open but the semilunar valves are closed. Once the ventricles are electrically excited, they begin contracting and the pressure within the ventricles rapidly increases. This marks the beginning of systole. When the pressure in the ventricles exceeds that in the atria, the AV valves are forced closed. The closure of the AV valves makes the "lub" sound of the familiar "lub-dub" heard through a stethoscope. Ventricular pressure continues to rise and finally exceeds the pressure in the arteries, which opens the semilunar valves. Blood is ejected out the semilunar valves into the arteries.

The pressure in the arteries increases during systole. As this is happening, the ventricles begin to return to their resting, unexcited state, and the pressure in the ventricles falls below that in the arteries. The higher pressure in the arteries closes the semilunar valves, which prevents blood from flowing back into the heart. Closure of the semilunar valves creates the second heart sound, "dub," heard through a stethoscope. Throughout systole, meanwhile, the atria continue to fill with blood, which raises the pressure in the atria. Soon the pressure in the atria exceeds that in the relaxed ventricles, and the AV valves open again, bringing a new volume of blood into the ventricles and starting a new diastole.

Blood pressure in the arteries is highest during systole and lowest during diastole. For this reason, blood pressure is measured with two numbers: the systolic and diastolic pressures. For historical reasons, the units are usually given as mmHg (millimetres of mercury). Blood pressures are highest in mammals and birds, and lowest in fish and invertebrates. A typical blood pressure in humans is around 120/80 mmHg (systolic/diastolic).

Unlike skeletal muscle, cardiac muscle does not fatigue. The vertebrate heart begins beating while an animal is still an embryo, and it never stops beating throughout life. The human heart beats about 70 times per minute. To envision how remarkable your heart is, try making a tight fist and relaxing it once every second for a few minutes. The muscles of your wrist and hand tire quickly, but the vertebrate heart does not. It continues beating steadily throughout life, with approximately 2 billion to 3 billion beats in an average lifetime.

An ECG Tracks Electrical Events During the Cardiac Cycle

An **electrocardiogram (ECG or EKG)** is a record of the electrical impulses generated during the cardiac cycle (**Figure 44.11**). Sensitive electrodes are placed on the surface of the body to monitor the wave of electricity initiated by the SA node, which travels through the atria, AV node, and ventricles. This procedure works because the body fluids that surround the heart conduct electricity, even the very weak impulses generated by a beating heart. The trace on an ECG reveals several waves of electrical excitation. The first is the P wave, which begins when the SA node fires and ends when the two atria completely depolarize. The next wave of excitation is a cluster of three waves, called the QRS complex. It begins when the branches from the AV node excite the ventricles and ends when both ventricles depolarize completely. The final wave is the T wave, which results from the repolarization of the ventricles back to their resting state. No wave is visible for atrial repolarization because it occurs simultaneously with the large QRS complex.

The ECG monitor displays both the amplitude (strength) of the electrical signal and the direction that the signal is moving in the chest. From this information, doctors can determine whether a person's heart is generating signals with a normal frequency, strength, duration, and direction.

Now that we have discussed the vertebrate heart, let's examine the vessels that transport blood to and from the heart and throughout the body.

44.4 BLOOD VESSELS

Learning Outcomes:

1. Explain the anatomic and functional distinctions among arteries, arterioles, capillaries, venules, and veins.
2. Describe the interaction of the lymphatic system with the circulatory system.

Figure 44.11 An electrocardiogram (ECG). Electrodes placed on the skin detect electrical impulses occurring in the heart, and an electrocardiogram visualizes them. The resultant waveform is a useful indicator of cardiac health. Note that the ventricular wave (QRS complex) is taller than the atrial wave (P wave). This is because the ventricles are larger than the atria and generate more electrical activity.

Concept check: *Why is it possible to detect electrical changes in the heart by using electrodes placed on the surface of the skin?*

Arteries Distribute Blood to Organs and Tissues

Figure 44.12 illustrates the route that blood follows in a closed circulatory system. Recall that arteries are thick-walled vessels that carry blood away from the heart. They consist of layers of smooth muscle and connective tissue wrapped around a single-celled inner layer, the **endothelium**, which forms a smooth lining in contact with the blood (**Figure 44.13**). Because of the thick layers of tissue surrounding the endothelium, most dissolved substances cannot diffuse across artery walls. Instead, arteries act as conducting tubes that distribute blood leaving the heart to all the organs and tissues of an animal's body.

In vertebrates, the walls of the largest arteries, such as the aorta, also contain one or more layers of proteins that have elastic properties (Figure 44.13). As the aorta stretches to accommodate blood entering from the heart, the elastic proteins also stretch. When the heart relaxes as it readies for another beat, the elastic proteins in the aorta recoil to their original state, something like releasing a stretched rubber band. The elasticity of the large arteries stabilizes blood pressure by minimizing the spike in pressure during the beginning of systole and helping maintain pressure during diastole.

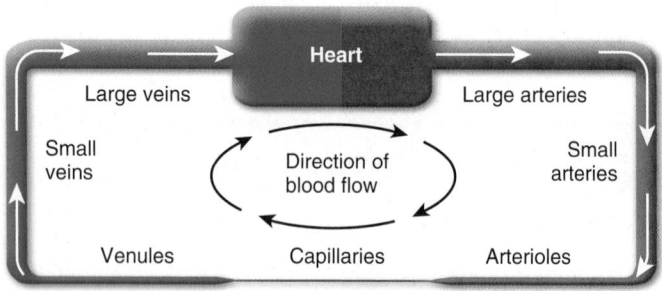

Figure 44.12 Overview of blood flow through vessels in a closed circulatory system. Regions of gas exchange have been omitted for clarity.

Arterioles Distribute Blood to Capillaries

As arteries carry blood away from the heart, they branch repeatedly and become narrower to penetrate to the smallest reaches of an organ or a tissue (**Figure 44.14**). Eventually, the vessels are little more than a single-celled layer of endothelium surrounded by one or two layers of smooth muscle and connective tissue. These **arterioles**, as they are called, deliver blood to the capillaries and distribute blood to regions of the body in proportion to metabolic demands. This is accomplished by changing the diameter of arterioles, such that they widen or dilate in areas of high metabolic activity, and narrow or constrict in inactive regions. Arterioles dilate when the smooth muscle cells around them relax, and they constrict when these cells contract.

Capillaries Are the Site of Gas and Nutrient Exchange

Arterioles branch into tiny thin-walled vessels called **capillaries**. At the capillaries, materials in the blood are delivered to the other cells of the body, and waste products and secretions from cells are delivered to the blood. Capillaries are tubes composed of a single-celled layer of endothelium resting on an extracellular matrix called a basement membrane. Continuous capillaries have smooth walls while fenestrated capillaries contain tiny openings called fenestrations (Figure 44.13). Capillaries are the smallest and narrowest blood vessels in the body, and they branch so extensively that essentially every cell in an animal's body is near one. The diameter of a capillary is about the same as the width of a red blood cell, so erythrocytes move through them in single file (**Figure 44.15**).

Blood enters capillaries under pressure that is created by the beating of the heart as blood is pumped into the arteries. This pressure forces some of the water in blood out through the fenestrations and other tiny openings in capillary walls into the interstitial space. These openings are wide enough to

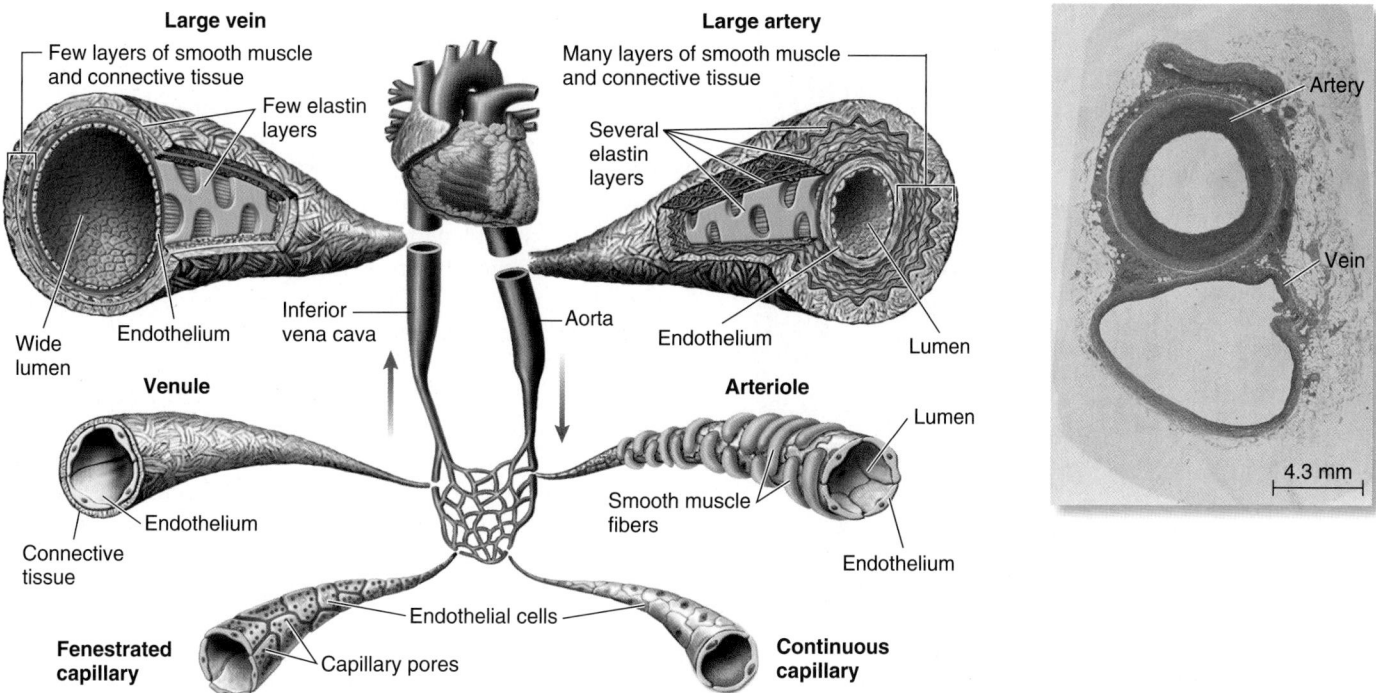

Figure 44.13 **Comparative features of blood vessels.**   Sizes are not drawn to scale. Inset: Light micrograph (enlarged four times) of a medium-sized artery near a vein. Note the difference between the two vessels in wall thickness and lumen diameter.

permit water and small solutes, but not red blood cells and most proteins, to move out of the capillary. Once in the interstitial space, the solutes diffuse into body cells. Conversely, body cells release secretions and metabolic waste products into interstitial fluid, where they diffuse into capillaries and enter the circulation to be carried away.

If the water that leaves a capillary were to remain in the interstitial space, the volume of plasma in the blood would decrease and the interstitial fluid would swell. Most of the water that leaves at the beginning of a capillary, however, is recaptured at the capillary's end, for two reasons (**Figure 44.16**). First, near the arteriole the blood pressure inside the capillary is higher than the fluid pressure of the surrounding interstitial space, which creates a force that moves water out of the capillary. However, by the time blood reaches the end of a capillary, its pressure has decreased considerably, partly as a result of the loss of water. Second, proteins are trapped within the

Figure 44.14 **Arteries and arterioles.**   Arteries branch into smaller arteries and into even smaller arterioles to penetrate to all the cells of tissues and organs.

Concept check: *What happens to the diameter of the arterioles of the animal's leg muscle when the animal is active?*

Figure 44.15 **Erythrocytes (red blood cells) moving through a capillary in single file.**

Figure 44.16 Water movement between capillaries and interstitial fluid. Water and dissolved solutes (other than proteins) exit capillaries near the arteriolar end because the capillary pressure is much greater than that of the interstitial fluid. As the volume of the water in the capillary decreases, however, the pressure within the capillary also decreases (but remains greater than interstitial fluid). Proteins remaining in the capillary contribute an osmotic force that tends to draw water back into the capillary. The combination of decreased pressure within the capillary and the osmotic force caused by proteins leads to the recapture of much of the water that left the capillary. Lymph vessels drain any excess fluid from the interstitial space. For clarity, the system shown here contains a single capillary connecting an arteriole and venule, instead of the typical situation where capillaries divide into numerous branching vessels.

capillary because they are too large to leak out through the capillary walls. This creates an osmotic force that draws water into the capillary from the interstitial fluid. Near the end of a capillary, the osmotic force drawing water into the capillary is greater than the pressure forcing water out, and thus water and dissolved solutes re-enter the capillary.

Despite the ability of capillaries to recapture their own fluid, the process is not 100% effective. Another set of vessels, those of the **lymphatic system**, collects excess fluid and returns it to the blood (see Chapter 50).

Venules and Veins Return Blood to the Heart

Once blood travels through the capillaries, picking up any substances secreted from the cells of the body, it then enters the **venules**, which are small, thin-walled extensions of the capillaries. The venules empty into veins, which return blood to the heart for another trip around the circulation.

The walls of veins are much thinner, less muscular, and more easily distended or stretched than those of arteries (Figure 44.13). Veins can fill with considerable volumes of blood, particularly veins in the lower parts of an animal's body, such as

the legs, where gravity tends to cause blood to pool. In this way, veins serve as a reservoir of blood. When an animal is active, this reservoir can be tapped to provide the heart with sufficient blood to meet the metabolic requirements of the animal. At such times, the sympathetic nervous system stimulates the smooth muscles in the large veins to contract. This compresses the veins and helps force blood back to the heart.

By the time blood has travelled through the capillaries and reached the veins, the pressure of the blood is very low. Consequently, several factors assist the blood on its way toward the heart when flowing against gravity. One is the stimulation of the smooth muscle in leg veins, just described, by the sympathetic nervous system. In addition, the activity of skeletal muscles in the limbs assists the return of venous blood to the heart. For example, each time the leg skeletal muscles contract, they squeeze the veins passing through them (**Figure 44.17a**). This alone would not move blood upward toward the heart, though, because each time a vein is squeezed blood could be forced both up and down (**Figure 44.17b**). However, this does not happen because one-way valves inside veins ensure that blood returning from below the heart moves in only one direction, toward the heart. By contrast, veins located above the heart, such as those in the necks of bipeds and some quadrupeds, lack valves because gravity pulls blood toward the heart.

You can easily observe the effects of gravity on venous blood flow. Hold your arms down by your side and look at the backs of your hands. The engorged blood vessels you see under the skin surface are veins. Now raise your arms above your head, and notice how the bulging veins quickly lose blood and become less visible. When blood from the veins returns to the heart, it must travel against gravity when your arms are at your sides and with gravity when your arms are elevated. As you just saw, blood drains from veins much more efficiently when gravity works in its favour.

44.5 RELATIONSHIPS BETWEEN BLOOD PRESSURE, BLOOD FLOW, AND RESISTANCE

Learning Outcomes:

1. Describe the relationship between blood pressure, blood flow, and resistance to flow.
2. Explain the effects of vasodilation and vasoconstriction on blood flow.
3. Explain how resistance and cardiac output determine blood pressure and flow.

Blood pressure is defined as the force exerted by blood on the walls of blood vessels, and it is responsible for moving blood through the vessels. It is not the same in all regions of an animal's body. As we saw earlier, for example, the blood pressure in arteries is higher than that in veins. For this reason, we generally speak only of arterial pressure when discussing blood pressure. In this section, we will examine how blood pressure is

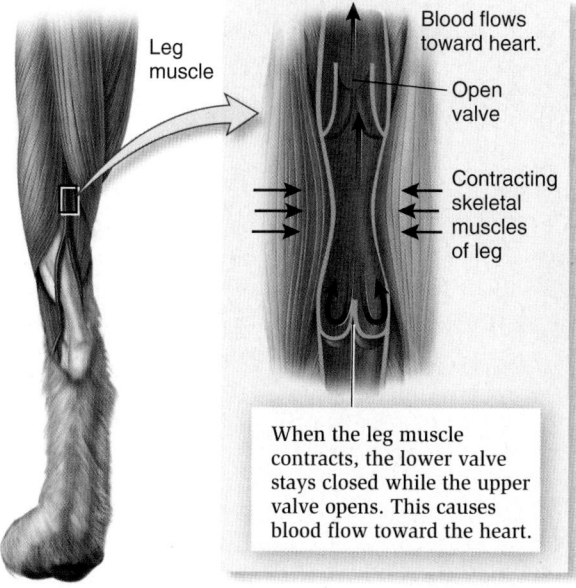

Leg muscle

Blood flows toward heart.

Open valve

Contracting skeletal muscles of leg

When the leg muscle contracts, the lower valve stays closed while the upper valve opens. This causes blood flow toward the heart.

(a) Vein with one-way valves

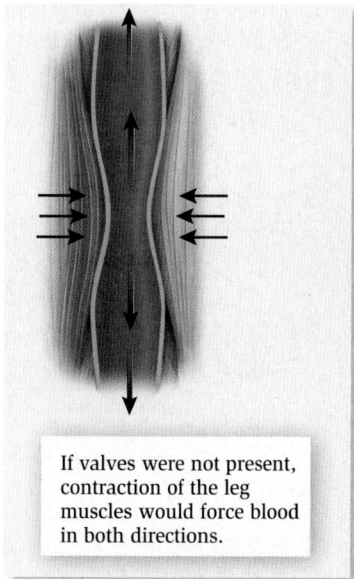

If valves were not present, contraction of the leg muscles would force blood in both directions.

(b) Vein without valves

Figure 44.17 **One-way valves.**
(a) In some veins, one-way valves assist the return of blood to the heart against the force of gravity. Valves are typically present in the limbs, as shown in this light micrograph of a leg vein with a closed valve directed toward the heart.
(b) Comparison of what would happen to blood flow through a vein with and without valves.

Concept check: *Giraffes have one-way valves in the veins of their long necks. Why?*

regulated, how blood flow is distributed through the body, and the relationship between pressure and flow.

Resistance Determines Blood Pressure and Blood Flow

Resistance (R) refers to the tendency of blood vessels to slow down the flow of blood through their lumens, and it is a function of three variables, including vessel radius and length, and blood viscosity. Wide, short tubes provide less resistance to flow than narrow, long tubes. Resistance is increased by the blood's viscosity, which is a measure of the blood's hematocrit. A high hematocrit increases the blood's viscosity—it makes the blood more sludgelike—and hinders its smooth flow through vessels.

The relationship among blood pressure, flow, and resistance is stated by Poiseuille's law, which is simplified here:

$$\text{flow (F)} = \Delta \text{ pressure (P)}/\text{resistance (R)}$$

Stated mathematically, blood flow through a blood vessel is directly proportional to the difference (Δ) in pressure of the blood at the beginning and end of the vessel and inversely proportional to the resistance created by that vessel. Changes in any of these three variables determine how much blood flows through different body regions at any moment. The equation can be rearranged as $\Delta P = F \times R$, which demonstrates that blood pressure depends on both blood flow and resistance. Poiseuille's law applies to blood flow through a single vessel, an organ, or the entire body.

Arteriole Radius Is the Major Factor That Regulates Resistance

As stated earlier, selective and changeable distribution of blood throughout the body is a key adaptation of closed circulatory systems. Changes in arteriolar resistance are the major

FEATURE INVESTIGATION

Furchgott Discovered a Vasodilatory Factor Produced by Endothelial Cells

As we have seen, the cells surrounding blood vessels can produce ions, acids, and gases that diffuse to arteriolar smooth muscle cells and cause these cells to relax and vasodilate. Beginning in the 1970s, American scientist Robert Furchgott provided evidence that an unidentified substance released from within an artery—that is, from the endothelial lining of the vessel—also played a key role in regulating blood vessel radius.

For many years, Furchgott had used flattened strips of rabbit aorta in a culture bath to test whether various compounds stimulated or inhibited contraction of the smooth

muscle in the artery. Although large arteries, like the aorta, do not show the dramatic vasodilation and vasoconstriction that arterioles do, they were more useful in experiments because of their larger size. Normally, when ACh is injected into an animal it causes vasodilation by relaxation of smooth muscle in arteriolar walls. However, in Furchgott's *in vitro* preparations, ACh caused the flattened strips of artery to contract. To determine if this apparent paradox could be the result of the method in which the tissues were prepared for *in vitro* tests, Furchgott compared the effects of ACh in different types of preparations. He discovered that ACh produced muscle relaxation when applied to circular rings of aorta, as described in step 1 of **Figure 44.18**.

HYPOTHESIS The endothelium of arteries produces a vasodilatory substance.

KEY MATERIALS Strips or rings of rabbit aorta, force transducers, acetylcholine.

	Experimental level	Conceptual level

1 Attach a ring of aorta to a pressure gauge. Add acetylcholine (ACh) to bath medium. Record change in force (increased force = increased muscle contraction; decreased force = decreased muscle contraction).

ACh added to medium   Force transducer

Intact aorta with endothelium

In the presence of endothelium, ACh relaxes the muscles of the aorta, causing the vessel to widen.

2 Denude ring of its endothelium. The muscle layer is left behind. Retest effect of ACh.

Wooden stick is used to scrape away endothelium.

Endothelial cells

Muscle layer

The denuded ring is then placed in recording apparatus as before.

In the absence of endothelium, ACh stimulates the muscles to contract, which narrows the vessel.

3 Perform "sandwich" experiment by combining denuded strip of aorta with an intact strip. Record effect of ACh on strip 1 alone, strip 2 alone, and strip 1 while part of a sandwich with strip 2.

Muscle layer only   Endothelium   Muscle layer

Strip 1

Strip 2

Sandwich

Strip 1   Strip 2

+ ACh →

Endothelium produces a vasodilating substance following ACh treatment that diffuses from strip 2 to strip 1, and causes strip 1 to relax.

4 THE DATA

Results of sandwich experiment

Force recorded on force transducer

Contraction / Relaxation

ACh

Time
Strip 1 alone: contraction

ACh

Time
Strip 2 alone: relaxation

ACh

Time
Strip 1 recorded while attached to strip 2: relaxation

Figure 44.18 Furchgott's discovery that endothelial cells produce a vasodilating substance.

5 **CONCLUSION** Endothelial cells release a factor that diffuses to the surrounding smooth muscle, causing it to relax. Relaxation of the vascular smooth muscle causes dilation of the blood vessel.

6 **SOURCE** Furchgott, R.F., and Zawadzki, J.V. 1980. The obligatory role of the endothelium in the relaxation of arterial smooth muscle by acetylcholine. *Nature* 288:373–376.

How did Furchgott explain the results of muscle contraction when ACh was applied to the flattened strips? After examining the two preparations of tissue, Furchgott realized that the lining of endothelial cells along the inner wall of the vessel had been scraped away during preparation of the strips, but the endothelial lining was still present in the rings. He hypothesized that the endothelial cells must produce a factor whose secretion was stimulated by ACh and that not only prevented contraction but also caused smooth muscles surrounding the blood vessel to relax. If so, this would explain the observation that ACh injected into rabbits resulted in vasodilation, because the intact vessels of the animals contained their endothelial lining and thus resembled Furchgott's aortic rings.

To confirm his hypothesis, Furchgott performed two experiments. As shown in step 2 of Figure 44.18, he used a wooden rod to scrape away the endothelium from circular rings of aorta and discovered that the relaxation effect of ACh was lost, as predicted. In step 3, he used a sandwich technique, in which he tested the effects of ACh on muscle contraction in a "denuded" strip of artery with the endothelium removed and then again on the same strip, which was attached ("sandwiched") to another strip, in which care was taken to ensure that the endothelium remained intact. When ACh was added to the water bath before the sandwich was formed, the denuded strip contracted, as expected. When the denuded strip was attached such that its muscle layer was exposed to the intact strip's endothelial surface, the denuded strip relaxed after ACh was added, demonstrating that the endothelium released a vasodilatory factor that diffused to the denuded strip and relaxed its muscles.

Two other scientists, Louis Ignarro and Ferid Murad, later determined that this factor was the gas nitric oxide (NO). The discovery of NO revealed a new category of signalling molecules. Ignarro and Murad also revealed that nitroglycerine, which had for many years been used to treat patients with cardiovascular disease, acted by generating NO in the blood to produce vasodilation and lower blood pressure. Today NO is considered one of the most potent and important naturally occurring vasodilators in animals. Knowledge of the NO signalling pathway has led to new therapies for treating a wide variety of health disorders associated with blood vessels, including high blood pressure, glaucoma (an eye disease), and erectile dysfunction. For their efforts, Furchgott, Ignarro, and Murad shared the 1998 Nobel Prize in Physiology or Medicine.

Experimental Questions

1. What observation did Furchgott make when testing the effects of acetylcholine on different treatments of rabbit aorta? How did he explain the results?
2. Based on his observations of the effects of acetylcholine on different preparations of rabbit aorta, what hypothesis did Furchgott propose to explain the relationship between acetylcholine and vasodilation? How did he test this hypothesis?
3. What did Furchgott conclude based on his experimental results?

mechanism for increasing or decreasing blood flow to a region. In the short term, the length of an arteriole and the viscosity of blood do not normally change. Therefore, the radii of arterioles become the most important factor in determining minute-to-minute resistance. The relationship between radius and resistance is not linear. Resistance is inversely proportional to the radius of the vessel raised to the fourth power: $R \propto 1/r^4$, where $\propto$ means "proportional to," and r is the radius of the arteriolar lumen. Let's consider an arteriole with a radius that increases by a factor of two. This would occur if the smooth muscles around the arteriolar wall relax sufficiently to allow the vessel to dilate and double its original radius. Because resistance is inversely proportional to the fourth power of vessel radius, an increase in radius by a factor of two will result in a decrease in resistance of 2^4 ($2 \times 2 \times 2 \times 2$), or 16-fold.

Vasodilation refers to an increase in blood vessel radius. **Vasoconstriction** refers to a decrease in blood vessel radius. Vasodilation and vasoconstriction are the most important mechanisms for directing blood flow to or away from specific regions of the body. The signals that control arteriolar radius come from three sources: locally produced substances, hormones, and nervous system inputs. Locally, metabolic by-products, such as carbon dioxide and lactic acid, as well as potassium ions and other substances secreted by metabolically active tissues, cause nearby arterioles to vasodilate immediately. According to Poiseuille's law, this permits more blood flow to the active region, facilitating oxygen and nutrient delivery and waste removal. Hormones secreted by glands throughout the body can also regulate arteriolar radius. For example, some hormones cause arterioles that deliver blood to the small intestine to vasoconstrict during fight-or-flight responses, routing blood away from the intestine and to areas of more immediate need, such as the heart and skeletal muscles. Finally, smooth muscle cells that make up the outer wall of arterioles receive inputs from nerves that can stimulate the muscles to contract or relax. One of the most important regulators of blood vessel diameters, however, is a gas, as we see next.

Heart Rate and Size Determine Cardiac Output

Because blood vessels provide resistance to blood flow, the heart must beat forcefully enough to overcome that resistance. **Cardiac output (CO)** is the amount of blood the heart pumps per unit time, usually expressed in units of L/min. The CO depends on the size of an animal's heart and how often it beats each minute. Each beat, or stroke, of the heart ejects an amount of blood known as the **stroke volume (SV)** that is roughly proportional to the size of the heart. Thus, if we know the stroke volume of a heart, and can measure the heart rate (HR: the number of beats per minute), we can determine the CO. Simply put, CO = SV × HR.

Naturally, the CO of an elephant is far greater than that of a mouse, a sparrow, or a salmon. Smaller animals have smaller hearts and therefore smaller stroke volumes (Table 44.1). The heart of the little brown bat, for example, is the size of a small pea, while the heart of a blue whale is as large as a cow. Their stroke volumes are similarly proportioned. However, small animals have faster heart rates than large animals. A hummingbird's or shrew's heart may beat more than 1,100 times per minute during intense activity, while a whale's heart may beat only 10 times per minute, although the amount of blood ejected with each of those beats is enormous. Recall from Chapter 40 that metabolic rate is relatively greater in smaller animals. The higher heart rates of small animals give them a greater cardiac output than would be predicted for the size of their hearts, which helps them meet the extraordinary oxygen and nutrient demands of such highly metabolic organisms.

Cardiac Output and Resistance Determine Blood Pressure

Poiseuille's law can be adapted to the whole body. In this case, pressure refers to arterial blood pressure (BP) recorded using a blood pressure cuff, flow refers to CO, and resistance refers to the sum of all the resistance in all the arterioles **(total peripheral resistance, or TPR)**. Thus, we have BP = CO × TPR. The CO and TPR determine the pressure the blood exerts in the arteries of a closed circulatory system. The greater the cardiac output and the higher the resistance, the higher the blood pressure. Imagine that the circulatory system is like a faucet (the heart) connected to a garden hose (the arteries) (**Figure 44.19**). If the faucet is fully open, analogous to maximal cardiac output, the amount of water rushing into the hose will increase and so will the water pressure. If the faucet is only partially open, the water pressure will be lower. However, if the faucet is partially open but the end of the hose (i.e., the arterioles) is

(a) Maximal cardiac output with low resistance

(b) Moderate cardiac output with low resistance

(c) Moderate cardiac output with high resistance

Figure 44.19   An analogy for how cardiac output, resistance, and blood pressure are related.   A hose analogy shows the way in which cardiac output (the faucet) and resistance (constriction of the hose) impact blood pressure.

constricted or squeezed, the pressure of the water in the hose will increase between the faucet and the point where the hose is squeezed.

Arterial blood pressure, therefore, is a function of how hard the heart is working, and how constricted or dilated the various arterioles are. Blood pressure must be high enough for blood to perfuse through all body tissues even at the farthest extremities, but not high enough to burst blood vessels or force excess plasma out of capillaries. Blood pressure is roughly similar among most mammals. Although species differences exist, they are not as diverse as, for example, species differences in heart rates.

Blood pressure is relatively low in nonmammalian vertebrates and in invertebrates, partly because of their smaller hearts.

44.6 ADAPTIVE FUNCTIONS OF CLOSED CIRCULATORY SYSTEMS

Learning Outcomes:

1. Describe how the circulatory system adapts to exercise.
2. Describe what a baroreceptor is, and why such receptors are important features in the ability to respond to a change in blood pressure.

It is not enough for a circulatory system to pump blood and return it to the heart. The system must also adapt to changing conditions, including sleep, sudden activity, and emergencies, such as blood loss or dehydration. In this section, we will examine how changes in the circulatory system help maintain cardiovascular activity when animals exercise or encounter changes in blood pressure arising from events such as blood loss following injury.

Circulatory Function Adapts to Exercise

Nearly all animals have periods of rest and activity. Therefore, the activity of the heart must adjust to fluctuating metabolic needs. For this reason, blood must be routed to different areas in proportion to their needs for oxygen and nutrients. Exercise provides a dramatic illustration of changes in circulatory function.

We often think of exercise as voluntary. In nature, exercise means an increase in locomotion for any reason. Typically, an animal exercises when it needs something, such as food or shelter, or when it is escaping something, such as a predator. The increased activity may be momentary and moderate, as when a fish briefly swims faster to avoid the tentacles of an anemone, or it may last longer and be more intense, as when a cheetah sprints after a gazelle. Exercise may last for long periods, as when a salmon migrates from the sea to its freshwater spawning grounds or a migratory goose flies thousands of kilometres over several weeks. The circulatory systems of animals must quickly adapt to these increased metabolic demands and adjust to the intensity, duration, and type of exercise.

We have already noted some adjustments, such as vasodilation and vasoconstriction. These are mediated by changes in arteriolar radius and therefore resistance. In addition, cardiac output increases during exercise, by increasing either stroke volume or heart rate, or both. Fish tend to increase stroke volume more than heart rate, while birds and mammals do the opposite. In humans, for example, stroke volume increases from approximately 75 mL at rest to 110 mL during exercise, a change of 1.5-fold, while heart rate may almost triple from 70 bpm to nearly 200 bpm. Thus, the combined effects of increasing stroke volume and heart rate raise the cardiac output by about 4.5-fold. Regardless of species, however, the result is the same: During exercise, cardiac output increases to supply more blood to the tissues that need it. As we will see in Chapter 45, the increased cardiac output is matched by an increase in the amount of oxygen obtained from the environment.

Whether cardiac output increases by changing stroke volume, heart rate, or both, one of the major mechanisms involved is an increase in blood levels of **epinephrine**, also known as adrenaline. Epinephrine is a hormone secreted by the adrenal glands, which receive input from the sympathetic nervous system during exercise. Epinephrine binds to receptors on heart muscle cells, making them contract more vigorously and thereby increasing stroke volume. In addition, epinephrine binds to receptors in the SA node cells of the atria, which stimulates the SA node to initiate impulses at a faster rate, thereby increasing heart rate. The latter effect of epinephrine is enhanced by the release of the neurotransmitter **norepinephrine** (or noradrenaline) directly from sympathetic nerve endings onto the SA node cells.

At rest, the heart does not pump out its entire content of blood. A reservoir of blood remains in each ventricle at the end of a beat. During exercise, this reservoir is tapped when epinephrine stimulates the heart muscles. In addition, the mechanical process of exercise itself enhances the return of blood to the heart, as skeletal muscles squeeze the veins within them and open their one-way valves. The combination of more blood getting returned to the heart and emptying the built-in reservoir of blood from the ventricles allows for increased stroke volume during exercise.

Because BP = CO × TPR, you might imagine that increased cardiac output would raise blood pressure to possibly harmful levels during exercise. Although blood pressure does increase somewhat, it does not rise as much as might be predicted. This is because resistance decreases in the blood vessels of skeletal muscles to allow more blood to enter and, in terrestrial animals, in vessels of the skin to dissipate heat and prevent overheating. Therefore, CO increases but the total peripheral resistance in the body decreases, negating some of the effect on blood pressure.

Baroreceptors Maintain Blood Pressure

Within the walls of certain arteries, notably the aorta and the carotid arteries, are pressure-sensitive regions that contain the endings of nerve cells. These regions, known as **baroreceptors** (from the Greek *baro*, pressure), are in constant communication with the brain (**Figure 44.20**). When the walls of these arteries stretch, the nerve cells stretch too, which increases the rate at which the nerves send action potentials to the brain. The brain interprets this increase as a signal that blood pressure is high—the arteries are being expanded more than normal. The brain responds by reducing the amount of norepinephrine released onto the cardiac SA node and inhibiting the glands that make epinephrine. The result is a decreased heart rate and stroke volume, resulting in lower cardiac output. In addition, nerves throughout the body release less vasoconstricting neurotransmitters onto the smooth muscle cells of arterioles, reducing total peripheral resistance. The combination of decreased cardiac output and resistance lowers blood pressure toward normal.

By contrast, if blood pressure falls below normal, the walls of these arteries would be less stretched than they normally are,

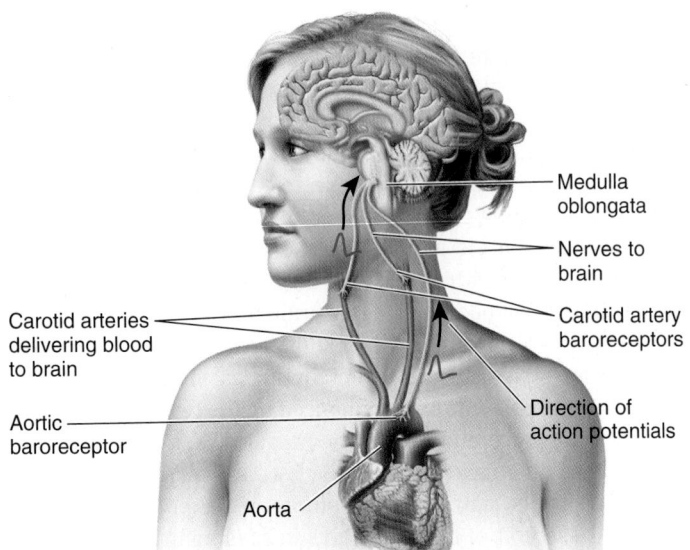

Figure 44.20 Location of the major baroreceptors. Increased blood pressure stretches arteries. This activates baroreceptors in the arteries, which send action potentials to the medulla oblongata in the brain. Nerve signals from the brain then initiate changes in heart function and total peripheral resistance that help restore blood pressure to normal.

BioConnections: *In Chapters 41–42, we discussed the different types of ion channels found in neurons, and the ways in which such channels open and close. What type of channels would you expect to be activated when baroreceptors are stimulated?*

and the baroreceptors would send fewer impulses to the brain. This results in a sequence of events that are opposite to those just described. More norepinephrine and epinephrine are secreted, thereby increasing cardiac output and vasoconstriction, thus increasing blood pressure toward normal. One situation that can cause blood pressure to drop is **dehydration**, which is a reduction in the amount of water in the body. Because blood is mostly water, dehydration reduces blood volume, and arteries—including those that contain baroreceptors—carry less blood than normal. Blood pressure can drop during **hemorrhage**, loss of blood from a ruptured blood vessel. Dehydration is primarily a problem for terrestrial animals, but hemorrhage can occur in any animal that has been injured. In a hemorrhage, there is a loss of both plasma and blood cells, and therefore hemorrhage may be more serious than dehydration. Like dehydration, though, hemorrhage results in reduced blood volume and therefore less baroreceptor activity.

Without baroreceptors, the circulatory system would have no means of relaying information about its status to the brain and the brain would be unable to initiate compensatory actions to maintain normal pressure. Baroreceptors even mediate nearly instantaneous adjustments to blood pressure, such as when you jump up quickly from a reclining position. When you stand suddenly, gravity causes blood to pool a bit in the lower legs, temporarily reducing the volume and pressure of blood reaching the brain. This is why you may sometimes feel woozy when you stand up quickly. Baroreceptors immediately detect the change in pressure in your neck arteries, however, and cardiac output is rapidly increased to bring pressure back to normal until the system stabilizes.

44.7   HUMAN HEALTH CONNECTION

Learning Outcomes:

1. Describe the impact of hypertension and atherosclerosis on human health.
2. Discuss the causes, symptoms, and current medical procedures for myocardial infarction (MI), or heart attack.

Cardiovascular disease—conditions affecting the heart and blood vessels—is the leading cause of death in Canada and is a major source of disability in seniors. Until recently, researchers concentrated on cardiovascular disease in men, but women are now increasingly at risk. Canada Research Chair Dr. Sandra Davidge of the University of Alberta is currently studying the long-term consequences of difficult pregnancies, especially those characterized by preeclampsia and hypertension, and the increased risk of developing cardiovascular disease later in life. Why is cardiovascular disease so devastating? One reason is that damage to these structures often occurs slowly, over many years, and without symptoms until the disease has reached late stages. In this section, we will consider several common cardiovascular disorders and their causes and treatments.

Systemic Hypertension and Atherosclerosis May Cause Heart and Blood Vessel Disease

Systemic hypertension, often called hypertension or high blood pressure, refers to an arterial blood pressure above normal. The normal range in humans varies from systolic/diastolic pressures of about 90/60 to 120/80 mmHg. A resting blood pressure above 140/90 mmHg defines hypertension and values between 140/90 and 120/80 mmHg are considered borderline. Hypertension can have many causes, including obesity, smoking, aging, kidney disease, excess male hormones, and genetic factors. It can often be treated with diet, exercise, and drugs that cause vasodilation, thereby reducing arterial resistance.

Hypertension may also occur in the pulmonary side of the circulation. **Pulmonary hypertension** usually results from a diseased or damaged left ventricle that fails to pump out the usual amount of blood with each beat. This causes blood to back up in the pulmonary vessels, raising their pressure. Pulmonary hypertension is dangerous because the increased pressure forces more water out of the capillaries in the lung, and this accumulation of water hinders the ability of oxygen to diffuse from lung cells into the bloodstream. One of the chief symptoms of pulmonary hypertension, therefore, is shortness of breath. The water in the

Figure 44.21 labels: Artery wall; Narrowed lumen; Plaque

0.2 mm

Figure 44.21 **An atherosclerotic plaque in an artery.** Compare this with the normal artery shown in the micrograph in Figure 44.13.

lungs gives them a congested sound in a stethoscope, and when the cause is failure of the heart to pump blood normally, this condition is called **congestive heart failure**.

Unlike pulmonary hypertension, systemic hypertension rarely has any symptoms. For this reason, it is important to have your blood pressure checked regularly. Systemic hypertension is dangerous because it can damage arteries, contributing to the formation of **plaques**—deposits of lipids, fibrous tissue, and smooth muscle cells—inside arterial walls and leading to a condition known as **atherosclerosis** ("hardening of the arteries") (**Figure 44.21**). Large plaques may occlude (block) the lumen of the artery entirely. In addition to hypertension, plaques are known to arise from a variety of factors, including calcium and fat deposits, and are correlated with obesity, high blood cholesterol levels, and smoking.

If plaques form in any artery, the regions of the body supplied with blood by that artery receive less oxygen and fewer nutrients. Although atherosclerosis is dangerous anywhere, it is especially significant if it affects the **coronary arteries**, which carry oxygen and nutrients to the thick heart muscle. **Coronary artery disease** occurs when plaques form in the coronary vessels, and it can be life threatening. One warning sign of coronary artery disease is **angina pectoris**, chest pain during exertion caused by the heart being deprived of oxygen.

Myocardial Infarction Results in Death of Cardiac Muscle Cells

If a region of the heart is deprived of blood for an extended time, the result may be a **myocardial infarction (MI)** or **heart attack**. Heart attacks occur at localized regions of heart muscle that have died from oxygen and fuel deprivation. Dead cardiac muscle tissue does not regenerate, diminishing the heart's ability to pump. If enough heart muscle dies, a heart attack can be deadly. According to the Heart and Stroke Foundation, each year more than 70,000 people experience a heart attack in Canada, and of these approximately 19,000 people die. Surprisingly, the discomfort of a small heart attack may not even alarm someone enough to seek medical attention. Procedures are available that allow physicians to monitor the status of the coronary vessels in people suspected of having heart disease. The coronary vessels can be visualized by injecting a dye into a person's veins and then taking an X-ray image of the chest, allowing a physician to determine if the vessels are narrowed by disease. This procedure is called cardiac angiography.

Several common treatments can restore blood flow through a blood vessel. One is **balloon angioplasty**, in which a thin tube with a tiny, inflatable balloon at its tip is threaded through the artery to the diseased area. Inflating the balloon compresses the plaque against the arterial wall, widening the lumen. In most cases, a wire-mesh device called a stent is inserted into the diseased artery after angioplasty has expanded it, providing a sort of lattice to hold the artery open (see the Appendix to this chapter, available on Connect™). Another treatment is a **coronary artery bypass**, in which a piece of healthy blood vessel is removed from one part of the body and surgically grafted onto the coronary circulation in such a way that blood bypasses the diseased artery.

Strokes Occur When Blood Flow to Part of the Brain Is Disrupted

If a blood vessel in the brain ruptures or is damaged by atherosclerosis, the result may be a **stroke**. In a stroke, the region of the brain normally receiving blood from the damaged vessel may die, resulting in permanent impairment. Depending on the region of the brain affected, this may reduce sensory function, such as vision or hearing, or motor function. Some strokes arise when a blood clot forms elsewhere within the circulatory system, breaks free, and lodges in an artery or arteriole in the brain. Clots can form, for example, during heart attacks when heart muscle is destroyed. To minimize the risk of a stroke, patients who have suffered a heart attack may take blood-thinning drugs known as anticlotting factors.

Summary of Key Concepts

44.1 Types of Circulatory Systems

- Circulatory systems transport necessary materials to all cells of an animal's body and transport waste products away from cells. The three basic types of circulatory systems are gastrovascular cavities, open systems, and closed systems.

- Cnidarians have a gastrovascular cavity that serves two functions: digestion of food and circulation of water containing the digested food. (Figure 44.1)

- An open circulatory system contains three components: hemolymph, vessels, and one or more hearts. The vessels open into the animal's body cavity. (Figure 44.2)

- In a closed circulatory system—found in earthworms, cephalopods (squids and octopi), and all vertebrates—blood and interstitial fluid are physically separated by blood vessel walls and differ in their components and chemical composition. (Figure 44.3)

- The closed circulatory systems of vertebrates can be divided into two major groups: single and double circulations. In crocodiles, birds, and mammals, oxygenated and deoxygenated blood are completely separated into the systemic circulation and pulmonary circulation. (Figure 44.4) The four-chambered heart requires a set of genes such as *Tbx5* for division of the heart into chambers. (Figure 44.5)

44.2 Blood and Blood Components

- Blood is a fluid connective tissue consisting of cells and (in mammals) cell fragments suspended in a solution of water containing dissolved nutrients, proteins, gases, and other molecules. Blood has four components: plasma, leukocytes, erythrocytes, and thrombocytes or platelets. (Figures 44.6, 44.7, 44.8)

44.3 The Vertebrate Heart and Its Function

- All vertebrate hearts have at least one atrium and one ventricle. In hearts with more than one atrium or ventricle, connective tissue separates the atria and ventricles. Blood enters the atria from systemic or pulmonary veins, moves down a pressure gradient through the AV valves into the ventricles, and is pumped out through the semilunar valves into the systemic and pulmonary arteries. (Figure 44.9, Table 44.1)

- Many arthropods and decapod crustaceans have a neurogenic heart that cannot beat without regular electrical impulses from the nervous system; all vertebrates have a myogenic heart, which beats on its own without electrical stimulation, but that can be regulated by the nervous system.

- The electrical signals of myogenic hearts are generated either at the junction of the veins and the single atrium (in fish) or at the sinoatrial (SA) node (in other vertebrates). The electrical impulses spread through the atria and ventricles and stimulate the heart muscle to contract. The cardiac cycle has two phases: diastole and systole. (Figures 44.10, 44.11)

44.4 Blood Vessels

- Arteries are thick-walled vessels that carry blood away from the heart. Arterioles distribute blood to capillaries, and capillaries are the site of gas and nutrient exchange. (Figures 44.12, 44.13, 44.14, 44.15, 44.16)

- Blood leaving the capillaries empties into venules and then into veins, which return it to the heart. One-way valves help to return blood to the heart. (Figure 44.17)

44.5 Relationships Between Blood Pressure, Blood Flow, and Resistance

- Blood pressure is the force exerted by blood on the walls of blood vessels, and it is responsible for moving blood through the vessels. Resistance refers to the tendency of blood vessels to slow down the flow of blood through their lumens.

- The endothelium of arteries produces a vasodilatory substance. (Figure 44.18)

- Blood flow through a vessel is directly proportional to the pressure of the blood entering the vessel, and inversely proportional to the resistance created by that vessel: flow (F) = pressure (P)/resistance (R). Arteriole radius is the major factor that regulates resistance.

- Cardiac output depends on the size of an animal's heart and how often it beats each minute. Cardiac output and total peripheral resistance determine blood pressure: BP = CO × TPR. Blood pressure must be high enough for blood to perfuse through all body tissues, but not high enough to burst vessels. (Figure 44.19)

44.6 Adaptive Functions of Closed Circulatory Systems

- The circulatory system adjusts to fluctuating metabolic needs through vasodilation, vasoconstriction, and increases in cardiac output. Baroreceptors maintain blood pressure by relaying information about circulatory system status to the brain, which initiates compensatory mechanisms. (Figure 44.20)

44.7 Human Health Connection

- Cardiovascular disease accounts for more deaths each year in Canada than any other cause. Cardiovascular conditions include systemic hypertension, atherosclerosis, congestive heart failure, coronary artery disease, angina pectoris, myocardial infarction (MI, or heart attack), and stroke. (Figure 44.21)

- Cardiovascular diagnostic techniques and treatments include cardiac angiography, balloon angioplasty, and coronary artery bypass.

Test to Assess Your Learning

1. Hemolymph differs from blood in that it
   a. does not contain blood cells.
   b. is a mixture of blood and interstitial fluid.
   c. circulates through closed circulatory systems only.
   d. functions only in defence of the body and not transport.
   e. does not pass through the heart.

2. The heart chamber that functions as the receiving chamber is
   a. the atrium.
   b. the ventricle.
   c. the aorta.
   d. the pulmonary artery.
   e. the coronary artery.

3. Amphibians are unique in that
   a. they are the only vertebrates with an open circulatory system.
   b. oxygen diffuses into their blood through gills.
   c. oxygen diffuses into the blood from the lungs or through the skin.
   d. they have a four-chambered heart.
   e. none of the above.

4. A major advantage of a double circulation is that
   a. blood can be pumped to the upper portions of the body by one circuit and to the lower portions of the body by the other circuit.
   b. each circuit can pump blood with differing pressures to optimize the function of each.
   c. the oxygenated blood can mix with the deoxygenated blood before being pumped to the tissues of the body.
   d. less energy is needed to provide nutrients and oxygen to the tissues of the body.
   e. all of the above.

5. The function of erythrocytes is to
   a. transport oxygen throughout the body.
   b. defend the body against infection and disease.
   c. transport chemical signals throughout the body.
   d. secrete the proteins that form blood clots.
   e. all of the above.

6. The mammalian heart is a myogenic heart, meaning
   a. it is composed of four chambers.
   b. it acts as two pumps for two different circulations.
   c. contraction is regulated solely by the nervous system.
   d. contraction is regulated by specialized cells of the heart.
   e. it contains valves that maintain a one-way flow of blood.

7. During systole of the cardiac cycle
   a. the ventricles of the heart are relaxed.
   b. the ventricles of the heart are filling.
   c. the ventricles of the heart are contracting.
   d. the atria of the heart are contracting.
   e. both (a) and (b).

8. Considering blood flow through a closed circulation, which of the following is the correct sequence of vessels beginning at the heart?
   a. arteriole, artery, capillary, vein, venule
   b. artery, capillary, arteriole, venule, vein
   c. vein, venule, capillary, arteriole, artery
   d. artery, arteriole, capillary, venule, vein
   e. artery, arteriole, capillary, vein, venule

9. Gas and nutrient exchange between the circulation and the tissues occurs at
   a. the arteries.
   b. the arterioles.
   c. the capillaries.
   d. the venules.
   e. the veins.

10. Which of the following factors determines blood pressure?
    a. cardiac output
    b. resistance
    c. arteriole diameter
    d. all of the above
    e. (a) and (b) only

Articulate to Assess Your Learning

1. What are the three basic components of a true circulatory system?
2. List and briefly explain the components of blood.

Collaborate to Assess and Extend Your Learning

1. In what ways would you expect the heart of a giraffe to differ from that of (a) a cod, (b) a musk ox, and (c) an earthworm? In what ways are they similar?
2. Explain the cardiac cycle. Why must heart valves open in only one direction?.
3. A principle of biology is that living organisms have mechanisms that maintain homeostasis. In what ways does the circulatory system contribute to homeostasis?

Visit McGraw-Hill Ryerson Connect™ for additional study resources.

Respiratory Systems

Chapter Outline

Llama (*Lama glama*) in the Andes Mountains.

I n the previous chapter we saw how circulatory systems function to transport blood or hemolymph throughout an animal's body. These fluids contain the nutrients that are absorbed from the digestive tract and must be delivered to all body cells. In addition, animals require oxygen, O_2. The oxygen is taken into the body by one of four major types of respiratory (breathing) structures, including the body surface, gills, lungs, or tracheae (in insects). It then dissolves in plasma, binds to a carrier protein, and diffuses into cells. As described in Chapter 7, O_2 is used by mitochondria in the formation of ATP. One of the waste products of that reaction is carbon dioxide—CO_2—which diffuses out of cells. On the return trip to the respiratory organ, CO_2 is released into the environment, either to the air or to water. The process of moving oxygen and carbon dioxide in opposite directions between cells and the environment is called **gas exchange** (**Figure 45.1**). This chapter deals with the mechanisms by which animals obtain and transport oxygen, rid themselves of carbon dioxide, and cope with the challenges imposed by their environments and their changing metabolic needs. We begin with an overview of the properties of gases in air and water, and why cells need oxygen.

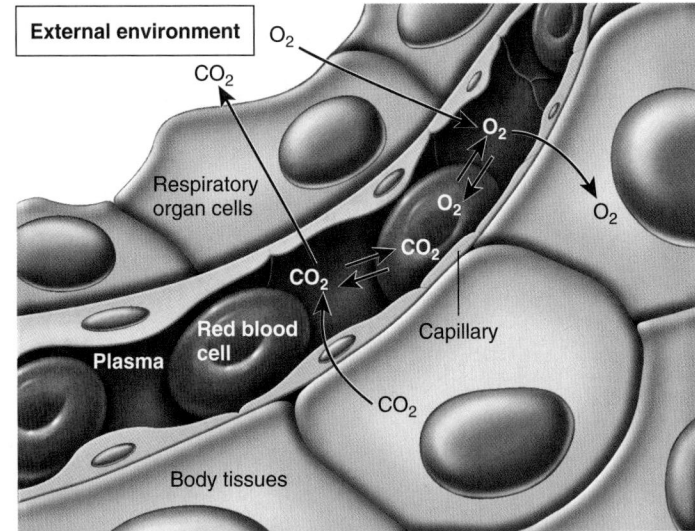

Figure 45.1 Overview of gas exchange between the environment, blood, and cells. In vertebrates, oxygen diffuses from the environment across the cells of a respiratory organ into the blood. From there, oxygen diffuses into tissue cells, where it is used during the formation of ATP. Cells generate carbon dioxide as a waste product, which diffuses out of cells and into blood, and then across the respiratory organ into the environment. In a vertebrate lung, the "external environment" is really the air that fills the lungs.

 Principle: *Living organisms have mechanisms to maintain homeostasis. Keep this principle in mind as you read this chapter. The exchange of oxygen and carbon dioxide illustrated here is absolutely essential for all homeostatic processes in animals, in part because oxygen is required for the production of much of an animal's ATP. The ATP, in turn, provides the energy required to sustain processes that contribute to homeostasis.*

45.1 PHYSICAL PROPERTIES OF GASES

Learning Outcomes:

1. List the relative amounts of each gas that make up the majority of the air we breathe.
2. Describe the relationship between altitude and atmospheric pressure.
3. Understand what is meant by partial pressure and how it is calculated.
4. Explain the influence of pressure, temperature, and the presence of other solutes on the solubility of gases in water.

In 1774 British physiologist Joseph Priestley demonstrated that heating mercuric oxide produced a pure gas that was "five or six times as good as common air," evidenced by its ability to sustain a burning candle or prevent a mouse from suffocating in an enclosed bell jar. Today, we know that the life-sustaining component of air is oxygen. Air is composed of about 21% oxygen, 78% nitrogen, and less than 1% carbon dioxide and other gases. From a respiratory standpoint, nitrogen gas can usually be ignored because it plays no role in energy production and is not created as a waste product of metabolism. In this section, we begin by examining some of the basic properties of the gases important in respiration.

Gases Exert Pressure, Which Depends on Altitude

The gases in air exert pressure on the body surfaces of animals, although the pressure is not perceptible unless it changes suddenly, like when your ears pop in a descending airplane. This pressure is called **atmospheric** (or **barometric**) **pressure**. It can be measured by noting how high a column of mercury is forced upward by the air pressure in a device called a mercury manometer. The traditional unit of gas pressure is mmHg, which is the same as for blood pressure.

At sea level, atmospheric pressure is 760 mmHg, and it decreases as we ascend to higher elevations (**Figure 45.2**). To visualize this, think how hydrostatic pressure increases at lower depths in an ocean. Now, imagine that you are standing at the bottom of an ocean of air. The closer you get to the surface (the top of the atmosphere), the lower the pressure exerted on your body. If you were stand at an elevation of 1,468 metres on the Cypress Hills Plateau at the Saskatchewan–Alberta border, the highest point of land between the Canadian Rockies and the Labrador Peninsula, the pressure is only 643 mmHg, while at the highest elevations continually inhabited by humans—in the Andes Mountains at 5,500 m—the pressure falls to 375 mmHg.

Atmospheric pressure is the sum of the pressures exerted by each gas in air, in exact proportion to their amounts. The individual pressure of each gas is its **partial pressure**, symbolized by a capital P and a subscript showing the specific gas.

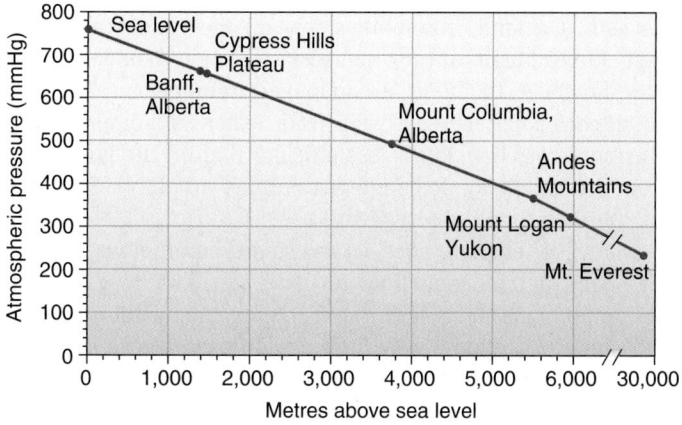

Figure 45.2 Atmospheric pressure decreases as altitude increases.

Thus, the partial pressure of oxygen (P_{O_2}) in the air we breathe is 21% of the atmospheric pressure at sea level, or 160 mmHg (0.21×760 mmHg).

The percentage of oxygen and other gases in air remains the same regardless of altitude, but the lower the atmospheric pressure, the lower the partial pressure of oxygen in air. The partial pressure of oxygen in the environment provides the driving force for its diffusion from air or water across the respiratory surface and into the blood. All gases diffuse along pressure gradients, from regions of high pressure to regions of lower pressure. This is analogous to the diffusion of dissolved solids from regions of high to low concentration, or the way heat moves from hotter to cooler regions. Consequently, the rate of oxygen diffusion into the bloodstream of a terrestrial animal at sea level decreases when the animal moves to a higher altitude, where the partial pressure of oxygen is lower.

Pressure, Temperature, and Other Solutes Influence the Solubility of Gases

Gases dissolve in solution, including fresh water, seawater, and all body fluids. It is while in solution that gases, like oxygen, exert their biological effects. However, most gases dissolve rather poorly in water. There is less oxygen in a given volume of water than in air, for example, which limits how active many aquatic organisms can be. Among the factors that influence the solubility of a gas in water, three are particularly important: the pressure of the gas, the temperature of the water, and the presence of other solutes.

The higher the pressure of a gas that comes into contact with water, the more of that gas that will dissolve, up to a limit that is specific for each gas at a given temperature. Not all gases dissolve equally. Oxygen is less soluble in water than carbon dioxide but more soluble than nitrogen. The partial pressure of gas in water is given in the same units as atmospheric pressure: mmHg. For example, if a solution of water is in contact with air that contains a P_{O_2} of 160 mmHg, the P_{O_2} of the water is also 160 mmHg.

Solubility also depends on the water's temperature, with more O_2 and CO_2 dissolved in 1 L of cold water than in 1 L of warm water. You can observe the effect of temperature with the following experiment. Open two bottles of a carbonated beverage and keep one on ice and the other at room temperature.

Note that the fizz (actually carbon dioxide gas that has been added to the drinks) of the room-temperature beverage disappears sooner as CO_2 escapes because of its lower solubility at that temperature. Why? At higher temperatures, gases in solution have more thermal energy and are therefore more likely to escape the liquid. In terms of biological systems, the effect of water temperature means that animals inhabiting very warm waters have less oxygen available to them than animals living, for example, in the waters off Antarctica. In addition, animals that live in shallow water such as ponds or tide pools, where the water temperature can fluctuate widely over a single day and night, must be able to adapt to dramatic daily swings in oxygen availability.

Finally, the presence of other solutes, namely salts, reduces the amount of gas that dissolves in water. Thus, warm salty blood dissolves less oxygen than does cold water. Likewise, less oxygen dissolves in seawater than fresh water at any given temperature and pressure. Animals living in cold freshwater lakes, therefore, typically have more oxygen available to them than do animals living in warm salty seas (although other factors can also influence the amount of oxygen, such as water depth and the amount of aquatic plant life).

45.2 TYPES OF RESPIRATORY ORGANS

Learning Outcomes:

1. List features that are common to all gas exchange surfaces in animals.
2. Discuss the different challenges faced by water- and air-breathing animals.
3. Describe how an animal's body surface can exchange gas with the environment.
4. Diagram the process of countercurrent flow in gill ventilation.
5. Understand the unique aspects of the tracheal system of ventilation in insects.

Despite the wide array of animal shapes, sizes, and habitats, animals obtain oxygen from their surroundings by only a few mechanisms. These include diffusion of oxygen across the body surface or across specialized respiratory or gas-exchange organs, including gills, tracheae, and lungs. **Ventilation** is the process of bringing oxygenated water or air into contact with a gas-exchange surface. In this section, we will examine the mechanisms of ventilation that are used by different animals.

The Structures of Respiratory Organs Are Adapted for Gas Exchange

Whether an animal uses respiratory organs or its body surface to obtain oxygen and expel carbon dioxide, all respiratory organs share certain common features. All have moist surfaces in which the gases can dissolve and diffuse. Further, all have adaptations that increase the amount of surface area available for gas exchange. As an example, if the gas-exchange regions of the human lungs were fully flattened, their total surface area would cover a tennis court.

The extensive surface area of respiratory organs is coupled with equally extensive blood flow, except in the special case of insects, described later in this chapter. The density of capillaries surrounding gills and lungs, for example, is among the highest found anywhere in an animal's body. The greater the amount of blood flowing to a respiratory surface, the more efficient is the delivery and removal of gases.

Thick barriers greatly slow the diffusion of a gas. As a result, respiratory organs tend to be thin, delicate structures, which also means that they are easily damaged. For instance, the inner structures of fish gills are so thin that they cannot support their own weight out of water, and they collapse when exposed to air.

Terrestrial and Aquatic Animals Face Different Challenges

Terrestrial and aquatic animals face different challenges to gas exchange. First, as noted earlier, aquatic animals generally have less available oxygen than do terrestrial animals, which means that an active aquatic animal requires a very efficient means of extracting oxygen from water. Second, unlike terrestrial animals, aquatic animals must adapt to fluctuating oxygen availability when the temperature changes. Terrestrial animals, by contrast, must cope with the dryness of air. Passing dry air over the lung surfaces runs the risk of drying out the lungs, which would damage them, dehydrate the animal, and reduce the ability of gases to dissolve.

Aquatic animals bring water, not air, over their respiratory surfaces and therefore do not usually risk dehydration in the way that terrestrial animals do. However, moving water over a gas-exchange surface creates its own challenges. First, because water is denser than air, more muscular work is required to move water than air. Second, cold seawater or fresh water moving over the richly vascular gills removes considerable heat from an animal's body because of the high heat capacity of water. Third, moving fresh or salt water over a gas-exchange surface can create osmotic movement of water across the surface, potentially resulting in water imbalances in an animal's body.

Some Animals Use Their Body Surface to Exchange Gases with the Environment

In those invertebrates that are only one or a few cell layers thick, oxygen and carbon dioxide can diffuse directly across the body surface. In this way, oxygen reaches all the interior cells, in some cases without any specialized transport mechanism or circulatory system. Even in some large, complex animals, the body surface may be permeable to gases (**Figure 45.3**). Amphibians and a few species of fish, including eels, have unusually permeable skin. On land, amphibians rely on their lungs and their moist skin to obtain oxygen and release carbon dioxide. Underwater, however, the lungs are no longer useful because they are not suited for extracting oxygen from water. Although oxygen diffusion across the skin is less efficient than in the lungs, this secondary ability to exchange gas permits amphibians to prolong the time spent underwater.

Many vertebrates, such as seals, are amphibious, in that they spend part of their lives on land and part in water, but only amphibians have skin that is highly permeable to gases. With some exceptions, very little gas diffuses across the body surfaces of fish, reptiles, birds, and mammals. Some reptiles, however, such as marine iguanas, can obtain oxygen from the water across the highly permeable mucous membranes of the nose, mouth, and anus. Although this provides less oxygen than

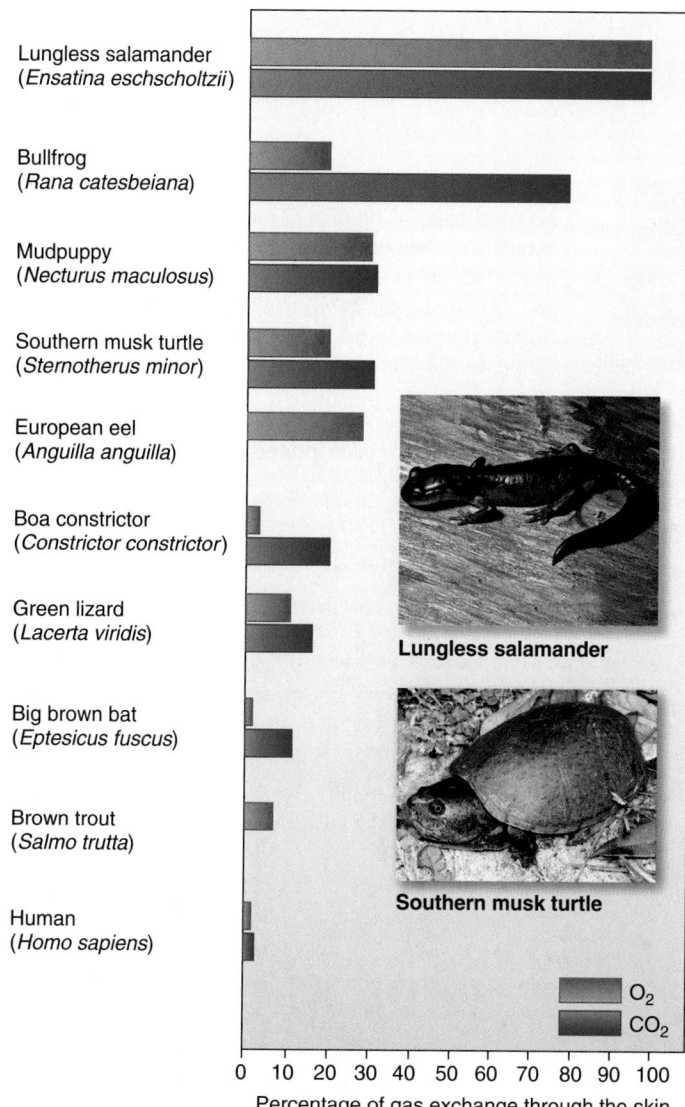

Lungless salamander

Southern musk turtle

O₂
CO₂

0 10 20 30 40 50 60 70 80 90 100
Percentage of gas exchange through the skin

Figure 45.3 Gas exchange across body surfaces. This occurs readily in amphibians and some fish. Among mammals, gas exchange occurs to a very limited extent in species with body features that have high surface area, such as bat wings. Note: CO₂ determinations were not made in all species.

air breathing, it nonetheless allows them to spend time underwater. Some animals have highly specialized body regions with considerable surface area—like the wings of a bat—that permit a small amount of gas exchange (Figure 45.3) but, except for amphibians, no vertebrates can rely for long periods of time exclusively on their skin to obtain oxygen and remain active.

Aquatic Animals Use Gills for Gas Exchange

Most aquatic animals use specialized respiratory structures called **gills**. External gills are uncovered extensions from the body surface, as occur in many invertebrates and the larval forms of some amphibians. Internal gills, which occur in fish, are enclosed in a protective cavity.

External Gills External gills vary widely in appearance, but all have a large surface area, often in the form of extensive projections (**Figure 45.4**). External gills may exist in one region of the body or be scattered over a large area. In many cases, they are ventilated by waving back and forth through the water. The ability to move external gills is particularly important for sessile invertebrates, which must otherwise rely on sporadic local water currents or muscular efforts of their bodies to create local currents for ventilation.

Despite the success of marine invertebrates, external gills have several limitations. First, they are unprotected and therefore susceptible to damage from the environment. Second, because water is much denser than air, considerable energy is required to continually wave the gills back and forth through the water (think of the difference between waving your hands through air or water). Finally, their appearance and motion may draw the attention of predators.

Internal Gills By contrast, fish have internal gills, which are covered by a bony plate called an operculum (**Figure 45.5a**). Fish gills have a more uniform appearance than external gills and are confined within the opercular cavity, which protects the gills and helps streamline the fish body.

The internal gills of fish contain numerous rows of **lamellae**, platelike structures that branch from structures called filaments (**Figure 45.5c**). The filaments, in turn, arise from the main support structure of the gills, the gill arches (**Figure 45.5b**). Blood vessels run the length of the filaments, with oxygen-poor blood travelling through the afferent vessel along one side of the filament, and oxygen-rich blood returning through the efferent vessel along the other side. Within the lamellae are numerous capillaries, all oriented with blood flowing in the same direction, from the oxygen-poor vessel to the oxygen-rich one.

Water enters the fish's mouth and flows between the lamellae in the opposite direction to blood flowing through the lamellar capillaries. This arrangement of water and blood flow is another example of a **countercurrent exchange mechanism** (see Chapter 40). As oxygenated water encounters the lamellae, it comes into contact with deoxygenated blood in the gill capillaries. Recall that oxygen diffuses along pressure gradients from a region of high oxygen pressure to low oxygen pressure. Thus, oxygen diffuses from the water into the capillaries of the lamellae. As water continues to flow across the lamellar surface, it encounters regions of capillaries that have not yet picked up oxygen—in other words, even as oxygen begins to diffuse from the water into the gill capillaries, a sufficient pressure gradient remains along the lamellae to permit diffusion of more of the remaining oxygen from the water. This is an extremely efficient way to remove as much oxygen from the water as possible before the water passes out of the operculum.

Fish use one of two mechanisms to ventilate their gills. The first method, **buccal pumping** (the buccal cavity refers to the mouth), makes use of the muscles of the mouth and operculum to create a hydrostatic pressure gradient for water to follow in one direction (**Figure 45.6a**). First, the jaw is lowered, which enlarges the buccal cavity and lowers the pressure in

(a) Mollusc (nudibranch) with clustered external gill tufts

(b) Larval salamander with external gills

Figure 45.4 **Examples of animals with external gills.** The gills of these animals have extensive projections to increase surface area, which facilitates oxygen diffusion from the surrounding water. **(a)** Mollusc (nudibranch) with clustered external gill tufts. **(b)** Larval salamander with external gills.

Principle: *Structure determines function. Note how the gills of the nudibranch and larval salamander have extensive surface modifications to increase the total area available for gas exchange. This is not unique to external gills; indeed, all gas-exchange surfaces have one or another type of surface area structural modification to increase their function.*

(a) Internal gills of a fish

As water flows across the lamellae, oxygen diffuses into the capillaries.

Operculum

Direction of H₂O flow

O₂-rich blood

Lamella

Direction of blood flow

O₂-poor blood

Afferent filament blood vessel

Blood flows through lamellae in the opposite direction of water flow.

Efferent filament blood vessel

Gill filaments

Gill arch

(b) Gill structure

Gill arch

Lamellae

Gill filament

Lamella

Water flow

40%   15%

70%

100%   30%   5%

60%

90%

Direction of O₂ movement

Blood flow

O₂ content

Afferent filament blood vessel

Efferent filament blood vessel

Direction of water flow

Countercurrent exchange in the lamellae results in a gradient for O₂ along the length of the capillaries.

0.4 μm

(c) SEM of gill filaments

Figure 45.5 **Structure of fish gills.** **(a)** The gills are protected beneath the operculum, which has been pulled open in this photo to reveal the gills underneath. **(b)** The gills are composed of gill arches, from which numerous pairs of filaments arise. Platelike lamellae with large amounts of surface area are arrayed along the filaments. Blood vessels from the filaments form capillaries in the lamellae. Blood flows through the capillaries in the opposite direction of water flowing between lamellae, a process called countercurrent exchange. **(c)** Lamellae as revealed in a scanning electron micrograph.

Concept check: *Why do fish die when out of water? (Hint: Consider the thin, delicate appearance of the water-covered lamellae.)*

BioConnections: *You have learned about countercurrent exchange before; look back to Figure 40.17a for a description of how countercurrent exchange can regulate heat loss in a vertebrate.*

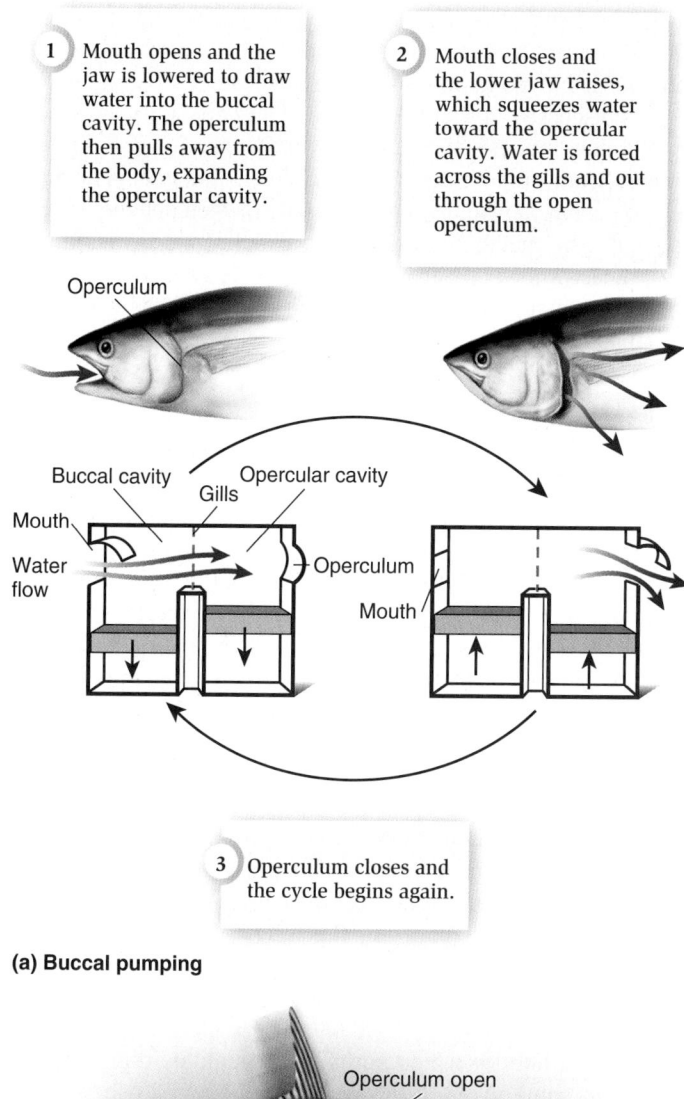

1 Mouth opens and the jaw is lowered to draw water into the buccal cavity. The operculum then pulls away from the body, expanding the opercular cavity.

2 Mouth closes and the lower jaw raises, which squeezes water toward the opercular cavity. Water is forced across the gills and out through the open operculum.

Operculum

Buccal cavity   Opercular cavity

Gills

Mouth

Water flow

Operculum

Mouth

3 Operculum closes and the cycle begins again.

(a) Buccal pumping

Operculum open

Mouth open

Water flow

(b) Ram ventilation

Figure 45.6 **Mechanisms of gill ventilation.** Some species use both buccal pumping and ram ventilation, while some can only use one. **(a)** Buccal pumping. The expansion of the buccal and opercular cavities acts like a suction pump, and closing these cavities acts like a pressure pump. During this process, flaps of tissue in the mouth, throat, and operculum help prevent water from moving in the reverse direction. **(b)** Ram ventilation. Many fish, such as this tuna, can ventilate their gills by swimming forward or facing upstream in moving water with their mouths open. This causes the water to move through the mouth and operculum.

the mouth, something like a suction pump. This draws water into the mouth, raising the water pressure again. At roughly the same time, the operculum begins to swing out from the body, enlarging the opercular cavity and lowering the water pressure there. This second suction pump is stronger than the buccal pump, so water flows down its hydrostatic pressure gradient from the outside to the mouth, through the opercular cavity. Next, the mouth closes and the buccal cavity constricts. This creates positive pressure that forces water across the gills and out through the operculum, which is now open. A flap of tissue at the back of the mouth helps prevent accidental flow of water down the esophagus. Thus, fish do not swallow the water they inhale but instead send it on a one-way journey across their gills. In buccal pumping, a fish can remain stationary and still ventilate even in stagnant water by drawing water into its mouth.

The second way in which some fish ventilate their gills is by swimming with their mouths open, in essence using their large swimming muscles to bring water into their buccal cavity and from there across their gills. This method of ventilation, called **ram ventilation** (**Figure 45.6b**), is more energy efficient than buccal pumping. Ram ventilation still requires energy expenditure, but in this case the energy is used for swimming or for using muscles to remain stationary while facing upstream in moving water. Many fish employ both methods of ventilation, using buccal pumping when swimming slowly or in stagnant water, and switching to ram ventilation when swimming quickly or facing upstream. Some fish—such as tuna—can only ram ventilate and therefore rarely stop moving.

Both buccal pumping and ram ventilation are **flow-through systems**—water moves unidirectionally such that the gills are constantly in contact with fresh, oxygenated water. As we will see, many air-breathing animals use a less efficient method of ventilating their lungs, called tidal ventilation, in which fresh air is breathed in and stale air is breathed out through the same route. Despite the efficiency of flow-through systems for maximizing oxygen extraction from water, they are energetically costly because of the work required to overcome the density of water. Fish may devote up to 10%–20% of their resting metabolic rate simply to ventilating their gills, while a typical air-breather may allocate only 1%–2% of its total energy usage to ventilating the lungs at rest.

Insects Use Tracheal Systems to Exchange Gases with the Environment

Except for terrestrial isopods, such as the pill bug (*Armadillidium vulgare*), which breathe air through very small, moist gills, the delicate nature of gill lamellae makes them unsuitable for gas exchange in air. Air-breathing probably evolved as an adaptation in aquatic animals inhabiting regions that were subject to periodic drought. One of the major mechanisms that animals evolved to breathe air is the tracheal system found in insects.

Running along the surface of both sides of an insect's body are tiny paired openings to the outside, called spiracles. Arising from the spiracles are **tracheae** (singular: trachea; **Figure 45.7**), sturdy tubes that are reinforced with chitin to keep them open. Tracheae branch extensively into ever-smaller tubes called tracheoles, eventually becoming small enough to bring their tips into contact with virtually every cell in the body. At their tips, tracheoles are filled with a small amount of fluid. Air moving down the tracheoles comes into contact with this fluid. Oxygen from the air dissolves in the fluid, and from there it diffuses across the tracheole wall and into nearby cells. Carbon dioxide diffuses in the opposite direction, from cells into the tracheoles, and from there to the environment.

When an insect's oxygen demands increase, muscular movements of its abdomen and thorax draw air into and out of the tracheae like a bellows, a phenomenon first demonstrated in the early twentieth century by Danish physiologist and Nobel Laureate August Krogh, who studied the mechanics of ventilation in locusts. Krogh showed that an insect's muscles and tracheal system match ventilation with the animal's exercise intensity and oxygen requirements. This is particularly important in flying insects, whose metabolic demands are high. The faster an insect flies, the more oxygen it uses. Likewise, the more intensely and rapidly the body wall muscles move, the more air is moved in and out of the tracheae.

As discussed in Chapter 44, the open circulatory system of insects does not participate in gas exchange. Oxygen diffuses directly from air to trachea to tracheoles and finally to body cells. This mechanism of ventilation and oxygen delivery is very efficient. The metabolic rate of insect flight muscles is among the highest known of any tissue in any animal, and the tracheal system supplies enough oxygen to meet those enormous demands.

Air-Breathing Vertebrates Use Lungs to Exchange Gases

Except for some rare amphibians, such as the lungless salamander, all air-breathing terrestrial vertebrates use **lungs** to bring oxygen into the circulatory system and remove carbon dioxide. Scorpions and some spiders are the only invertebrates to have lungs, although those structures—called *book lungs*—actually resemble gills more than lungs. Lungs are internal paired structures that arise from the pharynx (throat). All lungs receive deoxygenated blood from the heart and return oxygenated blood back to the heart. Depending on the class of vertebrate, lungs may be filled by using positive or negative pressure and be ventilated by a tidal system or flow-through system.

Most amphibians have lungs that are simple sacs with relatively little surface area, and thus they are less effective surfaces for oxygen diffusion than are the lungs of other vertebrates. A 30-gram mouse's lung, for example, has nearly 50 times as much gas exchange surface per cubic centimetre of lung tissue as a 30-gram frog's lung.

The method by which amphibians ventilate their lungs is similar in some ways to the buccal pumping of fish. A frog, for example, lowers its jaw, which decreases the air pressure inside the mouth cavity. According to Boyle's law, gas pressure and volume are inversely related (**Figure 45.8**). For example, when the volume in which a gas is contained increases, the pressure of the gas in that container decreases. By expanding its mouth cavity, therefore, a frog creates a pressure gradient for air to move from the atmosphere (higher pressure) into its mouth cavity (lower pressure). The mouth and nostrils are then closed, and the mouth cavity is constricted by raising the bottom jaw. This raises the air pressure in the mouth, forcing air through a series of valves down into the lungs. Thus, **positive pressure filling** means that frogs and most other amphibians gulp air and force it under pressure into the lungs, as if inflating a balloon. They may do this many times in a row before finally exhaling.

Except for a few species of reptiles that also depend on positive pressure filling, all other terrestrial vertebrates use a different method of ventilation, negative pressure filling. To understand how negative pressure filling works, we will first examine the anatomy of the respiratory tract in vertebrates, using the mammalian and avian systems as models.

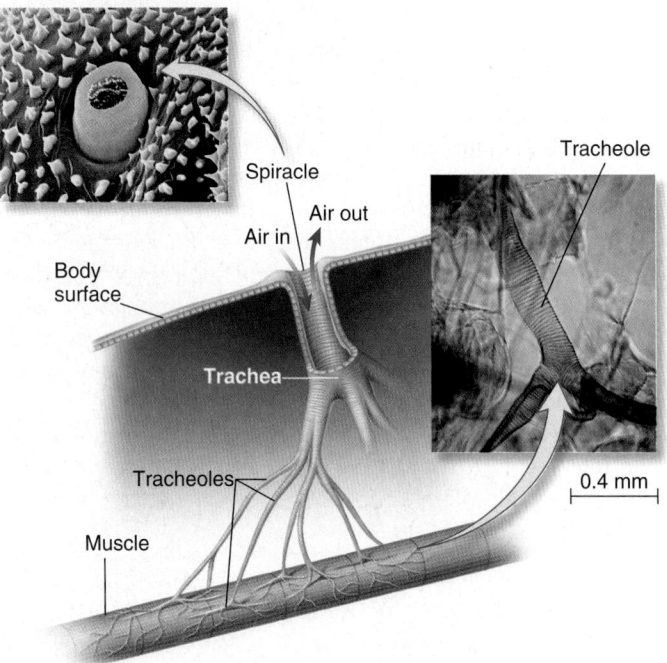

Figure 45.7   The tracheal system of insects. As shown in this house fly, air enters holes called spiracles. Oxygen diffuses directly from the fluid-filled tracheole tips to cells that come into contact with the tips. The circulatory system plays no role in gas exchange. The micrograph illustrates a few branching tracheoles.

Concept check: *How might the structure of the respiratory system of insects be related to why insects tend to be smaller than vertebrates?*

Rest

Pressure gauge

Piston

Increased volume
(analogous to inhaling)

Reduced volume
(analogous to exhaling)

Gas molecules have thermal energy and exert a pressure on the walls of the cylinder.

Fewer collisions of gas molecules occur with cylinder wall (decreased pressure).

Greater number of collisions of gas molecules occur with cylinder wall (increased pressure).

Figure 45.8 **Boyle's law.** At a constant temperature, the volume and pressure of a gas are inversely related. This relationship creates the gas pressure gradients needed to ventilate the vertebrate lungs.

45.3 STRUCTURE AND FUNCTION OF MAMMALIAN AND AVIAN RESPIRATORY SYSTEMS

Learning Outcomes:

1. Describe the components of the mammalian respiratory system, and the structure of the mammalian lung.
2. Describe the process of ventilation in mammalian lungs.
3. Compare and contrast tidal ventilation in mammals and the flow-through breathing cycle of birds.

The **respiratory system** includes all components of the body that contribute to the exchange of gas between the external environment and the blood. In mammals, this includes the nose, mouth, airways, lungs, and muscles and connective tissues that encase these structures within the thoracic (chest) cavity. In this section, we begin by examining the mechanisms by which mammals ventilate their lungs. We then contrast this with the highly specialized and unique way in which birds ventilate their lungs.

Air Is Warmed, Humidified, and Filtered in the Nose and Mouth

In humans and other mammals, air first enters the nose and mouth (**Figure 45.9a**), where it is warmed and humidified. These processes protect the lungs from drying out. While in the nose, the air is cleansed as it flows over a coating of sticky mucus in the nasal cavity. The mucus and hairs in the nasal cavity trap some of the larger dust and other particles that are inhaled with air. These are then removed by the body's defence cells or swallowed.

The inhaled air from the mouth and nose converges at the back of the throat, or **pharynx**. From there, air passes through the **larynx**. Within the larynx are the vocal cords, folds of tissue through which air passes to create sound. Air flows from the larynx to the **trachea**, which leads to the lungs. At the opening to the trachea, known as the glottis, a flap of tissue called the epiglottis prevents food from entering the trachea by closing when food is swallowed.

The trachea is ringed by cartilage that provides rigidity and ensures that the trachea always remains open. The inner walls of the trachea are lined with cilia and cells called goblet cells. These cells secrete mucus into the lumen of the trachea, coating the cilia (**Figure 45.9b**). This mucus layer captures potentially harmful or irritating particles that escaped the nasal cleaning mechanism. The cilia beat constantly toward the mouth and move the mucus and its trapped particles into the mouth, where it can be expelled or swallowed. Without these active cilia, it would require repeated coughing to force the mucus out of the trachea. This is why humans who smoke tobacco develop a chronic smoker's cough. The smoke and its components paralyze the cilia, causing mucus to pool in the trachea.

The trachea branches into two smaller tubes, called **bronchi** (singular: *bronchus*), which lead to each lung. The bronchi branch repeatedly into smaller and smaller tubes, eventually becoming thin-walled **bronchioles** surrounded by circular rings of smooth muscle (**Figure 45.9c**). Bronchioles can dilate or constrict in a manner analogous to that of arterioles (see Chapter 44). They may partially constrict when a damaging particle—such as a small bit of inhaled pollutant or dust—gets past the mucous layers of the upper airways. Constriction of a bronchiole prevents foreign particles from reaching delicate lung tissue. Once the body's defence cells have removed the particles, the bronchiole reopens to its normal diameter.

Figure 45.9 **The mammalian respiratory system.** **(a)** In this overview, the ribs have been removed in front, and the major airways have been drawn in the lungs. The thoracic cavity is bounded by the ribs and intercostal muscles, and the muscular diaphragm. **(b)** Ciliated epithelial cells and mucus-producing goblet cells line the trachea. The mucus traps inhaled particles, and the cilia help move the mucus toward the mouth, where it can be swallowed. **(c)** The bronchioles deliver air to clusters of alveoli. Note the smooth muscle cells around the bronchioles, which can cause the bronchioles to constrict or dilate. Capillaries surround the alveoli. Red represents oxygenated blood; blue represents deoxygenated blood. **(d)** Cross-section through a cluster of alveoli. Note the single layer of alveoli cells and their close proximity to the adjacent capillaries.

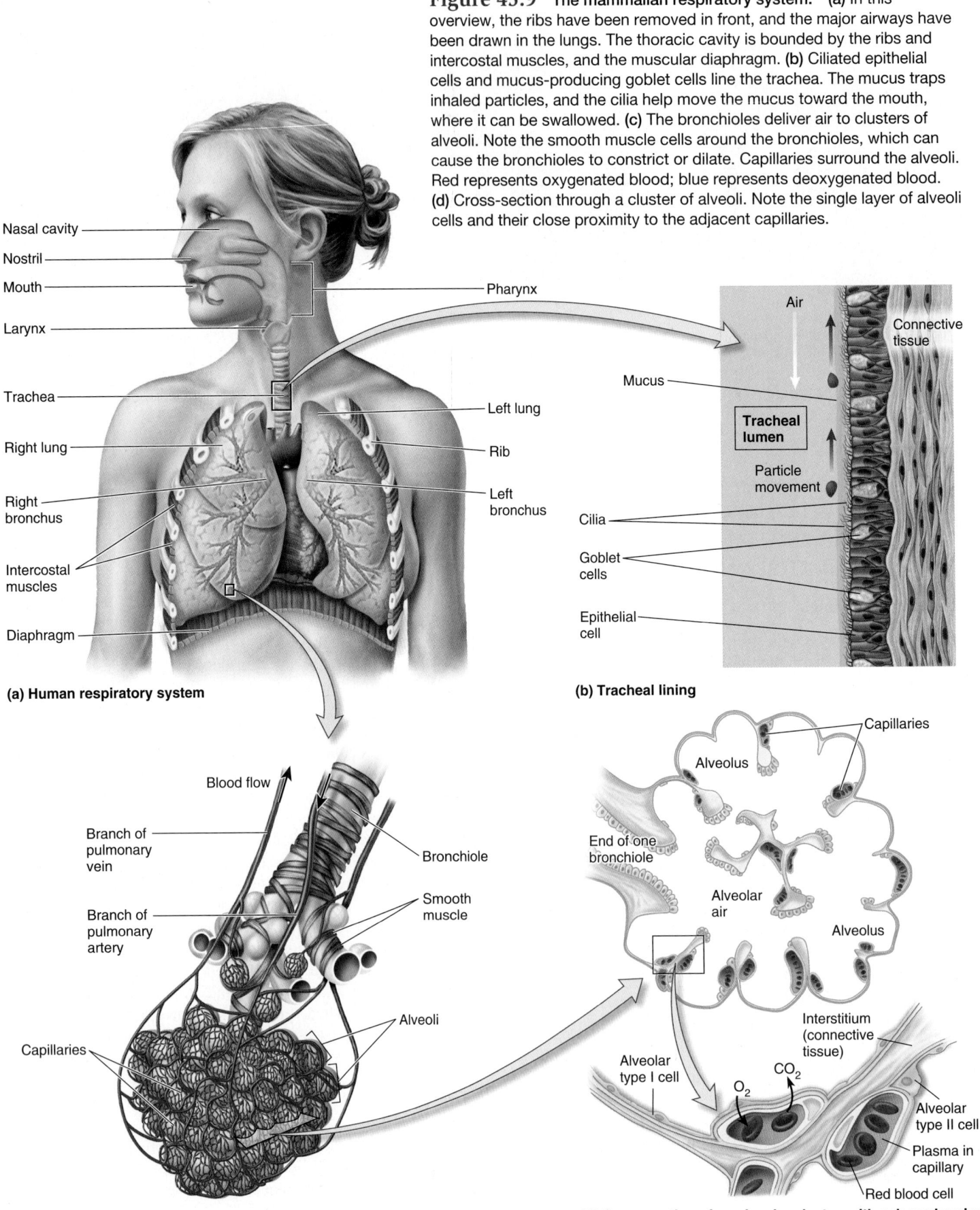

(a) Human respiratory system

(b) Tracheal lining

(c) Structure of a bronchiole and alveoli

(d) Cross-section of an alveolar cluster, with enlarged region

The bronchioles empty into the final, saclike regions of the lungs where gas exchange occurs—the **alveoli** (singular: alveolus; **Figure 45.9d**). Until now, air has flowed through the air tubes without any gas exchange taking place. The alveoli are highly adapted for gas exchange. They are only one cell thick and resemble extremely thin sacs, looking a little like bunches of grapes on a stem. Many capillaries containing deoxygenated blood pumped from the right ventricle of the heart surround the alveoli. Oxygen diffuses from the lumen of each alveolus across the alveolar cells, through the interstitial space outside the cells, and into the capillaries. Carbon dioxide diffuses in the opposite direction. The oxygenated blood from the lungs then flows to the left atrium of the heart and from there enters the left ventricle, where it is pumped out through the aorta to the rest of the body.

Surfactant Facilitates Lung Inflation by Reducing Surface Tension

Like all cells, those that make up the lining of the alveoli are coated with extracellular fluid. This fluid layer is where gases dissolve. Unlike other internal body cells, however, alveolar cells come into contact with air, creating an air/liquid interface along the inner surface of the alveoli. This results in surface tension within the alveoli, which would tend to make them collapse. If many or all the alveoli collapsed, however, the amount of surface area available for gas exchange in the lungs would be greatly reduced. What prevents them from collapsing? Certain alveolar cells produce **surfactant**, a mixture of proteins and amphipathic lipids, and secrete it into the alveolar lumen. There, it forms a barrier between the air and the fluid layer inside the alveoli. This barrier reduces surface tension in the alveolar walls, allowing them to remain open.

Surface tension is particularly important in the transition from fetal to postnatal life in mammals. Most mammalian fetuses are encased in fluid within the uterus. Consequently, their lungs do not have an air–liquid interface and they do not start producing surfactant until the final stages of pregnancy. If a human baby is born more than four to six weeks prematurely, before sufficient surfactant is produced, many alveoli will quickly collapse after birth. This condition, known as **respiratory distress syndrome of the newborn**, can be partially alleviated by inserting a tube in the trachea and injecting synthetic surfactant.

Membranes Protect the Lungs

The lungs are soft, delicate tissues that could easily be damaged by the surrounding bone, muscle, and connective tissue of the thoracic cavity if not protected. Each lung is encased in a **pleural sac**, a double layer of sheathlike moist membranes. Between the two layers of membrane is a microscopically thin layer of water that acts as a lubricant and makes the two membranes adhere to each other.

In addition to protecting the lungs, the inner pleural sac adheres to its lung, and the outer pleural sac adheres to the chest wall. In this way, movements of the chest wall result in similar movements of the lungs. This is important because the lungs are not muscular and cannot inflate themselves. Instead, as you will see, the lungs are inflated by the expansion of the thoracic cavity, which results from the contraction of muscles in the chest and abdomen.

Negative Pressure Ventilates Mammalian Lungs

The way in which you inflate a balloon, by forcing air from your mouth into the balloon, is called positive pressure filling. It is reminiscent of how amphibians ventilate their lungs. **Negative pressure filling** by contrast, is the mechanism by which reptiles, birds, and mammals ventilate their lungs (**Figure 45.10**). In this process, the volume of the lungs expands, creating a negative pressure that draws air into the lungs. The process differs in some ways among classes of vertebrates, but in mammals the work is provided by the **intercostal muscles**, which surround and connect the ribs in the chest, and a large muscle called the **diaphragm** (Figure 45.9a), which subdivides the thoracic

1 The external intercostal muscles contract during inhalation to increase chest volume.

2 The diaphragm lowers during inhalation.

3 Air flows in during inhalation because air pressure in the lungs is lower than that outside.

4 Air flows out when muscles relax.

Intercostal muscles

Diaphragm

KEY
- - - - - Inhalation
- - - - - Exhalation

(a) Action of muscles during ventilation

After inhaling

(b) Change in lung volume during ventilation

Figure 45.10 Ventilation of the mammalian lung by negative pressure filling. **(a)** The external intercostal muscles contract, which expands the chest cavity by moving the ribs up and out. The diaphragm also contracts, causing it to pull downward, further expanding the cavity. The muscular efforts require energy, whereas the return to the resting state by exhaling is primarily by recoil. **(b)** X-ray image of the chest of an adult man after inhaling. The volume of the lungs after exhaling is superimposed on the image using dashed lines to illustrate the relative change in lung volume.

cavity from the abdomen. At the start of a breath, the diaphragm contracts, pulling downward and enlarging the thoracic cavity. Simultaneously, the intercostal muscles contract, moving the chest upward and outward, which also helps to enlarge the thoracic cavity. Recall that the pleural sacs adhere the lungs to the chest wall, so that as the chest expands, the lungs expand with it. According to Boyle's law, as the volume of the lungs increases, the pressures of the gases within them must decrease. In other words, the pressure in the lungs becomes negative with respect to the outside air. Air, therefore, flows down its pressure gradient from outside the mouth and nose, into the lungs.

Once the lungs are inflated with air, the chest muscles and diaphragm relax and recoil back to their original positions as an animal exhales. This compresses the lungs and forces air out of the airways. Whereas inhaling requires the expenditure of significant amounts of energy, exhaling is mostly passive and does not require much energy. During exhalation, air leaves via the same route that it entered during inhalation, and no new oxygen is delivered to the airways at that time. This type of breathing is called **tidal ventilation** (think of air flowing in and out of the lungs like the tides of an ocean). Tidal ventilation is less efficient than the unidirectional, flow-through system of fish in which gills are always exposed to oxygenated water during all phases of the respiratory cycle.

As you know from experience, the lungs are neither fully inflated nor deflated at rest. For example, you could easily take a larger breath than normal if you wanted, or exhale more than the usual amount of air. The volume of air that is normally breathed in and out at rest is the **tidal volume**, about 0.5 litre in an average-sized human. Tidal volume is proportional to body size among humans and between species. A 183-centimetre-tall adult, for example, has a larger tidal volume than a 122-centimetre-tall child because the adult has larger lungs. Similarly, horses have larger tidal volumes than humans, and humans have larger tidal volumes than dogs (see the first four columns of **Table 45.1**). During exertion, the lungs can be inflated further than the resting tidal volume to provide additional oxygen. Likewise, the lungs can be deflated beyond their normal limits at rest, by exerting a strong effort during exhalation. The lungs never fully deflate, however, partly because they are held open by their adherence to the chest wall. This is important for a simple reason. Think again of our analogy of a balloon. It is much easier to fill a balloon that is already partly inflated than it is to inflate a completely empty balloon. The same is true of the lungs. The most difficult breath is the very first one that a newborn mammal takes—the only time its lungs are ever completely empty of air.

The Avian Lung Is a Flow-Through System

Unlike in mammals, ventilation in birds is a flow-through system. The avian respiratory system is unique among vertebrates in that it is supplemented with numerous **air sacs (Figure 45.11a)**,

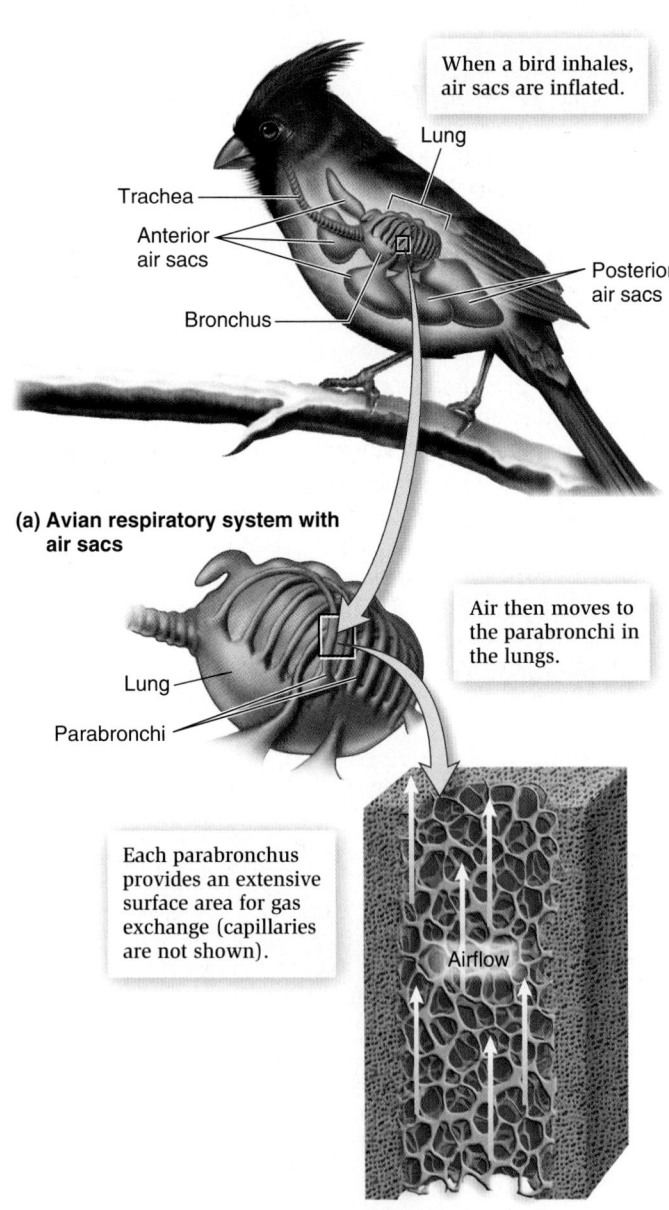

(a) Avian respiratory system with air sacs

When a bird inhales, air sacs are inflated.

Lung

Trachea

Anterior air sacs

Bronchus

Posterior air sacs

Air then moves to the parabronchi in the lungs.

Lung

Parabronchi

Each parabronchus provides an extensive surface area for gas exchange (capillaries are not shown).

Airflow

(b) Lung showing parabronchi and cross-section of a parabronchus

Figure 45.11 Respiratory system of a bird.

Table 45.1	Respiratory Characteristics of Different Mammals			
Animal	**Body mass**	**Breaths/min**	**Tidal volume**	**P_{50} value**
Shrew	0.0024 kg	700	30 μL	35 mmHg
Dog	25 kg	20	0.27 L	29 mmHg
Human	75 kg	12	0.50 L	26 mmHg
Horse	465 kg	9	6.50 L	24 mmHg

Note: All values are averages from resting animals. Tidal volume is the volume of air breathed in with each breath. Tidal volume increases as an animal's mass and therefore lung size increases. By contrast, breathing rate is higher in smaller animals. Similar relationships occur in other vertebrates, notably birds. As described later in the chapter, the P_{50} value is the oxygen pressure at which an animal's hemoglobin is 50% saturated with oxygen. Higher P_{50} values correspond to lower affinities of hemoglobin for oxygen (in other words, animals with high P_{50} values unload their oxygen from hemoglobin more readily).

Figure 45.12   Relationships between direction of flow of blood and water or air in different vertebrates.

which for simplicity we can lump together as those at the anterior or posterior regions of the body. The air sacs—not the lungs—expand when a bird inhales and shrink when it exhales. They expand by movements of the chest muscles, not by a diaphragm. The air sacs do not participate in gas exchange, as first demonstrated in a simple but elegant experiment by French physiologist J. Soum in 1896. Soum surgically plugged the openings of one of a pigeon's air sacs and then injected poisonous carbon monoxide (CO) gas into the sac. Birds are very sensitive to the toxic effects of CO, but in this experiment, the pigeon showed no signs of being poisoned. Soum concluded that gases do not diffuse from the air sacs into the blood.

Air enters the trachea of the avian respiratory system and moves from there into two bronchi. Instead of branching into bronchioles and then alveoli, however, avian bronchi branch into a series of parallel air tubes called **parabronchi** (**Figure 45.11b**) that make up the lungs. The parabronchi are the regions of gas exchange. They have enormous surface area and an extensive network of blood capillaries. Blood flows through the lungs in a crosscurrent direction with respect to movement of air (**Figure 45.12**). This is less efficient in extracting oxygen than the countercurrent flow arrangement in fish gills but more efficient than the tidal ventilation system of mammalian lungs.

FEATURE INVESTIGATION

Schmidt-Nielsen Mapped Airflow in the Avian Respiratory System

In 1967 Schmidt-Nielsen and co-workers conducted a series of experiments by using ostriches because of their large lung volumes. The researchers used O_2- and CO_2-sensitive probes to determine the concentrations of these gases in the birds' air sacs. In their first experiment, described in **Figure 45.13**, the investigators allowed the birds to breathe ordinary room air, which contained 21% oxygen. They used special syringes to extract a gas sample from the large air sacs of the birds and had the gas composition analyzed with the probes. They discovered that the O_2 content was high and the CO_2 content was low in the posterior air sacs, with the reverse pattern in the anterior sacs. They concluded that fresh air must move through the trachea and into the posterior air sacs, while stale

Figure 45.13   Schmidt-Nielsen and co-workers demonstrated the route that air travels in the avian (ostrich) lung.

Figure 45.13 *(Continued)*

2 | **THE DATA**

Results from Experiment 1:

Anterior air sacs

Low O$_2$; high CO$_2$

Posterior air sacs

21% O$_2$; low CO$_2$

The researchers proposed that air moves directly to posterior sacs, then through the lungs, and then to the anterior sacs.

How can this be demonstrated?

3 | **Experiment 2:**
Give ostriches a single breath of pure O$_2$, which can be tracked as it moves through the respiratory system. Then remove the mask and allow the bird to breathe normal air.

100% O$_2$

Tight-fitting mask

Gas analyzer

O$_2$ probe

100% O$_2$

Air from previous breath

Gas analyzer

O$_2$ probe

4 | **THE DATA**

Results from Experiment 2: Pure O$_2$ appears first in the posterior sacs and does not appear in anterior sacs until the next breath.

Volume of air in lungs

Inhalation | Exhalation | Inhalation | Exhalation | Inhalation | Exhalation

Time

O$_2$ content* in posterior sacs

Time

O$_2$ content* in anterior sacs

Time

*The O$_2$ shown in these graphs is from the pure O$_2$ inhaled on the first breath and is above the normal levels of O$_2$.

5 | **CONCLUSION**

Proposed pattern of avian ventilation*:

First inhalation

Anterior

Parabronchi

Sacs expand

Posterior

First exhalation

Sacs compress

Second inhalation

Second exhalation

*The blue colour indicates the location of gas taken on the first breath. The white arrows track the directional movement of air taken on the first breath.

6 | **SOURCE** Schmidt-Nielsen, K., et al. 1969. Temperature regulation and respiration in the ostrich. *The Condor* 71:341–352.

air, which had previously given up much of its oxygen in the lungs, must have entered the anterior sacs.

To test this hypothesis, they developed a method to track the movement of oxygen through the ostrich respiratory system, as shown in the second experiment of Figure 45.13. In this experiment, the scientists fitted ostriches with face masks, through which the birds inhaled a single breath of pure (100%) oxygen. O$_2$-sensitive probes were surgically inserted into the posterior and anterior air sacs to monitor when the pure oxygen gas appeared in each sac. The researchers discovered that

during the first inhalation, high levels of oxygen appeared in the posterior air sac but not the anterior sac. As the ostrich exhaled, some oxygen remained in the posterior air sac, but still no oxygen appeared in the anterior one. When the animal inhaled its next breath (this one of plain air, not pure oxygen), oxygen began appearing in the anterior sacs and disappearing from the posterior sacs. Finally, as the ostrich exhaled a second time, the oxygen in the anterior sacs decreased.

Schmidt-Nielsen concluded from this study that air flows through the trachea, down the bronchi, and into the posterior air sacs during inhalation. As a bird exhales, air exits the posterior sacs and flows through the parabronchi from the back to the front of the lungs. During its passage through the lungs, some of the oxygen diffuses into the capillaries, while CO_2 diffuses out of the capillaries and into the lungs. During the next inhalation, air at the anterior part of the lungs flows into the anterior air sacs, which serve as a sort of holding chamber. Finally, a second exhalation causes this air from the previous inhalation to exit the anterior sacs and leave the animal's body through the trachea.

Thus, it takes two complete breaths for air to move from the environment into the lungs and back out again to the environment. Air flows through the lungs during inhalation, as it is drawn by negative pressure through the parabronchi and into the expanding anterior sacs. Air is also forced through the

parabronchi by positive pressure during exhalation, as the posterior air sacs are compressed. The efficiency of the avian flow-through system, together with its crosscurrent blood supply, is a major reason why many birds are able to fly at altitudes with extremely low atmospheric pressures (even over Mt. Everest).

Experimental Questions

1. What was the purpose of these studies?
2. Considering the first experiment only, what were the results, and what conclusions did the researchers make based on these results?
3. Explain the purpose and procedure of the second experiment conducted by Schmidt-Nielsen and the conclusions he drew from his results.

The way in which air moves through avian lungs and the function of the air sacs remained a mystery to physiologists for many years, until the pioneering work of American physiologist Knut Schmidt-Nielsen.

45.4 | CONTROL OF VENTILATION IN MAMMALIAN LUNGS

Learning Outcomes:

1. Describe the role of respiratory centres and chemoreceptors in the regulation of ventilation.
2. Explain the link between ventilation rate and H^+ concentration.
3. Understand how the activity of the respiratory centres in the brain of vertebrates is related to an animal's metabolic rate.

Lungs are not muscles or electrically excitable tissue. Therefore, they are not capable of initiating and regulating their own expansion. Nonetheless, lungs require a mechanism to rhythmically expand and recoil, because animals cannot always consciously control breathing, such as during sleep. In this section, we examine the ways in which the brain and other structures control ventilation in mammals and how these control mechanisms are linked with metabolism.

The Nervous System Contains the Pacemaker for Ventilation

The pacemaker that initiates expansion of the lungs is a collection of nuclei in the nervous system. In mammals, these **respiratory centres** constitute several regions of the brainstem (**Figure 45.14**). Electrical impulses from the brainstem travel through two sets of nerves. The first set, called the intercostal nerves, stimulates the intercostal muscles, and the second

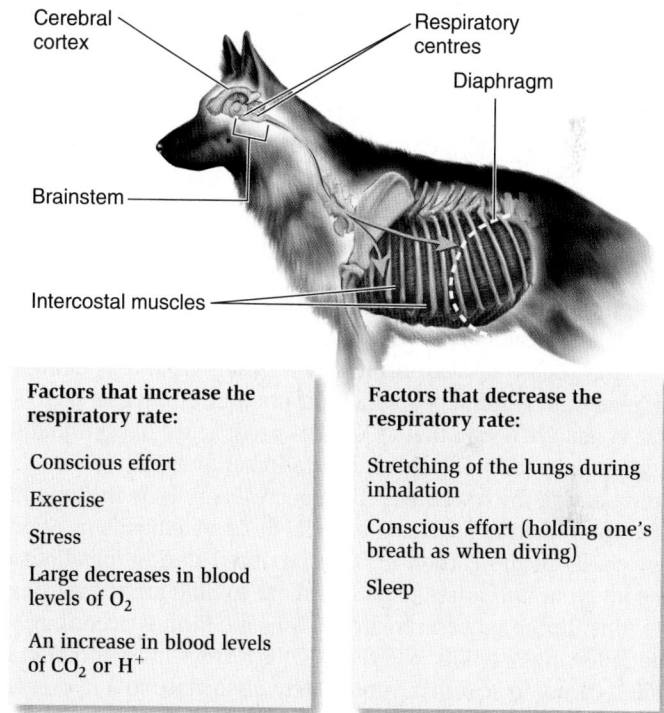

Factors that increase the respiratory rate:	Factors that decrease the respiratory rate:
Conscious effort	Stretching of the lungs during inhalation
Exercise	Conscious effort (holding one's breath as when diving)
Stress	Sleep
Large decreases in blood levels of O_2	
An increase in blood levels of CO_2 or H^+	

Figure 45.14 The control of breathing via respiratory centres in the mammalian brain. Neurons in the brainstem send action potentials via nerves that stimulate the intercostal muscles and diaphragm. The factors listed here can modulate the rate of action potential generation and thus the respiratory rate.

set, the phrenic nerves, stimulates the diaphragm. When the lungs expand in response to the contraction of these muscles, stretch-sensitive nerves in the walls of the lungs and chest send signals to the respiratory centres, informing them that the lungs are inflated. This temporarily turns off the stimulating signal until the animal exhales, whereupon a new signal is sent to the breathing muscles.

Although the brainstem controls breathing automatically, it can be overridden. Animals that dive underwater—including humans, when we go swimming—can hold their breath temporarily. We can also breathe faster than normal even while resting, at least for short periods. Normally, however, increased breathing occurs in response to exercise or stress. During exercise, a variety of factors converge on the respiratory centres to increase the rate and strength of signals to the breathing muscles, resulting in faster and deeper breaths.

Chemoreceptors Modulate the Activity of the Respiratory Centres

The concentrations of hydrogen ions (pH) in blood, and the partial pressures of carbon dioxide and oxygen, influence the respiratory centres. **Chemoreceptors**—special cells located in the aorta, carotid arteries, and the brainstem—detect the circulating levels of these substances and relay that information through nerves or interneurons to the respiratory centres.

Normally, the oxygen level is not the most important variable monitored by chemoreceptors. However, if the oxygen level falls far below normal, as might occur at high altitude or in certain respiratory diseases, the chemoreceptors signal the respiratory centres to increase the rate and depth of breathing to increase ventilation of the lungs. Similarly, a buildup of carbon dioxide in the blood, which would occur if an animal's ventilation was lower than normal (again, often the result of respiratory disease), signals the respiratory centres to stimulate breathing. Finally, hydrogen ions in the blood activate chemoreceptors, which signal the brain when the blood is too acidic. This leads to an increase in the rate of breathing.

One source of acid in the blood results from a by-product of anaerobic respiration, which occurs during intense exercise and is usually a sign that an animal needs more oxygen than it is getting. In addition, the concentration of hydrogen ions in the fluid bathing the brainstem chemoreceptors reflects the amount of carbon dioxide produced by cells during metabolism. About two-thirds of the carbon dioxide produced during metabolism is converted into a less toxic and more soluble form: bicarbonate ions. In the process, hydrogen ions are formed according to the following reaction, where H_2CO_3 is a short-lived compound called carbonic acid that immediately dissociates to a hydrogen ion and a bicarbonate ion:

$$CO_2 + H_2O \rightleftharpoons H_2CO_3 \rightleftharpoons H^+ + HCO_3^-$$

The left side of this reaction is readily reversible and is catalyzed in both directions by the enzyme carbonic anhydrase, which is present in high amounts in red blood cells. If CO_2 levels increase, the reactions move from left to right. Conversely, if the concentration of hydrogen ions rises or the levels of CO_2 decrease, the reactions move from right to left.

In body tissues, CO_2 levels are high because metabolism is generating the gas. Thus, the reactions move to the right, and CO_2 is converted to H^+ and (HCO_3^-). As blood flows through the lungs, however, dissolved CO_2 diffuses into the alveoli and is exhaled. Thus, CO_2 levels in the lung capillaries decrease, which makes the reactions proceed in the opposite direction, right to left so that (HCO_3^-) is converted back to CO_2 and exhaled.

In addition to being transported as bicarbonate ions, about 25% of the CO_2 in blood is bound to hemoglobin. The remainder—about 7%–10%—exists dissolved in solution in the plasma and within red blood cells.

Respiratory Centre Activity Varies Among Species with Different Metabolic Rates

The respiratory centres are sensitive to a variety of other factors besides gases and hydrogen ions, such as sleep, stress, hormones, and body size. Recall from Chapter 40 that small animals tend to have higher metabolic rates than larger animals. Thus, small animals would be expected to require more oxygen per unit mass than would larger animals. This is not achieved by having disproportionately large lungs in small animals. Instead, small animals have higher breathing rates than do large animals. The respiratory centres are set at a higher frequency in smaller, active animals. For example, a typical adult human takes about 12–14 breaths per minute at rest, while hummingbirds, small rodents, and shrews have astonishingly high rates of breathing, up to many hundreds of breaths per minute (Table 45.1). Thus, the respiratory activity of small, highly active animals is matched with their metabolism by increasing the resting breathing rate. This is similar to the differences in cardiac function among species. Small animals have hearts that are roughly proportional to their body size, but with higher heart rates than are found in larger animals (see Chapter 44). Parallel changes in the heart and breathing rates are adaptations that allow small animals to have small hearts and lungs yet achieve high metabolic rates.

45.5 MECHANISMS OF OXYGEN TRANSPORT IN BLOOD

Learning Outcomes:

1. Describe the characteristics of respiratory pigments in the blood of vertebrates and the hemolymph of many invertebrates.
2. Describe the oxygen-hemoglobin dissociation curve and factors that can modify the shape of the curve.
3. Write the equation for the bidirectional reaction between hemoglobin and oxygen.

Gases, such as oxygen, are soluble in the plasma component of blood, but as with all solutes, there are limits to how much of a gas can dissolve in a volume of water. The amount of gas dissolved in the body fluids is not sufficient to sustain life in most animals. In nearly all animals, therefore, the amount of oxygen in the body fluid compartments must be increased above that which can be physically dissolved. This is made possible because of the widespread occurrence in animals of oxygen-binding proteins, which increase the total amount of oxygen available to cells. In this section, we examine the nature, function, and evolution of these molecules.

Oxygen Binds to Respiratory Pigments

The amount of oxygen dissolved in blood under normal conditions is too low to provide the energy needed for the basal metabolic rate of most animals. Even the simple act of sleeping requires more oxygen than the amount dissolved in plasma. Therefore, animals have evolved a way to carry a reservoir of oxygen on plasma proteins. These proteins are called **respiratory pigments** because they have a colour (blue or red). In vertebrates, the pigments are contained within red blood cells, but in many invertebrates the pigments circulate in the plasma. Enclosing the pigments within blood cells is an efficient way to package them, because the pigments are in close proximity to various cellular enzymes that assist in binding and unbinding the gases to the pigments.

Respiratory pigments are proteins containing one or more metal atoms in their cores. The metal atom binds to oxygen. Typically, the metal is iron (Fe^{2+}) in vertebrates and many marine invertebrates, but in decapod crustaceans, arachnids, and many molluscs (including cephalopods and some gastropods), it is copper (Cu^+). The copper-containing pigment, **hemocyanin**, gives the blood or hemolymph a bluish tint. **Hemoglobin** is the major iron-containing pigment and gives blood a red colour when oxygen is bound.

Hemoglobin gets its name because it is a globular (soluble) protein, and it contains a chemical group called a heme in its core. An atom of iron is bound within the heme group. In vertebrates, hemoglobin consists of four protein subunits, each with its own heme group and iron atom. Thus, a single molecule of hemoglobin can bind up to four molecules of oxygen.

Respiratory pigments share certain characteristics that make them ideal for transporting oxygen in blood. First, they all have a high affinity for binding oxygen. Second, the binding between the pigment and oxygen is noncovalent and reversible. It would not do much good for a protein to bind oxygen if it could not unload the oxygen to cells that need it. Thus, the binding is reversible, as shown here:

$$O_2 + Hb \rightleftharpoons HbO_2$$

where Hb is hemoglobin, HbO_2 is called oxyhemoglobin, and the double arrows indicate that the reaction is reversible.

The amount of pigment present in the blood is great enough to provide sufficient oxygen to meet all but the most strenuous exertion. In humans, for example, the presence of hemoglobin gives blood about 45 times as much oxygen-carrying capacity as plasma alone. Differences exist among respiratory pigments, however, at the molecular level. For example, the amino acid sequences of hemoglobins from different species vary, in some cases considerably. Human hemoglobin is similar but not identical to that of other mammals, and mammalian hemoglobins have numerous amino acid differences from other vertebrate hemoglobins. The differences in amino acid sequences cause slight changes in the overall three-dimensional shape of hemoglobin, which alters its affinity for oxygen. As a general rule, animals with the highest metabolic rates tend to have hemoglobins with lower oxygen affinity, while animals with lower metabolic rates have higher affinities. That may sound paradoxical at first, but consider the preceding reactions again. Because the hemoglobin of small animals with high metabolic rates has lower oxygen affinity, the reverse reaction ($HbO_2 \rightarrow Hb + O_2$) will be more likely to occur when oxygen is diffusing from the blood to active cells. In other words, hemoglobin unloads its oxygen more readily in those animals whose cells use oxygen at the greatest rates.

The Amount of Oxygen Bound to Hemoglobin Depends on the P_{O_2} of Blood

Recall that partial pressure of (P_{O_2}) is a measure of its dissolved concentration. When P_{O_2} is high, more O_2 binds to hemoglobin, while fewer O_2 molecules are bound when P_{O_2} is low. **Figure 45.15** shows the relationship between O_2 binding and P_{O_2}, known as an **oxygen-hemoglobin dissociation curve**. At a P_{O_2} of 100 mmHg, which is found in the blood leaving the lungs, each hemoglobin protein binds four O_2 molecules. It is 100% saturated with oxygen. The P_{O_2} of blood leaving the

Figure 45.15   The human oxygen-hemoglobin dissociation curve.   Depending on the partial pressure of oxygen, oxygen is either loaded onto hemoglobin, as in the lungs, or unloaded from hemoglobin, as in the rest of the body tissues. When P_{O_2} is high, more Fe^{2+} atoms are bound to O_2 and the hemoglobin is more saturated with O_2.

Concept check: *Members of the Channichthyidae family of Antarctic icefish are the only vertebrates that do not have red blood cells and hemoglobin. How do they survive without the oxygen reservoir provided by hemoglobin? (Hint: Think about the effect of temperature on oxygen solubility and on an animal's metabolic rate.)*

tissue capillaries of other parts of the body is lower and depends on metabolic activity and exercise. At rest, the P_{O_2} of blood capillaries in these other parts of the body is typically around 40 mmHg. At this P_{O_2}, hemoglobin releases some O_2 molecules, becoming less saturated with O_2. At high levels of exercise, P_{O_2} drops even further (as low as 20 mmHg) and hemoglobin releases even more O_2. In this way, hemoglobin performs its role of oxygen delivery. In the lungs it binds O_2, and in other tissues of the body it releases some of the O_2 as needed.

You may have noticed that the curve in Figure 45.15 is not linear but S-shaped (sigmoidal). This is because the subunits of hemoglobin are said to cooperate with each other in binding oxygen. Once a molecule of oxygen binds to one subunit's iron atom, the shape of the entire hemoglobin molecule changes, making it easier for a second oxygen to bind to the next subunit, and so on. Thus, the relationship between oxygen pressure and the amount of oxygen bound to hemoglobin becomes very steep in the midrange of the curve, which are those pressures that occur in the tissue capillaries throughout the body except in the lungs. This steepness allows O_2 release to be very sensitive to changes in P_{O_2}, as occurs in exercise, for example.

One of the remarkable features of the oxygen-hemoglobin binding relationship is that it can be influenced by metabolic waste products, such as CO_2 and H^+, and also by temperature. **Figure 45.16a** shows three curves: one obtained under normal resting conditions and the others in the presence of low and high levels of CO_2. CO_2 binds to amino acids in the hemoglobin molecule (not to the iron, like O_2), and when it does, the ability of hemoglobin to continue binding oxygen decreases. Note how

increased CO_2 shifts the curve to the right, such that at any P_{O_2}, less O_2 is bound to hemoglobin. Another way of saying this is that at any P_{O_2}, more O_2 has been released from hemoglobin, thus becoming available to cells. Similar shifts in the curve occur in the presence of acid and increased temperature. Cells generate each of these products—CO_2, acid, and heat—when they are actively metabolizing fuel. The metabolic products enter the surrounding blood vessels, where they disrupt the normal shape of hemoglobin, causing it to release more of its oxygen than would normally occur at that oxygen pressure. This phenomenon is a way in which individual body tissues can obtain more oxygen from the blood to match their changing metabolic demands. Thus, when an animal exercises, the skeletal muscles generate more waste products and heat than does, say, the skin, and therefore the oxyhemoglobin in muscle blood vessels releases more oxygen to the cells where it is immediately needed.

The shift in the oxygen-hemoglobin dissociation curve occurs in all classes of vertebrates (although not in all species), but it has different magnitudes in different species. Not surprisingly, perhaps, the most metabolically active animals, such as mice, show a greater shift for a given increase in CO_2, H^+, or heat than do less active animals. Recall from Chapter 44 that these same waste products of metabolism also cause local vasodilation of arterioles. Thus, the more metabolically active a tissue is, the more blood flow it receives, which means more oxygen-bound hemoglobin. Moreover, the oxygen is unloaded from hemoglobin more readily because of the shift in the curve. This is another example of how adaptive changes in circulatory and respiratory functions often occur in parallel.

(a) Shifts in the oxygen-hemoglobin dissociation curve

(b) Oxygen-hemoglobin dissociation curves of different animals

Figure 45.16   Differences in oxygen-hemoglobin dissociation curves under different physiological conditions and among different species.   (a) Increasing or decreasing the amounts of carbon dioxide or hydrogen ions (acid), or the temperature of the blood, shift the oxygen-hemoglobin dissociation curve. Actively metabolic tissues generate these products. By shifting the curve, different tissues obtain oxygen from hemoglobin in proportion to their metabolic needs. (b) Oxygen-hemoglobin dissociation curves for three mammals with low (elephant), moderate (human), or high (mouse) relative metabolic rates. For any P_{O_2}, such as the one shown (40 mmHg), which is typical of the P_{O_2} of tissue capillaries, less oxygen is bound to mouse hemoglobin than to human or elephant and less is bound to human than to elephant hemoglobin. Thus, smaller animals unload O_2 from hemoglobin more readily.

The hemoglobins of metabolically active animals also have a lower affinity for oxygen (**Figure 45.16b**). Small, active animals have curves that are displaced to the right of the human curve, which itself is to the right of the curve for an elephant. At high oxygen pressures, such as those that occur in the lungs, these shifts have little relevance because nearly all the hemoglobin is bound to oxygen at those pressures. At lower oxygen pressures, however, such as those that would occur in the blood vessels of actively metabolic tissues, the difference in the curves becomes significant. For example, look at the three curves at an oxygen pressure of 40 mmHg, a typical value found in tissues that are using oxygen at a resting rate. The mouse hemoglobin has less oxygen bound (its hemoglobin is less saturated) at that pressure than the human hemoglobin, which in turn has less oxygen bound than the elephant hemoglobin. In other words, the mouse hemoglobin has released more of its oxygen to the hungry tissues than have the other animal hemoglobins.

A useful way to compare the relative affinities of hemoglobin for oxygen in different species is to compare the oxygen pressure required to half-saturate hemoglobin—the so-called P_{50} value of a species' hemoglobin (see the final column of Table 45.1).

GENOMES AND PROTEOMES

Hemoglobin Evolved More Than 500 Million Years Ago

Oxygen-carrying molecules are among the most ancient proteins found in animals. They appear to have begun as simple, single-subunit proteins, such as muscle myoglobin, which stores oxygen in muscle cells. Around 500 million years ago, the gene for this ancient molecule duplicated, resulting in one gene that coded for myoglobin and the other for an early form of hemoglobin. Thus, animals gained the ability to not only store oxygen in tissues but also transport it throughout the body via the circulation.

Modern hemoglobin in adult mammals contains four subunits, designated $\alpha 1$, $\alpha 2$, $\beta 1$, and $\beta 2$. The two alpha and two beta subunits are identical. Early in animal evolution, hemoglobin existed only as monomers (one subunit) or dimers (two subunits), which is still observed in lampreys. Later, gene duplication created the second set of subunits, leading to the four-subunit form, which first appeared in sharks and bony fish. As we have seen in this chapter, the subunit structure of hemoglobin enables one hemoglobin molecule to bind four oxygen molecules. Equally important, it allows the sigmoidal shape of the oxygen-hemoglobin dissociation curve.

As noted earlier, modern hemoglobins differ among species within the same class of vertebrates, and even more so between classes. This suggests that evolution of the hemoglobin genes continued even after the four-subunit structure appeared. The mutations that arose in the hemoglobin genes affected the structure of the hemoglobin molecule. One consequence is that the affinity of hemoglobin for oxygen differs among animals, as discussed earlier. The differences in affinity may result, for example, in better oxygen-capturing ability of animals living in regions of low oxygen pressure, for example, at high altitude. They also account, at least in part, for the ability of metabolically active animals to unload oxygen from hemoglobin more readily than less metabolically active organisms.

Despite the high frequency of mutations in the hemoglobin genes in vertebrates, certain regions of the molecule have remained well conserved. Not surprisingly, these are regions that are critically important for the function of the molecule. For instance, the amino acids that encase the heme group and iron atom of each subunit have changed little if at all during evolution. Similarly, the amino acid sequences associated with sites of subunit interactions have also resisted evolutionary change. Mutations that arise in these regions are typically not adaptive and may even be lethal.

Some mutations in the hemoglobin genes may appear to be detrimental because they negatively impact hemoglobin's function, and yet they provide a selective advantage under certain conditions. Consider the disease **sickle-cell anemia**. In this case, substitution of a thymine for an adenine at one position in the hemoglobin gene results in a single amino acid substitution. This produces an abnormal form of hemoglobin that tends to form polymers and precipitate under low oxygen conditions, particularly in capillaries and veins. The protein forms long fibrous strands that may permanently deform the red blood cell, making it sickle-shaped (**Figure 45.17**). Sickled cells are less able to move smoothly through capillaries and can block blood flow, resulting in severe pain and cell death of the surrounding tissue.

The sickled red blood cells are also fragile and easily destroyed. The loss of those cells and their hemoglobin results in anemia, meaning that people with the disease have less oxygen-carrying capacity in their blood. Only individuals who are homozygous for this mutation show the dramatic phenotype of the disease. Heterozygotes are relatively unaffected.

The sickle-cell gene mutation is present in up to a third of individuals living in malaria-prone regions of Africa and to lesser extents in the Middle East and Eastern Europe. The prevalence in the Canadian black community is unknown, but the Sickle-Cell Association of Ontario estimates that 1 in 12 black Canadians has the disease. Why would such an obviously harmful mutation persist in the human population?

Malaria, a mosquito-borne disease, is a global health threat that is responsible for more than 300 million severe illnesses and 1 million deaths every year. When an infected mosquito bites, it injects a parasitic protozoan (*Plasmodium falciparum*) into the circulation, where it spends part of its life cycle growing and multiplying within the host's red blood cells. The sickle-cell

3 μm

Figure 45.17 **Sickle-cell anemia.** A mutation in the hemoglobin gene can result in hemoglobin molecules that deform red blood cells, giving them a sickled appearance.

trait protects individuals from developing full-blown malaria, although the reason for this is uncertain. One favoured hypothesis states that the parasite lowers the oxygen pressure in red blood cells by consuming oxygen to support its own metabolism. This may render the red blood cell susceptible to sickling even in heterozygous individuals. The damaged cells are destroyed and removed from the circulation, which also removes the parasite and limits its ability to multiply. Another hypothesis states that the heterozygotic condition results in a more efficient immune response of the body to the presence of the parasite. Thus, although both malaria and homozygous sickle-cell anemia are life threatening, heterozygotes for the sickle-cell trait develop neither pronounced anemia nor severe malaria and therefore have an advantage in areas in which malaria is present. This heterozygote advantage explains why the sickle-cell mutation persists among certain human populations.

45.6 ADAPTATIONS TO EXTREME CONDITIONS

Learning Outcomes:

1. List adaptations of the respiratory and circulatory systems of animals living at high altitudes.
2. Discuss the adaptations of the respiratory and circulatory systems of diving animals.

Many animals are able to live permanently or temporarily in low-oxygen environments. Many humans, for instance, live in mountainous regions, and llamas and mountain goats spend most of their lives at extremely high altitudes. Other animals may only transiently encounter periods of oxygen deprivation, such as some reptiles, birds, and mammals that dive underwater to forage for food. As described in this section, several adaptations allow animals to exploit these environments, but all of them include changes in both cardiovascular and respiratory activities.

Life at High Altitudes Requires More Hemoglobin

Animals that live at high altitudes must have special adaptations that permit them to obtain the oxygen they need at such low atmospheric pressures. Llamas, such as the one shown in the chapter-opening photo, can live at altitudes up to 4,800 m, where the P_{O_2} is only about 85 mmHg (compared with 160 mmHg at sea level). Llama hemoglobin is quite different in amino acid sequence from that of other mammals, giving it an extraordinarily high affinity for binding oxygen even at very low atmospheric pressure. In other words, llamas' hemoglobin curves are well to the left of a human's. In addition, llamas have larger hearts and lungs than would be predicted for their body size and a higher number of red blood cells in a given volume of blood. These adaptations provide the oxygen-carrying capacity and cardiac output needed to deliver sufficient oxygen to the tissues, even at low partial pressures of oxygen.

When animals that normally inhabit lowland areas temporarily move to higher altitudes, they develop some of these same features. In humans, for example, the number of red blood cells increases from about 5.1×10^{12} cells/L to about 6.4×10^{12} cells/L. This is stimulated by the hormone erythropoeitin, which is secreted by the kidneys when the arterial P_{O_2} is low. This hormone acts on bone marrow to stimulate maturation of new red blood cells. Moving to higher elevations also increases ventilation because of a faster rate of breathing. The density of capillaries around the alveoli increases at high altitudes, an adaptation that facilitates oxygen diffusion into the blood. Finally, myoglobin content increases in muscle cells, expanding the reservoir of oxygen in the cytosol of those cells. Thus, after several days or weeks at high altitude, the cardiovascular and respiratory systems adapt together to maximize oxygen uptake, diffusion of oxygen into the blood, and the oxygen-carrying capacity of blood.

Diving Animals Have Adaptations That Permit Long Dives Underwater

Many birds, some reptiles, and a few mammals spend time underwater, foraging for food or escaping predators. During that time, the animal cannot breathe. In short dives, this is not a problem. We are all familiar with our own ability to stay underwater for a minute or so. After that time, the oxygen from our last breath is used up, blood levels of carbon dioxide begin to rise, and we must surface for air. Some marine mammals, however, have an astonishing ability to remain underwater for very long periods— up to nearly two hours in some species. During that time, they continue to be active and search for food. How do they do it?

Like high-altitude animals, many diving animals have unusually high numbers of red blood cells, allowing them to store more oxygen in their blood than nondiving animals. In some cases, such as seals, the extra blood cells are stored in the spleen until they dive, at which time the spleen contracts, like wringing a wet washcloth, and ejects the blood cells into the circulation. When seals resurface, the blood cells are sequestered again in the spleen until needed. In addition to having more erythrocytes, diving mammals typically have larger blood volumes than comparably sized mammals that live exclusively on land.

The muscles of diving mammals usually contain large quantities of myoglobin and its bound oxygen. This means that the muscles do not need to consume the precious stores of oxygen circulating in blood. Instead, the blood and its oxygen can be routed to other critical structures that lack myoglobin, such as the eyes, certain glands, the brain, and the placenta if the animal is pregnant.

Eventually, even with these adaptations, the oxygen in muscles and blood can become so depleted that the only way to prolong the dive is for cells to begin respiring anaerobically. Most of a long dive, in fact, occurs under anaerobic conditions.

Other adaptations to hypoxia (low oxygen levels) are found in fish, such as the cunner (*Tautogolabrus adspersus*), a western North Atlantic wrasse species that lives year-round in the inshore marine environments along the coast from Newfoundland and Labrador to Virginia. Chris Corkum and Kurt Gamperl of Memorial University of Newfoundland have recently shown that this wrasse species is capable of metabolic depression, allowing it to tolerate hypoxic conditions.

This concludes our examination of the ways in which animals obtain oxygen and eliminate carbon dioxide. We now address the importance of healthy lung function in humans and the ways in which humans are affected by respiratory diseases.

45.7 HUMAN HEALTH CONNECTION

Learning Outcomes:

1. Describe the causes, symptoms, and current treatments of several respiratory system diseases.
2. Describe the impact of smoking tobacco on respiratory health.

Respiratory diseases afflict more than 3 million people in Canada. Most of these diseases are chronic—once they appear, they last for the rest of a person's lifetime. Lifestyle factors, such as smoking tobacco and exposure to air pollution, can cause some respiratory disorders or make existing conditions worse. In this section, we examine a few of the most common respiratory disorders, as well as some of their causes and treatments.

Asthma Is a Disease of Hyperreactive Bronchioles

You learned earlier that the bronchioles deliver fresh air to the alveoli. Bronchioles are thin structures surrounded by smooth muscle cells that can contract in the presence of airborne pollutants or other potentially damaging substances. However, in the disease **asthma**, which affects 8%–10% of Canadians, the muscles around the bronchioles are hyperexcitable and contract more than usual. Contraction of the smooth muscles narrows the bronchioles, a process called bronchoconstriction. This makes it difficult to move air in and out of the lungs, because resistance to airflow increases when the diameter of the airways decreases. Often, the resistance to airflow can be so great that the movement of air creates a characteristic wheezing sound.

Asthma tends to run in families and therefore may have a genetic basis. Several known triggers can elicit wheezing, including exercise, cold air, and allergic reactions. The latter is of interest because asthma is believed to be partly the result of an imbalance in the immune system (see Chapter 50), which controls inflammation and other allergic responses. In fact, during flare-ups of asthma, a viscous, mucus-like fluid may clog the airways and make symptoms worse.

The symptoms of asthma can be alleviated by having the patient inhale an aerosol mist containing **bronchodilators**, compounds that bind to the muscles around bronchioles and cause them to relax and widen. To help reduce the inflammation of the lungs, patients may inhale a mist containing hormones with anti-inflammatory actions. There is no cure for asthma, but with regular treatment and the avoidance of known triggers, most asthmatics can lead normal lives.

Tobacco Smoke Can Cause Respiratory Health Problems and Cancer

Smoking tobacco products is one of the leading global causes of death, contributing to more than 37,000 deaths in Canada a year and more than 5 million per year worldwide. On average, people who smoke up to one pack of cigarettes per day live seven years less than nonsmokers, while heavy smokers lose 15 to 25 years of life. Pregnant women who smoke run a high risk of their babies being born underweight, a potentially serious condition that may affect the newborn's long-term health.

Up to 85% of all new cases of lung cancer diagnosed each year are attributable to smoking, making lung cancer the leading cause of preventable death. Equally important, however, is that smoking is estimated to be responsible for nearly 30% of all cancers, including cancer of the mouth and throat, esophagus, bladder, pancreas, and ovaries. Smoking is also a leading cause of cardiovascular disease, high blood pressure, atherosclerosis, and stroke. Smoking as few as three to five cigarettes per day raises the risk of heart disease.

Because the products of tobacco smoke are inhaled directly into the lungs, the chemicals in smoke can do considerable damage to lung tissue. Even adolescents who have only recently started smoking have increased mucus (phlegm) production in their airways (which inhibits the flow of air in and out of the airways), shortness of breath, and reduced lung growth. Thousands of chemicals, including more than 40 known cancer-causing compounds, have been identified in cigarette smoke. Some of these chemicals—such as formaldehyde—are toxic to all cells. Others, such as the odourless gas carbon monoxide (CO), have harmful effects on lung function in particular. CO competes with oxygen for binding sites in hemoglobin, thereby reducing hemoglobin saturation. Heavy smokers who smoke more than a pack of cigarettes per day may have up to 15% less oxygen-carrying capacity in their blood.

In addition to being a risk factor for lung cancer and cardiovascular disease, long-term smoking is the major cause of the serious and irreversible disease emphysema.

Emphysema Causes Permanent Lung Damage

Unlike asthma, in which the major problems are inflamed airways and hyperreactive bronchioles, emphysema involves extensive lung damage (**Figure 45.18**). The disease reduces the elastic quality of the lungs and the total surface area of the alveoli, which cuts the rate of oxygen diffusion from the lungs into the circulation. Consequently, one sign of emphysema is a lower than normal partial pressure of oxygen in the arteries. It is also physically harder to exhale because of the loss of elasticity, and therefore arterial CO_2 levels increase. Finally, the terminal ends of the bronchioles are often damaged, which increases resistance to airflow and creates asthma-like symptoms and shortness of breath.

Reduced blood oxygen and poor lung function limit the patient's ability to function, and in its late stages emphysema results in a person being essentially bedridden. Oxygen therapy, in which the person breathes a mixture of air and pure oxygen from a portable gas tank, can provide some help. The extra oxygen increases the pressure gradient for oxygen from the alveoli to the lung capillaries, promoting oxygen diffusion into the blood.

It is estimated that about 7% of the Canadian population has emphysema. Emphysema is a progressive disease that does not go away. As the years go by, the disease usually worsens, although medical care can slow the rate at which it worsens. In some cases, emphysema results from an enzyme deficiency in the lungs that destroys the protein that provides the recoil during exhalation, or it may result from chronic exposure to air or industrial pollution. However, the overwhelming majority of cases, 85%, are due to smoking. Toxins in cigarettes and other tobacco products damage the lungs by stimulating white blood cells to release proteolytic enzymes that degrade lung tissue. The likelihood of developing emphysema is tightly correlated with the number of cigarettes smoked during a person's lifetime.

Summary of Key Concepts

45.1 Physical Properties of Gases

- Gas exchange is the process of moving oxygen and carbon dioxide in opposite directions, such as between cells and blood, and between blood and the environment. The partial pressure of oxygen in the environment provides the driving force for its diffusion from air or water across a respiratory organ and into the blood. (Figures 45.1, 45.2)

- Three factors—the pressure of the gas, temperature of the water, and presence of any other solutes—are particularly important for affecting the solubility of a gas in water.

45.2 Types of Respiratory Organs

- Ventilation is the process of bringing oxygenated water or air into contact with a respiratory organ. All respiratory organs have moist surfaces in which gases can dissolve and diffuse, as well as other adaptations that increase the amount of surface area and blood flow. Terrestrial and aquatic animals face different challenges to gas exchange.

- The body surface may be permeable to gases in some invertebrates and in amphibians, eels, and a few other species of fish. (Figure 45.3)

- Most aquatic animals use external or internal gills for gas exchange. (Figures 45.4, 45.5, 45.6)

- Air-breathing animals have evolved two mechanisms to exchange gas with the environment: tracheal systems in insects, and lungs in many arachnids, some land snails, and all terrestrial vertebrates. In insects, air moving down the tracheoles comes into contact with fluid at the tracheole tips. Oxygen from the air dissolves in this fluid and diffuses across the tracheole wall and into nearby cells. (Figure 45.7)

- Except for some rare amphibians, all air-breathing terrestrial vertebrates use lungs to bring oxygen into the circulatory system and remove carbon dioxide. All lungs receive deoxygenated blood from the heart and return oxygenated blood to the heart.

- Frogs and most other amphibians ventilate their lungs with positive pressure filling. (Figure 45.8)

45.3 Structure and Function of Mammalian and Avian Respiratory Systems

- The mammalian respiratory system refers to all components of the body that contribute to the exchange of gas between the external environment and the blood. (Figure 45.9)

Broken alveoli   Note large areas without gas-exchange surfaces

Alveolus

|← 0.8 mm →| |← 0.5 mm →|
Normal lung   **Diseased lung**

Figure 45.18   The effects of emphysema.   The destruction of alveoli, caused by this disease, reduces the surface area for gas exchange in the lungs. These light micrographs compare a section of a normal lung (left) with a lung from a person who died of emphysema (right).

- Most reptiles and all birds and mammals ventilate their lungs by negative pressure filling. In mammals, the work is provided by the intercostal muscles and diaphragm. Tidal ventilation is less efficient than the unidirectional flow-through system of fish gills. Tidal volume is proportional to body size among humans and between species. (Figure 45.10, Table 45.1)

- The avian respiratory system, a flow-through system, is unique among vertebrates because it is supplemented with numerous air sacs. Blood flows through the lungs in a crosscurrent direction with respect to the movement of oxygen. This is less efficient in extracting oxygen than the countercurrent flow in fish gills but more efficient than the tidal ventilation system of mammals. (Figures 45.11, 45.12, 45.13)

45.4 Control of Ventilation in Mammalian Lungs

- In mammals, respiratory centres in the brainstem initiate the rhythmic expansion of the lungs. (Figure 45.14)

- Chemoreceptors detect blood levels of hydrogen ions and the partial pressures of carbon dioxide and oxygen, and they relay this information through nerves to the respiratory centres. The respiratory centres are also sensitive to other factors, such as sleep, stress, hormones, and body size.

45.5 Mechanisms of Oxygen Transport in Blood

- There are limits to how much of a gas can dissolve in water. These limits are overcome in nearly all animals by either transporting a gas reversibly bound to a protein carrier or by transforming the gas into a more soluble form.

- Animals have evolved a way to carry a reservoir of oxygen on respiratory pigments, large proteins containing one or more metal atoms that bind to oxygen. Typically, the metal is iron in vertebrates and many marine invertebrates, and copper in decapod crustaceans, arachnids, and many molluscs including cephalopods and some gastropods.

- The amount of oxygen bound to hemoglobin depends on the partial pressure of oxygen in the blood. Metabolic waste products can influence the oxygen-hemoglobin binding relationship. (Figures 45.15, 45.16, 45.17)

- The evolution of the globin gene family has resulted in several specialized hemoglobin proteins. Heterozygotes for the sickle-cell allele are resistant to malaria. (Figure 45.17)

45.6 Adaptations to Extreme Conditions

- Several adaptations in cardiovascular and respiratory activities allow animals to exploit low-oxygen environments. Animals that inhabit high altitudes have larger hearts and lungs, and hemoglobin with a high affinity for binding oxygen. Many diving animals have unusually high hematocrits and muscles with large quantities of myoglobin. Some fish can down-regulate their metabolism to tolerate low-oxygen conditions.

45.7 Human Health Connection

- In asthma, the muscles around the bronchioles contract more than usual, increasing resistance to airflow.

- Smoking tobacco products is one of the leading global causes of death. Smoking is strongly linked to cancer, cardiovascular disease, stroke, and emphysema. (Figure 45.18)

Test to Assess Your Learning

1. The driving force for diffusion of oxygen across the cells of a respiratory organ is
   a. the difference in the partial pressure of oxygen in the environment and in the blood.
   b. the humidity.
   c. the partial pressure of carbon dioxide in the blood.
   d. the air temperature.
   e. all of the above.

2. Carbon dioxide is considered a harmful by-product of cellular respiration because it
   a. lowers the pH of the blood.
   b. leads to damage of plasma membranes.
   c. competes with oxygen for transport in the blood.
   d. all of the above.
   e. (a) and (b) only.

3. The process of bringing oxygenated water or air into contact with a gas-exchange surface is
   a. respiration.
   b. inspiration.
   c. ventilation.
   d. resuscitation.
   e. exhalation.

4. The group of vertebrates that relies on gas exchange across the skin as well as in the lungs to maintain sufficient blood oxygen levels is
   a. the fish.
   b. the reptiles.
   c. the amphibians.
   d. the birds.
   e. the mammals.

5. The countercurrent exchange mechanism seen in the gills of fish
   a. maximizes oxygen uptake by the bloodstream.
   b. is a less efficient mechanism for gas exchange compared with mammalian lungs.
   c. occurs because the flow of blood is in the same direction as water flowing across the gills.
   d. increases the amount of energy necessary for respiration.
   e. requires that the fish swallow water.

6. The tracheal system of insects
   a. consists of several tracheae that connect to multiple lungs within the different segments of the body.
   b. consists of extensively branching tubes that are in close contact with all the cells of the body.
   c. allows oxygen to diffuse across the thin exoskeleton of the insect to the bloodstream.
   d. requires constant movement of the wings to move air into and out of the body.
   e. none of the above.

7. _____ is secreted by alveolar cells in the mammalian lung to prevent the collapse of alveoli caused by surface tension at the interface of air and extracellular fluid.
   a. Hemoglobin
   b. Myoglobin
   c. Mucus
   d. Hemolymph
   e. Surfactant

8. In negative pressure filling, air moves into the lungs when
   a. the volume of the thoracic cavity increases.
   b. the pressure in the thoracic cavity decreases.
   c. air is forced down the trachea by muscular contractions of the mouth and pharynx.

d. all of the above.

e. (a) and (b) only.

9. Which of the following factors does not alter the rate of breathing by influencing the respiratory centres of the brain?

a. carbon dioxide partial pressures in the blood

b. oxygen partial pressures in the blood

c. blood pH

d. blood glucose levels

e. hydrogen ion concentration in the blood

10. With rare exceptions, the majority of oxygen is transported in the blood of vertebrates

a. by binding to plasma proteins.

b. by binding to hemoglobin in erythrocytes.

c. as a component of large organic molecules that are broken down by the cells.

d. as dissolved gas in the cytoplasm in the erythrocytes.

e. by binding to myoglobin.

Articulate to Assess Your Learning

1. Define countercurrent exchange in the context of gas exchange.

2. Explain some of the special adaptations for life at high altitudes; why are such adaptations necessary?

Collaborate to Assess and Extend Your Learning

1. A lungless frog was recently discovered in Indonesia. What would happen to this frog (or to the lungless salamander) if the animal were placed on land and then allowed to dry out?

2. How does surface area in the lungs influence the mammalian respiratory system? What would happen if an infection were to destroy some of the lung tissue?

3. Two principles of biology are that new properties emerge from complex interactions and structure determines function. How are these principles related to what you have learned in this chapter about hemoglobin?

Visit McGraw-Hill Ryerson Connect™ for additional study resources.

Excretory Systems and Salt and Water Balance

Chapter Outline

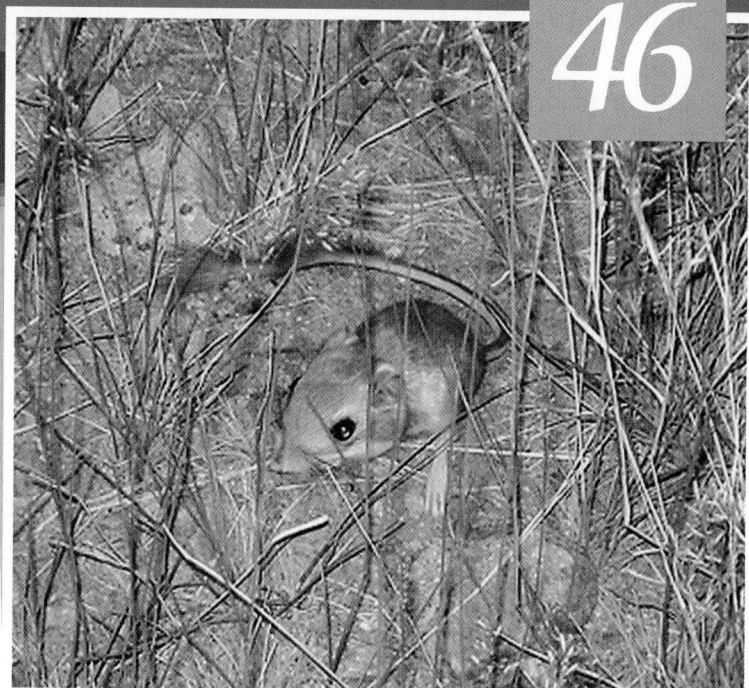

Ord's kangaroo rat (*Dipodomys ordii*). Found in the sand hill areas of southeastern Alberta and southwestern Saskatchewan, this rodent must conserve body stores of water.

Homeostasis has been a theme of the previous several chapters. Animals maintain a variety of physiological processes—including energy intake and usage, blood pressure, body temperature, and blood oxygen levels—within normal and often narrow ranges. Homeostasis is also critical in the regulation of salt and water levels in body fluid compartments. Changes in the concentrations of salts in the extracellular and intracellular fluids have the potential to disrupt proper cellular function, for example, by altering the potential difference across plasma membranes in the heart and brain. Salt concentrations and water volumes in the different body compartments are related to each other, because a major way in which water moves between compartments is by osmosis, which in turn depends on the dissolved solutes in water. Consequently, changes in salt concentrations in body fluids may also affect cell volume, which in turn can cause cell death.

As you have learned, homeostasis is an energy-requiring process. A significant portion of an animal's daily energy expenditure goes toward maintaining salt and water homeostasis. The ability to do so is complicated by many factors, such as the environment and climate in which an animal lives, and its access to sufficient supplies of drinking water. In addition, animals use water from their bodies to eliminate metabolic waste products through their excretory system, and that water needs to be regularly replenished.

In this chapter, we examine why salt and water balance is vital for survival, how it is affected by the requirement to eliminate metabolic wastes, and how different excretory organs participate in these processes. We then highlight some of the major features of the vertebrate and mammalian kidney, examine how the kidney eliminates wastes and regulates salt and water balance, and consider how kidney disease affects human health.

46.1   PRINCIPLES OF HOMEOSTASIS OF INTERNAL FLUIDS

Learning Outcomes:

1. Explain why a balance of water and electrolytes are critical for an animal's survival.
2. List ways in which water and ions (electrolytes) move across cell membranes and between body fluid compartments.
3. Describe the different kinds of nitrogenous wastes and their relative toxicities.
4. Compare and contrast osmotic adaptations of freshwater fish with those of marine fish.
5. List two ways of classifying animals according to how they adapt to osmotic challenges.

As we saw in Chapter 44, an animal's internal fluids exist in compartments within the body. In invertebrates, these fluids include the hemolymph and the intracellular fluid, and in vertebrates they include the plasma component of blood, the interstitial fluid surrounding cells, and the intracellular fluid. The major salts found in animals' bodies, and some of their chief functions, were summarized in Chapter 39 (refer back to Table 39.1). In solution, salts dissociate to form charged ions. Because ions are electrically charged, such salts are referred to as electrolytes. In this section, we will examine why this characteristic is so important and how an animal's electrolyte concentration and water volume are maintained within normal ranges.

Balance of Water and Electrolytes Is Critical for Survival

Maintenance of normal body water levels is of great importance for all animals. Not only is water the major portion of an animal's body mass, but it is also the solvent that permits dissolved solutes to interact in chemical reactions. Water is the transport vehicle that brings oxygen and nutrients to cells, and removes wastes generated by metabolism.

When an animal's water volume is reduced below the normal range, we say the animal is dehydrated. In terrestrial animals, dehydration may occur if sufficient drinking water is not available, or when water is lost by evaporation (perspiring or panting). Regardless of the cause, dehydration can be a serious, potentially life-threatening condition. For example, because blood is roughly 50% plasma (water), blood volume may decrease in dehydrated animals. Reduced fluid volume compromises the ability of the circulatory system to move nutrients and wastes throughout the body, and to help regulate body temperature on hot days (see Chapters 40 and 44).

Electrolyte balance is also very important for animals. A change of only a few percent in the extracellular fluid concentrations of K^+, for example, can trigger changes in nerve, heart, and skeletal muscle function by altering membrane potential (see Chapter 41). Other electrolytes, such as Ca^{2+}, Mg^{2+}, PO_4^{3-}, and SO_4^{2-}, participate in various biological activities. These include serving as cofactors for enzyme activation, participating in bone formation, forming part of the extracellular matrices around cells, and activating cellular events, such as exocytosis and muscle contraction. A serious imbalance in any of these ions can disrupt cellular activities and in some cases may result in death of the cells.

Water and Salts Move Between Fluid Compartments by Different Mechanisms

Water moves between adjacent body compartments by osmosis down an osmotic gradient (see Chapter 6). Changes in the salt concentration in one compartment will lead to changes in fluid distribution between the compartments. These changes can cause cells to shrink or swell. When, for example, the salt concentration of extracellular fluid increases, water moves by osmosis from inside cells to the extracellular fluid, causing the cells to shrink. Shrinking or swelling of cells in the brain, heart, and other vital organs can rupture plasma membranes, leading to cell death.

Whereas water moves between fluid compartments by osmosis, dissolved salts, such as sodium and potassium ions, move by different mechanisms. All ions have very limited ability to diffuse across plasma membranes, because of their high water solubility and low lipid solubility. As described in Chapter 6, ions may cross membranes through channels formed by proteins that create a pore in the membrane. Alternatively, ions may be actively transported across epithelial cells that line tubelike structures, such as those in the kidneys. Still other epithelia, such as those in gills, can actively transport salts between the surrounding salt or fresh water and the animal's body fluids. As this type

of transport is an active process, it requires energy stored in the chemical bonds of ATP. Animals that face exceptional challenges to maintaining salt balance, such as marine fish, must expend a considerable share of their daily energy budget to transport ions across epithelial cells.

Salt and Water Balance Occurs Despite Obligatory Exchanges with the Environment

Many vital processes—obtaining oxygen and eliminating carbon dioxide, consuming and metabolizing food, regulating body temperature, and eliminating nitrogenous wastes—have the potential to disturb salt and water balance. Therefore, these processes require additional energy expenditure to minimize or reverse the disturbance. Exchanges of salt and water with the environment that occur as a consequence of vital processes, such as respiration or the elimination of wastes, are called obligatory exchanges because the animal is "obliged" to make them (**Figure 46.1**). Next we will examine a few of these obligatory exchanges and how they are related to an animal's environment and life history.

Elimination of Nitrogenous Wastes   Proteins and RNA molecules exist for a finite period of time before they are broken down to smaller components. Among the degradation products of proteins and nucleic acids are **nitrogenous wastes** (**Figure 46.2**), molecules that include nitrogen from amino groups (NH_2). These wastes are toxic at high concentrations and must be eliminated from the body. Nitrogenous wastes are

Respiration: Water vapour exits during breathing.

Metabolism: Cells produce H_2O during metabolism.

Waste elimination: Salt and H_2O are lost in feces and urine.

Food ingestion: Food introduces salt and H_2O.

Body temperature regulation: H_2O is lost by evaporation.

Figure 46.1   Types of obligatory salt and water exchanges in a terrestrial animal.   Obligatory exchanges with the environment occur as the result of necessary life processes.

Concept check: *Can animals completely avoid all the losses resulting from obligatory exchanges?*

Animal group	Most aquatic animals	Mammals, most amphibians, some marine fishes, some reptiles, and some terrestrial invertebrates	Birds, insects, and most reptiles
Major form of nitrogenous waste	Ammonia (NH_3) or Ammonium ions (NH_4^+)	Urea	Uric acid
Energy required for production	None	Moderate	High
Amount of water required for excretion	High	Moderate	Low
Toxicity of waste	High	Low	Low

Figure 46.2 Nitrogenous wastes produced by different animal groups. The three forms of nitrogenous wastes, which are derived from the breakdown of proteins or nucleic acids, have different properties.

Principle: *Living organisms use energy. Energy from ATP is required to convert nitrogenous wastes into urea and uric acid. Different animals, therefore, must expend more or less energy each day to rid themselves of toxic nitrogenous wastes.*

usually found in three forms—ammonia and ammonium ions, urea, or uric acid—depending on the species and the environment in which it lives. The elimination of nitrogenous wastes occurs via excretory organs, such as the kidneys, or via other specialized structures, such as gills. Only certain species, including sharks, rays, and skates, can survive with high levels of nitrogenous wastes in their blood and other body fluids.

Ammonia (NH_3) and ammonium ions (NH_4^+) are the most highly toxic of the nitrogenous wastes because they disrupt pH, ion electrochemical gradients, and many chemical reactions that involve oxidations and reductions. Animals that excrete wastes in this form typically live in water. In marine invertebrates, NH_3 and NH_4^+ are continually excreted across the skin, whereas in freshwater fish these wastes are excreted via the gills and kidneys. Because ammonia is so toxic, aquatic animals excrete it as quickly as it is formed. However, some terrestrial snails and crustaceans can excrete ammonia in its gaseous form, which is less toxic and does not require water for elimination. The chief advantage of excreting nitrogenous wastes as NH_3 or NH_4^+ is that energy is not required to produce them, which is not the case for urea and uric acid, as described next.

All mammals, most amphibians, some marine fish, some reptiles, and some terrestrial invertebrates convert ammonia into **urea**, which is then excreted. Urea is less toxic than ammonia, and it does not require large volumes of water for its excretion. Animals can tolerate some accumulation of urea in their blood, tissues, and storage organs, such as the urinary bladder. This conserves water, removes the necessity for constant excretion, and reduces the likelihood of toxicity. One drawback of producing urea is that the enzymatic conversion of ammonia into urea requires a moderate expenditure of ATP and thus uses up part of an animal's total daily energy budget.

Birds, insects, and most reptiles produce **uric acid** or other nitrogenous compounds called purines. These compounds are less toxic than urea, but they are even more energetically costly to synthesize from ammonia. However, because they are poorly soluble in water, they are not excreted in watery urine. Instead, they are packaged with salts and other waste products into a semisolid, partly dried precipitate for excretion. The energy investment required to produce uric acid, therefore, is balanced against the water conserved by excreting nitrogenous wastes in this form.

Water and Electrolyte Exchanges During Respiration To ventilate its lungs, a terrestrial animal passes air in and out of its airways. Water in the form of water vapour in the mouth, nasal cavity, and upper airways exits the body with each exhalation. As an animal becomes more active, it requires more oxygen and produces more carbon dioxide. These changes are met by an increase in respiratory activity. Breathing becomes deeper and more rapid, which in turn increases the rate of water loss from the body. Thus, respiration in animals with lungs is associated with significant water loss, as can be observed in cold weather when we can see our breath.

As described in Chapter 45, small, active animals with high metabolic rates have higher breathing rates than do larger, less active animals. Consequently, the potential for water loss through respiration is considerably greater in small animals, particularly in endotherms. Hummingbirds, for example, may have 15 to 20 times the water loss per gram of body mass as a large goose does.

In aquatic animals, the osmoregulatory challenges are more complex, because fish and other aquatic animals move water, not air, over their respiratory organ (gills). Recall from Chapter 46 that gills, like all respiratory organs, are thin structures with large amounts of surface area and an extensive network of capillaries. These features make gills ideal for gas exchange by diffusion between the capillaries and the surrounding water. However, these same features also make gills ideal for salt and water movement by diffusion and osmosis, respectively.

When differences occur in salt concentration between an aquatic animal's body fluids and the surrounding salt or fresh water, respiration via the gills has the potential to disrupt salt and water balance. The solute concentration of a solution of water is known as the solution's **osmolarity**, expressed as milliosmoles/litre (mOsm/L). The number of dissolved solute molecules determines a solution's osmolarity. For example, a 150-mM NaCl solution has an osmolarity of 300 mOsm/L, because each NaCl molecule dissociates into two molecules, one Na^+ and one Cl^- ($2 \times 150 = 300$). The internal fluid osmolarity of most fish is usually within the range of 225–400 mOsm/L, similar to that of most other vertebrates. However, because freshwater lakes and rivers have very little salt content (usually <25 mOsm/L), a strong concentration gradient for salts could promote the loss of salts from a fish's body into the fresh water. Likewise, a strong osmotic gradient favours the movement of water into a freshwater fish. Water flows across the gills and into the underlying capillaries and bloodstream.

Freshwater fish, therefore, gain water and lose salt when ventilating their gills (**Figure 46.3a**). If left uncorrected, this would cause a dangerous decrease in blood salt concentrations. Freshwater fish avoid this problem using two different strategies. First, their kidneys are adapted to producing copious amounts of dilute urine—up to 30% of their body mass per day (an amount that would be equivalent to about 25 L per day in an average-sized man). Second, specialized gill epithelial cells actively transport Na^+ and Cl^- from the surrounding water into the fish's capillaries. Thus, these two important ions are recaptured from

the water. As the preceding discussion suggests, freshwater fish rarely if ever drink water, except for any that might be swallowed with food.

Other freshwater animals, such as frogs and other adult amphibians, have body surfaces that are permeable to water and used in gas exchange. Like freshwater fish, therefore, they tend to gain water by osmosis and compensate by excreting copious dilute urine. Epithelial cells of the skin actively transport necessary electrolytes from the water into the blood.

Saltwater fish have the opposite problem. They tend to gain salts and lose water across their gills, because seawater has a much higher osmolarity (about 1,000 mOsm/L) than that of their body fluids (**Figure 46.3b**). The gain of salts and the loss of water from the body are only partly offset by the kidneys, which in marine fish produce very little urine so that water can be retained in the body. The urine that is produced has a higher salt concentration than that of freshwater fish.

To prevent dehydration from occurring, marine fish must drink. However, the only water available to them to drink is seawater, which has a very high salt content. Paradoxically, therefore, marine fish drink seawater to replenish the water lost by osmosis through their gills. This creates a new problem: What does the fish do with all the salt it has ingested?

The ingested salt must be eliminated, and this process is accomplished by gill epithelial cells. In contrast to the gills of freshwater fish, which pump salt from the water into the fluids of the fish, gills of marine fish pump salt out of the fish and into the ocean. Thus, marine fish drink seawater to replace the water lost through their gills by osmosis and then expend energy to transport the excess salt out of the body.

Ingestion-Related Fluid and Electrolyte Balance Because foods contain minerals and water, eating also involves an

(a) Freshwater fish

(b) Saltwater fish

Figure 46.3 **Salt and water balance in water breathers.** Water breathing creates osmoregulatory challenges because of diffusion of salts and osmosis of water across gills. These challenges differ between **(a)** freshwater and **(b)** saltwater fish and are met by drinking or not drinking water, by active transport of salts across the gills, and by alterations in urine output.

 Principle: *Living organisms use energy* and *living organisms have mechanisms to maintain homeostasis. Energy from the hydrolysis of ATP is required for all of the active transport processes illustrated here. This energy is required to maintain homeostatic body fluid osmolarities despite the osmotic challenges imposed by the very different environments.*

obligatory exchange of salt and water. Some plant products are more than 95% water by weight, while other foods may contain high amounts of sodium or other minerals. Therefore, the type of diet an animal consumes determines how much salt and water it ingests.

Once food has been digested and absorbed, the unusable parts of food are excreted as solid wastes. Some water and salt are lost by this route in most animals, but exceptions exist. Desert-dwelling kangaroo rats (*Dipodomys ordii*) like the one shown in the chapter-opening photo, produce fecal pellets that are almost completely dry and urine that is very concentrated, which helps these animals conserve water. In addition, their nasal passages are highly convoluted to facilitate countercurrent heat exchange and promote condensation of moisture, thereby minimizing respiratory water loss.

As noted earlier, marine fish absorb some salt water. Other animals besides marine fish may also consume salt water, either because fresh water is unavailable or because they ingest some with the food they eat. Many marine reptiles and birds, for example, ingest seawater when consuming prey or, in some cases, when they spend prolonged periods at sea and thus have no access to fresh water for drinking. These animals have specialized epithelial cells that line structures called salt glands, located in groups around the nostrils, mouth, and eyes (**Figure 46.4**). Salts move from the blood into the interstitial fluid, from where they are actively transported by the epithelial cells of the salt glands into the tubules of the gland. The salts and a small amount of fluid then collect into a central duct and are excreted as highly concentrated solutions. Vertebrates without salt glands cannot survive by drinking seawater, because they have no means of creating and excreting a highly concentrated salt solution.

Use of Water to Regulate Body Temperature   Endotherms use body water to cool off (see Chapter 40). For example, sweating and panting are behaviours used for evaporative cooling. In the process, however, the animal loses salt and water. You know from tasting sweat that it is salty, but the saltiness of sweat and of blood are not the same. Sweat is a hypoosmotic (more dilute) solution compared with blood, so the fluid left behind in the body after perspiration has both a lower volume and a higher salt concentration.

Other than through perspiration and panting, very little water is gained or lost directly across the body surface of terrestrial vertebrates, because their skin is impermeable to water. An exception is the amphibians. Also, in invertebrates, the rate of water loss across the body surface depends on whether the animal is soft bodied, like worms, or covered in a waxy, water-impermeable cuticle, like most insects.

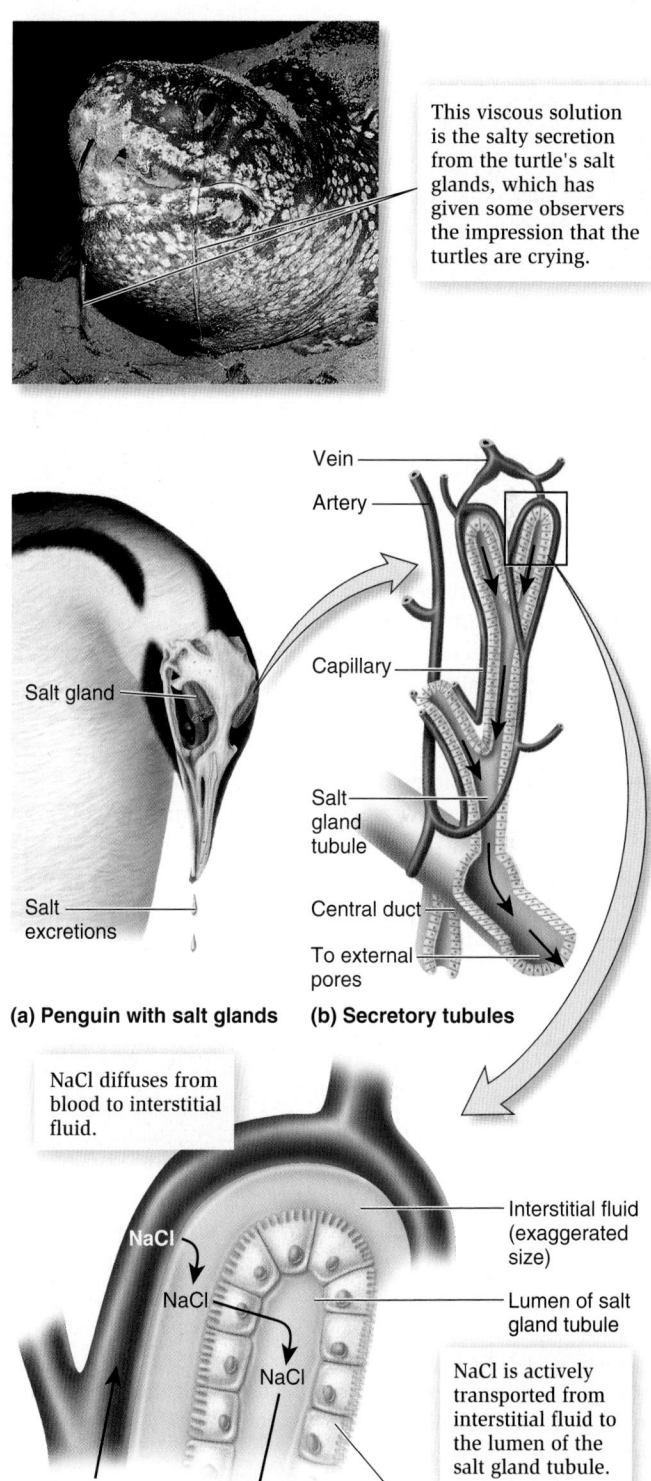

This viscous solution is the salty secretion from the turtle's salt glands, which has given some observers the impression that the turtles are crying.

Vein
Artery
Capillary
Salt gland
Salt gland tubule
Salt excretions
Central duct
To external pores

(a) Penguin with salt glands   **(b) Secretory tubules**

NaCl diffuses from blood to interstitial fluid.

Interstitial fluid (exaggerated size)

NaCl

NaCl

Lumen of salt gland tubule

NaCl

NaCl is actively transported from interstitial fluid to the lumen of the salt gland tubule.

Blood flow

To central duct

Epithelial cell

(c) Collection of salt solution in the tubule

Figure 46.4   Salt glands as an adaptation for marine life. Many marine birds and reptiles have salt glands, which contain a network of secretory tubules that actively transport NaCl from the interstitial fluid into the tubule lumen. The viscous solution then moves through a central duct and to the outside environment through pores in the nose, around the eyes, and in other locations. The black arrows indicate direction of flow of blood or salt gland secretions.

Concept check: *Why can't humans survive by drinking seawater?*

Effects of Metabolism on Water Balance   When food molecules are metabolized to provide the energy to synthesize ATP, water is generated when oxygen captures electrons and combines with hydrogen ions in mitochondria. This water is sometimes called *metabolic water* to indicate its origin. Some animals—especially desert dwellers, which lack ready access to drinking water—depend on this water to provide all or nearly all of their water requirements. In other animals, the production of metabolic water may result in more water than is needed at that time. This excess water is eliminated by the excretory organs or through other routes. As metabolism is ongoing and required for survival, the excretion or retention of metabolic water can be considered a type of obligatory exchange.

As described in the Feature Investigation, the significance of obligatory exchanges and their effects on homeostasis was dramatically illustrated by a long-term investigation by a research team at the University of Florida. Their discovery would lead to a revolution in our understanding of exercise physiology in humans.

Animals Adapt to Osmotic Challenges by Regulating or Conforming

Animals adapt to osmotic challenges posed by the environment in one of two major ways. Some animals regulate their internal osmolarity at a constant level, whereas others conform to the

FEATURE INVESTIGATION

Cade and Colleagues at the University of Florida Discovered Why Athletes' Performance Wanes on Hot Days

On a typical hot summer day in the early 1960s in Gainesville, Florida, the University of Florida football team was practising in full equipment. The players were rapidly becoming dehydrated and, unbeknown to them, the osmolarity of their body fluids was increasing as their bodies produced copious amounts of dilute sweat in an effort to maintain body temperature. The athletes became aware of two things. First, they discovered that they did not need to urinate for long periods after a tough practice session, and second, their performance on the field suffered as they became increasingly fatigued and more susceptible to muscle cramps. In fact, athletes exercising in these conditions have been known to occasionally develop seizures—uncontrolled activity of neurons in the brain. This situation did not escape the notice of the team physicians and, notably, university faculty member and kidney specialist Robert Cade.

Many of the symptoms experienced by the players could be readily explained. The fatigue was directly related to body water loss, which put a strain on the circulatory system and reduced blood flow to muscles and other organs. The muscle cramps and even occasional seizures arose from an imbalance in extracellular electrolytes—notably sodium and potassium—which are secreted in perspiration. The resulting change in extracellular salt concentrations caused a change in the electrical potential across muscle and nerve cell membranes, which triggered the spasms. Lastly, the decreased urine production is one of the body's mechanisms for reducing fluid loss when body water is decreasing.

The question was, How can these effects of extreme exercise best be reversed or prevented? The answer was simple and clever. Cade and his colleagues rejected the prevailing view that drinking any fluids during heavy exercise somehow contributed to cramps and other problems. Instead, they hypothesized that the best way to maintain salt and water homeostasis in a profusely sweating person is to restore to the body exactly what was lost; that is, the person should drink a solution of water and solutes that resembles sweat.

The first thing Cade needed to do was analyze precisely how much sodium, potassium, and other ions are actually present in sweat. Fortunately, he had an abundance of human sweat at his disposal to analyze. Once the players left the field, their jerseys were wrung out and the composition of the sweat was determined with an ion analyzer, such as one called a flame spectrophotometer, as shown in **Figure 46.5**. The concentrations could then be compared with known values of ion concentrations in human blood. The composition of human sweat is now known to change under certain conditions and to vary among people, but Cade's results were typical. The sweat of the athletes contained mostly Na^+, K^+, and Cl^- at concentrations that produced a dilute solution compared with blood. Once Cade completed this analysis, it was a relatively straightforward procedure to make a watery solution of a composition similar to human sweat. The next step was to give the solution to the players before and during the practice sessions and games. Improving its taste—adding some lemon flavouring and some sugar—removed any inhibitions the players may have had about drinking it, while also providing an energy boost.

For the first trial, Cade gave the solution to the freshman players during an intrasquad scrimmage against the more experienced varsity team, whose members received only pure water to drink as a control. Surprisingly, the freshman team outperformed the more experienced players and did not suffer the characteristic late-game fatigue the control subjects (the varsity) experienced. In subsequent years, Cade and other researchers would conduct carefully controlled experiments with humans and laboratory animals to confirm that a balanced solution of salts similar to that present in sweat effectively improves exercise performance and reduces the possibility of dehydration and its consequences.

Because the solution was envisioned as aid for the team known as the University of Florida Gators, the drink eventually came to be called Gatorade. After the team began using the drink, the Gators enjoyed their most successful season. In 1965 the Kansas City Chiefs of the former American Football League became the first professional sports team to try the drink, with

the same result. Today, Gatorade is used at sporting events around the world and for good scientific reason.

The effectiveness of a solution such as Gatorade is due to its ability to restore the correct amounts of water and ions lost during exercise. Importantly, it is very rapidly absorbed because its osmolarity is close to that of body fluids. Many of the other sports drinks subsequently invented contain additional solutes, such as vitamins and other minerals, and many contain higher amounts of sugar. Because of the presence of these other solutes, these drinks may be very hyperosmotic

HYPOTHESIS Athletic performance can be enhanced by maintaining the body's salt and H_2O balance during exercise.

KEY MATERIALS Supply of human sweat for analysis, ion analyzer, salt solutions.

Experimental level   Conceptual level

1 Obtain human sweat from exercising athletes.

Sweat

Dilute solution of salts of unknown composition

2 Analyze composition of sweat by using a flame spectrophotometer, which measures ion concentrations. Prepare artificial solution that mimics composition of sweat. Compare composition of both sweat and artificial solution to known ion concentration in human blood.

Flame spectrophotometer

Salts

Sweat   Artificial solution

3 Add flavouring and sugar to artificial solution.

Sugar

Artificial solution

Sugar improves flavour and provides energy.

4 Provide freshman team with the artificial solution and varsity B-team with water. Hold scrimmage.

Freshman team   Varsity B-team

Artificial solution   Water

Figure 46.5 Cade and colleagues discovered a way to improve athletic performance and prevent salt and water imbalance during strenuous exercise.

Figure 46.5   *(Continued)*

5   **THE DATA**

6   **CONCLUSION** Replacement of fluid with solute concentrations similar to those found in human sweat improves athletic performance compared with water replacement alone.

7   **SOURCE** Most of the original studies described here were published in expanded form in a later report. See Cade, R., et al. 1972. Effect of fluid, electrolyte and glucose replacement during exercise on performance, body temperature, rate of sweat loss, and compositional changes of extracellular fluid. *Journal of Sports Medicine and Physical Fitness* 12:150–156.

relative to body fluids. Therefore, when ingested, they initially tend to draw water out of the interstitial fluid and into the gut lumen by osmosis. This slows down the rate at which the water from the drink gets absorbed into the blood.

The story of Gatorade is one of good common sense based on solid scientific principles of osmolarity and salt and water homeostasis. You can now understand why drinking a dilute salt solution during strenuous exercise is better than drinking water. Although drinking pure water prevents dehydration, if drunk in excess it will actually reduce plasma salt concentrations to below normal. In other words, it will replace one type of salt imbalance with another.

Experimental Questions

1. What symptoms are commonly seen in athletes after strenuous exercise? How are these symptoms related to water loss during exercise? What did Robert Cade and his colleagues hypothesize about this?
2. How did the researchers test their hypothesis?
3. What was the result of consuming the drink during exercise?

osmolarity of their environment (e.g., the sea). Animals that maintain constant internal salt concentrations and osmolarities, even when living in water with very different osmolarities than their body fluids, are called **osmoregulators**. Such animals drink or excrete water and salt as necessary to maintain an internal osmolarity that is generally about 300 mOsm/L or about one-third that of salt water and at least 10 times that of fresh water. All terrestrial animals are osmoregulators, as are all freshwater animals and many marine animals, including bony fish and some crustaceans. Osmoregulators maintain stable cellular levels of ions and fluid, but this requires considerable expenditure of energy, primarily to pump ions into and out of epithelial cells.

Most marine invertebrates and some vertebrates—notably sharks—use a different means to control body fluid composition. In this case, the osmolarity of extracellular and intracellular fluids is matched with seawater. These animals are called **osmoconformers**, because their osmolarity conforms to that of their environment. The osmolarity of blood and other fluids of marine osmoconformers is like seawater, around 1,000 mOsm/L. An advantage of having body fluids conform to the osmolarity of the surrounding seawater is that there is much less tendency to gain or lose water across the skin or gills. Thus, sharks and other osmoconformers expend less energy to compensate for water gain or loss than do other aquatic animals. However, osmoconformers are generally limited to the marine environment, whereas many species of osmoregulators, such as salmon, can migrate between waters of different salinities.

Vertebrate osmoconformers employ a strategy in which they have a high concentration of uncharged molecules in their extracellular fluids. This allows the extracellular fluids and seawater to have similar osmolarities, but it prevents the excessive accumulation of ions in the body. The body fluids of sharks and other osmoconformers contain sugars, amino acids, and metabolic waste products—notably urea and an organic compound called trimethylamine oxide (TMAO). The total amount of salt and organic compounds in a shark's extracellular fluids produces an osmolarity very similar to that of seawater, even though the salt concentration is similar to that of osmoregulators.

Vertebrate osmoconformers cannot tolerate high ion concentrations in their body fluids any better than osmoregulators. One reason is that a proper ion balance is required for normal electrical signalling in their nerve and muscle cells. In addition, a second problem is that very high salt concentrations tend to disrupt the three-dimensional structure of many proteins, rendering them inactive. Consequently, the body fluids of vertebrate osmoconformers are less salty—that is, they have fewer ions—than seawater, as is also the case in all osmoregulators. Therefore, vertebrate osmoconformers tend to gain salt by diffusion across their gills. That excess salt is eliminated by the kidneys and a type of salt gland called the rectal gland.

Animals that cannot survive wide changes in the salinity of their surroundings—including most marine invertebrates and many types of fish—are said to be stenohaline ("narrow salt"). Other animals, such as migratory fish and some species of shellfish (oysters and mussels), can tolerate certain changes in the salinity of their surroundings and are said to be euryhaline ("broad salt"). One of the most dramatic examples of euryhaline animals is salmon, which migrate between fresh water and salt water without any ill effects. Although the mechanisms by which such animals adapt to changing salinities are not entirely understood, exposure to a sudden change in salinity is associated with large-scale changes in gene expression. A recent study in nematode worms, for example, reported more than 100 genes whose expression was altered by changing the salt concentration of the medium on which the worms were living. Presumably, some of the genes are associated with functions such as ion transport in skin and other tissue.

Next we will examine the excretory organs found in different animals and how such organs not only function to eliminate wastes but also are involved in salt and water homeostasis.

46.2 / A SURVEY OF EXCRETORY ORGANS

Learning Outcomes:

1. Describe the general processes of filtration, reabsorption, secretion, and excretion.
2. Identify several invertebrate osmoregulatory organs, and compare and contrast the process of elimination in each.
3. List general features of kidneys that are common to all vertebrates.
4. Relate kidney function to life history in vertebrates.

Although the mammalian kidney, and in particular that of humans, has been especially well studied, enough is known about other classes of animals to make general statements regarding the regulation of salt, water, and waste levels in the body's fluid compartments. This is an ancient and important function that arose early in evolution.

As just described, animals make use of one or more different organs to rid themselves of metabolic wastes, excess water and salts, and toxins from their environment. Most excretory organs contain tubular structures lined with epithelial cells that have the capacity to actively transport ions across their membranes. Wastes are secreted out of the body by means of these tubes. In some cases, animals may have considerable ability to regulate the rate at which waste is secreted and how much water is lost in the process. For example, even though a thirsty mammal on a hot, sunny day must continue to rid its body of soluble waste products, it must also conserve water. In this section, we examine general principles common to most excretory systems. Next, we consider invertebrate and vertebrate excretory organs.

Urine Production Involves the Processes of Filtration, Reabsorption, and Secretion

Most excretory organs operate by using one or more of the following processes: filtration, reabsorption, and secretion. In **filtration**, an organ acts like a sieve or filter, removing some of the water and its small solutes from the blood, interstitial fluid, or hemolymph, while leaving behind blood cells and large solutes like proteins. A typical filtration system is that seen in the mammalian kidney, in which the plasma component of blood is forced under pressure through leaky capillaries and into the kidney tubules (**Figure 46.6**). The material that passes through the filter and enters the excretory organ for either further processing or excretion is called a **filtrate**.

Some of the material in the filtrate can be recaptured and returned to the blood. This is an important feature of many excretory organs, because the formation of a filtrate is not selective, apart from the exclusion of proteins and blood cells. In other words, to filter the blood and remove soluble wastes, necessary molecules, such as salts, sugars, and amino acids, also are filtered in the process. Recapturing those useful solutes requires active transport pumps or other transport systems and

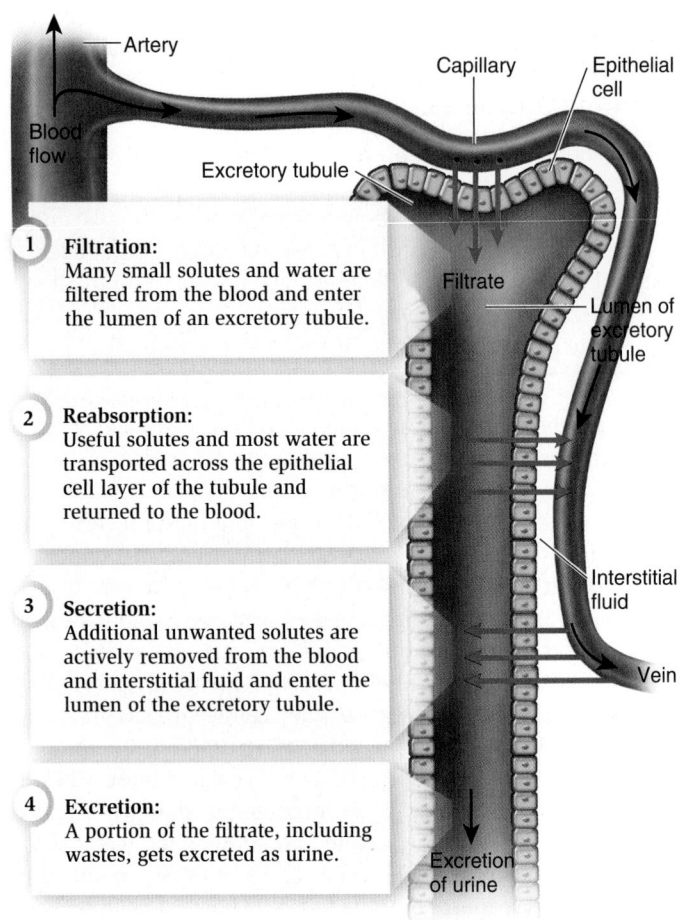

Figure 46.6   Basic features of the function of many excretory systems.

Concept check: *What is the benefit of secreting substances into the tubule?*

is known as **reabsorption**. The remaining part of the filtrate that is excreted is called **urine**.

In some cases, solutes may be excreted from the body in quantities greater than those found in the filtrate. How is this possible? Some solutes are actively transported from the interstitial fluid surrounding the epithelial cells of the tubules, into the tubule lumens. This process, called **secretion**, supplements the amount of a solute that would normally be removed by filtration alone. This is often a way in which excretory organs eliminate particularly toxic compounds from an animal's body, and it can be very effective. Some marine fish, for example, make use of secretion as the sole means of cleansing the blood. These animals do not form a filtrate at all.

Most Invertebrates Use a Filtration Mechanism to Cleanse the Blood

The simplest filtration mechanism in invertebrates is the **protonephridia** system of flatworms (**Figure 46.7**). A series of

Figure 46.7   The protonephridial filtration system of flatworms.   As the filtrate moves along the tubules, most solutes are reabsorbed. The final excreted fluid is typically hypoosmotic to the interstitial fluid.

branching tubules filters fluids from the body cavity into the tubule lumens by means of ciliated cells that cap the ends of the tubules. The beating of the cilia bears some resemblance to a flickering flame, which is why these cells are known as flame cells. As fluid is drawn through slitlike openings of the flame cells and into the lumen by the beating of the cilia, it percolates through the tubule, where most solutes are reabsorbed back into the interstitial fluid. Excess water and some wastes are emptied through tiny openings in the body wall called nephridiopores. Much of the nitrogenous waste in flatworms actually diffuses across the body surface into the surrounding water, and therefore the protonephridia are primarily osmoregulatory organs. The urine is generally hypoosmotic compared with the rest of the body fluids, an adaptation for life in fresh water.

Annelids, by contrast, use a different filtration mechanism, called a **metanephridial system** (**Figure 46.8**). In annelids, pairs of metanephridia are located in each body segment. They consist of a tubular network that begins with a funnel-like structure called a nephrostome. The nephrostomes are open to the body cavity and collect coelomic fluid, which contains nitrogenous wastes, through tiny pores that exclude large solutes. Na^+, Cl^-, and other solutes are reabsorbed by active transport along the

2 The filtrate moves through the metanephridial tubules, where useful solutes are reabsorbed into capillaries.

Metanephridium in capillary network

Capillaries

Coelomic fluid

Metanephridia tubules

Nephrostome

Nephridiopore

1 Coelomic fluid is filtered into the nephrostome.

3 A dilute urine is excreted via nephridiopores.

Figure 46.8 **The metanephridial filtration system of annelids.** Most internal body structures have been omitted for clarity. Only one of the two metanephridia in each segment is depicted; the other would be located behind the one shown.

length of the tubules that extend from the nephrostomes, and from there diffuse into nearby capillaries. The nitrogenous wastes remain behind in the tubules and are excreted through nephridiopores in the body wall. Many annelids live in watery environments and thus, like flatworms, excrete a hypoosmotic urine.

Filtration mechanisms also operate in the kidney-like structures of many molluscs, and in the crustacean excretory organs called antennal glands. As in worms, reabsorption of useful solutes occurs along the length of the excretory system. Research has clearly indicated that molluscs can reabsorb organic nutrients well enough that under most conditions these nutrients do not appear at all in the urine. Like the protonephridial and metanephridial systems just discussed, urine is excreted via nephridiopores in these other animals.

Insects Excrete Wastes by Means of Secretory Organs Rather Than Filtration

The insect excretory system is quite different from that of other invertebrates, because it does not involve filtration of body fluids. Instead, a series of narrow, extensive tubes called **Malpighian tubules** arises from the midgut and extends into the surrounding hemolymph (**Figure 46.9**). The cells lining the tubules actively transport potassium ions, along with uric acid and other purines from the hemolymph, into the tubule lumen. This secretion process creates an osmotic gradient that draws water into the tubules. The fluid moves from the tubules into the hindgut—the intestine and rectum—where much of the useful salt and water is reabsorbed. The nitrogenous wastes and

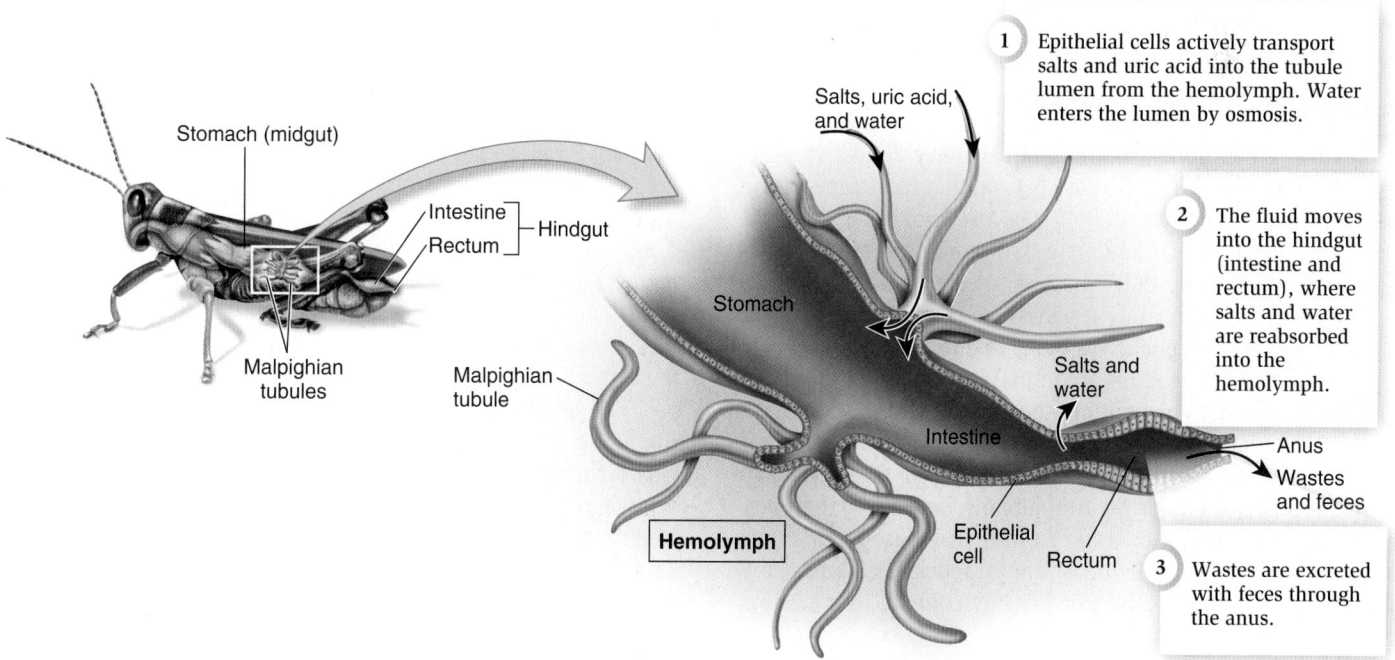

Stomach (midgut)

Intestine — Hindgut
Rectum

Malpighian tubules

Malpighian tubule

Salts, uric acid, and water

Stomach

Hemolymph

Intestine

Epithelial cell

Rectum

Salts and water

Anus

Wastes and feces

1 Epithelial cells actively transport salts and uric acid into the tubule lumen from the hemolymph. Water enters the lumen by osmosis.

2 The fluid moves into the hindgut (intestine and rectum), where salts and water are reabsorbed into the hemolymph.

3 Wastes are excreted with feces through the anus.

Figure 46.9 **Malpighian tubules from the excretory system of an insect.** The tubules, which are longer and more convoluted than shown in this simplified illustration, extend into the body cavity, where they are surrounded by hemolymph.

other waste compounds are excreted together with the feces through the anus.

Unlike other invertebrates, most terrestrial insects, apart from blood-sucking ones, excrete urine that is either isoosmotic or hyperosmotic to body fluids. This is a testament to the efficiency with which the insect hindgut reabsorbs water and reflects the fact that life in dry environments is associated with a risk of dehydration.

The Kidney Is the Major Excretory and Filtration Organ in Vertebrates

The major excretory organ found in all vertebrates is the kidney. The kidneys of all vertebrates have many features in common. They typically contain specialized tubules composed of epithelial cells that participate in both salt and water homeostasis by promoting active transport of sodium and other ions across their membranes. In addition, all kidneys participate in the excretion of wastes. In response to an animal's changing water and salt requirements, these processes can be controlled, that is, sped up or slowed down, by the actions of nerves and hormones. Most vertebrate kidneys are filtration kidneys, with the exception of purely secretory kidneys found in some marine fish. Finally, filtration in the kidneys is controlled by mechanical forces, such as the hydrostatic pressure exerted by blood entering the capillaries of the kidneys. The mammalian kidney has been especially well studied and is examined in detail later in this chapter.

The need to eliminate waste products while simultaneously maintaining salt and water homeostasis occurs in all animals. How animals achieve this balance in disparate environments, and with different life histories, is the subject of our next discussion.

The Diet and Life History of Vertebrates May Influence Renal Function

As previously mentioned, not all animals have similar requirements for salt and water. **Table 46.1** summarizes some of the special needs of different vertebrates and some major behavioural and physiological adaptations that allow them to maintain homeostasis. Note that when we refer to kidneys, we use the adjective renal, meaning "pertaining to the kidneys." For example, we refer to renal physiology and renal functions.

The demands placed on an animal by its environment can often be predicted by examining the activities of that animal's kidneys. For example, the kidneys of freshwater fish are specially adapted for rapid, large-scale filtering of the blood and producing a very dilute urine. Amphibians, because of their permeable skin, absorb fresh water from their environments, and consequently they have kidneys whose appearance and activity resemble those of freshwater fish. By contrast, the kidneys

of marine fish and desert mammals are adapted to produce urine that is more concentrated than that of freshwater fish and amphibians. This is an important adaptation that helps conserve as much water as possible.

Some animals have a diet that is extreme in one way or another, and this is often associated with differences in renal structure and function. Many mammals and insectivores, for example, subsist entirely or almost entirely on sporadic, high-protein meals. These animals consume so much protein at a single meal that the rate at which they generate nitrogenous waste is very high. Not surprisingly, perhaps, the rate at which blood is filtered through the kidneys of such animals tends also to be very high, an adaptation that helps eliminate the toxic waste.

At the other extreme, polar bears may go four to five months without feeding. During the nonfeeding periods, polar bears neither defecate nor urinate and subsist by breaking down stores of fat and protein in their bodies. Thus, even though they are not eating, they generate nitrogenous wastes, like urea. Despite the fact that they do not urinate during this time, however, the concentration of urea in their blood may actually drop. The explanation for this surprising phenomenon appears to be that polar bears have the extraordinary ability to recycle nitrogenous waste into synthesis of new protein, an ability that is of great interest to researchers who study the health consequences of kidney disease and consequent accumulation of urea in the bloodstream of humans.

Animals that subsist primarily on the blood of other animals, such as the vampire bat (*Desmodus rotundus*), face a special challenge because ingesting blood brings large amounts of water into the animal. The body mass of one of these bats may increase from around 30 grams before a blood meal to as much as 50 grams afterward. This is roughly equivalent to a 55-kilogram woman weighing more than 90 kilograms after a meal! Vampire bats engorged with blood can even become too heavy to fly. Consequently, their kidneys have become adapted to rapidly excrete a dilute urine. Most of the water portion of the blood they consume is quickly excreted, while the nutrients are retained. Increased urine production begins within a few minutes of feeding and can be produced at rates as high as 4 mL/kg body mass/minute. This is roughly 400 times as high as the rate at which urine is produced in a human being. This occurs only during and after a blood meal. At other times, the kidneys of vampire bats can produce a concentrated urine to conserve water when necessary.

The ability to respond to a blood meal by rapidly producing dilute urine has evolved on at least two separate occasions. Blood-sucking insects, such as mosquitoes, can also eliminate the water portion of their meal, even before they have finished ingesting a blood meal.

We turn now to an examination of one of the best understood excretory organs: the mammalian kidney.

| **Table 46.1** | **A Comparison of the Vertebrate Mechanisms of Osmoregulation in Different Environments** |

Type of animal		Blood concentration relative to environment	Urine concentration relative to blood	Main nitrogenous waste	Osmoregulatory mechanisms and special features
Marine fish		Hypoosmotic	Isoosmotic or hyperosmotic	Ammonia	Drinks seawater; secretes salt from gills
Freshwater fish		Hyperosmotic	Strongly hypoosmotic	Ammonia	Drinks no water; transports salt across gills
Amphibian (freshwater)		Hyperosmotic	Strongly hypoosmotic	Most secrete urea	Absorbs water through skin
Marine reptile		Hypoosmotic	Isoosmotic	Ammonia, urea, uric acid	Drinks seawater; hyperosmotic salt-gland secretion
Terrestrial reptile		—	Isoosmotic	Uric acid	Drinks fresh water
Marine bird		Hypoosmotic	Weakly hyperosmotic	Uric acid	Drinks seawater; hyperosmotic salt-gland secretion
Terrestrial bird		—	Weakly hyperosmotic	Uric acid	Drinks fresh water
Desert mammal		—	Strongly hyperosmotic	Urea	Drinks no water; very long loops of Henle; depends on water generated by cellular metabolism
Marine mammal		Hypoosmotic	Strongly hyperosmotic	Urea	Drinks no water
Other mammals		—	Strongly hyperosmotic	Urea	Drinks fresh water

Learning Outcomes:

1. Name the primary components of the urinary system in humans and the major anatomical features of the human kidney.
2. Describe the main parts of a nephron and outline the steps in which each contributes to the process of processing filtrate into urine.
3. Discuss how the actions of two hormones, aldosterone and antidiuretic hormone (ADH), mediate the final composition of urine.

All mammals have kidneys that are similar in structure and function, although some are more adapted to one type of life history and environment than another. Much of what we know today about the human kidney arose from observations made on the kidneys of rodents, dogs, and other mammals.

The two kidneys lie in the abdomen (**Figure 46.10a**). The urine formed in each kidney collects in the renal pelvis and from there flows through the **ureters** into the **urinary bladder**. Urine is eliminated via the **urethra**. Collectively, the kidneys, ureters, urinary bladder, and urethra constitute the **urinary system** in humans.

Each kidney is composed of an outer portion called the renal cortex and an inner portion called the renal medulla, which in turn is composed of outer and inner regions (**Figure 46.10b**). The cortex is the primary site of blood filtration. In the medulla, urine becomes concentrated by the reabsorption of water back into the blood. In this section, we will examine the structural features of the kidney that allow it to function as a filtration system.

The Functional Units of the Kidney Are Called Nephrons

Depending on its size, the mammalian kidney contains as many as several million similar, single-cell-thick structures called **nephrons**. (It is from the word *nephron* that we get the name of the medical specialty nephrology.) As shown in **Figure 46.10c**, each nephron consists of (1) an initial filtering component called the **renal corpuscle** and (2) a narrow tubule that extends out from the renal corpuscle. The tubule empties into a larger tubule called a **collecting duct**.

The renal corpuscle forms a filtrate from blood that is free of cells and proteins. This filtrate then leaves the renal corpuscle and enters the lumen of the tubule. As it flows through different regions along the length of the tubule, substances are secreted into it or reabsorbed from it. Ultimately the urine remaining at the end of each nephron combines into the collecting ducts.

The Renal Corpuscle Each renal corpuscle (**Figure 46.11a**) contains a cluster of interconnected, fenestrated capillaries called the **glomerulus** (plural: *glomeruli*) or glomerular capillaries. A fenestrated capillary has tiny holes in its walls that permit rapid flow of plasma out of the capillary (**Figure 46.11b**). Each glomerulus is supplied with blood under pressure by an **afferent arteriole**. The glomerulus protrudes into a fluid-filled space called Bowman's space, which lies within a capsule called **Bowman's capsule**. The combination of a glomerulus and a Bowman's capsule constitutes a renal corpuscle.

The Tubular Part of the Nephron The tubule of the nephron, which is continuous with Bowman's capsule, is made of a single layer of epithelial cells resting on a basement membrane. The epithelial cells differ in structure and function along the tubule's length, and 10 to 12 distinct segments are now recognized. For simplicity, however, it is possible to group two or more contiguous tubular segments when discussing function. Thus, the segment of the tubule that drains Bowman's capsule is the **proximal convoluted tubule** (*proximal* means "adjacent to," with respect to the beginning of the nephron; Figure 46.10c). The next portion of the tubule is the **loop of Henle**, which is a long, hairpinlike loop consisting of a descending limb coming from the proximal tubule and an ascending limb leading to the next tubular segment, the **distal** ("away from") **convoluted tubule**. Fluid flows from the distal convoluted tubule into one of the many collecting ducts in the kidney.

All along its length, each tubule is surrounded by capillaries. These include the **peritubular capillaries** in the cortex, and the **vasa recta capillaries** in the medulla (Figure 46.10c). These capillaries carry away reabsorbed solutes and water and return them to the bloodstream. Some of them also participate in the process of secretion in the nephron tubules.

Filtration: Blood Is Filtered by the Renal Corpuscle

Now that you have learned about the structural units of the mammalian kidney, we turn our attention to the mechanisms by which nephrons filter blood and produce urine for excretion, and how these activities are controlled under different conditions.

As blood flows through the glomerulus, about 20% of the plasma leaves the glomerular capillaries and filters into Bowman's space. The remaining blood then leaves the glomerulus by an **efferent arteriole** (Figure 46.11a). Proteins and blood cells are prevented from leaving the glomerular capillaries because the fenestrations are exceedingly tiny. In addition, the glomerular capillaries are surrounded by cells called podocytes (Figure 46.11b) that form filtration slits that act as a physical barrier to movement of large solutes and cells.

The fluid that leaves the glomerular capillaries and enters Bowman's space is called the glomerular filtrate. The rate at which the filtrate is formed is called the **glomerular filtration rate (GFR)**. GFR can be increased by dilation of the afferent arteriole. When the afferent arteriole widens, more blood enters the glomerulus, increasing the hydrostatic pressure in those capillaries and forcing more plasma through the fenestrations in the glomerular capillaries and into Bowman's space. This might happen, for example, when there is an excess of water in the body that must be excreted in the urine. By contrast, constriction

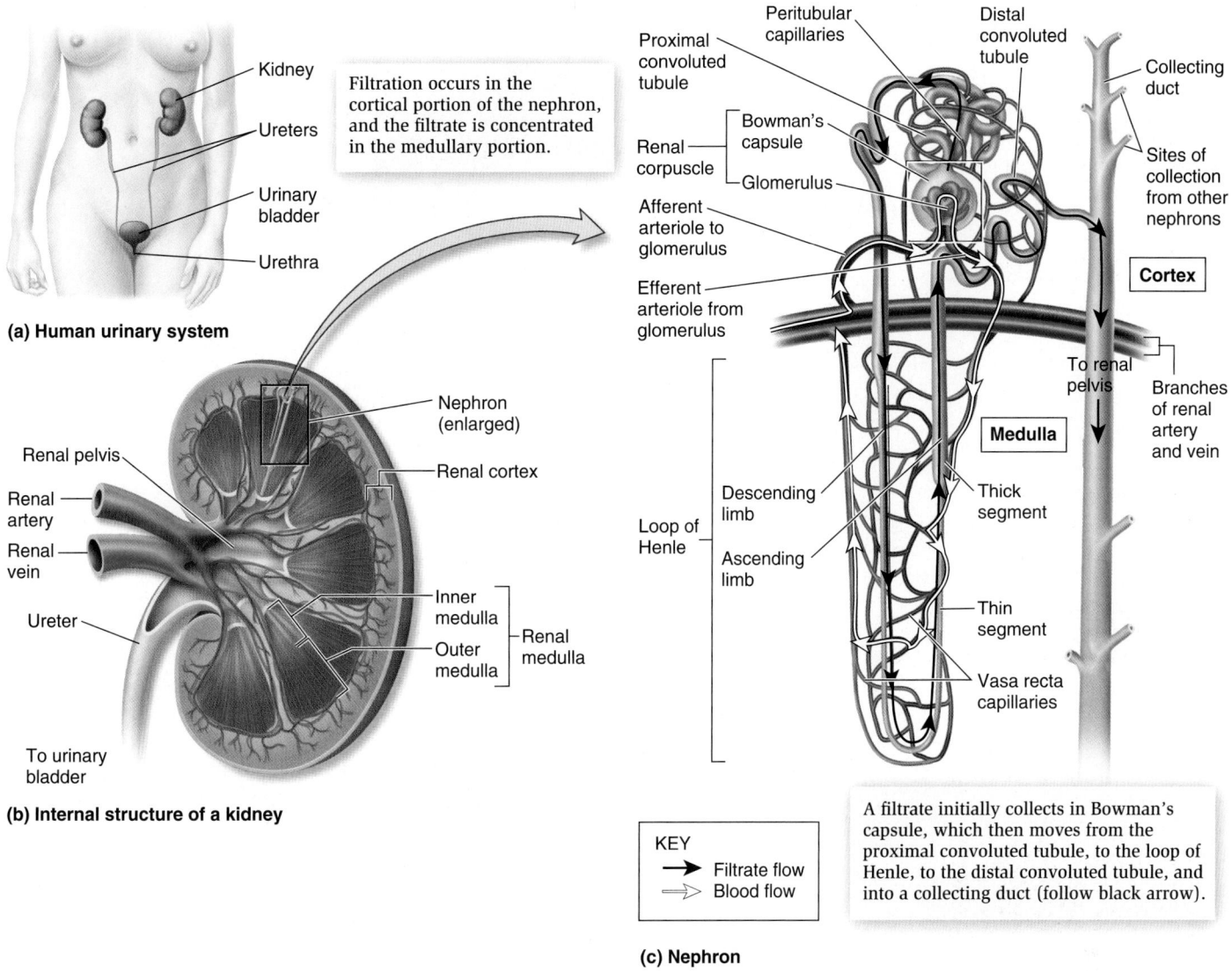

Filtration occurs in the cortical portion of the nephron, and the filtrate is concentrated in the medullary portion.

(a) Human urinary system

(b) Internal structure of a kidney

KEY
→ Filtrate flow
⇒ Blood flow

A filtrate initially collects in Bowman's capsule, which then moves from the proximal convoluted tubule, to the loop of Henle, to the distal convoluted tubule, and into a collecting duct (follow black arrow).

(c) Nephron

Figure 46.10   **The mammalian urinary system including the basic functional unit of the nephron.**   **(a)** The human urinary system in a woman. In the male, the urethra passes through the penis. **(b)** Enlarged view of a section through a kidney, showing the locations of the major internal structures and a single nephron (grossly enlarged; at the scale of this illustration, nephrons would be microscopic). **(c)** Structure of a nephron. The nephron begins at Bowman's capsule and terminates at a collecting duct. Many nephrons empty into a given collecting duct. Surrounding the nephron are capillaries called peritubular capillaries in the cortex and the vasa recta capillaries in the medulla.

of the afferent arteriole would reduce the amount of blood entering the glomerular capillaries, and therefore would reduce GFR. This might occur following a loss of blood from a severe injury. In such a scenario, reducing GFR results in less urine production, which in turn minimizes how much water is lost from the body and helps compensate for the blood lost through the injury.

Reabsorption: Most Reabsorption of Useful Solutes Occurs in the Proximal Tubule

Anywhere from two-thirds to 100 % of a particular solute is reabsorbed from the filtrate in the proximal tubule. This includes Na^+, K^+, Cl^-, HCO_3^-, and organic molecules, such as glucose and amino acids. Some ions diffuse through channels in the

membranes of the epithelial cells that form the single-cell-thick proximal tubule. Others are actively transported across the tubule. Organic molecules generally are reabsorbed by transporters, such as the Na^+/glucose symporter.

Most of the water in the filtrate leaves by osmosis as the ions and organic molecules are transported from the lumen of the proximal convoluted tubule (**Figure 46.12**) to the interstitial fluid outside the tubules. The amount of water reabsorbed is proportional to the amount of solutes reabsorbed. From there, the water and solutes enter peritubular capillaries to return to the blood. By the time the filtrate leaves the proximal tubule, its volume and composition have changed considerably. The amount of water and salts is much reduced, and the organic molecules have all been removed.

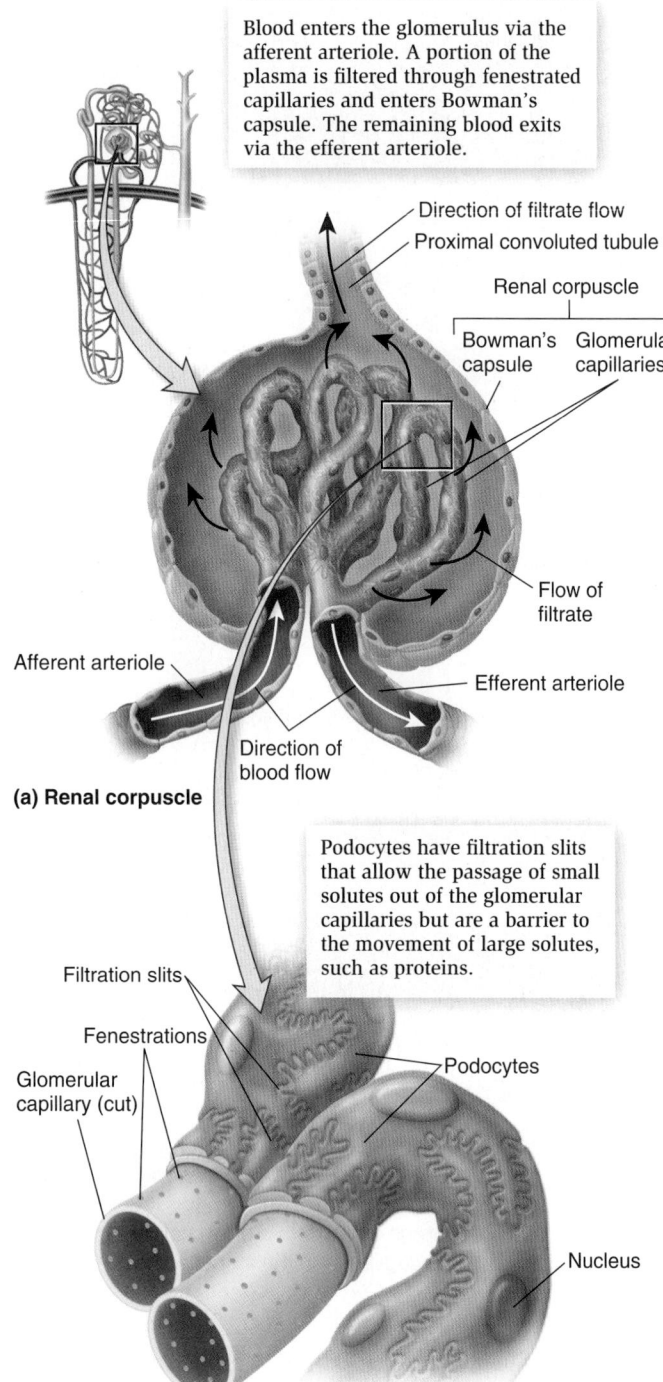

Blood enters the glomerulus via the afferent arteriole. A portion of the plasma is filtered through fenestrated capillaries and enters Bowman's capsule. The remaining blood exits via the efferent arteriole.

Direction of filtrate flow

Proximal convoluted tubule

Renal corpuscle

Bowman's capsule   Glomerular capillaries

Flow of filtrate

Afferent arteriole

Efferent arteriole

Direction of blood flow

(a) Renal corpuscle

Podocytes have filtration slits that allow the passage of small solutes out of the glomerular capillaries but are a barrier to the movement of large solutes, such as proteins.

Filtration slits

Fenestrations

Glomerular capillary (cut)

Podocytes

Nucleus

(b) Glomerular capillaries with podocytes

Figure 46.11   **The structure and function of the renal corpuscle.** (a) Renal corpuscle. (b) Glomerular capillaries with podocytes.

 Principle: *Structure determines function. The structure of the capillaries in the renal glomerulus is suited to the function of the capillaries. Fenestrations permit the passage of plasma but not blood cells. The structure of the podocytes is also suited to their function, in that filtration slits further filter out components of the plasma. Damage to the structure of the podocytes, for example, might cause protein to leak into the filtrate and be lost in the urine.*

Tubule lumen

Microvilli (brush border)

Figure 46.12   Electron micrograph of cuboidal epithelial cells of the proximal tubule of a rat nephron.   Note the extensive brush border microvilli on the lumenal surface of the cells.

BioConnections: *In what other organ have you learned about a brush border (see Figure 39.9 for a hint)? What general conclusions can you draw about the function of such specialized epithelia?*

Reabsorption: Water and Salt Reabsorption Continues Along the Loop of Henle

In the loop of Henle in the mammalian kidney, fluid moves down the descending limb of the loop, makes a U-turn at the bottom and then moves back up the ascending limb of the loop. The permeabilities and transport characteristics of the epithelial cells lining the loop change over its length as it descends from the cortex into the medulla and then ascends to the cortex again (**Figure 46.13**).

Let's begin upstream of the loop of Henle, in the proximal convoluted tubule. As you have seen, solutes and water are reabsorbed here; the osmolarity of the initial filtrate is about 300 mOsm/L. The descending limb of the loop of Henle is very permeable to water but not to solutes. Water leaves the tubular fluid by osmosis because the surrounding interstitial fluid is hyperosmotic compared to the tubule contents. The hyperosmolarity of the interstitial fluid originates from three sources. First, the initial upturn of the thin segment of the ascending limb of the loop of Henle is very permeable to sodium and chloride but not to water. Therefore, these ions diffuse at high rates out of the loop into the interstitial fluid, significantly increasing the osmolarity of the inner medulla. Second, the epithelial cells of the thick segment of the ascending limb of the loop of Henle actively transport some of the remaining sodium and chloride ions out of the lumen of the loop and into the interstitial fluid of the outer medulla. Third, although urea is a waste product that gets excreted, some of the urea that is present in the filtrate does not get excreted in the urine but instead diffuses out of the lower ends of the collecting ducts and into the inner medulla interstitial fluid. Collectively, these solutes create the osmotic force that draws water out of the descending limb. The water then enters local capillaries and rejoins the circulation.

1. Filtrate leaves the proximal tubule and enters the loop of Henle at the same osmolarity as blood. It becomes concentrated as water diffuses out of the water-permeable descending limb of the loop of Henle.

2. The thin segment of the ascending limb is permeable to Na^+ and Cl^-, but not to water. Na^+ and Cl^- diffuse out of the filtrate, making the filtrate more dilute. Epithelial cells in the thick segment actively transport Na^+ and Cl^- out of the filtrate, which further dilutes the filtrate.

3. By the time the filtrate enters the distal tubule, the total amounts of water and ions have been greatly decreased.

4. The filtrate becomes concentrated again during passage through the collecting duct, which is permeable to water but not to ions. The lower end of the collecting duct is also permeable to urea, which diffuses out and helps create the osmotic gradient in the inner medulla.

KEY

Filtrate osmolarity (mOsm/L)   ■ H_2O
— Simple diffusion   ■ Na^+, Cl^-
··· Active transport   ■ Urea

Figure 46.13   Tubule permeabilities and concentrations of the filtrate in the loop of Henle and collecting duct.

As water diffuses out of the descending limb of the loop of Henle, the osmolarity of the fluid in the tubule increases from 300 to about 1,200 (or higher in some species) mOsm/L. During its passage up the ascending limb, however, the osmolarity decreases as ions diffuse and are transported out of the tubule. Finally, the osmolarity of the tubule fluid increases a second time during passage along the collecting ducts, which are permeable to water but not to ions, allowing water to diffuse out of the tubules by osmosis.

Note that the osmolarity of the kidney interstitial fluid increases from cortex to inner medulla. This extracellular osmolarity gradient allows water to diffuse by osmosis from the descending limb of the loop of Henle all along its length. In other words, this is an example of a countercurrent exchange system, like those that operate in heat and gas exchange in some animals (see Chapters 40 and 46). A major difference between those countercurrent exchange systems and the one in the loop of Henle, however, is that the latter requires energy-dependent ion pumps to maintain the necessary gradient. Energy-requiring systems like that in the kidney are referred to as countercurrent multiplication systems, because energy is used to increase—or multiply—the gradient. Energy is not used to establish a heat or an oxygen gradient in those other countercurrent exchange systems.

The chief advantage to an animal provided by the loops of Henle is that urine volume can be reduced and concentrated by the recapture of water along the osmotic gradient. Animals in which total body water stores are regularly in danger of being depleted, such as desert mammals, tend to have very long loops of Henle with very large osmotic gradients in the medulla. By contrast, freshwater fish have no loops of Henle at all. In their case, it is advantageous to excrete as much water as possible to compensate for water entering the body by osmosis across the gills.

Reabsorption: The Medullary Blood Vessels Called the Vasa Recta Minimize the Loss of Solutes

Why does the blood flowing through the vasa recta capillaries of the medulla not eliminate the countercurrent osmotic gradient set up by the loops of Henle? You might think that when plasma, with an osmolarity of about 300 mOsm/L, enters the highly concentrated environment of the medulla, two types of massive net diffusion would occur: sodium and chloride into the capillaries, and water out of them. Thus, the interstitial gradient would be "washed away." However, this does not happen because the vasa recta form hairpin loops that run parallel to the loops of Henle and medullary collecting ducts. Near the top of the loop of Henle, blood in the vasa recta has a normal osmolarity. As the blood flows down the loop deeper and deeper into the inner medulla, sodium and chloride do indeed diffuse into, and water diffuses out of, the vasa recta. However, after the bend in the loop is reached, the blood then flows up the ascending vessel loop, where the process is almost completely reversed. Thus, the hairpin-loop structure of the vasa recta minimizes excessive loss of solutes from the interstitial fluid by diffusion.

At the same time, both the salt and the water being reabsorbed from the loops of Henle and collecting ducts are carried away in equivalent amounts by the passive movement of water and solutes between fluid compartments, and the steady-state countercurrent gradient set up by the loops of Henle is maintained.

Fine-Tuning of Urine Composition Occurs in the Final Portions of the Nephron

The tubule does not become highly permeable to water again until the distal tubule. By this point, most of the reabsorbed water and salt have already been restored to the blood. However, fine-tuning of the concentrations of sodium, chloride, and potassium, along with water, is mediated by the actions of **antidiuretic hormone (ADH)**, also known as vasopressin, and a hormone called aldosterone. Aldosterone acts on the basolateral surface of epithelial cells of the distal convoluted tubule to stimulate the active transport of three molecules of Na^+ out of the tubule and into the interstitial fluid (reabsorption) for every two molecules of K^+ it pumps into cells from the interstitial fluid (secretion; **Figure 46.14**). Water from the tubule lumen follows the Na^+ by osmosis into the interstitial fluid and blood. By contrast, ADH acts to remove water from the urine, as described next.

The Final Solute Concentration of Urine Is Largely Determined by Events Within the Collecting Ducts

The final place in which urine composition can be altered is within the collecting ducts. As previously described, cells along the collecting duct in the inner medulla are permeable to urea, which contributes to the osmotic gradient there. In addition, however, the permeability of the epithelial cells of the collecting ducts to water can be regulated, depending on the body's need at that moment for retaining or excreting water. This happens under the influence of ADH. When ADH is present in blood, it acts to increase the number of water channels called **aquaporins** in the luminal (apical) membranes of the collecting duct cells (**Figure 46.15**). It does this by stimulating intracellular signalling mechanisms that promote the fusion of storage vesicles containing aquaporins with the luminal membranes of the duct epithelial cells, resulting in the insertion of aquaporins into those membranes. Because the collecting ducts travel through the hyperosmotic medulla of the kidney, an osmotic gradient draws water from the filtrate in the duct into the duct epithelial cells. The water exits the cells on the other side (the basolateral surface), where another set of aquaporins is present. These aquaporins are always present in the basolateral membrane; unlike those on the luminal side of the cells, they do not require the presence of ADH for their insertion into the membrane. Once the water moves from the cells into the interstitial fluid, it enters the vasa recta capillaries and the blood. In this way, as the filtrate travels through the collecting ducts, the urine becomes greatly concentrated (hyperosmotic) compared with blood—as much as four to five times as concentrated.

Figure 46.14 **Action of aldosterone on distal convoluted tubule epithelial cells.** Aldosterone stimulates the Na^+/K^+-ATPase pumps in the cells of the distal tubule cells; these pumps are expressed only on the side of the cells facing the interstitial fluid (the basolateral surface). This activity creates an osmotic gradient, as three Na^+ ions are reabsorbed from the filtrate for every two K^+ ions secreted into it. Water then leaves the tubule by osmosis. The net effect is reabsorption of Na^+ ions and water, and secretion of K^+ ions, which are excreted in the urine. Na^+ ions and water enter the peritubular capillaries and are carried away in the bloodstream.

BioConnections: *What special property of epithelial cells is demonstrated by the action of aldosterone? Look back to Figure 38.4 for help.*

Figure 46.15 The effect of antidiuretic hormone (ADH) on water reabsorption in the collecting ducts of the kidney. Water molecules require a channel called an aquaporin to move through a membrane. The epithelial cells of the collecting duct express two sets of aquaporins. One set is always present on the basolateral side of the cells; the other set only inserts into the luminal membrane in the presence of ADH. ADH activates cell signalling mechanisms that stimulate the fusion of intracellular storage vesicles containing aquaporins with the luminal membrane. Water moves by osmosis across the cell and into the interstitial fluid, and from there enters the vasa recta capillaries to be transported into the circulation (not shown). When ADH concentrations in the blood decrease (e.g., when an animal is fully hydrated), the aquaporins on the luminal membrane are returned to the intracellular storage vesicles by the process of endocytosis.

ADH concentrations increase in the blood during situations where it is important to conserve water, such as when an animal is dehydrated. The ability of the kidneys to produce hyperosmotic urine is a major determinant of an animal's ability to survive in conditions where water availability is limited. When the body's stores of water are plentiful, the concentration of ADH in the blood decreases. This results in endocytosis of portions of the luminal membranes, along with their aquaporins. This, in turn, decreases the water permeability of the collecting ducts.

In such a case, urine increases in volume and becomes more dilute because water does not diffuse out of the collecting ducts.

Biological membranes, like the plasma membranes of animal cells, are composed of a lipid bilayer that inhibits the movement of water. The mysteries of how water moves rapidly across membranes like those of the collecting ducts and how ADH controls the amount of water reabsorption, were solved by the discovery in the early 1990s of the aquaporins (from the Latin, meaning water pores), as described next.

GENOMES AND PROTEOMES

Agre and Colleagues Discovered the Mechanism of Water Movement Across Biological Membranes

In the early 1990s American physiologist Peter Agre and his colleagues discovered the first of what would eventually be recognized as a new family of proteins, called aquaporins, a discovery that earned Agre the Nobel Prize in Chemistry in 2003. Aquaporins, it is now known, are a subfamily of an even larger family of proteins with membrane transport capabilities, found

in all kingdoms of living organisms. The functions of all the members of this family are not yet known, but some aquaporins can transport other small molecules, such as glycerol and urea. There are currently 11 known members of the aquaporin family in the human genome.

Aquaporins are proteins with six transmembrane helical domains and two short loops in the membrane (**Figure 46.16**). In animals, the two short loops come together to form the three-dimensional core of the water channel. The importance of the loops is reflected in the fact that these portions are the most highly conserved sequences of the channel among different species. Water must pass through a zone of constriction, created

(a) Secondary structure of aquaporin

H₂O pore formed by overlapping loops

(b) Three-dimensional (tertiary) structure of aquaporin

Figure 46.16 **Detailed aquaporin structure.** All proteins of the aquaporin family share a similar structure, with six membrane-spanning domains (represented as cylinders) and two loops that come together to form a water channel. **(a)** Secondary structure of aquaporin. This representation highlights the two separate regions of the molecule that come together to form the water pore. **(b)** Tertiary structure of aquaporin showing pore formation.

by the loops, that reduces the channel opening to a pore that is about 30 picometres, or just about the width of a water molecule. Scattered along the inner part of the channel are arginine amino acids, which are positively charged. The charged arginines participate in hydrogen bonding with water molecules, facilitating their single-file movement through each channel at rates that have been estimated to be up to billions of water molecules per second.

Within the various extracellular and intracellular domains of aquaporins are sites that can be modified by enzymes, such as protein kinases. This suggests that the opening and closing of these channels may be gated by stimuli, like the way ion channels are gated in neurons and other cells. In addition, the promoter region of certain aquaporin genes contains a site that is recognized by transcriptional activator proteins that are responsive to the presence of cAMP, a common intracellular signalling molecule and one that is generated by cells stimulated by ADH. Thus, in addition to its rapid effect on aquaporin insertion into cell membranes (see Figure 46.15), another mechanism by which ADH promotes osmosis of water out of the renal collecting ducts, reducing urine volume, is by stimulating the transcription of one or more aquaporin genes.

Our understanding of aquaporin function has allowed us to explain the molecular basis of one form of an inherited human disease in which patients are unable to produce a concentrated urine and who consequently lose large amounts of water. A mutation in one aquaporin gene results in a form of the protein expressing any of several abnormalities: improper folding into its correct shape, impaired ability of the molecule to enter the plasma membrane, or impaired ability of the molecule to form a channel core. In addition, the discovery of aquaporins may have widespread implications for other areas of biology and health research. For example, Canada research chair in genomics David Baillie, at Simon Fraser University, has shown that AQP-8, an aquaporin from the nematode worm *Caenorhabditis elegans*, is expressed in the worm's excretory cell and is involved in water balance. AQP-8 is orthologous to aquaporins that maintain water balance in vertebrates, which suggests that *C. elegans* may well be used as a model system to understand gene-regulatory networks in the developing vertebrate kidney.

The Reabsorption of Solutes Has Limits

Many of the reabsorptive mechanisms in the renal tubule have a limit to the amounts of material they can transport in a given amount of time, which is called the transport maximum (Tm). This occurs because the binding sites on the membrane transport proteins become saturated with their ligands. Occasionally, certain molecules may reach such high concentrations in the blood that they exceed the Tm for that molecule in the renal tubule and consequently are excreted in the urine. For example, most water-soluble vitamins are filtered in large amounts each day, but almost all these filtered molecules are reabsorbed by the proximal tubule. If the plasma concentration becomes high enough, however,

reabsorption of the filtered material will be less complete, and the substance will appear in the urine. Thus, people who ingest very large quantities of vitamin C, for example, have increased plasma concentrations of vitamin C. Eventually, the filtered load may exceed the tubular reabsorptive Tm for this substance, and any additional ingested vitamin C is excreted in the urine.

The mammalian kidney is a remarkably efficient organ that serves many functions, most of them related to various aspects of homeostasis. Because of its central role in homeostasis, it should not be surprising that kidney damage or disease can have devastating consequences. In the final section we consider some causes of kidney diseases in humans and their effects on the human condition.

46.4 HUMAN HEALTH CONNECTION

Learning Outcomes:

1. Describe several common health issues related to the diseases of the kidneys.
2. Diagram the process of hemodialysis, and explain its strengths and limitations.

Diseases and disorders of the kidney are a major cause of illness in the human population. According to statistics released by the Canadian Institute for Health Information's Canadian Organ Replacement Register, 1,113 kidney transplants were performed in Canada in 2004 and 1,204 kidney transplants in 2008. In the first half of 2009, 599 kidney transplants were performed. In Canadians aged 19 and under, the number of patients diagnosed with end-stage renal disease (ESRD) increased by 169% between 1981 and 2005. In this same period, the percentage of young patients receiving kidney transplants increased from 44% in 1981 to 77% in 2005; conversely, the percentage being treated with dialysis decreased from 56% in 1981 to 22% in 2005.

Kidney Damage and Disease Result in Disruption of Homeostasis

Many diseases affect the kidneys. Diabetes, bacterial infections, allergies, congenital defects, kidney stones (accumulation of mineral deposits in nephron tubules), tumours, and toxic chemicals are some causes of kidney damage or disease. A buildup of pressure caused by obstruction of the urethra or a ureter may damage one or both kidneys and increase the likelihood of a bacterial infection and eventual renal failure. In Canada diabetes is the fastest growing cause of ESRD, with type 2 diabetes—which is related to lifestyle—taking the lead. According to the Canadian Institute for Health Information, the number of ESRD patients with type 2 diabetes in 2004 was three times as high as it was in 1995. In addition, Aboriginal patients with ESRD were 2.5 times as likely to have type 2 diabetes as were non-Aboriginal Canadians.

The symptoms of renal malfunction are similar regardless of the cause of the disease and all stem from the condition known as **uremia**—literally, "urine in the blood." Assuming that a person with kidney disease continues to ingest a normal diet containing the usual quantities of nutrients and electrolytes, potentially toxic waste products that would normally enter the tubules by filtration instead build up in the blood, because kidney destruction significantly reduces the number of functioning nephrons. In addition, the excretion of potassium is impaired because too few nephrons remain capable of normal tubular secretion of this ion. Increased K^+ in the blood is an extremely serious condition, because of the importance of stable extracellular concentrations of K^+ ions in the control of heart and nerve function.

The kidneys are still able to perform their regulatory function quite well as long as 10% of the nephrons are functioning normally. The remaining nephrons undergo alterations in function—filtration, reabsorption, and secretion—to compensate for the missing nephrons. For example, each remaining nephron increases its rate of potassium secretion so that the total amount of potassium excreted by the kidneys can be maintained at normal levels. The kidneys' regulatory abilities are limited, however. If, for example, someone with severe renal disease were to eat a diet high in potassium, the remaining nephrons might not be able to secrete enough potassium to prevent its concentrations from increasing in the extracellular fluid.

Kidney Disease Is Treated with Hemodialysis and Transplantation

Kidney disease may eventually reach a point when the kidneys can no longer excrete and reabsorb water and ions at rates that maintain salt and water homeostasis, nor excrete waste products as fast as they are produced. Adjusting a person's diet can help reduce the severity of these problems. For example, lowering potassium intake reduces the amount of potassium to be excreted, but such alterations may not eliminate the problems. In that case, doctors use various procedures to artificially perform the kidneys' excretory functions. The most important of these procedures is **hemodialysis**. The general term *dialysis* means "to separate substances in solution by using a porous membrane."

An artificial kidney is an apparatus that removes excess substances from the blood by hemodialysis (**Figure 46.17**). During this procedure, blood from one of the patient's arteries flows to the dialyzer. Within the dialyzer, blood flows through cellophane tubing that is surrounded by a special dialysis fluid. The tubing is highly permeable to most solutes but relatively impermeable to protein and completely impermeable to blood cells. In fact, these characteristics are designed to be quite similar to those of the body's own capillaries. The dialyzer is filled with a solution with ion concentrations similar to those in normal plasma but without urea or other substances that are to be completely removed from the plasma.

As blood flows through the tubing, small solutes diffuse out into the surrounding solution in the dialyzer until an equilibrium is reached. If, for example, the patient's plasma potassium concentration is above normal, potassium diffuses out of the blood across the cellophane tubing and into the dialysis fluid. Similarly, waste products and excess amounts of other substances also diffuse into the dialysis fluid and thus are eliminated from the body. Note in Figure 46.17 that blood and dialysis fluid flow in opposite directions through the dialyzer. This establishes an artificial countercurrent exchange system that increases the efficiency by which the blood is cleansed. The dialyzed, purified blood is then returned to one of the patient's veins through another type of tubing that leaves the dialyzer.

Some patients with reversible, temporary forms of kidney disease may require hemodialysis for only days or weeks. However, patients with chronic, irreversible kidney disease require treatment for the rest of their lives, unless they receive a kidney transplant. Such patients undergo hemodialysis several times a week.

Figure 46.17   **Simplified diagram of hemodialysis.**   The dialyzer is composed of many strands of very thin, sievelike tubing. In the dialyzer, blood within the dialysis tubing and dialysis fluid bathing the tubing move in opposite directions (a countercurrent), which maximizes diffusion of substances out of the blood. The dialyzer thus provides a large surface area for diffusion of waste products out of the blood and into the dialysis fluid.

BioConnections: *Note that modern medical technology is using a feature found in many animals' countercurrent exchange. Refer back to Figures 40.17 and 45.5 for examples of countercurrent exchange in animals, and to the text of this chapter for a discussion of a countercurrent multiplication system in the kidneys.*

The treatment of choice for most patients with permanent kidney disease is kidney transplantation. Rejection of the transplanted kidney by the recipient's body is a potential problem with transplants, but great strides have been made in reducing the frequency of rejection. Many people who might benefit from a transplant, however, do not receive one, because the number of people needing a transplant exceeds the number of donors (at the beginning of 2005, about 2,900 people were still waiting for a kidney transplant). Currently, the major source of kidneys for transplanting is from recently deceased people, and improved public understanding may lead more individuals to give permission to have their kidneys and other organs donated following their death. Donation from a living donor has become more common, particularly with improved methods for preventing rejection. As noted earlier in this chapter, the mammalian kidney can perform its functions with only a small fraction of its nephrons intact. Because of this large safety factor, a person who donates one of his or her kidneys can function quite normally with only one kidney.

Summary of Key Concepts

46.1 Principles of Homeostasis of Internal Fluids

- Exchanges of salt and water with the environment resulting from vital processes, such as respiration or the elimination of wastes, are called obligatory exchanges. (Figure 46.1)

- Among the important products of the breakdown of proteins and nucleic acids are nitrogenous wastes, molecules that include nitrogen from amino groups (NH_2). Most aquatic animals produce ammonia (NH_3) and ammonium ions (NH_4^+), which are the most highly toxic nitrogenous wastes but require no energy to produce.

Many animals, including all mammals, convert ammonia into urea, which is less toxic than ammonia and requires moderate expenditures of water and energy. Birds, insects, and most reptiles produce uric acid or other nitrogenous compounds called purines. These nitrogenous wastes conserve water and are less toxic but energetically costlier than ammonia. (Figure 46.2)

- The solute concentration of a solution of water is known as the solution's osmolarity, expressed as milliosmoles/litre (mOsm/L). (Figure 46.3)

- Salt glands are adaptations found in marine birds and reptiles that permit these animals to eliminate excess salt from the body. (Figure 46.4)

- Robert Cade and colleagues discovered that fluid replacement during exercise is particularly beneficial if the fluid contains solutes at concentrations resembling those in sweat. (Figure 46.5)

- Animals that maintain constant internal salt concentrations and osmolarities, even when living in water with very different osmolarities than their body fluids, are called osmoregulators. Animals in which internal osmolarity conforms to the osmolarity of the environment are called osmoconformers.

46.2 A Survey of Excretory Organs

- Most excretory organs operate by one or more of three processes: (1) filtration, the passive removal of water and small solutes from the blood; (2) reabsorption, in which useful filtered solutes are returned to the blood via transport systems; and (3) secretion, in which unwanted solutes are actively transported from the blood and interstitial fluid and into the excretory tubule. (Figure 46.6)

- In the protonephridial system of flatworms, a series of branching tubules filters fluids from the body cavity into the tubule lumens via the actions of ciliated flame cells. (Figure 46.7)

- In the metanephridial system of annelids, pairs of metanephridia located in each body segment filter interstitial fluid through funnel-like structures called nephrostomes. A dilute urine is excreted via nephridiopores in the body wall. (Figure 46.8)

- In insects, cells of Malpighian tubules transport salts, uric acid, and water (by osmosis) from hemolymph into the tubule lumen. After useful salts and water are reabsorbed into the hemolymph, wastes are excreted from the body. (Figure 46.9)

- The mechanisms by which vertebrates osmoregulate vary depending on the animal's environment. (Table 46.1)

46.3 Structure and Function of the Mammalian Kidney

- The urinary system in humans consists of the kidneys, ureters, urinary bladder, and urethra. Each kidney is composed of an outer renal cortex and an inner renal medulla. The functional units of the kidney, called nephrons, are composed of a filtering component called the renal corpuscle and a tubule that empties into a collecting duct. Each renal corpuscle contains a cluster of interconnected, fenestrated capillaries called the glomerulus within a structure called Bowman's capsule. Each glomerulus is supplied with blood under pressure by an afferent arteriole. Filtration occurs in the renal corpuscle. Each tubule of a nephron is composed of a proximal convoluted tubule, a loop of Henle, and a distal convoluted tubule. Tubules are surrounded by peritubular capillaries in the cortex and by the vasa recta capillaries in the medulla. (Figures 46.10, 46.11)

- Different portions of the tubule have different permeabilities to solutes and water. Most reabsorption of useful solutes occurs in the proximal tubule. (Figure 46.12)

- Water and ion reabsorption continues along the loop of Henle, using a countercurrent exchange system. The reabsorption of solutes by the vasa recta minimizes the loss of solutes from the renal medulla. Fine-tuning of urine composition occurs in the distal tubule, and the final concentration of urine is formed within the collecting ducts. (Figures 46.13, 46.14)

- Peter Agre and colleagues discovered that water moves through plasma membranes through protein channels. Agre called these channels aquaporins. Aquaporins regulate water reabsorption in the kidneys. (Figures 46.15, 46.16)

46.4 Human Health Connection

- Regardless of the cause of renal malfunction, the symptoms are similar and stem from the condition known as *uremia*, which literally means "urine in the blood."

- One important treatment for kidney disease is hemodialysis, in which wastes in blood diffuse across a selectively permeable artificial membrane into a dialysis fluid. Hemodialysis uses a countercurrent exchange system. (Figure 46.17)

Test to Assess Your Learning

1. A change in electrolyte levels in the body may result in
   a. altered membrane potentials that disrupt normal cell function.
   b. disruption of certain biochemical processes that occur in the cell.
   c. cell death.
   d. (a) and (b) only.
   e. (a), (b), and (c).

2. Nitrogenous wastes are the by-products of the metabolism of
   a. carbohydrates.
   b. lipids.
   c. nucleic acids.
   d. proteins.
   e. both (c) and (d).

3. Marine fish avoid water balance problems by
   a. producing a large volume of dilute urine.
   b. not drinking water.
   c. having gill epithelial cells that recapture lost salts from the environment.
   d. producing small volumes of concentrated urine.
   e. (a), (b), and (c).

4. Metabolic water is water
   a. necessary to stimulate the process of cellular respiration.
   b. found within cells.
   c. produced during cellular respiration.
   d. produced by sweat glands.
   e. used by cells during the uptake of glucose.

5. Which of the following statements about osmoregulators and osmoconformers is false?
   a. Marine osmoregulators maintain an internal salinity lower than that of seawater.
   b. Freshwater osmoregulators maintain an internal salinity higher than that of fresh water.
   c. Osmoconformers are stenohaline ("narrow salt")—unable to tolerate much variation in environmental salinity.
   d. Sea stars are osmoconformers and their body fluids are similar to seawater in osmolarity.
   e. As osmoconformers, echinoderms grow well in estuaries where fresh and salt water meet and salinity fluctuates widely.

6. The excretory system found in insects is composed of
   a. protonephridia.
   b. metanephridia.
   c. Malpighian tubules.
   d. a filtration kidney.
   e. a secretory kidney.

7. In the mammalian kidney, filtration is driven by
   a. solute concentration in the tubular filtrate.
   b. solute concentration in the blood.
   c. water concentration in the blood.
   d. water concentration in the tubular filtrate.
   e. hydrostatic pressure in the blood vessels of the glomerulus.

8. In the mammalian urinary system, the urine formed in the kidneys is carried to the urinary bladder by
   a. the collecting duct.
   b. the renal tubule.
   c. the renal pelvis.
   d. the ureters.
   e. the urethra.

9. Which of the following causes an increase in sodium reabsorption in the distal convoluted tubule?
   a. an increase in aldosterone concentrations
   b. an increase in antidiuretic hormone concentrations
   c. a decrease in aldosterone concentrations
   d. a decrease in antidiuretic hormone concentrations
   e. none of the above

10. Aquaporins are
    a. ion channels.
    b. water channels.
    c. receptors for aldosterone.
    d. small pores in the fenestrated capillaries of the glomerulus.
    e. both (a) and (c).

Articulate to Assess Your Learning

1. Define nitrogenous wastes and list four types. What are some advantages and disadvantages of excreting different types of nitorgenous wastes?

2. List and define the three processes involved in urine production. Do all three processes occur for every substance that enters an excretory organ such as the kidney?

Collaborate to Assess and Extend Your Learning

1. Discuss two different types of filtration mechanisms found in invertebrates.

2. Briefly discuss the parts and functions of the nephron in the mammalian kidney.

3. A principle of biology is that living organisms have mechanisms that maintain homeostasis. Explain how salt glands are a homeostatic adaptation for marine life.

Visit McGraw-Hill Ryerson Connect™ for additional study resources.

Endocrine Systems

47

Chapter Outline

A section through a human brain, highlighting the pituitary gland (white) and its connection to the hypothalamus. Both of these structures are endocrine glands. Image is a three-dimensional MRI.

Communication takes several forms in nature and involves all the major sensory systems. It may occur over long distances, as when sound waves travel through the ocean from one whale to another over a kilometre or more, or when olfactory cues travel from one moth to another across hundreds of metres. At the other end of the scale, as you learned with neuronal synapses, communication can occur between individual cells across minute distances.

Between these two scales of communication lies yet another: that of long-distance cell-to-cell communication. **Endocrine glands** contain epithelial cells that secrete molecules called **hormones** into the bloodstream, where they circulate throughout the body. The hormones gain access to all the body's cells in this way and influence many different cellular activities. A single hormone can influence many parts of the body at the same time. Typically, hormones are produced in response to a homeostatic challenge, such as a change in an animal's blood pressure or body temperature. It is a chief function of hormones to counter these challenges and maintain the body's homeostasis. In this chapter, you will learn about the chemical nature of hormones and their mechanisms of action, how the endocrine and nervous systems interact, and the ways in which hormones influence diverse functions such as metabolism, growth, and reproduction. We conclude with a discussion of hormones and human health.

47.1 MECHANISMS OF HORMONE ACTION AND CONTROL

Learning Outcomes:

1. Be able to define what a hormone is and the characteristics that distinguish different types of hormones from each other.
2. List and give examples of the three different chemical classes of hormones.
3. Describe the cellular location of receptors for lipid-soluble hormones and receptors for water-soluble hormones.
4. Describe the factors that regulate the concentration of a hormone circulating in the blood.

In this section, we will examine some of the general characteristics of hormones, how they act, and how they are controlled.

Long-Distance Signalling Connects Remote Organs and Tissues

Suppose that an animal is injured and bleeding badly and that the total amount of fluid in its body decreases significantly. The animal's heart would not fill adequately with blood. As a consequence, blood pressure would decrease, creating a potentially life-threatening situation. In vertebrates, the major organs capable of minimizing the loss of fluid from the body during such times are the kidneys. After a loss of blood, the heart communicates with the kidneys, signalling them to retain water and produce more concentrated urine. This helps prevent the fluid levels of the body from dropping further. For this type of communication between organs, specific hormones are released from the heart—which detected the loss of blood—into the bloodstream, where they can be carried to the kidneys to exert their effects. Hormones are made by cells in nearly all the body's organs, including the heart. In many cases, though, hormone-producing cells are packaged into discrete glands of their own. In those cases, the glands are called endocrine

glands. Collectively, all the endocrine glands and other organs with hormone-secreting cells constitute the **endocrine system**, as depicted for a vertebrate in **Figure 47.1**. Unlike other organ systems, such as the urinary or respiratory systems, the endocrine system does not consist of physically connected tissues and organs.

Hormones Can Have Short-Term or Long-Term Effects

The effects of a given hormone may occur within seconds or require several hours to develop, and they may last for as short as a few minutes or as long as days. This is a key difference between the communication processes in the nervous and

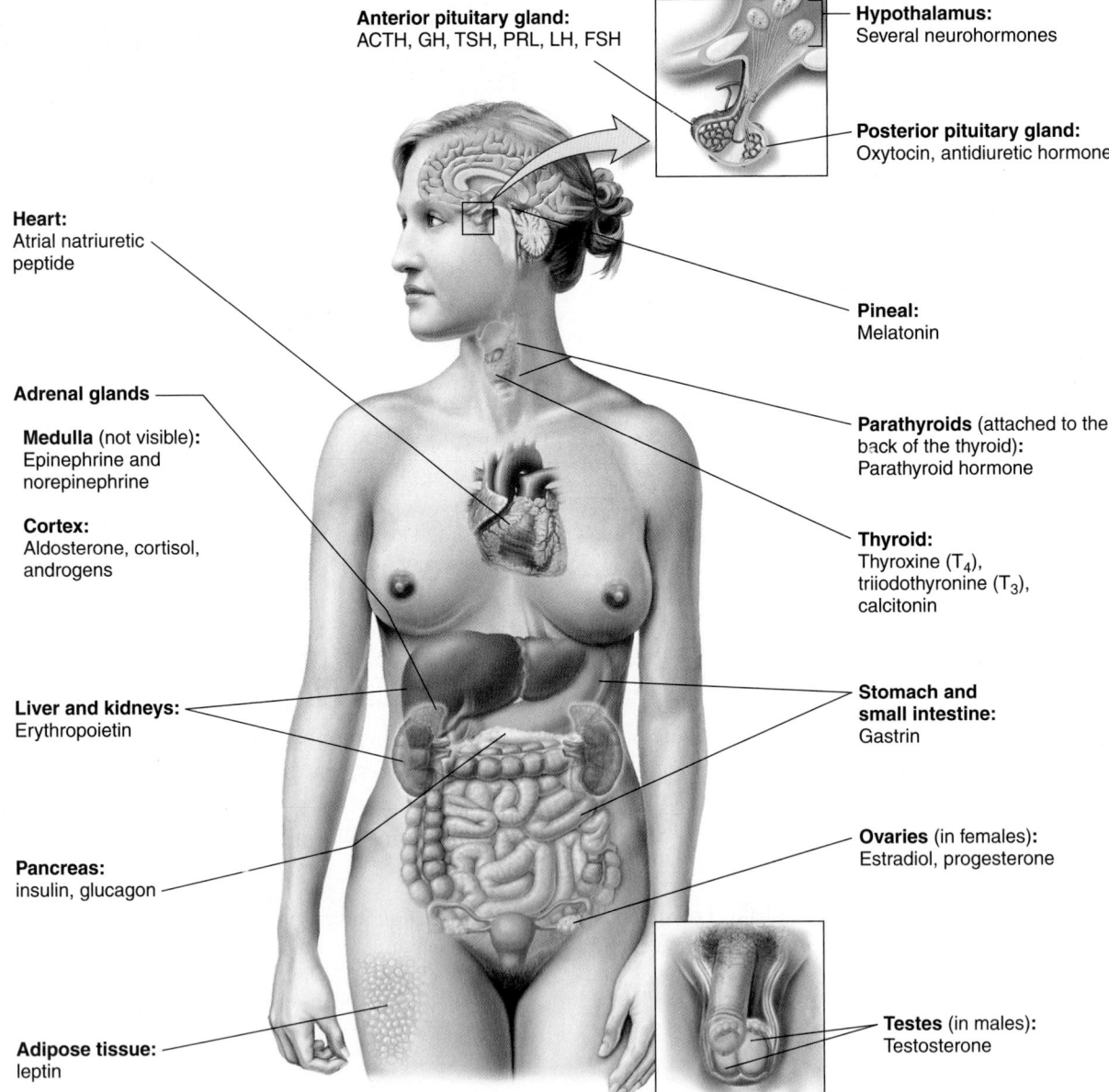

Anterior pituitary gland:
ACTH, GH, TSH, PRL, LH, FSH

Hypothalamus:
Several neurohormones

Posterior pituitary gland:
Oxytocin, antidiuretic hormone

Heart:
Atrial natriuretic peptide

Pineal:
Melatonin

Adrenal glands

Medulla (not visible):
Epinephrine and norepinephrine

Cortex:
Aldosterone, cortisol, androgens

Parathyroids (attached to the back of the thyroid):
Parathyroid hormone

Thyroid:
Thyroxine (T_4), triiodothyronine (T_3), calcitonin

Liver and kidneys:
Erythropoietin

Stomach and small intestine:
Gastrin

Pancreas:
insulin, glucagon

Ovaries (in females):
Estradiol, progesterone

Adipose tissue:
leptin

Testes (in males):
Testosterone

Figure 47.1   **Overview of the endocrine system in humans.**   This figure shows the location of the major human endocrine glands that constitute the human endocrine system, followed by the hormones produced by those glands.

endocrine systems. In the nervous system, signals are transmitted from one cell to another within milliseconds, and the effect on the postsynaptic cell occurs immediately. In the endocrine system, one hormone may act on a cell quickly and for a very short time, while another may act very slowly and have a lingering action. The explanation for these differences lies in the mechanisms by which different hormones act. To understand this, we first examine the different chemical types of hormones, because it is the chemical nature of hormones that determines their mechanisms of action.

The Three Classes of Hormones Differ in Composition and Modes of Action

Hormones fall into three broad classes: the amines, the proteins/peptides, and the steroids (**Table 47.1**). The amines and the proteins/peptides generally share similar chemical properties and modes of action, while the steroid hormones act very differently from the other classes.

The amine hormones are derived from an amino acid, either tyrosine or tryptophan. Tyrosine is the precursor for the hormones epinephrine and norepinephrine, which are produced in the adrenal medulla and are important in the body's response to stress (the so-called fight-or-flight reaction), and for dopamine, a hormone made by the brain. Tyrosine is also the chemical backbone of the hormones made by the thyroid gland, which are important regulators of metabolic rate, growth, and development. The only hormone derived from tryptophan is melatonin, which is produced within an endocrine gland called the pineal gland located in the brain. Melatonin is important for controlling seasonal reproduction in certain mammals, such as sheep and hamsters.

Most hormones are peptides (small, water-soluble polypeptides) or proteins. These hormones participate in numerous body functions, such as reproduction, metabolism, growth, and mineral balance.

The final group of hormones are the steroids, which are synthesized from the lipid cholesterol. All steroid hormones are lipids, unlike the other two classes of hormones. Steroids are less soluble in water than amines or protein and peptide hormones. Because of their limited solubility, steroids are usually bound to large, soluble proteins in the blood that serve as carriers. By combining with these proteins, steroid hormones can reach high concentrations in the blood. The major steroid hormones found in vertebrates include cortisol and aldosterone made by the adrenal cortex, androgens made by the testes, and estrogen and progesterone made by the ovaries. In insects, ecdysone is produced in the prothoracic gland.

Water-Soluble Hormones Act on Membrane Receptors

A hallmark of cell signalling by water-soluble molecules is that a ligand binds to a receptor protein located in the plasma membrane. This is the mechanism by which neurotransmitters act, for example. Similarly, all the amine and protein/peptide hormones, with one exception (thyroid hormones), act in this way. As these hormones diffuse from the blood into the interstitial fluid, they must bind to a specific receptor protein located on the cell surface. Only cells that have the proper receptors on their surfaces can respond to the hormone. Thus, although a hormone is released into the entire circulatory system, it activates only specific cells. The receptor interacts noncovalently and reversibly with the hormone. The reversibility of the binding between hormone and receptor is one way in which cells are prevented from being permanently stimulated.

Among cells throughout the body, different receptor proteins may be made that recognize the same hormone. These different receptors, called subtypes or isoforms, may be the product of different genes or be produced by alternative splicing, which is described in Chapter 12. In this way, one hormone can perform more than one action in the body by binding to receptor isoforms that differ slightly from each other. These receptors may have different affinities for the hormone, such that low concentrations of a hormone may cause one type of effect by binding to a high-affinity receptor on one cell, and higher concentrations may cause entirely new actions on different cells by binding to a low-affinity receptor on another cell. In this way, most hormones have evolved to serve more than one function.

The binding of a water-soluble hormone to its plasma membrane receptor initiates intracellular signalling (see Chapter 9). Three major signalling pathways that are activated by water-soluble hormones are the cyclic AMP pathway, the calcium/phosphatidylinositol pathway, and the tyrosine kinase pathway. These signal transduction processes may be rapid, occurring in some cases within seconds, and involve the activity of enzymes. Both of these features are important, since occasionally the rapidity of the cell response to a hormone can mean the

Table 47.1	Chemical Classes of Hormones			
Class	**Chemical properties**	**Location of target cell receptor**	**Mechanism of action**	**Examples**
Amines	Small, water soluble, derived from tyrosine or tryptophan	Plasma membrane (except thyroid hormones)	Second messengers (except thyroid hormones)	Epinephrine, norepinephrine, dopamine, melatonin, thyroid hormones
Proteins/Peptides	Water soluble	Plasma membrane	Second messengers	Insulin, glucagon, leptin
Steroids	Derived from cholesterol, mostly lipid soluble	Cytosol or nucleus	Usually stimulates gene transcription	Cortisol, testosterone, estradiol

difference between life and death, as may occur, for example, under conditions of extreme danger. The presence of enzymes in the signalling process ensures that a small amount of hormone has its signal amplified greatly, because a single signalling molecule results in the production of many intracellular messengers.

Activation of signalling pathways may also lead to changes in cellular activities that occur more slowly. These slower changes usually require activation or inhibition of various genes in the nucleus.

Lipid-Soluble Hormones Act on Intracellular Receptors

Because steroid hormones are lipids, they are soluble in plasma membranes and diffuse across the membrane into the cell cytosol. Unlike the case for water-soluble hormones, receptors for steroid hormones are located within the cell, either within the cytosol or, more commonly, within the nucleus. This is also true for the two thyroid hormones, which are poorly soluble in water.

The complex of a steroid hormone bound to its intracellular receptor functions as a transcriptional activator by binding to enhancers of particular genes (see Chapter 12). Once bound, transcription of a gene is greatly increased, which eventually increases the amount of that gene's protein product. These proteins may be important in any of a wide variety of cellular activities.

Steroid hormones can influence a number of genes within a single cell or in different cells. In this way, a single type of steroid hormone can exert a variety of actions throughout the body. The physical changes that accompany puberty result from the actions of two steroid hormones—androgens in males and estrogens in females—and are perhaps the most striking example of this widespread action.

We have learned that hormones act in all cases by binding to a receptor protein located on the cell surface, in the cytosol, or in the nucleus. This raises an interesting question: Which evolved first, a given hormone or its receptor? It would appear that there would be no selection pressure to evolve one without the other. However, recent research has generated intriguing new hypotheses regarding the evolution of these signalling systems, as described in Genomes and Proteomes.

Hormone Concentrations Depend on Rates of Synthesis and Removal

Although most hormones circulate in the blood at all times, their concentrations can increase or decrease dramatically when necessary. This can be accomplished in two major ways: by changing the rate of hormone production by an endocrine cell, and by changing the rates at which hormones are removed or inactivated.

Synthesis of amine hormones is mediated by enzymatic conversion of either tyrosine or tryptophan into their respective hormones. These reactions require several enzymes that add

GENOMES AND PROTEOMES

Hormones and Receptors Evolved as Tightly Integrated Molecular Systems

All hormones act by binding to a receptor. Without a receptor, a hormone has no function, and without a ligand, a receptor has no function. Hormones and their receptors function as tightly integrated molecular systems. Each molecule depends on the other for biological activity. How such systems could have evolved, or whether they evolved together, has long been a puzzle.

Joseph Thornton and his colleagues recently addressed this puzzle by examining how two structurally related steroid hormones evolved separate activities and distinct receptors. **Aldosterone**, as noted, is a steroid made by the adrenal cortex. Because it regulates the balance of certain minerals in the body, it is known as a **mineralocorticoid**. Cortisol is another steroid made by the adrenal cortex and is known as a **glucocorticoid** because one of its major functions is to regulate glucose balance. The actions of these hormones are mediated by intracellular receptors known as the mineralocorticoid receptor (MR) and the glucocorticoid receptor (GR), respectively. Phylogenetic analysis of the sequences of these two receptors suggests that they arose at least 450 million years ago by duplication of an ancient corticoid receptor (CR) gene.

The researchers analyzed the known sequences of the genes for the MR and GR of many vertebrate species, including the most ancient vertebrates, to deduce the theoretical sequence of an ancestral CR. They then synthesized this CR and tested its ability to bind aldosterone and cortisol. They discovered that the CR was capable of binding both hormones, particularly aldosterone. This was surprising, because aldosterone is present only in tetrapods, which arose long after the proposed gene duplication event that created the MR. Thus, it appears that a receptor with high affinity for aldosterone was present long before animals acquired the capacity to synthesize aldosterone. The receptor must have evolved to bind other steroids. Around 450 million years ago, the gene for the CR duplicated, and then the two resulting genes must have evolved such that one receptor gained high affinity primarily for mineralocorticoids and the other for glucocorticoids.

These studies suggest that the ability of an animal to respond to aldosterone evolved long before aldosterone did, because a receptor with high affinity was already in place in animals. When aldosterone evolved in tetrapods, the MR derivative of the ancestral CR was co-opted by aldosterone for its own use. In this example, therefore, the answer to the "which came first" question appears to be that the receptor evolved first and the hormone later.

or remove chemical side groups and achieve the desired product (**Figure 47.2**). The synthesis of the hormone depends on the amounts and activities of the synthesizing enzymes. These enzymes are always present in the cell, but the amounts and activities of the enzymes can be greatly stimulated when additional hormone is required.

Tyrosine:
Amino acid.

Enzyme 1

OH group added

L–dopa:
Inactive intermediate.

Enzyme 2

COOH group removed

Dopamine:
Important neurotransmitter and hormone made by the brain.

Enzyme 3

OH group added

Norepinephrine:
Important hormone for fight-or-flight reactions. Made in the adrenal medulla.

Enzyme 4

CH₃ group added

Epinephrine:
Important hormone for fight-or-flight reactions, similar to norepinephrine. Also made in the adrenal medulla.

Figure 47.2 Synthesis of the amine hormones dopamine, norepinephrine, and epinephrine.

The protein and peptide hormones are synthesized at a steady rate in an unstimulated cell, until additional hormone is needed. In that case, transcription factors within the cell direct the increased transcription of the gene coding for that hormone. Conversely, when less hormone is required, gene transcription is slowed or stopped. These hormones are too large to diffuse across the plasma membrane from the cytosol, where they are synthesized, out to the extracellular fluid. Instead, they are packaged into secretory vesicles much the same way as neurotransmitters are packaged in neuron terminals. This packaging provides a ready means of secreting the hormones by exocytosis and a reservoir of stored hormone available for immediate release when needed. When a cell is stimulated to secrete its stored protein or peptide hormones, it also is typically stimulated to synthesize new hormone molecules to replace them.

The synthesis of steroid hormones is quite different from that of other classes of hormones, because, as noted earlier, they are derived from cholesterol (**Figure 47.3**). To form steroid hormones, a cell must express enzymes capable of adding hydroxyl groups to specific carbons in the cholesterol skeleton. Other enzymes carry out reduction reactions, and still others can both hydroxylate a carbon and split carbon-carbon bonds. The activities and amounts of many of these enzymes change if more or less hormone is required.

Steroid hormones, unlike water-soluble hormones, are not packaged into secretory vesicles because the steroid would diffuse out across the lipid membrane of the vesicle. Instead, steroid hormones are made on demand, and no significant storage exists for them.

Although hormones carry out vital functions, excessive stimulation of cells by hormones can produce detrimental effects. For example, hormones that are activated if an animal loses blood typically help restore blood volume and pressure.

This cannot continue indefinitely, however, because once blood volume and pressure are restored, it would be harmful if they continued to increase until their concentrations were above normal. Therefore, once a hormone enters the blood and performs its functions, it must usually be prevented from exerting its effects indefinitely. This is accomplished in one or more ways:

- Hormones that bind to plasma membrane receptors may be engulfed by endocytosis into a cell, where lysosomal enzymes degrade the hormones.
- Small, water-soluble hormones are excreted in the urine.
- The liver chemically modifies many hormones to render them inactive and more easily excretable via the kidneys.
- Negative-feedback processes (see Chapter 38) turn off the signals that were responsible for stimulating the synthesis and secretion of the hormone.

Generally, these processes ensure that hormone concentrations in the blood remain within a normal range under most circumstances but have the capacity to be increased or decreased beyond that range if required. One of the ways in which changes in hormone concentrations are initiated is through sensory input to an animal's brain. As we see next, the nervous system and endocrine system are functionally linked in many animals, including all vertebrates.

Figure 47.3 Synthesis and major functions of the major steroid hormones in animals.

Principle: *Structure determines function. Notice how slight changes in the arrangements of side groups attached to the four-ring backbone create products with completely different functions. Keep in mind that the three-dimensional shape of a molecule may be changed much more by such chemical modifications than is visible in a two-dimensional depiction.*

47.2 LINKS BETWEEN THE ENDOCRINE AND NERVOUS SYSTEMS

Learning Outcomes:

1. Describe the anatomical connections between the hypothalamus, posterior pituitary, and anterior pituitary.
2. Explain the role of the hypothalamus and anterior pituitary in regulation of endocrine function.
3. List some of the major functions of the hormones of the posterior pituitary.

A key feature of the endocrine system in most animals is that the concentrations of many hormones in blood rise and fall with changes in an animal's environment. For this to happen, the endocrine system receives sensory input from an animal's nervous system, which in turn modulates the activity of one or more endocrine glands. In this section, we explore how this happens in vertebrates and how the hypothalamus and pituitary gland play the major roles in linking the nervous and endocrine systems.

The Hypothalamus and Anterior Pituitary Gland Have Integrated Functions

Sensory stimuli detected by the nervous system can activate the endocrine system. For example, when an antelope detects the presence of a nearby lion, visual and olfactory sense information is relayed to the antelope's brain. The brain initiates changes in certain endocrine glands that release hormones to prepare the antelope for the possibility of an attack. As another example, the concentrations of certain hormones fluctuate in the blood of migrating fish as they move back and forth between feeding grounds in the sea and freshwater spawning sites. These hormones are activated by different salinities in the environment,

which in turn are detected by sensory cells of the fish's nervous system. The hormones act to prepare the gills of the fish to handle the large swings in salinity of the water.

The common feature of these examples and many others is that a sensory cue, such as a predator or the salinity of water, must be perceived by a sensory receptor and converted into an endocrine response. Electrical signals are transmitted from the sensory receptors to different parts of the brain, including the hypothalamus. The hypothalamus sits at the bottom surface of the vertebrate brain and is vital for diverse functions such as reproduction, bodily rhythms, appetite and metabolism, and responses to stress (**Figure 47.4**). Within the hypothalamus are numerous neurons that synthesize a class of hormones called

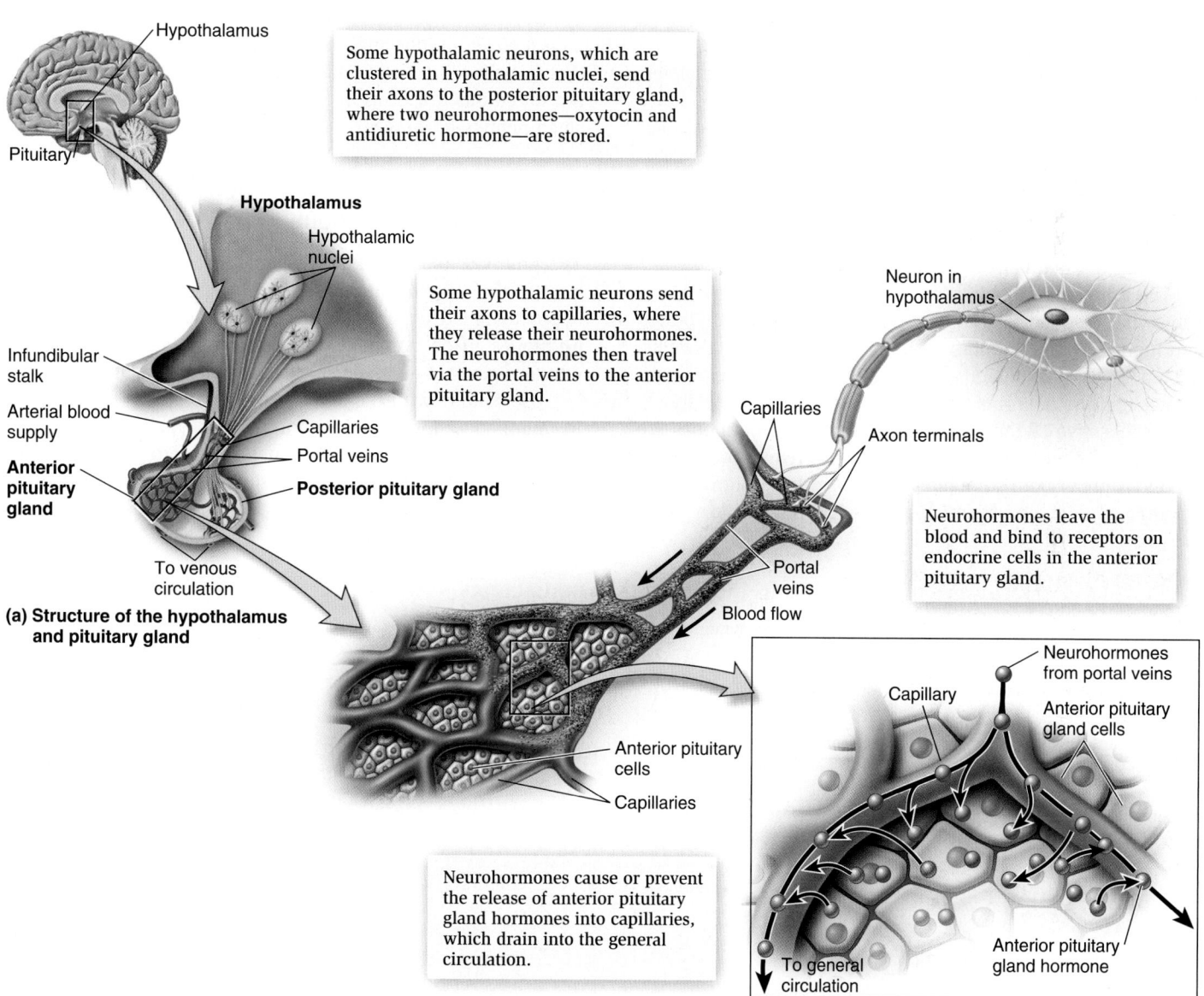

Some hypothalamic neurons, which are clustered in hypothalamic nuclei, send their axons to the posterior pituitary gland, where two neurohormones—oxytocin and antidiuretic hormone—are stored.

Some hypothalamic neurons send their axons to capillaries, where they release their neurohormones. The neurohormones then travel via the portal veins to the anterior pituitary gland.

Neurohormones leave the blood and bind to receptors on endocrine cells in the anterior pituitary gland.

(a) Structure of the hypothalamus and pituitary gland

Neurohormones cause or prevent the release of anterior pituitary gland hormones into capillaries, which drain into the general circulation.

(b) Stimulation of the anterior pituitary gland by the hypothalamus

Figure 47.4 Structure and function of the hypothalamus and pituitary gland.

BioConnections: *Recall the definition of neurotransmitter from Chapter 41 and take a look back at Figure 41.14. What determines whether a molecule such as dopamine is considered a neurotransmitter or a hormone?*

neurohormones, or hypothalamic releasing hormones, which are hormones made in and secreted by neurons. All neurohormones are either amines or peptides. Although they are produced within neurons, these molecular signals are not referred to as neurotransmitters, because the endings of the neurons do not terminate in a synapse with another cell. Instead, the neuron terminals end close to capillaries at the top of a structure known as the **infundibular stalk**. Here, the neurons secrete their neurohormones into the capillaries, which in turn collect into portal veins.

Portal veins differ from ordinary veins because they not only collect blood from capillaries—like all veins—but also form another set of capillaries, as opposed to returning the blood directly to the heart, like other veins. The portal veins extend through the length of the infundibular stalk before forming new capillaries. The stalk is physically connected to a multilobed endocrine gland sitting directly below the hypothalamus, called the **pituitary gland**, the highlighted structure in the chapter-opening photo. It is within the anterior lobe of the pituitary gland—often called simply the anterior pituitary gland—that the portal veins empty into a second set of capillaries. This arrangement of blood vessels bypasses the general circulation and allows for neurohormones to be delivered directly from the hypothalamus to the cells of the anterior pituitary gland in a quick, efficient manner.

The anterior pituitary gland synthesizes six different hormones that respond to the presence of the hypothalamic neurohormones in the capillaries arising from the portal veins. **Table 47.2** lists the major anterior pituitary hormones in vertebrates and the neurohormones that regulate them. As shown in the table, five of the anterior pituitary gland hormones are activated by neurohormones, one is inhibited by dopamine, and one is under both stimulatory and inhibitory control by the hypothalamus. The six hormones of the anterior pituitary gland are secreted into the general blood circulation, where they reach their target organs.

Adrenocorticotropic hormone (ACTH) stimulates the cells of the adrenal cortex to synthesize and release cortisol or related steroid hormones. Follicle-stimulating hormone (FSH) and luteinizing hormone (LH) act on the ovaries or testes to stimulate egg or sperm development and the synthesis and release of estrogens and androgens from the gonads. Growth hormone (GH) stimulates the growth of immature animals and participates in control of energy balance. Prolactin (PRL) concentrations are increased in mammals during late pregnancy and during lactation. This hormone stimulates milk production in mammals but affects salt and water balance in other vertebrates. Finally, thyroid-stimulating hormone (TSH) acts on cells of the thyroid gland to stimulate growth of the gland and production of thyroid hormones.

In addition to the anterior lobe, the pituitary gland contains a posterior lobe and, in some species, an intermediate lobe that is believed to be vestigial in primates. These lobes carry out numerous functions in the body, as described next for two small peptide hormones.

The Posterior Pituitary Gland Secretes Oxytocin and Antidiuretic Hormone

The posterior pituitary gland has a blood supply but, in contrast to the anterior pituitary gland, it is not connected to the hypothalamus by portal veins and does not respond to neurohormones made in the hypothalamus. Instead, the posterior pituitary gland is an extension from the hypothalamus that lies in close contact with the anterior pituitary gland (Figure 47.4). In mammals, the neuron terminals in the posterior pituitary contain one of two hormones: **oxytocin** or **antidiuretic hormone (ADH)**. When needed, these hormones are released directly from the neuron terminals into the bloodstream.

Table 47.2	Hormones of the Anterior Pituitary and Hypothalamus		
Pituitary hormone	**Stimulatory neurohormone from hypothalamus**	**Inhibitory neurohormone from hypothalamus**	**Major functions**
Adrenocorticotropic hormone (ACTH)	Corticotropin-releasing hormone (CRH)	None known	Stimulates adrenal cortex to make glucocorticoids
Follicle-stimulating hormone (FSH)	Gonadotropin-releasing hormone (GnRH)	None known	Stimulates germ cell development and sex steroid production in gonads
Luteinizing hormone (LH)	Gonadotropin-releasing hormone (GnRH)	None known	Stimulates release of eggs in females; stimulates sex steroid production from gonads
Growth hormone (GH)	Growth hormone–releasing hormone (GHRH)	Somatostatin	Promotes linear growth; regulates glucose and fatty acid balance in blood
Prolactin (PRL)	None known	Dopamine	Stimulates milk formation in mammals
Thyroid-stimulating hormone (TSH)	Thyrotropin-releasing hormone (TRH)	None known	Stimulates thyroid gland to make thyroid hormones

Oxytocin increases in the blood of pregnant mammals just before birth. It stimulates contractions of the smooth muscles in the uterus, which facilitates the birth process. After the offspring are born, oxytocin becomes important in the letdown of milk. When the mother's nipples are stimulated by the suckling of a newborn, neurons transmit a signal from the breast to the mother's hypothalamus, which stimulates the cells that produce oxytocin. Oxytocin, which is stored in the neuron terminals of the posterior pituitary gland, is released into the blood where it travels to smooth muscle cells surrounding the milk glands and ducts of the breast. This stimulates the secretion of milk. Thus, oxytocin has two important and different functions, one during birth and one during lactation. In both cases the hormone stimulates contraction of muscle cells.

Antidiuretic hormone gets its name because it acts on kidney cells to decrease urine production—a process known as antidiuresis. Diuresis is an increased loss of water in the urine, as happens, for example, when you drink large amounts of coffee or tea. If the fluid content of the body is low, such as during dehydration or after blood loss, ADH is secreted into the blood from the posterior pituitary gland. It acts to increase the number of water-channel proteins called aquaporins present in the membranes of kidney tubule cells (see Chapter 46). It is through the aquaporins that water is recaptured from the forming urine. Minimizing the volume of water used to form urine is an adaptation that conserves body water when necessary.

At high concentrations, ADH also increases blood pressure by stimulating vasoconstriction of blood vessels. Like oxytocin, therefore, ADH has more than one function. Both of its major functions are related in that they contribute to maintaining blood pressure and fluid levels in the body. The two actions of ADH are mediated by different receptor subtypes, a feature that has proven to be of medical value in humans. Researchers have synthesized versions of ADH that have been chemically modified to activate ADH receptors in the kidney but not those in blood vessels. One such compound is sometimes used to treat bed-wetting (**nocturnal enuresis**) in children by decreasing urine production without the unwanted side effect of increasing blood pressure.

Oxytocin and ADH are well-studied examples of the evolution of hormones. These two hormones are found only in mammals. However, many invertebrates and all nonmammalian vertebrates secrete one or more peptides that share chemical similarities with oxytocin and ADH but are not identical to the mammalian hormones. One of these is **vasotocin**, which combines some of the chemical structure of both oxytocin and ADH. It is believed that an ancestral gene duplicated at some point, and then the two new genes mutated slightly to produce two different and new hormones with new functions in mammals. Only mammals lactate, so the role of vasotocin must be different from that of oxytocin, for example, in birds, fish, and other vertebrates. Research has shown that vasotocin is responsible for regulating salt and water balance in the blood of nonmammalian vertebrates.

47.3 HORMONAL CONTROL OF METABOLISM AND ENERGY BALANCE

Learning Outcomes:

1. Describe the important anatomical features of the thyroid gland and the major function of thyroid hormones in adult animals.
2. List the hormones produced by the pancreas and adrenal glands, and provide a brief description of the major metabolic roles of each.
3. Explain the difference between type I diabetes mellitus and type II diabetes mellitus.

An important function of the endocrine system is to control metabolic rate and energy balance. Hormones are partly responsible for regulating energy use by cells by modulating appetite, digestion, absorption of nutrients, and the concentrations of energy sources, such as glucose, in the blood and their transport into cells. Although many hormones are involved in these processes, two from the thyroid gland, two from the pancreas, and one from adipose tissue play particularly important roles, as described in this section.

Thyroid Hormones Contain Iodine and Regulate Metabolic Rate

The thyroid gland lies within the neck of vertebrates. In mammals, it straddles the trachea just below the larynx (**Figure 47.5**). It consists of many small, spherical structures called follicles that contain in their core a gel-like substance called the **colloid**. The colloid consists primarily of large amounts of the protein **thyroglobulin**.

Thyroid hormones are produced when the neurohormone thyrotropin-releasing hormone (TRH; see Table 47.2) stimulates the secretion into the blood of thyroid-stimulating hormone (TSH) from the anterior pituitary gland. TSH in turn stimulates the follicle cells of the thyroid gland to begin the process of making thyroid hormones. Production of TRH and TSH is controlled by negative feedback actions of thyroid hormones on the hypothalamus and anterior pituitary.

During thyroid hormone synthesis, iodide—converted by the gut from dietary iodine—is transported from the extracellular fluid into the thyroid follicular cells. The iodide then enters the colloid, where it is oxidized and bonds to tyrosine side chains in thyroglobulin. When the thyroid follicle cells are stimulated by TSH, these tyrosines are enzymatically modified to form two active thyroid hormones, called **thyroxine** and **triiodothyronine**, which are cleaved from thyroglobulin and secreted from the cell. These molecules are unique among hormones in that they contain iodine molecules: four in the case of thyroxine, or T_4, and three in triiodothyronine, or T_3.

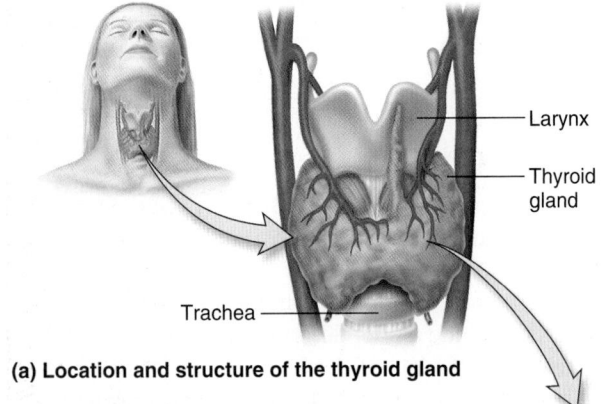

(a) Location and structure of the thyroid gland

- Larynx
- Thyroid gland
- Trachea

Figure 47.5 **(a) The thyroid gland.** Location and appearance of the gland in a mammal. Vertebrates contain thyroid tissue in the neck region, but it is not always consolidated into a single structure, as shown here. **(b)** The steps involved in the production of thyroid hormones. Shown is a cross-section through a small part of a single follicle in a thyroid gland, with a nearby capillary (not drawn to scale). The blood delivers iodide to the gland and picks up thyroid hormones secreted by the gland.

Capillary | **Interstitial fluid** | **Follicular cell of thyroid** | **Colloid**

- Iodide ion
- Basolateral membrane
- Apical membrane

1 Iodide is transported into the follicular cell.

Lysosome

4 The endocytotic vesicle fuses with lysosomes, which cleave off T_3 and T_4.

2 Iodides bond to tyrosine residues in thyroglobulin.

Iodinated TG

Thyroglobulin (TG)

T_3

T_4

Endocytotic vesicle

T_3

T_4

3 When the cell is stimulated by TSH, iodinated TG enters the cell by endocytosis.

5 T_3 and T_4 are secreted into the blood.

Triiodothyronine (T_3)   Thyroxine (T_4)

(b) Synthesis of thyroid hormones

A major action of thyroid hormones in adult animals is to stimulate energy consumption by many different cell types. This occurs in large part by increasing the number and activity of the Na^+/K^+-ATPase pumps in plasma membranes. As these pumps hydrolyze ATP, cellular levels of ATP decrease. This decrease is compensated for by increasing the cell's metabolism of glucose. Whenever metabolism is increased, heat production is increased. Consequently, a person with a hyperactive thyroid gland (**hyperthyroidism**; *hyper*, excessive) generally feels warm, while the opposite condition (**hypothyroidism**; *hypo*, less than normal) results in a sensation of coldness. It is estimated that up to 70% of the heat produced by some homeotherms is attributable solely to the actions of thyroid hormones on metabolic rate.

The fact that thyroid hormones cannot be made without iodine creates some interesting and unique features for these hormones. The availability of iodine in the diet of most animals is variable. As a consequence, the thyroid evolved the ability to store large amounts of thyroglobulin in the colloid. In this way, during times when iodine ingestion is high, many thyroglobulin molecules have their tyrosine amino acids bound to iodines, one of the first steps in forming T_4 and T_3. During times of low iodine availability, this reservoir of iodinated tyrosines in thyroglobulin molecules can be tapped. Humans, for example, have at least a two-month supply of thyroid hormones even in the absence of ingested iodine. In most industrialized countries, iodine deficiency is rarely a problem since the introduction of iodized salt in the mid-twentieth century. However, in some regions of the world this is still a major health problem.

The right side of **Figure 47.6a** shows the consequences that follow when thyroid hormones are not produced in normal amounts, for example, because of a lack of iodine in the diet.

The decreased T_4/T_3 concentrations remove the source of negative feedback on the hypothalamus and anterior pituitary gland, resulting in elevated TSH concentrations. The thyroid gland responds to the increased TSH by increasing the cellular machinery needed to produce more and more thyroglobulin, even though in the absence of iodine no additional T_4 or T_3 will be synthesized. What results is an overgrown gland that is nonetheless incapable of making thyroid hormone. This condition is known as an **iodine-deficient glucag (Figure 47.6b)**. In humans, the problem can be alleviated either by adding iodine to the diet or by taking T_4 pills. Goitres are not unique to humans. Iodine deficiency is relatively common among vertebrates, and

goitres are found frequently in reptiles and birds, particularly those that subsist on seeds, a diet generally low in iodine.

Hormones of the Pancreas and Adrenal Glands Regulate Fuel Concentrations in the Blood

Thyroid hormones regulate an animal's metabolism. For metabolism to proceed normally, however, body cells must have adequate energy available in the form of glucose, fatty acids, and amino acids. The brain, in particular, must have a constant supply of nutrients because brain cells have relatively limited storage capacity for fuel. Regulation of energy availability to cells is in large part the job of the hormones of the pancreas and the adrenal glands.

The pancreas is a complex organ consisting of two parts (**Figure 47.7**). Most of the mass of the pancreas comprises exocrine glands, which release their contents into the small intestine, where they aid digestion. The other part of the pancreas, the endocrine pancreas, produces the peptide hormones insulin and glucagons.

Spherical clusters of cells called **islets of Langerhans** are scattered in great numbers throughout the endocrine pancreas. Within the islets are alpha cells, which make glucagons, and beta cells, which make insulin. These two hormones are antagonistic with respect to each other. For example, insulin lowers and glucagon raises blood sugar concentrations. When glucose concentrations in the blood need to be raised, glucagon is released, whereas insulin is released when glucose concentrations are high.

(a) Thyroid function with and without normal iodine intake

(b) Woman with iodine-deficient goitre

Figure 47.6 **Consequences of normal and inadequate iodine in the diet.** (a) With normal iodine intake, as shown on the left, T_4 and T_3 concentrations inhibit TSH secretion. Without enough iodine, as shown on the right, less T_4 and T_3 are synthesized and the TSH concentration increases. This leads to enlargement of the thyroid gland. (b) An extreme example of an enlarged thyroid gland, or goitre, caused by iodine deficiency.

 Principle: *Living organisms have mechanisms that maintain homeostasis. Recall from Chapter 40 that a key way in which homeostasis is maintained is via negative feedback. Notice in this figure how a change in dietary intake of iodine results in decreased negative feedback and subsequent overgrowth of the thyroid gland.*

Figure 47.7 Location, appearance, and internal structure of the mammalian pancreas. The ducts of the pancreas empty into the small intestine. Amid the exocrine pancreas are scattered islets of Langerhans, which are endocrine tissue.

BioConnections: *The pancreas contains both exocrine and endocrine tissue. Is this property ever observed in other organs? (Hint: Think about the processes associated with digestion and absorption of food.)*

Maintaining normal glucose and other nutrient concentrations in the blood is a vital process that keeps cells functioning optimally. When an animal has not fed for some time and its energy stores are becoming depleted and blood glucose concentrations are falling, glucagons is secreted into the blood, where it acts on the liver to stimulate the production of glucose (**Figure 47.8**). The liver contains a limited supply of glucose in the form of stored glycogen, which is quickly broken down into many molecules of glucose, which are then secreted into the blood. This process, known as glycogenolysis (see Chapter 40), is stimulated within seconds by glucagons.

The adrenal glands, which sit atop the kidneys, also play a role in glucose metabolism by producing amine and steroid hormones. In addition to glucagons produced by the pancreas, epinephrine is secreted by the adrenal medulla and also stimulates glycogenolysis. Once the liver's glycogen is depleted, however, glucose must be produced in some other way if fasting continues or glucose concentrations continue to fall. In that case, cortisol is released from the adrenal cortex. Once in the blood, cortisol stimulates the liver to synthesize glucose from amino acids and glycerol. This process is vital to long-term survival in the absence of food. Because of the combined short-term and long-term actions of glucagons, epinephrine, and cortisol, blood glucose concentrations rarely fall or remain significantly below normal except in extreme circumstances.

In contrast to fasting, after an animal eats a meal the concentrations of glucose and other nutrients in the blood become elevated. Restoring the normal blood concentrations of glucose, fats, and amino acids is almost exclusively under the control of insulin, one of the very few hormones that is absolutely essential for survival in animals. The secretion of insulin is directly stimulated by increased concentrations of glucose in the blood (**Figure 47.8**). Once in the blood, insulin acts on plasma membrane receptors primarily in adipose and muscle tissues to facilitate the transport of glucose across the plasma membrane into the cytosol. Once in the cell, glucose is used for cellular functions or converted to stored energy forms, such as fat. As discussed in Chapter 40, the process of glucose transport involves the actions of proteins called glucose transporters. These molecules exist in membrane vesicles in the cytosol. The major function of insulin is to stimulate the movement of the vesicles with their glucose transporters to the plasma membrane. Once the vesicle fuses with the plasma membrane, its transporter molecules begin transporting glucose into the cell.

When blood glucose concentrations return to normal, the stimulus for insulin secretion disappears, and insulin concentrations in the blood decrease. This in turn results in a decrease in the number of glucose transporters in plasma membranes, because the glucose transporters are subjected to endocytosis and thereby return to membrane vesicles in the cytosol. The actions of insulin are not limited to glucose transport, however, because the hormone also stimulates movement of amino acids into cells and promotes fat deposition in adipose tissue. In other words, the broader role of insulin in the body is to facilitate the transfer of energy from the extracellular fluid into storage sites primarily in muscle and fat.

In the absence of sufficient insulin, as occurs in the disease **type 1 diabetes mellitus (T1DM)**, extracellular glucose cannot cross plasma membranes, and consequently glucose accumulates to very high concentrations in the blood.

T1DM occurs in many mammals and other vertebrates. It is caused when the body's immune system mistakenly attacks and destroys the insulin-producing cells of the islets of Langerhans. One consequence of the disease is that muscle and fat cells cannot receive their normal amount of glucose to provide the ATP they need. In addition, the unusually large amount of glucose in the blood overwhelms the kidneys' ability to reabsorb it from the kidney filtrate, and glucose appears in the urine. Fortunately, this form of the disease is treatable in humans with

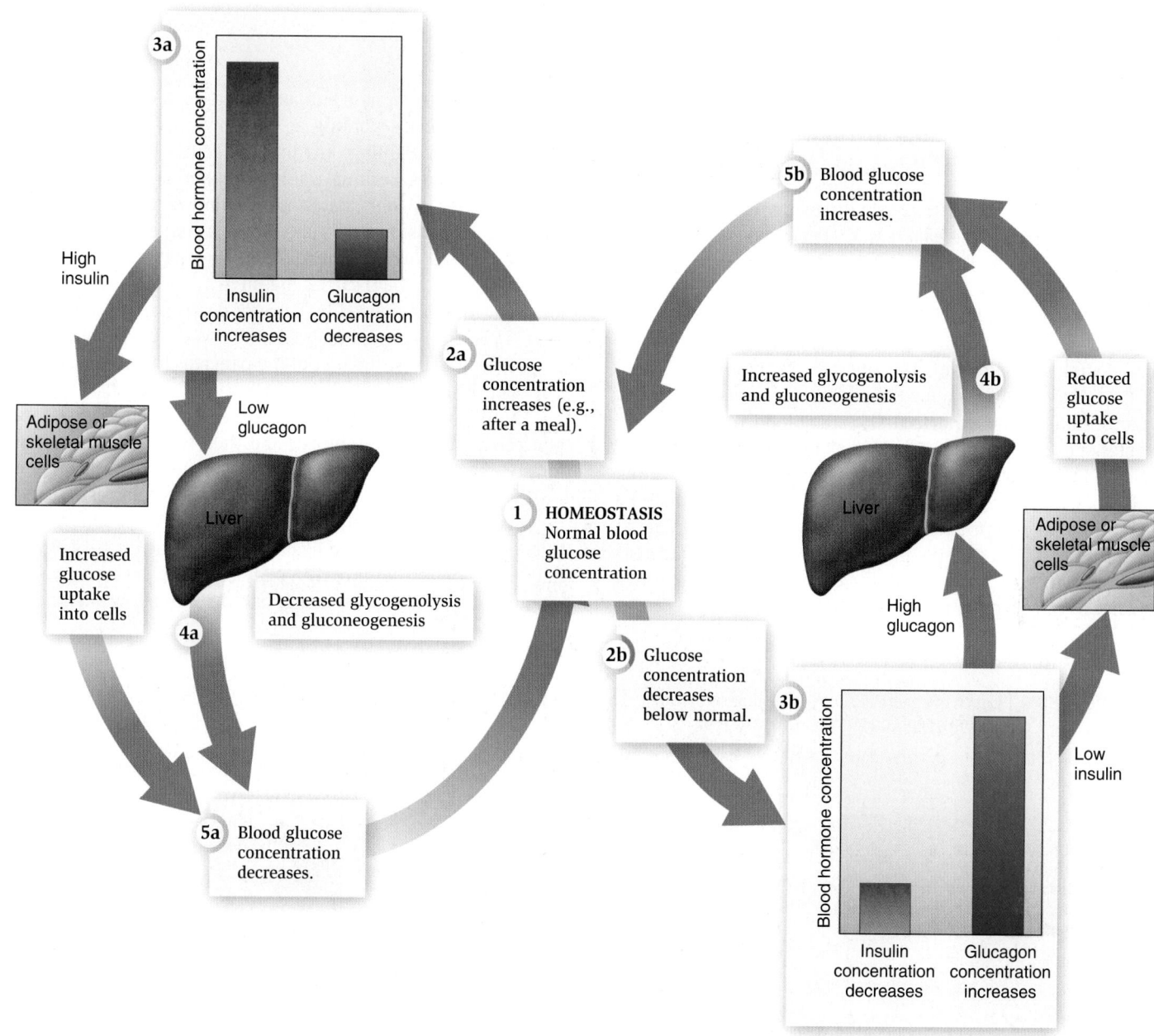

Figure 47.8 Mechanisms that help maintain glucose homeostasis in the blood. Glucagon and insulin respond in opposite ways to changes in plasma glucose concentrations. When the plasma glucose concentration decreases below normal (right), the insulin concentration decreases and glucagon increases. When plasma glucose concentration increases above normal (left), the insulin concentration increases and glucagon decreases. Both of these mechanisms return the plasma glucose concentration to normal.

regular monitoring of blood glucose concentrations and daily administration of insulin. Similar methods are used to treat the disease in pets.

In humans, the more common form of diabetes, which accounts for roughly 90% of all cases, is **type 2 diabetes mellitus (T2DM)**. In T2DM, the pancreas functions normally and is not attacked by the immune system. However, the cells of the body lose much of their ability to respond to insulin for reasons that are still unclear. T2DM is linked to obesity and can often be prevented or reversed with weight control. Drugs

are also available that improve the body's ability to respond to insulin. Formerly, T2DM was known as "adult-onset" diabetes, because it usually appeared in middle age. This name is no longer used, however, because the rising rates of childhood obesity in developed countries, such as Canada and the United States, have sparked a dramatic increase in the number of children and adolescents with the disease.

The discovery of insulin and its application to the human condition was one of the greatest and most influential achievements in the history of medical research, as described next.

FEATURE INVESTIGATION

Banting, Best, MacLeod, and Collip Isolated Active Insulin for the First Time in 1921 in Canada's Most Famous Medical Research Accomplishment

In the nineteenth century scientists discovered that in addition to the exocrine part of the pancreas, there existed spherical clusters of cells that were not associated with the exocrine digestive functions of this organ. These clusters were called islets by their discoverer, German physiologist Paul Langerhans. By the early twentieth century German scientists had discovered that, in dogs, complete removal of the pancreas resulted immediately in T1DM. Researchers assumed, therefore, that cells of the islets of Langerhans produced a factor of some kind that prevented diabetes—in other words, it helped maintain glucose homeostasis by preventing blood glucose concentrations from getting too high. The factor, however, proved impossible to isolate by using the chemical purification methods available at the time. It was assumed that during the process of grinding up a pancreas to produce an extract, the factor was destroyed by the digestive enzymes of the exocrine pancreas.

This problem was eventually solved in 1921 by a team of Canadian scientists working at the University of Toronto: surgeon Frederick Banting, medical student Charles Best, and biochemist James Bertram Collip. The work was performed in the laboratory of John MacLeod, a renowned expert in carbohydrate metabolism at the time. Banting had read a paper in a medical journal that described a deceased patient in whom the pancreatic duct, which carries digestive juices to the small intestine, had become clogged by calcium deposits. The closed duct caused pressure to build up behind the blockage, which eventually caused the exocrine part of the pancreas to atrophy and die. The islets of Langerhans, however, survived intact.

Banting hypothesized that if he were to tie off, or ligate, the pancreatic ducts of an animal, and then wait a sufficient time for the exocrine pancreas to die, he could more easily obtain an active glucose-lowering factor from the remaining islets without the problem of contamination by digestive enzymes. Banting and Best proceeded to ligate the pancreatic ducts of several dogs, as shown in **Figure 47.9**. After waiting seven weeks, an amount of time they previously had determined was sufficient

HYPOTHESIS Ligation of pancreatic ducts will cause atrophy of the exocrine pancreas, allowing extraction of an active glucose-lowering factor from the remaining portion of the pancreas.

KEY MATERIALS One group of dogs for ligation experiments; second group of dogs made diabetic by having pancreas removed.

Experimental level

Conceptual level

1. Ligate pancreatic ducts in one group of dogs by tying threads around the base of the ducts and pulling them tight.

Surgeon operating on midgut region of a dog.

Ligated ducts block flow of digestive juices, which damages exocrine pancreas.

Pancreas

Islets of Langerhans

Small intestine

2. Allow seven weeks for atrophy of pancreas.

Pancreas atrophies, but islets remain intact.

3. Remove atrophied pancreas. Prepare extract by grinding up tissue in acid. Purify by adding alcohol, filtering, removing lipids, and concentrating.

Acid and pancreatic tissue

Add alcohol

Filter

Evaporate alcohol

Remove lipids (see text)

- Factor
- Contaminating proteins
- Lipids

Mortar and pestle step only

More purified and concentrated factor

After further purification steps

Figure 47.9   The isolation of insulin by Banting, Best, McLeod, and Collip.

Figure 47.9 *(Continued)*

4 Remove pancreas from a second group of dogs.

Blood glucose levels increase because of diabetes.

Glucose appears in the urine, a sign of diabetes.

Urine puddle

5 Inject either purified extract or control solution into the diabetic dogs. Determine the levels of glucose in the blood and in the urine.

Diabetic dog

6 **THE DATA**

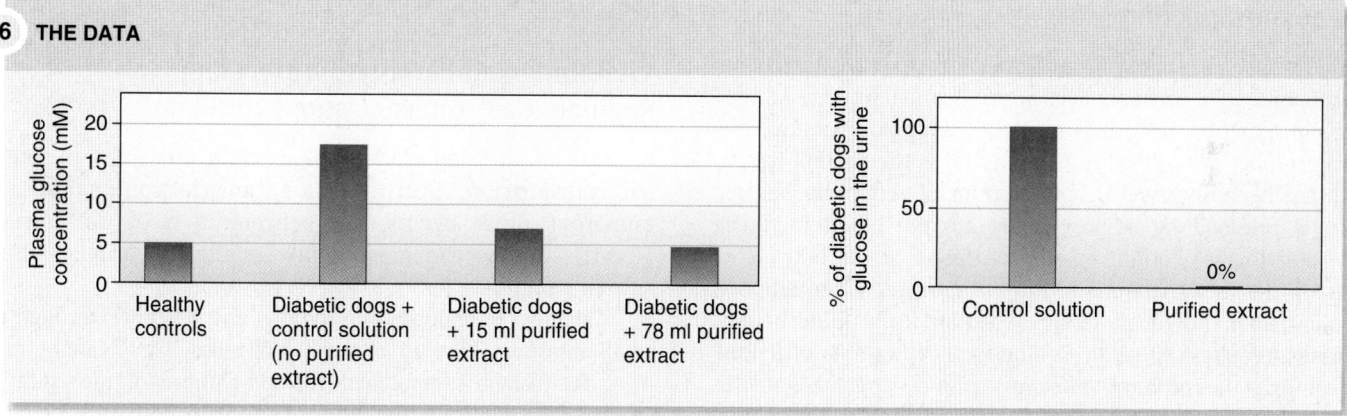

7 **CONCLUSION** Atrophy of the exocrine portion of the pancreas eliminated digestive enzymes that would have degraded the glucose-lowering factor (insulin) during its purification from the pancreas. Along with improved chemical purification procedures, this atrophy step allowed researchers to obtain a highly purified and fully active glucose-lowering factor.

8 **SOURCE** Banting, F.G., and Best, C.H. 1922. The internal secretion of the pancreas. *Journal of Laboratory and Clinical Medicine* 7:256–271.

for the exocrine part of the pancreas to atrophy, they prepared extracts of the remaining parts of the pancreas, including the islets of Langerhans. This was done by removing the atrophied pancreas from each dog and grinding it up with a mortar and pestle in an acid solution. The extract was then injected into a second group of dogs in which diabetes had previously been induced by surgically removing the pancreas. The researchers discovered that the extract was capable of keeping the diabetic dogs alive for a brief time. However, they were unable to isolate sufficient quantities of the active factor in the extract to keep the experiments going longer than a day or so, and they were unable to obtain sufficiently pure factor to prevent side effects, such as infection and fever.

This is where Collip's expertise came in. Collip developed a method to precipitate contaminating proteins from the extract by adding alcohol to the acid (Figure 47.9, step 3). This removed most of the contaminating proteins, leaving behind a much more purified and safe extract. The extract was then filtered

to remove debris and further extracted with hydrophobic solvents to remove lipids. This was done because the researchers believed that the factor was either a peptide or a protein, and by removing lipids they would obtain a more purified preparation. Finally, the purified extract was concentrated by evaporating the alcohol, which increased its potency. When this factor was injected into diabetic dogs, their blood glucose concentrations were normalized and there was no longer any glucose in their urine. Dogs that received only a control solution that did not contain the factor continued to show high glucose concentrations in the blood and urine.

In later experiments, two subsequent innovations enabled the researchers to obtain larger amounts of the factor and more accurately assess its potency even without the ligation procedure. First, the researchers chose the very large pancreases of cows, obtained at a local slaughterhouse, for their starting material from which to prepare the extracts. Second, Collip developed a highly sensitive assay to more precisely measure the concentration of glucose in the blood of an animal before and after injection of the purified factor. The combination of the improved chemical purification steps, large amounts of starting material, and improved assays for testing the extract proved to be the keys that enabled the team to test the factor, which they eventually named insulin, on human patients. The first successful test came in 1922 on a 14-year-old boy in Toronto, who was seriously ill from T1DM. In 1982, recombinant human insulin first became available for widespread use.

The success of the team in rapidly isolating insulin and proving its effectiveness was so significant that Banting and MacLeod were awarded the Nobel Prize in 1923. The Nobel committee apparently felt that Banting and MacLeod were the leaders of the project and that it was they who deserved the prize, but the two scientists disagreed. Banting shared the monetary portion of his award with Best, and MacLeod shared his with Collip.

Experimental Questions

1. How did Banting and Best propose to obtain the glucose-lowering factor produced by the pancreas?
2. What was Collip's contribution to the isolation of insulin?
3. What subsequent innovations led to large-scale production of insulin for human patients?

Adipose Tissue Secretes the Hormone Leptin to Regulate Appetite

Hormones also contribute to metabolism by exerting effects on appetite and, as a consequence, on food consumption. A chief source of appetite-regulating hormones is adipose tissue. One such hormone, introduced in Chapter 40, is the protein leptin, which has been observed in species from all vertebrate classes. Leptin is released by adipose cells into the blood in direct proportion to the amount of adipose tissue in the body, and it acts on the hypothalamus to inhibit appetite. When adipose stores are low, however, leptin secretion from adipose cells decreases, resulting in reduced blood concentrations of leptin. This removes the inhibitory effect of leptin on appetite, causing an animal to consume more food. In these ways, the amount of energy stored in an animal's body in the form of fat is communicated to the brain to regulate how hungry an animal feels.

We have seen that hormones influence energy homeostasis by regulating appetite, nutrient concentrations in the blood, transport of nutrients into cells, and metabolic rate. In the next section, we consider how hormones control another feature of homeostasis: regulating concentrations of key minerals in the blood.

47.4 | HORMONAL CONTROL OF MINERAL BALANCE

Learning Outcomes:

1. Describe the hormonal control of Ca^{2+} homeostasis.
2. Explain the regulation in the kidneys of Na^+ and K^+ balance by antidiuretic hormone, aldosterone, and atrial natriuretic factor.

All animals must maintain a proper balance in their cells and fluids of minerals such as Ca^{2+}, Na^+, and K^+. These ions participate in numerous functions common throughout much of the animal kingdom. For example, the partitioning of ions across plasma membranes determines in large part the electrical properties of cells such as neurons. In this section, we will see how maintaining a homeostatic balance of these ions in an animal's body is coordinated in large part by hormones.

Vitamin D and Parathyroid Hormone Regulate Ca^{2+} Concentrations in Blood

Because of the important roles calcium ions play in neuronal transmission, heart function, muscle contraction, and numerous other events, the concentration of Ca^{2+} in the blood is among the most tightly regulated variables in an animal's body.

Calcium is obtained from the diet and absorbed through the small intestine. Like all charged molecules, Ca^{2+} cannot readily cross plasma membranes, including those of the epithelial cells of the small intestine, and thus its transport must be facilitated. This process is controlled by the action of a derivative of **vitamin D**. In most mammals that receive regular exposure to the sun, skin cells produce vitamin D from a precursor called 7-dehydrocholesterol, a reaction that requires the energy of ultraviolet light (**Figure 47.10**). In addition, many animals obtain vitamin D from food or, in people today, from milk supplemented with the vitamin. This is especially important for people who live at latitudes that receive little sunlight for much or part of the year.

Before it can act, vitamin D must first be modified by two enzymes that both add one hydroxyl group to specific carbon atoms, first in the liver and then in the kidney. The final active product is called 1,25-dihydroxyvitamin D. This molecule is a hormone because it is secreted into the blood by one organ—the kidneys—and acts on a distant target tissue—the small intestine—where it stimulates the absorption of Ca^{2+}. The calcium ions then enter the blood, where they can be delivered to tissues for activities such as building bone and maintaining nerve, muscle, and heart functions. If the active form of vitamin D is not present in the blood, the bones lose calcium and become weakened. In children, this results in the weight-bearing bones of the legs becoming deformed, a condition called rickets.

When calcium is not present in the diet, or when 1,25-dihydroxyvitamin D is not formed in normal amounts because of insufficient exposure to sunlight, the blood concentrations of Ca^{2+} may decrease dramatically. This does not normally occur, however, because a hormone called

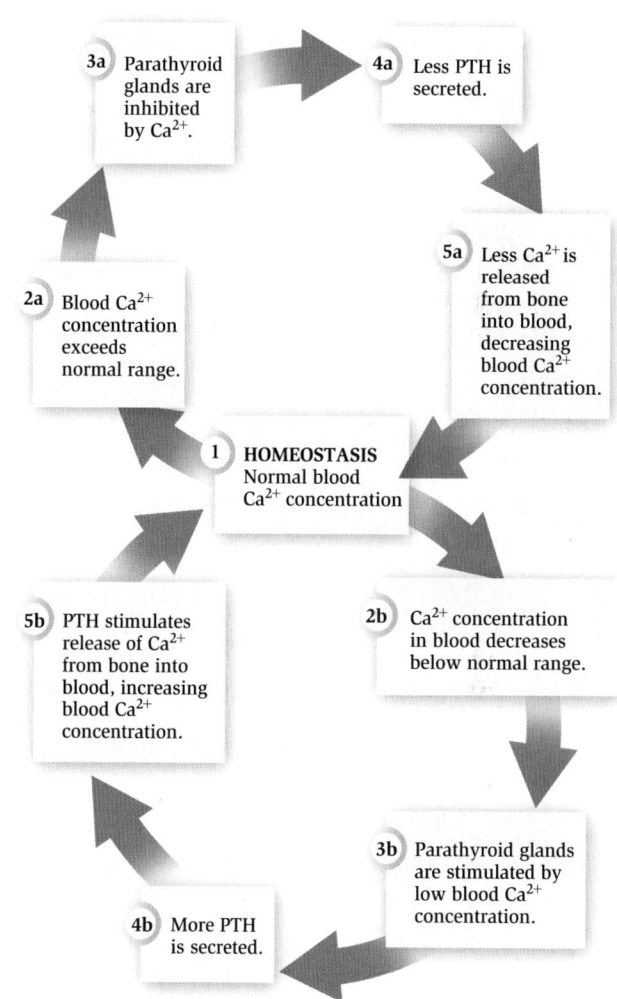

1 Vitamin D is consumed in food and made in the skin in the presence of sunlight.

Dietary vitamin D

Ultraviolet light

Vitamin D ← 7-dehydrocholesterol in the skin

2 An OH group is added to vitamin D in the liver.

Kidney

3 A second OH is added in the kidneys, producing the active hormone.

Liver

Small intestine

1,25-dihydroxyvitamin D (active hormone)

4 The active hormone reaches the small intestine; absorption of calcium from the small intestine into the blood is increased.

Figure 47.10 Synthesis of the active hormone formed from vitamin D or its precursor in skin.

Concept check: *Do you suppose that all mammals synthesize the active form of vitamin D using the energy of sunlight?*

parathyroid hormone (PTH) is secreted from several small glands called parathyroid glands located near the thyroid gland (**Figure 47.11a**). PTH acts on bone to stimulate the activity of cells that dissolve the mineral part of bone. This releases Ca²⁺, which then enters the blood (**Figure 47.11b**). Thus, besides providing a skeletal framework for the vertebrate body, bone also serves as an important reservoir of Ca²⁺. Without PTH, calcium homeostasis is not possible. The total absence of PTH is fatal in humans and other mammals.

Several Hormones Regulate Sodium and Potassium Ions in Vertebrates

Like calcium, concentrations of sodium and potassium ions in the body fluids of most animals are tightly regulated, because these ions play crucial roles in membrane potential formation

Pharynx (view from the back)

Thyroid gland

Parathyroid glands

Esophagus

Trachea

(a) Location of the parathyroid glands

3a Parathyroid glands are inhibited by Ca²⁺.

4a Less PTH is secreted.

2a Blood Ca²⁺ concentration exceeds normal range.

5a Less Ca²⁺ is released from bone into blood, decreasing blood Ca²⁺ concentration.

1 HOMEOSTASIS Normal blood Ca²⁺ concentration

5b PTH stimulates release of Ca²⁺ from bone into blood, increasing blood Ca²⁺ concentration.

2b Ca²⁺ concentration in blood decreases below normal range.

4b More PTH is secreted.

3b Parathyroid glands are stimulated by low blood Ca²⁺ concentration.

(b) Homeostatic control of blood Ca²⁺ concentration

Figure 47.11 Parathyroid glands and the role of parathyroid hormone in calcium homeostasis. (a) The four small parathyroid glands are found behind the thyroid. (b) The action of PTH: Steps 2A–5A occur when Ca²⁺ is in excess, while steps 2B–5B occur when Ca²⁺ is below normal.

 Principle: *Living organisms have mechanisms that maintain homeostasis. Homeostatic control of Ca²⁺ concentrations is vitally important to life in most living organisms, and in all animals. Because of hormones such as PTH, the Ca²⁺ concentration in the body fluids of humans rarely changes by more than a slight margin.*

1. NaCl (table salt) is ingested. NaCl dissolves in the gut and eventually is absorbed into the blood.

2a. Increased Na$^+$ stimulates the posterior pituitary to secrete more antidiuretic hormone (ADH).

2b. Increased Na$^+$ stimulates the heart to make more atrial natriuretic peptide (ANP).

Kidney

Less H$_2$O in urine

More Na$^+$ in urine

More Na$^+$ in urine

2c. Increased Na$^+$ inhibits aldosterone production by the adrenal glands.

3. The events described in step 2 collectively cause more Na$^+$ and less H$_2$O to be lost in urine. Blood concentration of Na$^+$ decreases.

Figure 47.12 An example of sodium balance achieved by the coordinated actions of three hormones.

Concept check: *Why is there more than one hormone to regulate sodium and potassium balance?*

and action potential generation (see Chapter 41), among other functions. Like calcium, sodium and potassium are ingested in the diet and excreted in the urine in vertebrates. Unlike calcium, however, no large reservoirs exist in the body for sodium and potassium. One of the key mechanisms that regulate the concentrations of these ions in the blood is altering the rate of sodium, potassium, and water reabsorption from the urine as it is being formed in the kidneys. This is accomplished in large part by the actions of three hormones: ADH, aldosterone, and atrial natriuretic peptide (**Figure 47.12**).

The vertebrate kidney normally reabsorbs most sodium and potassium from the fluid filtered through the kidney glomerulus (see Chapter 46). However, dietary and other changes can alter the concentrations of these ions in the blood. When this happens, it is the role of the kidney to restore the ions to their normal concentrations. For example, if blood sodium concentrations increase above normal, the osmolarity of the blood will increase. Osmoreceptors in the brain detect this and stimulate ADH secretion from the posterior pituitary gland. Recall from Chapter 46 that ADH acts on the kidney to reabsorb water from the forming urine. By increasing the amount of ADH available to act on the kidneys, less water is excreted in the urine. In addition, the secretion of the adrenal steroid hormone aldosterone is inhibited in response to an increase in Na$^+$ concentrations. Normally, aldosterone increases sodium reabsorption in the kidney, and therefore its absence results in more sodium excretion in the urine. Finally, **atrial natriuretic peptide (ANP)** is secreted from the atria of the heart whenever blood concentrations of sodium increase. ANP causes a natriuresis (a loss of sodium in the urine; from the Latin *natrium*, sodium) by decreasing sodium reabsorption. Thus, ANP and aldosterone have opposite effects on sodium balance in the body, which is why their concentrations in the blood tend to rise and fall in opposite directions. The combined effect of decreasing water loss in the urine and reabsorbing less sodium is to decrease the concentration of sodium in blood and other body fluids.

47.5 HORMONAL CONTROL OF GROWTH AND DEVELOPMENT

Learning Outcomes:

1. List and describe the function of the peptide/protein hormones involved in the regulation of growth and development in vertebrates.
2. Discuss the functions of the three major hormones that control growth and development in insects.

Hormones play a nearly universal role in controlling growth and development. In animals, growth occurs in brief spurts, slowly over long periods, or both. Many mammals, for example, grow slowly but steadily until puberty, and then experience a period of rapid growth, followed by slower rates of growth and finally cessation of growth. Many insects, conversely, grow only in spurts during moulting periods. Although growth is determined by many factors, notably adequate nutrition, it is regulated in large part by the endocrine system.

Growth is distinguished from development, which is the process by which cells form tissues with specific functions, and tissues form larger and more complex structures. In this section we describe how both processes depend in part on the endocrine system.

Figure 47.13 Acromegaly in one individual from a pair of identical twins.   This condition is caused by a high concentration of growth hormone, which leads to enlarged bones in the hands and feet.

Concept check: *Did the individual on the left develop a growth hormone disorder before or after puberty?*

Vertebrates Require a Balance of Several Hormones for Normal Growth

In vertebrates, the anterior pituitary gland produces **growth hormone (GH)**, which is under the control of the hypothalamus (see Table 47.2). GH acts on the liver to produce another hormone, called **insulin-like growth factor-1 (IGF-1)**. In mammals, IGF-1 stimulates the elongation of bones, especially during puberty, when mammals become reproductively mature. This growth is further accelerated by the steroid hormones of the gonads, leading to the rapid pubertal growth spurt. Eventually, however, the gonadal hormones cause the growth regions of bone to seal, preventing any further bone elongation.

GH, IGF-1, and gonadal steroid hormones continue to be produced in adult vertebrates—including humans—even though growth has ceased. In adulthood, GH in particular serves metabolic functions, such as helping regulate the concentrations of glucose and fatty acids in the blood. The gonadal steroids are important for reproduction in adults (see Chapter 48).

In rare cases, a tumour of the GH-secreting cells of the anterior pituitary gland produces excess GH during childhood and adulthood in humans and other mammals. In humans, a person with this disorder can grow very tall and is known as a **pituitary giant**. Soon after puberty, though, growth stops. If high GH concentrations occur after puberty, however, the excess GH causes many bones, like those of the hands and feet, to thicken and enlarge, a condition known as **acromegaly** (**Figure 47.13**). Acromegalics are generally treated with synthetic somatostatin, which, as you recall from Table 47.2, is the inhibitor of GH made by the hypothalamus.

By contrast, if the pituitary fails to make adequate amounts of GH during childhood, the concentrations of GH and IGF-1 in the blood will be lower than normal. In such cases, growth is stunted, resulting in **pituitary dwarfism**. Pituitary dwarfs can be treated with GH and will grow to relatively normal height, as long as treatment begins before puberty ends so that the bones can still elongate.

Hormones are also required during fetal life, not for growth but for development of the brain, lungs, and other tissues into fully mature, functional structures. For example, cortisol from the fetal adrenal gland is vital for proper lung formation. Premature babies born before the adrenal glands have matured have lungs that are not capable of expanding normally and therefore the infant must be hospitalized to survive.

As another example, thyroid hormones affect development among all vertebrates. In amphibians, thyroid hormones play a critical role in metamorphosis, notably in tadpoles, where they promote the resorption of the tail and development of the legs (**Figure 47.14**). This effect can be dramatically demonstrated by experimentally decreasing or increasing the tadpole's thyroid hormone concentrations, which results in a tadpole that does not transform into a frog, or a tadpole in which metamorphosis occurs sooner than normal, resulting in a tiny frog. In fish, thyroid hormones play an equally critical role in development. For example, among the hundreds of species of flatfish that live on the ocean floor, thyroid hormones are responsible for the characteristic change in appearance that occurs in these species as they settle into a sedentary existence on the ocean bottom. The fins and gill covers migrate to the dorsal surface facing the water, the dorsal body surface becomes pigmented, and most remarkably the eyes migrate to the same side of the head, so that one eye is not constantly unused on the side facing the ocean floor. Each of these metamorphic events is under the direct control of thyroid hormones.

Figure 47.14 **The effect of thyroid hormones on tadpole development.** Experimental manipulation of thyroid hormone concentrations can retard or accelerate this development.

Invertebrates Grow in Spurts Under the Control of Three Major Hormones

Like vertebrate endocrine pathways, hormonal control systems in insects and other invertebrates often involve multiple glands and neural structures acting in concert. In insects, for example, growth of larvae and their eventual development into pupae (in holometabolous insects) is under hormonal control (**Figure 47.15**). In the case of larval growth and metamorphosis, specialized nerve cells periodically secrete a hormone called **brain hormone**, which stimulates a pair of endocrine glands called the prothoracic glands. These glands synthesize and secrete a steroid hormone, **ecdysone**, not found in vertebrates. In response to each burst of ecdysone, the larva moults—sheds its cuticle—and begins a new growth period until it must shed its cuticle again in response to another episode of ecdysone secretion.

Throughout larval development, a structure behind the brain called the corpus allatum secretes another hormone, this one a protein called **juvenile hormone**. Ecdysone and juvenile hormone have opposing actions. Ecdysone stimulates growth and development of the larva, while juvenile hormone inhibits maturation of the larva into a pupa. As the larva ages, the amount of juvenile hormone it produces gradually declines until its concentrations are nearly zero. During this time, however, ecdysone continues to be periodically secreted. This imbalance eventually tips the scale in ecdysone's favour, and the larva progresses to the pupa stage and finally transforms into an adult.

47.6 HORMONAL CONTROL OF REPRODUCTION

Learning Outcomes:

1. List the male and female sex steroids, their sites of production, and their roles in reproductive development.
2. Explain how nutrition and reproduction are linked through hormones.

The topic of reproduction is covered in Chapter 48, but it is worth noting here that in all vertebrates and probably in most invertebrates, reproduction is closely linked with endocrine function. In this section, we describe the most common reproductive hormones and their actions in male and female animals.

The Gonads Secrete Sex Steroids That Influence Most Aspects of Reproduction

Hormones produced by the gonads of animals play vital roles in nearly all aspects of reproduction. These include sex-specific reproductive behaviours such as courtship displays and mating rituals, development of an animal's sex-specific physical characteristics, its transition from a reproductively immature to a mature state, and its ability to produce offspring. In males, the gonads are called testes. They house the gametes, called sperm cells.

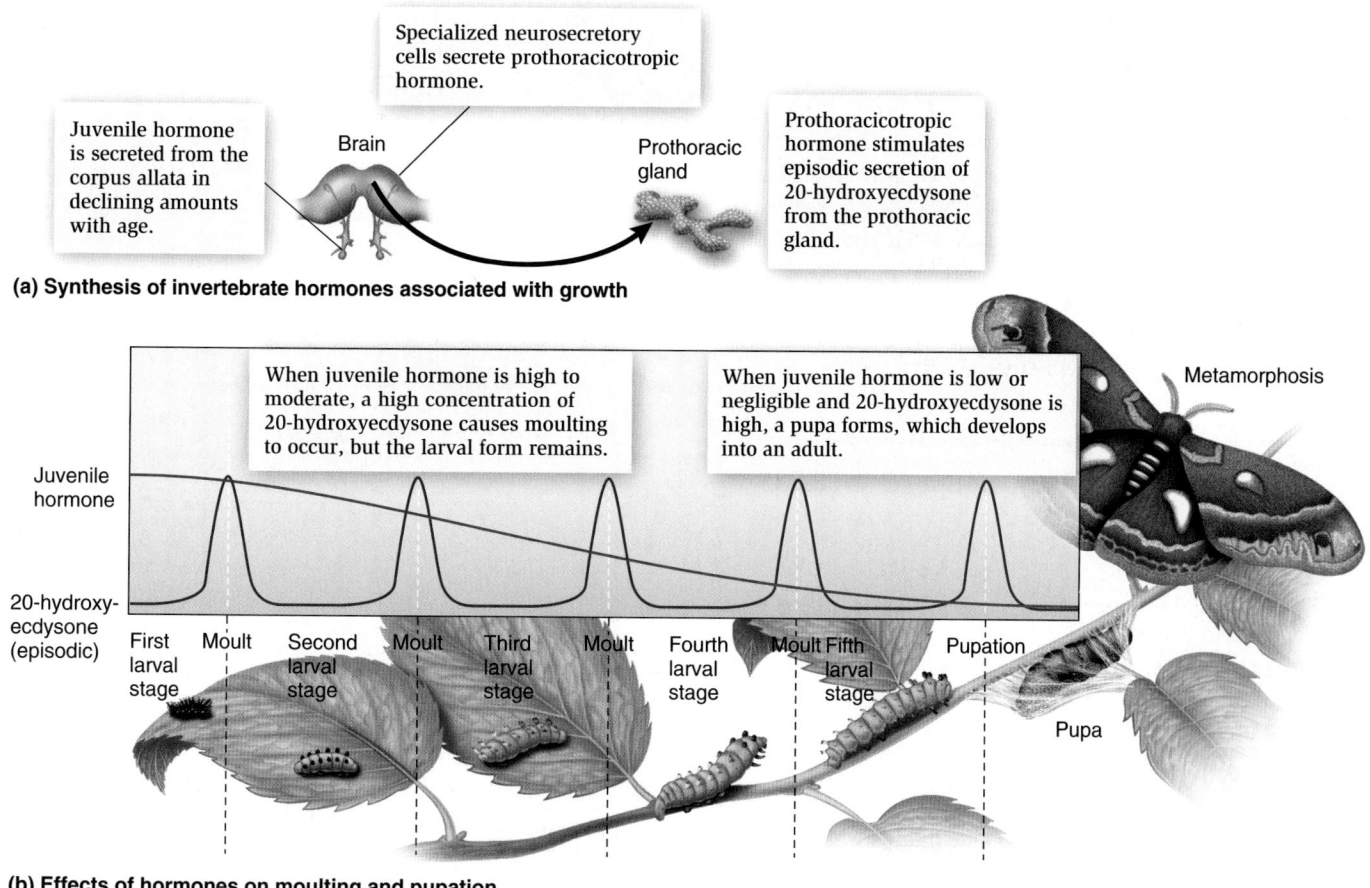

Juvenile hormone is secreted from the corpus allata in declining amounts with age.

Specialized neurosecretory cells secrete prothoracicotropic hormone.

Brain

Prothoracic gland

Prothoracicotropic hormone stimulates episodic secretion of 20-hydroxyecdysone from the prothoracic gland.

(a) Synthesis of invertebrate hormones associated with growth

When juvenile hormone is high to moderate, a high concentration of 20-hydroxyecdysone causes moulting to occur, but the larval form remains.

When juvenile hormone is low or negligible and 20-hydroxyecdysone is high, a pupa forms, which develops into an adult.

Metamorphosis

Juvenile hormone

20-hydroxy-ecdysone (episodic)

First larval stage | Moult | Second larval stage | Moult | Third larval stage | Moult | Fourth larval stage | Moult Fifth larval stage | Pupation

Pupa

(b) Effects of hormones on moulting and pupation

Figure 47.15 **Hormonal control of insect development.** Development of insects requires the coordinated actions of three hormones. Juvenile hormone suppresses pupa formation. Note the relative concentrations and patterns of 20-hydroxyecdysone and juvenile hormone in this figure are schematic and not representative of all insects.

In addition, though, the testes produce several related steroid hormones collectively termed **androgens**. In many vertebrates, including humans, the primary androgen is **testosterone**. The gonads of females are called the ovaries, which contain the female gametes, or egg cells. Other cells within the ovaries secrete two major steroid hormones, **progesterone** and a family of related hormones called **estrogens**. The major estrogen in many animals, including humans, is **estradiol**. Collectively, the male and female gonadal steroid hormones are referred to as the sex steroids.

The sex steroids are responsible for male- or female-specific reproductive behaviours associated with courtship and mating. In vertebrates, androgens from the developing testes are required for the development of the male phenotype. Exposure of fetuses to abnormal concentrations of male hormones or female hormones can lead to ambiguous phenotypes and sexual behaviour after birth. These steroids are also chiefly responsible for development of the secondary sex characteristics for each sex, which in humans include things such as growth of the appropriate external genitals, growth of the breasts, development of facial hair, and distribution and amount of fat and muscle in the body. Finally, the sex steroids are required for

maturation of gametes, the transition of a young animal to a reproductively mature one, and the ability of a female to produce young.

The ability of the testes and ovaries to produce the sex steroids depends on the presence of the gonadotropins, which are the same in both sexes and include **follicle-stimulating hormone (FSH)** and **luteinizing hormone (LH)** (see Table 47.2). Thus, the way in which the gonads are controlled in male and female animals is through identical anterior pituitary gland hormones.

Nutrition and Reproduction Are Linked Through Hormones

An interesting feature of the endocrine control of reproduction is the long-noted observation that puberty is delayed in mammals, including people, that are very undernourished. Similarly, fertility—the ability to produce offspring—is reduced in women and other adult female mammals under such conditions. This makes sense, because supporting the nutritional demands of a growing fetus would be difficult without good nutrition and energy stores. In such a case, it would be more advantageous for an animal to delay reproduction until sufficient food is available. How does the brain of a female mammal determine when sufficient energy is stored in her body to support a pregnancy? The answer appears to be partly the result of hormonal signals. For example, if the amount of fat in a woman's body decreases, so does the concentration of leptin in her blood, as described earlier. Leptin has been demonstrated to stimulate the synthesis and secretion of key reproductive hormones such as LH and FSH. Consequently, undernourishment causes a decrease in leptin, which in turn results in reduced production of reproductive hormones, and this contributes to a loss of fertility. Thus, leptin serves as a link between adipose tissue and the reproductive system.

47.7 HORMONAL RESPONSES TO STRESS

Learning Outcomes:

1. Define stress in a biological context and explain how it is linked with homeostasis.
2. Name the hormones produced by the different regions of the adrenal glands in response to acute and long-term stress and describe the major functions of each.

Stress in animal biology is often defined as any real or perceived threat to an animal's survival. This can take many forms depending on the species. To a crab, a passing shadow may indicate a hungry shark passing overhead, but to a human, a shadow may simply mean that a cloud has passed in front of the sun.

Similarly, a severe storm can be extremely stressful for birds in exposed nests but not to animals that live in sheltered environments. Overcrowding is adaptive for penguins trying to keep warm on ice floes, but it is very stressful to mice and rats.

In the 1930s while at McGill University, Hungarian Canadian endocrinologist Hans Selye made the remarkable discovery that regardless of the nature of the stress in any given species, a mammal's adaptive responses to stress were highly similar. One of the first responses was the enlargement of the adrenal glands. In this section, we describe how hormones made by the vertebrate adrenal glands are the common denominator of the vertebrate response to stress, and how these hormones act to prepare an animal to confront a challenge or escape it—the fight-or-flight response.

The Inner Core of the Adrenal Glands Makes Epinephrine

The adrenal glands, so named from the Latin *ad*, toward, and *renis*, kidney, because they sit atop the kidneys, and are multifunctional glands containing an inner region called the adrenal medulla and an outer region called the adrenal cortex (**Figure 47.16a**). The cells of the adrenal medulla secrete the amine hormones norepinephrine and epinephrine. Together, these two hormones are responsible for most of the fight-or-flight reactions that were described in Chapter 42 and are summarized here in **Table 47.3**.

(a) The location and structure of the adrenal glands

(b) Cellular organization and hormones of the adrenal cortex and medulla

Figure 47.16 Location and cellular arrangement of the adrenal glands.

The Outer Regions of the Adrenal Glands Make Steroid Hormones

Norepinephrine and epinephrine are only a part of the adrenal gland's response to stress, however. The outer part of the adrenal, the cortex, is itself subdivided into three zones (**Figure 47.16b**). The outer zone, the glomerulosa, is the region that makes aldosterone. Because this hormone acts to maintain

Table 47.3	Fight-or-Flight Response to Stress
System	**Responses**
Cardiovascular	Increase heart rate and strength of heart contractions to maximize pumping of blood to all parts of the body; dilate blood vessels entering tissues needing more oxygen—such as skeletal muscle—and constrict blood vessels to regions of less immediate importance—such as the gut and kidney
Respiratory	Dilate small airways (bronchioles) to reduce resistance to airflow in mammals; increase rate and depth of breathing to maximize oxygen intake and carbon dioxide elimination
Metabolic	Increase glycogenolysis in muscle to provide glucose for muscle cells and in liver to provide glucose to the blood, where it can reach all body cells; increase breakdown of adipose triglycerides into usable fuel (fatty acids) that can then enter the bloodstream; stimulate glucagon secretion, which acts on liver to promote gluconeogenesis
Nervous	Increase arousal and alertness; inhibit nonessential functions, such as appetite

Table 47.4	The Major Actions of Glucocorticoids in Stress
Site	**Actions**
Liver	Stimulate gluconeogenesis, thus providing glucose to the blood
Adipose tissue	Stimulate breakdown of triglycerides into fatty acids and glycerol for fuel
Muscle and adipose tissue	Inhibit sensitivity to insulin, making more glucose available to brain cells, which do not require insulin to move glucose across their plasma membranes
Bone	Inhibit bone growth and formation, because such processes require large amounts of nutrients that could be used to combat stress instead
Lungs	Stimulate lung maturation in the fetus
Immune system	Suppress immune system function and reduce inflammation
Other	Regulate sodium and chloride balance in migratory fish; stimulate nervous system development in most vertebrates; stimulate protein breakdown to provide amino acids to the liver for gluconeogenesis; inhibit reproduction

mineral balance, it is known as a mineralocorticoid. The innermost cortical zone is known as the reticularis, which functions in humans to make certain androgens, but whose function in other animals is not as clear. The bulk of the cortex is the middle zone, the fasciculata. It is here that the so-called glucocorticoid hormones are made, among them cortisol and other structurally related steroids.

Table 47.4 summarizes the major actions of glucocorticoids in vertebrates. Glucocorticoids are catabolic hormones; that is, they promote the breakdown of tissue. For example, they act on bone, immune, muscle, and fat tissue to break down proteins and lipids to provide energy for the body's cells. This is important for an animal that is facing an acute stress, because feeding and digestion both stop during fight-or-flight reactions, leaving internal stores as the only source of energy. In fact, these adrenal steroids are called glucocorticoids because one of their major actions is to promote gluconeogenesis in the liver during times of stress, thus providing glucose to the blood.

Responding to acute stress is an important function of glucocorticoids, but excessive production of these steroids can create serious problems. Such a situation might arise if an animal were chronically stressed for some reason, for example, because of habitat destruction, intraspecies fighting and aggression, or chronic infection. Glucocorticoids and the amines increase the activity of the heart and can raise blood pressure. Therefore, prolonged stress can lead to disorders of the heart and blood vessels. In addition, chronic increases in glucocorticoids can suppress the immune system because of the catabolic actions of glucocorticoids on immune tissue. This may compromise an animal's ability to fight infection. For example, the prolonged stress a salmon experiences when it makes its exhausting swim upriver to its spawning grounds causes massive suppression of its immune system, and many mature salmon that die after spawning are found to be riddled with infections. People who are chronically stressed also tend to be susceptible to infections,

or to having dormant viruses suddenly flare up, such as the herpes virus that causes cold sores.

Even an animal's ability to reproduce and grow is negatively affected by chronic stress, as noted most dramatically in medical situations involving humans. In children, for example, chronic exposure to high concentrations of glucocorticoids may stunt growth, at least temporarily. In women, chronic stress may result in the loss of monthly reproductive cycles. The explanation for this may be understood from an evolutionary perspective. Chronic stress generally suggests that an animal's fitness or survival is in jeopardy. Therefore, it is advantageous to have all energetically demanding activities—such as growth, reproduction, and even immune activity—come to a halt if these activities are not immediately required for staying alive.

The preceding discussion illustrates only a few ways in which the endocrine system can affect health and fitness in many animals, including humans. In the rest of this chapter, we highlight some aspects that are exerting a large impact on public health in humans.

47.8 HUMAN HEALTH CONNECTION

Learning Outcomes:

1. Name several hormones used therapeutically and the disease or health problem for which they are prescribed.
2. Describe the risks associated with the misuse of hormones and with exposure to endocrine disruptors in the environment.

Hormones have become very much a part of the news. The use of hormones to promote more efficient food production in dairy animals, for example, has created considerable controversy around the world. On the one hand, injecting cows with bovine growth hormone (BGH) makes for leaner, larger animals, which is of economic benefit to the dairy industry. On the other hand, many people are unsettled by the possibility that by-products of the hormone may find their way into our bodies, with unknown consequences. Note that the use of BGH in dairy cattle is banned in Canada but allowed in the United States. Let's look at two other ways in which factors that alter the function of the human endocrine system have important health implications and then consider how hormones are used therapeutically.

Synthetic Compounds May Act as Endocrine Disruptors

A recent phenomenon—disturbing because of its potential to affect reproduction in animals and people—is the growing amount of so-called **endocrine disruptors** found in lakes, streams, ocean water, and soil exposed to pollution runoff. These chemicals are derived in many cases from industrial waste and have molecular structures that in some cases resemble estrogen sufficiently to bind to estrogen receptors. If these compounds make their way into drinking water or food, they can exert estrogen-like actions or, in some cases, inhibit the actions of the body's own estrogen. This can lead to dramatic consequences on fertility and on development of embryos and fetuses. The extent of the risk from these **xenoestrogens** (from the Greek *xeno*, foreign) is hotly debated, but the number of mature, functional germ cells produced in animals as diverse as molluscs and human males has declined dramatically during the past 50 years in North America. In addition, researchers throughout the world have noted feminization of freshwater fish downstream of wastewater facilities. For example, male fish that were exposed to such conditions during development show increased production of proteins normally made by females bearing eggs. They also show changes in gonadal structures that resemble the female appearance.

Hormone Misuse Can Be Disastrous

Some individuals, typically those in competitive sports, self-administer hormones, such as androgens. This practice may increase muscle mass and improve athletic performance. However, the price is steep. First, androgens exert negative feedback actions on FSH and LH secreted by the anterior pituitary gland. As a consequence, the anterior pituitary gland stops producing and secreting FSH and LH while the user is taking supplements containing androgens. In males, this causes the testes to shrink, as they no longer are making sperm, and the man becomes infertile. Androgen administration has also been linked to extreme aggressive behaviour (**"roid" rage**), cardiovascular disease and heart attacks, skin problems, and certain cancers. Women using androgens run similar health risks as men but in addition develop masculinizing traits, including growth of body hair and thinning scalp hair.

Another example of hormone misuse is to boost the number of red blood cells in the circulation to increase the oxygen-carrying capacity of the blood (often called **blood doping**). This has become common among athletes participating in long-distance aerobic activities, such as cycling and cross-country skiing. It has replaced the former practice of actually transfusing suspensions of red blood cells into a person's circulation. The hormone that is used is **erythropoietin (EPO)**, which acts by stimulating the maturation of red blood cells in the bone marrow and their release into the blood. EPO is normally made by the liver and kidneys in response to any situation in which additional blood cells are required, such as following blood loss or when a person lives at high altitudes, where the oxygen pressure is low. When used abusively, however, the concentration of red blood cells reaches such high concentrations that the blood becomes much thicker than normal. This puts a serious strain on the heart, which must work harder to pump the thickened blood. Beginning the 1990s the international cycling community was stunned by the death of several world-class European cyclists who died of heart attacks. These individuals had been using EPO to gain an unfair and, as it turns out, unwise advantage. Testing continues to detect injected EPO in the blood of cyclists and other endurance athletes.

Hormones Are Used Therapeutically to Treat Millions of People

The list of endocrine-related diseases in the human population is a long one, ranging from relatively common disorders, such as diabetes and thyroid disease, to rare ones that may affect only 1 in every 100,000 or more individuals. Since the advent of large-scale hormone production, it has become routine to provide individuals with hormones that their own bodies fail to produce. For example, millions of people self-administer insulin each day, or take thyroxine to supplement their insufficient concentrations of thyroid hormones. Many women undergo hormone therapy to help induce pregnancy or control the symptoms of menopause. A growing number of men, too, take gonadal hormones if the concentrations produced by their bodies decline significantly in later life. Other examples include recombinant human growth hormone to treat abnormally short stature in prepubertal children, epinephrine inhalers to treat asthma, and glucocorticoids to treat inflammation, lung disease, and skin disorders, to name just a few.

Summary of Key Concepts

47.1 Mechanisms of Hormone Action and Control

- The endocrine glands and other organs with hormone-secreting cells constitute the endocrine system. Endocrine glands contain epithelial cells that secrete hormones into the bloodstream, where they circulate throughout the body. Although slower than the electrical signalling of nervous systems, chemical signalling complements nervous system regulation through its varying actions in multiple locations across widely ranging time frames. (Figure 47.1)

- Hormones fall into three broad classes: the amines, proteins/peptides, and steroids. Water-soluble hormones (amines and proteins/peptides) act on receptor molecules located in the plasma membrane, whereas lipid-soluble hormones (steroids) act on intracellular receptors. (Table 47.1)

- Blood concentrations of hormones can increase or decrease through two mechanisms: changing the rate of hormone production by an endocrine cell, and changing the rates at which hormones are removed or inactivated. (Figures 47.2, 47.3)

47.2 Links Between the Endocrine and Nervous Systems

- Sensory input from an animal's nervous system modulates the activity of certain endocrine glands and influences blood concentrations of many hormones.

- Within the hypothalamus are numerous neurons that synthesize neurohormones and stimulate the anterior pituitary. (Figure 47.4)

- The anterior pituitary gland synthesizes six different hormones that respond to the presence of hypothalamic neurohormones. They are adrenocorticotropic hormone, follicle-stimulating hormone, luteinizing hormone, growth hormone, prolactin, and thyroid-stimulating hormone. (Table 47.2)

- In mammals, the neuron terminals in the posterior pituitary gland secrete one of two hormones: oxytocin or antidiuretic hormone (ADH).

47.3 Hormonal Control of Metabolism and Energy Balance

- Hormones are partly responsible for regulating energy use by cells; that is, for modulating appetite, digestion, absorption of nutrients, and blood concentrations of energy sources, such as glucose. Although many hormones are involved in these processes, two from the thyroid gland (thyroxine and triiodothyronine), two from the pancreas (insulin and glucagon), and one from adipose tissue (leptin) play especially important roles.

- The thyroid gland makes thyroid hormones that contain iodide. A major action of thyroid hormones in adult animals is to stimulate energy consumption by many different cell types. (Figures 47.5, 47.6)

- The endocrine pancreas produces the peptide hormones insulin and glucagon, which have opposite effects on blood glucose concentrations. The adrenal glands produce steroid hormones known as glucocorticoids, which increase blood glucose concentrations. (Figure 47.7)

- Maintaining normal glucose and other nutrient concentrations in the blood is a vital process that keeps cells functioning optimally. The combined short-term and long-term actions of glucagon, epinephrine, and cortisol help maintain normal blood glucose concentrations during fasting. (Figure 47.8)

- Groundbreaking research by Banting, Best, MacLeod, and Collip isolated insulin for therapeutic use in treating diabetes mellitus. (Figure 47.9)

- Adipose tissue is an important source of appetite-regulating hormones, including the protein leptin, which acts on the hypothalamus to inhibit appetite. Adipose cells release leptin into the blood in direct proportion to the amount of adipose tissue in the body.

47.4 Hormonal Control of Mineral Balance

- Because of the important roles that calcium plays in neuronal transmission, heart function, muscle contraction, and numerous other events, the concentration of Ca^{2+} in the blood is among the most tightly regulated variables in an animal's body. Vitamin D and parathyroid hormone regulate blood concentrations of Ca^{2+} (Figures 47.10, 47.11)

- Sodium and potassium play crucial roles in membrane potential formation, action potential generation, and other functions. A key mechanism that regulates blood concentrations of these ions is to alter the rate of sodium, potassium, and water reabsorption from the urine as it is being formed in the kidneys. This is accomplished in large part by the actions of ADH, aldosterone, and atrial natriuretic peptide (ANP). (Figure 47.12)

47.5 Hormonal Control of Growth and Development

- Hormones play a crucial role in regulating growth and development. In vertebrates, normal growth depends on a balance among growth hormone, insulin-like growth factor-1 (IGF-1), and gonadal hormones. Thyroid hormones affect development in all vertebrates. (Figures 47.13, 47.14)

- In insects, brain hormone, ecdysone, and juvenile hormone control the growth of larvae and their development into pupae. (Figure 47.15)

47.6 Hormonal Control of Reproduction

- Hormones produced by the gonads play vital roles in nearly all aspects of reproduction. The ability of the testes and ovaries to produce the sex steroids depends on the presence of the gonadotropins, which are the same in both sexes and include luteinizing hormone (LH) and follicle-stimulating hormone (FSH).

- Leptin is a hormone produced by adipose cells that is required for fertility in mammals.

47.7 Hormonal Responses to Stress

- Regardless of the nature of the stress, animals' bodies respond to stress in similar ways. In vertebrates, hormones produced by the adrenal glands are the common denominator of the response to stress. Norepinephrine and epinephrine are responsible for most physiological reactions of the fight-or-flight response. (Figure 47.16, Table 47.3)

- Glucocorticoids promote the breakdown of storage compounds to provide energy for the body's cells during stress. (Table 47.4)

47.8 Human Health Connection

- Endocrine disruptors, such as chemicals derived from industrial waste, may bind to estrogen receptors in animals' bodies. They may exert estrogen-like actions or inhibit the actions of the body's own estrogen.

- Androgen misuse can disrupt normal hormone concentrations and cause health risks, such as aggression, cardiovascular disease, skin problems, cancer, infertility in men, and masculinizing traits in women. Blood doping with erythropoietin can make blood dangerously thick.

- Hormones are also used therapeutically to treat a variety of human disorders.

Test to Assess Your Learning

1. Which is the defining feature of hormones?
   a. They are produced only in endocrine glands.
   b. They are secreted by one type of cell into the blood, where they may simultaneously reach many distant target cells and thereby alter cell function throughout the body.
   c. They are released only by neurons.
   d. They are never released by neurons.
   e. They are secreted into ducts, where they are carried to another nearby gland or other structure.

2. Steroid hormones are derived from _____ and bind _____
   a. proteins; membrane receptors.
   b. cholesterol; membrane receptors.
   c. tyrosine; intracellular receptors.
   d. proteins; intracellular receptors.
   e. cholesterol; intracellular receptors.

3. Protein hormones are unable to diffuse across the membrane due to
   a. their large size.
   b. their hydrophilic nature.
   c. their electric charge.
   d. all of the above.
   e. (b) and (c) only.

4. Which is *not* correct about hormone control?
   a. Many are regulated by negative feedback.
   b. They may be controlled by changes in blood concentrations of certain nutrients such as glucose.
   c. They may be controlled by changes in blood concentrations of certain minerals.
   d. Their blood concentrations are controlled by their rates of synthesis and degradation.
   e. The rate of degradation of a hormone may go up or down, but synthesis is always constant.

5. The hypothalamus and the pituitary gland are physically connected by
   a. arteries.
   b. the infundibular stalk and portal vein system.
   c. the adrenal medulla.
   d. the spinal cord.
   e. the intermediate lobe.

6. The function of antidiuretic hormone is to
   a. increase water reabsorption at the kidneys.
   b. regulate blood pressure by constricting arterioles.
   c. decrease the volume of urine produced by the kidneys.
   d. increase blood pressure during times of high blood loss.
   e. all of the above.

7. Which of the following pairs of hormones are involved in the regulation of blood calcium concentrations in vertebrates?
   a. aldosterone and ANP
   b. insulin and glucagon
   c. parathyroid hormone and 1,25-dihydroxyvitamin D
   d. prolactin and oxytocin
   e. thyroxine and TSH

8. In invertebrates, growth of larvae is stimulated by
   a. growth hormone.
   b. cortisol.
   c. juvenile hormone.
   d. ecdysone.
   e. aldosterone.

9. Which of the following is *not* true of glucocorticoids?
   a. They stimulate maturation of the fetal lungs.
   b. They promote a decrease in blood glucose concentrations.
   c. They inhibit the sensitivity of cells to insulin.
   d. They are lipophilic.
   e. They reduce inflammation.

10. Endocrine disruptors are
   a. chemicals released by the nervous system to override the endocrine system.
   b. chemicals released by the male of a species to decrease the fertility of other males.
   c. drugs used to treat overactive endocrine structures.
   d. chemicals derived from industrial waste that may alter endocrine function.
   e. all of the above.

Articulate to Assess Your Learning

1. What is the function of leptin, and what is the benefit of an adipose-derived signalling molecule in this context? Why does an animal have an appetite?

2. Distinguish between type 1 and type 2 diabetes mellitus.

Collaborate to Assess and Extend Your Learning

1. Discuss how hormones help control invertebrate development.

2. Discuss the role of different steroid hormones and where they are produced in the vertebrate body.

3. A principle of biology is that living organisms have mechanisms to maintain homeostasis. How do the opposing actions of insulin and glucagon cooperate to maintain glucose homeostasis? When are they released into the blood? What might happen to a nonfasting mammal that was injected with a high dose of glucagon?

Visit McGraw-Hill Ryerson Connect™ for additional study resources.

Animal Reproduction

Chapter Outline

Most animals reproduce by sexual reproduction. These mud daubers, shown here mating, reproduce by sexual reproduction, which favours genetic variation in a species.

When we examine all forms of life, we discover that individuals of every species are part of an unbroken cycle of life and death. Perpetuation of all life requires **reproduction**: the processes by which organisms replicate themselves and multiply. Because reproduction is the only way in which a species can perpetuate itself, enormous evolutionary pressure has been exerted on the processes of reproduction, and demands made on organisms by their environments have influenced the means by which reproduction occurs.

The biological mechanisms that favour successful reproduction in the animal kingdom are extraordinarily diverse. Many of the observable differences in animal behaviour and anatomy are the result of adaptations to environmental pressures that increase an animal's chances of reproducing. Both the behaviours and the anatomical specializations that promote reproduction are under the control of a variety of factors, particularly hormones.

In this chapter, we will initially focus on the diverse means of reproduction that occur throughout the animal kingdom, including asexual and sexual reproduction. Later, we will highlight some of the anatomical, hormonal, and behavioural aspects of reproduction in mammals, including humans. We will conclude with a discussion of some key issues related to fertility (the ability to reproduce) in the human population today. We begin by examining how some animals reproduce without combining genetic material from two different sexes.

48.1 ASEXUAL AND SEXUAL REPRODUCTION

Learning Outcomes:

1. Describe several differences between asexual and sexual reproduction.
2. Classify the three types of asexual reproduction.
3. List the advantages and disadvantages of sexual reproduction and asexual reproduction.

Asexual Reproduction

Asexual reproduction occurs when offspring are produced from a single parent, without the fusion of gametes from two parents. The offspring are therefore clones of the parent. Although many kinds of animals use this type of reproductive strategy, it is more prevalent in species that live in very stable environments, with little selection pressure for genetic diversity in a population.

Asexual reproduction has numerous advantages. First, an animal can reproduce asexually even if it is isolated from others of its own species, either because the animal is sessile (nonmotile) or rarely encounters another member of its species. Another advantage is that individuals can reproduce rapidly because they need not seek out, attract, and mate with the opposite sex. In addition, all asexual individuals can produce offspring, whereas in sexual reproduction involving separate sexes, two parents are needed to produce offspring. Asexual reproduction, therefore, can be a very efficient way of generating large numbers of offspring.

Animals use one of three major forms of asexual reproduction: budding, regeneration, or parthenogenesis. **Budding**, which is seen in cnidarians, occurs when a portion of the parent organism pinches off to form a complete new individual. In this process, cells from the parent undergo mitosis and differentiate into specific types of structures before the new individual breaks away from the parent. At any one time, a parent organism may have one, two, or multiple buds forming simultaneously (**Figure 48.1a**). Each new animal is fully formed but continues to grow. Budding continues throughout an animal's lifetime.

Some animals, including certain species of sponges, echinoderms, and worms, reproduce by the **regeneration** of a complete organism from small fragments of their body. In the sea star, for example, an arm removed by injury or predation can

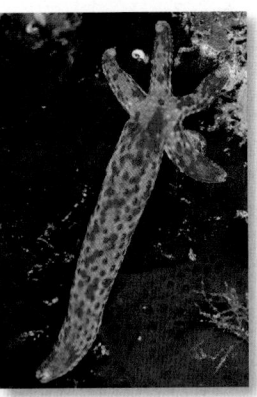

(a) Budding **(b) Regeneration**

Figure 48.1 **Examples of asexual reproduction.** Illustrated here are **(a)** budding, in a hydra, and **(b)** regeneration, shown in a sea star growing a complete new body from a single arm.

result in regrowth of a new individual (**Figure 48.1b**). Similarly, two new individuals regenerate if a flatworm is bisected.

As in budding, the ability to regenerate a new individual from a body part, or to regenerate a severed body part (as also occurs in many echinoderms and cnidarians), continues throughout an animal's lifetime. This suggests that the molecular mechanisms responsible for differentiation into a complete animal remain active over the course of such animals' lives. Many of the genes responsible for these events have been found to be homologous to genes expressed during the early developmental stages of vertebrates. Why these genes are expressed only during a brief time in most vertebrates, but remain active throughout life in many invertebrates, remains a key question in developmental animal biology (see Chapter 49).

The asexual process called **parthenogenesis** (from the Greek, virgin birth) is the development of offspring from an unfertilized egg. It occurs in several invertebrate classes and in a few species of fish and reptiles. Animals produced by parthenogenesis are usually haploid. Some species—such as rotifers, many social insects, and the freshwater crustacean *Daphnia*—may reproduce either parthenogenically or sexually, depending on the time of year or environmental conditions. In honeybees, ants, and wasps, for instance, haploid males (drones) are produced by parthenogenesis, and diploid females (workers and queens) by sexual reproduction. Production of drones, whose major function is to mate with a queen, usually occurs in late spring. The queen stores sperm cells from several drones for up to two years, during which time she may lay hundreds of thousands of eggs, most of which will be fertilized. As stored sperm runs out, the unfertilized eggs become new drones.

Sexual Reproduction

Sexual reproduction is the production of a new individual by the joining of two haploid **gametes**. The gametes are spermatozoa (usually shortened to **sperm**) from the male, and eggs or **ova** (singular: ovum) from the female. When a sperm unites with an **egg**—a process called **fertilization**—each haploid gamete contributes its set of chromosomes to produce a diploid cell called a **zygote**. As the zygote undergoes cell divisions and begins to develop, it is called an **embryo**. In this section, we will consider the advantages of sexual reproduction, how gametes are formed, and how two gametes join to form a new organism.

Advantages and Disadvantages of Asexual and Sexual Reproduction

Whereas asexual reproduction provides a relatively straightforward way for an organism to produce many copies of itself, sexual reproduction requires the joining of gametes from

---

FEATURE INVESTIGATION

Paland and Lynch Provided Evidence That Sexual Reproduction May Promote the Elimination of Harmful Mutations in Populations

Compared with asexual reproduction, sexual reproduction expends a lot more energy. Two types of gametes (sperm and eggs) must be made, and males and females need specialized body parts to mate with each other. Evolutionary biologists have speculated that these costs of sexual reproduction must somehow be outweighed by corresponding benefits.

In particular, sexual reproduction allows a species to redistribute alleles via crossing over and independent assortment across many generations. As a result, some offspring carry combinations of alleles that promote survival and reproduction, while other offspring may carry less favourable combinations. As described in Chapter 22, natural selection can favour those

combinations that promote greater reproductive success while eliminating offspring with lower fitness. By comparison, asexual organisms cannot reassort their alleles from generation to generation. As a result, it is more difficult to accumulate beneficial alleles within individuals and to eliminate harmful alleles from generation to generation. Evolutionary biologists have suggested that the inability of asexual species to reassort alleles may be a key disadvantage compared with sexually reproducing species.

To investigate this question, Susanne Paland and Michael Lynch studied the persistence of mutations in populations of *Daphnia pulex*, a freshwater organism known as the water flea. The researchers chose this organism because some natural populations reproduce asexually while others reproduce sexually.

In their experiment, shown in **Figure 48.2**, Paland and Lynch studied the sequences of several mitochondrial genes in 14 sexually reproducing and 14 asexually reproducing

HYPOTHESIS Sexual reproduction allows for greater mixing of alleles of different genes and thereby may prevent the accumulation of detrimental alleles in a population.

KEY MATERIALS The researchers collected samples of *Daphnia pulex* from many natural populations. A total of 14 sexual populations and 14 asexual populations were studied.

Experimental level   Conceptual level

1 Isolate mitochondrial DNA from members of 28 populations of *D. pulex*. This involves breaking open cells and extracting the DNA (refer back to Figure 19.1).

Daphnia   DNA   Segments of mitochondrial DNA

2 Amplify regions of mitochondrial genes, using PCR. Subject the regions to DNA sequencing. The techniques of PCR and DNA sequencing are described in Chapter 18.

PCR (refer back to Figure 18.8)   DNA sequencing (refer back to Figure 18.10)

```
TCGCCATCAG
TCAGGTTGGC
TCGCCATCAG
GTCGCCATCA
AGGTTGGCC
```

3 Using computer technology, align the sequences (refer back to Figure 19.12a) and determine the number of DNA changes that would cause amino acid substitutions. These amino acid changes were categorized as those that would be highly deleterious, moderately deleterious, mildly deleterious, or neutral for protein function. Compare the sexual and asexual populations for the persistence of these types of changes.

GGCACCTCACCC

GGCACCTAACCC

Stop codon

This change would be highly detrimental because it would put a stop codon into the gene.

4 **THE DATA**

Results from step 3:

Types of amino acid substitutions (The amino acid substitutions were due to rare mutations that occurred in the natural populations of *D. pulex*.)	% of total amino acid substitutions	Persisted in	
		Sexual populations	Asexual populations
Highly deleterious	73.2	No	No
Moderately deleterious	13.3	No	Yes
Mildly deleterious	4.4	Yes	Yes
Neutral	9.1	Yes	Yes

5 **CONCLUSION** Moderately deleterious mutations are less likely to persist in populations of animals that reproduce sexually.

6 **SOURCE** Paland, S., and Lynch, M. 2006. Transitions to asexuality result in excess amino acid substitutions. *Science* 311:990–992.

Figure 48.2 Paland and Lynch demonstrated the importance of sexual reproduction in reducing the frequency of harmful genetic mutations.

populations of *D. pulex*. The researchers hypothesized that sexual reproduction would prevent the accumulation of detrimental mutations in the population. As discussed in Chapter 22, random mutations that change the amino acid sequence of the encoded protein are much more likely to be harmful than beneficial. Sexually reproducing species can reassort their alleles from generation to generation, thereby producing succeeding generations in which the detrimental alleles are lost from the population. As seen in the data, the researchers discovered that both the sexual and the asexual strains could eliminate highly deleterious mutations from their populations. Organisms harbouring such mutations probably died rather easily. In addition, the sexual and asexual strains both perpetuated mildly deleterious and neutral mutations. However, moderately deleterious mutations

were not persistent in the sexual strains but they were persistent in asexual strains. One interpretation of these data is that sexual reproduction allowed for the reassortment of beneficial and detrimental alleles, making it easier for moderately detrimental mutations to have been eliminated from the sexual strains.

Experimental Questions

1. How did Paland and Lynch propose to test the hypothesis that sexual reproduction allowed for the reduction in deleterious mutations?
2. What did they discover?
3. What is the proposed evolutionary benefit of sexual reproduction?

---

two individuals to produce offspring. From a reproductive individual's perspective, it would seem to be more efficient to reproduce asexually than sexually, because more offspring can usually be produced per individual and reproduction can occur with only one parent. Yet given that most species reproduce sexually, a question has intrigued biologists since the time of Darwin: What is the advantage of sexual reproduction?

The major difference between asexual and sexual reproduction is that sexual reproduction allows for greater genetic variation through genetic recombination. Only certain alleles from each parent are passed on, and when genes from one parent mix with a different set from the other parent, the offspring are never exactly like either of their parents. Thus a hallmark of sexual reproduction is increased genetic variation between successive generations. One prevalent hypothesis about why sex evolved is that sexual reproduction allows more rapid adaptation to environmental changes than asexual reproduction. Alleles that confer a selective advantage arise independently in members of a population. Sexual reproduction provides the opportunity for two or more beneficial alleles to be inherited by the same offspring. Also, as described in the Feature Investigation, sexual reproduction may make it easier for populations to eliminate harmful alleles.

48.2 GAMETOGENESIS AND FERTILIZATION

Learning Outcomes:

1. Describe the processes of spermatogenesis and oogenesis.
2. Describe the advantages that internal fertilization provides.
3. Describe the two different types of hermaphroditism.
4. Compare viviparity, oviparity, and ovoviviparity.

Sperm and Ova Are Produced During the Process of Gametogenesis

Male and female gametes are formed within the **gonads**—the **testes** (singular: testis) in males and the ovaries (singular: **ovary**) in females. Some similarities are found in the ways gametes develop in the testes and the ovaries, as well as some differences.

Gametogenesis—the formation of gametes—begins with primordial cells called germ cells, which multiply by mitosis, resulting in diploid cells (denoted as $2n$) called **spermatogonia** (singular: spermatogonium) in males and **oogonia** (singular: oogonium) in females (**Figure 48.3**). Some of these cells become **primary spermatocytes** or **primary oocytes** that may begin the process of meiosis. Until this point, the development of sperm and eggs is similar. From then on, gametogenesis differs between the two types of gamete.

Spermatogenesis The formation of haploid sperm from the original diploid-germ cell is called **spermatogenesis**. As shown in **Figure 48.3a**, primary spermatocytes begin production of sperm by undergoing the first of two meiotic divisions (meiosis I). Meiosis I in the primary spermatocyte produces two haploid (n) cells called **secondary spermatocytes**. These cells also undergo meiosis (meiosis II), producing four haploid **spermatids** that eventually differentiate into mature sperm cells. Gametogenesis in males, therefore, results in four gametes from each spermatogonium.

The most striking change in each spermatid as it differentiates into a sperm is the formation of a flagellum or tail (**Figure 48.3b**), the movements of which require cellular energy and make the sperm motile. The chromosomes are in the head of the sperm, which is separated from the tail by a midpiece containing one or more mitochondria that produce the ATP required for tail movements. At the tip of the head is a special structure called the **acrosome** that (as we will discuss shortly) contains proteolytic enzymes that help break down the protective outer layers that surround the ovum.

(a) Spermatogenesis

(c) Oogenesis

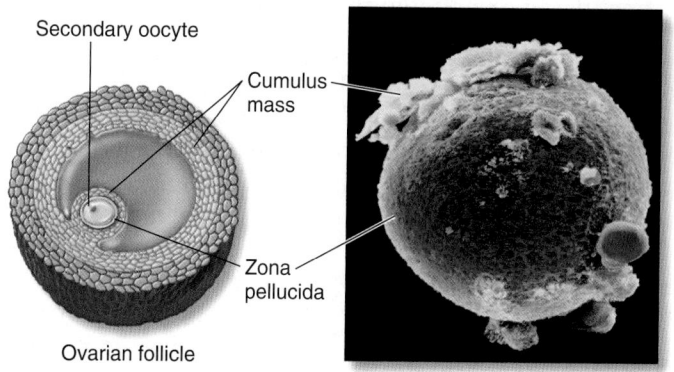

Acrosome

Nucleus

Mitochondrion

Head

Midpiece

Flagellum
(tail)

(b) Mature human sperm

Secondary oocyte

Cumulus mass

Zona pellucida

Ovarian follicle

(d) Mature human follicle and oocyte

Figure 48.3   **Gametogenesis and gametes in males and females.**   **(a)** In the process of spermatogenesis, male diploid (2n) germ cells undergo two meiotic divisions to produce mature haploid (n) sperm. **(b)** The characteristic head, midpiece, and tail of a mature human sperm, as seen in a drawing and the accompanying scanning electron micrograph (SEM). **(c)** The process of oogenesis in females, which produces a haploid secondary oocyte ready to be fertilized. **(d)** Mature oocyte. The drawing depicts a secondary oocyte within its follicle; the SEM shows an isolated human oocyte covered by its zona pellucida and remnants of the cumulus mass.

Principle: *Structure determines function. The structure of a sperm cell is a good example of this principle of biology at the cellular level. Notice how each of the three major structural elements of the sperm cell are suited for a particular function. When all three elements function together, the cell is capable of fertilizing an egg.*

BioConnections: *What happens during meiosis I that leads to greater genetic diversity among sexually produced offspring? (Refer back to Figure 14.14).*

Oogenesis Whereas spermatogenesis produces four gametes from each primary spermatocyte, gametogenesis in the female, called **oogenesis**, results in the production of a single gamete from each primary oocyte (**Figure 48.3c**). Each meiotic division in oogenesis results in one large cell—either a **secondary oocyte** (meiosis I) or an ovum (meiosis II)—plus a smaller cell, called a polar body, that eventually degenerates. Only the larger of the two daughter cells resulting from meiosis II (i.e., the ovum) contains the cellular machinery needed for development after fertilization.

Depending on the species, one or many ova can develop at a time. Within the ovaries, each ovum undergoes growth and development within a structure called a **follicle** before it leaves the ovary in the process of **ovulation**. Once ovulated, an egg cell can become fertilized if sperm are available. By the time ovulation occurs, the ovum is surrounded by two layers: an inner membranelike structure called the zona pellucida, which surrounds the surface of the ovum, and an outer layer of cells called the cumulus mass (**Figure 48.3d**). These two layers play important roles in fertilization of the egg.

In mammals, oogenesis begins in the female fetus before birth: Germ cells develop into primary oocytes and enter meiosis I, which is arrested partway through the process. Meiosis I does not resume until puberty, the time of a mammal's life when it first becomes capable of reproducing. In certain selected oocytes, meiosis I is completed, producing secondary oocytes. These cells then begin meiosis II and eventually develop into mature ova.

In a Given Species, Fertilization Occurs Either Inside or Outside the Female

For sperm to fertilize ova, the two gametes must physically come into contact. In some species, a sperm fertilizes the egg outside the female's body. This process, called **external fertilization**, occurs in aquatic environments, when eggs and sperm are released into the water in close enough proximity for fertilization to occur. The aqueous environment protects the gametes from drying out.

Animals that reproduce by external fertilization show species-specific behaviours that bring the eggs and sperm together. For instance, very soon after a female fish lays her eggs, a male deposits his sperm in the water nearby and they spread over the clump of eggs. When frogs mate, the clasping behaviour of the male stimulates the female to release her eggs into the water (**Figure 48.4a**); the male then releases sperm onto the eggs. The fertilized ova then develop outside the parent's body.

Although the aqueous environment protects against desiccation, fertilized eggs can be eaten by predators, washed downstream by currents, or subjected to potentially lethal changes in water temperature. To counteract such problems, many aquatic or amphibious animals release very large numbers of eggs at once.

In contrast to external fertilization, terrestrial animals use **internal fertilization**, in which sperm are deposited within the reproductive tract of the female during the act called **copulation**, as seen in the mud daubers in the chapter-opening photo.

(a)

(b) Stalked spermatophore of a collembolan

Figure 48.4 Examples of fertilization. (a) External fertilization. The male pickerel frog (*Rana palustris*) clasps the female, which stimulates her to release her eggs. He then releases his sperm (not visible here) over the eggs. This process occurs in aquatic environments, which protect gametes from drying out. In Canada, these frogs live in Ontario, Quebec, New Brunswick, Nova Scotia, and Prince Edward Island. (b) Internal fertilization without copulation. Insects called collembolans have internal fertilization without copulation. Males leave a spermatophore (sperm packet) on the ground and the female positions her genital opening over it to insert the spermatophore into her reproductive tract.

Concept check: *What kinds of environments are most suitable for external fertilization? How do you think the sperm in the collembolan spermatophore avoid dessication?*

Internal fertilization protects the delicate gametes from environmental hazards and predation, and also guarantees that sperm are placed and remain in very close proximity to ova. Once fertilization occurs within the female, the fertilized eggs then develop into offspring.

The behaviours and anatomical structures involved in achieving internal fertilization are extremely varied among species. Typically, mating involves accessory sex organs, which are reproductive structures other than the gonads. The external accessory sex organs involved in copulation are the genitalia (e.g., the **penis** and the **vagina**), which are used to physically join the male and female so that sperm can be deposited directly into the female's reproductive tract. A penis or an analogous structure is present in most insects, reptiles, some species of birds (rattites), and all mammals. However, males of other vertebrate species (such as most birds and turtles) that reproduce by internal fertilization lack a structure that can be inserted into the female, so they deposit sperm in the female by cloacal contact. The cloaca is a common opening for the reproductive, digestive, and excretory systems in these animals.

Another form of internal fertilization involves an indirect means of depositing sperm. In this circumstance, males produce small packets of sperm, called spermatophores, that are deposited externally and subsequently inserted into the female's reproductive tract by either the male or the female. When springtails (Order Collembola) reproduce, the male deposits a spermatophore on the ground, the female finds it and inserts it into her genital opening (**Figure 48.4b**). During copulation in squid and octopus, the male uses a tentacle to transfer a spermatophore into the mantle cavity of the female. In spiders, the male places a droplet of sperm on a web and then uses a foreleg to insert the droplet into the female's reproductive tract. Subsequently, the eggs are fertilized internally and deposited on the web or elsewhere in the environment.

Most female insects store sperm from one or more matings until it is time to oviposit (lay their eggs). Depending on the species, eggs are fertilized as the eggs pass down the oviducts, or within the genital chamber, before the eggs are released into the environment. This mode of fertilization allows some facultatively parthenogenetic species (such as aphids) to produce diploid females by fertilizing their own eggs with stored sperm or to produce haploid males by releasing unfertilized eggs.

Hermaphroditism Represents a Unique Form of Sexual Reproduction

In some species including many gastropods, worms, and some fish and reptiles, individuals have both male and female reproductive systems for part or all of their lives. This is called **hermaphroditism** (after the male and female Greek gods, Hermes and Aphrodite). In some hermaphroditic species, individuals can fertilize their own eggs with their own sperm, but in most hermaphroditic species individuals exchange sperm with another individual. The latter situation has the selective advantage of creating additional genetic diversity in the population. Because sperm and egg join to produce offspring, hermaphroditism is a form of sexual reproduction, and it is the one case in which all individuals of a sexually reproducing species can produce offspring.

Hermaphrodites are often sessile animals or burrowing animals, such as earthworms, which may live for long periods without encountering sexual partners. A single earthworm can fertilize its own eggs, or two earthworms can join together for several hours during which sperm from each worm fertilize the eggs of the other. In the latter case, individual worms act both as females (receiving sperm to fertilize their eggs) and males (giving sperm to fertilize another worm's eggs), so that the offspring carry genes from both individuals. This type of hermaphroditism is known as synchronous hermaphroditism, because individuals are simultaneously both male and female.

Another type of hermaphroditism, called sequential hermaphroditism, involves sex reversal, in which a female may change into a male or vice versa. In such animals, individuals of both sexes have reproductive structures capable of producing sperm or eggs, and the particular gamete an individual produces at any given time depends on which genes are being expressed. Sex reversal occurs in some species of animals with strong social hierarchies. In some reef-dwelling species of fish, for example, a single dominant male defends a harem of several females within a specific territory. When that dominant male dies, the largest of the females reverses sex and becomes a male. Thus, these fish are **protogynous**—that is, female first but capable of becoming males later during their life cycle. Oysters and clownfish are also sequential hermaphrodites, but they are **protandrous**; that is, they are males first and later become females. The advantage of protandrous hermaphroditism is that males change into females when they are older and larger—when they are likely to be capable of producing a greater number of eggs.

Fertilization Involves Union of Sperm with Egg

Fertilization is a complex series of events by which the haploid male and female gametes unite and become a diploid zygote. Several important cellular and molecular processes must occur before the nuclei of the gametes can fuse. First, the egg and sperm must come into contact. The mechanism by which this occurs has been studied extensively in sea urchins, and some evidence suggests that a similar process occurs in humans. When chemical attractant molecules emitted by sea urchin eggs bind to nearby sperm, cellular respiration (i.e., the breakdown of nutrients to synthesize ATP) within the sperm increases, which helps increase sperm motility. The sperm then swim toward the egg by following the attractant's concentration gradient. The attractants are species specific; that is, sperm will respond to the attractants produced only by ova of their own species.

For a sperm to reach the ovum, it must first penetrate the cellular layers surrounding the plasma membrane of the egg. When the head of the sperm contacts the layers surrounding the ovum, chemicals in the cumulus mass stimulate the breakdown of the membrane covering the acrosome of the sperm. Proteolytic enzymes released from the acrosome digest a local area of the zona pellucida, allowing the sperm to contact the plasma membrane of the ovum. The plasma membrane of the ovum then fuses with the sperm head, facilitating its movement into the egg cell cytoplasm.

Once a sperm fuses with the egg, it is important that other sperm be prevented from also fusing with the egg, because in that case the zygote will be polyploid, a condition that few zygotes survive. In mammals, the penetration of one sperm induces metabolic changes within the egg that prevent additional sperm from penetrating the zona pellucida and entering the egg (see Chapter 49).

Fertilized Eggs Are Laid or Retained Within the Mother

As we have seen, internal fertilization occurs within the female, and the fertilized eggs then continue their development into offspring. When the embryo develops within the mother, the process is called **viviparity**. Alternatively, fertilized eggs can be laid in a well-protected site in the environment. Development of the embryo within an egg is called **oviparity**. Some animals develop by a process called **ovoviviparity**, which features aspects of both modes of development. In that case, eggs covered with a shell that is little more than a thin sheath hatch inside the mother's body, but the offspring receive no nourishment from the mother. Ovoviviparity can occur in lizards, some sharks, some snakes, and some invertebrates.

Sharks are an amazing group of animals that reproduce sexually by internal fertilization. However, the embryos of different species have different fates. In viviparous species, such as the hammerhead shark (*Sphyrnidae sphyrna*), young are nourished in the female shark's uterus on a secretion called uterine milk, and then they are born (live birth). Oviparous species, such as the dogfish sharks (*Squalus* sp.), lay their eggs in thick cases (commonly called "Mermaid's purses") that are attached to rocks or seaweed. These cases protect the developing young from predators until they are ready to hatch. There are also ovoviviparous sharks, such as the mako shark (*Isurus* sp.), that protect the embryos by retaining them internally where they are nourished only on the egg's yolk sac. They then give birth to live young. Perhaps the most interesting shark is the mackerel shark, also ovoviviparous, in which the mother produces a stream of small, unfertilized eggs that are eaten by the developing embryos before their live birth.

Oviparity is the rule in avian species and is also common in reptiles, fish, and amphibians. Among mammals, only the echidna and the platypus lay eggs. Although some animals lay only a single egg at one time, snakes and turtles lay between several and hundreds of eggs at a time, frogs and fish can lay thousands of eggs, and honeybee queens produce an astounding 250,000 eggs during a nearly continuous laying cycle over one to two years.

Although oviparity reduces the female's metabolic investment in the young, it increases the incidence of predation. In many amphibian and reptile species, the large number of eggs laid increases the chances of some young surviving even if predation occurs. The energetic cost to the female of producing numerous eggs is high, but usually little or no parental care is involved, freeing the parent to devote energy to other activities. In birds, however, incubation of the eggs after laying requires additional energy expenditure in the form of parental care, which typically continues after the eggs have hatched, and thus relatively few eggs are laid.

All eggs are single cells. The ostrich egg is the largest single cell among all living species. Eggs include the yolk (which contains nutrients for the developing embryo), a surrounding membrane, and the cytoplasm. The nucleus of the egg is located within the yolk, usually close to the surface at one end. In general, the larger the egg, the longer it takes the young to develop, and more yolk is available to provide nutrition.

The eggs of aquatic tetrapods, such as frogs and other amphibians, lack shells so that external fertilization may occur. Such eggs are protected from drying out by their environment. In contrast, the group of terrestrial tetrapods known as the amniotes (see Chapter 32) produce eggs with shells that protect the future offspring from desiccation. The evolution of the amniotic egg was a critical innovation because it meant that tetrapods were no longer tied to water habitats for reproduction. Amniotic eggs may have leathery shells, as in snakes, lizards, some turtles, platypus, and echidna, or hard shells made from calcium carbonate, as in birds and other turtles (**Figure 48.5**). These eggs contain all the nutrients necessary for the development of the young. Oxygen enters, and carbon dioxide exits, through tiny pores in the shell.

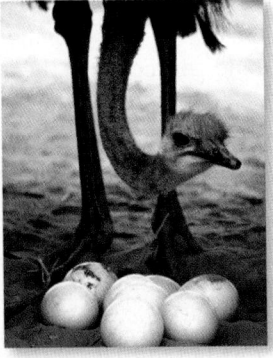

(a) Eggs with leathery shells   **(b) Eggs with hard shells**

Figure 48.5   **Oviparity in terrestrial animals.**   Terrestrial animals that lay eggs produce a wide range of egg types and sizes. (a) Snakes produce multiple eggs with leathery shells; such eggs can lose water and thus must be protected from desiccation. (b) Ostriches produce hard-shelled eggs that weigh up to 1.5 kg, including the shell.

48.3   MAMMALIAN REPRODUCTIVE STRUCTURE AND FUNCTION

Learning Outcomes:

1. Describe the structure of the human male reproductive tract.
2. Outline the process of hormonal control of the male reproductive system.
3. Describe the structure of the human female reproductive tract.
4. Diagram the events of the ovarian cycle.
5. Outline the process of hormonal control of the reproductive cycle of the human female.
6. Explain how maternal hormones prepare the uterus to accept the embryo.

We turn now to a detailed look at the mammalian reproductive system, including the processes by which gametes develop, and the establishment and maintenance of pregnancy. For both sexes, we will begin with a description of the anatomy of the reproductive system, including the gonads and the accessory sex structures. We will then examine the hormones that control the production of the gametes and the sexual behaviours that are important for internal fertilization.

The Male Reproductive Tract Is Specialized for Production and Ejaculation of Sperm

The external structures of the male reproductive tract—the genitalia—consist of the penis and the scrotum, the sac that contains the testes and holds them outside the body cavity (**Figure 48.6**). The testes develop within the body cavity, and just before birth in human males they descend into the scrotum, where the temperature is approximately 2°C lower than core body temperature. The lower temperature is optimal for spermatogenesis.

Figure 48.6 **Male reproductive structures in humans.** Side and front views of the male reproductive system (nonreproductive structures are identified in parentheses for orientation purposes).

Each testis is composed of tightly packed **seminiferous tubules** encased in connective tissue and surrounded by scattered Leydig cells—glandular cells that lie between the tubules and secrete the steroid hormone testosterone (**Figure 48.7**). Spermatogenesis takes place within the walls of the seminiferous tubules. Cells at the earliest stages of spermatogenesis, the spermatogonia, are located nearest the wall. Cells of more advanced stages are located progressively inward, such that the sperm are released into the tubule lumen. Cells within the seminiferous tubules are continuously developing from spermatogonia into spermatocytes and eventually to sperm, so at any one time, all types of cells are present along the seminiferous tubule. Support cells, called Sertoli cells, surround the developing spermatogonia and spermatocytes, providing them with nutrients and protection and playing a role in their maturation into sperm.

Sperm moving out of the seminiferous tubules are emptied into the **epididymis**, a coiled, tubular structure located on the surface of the testis (Figure 48.7). The epididymis is very long—approximately 6 metres in humans—and it takes about 20 days for new sperm to reach its end. It is here that the sperm complete their differentiation by becoming motile and gaining the capacity to fertilize ova.

Sperm leave the epididymis through the **vas deferens**, a muscular tube leading to the **ejaculatory duct**, which then connects to the urethra (Figure 48.6). As noted in Chapter 46, the urethra originates at the bladder and extends to the end of the penis. In

males, the urethra not only conducts urine but also carries **semen**, a mixture containing fluid and sperm, during **ejaculation**—the movement of semen through the urethra by contraction of muscles at the base of the penis. These contractions during ejaculation induce the pleasurable sensation of orgasm.

The liquid components of semen are important for the survival and movement of sperm through the female reproductive tract. This liquid is formed by three paired accessory glands that secrete substances into the urethra to mix with the sperm. The **seminal vesicles** secrete fructose, the main nutrient for sperm. The **bulbourethral glands** secrete alkaline mucus that protects sperm by neutralizing the acidity in the urethra. The **prostate gland** secretes a thin fluid that protects sperm once they are deposited within the female reproductive tract. Secretions constitute about 95% of semen, while sperm make up only about 5% of total semen volume. The volume of semen released at ejaculation in humans is about 2 to 5 mL and contains 20 million to 130 million sperm per millilitre. Although this seems like a huge excess of sperm to fertilize a single ovum, relatively few sperm actually reach the egg.

Introduction of sperm into the female reproductive system during copulation is made possible by erection of the penis. Erection occurs when blood fills spongy erectile tissue located along the length of the penis (see Figure 48.6). In a number of mammals (e.g., insectivores, bats, rodents, carnivores, and most primates except humans), the erection may be aided by the presence of a bone in the penis called a **baculum**.

Figure 48.7   The structure and function of the human testis.   The top of the drawing shows the internal structure of a testis. At the bottom, the stages of spermatogenesis within the seminiferous tubule are shown.

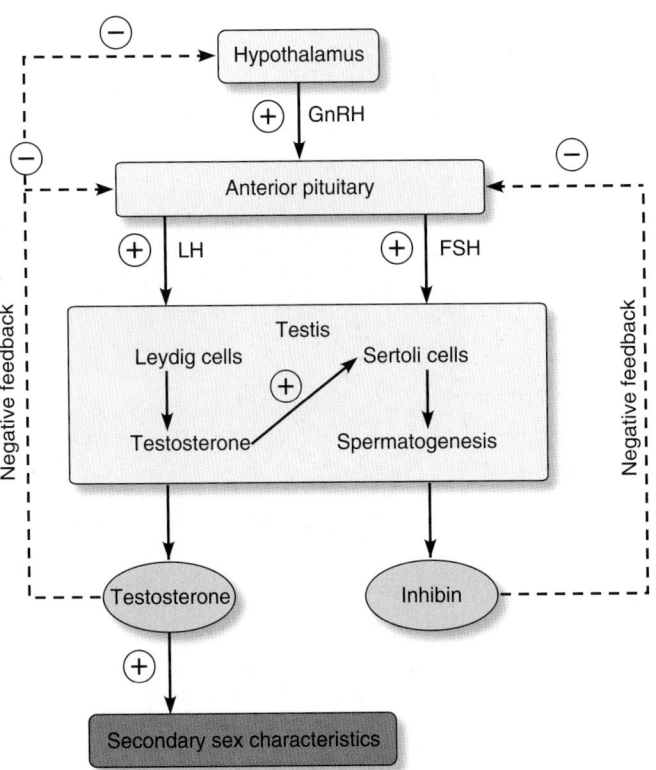

Figure 48.8   The endocrine control of spermatogenesis. In response to LH, Leydig cells in the testes secrete testosterone, which, along with FSH, acts on Sertoli cells to facilitate spermatogenesis. Negative signs indicate inhibitory effects via negative feedback.

Concept check: *What would happen to spermatogenesis in a man taking testosterone to increase muscle mass or improve athletic performance?*

Sexual arousal stimulates release of the gaseous neurotransmitter nitric oxide (NO) in the penis, causing vasodilation of arteries. The pressure of the blood flowing into the penis constricts nearby veins, causing a reduction in venous drainage from the penis, engorging it with blood. After ejaculation, NO release is reduced, causing a reversal of the vascular changes responsible for erection. Both physiological and psychological factors can result in an inability to achieve an erection, a condition known as erectile dysfunction (also called *impotence*). Orally administered drugs are available that increase the occurrence of erections by stimulating the same intracellular signalling events as NO in the smooth muscle cells of penile blood vessels.

Male Reproductive Function Requires the Actions of Testosterone

The role of hormones in male reproductive function is diagrammed in **Figure 48.8**. The hypothalamus produces gonadotropin-releasing hormone (GnRH), which stimulates the anterior pituitary gland to release two gonadotropic hormones: luteinizing hormone (LH) and follicle-stimulating hormone (FSH).

LH stimulates the Leydig cells of the testes to produce androgens, such as testosterone. In turn, testosterone acts on Sertoli cells and germ cells to stimulate spermatogenesis. Testosterone also stimulates the growth of the male reproductive tract and the genitalia during development and puberty, and the development of male secondary sex characteristics. In humans, these include facial hair growth, increased muscle size, and deepening of the voice. In other male mammals, they include things such as growth of the horns of a bull, enlargement of the nose of proboscis monkeys, and formation of cheek pads in some apes. Testosterone-dependent secondary sex characteristics are not unique to mammals, however. One familiar example is the bright coloration of extensive plumage in male birds, such as the peacock.

The other pituitary gonadotropin, FSH, functions along with testosterone to stimulate spermatogenesis. FSH does this by stimulating the activity of the Sertoli cells within the seminiferous tubules. The Sertoli cells provide the nutritional and structural support necessary for development of the sperm. They also respond to testosterone produced by the Leydig cells, by stimulating mitosis and meiosis of the germ cells associated with them in the tubules.

Production of sperm and testosterone is kept in check by negative feedback mechanisms that control the amount of gonadotropins produced (Figure 48.8). Testosterone inhibits the secretion of GnRH from the hypothalamus, so that both LH and FSH are inhibited when blood levels of testosterone are high. Testosterone also directly inhibits LH secretion by the pituitary gland. These feedback mechanisms maintain homeostatic levels of FSH and LH in the blood.

Before puberty, LH is not released in sufficient amounts to stimulate testicular production of testosterone, and the reproductive system is quiescent. Although the mechanisms that initiate puberty in mammals are still not completely understood, we know that increased GnRH production at that time initiates increased LH and FSH secretion from the pituitary. The testosterone induced by LH stimulates development of the secondary sexual characteristics, development of the internal reproductive organs, and stimulation of spermatogenesis. Testosterone is also responsible for an increased sex drive ("libido") at this time.

The Female Reproductive Tract Is Specialized for Fertilization of the Egg and Development of the Embryo

The female genitalia differentiate from the same embryonic tissues as the male genitalia. The female genitalia are composed of the large outer folds called the **labia majora** ("major lips"), which surround the external opening of the reproductive tract, plus the smaller, inner folds, called the **labia minora** ("minor lips"; **Figure 48.9**). The labia majora originate from the same embryonic tissue as the scrotum of the male, whereas the labia minora originate from urethral primordial tissue. At the anterior part of the labia minora is the **clitoris**, which is erectile tissue of the same origin as the penis. Like the penis, the clitoris becomes engorged with blood during sexual arousal (as do the labia minora) and is very sensitive to sexual stimulation. Unlike males, however, the openings of the reproductive tract and the urethra are separate in females. The opening of the urethra is beneath the clitoris and just anterior to the opening of the reproductive tract.

In mammals alone, the external opening of the reproductive tract leads to the **vagina**, a tubular, smooth muscle structure into which sperm are deposited during copulation. At the end of the vagina is a fibrous structure called the **cervix**, which forms the opening to the large, conical-shaped **uterus**. Sperm pass through the cervix into the uterus, which is specialized for carrying the developing fetus. It consists of an inner lining of glandular and secretory cells called the endometrium, and a thick muscular layer called the myometrium. We will discuss the functions of the uterus later in the chapter.

Eggs develop within one of the two bilateral ovaries (Figure 48.9), which are suspended within the abdominal cavity by connective tissue. In humans, each ovary is approximately the size of a ping-pong ball. Typically, one egg leaves the ovary and briefly enters the abdominal cavity. From there, the egg is

Figure 48.9 **Female reproductive structure and function in humans.** Side and front views of the female reproductive system (nonreproductive structures are identified in parentheses for orientation purposes). An oocyte moves from the ovary into the oviduct (also called the fallopian tube), where it may be fertilized. Subsequently the blastocyst enters the uterus, where it may implant in the endometrium, the inner lining of the uterus.

quickly drawn into a thin tube, the **oviduct** (also called the fallopian tube), by the actions of undulating fimbriae (fingers) of the oviduct that extend out to the ovary.

The egg is moved down the length of the oviduct by cilia on the oviduct's inner surface. Fertilization of the ovum by a sperm typically occurs within the oviduct. On fertilization, the ovum completes meiosis II, and the union of sperm and egg creates a zygote. The zygote undergoes several cell divisions to become a **blastocyst**, a ball of approximately 32 to 150 cells that enters the uterus, where it will develop into an embryo (see Chapter 49).

Gametogenesis in Females Is a Cyclical Process Within the Ovaries

The process of oogenesis occurs within the ovaries (**Figure 48.10**). In contrast to spermatogenesis, which continues throughout life in the testes in males, most female mammals appear to be born with all the primary oocytes they will ever have, although recent evidence in mice suggests that new oocytes may form later in life. At birth, each ovary in a human female has about 1 million primary oocytes, which are arrested in prophase of meiosis I. Most of these degenerate before the onset of puberty, when each ovary contains about 200,000 primary oocytes. Other than this degeneration, the ovaries are quiescent until puberty, at which time they begin to show cyclical activity.

The major estrogen produced by the mammalian ovaries is **estradiol**, which plays a critical role in ovulation and influences the secondary sexual characteristics of females. These secondary sexual characteristics, which begin to develop at puberty, include development of breasts, widening of the pelvis (an adaptation for giving birth), and a particular pattern of fat deposition.

The **ovarian cycle** involves the development of an ovarian follicle, the release of an ovum, and the formation and regression of a corpus luteum (**Figure 48.11**). During the first week of the ovarian cycle in humans, several primary oocytes begin to mature, each within a follicle. At the beginning of the second week, all but one of the growing follicles and its primary oocyte degenerate, and the single remaining follicle continues to develop and enlarge. During that time, the primary oocyte of that follicle completes meiosis I, becomes a secondary oocyte, and begins meiosis II. The developing secondary oocyte is surrounded by cells of the cumulus mass, which both protect and nurture it, and that secrete estradiol, the major form of estrogen in humans. The estradiol is secreted into the blood, where it functions to control the secretion of LH and FSH from the anterior pituitary gland. Some estradiol is also secreted into the follicle, where it stimulates fluid secretion into the inner core of the follicle, called the antrum. As the follicle grows in response to continued stimulation by LH and FSH, the fluid pressure inside the antrum increases, until the follicle begins to form a bulge. Eventually, ovulation occurs as the follicle ruptures and the egg, zona pellucida, and some surrounding supportive cells of the cumulus mass are released from the ovary.

Cells in the empty follicle subsequently undergo pronounced anatomical and physiological changes, developing into

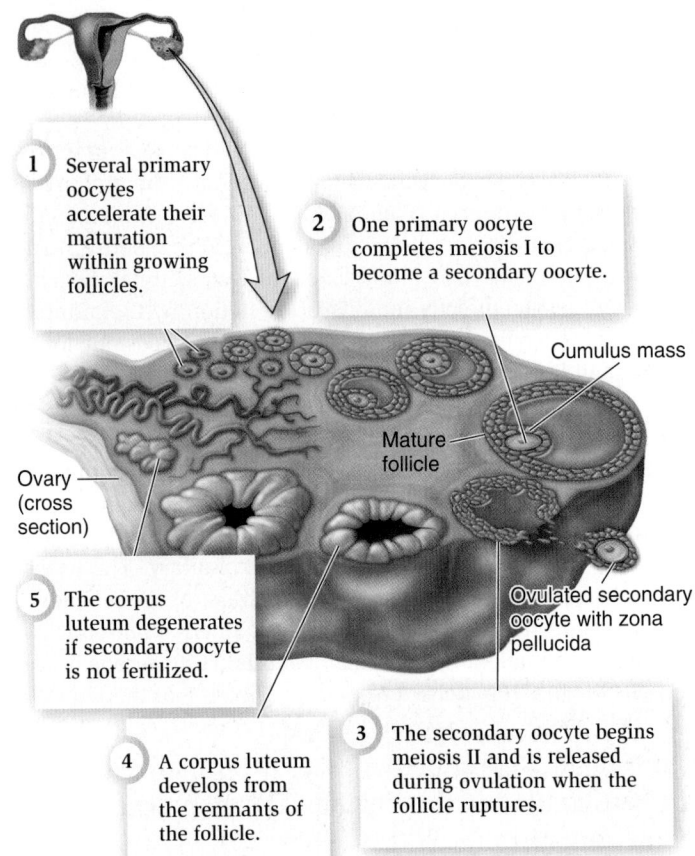

Figure 48.10 Follicle and oocyte development in humans. Development of an oocyte and corpus luteum within the ovary, illustrating the events that occur during a single ovarian cycle.

 Principle: *Living organisms grow and develop. This figure illustrates that growth and development do not necessarily stop in animals once they have reached maturity. Organs such as the human ovary can continue to develop throughout much of adulthood, as shown in this figure. Likewise, male gametes continue to develop throughout life in humans, as shown in Figure 48.8.*

a structure called the **corpus luteum**. In humans, the corpus luteum is active for approximately the second half of the ovarian cycle. It is responsible for secreting hormones that stimulate the development of the uterus needed for sustaining the embryo in the event of a pregnancy. If pregnancy does not occur, the corpus luteum degenerates, and subsequently a new group of follicles with their primary oocytes undergoes development.

The process of producing ova occurs as a cycle that may be as brief as a few days in small rodents, or as lengthy as 15 to 16 weeks in elephants. In humans, a typical cycle lasts approximately 28 days, during which time several oocytes in each ovary begin to mature. However, all but one of these oocytes usually degenerates, and only a single ovum fully matures and is released (ovulated) from the ovary each cycle. Thus, only 300 to 500 eggs are ovulated over a woman's 30- to 40-year reproductive lifetime.

Figure 48.11 **The ovarian and uterine cycles in a human female.** The ovarian cycle is divided into the follicular and luteal phases, while the uterine cycle is divided into menstruation and the proliferative and secretory phases.

Concept check: *Do similar surges in the concentrations of FSH and LH occur in human males?*

Ovulation and degeneration of additional primary oocytes continues throughout adulthood. Eventually, the oocytes become nearly depleted, and a woman stops having ovarian cycles, an event called **menopause**. The average onset of menopause among Canadian women is 51 years of age. After that time, a woman is no longer capable of becoming pregnant. At one time it was thought that menopause was unique to humans, but it appears that other female mammals, if they survive long enough, also become incapable of ovulation at some point.

The Ovarian Cycle Results from Changes in Hormone Secretion

We saw that in males, testosterone produced in the testes exerts a negative feedback on secretion of GnRH and LH. In females, however, the situation is more complicated. Although GnRH also stimulates release of LH and FSH, estradiol can have both negative and positive feedback effects on the gonadotropic hormones. To understand these events, let's examine hormone changes during the ovarian cycle (Figure 48.11).

The first half of the ovarian cycle is called the follicular phase of the cycle, because this is when the growth and differentiation of the follicle are occurring. The fairly low levels of LH that occur during follicular development stimulate the cells of the follicle to make estradiol. The estradiol that is produced is important for enlargement and growth of the oocyte, and it also is secreted into the blood, where it can influence the secretion of LH and FSH.

As the follicle develops, estradiol (and to a lesser extent, progesterone) production continues, and consequently levels of estradiol in the blood slowly but steadily increase. Initially, estradiol exerts a negative feedback action on LH and FSH secretion, preventing their blood levels from rising significantly until the follicle is nearly ready to ovulate. When the follicle is fully developed and ready for ovulation, its production of estradiol increases, such that the blood concentrations of estradiol increase sharply. At that time, the feedback action of estradiol on LH and FSH switches from negative to positive, by mechanisms that are still being investigated but involve increased GnRH secretion from the hypothalamus. This results in a sudden, sharp surge in gonadotropin levels in the blood, particularly LH.

The LH released from the pituitary as a result of positive feedback by estradiol induces rupture of the follicle and ovulation. This type of ovulation is known as spontaneous ovulation, because it happens regularly on a cyclical basis without requiring any external stimulus. Some mammals, including rabbits, cats, and camels, undergo ovarian cycles that turn off unless mating occurs. If mating occurs at a time in the ovarian cycle when eggs are ready, the mating act itself triggers ovulation. This mechanism, called induced ovulation, helps ensure that eggs are not wasted by being ovulated when the female has not mated with a male.

Ovulation marks the end of the follicular phase and the beginning of the luteal phase of the ovarian cycle, named after the corpus luteum. Estradiol production decreases, and the continuing high LH levels initiate development of the corpus luteum. The corpus luteum secretes progesterone, which is the dominant ovarian hormone of the luteal phase, plus some estradiol. Progesterone inhibits LH and FSH secretion, and it further prepares the uterus for receiving and nourishing the embryo. If fertilization of the ovum does not occur, the corpus luteum degenerates after two weeks, allowing LH and FSH to initiate development of a new set of oocytes. However, if fertilization does occur, the blastocyst develops a surrounding layer of cells that secrete an LH-like hormone, called **chorionic gonadotropin (CG)**, which maintains the corpus luteum.

Maternal Hormones Prepare the Uterus to Accept the Embryo

In humans, the ovarian cycle occurs in parallel with changes in the lining of the uterus called the **uterine cycle** or **menstrual** cycle. The hormones produced by the ovarian follicle influence the development of the endometrium, the glandular inner layer of the uterus. As depicted at the bottom left of Figure 48.11, a period of bleeding called **menstruation** (from the Latin *mensis*, month) marks the beginning of the uterine cycle and the follicular phase of the ovarian cycle. During menstruation, the endometrium is sloughed off and released from the body.

Menstruation is initiated when progesterone and estrogen levels decrease substantially as the corpus luteum degenerates near the end of a luteal phase in which pregnancy did not occur. Menstrual cycles are found in many primates, including humans. Other mammals also have uterine cycles, but without the bleeding associated with menstruation. These cycles are called estrous cycles and are usually associated with a period of sexual receptivity in females that is timed to coincide with the preovulatory period. Cyclical changes in female sexual receptivity may be present in some primates with menstrual cycles but does not occur in humans.

By about the end of the first week of the menstrual cycle in humans, the endometrium is ready to grow in response to newly increasing levels of estrogen secreted by a developing follicle. This phase of the menstrual cycle, which corresponds to the latter part of the ovarian follicular phase, is called the proliferative phase (Figure 48.11). During this time, the endometrium becomes thicker and more vascularized. During the subsequent luteal phase of the ovarian cycle, progesterone from the corpus luteum initiates further endometrial growth, including the development of glands that secrete nutritive substances that sustain the embryo during its first two weeks in the uterus. This part of the menstrual cycle is called the secretory phase. If fertilization does not occur, degeneration of the corpus luteum and the associated decrease in progesterone secretion initiates menstruation and the beginning of the next uterine cycle. If fertilization does occur, however, the blastocyst becomes embedded in the endometrium and pregnancy begins, as described in the next section.

48.4 | PREGNANCY AND BIRTH IN MAMMALS

Learning Outcomes:

1. Describe the major developmental events in the first trimester of pregnancy in mammals.
2. Explain the relationship between the fetal and maternal structures of the placenta.
3. Outline the hormonal control of the birth process.

Pregnancy, or gestation, is the time during which a developing embryo and fetus grows within the uterus of the mother. Physiologically, pregnancy is said to begin not at fertilization but when the embryo is established in the uterine lining. This occurs within days of fertilization in animals with short gestation lengths but may take weeks in large animals with long gestations.

In mammals, gestation length varies widely and is roughly related to the size of adults in a particular species. Thus, small animals such as hamsters and mice have gestation periods of 16 to 21 days, canines have longer pregnancies of about 60 to 65 days, humans average about 268 days, and the Asian elephant carries its fetus up to 660 days. The advantages of prolonging prenatal development are twofold: The embryo is protected while it is developing in the uterus, and the offspring can be more fully developed at birth. This is especially important for animals whose survival depends on mobility shortly after birth, such as horses and ruminants.

Gestation length is influenced not only by adult body size but also by the number of offspring in a single pregnancy. Rats, for example, which bear up to 12 or so offspring per litter, have a short gestation period and produce young that are relatively undeveloped at birth and are totally dependent on the mother. In this section, we will examine how mammals have evolved to retain their young in the uterus for extended periods, the structure and function of the placenta, and the role of hormones in pregnancy.

Most Mammals Retain Their Young in the Uterus and Nourish Them via a Placenta

Three types of pregnancies are found in mammals. Monotremes, such as the platypus, are the only mammals that lay eggs. In marsupials, such as the kangaroo, the young are born while still extremely undeveloped. They then crawl up the mother's abdomen to her pouch, where they attach to a nipple to suckle and obtain nourishment. They mature within the pouch. Compared with marsupials, humans and other eutherian mammals retain their young within the uterus a longer time and nourish them via transfer of nutrients and gases through a structure called the **placenta**.

During pregnancy, many physiological changes occur in both the embryo and the mother. The first event of pregnancy in nonegg-laying mammals is **implantation**, when the blastocyst embeds within the uterine endometrium, which occurs in humans within one to two weeks, typically around eight to ten days after fertilization. Initially, the implanted blastocyst receives nutrients directly from the endometrial glands. However, shortly after implantation, newly developing embryonic tissues merge with the endometrium to form the placenta (**Figure 48.12**), which remains in place and grows larger as the embryo matures into a **fetus**. (In humans, an embryo becomes a fetus after the eighth week of gestation.) The placenta, therefore, has a maternal portion and a fetal portion. However, different mammals exhibit different types of placentas (Figure 48.12 c,d,e,f).

The placenta is rich in blood vessels from both the mother and fetus. The maternal and fetal sets of vessels lie in close proximity. The fetal portion of the placenta, called the chorion, contains convoluted structures called chorionic villi that provide a large surface area containing capillaries for exchange of nutrients, gases, and other solutes. Nutrients and oxygen from the mother are carried through maternal arteries, where

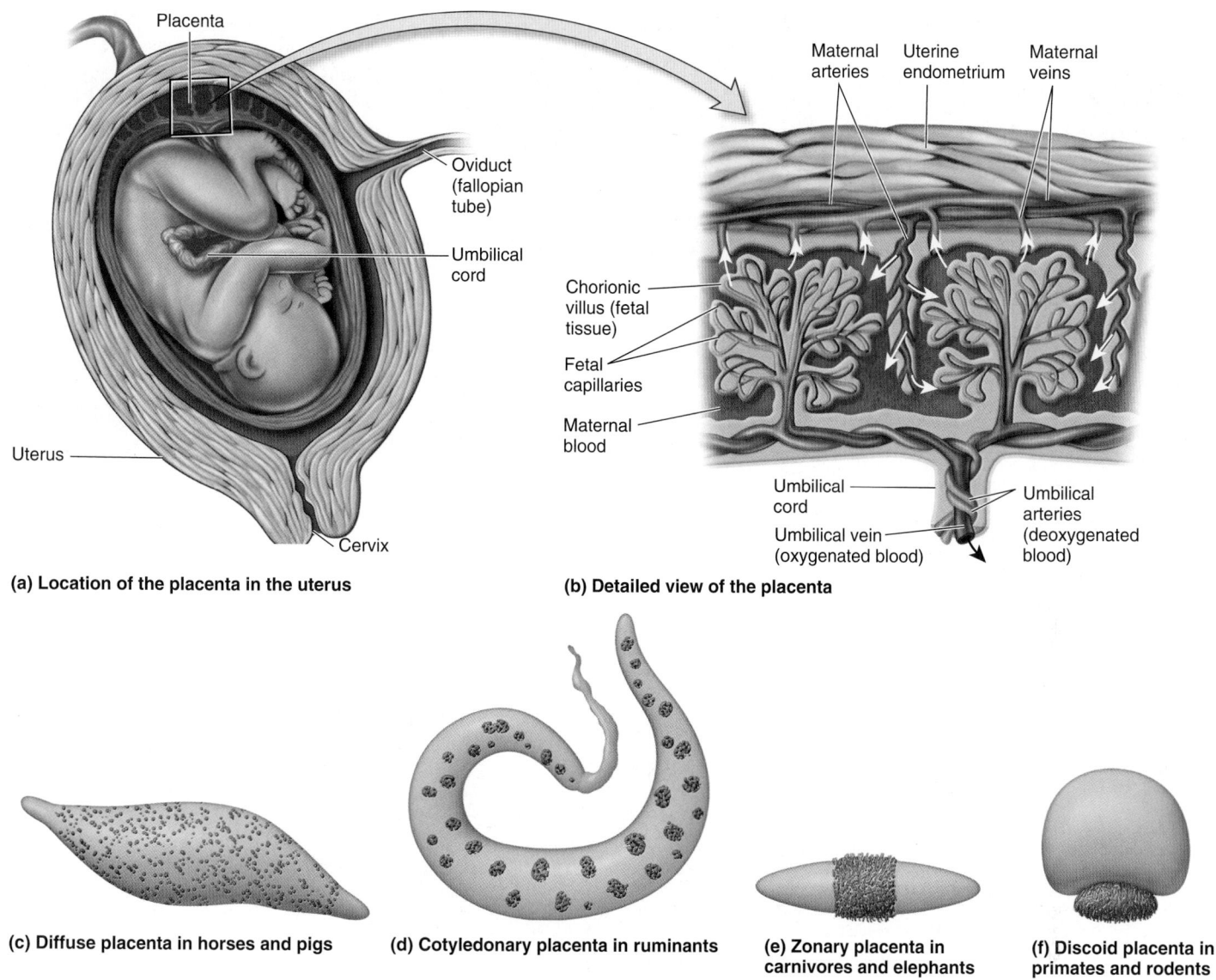

(a) Location of the placenta in the uterus

(b) Detailed view of the placenta

(c) Diffuse placenta in horses and pigs

(d) Cotyledonary placenta in ruminants

(e) Zonary placenta in carnivores and elephants

(f) Discoid placenta in primates and rodents

Figure 48.12 **The structure of the placenta.** In all mammals, the placenta is composed of both fetal and maternal tissues.
(a) Overview of placental structure in the human. **(b)** Enlarged view of the placenta showing the relationship between fetal and maternal structures. Note that in humans, blood in the fetal and maternal circulations does not mix. A variety of different placental types are found in mammals that differ in the shape and area of contact between maternal and fetal tissue: **(c)** diffuse, as seen in horses and pigs, **(d)** cotyledonary with numerous discrete areas of attachment, as seen in ruminants such as cattle, sheep, goats and deer, **(e)** zonary with a band of placental tissue surrounding the fetus, as seen in dogs, cats seals, and bears, **(f)** discoid with a single disc-shaped point of attachment, as seen in humans, apes, monkeys and rodents.

BioConnections: *Note that the umbilical arteries are shown in blue to signify that they carry deoxygenated blood, and the umbilical vein is shown in red to signify it carries oxygenated blood. Normally, arteries carry oxygenated blood, and veins carry deoxygenated blood, except in the pulmonary circulation (see Chapter 44). Why is the circulation through the placenta like that of the lungs?*

her blood pools in large areas of the fetal placenta surrounding the fetal capillaries. Solutes diffuse from the maternal blood into fetal capillaries, and from there flow into the umbilical vein, a portion of the fetal circulation. In turn, carbon dioxide and other waste products from the fetus are carried through the umbilical artery to the placenta, where they diffuse into the mother's circulation, from which they can be excreted.

Because of this placental organization, the blood of the mother and the fetus do not mix.

Prenatal development in humans is generally divided into three trimesters, each of which lasts about three months (**Figure 48.13**). During the first two months of pregnancy, the organs of the embryo develop. At the end of the first trimester, the rudiments of the organs are present, and the

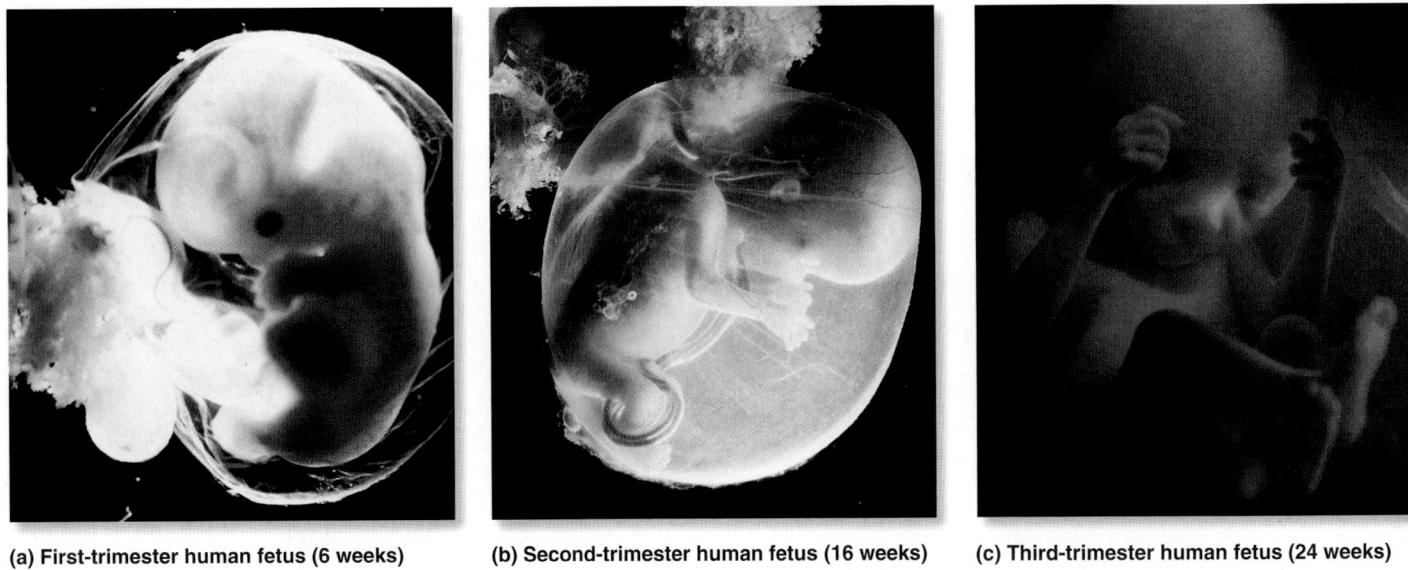

(a) First-trimester human fetus (6 weeks)   **(b)** Second-trimester human fetus (16 weeks)   **(c)** Third-trimester human fetus (24 weeks)

Figure 48.13 **Prenatal development in humans.** The photos show the developing fetus **(a)** in the first trimester, **(b)** in the second trimester, and **(c)** at the start of the third trimester.

2 The fetus's head pushing against the cervix activates stretch-sensitive sensory neurons that send stimulatory signals to the mother's hypothalamus.

Positive feedback

3 The hypothalamus stimulates secretion of oxytocin from the posterior pituitary gland.

Sensory nerves to hypothalamus

1 Estradiol from the placenta readies the uterus for a response to oxytocin.

Prostaglandins

Oxytocin

5 Prostaglandins secreted by the uterus also enhance contractions. Sensory input to the hypothalamus is further enhanced by contractions.

4 Oxytocin stimulates stronger uterine contractions.

Positive feedback

Figure 48.14 **Hormonal control of parturition.** Birth relies on neural signals from the uterus and on maternal hormones that act on the uterus. In response to sensory neural input arising from the push of the fetus on the cervix, the maternal posterior pituitary gland releases oxytocin, which stimulates uterine smooth muscle contractions. The secretion of prostaglandins by the uterus also increases the strength of the contractions. Sensory receptors in the uterus detect the more forceful contractions and signal the mother's posterior pituitary gland to secrete more oxytocin, thus completing a positive feedback loop that further strengthens the contractions.

developing fetus is about an inch long. The second trimester is an extremely rapid phase of growth. During the third trimester, the lungs of the fetus mature so that they are ready to function as gas-exchange organs, and the fetus positions itself with its head above the uterine cervix in preparation for birth.

Birth Is Dependent on Maternal and Fetal Hormones

Birth—also called **parturition**—is initiated by the actions of several hormones and other factors secreted by the mother (**Figure 48.14**). In humans and many other mammals, the initial event of parturition is an increase in estradiol and oxytocin levels in the mother's blood. Recall from Chapter 47 that oxytocin is a posterior pituitary gland hormone that stimulates contraction of uterine muscle. The high concentration of estradiol stimulates the production of oxytocin receptors within the smooth muscle layer of the uterus, making the uterus more sensitive to oxytocin. At the same time, the pressure of the fetus's head pressing on the cervix stretches the smooth muscle of the uterus and cervix. This stretch is detected by neurons in these structures. Signals from the stretch-sensitive neurons are sent to the mother's hypothalamus, triggering the release of still more oxytocin from the posterior pituitary gland.

The binding of oxytocin to its receptors initiates the strong uterine muscle contractions that are the hallmark of **labour**. In addition to its direct action on uterine muscle, oxytocin stimulates uterine secretion of prostaglandins that act with oxytocin to increase the strength of the muscle contractions. The stronger contractions elicit more oxytocin release from the mother's pituitary, which causes yet stronger contractions, setting up a positive feedback cycle that continues until the baby is pushed out of the uterus and through the vagina. The contractions continue for a short while after birth, helping to expel the placenta.

In most mammals, the young are nurtured for a period after birth by milk produced within the mother's mammary glands and secreted via the nipples. The monotremes, in which the young of some species use their pliable bills to attach to the breast of the mother and draw milk directly through the skin, are an exception. The production of milk is called **lactation**.

GENOMES AND PROTEOMES

The Evolution of the Globin Gene Family Has Been Important for Internal Gestation in Mammals

As discussed in Chapter 19, genes can become duplicated to create gene families. Gene families have been important in the evolution of complex traits because the various members of a gene family can enable the expression of complex, specialized forms and functions.

An interesting example is the globin gene family in animals. Globin genes encode polypeptides that are subunits of proteins that function in oxygen binding. Hemoglobin, which is made in erythrocytes, carries oxygen throughout the body in all vertebrates and many invertebrates, delivering oxygen to all of the body's cells (see Chapter 45). In humans, the globin gene family is composed of several homologous genes that were originally derived from a single ancestral globin gene (refer back to Figure 19.8).

Although all the globin polypeptides are subunits of proteins that play a role in oxygen binding, the various family members tend to have specialized functions. For example, certain globin genes are expressed only during particular stages of embryonic development. This has particular importance in placental mammals, in which prenatal development occurs in the uterus of females, because the oxygen demands of a rapidly growing embryo and fetus are quite different from the demands of its mother. These different demands are met by the differential expression of hemoglobin genes during prenatal development.

The hemoglobin protein of adult mammals is composed of four globin polypeptides—two encoded by the α-globin gene and two encoded by the β-globin gene. Altogether, five globin genes, designated α, β, γ, ζ, and δ encode the major subunits that are found in hemoglobin proteins at different developmental stages. During embryonic development, the δ-globin and ζ-globin genes are turned on, resulting in embryonic hemoglobin

Table 48.1	Globin Gene Expression During Mammalian Development		
Stage of development	**Globin genes expressed**	**Hemoglobin composition**	**Oxygen affinity (P_{50})***
Embryo	ε-globin and ζ-globin	Two ε-globin and two ζ-globin subunits	5–13.5 mmHg
Fetus	γ-globin and α-globin	Two γ-globin and two α-globin subunits	19.5 mmHg
Birth to adult	β-globin and α-globin	Two β-globin and two α-globin subunits	26.5 mmHg

*P_{50} values represent the partial pressure of oxygen required to half-saturate hemoglobin (see Chapter 45): A lower P_{50} indicates a higher affinity of hemoglobin for oxygen. The value for embryos is an estimate based on in vitro experiments. All values are for human hemoglobins.

with a very high affinity for oxygen (**Table 48.1**). At the fetal stage, these genes are turned off, and the α-globin and γ-globin genes are turned on, producing fetal hemoglobin with slightly less (but still high) affinity for oxygen. Finally, just before birth, expression of the γ-globin gene decreases, and the β-globin gene is turned on, resulting in adult hemoglobin, which has a lower affinity for oxygen than either the embryonic or fetal forms. The higher affinities of embryonic and fetal hemoglobins enable the embryo and fetus to remove oxygen from the mother's bloodstream and use that oxygen to meet their own metabolic demands. Thus the expression of different globin genes at particular stages of development enables placental mammals to develop in the uterus without either breathing on their own or being continually exposed to atmospheric oxygen (as occurs for vertebrate embryos that develop externally within eggs).

During pregnancy, elevated blood progesterone levels suppress the secretion of the anterior pituitary hormone prolactin, which is required for milk production. In humans, lactation begins shortly after birth in response to declining blood concentrations of progesterone previously provided by the placenta. Whereas the formation of milk is dependent on prolactin, the actual release of milk from the breast is dependent on activation of smooth muscle cells surrounding secretory ducts in the breast. These cells are stimulated to contract by the presence of oxytocin. Thus oxytocin plays a key role in two major processes: birth and nourishment of the young.

48.5 / TIMING OF REPRODUCTION WITH FAVOURABLE TIMES OF YEAR

Learning Outcomes:

1. Describe several mechanisms by which animals synchronize the production of offspring with favourable environmental conditions.

The likelihood that offspring will survive to adulthood and reproduce is influenced to a large degree by the environment into which they are born. For that reason, reproductive cycles often occur at times of the year when the likelihood of reproductive success is greatest—when the young will have sufficient nutrients to sustain them during their period of rapid growth. In general, animals that live under more uniformly favourable conditions—stable temperatures, ample rainfall, and abundant available food—have less dramatic cycles of reproductive activity. Many tropical species, for example, reproduce several times each year. By contrast, many temperate-zone animals have seasonal reproductive cycles that reflect large fluctuations in environmental conditions. For example, insects such as the mayfly live as underwater larvae for a year before emerging into the adult (reproductively active) stage, but the emergence occurs only during one or two favourable summer months.

Several means by which animals synchronize the production of offspring with favourable environmental conditions have evolved. In **sperm storage**, females store and nourish sperm in their reproductive tract for long periods of time, as long as two years in honeybees and four years in some turtles. Certain insectivorous, bats such as *Myotis lucifugus*, use a different strategy. These bats mate in the fall, but the ovarian cycle in females is halted before ovulation, and sperm are stored and nourished in the female's uterus over the winter. On arousal from hibernation in the spring, the female ovulates one or more eggs, which are fertilized by the stored sperm. This type of reproductive cycle, called **delayed ovulation**, means that bats mate when they are in prime condition, and that young are born when temperatures and food supplies are optimal.

Other animals have **delayed implantation**, in which a fertilized egg reaches the uterus but does not implant until later, when environmental conditions are more favourable for the newly produced young. This type of reproduction is common among carnivores, notably the mustelids (weasels) and some bears.

Finally, many animals (cats, some hamsters, sheep, and many birds) have seasonal periods of mating followed immediately by implantation and pregnancy. Such seasonal breeding results from neuroendocrine changes in the hypothalamus in response to changes in the length of daylight. As day length increases near the end of winter, neurohormone secretion and gamete development by the reproductive glands of some seasonal breeders increase, and these animals exhibit behavioural changes indicating their increased readiness to mate. Other seasonal breeders—sheep, for example—reproduce in response to shorter day length. Ewes are impregnated by rams in the fall, as the days grow shorter, and they carry the pregnancy through the winter. Lambs are born in the spring, providing a relatively long growth period before onset of the next winter. If sheep were to mate in summer, lambs would be born in late fall or winter, when conditions are much less favourable.

Unlike the examples just described, humans neither have a seasonal breeding cycle nor alter the timing of implantation or ovulation. Moreover, sperm can survive in a woman's reproductive tract for only a short time—two or three days. Human reproduction, therefore, is far less responsive to environmental changes, day length, or other factors. However, human reproductive success can be seriously curtailed by sickness and other factors, as we see next.

48.6 / HUMAN HEALTH CONNECTION

Learning Outcomes:

1. Explain the most common causes of human infertility.

Human reproduction can be affected by many factors, some voluntary and some not. At any given time, it is estimated that 7% of couples of childbearing age in Canada are experiencing infertility problems; that is, they cannot reproduce. In men and women alike, fertility can be compromised by a variety of factors. In this section, we discuss some of the common causes of **infertility**: the inability of a man to produce sufficient numbers or quality of sperm to impregnate a woman, or the inability of a woman to become pregnant or maintain a pregnancy.

Infertility May Result from Disease, Developmental Disorders, Inadequate Nutrition, and Stress

Approximately 20% of infertility in Canada is attributed to sexually transmitted infections (STIs). For example, some STIs may cause blockage in the ducts of the testes, preventing normal sperm transport.

A much rarer group of diseases that cause infertility are tumours. Tumours that form in the pituitary gland may prevent its normal functioning such that LH and FSH secretion is interrupted, resulting in decreased gamete development. Other tumours can form in a reproductive organ—for example, the uterus—and disrupt that organ's normal function.

Developmental disorders are conditions that are either present at birth or arise during childhood and adolescence. In some developmental disorders that affect fertility, inherited mutations of genes that code for enzymes involved in the biosynthesis of reproductive hormones cause abnormal expression of those genes. The result is either too much or too little of one or more of these hormones, notably estradiol or testosterone. Other developmental disorders that compromise fertility include malformations of the cervix or fallopian tubes.

Adequate nutrition is required for normal growth and development of all parts of the body, including the reproductive system. Because the reproductive system is not essential for the survival of any single organism, it often becomes inactive when nutrients are chronically scarce, such as during starvation. In this way, precious stores of energy in the body are preserved for vital functions, such as the operation of the brain and heart.

Nutrition can also affect reproduction before adulthood. Undernourished children may enter puberty several years later than other children. In light of recent evidence suggesting that the brains of mammals contain a centre that monitors the body's fat stores, one of the triggers that initiate puberty in girls may be a signal from adipose tissue to the brain. Very low fat levels in undernourished girls somehow signal the brain that her body does not contain sufficient fat stores to support the energetic demands of pregnancy, and puberty is delayed.

Stress—any real or perceived threat to an animal's homeostasis—can affect fertility. In the short term, stress can produce hormonal changes that are adaptive in meeting a crisis. However, long-term stress is damaging to many aspects of health, including reproductive health. Because reproduction is not necessary for an individual's survival, many nonessential functions—including the maintenance of menstrual cycles in women—are suppressed by chronic stress. The reproductive effects of stress, like those of starvation, appear to be much greater in females than in males, perhaps because only females bear the energetic cost of pregnancy. Interestingly, the human body responds to long-term strenuous exercise in a way that is similar to its response to long-term stress. This is why many young ballerinas and gymnasts experience delayed puberty and why in female marathon runners menstrual cycles may be abnormal or absent.

When the causes of infertility cannot be ascertained, a variety of factors come under suspicion. Among these possible causes of infertility are ingestion of toxins (e.g., certain heavy metals, such as cadmium), tobacco smoking, injuries to the gonads, occupational exposure to chemicals or radiation, the widespread presence of artificial hormones in the environment, and aging. Recall that as women age, they experience a loss of fertility, an event called menopause. Although reproductive function declines with age in men, they do not experience complete cessation of gamete production even at very advanced ages.

Summary of Key Concepts

48.1 Asexual and Sexual Reproduction

- Asexual reproduction occurs when offspring are produced from a single parent, without the fusion of gametes from two parents. Budding occurs when part of the parent organism pinches off to form a complete new individual. Some animals reproduce by the regeneration of a complete organism from small body fragments. Parthenogenesis is the development of offspring from an unfertilized egg. (Figure 48.1)

- Sexual reproduction is the production of a new individual by the joining of two haploid gametes: sperm and eggs. The union of a sperm and an egg—fertilization—produces a zygote, which develops into an embryo.

- Sexual reproduction was shown by Paland and Lynch to be more effective in eliminating deleterious mutations from a population of *Daphnia* than asexual reproduction. (Figure 48.2)

- In hermaphroditism, individuals can fertilize their own eggs with their own sperm, but in most hermaphroditic species individuals exchange sperm with another individual.

48.2 Gametogenesis and Fertilization

- Male and female gametes are formed within the gonads—the testes in males and the ovaries in females.

- Gametogenesis—the formation of gametes—begins with diploid primordial cells called germ cells. In spermatogenesis, one spermatogonium yields four sperm cells. In oogenesis, meiosis yields one egg (ovum). (Figure 48.3)

- In external fertilization, sperm and eggs are released into an aquatic environment where they unite and avoid desiccation. (Figure 48.4a). Terrestrial animals use internal fertilization, in which sperm are deposited within the reproductive tract of the female usually during copulation, but not always (Figure 48.4b).

- External accessory sex organs, such as the penis, are used to physically join the male and female during copulation so that sperm can be deposited directly into the female's reproductive tract.

- Development of an embryo within an egg is called oviparity. When an embryo develops within the mother, the process is called viviparity. In ovoviviparity, eggs covered with a thin shell are produced and hatch inside the mother's body, but the offspring receive no nourishment from the mother. (Figure 48.5)

48.3 Mammalian Reproductive Structure and Function

- Sperm produced within each testis move out of the seminiferous tubules and into the epididymis, which leads into the vas deferens, a muscular tube leading to the ejaculatory duct. The urethra conducts semen, a mixture containing fluid and sperm, during ejaculation. The fluid components of semen are produced in the seminal vesicles, the bulbourethral glands, and the prostate gland. (Figures 48.6, 48.7)

- Spermatogenesis is under hormonal control. (Figure 48.8)

- The external female genitalia are composed of large outer folds called the labia majora, plus smaller, inner folds called the labia minora, and the clitoris; the internal female reproductive tract includes the vagina, uterus, oviducts, and a pair of ovaries. The fertilized egg undergoes several cell divisions to become a blastocyst, a ball of cells that enters the uterus, where it will develop into an embryo. (Figures 48.9, 48.10)

- In females, changes in hormone secretion produce the ovarian cycle and control the uterine cycle or menstrual cycle. The latter name refers to menstruation, a period of bleeding at the beginning of the uterine cycle. (Figure 48.11)

- The event during which a woman stops having ovarian cycles is called menopause.

48.4 Pregnancy and Birth in Mammals

- The time during which a developing embryo grows within the uterus of the mother is termed *pregnancy* or gestation. Humans and other eutherian mammals retain and nourish their young within the uterus via transfer of nutrients and gases through a structure called the placenta. (Figure 48.12)

- The first event of pregnancy is implantation, when the blastocyst imbeds within the uterine endometrium. Newly developing embryonic tissues merge with the endometrium to form the placenta, which remains in place and grows larger as the embryo matures into a fetus. (Figure 48.13)

- Birth, or parturition, is initiated by the actions of hormones. The hormone oxytocin stimulates the strong uterine muscle contractions that characterize labour. (Figure 48.14). After the baby is born, contractions continue in order to expel the placenta.

- In most mammals, the young are nurtured for a period after birth by milk produced by lactation by the mother.

- The evolution of the globin gene family contributed to the ability of placental mammals to develop inside the mother's uterus. (Table 48.1)

48.5 Timing of Reproduction with Favourable Times of Year

- Animals synchronize the production of offspring with favourable environmental conditions by several means (depending on the species) including sperm storage, delayed ovulation, delayed implantation, and/or seasonal mating.

48.6 Human Health Connection

- Infertility is the inability of a man to produce sufficient numbers or quality of sperm to impregnate a woman, or the inability of a woman to become pregnant or maintain a pregnancy. A primary cause is STIs.

Test to Assess Your Learning

1. The development of offspring from unfertilized eggs is
   a. budding.
   b. cloning.
   c. fragmentation.
   d. parthenogenesis.
   e. implantation.

2. Which of the following is considered an advantage of sexual reproduction?
   a. necessity to locate a mate
   b. increased energy expenditure in producing gametes that may not be used in reproduction
   c. increased genetic variation
   d. decreased genetic variation
   e. both (a) and (b)

3. Spermatogonia are
   a. germ cells.
   b. diploid cells.
   c. male gametes.
   d. all of the above.
   e. (a) and (b) only.

4. Advantages of internal fertilization over external fertilization include
   a. ensuring that male gametes come into close proximity to female gametes.
   b. protection of gametes from predation or other harmful environmental factors.
   c. decreased likelihood of desiccation of gametes.
   d. all of the above.
   e. (a) and (b) only.

5. Which of the following is an example of ovoviviparity?
   a. Honeybees lay soft eggs within the hive.
   b. Sharks hatch from egg cases held within the female's body.
   c. Birds hatch from eggs laid within a nest.
   d. Kittens obtain nourishment from the mother through a placenta.
   e. Eggs are released into the water column, where they may be fertilized.

6. The fructose in semen is secreted by
   a. the epididymis.
   b. the seminiferous tubules.
   c. the seminal vesicles.
   d. the prostate gland.
   e. the bulbourethral glands.

7. The function of FSH in males is to
   a. stimulate the development of the gonads during early development.
   b. stimulate spermatogenesis.
   c. increase the secretion of testosterone by the testes.
   d. regulate the secretion of the bulbourethral glands.
   e. both (a) and (b).

8. During the human ovarian cycle, ovulation is stimulated by
   a. a decrease in FSH secretion.
   b. an increase in progesterone secretion.
   c. an increase in LH secretion.
   d. the presence of semen in the vagina.
   e. a decrease in estradiol levels in the bloodstream.

9. During the secretory phase of the menstrual cycle, endometrial glands secrete
   a. hormones that increase the likelihood of pregnancy.
   b. nutritive substances that sustain the embryo during the first two weeks of development.
   c. hormones that prevent ovulation.
   d. waste products into the lumen of the uterus.
   e. both (a) and (c).

10. Animals can synchronize the production of offspring with favourable environmental conditions by
    a. storing sperm.
    b. delaying ovulation.
    c. delaying implantation.
    d. seasonal mating.
    e. All of the above are correct.

Articulate to Assess Your Learning

1. Define asexual reproduction and give three examples

2. Many species of insects produce intersexual individuals (sometimes called gynandromorphs). What do you think these intersexes might look like?

Collaborate to Assess and Extend Your Learning

1. What are the advantages of sexual reproduction? Of asexual reproduction? What would you say is the most important difference between the two types of reproduction?

2. Within the insects, some species use internal fertilization and some use external fertilization. Under what conditions might you expect internal versus external fertilization to have evolved?

3. A principle of biology is that living organisms use energy. What are some of the energy costs associated with sexual reproduction? What outweighs those costs and accounts for the observation that most animals reproduce sexually?

Visit McGraw-Hill Ryerson Connect™ for additional study resources.

Animal Development

Chapter Outline

I n the previous chapter, we learned how animals reproduce. In this chapter, we will learn about the cellular and molecular processes that lead to the formation of an embryo. The biological information that controls embryonic development resides in both the organism's genetic material—its DNA—and in the cytoplasm of the egg. A fertilized egg first transforms into a cluster of cells without specialized functions and then, ultimately, into a complex organism containing organs with specific and evolutionarily conserved functions. These events occur during a period known as an animal's development. The process by which a fertilized egg is transformed into an organism with distinct physiological systems and body parts is called **embryonic development**. The process by which different cells within a developing organism acquire specialized forms and functions, through the expression of cell-specific genes, is called **cellular differentiation**.

In this chapter, we will first describe the five different stages of embryonic development. Next, we will examine the cellular and molecular mechanisms that control development. We conclude with an overview of how abnormal development affects the human condition.

How embryonic development can go wrong—a normal zebrafish embryo (top) and one exposed to ethanol (bottom).

Principle: *Living organisms interact with their environment. As you read this chapter, consider the many environmental factors that animals are exposed to during embryonic development.*

most animals have similar properties. As described in Chapter 30, most modern animals develop from embryos with three cell layers. Such triploblasts include vertebrates, arthropods, echinoderms, and molluscs. Development in these animals can be categorized into five general stages: fertilization, cleavage, gastrulation, neurulation, and organogenesis (**Figure 49.1**). Many species also go through a phase called metamorphosis, which is a transition from a feeding larval form to an adult. Metamorphosis occurs after organogenesis and facilitates the rapid growth of young organisms into mature ones. Examples of metamorphosis include the transformation of a caterpillar into a butterfly, and that of a tadpole into a frog. In this section, we will examine the key aspects of each of the five general stages of animal development.

49.1 / EVENTS OF EMBRYONIC DEVELOPMENT

Learning Outcomes:

1. List the five major events that take place during embryonic development and describe the end result of each.
2. Compare and contrast the fast block to polyspermy and the slow block to polyspermy.
3. Describe the process of cleavage, beginning at fertilization and leading into gastrulation.
4. Trace the fates of cells in a gastrula as they differentiate into the three major germ layers.
5. Outline the early development of the nervous system during neurulation.
6. Explain the migration and roles of neural crest cells.

Even though the adult forms of animals vary immensely in size and morphology (shape), embryonic developmental processes in

Event 1: Fertilization Involves a Union Between Sperm and Egg to Create a Zygote-Stage Embryo

The events in **fertilization** are quite similar in all triploblasts (**Figure 49.2**). The description that follows summarizes some of the hallmark events following fertilization in sea urchins, a well-studied echinoderm. As mentioned in Chapter 48, sperm can contact the egg either outside or inside the female, depending on the species. In all cases, the sperm must penetrate a jellylike layer before contacting the plasma membrane of the egg.

The initial contact is followed by the **acrosomal reaction**, in which hydrolytic enzymes are released from the acrosome in the tip of the sperm head onto the jelly coat of the egg (**Figure 49.2a**). These enzymes dissolve a localized region of the jelly coat, allowing the sperm head to bind to proteins in the egg's plasma membrane. Binding is followed by fusion of the sperm head with the

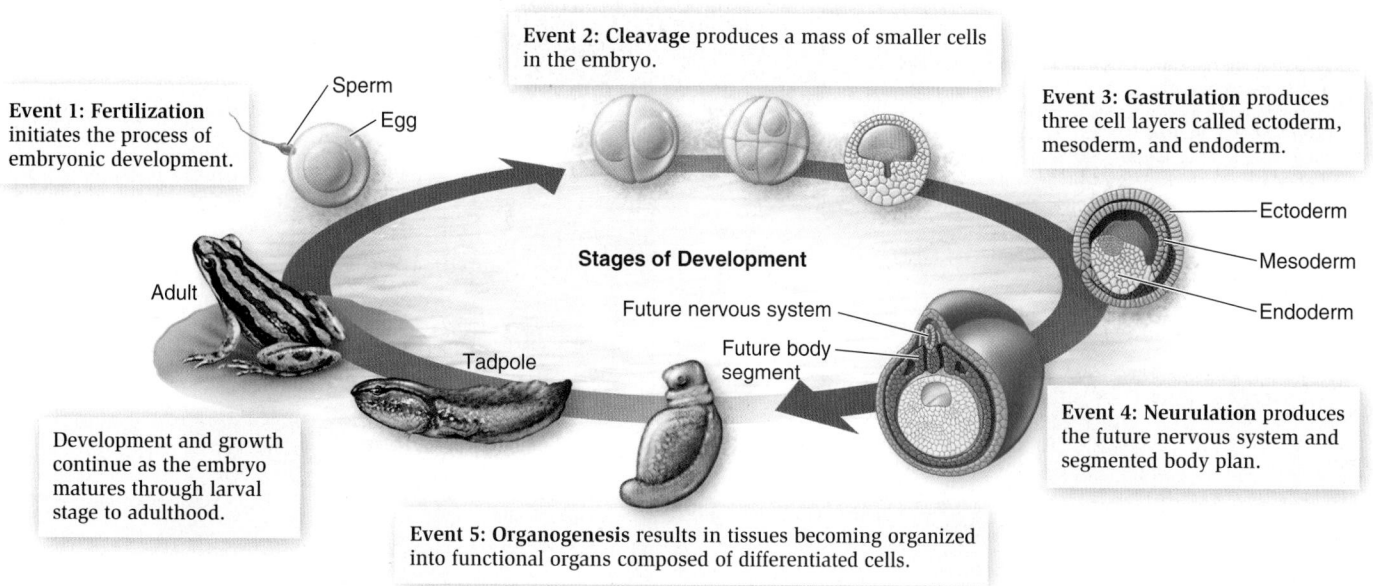

Figure 49.1 Overview of development of embryonic stages. This figure shows the stages that all vertebrate embryos go through, using a frog as an example.

egg membrane and, shortly after, by penetration of the sperm head and release of its nucleus into the egg. Additional sperm are prevented from fusing with the egg because the fusion of sperm and egg depolarizes the egg. This depolarization blocks other sperm from binding to egg membrane proteins and is known as the **fast block to polyspermy**. Without this block, a single egg could receive chromosomes from two or more sperm, resulting in zygotes that fail to develop normally or at all.

The acrosomal reaction is followed by the **cortical reaction** (**Figure 49.2b**). Normally, cytosolic calcium concentration in eggs, as in most cells, is kept at a low level by several mechanisms, some of which pump Ca^{2+} out of the cytosol and into the endoplasmic reticulum. With the binding of the sperm to the egg, inositol trisphosphate (IP_3) (see Chapter 9) is released from the region of the plasma membrane nearest to the sperm entry point. IP_3 then binds to nearby sites on the endoplasmic reticulum and opens Ca^{2+} channels. Within 10 seconds after a sperm cell binds to an egg, Ca^{2+} is released from the lumen of the endoplasmic reticulum and into the cytosol. This signal is propagated across the entire endoplasmic reticulum, resulting in the transmission of a calcium wave across the egg over a period of about 30 seconds. This calcium wave can be visualized by injecting the cytosol of an unfertilized egg with a calcium-sensitive fluorescent dye that becomes highly fluorescent when Ca^{2+} is released from the endoplasmic reticulum (**Figure 49.2c**).

The release of Ca^{2+} in the cortical reaction has several important effects. First, membrane-bound vesicles in the egg's cytosol, called cortical granules, release enzymes and other substances that inactivate the sperm-binding proteins on the plasma membrane. In addition, the outer coating of the egg cell, known as the vitelline layer in sea urchins, or the zona pellucida in vertebrates, becomes hardened and begins to separate

from the plasma membrane. These events create another barrier to more sperm fusing with the egg, a process called the **slow block to polyspermy**. Additionally, the burst of cytosolic Ca^{2+} leads to the activation of molecular signalling pathways that initiate the first cell cycle of the embryo and triggers an increase in protein synthesis and metabolism within the egg cell.

Shortly afterward, the nucleus of the sperm fuses with the nucleus of the egg, creating a diploid fertilized egg that is now called a zygote. The first cell division of the zygote occurs approximately 90 minutes after fertilization in sea urchins and amphibians, but it can take up to 24 hours after fertilization in mammals.

Event 2: Cell Divisions Without Cell Growth Create a Cleavage-Stage Embryo

The initial cell cycles of embryos are unique because they involve repeated cell divisions without cell growth. The developmental phase during which these cell cycles occur is called **cleavage**. The embryonic cells repeatedly split in two, resulting in several generations of daughter cells that are roughly half the size of the cells that gave rise to them. These early cell cycles that lack cell growth are characterized as "biphasic" because they alternate only between the mitotic (M) phase and DNA synthesis (S) phase of the cell cycle. Neither the G_1 nor G_2 phase occurs (see Chapter 9 for a discussion of the cell cycle).

In most species in which development occurs outside the mother, and thus eggs can be eaten by predators, cell division during cleavage represents some of the fastest cell cycles found in nature. The cell cycle during cleavage in amphibians, for example, requires only 20 minutes. During each 20-minute cell cycle, complete genome replication, mitosis, and duplication of the nuclear envelope are followed by cytokinesis. In eutherian

(a) Acrosomal reaction

1. When a sperm cell contacts an egg, the acrosome releases hydrolytic enzymes that dissolve the jelly coat.

2. This exposes sperm-binding proteins on the egg cell plasma membrane that bind to the sperm.

3. The sperm and egg plasma membranes fuse. The sperm nucleus will then enter the egg.

Sperm head
Sperm nucleus
Acrosome
Sperm-binding proteins
Jelly coat
Egg plasma membrane
Hydrolytic enzymes
Cortical granules
Vitelline layer
Egg cell cytoplasm

(b) Cortical reaction

1. IP_3 is released from the plasma membrane near the site of sperm fusion with the egg.

2. IP_3 stimulates Ca^{2+} release from the endoplasmic reticulum.

3. Ca^{2+} stimulates exocytosis of cortical granules.

4. The contents of the cortical granules destroy the sperm-binding proteins and cause the vitelline layer and plasma membrane to separate. The vitelline layer of the egg hardens. This prevents polyspermy.

Egg cell cytoplasm
IP_3
Ca^{2+}
Endoplasmic reticulum

(c) The Ca^{2+} wave of the cortical reaction in a sea urchin egg

Site of sperm entry

Time after sperm entry

15 seconds   25 seconds   31 seconds   36 seconds

Figure 49.2 **Fertilization of an egg by a sperm.** (a) Acrosomal reaction. The contact of a sperm with an egg initiates a series of events that permits the head of the sperm to bind to the plasma membrane of the egg. This depolarizes the egg and blocks other sperm from entering, in the fast block to polyspermy. (b) Cortical reaction. Sperm fusion leads to an increased level of cytosolic Ca^{2+} that ultimately causes the vitelline layer of the egg to harden, creating the slow block to polyspermy. (c) Calcium wave in a sea urchin egg. The increase in cytosolic Ca^{2+} begins near the site of sperm entry and propagates throughout the egg. The highest concentration of cytosolic Ca^{2+} released from the endoplasmic reticulum is indicated with brightest colour.

Concept check: *What is the final process called by which a tadpole develops into an adult frog?*

mammals, however, whose development occurs within the protective environment of the mother's body, biphasic cell divisions during cleavage are relatively slow, requiring about 12 hours to complete.

The two half-size daughter cells produced by each cell division during cleavage are known as **blastomeres**. Individual blastomeres are bound together, and the outer single-cell layer of blastomeres forms a sheet of epithelial cells that separates the embryo from its environment. After formation of the outer epithelial layer, the embryos of many animals take up water and form a cavity called a **blastocoel**. The embryo at this stage is called a **blastula**. The blastocoel provides a space into which cells will migrate to form the digestive tract and other structures of the embryo, as described later in event 3.

Meroblastic Cleavage (Birds and Fishes) Among triploblasts, cleavage-stage embryos can vary dramatically in size and appearance. This variation is in part related to the location and amounts of yolk that was deposited in the egg. Yolk is most concentrated toward one end—or pole—of the egg, called the **vegetal pole**. Much less yolk, and much more cytoplasm, is concentrated at the opposite pole, called the **animal pole** (**Figure 49.3**). These poles determine in part the future anteroposterior (head to tail) and dorsoventral (back to front or top to bottom, depending on the species) axes of the embryo.

In some animals, cleavage of the zygote is called incomplete because only the region of the zygote and embryo containing cytoplasm at the animal pole undergoes cell division. This incomplete type of cell cleavage, called **meroblastic cleavage**,

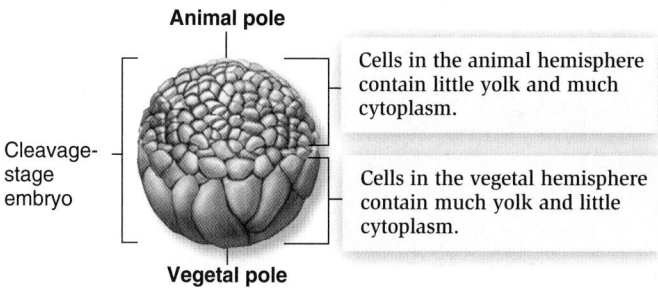

Animal pole

Cleavage-stage embryo

Cells in the animal hemisphere contain little yolk and much cytoplasm.

Cells in the vegetal hemisphere contain much yolk and little cytoplasm.

Vegetal pole

Figure 49.3 Polarity in an amphibian embryo. The cleavage-stage embryo contains an animal pole with little yolk and much cytoplasm, and a vegetal pole with large amounts of yolk and little cytoplasm.

occurs in birds, some fish, and some other vertebrates whose eggs contain large amounts of yolk (**Figure 49.4**). Instead of forming a ball of cells (a blastula), a flattened disk of blastomeres known as a **blastoderm** develops on top of the yolk mass.

Holoblastic Cleavage *(Amphibians and Mammals)* In animals whose eggs have smaller amounts of yolk, cleavage during the first cell division is complete and bisects the entire zygote into two equal-sized blastomeres. Such **holoblastic cleavage** occurs in amphibians and mammals (Figure 49.4). In amphibians, cleavage-stage embryos form a blastula, as previously noted. In mammals, however, cleavage-stage embryos undergo a process called compaction, in which the amount of physical contact between cells is maximized. At this stage, the embryo in these species is called a **morula**. The resulting blastomeres in mammals then proceed to form a **blastocyst**, the mammalian counterpart of a blastula.

In mammals, the events of fertilization and cleavage occur in the oviduct (**Figure 49.5**). The blastocyst has a different morphological appearance from the blastula or blastoderm embryos in nonmammalian species, and no animal-vegetal polarity that is analogous to that of other chordates exists. The blastocyst consists of an outer epithelial layer called the trophectoderm, which gives rise to the placenta, and an inner layer called the inner cell mass, which develops into the embryo. Upon reaching the uterus, the embryo "hatches" from the zona pellucida, the layer of glycoproteins that surrounds the secondary oocyte and is retained up to this time, preventing premature adhesion of the embryo to the oviduct. The embryo then becomes embedded in the endometrium of the mother's uterus, a process known as implantation (Figure 49.5; also see Chapter 48). This entire process takes four days in mice and about eight to ten days in humans.

Because cell cycles can be extremely rapid during early cleavage, the DNA is often maintained in a conformation that is incompatible with transcription, so little or no transcription occurs during early cleavage. Therefore, nearly all cellular division and differentiation processes during the cleavage stage are regulated by cytoplasmic components that resided in the egg before fertilization. Subcellular components that were synthesized before fertilization are called maternal factors and include many mRNAs and proteins that are stockpiled in the egg during oogenesis to facilitate cleavage in the absence of transcription.

Toward the end of the cleavage stage of embryonic development, cell cycles become less synchronous, and the embryo begins to express its own genes. The embryo's shift from existing exclusively on maternal factors to developing in response to products derived from its own genome begins 6 to 24 hours after fertilization in vertebrates. This is followed by the next event of development, called gastrulation.

Figure 49.4 Meroblastic and holoblastic cleavage. As seen in these electron micrographs, early embryos of birds and many fish undergo incomplete (meroblastic) cleavage, whereas most amphibian and mammalian embryos undergo complete (holoblastic) cleavage. The amount of yolk in the egg (not visible in these images) contributes to many of these morphological differences observed in various species.

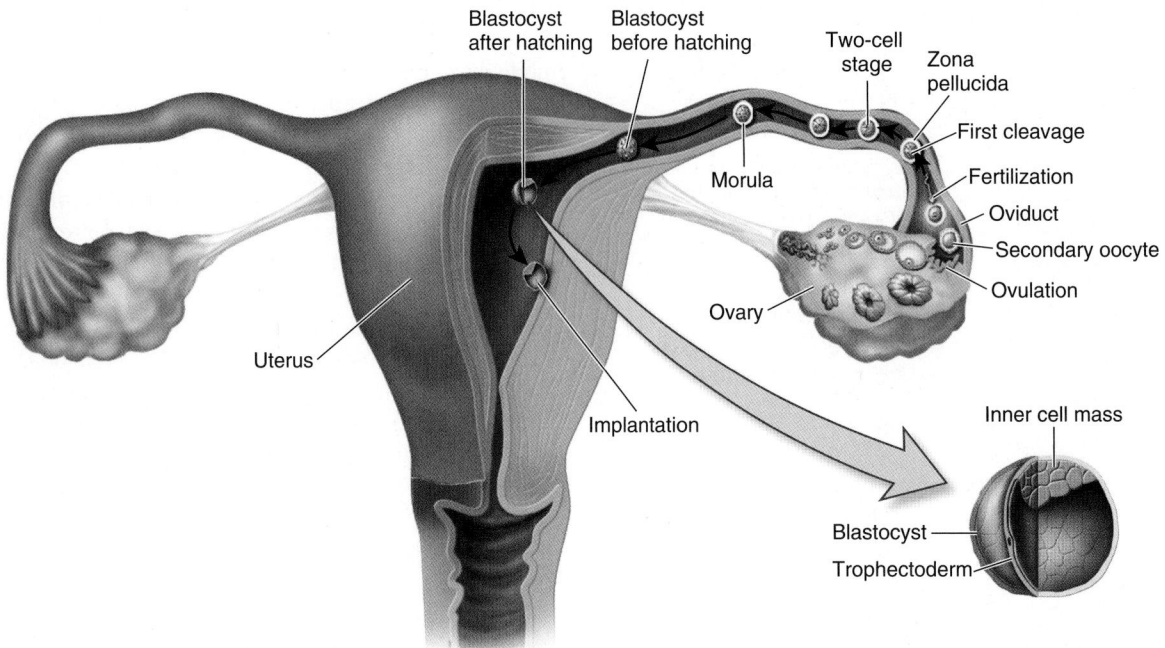

Figure 49.5 **The sites of early embryonic development in mammals.** After an ovulated secondary oocyte is fertilized, initial cleavage and development of the resulting zygote occur in the oviduct of the mother. The blastocyst hatches from the zona pellucida before implanting into the inner lining of the uterus. A blastocyst is composed of an outer epithelial layer called the trophectoderm, which gives rise to extra embryonic tissues, such as the placenta, and an inner cell mass, which develops into the embryo. This inner cell mass is where embryonic stem cells are found.

BioConnections: *Fertilization is internal in mammals. Is this true of all vertebrates? (Hint: Refer back to Figure 48.4.)*

Event 3: Gastrulation Establishes the Three Germ Layers in the Embryo

Following cleavage is **gastrulation**, one of the most dramatic events of embryonic development in animals. During gastrulation, the hollow ball of cells that makes up the blastula is developed into a highly organized structure in which the three germ layers—**ectoderm**, **mesoderm**, and **endoderm**—and the primordial germ cells are established. These distinct germ layers are partially differentiated tissues that are easily recognized by their appearance under a light microscope and ultimately give rise to specialized cells, tissues, and organs.

An embryo that has undergone gastrulation is called a **gastrula**. In the gastrula embryo, the three germ layers become clearly established and occupy discrete regions of the embryo, with an outer ectoderm, a middle mesoderm, and an inner endoderm layer. Each type of germ layer eventually gives rise to different structures, including the notochord, which is a key feature of all chordates described in a later section of this chapter. The organization that emerges during gastrulation is most evident by the clear establishment of the digestive tube and both body axes. Gastrulation is the first time when both the anteroposterior and the dorsoventral body axes are clearly evident in the embryo.

The ultimate fate of the three germ layers has been established by an experimental procedure called **fate mapping** (**Figure 49.6**). In this technique, a single cell or a small population of cells within an embryo is specifically labelled with a harmless dye, and the fate of these labelled cells is followed to a later stage of embryonic development. Use of this technique in a variety of vertebrates has shown that the ectoderm in the gastrula forms the epidermis and nervous system in the later embryo (**Figure 49.7**). The mesoderm gives rise to heart, limbs, muscles, kidneys, blood, and connective tissues. The endoderm becomes the epithelial lining of the gut, liver, pancreas, lungs, and bladder.

Some of our most detailed descriptions of the events in gastrulation come from the study of frog embryos, which are easy to observe under a dissecting microscope because they develop rapidly outside the mother and are relatively large (about 1.5 mm in diameter). The major events in gastrulation are depicted in **Figure 49.8** and described next.

Invagination and Involution: Formation of Germ Layers and Archenteron
Before gastrulation, the blastula is enclosed in a simple, spherical epithelial cell layer. Gastrulation begins when a band of tissue extending perpendicularly to the animal-vegetal axis at the widest part of the embryo invaginates (pinches in), creating a small opening called the **blastopore** (Figure 49.8, step 1). Invagination begins when a few epithelial cells located at the vegetal side of the blastula—called bottle cells—undergo a drastic change in their morphology, causing them to elongate toward their basal end and forcing the cells toward the centre of the embryo.

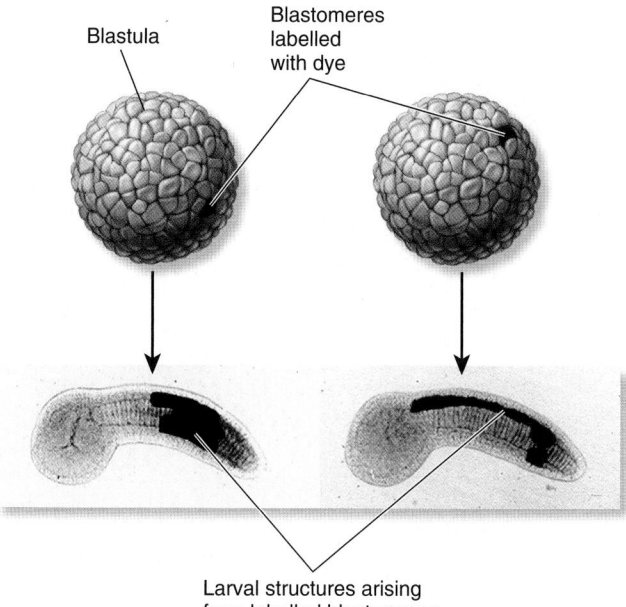

Blastula

Blastomeres labelled with dye

Larval structures arising from labelled blastomeres

Figure 49.6   Fate mapping during embryonic development. Fate mapping of single, labelled embryonic cells (blastomeres) shows that different cells in the embryo (in this case, a urochordate blastula) form different structures in the elongated larva, as shown by the dark regions. In the larva on the right, much of the dorsal nerve cord appears to be labelled.

The initiating site of invagination becomes the dorsal lip of the blastopore. This change in morphology of only a few key cells in the embryo initiates the gastrulation process in amphibians. Once the bottle cells change their shape and push into the interior of the embryo, other cell movements occur, and together these orchestrated movements establish the mesoderm and future digestive tract of the organism.

Just after invagination occurs, cells of the animal pole begin to spread out and are pushed toward the bottle cells at the dorsal lip of the blastopore. When cells from the animal pole reach the bottle cells, they are forced back toward the animal pole along the roof of the blastocoel. This folding back into the interior of the embryo is called *involution* (Figure 49.8, step 2). Both endodermal and mesodermal cells involute from the blastopore toward the opposite end of the embryo. After involution, dorsal mesodermal cells migrate toward the animal pole by crawling along the roof of the blastocoel, with endoderm following closely behind.

In chordates and echinoderms, the opening formed by the blastopore ultimately becomes the anus of the organism. As the opening from the blastopore extends into the embryo, a new cylindrically shaped cavity called the **archenteron** displaces the existing blastocoel (Figure 49.8, steps 2 and 3). The archenteron will become the organism's digestive tract. The blastopore opening remains sealed with a yolk-rich piece of tissue called the yolk plug until later in development.

Mechanisms for Changes in Cell Shape and Position   How do cells change shape and position during the process of embryonic development? For example, bottle cells initiate gastrulation

Ectoderm

Mesoderm

Endoderm

Ectoderm (outer layer)

Cells of epidermis

Neuron of brain

Neuron of peripheral nervous system

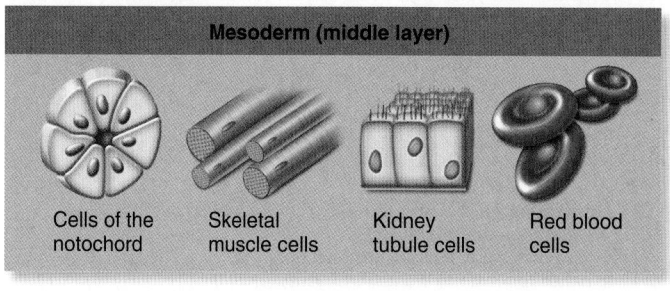

Mesoderm (middle layer)

Cells of the notochord

Skeletal muscle cells

Kidney tubule cells

Red blood cells

Endoderm (inner layer)

Pancreatic acinar cells

Thyroid follicular cells

Lung alveolar cells

Figure 49.7   Examples of cell types derived from ectoderm, mesoderm, and endoderm.

 Principle: *Living organisms grow and develop. The acquisition of specific cell types as shown here is an example of development; growth would entail an increase in the numbers of each of these cell types.*

through a process called **apical constriction** (**Figure 49.9a**). The spreading of ectoderm in the animal hemisphere toward the vegetal hemisphere is mediated by a cellular process called convergent extension. During this process, two rows of cells merge to form a single elongated layer (**Figure 49.9b**). Convergent extension produces movement of sheets of cells.

Formation of the Notochord   A distinguishing anatomical feature that forms at the end of gastrulation in all chordates is the **notochord**—a mesodermal structure that provides rigidity along the anteroposterior axis in the dorsal side of the gastrula (Figure 49.8, step 3). The presence of a notochord defines the phylum Chordates, which also includes the urochordates. Urochordates, such as the tunicates, form a tadpole-like larva but develop into adults that lack vertebrae. The similarities between urochordate and vertebrate

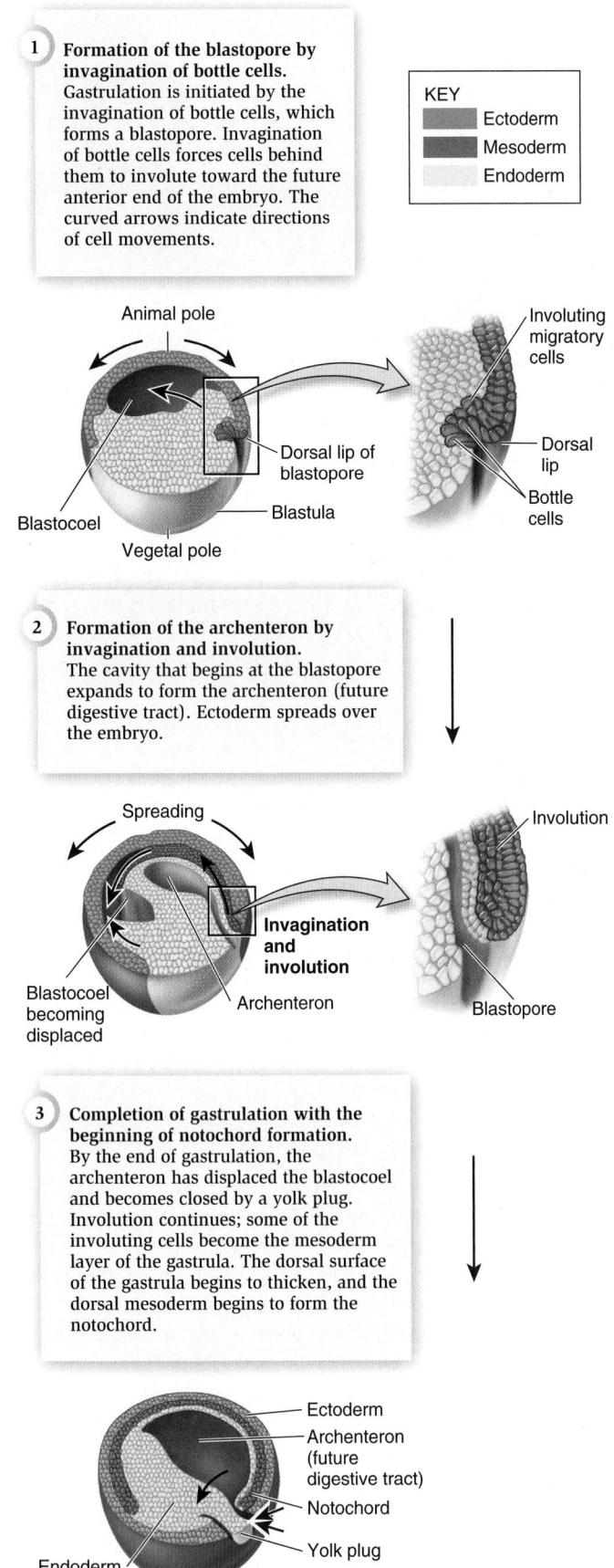

1 Formation of the blastopore by invagination of bottle cells. Gastrulation is initiated by the invagination of bottle cells, which forms a blastopore. Invagination of bottle cells forces cells behind them to involute toward the future anterior end of the embryo. The curved arrows indicate directions of cell movements.

KEY

Ectoderm
Mesoderm
Endoderm

Animal pole

Involuting migratory cells

Dorsal lip of blastopore

Dorsal lip

Bottle cells

Blastocoel

Blastula

Vegetal pole

2 Formation of the archenteron by invagination and involution. The cavity that begins at the blastopore expands to form the archenteron (future digestive tract). Ectoderm spreads over the embryo.

Spreading

Involution

Invagination and involution

Blastocoel becoming displaced

Archenteron

Blastopore

3 Completion of gastrulation with the beginning of notochord formation. By the end of gastrulation, the archenteron has displaced the blastocoel and becomes closed by a yolk plug. Involution continues; some of the involuting cells become the mesoderm layer of the gastrula. The dorsal surface of the gastrula begins to thicken, and the dorsal mesoderm begins to form the notochord.

Ectoderm

Archenteron (future digestive tract)

Notochord

Yolk plug

Endoderm

Figure 49.8 The events of gastrulation in amphibians.

Basal end

Contractile actin network

Apical end

(a) Apical constriction

(b) Convergent extension

Figure 49.9 Two mechanisms that affect cell shape and movement.

larva—including the formation of a notochord—have led many to believe that urochordates may be quite similar to the ancestor species of current-day vertebrates (see Chapter 24).

The notochord produces many signalling proteins that help establish tissue patterns in the embryo. During gastrulation, the notochord elongates through convergent extension, and proteins produced within it along the anteroposterior axis help further pattern the embryo and induce segment-specific expression of the *Hox* genes in subsequent stages of development. As described in Chapters 17 and 38, *Hox* genes are important for establishing structures along the anteroposterior axis. The notochord persists in the trunk and tail of fish and amphibians, but it is somewhat constricted within each vertebra. In birds and mammals, the notochord disappears by the time vertebrae have formed or remnants of it are retained as part of pulplike intervertebral discs.

Although the developmental steps vary among vertebrate species, gastrulation usually begins with invagination initiated by a small number of cells within an external epithelial cell layer that undergoes apical constriction. This leads to a morphologically distinct structure, such as the blastopore, that clearly defines the anteroposterior axis of the animal. The notochord then emerges from this structure. Since many of the genes responsible for specifying gastrulation processes are conserved from fish to humans, it appears that basic genetic mechanisms for gastrulation are evolutionarily conserved in vertebrates.

By the time the notochord has formed, the dorsal ectoderm overlying the notochord begins to thicken, which initiates the next event in development, called neurulation. Before we discuss that event, however, we consider another important event that occurs during gastrulation: the establishment of germ cells.

Primordial Germ Cells During gastrulation, a specialized group of cells called **primordial germ cells** (PGCs) migrates to the future site of gonad development in the embryo. These PGCs are highly specialized cells that often arise independently of the three germ layers in the embryo. This cell lineage has two primary functions: (1) to protect and propagate the genetic content of the species, and (2) to undergo meiosis and differentiate into gametes—sperm or eggs—in the adult organism. PGCs are stem cells that can divide through mitosis to make copies of themselves, and some of the resulting daughter cells differentiate into gametes.

The eggs and resulting embryos of some species contain certain cytoplasmic determinants—called the **germ plasm** (**Figure 49.10a**)—that help define and specify the PGCs in the gastrula stage. In amphibian eggs, for example, the germ plasm occupies a small region of cytoplasm at the vegetal pole and contains a specific subset of maternal mRNAs. These cytoplasmic determinants are inherited by a subpopulation of blastomeres during cleavage. At the beginning of gastrulation, blastomeres that inherit these cytoplasmic determinants differentiate into PGCs and migrate from the posterior end of the late gastrula to a region called the genital ridge near the primordial kidneys. The genital ridge is where primordial gonads and PGCs will form testes or ovaries. In flies, by contrast, PGCs are the first cells to form at the posterior end of the embryo and are called **pole cells** (**Figure 49.10b**).

In mammals, neither pole cells nor germ plasm have been identified. Instead, a few mesoderm-like cells begin to express PGC-specific genes early during gastrulation. These cells migrate along the hindgut during gastrulation and, as in amphibians, intermix with the gonad primordial cells at the genital ridge. Thus, the establishment of PGCs occurs during the earliest phases of animal development and presumably signifies the broad importance of this cell lineage for the propagation of species.

Event 4: Neurulation Involves Formation of the Central Nervous System and Segmentation of the Body

By studying development in several different vertebrate species, researchers are beginning to understand some of the fundamental steps in the formation of the central nervous system (CNS)—the brain and spinal cord—in vertebrates. The multistep embryological process responsible for initiating CNS formation is called **neurulation** (**Figure 49.11**). Neurulation occurs just after gastrulation and involves the formation of the **neural tube** from ectoderm located dorsal to the notochord. All neurons and their supporting cells in the CNS originate from neural precursor cells derived from the neural tube.

In the first step of neurulation shown in Figure 49.11, ectoderm overlaying the notochord thickens by the elongation of cells in the dorsal region to form the neural plate, with adjacent regions that will eventually form a structure called the neural crest (discussed shortly) and the epidermis. The neural plate then elongates by convergent extension, resulting in formation of a single, dorsal elongated epithelial cell layer that is aligned with the anteroposterior axis.

Germ plasm around the vegetal pole of an amphibian embryo

Pole cells at the posterior end of an early fly embryo

 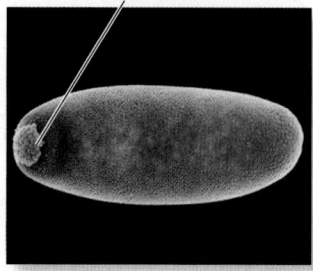

(a) Germ plasm   **(b) Pole cells**

Figure 49.10 Germ plasm and primordial germ cells (PGC) during gastrulation. **(a)** Germ plasm in an amphibian embryo visualized by labelling an mRNA that is specifically expressed in PGCs. **(b)** In fly embryos, the PGCs are called pole cells.

The neural plate forms the neural tube through a series of apical constrictions (Figure 49.11, steps 2 and 3). First, a column of cells along the midline of the neural plate—the medial hinge point—undergoes apical constriction. This initiates the folding phase of neurulation and leads to the formation of the neural groove characteristic of early neurula embryos. Two bilateral columns of cells in the dorsal lateral hinge points then undergo apical constriction after folding, leading to convergence of the two sides of the neural groove and generation of a tubelike structure that is not yet sealed on the dorsal side.

In a fourth step of neurulation, called fusion, the dorsal-most cells on either side of the neural tube are released from adjacent ectoderm and fuse with each other, culminating in the closure of the neural tube (Figure 49.11, step 4). At the same time, ectoderm on either side of the neural tube moves toward the centreline, then up and over the neural tube, where it fuses and forms the dorsal epidermis of the embryo.

Neural Crest Formation Another important cell lineage that arises during neurulation is the **neural crest**, which is unique to vertebrates. It consists of cells that originate from the ectoderm overlaying the dorsal side of the newly formed neural tube and that migrate to other regions of the embryo (Figure 49.11, step 5). Once these cells reach their final destination in the embryo, they differentiate into a variety of cell types different from those that arise from the rest of the ectoderm. All neurons and supporting cells of the peripheral nervous system in vertebrates are derived from neural crest cells. In addition, the neural crest gives rise to melanocytes—specialized cells that provide pigmentation to the skin of vertebrates—and to cells that form facial cartilage and parts of the adrenal glands. The neural crest is so important that some refer to it as the "fourth germ layer" of vertebrates.

Segmentation and the Formation of Somites As embryos develop, distinct tissues acquire recognizable shapes and patterns, and the body often becomes segmented along the anteroposterior axis of the embryo. **Segmentation** allows individual body segments to have more specialized functions. In some species, such as insects, body segments are found in the adult

Future neural crest   Future epidermis

Neural plate

Future neural crest

Notochord

Neural groove

Medial hinge point

Unsealed dorsal surface

Dorsal lateral hinge points

Neural crest
Neural tube

Epidermis

Migrating neural crest cells

1 **Thickening and elongation:**
Ectoderm over the notochord thickens to form the neural plate, which elongates. Adjacent regions will form a neural crest and epidermis.

2 **Folding:**
Cells along the medial hinge point undergo apical constriction, causing the formation of a neural groove.

3 **Convergence:**
Two dorsal lateral hinge points undergo apical constriction to produce a tubelike structure.

4 **Fusion:**
The dorsal-most cells on each side of the neural tube begin to fuse. Epidermis also fuses dorsal to the neural tube.

5 Neural crest cells migrate away as fusion is completed.

Figure 49.11   Neurulation and the beginning of neural crest formation in vertebrates.   The four steps of neurulation are thickening and elongation; folding, which creates the neural groove; convergence, in which the neural tube begins to take shape; and fusion, in which the neural tube is completed. In the fifth step, the neural crest cells migrate away from the neural tube to form several other structures including the neural crest.

animal. In vertebrates, the segmentation process helps define repeated structures, such as vertebrae and ribs, which form later during development. Segmentation of the body plan along the anteroposterior axis becomes apparent during neurulation.

During neurulation, the mesoderm becomes segmented from the anterior end first, giving rise to blocklike structures of mesoderm called **somites** (**Figure 49.12**). The segmentation of somitic mesoderm continues toward the posterior end of the animal and into the tail, as can be seen in **Figure 49.12b**. The number of somite pairs that forms in a given species is relatively constant, but the number can vary considerably among species (50 in chicks, 65 in mice, 500 in some snakes, and 32 to 34 in humans). Because the rate of embryonic development within a given species often varies with temperature and other environmental factors, stages of embryo development are often standardized according to the number of somites that have formed.

Somites arise from a group of loosely packed mesodermal cell aggregates that condense into epithelial somites, which consist of a hollow ball or vesicle enclosed by an epithelial layer. The scanning electron micrograph in **Figure 49.12a** shows a dorsal view of a chick embryo undergoing somite formation. These epithelial somites are located toward the anterior end,

and unsegmented mesoderm can be seen extending toward the posterior end. The epithelial somites are transient structures, and the cells within them soon undergo transformation into two morphologically distinct structures that eventually form the ribs and skeletal muscle and the vertebrae, respectively.

Event 5: Organs Are Formed During Organogenesis

As described in Chapter 38, organs are specialized structures that consist of arrangements of two or more tissue types. Most organs, such as the kidney, contain all four tissue types: nervous, muscle, epithelial, and connective tissue (see Chapter 38). The developmental event during which cells and tissues form organs is called **organogenesis**. Each germ layer gives rise to different organs (Figure 49.7). Many organs begin to form during or just after neurulation.

However, these organs become functional at different times during development. For example, the lungs of mammals do not acquire the ability to function until shortly before birth. By contrast, the heart is the first functional organ to form in the vertebrate embryo. It begins to beat and pump blood before all the embryo's somites have formed (by 2.5 days after fertilization in chicks, 9 days in mice, and about 22 days in humans).

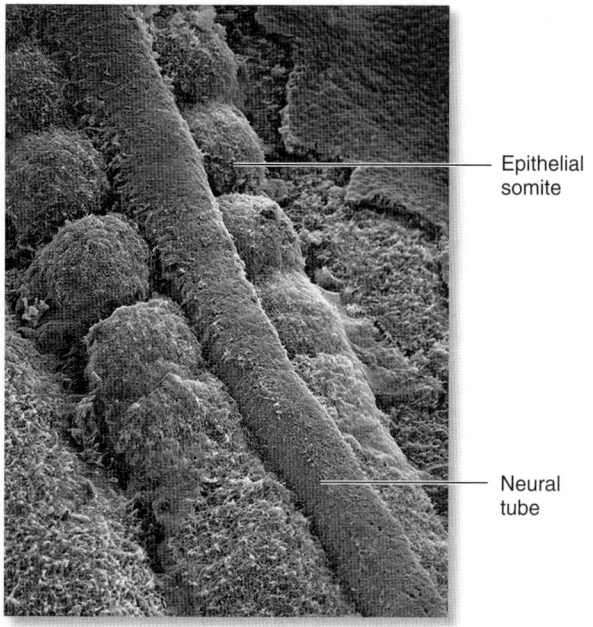

(a) **Segmentation of mesoderm starts at anterior end first**

(b) **Segmentation continues toward the posterior end**

Figure 49.12 Segmentation of mesoderm during neurulation.   (a) This scanning electron micrograph shows early events in the segmentation process: the formation of epithelial somites at the anterior end of a chick embryo. (b) Light microscope image of a chick embryo, showing body segments along the anteroposerior axis.

As we saw in Chapter 38, the development of different organs in animals is controlled by genes in the embryo, notably the *Hox* genes, which are important for establishing structures along the anteroposterior axis. Many of the genes controlling the processes of gastrulation, neurulation, and organogenesis encode secreted proteins or growth factors that induce cells in their local vicinity to differentiate along a specific developmental pathway. Next, we will see how such growth factors can be studied in the context of embryonic development.

49.2 CONTROL OF CELL DIFFERENTIATION AND MORPHOGENESIS DURING ANIMAL DEVELOPMENT

Learning Outcomes:

1. Distinguish between autonomous and conditional specification.
2. Explain how the direct contact between the plasma membranes of neighbouring cells affects embryonic development.
3. Describe how organizers can influence cells to differentiate.

Thus far, we have examined the five events of embryonic development. In this section, we will turn our attention to certain molecular mechanisms that are crucial for cell differentiation and morphogenesis.

Cytosolic Factors and Extracellular Signals Drive Cell Differentiation During Embryonic Development

The process of embryonic development requires that cells move to specific sites and acquire distinct functional properties (i.e., differentiate). After the unicellular fertilized egg (zygote) divides into two cells, those cells then divide into four, then into eight, and soon the rates of cell divisions become asynchronous and more uniquely specified. The fate of each cell within this ever-growing collection of cells is determined through the cell's response to two primary mechanisms of cell differentiation. The first mechanism is the differential acquisition of various cytoplasmic factors during cell division, a process known as autonomous specification (**Figure 49.13a**). The second is the acquisition of properties through a variety of cell-to-cell signalling mechanisms, a process called conditional specification (**Figure 49.13b**). These two mechanisms provide embryonic cells with a continuously changing internal and external environment, in which cells ultimately fulfill their unique functional and spatial fates. This differentiation process involves alterations of gene expression such that specific cells may express a unique set of genes required for a particular function.

Throughout development, autonomous and conditional specification work together such that distinct cells differentiate into each of the numerous diverse cell types with unique functions in the developing organism. Such differentiation involves changes in both gene expression and subcellular organization. Identifying the precise conditional and autonomous signals that specify each cell lineage in the embryo is one of the biggest challenges facing developmental biologists.

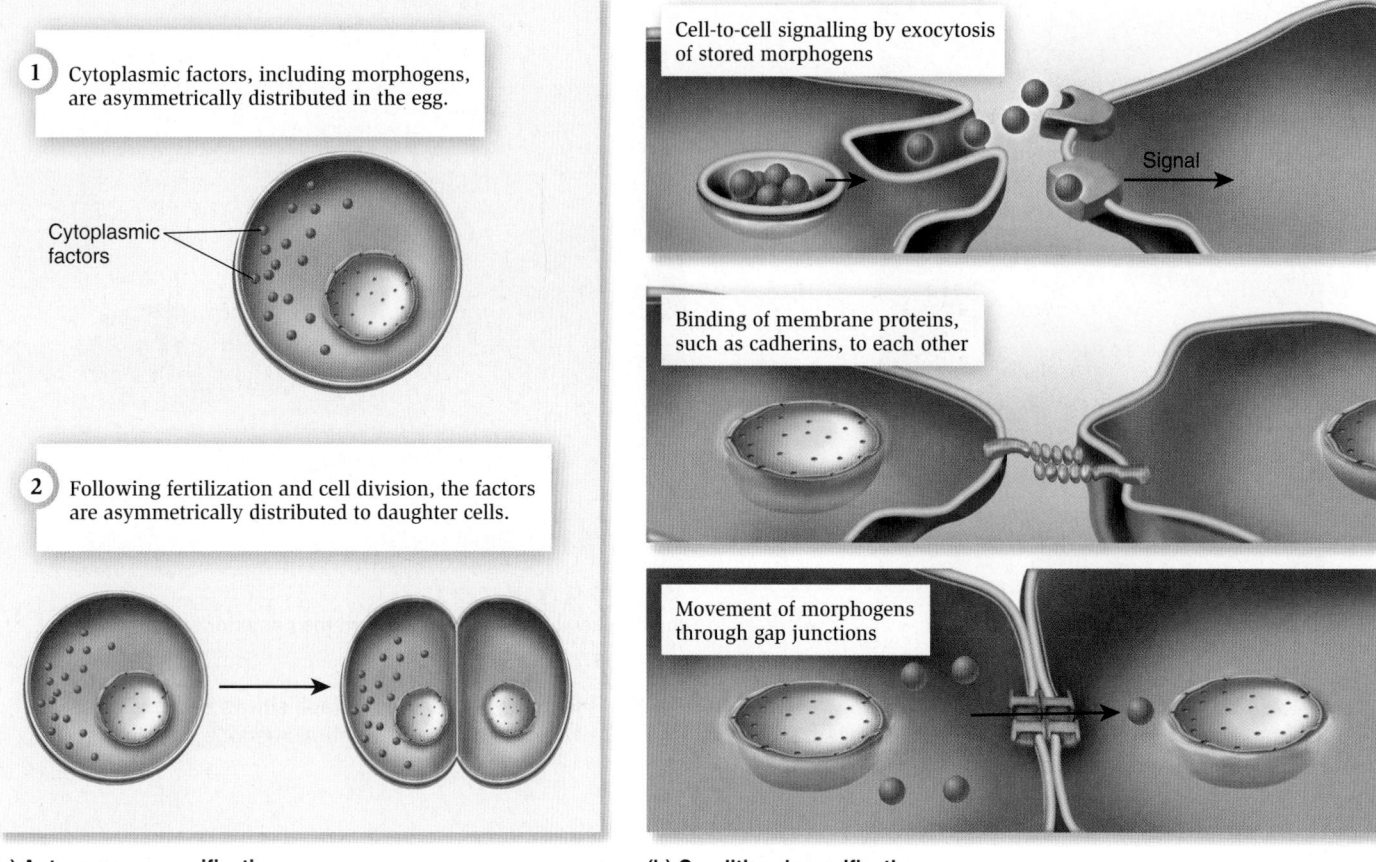

(a) **Autonomous specification**

(b) **Conditional specification**

Figure 49.13 **Mechanisms that convey positional information during embryonic development.** **(a)** In autonomous specification, cell fate is determined through the unequal segregation of subcellular components during mitosis. **(b)** In conditional specification, cells respond to one of at least three types of chemical signals generated by neighbouring embryonic cells.

Concentration Gradients of Morphogens Control Cell Differentiation in Vertebrate Embryos

The substances that elicit different cellular responses at distinct concentrations in an embryo are proteins called **morphogens**. For the biochemical identification of morphogens, researchers have often focused on amphibians. Three features of amphibians make them ideal for analyzing embryonic development by using nongenetic mechanisms. First, fertilization and embryonic development occur outside the mother, making it easy to observe and manipulate embryos as they develop. Second, eggs are abundant—adult females carry thousands of eggs and can be induced to lay them by injecting a specific hormone—and are easily fertilized, usually by simply placing a male in an aquarium with an ovulating female. Third, amphibian embryos develop rapidly. In frogs, for example, development from fertilized egg to tadpole formation—including cleavage, gastrulation, neurulation, and complete organogenesis—takes only about 35 hours. Several types of experiments performed with amphibian embryos demonstrate how conditional specification directs cell differentiation in vertebrate embryos.

Conditional specification often involves the synthesis by a cell or group of cells of a signalling protein, a morphogen, that induces a response in another group of cells in the embryo. The idea of cellular induction during embryonic development arose from experiments in which cells isolated from one part of an embryo were analyzed in the presence or absence of cells isolated from a different region of the embryo.

An example of cellular induction was observed in experiments performed by Dutch developmental biologist Pieter Nieuwkoop during the 1950s. Nieuwkoop isolated cells from either the animal pole or the vegetal pole of late blastula (cleavage-stage) amphibian embryos. When cells from the animal pole, called an animal cap, were cultured in an appropriate growth medium, they formed undifferentiated spherical structures composed primarily of ectodermal cells. When cells isolated from the vegetal pole were cultured, undifferentiated clumps of endodermal cells resulted. However, when animal and vegetal cells were cultured together, Nieuwkoop observed the formation of mesodermal derivatives from the animal pole cells. This suggested that factors released by vegetal pole cells could induce differentiation of animal pole cells. This type of experiment, called an **animal cap assay**, has been used extensively to identify proteins secreted by embryonic cells that induce cells in the animal pole to differentiate into mesoderm. Nieuwkoop went on to show that

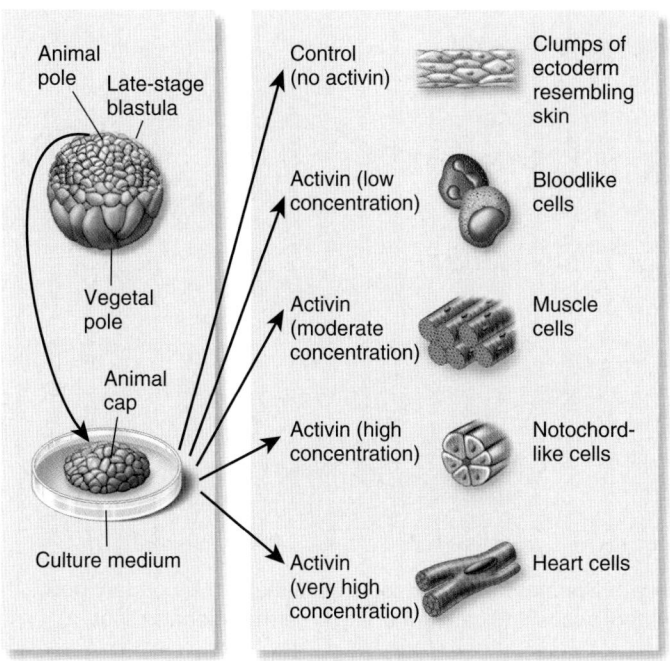

Figure 49.14 **Figure 49.14** Use of an animal cap assay to demonstrate morphogen activity in conditional specification. Activin, a member of the TGFβ protein family, functions as a morphogen in an animal cap assay by inducing different types of mesoderm at different concentrations. In the absence of activin, no mesodermal derivatives form and the animal caps form cells resembling skin cells. Low concentrations of activin induce mesodermal derivatives resembling blood cells, whereas moderate concentrations induce muscle cells, and higher concentrations induce such as mesodermal derivatives notochord and heart cells.

Concept check: *How might it be possible for a single molecule to exert different effects on cells at different concentrations?*

in culture to form clumps of ectodermal tissue that resemble skin cells. However, when purified TGFβs are added to these cells, they differentiate into mesoderm. TGFβ proteins bind to a specific receptor molecule expressed on the surface of animal cap cells, inducing them to differentiate into mesoderm.

A key question was whether different TGFβ proteins specify different types of mesoderm or whether a single protein at different concentrations induced all types of mesoderm. The morphogenic activity of one TGFβ protein—activin—in an animal cap assay is shown in **Figure 49.14**. At low concentrations, activin induces mesoderm consisting of bloodlike cells. However, at incrementally higher concentrations, muscle cells, mesoderm resembling the notochord, and fully differentiated heart cells are induced. These results show that certain TGFβ proteins exert different effects depending on their concentrations.

different vegetal cells isolated from various positions along the dorsoventral axis induced specific types of mesoderm.

One family of proteins—named transforming growth factor betas (TGFβs)—soon emerged as important factors involved in the induction of mesoderm. By purifying these proteins and then adding them to a culture medium containing animal caps, researchers demonstrated that TGFβ proteins have mesoderm-inducing activity. In the absence of TGFβs, animal caps grow

GENOMES AND PROTEOMES

Groups of Embryonic Cells Can Produce Specific Body Structures Even When Transplanted into Different Animals

One of the more interesting ideas to emerge from the study of developmental biology is the concept of the **morphogenetic field**, a group of embryonic cells that ultimately produce a specific body structure. Long before genes and their encoded proteins were identified, embryologists working with amphibians discovered that particular groups of embryonic cells have a striking characteristic: they form complete body structures when transplanted to another site in the embryo. This is true for cells that form the eyes, limbs, and heart in vertebrates, and the eyes, antennae, legs, and wings in insects. In insects, these morphogenetic fields are called imaginal discs.

One of the first morphogenetic fields discovered in vertebrates was the limb field. Between 1910 and 1930, two important observations were made concerning the limb field. First, removing this group of cells from either side of an early developing embryo led to an embryo that lacked a limb at the corresponding position. Second, transplanting a limb field to a

new location within prelimb embryos led to the development of an additional limb at the new location. Fate-mapping studies showed that certain cells within the field give rise to specific regions of the limb. These types of experiments revealed that cells within morphogenetic fields are uniquely specified to become particular embryonic structures before any physical evidence for the structure itself can be observed in the embryo.

It is thought that morphogenetic fields in amphibians are particularly sensitive to environmental pollutants. Over the past decade, a growing number of amphibians with limb deformities have been observed in Quebec and across Canada, leading many scientists to consider these species to be reliable bioindicators of environmental pollution.

In the 1920s German zoologists Hans Spemann and Hilde Mangold discovered in an early gastrula an extremely important morphogenetic field with amazing properties. This morphogenetic field is now known as **Spemann's organizer**. Their experiments involved dissecting a small piece of tissue from the dorsal lip of the blastopore in an early gastrula of a newt and transplanting it to the opposite side of another gastrula (**Figure 49.15**). The result was the formation of a second notochord and neural tube

1 Transplantation

Pigmented gastrula of donor embryo (*Triton taeniatus*)

Dorsal lip of blastopore

Nonpigmented gastrula of host embryo (*Triton cristatus*)

2 Completion of embryonic development

Primary structures (nonpigmented cells)
- Neural tube
- Notochord

Secondary structures (mostly nonpigmented cells)
- Notochord
- Neural tube

Primary embryo

Secondary (induced) nonpigmented embryo

Figure 49.15   Experiment on newt embryos that led to the discovery of Spemann's organizer.   Note that the secondary body axis formed by the transplanted organizer is composed of host (nonpigmented) tissue, indicating that the organizer (donor) tissue induced the host tissue to differentiate.

during gastrulation and neurulation in the host embryo, and ultimately the formation of an entirely new body axis—the resulting embryo developed two bodies.

Though technically difficult because the gastrulas were only about 2 mm wide, these experiments yielded clear results because the researchers used two very closely related species of newts. *Triton taeniatus*, which is pigmented, served as the tissue donor, and *Triton cristatus*, which is nonpigmented, served as the host embryo. By transplanting pigmented tissue from the donor embryo into a nonpigmented host embryo, Spemann and Mangold were able to visually track the origin of the newly developed tissue. The results showed that the secondary notochord and neural tube were composed in large part of host (nonpigmented) cells, with some pigmented cells remaining from the transplanted tissue. This indicated that the transplanted tissue—which they named the *organizer*—had induced cells in the host to differentiate into neural tissue on the transplanted side of the embryo. More recent work has shown that the organizer secretes morphogens—unknown at the time of Spemann's experiments—responsible for inducing the formation of a new embryonic axis. In 1935 Spemann was acknowledged for his important discovery of cellular induction by being awarded the Nobel Prize in Physiology or Medicine, the first to be awarded for studies in developmental biology.

In the past two decades, scientists have identified several genes expressed specifically in Spemann's organizer. Strikingly, many of these genes, which were first discovered in amphibians, are evolutionarily conserved in all vertebrates. These organizer-specific genes are expressed in very small regions of early gastrula embryos, allowing researchers to identify the equivalent of Spemann's organizer in these other species. The names given the organizer in different species vary. In chicks, it is called Hensen's node, whereas in mice it is simply referred to as the node.

With advances in molecular genetics during the 1960s and 1970s, molecular biologists began to re-examine the work of Hans Spemann and his contemporaries. A major quest of this new generation of molecular biologists was to identify the specific genes transcribed within Spemann's organizer that give this morphogenetic field the ability to form an entirely new body structure. Identifying the genes expressed exclusively in Spemann's organizer, it was thought, would give key insights into the genetic control systems that govern embryonic patterning during gastrulation in vertebrates. However, identifying unknown genes and their protein products was a daunting challenge. In 1992 the first secreted morphogen expressed specifically in the organizer was isolated, as we see next.

FEATURE INVESTIGATION

Richard Harland and Coworkers Identified Genes Expressed Specifically in the Organizer

Richard Harland and his colleagues hypothesized in the early 1990s that morphogens expressed in the organizer should promote the formation of dorsal structures, such as those found

in the head. To search for genes that promote the formation of dorsal structures and are expressed in the organizer during gastrulation, Harland's group took advantage of the fact that unfertilized *Xenopus* (frog) eggs exposed to UV light at their vegetal pole fail to form tadpoles. However, embryos derived from UV-treated eggs do form primitive mesoderm but only ventral mesoderm forms. Dorsal mesoderm, which normally gives rise to the notochord and somites, does not form in UV-treated eggs, and the resulting "ventralized" embryos soon die. The embryos appear to be lacking one or more morphogens needed for proper dorsal development.

To identify genes in the organizer that encode morphogens that promote the formation of structures such as the notochord, Harland and colleagues used a strategy called expression cloning, as shown in **Figure 49.16**. First, after dissecting a frog embryo, they isolated and purified mRNA from dorsal-lip tissue containing the organizer. They next constructed a cDNA library (see Chapter 18) from the purified mRNA. This resulted in approximately 15,000 different cDNAs, each of which corresponded to a single gene. Their next task was to transcribe each of these cDNAs back into mRNA *in vitro*. In a third step, the researchers injected these different mRNAs into thousands of unfertilized UV-treated eggs, which they then fertilized. Each egg was injected with a single type of mRNA. Their idea was that any mRNA that produced a protein with dorsal

mesoderm-promoting activity might "rescue" the embryos and result in free-swimming tadpoles.

By using this procedure, the researchers identified one mRNA whose protein product rescued the embryo. They then injected increasing amounts of this mRNA into UV-treated eggs, fertilized the eggs, and then examined the morphology of the resultant tadpoles. They discovered that the protein product from this mRNA acted as a morphogen because it induced different embryonic structures at different concentrations. At low concentrations, it partially rescued the embryos. At moderate concentrations, it resulted in the formation of normal embryos. However, at very high concentrations, the embryos developed too much dorsal mesoderm and not enough ventral mesoderm. These abnormal embryos developed large heads and extremely small trunks. Further studies identified the gene (which they called *noggin*) that coded for this mRNA, and verified that it was transcribed in Spemann's organizer.

Later work revealed that noggin protein promotes dorsal development by inhibiting ventral development. Noggin protein

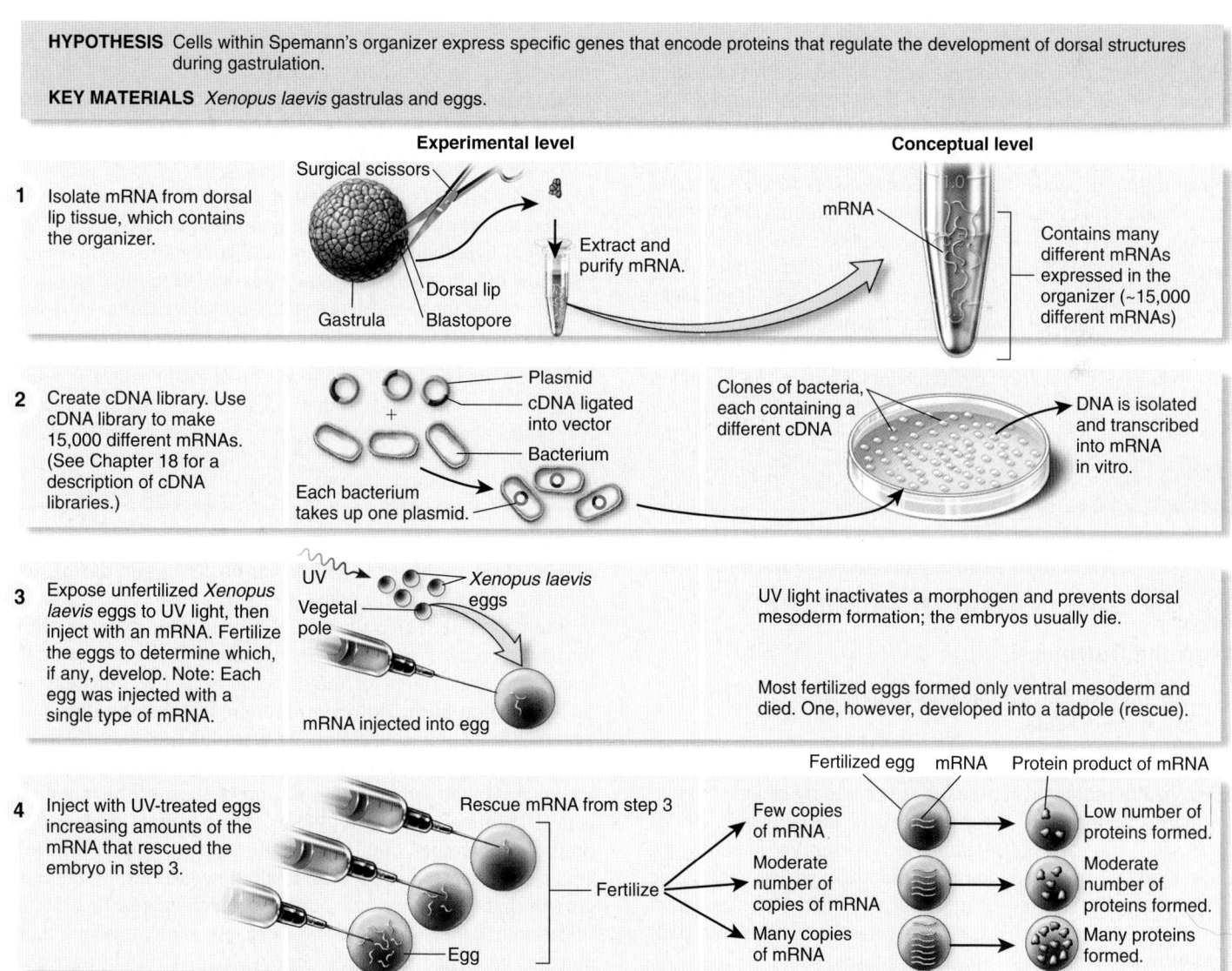

HYPOTHESIS Cells within Spemann's organizer express specific genes that encode proteins that regulate the development of dorsal structures during gastrulation.

KEY MATERIALS *Xenopus laevis* gastrulas and eggs.

Experimental level   **Conceptual level**

1 Isolate mRNA from dorsal lip tissue, which contains the organizer.

Surgical scissors

Dorsal lip

Gastrula   Blastopore

Extract and purify mRNA.

mRNA

Contains many different mRNAs expressed in the organizer (~15,000 different mRNAs)

2 Create cDNA library. Use cDNA library to make 15,000 different mRNAs. (See Chapter 18 for a description of cDNA libraries.)

Plasmid

cDNA ligated into vector

Bacterium

Each bacterium takes up one plasmid.

Clones of bacteria, each containing a different cDNA

DNA is isolated and transcribed into mRNA in vitro.

3 Expose unfertilized *Xenopus laevis* eggs to UV light, then inject with an mRNA. Fertilize the eggs to determine which, if any, develop. Note: Each egg was injected with a single type of mRNA.

UV

Vegetal pole

Xenopus laevis eggs

mRNA injected into egg

UV light inactivates a morphogen and prevents dorsal mesoderm formation; the embryos usually die.

Most fertilized eggs formed only ventral mesoderm and died. One, however, developed into a tadpole (rescue).

4 Inject with UV-treated eggs increasing amounts of the mRNA that rescued the embryo in step 3.

Rescue mRNA from step 3

Egg

Fertilize

Fertilized egg   mRNA   Protein product of mRNA

Few copies of mRNA

Moderate number of copies of mRNA

Many copies of mRNA

Low number of proteins formed.

Moderate number of proteins formed.

Many proteins formed.

Figure 49.16   Harland and colleagues discovered the morphogen noggin using expression cloning.

Figure 49.16 *(Continued)*

5   THE DATA

Embryo from UV-treated egg | Partial rescue | Normal tadpole | Abnormal tadpoles with excess dorsal and anterior development

Increasing amounts of dorsal mesoderm-promoting mRNA and its protein product

6   CONCLUSION Cells in Spemann's organizer secrete a morphogen—termed noggin—that directs normal dorsal development in *Xenopus laevis* embryos.

7   SOURCE Smith, W.C., and Harland, R.M. 1992. Expression cloning of noggin, a new dorsalizing factor localized to the Spemann organizer in *Xenopus* embryos. *Cell* 70:829–840.

inhibits at least two other morphogens that are known to induce ventral but not dorsal mesoderm. These studies showed that antagonistically acting proteins expressed and secreted from certain cells in the organizer can specify precise structures in a concentration-dependent fashion. Further work in mice revealed that *noggin* is expressed in the node of mammals. Moreover, specific deletion of the *noggin* gene in mice leads to defects in dorsal structures. This indicates that *noggin* plays a fundamental role during gastrulation in mammals as well as amphibians.

The discovery of *noggin* and its mechanism of action revealed that the normal development of embryos requires a balance between stimulatory and inhibitory factors. The inhibition of developmental processes—such as the suppression of ventral mesoderm by *noggin*—appears to be a normal part of the mechanism by which development of an organism occurs. This

important control mechanism has since been observed in other developmental pathways, one example of which is described next.

Experimental Questions

1. Why were scientists interested in identifying genes expressed exclusively in Spemann's organizer?
2. What hypothesis did Harland and colleagues test?
3. How did the scientists identify possible genes that are important for the development of dorsal structures, and how did they test the gene products to determine their activity?

Given the complexity and precision of the five developmental events we have described in this chapter, it may not be surprising that on occasion these processes fail to work properly. When this happens in humans, its impact can be devastating, as we see next.

49.3 | HUMAN HEALTH CONNECTION

Learning Outcomes:

1. Describe the cause of the human birth defect called spina bifida.

Many health problems in humans are caused by genetic or environmental factors that disrupt embryonic development. As we have seen, the early development of an embryo is among the most complex processes found in nature. Because embryonic development is affected by genetic as well as environmental factors, a number of diseases and disorders in humans stem from problems that arise during this process.

An example of a condition involving defective embryonic development is spina bifida, caused by the failure of the neural

tube to close at either the anterior or posterior end during neurulation. Signs and symptoms of spina bifida vary depending on the degree to which the neural tube fails to close. In minor forms there may be gaps in a few vertebrae at the bottom of the back, and impairment of motor or sensory function may not be apparent at birth. However, neurological deterioration often becomes evident during childhood or adulthood. Surgical procedures soon after birth can improve the long-term quality of life for patients with spina bifida, but prevention of this condition is much more effective. Up to 75% of spina bifida cases may be prevented if women in the first trimester of pregnancy take folic acid supplements, a common B vitamin needed during the rapid growth that occurs during embryonic development. In 1998 fortification of cereals with folic acid became mandatory in Canada and the incidence of babies born with spina bifida decreased from 1.58 per 1,000 births before fortification to 0.86 per 1,000 births after fortification.

Whereas spina bifida appears to be caused by deficient folic acid levels during neurulation, other embryonic defects are caused by foreign chemicals introduced during pregnancy. One of the more tragic examples involved a drug called thalidomide, which originally was developed in Europe during the late 1950s and early 1960s as an anticonvulsive drug for epilepsy and was later prescribed as an antihistamine for allergies. Although further testing revealed no beneficial effects on these conditions, it was noted that thalidomide seemed to qualm nausea and help people sleep. In 1961 thalidomide was the most widely used sleeping medication in Europe, where it was also prescribed to combat morning sickness (nausea) in pregnant women.

Soon afterward, however, physicians in Europe and Australia noticed that babies born to mothers who had taken thalidomide sometimes had malformed limbs, with hands and feet often emanating directly from the body. It became clear that cells within the limb fields in human embryos are selectively and adversely affected by this toxic compound. Ultimately, thousands of babies worldwide were deformed because of thalidomide. The drug was quickly eliminated from pharmaceutical markets, and only a few hundred thalidomide babies were born in Canada. Such tragedies underscore the importance of continued research into the mechanisms that regulate embryonic development in mammals.

Summary of Key Concepts

- The process by which a fertilized egg is transformed into an organism with distinct physiological systems and body parts is called embryonic development.

- The process by which different cells within a developing organism acquire specialized forms and functions, due to the expression of cell-specific genes, is called cellular differentiation.

49.1 Events of Embryonic Development

- Development in many animals, including vertebrates, involves five general events: fertilization, cleavage, gastrulation, neurulation, and organogenesis. (Figure 49.1)

- Major events in fertilization include the acrosomal reaction and the cortical reaction. During the acrosomal reaction, the binding of a sperm with the egg membrane triggers a series of events producing the fast block to polyspermy, which prevents other sperm from binding to the egg. During the cortical reaction, events involving IP$_3$ and calcium produce additional barriers to more sperm, a process called the slow block to polyspermy. (Figure 49.2)

- During cleavage, which involves cell divisions without cell growth, the daughter cells are called blastomeres. When the embryo forms an outer epithelial layer and an inner cavity, it is called a blastula. The mammalian counterpart of a blastula is called a blastocyst.

- Cleavage-stage embryos in triploblast organisms have an animal pole and a vegetal pole. The poles determine in part the future anteroposterior and dorsoventral axes of the embryo. (Figure 49.3)

- Incomplete or meroblastic cleavage occurs in birds, some fish, and some other vertebrates whose eggs contain large amounts of yolk. Complete or holoblastic cleavage occurs in amphibians and mammals, whose eggs have smaller amounts of yolk; the cleavage-stage embryo in mammals is called a morula. In mammals, cleavage occurs in the oviduct. (Figures 49.4, 49.5)

- In fate mapping, a small population of embryonic cells is specifically labelled with a harmless dye, and the fate of these labelled cells is followed to a later event of embryonic development. (Figure 49.6)

- During gastrulation, the hollow ball of cells that makes up the blastula is converted into a highly organized structure in which the three germ layers—endoderm, mesoderm, and ectoderm—and the primordial germ cells are established. Each germ layer gives rise to specific structures. An embryo that has undergone gastrulation is called a gastrula. (Figure 49.7)

- Gastrulation begins when a band of tissue invaginates (pinches in), creating a small opening called the blastopore. During gastrulation, the embryo forms a cavity called the archenteron, which will become the organism's digestive tract. (Figure 49.8)

- During gastrulation, two cellular processes are crucial to development: apical constriction, in which a reduction in the diameter of the actin rings connected to the adherens junctions causes the cells to elongate toward their basal end, and convergent extension, in which two rows of cells merge to form a single elongated layer. (Figure 49.9)

- A distinguishing anatomical feature that forms at the end of gastrulation in all chordates is the notochord, which produces many signalling proteins that help establish tissue patterns in the embryo.

- During gastrulation, primordial germ cells (PGCs) become established. Amphibian eggs contain certain cytoplasmic determinants, called the germ plasm, that help define and specify the PGCs in the gastrula stage. In flies, PGCs are the first cells to form at the posterior end of the embryo and are called pole cells. (Figure 49.10)

- Neurulation is the multistep embryological process responsible for initiating CNS formation. Neurulation occurs just after gastrulation and involves the formation of the neural tube from ectoderm located dorsal to the notochord. (Figure 49.11)

- Another important cell lineage that arises during neurulation is the neural crest, which gives rise to all neurons and supporting cells of the peripheral nervous system in vertebrates.

- During neurulation, the mesoderm becomes segmented from the anterior end first, giving rise to blocklike structures of mesoderm called somites. (Figure 49.12)

- The developmental event during which cells and tissues form organs is called organogenesis.

49.2 Control of Cell Differentiation and Morphogenesis During Animal Development

- The process of cell differentiation during embryonic development is driven by two mechanisms: autonomous specification, which involves cytosolic factors, and conditional specification, which involves cell-to-cell signals. (Figure 49.13)

- The substances that elicit different cellular responses at distinct concentrations in an embryo are proteins called morphogens.

- A type of experiment called an animal cap assay has been used extensively to identify factors (proteins) secreted by embryonic cells that induce cells in the animal pole to differentiate into mesoderm. (Figure 49.14)

- A group of embryonic cells called a morphogenetic field controls the formation of certain body structures.

- An extremely important morphogenetic field in the early gastrula is known as Spemann's organizer. The organizer secretes morphogens responsible for inducing the formation of a new embryonic axis. (Figure 49.15)

- Richard Harland his and co-workers discovered the *noggin* gene in frog embryos and demonstrated that it acted to promote dorsal development by inhibiting ventral development. (Figure 49.16)

49.3 Human Health Connection

- An important example of a condition involving defective embryonic development is spina bifida, caused by the failure of the neural tube to close completely during neurulation.

- Thalidomide is toxic to cells within the limb fields in human embryos; some babies born to mothers who had taken thalidomide to treat the symptoms of morning sickness had malformed limbs.

Test to Assess Your Learning

1. The acrosomal and cortical reactions occur during which stage of development?
   a. fertilization
   b. cleavage
   c. gastrulation
   d. neurulation
   e. organogenesis

2. Cadherins are
   a. adhesion protein molecules that attach cells to extracellular material.
   b. genes necessary for proper germ layer formation.
   c. adhesion protein molecules that allow cells of a given germ layer to adhere to each other.
   d. diploblastic germ layers.
   e. proteins that provide structural support to the cytoplasm of cells.

3. Cell differentiation that results from cell-to-cell signalling is
   a. autonomous specification.
   b. conditional specification.
   c. communicative specification.
   d. gastrulation.
   e. embryogenesis.

4. The three germ layers of triploblasts are established during
   a. fertilization.
   b. cleavage.
   c. blastula formation.
   d. gastrulation.
   e. neurulation.

5. The limbs of vertebrates are formed from
   a. the endoderm.
   b. the mesoderm.
   c. the ectoderm.
   d. all of the above.
   e. both (b) and (c).

6. In vertebrates, the digestive tract forms from
   a. the blastopore.
   b. the dorsal lip.
   c. the archenteron.
   d. the mesoderm.
   e. both (a) and (d).

7. The cells that give rise to gametes
   a. are derived from the mesoderm.
   b. often arise independently from the three germ layers.
   c. originate directly from the tissue that will develop into the gonads.
   d. are some of the last cells of the embryo to differentiate.
   e. are formed the same way in all vertebrates.

8. Cells of the neural crest
   a. form the central nervous system.
   b. originate from the ectoderm.
   c. migrate to different areas of the body and differentiate into a variety of cells, including neurons of the peripheral nervous system.
   d. all of the above.
   e. (b) and (c) only.

9. The first functional organ to form in an embryo is
   a. the lungs.
   b. the brain.
   c. the heart.
   d. the kidneys.
   e. the liver.

10. Morphogens
    a. are proteins that stimulate responses in the cells of an embryo.
    b. are important signalling proteins in the process of embryonic development.
    c. can elicit different cell responses at different concentrations.
    d. all of the above.
    e. (a) and (c) only.

Articulate to Assess Your Learning

1. What are the differences between autonomous and conditional specification?

2. During organogenesis in vertebrates, some organs develop and become functional sooner than others. Why is it important, for example, that the heart of a terrestrial vertebrate develop sooner than its lungs?

Collaborate to Assess and Extend Your Learning

1. Discuss the major events of gastrulation in terms of the movement of cells that will be involved in neurulation.

2. What are the three primary germ layers? Give two examples of tissues, organs, or organ systems that are derived from each germ layer in humans.

3. A principle of biology is that living organisms grow and develop. Distinguish between embryonic development, differentiation, and growth.

Visit McGraw-Hill Ryerson Connect™ for additional study resources.

Immune Systems

Chapter Outline

In an immune system response, a macrophage engulfs numerous bacteria (false-colour SEM).

All animals must defend themselves against environmental factors that threaten their survival, including predation, intraspecific conflict, accidents, and hazardous substances. In addition, animals must contend with various threats within their internal environment, including the invasion of potentially harmful microorganisms, such as bacteria; the presence of foreign molecules, such as the products of microorganisms; and the presence of abnormal cells, such as cancer cells. The ability of an animal to ward off these internal threats—an animal's **immunity**, or immune defences—is the subject of this chapter. The cells and organs within an animal's body that contribute to immune defences collectively constitute an animal's **immune system**.

The study of immunity is called immunology. Immunologists examine the processes by which the immune system protects an animal from foreign matter, whether living or nonliving. In these processes, the body's immune defences recognize the body's own molecules as "self" and attack anything it recognizes as foreign, or "nonself."

Immune defences are often divided into two types. In **innate (nonspecific) immunity**, the body's defences are present at birth and act against foreign materials in much the same way regardless of the specific identity of the invading material. Innate immunity includes the body's external barriers (skin and mucous membranes) and a set of cellular and chemical defences that oppose substances that breach those barriers. All animals have innate immune defences. In contrast, **acquired (specific) immunity** develops only after the body is exposed to foreign substances. The specificity of this type of immunity results from the ability of certain cells of the immune system to recognize a foreign substance and initiate a response that targets that substance specifically. Such immune defences have been identified in all vertebrates except for jawless fish, but they have not been unequivocally identified in invertebrates.

We begin the chapter with a brief overview of the different microorganisms that cause disease in animals. We then consider the mechanisms that provide animals with innate (nonspecific) and acquired (specific) defences against harmful microorganisms and conclude with a discussion of the public health implications of some selected immunity-related conditions in humans.

50.1 | TYPES OF PATHOGENS

Learning Outcomes:

1. List the three main types of pathogens that elicit immune responses and how each damages its host organism.

As just noted, the body's immune defences must protect against a variety of foreign materials, but most important among them are disease-causing microorganisms or pathogens. Pathogens exist in nearly every possible ecological niche on Earth. Both terrestrial and aquatic animals, including invertebrates and vertebrates, encounter each of the three major types of pathogens: bacteria, viruses, and parasites.

Bacteria can either damage tissues at open wound sites or release toxins that enter the bloodstream and disrupt functions in other parts of the body. Bacteria are responsible for many diseases and infections, including typhoid fever, strep throat, skin infections, middle ear infections, and food poisoning. The major ways in which bacteria gain entry into an animal's body are through direct bodily contact, open wounds, inhalation through the respiratory tract, and ingestion via fecal contamination of food or water. The latter situation may arise because many infectious bacteria enter the intestines and are excreted in feces, which may be deposited near food or water sources for some animals.

A **virus** is a nucleic acid enclosed within a protein coat. Viruses are much smaller than bacteria and lack the metabolic machinery to synthesize the proteins they need to replicate themselves. Instead, viruses must infect a host cell and use the cell's biochemical and genetic apparatus, including nucleotides and energy sources, to make more viruses. The viral nucleic acid directs the host cell to synthesize the proteins required for viral replication. After entering a cell, some viruses, such as the common cold virus, multiply rapidly, kill the cell, and then infect other cells. Other viruses can lie dormant within host cells before suddenly undergoing rapid replication, which causes cell damage. Finally, certain viruses can transform their host cells into cancer cells. Viruses are responsible for a great variety of illnesses, including some sexually transmitted infections. Viral infections can spread rapidly among animals and can be lethal. Although viruses typically enter the body through the respiratory tract or through open wounds in skin and mucous membranes, some, such as West Nile virus, are mosquito borne. Although West Nile virus first arrived in North America in 1999, it spread rapidly among the native bird and human populations, and it reached epidemic proportions in humans in Ontario in 2002 and in Saskatchewan in 2003. West Nile virus strains from Kenya (KEN 1998) are not particularly virulent, whereas the New York 1999 (NY99) strain results in rapidly induced viremia and death in American crows. Researchers have determined that a single amino acid substitution (from threonine to proline) at residue 249 in the NS3 *helicase* gene is correlated with this increase in virulence.

Parasites—whether protozoa, fungi, or multicellular eukaryotic organisms, such as worms—damage a host by using the host's nutrients for their own growth and reproduction or by secreting toxic chemicals. In humans, parasites account for an enormous number of cases of disease annually. For example, several hundred million people worldwide are infected with *Plasmodium* sp., a mosquito-borne protozoan that causes malaria. Parasitic infections can enter a host through the bite of an infected insect, as in malaria, by ingestion of food or water containing parasitic organisms (many roundworms), or in some cases by penetrating the skin, as in blood flukes.

50.2 INNATE (NONSPECIFIC) IMMUNITY

Learning Outcomes:

1. Identify the main innate defence mechanisms in animals, and understand why innate immunity is also called nonspecific immunity.
2. Explain how an animal's body surface provides protection from pathogens.
3. Describe the process of phagocytosis and explain its importance in innate immune responses.
4. List the cell types involved in innate immunity and the functions of each.
5. Describe the sequence of events in the inflammatory response.

Innate (nonspecific) immune defences protect against foreign cells or matter without having to recognize the invaders' specific identities. This type of defence mechanism is called innate

because animals inherit the ability to perform these protective functions and because this type of immunity does not require prior exposure to invaders. Instead of distinguishing among foreign materials, innate defences recognize some general, conserved property marking the invader as foreign, such as a particular class of carbohydrate or lipid present in the cell walls of many different kinds of microbes.

In this section, we will consider the innate immune defences, which include defences at the body surfaces, the actions of phagocytic cells, the response to injury known as inflammation, and various antimicrobial proteins.

The Body Surface Is an Initial Line of Defence

An animal's initial defences against pathogens are the barriers provided by surfaces exposed to the external environment. Very few microorganisms can penetrate the intact skin or body surface of most animals, particularly the tough, thick, or scaly skin characteristic of many vertebrates or the rigid exoskeleton of many arthropods. Moreover, glands in the body surfaces of both invertebrates and vertebrates secrete a variety of antimicrobial molecules, including mild acids and enzymes, such as lysozyme, that destroy bacterial cell walls.

The mucus secreted by cells in the mucous membranes lining the respiratory and upper gastrointestinal tracts of vertebrates also contains antimicrobial molecules, but more important, mucus is sticky. Microbes that become stuck in it are prevented from penetrating the mucous membrane barrier. They are either swept up into the pharynx and swallowed or engulfed by cells that are present in both tracts. Pathogens ingested with food are often destroyed by the acidic environment of an animal's midgut.

If a pathogen is able to penetrate a barrier and gain entry into an animal's internal tissues and fluids, other innate defence mechanisms are activated. These mechanisms are mediated by several types of cells that reside in the body fluids and tissues, as described next.

Phagocytic Cells Defend Against Pathogens That Enter the Body

Several different types of cells in vertebrates play key roles in innate immunity (**Figure 50.1**). Many of these cells are **phagocytes**—cells capable of **phagocytosis**. Phagocytosis is a type of endocytosis in which the cell engulfs particulate matter, which usually is then destroyed by proteases or oxidizing agents, such as hydrogen peroxide. Phagocytes are found in the body fluids, such as hemolymph and blood, and also within various tissues and organs. Phagocytes are present in all classes of animals and are among the most fundamental and ancestral forms of body defences. In vertebrates, most phagocytes belong to the type of blood cells called white blood cells, or **leukocytes** (Figure 50.1). All leukocytes are derived from a common type of stem cell (see Chapter 17), which in mammals and birds resides in the bone marrow. These stem cells give rise to several types of leukocytes and other cells that have specialized functions.

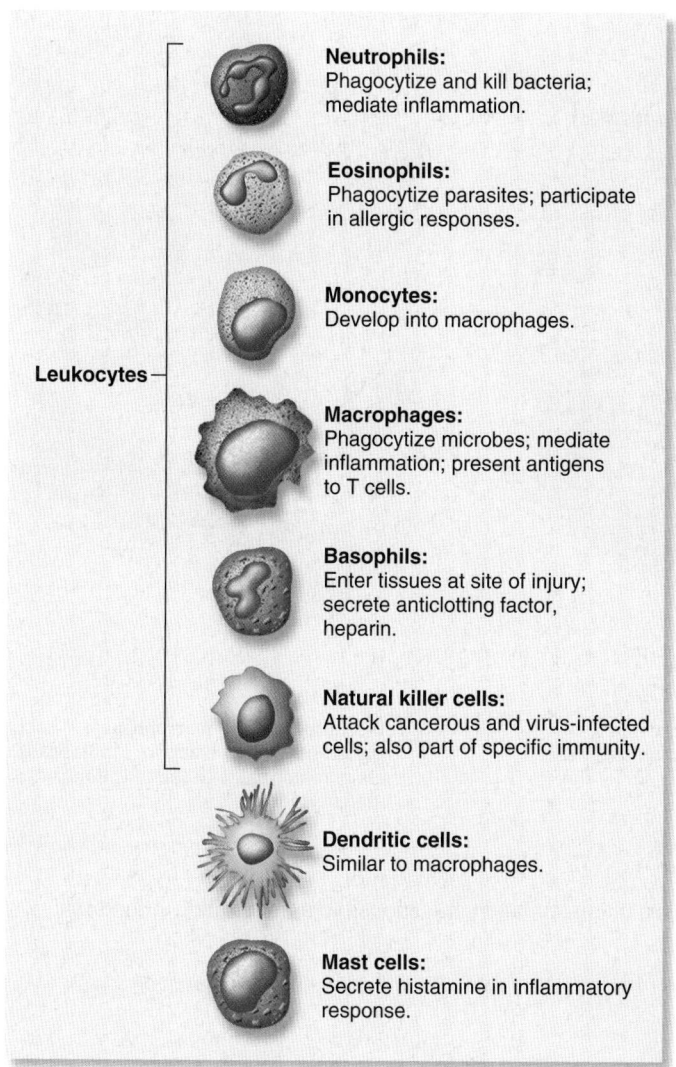

Figure 50.1 Cells involved in innate immunity in vertebrates. Note that five of these types of cells are leukocytes.

The leukocytes involved in innate immunity include neutrophils, eosinophils, monocytes, macrophages, and basophils.

Neutrophils are phagocytes and the most abundant leukocytes. They are found in blood and within tissues. Neutrophils engulf bacteria by endocytosis. The bacteria are destroyed within endocytotic vacuoles by proteases, oxidizing agents, and antibacterial proteins called defensins. The production and release of neutrophils from bone marrow is greatly stimulated during the course of an infection. **Eosinophils** are phagocytes found in large numbers in mucosal surfaces lining the gastrointestinal, respiratory, and urinary tracts, where they fight off parasitic invasions. **Monocytes** are phagocytes that circulate in the blood for only a few days, after which they take up permanent residence as **macrophages** in virtually all organs and tissues. Macrophages are strategically located where they will encounter invaders, including epithelia in contact with the external environment, such as skin and the linings of respiratory and digestive tracts, and in many organs at sites through which blood or lymph flows. Macrophages are large phagocytes capable of engulfing viruses and bacteria (see the chapter-opening photo).

In contrast to these other leukocytes, **basophils** are secretory cells. They secrete the anticlotting factor heparin at the site of an infection, which helps the circulation flush out the infected site. Basophils also secrete histamine, which attracts infection-fighting cells and proteins to the site.

Natural killer (NK) cells are another type of leukocyte called lymphocytes, of which there are several types. NK cells participate in both innate and acquired immunity. These cells are part of the body's innate defences because they recognize general features on the surface of cancer cells or any virus-infected cells. NK cells arise in the bone marrow, but their life history remains unclear. They act by releasing chemicals into the vicinity of cancer or virus-infected cells and thereby kill those cells.

In addition to leukocytes, two other types of cells derived from bone marrow stem cells play important roles in innate immunity. **Dendritic cells** are scattered throughout most tissues, where they perform various macrophage functions. **Mast cells** are found throughout connective tissues, particularly beneath the epithelial surfaces of the body. Mast cells secrete many locally acting molecules, including histamine. Histamine and other substances are involved in inflammation, a fundamental component of the innate defence mechanism to which we now turn.

Inflammation Is an Innate Response to Infection or Injury

Inflammation is an innate local response to infection or injury. The functions of inflammation are to destroy or inactivate foreign invaders, to clear the infected region of dead cells and other debris, and to set the stage for tissue repair. The key cellular mediators are phagocytes, primarily neutrophils, macrophages, dendritic cells, and mast cells.

The sequence of local events in a typical inflammatory response to a bacterial infection is summarized in **Figure 50.2**. The familiar signs and symptoms of tissue injury and inflammation are local redness, swelling, heat, and pain.

The events of inflammation are induced and regulated by chemical mediators. These include a family of proteins called **cytokines** that function in both nonspecific and specific immune defences. Cytokines provide a chemical communication network that synchronizes the components of the immune response. Most cytokines are secreted by more than one type of immune system cell and also by nonimmune cells, such as endothelial cells and fibroblasts. Cytokine-like molecules have been identified in all vertebrates and in several evolutionarily distant invertebrate orders, in which they serve functions similar to some of those seen in vertebrates.

Substances secreted into the extracellular fluid from injured tissue cells, mast cells, and neutrophils also contribute to the inflammatory response (**Figure 50.2, step 1**). For example,

1) An injury introduces bacteria beneath the skin. Mast cells secrete histamine, and endothelial cells secrete nitric oxide.

2) Capillaries dilate and become leaky. Fluid and neutrophils exit the capillaries and enter the site of the wound.

3) As neutrophils and macrophages engulf and destroy bacteria, capillaries return to normal, and the infection is brought under control.

Figure 50.2 The events in inflammation.   Shown are the initial stages of inflammation in response to a penetrating wound that introduces bacteria beneath the skin.

Concept check: *Inflammation often is associated with swelling of the inflamed area. Does this swelling have an adaptive value?*

histamine from mast cells and nitric oxide from endothelial cells cause dilation of the small blood vessels in an infected or damaged area, and the vessels become leaky (**Figure 50.2, step 2**).

These vascular changes provide two benefits. First, the increased blood flow to the inflamed area, which accounts for the redness and heat, increases the delivery of beneficial proteins and leukocytes. Second, the increased vascular permeability ensures that the plasma proteins that participate in inflammation can gain entry to the interstitial fluid. The swelling in an inflamed area also results from this increased leakiness of blood vessels, but it has no adaptive value of its own.

Once neutrophils and macrophages arrive at the site of an injury, they begin the process of phagocytizing and destroying invading microbes (**Figure 50.2, step 3**). The initial step in phagocytosis involves the interaction of phagocyte surface receptors with certain carbohydrates or lipids in the microbial cell walls. Subsequently, the neutrophils and macrophages also release into the extracellular fluid antimicrobial substances that can destroy microbes even before phagocytosis occurs. Other secreted substances, such as nitric oxide, function as inflammatory mediators. The result is positive feedback: Once phagocytes enter the area and encounter microbes, they release

inflammatory mediators that bring even more phagocytes into the area.

Inflammation sets the stage for tissue repair. In some tissues, undamaged cells surrounding an injury can multiply to replace destroyed cells and thereby restore tissue function, while in others they cannot. Liver cells, for example, multiply following injury or damage, but skeletal muscle cells do not. In either case, nearby connective tissue cells called fibroblasts divide rapidly and secrete large quantities of collagen, the major component of extracellular matrices, and nearby blood vessel cells proliferate to restore blood supply. Ultimately, tissue repair may be imperfect, leaving a scar largely composed of fibroblasts, collagen, and other proteins.

Inflammation—indeed any stage of an illness—may be accompanied by **fever**, an increase in an animal's body temperature that results from an infection. In humans, a temperature greater than 38°C is considered to be a fever (normal is about 37°C). The precise mechanisms by which a fever arises are not completely understood. It is clear, however, that in mammals, cytokines released into the circulation by activated macrophages act within the hypothalamus to raise the body's set point for temperature. The result is a decrease in heat dissipation and an increase in heat generation. Whereas a sustained high fever requires medical attention because of the damaging effects of high temperature on membrane function and enzyme activity, it appears from animal models that a low or moderate increase in temperature stimulates leukocyte activity and proliferation and provides a less hospitable environment for at least some types of pathogens.

Antimicrobial Proteins Include Interferons and Complement Proteins

Interferons are proteins that generally inhibit viral replication inside host cells. In response to viral infection, most cell types produce interferons and secrete them into the extracellular fluid. When the interferons bind to plasma membrane receptors on the secreting cell and on other cells, the cell synthesizes a variety of proteins that interfere with the ability of the viruses to replicate. Interferons are not specific. Many kinds of viruses induce interferon synthesis, and the same interferons in turn can inhibit the multiplication of many different kinds of viruses.

The family of plasma proteins known as **complement** provides another means for extracellular killing of microbes without prior phagocytosis. Inactive complement proteins normally circulate in the blood at all times. When they contact the surface of microbes, a cascade of events results in the formation of active complement proteins. Five of the active proteins generated in the complement cascade form a multi-unit protein called the **membrane attack complex** (**MAC**), which, by embedding itself in the microbial plasma membrane, creates porelike channels. Water and salts enter the microbe through the channels, and the microbe bursts.

We turn now to the type of immunity that is present in all jawed vertebrates and that is distinguished by an ability to recognize great numbers of specific foreign molecules.

50.3 | ACQUIRED (SPECIFIC) IMMUNITY

Learning Outcomes:

1. Describe the components of the immune system including the major classes of lymphocytes.
2. Describe the three stages of the acquired immune response.
3. Compare and contrast the humoral immune response with the cell-mediated immune response.
4. Explain how antibody structure and genetic rearrangement lead to the diverse set of antibodies found in mammals.
5. Describe the typical inflammatory and humoral immune responses.
6. Describe the importance of secondary immune responses.

In acquired or specific immunity, cells of the immune system first encounter and later recognize a specific foreign cell or protein to be attacked, as opposed to recognizing some general feature of pathogens. Because this type of immunity requires exposure to foreign substances, it is also called acquired immunity. Foreign molecules that can trigger a specific immune response are called **antigens**. An antigen is any molecule that the host does not recognize as self. Most antigens are either proteins or very large polysaccharides. Antigens include the protein coats of viruses, specific macromolecules on pollens and other allergens, cancer cells, transplanted cells, toxins, and vaccines.

This type of immunity is found in all classes of vertebrates except jawless fish and was once thought to be absent in invertebrates. Recently, however, scientists who study the evolution of immune systems have uncovered several interesting features of invertebrate immune function that suggest that some invertebrates have a limited ability to adapt immune activity to a specific invader. Despite this intriguing finding, however, we will consider specific immune responses in the context in which they are best understood, the jawed vertebrates.

Lymphocytes Provide Acquired Immunity Against Antigens

Lymphocytes are a type of leukocyte that are responsible for acquired (specific) immunity (**Figure 50.3**). The two types of lymphocytes are **B cells** and **T cells**. B cells were first observed

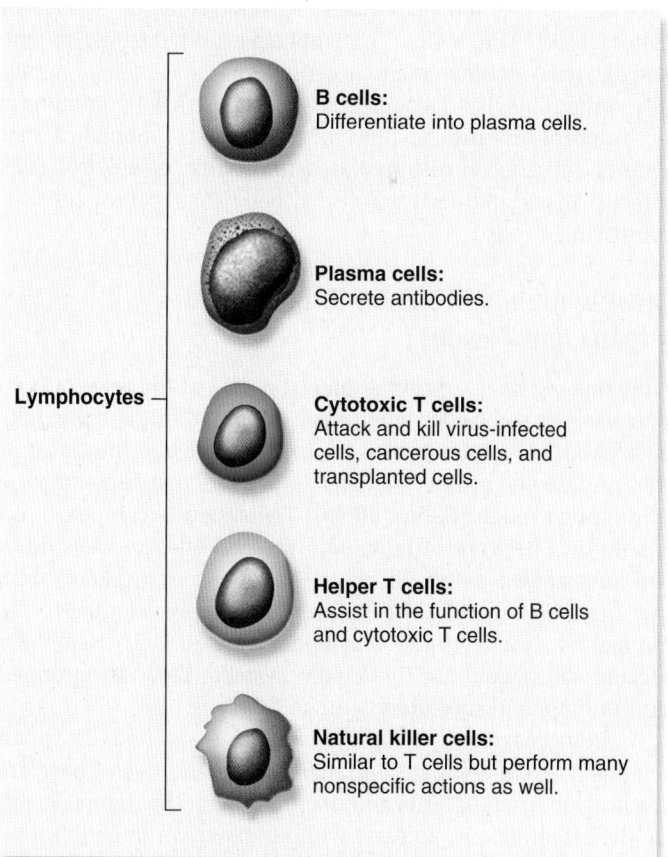

Figure 50.3 Cells involved in acquired immunity in vertebrates. Some important functions of each type of leukocyte are included.

to mature in an avian organ called the bursa of Fabricius—thus the name B cells. In mammals, B cells mature within bone marrow. Some B cells differentiate further into **plasma cells**, which synthesize and secrete antibodies, proteins that bind to and help destroy foreign molecules, as described later. T cells are so named because they mature within the thymus gland.

Most T cells directly kill infected, mutated, or transplanted cells. T cells include two distinct types of lymphocytes: cytotoxic T cells and helper T cells. **Cytotoxic T cells** travel to the location of their targets, bind to these targets by combining with an antigen on them, and directly kill those targets via secreted chemicals. Responses mediated by cytotoxic T cells are directed against body cells that have become cancerous or infected by pathogens. Natural killer cells also destroy such cells by secreting toxic chemicals.

As the name **helper T cells** implies, these cells do not themselves function as "attack" cells. Instead, they assist in the activation and function of B cells and cytotoxic T cells. With only a few exceptions, B cells and cytotoxic T cells cannot function adequately unless they are stimulated by cytokines secreted from helper T cells. Helper T cells can be identified by the presence of a unique protein on their surface called CD4, which plays a role in the cell's ability to interact with other lymphocytes. Cytotoxic T cells are identified by a different membrane protein: CD8.

Lymphocytes carry out their role by recognizing antigens, such as those found on viruses, bacteria, and the surface of cancer cells. The ability of lymphocytes to distinguish one antigen from another plays a central role in acquired immunity. Immunologists recognize two types of specific immunity. In **humoral immunity**, plasma cells secrete antibodies that bind to antigens. In **cell-mediated immunity**, cytotoxic T cells directly attack and destroy infected body cells, cancer cells, or transplanted cells.

Most Lymphocytes Exist in Lymphoid Organs and Tissues

Now that we have a general understanding of the roles of lymphocytes, let's consider where they are found in the body. Like all leukocytes, lymphocytes circulate in the blood, but most of them reside in a group of organs and tissues that constitute the **lymphatic system** (**Figure 50.4a**). The system is composed primarily of a network of lymphatic vessels. These vessels drain the fluid known as lymph, which filters out of capillaries into the interstitial spaces. The lymph is eventually returned to the circulatory system. Various lymphoid organs and tissues are located throughout the lymphatic system. They are grouped into primary and secondary lymphoid organs.

The primary lymphoid organs are the structures in which lymphocytes differentiate into mature immune cells. These are the bone marrow in birds and mammals, and the thymus gland in all vertebrates. In animals without extensive bone marrow, specialized regions of other organs, such as the kidney and liver, serve as primary lymphoid organs.

The primary lymphoid organs supply mature lymphocytes to secondary lymphoid tissues and organs, where the lymphocytes multiply. These include the lymph nodes of mammals

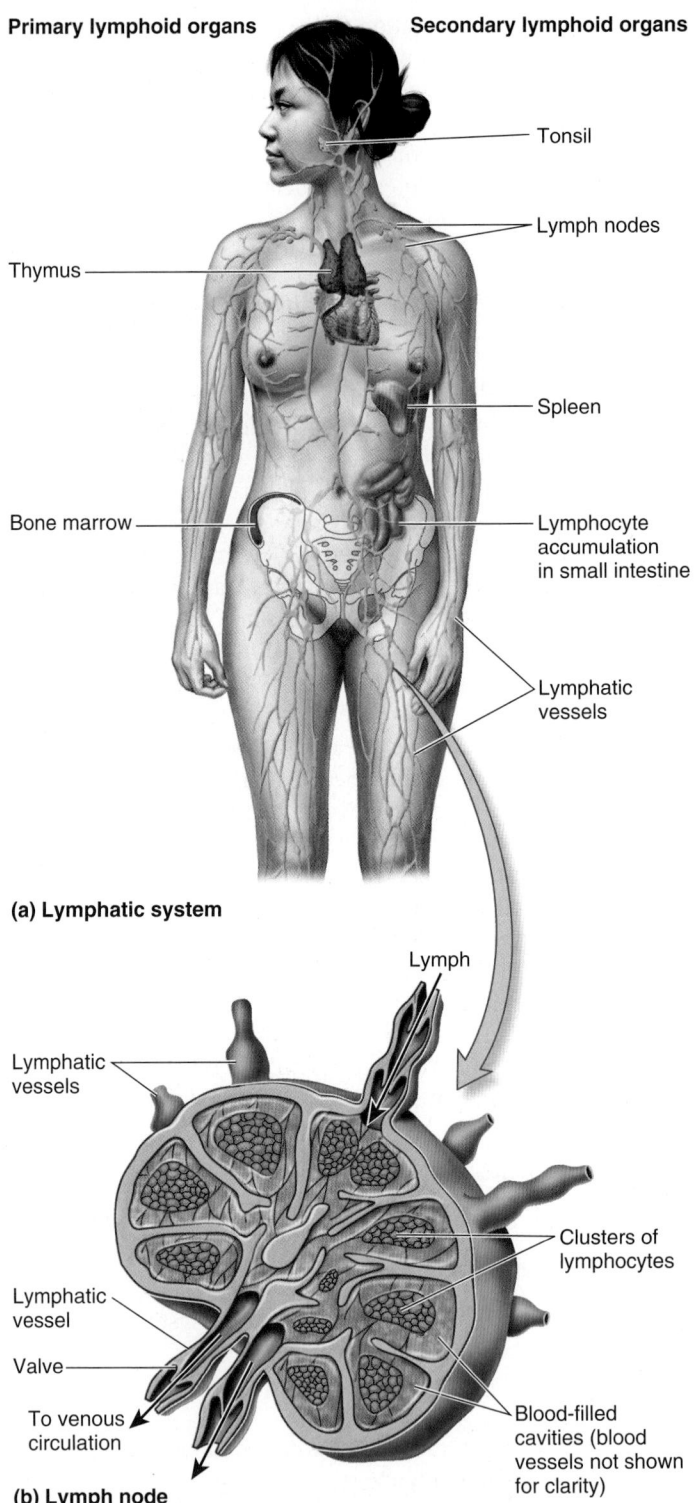

Figure 50.4 **The lymphatic system in humans.** (a) The major components of the lymphatic system. Primary lymphoid organs are shown in red, and secondary lymphoid structures are shown in green. In adult humans, the primary lymphoid organs in bone are found in the sternum, ribs, parts of the skull, small regions of the femur and humerus, and, as shown here, the hip bones. (b) The structure of a lymph node. Lymph nodes occur along the course of lymphatic vessels, which drain interstitial fluid from tissues and return it to the venous circulation. Within a lymph node, lymph percolates through open cavities containing clusters of lymphocytes.

(**Figure 50.4b**), the spleen (found in all jawed vertebrates and the largest secondary lymphoid structure), the tonsils (small, rounded lymphoid organs in the pharyngeal region of mammals), and scattered lymphocyte accumulations in the linings of the intestinal, respiratory, genital, and urinary tracts.

At any moment, some lymphocytes are circulating from the bone marrow or thymus to the secondary lymphoid organs. The vast majority of lymphocytes, though, are in transit between the secondary lymphoid organs, blood, lymph, and all the tissues of the body. Lymphocytes from all the secondary lymphoid structures continually enter the lymphatic vessels draining those structures and are carried to the bloodstream. Simultaneously, some circulating lymphocytes are exiting venules all over the body to enter the interstitial fluid. From there, they enter into lymphatic vessels and are carried to secondary lymphoid organs. They may then leave the lymphatic vessels to take up residence in a lymph node or other structure.

This recirculation is going on all the time, but during an infection the migration of lymphocytes into an inflamed area is greatly increased. Lymphocyte recirculation increases the likelihood that any given lymphocyte will encounter an antigen it is specifically programmed to recognize.

Acquired Immune Responses Occur in Three Stages

Thus far, we have considered the types of lymphocytes involved in an acquired immune response and how they circulate through the body. An acquired immune response can usually be divided into three stages (**Figure 50.5**): (1) antigen encounter and recognition by lymphocytes, (2) activation and proliferation of lymphocytes (which includes cell division to produce effector cells and memory cells), and (3) the attack launched by the activated lymphocytes and their secretions.

Stage 1: Recognition of Antigen During its development, each lymphocyte synthesizes a type of membrane receptor that can bind to a specific antigen. If, subsequently, the lymphocyte encounters that antigen, the antigen becomes bound to the receptor. This specific binding is the meaning of the word *recognize* in immunology. Antigens that bind to a lymphocyte receptor are said to be recognized by the lymphocyte. The ability of lymphocytes to distinguish one antigen from another, therefore, is determined by the nature of their plasma membrane receptors. Each lymphocyte is specific for just one type of antigen.

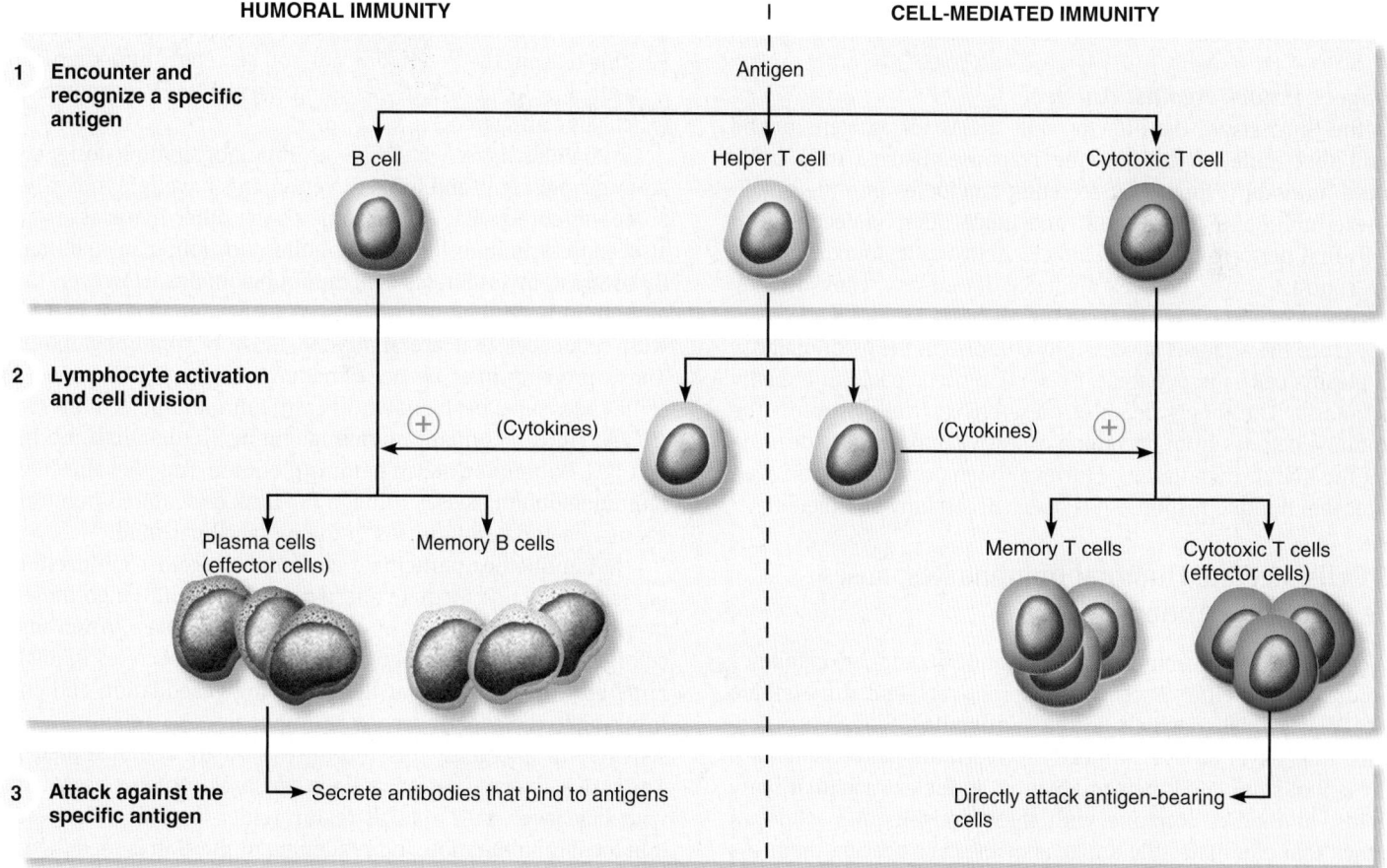

Figure 50.5 **The three stages of an acquired immune response.** All three cell types in step 1 recognize the same antigen. Helper T cells secrete cytokines that activate B cells and cytotoxic T cells, as indicated by the plus (+) symbol. Both B cells and T cells undergo cell division to form clones when activated, and in both cases a portion of the cells are set aside as memory cells to fight off a future infection of the same type.

Stage 2: Activation of Lymphocytes

In the second stage, the binding of an antigen to a receptor on a lymphocyte activates the lymphocyte. On binding to an antigen, the lymphocyte undergoes multiple cycles of cell division. The result is the formation of many lymphocytes that express receptors identical to the receptor that first recognized the antigen. When an antigen-stimulated lymphocyte divides and replicates itself, the progeny of this lymphocyte—all of which express the same receptor—are called clones, and the process by which these clones are formed is called **clonal selection**. This term emphasizes that lymphocyte proliferation is selected by exposure to an antigen, an idea first established by Niels Jerne, Sir Frank MacFarlane, and Joshua Lederberg in the 1950s. The chemical nature of the antigen determines which individual lymphocytes will be activated to form clones. In a typical person, the size of the lymphocyte population is staggering. More than 100 million different lymphocytes, each with the ability to recognize a unique antigen, are found in a person's immune system. This vast population explains why our bodies are able to recognize so many different antigens as foreign and eventually destroy them. The process of clonal selection requires the function of helper T cells that secrete cytokines—chemicals that promote cell division.

After activation, some of the cloned lymphocytes become **effector cells**, which carry out the attack response. Other cells function as **memory cells**, which remain poised to recognize the antigen if it returns in the future.

Stage 3: Attack Against Antigen

In the third stage, the effector cells attack all antigens of the kind that initiated the immune response. Plasma cells carry out a humoral response by secreting antibodies into the blood. These antibodies then recruit and guide other molecules and cells that perform the actual attack. Activated cytotoxic T cells, by contrast, carry out cell-mediated immunity. They directly attack and kill the cells bearing the antigens.

Once the attack is successfully completed, the great majority of plasma cells and cytotoxic T cells that participated in it die by apoptosis. The timely death of these effector cells prevents the immune defence from becoming excessive and possibly destroying the body's own tissues. However, memory cells persist even after the immune response has been successfully completed.

B Cells Mediate Humoral Immune Responses by Producing Antibodies

When B cells are activated by an antigen and by cytokines produced by helper T cells, they proliferate and differentiate into plasma cells, which secrete **antibodies**. These are proteins that travel all over the body to reach antigens identical to those that stimulated their production. In the extracellular body fluids, antibodies combine with these antigens and guide an attack that eliminates the antigens or the cells bearing them. As mentioned, such antibody-mediated responses are also called humoral immune responses, the adjective *humoral* denoting communication by way of soluble chemical messengers.

Antibody mediated responses are the major defence against bacteria, viruses, and other microbes in the extracellular fluid and against toxin molecules.

Antibodies are members of a family of proteins called **immunoglobulins**. Some immunoglobulins, such as antibodies, are soluble proteins that are secreted from plasma cells (**Figure 50.6a**). Other immunoglobulins have a transmembrane domain that anchors them in the membrane. These immunoglobulins function as receptors for antigens (**Figure 50.6b**).

Each immunoglobulin molecule is composed of four interlinked polypeptides: two long **heavy chains** and two short **light chains** (Figure 50.6a). A hinge region that provides the molecule with flexibility separates the light chains and upper parts of the heavy chains from the lower parts of the heavy chains. A key feature of immunoglobulins is their variable region, which varies among different B cells. The variable region is the site that specifically recognizes an antigen. The mechanism for variation in this region of the immunoglobulin will be described later.

Before activation, B cells produce B-cell receptors but do not secrete antibodies. On activation, the resulting plasma cells begin to synthesize massive amounts of antibodies, which are secreted from the cell. Interestingly, the B-cell receptor and the antibodies made by plasma cells are encoded by the same genes. On B-cell activation, the pre-mRNA for the heavy chain is alternatively spliced, a phenomenon described in Chapter 12, so that the transmembrane domain is not present in the protein. For this reason, the B-cell receptor and secreted antibodies from a particular B cell and its resulting plasma cells recognize the exact same antigen.

Mammals have five classes of immunoglobulins designated IgM, IgG, IgE, IgA, and IgD. All vertebrates have IgM molecules. Some vertebrates have only some of the other five classes and also express unique immunoglobulins not found in mammals. By contrast, invertebrates lack immunoglobulins. However, they have proteins containing regions called Ig-domains (or Ig-folds) with sequences that are similar to those of immunoglobulins. These proteins may be ancestral to immunoglobulins and in some cases have been shown to carry out immune activities.

The most abundant immunoglobulins in mammals are IgM and IgG, commonly called gamma globulin. Together these two immunoglobulin classes provide the bulk of acquired immunity against bacteria and viruses in the extracellular fluid.

IgE antibodies participate in defences against multicellular parasites and also mediate allergic responses. Although present in blood, they also exist in mast cell membranes. When mast cell IgE molecules bind antigen, the mast cell secretes its histamine into the extracellular fluid, causing vasodilation and contributing to the allergic response. In people who are particularly sensitive to allergens, this response is easily demonstrated by a pinprick injection of an antigen, such as proteins associated with hay fever, into a small region under the skin. The resultant local inflammation and reddening of the skin is mediated in large part by IgE molecules.

IgA antibodies are secreted by plasma cells in the linings of the gastrointestinal, respiratory, and genitourinary tracts, and

Antigen

Plasma membrane of B cell

Transmembrane domain

Cytosol

(a) B-cell receptor

Antigen

Specific antigen-binding sites

Light chain

Hinge regions

Disulphide bond

Heavy chain

Variable region

Constant region

(b) Secreted antibody

Figure 50.6   Immunoglobulins.   (a) B-cell receptor and (b) secreted antibody. Immunoglobulins are composed of two heavy chains and two light chains. Disulphide bonds hold the chains together. Within each immunoglobulin class, the constant regions, including the Fc regions (stems), have identical amino acid sequences. In contrast, the antigen-binding sites formed by the light- and heavy-chain variable regions have unique amino acid sequences and give each antibody its specificity for a particular antigen.

in tear ducts and salivary glands. They act locally in the linings of these structures or on their surfaces. For example, IgA molecules secreted into saliva help keep animals' mouths relatively free of pathogens. IgA molecules are also secreted by the mammary glands of mammals shortly after birth and therefore are the major antibodies in milk. Although the functions of IgD are still unclear, IgD molecules are present both in blood and on the surface of B cells, and they are known to bind antigen on B cells, thus possibly contributing to B-cell activation.

The immunoglobulin's two heavy chains have a stem called the Fc region (Figure 50.6a), which contains two or three domains depending on the class of immunoglobulin. The amino acid sequences of the Fc domains are identical for all immunoglobulins of a given class and are therefore known as **constant regions**.

Another part of each heavy chain and its associated light chain contain a constant domain, plus a domain called the **variable region** that serves as the antigen-binding site. In contrast to the constant domains of the heavy and light chains, the amino acid sequences of the variable domains vary widely from immunoglobulin to immunoglobulin in a given Ig class. The enormous number of variable sequences results in countless unique structures of immunoglobulins within each class. Thus, each of the five classes of antibodies contains up to millions of unique immunoglobulins, each capable of combining with only one specific antigen or, in some cases, with several antigens whose structures are very similar. The genetic basis for this remarkable array of immunoglobulins was first identified in the 1970s, as we see next.

GENOMES AND PROTEOMES

Recombination and Hypermutation Produce an Enormous Number of Different Immunoglobulin Proteins

The existence of so many different types of immunoglobulins raises an interesting question, because the human genome contains only about 200 genes that code for immunoglobulins: How can the body produce immunoglobulins having millions of different antigen-binding sites, when each immunoglobulin

protein requires coding by a distinct gene? The answer is that immunoglobulin diversity is in part the result of a genetic process unique to lymphocytes.

Beginning in the 1970s work by Susumu Tonegawa and others demonstrated that segments of genes that code for antigen-binding sites of immunoglobulin light and heavy chains are cut by lymphocyte-specific enzymes, a segment is removed, and then the ends of the genes are rejoined to form new genes (**Figure 50.7**). The sites within the immunoglobulin genes

Organization of gene segments in a light-chain gene

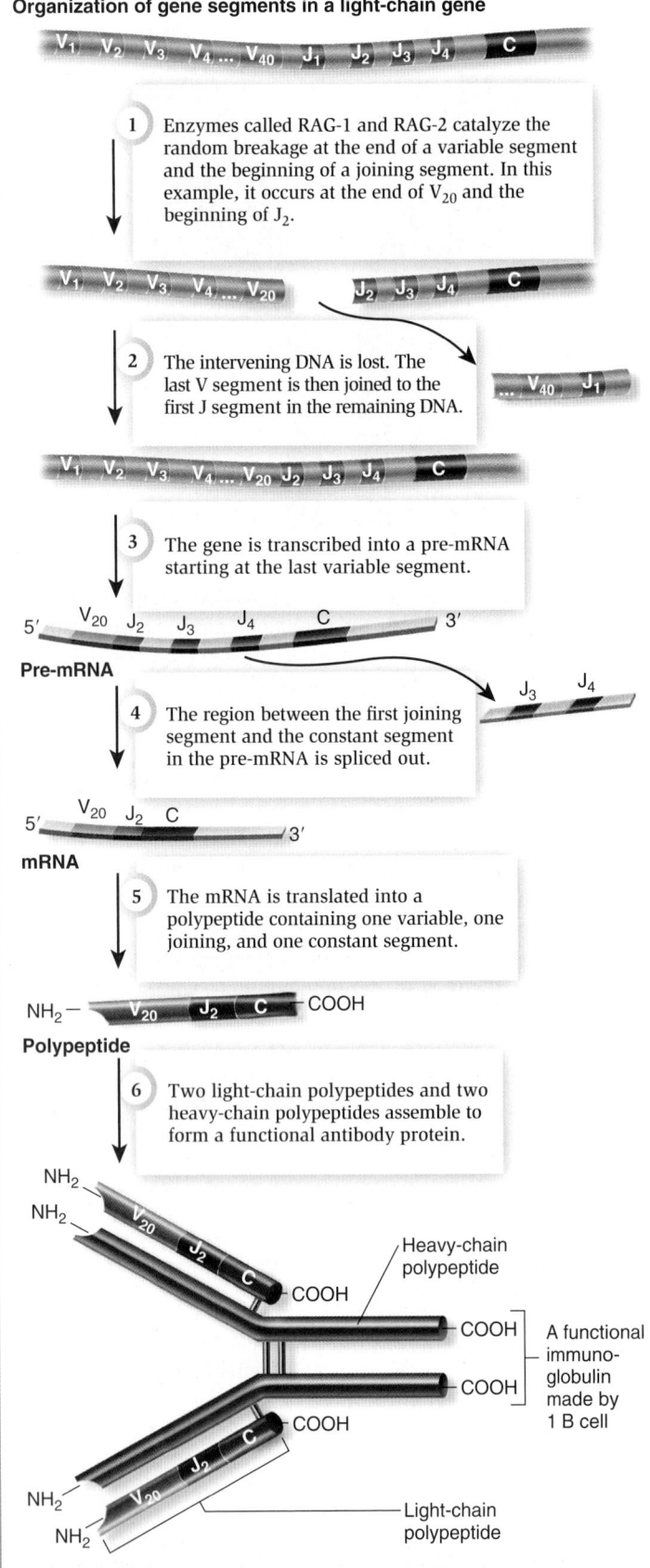

1 Enzymes called RAG-1 and RAG-2 catalyze the random breakage at the end of a variable segment and the beginning of a joining segment. In this example, it occurs at the end of V_{20} and the beginning of J_2.

2 The intervening DNA is lost. The last V segment is then joined to the first J segment in the remaining DNA.

3 The gene is transcribed into a pre-mRNA starting at the last variable segment.

Pre-mRNA

4 The region between the first joining segment and the constant segment in the pre-mRNA is spliced out.

mRNA

5 The mRNA is translated into a polypeptide containing one variable, one joining, and one constant segment.

Polypeptide

6 Two light-chain polypeptides and two heavy-chain polypeptides assemble to form a functional antibody protein.

Heavy-chain polypeptide

A functional immuno-globulin made by 1 B cell

Light-chain polypeptide

Figure 50.7   The mechanism of immunoglobulin diversity. Events similar to those depicted here also occur in the heavy chains.

where cutting and rejoining occur, vary randomly from B cell to B cell, resulting in great diversity of the genes coding for the immunoglobulins that are produced by different B cells. In this way, immunoglobulin diversity is generated in somatic cells, not by inheritance through gametes.

Along the length of a typical immunoglobulin gene are numerous domains that code for a piece of the final immuno-globulin molecule. In light chains, these domains are of three types, called the variable, joining, and constant domains. A total of about 300 variable (V) domains code for the N-terminal region of the antigen-binding site. These are next to four joining (J) domains and a single constant (c) domain. Each domain along the length of the gene is flanked by rec-ognition sequences that bind two enzymes, called RAG-1 and RAG-2 (for recombination-activating gene). These enzymes, which are expressed only in developing lymphocytes, cut a random V domain and paste it to a random J domain. The result is a new, permanent immunoglobulin gene for that B cell. Because any V domain can be linked with any J domain, the number of possible final genes among different B cells is huge. Additionally, heavy chains have multiple domains that are spliced together in this way, except that they have yet another domain (designated D) and more V domains, yield-ing an even greater number of possible heavy-chain genes. Because any heavy chain can combine with any light chain in a given B cell, the number of possible combinations of immu-noglobulins is immense.

The number of possible immunoglobulins is increased even further in two more important ways within B cells. First, the joining process of the V, D, and J domains is not always precise. Occasionally, a few nucleotides may be lost at a joining end, resulting in a different amino acid sequence in the immunoglob-ulin protein. Second, in a subset of activated B cells, the DNA coding for the variable antigen-binding sites of immunoglobulins undergoes a process known as **hypermutation**, which primar-ily produces point mutations. During this process, cytosines are deaminated into uracils, leading to numerous C to T mutations during DNA replication. In addition, the presence of numerous uracils within the DNA recruits error-prone DNA polymerases, leading to several additional types of mutations. The result is a hypervariable region of the light and heavy chains of all immuno-globulins. Hypermutation in lymphocytes appears to arise from lymphocyte-specific expression of a novel enzyme capable of deaminating cytosine.

The three processes of gene recombination, imprecise joining of domains, and hypermutation cause lymphocytes to produce an incredibly diverse array of antibodies capable of rec-ognizing many different antigens. Because the body makes hun-dreds of millions of different types of lymphocytes, nearly any foreign antigen that is taken into the body will be recognized by some lymphocytes in this large population.

T-Cell Receptors Are Present in Plasma Membranes and Are Not Secreted

Like immunoglobulins, T-cell receptors for antigens have specific regions that differ from one T cell clone to another. As shown in **Figure 50.8a**, they are composed of two polypeptides, each with a variable and constant region, along with a transmembrane domain. The variable regions recognize an antigen. As in B-cell development, multiple DNA rearrangements occur during T-cell maturation, leading to millions of distinct clones of T cells, each possessing receptors of a unique specificity. For T cells, this maturation occurs during their development in the thymus.

In addition to their general structural differences, the B-cell receptors and T-cell receptors differ in a much more important way. T-cell receptors cannot combine with antigen unless the antigen is first complexed with certain of the body's own plasma membrane proteins. The T-cell receptor then combines with the entire self-protein–antigen complex.

The plasma membrane self-proteins that must be complexed with the antigen in order for T-cell recognition to occur are encoded by a gene family known as the **major histocompatibility complex** (**MHC**), and thus the proteins are called MHC proteins. Other than identical twins, no two individuals have the same sets of MHC genes, so no two individuals have the same MHC proteins on the plasma membranes of their cells. MHC proteins are cellular "identity tags" that serve as genetic markers of self.

Two classes of MHC proteins are known. Class I MHC proteins are found on the surface of all human body cells except erythrocytes. Class II MHC proteins are found only on the surface of macrophages, B cells, and dendritic cells.

The two different types of T cells have different MHC requirements. Cytotoxic T cells require antigen to be associated with class I MHC proteins, whereas helper T cells require class II MHC proteins. One reason for this difference stems from the presence, as described earlier, of CD4 proteins on helper T cells and CD8 proteins on cytotoxic T cells; CD4 binds to class II MHC proteins, whereas CD8 binds to class I MHC proteins.

How do antigens, which are foreign, end up complexed with MHC proteins on the surface of the body's own cells? The answer involves the process known as antigen presentation, described next.

Antigen Presentation to Helper T Cells As previously noted, T cells can bind antigen only when the antigen appears on the plasma membrane of a host cell complexed with the cell's MHC proteins. Cells bearing these complexes, therefore, function as **antigen-presenting cells** (**APCs**). Helper T cells require class II MHC proteins to function. Because only macrophages, B cells, and dendritic cells express class II MHC proteins, only these cells can function as APCs for helper T cells.

Let's consider the function of macrophages as APCs for helper T cells (**Figure 50.8b**). After a microbe or noncellular

(a) T-cell receptor

(b) Antigen presentation

Figure 50.8 **The T-cell receptor and antigen presentations.** (a) Structure of a T-cell receptor. (b) Antigen presentation. In the initial events in helper T-cell activation, antigen fragments are complexed with a class II MHC protein within an antigen-presenting cell, such as a macrophage. The complex is then displayed on the cell surface and binds to a helper T-cell receptor. Also required for T-cell activation are the binding of nonantigenic proteins between the APC and the attached helper T cell, and the actions of the cytokines IL-1 and TNF.

antigen has been phagocytized by a macrophage in an innate response, antigens, such as proteins, are partially broken down into smaller peptide fragments by the macrophage's proteolytic enzymes within intracellular vesicles called endosomes. The resulting digested fragments then bind in the endosome to class II MHC proteins synthesized by the macrophage. Each fragment-MHC complex is then transported to the cell surface, where it is displayed in the plasma membrane. It is to this entire complex on the cell surface of the macrophage that a specific helper T-cell receptor binds. The CD4 protein helps link the two cells together. What is complexed to MHC proteins and presented to the helper T cells are not the intact antigens but instead the peptide fragments of the antigen—called antigenic determinants, or **epitopes**. Even so, it is customary to call this antigen presentation rather than epitope presentation.

B cells process antigen and present it to helper T cells in essentially the same way as occurs in macrophages. The ability of B cells to present antigen to helper T cells is a second function of B cells in response to antigenic stimulation, in addition to their differentiation into antibody-secreting plasma cells.

The binding between the helper T-cell receptor and antigen bound to class II MHC proteins on an APC is the essential antigen-specific event in helper T-cell activation. However, by itself this specific binding will not result in T-cell activation. In addition, interactions occur between nonantigenic pairs of proteins on the surfaces of the attached helper T cell and the APC, and these interactions provide a necessary costimulus for T-cell activation (Figure 50.8).

Finally, the antigenic binding of the APC to the T cell plus the costimulus induce the APC to secrete large amounts of two cytokines—interleukin 1 (IL-1) and tumour necrosis factor (TNF). These molecules also stimulate the attached helper T cell.

Thus, the APC participates in the activation of a helper T cell in three ways: (1) antigen presentation, (2) provision of a costimulus in the form of a matching nonantigenic plasma membrane protein, and (3) secretion of IL-1 and TNF. As discussed later, activated T cells secrete molecules that stimulate other cells, such as B cells.

Antigen Presentation to Cytotoxic T Cells   Unlike helper T cells, cytotoxic T cells require class I MHC proteins for activation. Class I MHC proteins are synthesized by all nucleated cells, and therefore any such cell can act as an APC for a cytotoxic T cell. This distinction helps explain the major function of cytotoxic T cells—destruction of any of the body's own cells that have become cancerous or infected with viruses. The crucial point is that the antigens that complex with class I MHC proteins arise within body cells. They are endogenous antigens, synthesized by a body cell.

How do such antigens arise? In viral infections, once a virus has entered a host cell, the viral nucleic acid instructs the host cell to manufacture viral proteins, which are foreign to the cell. In cancerous cells, one or more of the cell's genes have become altered by chemicals, radiation, or other factors. The altered genes, called oncogenes, code for proteins that are not normally found in the body. Such abnormal proteins act as antigens.

In both virus-infected cells and cancerous cells, cytosolic enzymes hydrolyze some of the endogenously produced antigenic proteins into peptide fragments, which are transported into the endoplasmic reticulum. There the fragments are complexed with the host cell's class I MHC proteins and then shuttled by exocytosis to the plasma membrane, where a cytotoxic T cell specific for the antigen–MHC protein complex can bind to it. Once binding occurs, cytotoxic T cells release into the extracellular fluid chemicals that kill the infected or cancerous cell. This process will be discussed later.

Humoral Immune Responses Involve B Cells and T Cells Working Together

One classic humoral immune response results in the destruction of bacteria. The sequence of events, which is quite similar to the response to a virus in the extracellular fluid, is summarized in **Figure 50.9**. For this example, we consider the response in mammals, in which lymph nodes are present. Many features of the response, however, are similar in other vertebrates.

This process starts the same way as for innate responses, with the bacteria penetrating one of the body's linings and entering the interstitial fluid (Figure 50.9, step 1). The bacteria then move with lymph into the lymphatic system and are carried to lymph nodes (Figure 50.9, step 2). Within the lymph node, a macrophage and a B cell recognize the bacteria as a foreign substance and bind to the bacteria.

The process of B-cell activation usually requires the activation of helper T cells, which was depicted in Figure 50.8 and is also shown in step 3 of Figure 50.9. The helper T cell binds to a complex of antigen and class II MHC protein on an APC. In this case, the APC is a macrophage that has phagocytized one of the bacteria, hydrolyzed its proteins into peptide fragments, complexed the fragments with class II MHC proteins, and displayed the complexes on its surface. Once a helper T cell specific for the complex binds to it, the helper T cell becomes activated. The macrophage helps this activation process in two other ways: It provides a costimulus via nonantigenic plasma membrane proteins, and it secretes IL-1 and TNF.

IL-1 and TNF stimulate the helper T cell to secrete another cytokine, named interleukin 2 (IL-2). IL-2 stimulates the activated helper T cell to divide. This leads eventually to the formation of a clone of activated helper T cells (Figure 50.9, step 4), which bind to B cells and also secrete IL-2 and other cytokines. Certain of these cytokines provide the additional signals (Figure 50.9, step 5) that are usually required to activate nearby antigen-bound B cells to proliferate and differentiate into plasma cells (Figure 50.9, step 6), which then secrete specific antibodies (Figure 50.9, step 7). Some B cells are set aside to become memory cells to help ward off possible future attacks by the same antigen. Thus, helper T cells are so named because their secretions help activate B cells that have bound antigen.

The secreted antibodies circulate through the lymphatic system and then the bloodstream, through which they reach the site of bacterial infection and inflammation. There the antibodies leave the blood and combine with the bacterial surface

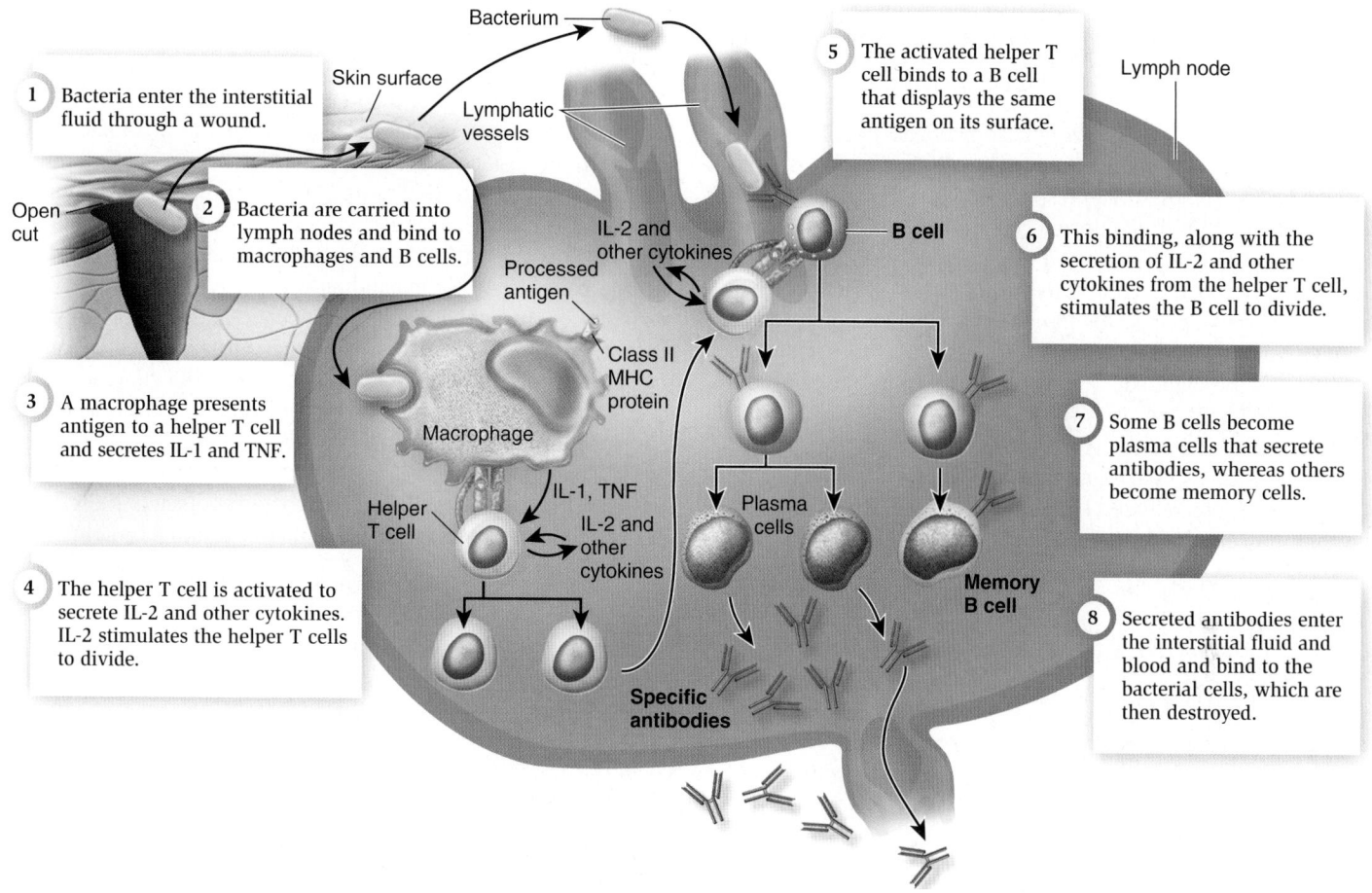

Figure 50.9   Summary of events in a typical humoral immune response.   Most of the events depicted occur within a lymph node.

antigen that initiated the immune response. These antibodies then direct the attack against the bacteria to which they are now bound (Figure 50.9, step 8). Thus, immunoglobulins play two distinct roles in humoral immune responses. First, during antigen recognition, immunoglobulins on the surface of B cells (B-cell receptors) bind to antigen brought to them. Second, immunoglobulins secreted by the resulting plasma cells (antibodies) bind to bacteria bearing the same antigens, marking them as the targets to be attacked.

Instead of directly killing the microbes, antibodies bound to antigen on the microbial surface inactivate the microbes in various ways. Antibodies may physically link the microbes to phagocytes (neutrophils and macrophages), complement proteins, or NK cells. This linkage—called opsonization—triggers the attack mechanism and ensures that only the microbes and not nearby body cells are killed.

In a second mechanism, antibodies directed against bacterial toxins in the extracellular fluid bind to the toxins, thereby preventing them from harming susceptible body cells. The antibody-antigen complexes that are formed are then destroyed by phagocytes.

In a similar way, antibodies produced against certain viral surface proteins bind to the viruses in the extracellular fluid, preventing them from attaching to the plasma membranes of potential host cells. As with bacterial toxins, the antibody–virus complexes that are formed are subsequently phagocytized. Thus the body can eliminate viruses in two ways: through the humoral actions of antibodies in body fluids, and through the cell-mediated killing of virus-infected cells by cytotoxic T cells.

In Cell-Mediated Immunity, Cytotoxic T Cells Kill Infected or Cancer Cells

The previous sections described how immune responses provide long-term defences against bacteria, viruses, and individual foreign molecules that enter the body's extracellular fluid. We now describe in detail how the body's own cells that have become infected by viruses or transformed into cancer cells are destroyed by cell-mediated immune responses.

What is the value of destroying virus-infected host cells? First, such destruction prevents cells from making more viruses. Second, for cells that already are making mature viruses, it results in the release of the viruses into the extracellular fluid, where they can then be directly neutralized by circulating antibody, as just described. Generally, only a few host cells are sacrificed in this way. Once viruses have had a chance to replicate and spread from cell to cell, however, so many virus-infected host cells may be killed by the body's own defences that organ malfunction may occur.

Role of Cytotoxic T Cells A typical cytotoxic T-cell response triggered by viral infection of a vertebrate's body cells is summarized in **Figure 50.10**. The response triggered by a cancer cell would be similar. A virus-infected cell produces foreign proteins, viral antigens that are processed and presented on the plasma membrane of the cell complexed with class I MHC proteins. Cytotoxic T cells specific for the particular antigen bind to the complex. As with B cells, binding to antigen alone does not cause activation of the cytotoxic T cell. Cytokines from adjacent activated helper T cells are also needed.

How are the helper T cells brought into play in these cases? Macrophages phagocytize extracellular viruses (or, in the case of cancer, antigens released from the surface of cancerous cells) and then process and present antigen, in association with class II MHC proteins, to the helper T cells. In addition, the macrophages provide a costimulus and also secrete IL-1 and TNF. The activated helper T cell releases IL-2 and other cytokines, which stimulate proliferation of the helper T cell.

IL-2 and other cytokines also act on the cytotoxic T cell bound to the surface of the virus-infected or cancer cell, stimulating this attack cell to proliferate. Why is proliferation important if a cytotoxic T cell has already located and bound to its target? The answer is that there is rarely just one virus-infected cell or one cancer cell. By expanding the clone of cytotoxic T cells capable of recognizing the particular antigen, proliferation increases the likelihood that the other virus-infected or cancer cells will be encountered by the specific type of cytotoxic T cell.

Target cell killing by activated cytotoxic T cells occurs by several mechanisms, but one of the most important is as follows. The cytotoxic T cell releases the contents of its secretory vesicles into the extracellular space between itself and the target cell to which it is bound. These vesicles contain a protein called

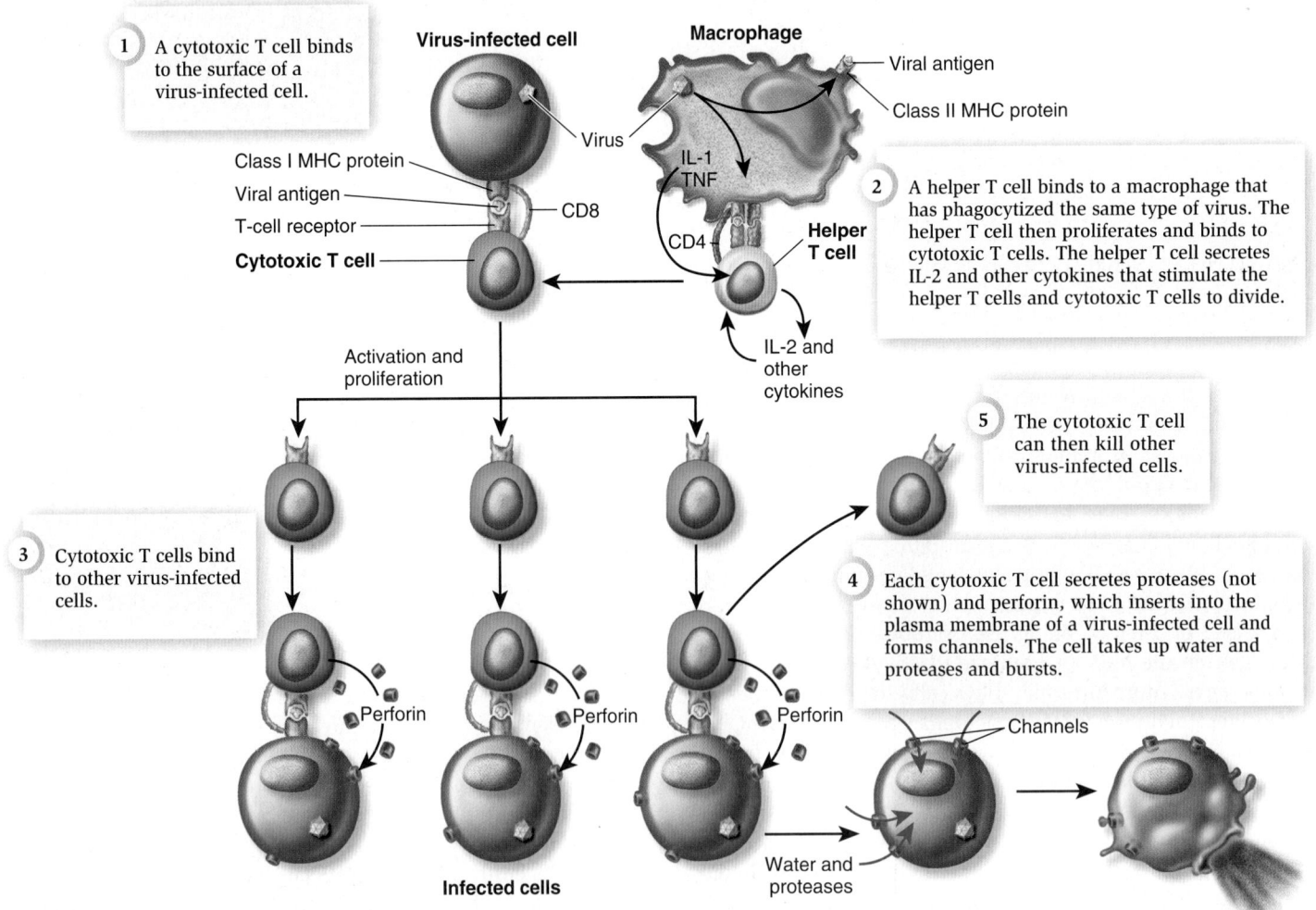

Figure 50.10 Summary of events in the killing of virus-infected cells by cytotoxic T cells. These events occur in the extracellular fluid. The sequence is similar for cancerous cells attacked by a cytotoxic T cell.

perforin, which is similar in structure to the proteins of the complement system's membrane attack complex. Perforin inserts into the target cell's membrane and forms channels ("perforations") through the membrane. In this manner, it causes the attacked cell to take in water and burst. The fact that perforin is released directly into the space between the tightly attached cytotoxic T cell and the target ensures that other nearby host cells will not be killed.

Role of Natural Killer (NK) Cells   Although cytotoxic T cells are very important attack cells against virus-infected and cancer cells, they are not the only ones. NK cells also destroy such cells by secreting toxic chemicals.

As mentioned earlier, NK cells can recognize general features on the surface of virus-infected cells or cancer cells, and participate in innate immunity. In addition, NK cells can be linked to target cells by antibodies, and this constitutes another potential mechanism for bringing them into play against virus-infected or cancer cells.

B Cells and T Cells That Recognize Self-Molecules Must Be Killed or Inhibited

As we have seen, the lymphocytes responsible for the acquired immune response in vertebrates are very capable killers of pathogens—so capable, in fact, that it raises a question: Why don't these cells attack and kill normal self-cells? In other words, how does the body distinguish between self- and nonself-components and develop what is called **immune tolerance?**

Recall that the huge diversity of lymphocyte receptors is ultimately the result of multiple random DNA cutting and recombination processes. It is virtually certain, therefore, that every animal possessing acquired immune defences would have clones of lymphocytes with receptors that could bind to that individual's own proteins. The continued existence and functioning of such lymphocytes would be disastrous because such binding would launch an immune attack against all body cells expressing these proteins.

At least two mechanisms explain why individuals normally lack active lymphocytes that respond to self-components. First, during early development in vertebrates, T cells are exposed to a wide mix of self-proteins in the thymus. Those T cells with receptors capable of binding self-proteins are destroyed by apoptosis in a process termed **clonal deletion**. The second process, termed **clonal inactivation**, occurs outside the thymus and causes potentially self-reacting T cells to become nonresponsive. B cells undergo similar processes. The mechanisms by which these two events occur are still under investigation.

Occasionally, however, these mechanisms fail, and the body's immune cells attack the body's own cells. When this happens in humans, it is known as an **autoimmune disease**. Autoimmune diseases are conditions in which the body's normal state of immune tolerance somehow breaks down, with the result that both humoral and cell-mediated attacks are directed against the body's own cells and tissues. A growing number of human diseases are being recognized as autoimmune in origin. Examples are multiple sclerosis, in which myelin is attacked; myasthenia gravis, in which the receptors for acetylcholine on skeletal muscle cells are the targets; rheumatoid arthritis, in which joints are damaged; and type 1 diabetes mellitus, in which the insulin-producing cells of the pancreas are destroyed.

Treatments for autoimmune disease range from treating the symptoms (for example, administering insulin to individuals with diabetes), to suppressing the immune system with drugs. Currently, researchers are investigating the possible use of transplanted hematopoietic stem cells that do not recognize the target protein as being foreign and thus antigenic.

Autoimmune diseases affect a large number of people, but many other immune disorders have far greater impacts on public health, as described in section 50.4.

Immunological Memory Is an Important Feature of Acquired Immunity

As we have learned, the acquired immune response to a given antigen depends on whether or not the body has previously been exposed to that antigen. Consider, for example, the humoral immune response. In mammals, antibody production in response to first contact with an antigen occurs slowly, over a few weeks (**Figure 50.11**). This response to an initial exposure to an antigen is termed a **primary immune response**. Any

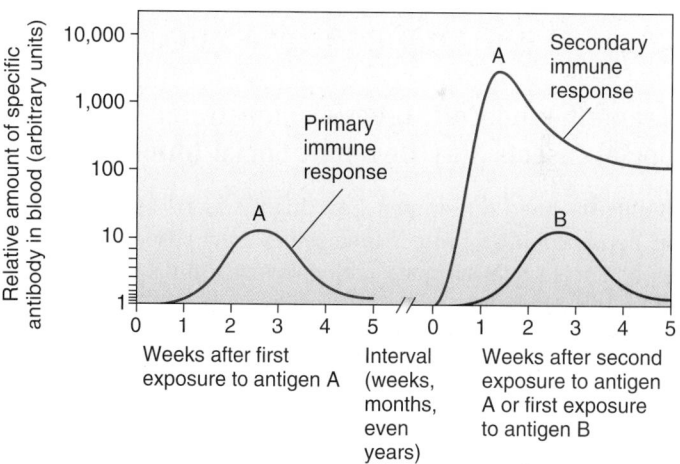

Figure 50.11   Primary and secondary immune responses. In a primary response, as shown in this graph, an initial exposure to an antigen produces modest levels of specific antibody over a period of weeks. In a secondary response, subsequent exposure to the same antigen results in greater antibody production (note that the scale of the Y-axis on the graph is logarithmic) that occurs more rapidly and lasts longer than a primary response. The secondary response is specific for that antigen. Exposure at that time to other antigens for the first time produces the usual primary response.

Concept check: *What is the advantage of a secondary immune response?*

subsequent infection by the same pathogen elicits an immediate and heightened production of additional specific antibodies against that particular antigen, a reaction termed a **secondary immune response**.

In the case of humoral immunity, this secondary response occurs more quickly, is stronger, and lasts longer because memory B cells that had been produced in response to initial antigen exposure are quickly stimulated to multiply and differentiate into thousands of plasma cells. These cells then produce large amounts of specific antibodies. The immune system's ability to produce this secondary response is called **immunological memory**.

Immunological memory explains why we and other animals are able to fight off many illnesses to which we have been previously exposed, such as many common childhood diseases. The acquired response to exposure to any type of antigen is known as **active immunity**. Active immunity not only results from natural exposure to antigens but also is the basis for the artificial exposures to antigen that occur in vaccinations and immunizations.

In **vaccinations** and **immunizations**, small quantities of living or dead microbes, small quantities of toxins, or harmless antigenic molecules derived from a microorganism or its toxin are injected into the body, resulting in a primary immune response including the production of memory cells. Subsequent natural exposure to the immunizing antigen results in a rapid, effective response that can prevent or reduce the severity of disease.

In contrast to active immunity is another type of acquired immunity called **passive immunity**, which confers protection against disease through the direct transfer of antibodies from one individual to another. Passive immunity can occur naturally, as when IgG molecules cross the mammalian placenta to protect a fetus from various pathogens, or when a newborn mammal receives antibodies from breast milk. It can also occur artificially, as when a human patient is given an injection of IgG molecules against hepatitis shortly after exposure to hepatitis viruses. Because antibodies are proteins with a limited lifespan, the protection afforded by the transfer of antibodies in passive immunity is relatively short lived, usually lasting only a few weeks or months.

Immunizations are very important in preventing disease among humans and domesticated animals. This is especially important when humans or other animals live in dense populations. A good example is seen in certain invertebrates, such as social insects, which live in populations with enormous numbers of individuals in confined areas. Do such populations have any naturally occurring protection against widespread disease that could otherwise ravage an entire colony of animals? This question has been explored recently by biologists studying social insects like ants and termites, as described next.

FEATURE INVESTIGATION

Traniello and Colleagues Demonstrated That Social Insects May Develop "Social Immunity"

Biologists have questioned how highly social animals living in dense colonies protect themselves from disease transmission. Such social animals include wood-eating termites that exist in very large numbers in complex nests. Termites may encounter a range of pathogens because they nest in moist, decaying wood, which provides a favourable environment for bacteria, fungi, and other parasites. A single infected termite could rapidly spread disease from insect to insect in a densely populated colony, but rarely are entire colonies wiped out by infection. In part, this occurs because termites kill microbes by producing antimicrobial secretions that are used to line their nests. In addition, behavioural adaptations, such as grooming to remove pathogens from nest mates' cuticles and removing sick or dead animals from the nest, help reduce disease transmission.

Recently, however, James Traniello and colleagues identified in termites another possible mechanism of protection from disease. "Social immunity," which involves the transfer of infection resistance from immunized to naive (susceptible) nest mates, is shown in **Figure 50.12**. These investigators first discovered that *Zootermopsis angusticollis* termites survive a pathogen challenge better when they are living in a group than when they are isolated as individuals. This indicates that an individual's immunity is enhanced when they are surrounded by nest mates. How might this occur? Individuals of this species are highly susceptible to parasitic fungi. Traniello and his colleagues divided animals into two groups. To distinguish the groups from each other, one group was fed on paper that contained a dye that marked the animals with a visible colour. The investigators then exposed this group of termites to a sublethal dose of fungal spores to immunize them against the fungus. The other (uncoloured) group was exposed only to a control solution. One week following exposure to spores or control solutions, half of the control group of animals was combined into a single nest with the immunized animals, while the other half of the control group remained in a separate nest.

One week later, the animals in each group were exposed to a potentially lethal dose of fungal spores, and their survival was recorded after six days. Uncoloured termites that had not experienced an initial exposure to spores but had later nested with animals that were exposed and thus immunized, had a significantly higher survival rate following exposure to the lethal dose of spores, compared with animals that did not nest with immunized animals. Thus, the investigators concluded that social contact between nonimmunized and immunized animals resulted in a transfer of immunity to the more susceptible members of the group.

HYPOTHESIS Sociality promotes disease resistance in termites.

KEY MATERIALS Termites (*Zootermopsis angusticollis*), pathogenic fungus spores.

Experimental level

Conceptual level

1 Feed termites dyed or undyed filter paper.

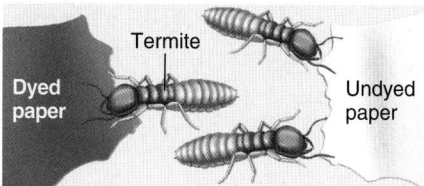

Dyed paper   Termite   Undyed paper

These termites were fed dyed paper and turned blue.   These termites were fed undyed paper.

2 Expose dyed termites to a suspension of pathogenic fungal spores at a sublethal concentration. Undyed termites receive a control solution.

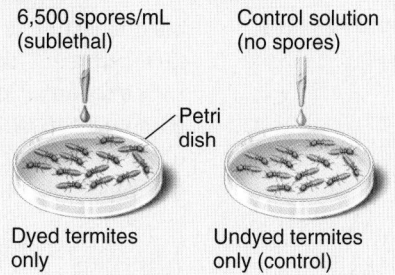

6,500 spores/mL (sublethal)   Control solution (no spores)

Petri dish

Dyed termites only   Undyed termites only (control)

Only the dyed termites have been exposed to the pathogen and will have an immune response.

3 One week after exposure, some of the unexposed (undyed) termites were grouped with some of the exposed (dyed) termites. This is called group 1. Group 2 consists of only undyed termites.

Group 1   Group 2

Allowed to coexist for one week.

Close contact between exposed and unexposed termites may transfer immunity.

4 Expose group 1 and group 2 to a potentially lethal concentration of fungal spores. Measure the percentage of undyed termites that survive after six days.

65,000 spores/mL

If immunity is transferred, a higher percentage of undyed animals in group 1 should survive exposure to the spores.

5 **THE DATA**

Results from step 4:

Percentage of undyed animals surviving after 6 days (y-axis: 0, 20, 40, 60, 80, 100)

From group 1   From group 2

6 **CONCLUSION** Immunity against deadly pathogens can be transferred from exposed termites to unexposed termites.

7 **SOURCE** Traniello, J.F., Rosengaus, R.B., and Savoie, K. 2002. The development of immunity in a social insect: evidence for the group facilitation of disease resistance. *Proceedings of the National Academy of Sciences USA* 99:6838–6842.

Figure 50.12 Traniello and his colleagues demonstrated that social insects may develop "social immunity."

Concept check: *What other animals besides social insects live in extremely dense colonies and require protection against devastating illnesses sweeping through the entire population?*

The mechanism of social immunization is not known but could be related to either the oral exchange of secretions or contact with inactivated spores remaining on the bodies of immunized animals. Whatever the mechanism may prove to be, the consequence is striking: The close physical contact that is characteristic of social insect behaviour helps propagate colonywide immunization against potentially deadly pathogens.

Experimental Questions

1. What features of termite physiology and behaviour reduce the chance that an infection will spread throughout the colony?
2. What hypothesis was tested by Traniello and his colleagues?
3. How did the researchers test this hypothesis, and what were the results of the study?

50.4 HUMAN HEALTH CONNECTION

Learning Outcomes:

1. Explain the role of the immune system in organ transplant rejection and allergic reactions.
2. Characterize the effects of HIV on a human immune system and describe current methods of treating HIV infection.

In this section, we describe a few ways in which immune responses affect human health.

Organ Transplants and Blood Transfusions Require Matching of Donor and Recipient

Since the mid-twentieth century, organ transplants from a healthy or recently deceased donor to a recipient have become widespread. The Canadian Institute for Health Information, through its Canadian Organ Replacement Register, reported that approximately 2,000 organs are transplanted in Canada each year; in 2008, there were kidney (1,204), liver (445), heart (162), lung (131), and pancreas (56) transplants. The major obstacle to successful transplantation of tissues and organs is a reaction called graft rejection, in which the immune system recognizes the transplants (also called grafts) as foreign and attacks them as it would any other foreign cells. Although B cells and macrophages play some role in graft rejection, cytotoxic T cells and helper T cells are mainly responsible. To minimize this possibility, patients are given drugs that suppress immune function.

Except for identical twins, the class I MHC proteins on graft cells differ from those on the recipient's cells, as do the class II MHC proteins present on macrophages in the graft. Consequently, the recipient's T cells recognize the MHC proteins in the graft as foreign, and cytotoxic T cells (with the aid of helper T cells) destroy the graft cells.

Blood transfusion reactions, in which erythrocytes are destroyed after the transfusion, are a special example of tissue rejection in that antibodies, rather than cytotoxic T cells, are the major factor in rejection. Although erythrocytes lack MHC proteins, they have plasma membrane components that can function as antigens when transfused into another person's blood. Of the more than 400 erythrocyte antigens, the ABO system (see Chapter 15) of carbohydrates is the most important for transfusion reactions.

Allergies

An allergy (also known as hypersensitivity) is a condition in which immune responses to environmental antigens cause inflammation and damage to body cells. Antigens that induce allergic reactions are called allergens. Common examples of allergens include ragweed pollen and poison ivy. Most allergens themselves are relatively or completely harmless. It is the immune responses to them that cause the damage. In essence, then, allergy is immunity gone awry, for the response is of inappropriate strength and duration for the stimulus. In Canada alone, as many as 10 million people have allergies.

For any allergy to develop, a genetically predisposed person must first be exposed to the allergen—a process called sensitization. Subsequent exposures elicit the damaging immune responses we recognize as an allergy.

Allergies can be broadly classified according to the speed of the reaction. Allergies that take up to several days to develop are considered delayed hypersensitivities. The skin rash that appears after contact with poison ivy is an example. More common are reactions considered immediate hypersensitivities, which can develop in minutes or up to a few hours. These allergies are also called IgE-mediated hypersensitivities because they involve IgE antibodies.

In immediate hypersensitivity, sensitization to the allergen leads to the production of specific antibodies and a clone of memory B cells. In individuals who are genetically susceptible to allergies, antigens that elicit immediate hypersensitivity reactions stimulate the production of IgE antibodies. On their release from plasma cells, these IgE molecules circulate throughout the body and attach themselves to mast cells in connective tissue. When the same antigen subsequently enters the body at some future time and binds with IgE bound to mast cells, the mast cell is stimulated to secrete many inflammatory

Figure 50.13 A mast cell, which produces the symptoms of a hypersensitivity reaction. When antigen binds to IgE molecules on the mast cell membrane, the cell is activated and releases the contents of its vesicles by exocytosis to extracellular fluid. An unstimulated mast cell contains many secretory vesicles.

mediators, including histamine, that then initiate an inflammatory response.

The signs and symptoms of IgE-mediated allergy reflect both the effects of the inflammatory mediators and the body site in which the antigen–IgE–mast cell binding occurs. When, for example, a previously sensitized person inhales ragweed pollen, the antigen combines with IgE on mast cells in the respiratory passages (**Figure 50.13**). The mast cells release their contents, which induce increased mucus secretion, increased blood flow, swelling of the epithelial lining, and contraction of the smooth muscle surrounding airways. These effects produce the congestion, runny nose, sneezing, and difficulty in breathing characteristic of hay fever.

Acquired Immune Deficiency Syndrome (AIDS)

AIDS is caused by the **human immunodeficiency virus** (**HIV**), which incapacitates the immune response by preferentially infecting helper T cells. HIV is a retrovirus; such viruses have a nucleic acid core of RNA rather than DNA. Once inside a helper T cell, HIV uses the enzyme reverse transcriptase to transcribe the virus's RNA into DNA, which is then integrated into the T cell's chromosomes. Later, viral replication within the T cell results in the death of the cell (see Chapter 16).

HIV infects helper T cells because the CD4 protein in their plasma membranes acts as a receptor for an HIV capsid protein. But the binding to CD4 is not sufficient to enable HIV to enter the helper T cell. Another T-cell surface protein, which

normally acts as a receptor for certain cytokines, must serve as a coreceptor. Interestingly, individuals possessing a mutation in this cytokine receptor are highly resistant to HIV infection, so much research is now focused on the possible therapeutic use of chemicals that can bind to and block this coreceptor.

HIV not only directly kills helper T cells but also indirectly causes additional helper T cell death by inducing cytotoxic T cells to kill HIV-infected helper T cells. In addition, by still poorly understood mechanisms, HIV causes the death of many uninfected helper T cells by apoptosis. Without adequate numbers of helper T cells, neither B cells nor cytotoxic T cells can function normally. Both humoral and cell-mediated immunity are compromised. Many individuals with AIDS die from infections and cancers that ordinarily would be readily handled by a fully functional immune system.

AIDS, first described in 1981, has since reached epidemic proportions. About 40 million people worldwide are infected with HIV, and nearly 15,000 new infections occur each day. The great majority of individuals now infected with HIV show no signs of AIDS. Their infections are diagnosed by the presence of anti-HIV antibodies or HIV RNA in the blood. However, most individuals infected with HIV will eventually develop AIDS.

If left untreated, HIV infection commonly develops into AIDS in about 10 years. During the first five years, killed helper T cells are typically replaced by new cells, so T-cell levels remain normal, and the individual remains asymptomatic. Over the next five years T-cell levels begin to decline, until at some point AIDS reveals itself in the form of opportunistic viral, bacterial, and fungal infections. Certain unusual cancers, such as Kaposi's sarcoma, also occur with high frequency. In untreated individuals, death usually ensues within two years after the onset of AIDS symptoms.

The major routes of HIV transmission are (1) unprotected sexual intercourse with an infected partner; (2) transfer of contaminated blood or blood products between individuals, such as during a blood transfusion or the sharing of needles among intravenous drug users; (3) transfer from an infected mother to her child across the placenta or during delivery; or (4) transfer via breast milk during nursing.

Treatment for HIV-infected individuals has two components: one directed against the virus itself to delay progression of the disease, and one to prevent or treat the opportunistic infections and cancers that ultimately cause death. One current antiviral approach involves administering a "cocktail" of four drugs, known as HAART (highly active anti-retroviral therapy). Two of the drugs inhibit the action of reverse transcriptase in converting viral RNA into DNA within the host cell, a third drug inhibits an HIV enzyme required for assembling new viruses, and a recently developed fourth class of drugs called fusion inhibitors prevents the virus from entering T cells. These treatments have proven to be effective in slowing the rate at which infection with HIV leads to AIDS.

Summary of Key Concepts

- An animal's cells and organs that collectively contribute to its immune defences, or immunity, constitute the animal's immune system.

- In innate (nonspecific) immunity, the body's defences are present at birth and act against foreign materials in much the same way regardless of the specific identity of the invading material. Acquired (specific) immunity develops only after the body is exposed to foreign substances and targets those foreign substances specifically.

50.1 Types of Pathogens

- Three major types of pathogens elicit an immune response: bacteria, viruses, and parasites.

50.2 Innate (Nonspecific) Immunity

- An important innate defence is composed of phagocytes—cells capable of phagocytosis. In vertebrates, most phagocytes belong to the blood cells called leukocytes. The leukocytes involved in innate immunity include neutrophils, eosinophils, monocytes, macrophages, basophils, and natural killer (NK) cells. (Figure 50.1)

- Two other types of cells play important roles in innate immunity: dendritic cells and mast cells.

- Inflammation is an innate local response to infection or injury characterized by local redness, swelling, heat, and pain. The events of inflammation are induced and regulated by chemical mediators called cytokines. (Figure 50.3)

- Antimicrobial proteins include interferons, which inhibit viral replication, and complement proteins, which kill microbes without prior phagocytosis. Activation of the complement proteins results in the formation of a membrane attack complex (MAC), which creates water channels in the microbial plasma membrane and causes the microbe to swell and burst.

50.3 Acquired (Specific) Immunity

- Any foreign molecule that the host does not recognize as self and that triggers a specific immune response is called an antigen.

- The lymphocytes responsible for specific immunity are B cells, which differentiate into antibody-producing cells called plasma cells, and T cells, which directly kill infected, mutated, or transplanted cells. T cells include cytotoxic T cells, which directly kill target cells via secreted chemicals, and helper T cells, which assist in the activation and function of B cells and cytotoxic T cells. (Figure 50.3)

- Immunologists recognize two types of specific immunity. In humoral immunity, plasma cells secrete antibodies that bind to antigens. In cell-mediated immunity, cytotoxic T cells directly attack and destroy infected body cells, cancer cells, or transplanted cells.

- Although lymphocytes circulate in the blood, most of them reside in a group of organs and tissues that constitute the lymphatic system. (Figure 50.4)

- When a lymphocyte is stimulated by an antigen, it divides and produces clones of itself, all of which express the same receptor. The process by which these clones are formed is called clonal selection. After activation, some of the cloned lymphocytes function as effector cells, which carry out the attack response; other cells function as memory cells, which remain poised to recognize the antigen if it returns in the future. (Figure 50.5)

- B cells that are activated by an antigen and by cytokines produced by helper T cells differentiate into plasma cells, which secrete antibodies—proteins that combine with the antigen and guide an attack that eliminates the antigen or the cells bearing it.

- Immunoglobulins (including antibodies and B-cell receptors) are Y-shaped proteins that include two heavy chains and two light chains. The lower halves of the heavy chains contain constant regions, which are identical for all immunoglobulins of a given Ig class. At the other end of the Ig molecule, the two chains form a variable region that serves as the antigen binding site. (Figures 50.6, 50.7)

- The process known as hypermutation, which primarily involves numerous C to T point mutations, is crucial to enabling lymphocytes to produce a diverse array of antibodies capable of recognizing many different antigens.

- Major histocompatibility complex (MHC) proteins are cellular identity tags that serve as genetic markers of self. Class I MHC proteins are found on the surface of all human body cells except erythrocytes. Class II MHC proteins are found only on the surface of macrophages, B cells, and dendritic cells.

- Antigen-presenting cells (APCs) are cells bearing fragments of antigen, called antigenic determinants or epitopes, complexed with the cell's MHC proteins. (Figure 50.8)

- The process by which the body distinguishes between self- and nonself-components is called immune tolerance. Individuals normally lack active lymphocytes that respond to self-components because of two mechanisms. T cells with receptors capable of binding self-proteins are destroyed by apoptosis in a process termed *clonal deletion*. Clonal inactivation causes potentially self-reacting lymphocytes to become nonresponsive.

- Humoral immune responses are mediated by B cells and plasma cells, while cell-mediated immune responses are mediated by cytotoxic T cells. In both types of responses, helper T cells are required. (Figures 50.9, 50.10)

- When the body's immune cells attack the body's own cells, the result is called an autoimmune disease.

- On initial exposure to an antigen, the body produces a primary immune response. Any subsequent exposure to the same antigen elicits an immediate and heightened response termed a *secondary immune response*. The immune system's ability to produce this secondary response is called immunological memory. (Figure 50.11)

- The acquired response to exposure to any type of antigen is known as active immunity. The artificial exposures to antigen that occur in vaccinations and immunizations also induce active immunity. In contrast, passive immunity confers protection against disease through the direct transfer of antibodies from one individual to another.

- Some animals, such as social insects, can confer immunity on each other through social contact, called social immunity. (Figure 50.12)

50.4 Human Health Connection

- Organ transplant rejections can be minimized by attempting to match the MHC I and II types of donor and recipient. Other areas in which immune responses are involved include allergies, and AIDS, caused by the human immunodeficiency virus (HIV). AIDS reduces the body's immunity by killing helper T cells. (Figure 50.13)

Test to Assess Your Learning

1. Which of the following is *not* an example of a barrier defence in animals?
   a. skin
   b. secretions from skin glands
   c. exoskeleton
   d. mucus
   e. antibodies

2. The leukocytes that are found in mucosal surfaces and play a role in defending the body against parasitic infections are
   a. neutrophils.
   b. eosinophils.
   c. basophils.
   d. monocytes.
   e. NK cells.

3. The vascular changes of inflammation
   a. lead to an increase in bacterial cells at the injury site.
   b. decrease the number of leukocytes at the injury site.
   c. allow plasma proteins to move easily from the bloodstream to the injury site.
   d. increase the number of antibodies at the injury site.
   e. activate lymphocytes.

4. Which of the following statements is correct regarding specific immunity?
   a. Specific immunity requires only the presence of helper T cells to function properly.
   b. Specific immunity does not require exposure to a foreign substance.
   c. Specific immunity is triggered by contact with a particular antigen.
   d. Specific immunity includes inflammation.
   e. All of the above are correct.

5. Memory B cells are
   a. cloned lymphocytes that are active in subsequent infections.
   b. cloned lymphocytes that are active during a primary infection.
   c. NK cells that recognize cancer cells and destroy them.
   d. cells that produce antibodies.
   e. macrophages that have recognized self-antigens.

6. The immunoglobulin that is passed from mother to fetus across the placenta is
   a. IgA.
   b. IgD.
   c. IgE.
   d. IgG.
   e. IgM.

7. The region of an antibody that serves as the antigen binding site is
   a. the constant region.
   b. the variable region.
   c. the heavy chain.
   d. the light chain.
   e. the hinge point.

8. A major difference between the activation of B cells and T cells is that
   a. T cells must interact with antigens bound to plasma membranes.
   b. B cells interact with only free antigens.
   c. B cells are not regulated by helper T cells.
   d. T cells produce antibodies.
   e. none of the above.

9. Cells that process foreign proteins and complex them with their MHC proteins are called
   a. cytotoxic T cells.
   b. plasma cells.
   c. NK cells.
   d. antigen presenting cells.
   e. helper T cells.

10. HIV causes immune deficiency because the virus
    a. destroys all the cytotoxic T cells.
    b. preferentially destroys helper T cells that regulate the immune system.
    c. directly inactivates plasma cells.
    d. causes mutations that lead to autoimmune diseases.
    e. all of the above.

Articulate to Assess Your Learning

1. Distinguish between *innate immunity* and *acquired immunity*.
2. Explain the function of cytotoxic T cells.

Collaborate to Assess and Extend Your Learning

1. Discuss the basic structure of an immunoglobulin.
2. Describe the major difference between invertebrate and vertebrate immune systems.
3. A principle of biology is that living organisms interact with their environment. Such interactions include potentially threatening environmental factors such as pathogens. Discuss three types of pathogens that affect the health of animals.

Visit McGraw-Hill Ryerson Connect™ for additional study resources.

WHAT'S NEW?

An interview with Dr. Glenn Tattersall from Brock University by Aileen Hutson, a fourth-year student at Brock University.

Dr. Tattersall is an Associate Professor in the Department of Biological Sciences at Brock University.

▶ What made you decide to go into scientific research?

It started with a childhood curiosity of the natural world. I spent a lot of time when I was younger wandering in the wild and developed an appreciation and curiosity for all things natural. Based on this curiosity, I wanted to be a scientist, even before I understood exactly what a scientist really does. It wasn't until university that I fully realized what scientific researchers do (quite different from a childhood impression), but by then I was hooked, and was sure that was what I wanted to become.

▶ What led you to study the thermoregulation and metabolic control of animals?

When I was younger, my family and I would help frogs overwinter in our backyard pond; that is probably what sparked my interest in the study of hibernation and thermoregulation. During my undergraduate years I worked as a research assistant in various labs during the summers, and one year I studied the effects of acidic environments on amphibians. Those jobs led me toward doing my PhD in zoology and studying overwintering in frogs, which unfolded into more fundamental questions about thermoregulation and metabolic control.

▶ What makes a good scientific researcher?

A good scientific researcher should be perseverant, patient, self-motivated, and logical. You have to be willing to repeat the same experiment over and over after the initial excitement from a positive result has faded. Research also involves discovering a lot of things that do not necessarily answer the initial question, so you should be open to new ideas. You cannot be discouraged when a particular experiment does not go as expected. Usually, this means you are not looking at the problem from the right perspective. Perhaps the most important thing is to be curious about the world around you.

▶ What skills should students develop if they are thinking about going into research?

You should know the fundamentals. Mathematical and logical skills are the primary skill sets for any researcher. In my field, physiology, physics, and chemistry play critical roles. You will also have to develop your writing and communication skills. It is important to write clearly, since writing communicates ideas more accurately than speaking. The most important thing is to find the area of research that you are most passionate about so you will still be interested after many years. You can use your textbooks and courses to find research that interests you and then read many research articles to learn about the research methods and the other details of those specific areas of research. Many students feel that they cannot get started in research unless they start full of original ideas. Those ideas will develop over time, particularly for people who are passionate about their research.

▶ What would be the ultimate discovery in your research?

I suppose what we really want to discover is taking a leap from the basic research into an artificial means to suppress metabolism and body temperature in mammals, for human application. Finding a safe means to reversibly suppress metabolism would be an exciting discovery that would change biomedical research and life as we know it.

▶ What are some of the applications for artificial suppression of metabolism?

There are many surgical applications, such as use in cardiac bypass surgery or heart and lung transplant surgery. It could also be useful for assisting premature infants who suffer respiratory ailments. One of the current applications being researched is for stroke treatment and prevention of further brain damage from stroke. Researchers are currently investigating how whole-head cooling can reduce the brain damage caused by a stroke. The more exotic applications are for prolonged stasis for use in space travel and life preservation.

▶ Which animal do you find the most fascinating and why?

Probably the toucans I researched. The extremely large beak is what fascinated me, and although we have numerous ideas for what the beak can do, its evolutionary origins are still somewhat of a mystery.

❯ **Can you tell us about your favourite field research trip?**

My favourite was spending four days on a small, 2-square-kilometre, island off the coast of Brazil. This little island, called Queimada Grande, is (or we should say 'was' because the species may now be in decline) home to a rare species of pit viper. These snakes live in high density in the forested area of the island, while along the coastal margin of the island are enormous numbers of nesting seabirds. So, within 100 metres you can go from observing the small critters like insects on the ground of the forest (while avoiding the snakes!) to observing the ridiculous nests built by the Brown Boobies.

❯ **Is all of your research noninvasive? Is this important to you?**

Not all of my research is noninvasive, but I view this as an important challenge. Many researchers are attempting to answer important questions using modern, noninvasive approaches. I believe that in addition to discovery and generating new knowledge, scientists are also always trying to refine and invent new ways to look at our science. In my case, I view this approach as refinement. Nevertheless, it is important to me, as well as all my scientific colleagues, to ensure that we do little harm when studying animals, so I have adopted noninvasive research methods whenever possible.

❯ **Will animals adapt quickly enough to survive the rapid temperature changes associated with Global Climate Change?**

This is the burning question in biology for the twenty-first century. If the question is, "In light of climate change, will all animals remain as they are in the next century"? I doubt it. Certainly many species are already migrating poleward. Some are already being affected physiologically and morphologically. Will they adapt? Evolution is ongoing and many evolutionary traits in those groups within which it has been studied do change quite rapidly. The consensus in the field of biology is that these rates of climate change are faster than most species have experienced before, so I certainly do not think that life will adapt in a manner that we, as humans, may appreciate. Remember as well that life also includes organisms that cause infectious diseases. Disease vectors will move poleward as well and disturb ecosystems or human health as the climate changes. The question is never a simple temperature-based question, but one that involves many interacting levels.

Unit VIII
Ecology

Ecology is the study of interactions among organisms and between organisms and their environment. These interactions govern the number of species in an area and their population densities. Ecologists work at the largest scales of any biologists.

In Chapter 51, we introduce the field of ecology, discuss the effects of physical variables such as temperature and moisture, and introduce the different scales at which ecologists work. At the largest scales, variation in temperature and moisture create distinct large-scale habitats, called biomes. Chapter 52 discusses behavioural ecology and how behaviour contributes to the fitness of organisms. The next two chapters examine population growth and the constraints to growth provided by competitors and natural enemies. In Chapter 53, we introduce the demographic tools needed to study population growth, provide simple mathematical models of growth, and examine the special case of human population growth. In Chapter 54, we discuss the effects of competition, predation, herbivory, parasitism, mutualism, and commensalism on populations. In Chapter 55, we consider the factors that influence the number of species in a community, and we examine different measures of diversity. Chapter 56 addresses the flow of energy and nutrients through the living and nonliving components of the environment. Finally, in Chapter 57 we address the conservation of life on Earth and the various strategies used to protect genetic, species, and ecosystem diversity. Throughout the unit, we examine the effects of humans on the environment, including pollution, global climate change, and the introduction of exotic species of plants and animals.

 The following biology principles will be emphasized this unit:

- *Living organisms use energy:* In Chapter 56 we discuss the cycle of nutrients and energy flow in ecosystems.

- *Living organisms interact with their environment:* Chapter 51 provides examples of the influence of temperature, water, pH, salt concentration, and light on the distribution and abundance of organisms.

- *New properties of life emerge from complex interactions:* In Chapter 57, we see how the effects of natural enemies and abiotic factors can cascade through natural communities.

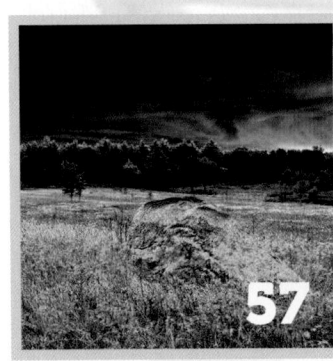

An Introduction to Ecology and Biomes

Chapter Outline

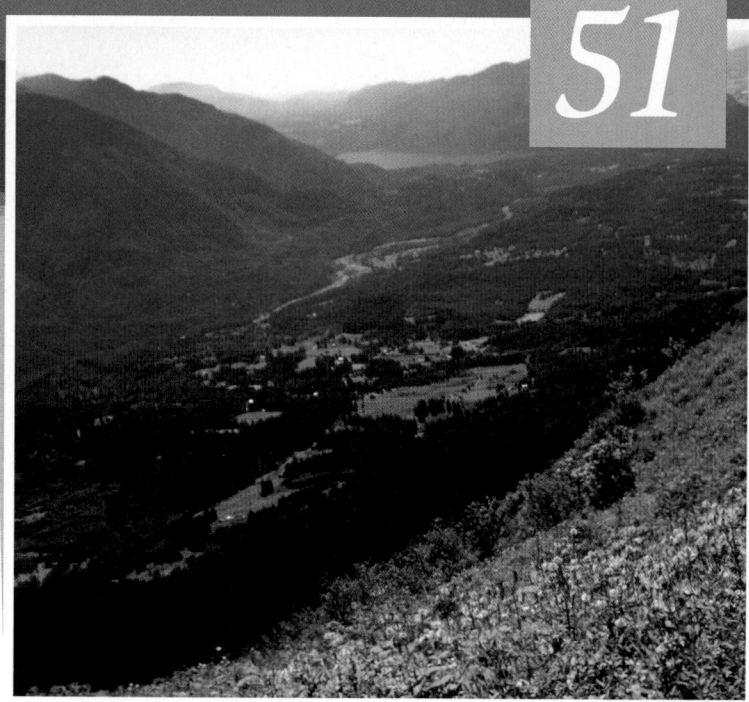

What controls the densities of these flowering plants on Mt. Thurston, British Columbia? Is it temperature or rainfall? Or is it the availability of pollinators, herbivory by insects or vertebrates, or competition with other plant species for resources? Ecology seeks to answer questions such as these.

In 2006 a study led by J. Alan Pounds of the Monteverde Cloud Forest Preserve in Costa Rica reported that fully two-thirds of the 110 species of harlequin frogs in mountainous areas of Central and South America had become extinct over the previous 20 years. The researchers noted that populations of other species, such the Panamanian golden frog (*Atelopus zeteki*), had been greatly reduced (**Figure 51.1**). The question was why. The culprit was identified as a disease-causing chytrid fungus, *Batrachochytrium dendrobatidis* (see Chapter 27), but this study implicated global climate change as the agent causing outbreaks of the fungus. One effect of global climate change is to increase the cloud cover, which reduces daytime temperatures and raises nighttime temperatures. Researchers believe that this combination has created favourable conditions for the spread of *B. dendrobatidis*, which thrives in cooler temperatures. Pounds, the lead ecologist, was quoted as saying, "Disease is the bullet killing frogs, but climate change is pulling the trigger." Chytrid fungi may also be contributing to amphibian declines in Canada, according to work being done by Purnima Govindarajulu (BC Ministry of the Environment and University of Victoria) to determine the effects on native frog populations in British Columbia.

Ecology is the study of interactions among organisms and between organisms and their environments. The interactions among organisms are called **biotic** interactions, while those between organisms and their nonliving environment are termed **abiotic** interactions. These interactions in turn govern the population densities of plants and animals and the numbers of species in an area. In this first chapter of the ecology unit, we will introduce you to four broad areas of ecology: organismal, population, community, and ecosystem ecology. Next, we will explore how ecologists approach and conduct their work. We will then turn our focus to abiotic interactions and examine the effects of factors such as temperature, water, light, pH, and salt concentrations on the distributions of organisms. We conclude with a consideration of climate and its large influence on the major types of habitats, called biomes, where organisms are found.

Ecological studies have important implications in the real world, as will be amply illustrated by examples discussed throughout the unit. However, a distinction must be made between ecology and **environmental science**, the application of ecology to real-world problems. To use an analogy: Ecology

Figure 51.1　Diminishing and disappearing populations. Population sizes of the Panamanian golden frog (*Atelopus zeteki*) have diminished greatly over the past 20 years, while populations of many other species of harlequin frogs have disappeared entirely. Ecologists are investigating the reasons for this decline.

BioConnections: *Look ahead to section 57.2. What are the main threats to species? Are they natural or human induced?*

is to environmental science as physics is to engineering. Both physics and ecology provide the theoretical framework on which to pursue more applied studies. Engineers rely on the principles of physics to build bridges. Environmental scientists rely on the principles of ecology to solve environmental problems.

Ecology describes the necessary framework for understanding how populations are affected by features of the physical environment, such as temperature and moisture, and by other organisms. In this unit, we'll also learn how plants compete with one another, how herbivores affect plant abundance, and how natural enemies affect prey populations. We'll examine the effects of humans on the environment, including pollution, global climate change, and the introduction of exotic species of plants and animals.

51.1 THE SCALE OF ECOLOGY

Learning Outcomes:

1. Describe and differentiate between the different scales at which ecologists work.
2. Discuss how the five steps of hypothesis testing can be applied to an ecological research project.

Ecology ranges in scale from the study of an individual organism through the study of populations to the study of communities and ecosystems (**Figure 51.2**). Figure 51.2 shows the different scales of ecology using locusts as an example. Swarms of the migratory grasshopper, *Melanoplus sanguinipes*, are also observed in the Canadian prairies with devastating agricultural effects. George Khachatourians at the University of Saskatchewan has developed a fungal biocontrol agent that can infect and kill these grasshoppers. In this section, we

introduce each of the broad areas of organismal, population, community, and ecosystem ecology. We will provide an investigation that helps illuminate the field of population ecology and conclude with an exploration of how ecologists conduct their experiments.

Organismal Ecology Investigates How Adaptations and Choices by Individuals Affect Their Reproduction and Survival

Organismal ecology can be divided into two subdisciplines. The first, physiological ecology, investigates how organisms are physiologically adapted to their environment and how the environment affects the distribution of species. Much of this chapter discusses physiological ecology.

The second area, **behavioural ecology**, focuses on how the behaviour of an individual animal contributes to its survival and reproductive success, which in turn eventually affects the population density of the species.

Population Ecology Describes How Populations Grow and Interact with Other Species

Population ecology focuses on groups of interbreeding individuals, called populations. A primary goal is to understand the factors that affect a population's growth and determine its size and density. Although the attention of a population ecologist may be aimed at studying the population of a particular species, the relative abundance of that species is often influenced by its interactions with other species. Thus, population ecology includes the study of **species interactions** such as predation, competition, and parasitism. Much of the theory of ecology is built upon the ecology of populations. Knowing what factors affect populations can help us maintain biodiversity, stop extinctions, and control invasive species.

(a)

(b)

(c)

(d)

Figure 51.2 **The scales of ecology.** (a) Organismal ecology. What is the temperature tolerance of this desert locust, *Schistocerca gregaria*? (b) Population ecology. What factors, such as the amount and quality of vegetation, influence the growth of desert locust populations? (c) Community ecology. What factors influence the interaction of species in functional communities? Desert locusts are in competition with other herbivores, such as these goats, for grass to eat. (d) Ecosystem ecology. How does energy flow among organisms, and how do nutrients cycle between organisms and the environment in the desert ecosystem? These desert locusts have died over the ocean and have been washed ashore.

FEATURE INVESTIGATION

Callaway and Aschehoug's Experiments Showed That the Secretion of Chemicals Gives Exotic Plants a Competitive Edge over Native Species

One important topic in the area of population ecology concerns **exotic species**, species moved from a native location to another location, usually by humans. Such species sometimes spread or invade so aggressively that they crowd out native species. It is estimated that more than 800 of the 5,000 plant species found in Canada are actually exotic introductions that have successfully established populations in the wild. Over half were brought in for gardening, horticulture, or landscaping purposes. Invasive exotic plants have traditionally been thought to succeed because they have escaped their natural enemies, primarily insects that remained in the country of origin and were not transported to the new locale. One way of controlling exotic species, therefore, has been to import the plant's natural enemies. This is known as **biological control**. However, new research on the population ecology of diffuse knapweed (*Centaurea diffusa*), an invasive Eurasian plant that has established itself in many areas of North America and causes serious problems in the arid southwestern interior of Canada, especially British Columbia, suggests a different reason for their success.

Researchers Ragan Callaway and Erik Aschehoug hypothesized that this particular species secretes powerful root exudates called **allelochemicals** that kill the roots of other species, allowing *Centaurea* to proliferate. To test their hypothesis, Callaway and Aschehoug collected seeds of three native Montana grasses, *Koeleria cristata*, *Festuca idahoensis*, and *Agropyron spicata*, and grew them both without other species and with the exotic *Centaurea* species (**Figure 51.3**). As hypothesized, *Centaurea* depressed the biomass of the native grasses. When

HYPOTHESIS Exotic plants from Eurasia outcompete native Montana grasses by secreting allelochemicals from their roots.

STARTING LOCATION *Centaurea diffusa*, a Eurasian plant, is invading Montana grasslands because it outcompetes three native grasses: *Koeleria cristata*, *Festuca idahoensis*, and *Agropyron spicata*.

	Experimental level	**Conceptual level**
1 Collect seeds of native Montana grasses and plant with and without seeds of invasive *C. diffusa* from Eurasia. Three months after sowing seeds, the plants are harvested, dried, and weighed.		*C. diffusa* significantly reduces biomass of native Montana grasses.
2 Collect seeds of grasses from Eurasia of the same three genera as the Montana grasses and plant with and without *C. diffusa*. Three months after sowing seeds, the plants are harvested, dried, and weighed.		*C. diffusa* doesn't depress the biomass of grasses native to Eurasia as much.

3 THE DATA*

*The biomass is that of the genus noted at the top of each graph.

Figure 51.3 Experimental evidence of the effect of allelochemicals on plant production.

Figure 51.3 *(Continued)*

> **4**   **CONCLUSION** *Centaurea diffusa*, a Eurasian grass, is invasive in the U.S. because it secretes allelochemicals, which inhibit the growth of native plants.
>
> **5**   **SOURCE** Callaway, R.M., and Aschehoug, E.T. 2000. Invasive plants versus their old and new neighbors. *Science* 290:521–523.

the experiments were repeated with grasses native to Eurasia—*Koeleria laerssenii*, *Festuca ovina*, and *Agropyron cristatum*—the species were affected, but to a significantly lesser degree than the Montana species were.

In other experiments not described in Figure 51.3, Callaway and Aschehoug added activated carbon, which absorbs the chemical excreted by the *Centaurea* roots. With activated carbon added to the soil, the Montana grass species increased in biomass compared to the previous experiments. The researchers concluded that *C. diffusa* outcompetes Montana grasses by secreting an allelochemical and that Eurasian grasses are not as susceptible to the chemical's effect, since they coevolved with it. If the reason for the success of invasive plants can be attributed to the chemicals they secrete, this calls into question the effectiveness of biological control of exotic weeds by importation of their natural enemies. This study on the population biology of an exotic plant has changed the way we think about why invasive exotic species succeed and could affect the way we attempt to control them in the future.

Experimental Questions

1. Prior to Callaway and Aschehoug's study, what was the prevailing hypothesis of why invasive species succeed in new environments?
2. Briefly describe the evidence collected to support the allelochemical hypothesis.
3. What was the function of the activated carbon used in a subsequent test of the hypothesis?

Community Ecology Focuses on What Factors Influence the Number of Species in a Given Area

We've just seen how a population of an exotic grass may produce allelochemicals that give it a growth advantage over populations of other species. On a larger scale, **community ecology** studies how populations of species interact and form functional communities. In a forest, there are many populations of trees, herbs, shrubs, grasses, the herbivores that eat them, and the carnivores that in turn prey on the herbivores. Community ecology focuses on why certain areas have high numbers of species (that is, are species rich), while other areas have low numbers of species (that is, are species poor).

While ecologists are interested in species richness for its own sake, a link also exists between species richness and community function. Ecologists generally believe that species-rich communities perform better than do species-poor communities in terms of net productivity.

It has also been posited that more species make a community more stable; that is, more resistant to disturbances such as introduced species. Community ecology also considers how species composition and community structure change over time and in particular after a disturbance, a process called succession.

Ecosystem Ecology Describes the Passage of Energy and Nutrients Through Communities

Ecosystem ecology deals with the flow of energy and cycling of nutrients among organisms within a community and between organisms and the environment. As such, it is concerned with both the biotic and abiotic components of the environment. Following this flow of energy and nutrients necessitates an understanding of feeding relationships between species, called food chains. In food chains, each level is called a trophic level and many food chains interconnect to form complex food webs.

The second law of thermodynamics states that in every energy transformation, free energy is reduced because heat energy is lost from the ecosystem in the process, and the entropy of the universe increases. There is, therefore, a unidirectional flow of energy through an ecosystem, with energy dissipated at every step. An ecosystem needs a recurring input of energy from an external source—in most cases, the sun—to sustain itself. In contrast, chemicals such as mercury cycle between abiotic and biotic components of the environment, often becoming more concentrated in organisms in higher trophic levels.

Ecological Methods Focus on Observation and Experimentation

How do ecologists go about studying their subject? Let's suppose you are employed by the United Nations' Food and Agricultural Organization (FAO), which operates internationally out of Rome, Italy. As an ecologist, you are charged with finding out what causes outbreaks of locusts that periodically erupt in Africa and other parts of the world, destroying crops and other vegetation. First, you might draw up a possible web of

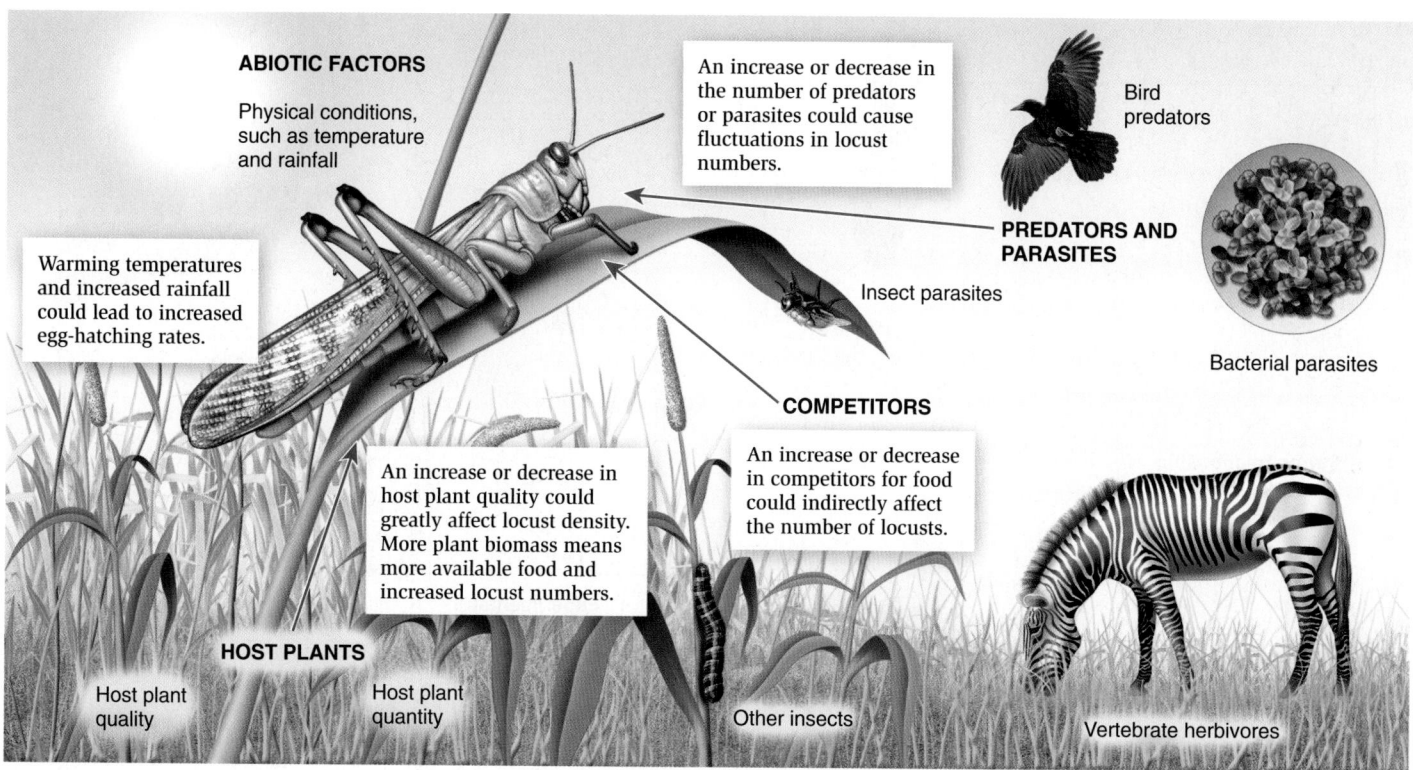

ABIOTIC FACTORS

Physical conditions, such as temperature and rainfall

An increase or decrease in the number of predators or parasites could cause fluctuations in locust numbers.

Bird predators

PREDATORS AND PARASITES

Insect parasites

Bacterial parasites

Warming temperatures and increased rainfall could lead to increased egg-hatching rates.

An increase or decrease in host plant quality could greatly affect locust density. More plant biomass means more available food and increased locust numbers.

COMPETITORS

An increase or decrease in competitors for food could indirectly affect the number of locusts.

HOST PLANTS

Host plant quality

Host plant quantity

Other insects

Vertebrate herbivores

Figure 51.4 Interaction web of factors that might influence locust population size.

interaction among the factors that could affect locust population size (**Figure 51.4**). These interactions are many and varied, and they include

- abiotic factors such as temperature, rainfall, wind, and soil pH;
- host plants, including increases or decreases in either the quality or quantity of the plants;
- predators, including bird predators, insect parasites, and bacterial parasites; and
- competitors, including other insects and larger vertebrate grazers.

With such a vast array of factors to be investigated, where is the best place to start? As discussed in Chapter 1, hypothesis testing involves a five-stage process: (1) observations, (2) hypothesis formation, (3) experimentation, (4) data analysis, and (5) acceptance or rejection of the hypothesis. In our study of locusts, we begin by careful observation of the organism in its native environment. We can analyze the fluctuations of locusts and determine if the populations vary with fluctuations in the other phenomena such as levels of parasitism, numbers of predators, or food supply. Imagine we found that locust numbers are affected by bird predation levels, and that an inverse relationship exists between predation levels and locust numbers. As predation levels increase, locust numbers decrease. If we plotted

this relationship graphically, the resulting graph would look like that depicted in **Figure 51.5a**. This result would give us some confidence that predation levels determined locust numbers and this would be our hypothesis. In fact, we would have so much confidence that we could create a "line of best fit" to represent a summary of the relationship between these two variables.

However, if the points were not highly clustered, as in **Figure 51.5b**, we would have little confidence that predation affects locust density. Many statistical tests are used to determine whether or not two variables are significantly correlated. In the studies in this unit, unless otherwise stated, most graphs like Figure 51.5b imply that a meaningful relationship exists between the two variables. We call this type of relationship a significant **correlation**. If locust density shows a linear relationship with predation, we say that locust density is correlated with predation.

We have to be cautious when forming conclusions based on correlations. For example, large numbers of locusts could be associated with large, dense plants. We might conclude from this that food availability controls locust density. However, an alternative conclusion would be that large plants provide locusts refuge from bird predators, which cannot attack them in the dense interior. While it would appear that plant biomass affects locust density by providing abundant food, in actuality, predation would still be the most important factor affecting locust density. Thus, correlation does not always mean causation. For

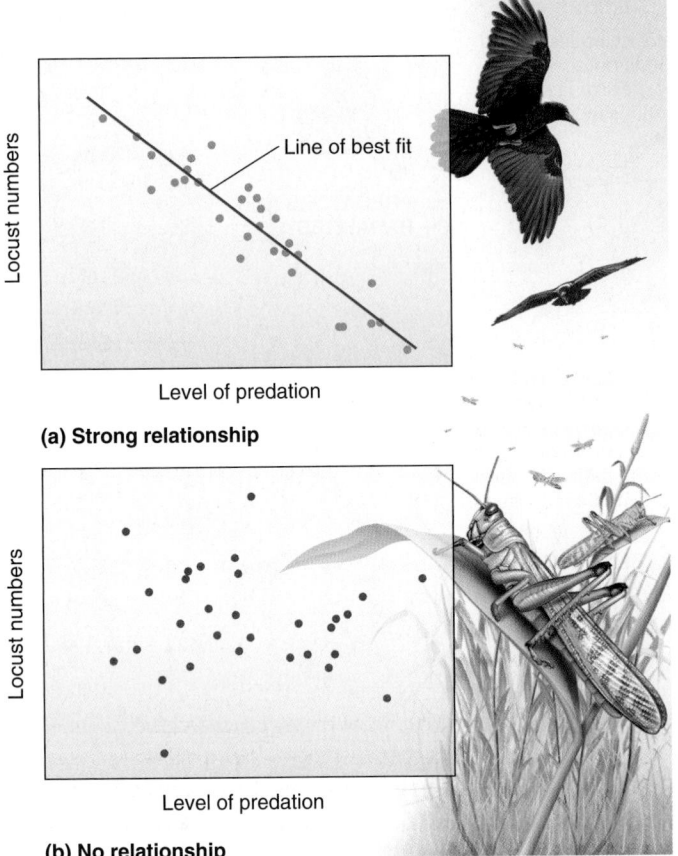

Figure 51.5 Correlation of locust numbers with predation. Higher locust numbers are found in nature where predation levels are lowest. We can draw a line of best fit **(a)** to represent this relationship. In **(b)**, the relationship between locust numbers and predation levels might be so weak that we would not have much confidence in a linear relationship between the variables.

Concept check: *What would it mean if the line of best fit sloped in the opposite direction?*

this reason, after conducting observations, ecologists usually turn to experiments to test their hypotheses.

Continuing with our example, an experiment might involve removing predators from locust populations. If predators are having a significant effect, then removing them should cause an increase in locust numbers. Thus, we would have two groups: a group of locusts with predators removed (the experimental group) and a group of locusts with predators still intact (the control group), with equal numbers of locusts in both groups at the start of the experiment. Any differences in locust population density would be due solely to differences in predation. Reduced predation might be achieved by putting a cage made of chicken wire over and around bushes containing locusts, so that birds are denied access. We could look at locust survivorship over the course of one generation of locust and predator.

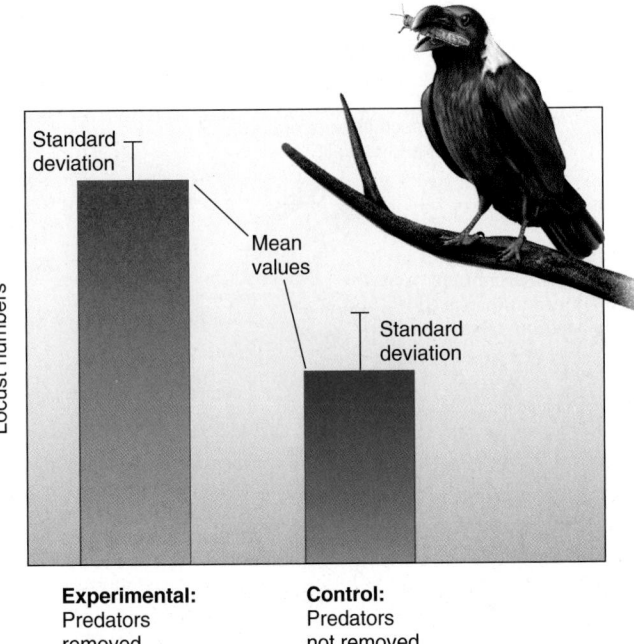

Figure 51.6 Graphic display of hypothetical results of a predator removal experiment. The two bars represent the average number of locusts where predators are removed (experimental) and where predators are not removed (control). The vertical lines (the standard deviations) give an indication of how tightly the individual replicate results are clustered around the mean. The shorter the lines, the tighter the cluster, and the more confidence we have in the result.

Performing the experiments several times is called **replication**. We might replicate the experiment 5 times, 10 times, or even more. At the end of the replications, we would add up the total number of living locusts and calculate the mean. In the experimental group, let's suppose that the surviving numbers of locusts in each replicate are 5, 4, 7, 8, 12, 15, 13, 6, 8, and 10; the mean number surviving would be 8.8. In the control group, which still allows predator access, the numbers surviving might be 2, 4, 7, 5, 3, 6, 11, 4, 1, and 3, with a mean of 4.6. Without predators, the mean number of locusts surviving would therefore be almost double the average number surviving with predators. Our data analysis would give us confidence that predators were indeed the cause of our changes in locust numbers. The results of such experiments can be illustrated graphically by a bar graph (**Figure 51.6**). Ecologists can use a variety of tests to see if these differences are statistically significant. We won't look at the mechanics of these tests, but in this unit, when experimental and control groups are presented as differing, these are considered to be statistically significant differences unless stated otherwise.

By the way, it turns out that predation is not really the primary factor that controls locust populations. The results we have been discussing were hypothetical. Weather, in particular rain, is the most important feature governing locust population

Figure 51.10 Prescribed burn in Pukaskwa National Park. Periodic, controlled human-made fires mimic the sporadic wildfires that normally burn natural areas. Such fires are vital to the health of fire-dependent jack pine and white pine populations, since they serve to open the pine cones and release the seeds.

Concept check: *Why are some fires very destructive to natural systems?*

determined that there were far fewer and smaller forest fires from 1960 onwards than there had been in previous decades. As a result, populations of young fire-dependent trees (such as jack pine and white pine) were on the decline and insect infestations of older trees were on the increase. Therefore, Parks Canada has initiated a prescribed-burn management program in the park (**Figure 51.10**). These fires are designed both to enhance the release of seeds and to clear out competing vegetation at the base of the tree so that seeds can germinate. Fire-suppression practices that attempt to protect forests from fires actually can have the opposite result by preventing the regeneration of fire-dependent species. Furthermore, fire prevention can result in more growth of vegetation beneath the canopy (that is, in the understory) that may later fuel hotter and more damaging fires.

Keep in mind that it is not mean average temperatures that usually limit the range of species but rather the frequency of occasional extremes, such as freezes for the saguaro cacti. Farmers know this only too well. The frequency and strength of periodic freezes, and not average temperatures for the coldest months, limit the northern distribution of peaches in southern

Ontario and British Columbia and the southern distribution of coffee in Brazil.

Despite the obvious relationships between species distributions and temperature, we need to realize that there may also be other factors affecting distributions. The temperatures measured for constructing isotherm maps are not always the temperatures that the organisms experience. In nature, an organism may choose to lie in the sun or hide in the shade, both of which affect the temperatures it experiences. Such local variations of the climate within a given area, or **microclimate**, can be important for a particular species. For example, the rufous grasshopper (*Gomphocerippus rufus*) is distributed widely in Europe, but in Great Britain it reaches its northern limit only 150 metres from the south coast, where it is restricted to steep, south-facing, and therefore relatively sun-drenched and warm grassy slopes.

Because so many species are limited in their distribution patterns by global temperatures, ecologists are concerned that if global temperatures rise, many species will be driven to extinction or that their geographic ranges will shrink and the location of centres of agriculture and forestry will be altered. The increase in the average temperature of Earth's atmosphere and oceans is called global warming.

The Greenhouse Effect The Earth is warmed by the **greenhouse effect**. In a greenhouse, sunlight penetrates the glass and raises temperatures, with the glass acting to trap the resultant heat inside. Similarly, solar radiation in the form of short-wave energy passes through the atmosphere to heat the surface of the Earth. At night this energy is radiated from the Earth's warmed surface back into the atmosphere, but in the form of long-wave infrared radiation. Instead of letting it escape back into space, however, atmospheric gases absorb much of this infrared energy and reradiate it to the Earth's surface, causing its temperature to rise further (**Figure 51.11**). Without some type of greenhouse effect, life on Earth would not exist. Global temperatures would be much lower than they are, perhaps averaging only $-17°C$ compared with the existing average of $+15°C$.

The greenhouse effect is caused by a small group of gases that together make up less than 1% of the total volume of the atmosphere. The four most significant greenhouse gases are carbon dioxide, methane, nitrous oxide, and chlorofluorocarbons (**Table 51.1**). Ecologists are concerned that human activities are changing the atmosphere's composition and intensifying the greenhouse effect.

Global Climate Change It should be noted that the term climate differs from weather; climate refers to averages taken over a long time period (usually 30 years). Therefore, **climate change** refers to a gradual change in multiple variables such as precipitation, ocean currents, and temperature. Although the term global warming is often used interchangeably with climate change, the former refers only to changes in temperature, and does not encompass the complexity of the global system.

The observable effects of climate change include an overall increasing temperature (particularly pronounced at higher,

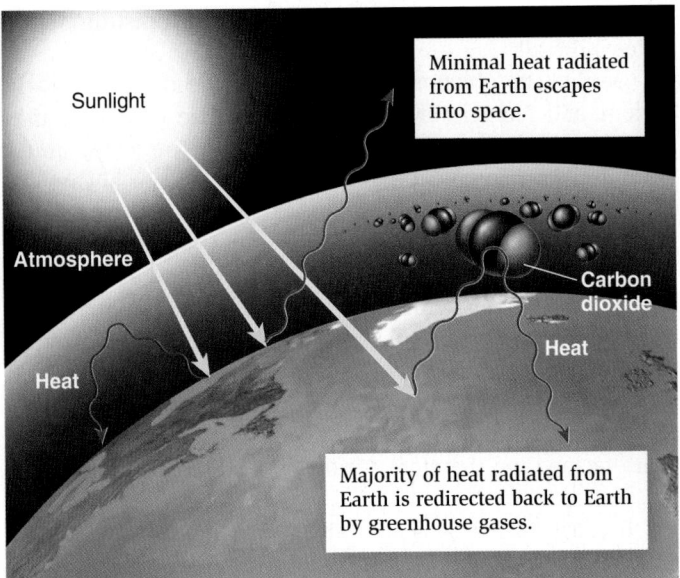

Figure 51.11 **The greenhouse effect.** Solar radiation, in the form of short-wave energy, passes through the atmosphere to heat the Earth's surface. Long-wave infrared energy is radiated back into the atmosphere. Most infrared energy is reflected by atmospheric gases, including carbon dioxide molecules, back to Earth, causing global temperatures to rise.

northern latitudes); an increase in heat absorption by the oceans; an increased frequency of extreme weather events; a global average increase in sea level; a decline in ice and snow extent; an increased precipitation in eastern North and South America, northern Europe and Asia; and a decreased rainfall in northern and southern Africa, the Mediterranean, and parts of southern Asia. Major changes to climate correspond to the timing of intensive industrialization of human civilizations. Human-mediated climate change has been attributed to increased carbon dioxide from fossil fuel use and deforestation, as well as to methane production.

All greenhouse gases have increased in atmospheric concentration since industrial times. The most important of these gases is carbon dioxide (CO_2). As Table 51.1 shows, CO_2 has a lower global warming potential per unit of gas (relative absorption) than any of the other major greenhouse gases, but its concentration in the atmosphere is much higher. Concentrations of atmospheric CO_2 have increased by about 24% between 1957 and 2011.

To predict the effect of global climate change, most scientists focus on a future point, about 2100, when the concentration of atmospheric CO_2 will have doubled—that is, increased to about 700 ppm compared with the late-twentieth-century level of 350 ppm. Ecologists argue that at that time, average global temperatures will be about 1°C–6°C (about 2°F–10°F) warmer than present and will increase an additional 0.5°C each decade. This increase in heat might not seem like much, but it is comparable to the warming that ended the last ice age.

Assuming this scenario of gradual global climate change is accurate, we need to consider what the consequences on natural and human-made ecosystems might be. Ecological systems are responding to climate change in complex ways, including geographic range shifts, changes to community structure, the successful establishment of invasive species, and changed interactions among trophic levels. Although many species can adapt to slight changes in their environment, the anticipated changes in global climate are expected to occur too rapidly to be compensated for by normal evolutionary processes such as natural selection. Plant species cannot simply disperse and move north or south into the newly created climatic regions that will be suitable for them. Many tree species take hundreds, even thousands, of years for seed dispersal. Paleobotanist Margaret Davis predicted that in the event of a CO_2 doubling, the sugar maple (Acer saccharum), which is currently distributed throughout the midwestern and northeastern United States and southeastern Canada, would die back in all areas except in northern Maine, northern New Brunswick, and southern Quebec (**Figure 51.12**). Of course, this contraction in

Table 51.1	Greenhouse Gases and Their Contribution to Global Climate Change			
	Carbon dioxide (CO_2)	Methane (CH_4)	Nitrous oxide (N_2O)	Chlorofluorocarbons (CFCs)
Relative absorption per ppm of increase*	1	21	310	10,000
Atmospheric concentration ppm†	385	1.75	0.315	0.0005
Contribution to global warming	73%	7%	19%	1%
Percent from natural sources; type of source	20–30%; volcanoes	70–90%; swamps, gas from termites and ruminants	90–100%; soils	0%
Major human-made sources	Fossil fuel use, deforestation	Rice paddies, landfills, biomass burning, coal and gas exploitation	Cultivated soil, fossil-fuel use, automobiles, industry	Previously manufactured products (for example, as aerosol propellants) but now banned in the United States and the E.U.

* Relative absorption is the warming potential per unit of gas.

† ppm parts per million.

45°N

30°N

Figure 51.12   The range of sugar maples could be reduced by global climate change.   The present geographic range of the sugar maple (blue shading) and its potential range under doubled CO_2 levels (red shading) in North America. Purple shading indicates the region of overlap, which is the only area where the sugar maple would be found before it spread into its new potential range.

Concept check: *What abiotic factors that influence sugar maple distribution might change in a world with elevated levels of CO_2?*

the tree's distribution could be offset by the creation of new favourable habitats in central Quebec. However, most scientists believe that the climatic zones would shift toward the poles faster than trees could migrate via seed dispersal, hence extinctions would occur. Interestingly, scientists are beginning to be able to genetically modify organisms to change their temperature tolerances.

Wind Can Amplify the Effects of Temperature

Wind is created by temperature gradients. As air heats up, it becomes less dense and rises. As hot air rises, cooler air rushes in to take its place. Hot air rising in the tropics is replaced by cooler air flowing in from more temperate regions, thereby creating northerly or southerly winds.

GENOMES AND PROTEOMES

Temperature Tolerance May Be Manipulated by Genetic Engineering

Below-freezing temperatures can be very damaging to plant tissue, either killing the plant or greatly reducing its productivity. Globally, frost injury causes losses to agriculture of 5%–15% annually. While frost has been considered an unavoidable result of subfreezing temperatures, genetic engineering is beginning to change this view.

Between 0°C and −40°C, pure water will be a liquid unless provided with an ice nucleus or template on which an ice crystal can be built. Researchers discovered that some bacteria commonly found on leaf surfaces act as ice nuclei, triggering the formation of ice crystals and eventually causing frost damage. The genes that confer ice nucleation have been identified, isolated, and prevented from working in an engineered strain of the bacteria *Pseudomonas syringae*. When this strain is allowed to colonize strawberries, frost damage is greatly reduced and plants can withstand an additional 5°C drop in temperature before frost forms. The promise of this technique for increasing agricultural yields and altering normal plant-distribution patterns is staggering.

At the other end of the temperature spectrum, heat shock proteins (HSPs) function as "molecular chaperones" to help organisms cope with the stress of high temperatures. At high temperatures, proteins may either unfold or bind to other proteins to form misfolded protein aggregations. HSPs act to prevent this type of event from taking place or to help aggregated proteins regain their normal configuration. HSPs normally constitute only about 2% of the cell's soluble protein content, but this can increase to 20% when a cell is stressed, whether by heat, cold, drought, or other stressors. In fact, HSPs are extremely common and are found in all organisms, from bacteria to plants and animals.

In the tropics, high temperatures can substantially decrease the growth rates and productivity of many crop species. There is now substantial interest in identifying crop strains with naturally high HSP levels and identifying thermally tolerant varieties for use in crop-breeding programs. Given the seemingly inevitable prospect of global warming, such research seems particularly timely.

(a)

(b)

Figure 51.13 Animals and plants of the intertidal zone adhering to their rocky surface. **(a)** The brown alga (*Laminaria digitata*) has a holdfast that enables it to cling to the rock surface. **(b)** The mussel (*Mytilus edulis*) attaches to the surface of a rock by proteinaceous threads (byssal threads) that extend from the animal's muscular foot.

Wind affects living organisms in a variety of ways. It increases heat loss by evaporation and convection (the wind-chill factor). Wind also contributes to water loss in organisms by increasing the rate of evaporation in animals and transpiration in plants. For example, the treeline in alpine areas is often determined by a combination of low temperatures and high winds such that transpiration exceeds water uptake.

Winds can also intensify oceanic wave action, with resulting effects for organisms. On the ocean's rocky shore, seaweeds survive heavy surf by a combination of holdfasts and flexible structures. The animals of this zone have powerful organic glues and muscular feet to hold them in place (**Figure 51.13**).

The Availability of Water Has Important Effects on the Abundance of Organisms

Water has an important effect on the distribution of organisms. Cytoplasm is 85%–90% water, and without moisture there can be no life. As noted in Chapter 3, water performs crucial functions in all living organisms. It acts as a solvent for chemical

Figure 51.14 The relationship between the amount of rainfall and the density of buffalo. In the Serengeti area of Africa, buffalo density is very much dependent on grass availability, which itself is dependent on annual rainfall. The main exception is where there is permanent water, such as Lake Manyara, where greater water availability leads to greater grass growth and buffalo densities.

reactions, takes part in the reactions of hydrolysis, is the means by which animals eliminate wastes, and is used for support in plants and in some invertebrates as part of a hydrostatic skeleton.

The distribution patterns of many plants are limited by available water. Some plants, such as the water tupelo tree (*Nyssa aquatica*) in the southeast United States, do best when completely flooded and are thus found predominantly in swamps. Others, for example, coastal plants that grow on sand dunes, experience very little fresh water. Their roots penetrate deep into the sand to extract moisture. In cold climates, water can be present but locked up as permafrost and, therefore, unavailable—this is termed a frost-drought situation. Alpine trees can be affected by frost drought. The trees stop growing at a point on the mountainside where they cannot take up enough moisture to offset transpiration losses. This point, known as the timberline, is readily apparent on many mountainsides. Not surprisingly, the density of many plants is limited by the availability of water. For example, a significant correlation is observed between increased rainfall and increased creosote bush density in the Mojave Desert.

Animals face problems of water balance, too, and their distribution and population density can be strongly affected by water availability. Because most animals depend ultimately on plants as food, their distribution is intrinsically linked to those of their food sources. Such a phenomenon regulates the number of buffalo (*Syncerus caffer*) in the Serengeti area of Africa. In this area, grass productivity is related to the amount of rainfall in the previous month. Buffalo density is governed by food availability, so a significant correlation is found between buffalo density and rainfall (**Figure 51.14**). The only exception occurs in the vicinity of Lake Manyara, where groundwater promotes plant growth.

Light Can Be a Limiting Resource for Plants and Algae

Because light is necessary for photosynthesis, it can be a limiting resource for plants. However, what may be sufficient light to support the growth of one plant species may be insufficient for another. Many plant species grow best in shady conditions, such as eastern hemlock (*Tsuga canadensis*). Its saplings grow in the understory below the forest canopy, reaching maximal photosynthesis at one-quarter of full sunlight. Other plants, like sugarcane (*Saccharum officinarum*) or the desert shrub *Larrea*, continue to increase their photosynthetic rate as light intensity increases.

One reason photosynthetic rates vary among plants is related to three different biochemical pathways by which carbon fixation can occur: C_3, C_4, and CAM (see Chapter 8). Because C_4 plants such as sugarcane grow faster in areas with high daytime temperatures and intense sunlight, those species outcompete C_3 plants and are more common in tropical areas than in temperate areas. On the other hand, in cooler, cloudier temperate areas, C_3 species can tolerate lower light and live in areas where C_4 plants cannot. Thus, C_3 plants are much more common in areas outside the tropics. CAM plants, such as some desert succulents, are the opposite of typical plants in that they open their stomata to take up CO_2 at night, presumably as an adaptation to minimize water loss in the day. The absorbed CO_2 is stored as malic acid, which is then used to complete photosynthesis during the day. These plants are adapted to live in very dry desert areas where little else can grow.

In aquatic environments, light may be an even more limiting factor because water absorbs light, preventing photosynthesis at depths greater than 100 metres. Most aquatic plants and algae are limited to a fairly narrow zone close to the surface, where light is sufficient to allow photosynthesis to exceed respiration. This zone is known as the **euphotic zone**. In marine environments, seaweeds at greater depths have wider thalli (leaflike light-gathering structures) than those nearer the surface, because wide thalli can collect more light. In addition, in aquatic environments, plant colour changes with depth. At the surface, plants and algae appear green, as they are in terrestrial conditions, because they absorb red and blue light but not green. At greater depths, red light is mostly absorbed by water, leaving predominantly blue-green light. Red algae occur in deeper water because these possess pigments that enable them to utilize blue-green light efficiently (**Figure 51.15**).

The Concentration of Salts in Soil or Water Can Be Critical

Salt concentrations vary widely in aquatic environments and have a great impact on osmotic balance in animals. Oceans contain considerably more dissolved minerals than rivers. Oceans continually receive the nutrient-rich waters of rivers, and the sun evaporates pure water from ocean surfaces, making concentrations of minerals such as salt even higher.

(a)

(b)

Figure 51.15 Green algae of surface marine waters compared to red algae of deeper marine waters. (a) In Queen Charlotte Strait, British Columbia, this kelp forest is green, just like terrestrial plants. (b) In contrast, at 75-metre depth, in the McGrail Bank off the Gulf of Mexico, most seaweeds are pink and red because the pigments can absorb the blue-green light that occurs at such depths.

The phenomenon of osmosis influences how living organisms cope with different environments. Freshwater fish cannot live in salt water, and saltwater fish cannot live in fresh water. Each employs different mechanisms to maintain an osmotic balance with its environment. Freshwater fish are hyperosmotic (having a higher concentration of ions) to their environment and tend to gain water by osmosis as it passes over the thin tissue of the gills and mouth. To counter this, the fish continually eliminate water in the urine. However, to avoid losing all dissolved ions, many ions are reabsorbed into the bloodstream at the kidneys. Many marine fish are hypoosmotic (having a lower concentration of ions) to their environment and tend to lose water as seawater passes over the mouth and gills. They drink more water to compensate for this loss, but the water contains a higher concentration of salts, which must then be excreted at the gills and kidneys (look back to Chapter 46).

Salt in the soil also affects the growth of plants. In arid terrestrial regions, crystalline salt accumulates in soil where water evaporates. This can be of great significance in

Figure 51.16 Plant adaptations for salty conditions.
Special salt glands in *Spartina* leaves exude salt, enabling this
grass to exist in saline intertidal conditions.

BioConnections: *Look back to section 38.2. Why can't most*
plants grow in salty habitats?

agriculture, where continued watering in arid environments,
together with the addition of salt-based fertilizers, greatly
increases salt concentration in soil and reduces crop yields.
A very few terrestrial plants are adapted to live in saline
soil along seacoasts. Here the vegetation consists largely of
halophytes, species that can tolerate higher salt concentrations in their cell sap than regular plants. Species such as
mangroves and *Spartina* grasses have salt glands that excrete
salt to the surface of the leaves, where it forms tiny white salt
crystals (**Figure 51.16**).

The pH of Soil or Water Can Limit the Distribution of Organisms

As discussed in Chapter 2, the pH of water can be acidic, alkaline, or neutral. Variation in pH can have a major impact on
the distribution of organisms. Normal rainwater has a pH of
about 5.6, which is slightly acidic because the absorption of
atmospheric CO_2 and SO_2 into rain droplets forms carbonic and
sulphuric acids. However, most plants grow best at a soil water
pH of about 6.5, a value at which soil nutrients are most readily
available to plants. Only a few genera, such as rhododendrons
(*Rhododendron*) and azaleas (*Azalea*), can live in soils with a
pH of 4.0 or less. Furthermore, at a pH of 5.2 or less, nitrifying bacteria do not function properly, which prevents organic
matter from breaking down. In general, soils containing chalk
and limestone, the so-called high-lime soils, have a higher pH
and sustain a much richer flora (and associated fauna) than do
acidic soils (**Figure 51.17**).

Generally, the number of fish and other species also
decreases in acidic waters. The optimal pH for most freshwater
fish and bottom-dwelling invertebrates is between 6.0 and 9.0.
Acidity in lakes increases the amount of toxic metals, such as
aluminum, mercury, and lead, which can leach into the water
from surrounding soil and rock. Both too much mercury and

(a) Rich flora on alkaline soil　　**(b) Sparse flora on acidic soil**

Figure 51.17 Species-rich floras of chalk grassland
compared to species-poor floras of acid soils. (a) At Mount
Caburn, in the lime-rich chalk hills of Sussex County, England,
there is a much greater variety of plant and animal species than
at (b) a heathland site in England. Heathlands are a product of
thousands of years of human clearance of natural forest areas
and are characterized by acidic, nutrient-poor soils.

Concept check: *Why do acidic soils support fewer*
species of plants and animals than lime-rich soils?

too much aluminum can interfere with gill structure and function, causing fish to suffocate.

The susceptibility of both aquatic and terrestrial organisms
to changes in pH explains why ecologists are so concerned
about **acid precipitation** (sometimes referred to simply as acid
rain), precipitation with a pH of less than 5.6. Acid precipitation results from the burning of fossil fuels such as coal, natural gas, and oil, which releases sulphur dioxide and nitrogen
oxide into the atmosphere. These react with oxygen in the air
to form sulphuric acid and nitric acid, which falls to the surface in rain or snow. When this precipitation falls on rivers and
especially lakes, it can turn them more acidic and they lose
their ability to sustain fish and other aquatic life. For example, lake trout disappear from lakes in Ontario and the eastern
United States when the pH falls below about 5.2. Although this
low pH does not affect survival of the adult fish, it affects the
survival of juveniles.

Acid precipitation is important in terrestrial systems, too.
For example, acid precipitation can directly affect forests by killing leaves or pine needles, as has happened on some mixed
hardwood forests in Ontario. It can also greatly depress soil pH,
which can result in a loss of essential nutrients such as calcium
and nitrogen. Low calcium in the soil results in calcium deficiencies in plants, in the snails that consume the plants, and in
the birds that eat the snails, ultimately causing weak eggshells
that break before hatching. Decreased soil pH also kills certain
soil microorganisms, preventing decomposition and recycling
of nitrogen in the soil. Decreases in soil calcium and nitrogen

weaken trees and other plants, and may make them more susceptible to insect attack.

Acid precipitation is a common problem in northeastern North America and Scandinavia, where sulphur-rich air drifts over from the Midwest and the industrial areas of Britain, respectively, causing the deposition of highly acidic rain. The problem was particularly acute during the 1960s and 1970s, but decreased manufacturing and the use of low-sulphur coal and the introduction of sulphur-absorbing scrubbers on the smokestacks of coal-burning power plants have reduced the problem somewhat in recent years. Acid precipitation is clearly a problem with a wide-ranging impact on ecological systems.

51.3 | CLIMATE AND ITS RELATIONSHIP TO BIOLOGICAL COMMUNITIES

Learning Outcomes:

1. Explain how global temperature differentials drive atmospheric circulation.
2. Explain how both mountains and large bodies of water can change local temperature and precipitation patterns.
3. List 10 major terrestrial communities, noting the temperature and rainfall pattern of each.
4. Discuss how changes in water salinity, oxygen content, depth, and current affect aquatic biomes.

Temperature, water, wind, and light are components of **climate**, the prevailing weather pattern in a given region. Because the distribution and abundance of organisms are often limited by the abiotic environment, to understand the patterns of abundance of life on Earth ecologists need to study the global climate. We begin this section by examining global climate patterns, focusing on how temperature variation drives atmospheric circulation and how features such as elevation and land mass can alter these patterns. Knowing how and why climate changes around the world enables us to understand and predict the occurrence of different **biomes**, the major community types on Earth such as tropical forests and hot deserts. In this section, we also explore the main characteristics of Earth's major terrestrial and aquatic biomes.

Atmospheric Circulation Is Driven by Global Temperature Differentials

Substantial differences in temperature occur over the Earth, mainly due to variations in the incoming solar radiation. In higher latitudes, such as northern Canada and Russia, the sun's rays hit the Earth obliquely and are spread out over more of the planet's surface than they are in equatorial areas (**Figure 51.18**). More heat is also lost in the atmosphere of higher altitudes because the sun's rays travel a greater distance through the atmosphere, allowing more heat to be dissipated

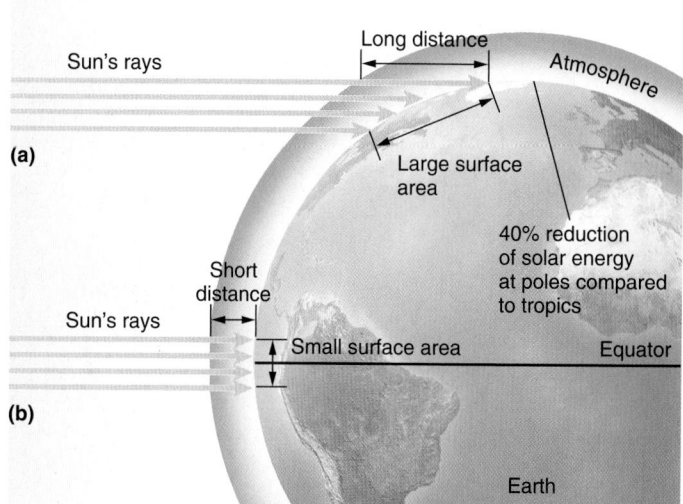

Figure 51.18 The intensity of solar radiation at different latitudes. In polar areas **(a)**, the sun's rays strike the Earth at an oblique angle and deliver less energy than at tropical locations. In tropical areas **(b)**, the energy is concentrated over a smaller surface and travels a shorter distance through the atmosphere.

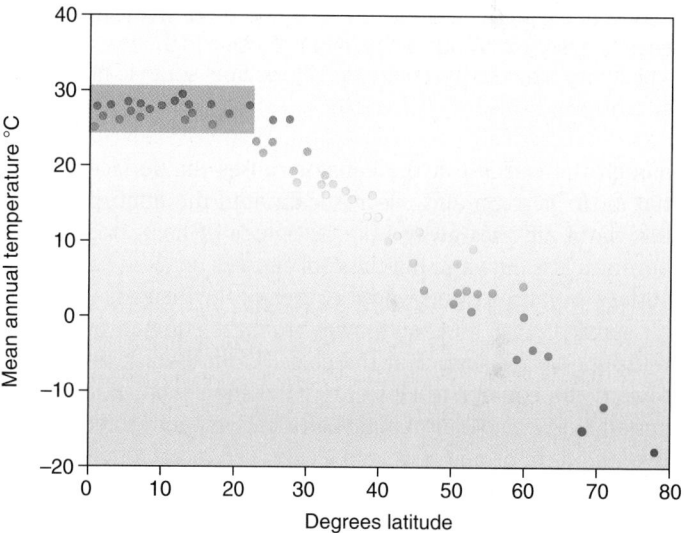

Figure 51.19 Variation of the Earth's temperature. The temperatures shown in this figure were measured at moderately moist continental locations of low elevation. Note the wide band of similar temperatures at the tropics.

by cloud cover. The result is that a much smaller amount of solar energy (40% less) strikes polar latitudes than equatorial areas. Generally, temperatures increase as the amount of solar radiation increases (**Figure 51.19**). However, at the tropics both cloudiness and rain reduce average temperature, so that temperatures do not continue to increase toward the equator.

The English meteorologist George Hadley made the initial contribution to a model of general atmospheric circulation in 1735. Hadley proposed that solar energy drives winds, which in turn influence the global circulation of the atmosphere. In his

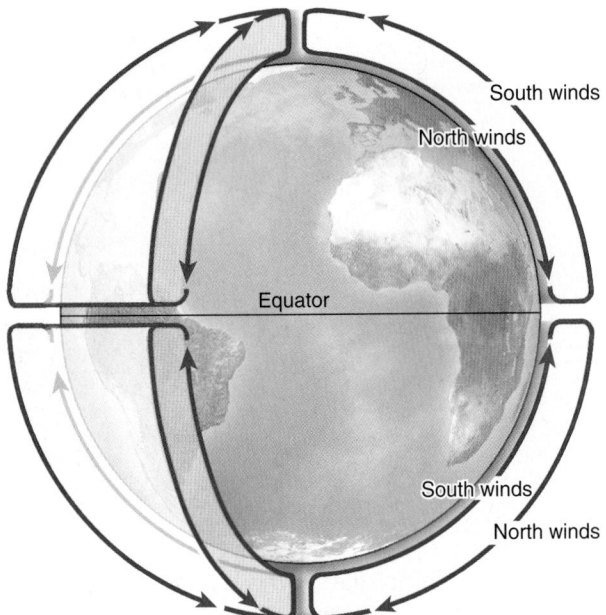

Figure 51.20 George Hadley's 1735 model of atmospheric circulation. In Hadley's model, simple convective circulation of air on a uniform, nonrotating Earth, heated at the equator and cooled at the poles, took the form of one large convection cell in each hemisphere. Winds are named according to the direction from which they blow, so the south wind blows from south to north.

model, the warmth at the equator causes the surface equatorial air to heat up and rise vertically into the atmosphere. As the warm air rises away from its source of heat, it cools and becomes less buoyant, but the cool air does not sink back to the surface because of the warm air behind it. Instead, the rising air spreads north and south away from the equator, eventually returning to the surface at the poles. From there it flows back toward the equator to close the circulation loop. Hadley suggested that on a nonrotating Earth this air movement would take the form of one large convection cell in each hemisphere, as shown in **Figure 51.20**.

When the effect of the Earth's rotation is added, however, the surface flow is deflected toward the west. This consequence is known as the **Coriolis effect**. Hadley's one-cell circulation has since been modified to account for the Coriolis effect and other more modern data. In the 1920s a three-cell circulation in each hemisphere was proposed to fit the Earth's heat balance (**Figure 51.21**). The contribution of George Hadley is still recognized, in that the most prominent of the three cells, the one nearest the equator, is called the **Hadley cell**. In the Hadley cell, the warm air rising near the equator forms towers of cumulus clouds that provide rainfall, which in turn maintains the lush vegetation of the equatorial rain forests. As the upper flow in this cell moves toward the poles, it begins to subside, or fall back to Earth, at about 30° north and south of the equator. These **subsidence zones** are areas of high pressure and are the sites of the world's tropical deserts, because

the subsiding air is relatively dry, having released all of its moisture over the equator. Winds are generally weak and variable near the centre of this zone of descending air. Subsidence zones have popularly been called the horse latitudes. The name is said to have been coined by Spanish sailors crossing the Atlantic, whose ships were sometimes rendered motionless in these waters and who reportedly were forced to throw horses overboard, or eat them, as they could no longer water or feed them.

From the centre of the subsidence zones, the surface flow splits into the westerlies that flow toward the poles, and the equatorial flow, which is deflected by the Coriolis effect and forms the reliable trade winds. In the northern hemisphere, the trades are from the northeast, the direction from which they provided the sail power to explore the New World; in the southern hemisphere, the trades are from the southeast. The trade winds from both hemispheres meet near the equator in a region called the intertropical convergence zone (ITCZ), also known as the doldrums. Here the light winds and humid conditions provide the monotonous weather that may be the basis for the expression "in the doldrums."

In the three-cell model, the circulation between 30° and 60° latitude, called the **Ferrell cell**, is opposite that of the Hadley cell. The net surface flow is poleward, and because of the Coriolis effect, the winds have a strong westerly (flowing from west to east) component. Secondary zones of high precipitation can come anywhere from about 45° to 60°, with between 45° and 55° being most common. The final circulation cell is known as the **polar cell**. At the poles, the air has cooled and descends, but it has little moisture left, explaining why many high-latitude regions are actually desert-like in condition.

Thus, the distributions of the major biomes are determined by temperature differences and the wind patterns they generate. Hot, tropical forest blankets the tropics, where rainfall is high. At about 30° latitude, the air cools and descends, but it is without moisture, so the hot deserts occur around that latitude. The middle cell of the circulation model shows us that at about 45° to 55° latitude the air has warmed and gained moisture, so it ascends, dropping rainfall over the wet, temperate forests of this region in the Pacific northwest and Western Europe in the northern hemisphere and over New Zealand and Chile in the southern hemisphere.

Elevation and Other Features of a Land Mass Can Also Affect Climate

Thus far, we have considered how global temperatures and wind patterns affect climate. The geographic features of a land mass can also have an important impact. For example, the elevation of a region greatly influences its temperature range. On mountains, temperatures decrease with increasing elevation. This decrease is a result of a process known as **adiabatic cooling**, in which increasing elevation leads to a decrease in air pressure. When air is blown across the Earth's surface and up over mountains, it expands because of the

Figure 51.21 **Patterns of atmospheric circulation and biome positions.** Three-cell model of the atmospheric circulation on a uniform, rotating Earth heated at the equator and cooled at the poles. Tropical forests exist mainly in a band around the equator, where it is hot and rainy. At around 30° north and south, the air is hot and dry, and deserts exist. A secondary zone of precipitation exists at around 45° to 55° north and south, where temperate forests are located. The polar regions are generally cold and dry.

reduced pressure. As it expands, it cools at a rate of about 10°C for every 1,000 metres in elevation, as long as no water vapour or cloud formation occurs. (Adiabatic cooling is also the principle behind the function of a refrigerator, in which Freon gas cools as it expands coming out of the compressor.) A vertical ascent of 600 metres produces a temperature change roughly equivalent to that brought about by an increase in latitude of 1,000 kilometres. This explains why mountaintop vegetation, even in tropical areas, can have the characteristics of tundra.

Mountains can also influence patterns of precipitation. For example, when warm, moist air encounters the windward side of a mountain, it flows upward and cools, releasing precipitation in the form of rain or snow. On the side of the mountain sheltered from the wind (the leeward side), drier air descends, producing what is called a **rain shadow**, an area where precipitation is noticeably less (**Figure 51.22a**). In this way, the

western side of the Coast Mountains and Cascade Range (found in both British Columbia and Washington State) receives more than 500 centimetres of annual precipitation, whereas the eastern side receives only 50 centimetres.

The proximity of a land mass to a large body of water can affect climate because land heats and cools more quickly than the sea does. The specific heat capacity of the land is much lower than that of the water, allowing the land to warm more quickly in the day. The warmed air rises and cooler air flows in to replace it. This pattern creates the familiar onshore sea breezes in coastal areas (**Figure 51.22b**). At night, the land cools quicker than the sea, and so the pattern is reversed, creating offshore breezes. The sea, therefore, has a moderating effect on the temperatures of coastal regions and especially islands. The climates of coastal regions may differ markedly from those of their climatic zones. Many never experience frost, and fog is often evident. Thus, along coastal areas,

As moist air blows across the windward side of a mountain, it rises and cools, and precipitation falls as rain or snow.

Moist air

Dry air

On the leeward side of a mountain, the cooler air descends and becomes warmer; little precipitation occurs.

(a) Rain shadow

Cool air

Warm air

During the day, as warm air rises, cooler air rushes in from the ocean to replace it.

(b) Sea breezes

Figure 51.22   The influence of elevation and proximity to water on climate.

different vegetation patterns may occur compared to those in areas farther inland. In fact, some areas of the United States, including Florida, would be deserts were it not for the warm water of the sea and the moisture-laden clouds that form above them.

Together with the rotation of the Earth, winds also create ocean currents. The major ocean currents act as "pinwheels" between continents, running clockwise in the ocean basins

of the northern hemisphere and counter-clockwise in those of the southern hemisphere (**Figure 51.23**). Thus, the Gulf Stream, equivalent in flow to 50 times the world's major rivers combined, brings warm water from the Caribbean and the United States east coast across to Europe, the climate of which is correspondingly moderated. The Humboldt Current brings cool conditions almost to the equator along the western coast of South America.

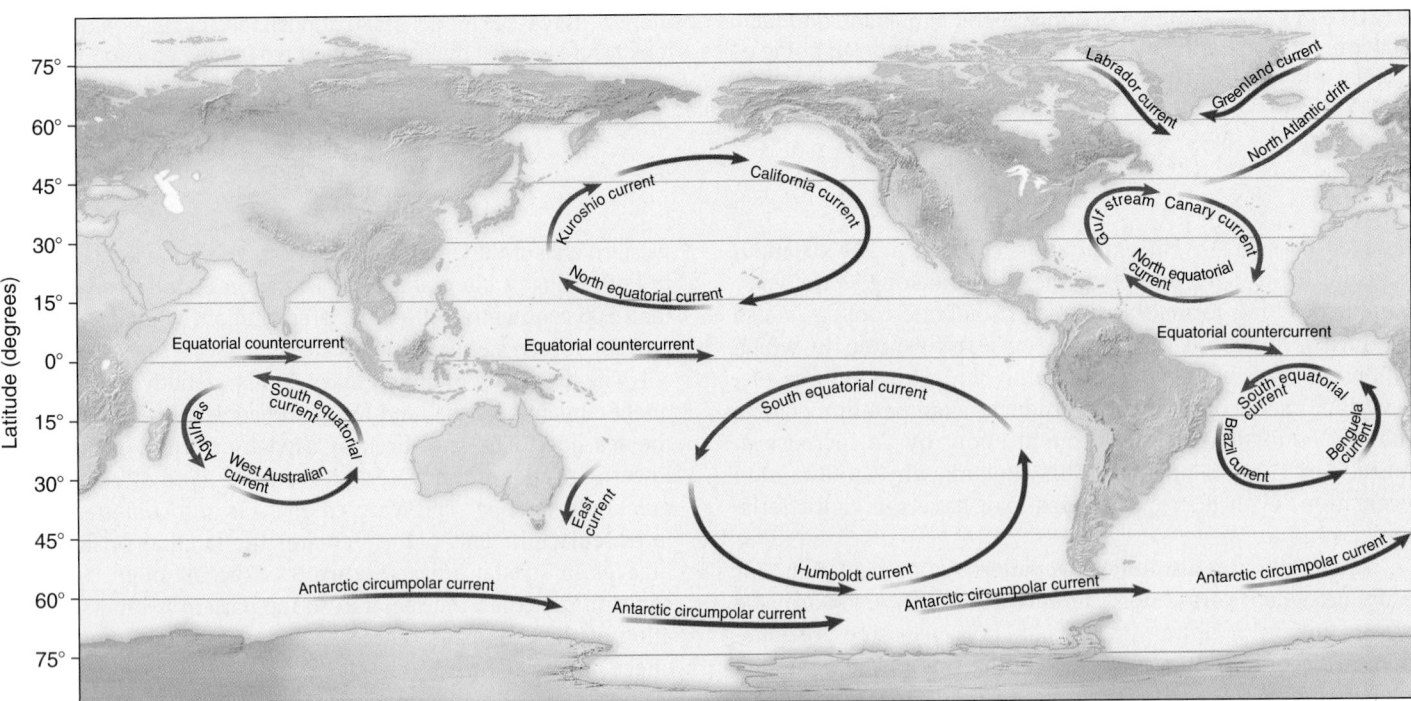

Figure 51.23   Ocean currents of the world.   The red arrows represent warm water; the blue arrows, cold water.

Terrestrial Biome Types Are Dictated by Climate Patterns

Differences in climate on Earth help to define its different terrestrial biomes. Many types of classification schemes are used for mapping the geographic extent of biomes, but one of the most useful was developed by the American ecologist Robert Whittaker, who classified biomes according to the physical factors of average annual precipitation and temperature (**Figure 51.24**). In this scheme, we can recognize 10 terrestrial biomes (**Figure 51.25**):

1. tropical rain forest;
2. tropical deciduous forest;
3. temperate rain forest;
4. temperate deciduous forest;
5. temperate coniferous forest (taiga or boreal forest);
6. tropical grassland (savannah);
7. temperate grassland (prairie);
8. hot desert;
9. cold desert;
10. tundra.

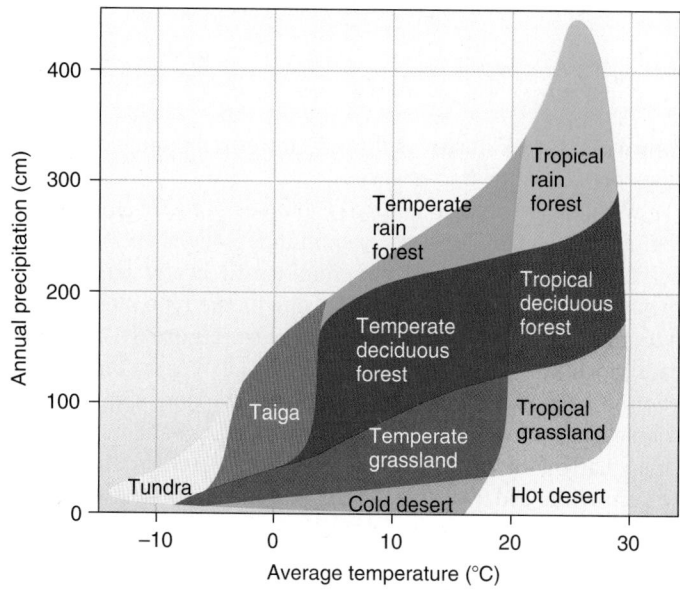

Figure 51.24 The relationship between the world's terrestrial biome types and temperature and precipitation patterns.

Concept check: *What other factors may influence biome types?*

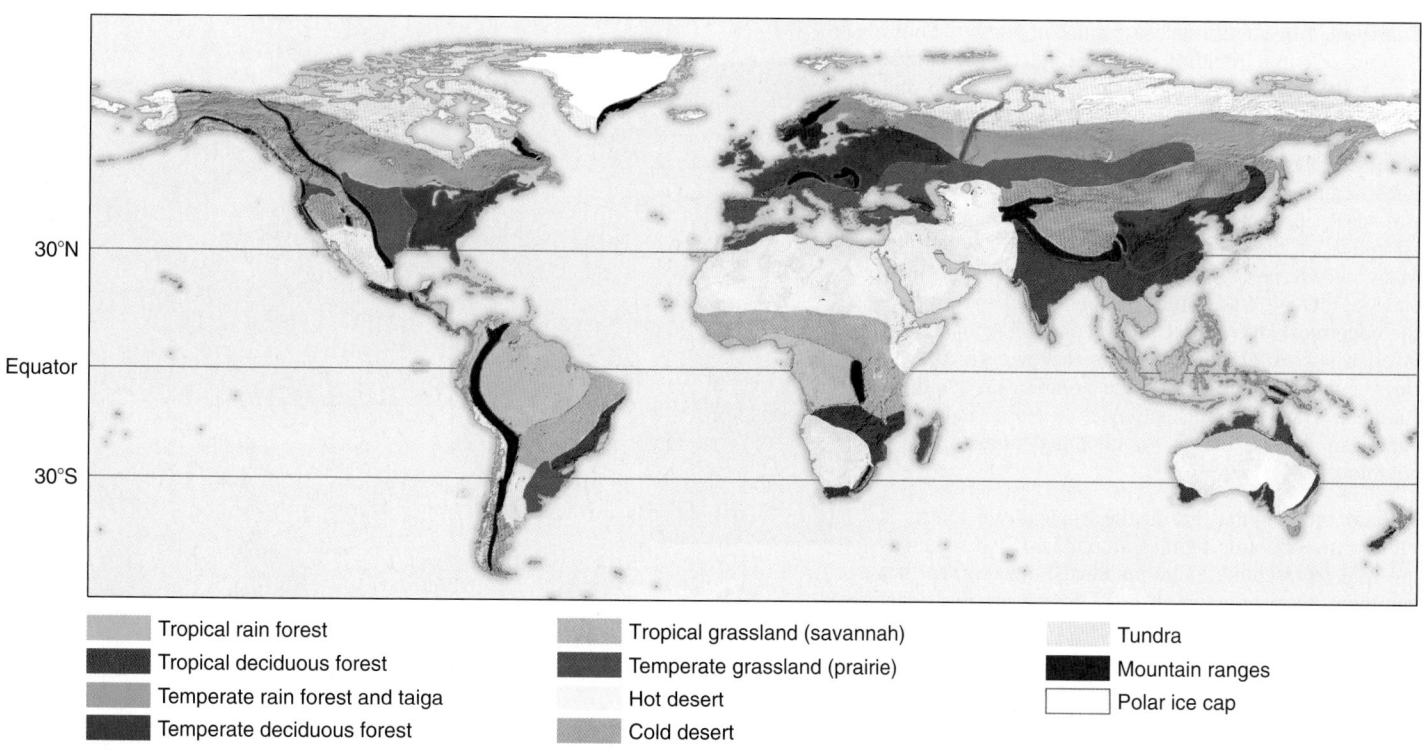

Tropical rain forest
Tropical deciduous forest
Temperate rain forest and taiga
Temperate deciduous forest
Tropical grassland (savannah)
Temperate grassland (prairie)
Hot desert
Cold desert
Tundra
Mountain ranges
Polar ice cap

Figure 51.25 **Geographic location of terrestrial biomes.** The distribution patterns of taiga and temperate rain forest are combined because of their similarity in tree species and because temperate rain forest is actually limited to a very small area.

Concept check: *If global climate change continues, what biome might expand into areas currently occupied by tundra?*

Figure 51.26a–j illustrates these 10 terrestrial biomes and identifies their main characteristics.

While these broad terrestrial biomes are a useful way of defining the main types of communities on Earth, ecologists acknowledge that not all communities fit neatly into one of these 10 major biome types. Also, one biome type often grades into another, as seen on mountain ranges (**Figure 51.26k**). Soil conditions can also influence biome type. For example, serpentine soils, which are dry and nutrient poor, support only sparse vegetation. Along the Niagara Escarpment in Ontario, Doug Larson of the University of Guelph studies an ancient eastern white cedar (*Thuja occidentalis*) forest that clings to the hollows, cracks, and ledges of the limestone cliffs. Although the trees are hundreds of years old, they are generally less than 2.5 metres high and often hang downwards from the cliff face.

Some ecologists recognize chaparral, a type of temperate grassland, as a distinct biome type. Winters are cool and wet, and summers warm and dry. Summer conditions are so dry that fires occur normally and frequently at this time. Such conditions are most commonly seen on the west coast at around 30°N and S latitudes, where cool ocean waters moderate the climate, as along the coasts of California, South Africa, Chile, and southwest Australia and in countries surrounding the Mediterranean Sea.

TROPICAL RAIN FOREST	Figure 51.26a

Tropical rain forest in Fiji

Physical Environment: Rainfall exceeding 230 centimetres per year, temperature hot year-round, averaging 25°C–29°C, soils often shallow and nutrient poor.

Location: Equatorial, between the Tropics of Cancer and Capricorn. Tropical forests cover much of northern South America, Central America, western and central Africa, Southeast Asia, and various islands in the Indian and Pacific Oceans.

Plant Life: The numbers of plant species found in tropical forests can be staggering, often reaching as many as 100 tree species per square kilometre. Leaves often narrow to "drip-tips" at the apex so that rainwater drains quickly. Many trees have large buttresses that help support their shallow root systems. Little light penetrates the **canopy**, the uppermost layer of tree foliage, and the ground cover is often sparse. Epiphytes, plants that live perched on trees and are not rooted in the ground, are common. Bromeliads are common epiphytes in North and South American forests. Lianas, or climbing vines, are also common.

Animal Life: Animal life in the tropical rain forests is diverse: insects, birds, reptiles, amphibians, and mammals are well represented. Large mammals, however, are not common. Because many of the plant species are widely scattered in tropical forests, it is risky for plants to rely on wind for pollination or to disperse their seed. This means that animals are important in pollinating flowers and dispersing fruits and seeds. Mimicry and bright protective coloration, warning of bad taste or the existence of toxins, are rampant.

Effects of Humans: Human disturbance of the tropical rainforest biome began in preindustrial and precolonial periods by early civilizations, but has been exacerbated by twentieth-century industrialization and climate change. The major losses of rainforest lands result from agricultural intensification, where regions are deforested to create crop fields or pasture for cattle. Alternatively, regions of forest are converted to agroforestry land uses, where farmers combine crops (e.g., coffee and cacao) and sometimes pasture under the shade from existing trees.

TROPICAL DECIDUOUS FOREST

Figure 51.26b

Tropical deciduous forest in Bandhavgarh National Park, India

Physical Environment: Rainfall is substantial, at around 130–280 centimetres a year, but the dry season is distinct, often two to three months or longer. Soil water shortages can occur in the dry season. Temperatures are hot year-round, averaging 25°C–39°C.

Location: Equatorial, where rainfall is more seasonal. Much of India consists of tropical deciduous forest, containing teak trees. Brazil, Thailand, and Mexico also contain tropical deciduous forest. At the wet edges of this biome, it may grade into tropical forests; at the dry end, it may grade into tropical grasslands or savannahs.

Plant Life: Because of the distinct dry season, many of the trees in tropical deciduous forests shed their leaves, just as they do in temperate forests, and an understory of herbs and grasses may grow during this time. Indeed, because the canopy is often more open than in the tropical rain forest, a denser closed forest—what we might think of as a "tropical jungle"—exists at the forest floor. Where the dry season is six to seven months long, tropical deciduous forests may contain shorter, thorny plants such as acacia trees and the forest is referred to as a tropical thorn forest.

Animal Life: The diversity of animal life is high, and species such as monkeys, antelopes, wild pigs, and tigers are present. However, as with plant diversity, animal diversity is less than in tropical rain forests. Tropical thorn forests may contain more browsing mammals; hence, the development of plant thorns as a defence.

Effects of Humans: Logging and agriculture have had a large impact on tropical deciduous forests. The litter layer of dead, decaying leaves is much thicker than in tropical rain forests and renders the soil more fertile.

TEMPERATE RAIN FOREST

Figure 51.26c

Rain forest in Pacific Rim National Park, Vancouver Island, British Columbia

Physical Environment: Temperatures are 5°C–25°C, on average, and winters are mild, but there is abundant rainfall, usually exceeding 200 centimetres a year. The condensation of water from dense coastal fogs augments the normal rainfall.

Location: The coverage of this biome type is small, consisting of a thin strip along the northwest coast of North America from northern California through Washington State, British Columbia, and into southeast Alaska (here called Tongass). It also exists in southwestern South America along the Chilean coast. Indeed, it is found only in coastal situations because of the moderating influence of the ocean on air temperature.

Plant Life: The dominant vegetation type, especially in North America, consists of large evergreen trees such as western hemlock, Douglas fir, and Sitka spruce. The high moisture content allows epiphytes to thrive. Cool temperatures slow the activity of decomposers, so that the litter layer is thick and spongy.

Animal Life: In North America, the temperate rain forest is rich in species such as mule deer, elk, squirrels, and numerous birds such as jays and nuthatches. Because of the abundant moisture and moderate temperatures, reptiles and amphibians are also common.

Effects of Humans: This biome is a prolific producer of wood and supplies much timber, although logging threatens the survival of the forest in some areas.

TEMPERATE DECIDUOUS FOREST

Figure 51.26d

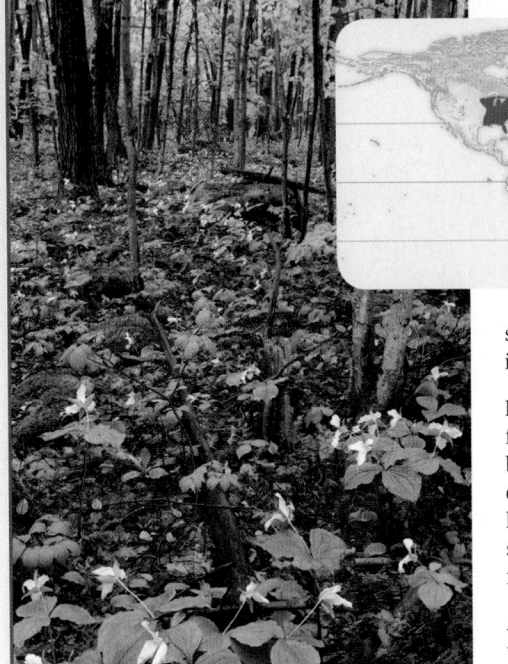

Temperate deciduous forest in southeastern Canada

Physical Environment: Temperatures fall below freezing each winter but not usually below −12°C, and annual rainfall is generally between 75 centimetres and 200 centimetres.

Location: Large tracts of temperate deciduous forest are evident in the eastern United States and Canada, eastern Asia, and western Europe. In the southern hemisphere, eucalyptus forests occur in Australia, and stands of southern beech are found in southern South America, New Zealand, and Australia.

Plant Life: Species diversity is much lower in temperate deciduous forests than in the tropical forests, with about only three to four species per square kilometre, and several tree genera may be dominant in a given locality—for example, beech–maple forests predominate in the temperate deciduous forests of Canada. Commonly, leaves are shed in the fall and reappear in the spring. Many herbaceous plants flower in spring before the trees leaf out and block the light, though even in the summer the forest is not as dense as in tropical forests so there is abundant ground cover. There are few epiphytes and lianas.

Animal Life: Animals are adapted to the vagaries of the climate; many mammals hibernate during the cold months, birds migrate, and insects enter diapause, a condition of dormancy passed usually as a pupa. Reptiles, which are dependent on solar radiation for heat, are relatively uncommon. Mammals in North American temperate deciduous forests include squirrels, wolves, bobcats, foxes, white-tailed deer, bears, and mountain lions.

Effects of Humans: Logging has eliminated much temperate forest from heavily populated portions of Europe and North America. Soils are rich because the annual leaf drop promotes high soil nutrient levels. With careful agricultural practices, soil richness can be conserved, and as a result agriculture can flourish.

TEMPERATE CONIFEROUS FOREST (TAIGA OR BOREAL FOREST)

Figure 51.26e

Temperate coniferous forest in Canada

Physical Environment: Precipitation is generally between 30 centimetres and 70 centimetres per year, often occurring in the form of snow. Temperatures are very cold, below freezing for long periods of time.

Location: The biome of coniferous forests, known commonly by its Russian name, taiga, lies north of the temperate-zone forests and grasslands. Vast tracts of taiga exist in North America and Russia, and mountain taiga exists at high elevations. In the southern hemisphere, little land area occurs at latitudes at which one would expect extensive taiga to exist.

Plant Life: Most of the trees are evergreens or conifers with tough needles, hence this biome's similarity to temperate rain forest. In this biome, spruces, firs, and pines generally dominate, and the number of tree species is relatively low. Many of the conifers have conical shapes to reduce bough breakage from heavy loads of snow. As in tropical forests, the understory is sparse because the dense year-round canopies prevent sunlight from penetrating. Soils are poor because the fallen needles decay so slowly in the cold temperatures that a layer of needles builds up. This layer of needles acidifies the soil, further reducing the numbers of understory species.

Animal Life: Reptiles and amphibians are rare because of the low temperatures. Insects are strongly periodic but may often reach outbreak proportions in times of warm temperatures. Mammals that inhabit this biome such as bears, lynxes, moose, beavers, and squirrels are heavily furred.

Effects of Humans: Humans have not extensively settled these areas, but they have been quite heavily logged.

TROPICAL GRASSLAND (SAVANNAH)

Figure 51.26f

Tropical grassland of the Masai Mara Game Reserve in Kenya

Physical Environment: Hot, tropical areas, averaging 24°C–29°C with a low or seasonal rainfall of between 50 centimetres and 130 centimetres per year. There is often an extensive dry season.

Location: Extensive savannahs occur in Africa, South America, and northern Australia.

Plant Life: Wide expanses of grasses dominate savannahs but occasional thorny trees, such as acacias, may occur. Fire is prevalent in this biome, so most plants have well-developed root systems that enable them to resprout quickly after a fire.

Animal Life: The world's greatest assemblages of large mammals occur in the savannah biome. Herds of antelope, zebras, and wildebeest are found, together with their associated predators: cheetah, lion, leopard, and hyena. Termite mounds dot the landscape in some areas. The extensive herbivory of large grazers, together with frequent fires, may help maintain savannahs and prevent their development into forests.

Effects of Humans: Savannah soils are often poor because the occasional rain leaches nutrients out. Nevertheless, conversion of this biome to agricultural land is rampant, especially in Africa. Overstocking of land for domestic animals can greatly reduce grass coverage through overgrazing, turning the area more desertlike. This process is known as **desertification**.

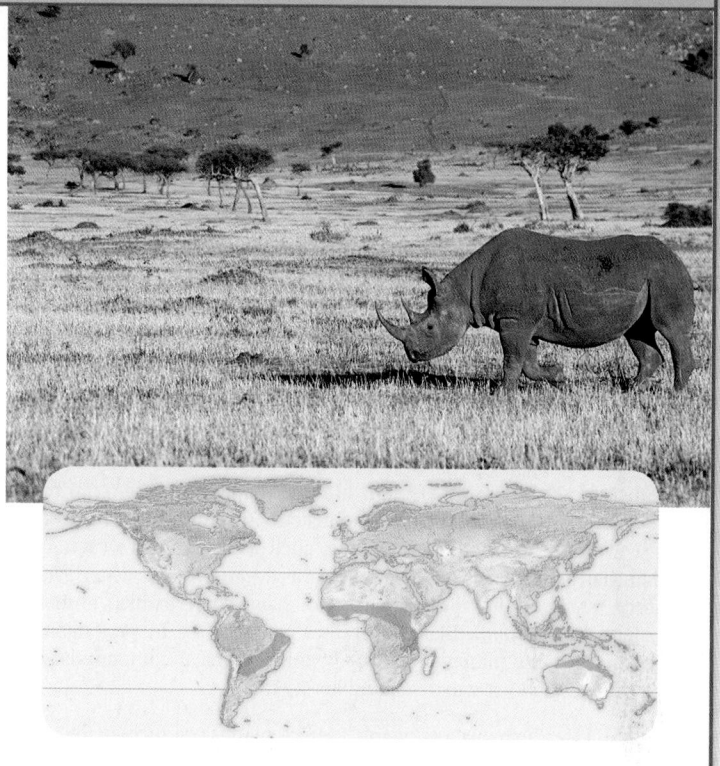

TEMPERATE GRASSLAND (PRAIRIE)

Figure 51.26g

Temperate grassland in Saskatchewan

Physical Environment: Annual rainfall is generally between 25 centimetres and 100 centimetres, too low to support a forest but higher than that in deserts. Temperatures in the winter often fall below 10°C, while summers may be very hot, approaching 30°C.

Location: Temperate grasslands include the prairies of North America, such as those found in Manitoba, Saskatchewan, and Alberta, the steppes of Russia, the pampas of Argentina, and the veldt of South Africa. In addition to the limiting amounts of rain, fire and grazing animals may also prevent the establishment of trees in the temperate grasslands. Where temperatures rarely fall below freezing and most of the rain falls in the winter, chaparral, a fire-adapted community featuring shrubs and small trees, occurs.

Plant Life: From east to west in North America and from north to south in Asia, grasslands show differentiation along moisture gradients. In the tallgrass prairie of southern Manitoba, with annual precipitation of 50 centimetres to 80 centimetres, grasses such as big bluestem and switchgrass grow to about 2 metres high. Along the eastern base of the Rockies in Alberta, where rainfall is 5 centimetres to 25 centimetres, mixed prairie grasses such as buffalo grass and blue grama rarely exceed 0.5 metres in height. Similar gradients occur in South Africa and Argentina.

Animal Life: Where the grasslands remain, large mammals are the most prominent members of the fauna: bison (buffalo) and pronghorn antelope in North America, wild horses in Eurasia, and large kangaroos in Australia. Burrowing animals such as North American prairie dogs and ground squirrels and African mole rats are also common. On the Canadian prairies, birds of prey include ferruginous hawks and the endangered burrowing owl.

Effects of Humans: Prairie soil is among the richest in the world, having 12 times the humus layer of a typical forest soil. Worldwide, most prairies have been converted to agricultural cropland, and original grassland habitats are among the rarest biomes in the world.

HOT DESERT

Figure 51.26h

Saguaro National Park in Arizona, part of the Sonoran Desert

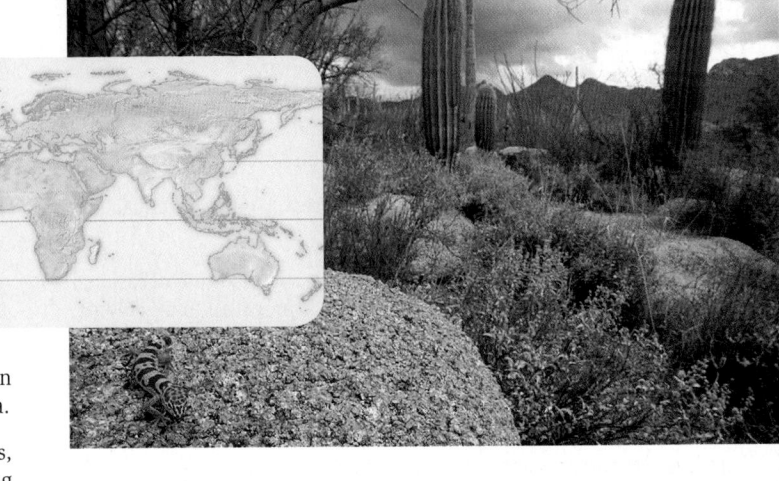

Physical Environment: Temperatures are variable, from below freezing at night to as much as 50°C in the day. Rainfall is less than 30 centimetres per year.

Location: Hot deserts are found around latitudes of 30° north and south. Prominent deserts include the Sahara of North Africa, the Kalahari of southern Africa, the Atacama of Chile, the Sonoran of northern Mexico and the southwest United States, and the Simpson of Australia.

Plant Life: Three forms of plant life are adapted to deserts: annuals, succulents, and desert shrubs. Annuals circumvent drought by growing only when there is rain. Succulents, such as the saguaro cactus and other barrel cacti of the southwestern deserts, store water. Desert shrubs, such as the spraylike ocotillo, have short trunks, numerous branches, and small, thick leaves that can be shed in prolonged dry periods. In many plants, spines or volatile chemical compounds serve as a defence against water-seeking herbivores.

Animal Life: To conserve water, desert plants produce many small seeds, and animals that eat those seeds, such as ants, birds, and rodents, are common. Reptiles are numerous because high temperatures permit these ectothermic animals to maintain a warm body temperature. Lizards and snakes are important predators of seed-eating mammals.

Effects of Humans: Ambitious irrigation schemes and the prolific use of underground water have allowed humans to colonize deserts and grow crops there. However, salinization of soils is prevalent. Off-road vehicles can disturb the fragile desert communities.

COLD DESERT

Figure 51.26i

The Gobi Desert of Mongolia

Physical Environment: Precipitation is less than 25 centimetres a year, often in the form of snow. Rainfall usually comes in the spring. In the daytime, temperatures can be high in the summer, 21°C–26°C, but average around freezing, 2°C–4°C, in the winter.

Location: Cold deserts are found in dry regions at middle to high latitudes, especially in the interiors of continents and in the rain shadows of mountains. Cold deserts are found in North America (the Great Basin Desert), in eastern Argentina (the Patagonian Desert), and in central Asia (the Gobi Desert).

Plant Life: Cold deserts are relatively poor in terms of numbers of species of plants. Most plants are small in stature, being only between 15 centimetres and 120 centimetres tall. Many species are deciduous and spiny. The Great Basin Desert in Nevada, Utah, and bordering states is a cold desert dominated by sagebrush.

Animal Life: As in hot deserts, large numbers of plants produce small seeds on which numerous ants, birds, and rodents feed. Many species live in burrows to escape cold and to keep warm. In the Great Basin Desert, pocket mice, jackrabbits, kit fox, and coyote are common. In the Gobi Desert, wild Bactrian (two-humped) camels are found as are the only desert-inhabiting bears, Gobi bears.

Effects of Humans: Agriculture is hampered because of low temperatures and low rainfall, and human populations are not extensive. If the top layer of soil is disturbed by human intrusions such as off-road vehicles, erosion occurs rapidly and even less vegetation is able to exist.

TUNDRA

Figure 51.26j

Tuktut Nogait National Park, Northwest Territories, Canada

Physical Environment: Precipitation is generally less than 25 centimetres per year and is often locked up as snow and unavailable for plants. Deeper water can be locked away for a large part of the year in **permafrost**, a layer of permanently frozen soil. The growing season here is short, only 50–60 days. Summer temperatures are only 3°C–12°C, and even during the long summer days the ground thaws to less than 1 metre in depth. Midwinter temperatures average 32°C.

Location: Tundra (from the Finnish *tunturia*, treeless plain) exists mainly in the northern hemisphere, north of the taiga, because there is very little land area in the southern hemisphere at the latitude where tundra would occur.

Plant Life: With so little available water, trees cannot grow. Vegetation occurs in the form of fragile, slow-growing lichens, mosses, grasses, sedges, and occasional shrubs, which grow close to the ground. Plant diversity is very low. In some places desert conditions prevail because so little moisture falls.

Animal Life: Animals of the arctic tundra have adapted to the cold by having good insulation. Many birds, especially shorebirds and waterfowl, migrate. The fauna is much richer in summer than in winter. Many insects spend the winter at immature stages of growth, which are more resistant to cold than the adult forms. The larger animals include herbivores such as musk oxen and caribou in North America, called reindeer in Europe and Asia, as well as the smaller hares and lemmings. Common predators include arctic fox, wolves, and snowy owls, and polar bears near the coast.

Effects of Humans: Though this area is sparsely populated, mineral extraction, especially of oil, has the potential to significantly impact this biome. Ecosystem recovery from such damage would be very slow.

MOUNTAIN RANGES

Figure 51.26k

Rocky Mountains of British Columbia

Physical Environment: Mountain ranges must be treated differently than the 10 biomes listed above. Biome type relies predominantly on climate. On mountains, temperature decreases with increasing elevation through adiabatic cooling, as discussed in the text. Thus, precipitation and temperature may change dramatically, depending on elevation and whether the mountainside is on the windward or leeward side.

Location: Mountain ranges exist in many areas of the world, but among the largest are the Himalayas in Asia, the Rockies in North America, and the Andes in South America.

Plant Life: Biome type may change from temperate forest through taiga and into tundra on an elevation gradient in the Rocky Mountains, and even from tropical forest to tundra on the highest peaks of the Andes in tropical South America. In tropical regions, daylight varies little from the 12 hours per day throughout the year. Instead of an intense period of productivity, vegetation in the tropical alpine tundra exhibits slow but steady rates of photosynthesis and growth all year.

Animal Life: The animals of this biome are as varied as the number of habitats they contain. Generally, more species of plants and animals are found at lower elevations than at higher ones. At higher elevations, animals such as bighorn sheep and mountain goats have to be very sure-footed to climb the craggy slopes and have skidproof pads on their hooves. Despite the often-strong winds, birds of prey, such as eagles, are frequent predators of the furry rodents found at higher elevations, including guinea pigs and marmots.

Effects of Humans: Logging and agriculture at lower elevations can cause habitat degradation. Because of the steep slopes, mountain soils are often well drained, thin, and especially susceptible to erosion.

Aquatic Biomes Consist of Marine and Freshwater Regions

Freshwater and marine ecology comprises a combined study of the interactions of water and substrate chemistry, vegetation, and organisms ranging in size from bacteria to blue whales. The study of freshwater lakes and marine ecosystems has allowed scientists to address major environmental issues affecting the entire globe. In addition, biodiversity of these ecosystems is increasingly important: freshwater-dwelling organisms comprise approximately 6% of all described species, yet may live in one of the most endangered ecosystems in the world. Many Canadian researchers show strong leadership in the field of freshwater ecology. For example, David Schindler's work studying the ecology of Canadian Shield Lakes in the 1980s provided strong evidence for lake acidification due to acid rain. More recently, John Smol's work on diatoms in lake sediments in high Arctic lakes have shown increasingly longer growing seasons consistent with predictions from global climate change.

Freshwater ecosystems are under substantial threat from overexploitation, pollution, changes to flow patterns, habitat destruction, and invasion by exotic species. Similarly, our oceans are facing degradation from continued pollution, overharvesting, and climate change. Understanding how these major pressures affect fresh and saltwater ecosystems will be paramount in adapting to global changes.

Specific terminology is used within freshwater and marine ecology, often referring to the physical structure of the ecosystem or characteristics therein. The **littoral** region refers to the shallow area along the shore between high tide and low tide, characterized by the presence of emerged, floating, and submerged plants. This depth, to which light

---

INTERTIDAL ZONE

Figure 51.27a

Pacific Rim National Park, British Columbia

Physical Environment: The **intertidal zone**, the area where the land meets the sea, is alternately submerged and exposed by the daily cycle of tides. The resident organisms are subject to huge daily variation in temperature, light intensity, and availability of seawater, which makes life difficult.

Location: Throughout the world, the area where the land meets the sea consists of sandy shore, mudflats, or rocky shore. Commonly, there is a vertical zonation consisting of three broad zones, most evident on rocky shores. The upper intertidal zone is submerged only during the highest tides. The middle intertidal zone is submerged during the highest regular tide and exposed during the lowest tide each day. The lower intertidal zone is exposed only during the lowest tide.

Plant Life: Plant life may be quite limited because the sand or mud is constantly shifted by the tide. Mangroves may colonize mudflats in tropical areas, and salt marsh grasses may colonize mudflats in temperate locations. On the rocky shore, primary producers include green algae and seaweeds.

Animal Life: Animal life may be quite diverse. On the rocky shore, sea anemones, snails, hermit crabs, and small fishes live in tide pools. On the rock face, there may be a variety of limpets, mussels, sea stars, sea urchins, snails, sponges, tube worms, whelks, isopods, and chitons. At low tides, organisms may be dry and vulnerable to predation by a variety of animals, including shorebirds and mammals. High tides bring predatory fish. In sandy or muddy shores, the biome may contain burrowing marine worms, crabs, and small isopods.

Effects of Humans: Urban development has greatly reduced the beach area available to breeding turtles and shorebirds. Oil spills have greatly impacted some rocky intertidal areas.

can still penetrate, is also called the photic zone, while the **limnetic** region refers to the deeper, open water where light no longer penetrates to the substrate and no vegetation grows. The depth below which no light can penetrate is called the aphotic zone. The **benthic zone** refers to the thick organic layer comprising the substrate, often populated by small aquatic invertebrate communities. The section of open water, by contrast, in which organisms must swim or float, is called the **pelagic** region. Marine ecology is often separated into studies of the **continental shelf** region, the shallow ocean section along continental ridges that were exposed during ice ages, or the **open ocean** region, which comprises the remaining deeper regions of the ocean.

During the warmer months of the year in temperate regions, freshwater lakes are stratified by a temperature barrier called a thermocline, where warmer water becomes trapped within a surface layer and does not mix with the lower, cooler layer of water. In the winter, following the fall turnover, the surface region becomes cooler and may turn to ice, while the water below the thermocline remains warmer. The thermocline functions to provide thermally suitable habitat to specific organisms as well as to prevent the rapid depletion of nutrients introduced through detritus during winter months. Turnover also serves to resuspend particulate matter from the substrate and regulate the extent of the littoral zone. Climate change has been shown to affect the depth at which the thermocline forms. In smaller lakes, summer thermoclines have been established at increasingly deeper depths, particularly during El Niño years.

Within aquatic environments, several different biome types are also recognized, including marine aquatic biomes (the intertidal zone, coral reef, and open ocean) and freshwater lakes, rivers, and wetlands. These biomes are distinguished by differences in parameters such as salinity, oxygen content, depth, current strength, and availability of light (**Figures 51.27a–f**).

CORAL REEF

Figure 51.27b

Caribbean coral reef

Physical Environment: Corals need warm water of at least 20°C but less than 30°C. They are also limited to the euphotic zone, where light penetrates. Sunlight is important because many corals harbour symbiotic algae, or dinoflagellates, that contribute nutrients to the animals and require light to live.

Location: Coral reefs exist in warm tropical waters where there are solid substrates for attachment and water clarity is good. The largest coral reef in the world is the Great Barrier Reef off the Australian coastline, but other coral reefs are found throughout the Caribbean Sea and Pacific Ocean.

Plant Life: Dinoflagellate algae live within the coral tissue, and a variety of red and green algae live on the coral reef surface.

Animal Life: An immense variety of microorganisms, invertebrates, and fish live among the coral, making the coral reef one of the most interesting and species-rich biomes on Earth. Probably 30%–40% of all fish species on Earth are found on coral reefs. Prominent herbivores include snails, sea urchins, and fish. These are in turn consumed by octopus, sea stars, and carnivorous fish. Many species are brightly coloured, warning predators of their toxic nature.

Effects of Humans: Collectors have removed many corals and fish for the aquarium trade, and marine pollution threatens water clarity in some areas. Perhaps the greatest threat is from global climate change. Water temperatures that are too high (over 30°C) can cause coral bleaching.

OPEN OCEAN

Figure 51.27c

Manta ray in the open ocean

Physical Environment: In the open ocean, sometimes called the **pelagic zone**, water depth averages 4,000 metres and nutrient concentrations are typically low, though the waters may be periodically enriched by ocean **upwellings**, which carry mineral nutrients from the bottom waters to the surface. Pelagic waters are mostly cold, warming only near the surface.

Location: Across the globe, covering 70% of the Earth's surface.

Plant Life: Where light levels are high at the surface, many microscopic, photosynthetic organisms (**phytoplankton**) grow and reproduce. Phytoplankton account for nearly half the photosynthetic activity on Earth and produce much of the world's oxygen.

Animal Life: Open-ocean organisms include **zooplankton**, minute animal organisms consisting of some worms, copepods (tiny shrimplike creatures), tiny jellyfish, and the small larvae of invertebrates and fish that graze on the phytoplankton. The open ocean also includes free-swimming animals collectively called **nekton**, which can swim against the currents to locate food. The nekton include large squids, fish, sea turtles, and marine mammals that feed on phytoplankton, zooplankton, or each other. Only a few of these organisms live at any great depth. In some areas, there exists a unique assemblage of animals associated with deep-sea hydrothermal vents that spew out hot (350°C) water rich in hydrogen sulphide. In this dark, oxygen-poor environment, large polychaete worms exist together with other organisms that are chemoautotrophs (see Figure 56.3).

Effects of Humans: Oil spills and a long history of garbage disposal have polluted the ocean floors of many areas. Overfishing has caused many fish populations to crash, and the whaling industry has greatly reduced the numbers of most species of whales.

FRESHWATER LENTIC HABITATS

Figure 51.27d

Location: Throughout all the continents of the world. The Great Lakes of Canada represent the largest series of freshwater habitats on Earth.

Freshwater lake, Canada

Physical Environment: Freshwater habitats are traditionally divided into **lentic**, or standing-water, habitats (from the Latin *lenis*, calm), and **lotic**, or running-water, habitats (from the Latin *lotus*, washed). The lentic habitat consists of still, often deep water. Its physical characteristics depend greatly on the surrounding land, which dictates what nutrients collect in the lake. Young lakes often start off clear and with little plant life. Such lakes are called **oligotrophic**. With age, the phytoplankton bloom and algae spread, reducing the water clarity. Such lakes are termed **eutrophic**. The process of eutrophication is discussed more thoroughly in Chapter 56.

Plant Life: In addition to free-floating phytoplankton and algae, lentic habitats may have rooted vegetation, which often emerges above the water surface (emergent vegetation), such as cattails, plus deeper-dwelling aquatic plants and algae.

Animal Life: Animals include fish, frogs, turtles, crayfish, and many species of insects (including aquatic insect larvae). In tropical and subtropical lakes, alligators and crocodiles commonly are seen.

Effects of Humans: Agricultural runoff, including fertilizers and sewage, can greatly increase lake nutrient levels and speed up the process of eutrophication. This may result in algal blooms and fish kills. In some areas, exotic species of invertebrates and fish are outcompeting native species.

FRESHWATER LOTIC HABITATS Figure 51.27e

Fast-flowing waters of the Humber River, Newfoundland, are a challenge to Atlantic salmon migrating upstream to their spawning grounds

Physical Environment: In lotic habitats, flowing water prevents nutrient accumulations and phytoplankton blooms. The current also mixes water thoroughly, providing a well-aerated habitat of relatively uniform temperature. However, current, oxygen level, and clarity are greater in headwaters than in the lower reaches of rivers. Nutrient levels are generally less in headwaters.

Location: On all continents except Antarctica.

Plant Life: In slow-moving streams and rivers, algae and rooted plants may be present; in swifter-moving rivers, leaves from surrounding forests are the primary food source for animals.

Animal Life: Lotic habitats have a fauna completely different from that of lentic waters. Animals are adapted to stay in place despite an often-strong current. Many of the smaller organisms are flat and attach themselves to rocks to avoid being swept away. Others live on the underside of large boulders, where the current is much reduced. Fish such as trout may be present in rivers with cool temperatures, high oxygen, and clear water. In warmer, murkier waters, catfish and carp may be abundant.

Effects of Humans: Animals of lotic systems are not well adapted for low-oxygen environments and are particularly susceptible to oxygen-reducing pollutants such as sewage. Dams across rivers have prevented the passage of migratory species such as salmon.

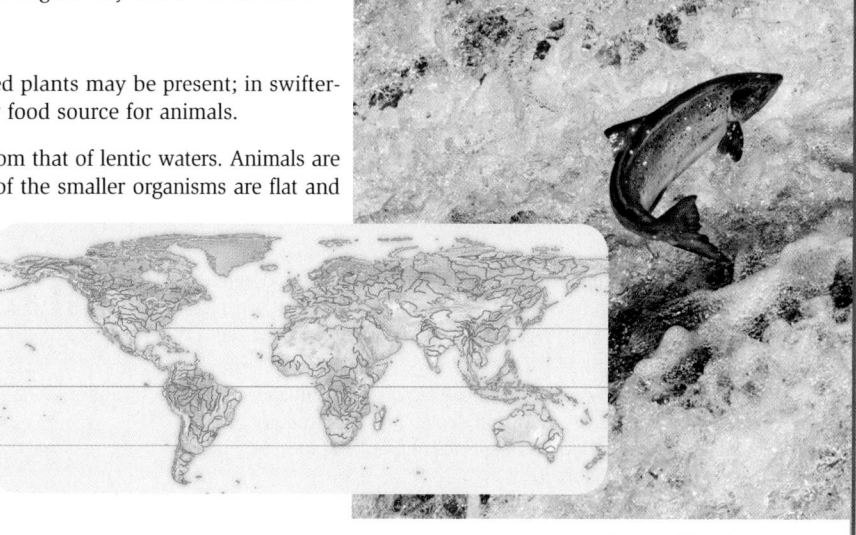

WETLANDS Figure 51.27f

Wetlands in Canada

Physical Environment: At the margins of both lentic and lotic habitats, wetlands may develop. Wetlands are areas regularly saturated by surface water or groundwater. They can range from marshes and swamps to bogs. Many are seasonally flooded when rivers overflow their banks or lake levels rise. Some wetlands also develop along estuaries, where rivers merge with the ocean and high tides can flood the land. Here, salt marshes or, in tropical areas, stands of mangroves can develop. Because of generally high nutrient levels, oxygen levels are fairly low. Temperatures vary substantially with location. Prairie potholes are also a type of wetland.

Location: Worldwide, except in Antarctica.

Plant Life: Wetlands are among the most productive and species-rich areas in the world. In North America, floating plants such as lilies and rooted species such as sedges, cattails, cypress, and gum trees predominate.

Animal Life: Most wetlands are rich in animal species. Wetlands are a prime habitat for wading and diving birds. In addition, they are home to a profusion of insects, from mosquitoes to dragonflies. Vertebrate predators include many amphibians, reptiles, and mammals such as otters.

Effects of Humans: Long mistakenly regarded as wasteland by humans, many wetlands have been drained and developed for subdivisions and industry.

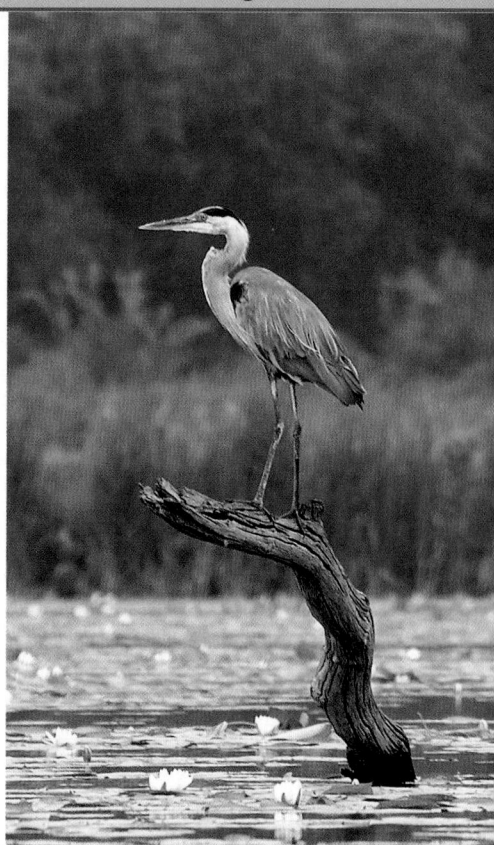

In this chapter we have discussed how the physical environment profoundly influences the distribution and abundance of life on Earth and the existence of different biome types. In subsequent chapters, we will learn how other factors influence the distribution of plants and animals. On a smaller scale, the presence of predators, parasites, or competitors can also influence where organisms are found. Part of an organism's fundamental niche may be occupied by a competitively superior species.

We will examine the influences of such factors in Chapter 53. For animals, social interactions with other members of the same species such as fights over territory or mates can also influence population distributions. To discuss these issues, the next chapter examines animal behaviour.

Summary of Key Concepts

51.1 The Scale of Ecology

- Ecologists study the interactions among organisms and between organisms and their environments. (Figure 51.1)

- The field of ecology can be subdivided into broad areas of organismal, population, community, and ecosystem ecology. (Figure 51.2)

- Organismal ecology considers how individuals are adapted to their environment and how the behaviour of an individual organism contributes to its survival and reproductive success and the population density of the species.

- Population ecology explores those factors that influence a population's growth, size, and density, and community ecology studies how populations of species interact and form functional communities. (Figure 51.3)

- Ecosystem ecology examines the flow of energy and cycling of nutrients among organisms within a community and between organisms and the environment.

- Ecological methods focus on observation and experimentation. Interactions among species are often observed and analyzed graphically, and an hypothesis is formed. Ecologists often test their hypotheses using well-replicated experiments. The results are often presented graphically and analyzed via a variety of statistical tests. (Figures 51.4, 51.5, 51.6)

51.2 The Environment's Impact on the Distribution of Organisms

- Abiotic factors such as temperature, wind, water, light, salinity, pH, and water currents can have powerful effects on ecological systems.

- Temperature exerts important effects on the distribution of organisms because of its effect on biological processes and the inability of most organisms to regulate their body temperature. (Figures 51.7, 51.8, 51.9, 51.10)

- Life on Earth is made possible by the greenhouse effect, in which short-wave solar radiation passes through the atmosphere to warm the Earth but is radiated back to space as long-wave infrared radiation. Much of this radiation is absorbed by atmospheric gases and reradiated back to Earth's surface, causing its temperature to rise. (Figure 51.11)

- The major atmospheric gases causing the greenhouse effect are carbon dioxide, methane, nitrous oxide, and chlorofluorocarbons. (Table 51.1)

- An increase in atmospheric gases is increasing the greenhouse effect, causing global warming, a gradual elevation of the Earth's surface temperature. Ecologists expect that global warming will have a large effect on the distribution of the world's organisms. (Figure 51.12)

- Wind can amplify the effects of temperature and modify wave action. (Figure 51.13)

- The availability of water has an important effect on the abundance of organisms. (Figure 51.14)

- Light can be a limiting resource for plants in both terrestrial and aquatic environments. (Figure 51.15)

- The concentration of salts and the pH of soil and water can limit the distribution of organisms. (Figures 51.16, 51.17)

51.3 Climate and Its Relationship to Biological Communities

- Global temperature differentials are caused by variations in incoming solar radiation and patterns of atmospheric circulation. (Figures 51.18, 51.19, 51.20, 51.21)

- Elevation and the proximity between a land mass and large bodies of water can similarly affect climate. (Figures 51.22, 51.23)

- Climate has a large effect on biomes, major types of habitats characterized by distinctive plant and animal life. (Figures 51.24, 51.25)

- Terrestrial biomes are generally named for their climate and vegetation type and include tropical rain forest, tropical deciduous forest, temperate rain forest, temperate deciduous forest, temperate coniferous forest (taiga), tropical grassland (savannah), temperate grassland (prairie), hot and cold deserts, and tundra. In mountain ranges, biome type may change on an elevation gradient. (Figure 51.26)

- Within aquatic environments, biomes include marine aquatic biomes (the intertidal zone, coral reef, and open ocean) and freshwater lakes, rivers, and wetlands. These are distinguished by differences in parameters including salinity, oxygen content, depth, current strength (lentic versus lotic), and availability of light. (Figure 51.27)

Test to Assess Your Learning

1. Which of the following is probably the most important factor in the distribution of organisms in the environment?
   a. light
   b. temperature
   c. salinity
   d. water availability
   e. pH

2. The greenhouse effect is
   a. a new phenomenon resulting from industrialization.
   b. due to the absorption of solar radiation by atmospheric gases.
   c. responsible for the natural warming of the Earth.

d. all of the above.

e. b and c only.

3. Which of the following is not a component of climate?

a. temperature

b. vegetation

c. water

d. wind

e. light

4. The study of how groups of different species interact in their common environment is

a. ecology.

b. organismal ecology.

c. community ecology.

d. population ecology.

e. environmental ecology.

5. In aquatic environments, plants and algae are usually found in the _____ zone near the surface of the water, where light is able to penetrate.

a. aphotic

b. littoral

c. euphotic

d. limnetic

e. photosynthetic

6. What is the driving force that determines the circulation of the atmospheric air?

a. temperature differences of the Earth

b. winds

c. ocean currents

d. mountain ridges

e. all of the above

7. The distribution of the major biomes of the Earth is determined by

a. temperature differences.

b. mountain ridges.

c. ocean currents.

d. temperature and moisture differences.

e. all of the above.

8. What characteristics are commonly used to identify the biomes of the Earth?

a. temperature

b. precipitation

c. vegetation

d. all of the above

e. a and b only

9. Terrestrial areas that are regularly saturated by surface water or groundwater are called

a. chaparral.

b. lakes.

c. wetlands.

d. deserts.

e. grasslands.

10. Which is the most important contribution to human-caused global warming?

a. carbon dioxide

b. nitrous oxide

c. sulphur dioxide

d. methane

e. chlorofluorocarbons

Articulate to Assess Your Learning

1. If mountains are closer to the sun than valleys, why aren't they hotter?

2. Why are fires generally more frequent in prairies than in hotter, drier deserts?

Collaborate to Assess and Extend Your Learning

1. The Okanagan Mountain Park fire in 2003 was one of the worst interface wildfires in British Columbia's history, burning approximately 256 square kilometres. What could be done to prevent such a catastrophic fire in the park?

2. Based on your knowledge of biomes, identify the biome in which you live. In your discussion, list and describe the organisms that you have observed in your biome. Why might your observations not fit the biome predicted to occur from temperature/precipitation profiles?

3. A principle of biology is that living organisms interact with their environment. Why are invasive species of insects able to succeed in new environments?

Visit McGraw-Hill Ryerson Connect™ for additional study resources.

Behavioural Ecology

Chapter Outline

A redback spider *(Latrodectus hasselti)* on a web with one courting male and one cannibalized male.

Behaviour is the observable response of organisms to external or internal stimuli. Defined as such, behaviour takes into account a very broad range of activities. In this chapter, we focus our attention on the field of **behavioural ecology**, the study of how behaviour contributes to the differential survival and reproduction of organisms. For example, nesting black-headed gulls (*Larus ridibundus*) always pick up broken eggshells after a chick has hatched and carry them away from the nest. One might think that they are being neat and tidy, or are minimizing the risk of bacterial infection to the chicks, but there is more to the behaviour than this. The chicks and unhatched eggs are well camouflaged in the nest, but the white colour of the empty eggshell quickly attracts the attention of predators such as crows that would kill and eat the chicks or remaining eggs. By removing the old eggshells, the gull parents are increasing the chances that their offspring—and thus their genes—will survive.

In the early twentieth century, **ethology** (from the Greek *ethos*, habit, manner), the study of animal behaviour, addressed questions about both *how* animals behave (**proximate causation**) and *why* animals behave in particular ways (**ultimate causation**). Factors that focus on specific genetic and physiological mechanisms of behaviour are called proximate causes. For example, we could hypothesize that in the fall, male deer rut or fight with other males because a change in day length stimulates the eyes, brain, and pituitary gland and triggers hormonal changes in their bodies. Factors that focus on the adaptive significance of behaviours or the evolutionary basis of behaviours are called ultimate causes. Thus, asking questions about why fighting evolved among male deer leads to the hypothesis that male deer fight to determine which deer get to mate with female deer and pass on their genes. This hypothesis leads to a different answer than the one that is concerned with changes in day length. This answer focuses on the adaptive significance of fighting to the deer; that is, on why a particular behaviour evolved, in terms of its effect on reproductive success.

In this chapter, we will explore the role of both proximate and ultimate causes of behaviour. We begin the chapter by investigating how behaviour is achieved; that is, we look at the role of both genetics and the environment. In doing so, we will examine the important contributions of Karl von Frisch, Konrad Lorenz, and Niko Tinbergen, who shared the 1973 Nobel Prize in Physiology or Medicine for their pioneering discoveries in ethology. We consider how different behaviours are involved in movement, gathering food, and communication. Later, we investigate how organisms interact in groups, whether an organism can truly behave in a way that benefits others at a cost to itself, and how behaviour shapes different mating systems. The current field of behavioural ecology concentrates almost exclusively on the ultimate causes of behaviour.

52.1 THE IMPACT OF GENETICS AND LEARNING ON BEHAVIOUR

Learning Outcomes:

1. Describe the differences between innate behaviour, conditioning, and learning.
2. Distinguish between classical conditioning and operant conditioning.
3. Give examples of how genetics and learning influence most behaviours.

Behaviour is rarely due solely to genes (nature) or solely to environmental influences (nurture), but is usually due to a combination of both. Determining to what degree a behaviour is influenced by genes versus the environment will depend on the particular

GENOMES AND PROTEOMES

Some Behaviour Results from Simple Genetic Influences

An excellent example of the effect of a single gene on complex behaviour was demonstrated in W. C. Rothenbuhler's 1964 work on honeybees. Some strains of bees are termed hygienic; that is, they detect and remove diseased larvae from the nest. This behaviour involves two distinct manoeuvres: uncapping the wax cells and then discarding the dead larvae. Other strains are not hygienic and do not exhibit such behaviour. Rothenbuhler demonstrated, by genetic crosses, that one gene (u) controlled cell uncapping and another gene (r) controlled larval removal. Double recessives (*uurr*) were hygienic strains, and double dominants (*UURR*) were nonhygienic strains. When the two strains were crossed, all the F_1 hybrids were nonhygienic (*UuRr*). When the F_1 hybrids were backcrossed with the pure hygienic strain (*uurr*), four different genotypes were produced, as Mendel's law of independent assortment predicts (Chapter 15): one-quarter of the offspring were hygienic (*uurr*), one-quarter were nonhygienic and showed neither behaviour (*UuRr*), one-quarter uncapped the cells but failed to remove the larvae (*uuRr*), and one-quarter removed the larvae but only if the cells were uncapped for them (*Uurr*).

Genes for behaviour actually act on the development of nervous systems and musculature, physical traits that evolve through natural selection. Many genes are needed for the proper development and function of the nervous system and musculature. Even so, variation in a single gene can have a dramatic impact on behaviour.

genes and environment examined. In a few cases, changes in behaviour may be caused by variation in just one gene. Even if a given behaviour is influenced by many genes, if one gene is altered it is possible that the entire behaviour can change.

In this section, we begin by examining the effect that a single gene can exert on behaviour and consider several examples of simple, genetically programmed behaviours. Later, we explore several types of learned behaviour, including classical and operant conditioning and cognitive learning, and conclude the section by exploring an example of the interaction of genetics and learning on behaviour.

Fixed Action Patterns Are Genetically Programmed

Behaviours that seem to be genetically programmed are referred to as **innate** (also called instinctual). While we recognize that expression of genes varies, often in response to environmental stimuli, some behaviour patterns evidently are genetically quite fixed. Most individuals will exhibit the same behaviour regardless of the environment. A spider will spin a specific web without ever seeing a member of its own species build one. The courtship behaviours of many bird species are so stereotyped as to be virtually identical.

A classic example of innate behaviour is the egg-rolling response in geese (**Figure 52.1**). If an incubating goose notices an egg out of the nest, she will extend her neck toward the egg, get up, and then roll the egg back to the nest using her beak. Such behaviour functions to improve fitness because it increases the survival of offspring. Eggs that roll out of the nest get cold and fail to hatch. Geese that fail to exhibit the egg-rolling response would pass on fewer of their genes to future generations. Egg-rolling behaviour is an example of what ethologists term a **fixed action pattern (FAP)**, a behaviour that, once initiated, will continue until completed. For example, if the egg is removed while the goose is in the process of rolling it back toward the nest, the goose still completes the FAP, as though she were rolling back the now-absent egg to the nest. The stimulus to initiate this behaviour is obviously a strong

1. The female goose extends her neck toward the egg.
2. The goose gets up from the nest and approaches the egg.
3. The goose places her neck above the egg.
4. The goose rolls the egg back to the nest with her beak and neck.

Figure 52.1 **A fixed action pattern as an example of innate behaviour.** Female geese retrieve eggs that have rolled outside the nest through a set sequence of movements. The goose will complete this entire sequence even if a researcher takes the egg away before the goose has rolled it back to the nest.

one, which ethologists term a **sign stimulus**. The sign stimulus for the goose is an egg that has rolled out of the nest. According to ethologists, this stimulus acts on the goose's central nervous system, which provides a neural stimulus to initiate the motor program or FAP. Interestingly, any round object will elicit the egg-rolling response, from a wooden egg to a volleyball. While sign stimuli usually have certain key components, they are not necessarily very specific.

Niko Tinbergen's study of male stickleback fish provides another classic example of FAPs and sign stimuli. Male sticklebacks, which have a characteristic red belly, will attack other male sticklebacks that invade their territory. Tinbergen found that sticklebacks attacked small, unrealistic model fish having a red ventral surface, while ignoring a realistic male stickleback model that lacked a red underside (**Figure 52.2**).

Learning

Although many of the behavioural patterns exhibited by animals are largely innate, sometimes animals can make modifications to their behaviour based on previous experience, a process called **learning**. Perhaps the simplest form of learning is **habituation**, in which an organism learns to ignore a repeated stimulus. For example, birds can become habituated to the presence of a scarecrow. Habituation can be a problem at airfields, where birds eventually ignore the alarm calls designed to scare them away from the runways.

When an association develops between a stimulus and a response, a change in behaviour can occur; this is termed **associative learning**. The two main types of associative learning are classical conditioning and operant conditioning and are dealt with in most introductory psychology texts.

In **classical conditioning**, an involuntary response comes to be associated positively or negatively with a stimulus that did not originally elicit the response. This type of learning is generally associated with the Russian psychologist Ivan Pavlov and is discussed in Chapter 38. In classical conditioning, organisms learn to associate a particular stimulus, such as the sound of a bell, with a subsequent event. In this case, the learned association is maintained by the antecedent stimulus. Classical conditioning is widely observed in nature. For example, many insects quickly learn to associate certain flower odours with nectar rewards that elicit floral probing behaviour, whereas other flower odours, associated with no rewards, will not elicit probing behaviour.

In **operant conditioning**, an animal's behaviour is reinforced by a consequence, either a reward or a punishment, and is also called trial-and-error learning. Organisms associate a specific behaviour with particular consequences, such as a punishment. In this case, the behaviour is modified by the subsequent stimulus (i.e., the consequence), and behaviour may be modified slowly over time with repeated exposure to the consequence. For example, toads will eventually refuse to strike at insects that sting, such as wasps and bees, and birds will learn to avoid bad-tasting butterflies (**Figure 52.3**).

Cognitive Learning Involves Conscious Thought

Cognitive learning refers to the ability to solve problems with conscious thought and without direct environmental feedback. In the 1920s psychologist Wolfgang Kohler conducted a series of classic experiments with chimpanzees that suggested animals could

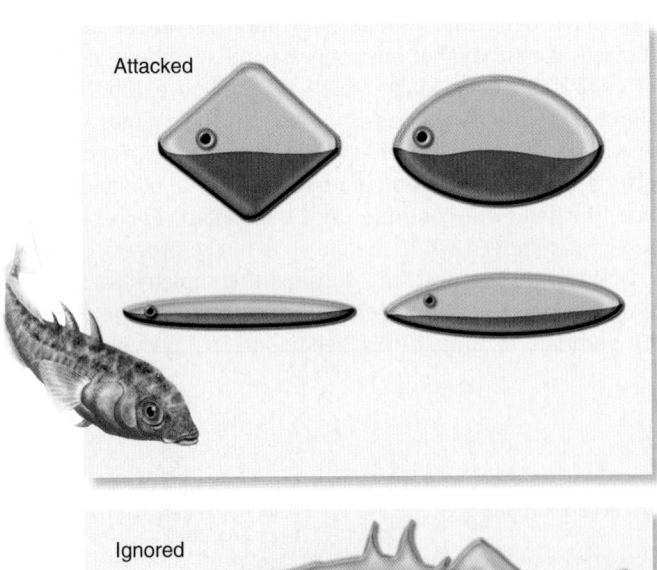

Figure 52.2   A fixed action pattern elicited by a sign stimulus.   The sign stimulus for male sticklebacks to attack other males entering their territory is a red ventral surface. In experiments, male sticklebacks attacked all models that had a red underside, while ignoring a realistic model of a stickleback that lacked the red belly.

(a) Blue jay eating monarch   **(b) Vomiting reaction**

Figure 52.3   Operant conditioning, also known as trial-and-error learning.   (a) A young blue jay will eat a monarch butterfly, not knowing that it is noxious. (b) After the first experience of vomiting after eating a monarch, a blue jay will avoid the insects in the future.

Concept check: *What's the difference between operant conditioning and classical conditioning?*

BioConnections: *Look forward to Figure 54.11d. How might operant conditioning influence the similar appearance of king snakes and coral snakes?*

exhibit cognitive learning. In the experiments, a chimpanzee was left in a room with a banana hanging from the ceiling and out of reach (**Figure 52.4**). Also present in the room were several wooden boxes. At first, the chimp tried in vain to jump up and grab the bananas. After a while, however, it began to arrange the boxes one on top of another underneath the fruit. Eventually, the chimp climbed the boxes and retrieved the fruit. This clearly looks like an example of problem solving that involves cognitive learning.

In fact, many other examples of such behaviour exist. Chimps strip leaves off twigs and use the twigs to poke into ant nests, withdrawing the twig and licking the ants off. Captive ravens have been shown to retrieve meat suspended from a branch by a string, even though they have never encountered the problem before. They pull up on the string, step on it, and then pull up on the string again, repeating the process until the meat is within reach.

The Interaction of Genetics and Learning on Behaviour Often Involves Imprinting

Much of the behaviour we have discussed so far has been presented as either innate or learned, but the behaviour we observe in nature is often a mixture of both. Bird songs present a good example. Many birds learn their songs as juveniles, when they hear their parents sing. If juvenile white-crowned sparrows are raised in isolation, their adult songs do not resemble the typical species-specific song (**Figure 52.5**). If they hear only the song of a different species, such as the song sparrow, they again sing a poorly developed adult song. However, if they hear the song of the white-crowned sparrow, they will learn to sing a fully developed white-crowned sparrow song. The birds are genetically programmed to learn, but they will sing the correct song only if they are exposed to the appropriate song from which to learn.

Another example of how innate behaviour interacts with learning can occur during a limited time period of development,

called a **critical period**. At this time, many animals develop species-specific patterns of behaviour. This process is called **imprinting**. One of the best examples of imprinting was demonstrated by the Austrian ethologist Konrad Lorenz in the 1930s.

Lorenz noted that young birds of some species imprint on their mother during a critical period, usually within a few hours after hatching. This behaviour serves them well, because in many species of ducks and geese it would be hard for the mother to keep track of all her offspring as they walk or swim. After imprinting takes place, the offspring keep track of the mother.

The survival of the young ducks requires that they quickly learn to follow their mother's movements. Lorenz raised greylag geese from eggs, and soon after they hatched, he used himself as the model for imprinting. As a result, the young goslings imprinted on Lorenz and followed him around. For the rest of their life, they preferred the company of Lorenz and other humans to geese. In nature, if the young geese failed to be provided with any stimulus during the critical period, they would fail to imprint on anything, and without parental care they would almost certainly die.

Other animals imprint in different ways. Newborn shrews imprint on the scent of their mother. Mothers also can imprint on their own young within a few hours. For example, if sheep mothers are kept apart from their offspring for only a few hours after birth, they will reject them. In these situations, the innate behaviour is the ability to imprint soon after birth, and the factors in the environment are the stimulus to which the imprinting is directed.

Finally, innate behaviour can interact with learning during animal migration. Inexperienced juvenile birds will migrate in a particular direction but will fail to correct for deviations if they are blown off course. Experienced adult birds, on the other hand, can often correct for storm-induced displacement, indicating they have more complex navigational skills. There are in fact many complex behaviours involved in movement, as we will explore in the next section.

Figure 52.4 **Cognitive behaviour involves problem-solving ability.** This chimp has devised a solution to the problem of retrieving bananas that were initially out of its reach.

Song heard by juvenile

No song heard

Song of song sparrow

Song of white-crowned sparrow

Song sung by juvenile

Abnormal song

Abnormal song

Normal song

Figure 52.5   The interaction between genetics and learning.   The juvenile white-crowned sparrow will sing an abnormal song if it is kept in isolation or hears only the song of a different species. However, the juvenile will sing the normal white-crowned sparrow song if exposed to it.

Concept check: *Cuckoos lay their eggs in other birds' nests, so their young are reared by parent birds of a different species. However, unlike the white-crowned sparrow, adult cuckoos always sing their own distinctive song, not that of the host species they hear as juveniles. How is this possible?*

FEATURE INVESTIGATION

Tinbergen's Experiments Show That Digger Wasps Use Landmarks to Find Their Nests

In the sandy, dry soils of Europe, the solitary female digger wasp (*Philanthus triangulum*) digs four to five nests in which to lay her eggs. Each nest stretches obliquely down into the ground for 40 to 80 centimetres. The wasp, sometimes called a bee wolf, follows this by performing a sequence of apparently genetically programmed events. She catches and stings a honeybee, which paralyzes it; returns to the nest; drags the bee into the nest; and lays an egg on it. The egg hatches into a larva, which feeds on the paralyzed bee. However, the larva needs to ingest five to six bees before it is fully developed. This means the wasp must catch and sting four to five more bees for each larva. She can only carry one bee at a time. After each visit, the wasp must seal the nest, find a new bee, relocate the nest, open it, and add the bee. How does the wasp relocate the nest after spending considerable time away? Niko Tinbergen observed the wasps hover and fly around the nest each time they took off. He hypothesized that they were learning the nest position by creating a mental map of the landmarks in the area.

To test his hypothesis, Tinbergen experimentally adjusted the landmarks around the burrow that the wasps might be using as cues (**Figure 52.6**). First, he put a ring of pinecones

HYPOTHESIS Digger wasps (*Philanthus triangulum*) use visual landmarks to locate their nests.

STARTING LOCATION The female digger wasp excavates an underground nest, to which she returns daily, bringing food to the larvae located inside.

Experimental level

1   Place a ring of pinecones around the nest to train the wasp to associate pinecones with the nest.

Pinecones

Digger wasp

Figure 52.6   How Niko Tinbergen discovered the digger wasp's nest-locating behaviour.

Concept check: *How would you test what type of spatial landmarks are used by female digger wasps?*

Figure 52.6 *(Continued)*

2 After the wasp leaves the nest to hunt, move the pinecones 30 cm from the real nest. The wasp returns and flies to the centre of the pinecone circle instead of the real nest. Repeated experiments yield similar results (see data), indicating that the wasp uses landmarks as visual cues.

Move pinecones 30 cm from the nest.

3 To test whether it is the shape or the smell of the pinecones that elicits the response, perform the same experiment as above, except use pinecones with no scent and add two small pieces of cardboard coated with pine oil.

Pine oil

Cardboard

4 After the wasp leaves the nest, move the pinecones 30 cm from the nest, but leave the scented cardboard at the nest. The wasps again fly to the pinecone nest (see data), indicating that it is the arrangement of cones, not their smell, that elicits the learning.

Move pinecones 30 cm from the nest.

5 **THE DATA***

Results from steps 1 and 2:

Wasp #	Number of return visits per wasp to real nest without pinecones	Number of return visits per wasp to sham nest with pinecones
1–17	0	~9

Results from steps 3 and 4:

Wasp #	Number of return visits per wasp to real nest with scented cardboard	Number of return visits per wasp to sham nest with pinecones
18–22	0	~6

*Seventeen wasps, numbered 1–17, were studied as described in steps 1 and 2. Five wasps, numbered 18–22, were studied as described in steps 3 and 4.

6 **CONCLUSION** Digger wasps remember the positions of visual landmarks and use them as aids in local movements.

7 **SOURCE** Tinbergen, N. 1951. *The study of instinct.* Clarendon Press, Oxford.

around the nest entrance to train the wasp to associate the pinecones with the nest. Then, when the wasp was out hunting, he moved the circle of pinecones a distance from the real nest and constructed a sham nest, making a slight depression in the sand and mimicking the covered entrance of the burrow. On returning, the wasp flew straight to the sham nest and tried to locate the entrance. Tinbergen chased it away. When it returned, it again flew to the sham nest. Tinbergen repeated this nine times, and every time the wasp chose the sham nest. Tinbergen got the same result with 16 other wasps and not once did they choose the real nest.

Next Tinbergen experimented with the type of stimulus that might be eliciting the learning. He hypothesized that the wasps could be responding to the distinctive scent of the pinecones rather than their appearance. He trained the wasps by placing a circle of pinecones that had no scent and two small pieces of cardboard coated in pinecone oil around the real nest. He then moved the cones to surround a sham nest and left the scented cardboard around the real nest. The returning wasps again ignored the real nest with the scented cardboard and flew to the sham. He concluded that for the wasps, sight was apparently more important than smell in determining landmarks.

Experimental Questions

1. What observations were important for the development of Niko Tinbergen's hypothesis explaining how digger wasps located their nests?
2. How did Tinbergen test the hypothesis that the wasps were using landmarks to relocate the nest? What were the results?
3. Did the Tinbergen experiment rule out any other cue the wasps may have been using besides the sight of pinecones?

52.2 LOCAL MOVEMENT AND LONG-RANGE MIGRATION

Learning Outcomes:

1. Distinguish between kinesis and taxis, two different types of local movement.
2. Describe the three mechanisms animals use during migration.

Organisms need to find their way, both locally and over what can be extremely long distances. Locally, organisms continually need to locate sources of food, water, and perhaps nesting sites. Migration involves the longer-distance seasonal movement of animals between overwintering areas and summer breeding sites; these are often hundreds or even thousands of kilometres apart. Several different types of behaviour may be involved in these movements. In this section, we begin by exploring local movement and, in particular, how one species uses landmarks to guide its movements. We then consider the longer-range seasonal movement called migration and examine three possible mechanisms used by migrating animals to find their way.

Local Movement Can Involve Kinesis, Taxis, and Memory

The simplest forms of movement are mere responses to stimuli. A **kinesis** is a movement in response to a stimulus, but one that is not directed toward or away from the source of the stimulus. A simple experiment often done in classrooms is to observe the activity levels of woodlice, sometimes called sow bugs or pill bugs, in dry areas and moist areas. The woodlice move faster in drier areas, and they slow down when they reach moist environments. This behaviour tends to keep them in damper areas, which they prefer in order to avoid desiccation.

A **taxis** is a more directed type of response either toward or away from a stimulus. Cockroaches exhibit negative phototaxis, meaning they tend to move away from light. Under low-light conditions, the photosynthetic unicellular flagellate *Euglena gracilis* shows positive phototaxis and moves toward a light source. Sea turtle hatchings are also strongly attracted to light. On emerging from their nests, they crawl toward the brightest location, traditionally the reflected moonlight on the ocean's surface. Lighted houses on the shore can confuse

the hatchlings, however, and cause them to lose their way, with sometimes disastrous results. Male silk moths orient themselves in relation to wind direction (anemotaxis). If the air current carries the scent of a female moth, they will move upwind to locate it. Some freshwater fish orient themselves to the currents of streams. Many fish exhibit positive rheotaxis (from the Greek *rheos*, current), in that they swim against the water current to prevent being washed downstream.

Sometimes memory and landmarks may be used to aid in local movements. The prominent Dutch-born ethologist Niko Tinbergen showed how the female digger wasp uses landmarks to relocate her nests. Tinbergen's experiments are described in the Feature Investigation.

Migration Involves Long-Range Movement and More Complex Spatial Navigation

As well as learning to navigate over short-range distances, many animals undergo **migration**, long-range seasonal movement. Migrations occur in many species and usually involve a movement away from a birth area to feed and a return to the birth area to breed, with the movement generally being linked to seasonal availability of food. For example, nearly half the breeding birds of North America migrate to Central America and Mexico to escape the cold winters and feed, and then they return to North America in the spring to breed. Arctic terns that breed in Arctic Canada and Asia migrate to the Antarctic to feed in the winter and then return to breed. This staggering journey involves a 40,000-kilometre round trip, most of it over the open ocean, during which the birds must stay airborne for days at a time! Many mammals, including wildebeest and caribou, make migrations that track the appearance of new vegetation on which they feed. The monarch butterfly of North America migrates to overwinter in California, Mexico, and probably south Florida and Cuba (**Figure 52.7**). This migration is unique in that none of the individuals has ever been to the migration sites before. An interesting point about the return journey of the monarch is that it involves several generations of butterflies to complete. On their way back to the northern United States and Canada, they lay eggs and die. The caterpillars develop on milkweed plants, and the resultant adults continue to journey farther north. This happens several times in the course of the return journey. Monarch migration is now well understood, but it took over 40 years of study by Fred Urquhart (of the Royal Ontario Museum and University of Toronto), his wife, Norah (**Figure 52.8**), and hundreds of volunteers who

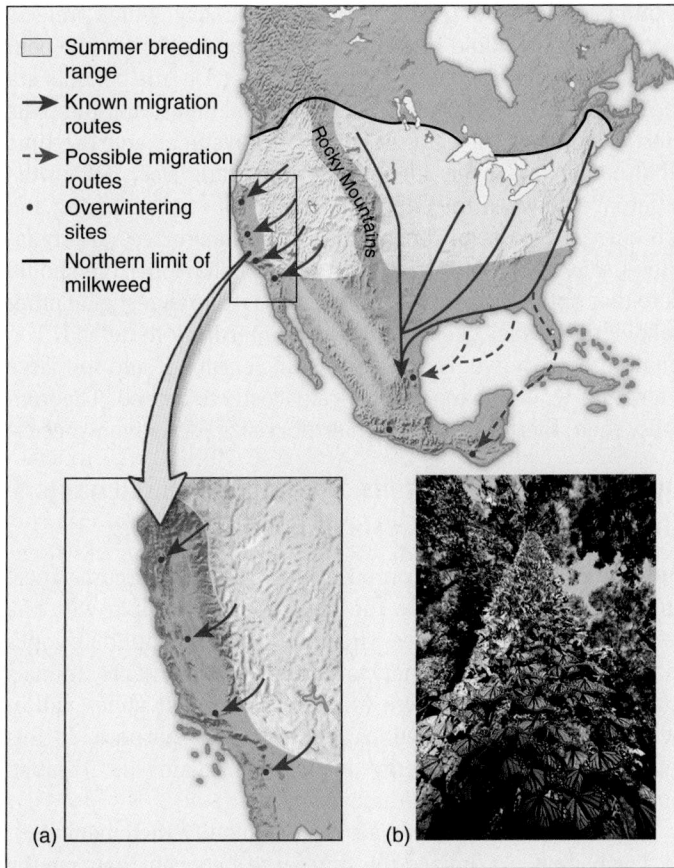

Figure 52.7 Monarch butterfly migration. (a) Many monarch butterflies east of the Rocky Mountains migrate to a small area in Mexico to avoid the cold northern weather. Here they roost together in large numbers in fir trees. Some butterflies may stay in Florida and Cuba. Butterflies west of the Rockies overwinter in mild coastal California locations. (b) Aggregation of monarch butterflies in their overwintering site in Mexico.

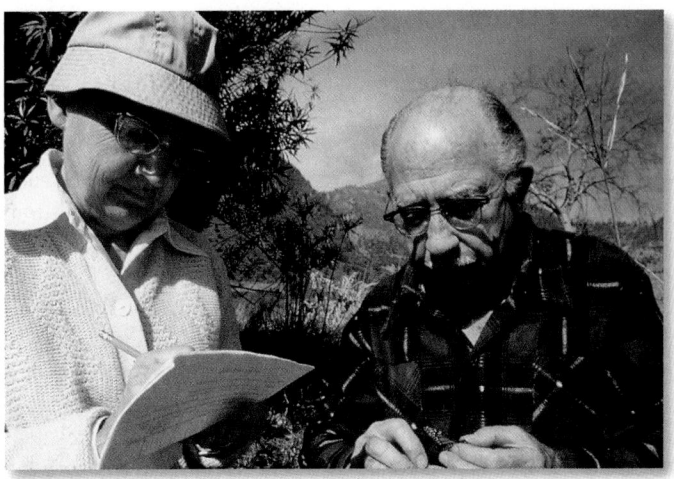

Figure 52.8 Fred and Norah Urquhart. The Urquharts were instrumental in unravelling the mystery of the monarch butterfly's migration.

Figure 52.9 Orientation versus navigation. Starlings normally migrate from breeding grounds in Scandinavia and northeastern Europe through the Netherlands and northern Germany to overwintering sites in northern France and southeast England. This involves a southwest flight. When juveniles were captured in the Netherlands and moved to Switzerland, they continued on in a southwestern direction and ended up in Spain. When experienced birds were captured and moved, they flew to the normal overwintering areas.

helped stick tiny tags on the hind wings of the butterflies that read "Send to Zoology University Toronto Canada."

How do migrating animals find their way? Three mechanisms have been proposed: piloting, orientation, and navigation. In **piloting**, an animal moves from one familiar landmark to the next. For example, many whale species migrate between overwintering areas and summer calving grounds. Grey whales migrate between the Bering Sea near Alaska and coastal areas of Mexico. Features of the coastline, including mountain ranges and rivers, may aid in navigation. In **orientation**, animals have the ability to follow a compass bearing and travel in a straight line. **Navigation** involves the ability not only to follow a compass bearing but also to set or adjust it.

An experiment with starlings helps illuminate the difference between orientation and navigation (**Figure 52.9**). European starlings breed in Scandinavia and northeastern Europe and migrate in a southwest direction toward coastal France and southern England to spend the winter. Migrating starlings were captured and tagged in the Netherlands and then transported south to Switzerland and released. Juvenile birds, which had never made the trip before, flew southwest in their migration and were later recaptured in Spain. Adult birds, with more experience, returned to their normal wintering range by adjusting their course by approximately 90°. This implies that the adult birds can actually navigate, whereas the juveniles rely on orientation.

Many species use a combination of navigational reference points, including the position of the sun, the stars (for nighttime travel), and the Earth's magnetic field. Homing pigeons have magnetite in their beaks that acts as a compass to tell direction (look back to section 42.6, Thermoreception, Nociception, and Electromagnetic Sensing).

Navigation by the sun or the stars also requires the use of a timing device to compensate for the ever-changing position of these reference points. Many migrants, therefore, possess the equivalent of an internal clock. Pigeons integrate their internal clock with the position of the sun. Researchers have altered the internal clock of pigeons by keeping them under artificial lights for certain periods of time. When the pigeons are released, they display predictable deviations in their flight. For every hour that their internal clock is shifted, the orientation of the birds shifts about 15°.

The heritability of migration behaviour in birds was evaluated experimentally by Peter Berthold using the blackcap Sylvia atricapilla. Blackcaps migrate from central Europe to their breeding grounds in Africa. During this migration, some birds migrate south through the Middle East, some birds migrate toward the western Mediterranean region of Spain and Portugal, and some do not migrate at all. Berthold was able to selectively breed migrants with other migrants and nonmigrants with other nonmigrants, and after several generations, was able to produce populations of birds that either all migrated or did not, thereby demonstrating the heritable nature of migration.

Not all examples of animal migration are well understood. Green sea turtles feed off the coast of Brazil yet swim east for 2,300 kilometres to Ascension Island, an 8-kilometre-wide island in the centre of the Atlantic Ocean between Brazil and Africa, to lay their eggs. It is not known why the turtles lay their eggs on this speck of an island or how they succeed in finding it. Perhaps fewer predators exist on Ascension than on other beaches. Thus, while scientists have made many discoveries about animal navigation, much remains to be learned about how animals acquire a "map sense."

To a large extent, local and long-distance movement involves searching for food. Organisms are constantly faced with a decision of how long to stay in a food patch and when to look for a new source of food. In the next section, we will investigate how such foraging decisions are made.

52.3 FORAGING BEHAVIOUR

Learning Outcomes:

1. Describe and give examples of optimal foraging.
2. Outline the costs and benefits of defending a territory.

Food gathering, or foraging, often involves decisions about whether to remain at a resource patch and look for more food or look for a completely new patch. The analysis of these decisions is often performed in terms of **optimality theory**, which predicts that an animal should behave in a way that maximizes the benefits of a behaviour minus its costs. In this case, the benefits are the nutritional or calorific value of the food items, and the costs are the energetic or calorific costs of movement and the time (that could have been spent doing something else). When the difference between the energetic benefits of food gathering and the energetic costs of food gathering is maximized, an organism is said to be optimizing its foraging behaviour. We should note that optimality theory can also be used to investigate other behavioural issues such as how large a territory to defend. Too small a territory would contain insufficient food, and too large a territory would be too energetically costly to defend. Theoretically, then, there is an optimal territory size for a given species.

Optimal Foraging Entails Maximizing the Benefits and Minimizing the Costs of Food Gathering

Optimal foraging theory proposes that in a given circumstance, an animal seeks to obtain the most energy possible with the least expenditure of energy. The underlying assumption of optimal foraging theory is that natural selection favours animals that are maximally efficient at propagating their genes and at performing all other functions that serve this purpose. In this model, the more net energy an individual gains in a limited time, the greater the reproductive success.

Studies show that animals tend to modify their behaviour in a way that maximizes the difference between their energy uptake and their energy expenditure. For example, shore crabs (*Carcinus maenas*) will eat many different-sized mussels but tend to feed preferentially on intermediate-sized mussels, which give them the highest rate of energy return (**Figure 52.10**). Very large mussels yield more energy, but they take so long for the crab to open that they are actually less profitable, in terms of energy yield per unit time spent, than smaller sizes. Very small mussels are easy to crack open but contain so little flesh that they are not worth the effort. This leaves intermediate-sized mussels as the preferred size. Of course, the intermediate-sized mussels may take a longer time to locate, because more crabs are looking for them, so crabs eat some less profitable but more frequently encountered sizes. The result is that the diet consists of mussels in a range of sizes around the preferred optimal size.

In some cases, animals do not always attempt to maximize the rate of energy intake. For example, animals seek not only to forage but also to minimize the risk of predation. Some species may dart out to take food only from time to time. The risk of predation thus has an influence on foraging behaviour. Many animals also maintain territories to minimize competition with other individuals and control resources, whether food, nesting sites, or mates. However, as we will see, defending these territories also has an energetic cost.

Defending Territories Has Costs and Benefits

Many animals, or groups of animals, such as a pride of lions, actively defend a **territory**, a fixed area in which an individual or group excludes other members of its own species, and sometimes other species, by aggressive behaviour or territory marking. Territory owners tend to optimize territory size according to

Figure 52.10 **Optimal foraging behaviour in shore crabs.** In an aquarium setting, when offered a choice of equal numbers of each size mussel, the shore crab (*Carcinus maenas*) prefers intermediate-sized mussels that provide the highest rate of energy return. Profitability is the energy yield (joules) per second of time used in breaking open the shell.

the costs and benefits involved. The primary benefit of a territory is that it provides exclusive access to a particular resource, whether it be food, mates, or sheltered nesting sites. Large territories may provide more of a resource but may be costly to defend, while small territories that are less costly to defend may not provide enough of a resource.

In studies of the territorial behaviour of the golden-winged sunbird (*Nectarinia reichenowi*) in East Africa, researchers measured the energy content of nectar as the benefit of maintaining a territory while the energy costs included activities such as perching, foraging, and defending (**Figure 52.11a**). Defending the territory

ensured that other sunbirds did not take nectar from available flowers, thus increasing the amount of nectar in each flower. In defending a territory, the sunbird saved 780 calories a day in reduced foraging activity. However, the sunbird also spent 728 calories in defence of the territory, yielding a net gain of 52 calories a day.

Territory size differs considerably among species, and optimality theory predicts that it should evolve to maximize the difference between benefits and costs, thus maximizing the fitness "profit" to the territory holder. Because cheetahs need large areas to be able to hunt successfully, they establish large territories relative to their size (**Figure 52.11b**). In contrast, territories set up solely to defend areas for mating or nesting are often relatively small. For example, male sea lions defend small areas of beach. The preferred areas contain the largest number of females and are controlled by the largest breeding bulls. The size of the territory of some nesting birds, such as gannets, is determined by how far the bird can reach to peck its neighbour without leaving its nest (**Figure 52.11c**).

Territories may be held for a season, a year, or the entire lifetime of the individual. Ownership of a territory needs to be periodically proclaimed, and thus communication between individuals is necessary for territory owners. This may involve various types of signalling, which we discuss next.

52.4 COMMUNICATION

Learning Outcome:

1. Give examples of how animals use chemical, auditory, visual, and tactile communication.

Communication is the use of specially designed signals or displays to modify the behaviour of others. It may be used for many purposes, including defining territories, maintaining contact with offspring, courtship, and contests between males. The use of different forms of communication between organisms depends on the environment in which they live. For example,

(a) Golden-winged sunbird

(b) Cheetah

(c) Nesting gannets

Figure 52.11 **Territory sizes differ among animals.** (a) The golden-winged sunbird of East Africa (*Nectarinia reichenowi*) has a medium territory size that is dependent on the number of flowers it can obtain resources from and defend. (b) Cheetahs (*Acinonyx jubatus*) hunt over large areas and can have extensive territories. This male is urine-marking part of his territory in the southern Serengeti, near Ndutu, Tanzania. (c) Nesting gannets (*Morus bassanus*) have much smaller territories, in which each bird is just beyond the pecking range of its neighbour.

visual communication plays little role in the signals of nocturnal animals. Similarly, animals in dense forests often cannot see each other, so sounds are of prime importance in mapping out territories. Sound, however, is a temporary signal. Scent can last longer and is often used to mark the large territories of some mammals. In this section, we outline the various types of communication—chemical, auditory, visual, and tactile—that occur among animals.

Chemical Communication Is Often Used to Mark Territories or Attract Mates

The chemical marking of territories is common among mammals, especially among members of the canine and feline families (see Figure 52.11b). Scent trails are often used by social insects to recruit workers to help bring prey to the nest. Fire ants (*Solenopsis* spp.) attack large, living prey, and many ants are needed to drag the prey back to the nest. In this case, the scout that finds the prey lays down a scent trail from the prey back to the nest. The scent excites other workers, which follow the trail to the prey. The scent marker is very volatile, and the trail effectively disappears in a few minutes to avoid mass confusion over old trails.

Animals frequently use chemicals, called **pheromones**, for intraspecific communication. For example, female moths attract males for mating using sex pheromones. Among social organisms, some individuals use pheromones to manipulate the behaviour of others. A queen bee releases pheromones that suppress the reproductive system of workers, which ensures that she is the only reproductive female in the hive.

Auditory Communication Is Often Used to Attract Mates and Deter Competitors

Many organisms communicate by making sound. Because the Earth itself can absorb sound waves, sound travels farther in the air, which is why many birds and insects use elevated perches when singing. Air is on average 14 times less turbulent at dawn and dusk than during the rest of the day, which helps explain the preference of most animals for calling at these times. Some insects utilize the very plants on which they feed as a medium of song transmission. Many male leafhopper and planthopper insects vibrate their abdomens on leaves and create species-specific courtship songs that are transmitted by adjacent and touching vegetation and are picked up by nearby females of the same species.

While many males use auditory communication to attract females, some females use calls to attract the attention of males. Female elephant seals use this behaviour to their advantage. When a nondominant male attempts to mate with a female, she screams loudly, attracting the attention of the dominant male, which drives the nondominant male away. In this way, she is guaranteed a mating with the strongest male. Sound production can attract predators as well as mates. Some bats listen for the mating calls of male frogs to find their prey. Parasitic flies detect and locate chirping male crickets and then deposit tiny maggots on or near them. The maggots latch onto and penetrate the cricket, and eventually kill it. Sound may also be used by males during competition over females. In many animals, lower-pitched sounds come from bigger males, so by calling to one another, males can gauge the size of their opponents and save fighting energy.

Visual Communication Is Often Used in Courtship and Aggressive Displays

In courtship, animals use a vast number of visual signals to identify and select potential mates. Competition among males for the most impressive displays to attract females has led to elaborate coloration and extensive ornamentation in some species. For example, sexual selection in male peacocks has resulted in elaborate plumage to attract females.

Male fireflies have developed light flashes that are species-specific with regard to number and duration of flashes (**Figure 52.12**). Females respond with a flash of their own.

(a) (b) (c)

Figure 52.12 Visual communication in fireflies. (a) Communication between fireflies is conducted by species-specific light flashes emitted by organs located on the underside of the abdomen. (b) At dusk, many different light flashes can be seen. (c) Sometimes females, such as this large *Photuris versicolor*, mimic the displays of other species, luring an unwitting male, such as this *Photinus tanytoxus*, and then eating him.

 Principle: *Structure determines function. In the firefly a morphological feature (the light emitting organ) influences animal behaviour.*

Such bright flashes are also bound to attract predators. Some female fireflies use mimicry to their advantage. Female *Photuris versicolor* fireflies mimic the flashing responses normally given by females of other species, such as *Photinus tanytoxus*, in order to lure the males of those species close enough to eat them.

Visual signals are also used to resolve disputes over territories or mates. Deer and antelope have antlers or horns that they use to display and spar over territory and females. Most of these matches never develop into outright fights, since the males gauge their opponent's strength by the size of these ornaments. Among insects, the "horns" of rhinoceros beetles and the eye stems of stalk-eyed flies send similar signals.

Tactile Communication Is Used to Strengthen Social Bonds and Convey Information About Food

Animals often use tactile communication to establish bonds between group members. Primates frequently groom one another, while canines and felines may nuzzle and lick each other. Many insects use tactile communication to convey information on the whereabouts of food. Members of the ant genus *Leptothorax* feed on immobile prey such as dead insects. When a scouting ant encounters such prey, it usually needs an additional worker to help bring it back to the nest. Rather than laying a scent trail, which is energetically costly, the scout ant recruits a helper and physically leads it to the food source. The helper runs in tandem with the scout, its antennae touching the scout's abdomen.

Perhaps the most fascinating example of tactile communication among animals is the dance of the honeybee, elegantly studied by German ethologist Karl von Frisch in the 1940s. Bees commonly live in large hives; in the case of the European honeybee (*Apis mellifera*), the hive consists of 30,000 to 40,000 individuals. The flowering plants on which the bees forage are sometimes located miles from the hive and are distributed in a patchy manner, with any given patch usually containing many flowers that store more nectar and pollen than an individual bee can carry back to the nest. The scout bee that locates the resource patch returns to the hive and recruits more workers to join it (**Figure 52.13a**). Because it is dark inside the hive, the bee uses a tactile signal. The scout dances on the vertical side of a honeycomb, and the dance is monitored by other bees, which follow and touch her to interpret the message. If the food is relatively close to the hive, less than 50 m away, the scout performs a round dance, rapidly moving in a circle, first in one direction and then the other. The other bees know the food is relatively close at hand, and the smell of the scout tells them what flower species to look for (**Figure 52.13b**).

If the food is more than 50 metres away, the scout will perform a different type of dance, called a "waggle dance." In this dance, the scout traces a figure 8, in the middle of which she waggles her abdomen and produces bursts of sound. Again, the other bees maintain contact with her. Occasionally, the scout will regurgitate a small sample of nectar so the bees know the type of food source they are looking for. The truly amazing part of the waggle dance is that the angle at which the central part of the figure 8 deviates from the vertical direction of the comb represents the same angle at which the food source deviates from the sun (**Figure 52.13c**). The direction is always up-to-date, because the bee adjusts the dance as the sun moves across the sky.

As we have seen, much communication occurs not only to defend territories but also to communicate information to other individuals in the population, including potential mates. While living on your own and maintaining a territory has advantages, living in a group also has its benefits, including ready availability of mates and increased protection from predators. In the following section, we examine group living and the behaviour it engenders.

(a) Bees clustering around a recently returned worker, shown on the right

(b) Round dance

(c) Waggle dance: The angle of the waggle to the vertical orientation of the honeycomb corresponds to the angle of the food source from the sun.

Figure 52.13 Tactile communication among honeybees regarding food sources. (a) Bees gather around a newly returned scout to receive information about nearby food sources. (b) If the food is less than 50 metres away, the scout performs a round dance. (c) If the food is more than 50 metres away, the scout performs a waggle dance, which conveys information about its location. If the dance is performed at a 30° angle to the right of the hive's vertical plane, then the food source is located at a 30° angle to the right of the sun.

52.5 LIVING IN GROUPS

Learning Outcomes:

1. Discuss the costs and benefits of living in groups.

Much animal behaviour is directed at other animals. As such, some of the more complex behaviour occurs when animals live together in groups such as flocks or herds. If a central concern of ecology is to explain the distribution patterns of organisms, then one of our most important tasks is to identify and understand the behaviour that results from group living. While congregations promote competition for food, there are also benefits of group living that compensate for the costs involved. As we discuss in this section, many of these benefits relate to group defence against predators. Group living can reduce predator success in at least two ways: through increased vigilance and through protection in numbers.

Living in Large Groups May Reduce the Risk of Predation Because of Increased Vigilance

For many predators, success depends on surprise. If an individual is alerted to an attack, the predator's chance of success is lowered. A woodpigeon (*Columba palumbus*) will take to the air when it spots a goshawk (*Accipiter gentilis*). Once one pigeon takes flight, the other members of the flock are alerted and follow suit. If each pigeon occasionally looks up to scan for a hawk, the bigger the group, the more likely that one bird will spot the hawk early enough for the flock to take flight. This is referred to as the **many-eyes hypothesis** (**Figure 52.14**). By living in groups, individuals may decrease the amount of time scanning for predators and increase the time they have to feed. Of course, cheating is a possibility, because some birds might never look up, relying on others to keep watch while they keep feeding. However, the individual that happens to be scanning when a predator approaches is most likely to escape, a fact that tends to discourage cheating.

Living in Groups Offers Protection by the "Selfish Herd"

Group living also provides protection in sheer numbers. Typically, predators take one prey animal per attack. In any given attack, an individual antelope in a herd of 100 has a 1 in 100 chance of being selected, whereas a single individual has a 1 in 1 chance. Large herds may be attacked more frequently than a solitary individual, but a herd is unlikely to attract 100 times more attacks than an individual, often because of the territorial nature of predators. Furthermore, large numbers of prey are able to defend themselves better than single individuals, which usually choose to flee. For example, groups of nesting

blackheaded gulls will mob a crow relentlessly, thereby reducing the crow's ability to steal the gulls' eggs.

Research has shown that within a group, each individual can minimize the danger to itself by choosing the location that is as close to the centre of the group as possible. This was the subject of a famous paper, "The Geometry of the Selfish Herd," by the British evolutionary biologist W. D. Hamilton. The explanation of this type of defence is that predators are likely to attack prey on the periphery because they are easier to isolate visually. Many animals in herds tend to bunch close together when they are under attack, making it physically difficult for the predator to get to the centre of the herd.

In the end, group size may be the result of a trade-off between the costs and benefits of group living. Although much group behaviour serves to reduce predation, other complex behaviour occurs in groups, including grooming behaviour and behaviour that appears to benefit the group at the expense of the individual. For example, a honeybee will sting a potential hive predator to discourage it. The bee's stinger is barbed, and once it has penetrated the predator's skin, the bee cannot withdraw it. The bee's only means of escape is to tear away part of its abdomen, leaving the stinger behind and dying in the process. In the next section, we explore the reasons for altruistic behaviour, in which an individual risks its life for the benefit of others.

Figure 52.14   Living in groups and the many-eyes hypothesis.   The larger the number of woodpigeons, the less likely an attack will be successful.

Concept check: *What other advantages are there to large groups of individuals when being attacked by a predator?*

Learning Outcomes:

1. List the arguments in favour and against the concept of group selection.
2. Describe how the concept of kin selection can explain altruistic behaviour.
3. Discuss eusociality as an example of altruism.

In Chapter 21, we learned that a primary goal of an organism is to pass on its genes, yet we see many instances in which some individuals forgo reproducing altogether, apparently to benefit the group. How do ecologists explain **altruism**, behaviour that appears to benefit others at a cost to oneself? In this section, we begin by discussing whether such behaviour evolved for the good of the group or for the good of the individual. As we will see, most altruistic acts serve to benefit the individual's close relatives. We explore the concept of kin selection, which argues that acts of self-sacrifice indirectly promote the spread of an organism's genes, and see how this plays out in an extreme form in the genetics of social insect colonies. We conclude by examining reciprocal altruism as an attempt to explain the evolution of altruism among non-kin.

In Nature, Individual Selfish Behaviour Is More Likely Than Altruism

One of the first attempts to explain the existence of altruism was called **group selection**, the premise that natural selection produces outcomes beneficial for the whole group or species. In 1962 the British ecologist V. C. Wynne-Edwards argued that a group containing altruists, each willing to subordinate its interests for the good of the group, would have a survival advantage over a group composed of selfish individuals. In concept, the idea of group selection seemed straightforward and logical: a group that consisted of selfish individuals would overexploit its resources and die out, while the fitness of a group with altruists would be enhanced.

In the late 1960s the idea of group selection came under severe attack. Leading the charge was the biologist G. C. Williams, who argued that evolution acts through **individual selection**, which proposes that adaptive traits generally are selected for because they benefit the survival and reproduction of the individual rather than the group. Williams's arguments against group selection follow.

Mutation Mutant individuals that readily use resources for themselves or their offspring will have an advantage in a population where individuals limit their resource use. Consider a species of bird in which a pair lays only two eggs; that is, it has a clutch size of two and there is no overexploitation of resources. Two eggs would ensure a replacement of the parent birds but would prevent a population explosion. Imagine a

mutant bird arises that lays three eggs. If the population is not overexploiting its resources, sufficient food may be available for all three young to survive. If this happens, the three-egg genotype will eventually become more common than the two-egg genotype. This process would work for even larger brood sizes, such as four eggs or five eggs, and brood sizes would tend to increase until they became so large that the parents could not look after all their young. Field studies of great tits in Wytham Woods, England, show a median clutch size of eight to nine eggs, not because females couldn't incubate more, but because adult birds cannot reliably supply sufficient food for more than eight or nine chicks to survive.

Immigration Even in a population in which all pairs laid two eggs and no mutations occurred to increase clutch size, selfish individuals that laid more could still immigrate from other areas. In nature, populations are rarely sufficiently isolated to prevent immigration of "selfish" mutants from other populations.

Individual Selection For group selection to work, some groups must die out faster than others. In practice, groups do not become extinct very frequently. Individuals die off more frequently than groups, so individual selection will be the more powerful evolutionary force.

Resource Prediction Group selection assumes that individuals are able to assess and predict future food availability and population density within their own habitat. There is little evidence that they can. For example, it is difficult to imagine that songbirds would be able to predict the future supply of the caterpillars that they feed to their young and adjust their clutch size accordingly.

Most ecologists accept individual gain as a more plausible result of natural selection than group selection. Population size is more often controlled by competition in which individuals strive to command as much of a resource as they can. Such selfishness can cause some seemingly surprising behaviours. For example, male Hanuman langurs (*Semnopithecus entellus*) kill infants when they take over groups of females from other males (**Figure 52.15**). The reason for the behaviour is that when they are not nursing their young, females become sexually receptive much sooner, hastening the day when the male can father his own offspring. Infanticide ensures that the male will father more offspring, and the genes governing this tendency spread by natural selection.

If individual selfishness is more common than group selection, how do we account for what appear to be examples of altruism in nature?

Apparent Altruistic Behaviour in Nature Is Often Associated with Kin Selection

All offspring have copies of their parents' genes, so parents taking care of their young are actually caring for copies of their own genes. Genes for altruism toward one's young are

Figure 52.15 **Infanticide as selfish behaviour.** Male Hanuman langurs (*Semnopithecus entellus*) can act aggressively toward the young of another male, even killing them, hastening the day the females come into estrus and the time when the males can father their own offspring. Note that the mother is running with the infant.

favoured by natural selection and will become more numerous in the next generation, because offspring have copies of those same genes.

The probability that any two individuals will share a copy of a particular gene is a quantity, r, called the **coefficient of relatedness**. During meiosis any given copy of a gene has a 50% chance of going into an egg or sperm. A mother and father are related to their children by an amount $r = 0.5$, because half of a child's genes come from its mother and half from its father. By similar reasoning, brothers or sisters are related on average by an amount $r = 0.5$ (they share half their mother's genes and half their father's); grandchildren and grandparents, on average by 0.25; and cousins, on average, by 0.125 (**Figure 52.16**). In 1964 ecologist W. D. Hamilton realized the implication of the coefficient of relatedness for the evolution of altruism. An organism can pass on its genes not only through having offspring, but also through ensuring the survival of siblings, nieces, nephews, and cousins. This means an organism has a vested interest in protecting its brothers and sisters, and even their offspring.

The term **inclusive fitness** is used to designate the total number of copies of genes passed on through one's relatives, as well as one's own reproductive output. Selection for behaviour that lowers an individual's own fitness but enhances the reproductive success of a relative is known as **kin selection**. Hamilton proposed that an altruistic gene will be favoured by natural selection when

$$rB > C$$

where r is the coefficient of relatedness of donor (the altruist) to the recipient, B is the benefit received by the recipients of the altruism, and C is the cost incurred by the donor. This is known as **Hamilton's rule**.

Imagine two sisters who are not yet mothers. One has a rare kidney disease and needs a transplant from her sister. Let's

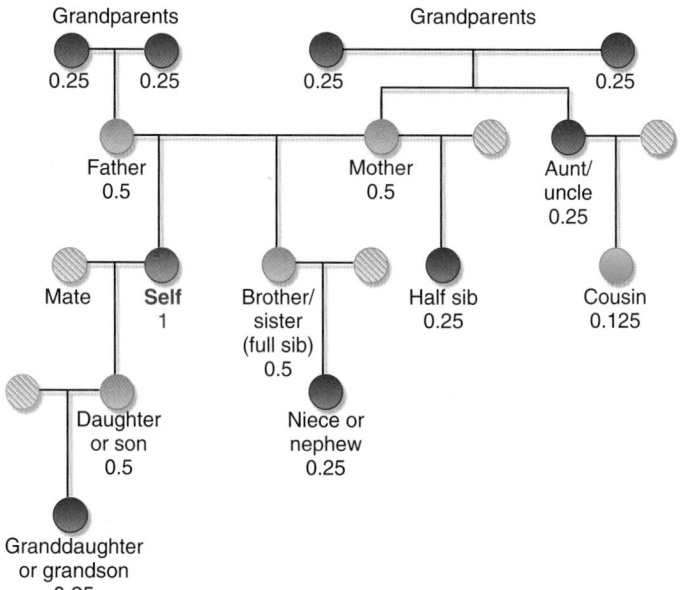

Figure 52.16 **Degree of genetic relatedness to self in a diploid organism.** Pink circles represent completely unrelated individuals.

Concept check: *In theory, should you sacrifice your life to save two sisters or nine cousins?*

assume both sisters will have two children of their own. The risk of the transplant to the donor involves a 1% chance of dying, but the benefit to the recipient involves a 90% chance of living and having children. In this example, $r = 0.5$, $B = 0.9 \times 2 = 1.8$, and $C = 0.01 \times 2 = 0.02$. Since the genetic benefit (rB) of 0.9 is much greater than the genetic cost (C) of 0.02, it makes evolutionary sense to proceed with the transplant. While humans are unlikely to do this type of calculation before deciding whether to risk their lives to save their brothers or sisters from a life-threatening event, this example shows how such behaviour could arise and spread in nature.

Let's examine a situation involving altruism within a group of animals. Many insect larvae, especially caterpillars, are soft-bodied creatures. They rely on a bad taste or toxin to deter predators, and advertise this condition with bright warning colours. For example, noxious *Datana ministra* caterpillars, which feed on oaks and other trees, have bright red and yellow stripes and adopt a specific posture with head and tail ends upturned when threatened (**Figure 52.17**). Unless it is born with an innate avoidance of this prey type, a predator has to kill and eat one of the caterpillars in order to learn to avoid similar individuals in the future. It is of no personal use to the unlucky caterpillar to be killed. However, animals with warning colours often aggregate in kin groups because they hatch from the same egg mass. In this case, the death of one individual is likely to benefit its siblings, which are less likely to be attacked in the future, and thus its genes will be preserved. This explains why the genes for bright colour and a warning posture are successfully passed on from generation to generation. In a case

Figure 52.17 Altruistic behaviour or kin selection? *Datana ministra* caterpillars exhibit a bright, striped warning pattern to advertise their bad taste to predators. All the larvae in the group are likely to be the progeny of one egg mass from one adult female moth. The death of the one caterpillar it takes to teach a predator to avoid the pattern benefits the caterpillar's close kin.

where $r = 0.5$, B might be 50, and $C = 1$, the benefit of 25 is greater than 1, so the genes for this behaviour will be favoured by natural selection.

A common example of altruism in social animals occurs when a sentry raises an alarm call in the presence of a predator. This behaviour has been observed in Belding's ground squirrels (*Spermophilus beldingi*) (**Figure 52.18**). The squirrels feed in groups, with certain individuals acting as sentries and watching for predators. As a predator approaches, the sentry typically gives an alarm call and the group members retreat into their burrows. In drawing attention to itself, the caller is at a higher risk of being attacked by the predator. However, in many groups, those closest to the sentry are most likely to be offspring or brothers or sisters; thus, the altruistic act of alarm calling is reasoned to be favoured by kin selection. Supporting this is the fact that most alarm calling is done by females, because they are more likely to stay in the colony where they

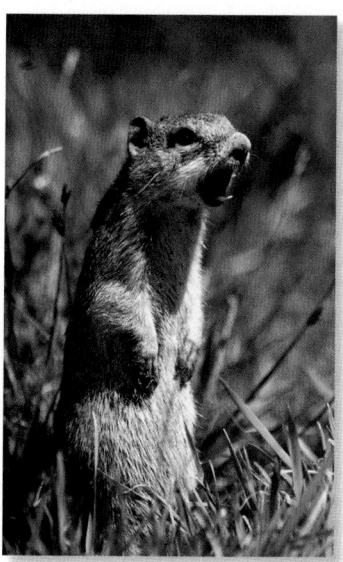

Figure 52.18 Alarm calling, a possible example of kin selection. This Belding's ground squirrel sentry is emitting an alarm call to warn other individuals, which are often close kin, of the presence of a predator. It is believed that by doing so, the sentry draws attention away from the others but becomes an easier target itself.

were born and thus have kin nearby, whereas the males are more apt to disperse far from the colony. James Hare of the University of Manitoba has been able to demonstrate that in some species of ground squirrel individuals do not recognize kin per se, but they are able to recognize litter mates; in other species, individuals can recognize kin even if they have been transported to other locations. This raises interesting questions of proximate causation!

Altruism in Social Insects Arises Partly from Genetics and Partly from Lifestyle

Perhaps the most extreme form of altruism is the evolution of sterile castes in social insects, in which the vast majority of females, known as workers, rarely reproduce themselves but instead help one reproductive female (the queen) to raise offspring, a phenomenon called **eusociality**. The explanation of eusociality lies partly in the particular genetics of most social insect reproduction. Females develop from fertilized eggs and are diploid, the product of fertilization of an egg by a sperm. Males develop from unfertilized eggs and are haploid.

Such a genetic system is called **haplodiploidy**. If they have the same parents, each daughter receives an identical set of genes from her haploid father. The other half of a female's genes come from her diploid mother, so the coefficient of relatedness (r) of sisters is 0.50 (from father) + 0.25 (from mother) = 0.75. The result is that females are more related to their sisters (0.75) than they would be to their own offspring (0.50). This suggests it is evolutionarily advantageous for females to stay in the nest or hive and care for other female offspring of the queen, which are their full sisters.

However, not all haplodiploid bees are eusocial. Laurence Packer from York University, Ontario, studied the social structure and nest architecture among eight species of closely related *L-asioglossum* (*Evylaeus*) sweat bees in the family Halictidae. These bees display a range of behaviours, with some species being social and forming large colonies each year, some species being completely solitary, and other species forming perennial colonies. Packer reconstructed the phylogeny of the halictids using allozyme data and then mapped the behaviours onto the cladogram. He was the first to demonstrate that social behaviour in these sweat bees was shared by descent from a common eusocial ancestor and that solitary behaviour was, in fact, a derived condition. This discovery encouraged other scientists to seek ecological explanations for a lack of sociality in some of these haplodiploid organisms.

Altruism Can Arise in Diploid Organisms for Ecological Reasons

Naked mole rats are diploid species that live in arid regions of Kenya, Somalia, and Ethiopia in large underground colonies where only one female, the queen, produces offspring (**Figure 52.19**). A renewable food supply is present in the form of tubers of the plant *Pyrenacantha kaurabassana*. These weigh up to 50 kilograms and provide food for a whole

Figure 52.19 A naked mole rat colony. In this mammal species, females do not reproduce and only the queen (shown resting on workers) has offspring.

colony, though the food would be insufficient if all the mole rats reproduced. Because the burrows are as hard as cement there are few ways to attack them, and a heroic effort by a mole rat blocking the entrance can effectively stop a predator (commonly a rufous-beaked snake). The queen mole rat does indeed manipulate the colony members; she suppresses reproduction in other females by producing a pheromone in her urine that is passed around the colony by grooming. Hence, it appears that diploid mole rats have evolved eusocial behaviour to exploit their unique ecological niche.

Unrelated Individuals May Engage in Altruistic Acts If the Altruism Is Likely to Be Reciprocated

Even though we have argued that kin selection can explain instances of apparent altruism, cases of altruism are known to exist between unrelated individuals. What drives this type of behaviour appears to be a "You scratch my back, I'll scratch yours" type of reciprocal altruism, in which the cost to the animal of behaving altruistically is offset by the likelihood of a return benefit. This occurs in nature, for example, when unrelated chimps groom each other and when unrelated vampire bats exhibit reciprocal altruism via food sharing.

Vampire bats can die after 60 hours without a blood meal, because they can no longer maintain their correct body temperature. Adult females will share their food with their young, the young of other females, and other unrelated females that have not fed. The females roost together in groups of 8 to 12 and their dependent young. A hungry female will solicit food from another female by approaching and grooming her. The female being groomed then regurgitates part of her blood meal for the other. The roles of blood donor and recipient are often reversed, and researchers have shown that unrelated females are more likely to share with those that had recently shared with them. The probability of a female getting a free lunch is increased because the roost consists of individuals that remain associated with each other for long periods of time.

Learning Outcomes:

1. Compare and contrast promiscuous, monogamous, polygynous, and polyandrous mating systems.
2. List and describe the two forms of sexual selection.

In nature, most males seem superfluous because one male could mate with many females in a local area. If one male can mate with many females, why are there few species with a sex ratio of, say, 1 male: 20 females? The sex ratio is more often about 1:1. The answer lies with natural selection. Let's consider a hypothetical population that contains 20 females for every male; each male mates, on average, with 20 females. A parent whose children were exclusively sons could expect to have 20 times the number of grandchildren compared to a parent with the same number of daughters. Under such conditions, natural selection would favour the production of sons, and males would become prevalent in the population. However, if the population were mainly males, females would be at a premium, and natural selection would favour their production. Such constraints operate on the numbers of both male and female offspring, keeping the sex ratio at about 1:1.

Even though the sex ratio is fairly even in most species, that doesn't mean that one female always mates with one male or vice versa. Several different types of mating systems occur among animals. In monogamy, each individual mates exclusively with one partner over at least a single breeding cycle and sometimes for longer. In contrast, polygamy, a system in which individuals mate with more than one partner in a breeding season, is much more common among animals. There are two types of polygamy. In polygyny ("many females"), one male mates with more than one female, but females mate only with one male. In polyandry ("many males"), one female mates with several males, but males mate with only one female.

In this section, we examine the characteristics of these mating systems and explore the role of sexual selection, a type of natural selection in which competition for mates drives the evolution of certain traits.

Sexual Selection Involves Mate Choice and Mate Competition

As we learned in Chapter 22, sexual selection promotes traits that will increase an organism's mating success. You will recall that sexual selection can take two forms. In intersexual selection, members of one sex, usually females, choose mates based on particular characteristics such as colour of plumage or sound of courtship song. In intrasexual selection, members of one sex, usually males, compete over partners, and the winner performs most of the matings. Let's explore each of these in a little more detail.

Intersexual Selection Females have many different ways to choose their prospective partners. Female hangingflies (*H-ylobittacus* spp.) demand a nuptial gift of a food package, an insect prey item that the male has caught (**Figure 52.20**). Such a nutrient-rich gift may permit females to produce more eggs. The bigger the gift, the longer it takes the female to eat it and the longer the male can copulate with her. Females will not mate with males that do not offer such a package. Female spiders and mantids will sometimes eat their mate during or after copulation, with the male's body constituting the ultimate nuptial gift. Female redback spiders (*Latrodectus hasselti*) have been studied by Maydianne Andrade and her students at the University of Toronto (Scarborough campus). When a male attempts copulation too quickly, the female will kill and eat the "lazy suitor." However, if the male invests up to five hours in a lengthy courtship (by alternately plucking the web and beating on the female's abdomen before attempting copulation), she is more likely to allow him to mate a second time, thereby fathering more of her young. In the chapter-opening photo, the size difference between the males and the female is obvious. One of the males has already been eaten by the female.

Males may also have parenting skills that females desire. Among 15-spined sticklebacks (*Spinachia spinachia*), males perform nest fanning, cleaning, and guarding of the offspring. Males display their parental skills through body shakes during courtship, and females prefer to mate with males that shake their bodies the most energetically, apparently using this cue to assess the quality of the male as a potential father.

Often, females choose mates without the offering of obvious material benefits and make their choices based on plumage colour or courtship display. The male African long-tailed widowbird (*Euplectes progne*) has long tail feathers that he displays to females via aerial flights. When the tails of some birds were experimentally shortened (by clipping their tail feathers), and the tails of others were artificially lengthened (by gluing on the clippings from the first set of birds), the males with long tails attracted four times as many females as males with short tails and they fathered more clutches of eggs (**Figure 52.21**).

Figure 52.20 Female choice of males based on nuptial gifts. A male hangingfly presents a nuptial gift, a small moth, to a female.

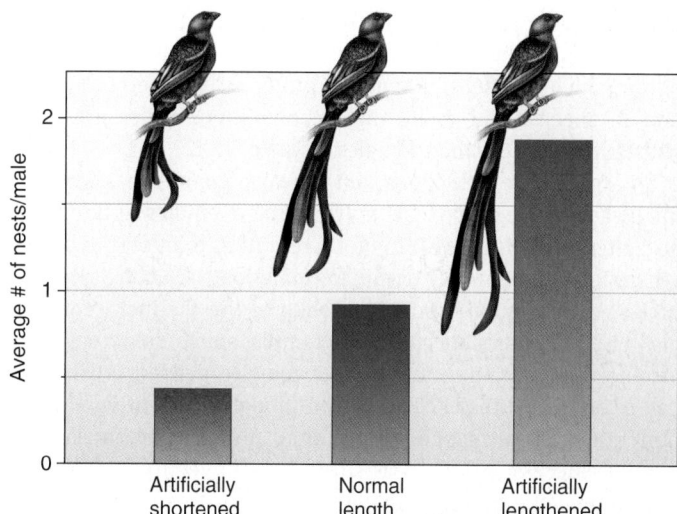

Figure 52.21 Female choice based on male appearance. Males with artificially lengthened tails mate with more females, and therefore have more nests, than males with a normal or artificially shortened tail.

Concept check: *Why do you think it is rarer for female birds or mammals to have more colourful plumage or elaborate adornments than males of the same species?*

Some researchers have suggested that ornaments such as excessively long tail feathers function as a sign of an individual's genetic quality, in that the bearer must be very healthy in order to afford such energetically costly traits. This hypothesis is called the handicap principle. However, other important benefits may be associated with plumage quality. Bright colours are often caused by pigments called carotenoids that help stimulate the immune system to fight diseases. In zebra finches and red jungle fowl, colourful plumage has been associated with heightened resistance to disease, suggesting that females that choose such males are choosing genetically healthier mates.

On rare occasions, a sex role reversal occurs and the male discriminates among females. In the Mormon cricket (*Anabrus simplex*), males mate only once because they provide a nutrient-rich nuptial gift of a spermatophore to females, which is energetically costly to produce. In fact, spermatophore production may reduce the male's weight by as much as 30%. Here, males choose heavier females to mate with because these females have more eggs and the males can father more offspring.

Intraspecies Selection In many species, females do not actively choose their preferred mate; instead, they mate with competitively superior males. In such cases, dominance is determined by fighting or by ritualized sparring. Outcomes may be dictated by the size of weapons such as antlers or horns, or by body size. In the southern elephant seal (*Mirounga leonina*), females haul up onto the beach to give birth and gain safe haven for their pups from marine predators. Following birth, the mothers are ready to re-mate. In this situation, dominant males are able to command a substantial group and constantly lumber across the beach to fight other males and defend their harem. Such competition tends to promote increased body size, and in species with male–male competition, males are often substantially larger than females (**Figure 52.22**).

Large body size does not always guarantee paternity. Smaller male elephant seals may intercept females in the ocean and attempt to mate with them there, rather than on the beach, where the competitively dominant males patrol. Such "satellite" males, which move around the edge of the mating arena, are also visible in other species. For example, small male frogs hang around ponds waiting to intercept females headed toward the call of dominant males. Thus, even though competitively dominant males father most offspring, smaller males can have reproductive success. Mart Gross, from the University of Toronto, has studied the mating behaviour of bluegill sunfish (*Lepomis m-acrochirus*) for many years at Lake Opinicon in Ontario. He and his students have shown that bluegill males can adopt one of three alternative mating tactics: parentals, sneakers, or satellites. Parentals are specialized nest and mate guarders, they mature at seven years of age, and 80% to 90% of the time spawn with females at their nests without interruption; their sperm is thus used to fertilize all eggs in a batch. In the remaining 10% to 20% of spawnings, sneakers or satellites also release their sperm near the female's eggs. Sneaker males mature when small, at two to three years, and use a sneaking, ambush tactic. Satellite males are larger, maturing at four to five years, and use female mimicry to obtain access to spawning females. Interestingly, the sperm of sneakers and satellites can outcompete

that of parental males; sneaker sperm can fertilize up to 89% of eggs and satellite sperm can fertilize up to 67% of eggs when in direct competition with parental sperm.

In Monogamous Mating Systems, Males and Females Are Paired for at Least One Reproductive Season

Mating success is also dependent on the type of the particular species' mating system. In **monogamy**, one male mates with one female, and most individuals have mates. Males and females are generally similar in body size and appearance (**Figure 52.23a**). Several hypotheses explain the existence of monogamy. The first is the **mate-guarding hypothesis**, which suggests that males stay with a female to protect her from being fertilized by other males. Such a strategy may be advantageous when receptive females are widely scattered and difficult to find.

The **male assistance hypothesis** maintains that males remain with females to help them rear their offspring. Monogamy is common among birds, about 70% of which are socially monogamous; that is, the pairings remain intact during at least one breeding season. According to this hypothesis, monogamy is prevalent in birds because eggs and chicks take a considerable amount of parental care. Most eggs need to be incubated continuously if they are to hatch, and chicks require almost continual feeding. It is therefore in the male's best interest to help fledge his young, because he would have few surviving offspring if he did not.

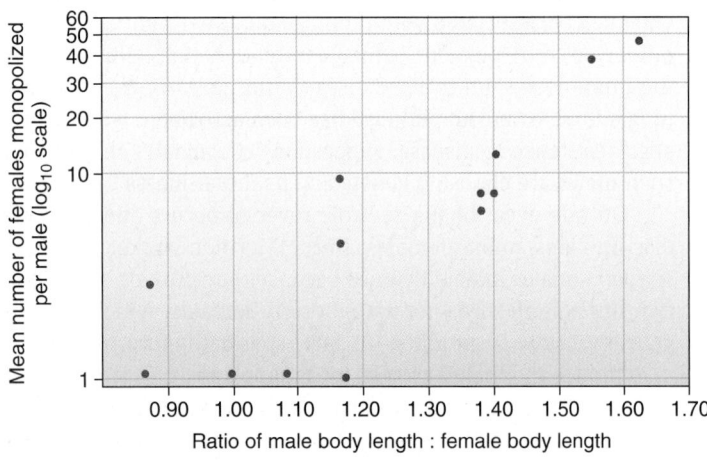

(a) Relationship between body size and mating success

(b) Male competition for mates

Figure 52.22   **Large male size and mating success.**   **(a)** In southern elephant seals, the larger the male, in relation to female size, the greater the number of females that can be mated with and monopolized. **(b)** These male elephant seals are fighting to maintain control of their female harems.

Concept check: *During fights between males, some pups are crushed as the males lumber across the beach. Why aren't the males careful to avoid the pups?*

BioConnections: *Look back to Figure 22.7. What anatomical feature of male fiddler crabs is enlarged as a result of intrasexual selection?*

(a) Monogamous species

(b) Polygynous species

(c) Polyandrous species

Figure 52.23 Sexual dimorphism in body size and mating system. **(a)** In monogamous species, such as these Manchurian cranes, *Grus japonensis*, males and females appear very similar. **(b)** In polygynous species, like white-tailed deer, *Odocoileus virginianus*, males are bigger than females and have large horns with which they engage in combat over females. **(c)** In polyandrous species, there is often sex-role reversal, as in the northern pipefish, *Syngnathus fuscus*. Males look after the developing young in a brood pouch.

The **female-enforced monogamy hypothesis** suggests that females stop their male partners from being polygynous. Male and female burying beetles (*Nicrophorus defodiens*) work together to bury small, dead animals, which will provide a food resource for their developing offspring. Males will release pheromones to attract other females to the site. However, while an additional female might increase the male's fitness, the additional developing offspring might compete with the offspring of the first female, decreasing her fitness. As a result, on smelling these pheromones, the first female will interfere with the male's attempts at signalling, preserving the monogamous relationship.

Interestingly, fidelity may have a genetic basis. The fidelity of male voles depends on the length of repeating, short genetic sequences, once considered junk DNA, in a gene that codes for a key hormone receptor. Adult male voles with the long version of the sequence were more apt to form pair bonds with female partners and nurture their offspring than were voles with the short version.

In Polygynous Mating Systems, One Male Mates with Many Females

In **polygyny**, one male mates with more than one female in a single breeding season, but females mate only with one male. Physiological constraints often dictate that female organisms must care for the young, because they are the ones most often left "holding the baby." Because of these constraints, at least in many organisms with internal fertilization, such as mammals and some fish, males are able to desert and mate with more females. Polygynous systems are therefore associated with uniparental care of young, with males contributing little. Sexual dimorphism is typical in polygynous mating systems, particularly when males engage in competition over mates (**Figure 52.23b**). Sexual maturity is often delayed in males that fight because of the considerable time it takes to reach a sufficiently large size to compete for females.

Polygyny is influenced by the spatial or temporal distribution of breeding females. In cases where all females are sexually receptive within the same narrow period of time, little opportunity exists for a male to garner all the females for himself. Where female reproductive receptivity is spread out over weeks or months, there is much more opportunity for males to mate with more than one female. For example, females of the common toad (*Bufo bufo*) all lay their eggs within a week, and males generally have time to mate with only one female. In contrast, female bullfrogs (*Rana catesbeiana*) have a breeding season of several weeks, and males may mate with as many as six females in a season.

In some polygynous species, such as water striders, a conflict arises between specific males and females. Females generally receive enough sperm from a single mating to fertilize all of their eggs; the act of mating reduces the amount of time they can spend foraging and increases the likelihood that an aquatic predator will find and eat the female. During copulation the female is on the bottom and, by resisting copulation too strenuously, she is often eaten by an underwater predator. Males, on the other hand, achieve greater fitness if they mate with as many females as possible (preferably being the last male to mate with a female so that his sperm are used first to fertilize her eggs). Locke Rowe from the University of Toronto has studied water striders extensively and has found that males and females have evolved counterstrategies to one another in the form of armaments. Males have armaments to increase their success in clasping females and females have armaments to resist the clasping of males.

Resource-based Polygyny Where some critical resource is patchily distributed and in short supply, certain males may dominate the resource and breed with more than one visiting female. In the lark bunting (*Calamospiza melanocorys*), which mates in North American grasslands, males arrive at the grasslands first, compete for territories, and then display with special courtship flight patterns and songs to attract females. The major source of nestling death in this species is overheating from too much exposure to the sun. Prime territories are therefore those with abundant shade, and some males with shaded territories attract two females, even though the second female can expect no help from the male in the process of rearing young. Males in some exposed territories remain bachelors for the season. From the dominant male's point of view, resource-based polygyny is advantageous; from the female's point of view, there may be costs. Although by choosing dominant males a female may be gaining access to good resources, she may also have to share these resources with other females.

Harem Mating Structures Sometimes males defend a group of females without commanding a resource-based territory. This pattern is more common when females naturally congregate in groups or herds, perhaps to avoid predation, as with southern elephant seals (see Figure 52.22). Usually the largest and strongest males command most of the matings, but being a harem master is usually so exhausting that males may manage to remain the dominant male for only a year or two.

Communal Courting Polygynous mating can occur where neither resources nor harems are defended. In some instances, particularly in birds and mammals, males display in designated communal courting areas called **leks** (**Figure 52.24**). Females come to these areas specifically to find a mate, and they choose a prospective mate after the males have performed elaborate displays. Most females seek to mate with the best males, so a few successful males perform the vast majority of the matings. On the southernmost prairies of Alberta and Saskatchewan, where sagebrush grows, leks of the greater sage grouse (*Centrocercus urophaianus*) may contain between 15 and 75 males displaying (**Figure 52.24a**). Despite the rigorous displays that are performed (**Figure 52.24b**) only about 15% of the males are successful at gaining copulations.

In Polyandrous Mating Systems, One Female Mates with Many Males

In most systems in which one individual mates with more than one individual of the opposite sex, the polygamous sex is the male. The opposite condition, **polyandry**, in which one female mates with several males, is much more rare. Nevertheless, it is practised by some species of birds, fish, and insects. Sexual dimorphism is present, with the females being the larger of the sexes (see chapter-opening photo). The productivity of the breeding grounds of the spotted sandpiper (*Actitis macularia*) is so high that the female becomes rather like an egg factory, laying up to five clutches of four eggs each in 40 days. Her reproductive success is limited not by food but by the number of males she can find to incubate the eggs, and females compete for males, defending territories where the males sit.

Polyandry is also seen in some species where egg predation is high and males are needed to guard the developing

(a)

(b)

Figure 52.24 **Some male birds and mammals congregate in communal courting grounds called leks.** (a) Large numbers of male greater sage grouse (*Centrocercus urophasianus*) gather on display grounds, leks, to perform a strutting display for gathering females. If a female is interested in a particular male, she will solicit a copulation from him. (b) Males fan their pointed tail feathers, hold their head feathers erect, strut around, swish their wings, and produce air sac "plops" to get the attention of females.

young. For example, in the northern pipefish (*Syngnathus fuscus*) found in the Gulf of St. Lawrence, males have brood pouches that provide eggs with safety and a supply of oxygen and nutrient-rich water (**Figure 52.23c**). Females fill the brood pouch of one male and then try to find another male with which to mate.

Ultimately, as we have seen, most behaviours have evolved to maximize an individual's reproductive output. In a successful group of individuals, this leads to population growth. But we are not knee-deep in sandpipers or elephant seals, so there must be some constraints on reproductive output. In Chapter 53, we next turn to the realm of population ecology to explore how populations grow and what factors limit their growth.

Summary of Key Concepts

52.1 The Impact of Genetics and Learning on Behaviour

- Behaviour is usually due to the interaction of an organism's genes and the environment.
- Genetically programmed behaviours are termed innate and often involve a sign stimulus that initiates a fixed action pattern. (Figures 52.1, 52.2)
- Organisms can often make modifications to their behaviour based on previous experience, a process called learning. Some forms of learning include habituation, classical conditioning, operant conditioning, and cognitive learning. (Figures 52.3, 52.4)
- Much behaviour is a mixture of innate and learned behaviours. A good example of this occurs in a process called imprinting, in which animals develop strong attachments that influence subsequent behaviour. (Figures 52.5, 52.6)

52.2 Local Movement and Long-Range Migration

- The simplest forms of local movement involve kinesis, taxis, and memory.
- Many animals undergo long-range seasonal movement called migration in order to feed or breed. They do this using three proposed mechanisms: piloting, the ability to move from one landmark to the next; orientation, the ability to follow a compass bearing; and navigation, the ability to set, follow, and adjust a compass bearing. (Figures 52.7, 52.8, 52.9)

52.3 Foraging Behaviour

- Animals use complex behaviour in food gathering or foraging. Optimality theory views foraging behaviour as a compromise between the costs and benefits involved.
- The theory of optimal foraging assumes that animals modify their behaviour to keep the ratio of their energy uptake to energy expenditure high. (Figure 52.10)
- The size of a territory, a fixed area in which an individual or group excludes other members of its own species, tends to be optimized according to the costs and benefits involved. (Figure 52.11)

52.4 Communication

- Communication is a form of behaviour. The use of different forms of communication between organisms depends on the environment in which they live.
- Chemical communication often involves marking territories; auditory and visual forms of communication are often used to attract mates. A fascinating form of tactile communication involves the dance of the honeybee. (Figures 52.12, 52.13)

52.5 Living in Groups

- Many benefits of group living relate to defence against predators, offering protection through sheer numbers and through what is called the many-eyes hypothesis or the geometry of the selfish herd. (Figure 52.14)

52.6 Altruism

- Infanticide is an example of selfish behaviour. (Figure 52.15)
- Altruism is behaviour that benefits others at a cost to oneself. One of the first explanations of altruism, called group selection, posited that natural selection produced outcomes beneficial for the group.

Biologists now believe that most apparently altruistic acts are often associated with outcomes beneficial to those most closely related to the individual, a concept termed *kin selection*. (Figures 52.16, 52.17, 52.18)

- Altruism among eusocial animals may arise partly from the unique genetics of the animals and partly from lifestyle. (Figure 52.19)
- Altruism is known to exist among nonrelated individuals that live in close proximity for long periods of time.

52.7 Mating Systems

- Sexual selection takes two forms: intersexual selection, in which the female chooses a mate based on particular characteristics, or intrasexual selection, in which males compete with one another for the opportunity to mate with a female. (Figures 52.20, 52.21, 52.22)
- Several types of mating systems are found among animals, including monogamy, polygyny, and polyandry. (Figure 52.23)
- Polygynous mating can often occur in situations where males dominate a resource, defend groups of females (harems), or display in common courting areas called leks. (Figure 52.24)

Test to Assess Your Learning

1. Behavioural ecology is the study of
   a. how organisms interact with their environment.
   b. courtship behaviour.
   c. how an individual's behaviour affects reproductive success.
   d. how an individual's behaviour affects survival.
   e. both c and d.

2. Geotaxis is a response to the force of gravity. Fruit flies placed in a vial will move to the top of the vial. This is an example of _____ geotaxis.
   a. positive
   b. neutral
   c. innate
   d. negative
   e. learned

3. Certain behaviours seem to have very little environmental influence. Such behaviours are the same in all individuals regardless of the environment and are referred to as _____ behaviours.
   a. genetic
   b. instinctual
   c. innate
   d. (b) and (c) only
   e. all of the above

4. Patrick has decided to teach his new puppy a few tricks. Each time the puppy responds correctly to Patrick's command, the puppy is given a treat. This is an example of
   a. habituation.
   b. classic conditioning.
   c. operant conditioning.
   d. imprinting.
   e. orientation.

5. An animal using landmarks to move from one area to another is exhibiting
   a. navigation.
   b. classic conditioning.
   c. migration.
   d. piloting.
   e. orientation.

6. For group living to evolve, the benefits of living in a group must be greater than the cost of group living. Which of the following is an example of a benefit of living in a group?
   a. reduced spread of disease and/or parasites
   b. increased food availability
   c. reduced competition for mates
   d. decreased risk of predation
   e. all of the above

7. The modification of behaviour based on prior experience is called
   a. a fixed action pattern.
   b. learning.
   c. navigation.
   d. adjustment behaviour.
   e. innate.

8. When an individual behaves in a way that reduces its own fitness but increases the fitness of others, the organism is exhibiting
   a. kin selection.
   b. group selection.
   c. altruism.
   d. selfishness.
   e. ignorance.

9. Hamilton's theory of kin selection suggests that altruism could evolve in a population if the altruistic behaviour of one individual increased the reproductive behaviour of
   a. all members of the group.
   b. only the females of the group.
   c. relatives.
   d. nonrelatives.
   e. the youngest individuals of the group.

10. When each female in the population mates with several males, but each male mates with only one female, the mating system is referred to as
    a. polygamy.
    b. polyandry.
    c. polygyny.
    d. monogamy.
    e. harem mating.

Articulate to Assess Your Learning

1. Define ethology.
2. Why does male parental care occur in only 7% of fish and amphibian families with internal fertilization but in 69% of families with external fertilization?
3. Describe the distinguishing features of the different mating systems.

Collaborate to Assess and Extend Your Learning

1. Whooping cranes (*Grus americana*) are an endangered species bred in captivity to increase their numbers. One problem is that these cranes are migratory. In the absence of other cranes, can you think of an innovative way human researchers might have used crane behaviour to ensure their safe passage to overwintering sites?
2. Discuss several ways in which organisms communicate with each other.
3. A principle of biology is that populations of organisms evolve from one generation to the next. Discuss how altruism functions in maintaining evolution according to natural selection.

Visit McGraw-Hill Ryerson Connect™ for additional study resources.

Population Ecology

Chapter Outline

A population of colonial nesting Northern gannets (*Morus bassanus*) on Bird Rock, Cape St. Mary's Sanctuary, Newfoundland and Labrador.

A **population** can be defined as a group of interbreeding individuals occupying the same area at the same time. In this way, we can think of a population of water lilies in a particular lake, the lion population in the Ngorongoro crater in Africa, or the human population of Prince Edward Island. However, the boundaries of a population can often be difficult to define, though they may correspond to geographic features such as the boundaries of a lake or forest or be contained within a mountain valley or a certain island. Individuals may enter or leave a population, such as the human population of Vancouver Island or the grizzly bear population in Banff National Park. Thus, populations are often fluid entities, with individuals moving into (immigrating) or out of (emigrating) an area. For the purposes of simplicity, in our discussion we will assume that immigration and emigration cancel each other out as factors.

This chapter explores **population ecology**, the study of how populations grow and what factors promote and limit growth. To study populations, we need to employ some of the tools of **demography**, the study of birth rates, death rates, age distributions, and the sizes of populations. We begin our discussion by exploring characteristics of populations, including density and how it is quantified, dispersion, reproductive strategies, and age classes. We will consider how life tables and survivorship curves help summarize demographic information such as birth and death rates. Similarly, growth rates will be examined by determining how many reproductive individuals are in the population and their fertility rate. The data are then used to construct simple mathematical models that allow us to analyze and predict population growth. We will also look at the factors that limit the growth of populations, and conclude the chapter by using the population concepts and models to explore the growth of human populations.

53.1 / UNDERSTANDING POPULATIONS

Learning Outcomes:

1. List the different techniques ecologists use to measure population density.
2. Identify the three main patterns of dispersion observed in nature.
3. Describe the difference between semelparity and iteroparity, two different reproductive strategies.

Within their areas of distribution, organisms occur in varying numbers. We recognize this pattern by saying a plant or animal is "rare" in one place and "common" in another. For more precision, ecologists quantify commonness further and talk in terms of population **density**, the numbers of organisms in a given unit area. Population growth affects population density, and knowledge of both can help us make decisions about the management of species. How long will it take for a population of an endangered species to recover to a healthy level if we protect it from its most serious threats? For example, in Alberta and Saskatchewan the greater short-horned lizard (*Phrynosoma hernandesi*) is listed as endangered as a result of severely fragmented populations threatened by ongoing oil and gas development, road construction, and proposed mineral development. Detailed knowledge of greater short-horned lizard population growth rates and population densities would allow species-at-risk recovery teams to determine at what point populations can no longer recover from such losses and could help determine when and where to intervene. In July 1992 a moratorium was placed on the Northern cod fishery along Canada's east coast, ending almost 500 years of fishing activity in Newfoundland and Labrador—due, presumably, to commercial overfishing. However, the moratorium was lifted, and in 2008 17.500 metric tons of Atlantic cod was harvested from Newfoundland alone. Can a cod fishery be sustained at these levels? How many fish can we reasonably trawl from the sea and still ensure that an adequate population will exist for future use? Such information is vital in making determinations of size limits, catch quotas, and length of season for fisheries to ensure an adequate future population size.

In this section, we discuss density and other characteristics of populations within their habitats. We will also discuss the different reproductive strategies organisms use and assign individuals to different groups called age classes. Population growth can be predicted using knowledge of age classes, reproductive age, and reproductive strategies. We then analyze survivorship and fertility data, which can tell us at what rates populations may grow. Let's begin our exploration of populations by considering density and the various ways that ecologists attempt to quantify it.

Ecologists Use Many Different Methods to Quantify Population Density

The simplest method to measure population density is to visually count the number of organisms in a given area. We can reasonably do this only if the area is small and the organisms are relatively large. For example, we can determine the number of pitcher plants (*Sarracenia purpurea*) in a bog in Newfoundland. Normally, however, population ecologists calculate the density of plants or animals in a small area and use this figure to estimate the total abundance over a larger area. Several different sampling methods exist for quantifying density in this way, including the use of traps to catch animals from insects to mammals. Suction traps, like giant aerial vacuum cleaners, can suck flying insects from the sky. Pitfall traps set into the ground can catch species wandering over the surface, such as spiders, lizards, or beetles. Mist nets, consisting of very fine netting spread between poles, can entangle flying birds and bats. Simple baited snap traps, such as mouse traps, or live traps, can catch small mammals. Population density can thus be estimated as the number of animals caught per unit area per habitat where the traps were set.

Sometimes population biologists will capture animals and then tag and release them (**Figure 53.1**). The rationale behind the **mark-recapture technique** is that after the tagged animals are released, they mix freely with unmarked individuals and within a short time are randomly mixed within the population. The population is resampled and the numbers of marked and unmarked individuals are recorded. We assume that the ratio of marked to unmarked individuals in the second sample is the same as the ratio of marked individuals in the first sample to the total population size. We are then able to rearrange the equation to solve for *N*, the total population size.

$$\frac{\text{Number of marked individuals in first catch}}{\text{Total population size, } N} = \frac{\text{Number of marked recaptures in second catch}}{\text{Total number of second catch}}$$

$$\text{Total population size, } N = \frac{\text{Number of marked individuals in first catch} \times \text{Total number in second catch}}{\text{Number of marked recaptures in second catch}}$$

However, the mark-recapture technique can have drawbacks. Some animals that have been marked may learn to avoid the traps. Recapture rates will then be low, resulting in an overestimate of population size. On the other hand, some animals can become trap-happy, particularly if the traps are baited with food. This would result in an underestimate of the population size.

Because of the limitations of the mark-recapture technique, ecologists also use other, more novel methods to estimate population density. For many species with valuable pelts we can track population densities through time by examining pelt records taken from trading stations. We can also estimate relative population density by examining catch per unit effort, which is especially valuable in commercial fisheries. We can't easily expect to count the number of fish in an area of ocean, but we can count the number caught, say, per 100 hours of trawling. For some species that leave easily recognizable fecal pellets;

Figure 53.1 **The mark-recapture technique is often used to estimate population size.** An ear tag identifies this Rocky Mountain goat (*Oreamnos americanus*) in Olympic National Park, Washington. Recapture of such marked animals permits accurate estimates of population size.

Concept check: *If we mark 110 Rocky Mountain goats and recapture 100 goats, 20 of which have ear tags, what is the estimate of the total population size?*

such as rabbits or deer, we can count pellet numbers. For frogs or birds, we can count chorusing or singing individuals. Many plant individuals are clonal; that is, they grow in patches of genetically identical individuals, so that rather than count individuals we can use the amount of ground covered by plants as an estimate of vegetation density. We can also count leaf scars or chewed leaves as an estimate of the density of the animals that feed on them.

Patterns of Spacing Individuals within a population can show different patterns of spatial **dispersion**; that is, they can be clustered together or spread out to varying degrees. The three basic kinds of dispersion pattern are clumped, uniform, and random.

The type of dispersion observed in nature can tell us a lot about what processes shape group structure. The most common dispersion pattern is **clumped**, likely because resources tend to be clustered in nature. For example, certain plants may do better in moist conditions, and moisture is greater in low-lying areas (**Figure 53.2a**). Social behaviour between animals may also promote a clumped pattern. Many animals are clumped into flocks or herds.

On the other hand, competition may cause a **uniform** dispersion pattern between individuals, as between trees in a forest. At first, the pattern of trees and seedlings may appear random as seedlings develop from seeds dropped at random, but competition between roots may cause some trees to be outcompeted by others, causing a thinning out and resulting in a uniform distribution. Thus, the dispersion pattern starts out random but ends up uniform. Uniform dispersions may also result from social interactions, as between some nesting birds, which tend to keep an even distance from each other (**Figure 53.2b**).

Perhaps the rarest dispersion pattern is **random** because resources in nature are rarely randomly spaced. Where resources are common and abundant, as in moist, fertile soil, the dispersion patterns of plants may be random and lacking a pattern (**Figure 53.2c**).

Reproductive Strategies To better understand how populations grow in size, let's consider their reproductive strategies. For example, some organisms produce all of their offspring in a single reproductive event. This pattern, called **semelparity** (from the Latin *semel*, once, and *parere*, to bear), is common in insects and other invertebrates and also occurs in organisms such as salmon, bamboo grasses, and agave plants (**Figure 53.3a**). These individuals reproduce once only and die. Semelparous organisms may live for many years before reproducing, like the agaves, or they may be annual plants that develop from seed, flower, and drop their own seed within a year.

Other organisms reproduce in successive years or breeding seasons. The pattern of repeated reproduction at intervals throughout the life cycle is called **iteroparity** (from the Latin *itero*, to repeat), and it is common in most vertebrates and perennial plants such as trees. Among iteroparous organisms much variation occurs in the number of reproductive events and in the number of offspring per event. Many species, such as temperate birds or temperate forest trees, have distinct breeding seasons (seasonal iteroparity) that lead to distinct generations (**Figure 53.3b**). For a few species, individuals reproduce repeatedly and at any time of the year. This is termed continuous iteroparity and is exhibited by some tropical species, many parasites, and many mammals (**Figure 53.3c**).

Age Classes The reproductive strategy employed by an organism has a strong effect on the subsequent age classes of

(a) Clumped

(b) Uniform

(c) Random

Figure 53.2 **Three types of dispersion.** (a) A clumped distribution pattern, as in these plants clustered around an oasis, often results from the uneven distribution of a resource, in this case water. (b) A uniform distribution pattern, as in these nesting black-browed albatrosses (*Diomedea melanophris*) on the Falkland Islands, may be a result of competition or social interactions. (c) A random distribution pattern, as in these bushes at Leirhnjukur Volcano in Iceland, is the least common form of spacing.

Concept check: *What is the distribution pattern of students in a half-empty classroom?*

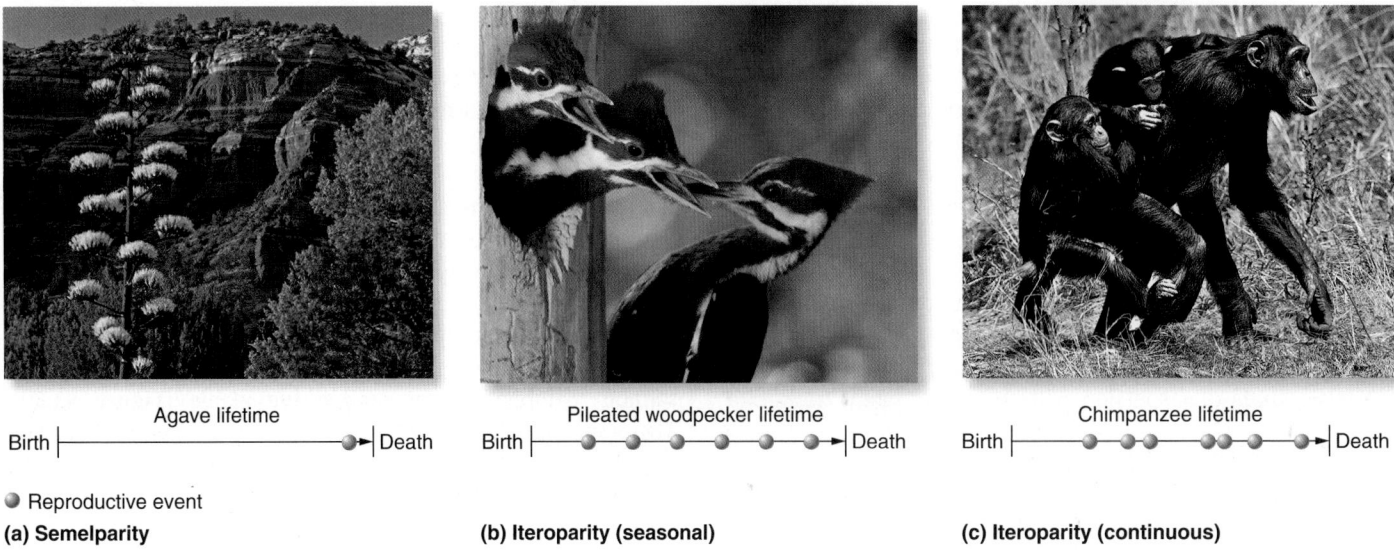

Birth |————————————————————●—|Death
Agave lifetime

Birth |———●——●——●——●——●——●——►|Death
Pileated woodpecker lifetime

Birth |———●——●●——●——●●—●——●—►|Death
Chimpanzee lifetime

● Reproductive event

(a) Semelparity   **(b) Iteroparity (seasonal)**   **(c) Iteroparity (continuous)**

Figure 53.3   Differences in reproductive strategies.   Species such as **(a)** agave plants are semelparous, meaning they breed once in their lifetime and then die (century plant, *Agave shawii,* Baja, California). This contrasts with **(b)** pileated woodpeckers, *Dryocopus pileatus,* found in the boreal forests of Canada, and **(c)** chimpanzees, *Pan troglodytes,* Chimfunshi Chimp Reserve, Zambia, which are iteroparous and breed more than once in their lifetime.

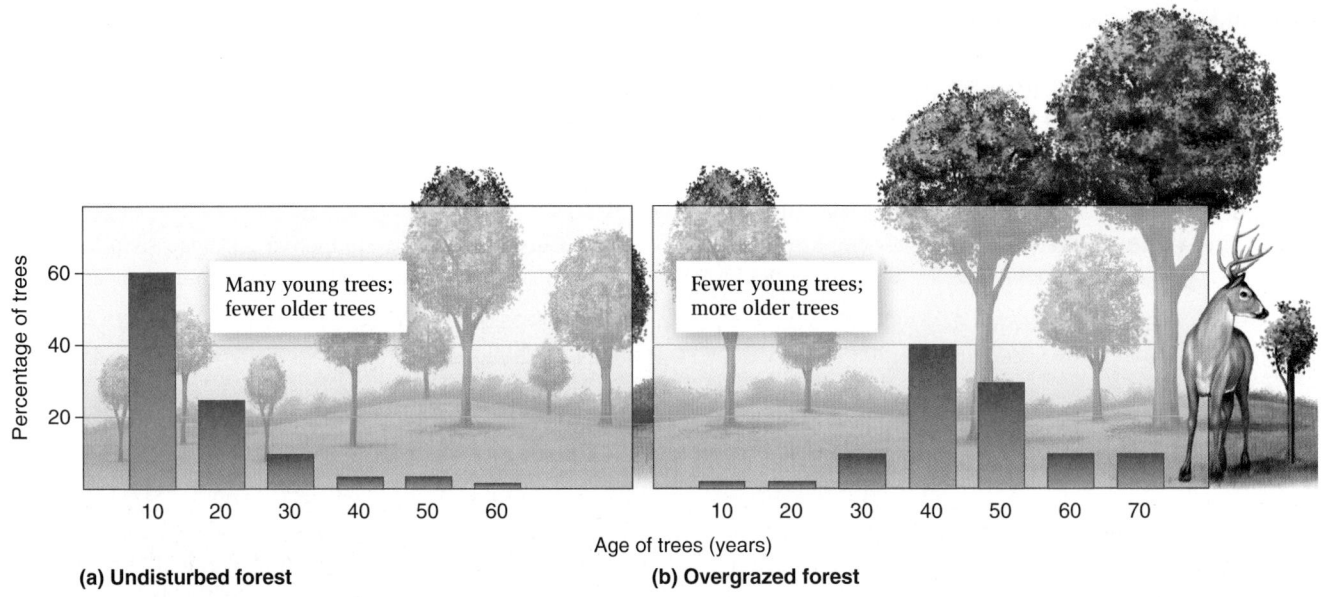

(a) Undisturbed forest   **(b) Overgrazed forest**

Figure 53.4   Theoretical age distribution of two forest populations.   **(a)** Age distribution of an undisturbed forest with numerous young trees, many of which die as the trees age and compete with one another for resources, leaving relatively few big, older trees. **(b)** Age distribution of a forest where overgrazing has reduced the abundance of young trees, leaving mainly trees in the older age classes.

a population. Semelparous organisms often produce groups of same-aged young called **cohorts**, which may grow at similar rates. Iteroparous organisms generally have many young of different ages because the parents reproduce frequently. The age classes of populations can be characterized by specific categories, such as years in mammals, stages (eggs, larvae, or pupae) in insects, or size in plants.

We expect that a population increasing in size should have a large number of young, whereas a decreasing population should have few young. An imbalance in age classes can have a profound influence on a population's future. For example, in an overexploited fish population, the bigger, older reproductive age classes are often removed. If the population experiences reproductive failure for one or two years, there will be no young fish to move into the reproductive age class to replace the removed fish, and the population may collapse. Other populations experience removal of younger age classes. Where populations of white-tailed deer are high, they overgraze the vegetation and eat many young trees, leaving only older trees, whose foliage is too tall for them to reach (**Figure 53.4**). This can have disastrous effects on the future population of trees, for while the forest might consist of healthy mature trees, when these die there will be no replacements. Removal of deer predators such as cougars and wolves often allows deer numbers to skyrocket and survivorship of young trees in forests to plummet. To accurately examine how populations grow, we need to examine and understand the demography of the population. We will look at an example of different age classes when we get to Table 53.1.

53.2 DEMOGRAPHY

Learning Outcomes:

1. Describe the difference between information summarized in a life table and in a survivorship curve.
2. Differentiate between type I, II, and III survivorship curves and give examples of organisms that exhibit these survivorship curves.
3. Explain how age-specific fertility data can help predict a population's growth.

One way to determine how a population will grow is to examine a cohort of individuals from birth to death. For most animals and plants this involves marking a group of individuals in a population as soon as they are born or germinate and following their fate through their lifetime. For some long-lived organisms such as tortoises, elephants, or trees, this is impractical, so a snapshot approach is used in which researchers examine the age structure of a population at one point in time. Recording the presence of juveniles and mature individuals, researchers

use this information to construct a life table. A **life table** provides data on the number of individuals alive in each particular age class. Age classes can be created for any time period, but they often represent one year. Males are not usually included in these tables, since they are typically not the limiting factor in population growth. **Demography** is the study of how births and deaths change population sizes over time. In the next section, we will determine how to construct life tables and plot survivorship curves that show at a glance the general pattern of population survival over time. With a knowledge of life tables and additional information on birth rates, we can predict how populations will grow.

Life Tables and Survival Curves Summarize Survival Patterns

Let's examine a life table for the North American beaver (*Castor canadensis*). Prized for their pelts, by the mid-nineteenth century these animals had been hunted and trapped to near extinction. Beavers began to be protected by laws in the twentieth century, and populations recovered in many areas, often growing to what some considered to be nuisance status. In Newfoundland, legislation supported trapping as a management technique. From 1964 to 1971, trappers provided mandibles from which teeth were extracted for age classification. If many teeth were obtained from, say, one-year-old beavers, then such animals were probably common in the population. If the number of teeth from two-year-old beavers was low, then we know there was high mortality for the one-year-old age class. From the mandible data, researchers constructed a life table (**Table 53.1**). The number of individuals alive at the start of the time period (in this case, a year) is referred to as n_x, where n is

Table 53.1	Life Table for the Beaver (*Castor canadensis*) in Newfoundland				
Age (years)	Number alive at start of year, n_x	Number dying during year, d_x	Proportion alive at start of year l_x	Age-specific fertility, m_x	$l_x m_x$
0–1	3,695	1,995	1.000	0.000	0
1–2	1,700	684	0.460	0.315	0.145
2–3	1,016	359	0.275	0.400	0.110
3–4	657	286	0.178	0.895	0.159
4–5	371	98	0.100	1.244	0.124
5–6	273	68	0.074	1.440	0.107
6–7	205	40	0.055	1.282	0.071
7–8	165	38	0.045	1.280	0.058
8–9	127	14	0.034	1.387	0.047
9–10	113	26	0.031	1.080	0.033
10–11	87	37	0.024	1.800	0.043
11–12	50	4	0.014	1.080	0.015
12–13	46	17	0.012	1.440	0.017
13–14	29	7	0.007	0.720	0.005
14+	22	22	0.006	0.720	0.004

Net reproductive rate, $\Sigma l_x m_x = 0.938$

Figure 53.5 Survivorship curve for the North American beaver.   The survivorship curve is generated by plotting the number of surviving beavers, n_x, from any given cohort of young, usually measured on a log scale, against age.

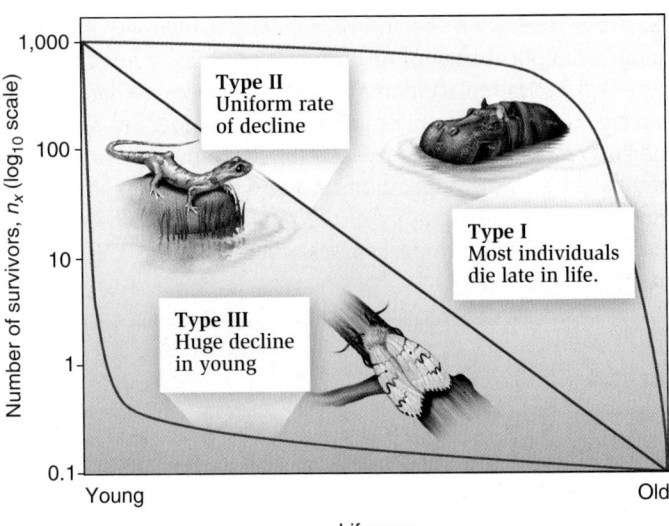

Figure 53.6 Idealized survivorship curves.

Concept check: *Which type of survivorship curve would you expect in (a) mussels and (b) snapping turtles?*

the number and x refers to the particular age class. By subtracting the value of n_x from the number alive at the start of the previous year, we can calculate the number dying in a given age class or year, d_x. Thus $d_x = n_x - n_{x+1}$. For example, in Table 53.1, 273 beavers were alive at the start of their sixth year (n_5) and only 205 were alive at the start of the seventh year (n_6); thus, 68 died during the fifth year: $d_5 = n_5 - n_6$, or $d_5 = 273 - 205 = 68$.

A simple but informative exercise is to plot numbers of surviving individuals at each age, creating a **survivorship curve** (**Figure 53.5**). The value of n_x, the number of individuals, is typically expressed on a log scale. Ecologists use a log scale to examine rates of change with time, not change in absolute numbers. Although we could accomplish the same thing with a linear scale, the use of logs makes it easier to examine a wide range of population sizes. For example, if we start with 1,000 individuals and 500 are lost in year 1, the log of the decrease is

$$\log_{10}1,000 - \log_{10}500 = 3.0 - 2.7 = 0.3 \text{ per year}$$

If we start with 100 individuals and 50 are lost, the log of the decrease is similarly

$$\log_{10}100 - \log_{10}50 = 2.0 - 1.7 = 0.3 \text{ per year}$$

In both cases the rates of change are identical even though the absolute numbers are different. Plotting the n_x data on a log scale ensures that regardless of the size of the starting population, the rate of change of one survivorship curve can easily be compared to that of another species. The survivorship curve for the beaver follows a fairly uniform rate of death over the lifespan.

Survivorship curves generally fall into one of three patterns (**Figure 53.6**). In a type I curve, the rate of loss for juveniles is relatively low, and most individuals are lost later in life, as they become older and more prone to sickness and predators (see the Feature Investigation that follows). Organisms that exhibit type I survivorship have relatively few offspring but invest much time and resources in raising their young. Many large mammals, including humans, exhibit type I curves. At the other end of the scale is a type III curve, in which the rate of loss for juveniles is relatively high, and the survivorship curve flattens out for those organisms that have survived early death. Many fish and marine invertebrates fit this pattern. Most of the juveniles die or are eaten, but a few reach a favourable habitat and thrive. For example, once they find a suitable rock face on which to attach themselves, barnacles grow and survive very well. Many insects and plants also fit the type III survivorship curve, because they lay many eggs or release hundreds of seeds, respectively. Type II curves represent a middle ground, with fairly uniform death rates over time. Species with type II survivorship curves include many birds, small mammals, reptiles, and some annual plants. The beaver population most closely resembles this survivorship curve. Keep in mind, however, that these are generalized curves and that few populations fit them exactly.

FEATURE INVESTIGATION

Murie's Collections of Dall Mountain Sheep Skulls Permitted Accurate Life Tables to Be Constructed

The Dall mountain sheep (*Ovis dalli*) lives in mountainous regions, including the Arctic and sub-Arctic regions of Alaska. In the late 1930s the United States National Park Service was bombarded with public concerns that wolves were responsible for a sharp decline in the population of Dall mountain sheep in Denali National Park (then Mt. McKinley National Park). Shooting the wolves was advocated as a way of increasing the number of sheep. Because meaningful data on sheep mortality were nonexistent, the Park Service enlisted biologist Adolph

Murie to collect relevant information. In addition to spending many hours observing interactions between wolves and sheep, Murie also gathered data on sheep age at death. To do this, he collected sheep skulls in Denali National Park. He determined their age by counting annual growth rings on the horns. Thus, the analysis of skulls gave a snapshot of the age of the animals when they died.

In 1947 Edward Deevey put Murie's data in the form of a life table that listed each age class and the number of skulls in it (**Figure 53.7**). While Murie had collected 608 skulls, Deevey expressed the data per 1,000 individuals to allow for comparison with other life tables. From the data, Deevey constructed a survivorship curve. For the Dall mountain sheep, there was a slight initial decline in survivorship as young lambs were lost and then the survivorship curve flattened out, indicating that the sheep survived well through about age 7 or 8.

Then the number of sheep declined rapidly as they aged. These data underlined what Murie had previously observed, which was that wolves preyed primarily on the most vulnerable members of the sheep population, the youngest and the oldest. The Park Service ultimately ended a limited wolf control program that had been in effect since 1929. It also determined that the decline in the Dall mountain sheep had actually been precipitated by a series of cold winters that killed many sheep and weakened others, making them easier prey for the wolves, but that wolf predation per se was not to blame.

HYPOTHESIS Culling the wolf population would protect reproductively active adults in the Dall mountain sheep population.

STARTING LOCATION Denali National Park (formerly known as Mt. McKinley National Park) in Alaska, where wolf predation of sheep is common.

Experimental level

Conceptual level

1 Collect sheep skulls lying on the ground.

Only skulls with horns are collected in this sampling technique.

2 Determine the age of the skulls by counting their growth rings.

Annuli are the annual growth rings used to estimate a horned animal's age.

3 Organize the data into a life table (see step 4) and construct a survivorship curve using the data.

Survivorship curve for the Dall mountain sheep shows the number of sheep alive in each age class on a log scale, plotted against age in years.

Figure 53.7 Examining the survivorship curve of a Dall mountain sheep population reveals information on the cause of death.

Figure 53.7 *(Continued)*

4   THE DATA

Results used in step 3:

Age class	Number alive, n_x	$\log_{10} n_x$	Age class	Number alive, n_x	$\log_{10} n_x$
0–1	1,000	3.00	7–8	640	2.81
1–2	801	2.90	8–9	571	2.76
2–3	789	2.90	9–10	439	2.64
3–4	776	2.89	10–11	252	2.40
4–5	764	2.88	11–12	96	1.98
5–6	734	2.86	12–13	6	0.78
6–7	688	2.84	13–14	3	0.48

5   CONCLUSION Most Dall mountain sheep die when very young or very old. Culling the wolf population would not greatly increase sheep survival.

6   SOURCE Deevey, E.S. Jr. 1947. Life tables for natural populations of animals. *Quarterly Review of Biology* 22:283–314.

Experimental Questions

1. What problem led to the study conducted by Murie on the Dall mountain sheep population of Denali National Park?

2. Describe the survivorship curve developed by Deevey based on Murie's data.

3. How did the Murie and Deevey data affect the decision of the Park Service on the control of the wolf population?

Age-Specific Fertility Data Can Tell Us When to Expect Growth to Occur

To calculate how a population grows, we need information on birth rates as well as mortality and survivorship rates. For any given age, we can determine the proportion of female offspring that are born to females of reproductive age. Using these data we can determine an **age-specific fertility rate**, called m_x. For example, if 100 females produce 75 female offspring, $m_x = 0.75$. With this additional information, we can calculate the growth rate of a population.

First, we use the survivorship data to find the proportion of individuals alive at the start of any given age class. This age-specific survivorship rate, termed l_x, equals n_x/n_0, where n_0 is the number alive at time 0, the start of the study, and n_x is the number alive at the beginning of age class x. Let's return to the beaver life table in Table 53.1. The proportion of the original beaver population still alive at the start of the sixth age class, l_5, equals $n_5/n_0 = 273/3,695$, or 0.074. This means that 7.4% of the original beaver population survived to age 5. Next we multiply the data in the two columns, l_x and m_x, for each row, to give us a column $l_x\,m_x$. This column represents the contribution of each age class to the overall population growth rate. An examination of the beaver age-specific fertility rates illustrates a couple of general points. First, for this beaver population in particular, and for many organisms in general, there are no babies born to young females. As females mature sexually, age-specific fertility goes up and it remains fairly high until later in life, when females reach postreproductive age.

The number of offspring born to females of any given age class depends on two things: the number of females in that age class and their age-specific fertility rate. Thus, although fertility of young beavers is very low, there are so many females in the age class that $l_x\,m_x$ for one-year-olds is quite high. Age-specific fertility for older beavers is much higher, but the relatively few females in these age classes cause $l_x\,m_x$ to be low. Maximum values of $l_x\,m_x$ occur for females of an intermediate age, three to four years old in the case of the beaver. The overall growth rate per generation is then the number of offspring born to all females of all ages, where a generation is defined as the mean period between birth of females and birth of their offspring. Thus, to get the generational growth rate, we sum all the values of $l_x\,m_x$; that is, $\Sigma\,l_x\,m_x$, where the symbol Σ means "sum of." We term this summed value R_0 and refer to it as the **net reproductive rate**.

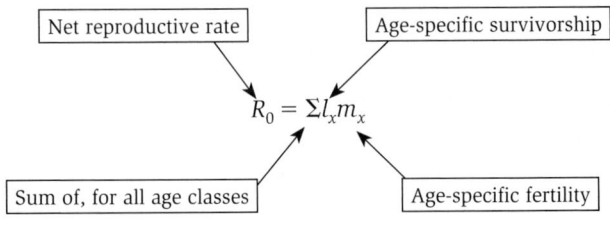

$$R_0 = \Sigma l_x m_x$$

Net reproductive rate | Age-specific survivorship | Sum of, for all age classes | Age-specific fertility

To calculate the future size of a population, we simply multiply the number of individuals in the population by the net reproductive rate. Thus, the population size in the next generation, N_{t+1}, is determined by the number in the population now, at time t, which is given by N_t multiplied by R_0.

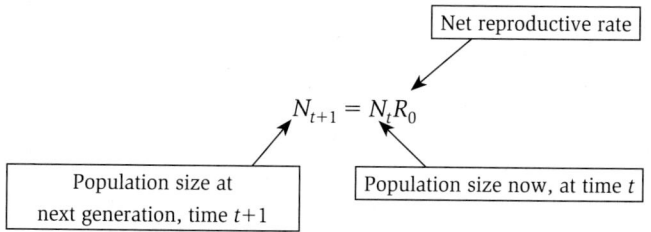

Let's consider an example in which the number of beavers alive now, N_t, is 1,000 and $R_0 = 1.1$. This means the beaver population is reproducing at a rate that is 10% greater than simply replacing itself. The size of the population next generation, N_{t+1}, is given by

$$N_{t+1} = N_t R_0$$
$$N_{t+1} = 1,000 \times 1.1$$
$$= 1,100$$

Thus, the number of beavers in the next generation is 1,100 and the population will have grown larger.

In determining population growth, much depends on the value of R_0. If $R_0 > 1$, then the population will grow. If $R_0 < 1$, the population is in decline. If $R_0 = 1$, then the population size stays the same and we say it is at **equilibrium**. In the case of the beavers, Table 53.1 reveals that $R_0 = 0.938$, which is less than 1, and therefore the population is in decline. This is valuable information, because it tells us that at that time, the beaver population in Newfoundland needed more protection (perhaps in the form of bans on trapping and hunting) in order to attain a population level at equilibrium.

53.3 / HOW POPULATIONS GROW

Learning Outcomes:

1. Explain how the population growth of continuously breeding organisms can be predicted using the per capita growth rate (r).
2. Distinguish between exponential growth and logistic growth.
3. Describe how density-dependent factors and density-independent factors can regulate population size.
4. Compare and contrast life history strategies of r-selected and K-selected species.

Life tables can provide us with accurate information about how populations can grow from generation to generation. However, other population growth models can provide us with valuable insights into how populations grow over shorter time periods.

The most simple of these assumes that populations grow if, for any time interval, the number of births is greater than the number of deaths. In this section, we will examine two different types of these simple models. The first assumes resources are not limiting, and it results in prodigious growth. The second, and perhaps more biologically realistic, assumes resources are limiting, and it results in limits to growth and eventual stable population sizes. We then consider what other factors might limit population growth, such as natural enemies, and discuss the overall life history strategies employed by different species to enable them to exist on Earth.

Per Capita Growth Rate

The change in population size over any time period can be written as the number of births per unit time interval minus the number of deaths per unit time interval. Ecologists are often interested in the number of births (b) or deaths (d) per individual in the population and refer to the **per capita growth rate (r)**, where $r = b - d$. Knowing r helps predict how populations will grow, with population growth rates expressed as $dN/d_t = rN$.

Exponential Growth Occurs When the Per Capita Growth Rate Remains Above Zero

How do populations grow? Clearly, much depends on the value of r. When $r < 0$, the population decreases; when $r = 0$, the population remains constant; and when $r > 0$, the population increases. When $r = 0$ the population is often referred to as being at equilibrium, where no changes in population size will occur and there is **zero population growth**.

Even if r is only fractionally above 0, population increase is rapid and, when plotted graphically, a characteristic J-shaped curve results (**Figure 53.8**). We refer to this type of population growth as geometric or **exponential growth**. When conditions are optimal for the population, r is at its maximum rate and is called the **intrinsic rate of increase** (denoted r_{max}). Thus, the rate of population growth under optimal conditions is $dN/d_t = r_{max} N$. Again, the larger the value of r_{max}, the steeper the slope of the curve. Because population growth depends on the value of N as well as the value of r, the population increase is even greater as time passes.

Increasing K, the carrying capacity, will cause the change in population over time to increase in value as well. Therefore, as N (the population density), approaches K (the carrying capacity), the rate of increase will approach zero, levelling off population growth. In this way, population sizes are stabilized through density-dependent feedback, and will decline if they grow beyond the maximum carrying capacity of the environment.

How do field data fit this simple model for exponential growth? Clearly population growth cannot go on forever, as envisioned under exponential growth. But, initially at least, exponential growth is often observed in a new and expanding population where resources are not limited. Let's look at a few examples.

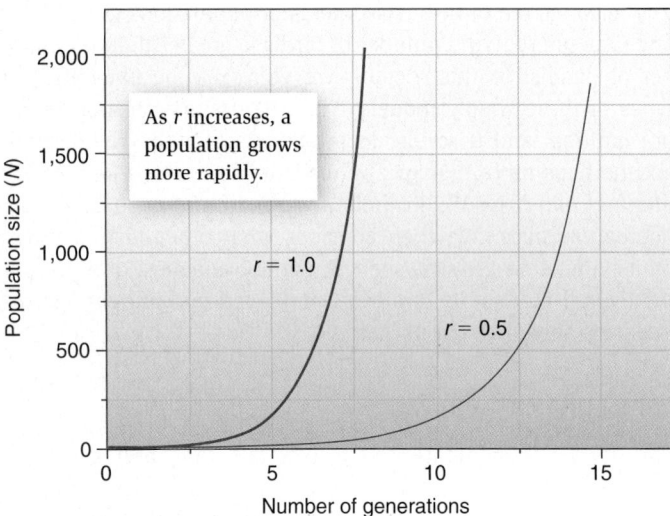

Figure 53.8 **Exponential population growth.** As the value of *r* increases, the slope of the curve gets steeper. In theory, a population with unlimited resources could grow indefinitely.

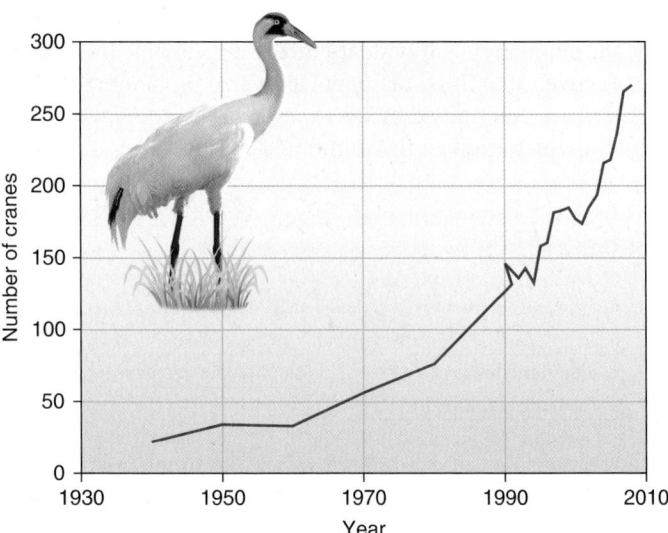

Figure 53.9 **Exponential growth in the Canadian migratory population of the whooping crane after 70 years of conservation efforts.** The population appears to be increasing at about 4.5% per year.

The migratory whooping crane (*Grus americana*) was introduced in Chapter 22. Once numbering in the several thousands, the whooping crane approached the brink of extinction in the 1940s, when only 21 remained in the world. Most of the wetlands in its historical range have been drained for agriculture and additional habitat loss was caused by oil and gas development and the construction of intercoastal waterways for barge traffic. Furthermore, it was hunted for its meat and for its feathers. Luckily, these large majestic birds were saved from extinction, and by March 2007 the Canadian migratory whooping crane population had grown to 237 birds. The Canadian migratory population breeds in Wood Buffalo National Park (which straddles the border between the Northwest Territories and Alberta) and overwinters in Aransas National Wildlife Reserve, on the Texas Gulf Coast. Due to strict conservation efforts in both Canada and the United States, the migratory whooping crane population has made a remarkable recovery (**Figure 53.9**). The whooping crane currently exists in the wild at three locations and in captivity at seven sites. The total wild population was estimated at 344 in March 2007, including the 237 individuals in the Canadian migratory population, 45 captive-raised and released individuals in the Florida population, and 62 individuals in the eastern United States that migrate between Wisconsin and Florida. The captive population consisted of 145 birds in March 2007.

The growth of some exotic species introduced into new habitats also seems to fit the pattern of exponential growth. The rapid expansion of rabbits after their introduction into South Australia in the late nineteenth century is a case in point. In 1859 Thomas Austin received two dozen European rabbits from England. Rabbit gestation lasts a mere 31 days, and in South Australia each doe could produce up to 10 litters of at least six young each year. The rabbits had essentially no enemies and ate the grass used by sheep and other grazing animals. Even when two-thirds of the population was shot for sport, which was the purpose of the initial introduction, the population grew into the millions in a few short years. By 1875 rabbits were reported

on the west coast, having moved more than 1,760 kilometres across the continent despite the deployment of huge, thousand-kilometre-long fences meant to contain them.

Finally, one of the most prominent examples of exponential growth is the growth of the global human population, which, because of its large importance, we will examine separately later in the chapter.

Logistic Growth Occurs in Populations in Which Resources Are Limited

Despite its applicability to rapidly growing populations, the exponential growth model is not appropriate in many situations. The model assumes unlimited resources, which is not often the case in the real world. For most species, resources become limiting as populations grow. Thus the per capita growth rate decreases as resources are used up. The upper boundary for the population size is known as the **carrying capacity (K)**. Thus, a more realistic equation to explain population growth, one that takes into account the amount of available resources, is where $(K - N)/K$ represents the proportion of unused resources remaining. This equation is called the **logistic equation**.

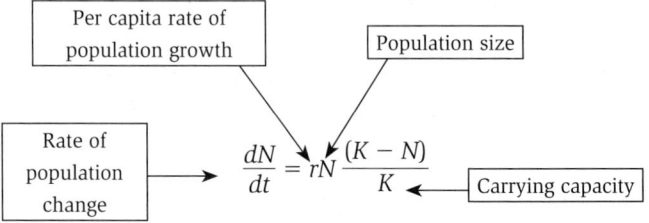

$$\frac{dN}{dt} = rN\frac{(K - N)}{K}$$

In essence, this equation means that the larger the population size, *N*, the closer it becomes to the carrying capacity, *K*, and the fewer the available resources for population growth. At large values of *N*, $(K - N)/K$ becomes small and thus population growth is small. It turns out that growth is greatest when $N = K/2$.

Let's consider how an ecologist would use the logistic equation. First, the value of K would come from intense field and laboratory work where researchers would determine the amount of resources, such as food, needed by each individual and then determine the amount of available food in the wild. Field censuses would determine N, and field censuses of births and deaths per unit time would provide r. When this type of population growth is plotted over time, an S-shaped growth curve results (**Figure 53.10**). This pattern, in which the growth of a population typically slows down as it approaches K, is called **logistic growth**.

Does the logistic growth model provide a better fit to growth patterns of plants and animals in the wild than the exponential model, which is also shown in Figure 53.10? In some instances, such as laboratory cultures of bacteria and yeasts, the logistic growth model provides a good fit (**Figure 53.11**). However, for many other populations, including those of the shrews, voles, and red squirrels shown in **Figure 53.12**, there is much variation. If the logistic model held true for these species, we would expect to see population growth levelling off, indicative of the populations having reached their equilibrium densities. However, in nature variations in temperature, rainfall, or resources cause changes in carrying capacity and thus in population densities. The uniform conditions of temperature and resource levels of the laboratory do not exist. In fact, when studying the population patterns of short-tailed shrews, researchers at the Konza Prairie Biological Station in Kansas found a tight relationship between available soil moisture and the relative abundance of shrews (**Figure 53.13**). One hypothesis is that increased soil moisture provides more free water for drinking and an increased amount of invertebrate prey such as worms. This reminds us again of the influence of abiotic factors on population densities, as we explored in Chapter 51.

Figure 53.11 **Growth of yeast cells in culture fits the logistic growth model.** Early tests of the logistic growth curve were validated by growth of yeast cells in laboratory cultures. These populations showed the typical S-shaped growth curve.

Is the logistic model of little value because it fails to describe population growth accurately? Not really. It is a useful starting point for thinking about how populations grow, and it seems intuitively correct. However, the carrying capacity is a difficult feature of the environment to identify for most species, and it also varies temporally, according to climatic and local weather patterns; thus, logistic growth is difficult to measure accurately.

Also, as we will discover, populations are affected by predators, parasites, or competition with other species. In Chapter 54, we will examine how natural enemies and competitors affect population densities and explore whether species interactions commonly limit population growth. However, it is instructive to first see how these natural enemies can reduce population size. Such population reductions are often caused by a process known as density dependence.

Density-Dependent Factors May Regulate Population Sizes

Factors that influence birth and death rates, and thus regulate population size, can be either density dependent or density independent. A **density-dependent factor** is a mortality factor whose influence varies with the density of the population. Parasitism, predation, and competition are some of the many density-dependent factors that may reduce the population densities of living organisms and stabilize them at equilibrium levels. Such factors can be density dependent in that their impact depends on the density of the population; they kill relatively more of a population when densities are higher and less of a population when densities are lower. For example, many predators develop a visual search image for a particular prey. When a prey is rare, predators tend to ignore it and kill relatively few. When a prey is common, predators key in on it and kill relatively more. In England, for example, predatory shrews kill proportionately more moth pupae in leaf litter when the pupae are common compared to when they are rare.

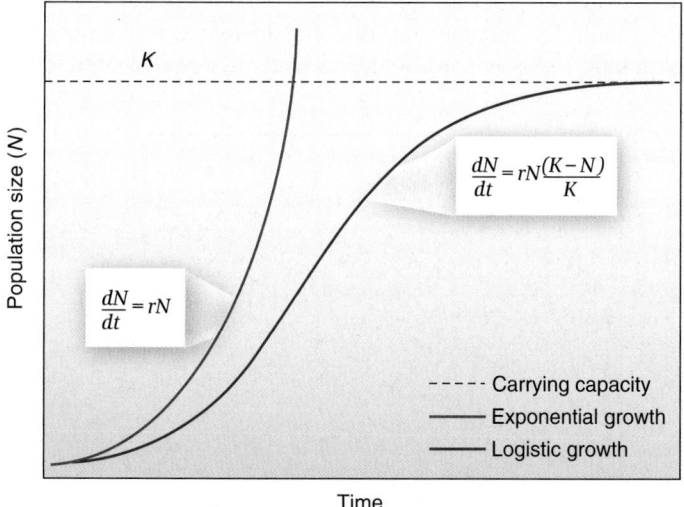

Figure 53.10 **Exponential versus logistic growth.** Exponential (J-shaped) growth occurs in an environment with unlimited resources, while logistic (S-shaped) growth occurs in an environment with limited resources.

Concept check: *What is the population growth per unit of time when r = 0.1, N = 200, and K = 500?*

(a) Short-tailed shrews at Konza Prairie, Kansas

(b) Voles in Sweden

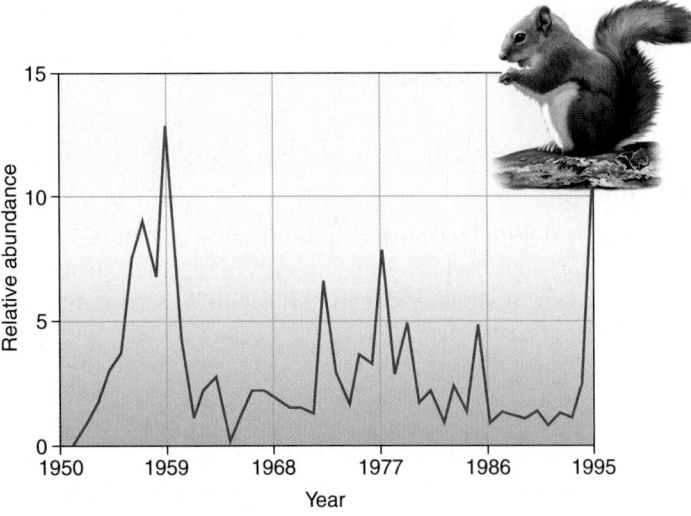

(c) Red squirrels in Ontario

Density dependence can be detected by plotting mortality, expressed as a percentage, against population density (**Figure 53.14**). If a positive slope results and mortality increases with density, the factor tends to have a greater effect on dense populations than on sparse ones and is clearly acting in a density-dependent manner.

Figure 53.12 The logistic growth model does not describe all populations. Variation in abundance of different species of small mammal populations over many years of data collection shows great variability and a lack of fit to the idealized logistic growth curve. Data reflect relative abundance in a set number of traps at different sampling points.

BioConnections: *Look ahead to Figure 54.12 to see how population curves of small mammals can be influenced by predators.*

A **density-independent factor** is a mortality factor whose influence is not affected by changes in population size or density. In general, density-independent factors are physical factors, including weather, drought, freezes, floods, and disturbances such as fire. For example, in hard freezes the same proportion of organisms such as birds or plants are usually killed, no matter how large the population size. However, even physical factors such as weather can act in a density-dependent manner. For example, in an environment where there were many beavers and a limited number of rivers to dam, some individuals would not have a lodge. In such a situation, a cold winter could kill a high percentage of beavers. If, on the other hand, there were few beavers, most would have a lodge to provide them with protection from a hard freeze. In this case, the cold would kill a lower percentage.

Determining which factors act in a density-dependent fashion has large practical implications. Foresters, game managers, and conservation biologists alike are interested in learning how to maintain populations at equilibrium levels. For example, if disease were to act in a density-dependent manner on white-tailed deer, there wouldn't be much point in game managers attempting to kill off predators such as mountain lions to increase herd sizes for hunters, because proportionately more deer would be killed by disease.

Finally, a source of mortality that decreases with increasing population size is considered an **inverse density-dependent**

Figure 53.13 Abiotic factors influence population densities. The number of short-tailed shrews at Konza Prairie, Kansas, increases as precipitation and thus soil moisture increases because of a greater availability of drinking water and invertebrate prey. Each point refers to a year from Figure 53.12a.

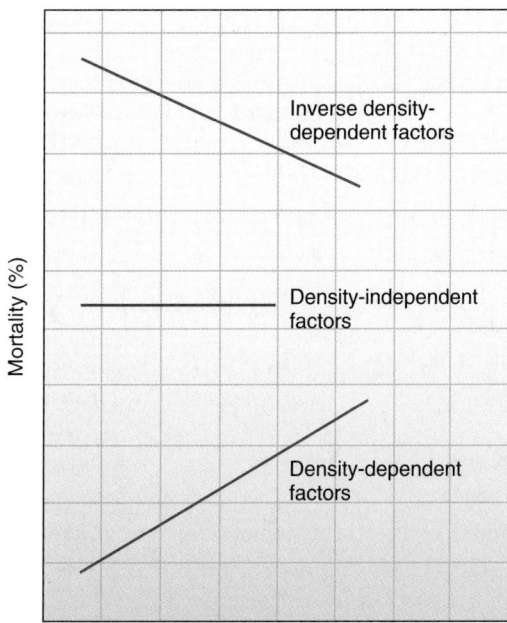

Figure 53.14 **Three ways that factors affect mortality in response to changes in population density.** For a density-dependent factor mortality increases with population density; for a density-independent factor mortality remains unchanged. For an inverse-dependent factor, mortality decreases as a population increases in size.

factor. For example, if a territorial predator such as a lion always ate the same number of wildebeest prey, regardless of wildebeest density, it would be acting in an inverse density-dependent manner, because it is taking a smaller proportion of the population at higher density. Some mammalian predators, being highly territorial, often act in this manner on herbivore density.

Thus, natural enemies can act in a density-dependent manner and control prey populations, or they can act in a density-independent or inverse density-dependent manner and not regulate them. In order to make generalizations about which factors control populations in nature, we need to know the frequency of density dependence in natural systems.

Which factors tend to act in a density-dependent manner? In the 1980s a broad review of many research studies, which considered 51 populations of insects, 82 populations of large mammals, and 36 populations of small mammals and birds, showed a wide variety of density-dependent factors. No single process such as parasitism, competition, or predation could be regarded as a regulatory factor of overriding importance. Even for individual taxa, such as insects, density dependence varied from parasitism and predation to competition and abiotic factors. This finding is disconcerting to ecologists interested in species management, because it means that generalizations about which factors are likely to act in a density-dependent manner are not easily made. Each species has to be analyzed on a case-by-case basis.

Life History Strategies Incorporate Traits Relating to Survival and Competitive Ability

The population parameters we have discussed—including iteroparity versus semelparity, continuous versus seasonal iteroparity, and density-dependent versus density-independent factors—have important implications for how populations grow and indeed for the reproductive success of populations and species. However, these reproductive strategies can be viewed in the context of a much bigger picture of life history strategies, sets of physiological and behavioural features that incorporate not only reproductive traits but also survivorship and length of life characteristics, habitat type, and competitive ability. Life history strategies can be considered a continuum (**Figure 53.15**). At the one end are species, termed ***r*-selected species**, that have a high rate of per capita population growth, *r*, but poor competitive ability. An example is a weed that quickly colonizes vacant habitats (such as barren land), passes through several generations, and then is outcompeted. Weeds produce huge numbers of tiny seeds and therefore have high values of *r*. At the other end are species, termed ***K*-selected species**, that have more or less stable populations adapted to exist at or near the carrying capacity, *K*, of the environment. An example is a tree that exists in a mature forest. While trees do not have a high reproductive rate, they tend to compete well and eventually displace many species by overtopping them and shading them out. The *r*- and *K*-selection continuum brings together various life history features including reproductive strategy, dispersal ability, growth rates, and population size (**Table 53.2**).

Let's return to our previous comparison of weeds versus trees. Weeds exist in disturbed habitats such as gaps in a forest canopy where trees have blown down, allowing light to penetrate to the forest floor. An *r*-selected species such as a weed grows quickly and reaches reproductive age early, devoting much energy to producing a large number of seeds that disperse widely. These weed species remain small and do not live long, perhaps passing a few generations in the light gap before it closes.

A mature forest tree, on the other hand, often exists in undisturbed native habitats. Forest trees grow slowly and reach reproductive age late, having to devote much energy to growth and maintenance. A *K*-selected species such as a tree grows large and shades out *r*-selected species such as weeds, eventually outcompeting them. Such trees live a long time and produce seeds repeatedly every year when mature. These seeds are bigger than those of *r*-selected species; consider the acorns of oaks versus the seeds of dandelions. Acorns contain a large food reserve that helps them grow, whereas dandelion seeds must rely on whatever nutrients they can gather from the soil.

As you might expect, a trade-off exists between seed size and number—a plant can produce a few big seeds or lots of small ones. While the weed–tree example is a useful way to think about the *r*- and *K*-selection continuum, we must remember that other organisms can be *r*- or *K*-selected, too. For example, insects can be considered small, *r*-selected species that produce many young and have short life cycles. Mammals, such as elephants, that grow slowly, have few young, and reach large sizes are typical of *K*-selected species.

- Small size
- Rapid growth
- Short lifespan

- Many small seeds
- Good seed dispersal

(a) *r*-selected species

- Large size
- Slow growth
- Long lifespan

- Few large seeds
- Poor seed dispersal

(b) *K*-selected species

Figure 53.15 **Life history strategies.** Differences in traits of a dandelion (*top*) and an oak tree (*bottom*) illustrate some of the differences between *r*- and *K*-selected species.

BioConnections: *Look back at Figure 37.23. What is unusual about the reproductive strategy of the mother of thousands plant?*

In a human-dominated world, almost every life history attribute of a *K*-selected species sets it at risk of extinction. First, *K*-selected species tend to be bigger, so they need more habitat in which to live. Florida panthers need huge tracts of land to establish their territories and hunt for deer. There is only room for about 22 panthers on publicly owned land in South Florida. Privately owned land currently supports another 50 panthers. As the amount of land shrinks through development, so does the number of panthers. Second, *K*-selected species tend

Table 53.2	Characteristics of *r*- and *K*-Selected Species	
Life history feature	***r*-selected species**	***K*-selected species**
Development	Rapid	Slow
Reproductive rate	High	Low
Reproductive age	Early	Late
Body size	Small	Large
Length of life	Short	Long
Competitive ability	Weak	Strong
Survivorship	High mortality of young	Low mortality of young
Population size	Variable	Fairly constant
Dispersal ability	Good	Poor
Habitat type	Disturbed	Not disturbed
Parental care	Low	High

to have fewer offspring and so their populations cannot recover as quickly from disturbances like fire or overhunting. California condors, for example, produce only a single chick every other year. Third, *K*-selected species breed at a later age, and their generation time and time to grow from a small population to a larger population is long. Gestation time in elephants is 22 months, and elephants take at least seven years to become sexually mature. Large trees such as the giant sequoia; large terrestrial mammals like elephants, rhinoceros, and grizzly bears; and large marine mammals like blue whales and sperm whales all run the risk of extinction. Interestingly, the coast redwood seems to be an exception, a fact perhaps attributable to its unusual genome (see the following Genomes and Proteomes section).

What are the advantages to being a *K*-selected species? In a world not perturbed by humans, *K*-selected species would fare well. Being a *K*-selected species is as viable an option as being *r*-selected. However, in a human-dominated world, many *K*-selected species are selectively logged or hunted or their habitat is altered, and the resulting small population sizes make extinction a real possibility.

Although the majority of organisms do not fit into the *K*-selected versus *r*-selected dichotomy, an understanding of these terms is still useful. In the 1990s this paradigm was largely replaced with demographic theory, which emphasized age-structured populations under pressure from natural selection. Additionally, since life history strategies are frequently extremely flexible in the presence of external factors, more recent life history strategy papers typically relate environmental parameters or external pressures such as predation to organism body size and reproductive characteristics.

From an evolutionary perspective, why do aging and senescence occur? The classic theory of aging is that natural selection acts on individuals in their younger years when they are reproductively active, rather than later in life, once reproductive activities have ceased. Therefore, individuals will expend vigour in their youth, and as a trade-off, have declined vigour in later years.

GENOMES AND PROTEOMES

Hexaploidy Increases the Growth of Coast Redwood Trees

Besides having the world's most massive tree, the giant sequoia (*Sequoiadendron giganteum*), California is also home to the world's tallest tree, the coast redwood (*Sequoia sempervirens*), a towering giant that can grow to over 90 metres and can live for up to 2,000 years (**Figure 53.16**). These trees are currently confined to a relatively small 700-kilometre strip along the Pacific coast from California to southern Oregon, an area characterized by temperatures that are moderate year-long, heavy winter rains, and dense summer fog. Interestingly, because this climate was far more common in earlier eras, these trees were once dispersed throughout the northern hemisphere. As of today, however, over 95% of the old-growth coast redwoods are gone, the result of extensive logging.

How is this huge species different from other tree species? In 1948 researchers made the startling discovery that the tree is a hexaploid; that is, each of its cells contains six sets of chromosomes, with 66 chromosomes in total. While hexaploidy is not unknown in grasses and shrubs, it is unusual in trees. Of all the conifers on Earth, the coast redwood is the only hexaploid. Having this quality means each tree may have several different alleles for any given gene, which leads to a very genetically diverse population. Molecular biologist Chris Brinegar has found that hardly any two trees have exactly the same genetic constitution. Such genetic diversity allows greater adaptation to environmental conditions and more adaptations against insect or fungal pests. Indeed, living redwoods have no known lethal diseases, and pests do not cause significant damage. What's more, with six different sets of genes, trees also have the potential for great variety in their gene products, the proteins, which may help explain their prodigious growth.

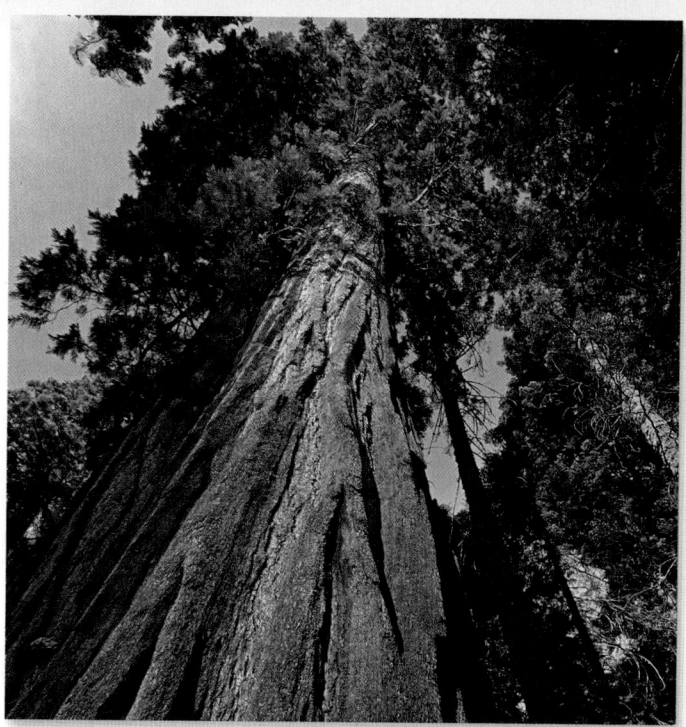

Figure 53.16 The coast redwood (*Sequoia sempervirens*) is a hexaploid conifer. The coast redwood can grow to over 90 metres, and the oldest living trees are over 2,000 years old. Their great genetic variation may help explain their incredible growth and longevity.

 Principle: *The genetic material provides a blueprint for sustaining life. Despite being large, K-selected species, coastal redwoods grow faster than any other known conifer and this is due to their unusual hexaploid genome.*

53.4 / HUMAN POPULATION GROWTH

Learning Outcomes:

1. Describe the pattern of human population growth.
2. Graph the demographic transition.
3. Discuss differences in age structure and human fertility across different countries.
4. Explain the concept of an ecological footprint.

In 2005 the world's population was estimated to be increasing at the rate of 153 people every minute, with 151 of those in less developed nations. The United Nations' 2005 projections pointed to a world population stabilizing at around 10 billion near the year 2150, as would happen with logistic growth. However, until now, human population growth has better fit an exponential growth pattern than a logistic one. In this section, we examine human population growth trends in more detail and discuss how knowledge of a population's age structure can help predict its future growth. We then investigate the carrying capacity of the Earth for humans and explore how the concept of an ecological footprint, which measures human resource use, can help us determine this carrying capacity.

Human Population Growth Fits an Exponential Pattern

Until the beginning of agriculture and the domestication of animals, about 10,000 BCE, the average rate of population growth was very low. With the establishment of agriculture, the world's population grew to about 300 million by 1 CE and to 800 million by the year 1750. Between 1750 and 1998, a relatively tiny period of human history, the world's human population surged from 800 million to 6 billion (**Figure 53.17**). In 2006 the number

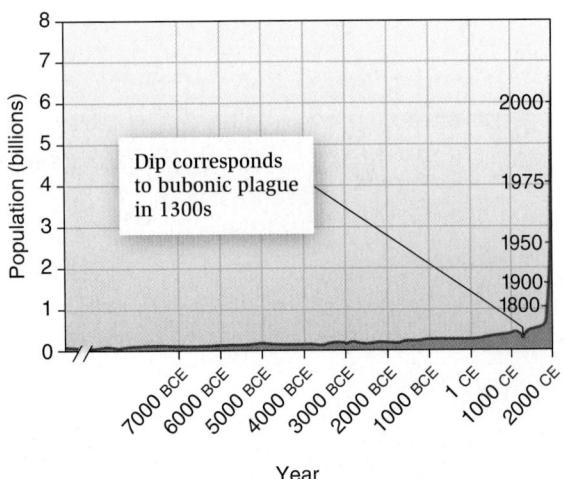

Figure 53.17 World human population growth through history illustrates an exponential growth pattern. If and when human population growth will level off are issues of considerable debate.

of humans was estimated at 6.5 billion, with two people added to the world's population every second. Considering this phenomenal increase in growth, the biggest questions remain: When will the human population level off—and at what level?

Human populations can exist at equilibrium densities in one of two ways:

1. *High birth and high death rates.* Before 1750 this was often the case, with high birth rates offset by deaths from wars, famines, and epidemics.
2. *Low birth and low death rates.* In Europe, beginning in the 18th century, better health and living conditions reduced the death rate. Eventually, social changes such as increasing education for women and marriage at a later age reduced the birth rate.

The shift in birth and death rates with development is known as the **demographic transition** (**Figure 53.18**). In the first stage of the transition, birth and death rates are both high, and the population remains in equilibrium. In the second stage of this transition,

which first occurred in Western Europe beginning in the late eighteenth century, the death rate declines first, while the birth rate remains high. High rates of population growth result. In the third stage, the birth rates drop and death rates stabilize, so that low population growth ensues. In the fourth stage, both birth and death rates are low, and the population is again at equilibrium.

The exact pace of the demographic transition between countries differs, depending on culture, economics, politics, and religion. This is illustrated by examining the demographic transition in Sweden and Mexico (**Figure 53.19**). In Mexico, the demographic transition occurred more recently and was typified by a faster decline in the death rate, reflecting rapid improvements in public health. A relatively longer lag occurred between the decline in the death rate and the decline in the birth rate, however, with the result that Mexico's population growth rate is still well above Sweden's, perhaps reflecting differences in culture or the fact that in Mexico the demographic transition is not yet complete.

Knowledge of a Population's Age Structure Can Help Predict Its Future Growth

Changes in the age structure of a population also characterize the demographic transition. In all populations, **age structure** refers to the relative numbers of individuals of each defined age group. This information is commonly displayed as a population pyramid (**Figure 53.20**). In West Africa, for example, children under the

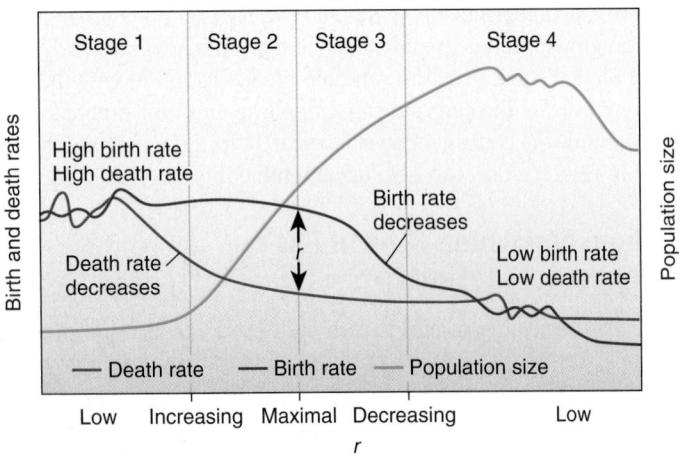

Figure 53.18 The classic stages of the demographic transition. The difference in the birth rate and the death rate equals the rate of natural increase or decrease.

Figure 53.19 The demographic transition in Sweden and Mexico. While the transition began earlier in Sweden than it did in Mexico, the transition was more rapid in Mexico and the overall rate of population increase remains higher. (The spike in the death rate in Mexico prior to 1920 is attributed to the turbulence surrounding the Mexican revolution.)

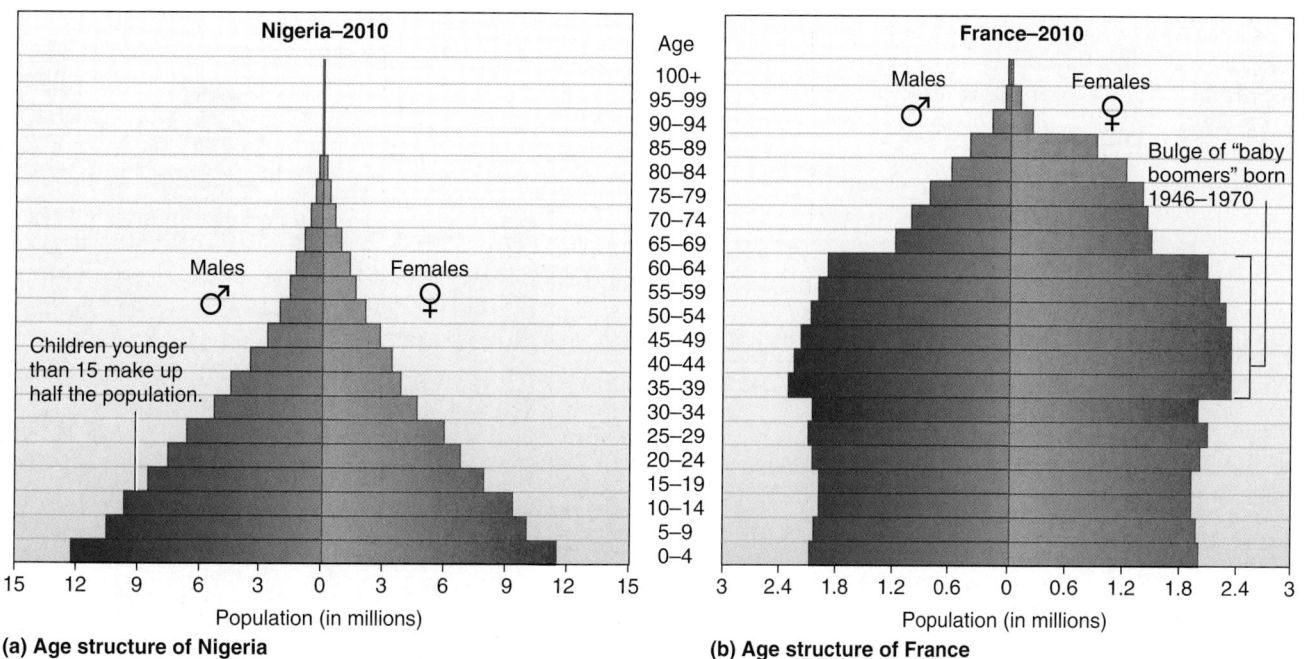

(a) Age structure of Nigeria

(b) Age structure of France

Figure 53.20   The age structure of human populations in West Africa and Western Europe, as of 2010.   (a) In developing areas of the world such as West Africa there are far more children than any other age group. (b) In the developed countries of Western Europe, the age structure is more even. The bulge represents those born in the post–World War II baby boom, when birth rates climbed due to stabilization of political and economic conditions.

age of 15 make up nearly half of the population, creating a pyramid with a wide base and narrow top. Thus, even if fertility rates decline, there will still be a huge increase in the population as these children move into child-bearing age. The age structure of Western Europe is much more balanced. Even if the fertility rate of young women in Western Europe increased to a level higher than that of their mothers, the annual numbers of births would still decline because of the low number of women of child-bearing age.

Predicting the Earth's Carrying Capacity for Humans Is a Difficult Task

What is the Earth's carrying capacity for humans and when will it be reached? Estimates have been quite varied. Much of the speculation on the future size of the world's population centres on lifestyle. To use a simplistic example, if everyone on the planet ate meat extensively and drove large cars, then the carrying capacity would be a lot less than if people were vegetarians and used bicycles as their main means of transportation.

Most estimates propose that the human population will grow to between 10 to 15 billion people by the end of the twenty-first century. Global population growth can be examined by looking at **total fertility rates (TFR)**, the average number of live births a woman has during her lifetime (**Figure 53.21**). The global fertility rate has been declining, from almost 5.0 in the 1960s to 2.9 in the late 1990s. This is still greater than the 2.1 needed for zero population growth. (The fact that the replacement rate is slightly higher than 2.0, to replace mother and father, reflects mortality before individuals reach reproductive age.) The fertility rate differs considerably among geographic areas. In Africa the total fertility rate of 5.2 in 2003 has declined relatively little since

the 1950s, when it was around 6.7 children per woman. In Latin America and Southeast Asia, the rates have declined considerably from the 1950s and are now at around 2.7 and 2.6, respectively. Sweden and most other countries in Europe and North America have a TFR of less than 2.1; in Russia, fertility rates have dropped to a low of 1.1. In China, while the TFR is only 1.8, the population there will still continue to increase until at least 2025 because of the large number of women of reproductive age.

Total fertility rates of less than 2.1 will lead to population decline over the long term. The results illustrate that in highly industrialized or developed countries, the population has nearly stabilized at a little over 1 billion people, while in less developed countries the population is still increasing dramatically.

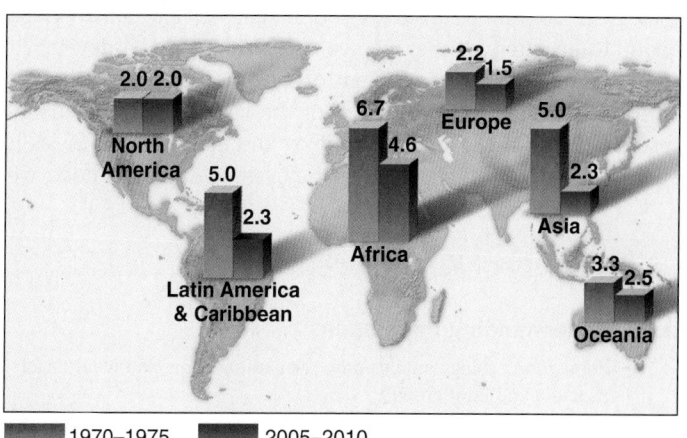

Figure 53.21   Total fertility rates (TFRs) among major regions of the world.   Data refer to the average number of children born to a woman during her lifetime.

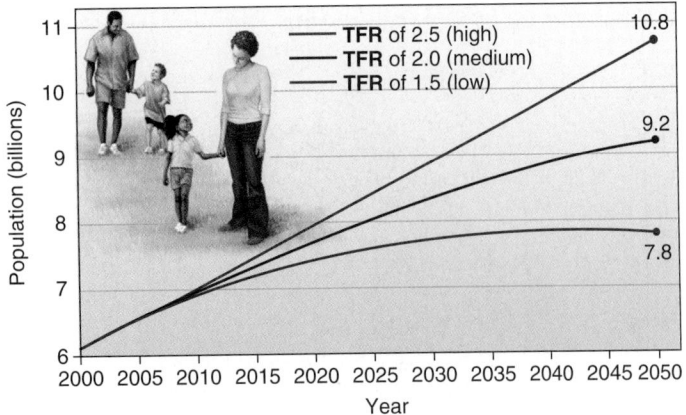

Figure 53.22 Population predictions for 2000–2050, using three different total fertility rates (TFRs).

A recent United Nations report shows world population projections to the year 2050 for three different growth scenarios: low, medium, and high (**Figure 53.22**). The three scenarios are based on three different assumptions about fertility rate. Using a low fertility rate estimate of only 1.5 children per woman, the population would reach a maximum of about 7.4 billion people by 2050. A more realistic assumption may be to use the fertility rate estimate of 2.0 or even 2.5, in which case the population would continue to rise to 7.8 or 10.8 billion, respectively.

The Concept of an Ecological Footprint Helps Estimate Carrying Capacity

In the 1990s researcher Mathis Wackernagel from the University of British Columbia calculated how much land is needed for the support of each person on Earth. Everybody has an impact on the Earth because they consume the land's resources, including crops, wood, oil, and other supplies. Thus, each person has an **ecological footprint**, the aggregate total of land needed for survival in a sustainable world. The average footprint size for everyone on the planet is about 2 hectares or 5 acres (1 ha = 10,000 m²), but a wide variation is found around the globe (**Figure 53.23**). The ecological footprint of the average Canadian is 7.5 hectares versus about 10 hectares for the average American. In most developed countries, the largest component of land is for energy, followed by food and then forestry. Much of the land needed for energy serves to absorb the CO_2 emitted by the use of fossil fuels. If everyone required 10 hectares, as the average American does, we

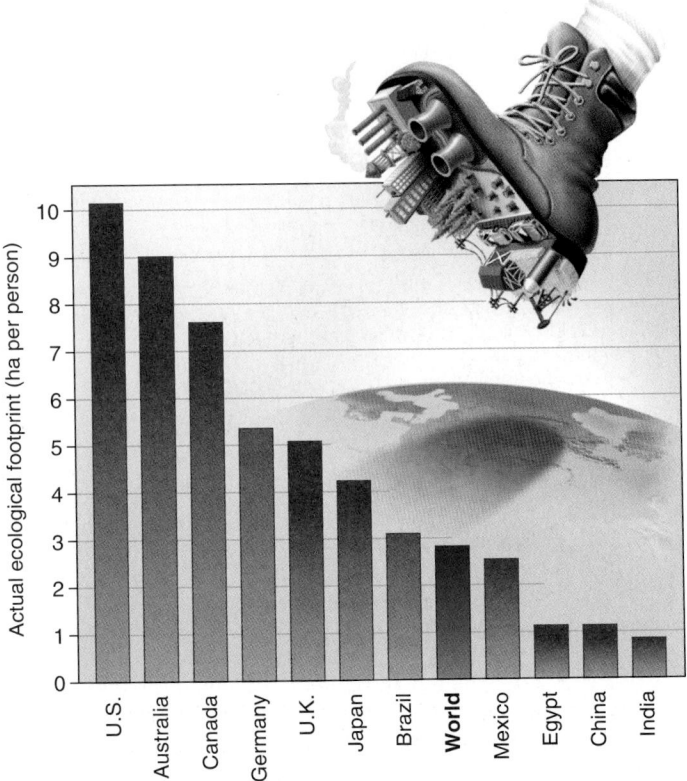

Figure 53.23 Ecological footprints of different countries. The term *ecological footprint* refers to the amount of productive land needed to support the average individual of that country.

Concept check: *What is your ecological footprint?*

would need three Earths to provide us with the needed resources. Many people in less developed countries are much more frugal in their use of resources. However, globally we are already in an ecological deficit. This is possible because many people currently live in an unsustainable manner, using supplies of nonrenewable resources, such as groundwater and fossil fuels.

What's your personal ecological footprint? Several different calculators are available on the Internet that you can use to find out. Just type "ecological footprint" (in quotation marks) into a search engine. A rapidly growing human population combined with an increasingly large per capita ecological footprint makes it increasingly difficult to conserve other species on the planet, a subject we will examine further in our discussion of conservation biology (Chapter 57).

Summary of Key Concepts

53.1 Understanding Populations

- Population ecology studies how populations grow and what factors promote and limit growth.
- Ecologists measure population density, the numbers of organisms in a given unit area, in many ways, including the mark-capture technique. (Figure 53.1)
- Individuals within populations show different patterns of dispersion, including clumped (the most common), uniform, and random; different reproductive strategies; and different age classes. (Figures 53.2, 53.3, 53.4)

53.2 Demography

- Life tables summarize the survival pattern of a population. (Table 53.1)
- Survivorship curves illustrate life tables by plotting the numbers of surviving individuals at different ages. (Figures 53.5, 53.6, 53.7)
- Age-specific fertility and survivorship data help determine the overall growth rate per generation, or the net reproductive rate (R_0).

53.3 How Populations Grow

- The per capita growth rate (r) helps determine how populations grow over any time period.

- When r is > 0, exponential (J-shaped) growth occurs. Exponential growth can be observed in an environment where resources are not limited. (Figures 53.8, 53.9)

- Logistic (S-shaped) growth takes into account the upper boundary for a population, called carrying capacity, and occurs in an environment where resources are limited. (Figures 53.10, 53.11)

- Variations in temperature, rainfall, or resource quantity or quality cause changes in population densities, and thus the idealized logistic growth model does not describe all populations. (Figures 53.12, 53.13)

- Density-dependent factors are mortality factors whose influence varies with population density. (Figure 53.14)

- Life history strategies are a set of features including reproductive traits, survivorship and length of life characteristics, habitat type, and competitive ability.

- Life history strategies can be viewed as a continuum, with r-selected species (those with a high rate of population growth but poor competitive ability) at one end and K-selected species (those with a lower rate of population growth but better competitive ability) at the other. (Figures 53.15, 53.16, Table 53.2)

53.4 Human Population Growth

- Up to the present, human population growth has fit an exponential growth pattern. (Figure 53.17)

- Human populations have been moving from states of high birth and death rates to low birth and death rates, a shift called the demographic transition. (Figures 53.18, 53.19)

- Differences in the age structure of a population, the numbers of individuals in each age group, are also characteristic of the demographic transition. (Figure 53.20)

- Though they have been declining worldwide, total fertility rates (TFRs) differ markedly in less developed and more developed countries. Predicting the growth of the human population depends on the total fertility rate that is projected. (Figures 53.21, 53.22)

- The ecological footprint refers to the amount of productive land needed to support each person on Earth. Because people in many countries live in a nonsustainable manner, globally we are already in an ecological deficit. (Figure 53.23)

Test to Assess Your Learning

1. The number of organisms in a given unit area is termed population
   a. dispersion.
   b. dispersal.
   c. density.
   d. ecology.
   e. growth.

2. A student decides to conduct a mark-recapture experiment to estimate the population size of sunfish in a small pond near his home. In the first catch, he marked 45 individuals. Two weeks later he captured 62 individuals, of which 8 were marked. What is the estimated size of the population based on these data?
   a. 134
   b. 349
   c. 558

   d. 1,016
   e. 22,320

3. Which of the following factors often results in a clumped pattern of dispersion?
   a. competition over limited resources
   b. random dispersal of seed
   c. social behaviour among members of a population
   d. all of the above
   e. a and c only

4. A life table usually contains information about
   a. the number of surviving individuals of a particular age class.
   b. fertility for specific age classes.
   c. dispersal patterns of a population.
   d. all of the above.
   e. a and b only.

5. _____ survivorship curves are usually associated with organisms that have high mortality rates in the early stages of life.
   a. Type I
   b. Type II
   c. Type III
   d. Types I and II
   e. Types II and III

6. If the net reproductive rate (R_0) is equal to 0.5, what assumptions can we make about the population?
   a. This population is essentially not changing in numbers.
   b. This population is in decline.
   c. This population is growing.
   d. This population is in equilibrium.
   e. None of the above.

7. The maximum number of individuals a certain area can sustain is known as
   a. the intrinsic rate of growth.
   b. the resource limit.
   c. the carrying capacity.
   d. the logistic equation.
   e. the equilibrium size.

8. Which of the following factors may alter carrying capacity over time?
   a. weather pattern changes
   b. numbers of other species that are present in the habitat
   c. deforestation
   d. soil chemistry changes
   e. all of the above

9. A mortality factor whose influence does not vary with the density of the population is known as a _____ factor.
   a. limiting
   b. density-independent
   c. resource-partitioning
   d. density-dependent
   e. inverse density-dependent

10. The amount of land necessary for survival for each person in a sustainable world is known as
    a. the sustainability level.
    b. an ecological impact.
    c. an ecological footprint.
    d. survival needs.
    e. all of the above.

Articulate to Assess Your Learning

1. According to the logistic equation, growth is greatest when $N = K/2$. Try some calculations to verify this for yourself and then try to prove this using your knowledge of introductory calculus.

2. As a researcher, you are using the mark-recapture procedure with large mouth bass. Say you do a poor job tagging the fish, and 20% of the tags fall off. How does this influence your estimate of population size?

Collaborate to Assess and Extend
Your Learning

1. Discuss the two main types of life history strategies.
2. Refer back to the section on Reproductive Strategies and try to come up with a hypothesis to explain why Atlantic salmon are iteroparous whereas Pacific salmon are semelparous.

3. A principle of biology is that living organisms interact with their environment. Imagine two types of ponds. In one, the pond dries out when there is little rain, while in the other the water levels fluctuate but there is always some water present. Contrast the reproductive strategies of organisms that might live in each pond.

Visit McGraw-Hill Ryerson Connect™ for additional study resources.

Species Interactions

Chapter Outline

Species interactions are numerous and varied. This white-coloured black bear, also known as a Spirit Bear, is feeding on a fish that had, in turn, fed on aquatic invertebrates.

I n this chapter we introduce different types of interactions experienced by species. Keep in mind that some of the terms are applicable both to **intraspecific** interactions (those that take place among members or populations of the same species) and to **interspecific** interactions (how individuals or populations of one species interact with individuals or populations of other species that live in the same locality). Emphasis in this chapter will be on interspecific interactions and these can take a variety of forms (**Table 54.1**). **Competition** is an interaction that affects both species negatively (−/−), as both species compete over food or other resources. Sometimes this interaction is quite one-sided, where it is detrimental to one species but not to the other, an interaction called **amensalism** (+/0). **Predation**, **herbivory**, and **parasitism** all have a positive effect on one species, the predator, herbivore, or parasite, and a negative effect on another species, the prey, plant, or host (+/−). However, while predators always kill their prey (an extremely negative effect), the hosts of parasites and herbivores often survive their attacks (with the negative effect being lost or damaged tissues or ill health). At a population level, one species could increase in population size or rate of population growth (positive effects), whereas the other species could decrease in population size or have a lowered rate of population increase (negative effects). **Mutualism** is an interaction in which both species benefit (+/+), while **commensalism** benefits one species and leaves the other unaffected (+/0). Last is the interaction, or rather lack of interaction, termed **neutralism**, when two species occur together but do not

interact in any measurable way (0/0). Neutralism may be quite common, but few people have quantified its occurrence.

To illustrate how species interact in nature, let's consider a rabbit population in a woodland community (**Figure 54.1**). To determine what factors influence the size and density of the

Table 54.1	Summary of the Types of Species Interactions	
Nature of interaction	**Species 1***	**Species 2***
Competition	−	−
Amensalism	−	0
Predation, herbivory, parasitism	+	−
Mutualism	+	+
Commensalism	+	0
Neutralism	0	0

* + = positive effect; − = negative effect; 0 = no effect.

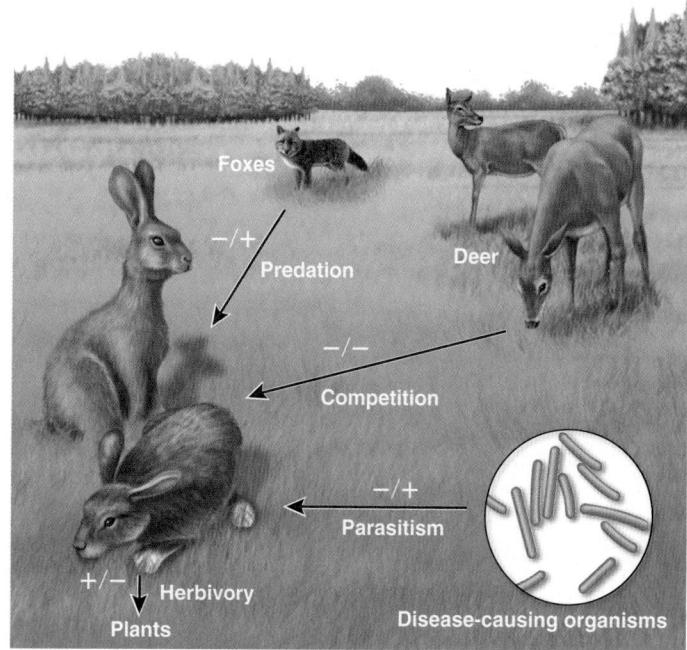

Figure 54.1   Species interactions. These rabbits can interact with a variety of species, experiencing competition with deer for food, predation by foxes, and parasitism from various disease-causing organisms. Understanding what factors affect the rabbit population size requires an understanding of each of these species' interactions.

rabbit population, we need to understand the range of its possible species interactions. For example, the rabbit population could be limited by the quality of available food. It is also likely that other species, such as deer, use the same resource and thus compete with the rabbits. The rabbit population could be limited by predation from foxes or by a virus that causes disease. It is also possible that other associations, such as mutualism or commensalism, may occur. This chapter examines each of these species interactions in turn, beginning with competition, an important interaction among species. We conclude with a discussion of models of species interactions that ecologists use when trying to determine which factors are most important in influencing population densities within ecological systems.

54.1   COMPETITION

Learning Outcomes:

1. Describe the different types of competition that occur in nature.
2. Discuss how changes in the abiotic environment can alter the outcome of competitive interactions.
3. Explain how the competitive exclusion principle can lead to resource partitioning among species.
4. Give examples of how morphological differences may allow species to coexist.

In this section, we will see how ecologists have studied different types of competition and how they have shown that the competitive effects of one species on another can change as the environment changes or as different predators or parasites are present. Although species may compete, we will also learn how sufficient differences in lifestyle or morphological traits can exist that reduce the overlap in their ecological niches, thus allowing them to coexist.

Several Different Types of Competition Occur in Nature

Several different types of competition are found in nature (**Figure 54.2**). Competition may be **intraspecific**, between individuals of the same species, or **interspecific**, between individuals of different species. Competition can also be characterized as exploitation competition or as interference competition. In **exploitation**

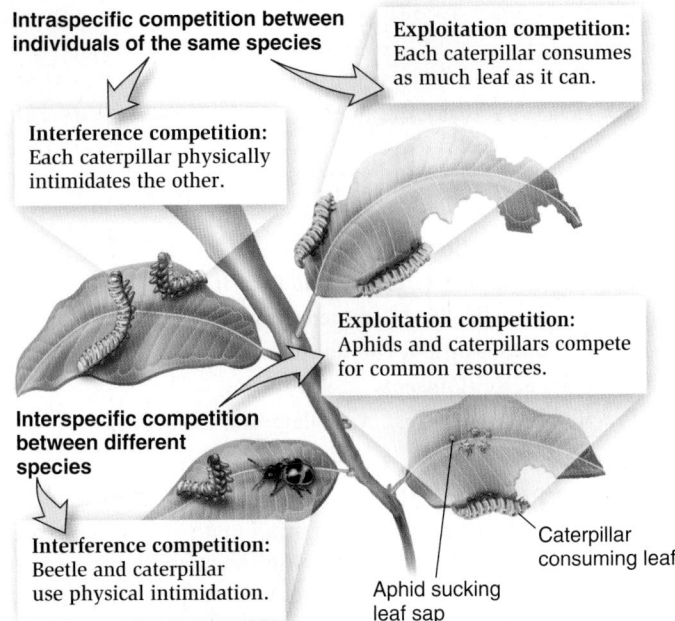

Figure 54.2   The different types of competition in nature.

Concept check: *How would you classify competition among vultures feeding on roadkill?*

competition, organisms compete indirectly through the consumption of a limited resource, with each obtaining as much as it can. For example, when fly maggots compete in a mouse carcass (an example of intraspecific exploitation competition), not all the individuals can command enough of the resource to survive and become adult flies. In **interference competition**, individuals interact directly with one another by physical force or intimidation. Often this force is ritualized into aggressive behaviour associated with territoriality (an example of intraspecific interference competition as discussed in Chapter 52). In these cases, large or strong individuals survive and take the best territory, and smaller and weaker ones perish or at best survive under suboptimal conditions.

In interspecific competition, competition between the species is not always equal. Researchers have established that one of the best methods of studying competition between two species is to remove one of them temporarily and examine the effect on the other species. A now-classic example of this method involved a study of the interactions between two species of barnacles conducted on the west coast of Scotland, as described in the Featured Investigation.

FEATURE INVESTIGATION

Connell's Classic Experiments with Barnacle Species Showed That One Species Can Competitively Exclude Another in a Natural Setting

The most direct method of assessing the effect of competition is to remove individuals of species A and measure the response of species B. Often, however, such manipulations are difficult to conduct outside the laboratory. If individuals of species A are removed, what is to stop them from migrating back into the area of removal?

In 1954 ecologist Joseph Connell conducted an experiment that overcame this problem. *Chthamalus stellatus* and *Semibalanus balanoides* (formerly known as *Balanus balanoides*) are two species of barnacles that dominate the Scottish coastline. Each organism's **niche**, or physical distribution and ecological role, on the intertidal zone was well defined, with *Chthamalus* occurring in the upper intertidal zone, and *Semibalanus* restricted to the lower intertidal zone. Connell sought to determine what the range of *Chthamalus* adults might be in the absence of competition from *Semibalanus* (**Figure 54.3**).

To do this, Connell obtained rocks from high on the rock face, just below the high-tide level, where only *Chthamalus* grew. These rocks already contained young and mature *Chthamalus*. He then moved the rocks into the *Semibalanus* zone, fastened them down with screws, and allowed *Semibalanus* to also colonize them. Once *Semibalanus* had colonized these rocks,

he took the rocks out, removed all the *Semibalanus* organisms from one side of the rocks with a needle, and then returned the rocks to the lower intertidal zone, screwing them down once again. As seen in the data, the mortality of *Chthamalus* on rock halves with *Semibalanus* was fairly high. On the *Semibalanus*-free halves, however, *Chthamalus* survived well.

Connell also monitored survival of natural patches of both barnacle species where both occurred on the intertidal zone at the upper margin of the *Semibalanus* distribution. In a period of unusually low tides and warm weather, when no water reached any barnacles for several days, desiccation became a real threat to the barnacles' survival. During this time, young

HYPOTHESIS Adult *Chthamalus stellatus* were being competitively excluded from the lower intertidal zone by the species *Semibalanus balanoides*.

STARTING LOCATION The intertidal zone of the rocky shores of the Scottish coast, where the two species of barnacles occur.

Experimental level

1. Transfer rocks containing young and mature *Chthamalus* from the upper intertidal zone to the lower intertidal zone, and fasten them down in the new location with screws.

2. Allow *Semibalanus* to colonize the rocks.

3. After the colonization period is over, remove *Semibalanus* from half of each rock with a needle (leaving the other half undisturbed). Return the rocks to the lower intertidal zone, and fasten them down once again.

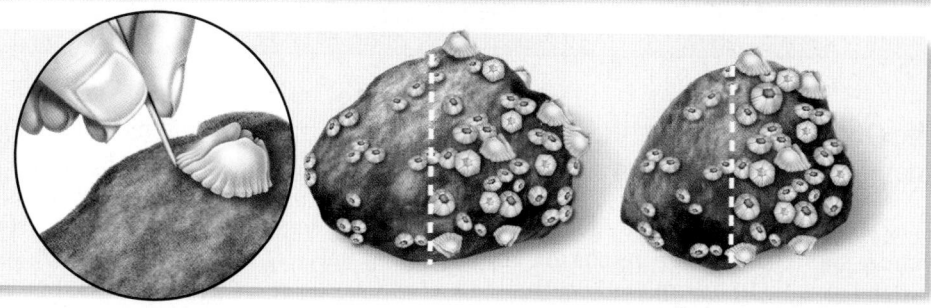

4. Monitor the survival of *Chthamalus* on both sides of the rocks.

Chthamalus grows on the side where *Semibalanus* has been removed, indicating that *Semibalanus* may exclude *Chthamalus* from certain habitats.

Figure 54.3 Connell's experimental manipulation of species indicated the presence of competition.

Figure 54.3   *(Continued)*

Rock No.	Side of rock	% *Chthamalus* mortality over 1 year	
		Young barnacles	**Mature barnacles**
13b	*Semibalanus* removed	35	0
	Semibalanus not removed	90	31
12a	*Semibalanus* removed	44	37
	Semibalanus not removed	95	71
14a	*Semibalanus* removed	40	36
	Semibalanus not removed	86	75

6   CONCLUSION The data from this study indicate that *Semibalanus* is found on the lower rock face because it outcompetes *Chthamalus*. Other studies indicate that *Chthamalus* occupies the upper rock face because it is more resistant to desiccation.

7   SOURCE Connell, J.H. 1961. The influence of interspecific competition and other factors on the distribution of the barnacle *Chthamalus stellatus*. *Ecology* 42:710–732.

Semibalanus suffered a 92% mortality rate and older individuals a 51% mortality rate. At the same time, young *Chthamalus* experienced a 62% mortality rate compared with a rate of only 2% for more resistant older individuals. Clearly, *Semibalanus* is not as resistant to desiccation as *Chthamalus* and thus could not survive in the upper intertidal zone where *Chthamalus* occurs. *Chthamalus* is more resistant to desiccation than *Semibalanus* and thus can be found higher in the intertidal zone.

Thus, while the potential distribution (the fundamental niche) of *Chthamalus* extends over the entire intertidal zone, its actual distribution (the realized niche) is restricted to the upper zone. Connell's experiments were among the first to show that, in a natural environment, one species can actually outcompete another, affecting its distribution within a habitat. Interestingly,

30 years later, in the 1980s, Connell repeated his competition experiments in the same area of the Scottish coast and once more observed strong evidence for competition.

Experimental Questions

1. Describe the realized niches for the two species of barnacles used in Connell's experiment.
2. Outline the procedure that Connell used in the experiments.
3. How did Connell explain the presence of *Chthamalus* in the upper intertidal zone if *Semibalanus* was shown to outcompete the species in the first experiment?

The Outcome of Competition Can Vary with Changes in the Biotic and Abiotic Environments

Using experiments to remove individuals of one species temporarily and examine the results on the remaining species, as Connell did, is often the most direct method to investigate the effects of competition. It is especially valuable to do such manipulations in the field because organisms can then also interact with all other organisms in their environment, or, as ecologists say, natural variation can be factored in.

In the late 1940s biologist Thomas Park began a series of laboratory experiments examining competition between two flour beetles, *Tribolium castaneum* and *Tribolium confusum*, under a variety of biotic and abiotic conditions. These beetles were well suited to study in the laboratory, since large colonies could be grown in relatively small containers containing dry

food medium. Thus, many replicates of each experiment were possible to confirm that results were consistent.

Park conducted the experiments by putting the same number of beetles of both species into a container and counting the number of each that were still alive after a given time interval. *T. confusum* usually won, but in initial experiments, the beetle cultures were infested with a protozoan parasite that preferentially killed *T. castaneum* beetles. Subsequently, when the parasite was removed, *T. castaneum* usually won. Two things were evident from this experiment. First, the presence of a parasite (a biotic factor) was shown to alter the outcome of competition. Second, with or without the parasite, there was no absolute victor. For example, even with the parasite present, sometimes *T. castaneum* won. Thus, some random variation, which we call stochasticity, was evident.

Park varied the abiotic environment and found that competitive ability was greatly influenced by climate (**Figure 54.4**). Generally,

Figure 54.4 **Influence of abiotic factors on competition between *T. castaneum* and *T. confusum*.** Results of competition between the flour beetles *Tribolium castaneum* and *Tribolium confusum* show that each species usually performs better in a given habitat; for example, *T. confusum* does better in dry conditions.

T. confusum did better in dry conditions, and *T. castaneum* in moist conditions. However, *T. confusum* also won in cold-wet conditions. Once again, some stochasticity occurred, and victory was not always absolute.

In summary, Park's important series of experiments illustrated that the results of competition could vary as a function of at least three factors: parasites, temperature, and moisture. The experiments also showed that stochasticity occurred, even in controlled laboratory conditions. But what of systems in nature, where far more variability exists? Is competition a common

occurrence? One line of evidence shows that competition is frequent in nature and a strong enough force to cause the extinction of one of two competing species that share the same niche. Researchers have proposed several mechanisms by which two competing species can coexist. One states that similar species can coexist if they occupy different niches. Another is that species may occupy similar niches but undergo physical changes in form, termed *character displacement*, that allow them to utilize different resources. Let's explore each of these concepts in more detail.

Field Studies Show Competition Occurs Frequently in Nature

By reviewing studies that have investigated competition in nature, we can see how frequently it occurs and in what particular circumstances it is most important. In one 1983 review by Joseph Connell, competition was found in 55% of 215 species surveyed, demonstrating that it is indeed frequent in nature. Generally in studies of single pairs of species utilizing the same resource, competition is almost always reported (90%), whereas in studies involving more species, the frequency of competition drops to 50%. Why should this be the case? Imagine a resource such as a series of different-sized grains with four species—ants, beetles, mice, and birds—feeding on it. The ants feed on the smallest grain, the beetles and mice on the intermediate sizes, and the birds on the largest. If only adjacent species competed with each other, competition would be expected only between the ant-beetle, beetle-mouse, and mouse-bird. Thus, competition would be found in only three out of the six possible species pairs (50%) (**Figure 54.5**). Naturally, the percentage would vary according to the number of species on the axis. If there were only three species along the axis, we would expect competition in two of the three pairs (67%).

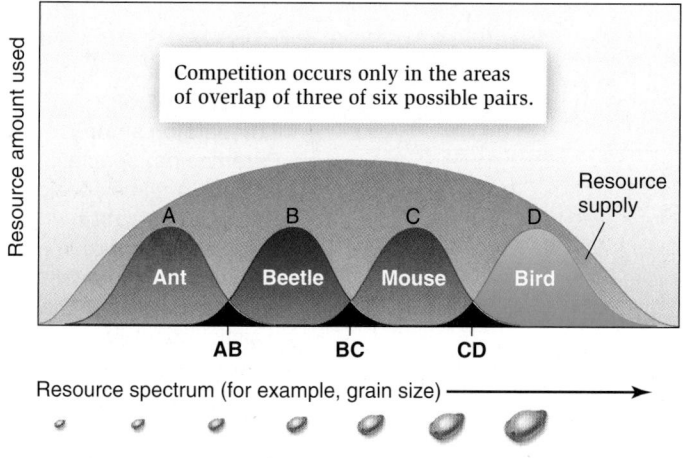

(a) Competition among four species for a resource

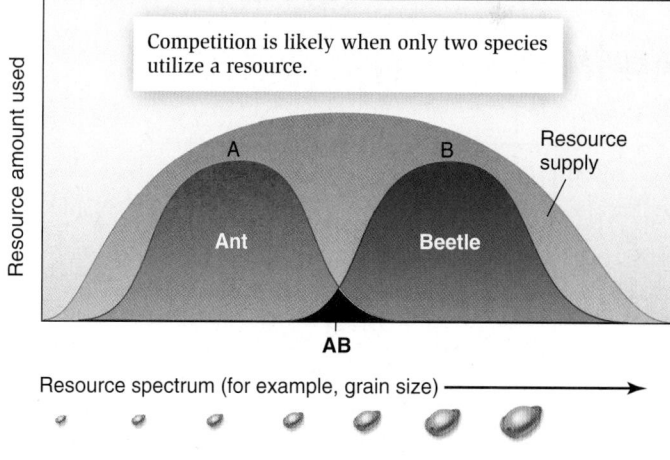

(b) Competition between two species for a resource

Figure 54.5 **The frequency of competition according to the number of species involved.** (a) Resource supply and utilization curves of four species, A, B, C, and D, along the spectrum of a hypothetical resource such as grain size. If competition occurs only between species with adjacent resource utilization curves, competition would be expected between three of the six possible pairings: A and B; B and C; and C and D. (b) When only two species utilize a resource set, competition would nearly always be expected between them.

Concept check: *If five species utilized the resource set in part (a), what would be the expected frequency of competition observed?*

Some other general patterns were evident from Connell's review. Plants showed a high degree of competition, perhaps because they are rooted in the ground and cannot easily escape or perhaps because they are competing for the same set of limiting nutrients—water, light, and minerals. Marine organisms tended to compete more than terrestrial ones, perhaps because many of the species studied lived in the intertidal zone and were attached to the rock face in a manner similar to that of plants. Because the area of the rock face is limited, competition for space is quite important. However, even though we see competition frequently in nature, we often see apparent competitors occupying the same general areas. How is this possible?

Species May Coexist If They Do Not Occupy Identical Niches

In 1934 the Russian microbiologist Georgyi Gause began to study competition among three protist species, *Paramecium*

aurelia, *Paramecium bursaria*, and *Paramecium caudatum*, all of which fed on bacteria and yeast, which in turn fed on an oatmeal medium in a culture tube in the laboratory. The bacteria occurred more in the oxygen-rich upper part of the culture tube, and the yeast in the oxygen-poor lower part of the tube. Because each species was a slightly different size, Gause calculated population growth as a combination of numbers of individuals per millilitre of solution multiplied by their unit volume to give a population volume for each species. When grown separately, population volume of all three *Paramecium* species followed a logistic growth pattern (**Figure 54.6a**). When Gause cultured *P. caudatum* and *P. aurelia* together, *P. caudatum* went extinct (**Figure 54.6b**). Both species utilized bacteria as food but *P. aurelia* grew at a rate six times faster than *P. caudatum* and was better able to convert the food into offspring.

However, when Gause cultured *P. caudatum* and *P. bursaria* together (**Figure 54.6c**), neither went extinct. The population volume of each was much less compared to when they

(a) Each *Paramecium* species grown alone

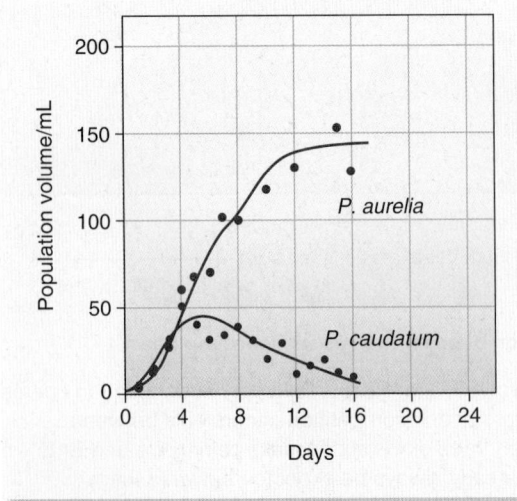

(b) Competition between *P. aurelia* and *P. caudatum*

(c) Competition between *P. caudatum* and *P. bursaria*

Figure 54.6
Competition among *Paramecium* species.
(a) Each of three species, *Paramecium aurelia*, *Paramecium bursaria*, and *Paramecium caudatum*, grows according to the logistic model when grown alone. **(b)** When *P. aurelia* is grown with *P. caudatum*, the density of *P. aurelia* is lowered compared to when grown alone, and *P. caudatum* goes extinct. **(c)** When *P. aurelia* is grown with *P. bursaria*, the population densities of both are lowered but they coexist.

were grown alone, because some competition occurred between them. Gause discovered, however, that *P. bursaria* was better able to utilize the yeast in the lower part of the culture tubes. From these experiments Gause concluded that two species with exactly the same requirements cannot live together in the same place and use the same resources, that is, occupy the same niche. His conclusion, later termed the **competitive exclusion hypothesis**, essentially means that complete competitors cannot coexist.

If complete competitors drive one another to extinction, how different do they have to be to coexist and in what features do they usually differ? To address such questions, in 1958 ecologist Robert MacArthur examined coexistence among five species of warblers feeding within spruce trees in New England. All belonged to the genus *Dendroica*, so one would expect these closely related bird species to compete strongly, possibly sufficiently strongly to cause extinctions. MacArthur found that the species occupied different heights and portions in the tree and thus each probably fed on a different range of insects (**Figure 54.7**).

The term **resource partitioning** describes the differentiation of niches, both in space and time, that enables similar species to coexist in a community, just as *Chthamalus* and *Semibalanus* live on different parts of the intertidal zone in Scotland. In a way, we can think of resource partitioning as reflecting the results of past competition. British ornithologist David Lack examined competition and coexistence among about 40 species of British passerines, or perching birds (**Figure 54.8**). As a group, these perching birds had fairly similar lifestyles. Most segregated according to some resource factor, with habitat being the most common one. For example, while all the passerines fed on insects, some would feed exclusively in grasslands,

others in forests, some low to the ground, and others high in trees, where the insects present would likely be different. Birds also segregated by size, so that bigger species would take different-sized food than smaller species, and by feeding habit, with some feeding on insects on tree leaves, others on tree trunks, and so on. Some species also fed in different winter ranges, while others occurred in different parts of the country (separation by geography). About 15% of bird species showed no segregation at all.

What about the species that do not appear to live in different habitats or have different food habits? To answer this question, researchers have looked at differences in physical form, or morphology, between coexisting species.

Morphological Differences May Allow Species to Coexist

Although the competitive exclusion principle acknowledges that complete competitors cannot coexist, some partial level of competition may exist that is not severe enough to drive one of the competitors to extinction. When two species live in **allopatry** (different geographic areas) they may be nearly identical in form and function, but when they live in **sympatry** (same geographic area), competition will cause some meaningful differences between them. The tendency for two species to diverge

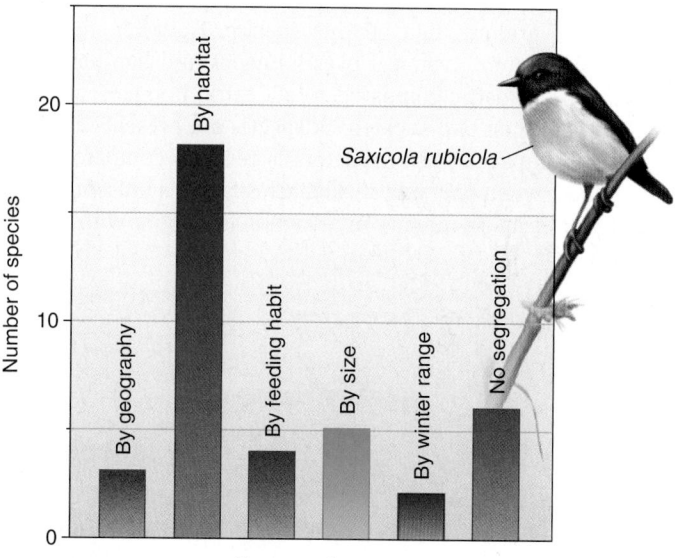

Figure 54.8 Segregation according to resource factor among 40 species of British passerine birds. Most segregation is by habitat, followed by size, feeding habit, geography, and type of winter range in which they forage. In about 15% of cases, no obvious segregation was observed. More than half of all bird species, including *Saxicola rubicola*, are passerines, also known as perching birds.

Concept check: *Do you think these results for passerine birds are typical for most other species? For example, do most other species segregate by habitat?*

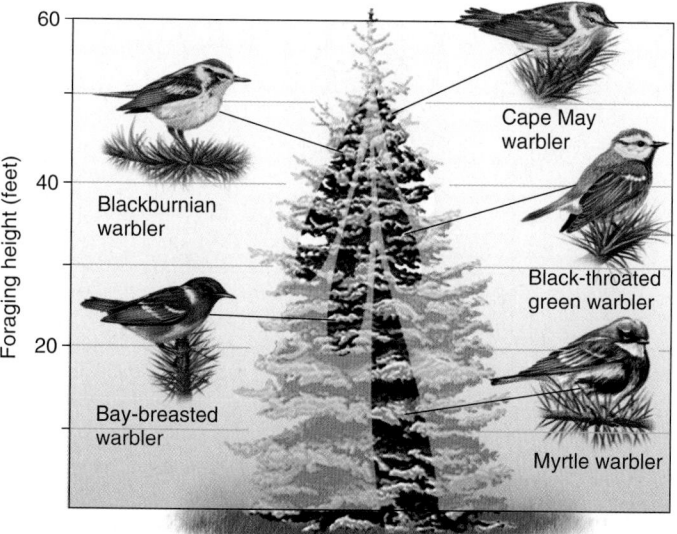

Figure 54.7 Resource partitioning among five species of warblers feeding in North American spruce trees. Each warbler species prefers to feed at a different height and portion of the tree, thus reducing competition.

structurally is called **character displacement** and it may involve divergence in their resource use because of competition or even divergence in antipredator tactics, as shown below.

Dolph Schluter and his students at the University of British Columbia have studied character displacement in species pairs of stickleback fish (*Gasterosteus aculeatus* complex) in a series of small lakes in coastal British Columbia. Sympatric species pairs exhibit ecological character displacement in traits related to resource use. The benthic species feed on benthic organisms living in the sediments and on the vegetation, whereas the limnetic species feed on planktonic species in the limnetic (open water) zone. The benthic species have few, short gill rakers and a wide gape, whereas the limnetic species have many long gill rakers and a narrow gape (**Figure 54.9a**). However, when related species live allopatrically, the morphological differences are lacking and they display intermediate phenotypes. In addition, they feed in both limnetic and benthic zones in the absence of competition.

More recently, Vamosi and Schluter have gone on to demonstrate that natural enemies such as predatory fish, *Oncorhynchus* sp., may contribute to morphological character displacement in sympatric species pairs of sticklebacks. By measuring defensive armour traits (such as lengths of the first dorsal spine, pelvic spine, and pelvic girdle) in sympatric benthic and limnetic stickleback species and comparing them with the same traits in nearby allopatric populations—all which coexisted with the predator—they found evidence of character displacement in defensive armour. In sympatry, limnetic species had consistently more armour than benthic species. However, the total amount of armour, averaged over limnetics and benthics, was reduced in sympatric compared to allopatric populations, suggesting that when two stickleback species are present in a lake the overall impact of fish predators is reduced compared with their impact when only one stickleback species is present. Notably, there was an asymmetry in reduction in armour with a large

downward shift in sympatric benthics, but only a small shift in limnetics (**Figure 54.9b**).

In summary, competition occurs frequently in nature and several different competitive mechanisms are involved. Competition over the same limited resource can lead to the extinction of one of two species occupying the same niche. However, species may coexist if their niche overlap is reduced through resource partitioning or character displacement. We also saw that the outcome of competitive interactions may vary according to both abiotic and biotic factors in the environment. Biotic factors such as parasitism, herbivory, and predation may be powerful mortality factors in their own right and could be sufficient to reduce population densities to the extent that competition does not occur. In the following sections we will examine the strength of these factors, beginning with predation.

54.2   PREDATION, HERBIVORY, AND PARASITISM

Learning Outcomes:

1. List and describe strategies animals use to avoid predation.
2. Give examples of the effects of predators on prey populations.
3. Explain why plants and herbivores are said to be in an "evolutionary arms race."
4. Describe variations on the parasitic lifestyle.

Several interactions between species have a positive effect for one species and a negative effect for the other. The traditional view of predation is one of carnivory, in which a predator, typically an animal, feeds on another animal. However, herbivory

(a)

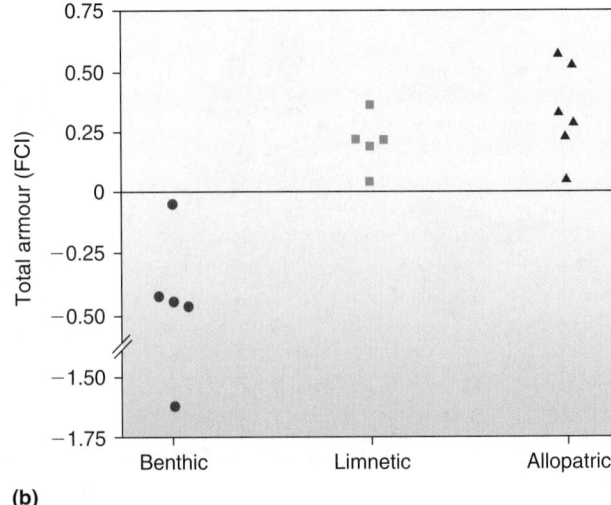

(b)

Figure 54.9 Adaptive radiation in stickleback fish. The fish shown here are the limnetic (upper) and benthic (lower) forms of sticklebacks from British Columbia. The first gill arch with its characteristic gill rakers is shown for each fish. FD refers to first dorsal spine, SD to second dorsal spine, and PS to pelvic spine.

and parasitism are also interactions in which one species benefits and the other is harmed, and while they can be viewed in the broad context of predation, each has special characteristics that set it apart.

Herbivory usually involves nonlethal predation on plants (except in the case of seed eating), while predation generally results in the death of the prey. Parasitism, like herbivory, is typically nonlethal, and differs from predation in that the adult parasite typically lives and reproduces in the living host, as in Chinese liver flukes (refer back to Figure 31.9). Parasitoids, insects that lay eggs in living hosts, have features in common with both predators and parasites. They always kill their hosts, as predators do, but one host can support the development of one or more than one parasitoid, just as in parasitism. Parasitoids are common in the insect world and include parasitic wasps and flies that feed on many other insects or spiders. Omnivores are individuals that can feed on both plants and animals. For example, bears feed on both berries and fish. These varied categories of predation can be classified according to how lethal they are for the prey and how close is the association between predator and prey (**Figure 54.10**).

In this section we begin by looking at antipredator strategies and how, despite such strategies, predation remains a factor affecting the density of prey. We survey the strategies plants use to deter herbivores and how, in turn, herbivores overcome host plant defences. Finally, we investigate parasitism, which may be the predominant lifestyle on Earth, and explore the growing role of genomics in the fight against parasites.

Figure 54.10 **Possible interactions among populations.** Lethality represents the probability that an interaction results in the death of the prey. Intimacy represents the closeness and duration of the relationship between the consumer and the prey.

Concept check: *Where might omnivores fit in this figure?*

Animals Have Evolved Many Antipredator Strategies

The variety of strategies that animals have evolved to avoid being eaten underscores the fact that predation is a strong selective force.

Chemical Defence A great many species have evolved chemical defences against predation. One of the classic examples of a chemical defence involves the bombardier beetle (*Stenaptinus insignis*). These beetles possess reservoirs of hydroquinone and hydrogen peroxide in their abdomen. When threatened, they eject the chemicals into an "explosion chamber," where the subsequent release of oxygen causes the whole mixture to be violently ejected as a hot spray (about 88°C) that can be directed at the beetle's attackers (**Figure 54.11a**). Many other arthropods, such as millipedes, have chemical sprays too, and the phenomenon is also found in vertebrates—as anyone who has had a close encounter with a skunk can testify.

Often associated with a chemical defence is an **aposematic coloration**, or warning coloration, which advertises an organism's unpalatable taste. For instance, the ladybird beetle's bright red colour warns of the toxic defensive chemicals it exudes when threatened, and many tropical frogs have bright warning coloration that calls attention to their skin's lethality (**Figure 54.11b**). In the 1960s researchers showed that after inexperienced blue jays ate a monarch butterfly and suffered a violent vomiting reaction, they learned to associate the striking orange-and-black appearance of the butterfly with a noxious reaction (refer back to Figure 52.3). While some animals, such as rattlesnakes, synthesize toxins using their own metabolic processes, other animal poisons are actually acquired from plants. For example, the monarch butterfly caterpillars accumulate toxic chemicals called cardiac glycosides from milkweed that they eat.

Cryptic Coloration **Cryptic coloration** is an aspect of camouflage, the blending of an organism with the background of its habitat. Cryptic coloration is a common method of avoiding detection by predators. For example, many grasshoppers are green and blend in with the foliage on which they feed. Stick insects mimic branches and twigs with their long, slender bodies. In most cases, these animals stay perfectly still when threatened, because movement alerts a predator. Behaviour that allows an animal to blend into its environment is referred to as **catalepsies**. Cryptic coloration is prevalent in the vertebrate world, too. Many seahorses adopt a body shape and colour pattern similar to the habitats in which they are found (**Figure 54.11c**).

Mimicry **Mimicry**, the resemblance of an organism (the mimic) to another organism (the model), also secures protection from predators. There are two major types of mimicry. In **Müllerian mimicry**, many noxious species converge to look the same, thus reinforcing the basic distasteful design. One example is the black and yellow striped bands of several different types

(a) As it is held by a tether attached to its back, this bombardier beetle (*Stenaptinus insignis*) directs its hot, stinging spray at a forceps "attacker."

(b) Aposematic coloration advertises the poisonous nature of this blue poison arrow frog (*Dendrobates azureus*) from South America.

(c) Cryptic coloration allows this Pygmy sea horse (*Hippocampus bargibanti*) from Bali to blend in with its background.

(d) In this example of Batesian mimicry, an innocuous scarlet king snake (*Lampropeltis triangulum*) (*left*) mimics the poisonous coral snake (*Micrurus nigrocinctus*) (*right*).

(e) In a display of intimidation, this porcupinefish (*Diodon hystrix*) puffs itself up to look threatening to its predators.

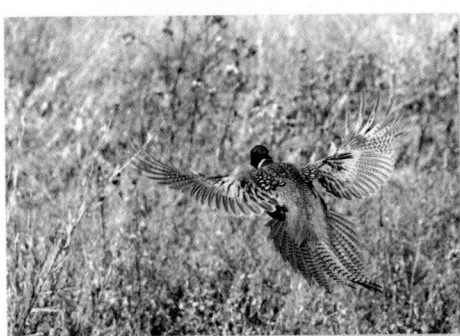

(f) Ground birds, such as galliforms, flush from the undergrowth to startle predators and avoid capture.

(g) The armour of sticklebacks may protect them from predators such as this pike.

Figure 54.11   Antipredator adaptations.

Concept check: *According to the classification of species interactions in Table 54.1, how would you classify Batesian and Müllerian mimicry?*

BioConnections: *Refer back to Figure 31.14. Which types of antipredator adaptations are possessed by mollusks?*

of bees and wasps. Müllerian mimicry is also found among noxious Amazonian butterflies. **Batesian mimicry** is the mimicry of an unpalatable species (the model) by a palatable one (the mimic). Some of the best examples involve flies, especially hoverflies of the family Syrphidae, which are striped black and yellow to resemble stinging bees and wasps but are themselves harmless. The nonvenomous scarlet king snake (*Lampropeltis triangulum*) mimics the venomous coral snake (*Micrurus nigrocinctus*), thereby gaining protection from would-be predators (**Figure 54.11d**).

Negative frequency-dependent selection refers to the phenomenon whereby phenotypes increase in fitness as they become more rare within a population; it is an example of balancing selection, favouring diversity within a population. Negative frequency-dependent selection is responsible for Batesian mimicry, where harmless species have evolved the same warning symbols (e.g., coloration) as harmful species in relation to a common predator. As long as the harmless species is much less abundant than the harmful species in the environment, the predator will continue to avoid feeding on both.

It is sometimes difficult to distinguish between Batesian and Müllerian mimics. For a long time, the viceroy butterfly was believed to be an example of Batesian mimicry because of its striking resemblance to the unpalatable monarch. However, it was subsequently shown that the viceroy was equally as unpalatable as the monarch and is actually an example of Müllerian mimicry. In theory, Batesian mimics should lose their protection when they are common, because they need plenty of distasteful models whose unpalatability maintains the validity of their warning colours. If the edible mimic became too common, predators would learn to ignore the coloration, which would also harm the model.

Displays of Intimidation Some animals put on displays of intimidation in an attempt to discourage predators. For example, a toad swallows air to make itself appear larger, frilled lizards extend their collars when frightened to create this same effect, and porcupine fish inflate themselves to large proportions when threatened (**Figure 54.11e**). All of these animals use displays to deceive potential predators about the ease with which they can be eaten.

Fighting Many animals have developed horns and antlers, which although primarily used in competition over mates can also be used in defence against predators (refer back to Figure 32.27). Invertebrate species often have powerful claws, pincers, or, in the case of scorpions, venomous stingers that can be used in defence as well as offence.

Agility Some groups of insects, such as grasshoppers, have a powerful jumping ability to escape the clutches of predators. Many frogs are prodigious jumpers, and flying fish can glide above the water to escape their pursuers. Ground birds, such as galliforms, flush from the undergrowth and make short, rapid flights to avoid terrestrial predators (**Figure 54.11f**).

Armour The shells of tortoises and turtles are a strong means of defence against most predators, as are the quills of porcupines (refer back to Figure 32.25c). Many beetles have a tough exoskeleton that protects them from attack from other arthropod predators, such as spiders. As we saw earlier, the spines and plates of stickleback fish are a form of armour that protects the fish from not only fish predators but also bird predators (**Figure 54.11g**).

Predator Satiation **Predator satiation** is the synchronous production of many progeny by all individuals in a population to satiate predators and thereby allow some progeny to survive. Predator satiation is commonly called masting when discussed in relation to seed herbivory in trees, which tend to have years of unusually high seed production that reduces predation. However, a similar phenomenon is exhibited by the emergence of 13-year and 17-year periodical cicadas (*Magicicada* spp.). These insects are termed *periodical* because the emergence of adults is highly synchronized to occur once every 13 or 17 years. Adult cicadas live for only a few weeks, during which time females mate and deposit eggs on the twigs of trees. The eggs hatch 6 to 10 weeks later, and the nymphs drop to the ground and begin a long subterranean development, feeding on the contents of the xylem of roots. Because the xylem is low in nutrients, it takes many years for nymphs to develop, though there appears to be no physiological reason that some cicadas couldn't emerge

after, say, 12 years of feeding, and others after 14. Their synchrony of emergence is thought to maximize predator satiation. Worth noting in this context is the fact that both 13 and 17 are prime numbers, and thus predators on a shorter multiannual cycle cannot repeatedly utilize this resource. For example, a predator that bred every three years could not rely on cicadas always being present as a food supply.

How common is each of these defence types? No one has done an extensive survey over the entire animal kingdom. However, half of the common antipredator mechanisms in insects (and related arthropods) are chemical defences and associated aposematic coloration. All other types of defence mechanisms occurred with considerably less frequency.

Despite the Impressive Array of Defences, Predators Can Still Affect Prey Densities

The importance of predation on prey populations may be dependent on whether the system is donor controlled or predator controlled. In a donor-controlled system, prey supply is determined by factors other than predation, such as food supply, so that removal of predators has no effect on prey density. Examples include predators that feed on intertidal communities in which space is the limiting factor that controls prey populations.

In a predator-controlled system, the action of predator feeding eventually reduces the supply of prey. The removal of predators in a donor-controlled system is thus likely to have little effect, whereas in a predator-controlled system such an action would probably result in large increases in prey abundance. Research studies have shown that many predators can have a significant effect on many prey populations. Considerable data exist on the interaction of the Canada lynx (*Lynx canadensis*) and its prey, snowshoe hares (*Lepus americanus*), because of the value of the pelts of both animals. In 1942 British ecologist Charles Elton analyzed the records of furs traded by trappers to the Hudson's Bay Company in Canada over a 100-year period. Analysis of the records showed that a dramatic 9- to 11-year cycle existed for as long as records had been kept (**Figure 54.12a**). This cycle appears to be an example of a stable predator–prey oscillation that is predator controlled: the hares go up in density, followed by an increase in density of the lynx, which then depresses hare numbers. This is followed by a decline in the number of lynx, and the cycle begins again.

From 1977 to 2001, the lynx–hare cycle was monitored by Charles Krebs and his students from the University of British Columbia on Jacquot Island in Kluane Lake, southwestern Yukon, and on neighbouring mainland control sites. Both the island and mainland sites showed 10-year population fluctuations or oscillations, but the island populations fluctuated with much lower amplitudes than did mainland populations (**Figure 54.12b**). Although the overall cyclic trends were broadly similar on the island and the mainland over the 25 years of study, there was a five-fold difference in hare densities during the low-cycle phase. On the island, in eight years of low numbers, hare densities averaged 0.57 hares per hectare as compared to 0.11 hares per hectare on the mainland during the same years. Hare reproductive

(a)

(b)

Figure 54.12   **Effect of predator on prey populations.**
(a) The 9- to 11-year oscillation in the abundance of the
snowshoe hare (*Lepus americanus*) and the Canada lynx (*Lynx
canadensis*) was revealed from pelt trading records of the
Hudson's Bay Company. **(b)** Prey (snowshoe hare) abundance
shows lower fluctuation amplitude on island versus mainland
populations.

rates were not different between mainland and island populations, but differences in hare survival did exist. Lack of food on
the island was ruled out as a cause of differential survival. However, differences in predation pressure between mainland and
island populations were sufficient to explain why the cyclic lows
were not as low on the island as compared to the mainland. On
the mainland, lynx, coyote, great-horned owls, goshawks, red
squirrels, and Arctic ground squirrels were common predators.
In contrast, there was only a single year when a lynx was active
on the island, great-horned owls and red squirrels were rare,
and Arctic ground squirrels were never seen. Thus, improved
survival on the island was correlated with a reduction in the
numbers and types of predators found on the island compared
to the mainland.

Invasive species have provided striking examples of the
effects of predators. The brown tree snake (*Boiga irregularis*)
was inadvertently introduced by humans to the island of Guam,
in Micronesia, shortly after World War II. The growth and
spread of its population over the next 40 years closely coincided
with a precipitous decline in the island's forest birds. The snake
is a new predator with no natural predators on Guam to control
it, and since the birds did not evolve with the snake, they have
no defences against it. Eight of the island's 11 native species of
forest birds went extinct by the 1980s (**Figure 54.13**).

One of the biggest reductions in prey in response to predation has been the systematic decline of whales of various species in response to the human whaling industry. The history of
whaling has been characterized by a progression from larger,
more valuable or easily caught species to smaller, less valuable or easily caught ones, as numbers of the original targets
have been depleted (**Figure 54.14**). Belatedly, the International
Whaling Commission enacted a moratorium on all commercial
whaling in 1986. Following the moratorium, the populations of

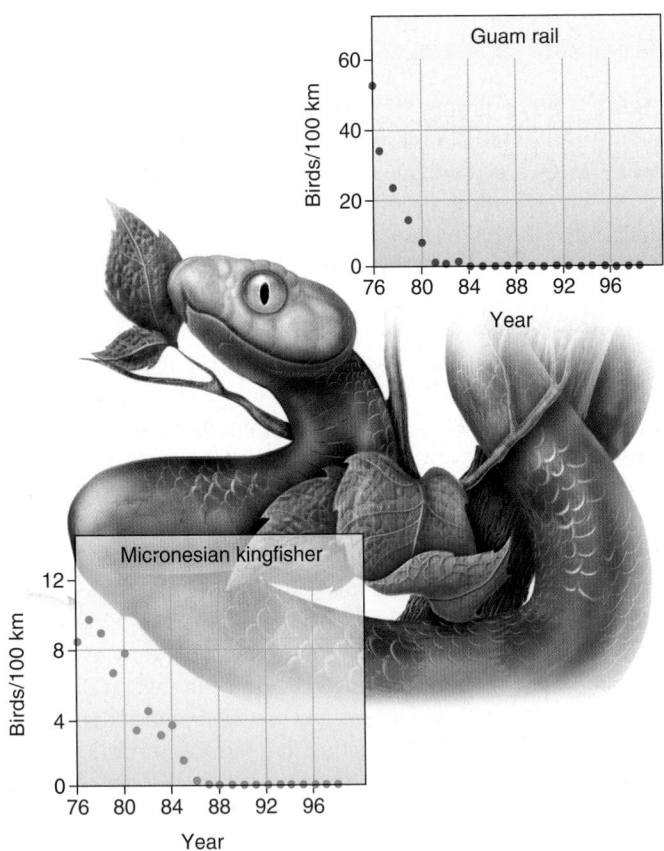

Figure 54.13   **Invasive species provide an example of
predator pressure.**   Population trends for two native Guam
birds, as indicated by 100-kilometre roadside surveys conducted
from 1976 to 1998, show a precipitous decline because of
predation by the introduced brown tree snake.

Concept check: *Why can invasive predators have such
strong effects on native prey?*

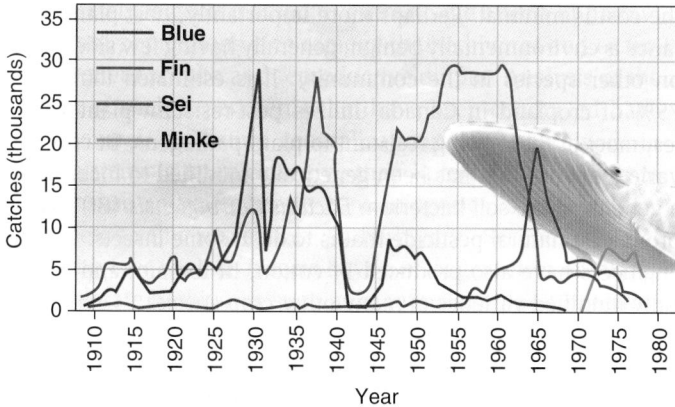

Figure 54.14 Sequential decline of whale catches in the Antarctic shows the strong effect of human predators. Whale catches are believed to be directly related to whale population sizes. The catches of blue whale, the first species to be strongly affected by human predation, started a precipitous decline in the 1940s, as the whale was hunted to very low levels. Humans then began hunting more abundant fin whales, and in turn sei and minke whales, as each species became depleted.

some whales have increased. Blue whales are thought to have quadrupled their numbers off the California coast during the 1980s, and numbers of the California gray whales have recovered to prewhaling levels, showing the impact that an absence of a predator can have.

Ecologists have found that in nearly 1,500 predator–prey studies, more than two-thirds (72%) showed a large depression of prey density by predators. Thus, we can conclude that in the majority of cases, predators influence the abundance of their prey in their native environment. The variety of antipredator mechanisms discussed earlier also shows how predation is important enough to select for the evolution of chemical defences, camouflage, and mimicry in prey. Taken together these data indicate that predation is a powerful force in nature.

Plants and Herbivores May Be Engaged in an Evolutionary Arms Race

Herbivory involves the predation of plants or similar species such as algae. Such herbivory can be lethal to the plants, especially for small species, but often it is nonlethal, since many plant species, particularly larger ones, can regrow. We can distinguish two types of herbivores: generalist herbivores and specialist herbivores. Generalist herbivores can feed on many different plant species and are usually mammals. Specialist herbivores are often restricted to one or two species of host plants and are usually insects. There are, however, exceptions. Pandas are specialists because they feed on only bamboo, and koalas specialize on eucalyptus trees. On the other hand, grasshoppers are generalists, because they feed on a wide variety of plant species, including crops.

Plants appear to present a luscious green world of food to any organism versatile enough to use it, so why don't we see more plants being eaten by herbivores? After all, unlike most animals, plants cannot move to escape being eaten. Two hypotheses have

been proposed to answer the question of why more plant material is not eaten. First, predators and parasites might keep herbivore numbers low, thereby sparing the plants. The many examples of the strength of predation provide evidence for this view. Second, the plant world is not as helpless as it appears; the sea of green is in fact armed with defensive spines, tough cuticles, and noxious chemicals. Let's take a closer look at plant defences against herbivores and the ways that herbivores attempt to overcome them.

Plant Defences Against Herbivores As described in Chapter 7, an array of unusual and powerful chemicals is present in plants, including alkaloids (nicotine in tobacco, morphine in poppies, cocaine in coca, and caffeine in tea), phenolics (lignin in wood and tannin in leaves), and terpenoids (in peppermint) (**Figure 54.15a–c**). Two general chemical classes can

(a) Alkaloids in tobacco   **(b) Phenolics in tea**

(c) Terpenoids in peppermint   **(d) Thorns on rose stems**

Figure 54.15 Defences against herbivory. Plants possess an array of unusual and powerful chemicals, including **(a)** alkaloids, such as nicotine in tobacco, **(b)** phenolics, such as tannins in tea leaves (near Mount Fuji, Japan), and **(c)** terpenoids in peppermint leaves. **(d)** Mechanical defences include plant spines and thorns, as on this shrub, *Rosa multiflora*.

Concept check: *Which type of defence would be most effective in deterring invertebrate herbivores?*

BioConnections: *Capsaicin is an alkaloid produced by which species of plant? Refer back to Figure 29.22.*

Figure 54.17 *Rafflesia arnoldii*, the world's biggest flower, lives as a parasite in Indonesian rain forests.

BioConnections: *More than 4,500 species of plants live as complete or partial parasites. What is an example of another important parasitic plant? Refer back to Figure 35.21.*

Last, we can distinguish **ectoparasites**, such as ticks and fleas, which live on the outside of the host's body, from **endoparasites**, such as pathogenic bacteria and tapeworms, which live inside the host's body. Problems of definition arise with regard to plant parasites, which seem to straddle both camps. For example, some parasitic plants, such as dodder (*Cuscuta* spp.), an orange, stringlike plant, exist partly outside the host's body and partly inside (refer back to Figure 35.21a). Outgrowths called haustoria penetrate inside the host plant to tap into nutrient supplies. Being endoparasitic on a host seems to require greater specialization compared to ectoparasitism. Thus, ectoparasitic animals such as leeches feed on a wider variety of hosts than do internal parasites such as liver flukes.

As we have seen throughout this textbook, there are vast numbers of species of parasites, including viruses, bacteria, protozoa, flatworms (flukes and tapeworms), nematodes, and various arthropods (ticks, mites, and fleas). Therefore, parasitism is a common way of life. Parasites may outnumber free-living species by four to one. Most plant and animal species harbour many parasites. For example, leopard frogs have nematodes in their ears and veins, and flukes in their bladders, kidneys, and intestines. A free-living organism that does not harbour parasitic individuals of a number of species is a rarity.

As with studies of other species interactions, a good method to determine the effect of parasites on their host populations is to remove the parasites and to re-examine the system. However, this is difficult to do, primarily because of the small size and unusual life histories of many parasites, which makes them difficult to remove from a host completely. The few cases of experimental removal confirm that parasites can reduce host population densities. The nests of birds such as blue tits are often infested with parasitic blowfly larvae that feed on the blood of nestlings. In 1997 Sylvie Hurtrez-Boussès and colleagues experimentally reduced blowfly larval parasites of young blue tits in nests in Corsica. Parasite removal was cleverly achieved by taking the nests

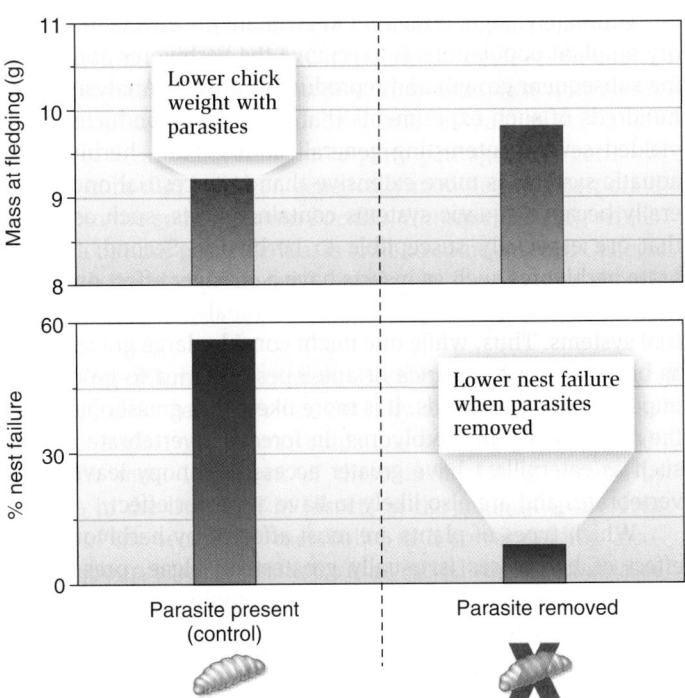

Figure 54.18 Parasite removal experiments. The left side shows the results when blowfly larvae were present in the nests of young blue tits, while the right side shows the results when these parasites were removed.

from 145 nest boxes, removing the young, microwaving the nests to kill the parasites, and then returning the nests and chicks to the wild. The success of chicks in microwaved nests was compared to that in nonmicrowaved (control) nests, and it was found that parasite-free blue tit chicks had greater body mass at fledging, the time when feathers first grow (**Figure 54.18**). Perhaps more important was that complete nest failure, that is, death of all chicks, was much higher in control nests than in treated nests.

Because parasite removal studies are difficult to do, ecologists have also examined the strength of parasitism as a mortality factor by studying introduced parasite species. Evidence from natural populations suggests that introduced parasites have substantial effects on their hosts. Chestnut blight, a fungus from Asia that was accidentally introduced to New York around 1904, virtually eliminated chestnut trees (*Castanea dentata*) in North America. Although the fungus took many years to spread throughout North America, by the 1950s it had significantly reduced the density of American chestnut trees in North Carolina (**Figure 54.19**). In Europe and North America, Dutch elm disease has similarly devastated populations of elms. The disease wiped out 25 million of Britain's original 30 million elm trees between the 1960s and the 1990s. In Italy, canker has had similar severe effects on cypress. Fortunately, as we will discuss shortly, the field of genomics is helping greatly in the fight against plant diseases.

Introduced parasites have a strong effect on native animals as well as plants. Conservationists are particularly concerned that many endangered animals are threatened by disease from domestic animals. In 1994 one-third of the population of lions in Serengeti National Park was wiped out by canine distemper virus,

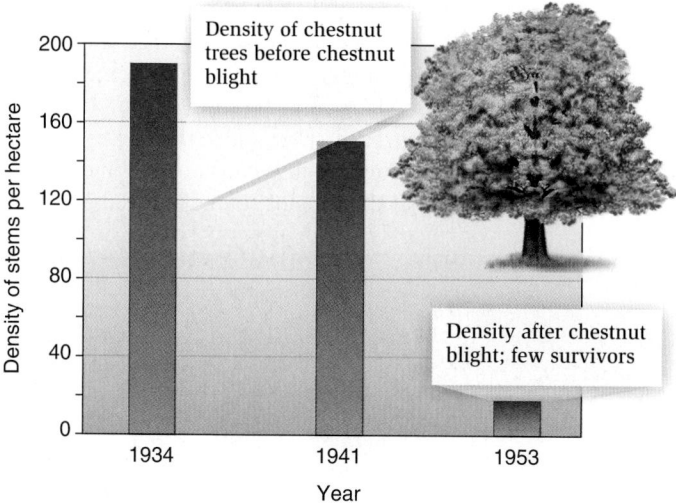

Figure 54.19 Effects of introduced parasites on American chestnut trees. The reduction in density of American chestnut trees in North Carolina following the 1904 introduction of chestnut blight disease from Asia shows the severe effect that parasites can have on their hosts. By the 1950s, this once-prevalent species was virtually eliminated.

presumably contracted from domestic dogs. Some believe that the early-twentieth-century extinction of the thylacine (*Thylacinus cynocephalus*), a Tasmanian marsupial that resembled a wolf, was caused by a distemper-like disease spread by dogs. To prevent the threat of disease among endangered species, some populations have been vaccinated; for example, the Ethiopian wolf (*Canis simensis*) has been vaccinated against rabies, and mountain gorillas (*Gorilla gorilla*) have been vaccinated against measles.

54.3 MUTUALISM AND COMMENSALISM

Learning Outcomes:

1. Distinguish between the different types of mutualisms in nature.
2. Give examples of the species interaction called commensalism.

Mutualism and commensalism are interactions that are beneficial to at least one of the species involved. The unique feature of mutualism is that both species benefit from the interaction.

GENOMES AND PROTEOMES

Transgenic Plants May Be Used in the Fight Against Plant Diseases

Many important native forest trees, which are also grown in urban landscapes, have been almost entirely wiped out by diseases spread by the importation of exotic plants. Sudden oak death is a recently recognized disease that is killing tens of thousands of oak trees and other plant species in California. The symptoms vary between species but include leaf spots, oozing of a dark sap through the bark, and twig dieback. Although sudden oak death is a forest disease, the organism causing this disease is known to infect many woody ornamental plants, such as rhododendrons, that are commonly sold by nurseries. In March 2004 a California nursery was found to have unknowingly shipped plants infected with sudden oak death to all 50 states. Following this discovery, California nurseries halted shipments of trees to other states in an attempt to stop the spread of the disease, originally thought to have been imported on rhododendrons. In 2004 scientists mapped out the genome sequence of the disease-carrying fungus, *Phytophthora ramorum*. They are hoping that identifying the genes and their proteins will help them develop specific diagnostic tests to quickly detect the presence of sudden oak death in trees, which is currently impossible to detect until a year or more after the tree is infected.

However, scientists hope for much more from the field of genomics in their fight against plant diseases. Many scientists

have suggested limited, cautious transfer of resistance genes from the original host species in the source regions of the disease to threatened species. Original host species have usually evolved over millions of years of exposure to these diseases and have acquired genes that provide resistance. In the regions of recent introduction of parasites, there has been no selection for resistance, so the host plants are often killed en masse. Transgenic trees that have received resistance genes could be produced and then be replanted in forests or urban areas. An advantage of this technique over traditional cross-breeding strategies involving two different species is that transgenic methods involve the introduction of fewer unnecessary genes of the nonnative species. Also, fewer tree generations would be required to develop resistance. For example, using traditional breeding technology, Asian chestnut trees (*Castanea mollissima*) are being bred with American chestnuts (*C. dentata*) to reduce the susceptibility of the latter to chestnut blight, but the resultant hybrid is often significantly altered in appearance from the traditional American chestnut and the process takes more than a decade to produce trees that are ready to plant. Transgenic technology could minimize these drawbacks. William Powell and colleagues are working to enhance the American chestnut's resistance by inserting a gene taken from wheat. The gene, oxalate oxidase, destroys a toxin produced by the fungus that causes chestnut blight.

For example, in mutualistic pollination systems both plant and pollinator benefit, the former by the transfer of pollen and the latter typically by a nectar meal. In commensalism, one species benefits and the other remains unaffected. For example, in some forms of seed dispersal, barbed seeds are transported to new germination sites in the fur of mammals. The seeds benefit, but the mammals are generally unaffected. In this section we will examine the major types of mutualism and commensalism.

It is interesting to note that humans have entered into mutualistic relationships with many species. For example, the mutualistic association of humans with plants has resulted in some of the most far-reaching ecological changes on Earth. Humans have planted huge areas of the Earth with crops, allowing these plant populations to reach densities they never would on their own. In return, the crops have led to expanded human populations because of the increased amounts of food they provide.

Mutualism Is an Association Between Two Species That Benefits Both Species

Many close associations are known between species in which both species benefit. One example is found in the leaf-cutting ants of the tribe Attini, which enter into a mutualistic relationship with a fungus. A typical colony of about 9 million ants has the collective biomass of a cow and harvests the equivalent of a cow's daily requirement of fresh vegetation. Instead of consuming it directly, the ants chew it into a pulp, which they store underground as a substrate on which the fungus grows. The ants shelter and tend the fungus, protecting it from competing fungi and helping it reproduce and grow. In turn, the ants feed on specialized structures produced by the fungus. In this way, the ants circumvent the chemical defences of the leaves, which are digested by the fungus. The ant–fungus mutualism permits both species to use a common resource.

Other different types of mutualisms occur in nature. Classic mutualisms include microbes in the guts of herbivores (see Chapter 39), lichens (see Chapter 27), mycorrhizal associations (see Chapter 27), and nitrogen fixing bacteria associated with the roots of legumes (see Chapter 35). **Defensive mutualisms** often involve an animal defending a plant or a herbivore. **Dispersive mutualisms** include plants and pollinators that disperse their pollen, and plants and fruit eaters that disperse the plant's seeds.

Defensive Mutualism   One of the most commonly observed mutualisms occurs between ants and aphids. Aphids are fairly defenceless creatures and are easy prey for most predators. The aphids feed on plant sap and have to process a significant amount of it to get their required nutrients. In doing so, they excrete a lot of fluid, and some of the sugars still remain in the excreted fluid, which is called honeydew. The ants drink the honeydew and, in return, protect the aphids from an array of predators, such as ladybird beetle larvae, by driving the predators away. In some cases, the ants herd the aphids like cattle, moving them from plant to plant (**Figure 54.20a**).

In other cases, ants enter into a mutualistic relationship with a plant itself. One of the most famous cases involves acacia trees in Central America, whose large thorns provide food and nesting sites for *Pseudomyrmex ferruginea* ants (**Figure 54.20b**). In return, the ants bite and discourage both insect and vertebrate herbivores from feeding on the trees. The ants also consume modified leaflet tips called Beltian bodies as their major source of dietary protein.

(a)

(b)

Figure 54.20   Defensive mutualism involves species that receive food or shelter in return for providing protection. **(a)** This red carpenter ant, *Camponotus pennsylvanicus*, tends aphids feeding on a twig. The ants receive sugar-rich honeydew produced by the aphids and in return they protect the aphids from predators. **(b)** Ants, usually *Pseudomyrmex ferruginea*, make nests inside the large, hornlike thorns of the bull's horn acacia and defend the plant against insects and mammals. In return, the acacia (*Acacia collinsii*) provide two forms of food to the ants: protein-rich granules called Beltian bodies and nectar from extrafloral nectaries (nectar-producing glands that are physically apart from the flower).

Concept check: *Is the relationship between red carpenter ants and aphids an example of facultative or obligatory mutualism?*

BioConnections: *Refer back to Figure 27.17. What is the name given to the association between the hyphae of certain fungi and the roots of most plants that exist together in a trophic mutualism?*

Laboratory studies have shown that while alternative food can be provided to the ants for a short while, they do require the specific proteins found in Beltian bodies for survival. In addition, the ants trim away foliage from competing plants and kill neighbouring plant shoots, ensuring more light, water, and nutrient supplies for the acacias. When ants were experimentally removed from acacia trees, the acacias were quickly, severely defoliated by native phytophagous insects, resulting in rapid death of the trees. In this mutualistic relationship, neither species can live without the other, a concept called **obligatory mutualism**.

This contrasts with **facultative mutualism**, in which the interaction is beneficial but not essential to the survival and reproduction of either species. For example, the ant–aphid mutualisms are generally facultative. Both species benefit from the association, but each could live without the other.

Dispersive Mutualism   Many examples of plant–animal mutualism involve pollination and seed dispersal. From the plant's perspective, an ideal pollinator would be a specialist, moving quickly among individuals but retaining a high fidelity to a plant species. One way that plant species in an area encourage the pollinator's species fidelity is by sequential flowering of different species through the year and by synchronized flowering within a species. The plant should provide just enough nectar to attract a pollinator's visit. From the pollinator's perspective, it would be best to be a generalist and obtain nectar and pollen from as many flowers as possible in a small area, thus minimizing the energy spent on flight between patches. This suggests that although mutualisms are beneficial to both species, their optimal needs are quite different.

Mutualistic interactions are also highly prevalent in the seed-dispersal systems of plants. Fruits often provide a diet rich in carbohydrates and vitamins. In return for this juicy meal, animals unwittingly disperse the enclosed seeds, which pass through the digestive tract unharmed. Fruits taken by birds and primates often have attractive colours (**Figure 54.21**); generally, those dispersed by nocturnal bats and other mammals are not brightly coloured but instead give off a pungent odour that attracts the bats.

In Commensalism, One Partner Receives a Benefit While the Other Is Unaffected

In commensalism, one member derives a benefit while the other neither benefits nor is harmed. Such is the case when orchids or other epiphytes grow in forks of tropical trees. The tree is unaffected, but the orchid gains support and increased exposure to sunlight and rain. Cattle egrets feed in pastures and fields among cattle, whose movements stir up insect prey for the birds. The egrets benefit from the association, but the cattle generally do not. One of the best examples of commensalism involves **phoresy**, in which one organism uses a second organism for transportation. Flower-inhabiting mites travel between flowers in the nostrils (nares) of hummingbirds. The flowers the mites inhabit live only a short while before dying, so the mite relocates to distant flowers by scuttling into the nares of visiting hummingbirds and hitching a ride to the next flower. Presumably the hummingbirds are unaffected.

Figure 54.21   Dispersive mutualism.   The American robin (*Turdus migratorius*), found across Canada, is an effective seed disperser. In the fall and winter it feeds on chokecherries, hawthorn, dogwood, and sumac fruits, as well as on juniper berries.

BioConnections: *Refer back to Table 29.2. Birds have excellent colour vision and are also involved in the pollination of flowers. What is a common colour of bird-pollinated plants?*

Some commensalisms involve one species "cheating" on the other without harming it. In sphagnum bogs from Ontario eastward to Newfoundland, the grass-pink orchid (*Calopogon pulchellus*) produces no nectar, but it mimics the nectar-producing rose pogonia (*Pogonia ophioglossoides*) and is therefore still visited by bees. Bee orchids mimic the appearance and scent of female bees; males pick up and transfer pollen while trying to copulate with the flowers (**Figure 54.22a**). The stimuli of flowers of the orchid genus *Ophrys* are so effective that male bees prefer to mate with them even in the presence of actual female bees! Many plants have essentially cheated their potential mutualistic seed-dispersal

(a)   (b)

Figure 54.22   Commensalisms that involve cheating. **(a)** Bee orchids (*Ophrys apifera*) mimic the shape of a female bee. Male bees copulate with the flowers, transferring pollen but getting no nectar reward. **(b)** Hooked seeds of burdock (*Arctium minus*) have lodged in the fur of a white-footed mouse (*Peromyscus leucopus*). The plant benefits from the relationship by the dispersal of its seeds, and the animal is not affected.

agents out of a meal by developing seeds with barbs or hooks to lodge in the animals' fur or feathers rather than their stomachs (**Figure 54.22b**). In these cases, the plants receive free seed dispersal, and the animals receive nothing, except perhaps minor annoyance. This type of relationship is fairly common; most hikers and dogs have at some time gathered spiny or sticky seeds as they wandered through woods or fields.

54.4 BOTTOM-UP AND TOP-DOWN CONTROL

Learning Outcomes:

1. Describe bottom-up control and top-down control as conceptual models of how species interactions limit population size.

In this chapter, we have seen that competition, predation, herbivory, parasitism, mutualism, and commensalism are important in nature. How can we determine which of these factors, along with abiotic factors such as temperature and moisture, is the most important in regulating population size? The question is one asked by many applied biologists, such as foresters, marine biologists, and conservation biologists, who are interested in reducing population mortality in order to maximize a population's size. Many different theoretical models have been proposed to describe which mortality factors are the most significant in limiting population size. Some models stress the importance of so-called bottom-up factors such as plant or prey quality and abundance in controlling the herbivores or predators that feed on them. Others stress the importance of top-down factors, such as predators and parasites, acting on their animal or plant prey (**Figure 54.23**). Still others incorporate components of both these models. In this section, we will briefly discuss some of the evidence for the existence of bottom-up versus top-down control.

Bottom-Up Control Suggests That Food Limitation Influences Population Densities

At least two lines of evidence exist to suggest that bottom-up effects are important in limiting population sizes. First, we know there is a progressive lessening of available energy passing from plants through herbivores to carnivores and to the carnivores that eat carnivores (termed *secondary carnivores*). This line of evidence, based on the thermodynamic properties of energy transfer, suggests that plants usually regulate the population size of all species that rely on them.

Second, much evidence supports the **nitrogen-limitation hypothesis** that organisms select food in terms of the nitrogen content of the tissue. This is largely due to the different proportions of nitrogen in plants and animals. Animal tissue generally contains about 10 times as much nitrogen as plant tissue; thus, animals favour high-nitrogen plants. For example, red deer feed

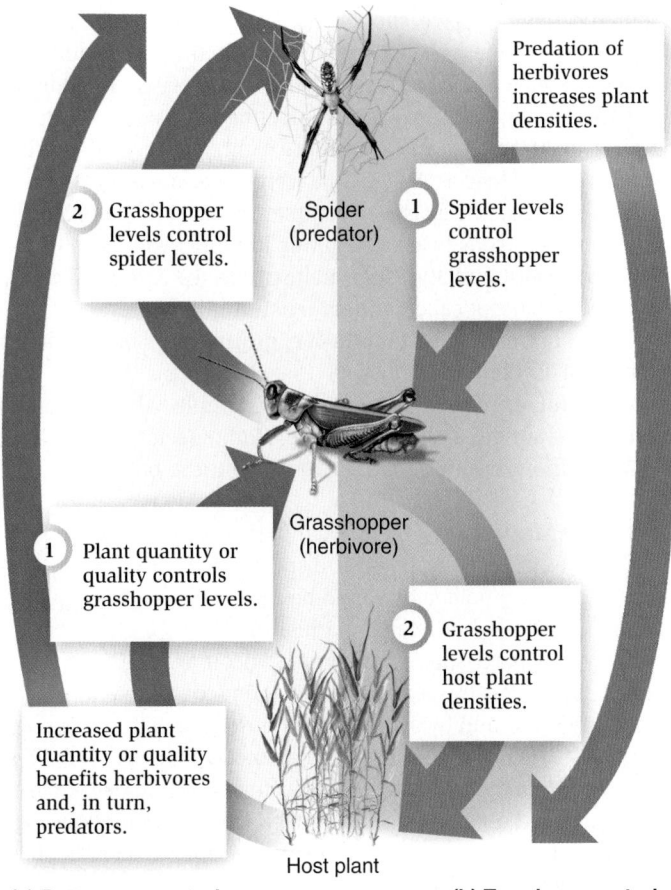

(a) Bottom-up control   **(b) Top-down control**

Figure 54.23 Bottom-up control versus top-down control. **(a)** Bottom-up control proposes that host plant quantity or quality limits the density of herbivores, which in turn sets limits on the abundance of predators. Taken together, this means that high quantity and quality of host plants would result in increased numbers of predators because of higher densities of the herbivores they prey on. **(b)** Top-down control proposes that plant densities are limited by their herbivores and that herbivores are limited by their predators. Taken together, this means that high levels of predation would result in high densities of host plants because there would be fewer herbivores.

preferentially on grasses defecated upon by herring gulls (*Larus argentatus*). Where the number of gull droppings increases, so does the vegetation nitrogen content. Fertilization has repeatedly been shown to benefit herbivores. Nearly 60% of 186 studies investigating the effects of fertilization on herbivores reported that increasing a plant's tissue nitrogen concentration through fertilization had strong positive effects on herbivore population sizes, survivorship, growth, and fecundity.

Top-Down Control Suggests That Natural Enemies Influence Population Densities

Top-down models suggest that predators control populations of their prey and that herbivores control plant populations. Supporting evidence comes from the world of biological control,

(a)   **(b)**

Figure 54.24 Successful biological control of leafy spurge. Leafy spurge (*Euphorbia esula*) in Saskatchewan before **(a)** and after **(b)** top-down control by the black dot spurge beetle (*Aphthona nigriscutis*).

where natural enemies are released to control pests of agriculture. Many weeds are invaders that were accidentally introduced to an area from a different country, as seeds in ships' ballasts or in agricultural shipments. For example, over 50% of the 190 major weeds in the United States are invaders from outside the country. Many of these weeds have become separated from their native natural enemies; this is one reason the weeds become so prolific. Because chemical control is expensive and may have unwanted environmental side effects, many land managers have adopted biological control, in which the invading weed is reunited with its native natural enemy.

Ecologists have noted many successes in the biological control of weeds. Klamath weed or St. John's wort (*Hypericum perforatum*), a pest in California pastures, was controlled by two beetles from its homeland in Europe. The Brazilian weevil, *Cyrtobagous salviniae*, is a proven biological control agent for the floating fern (*Salvinia molesta*), which has invaded lakes in Australia and New Guinea. Alligator weed has been controlled in Florida's rivers by the alligatorweed flea beetle (*Agasicles hygrophila*) from South America. Leafy spurge (*Euphorbia esula*), a deep-rooted, noxious perennial weed, was accidentally introduced to North America in the early 1800s. It outcompetes forage plants on the

prairies and can cause mouth and throat blisters in cattle that feed on it. Black dot spurge beetle (*Aphthona nigriscutis*) has been successfully used as a biocontrol agent in Saskatchewan, resulting in a 99% reduction in spurge stand density (**Figure 54.24**). The numerous examples showing that these pest populations are controlled when reunited with their natural enemies provide strong evidence of top-down control in nature.

Modern Models Suggest Both Top-Down and Bottom-Up Effects Are Important

More recently, different models have been proposed that take into account the effects of both natural enemies and limited resources on species. In 1981 Lauri Oksanen and colleagues suggested that the strength of mortality factors varies with availability of plant biomass involved, a model they termed *the ecosystem exploitation hypothesis* (**Table 54.3**). Thus, for very simple systems where mainly plants exist, such as Arctic tundra, not enough plant material is available to support herbivores and plants must be resource limited (i.e., limited by competition with each other). As plant biomass increases, some herbivores can be supported but there are too few herbivores

Table 54.3	Primary Mortality Factors According to Availability of Plant Biomass			
	Low ——————→ Plant biomass ————————————→ High			
Taxa	**Plants only**	**Plants and herbivores**	**Plants, herbivores, and carnivores**	**Plants, herbivores, carnivores, and secondary carnivores**
Plants	Competition	Herbivory	Competition	Herbivory
Herbivores		Competition	Predation	Competition
Carnivores			Competition	Predation
Secondary carnivores				Competition

to support carnivores. In the absence of carnivores, levels of herbivory can be quite high. Plant abundance becomes limited primarily by herbivory, not competition. The abundance of herbivores, in the absence of carnivores, is limited by competition for plant resources. As plant biomass increases still further and herbivores become common, carnivores become abundant and reduce the number of herbivores, which in turn increases plant abundance. Plants, being abundant, endure severe competition for resources, but herbivores, suffering high rates of mortality from natural enemies, are not abundant enough to compete.

The predators, being limited only by the availability of their prey, are also common and thus experience competition. Ecologists are currently examining the degree to which such a model holds true in nature.

Species interactions can clearly be very important in influencing both population growth and community structure. What factors determine the numbers of species in a given area? What factors influence the stability of a community, and what are the effects of disturbances on community structure? In the next chapter, on community ecology, we will explore these and other questions.

Summary of Key Concepts

- Species interactions can take a variety of forms that differ based on their effect on the species involved. (Table 54.1, Figure 54.1)

54.1 Competition

- Competition can be categorized as intraspecific (between individuals of the same species) or interspecific (between individuals of different species). Competition can also be categorized as resource competition or interference competition. (Figure 54.2)

- One species can exclude the other in a natural environment, affecting its distribution within a habitat. (Figure 54.3)

- Laboratory and field experiments show that competition occurs frequently in nature, and varies as a function of both abiotic and biotic factors. (Figures 54.4, 54.5)

- The competitive exclusion hypothesis states that two species with the same resource requirements cannot occupy the same niche. (Figure 54.6)

- Resource partitioning and morphological differences between species allow them to coexist in a community. (Figures 54.7, 54.8, 54.9)

54.2 Predation, Herbivory, and Parasitism

- Many antipredator strategies have evolved in animals. Of these strategies, chemical defence and aposematic coloration are the most common. (Figures 54.10, 54.11)

- Despite these defences, oscillations in predator–prey cycles, the effect of introduced species, and examples of human predation illustrate that predators can have a large effect on prey densities. (Figures 54.12, 54.13, 54.14)

- Plants have also evolved an array of defences against predators, termed *host plant resistance*, which includes chemical defences such as secondary metabolites and mechanical defences such as thorns and spines. (Figure 54.15, Table 54.2)

- Parasitism is a common lifestyle on Earth, and some parasites have complex life cycles involving multiple hosts. (Figures 54.16, 54.17)

- Evidence from experimental removal of parasites and from the study of introduced plant and animal parasites confirms that parasites can greatly reduce prey densities. (Figures 54.18, 54.19)

54.3 Mutualism and Commensalism

- Mutualism is an association between two species that benefits both. Defensive mutualisms typically involve an animal defending either a plant or herbivore; dispersive mutualisms involve plants and pollinators that disperse their pollen, and plants and fruit eaters that disperse the plant's seeds. (Figures 54.20, 54.21)

- In commensal relationships, one partner receives a benefit while the other is not affected. (Figure 54.22)

54.4 Bottom-up and Top-down Control

- Models of species interactions describe the importance of factors such as competition and predation. Bottom-up models propose that plant quality or quantity regulates the abundance of all herbivore and predator species; top-down models propose that the abundance of predators controls herbivore and plant densities. (Figures 54.23, 54.24)

- Modern models, which incorporate components of both bottom-up and top-down models, propose that mortality varies according to productivity of plant biomass. (Table 54.3)

Test to Assess Your Learning

1. Two species of birds feed on similar types of insects and nest in the same tree species. This is an example of
   a. intraspecific competition.
   b. interference competition.
   c. resource competition.
   d. mutualism.
   e. none of the above.

2. The experiments conducted by Thomas Park using flour beetles provided evidence that the results of competition are influenced by
   a. moisture.
   b. temperature.
   c. parasitism.
   d. stochasticity.
   e. all of the above.

3. According to the competitive exclusion hypothesis
   a. two species that use the exact same resource show very little competition.
   b. two species with the same niche cannot coexist.
   c. one species that competes with several different species for resources will be excluded from the community.
   d. all competition between species results in the extinction of at least one of the species.
   e. none of the above.

4. In Lack's study of British passerine birds, different species seem to segregate based on resource factors, such as location of prey items. This differentiation among the niches of these passerine birds is known as
   a. competitive exclusion.
   b. intraspecific competition.

c. character displacement.

d. resource partitioning.

e. allelopathy.

5. Divergence in morphology that is a result of competition is termed
   a. competitive exclusion.
   b. resource partitioning.
   c. character displacement.
   d. amensalism.
   e. mutualism.

6. Some organisms have bright coloration that serves as a warning to predators of the organism's bad taste. This type of signal is called
   a. Batesian mimicry.
   b. aposematic coloration.
   c. allelopathy.
   d. cryptic coloration.
   e. masting.

7. Batesian mimicry differs from Müllerian mimicry in that
   a. in Batesian mimicry, both species possess the chemical defence.
   b. in Batesian mimicry, one species possesses the chemical defence.
   c. in Müllerian mimicry, one species has several different mimics.
   d. in Müllerian mimicry, aposematic coloration is always found.
   e. in Batesian mimicry, cryptic coloration is always found.

8. Secondary metabolites
   a. are produced as chemical defences by plants.
   b. are by-products of cellular respiration.
   c. are typically produced by organisms that exhibit Batesian mimicry.
   d. play an important role in energy production in plants.
   e. can be used as alternative reactants in photosynthesis.

9. Parasitic plants that rely solely on their host for nutrients are called
   a. hemiparasites.
   b. fungi.
   c. holoparasites.
   d. monophagous.
   e. polyphagous.

10. A species interaction in which one species benefits but the other species is unharmed is called
    a. mutualism.
    b. amensalism.
    c. parasitism.
    d. commensalism.
    e. mimicry.

Articulate to Assess Your Learning

1. Define the competitive exclusion hypothesis.

2. Distinguish between Müllerian and Batesian mimicry.

3. Describe some plant defences against herbivory.

Collaborate to Assess and Extend Your Learning

1. Discuss different types of competition found in nature.

2. Discuss several antipredator strategies that animals have evolved.

3. Can you think of examples of mimicry used by predators to catch prey rather than used by prey to avoid being eaten? Look back to Figure 52.12 and the associated text.

4. A principle of biology is that living organisms grow, develop, and reproduce. Describe density-dependent factors that can affect population growth and size.

Visit McGraw-Hill Ryerson Connect™ for additional study resources.

Community Ecology

Chapter Outline

So far in this unit, we have examined ecology in terms of the behaviour of individual organisms, the growth of populations, and interactions between pairs of species. Most populations, however, exist not on their own but together with populations of many other species. This assemblage of many populations that live in the same place at the same time is known as a **community**. For example, a tropical forest community consists not only of the tree species, vines, and other vegetation but also of the insects that pollinate them, the herbivores that feed upon the insects, and the predators and parasites of the herbivores. Communities can occur on a wide range of scales and can be nested. The tropical forest community also encompasses smaller communities such as the water-filled recesses of bromeliads, which form a microhabitat for different species of insect and their larvae. Both of these entities—the tropical forest and the bromeliad tank—are viable communities, depending on one's frame of reference with regard to scale.

Community ecology studies how groups of species interact and form functional communities. In Chapter 54, we looked in detail at interactions between individual species. In this chapter, we widen our focus to explore the factors that influence the number and abundance of species in a community. We begin by examining the nature of ecological communities. Are communities loose assemblages of species that happen to live in the same place at the same time, or are they more tightly organized groups of mutually dependent species? We explore why, on a global scale, the number of species is usually greatest in the tropics and declines toward the poles. Community ecology also addresses what factors act to stabilize species richness in a community. However, ecologists recognize that communities may change, for example, following a disturbance such as a fire. This recovery tends to occur in a predictable way that ecologists have termed *succession*. Finally, in certain situations, for example, on islands recovering from physical disturbance, succession has been postulated to occur via waves of colonization of species from neighbouring land masses, followed by extinctions of some species. The equilibrium model of island biogeography holds that island size and distance from the mainland govern the process of succession.

Waterhole with lion pride and elephants, Savuti Reserve, Botswana.

55.1 DIFFERING VIEWS OF COMMUNITIES

Learning Outcomes:

1. Distinguish between Clements's organismic model and Gleason's individualistic model to explain the nature of an ecological community.
2. Describe the principle of species individuality.

Ecologists have long held differing views on the nature of a community and how it is structured and functions. Some of the initial work in the field of community ecology considered a community to be equivalent to a superorganism, in much the same way that the body of an animal is more than just a collection of organs. In this view, individuals, populations, and communities have a relationship to each other that resembles the associations found among cells, tissues, and organs. Indeed, American botanist Frederic Clements, the champion of this viewpoint, suggested in 1905 that ecology was to the study of communities what physiology was to the study of individual organisms. This view of community, with predictable and integrated associations of species separated by sharp boundaries, is termed the **organismic model**. Some modern-day ecologists still depict the community as a superorganism. As we will see later in this chapter, Clements's hypotheses on communities were also linked to his study of succession, the changes in the types of plant and animal species that occupy a given area through time.

Clements's ideas were challenged in 1926 by botanist Henry Allan Gleason. Gleason proposed an **individualistic model**, which viewed a community as an assemblage of species coexisting primarily because of similarities in their physiological requirements and tolerances. While acknowledging that some assemblages of species were fairly uniform and stable over a given region, Gleason suggested that distinctly structured ecological communities usually do not exist. Instead, species distribute independently along an environmental gradient. Viewed in this way, communities do not necessarily have sharp boundaries, and associations of species are much less predictable and integrated than in Clements's organismic model.

By the 1950s many ecologists had abandoned Clements's view in favour of Gleason's. In particular, Robert Whittaker's studies asserted the **principle of species individuality**, which stated that each species is distributed according to its physiological needs and population dynamics, that most communities intergrade continuously, and that competition does not create distinct vegetational zones. For example, let's consider an environmental gradient such as a moisture gradient on an uninterrupted slope of a mountain. Whittaker proposed that four hypotheses could explain the distribution patterns of plants and animals on the gradient (**Figure 55.1**):

1. Competing species, including dominant plants, exclude one another along sharp boundaries. Other species evolve toward a close, perhaps mutually beneficial association with the dominant species. Communities thus develop along the gradient, each zone containing its own group of interacting species giving way at a sharp boundary to another assemblage of species. This corresponds to Clements's organismic model.
2. Competing species exclude one another along sharp boundaries but do not become organized into groups of species with parallel distributions.
3. Competition does not usually result in sharp boundaries between species. However, the adaptation of species to similar physical variables will result in the appearance of groups of species with similar distributions.
4. Competition does not usually produce sharp boundaries between species, and the adaptation of species to similar physical variables does not produce well-defined groups of species with similar distributions. The centres and boundaries of species populations are scattered along the environmental gradient. This corresponds to Gleason's individualistic model.

To test these possibilities, Whittaker examined the vegetation on various mountain ranges in the western United States. He sampled plant populations along an elevation gradient from the tops of the mountains to the bases and collected data on various physical variables, such as soil moisture.

The results supported the fourth hypothesis, that competition does not produce sharp boundaries between species and that adaptation to physical variables does not result in defined groups of species. Whittaker concluded that his observations agreed with Gleason's predictions that (1) each species is distributed in its own way, according to its genetic, physiological, and lifecycle characteristics; and (2) the broad overlap and scattered centres of species populations along a gradient implies that most communities grade into each other continuously rather than form

Figure 55.1   **Four hypotheses on how populations might relate to one another along an environmental gradient.**   Each curve in each part of the figure represents one species and the way its population might be distributed along an environmental gradient such as a moisture gradient on a mountain slope.

BioConnections: *Look back to Section 1.3. What's the difference between a hypothesis and a theory?*

distinct, clearly separated groups. Thus, Whittaker's observations showed that the composition of species at any one point in an environmental gradient was largely determined by factors such as temperature, water, light, pH, and salt concentrations (features discussed in Chapter 51).

55.2 | PATTERNS OF SPECIES RICHNESS

Learning Outcomes:

1. Identify the latitudinal gradient of species richness.
2. List and describe four hypotheses for observed patterns of species richness.

Even though most communities intergrade along environmental gradients such as a mountain slope, ecologists recognize distinct differences between communities. The community at

Figure 55.2   An example of a sharp boundary between two communities.   In New Zealand's Dun Mountain area, we can contrast the sparse vegetation on the serpentine soil to the left to that of the beech forest on the nonserpentine soil on the right.

Principle: *Living organisms interact with their environment. Serpentine soil is nutrient poor and relatively few plants species are adapted to live in it.*

Figure 55.3   Species richness of birds in North America. The values indicate the numbers of different species in a given area. Contour lines show equal numbers of bird species. Note the pronounced latitudinal gradient heading south toward the tropics and the high diversity in California and northern Mexico, regions of considerable topographical variation and habitat diversity.

the top of a mountain will be quite different from that at the bottom, so distinguishing between communities on a broad scale is useful. Also, some sharp boundaries between groups of species sometimes do exist—especially related to physical differences such as water quality and soil type—that cause distinct communities to develop. For example, serpentine soils are rich in metals, including magnesium, iron, and nickel, but poor in plant nutrients. The species that have adapted to these harsh conditions form a unique community restricted to this area (**Figure 55.2**).

One of the most straightforward means of describing communities is to determine the number of species in each community, or **species richness**. The number of species of most taxa varies according to geographic location, generally increasing from polar areas to temperate areas and reaching a maximum in the tropics. For example, the species richness of North American birds increases from Arctic Canada to Panama (**Figure 55.3**). A similar pattern exists for mammals and reptiles. Species richness is also increased by topographical variation. More mountains mean more hilltops, valleys, and differing habitats; thus, there is an increased number of birds in the mountainous western United States. However, species richness is reduced by the peninsular effect, in which diversity decreases as a function of distance from the main body of land, and thus we see a decrease in the number of species in Florida and in Baja California.

Many hypotheses for the polar-equatorial gradient of species richness have been advanced. We will consider three of the most important, which propose that communities diversify with increased time, area, and productivity, respectively. Although they are treated separately here, it is important to note that these hypotheses are not mutually exclusive and that all can contribute to patterns of species richness.

The Time Hypothesis Suggests Communities Diversify with Age

Many ecologists argue that communities diversify—that is, gain species—with time and that temperate regions have less rich communities than tropical ones because they are younger and have only more recently (relatively speaking) recovered from recent glaciations and severe climatic disruption. The time hypothesis has two variations. It proposes first that resident species have not yet evolved new forms to exploit vacant niches, and second that species that could possibly live in temperate regions have not migrated back from the unglaciated areas into which the ice ages drove them.

In support of the time hypothesis, ecologists compared the species richness of bottom-dwelling invertebrates such as oligochaete worms in historically glaciated (covered with ice) and unglaciated lakes in the northern hemisphere that occur at similar latitudes. Lake Baikal in Siberia is an ancient unglaciated temperate lake (~25 to 30 million years old) and contains a very diverse fauna; for example, there are 580 species of invertebrates in the bottom zone. Great Slave Lake, a comparable-sized lake in northern Canada that was glaciated as recently as 12,000 years ago, contains only four species in the same zone.

There are, however, drawbacks to the utility of the time hypothesis. For example, the time hypothesis may help explain variations in the species richness of terrestrial organisms, but it has limited applicability to marine organisms. While we might not expect terrestrial species to redistribute themselves quickly following a glaciation—especially if there is a barrier such as the English Channel to overcome—there seems to be no reason that marine organisms couldn't relatively easily shift their distribution patterns during glaciations, yet the polar-equatorial gradient of species richness still exists in marine habitats.

The Area Hypothesis Suggests Large Areas Support More Species

The **area hypothesis** proposes that larger areas contain more species than smaller areas because they can support larger populations and a greater range of habitats. Much evidence supports the area hypothesis. For example, in 1974, Donald Strong showed that insect species richness on tree species in Britain was better correlated with the area over which a tree species could be found than with time of habitation since the last ice age. The relationship between the amount of available area and the number of species present is called the **species–area effect** (**Figure 55.4**). Some introduced tree species, such as apple and lime, were relatively new to Britain but they bore many different insect species, a fact Strong argued did not support the time hypothesis.

As we saw in Chapter 51, the three-cell model of atmospheric circulation leads to a symmetry of climates between polar regions and temperate areas in the northern and southern hemispheres (refer back to Figure 51.21). Symmetrically similar climates are only adjacent in the tropics, however, which creates one large area. This has been proposed as a reason the tropics have greater species richness. However, the area hypothesis seems unable to explain why, if increased richness is linked to increased area, there are not more species in the vast contiguous land mass of Asia. Furthermore, while tundra may be the

world's largest land biome, it has low species richness. Finally, the largest marine system, the open ocean, which has the greatest volume of any habitat, has fewer species than tropical surface waters, which have a relatively small volume.

The Productivity Hypothesis Suggests That More Energy Permits the Existence of More Species

The **productivity hypothesis** proposes that greater production by plants results in greater overall species richness. An increase in plant biomass, the total weight of plant material produced, leads to an increase in the number of herbivores and hence an increase in the number of predator, parasite, and scavenger species.

Production itself is influenced by factors such as temperature and rainfall, because many plants grow better where it is warm and wet. For example, in 1987, David Currie and colleagues at the University of Ottawa showed that the species richness of trees in North America is best predicted by the **evapotranspiration rate**, the rate at which water moves into the atmosphere through the processes of evaporation from the soil and transpiration of plants (**Figure 55.5**).

Once again, however, there are exceptions to this rule. Some tropical seas, such as the southeast Pacific off Colombia and Ecuador, have low productivity but high species richness. On the other hand, the sub-Antarctic Ocean has a high productivity but low species richness. Estuarine areas, where rivers empty into the sea, are similarly very productive yet low in species, presumably because they represent a stressful environment for many organisms that are alternately inundated by fresh water and salt water with daily changes in the tide. Some lakes that are polluted with fertilizers have high productivity but low species richness.

Last, Robert Latham and Robert Ricklefs showed in 1993 that while patterns of tree diversity in North America support

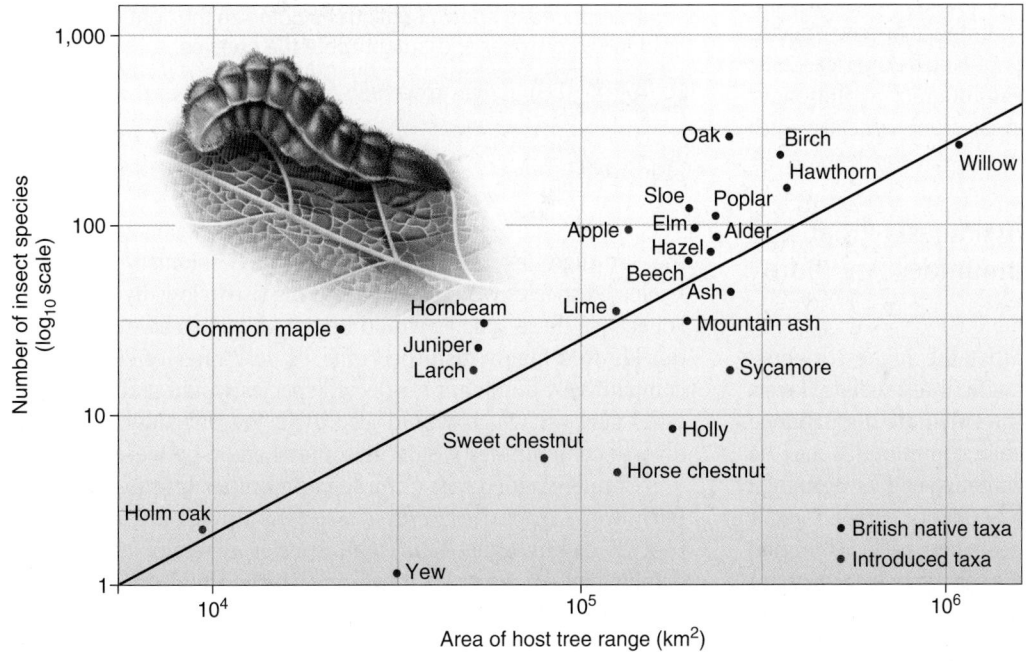

Figure 55.4 Insect species diversity on British host trees supports the area hypothesis. A positive correlation is found between insect species richness and the host tree's present range (in km²). Here, the range represents an area in Britain known to contain trees of each species.

Figure 55.5 Tree species richness in North America is correlated with evapotranspiration rate. Contour lines show equal numbers of tree species.

Concept check: *Why doesn't the species richness of trees increase in mountainous areas of the West, as it does for birds?*

the productivity hypothesis, the pattern does not hold for broad comparisons between continents: the temperate forests of eastern Asia support substantially higher numbers of tree species (729) than do climatically similar areas of North America (253) or Europe (124). These three areas have different evolutionary histories and different neighbouring areas from which species might have invaded.

The Intermediate-Disturbance Hypothesis Proposes That Moderately Disturbed Communities Are More Diverse

Ecologist Joseph Connell has argued that the highest diversities are maintained in communities with intermediate levels of disturbance, a concept called the **intermediate-disturbance hypothesis** (**Figure 55.6a**). Disturbance in communities may be brought about by many different phenomena such as droughts, fires, floods, and hurricanes, or even herbivory, predation, or parasitism. Recall from Chapter 53 that some species, termed *r*-selected species, are better dispersers than other species, and that *K*-selected species are better competitors. Connell reasoned

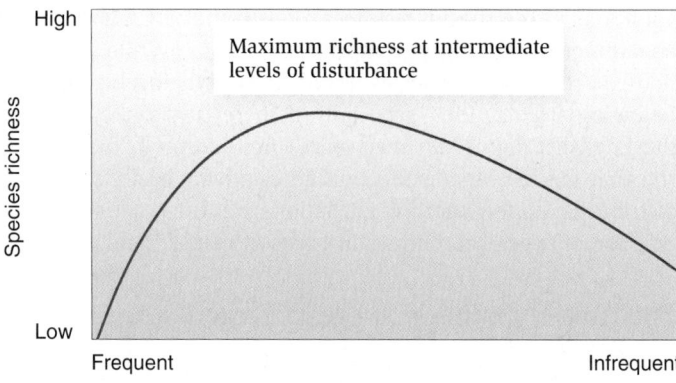

(a) Relationship between species richness and disturbances

(b) Light gap in a tropical rain forest

Figure 55.6 The intermediate-disturbance hypothesis of community organization. **(a)** This hypothesis proposes that species richness is highest at intermediate levels of disturbances caused by events such as fires or windstorms. **(b)** A light gap in a tropical rain forest in Costa Rica promotes the growth of small herbaceous species until trees colonize the light gap and gradually grow over and outcompete the species.

Concept check: *According to the intermediate-disturbance hypothesis, why are there so many species in the tropics?*

that at high levels of disturbance only colonists that were *r*-selected species would survive, giving rise to low diversity. This is because these species would be the only ones able to disperse quickly to a highly disturbed area. At low rates of disturbance, competitively dominant *K*-selected species would outcompete all other species, which would also yield low diversity. The most diverse communities would lie somewhere in between.

Connell argued that natural communities fit into this model fairly well. Tropical rain forests and coral reefs are both examples of communities with high species diversity. Coral reefs exhibit highest diversity in areas disturbed by hurricanes, and the richest tropical forests occur where disturbance by storms causes landslides and tree falls. The fall of a tree creates a hole in the rain forest canopy known as a light gap, where direct sunlight is able to reach the rain forest floor. The light gap is rapidly colonized by *r*-selected species, such as small herbaceous plants, which are well adapted for rapid growth. While these pioneering species grow rapidly, they are overtaken by hardier *K*-selected species, such as mature trees, which fill in the gap in the canopy (**Figure 55.6b**). Although events such as hurricanes and tree falls are fairly frequent events in these communities, their occurrence in any one area is usually of intermediate frequency.

In 1979 Wayne Sousa provided an elegant experimental verification of the intermediate-disturbance hypothesis in the marine intertidal zone. He found that small boulders, which were easily disturbed by waves, carried a mean of 1.7 sessile plant and animal species. These frequently moving boulders crushed or dislodged most colonizing species. Large boulders, which were rarely moved by waves, had a mean of 2.5 species. On these boulders, competitively dominant species supplanted many other species. Sousa found that intermediate-sized boulders had the most species, an average of 3.7 species per boulder, because they contained a mix of *r*- and *K*-selected species. To test the hypothesis, Sousa cemented small boulders to the ocean floor and obtained an increase in species richness to near the value for large boulders, showing that the resulting number of species was a result of rock stability, not rock size.

When comparing the time, area, productivity, and intermediate disturbance hypotheses, each has some evidence to support it and some to contradict it. Different processes may occur over different scales. On a regional scale, we know that the time since the last glaciation has the potential to change patterns of species richness. On a more local scale, area, productivity of available habitat, and disturbance level may be important. At any given point on the globe, species richness may be affected by the interaction of these different factors.

55.3 CALCULATING SPECIES DIVERSITY

Learning Outcomes:

1. Define species diversity and how it is calculated.

So far, we have discussed communities in terms of variations in species richness. However, to measure species diversity, ecologists need to take into account not only the number of species in a community but also their frequency of occurrence, or **relative abundance**. For example, imagine two hypothetical communities, A and B, both with two species and 100 total individuals.

	Number of individuals of species 1	Number of individuals of species 2
Community A	99	1
Community B	50	50

The species richness of community B equals that of community A, because they both contain two species. However, community B is considered more diverse because the distribution of individuals between species is more even. One would be much more likely to encounter both species in community B than in community A, where one species dominates.

To measure the diversity of a community, therefore, ecologists calculate what is known as a diversity index. Three levels of species diversity have been proposed at different spatial levels. Alpha diversity refers to the number of species within a particular habitat or community (e.g., at a local level). Beta diversity refers to the change in species composition over space or time, as one passes from one community to the next, across a landscape. Gamma diversity is the number of species across an entire landscape, thus incorporating a combination of alpha and beta diversity. There are many indices of diversity in use by ecologists today, and studies of species diversity usually incorporate a few different indices. Some indices include an element of heterogeneity in the distribution of species (e.g., Simpson's index, which provides the probability that two individuals sampled from a population will belong to the same species). Others incorporate an element of evenness in the number of members of different species in a community (e.g., Pielou's evenness index). Modern mathematical techniques such as rarefaction curves allow ecologists to estimate species diversity in more species-rich or hard-to-sample taxa based on a smaller subsample of individuals. Although there are a great many of these indices, the most widely used is the **Shannon diversity index (H_S)**, which is calculated as

$$H_s = -\Sigma p_i \ln p_i$$

where p_i is the proportion of individuals belonging to species i in a community, ln is the natural logarithm, and the Σ is a summation sign. For example, for a species in which there are 50 individuals out of a total of 100 in the community, p_i is 50/100, or 0.5. The natural log of 0.5 is -0.693. For this species, $p_i \ln p_i$ is then $0.5 \times -0.693 = -0.347$. For a hypothetical community with 5 species and 100 total individuals, the Shannon diversity index would be calculated as follows:

	Species	Abundance	p_i	$p_i \ln p_i$
	1	50	0.5	−.347
	2	30	0.3	−.361
	3	10	0.1	−.230
	4	9	0.09	−.217
	5	1	0.01	−.046
Total	5	100	1.00	$\Sigma p_i \ln p_i$ −1.201

In this example, even the rarest species, species 5, contributes some value to the index, so that if there were many such rare species their contributions would accumulate. This makes the Shannon diversity index very valuable to conservation biologists, who often study rare species and their importance to the community. Remember too that the negative sign in front of the summation changes these values to positive, so the index actually becomes 1.201, not −1.201. (The minus sign in the equation is used to give us a positive number for the index, which is more appealing than an index with a negative number.) Values of the Shannon diversity index for real communities often fall between 1.5 and 3.5, with the higher the value, the greater the diversity.

An accurate determination of community diversity depends on detailed knowledge of which and how many of each species are present. While this is relatively easy to determine for communities of vertebrates and some invertebrates, it is much more difficult for microbial communities. Yet knowledge of microbial communities is of vital importance if only because of the decomposition functions they perform. As described next, with the advent of modern molecular tools, our knowledge of the diversity of microbial communities is beginning to expand.

GENOMES AND PROTEOMES

Metagenomics May Be Used to Measure Community Diversity

Bacteria are abundant members of all communities and are vital to their functioning. They serve as food sources for other organisms and participate in the decomposition process. However, most microorganisms are taxonomically unknown, mainly because they cannot be cultivated on known culture media. The new field of **metagenomics** seeks to identify and analyze the collective microbial genomes contained in a community of organisms, including those that are not easily cultured in the laboratory. This technique has been in existence only since the early 1990s, but significant progress has already been made in providing libraries that have advanced our understanding of which bacteria are present in various communities and how they function.

The process involves four main steps (**Figure 55.7**). First, an environmental sample containing many bacterial species is collected and its DNA is isolated from the cells using chemical or physical methods. Because the genomic DNA of each species is relatively large, it is cut up into fragments with enzymes called restriction endonucleases (see Chapter 18). Second, the

Figure 55.7 **The standard protocol of a metagenomics experiment.** (1) Isolation and fragmentation of DNA from the sample, (2) insertion of fragments into bacterial vectors, (3) insertion of cloned DNA into host cell and culturing in selective growth media to create a library, and (4) analysis of DNA sequences and protein expression.

fragments are combined with vectors, small units of DNA that can be inserted into a model organism, usually a bacterium. The third step is transformation, the physical insertion of the foreign DNA into a host bacterial cell. Individual bacteria are then grown on a selective medium so that only the transformed cells survive, and they grow into a colony of cloned cells. A collection of thousands of clones, each containing a different piece of microbial DNA, is called a metagenomic library. Lastly, the DNA from the metagenomic libraries is analyzed. In some cases, expression of the new DNA results in the synthesis of a new protein that changes the phenotype of the host; for example, a new enzyme that is detected by a chemical technique or an unusual colour or shape in the model organism.

Metagenomics is helping determine the identity and activities of bacteria in diverse habitats, from the soil to deep-sea sediments to the oral cavity of humans. Recent studies have used shotgun DNA sequencing (see Chapter 19) to analyze bacterial genomes directly from soil and ocean samples. Sampling of deep-sea and ocean sediment has permitted sequencing of particular genes, most often the 16S ribosomal RNA (16S rRNA) that all bacteria possess. A sample of many different bacterial species will yield many different 16S rRNA gene sequences.

These are then compared to a database containing all known sequences of this gene. Larger DNA segments will be compared to corresponding genomes of cultured bacteria to see if we can assign a tentative metabolic function to each segment. In this way, we can determine the community diversity of soil, sediment, or water samples and make better determinations of how the community is functioning.

In 2004 Jill Banfield and colleagues used metagenomics techniques to identify the five dominant species of bacteria living at temperatures of 42°C and pH 0.8 in the acidic waste water (called acid mine drainage) from a mine in California. They detected 2,036 proteins from these species, including proteins from the most abundant bacterial species, a *Leptospirillum* group II bacterium. This represented the first large-scale proteomics-level expression of a natural microbial community. One of the proteins, a cytochrome, oxidizes iron and probably influences the rate of breakdown of acid mine drainage products. Many other proteins appear responsible for defending against free radicals, suggesting that this is a challenging task. The hope is that the team can now identify enzymes and metabolic pathways that will help in the cleanup of this and other contaminated sites in the future.

55.4 | SPECIES RICHNESS AND COMMUNITY STABILITY

Learning Outcomes:

1. Describe the diversity–stability hypothesis and evidence supporting it.

A community is often seen as stable when little to no change can be detected in the number of species and their abundance over a given time period. The community may then be said to be in equilibrium. The frame of reference for detecting change may encompass a study of a few years or, preferably, several decades. For example, long-term data from Bookham Common, England, revealed bird communities in which the number of species appeared stable for nearly 30 years. Community stability is an important consideration in conservation biology, as we will discuss further in Chapter 57. A decrease in the stability of a community over time may alert us to a possible problem. In the 1970s the populations of many fish-eating birds that nest on lakes, including eagles, osprey, and cormorants, declined precipitously. Eventually, the decline was traced to the pesticide DDT (dichlorodiphenyltrichloroethane), which caused eggshells to become thin and break before the birds could hatch. After DDT was banned later in the decade, bird populations began to recover.

In this section, we consider the relationship between species richness and community stability. We begin by exploring the question of whether communities with more species are

more stable than communities with fewer species. We then examine the link between diversity and stability, using evidence from the field. In a final consideration, we look at the relationship from a different angle and consider whether or not undisturbed communities are more species rich than communities that have been disturbed.

The Diversity–Stability Hypothesis States That Species-Rich Communities Are More Stable Than Those with Fewer Species

Community stability may be viewed in several different ways. Some communities, such as extreme deserts, are considered stable because they are resistant to change by anything other than water. Other communities, such as river communities, are considered stable because they can recover quickly after a disturbance, such as pollution, being cleansed by the rapid flow of fresh water. Lake communities, on the other hand, may be less stable because there is no drainage outlet and pollutants can accumulate quickly.

Because maintaining community stability is seen as important, much research has gone into understanding the factors that enhance it. This work has produced the prevailing idea that species-rich communities are more stable than species-poor communities. There is much debate, for example, over whether species-rich communities are more resistant to invasion by undesirable exotic species, such as weeds, than species-poor communities.

The link between species richness and stability was first explicitly proposed by English ecologist Charles Elton in the

1950s. He suggested that a disturbance in a species-rich community would be cushioned by large numbers of interacting species and would not produce as drastic an effect as it would on a species-poor community. Thus, an introduced predator or parasite could cause extinctions in a species-poor system but possibly not in a more diverse system, where its effects would be buffered by interactions with more species in the community. Elton argued that outbreaks of pests are often found on cultivated land or land disturbed by humans, both of which are species-poor communities with few naturally occurring species. His argument became known as the **diversity–stability hypothesis**.

However, some ecologists began to challenge Elton's association of diversity with stability. They pointed out many examples of introduced species that have assumed pest proportions on continents, not just islands, including rabbits in Australia and pigs in North America. They noted that disturbed or cultivated land may suffer from pest outbreaks not because of its simple nature but because individual species, including exotic pest species and native species of natural enemies, often have no evolutionary history with one another, in contrast to the long associations between pests and natural enemies evident in natural biomes. For example, in Europe coevolved predators such as foxes prevent rabbit populations from increasing to pest proportions. What was needed was an experiment to determine whether a link existed between diversity and stability.

In 1996 ecologist David Tilman reported the relationship between species richness and stability from an 11-year study of 207 grassland plots in Minnesota. He measured the biomass of every species of plant, in each plot, at the end of every year and obtained the average species biomass. He then calculated how much this biomass varied from year to year through a statistical measure called the coefficient of variation. Year-to-year variation in plant community biomass was significantly lower in plots with greater plant species richness (**Figure 55.8**). Tilman's results showed that community stability is positively correlated with diversity.

Tilman suggested that diversity stabilizes communities because diverse plots were more likely to contain disturbance-resistant species that in the event of a disturbance could grow and compensate for the loss of disturbance-sensitive species. For example, when a change in climate such as drought harmed competitively dominant species that thrived in normal conditions, decreasing their abundance, unharmed drought-resistant species increased in mass and replaced them. Such decreases in susceptible species and compensatory increases in other species acted to stabilize total community biomass.

55.5 / SUCCESSION: COMMUNITY CHANGE

Learning Outcomes:

1. Distinguish between primary and secondary succession.
2. Compare and contrast facilitation, inhibition, and tolerance as mechanisms of succession.

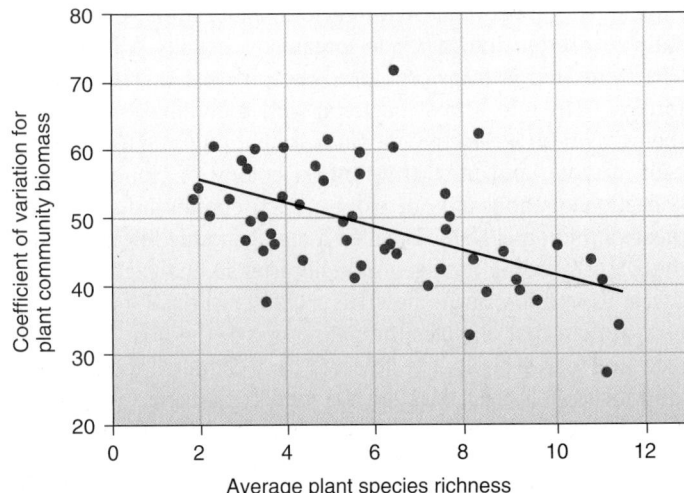

Figure 55.8   Relationships between biomass variation and species diversity.   Tilman's 11-year study of grassland plots in Minnesota revealed that year-to-year variability in community biomass was lower in species-rich plots. Each dot represents an individual plot, although only the plots from one field are graphed.

At 8:32 a.m. on May 18, 1980, Mount St. Helens, a previously little-studied peak in the Washington Cascades, erupted. The blast felled trees over a 600-square-kilometre area, and the landslide that followed—the largest in recorded history—destroyed everything in its path, killing nearly 60 people and thousands of animals. However, since the eruption much of the area has experienced a relatively rapid recovery of plant and animal communities (**Figure 55.9**).

Ecologists have developed several terms to describe how community change occurs. The term **succession** describes the gradual and continuous change in species composition and community structure over time. **Primary succession** refers to succession on a newly exposed site that was not previously occupied by soil and vegetation, such as bare ground caused by a volcanic eruption or the rubble created by the retreat of glaciers. In primary succession on land, the plants must often build up the soil, and thus a long time—even hundreds of years—may be required for the process. Only a tiny proportion of the Earth's surface is currently undergoing primary succession; for example, around Mount St. Helens and the volcanoes in Hawaii and off the coast of Iceland, and behind retreating glaciers in Alaska and Canada.

Secondary succession refers to succession on a site that has already supported life but has undergone a disturbance, such as a fire, tornado, hurricane, or flood (as in the 2004 tsunami in Indonesia). Clearing a natural forest and farming the land for several years is an example of a severe forest disturbance that does not kill all native species; some plants and many soil bacteria, nematodes, and insects are still present. Cessation of farming may lead to a distinct secondary succession. The secondary succession in abandoned farmlands also can lead to a pattern of vegetation quite different from one that develops after primary succession following glacial retreat. For

(a) 1980   **(b) 1997**

Figure 55.9 Succession on Mount St. Helens. (a) The initial blast occurred on May 18, 1980. (b) By 1997, 17 years later, many of the areas initially overrun by lava had developed low-lying vegetation and new trees sprouted up between the old dead tree trunks.

example, the plowing and added fertilizers, herbicides, and pesticides may have caused substantial changes in the soil of an old field, allowing species that require a lot of nitrogen to colonize. These species would not be present for many years in newly created glacial soils. Typically in old-field studies, following disturbance, annual plants colonize a region initially, followed after approximately two years by perennial forbs, and finally, woody plants. The rate at which plants return to an area is related to both the distance to existing plants and their method of propagation, as well as the size and extent of the disturbed patch. The pattern of succession is closely linked to the increasing availability of nitrogen in the soil, where major plant species show specific soil nitrogen requirements. There is also a tendency for species richness to increase over time; however, sometimes early-colonizing plants can be more speciose. However, patterns of succession vary among ecosystems and climates, and require localized studies to determine the length of time until the system returns to a mature state.

Frederic Clements is often viewed as the founder of successional theory as well as community ecology in general. His work in the early twentieth century emphasized succession as proceeding to a distinct end point or **climax community**. Each phase of succession was called a **sere**, or seral stage. The initial sere was known as the pioneer seral stage. While disturbance could return a community from a later seral stage to an earlier seral stage, generally the community headed toward climax.

A key assumption of Clements was that each colonizing species made the environment a little different—a little more shady or a little more rich in soil nitrogen—so that it became more suitable for other species, which then invaded and outcompeted the earlier residents. This process, known as **facilitation**, supposedly continued until the most competitively dominant species had colonized, when the community was said to be at climax. The composition of the climax community for any given region was thought to be determined by climate and soil conditions. While Clements' ideas on succession focused on the mechanism of facilitation, two other mechanisms affecting

succession—inhibition and tolerance—have since been proposed. Next, we'll examine the evidence for each of them.

Facilitation Assumes Each Invading Species Creates a More Favourable Habitat for Succeeding Species

Succession following the gradual retreat of Alaskan glaciers is often used as a specific example of facilitation as a mechanism of succession. Over the past 200 years, the glaciers in Glacier Bay have undergone a dramatic retreat of nearly 100 kilometres (**Figure 55.10**). This is one of the few instances where we can trace the chronology of physical change in an area—from 1794, when Captain George Vancouver visited the inlet and made notes on the positions of the glaciers, to the present.

Succession in Glacier Bay follows a distinct pattern of vegetation. As glaciers retreat, they leave moraines, deposits of stones, pulverized rock, and debris that serve as soil. In Alaska, the bare soil has a low nitrogen content and scant organic matter. In the pioneer stages, the soil is first colonized by a black crust of cyanobacteria, lichens, moss, horsetail (*Equisetum variegatum*), and the occasional river beauty (*Epilobium latifolium*) (**Figure 55.11a**). Because the cyanobacteria are nitrogen fixers, the soil nitrogen increases a little, but soil depth and litterfall (fallen leaves, twigs, and other plant material) are still minimal. At this stage there may be a few seeds and seedlings of dwarf shrubs of the rose family commonly called mountain avens (*Dryas drummondii*), alders, and spruce, but they are rare in the community. After about 40 years, *D. drummondii* dominates the landscape (**Figure 55.11b**). Soil nitrogen increases, as does soil depth and litterfall, and alder trees begin to invade.

At about 60 years, alders (*Alnus sinuata*) form dense, close thickets (**Figure 55.11c**). Alders have nitrogen-fixing bacteria that live mutualistically in their roots and convert nitrogen from the air into a biologically useful form. The excess nitrogen fixed by these bacteria accumulates in the soil. Soil nitrogen dramatically increases, as does litterfall. Spruce trees (*Picea sitchensis*) begin to invade at about this time. After about 75 to 100 years,

(a) Glacier Bay, Alaska

(b) Glacial retreat

Figure 55.10   The degree of glacier retreat at Glacier Bay, Alaska, since 1794.   (a) Primary succession begins on the bare rock and soil evident at the edges of the retreating glacier. (b) The lines reflect the position of the glacier in 1794 and its subsequent retreat.

Concept check: *Why do ecologists sometimes view walking through Glacier Bay as the equivalent of being in a time machine?*

the spruce trees begin to overtop the alders, shading them out. The litterfall is still high and the large volume of needles turns the soil acidic. The shade causes competitive exclusion of many of the original understory species, including alder, and only mosses carpet the ground. At this stage, seedlings of western hemlock (*Tsuga heterophylla*) and mountain hemlock (*Tsuga mertensiana*) may also occur, and after 200 years a mixed spruce–hemlock climax forest results (**Figure 55.11d**).

What other evidence is there of facilitation? Experimental studies of early primary succession on Mount St. Helens, which show that decomposition of fungi allows mosses and other fungi to colonize the soil, provide evidence of facilitation. In

New England salt marshes, *Spartina* grass facilitates the establishment of beach plant communities by stabilizing the rocky substrate and reducing water velocity, which enables other seedlings to emerge. Succession on sand dunes also supports the facilitation model, in that pioneer plant species stabilize the sand dunes and facilitate the establishment of subsequent plant species. The foredunes, those nearest the shoreline, are the most frequently disturbed and are maintained in a state of early succession, while more stable communities develop farther away from the shoreline.

Succession also occurs in aquatic communities. Although soils do not develop in marine environments, facilitation may still be encountered when one species enhances the quality of settling and establishment sites for another species. When experimental test plates used to measure settling rates of marine organisms were placed in the Delaware Bay, researchers discovered that certain cnidarians enhanced the attachment of tunicates, and both facilitated the attachment of mussels, which were the dominant species in the community. In this experiment, the smooth surface of the test plates prevented many species from colonizing, but once the surface became rougher because of the presence of the cnidarians many other species were able to colonize. In a similar fashion, early colonizing bacteria, which create biofilms on rock surfaces, can facilitate succession of other organisms.

Inhibition Implies That Early Colonists Prevent Later Arrivals from Replacing Them

Although data on succession in some communities fit the facilitation model, researchers have proposed alternative hypotheses of how succession may operate. Another view is that possession of space is all important, and that what gets there first determines subsequent community structure. In this process, known as **inhibition**, early colonists may exclude subsequent colonists. For example, removing the litter of *Setaria faberi*, an early successional plant species in New Jersey old fields, causes an increase in the biomass of a later species, *Erigeron annuus*. The release of toxic compounds from decomposing *Setaria* litter or physical obstruction by the litter itself contributes to the inhibition of *Erigeron*. Without the litter present, *Erigeron* dominates and reduces the biomass of *Setaria*. Plant species that grow in dense thickets, such as some grasses, ferns, vines, pine trees, and bamboo, can inhibit succession, as can many introduced plant species.

Inhibition has been seen as the primary method of succession in the marine intertidal zone, where space is limited. In this habitat, early successional species are at a great advantage in maintaining possession of valuable space. In 1974 ecologist Wayne Sousa created an environment for testing how succession works in the intertidal zone by scraping rock faces clean of all algae or putting out fresh boulders or concrete blocks. The first colonists of these areas were the green algae *Ulva*. By removing *Ulva* from the substrate, Sousa showed that the large red alga *Gigartina canaliculata* was able to colonize more

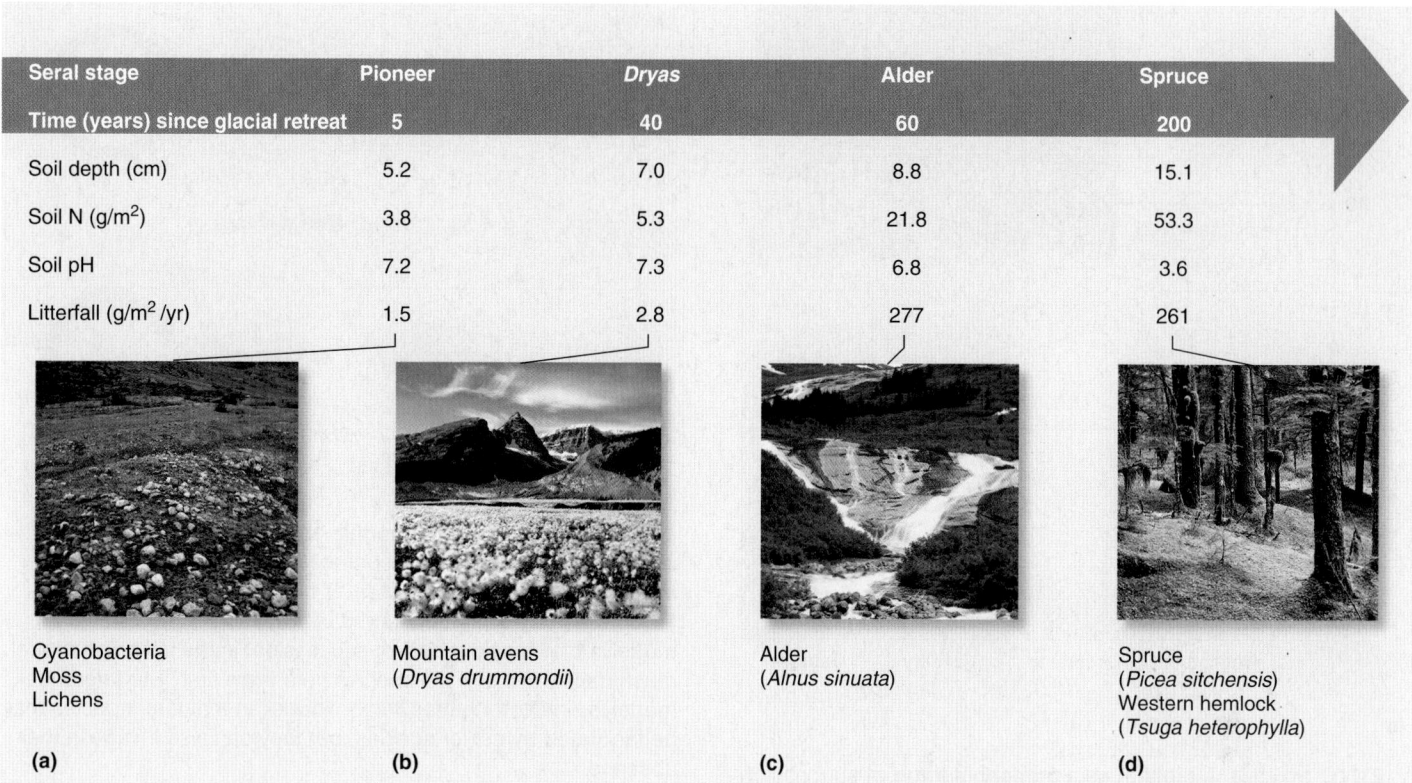

Seral stage	Pioneer	*Dryas*	Alder	Spruce
Time (years) since glacial retreat	5	40	60	200
Soil depth (cm)	5.2	7.0	8.8	15.1
Soil N (g/m²)	3.8	5.3	21.8	53.3
Soil pH	7.2	7.3	6.8	3.6
Litterfall (g/m²/yr)	1.5	2.8	277	261

Cyanobacteria
Moss
Lichens

(a)

Mountain avens
(*Dryas drummondii*)

(b)

Alder
(*Alnus sinuata*)

(c)

Spruce
(*Picea sitchensis*)
Western hemlock
(*Tsuga heterophylla*)

(d)

Figure 55.11 **The pattern of primary succession at Glacier Bay, Alaska.** **(a)** The first species to colonize the bare Earth following retreat of the glaciers are small species such as cyanobacteria, moss, and lichens. **(b)** Mountain avens (*Dryas drummondii*) is a flower common in the *Dryas* seral stage. **(c)** Soil nitrogen and litterfall increase rapidly as alder (*Alnus sinuata*) invade. Note also the appearance of a few spruce trees higher up the valley. **(d)** Spruce (*Picea sitchensis*) and hemlock (*Tsuga heterophylla*) trees comprise a climax spruce–hemlock forest at Glacier Bay, with moss carpeting the ground. Two hundred years ago, glaciers occupied this spot.

Concept check: *Is facilitation the only mechanism fuelling succession at Glacier Bay?*

BioConnections: *Refer back to section 35.3. In what genus are the nitrogen-fixing bacteria that occur in nodules on the roots of alder trees?*

quickly (**Figure 55.12**). The results of Sousa's study indicate that early colonists can inhibit rather than facilitate the invasion of subsequent colonists. Succession may eventually occur because early colonizing species, such as *Ulva*, are more susceptible to the rigours of the physical environment and to attacks by herbivores, such as crabs (*Pachygrapsus crassipes*), than later successional species, such as *Gigartina*.

Tolerance Suggests That Early Colonists Neither Facilitate Nor Inhibit Later Colonists

The huge differences between facilitation and inhibition as mechanisms of succession prompted Joseph Connell and Ralph Slatyer to view the two as extremes on a continuum. In 1977 the two researchers proposed a third mechanism of succession, which they termed **tolerance**. In this process, any species can start the succession, but the eventual climax community is

reached in a somewhat orderly fashion. Early species neither facilitate nor inhibit subsequent colonists. Connell and Slatyer found the best evidence for the tolerance model in Frank Egler's earlier work on floral succession. In the 1950s Egler showed that succession in plant communities is determined largely by species that already exist in the ground as buried seeds or old roots. Whichever species germinates first, or regenerates from roots, initiates the succession sequence.

The key distinction among the three models is in the manner in which succession proceeds. In the facilitation model, species replacement is facilitated by previous colonists; in the inhibition model, it is inhibited by the action of previous colonists; and in the tolerance model, species may be unaffected by previous colonists but they do not require them (**Figure 55.13**). Subsequent research has suggested that other factors may also influence succession, especially on islands. The study of succession on islands is often referred to as *island biogeography*, which is described next.

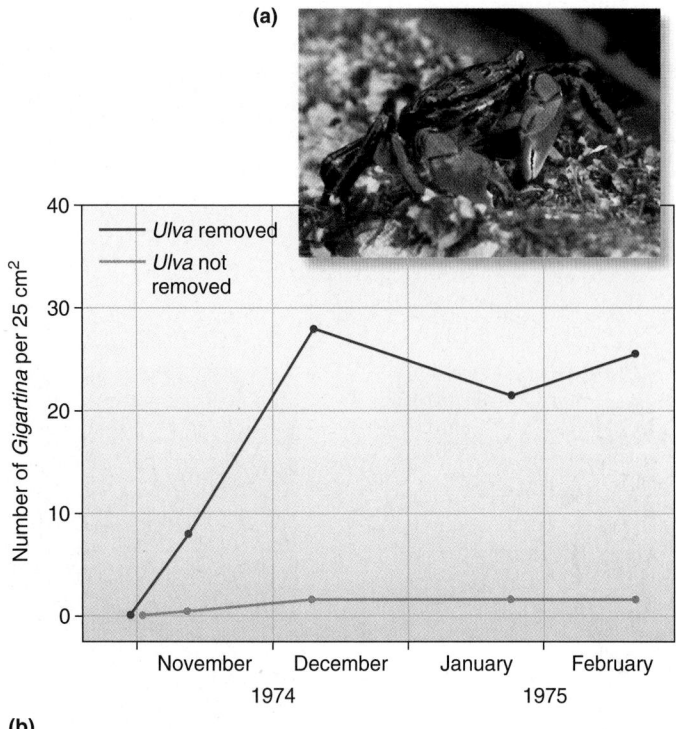

(a)

(b)

Figure 55.12 **Inhibition as a primary method of succession in the marine intertidal zone.**   (a) *Gigartina* on rock face with the herbivorous crab, *Pachygrapsus crassipes*. (b) Removing *Ulva* from intertidal rock faces allowed colonization by *Gigartina*.

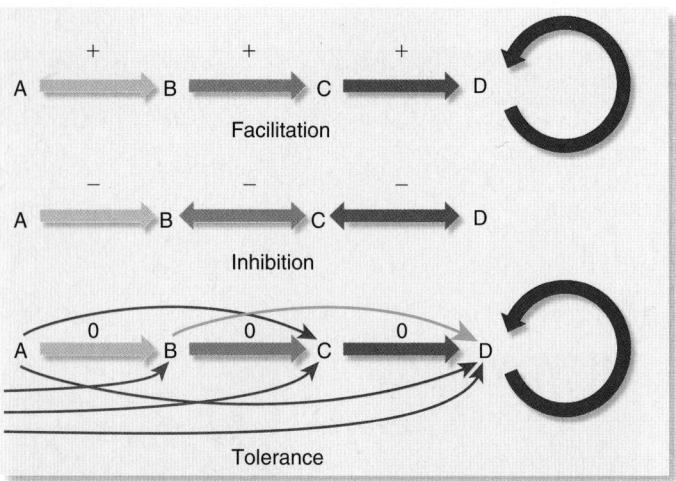

Figure 55.13   **Three models of succession.**   A, B, C, and D represent four stages or seres. D represents the climax community. An arrow indicates "is replaced by," and + = facilitation, − = inhibition, and 0 = no effect. The facilitation model is the classic model of succession. In the inhibition model, much depends on which species gets there first. The tolerance model is similar to the facilitation model, in that later species may be facilitated by earlier species, but they can also invade in their absence.

Concept check: *Inhibition implies competition between species with early-arriving species tending to outcompete later arrivals, at least for a while. Does competition or mutualism feature more prominently in facilitation?*

55.6 ISLAND BIOGEOGRAPHY

Learning Outcomes:

1. Describe the equilibrium model of island biogeography.
2. List the predictions of the model and discuss how well evidence supports them.

In the 1960s two eminent ecologists, Robert MacArthur and E. O. Wilson, developed a comprehensive model to explain the process of succession on new islands, where a gradual buildup of species proceeds from a sterile beginning. Their findings, termed the **equilibrium model of island biogeography**, hold that the number of species on an island tends toward an equilibrium number that is determined by the balance between two factors: immigration rates and extinction rates. In this section, we explore island biogeography and how well the model's predictions are supported by data, particularly that provided by classic experiments in the Florida Keys.

The Island Biogeography Model Suggests That During Succession Losses from Extinction Are Balanced by Gains in Immigration

MacArthur and Wilson's model of island biogeography suggests that species repeatedly arrive on an island and either thrive or become extinct. Thus, the number of species tends toward an equilibrium number, Ŝ, which reflects a balance between the rate of immigration and the rate of extinction. The rate of immigration of new species is highest when no species are present on the island, so that each species that invades the island is a new species. As species accumulate, subsequent immigrants are less likely to represent new species. The rate of extinction is low at the time of first colonization, because few species are present and many have large populations. With the addition of new species, the populations of some species diminish, so the probability of extinction by chance alone increases. Species may continue to arrive and go extinct, but the number of species on the island remains approximately the same.

MacArthur and Wilson reasoned that both the immigration and extinction lines would be curved, for several reasons (**Figure 55.14a**). First, species arrive on islands at different rates. Some organisms, including plants with seed dispersal mechanisms and winged animals, are more mobile than others and will arrive quickly. Other organisms will arrive more slowly. This pattern causes the immigration curve to start off steep but get progressively shallower. On the other hand, extinctions rise at accelerating rates, because as later species arrive, competition increases and more species are likely to go extinct. As noted previously, earlier-arriving species tend

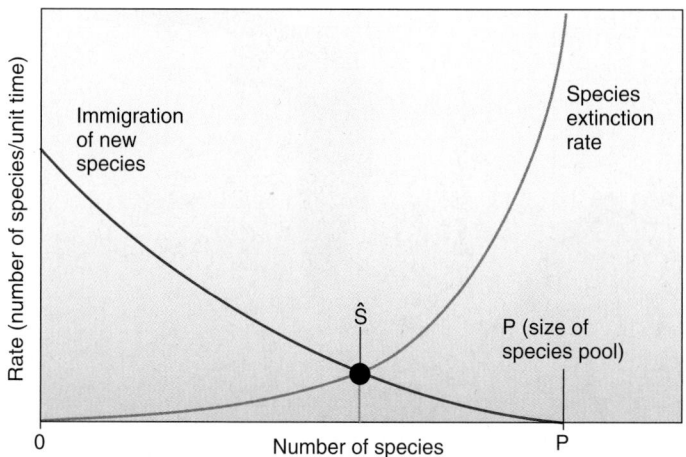

(a) Effects of immigration and extinction on species number

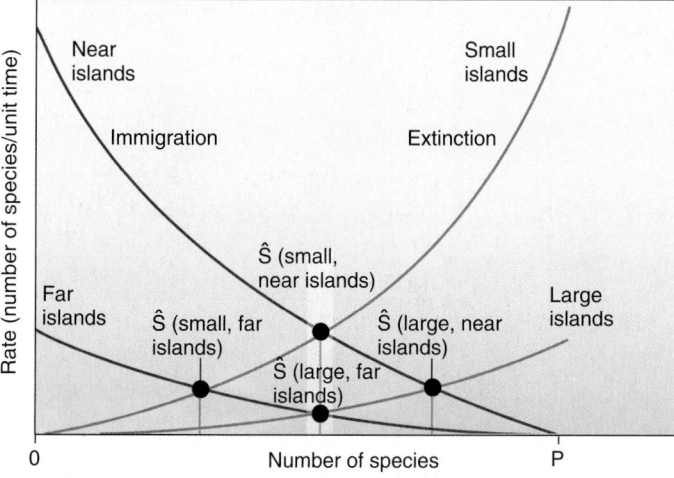

(b) Added effects of island size and proximity to the mainland on species number

Figure 55.14 MacArthur and Wilson's theory of island biogeography. (a) The interaction of immigration rate and extinction rate produces an equilibrium number of species on an island, Ŝ. Ŝ varies from 0 species to *P* species, the total number of species available to colonize. (b) Ŝ varies according to the island's size and distance from the mainland. An increase in distance (near to far) lowers the immigration curve, while an increase in island area (small to large) lowers the extinction rate.

Concept check: *Can you think of a scenario where there would be large numbers of species on a small island?*

BioConnections: *Look forward to Figure 57.12. How might the model of island biogeography be useful in the design of nature reserves?*

to be *r*-selected species, which are better dispersers, whereas later-arriving species are generally *K*-selected species, which are better competitors. Later-arriving species usually outcompete earlier-arriving ones, causing an increase in extinctions.

The strength of the island biogeography model was that it generated several falsifiable predictions:

1. The number of species should increase with increasing island size. This is also known as the species–area effect (see Figure 55.4). Extinction rates would be greater on smaller islands because population sizes would be smaller and more susceptible to extinction (**Figure 55.14b**).
2. The number of species should decrease with increasing distance of the island from the mainland, or the **source pool**, the pool of species available to colonize the island. Immigration rates would be greater on islands near the source pool because species do not have as far to travel (Figure 55.14b).
3. The turnover of species should be considerable. The number of species on an island might remain the same, but the composition of the species should change continuously as new species colonize the island and others become extinct.

Let's examine these predictions one by one and see how well the data support them.

The Number of Species Increases with Increasing Island Size

The West Indies has traditionally been a key location for ecologists studying island biogeography. This is because the physical geography and the plant and animal life of the islands are well known. Furthermore, the Lesser Antilles, from Anguilla in the north to Grenada in the south, enjoy a similar climate and are surrounded by deep water (**Figure 55.15a**). In 1999 Robert Ricklefs and Irby Lovette summarized the available data on the richness of species of four groups of animals—birds, bats, reptiles and amphibians, and butterflies—over 19 islands that varied in area over two orders of magnitude (13–1,510 square kilometres). In each case, a possible correlation occurred between area and species richness (**Figure 55.15b**). Note that these relationships are traditionally plotted on a double logarithmic scale, a so-called log-log plot, in which the horizontal axis is the logarithm to the base 10 of the area and the vertical axis is the logarithm to the base 10 of the number of species. A linear plot of the area versus the number of species would be difficult to produce, because of the wide range of area and richness of species involved. Logarithmic scales condense this variation to manageable limits.

Apart from Ricklefs and Lovette's study, species–area relationships exist for birds of the East Indies, beetles on West Indian islands, ants in Melanesia, and land plants of the Galápagos, providing strong support for this prediction of the equilibrium model of island biogeography.

The Number of Species Decreases with Increasing Distance from the Source Pool

MacArthur and Wilson also provided evidence for the effect of the distance of an island from a source pool of colonists, usually the mainland. In studies of the numbers of lowland forest bird species in Polynesia, they found that the number of species

Figure 55.15 Species richness increases with island size. (a) The Lesser Antilles extend from Anguilla in the north to Grenada in the south. (b) The number of bird, bat, reptile and amphibian, and butterfly species increases with the area of an island.

Concept check: *How large is the change in bird species richness across islands in the Lesser Antilles?*

decreased with the distance from New Guinea, the source pool in this case (**Figure 55.16**). They expressed the richness of bird species on the islands as a percentage of the number of bird species found on New Guinea. There was a significant decline in this percentage with increasing distance, with more distant islands containing lower numbers of species than nearer islands. This research substantiated the prediction of species richness declining with increasing distance from the source pool.

Species Turnover on Islands Is Generally Low

Studies involving species turnover on islands are difficult to perform because detailed and complete species lists are needed over long periods of time, usually many years and often decades. The lists that do exist are often compiled in a casual way and are not usually suitable for comparison with more modern data. In 1980 British researcher Francis Gilbert reviewed 25 investigations carried out to demonstrate turnover and found a lack of this type of rigour in nearly all of them. Furthermore, most of

the observed turnover in these studies, usually less than 1% per year, or less than one species per year, appeared to be due to immigrants that never became established, not due to the extinction of well-established species. More recent studies have revealed similar findings. The take-home message from most studies is that recorded rates of turnover are low, giving little conclusive support to this prediction of the equilibrium model of island biogeography.

Conservation and the Theory of Island Biogeography

In conservation biology, habitat fragmentation has been related to the theory of island biogeography, where islands (e.g., forest patches) separated from the mainland (e.g., main forest) undergo individual selection pressures and therefore experience extinction or evolution in isolation. The fragmentation of habitat is a continuous landscape process affecting all natural environments (although it is most typical in the case of deforestation)

(a) New Guinea and neighbouring islands

Figure 55.16 Species richness decreases with distance from the source pool.   (a) Map of Australia, New Guinea, and these Polynesian Islands: New Caledonia, Fiji Islands, Cook Islands, Marquesas Islands, Pitcairn, and Easter Island. (b) The numbers of bird species on islands with increasing distance from the source pool, New Guinea, expressed as the percentage of bird species on New Guinea.

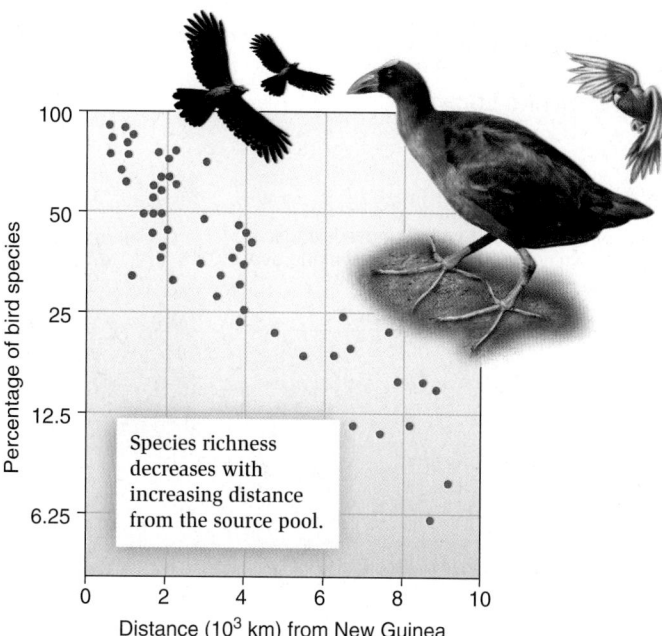

Species richness decreases with increasing distance from the source pool.

(b) Relationship between species richness and distance from source

with variable effects upon different species and among different regions. The use of island biogeography concepts to study habitat fragmentation has provided a spatial ecology framework for the field of conservation biology, and some of the basic principles are directly transferable. However, habitat fragmentation differs from island biogeography in that it also incorporates a loss of habitat, as well as spaces between original habitats varying in suitability for species. Therefore, although an island biogeography approach has some uses in the study of habitat fragmentation, a regional and specific approach is also necessary in conservation biology.

FEATURE INVESTIGATION

Wilson and Simberloff's Experiments Tested the Predictions of the Equilibrium Model of Island Biogeography

E. O. Wilson and Daniel Simberloff conducted possibly the best test of the equilibrium model of island biogeography ever performed using islands in the Florida Keys. They surveyed four small red mangrove (*Rhizophora mangle*) islands, 11–25 m in diameter, for all terrestrial arthropods. They then enclosed each island with a plastic tent and had the islands fumigated with methyl bromide, a short-acting insecticide, to remove all arthropods on them. The tents were removed, and periodically thereafter Wilson and Simberloff surveyed the islands to examine recolonization rates. At each survey, they counted all the species present, noting any species not there at the previous census and the absence of others that were previously there but had presumably gone extinct (results for four of the islands shown in **Figure 55.17**). In this way, they estimated turnover of species on islands.

After 250 days, all but one of the islands had a similar number of arthropod species as they had to begin with, even though population densities were still low. The data indicated that colonization rates were higher on islands nearer to the mainland than on far islands—as the island biogeography model predicts. However, the data, which consisted of lists of species on islands before and after extinctions, provided little support for the prediction of high turnover. Rates of turnover were low, only 1.5 extinctions per year, compared to the 15 to 40 species found on the islands within a year. Wilson and Simberloff concluded that turnover probably involves only a small subset of transient or unimportant species, with the more important species being permanent after colonization.

In summary, MacArthur and Wilson's equilibrium model of island biogeography has stimulated much research that confirms the strong effects of area and distance on species richness. However, species turnover appears to be low rather than considerable, which suggests that succession on most islands is a fairly orderly process. This means that colonization is not a random process and that the same species seem to always colonize first and other species gradually reappear in the same order.

It is also important to note that the principles of island biogeography have been applied to wildlife preserves, which are essentially islands in a sea of developed land, either agricultural fields or urban sprawl. Conservationists have utilized island biogeography modelling in the design of nature preserves, a topic we will return to in Chapter 57.

HYPOTHESIS Island biogeography model predicts higher species richness for islands closer to the mainland and significant turnover of species on islands.

STARTING LOCATION Mangrove islands in the Florida Keys.

| Experimental level | Conceptual level |

1   Take initial census of all terrestrial arthropods on four mangrove islands. Erect a framework over each mangrove island.

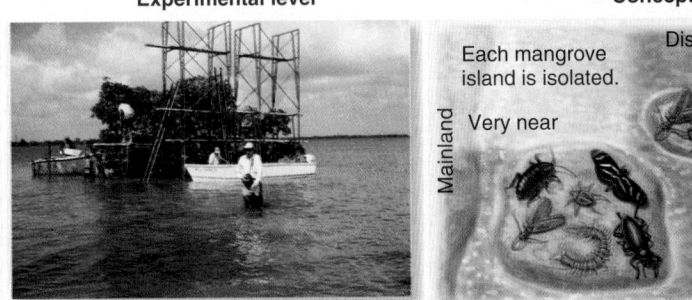

Each mangrove island is isolated.

2   Cover the framework with tents and fumigate with methyl bromide to kill all arthropod species.

Methyl bromide is a low-persistent insecticide that at low levels will not kill plant life.

3   Remove the tents and conduct censuses every month to monitor recolonization of arthropods and to determine extinction rates.

Mangrove islands are recolonized.

4   **THE DATA**   Island E2 was closest to the mainland and supported the highest number of species both before and after fumigation. E3 and ST2 were at an intermediate distance from the mainland, and E1 was the most distant.

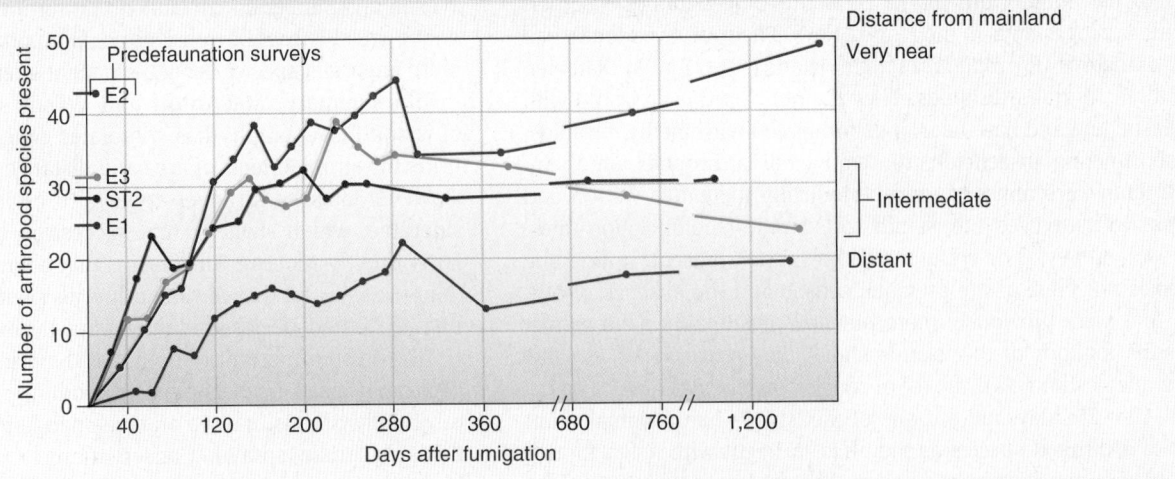

Figure 55.17   Wilson and Simberloff's experiments on the equilibrium model of biogeography.

5   CONCLUSION Island size and distance from the mainland influence species richness on mangrove islands in the Florida Keys. However, species turnover is minimal, and species richness changes little following initial recolonization.

6   SOURCE Simberloff, D.S. 1978. Colonization of islands by insects: immigration, extinction and diversity. pp. 139–153 in L.A. Mound and N. Waloff (eds.) *Diversity of insect faunas*. Blackwell Scientific Publications, Oxford, U.K.

Experimental Questions

1. What was the purpose of Simberloff and Wilson's study?
2. Why did the researchers conduct a thorough species survey of arthropods before experimental removal of all the arthropod species?

3. What did the researchers conclude about the relationship between island proximity to the mainland and species richness and turnover?

In this chapter, we have seen how important species richness is to community function. It affects not only stability but also, as we shall see, many other features of a community such as nutrient uptake, biomass, and productivity. In order to know how diversity affects these properties, we need to understand the basic processes of energy flow and chemical cycling within a community and its surrounding environment, and for that we turn to a discussion of ecosystems ecology.

Summary of Key Concepts

55.1 Differing Views of Communities

- Community ecology studies how groups of species interact and form functional communities. Ecologists have differing views on the nature of a community. In one view, communities are tightly organized groups of mutually dependent species, and in another, they are loose assemblies of species that happen to live in the same place at the same time. (Figure 55.1)

55.2 Patterns of Species Richness

- While many observations support the idea that communities are loose assemblages of species, sharp boundaries between groups of species do exist, especially related to physical differences that cause distinct communities to develop. (Figure 55.2)
- The number of species of most taxa varies according to geographic location, generally increasing from polar areas to tropical areas. (Figure 55.3)
- Varying hypotheses for the polar-equatorial gradient have been advanced, including the time hypothesis, the area hypothesis, the productivity hypothesis, and the intermediate-disturbance hypothesis. (Figures 55.4, 55.5, 55.6)

55.3 Calculating Species Diversity

- The most widely used measure of the diversity of a community, called the Shannon diversity index, takes into account both species richness and species abundance.
- The field of metagenomics seeks to identify and analyze the genomes contained in a community of microorganisms. (Figure 55.7)

55.4 Species Richness and Community Stability

- Community stability is an important consideration in ecology. The diversity–stability hypothesis maintains that species-rich communities are more stable than communities with fewer species.

- Tilman's field experiments, which showed that year-to-year variation in plant biomass decreased with increasing species diversity, established a link between diversity and stability. (Figure 55.8)

55.5 Succession: Community Change

- Succession describes the gradual and continuous change in community structure over time. Primary succession refers to succession on a newly exposed site not previously occupied by soil; secondary succession refers to succession on a site that has already supported life but has undergone a disturbance. (Figures 55.9, 55.10)
- Three mechanisms have been proposed for succession: in facilitation, each species facilitates or makes the environment more suitable for subsequent species. In inhibition, initial species inhibit later colonists. In tolerance, any species can start the succession, and species replacement is unaffected by previous colonists. (Figures 55.11, 55.12, 55.13)

55.6 Island Biogeography

- In the equilibrium model of island biogeography, the number of species on an island tends toward an equilibrium number determined by the balance between immigration rates and extinction rates. (Figure 55.14)
- The model predicts that the number of species increases with increasing island size, and that the number of species decreases with distance from the source pool. (Figures 55.15, 55.16)
- Wilson and Simberloff's experiments on mangrove islands in the Florida Keys provided some support for the island biogeography model. (Figure 55.17)

Test to Assess Your Learning

1. The number of species in a community is called
   a. species complexity.
   b. community complexity.
   c. species richness.
   d. species diversity.
   e. species abundance.

2. Which of the following statements best represents the productivity hypothesis regarding species richness?
   a. The larger the area, the greater the number of species that will be found there.
   b. Temperate regions have a lower species richness due to the lack of time available for migration after the last ice age.
   c. The number of species in a particular community is directly related to the amount of plant biomass available for consumers.
   d. As invertebrate productivity increases, species richness will increase.
   e. Species richness is not related to primary productivity.

3. The Shannon diversity index is a measure of
   a. the number of different species in a community.
   b. the abundance of a species in a community.
   c. the types of species found in a typical climate.
   d. the number of different species and their relative abundance in a community.
   e. the distribution of members of a species in a community.

4. Metagenomics is a field of study that
   a. determines the similarities of the genomes of all species in a community.
   b. focuses on the microbial genomes contained in a community.
   c. compares the genomes of similar species in different communities.
   d. none of the above.
   e. both (a) and (b).

5. Extreme fluctuations in species abundance
   a. lead to more diverse communities.
   b. are usually seen in early stages of community development.
   c. may increase the likelihood of extinction.
   d. have very little effect on species richness.
   e. are characteristic of stable communities.

6. Which of the following statements best represents the relationship between species diversity and community disturbance?
   a. Species diversity and community stability have no relationship.
   b. Communities with high levels of disturbance are more diverse.
   c. Communities with low levels of disturbance are more diverse.
   d. Communities with intermediate levels of disturbance are more diverse.
   e. Communities with intermediate levels of disturbance are less diverse.

7. The process of primary succession occurs
   a. around a recently erupted volcano.
   b. on a newly plowed field.
   c. on a hillside that has suffered a mudslide.
   d. on a recently flooded riverbank.
   e. none of the above.

8. When the early colonizers exclude subsequent colonists from moving into a community, this is referred to as
   a. facilitation.
   b. competitive exclusion.
   c. secondary succession.
   d. inhibition.
   e. natural selection.

9. Which of the following statements is not true concerning island biogeography?
   a. Diversity on islands is directly related to the size of the island.
   b. Diversity on islands is inversely related to the distance of the island from the source for colonizing species.
   c. The number of species on an island represents the balance between immigration and extinction rates.
   d. The number of species on an island increases with increasing distance from the source pool.
   e. The number of species on an island increases with increasing island size.

10. The equilibrium model of island biogeography
    a. is a method of mapping islands in the Pacific Ocean.
    b. is a method of identifying particular species on particular islands.
    c. describes factors that influence succession on new islands.
    d. describes the pattern of species types that first colonize an island.
    e. predicts that the first colonizers of an island will become extinct.

Articulate to Assess Your Learning

1. Define a community and community ecology.
2. List some possible ecological disturbances, their likely frequency in natural communities, and the severity of their effects.
3. In the nutrient-poor heathlands of Europe, scotch heather (*Calluna vulgaris*) and cross-leaved heath (*Erica tetralix*) are gradually replaced by variegated purple moor grass (*Molinia caerulea*) and wavy hair grass (*Deschampsia flexuosa*). Adding Calluna litter or nitrogen fertilizer speeds up this process. Explain this phenomenon and which mechanism of succession is supported.

Collaborate to Assess and Extend Your Learning

1. Distinguish between the time hypothesis, area hypothesis, and productivity hypothesis as explanation for the latitudinal gradient in species richness.
2. Calculate the species diversity of the following four communities. Which community has the highest diversity? What is the maximum diversity each community could have?

Community	Relative Abundance of Species H_S			Maximum Possible Diversity
	Species 1	Species 2	Species 3	
1	90	10	–	
2	50	50	–	
3	80	10	10	
4	33.3	33.3	33.3	

3. A principle of biology is that populations of organisms evolve from one generation to the next. Use examples provided in this chapter to describe how populations might change and evolve during succession in a community. Include primary and secondary succession, and the three mechanisms that have been proposed for succession.

Visit McGraw-Hill Ryerson Connect™ for additional study resources.

Ecosystem Ecology

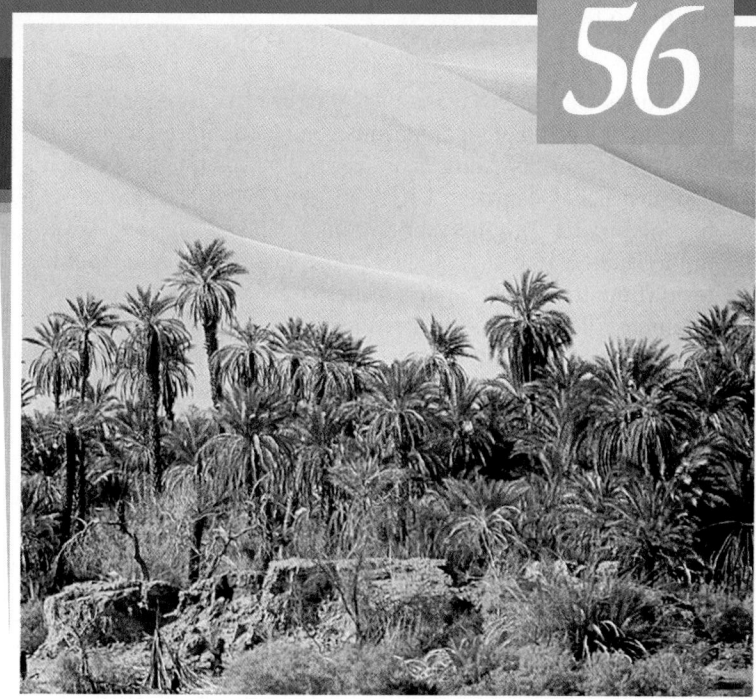

The term **ecosystems** was coined in 1935 by the British plant ecologist A. G. Tansley. An ecosystem includes not only the biotic community of organisms in an area but also the abiotic environment affecting that community. **Ecosystem ecology** is concerned with the movement of energy and materials through organisms and their communities. Just like the concept of a community, the ecosystem concept can be applied at any scale: A small pond inhabited by protozoa and insect larvae is an ecosystem, and an oasis with its plants, frogs, fish, and birds constitutes another. Most ecosystems cannot be regarded as having definite boundaries. Even in a clearly defined pond ecosystem, amphibians may be moving in and out (**Figure 56.1**). Nevertheless, studying ecosystem ecology allows us to use the common currency of energy and chemicals, or nutrients, to compare the functions between and within ecosystems. As we will see, energy moves in one direction through an ecosystem (from producers to consumers), whereas nutrients are moved through both biotic and abiotic compartments of the ecosystem, in effect being constantly recycled.

In investigating the different processes of an ecosystem, at least three major constituents can be measured: energy flow, biomass production, and biogeochemical cycling. We begin the chapter by exploring **energy flow**, the movement of energy through the ecosystem. In examining energy flow, the main tasks are to document the complex networks of feeding relationships, called food webs, and to measure the efficiency of energy transfer between organisms in an ecosystem. We also consider the tendency of chemical elements to accumulate in organisms, a process called biomagnification.

Next, we focus on the measurement of **biomass**, a quantitative estimate of the total mass of living matter in a given area, usually measured in grams or kilograms per square metre. We will examine the amount of biomass produced through photosynthesis, termed *primary production*, and the amount of biomass produced by the organisms that are the consumers of primary production.

The functioning of an ecosystem can sometimes be most limited by the availability of a scarce chemical or mineral. In the last section, we examine the movement of limiting chemicals through ecosystems, called **biogeochemical cycles**. We explore the cycling of chemical elements such as nitrogen, carbon, sulphur, and phosphorus and the effect that human activities have on these ecosystemwide processes.

Mandara Lake Oasis, Libya.

56.1 / FOOD WEBS AND ENERGY FLOW

Learning Outcomes:

1. Distinguish between autotrophs and heterotrophs and between primary, secondary, and tertiary consumers.
2. Describe two ways to measure the efficiency of consumers as energy transformers.
3. List and describe the different types of ecological pyramids.
4. Explain how the process of biomagnification can occur at higher trophic levels.

Figure 56.1 A small ecosystem. Even in this pond ecosystem, insects, frogs, or other species such as birds may move in and out, importing or exporting nutrients and energy with them.

Most organisms either make their own food using energy from sunlight or feed on other organisms. Simple feeding relationships between organisms can be characterized by an unbranched **food chain**, a linear depiction of energy flow, with each organism feeding on and deriving energy from organisms one step lower in the chain. Each feeding level in the chain is called a **trophic level** (from the Greek *trophos*, feeder), and different species feed at different levels. In a food chain diagram, an arrow connects each trophic level with the one above it (**Figure 56.2**).

In this section, we will examine trophic relationships and the flow of energy in a food chain and a food web, a more complex model of interconnected food chains. We will then explore two of the most important features of food webs—chain length and the pyramid of numbers—and learn how the passage of nutrients through food webs can result in the concentration of harmful chemicals in the tissues of organisms at higher trophic levels.

The Main Trophic Levels Within Food Chains Consist of Primary Producers, Primary Consumers, and Secondary Consumers

Food chains typically consist of organisms that obtain energy in different ways. **Autotrophs** harvest light or chemical energy and store that energy in carbon compounds. Most autotrophs, including plants, algae, and photosynthetic prokaryotes, use sunlight for this process. These organisms, called **primary producers**, are at the base of the food chain. They produce the energy-rich tissue upon which nearly all other organisms depend. Note that not all primary producers utilize sunlight; some organisms, called chemoautotrophs (see Chapter 25), obtain their energy by oxidizing inorganic compounds such as sulphides (**Figure 56.3**).

Organisms in trophic levels above the primary producers are termed **heterotrophs**. These organisms receive their nutrition by eating other organisms. Organisms that obtain their food by eating primary producers are **primary consumers** and include animals, most protists, and even some plants. They are also called **herbivores**. Organisms that eat primary consumers are **secondary consumers**, also called **carnivores** (from the Latin, *carn*, flesh). Organisms that feed on secondary consumers are called **tertiary consumers**, and so on. Thus, energy enters a food chain through primary producers, generally via photosynthesis, and is passed up the food chain to primary, secondary, and tertiary consumers (see Figure 56.2). However, some consumers may feed at several different trophic levels. Omnivores, for instance, may feed on both primary producers and primary consumers.

Much energy from the first trophic level, the plants, goes unconsumed by herbivores. Instead, unconsumed plants die and decompose in place. This material, along with dead remains of animals and waste products, is called **detritus**. Consumers that get their energy from detritus, called **detritivores** or **decomposers**, break down dead organisms from all trophic levels (**Figure 56.4**). Detritivores probably carry out 80%–90% of the consumption of plant matter, with different species working in concert to extract most of the energy. Detritivores may in turn support a community of predators that feed on them.

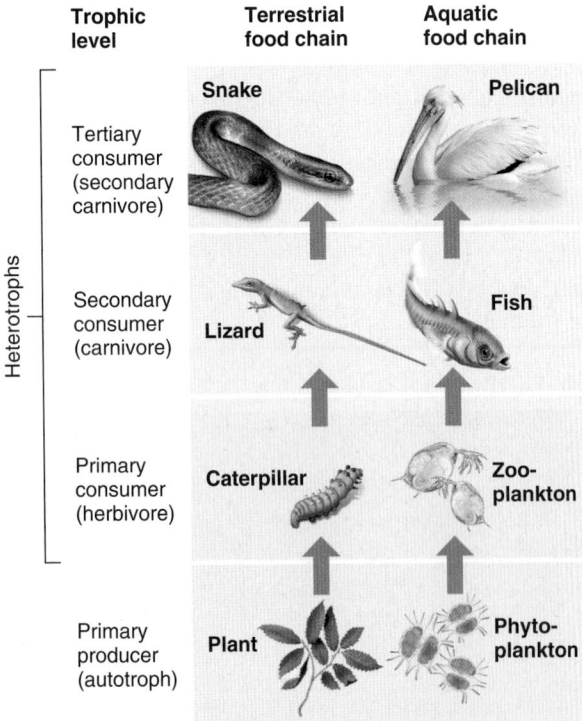

Figure 56.2 **Food chains.** Two examples of the flow of food energy up the trophic levels: a terrestrial food chain, and an aquatic food chain.

BioConnections: *In these two food chains, plants and protists (phytoplankton) are the producers. Look back at section 25.5. What other organisms are producers and could also support food chains?*

Figure 56.3 **Chemoautotrophic organisms living around deep-sea hydrothermal vents.** Some bacteria obtain their energy from the sulphur-rich emissions of hydrothermal vents on the ocean floor, also called black smokers.

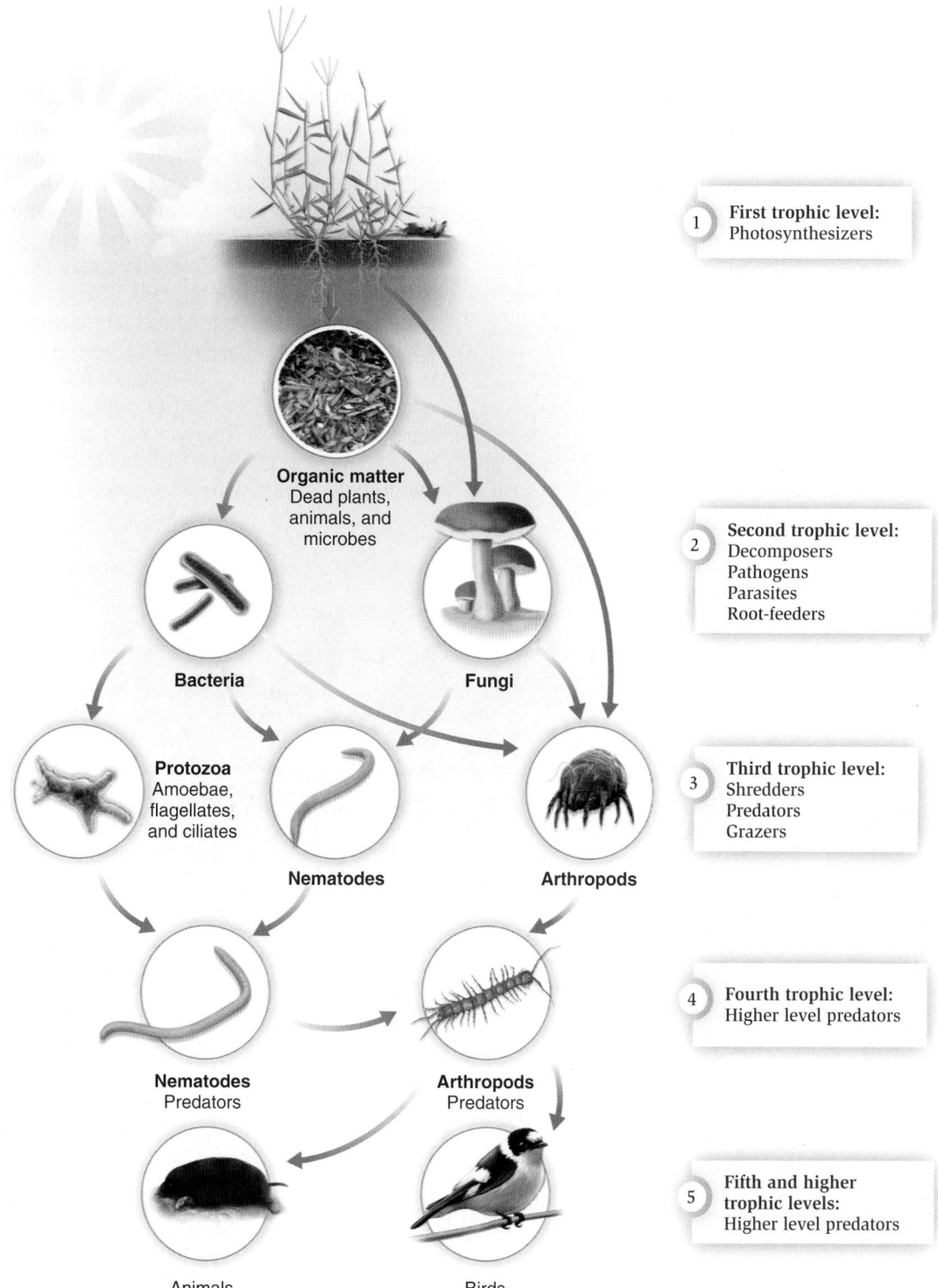

First trophic level:
Photosynthesizers ... 1

Second trophic level: ... 2
Decomposers
Pathogens
Parasites
Root-feeders

Third trophic level: ... 3
Shredders
Predators
Grazers

Fourth trophic level: ... 4
Higher level predators

Fifth and higher ... 5
trophic levels:
Higher level predators

Organic matter
Dead plants,
animals, and
microbes

Bacteria

Fungi

Protozoa
Amoebae,
flagellates,
and ciliates

Nematodes

Arthropods

Nematodes
Predators

Arthropods
Predators

Animals

Birds

Figure 56.4 Decomposers (detritivores) feeding on dead plant and animal matter. Many dead plants and animals are eaten by a variety of organisms. Here, pill bugs and fungi feed on dead wood and rotting plant material, while earthworms, nematodes, and bacteria decompose organic matter in the soil. Dead animals, or carrion, may be fed upon by blowfly larvae, carrion beetles, and other scavengers. These may, in turn, support a variety of predators, including centipedes or larger predators such as birds, which will also feed on the animal carcass.

Concept check: *At which trophic level do decomposers feed?*

BioConnections: *Name two fungal phyla that are active in decomposition. (Hint: Refer back to Table 27.1.)*

Usually, many herbivore species feed on the same plant species. For example, one may find many insect species and vertebrate grazers all feeding on one type of plant. Also, many species of herbivores eat several different plant species. Such branching of food chains also occurs at other trophic levels. For instance, on the African savannah, cheetahs, leopards, lions, and wild dogs all eat a variety of prey including giraffes, gazelles, baboons, zebras, and wildebeest. These, in turn, eat a variety of grasses and trees. It is more correct, then, to draw relationships between these plants and animals not as a simple chain but as a more elaborate interwoven **food web**, in which there are multiple links among species (**Figure 56.5**).

In Most Food Webs, Chain Lengths Are Short and a Pyramid of Numbers Exists

Now that we have introduced the structure of food webs, let's examine some of their characteristics in more detail. In food webs, the concept of chain length refers to the number of links between the trophic levels involved. For example, if a lion feeds on a zebra, and a zebra feeds on grass, the chain length would be two. For most food webs, chain lengths tend to be short, usually fewer than five. The main reason why they are short comes from the well-established laws of physics and chemistry that we discussed in Chapter 2. The first law of thermodynamics states that energy cannot be created or destroyed, only transformed. We can thus construct energy budgets for food webs that trace energy flow from green plants to tertiary consumers (and, if needed, beyond). The second law of thermodynamics states that energy conversions are not 100% efficient. In any transfer process, some useful energy, which can do work, is lost (**Figure 56.6**). This suggests that we can compare the efficiency of energy transfer through trophic levels in different types of food webs. The two main measures of the efficiency of consumers as energy transformers are production efficiency and trophic-level transfer efficiency.

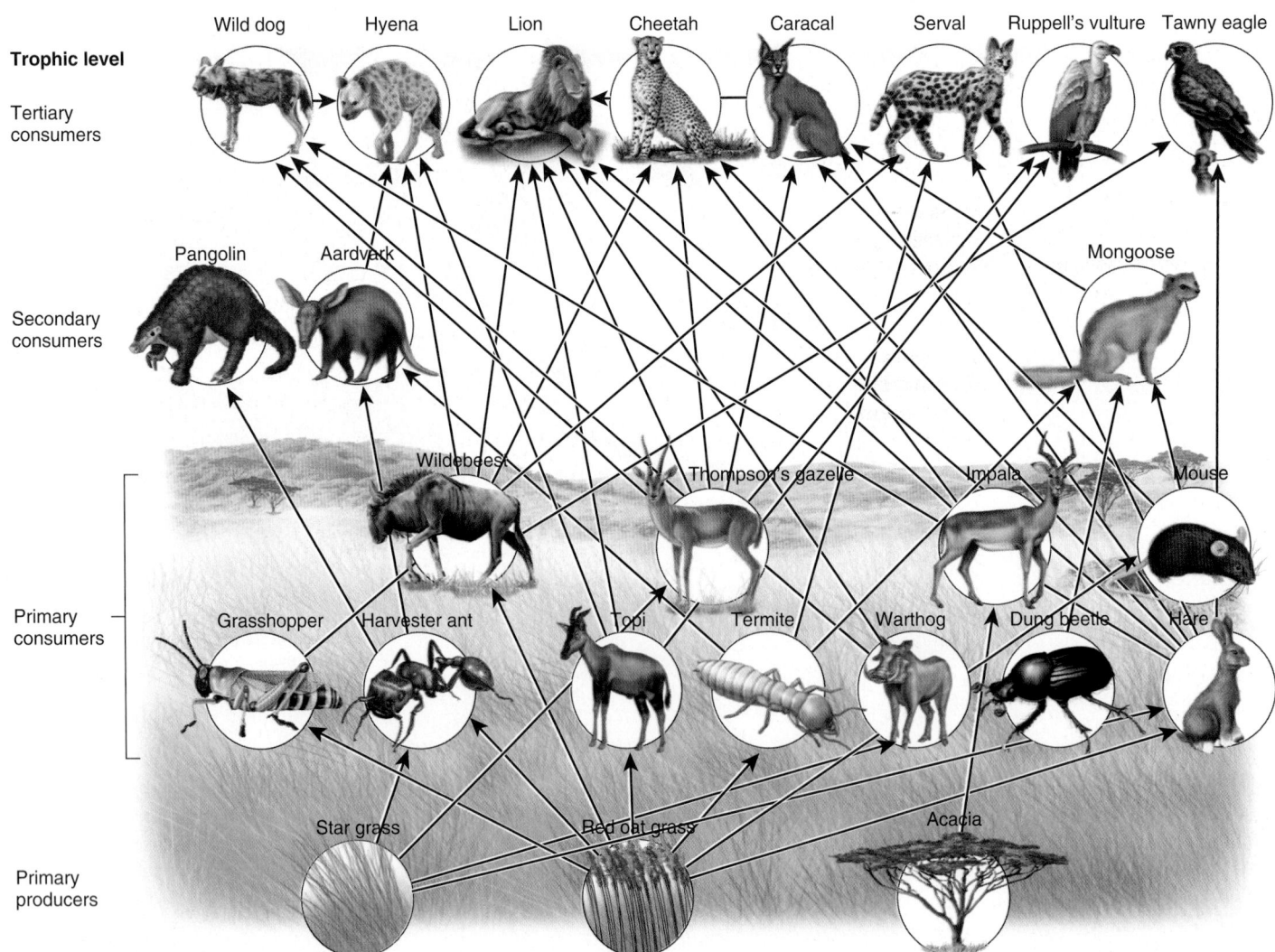

Figure 56.5 **A simplified food web from an African savannah ecosystem.** Each trophic level is occupied by different species. Generally, each species feeds on, or is fed upon by, more than one species.

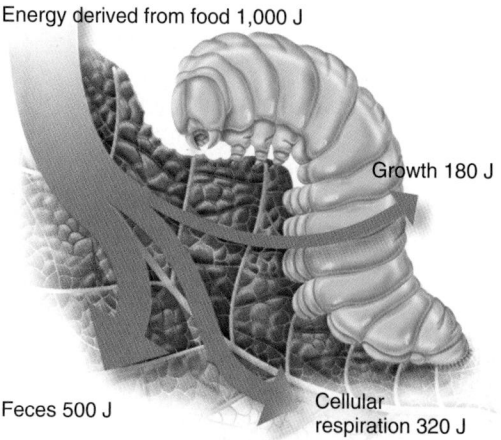

(a) High production efficiency of an invertebrate

(b) Low production efficiency of a vertebrate

Figure 56.6 **Energy flow through an ecosystem.** **(a)** Energy lost as heat in a single trophic level. **(b)** Energy lost in the conversion between one trophic level and another.

 Principle: *Living organisms use energy. Within trophic levels, energy is lost to maintenance, and between trophic levels, energy is lost to imperfect efficiency of transfer.*

Production Efficiency **Production efficiency** is defined as the percentage of energy assimilated by an organism that becomes incorporated into new biomass.

$$\text{Production efficiency} = \frac{\text{Net productivity}}{\text{Assimilation}} \times 100$$

Here, net productivity is the energy, stored in biomass, that has accumulated over a given time span, and assimilation is the total amount of energy taken in by an organism over the same time span. Invertebrates generally have high production efficiencies that average about 10%–40% (**Figure 56.7a**). Microorganisms also have relatively high production efficiencies. Vertebrates tend to have lower production efficiencies than invertebrates, because they devote more energy to sustaining their metabolism than to new biomass production. Even within vertebrates, much variation occurs. Fish, which are ectotherms, typically have production efficiencies of around 10%, and birds and mammals, which are endotherms, have production efficiencies in the range of 1%–2% (**Figure 56.7b**). In large part, the difference reflects the energy cost of maintaining a constant body temperature.

One consequence of these differences is that sparsely vegetated deserts can support healthy populations of snakes and lizards while mammals might easily starve. The largest living lizard known, the Komodo dragon, eats the equivalent of its own weight every two months, whereas a cheetah consumes approximately four times its own weight in the same period. It is also interesting to note that production efficiencies are higher in young animals, which are rapidly accruing biomass, than in older animals, which are not. This is the main reason behind the practice of raising young chickens and calves for meat.

Trophic-Level Transfer Efficiency The second measure of efficiency of consumers as energy transformers is **trophic-level transfer efficiency**, which is the amount of energy at one trophic level that is acquired by the trophic level above and

Figure 56.7 **Production efficiency.** **(a)** This caterpillar, an invertebrate and ectotherm, chews leaves to obtain its energy. If a mouthful of food contains 1,000 joules (J) of energy, about 320 J is used to fuel metabolic processes (32%) and 500 J (50%) is lost in feces. This leaves about 180 J to be converted into insect biomass, a production efficiency of 18%. **(b)** The production efficiency of this squirrel, a vertebrate and endotherm, is much lower.

Concept check: *What is the production efficiency of the squirrel, using the numbers in the figure?*

 Principle: *Living organisms have mechanisms to maintain homeostasis. For the squirrel, maintaining a constant body temperature reduces its production efficiency.*

incorporated into biomass. This provides a way to examine energy flow between trophic levels, not just in individual species. Trophic-level transfer efficiency is calculated as:

$$\text{Trophic-level transfer efficiency} = \frac{\text{Production at trophic level } n}{\text{Production at trophic level } n-1} \times 100$$

For example, if there were 14 g/m^2 of zooplankton in a lake (trophic level n) and 100 g/m^2 of phytoplankton production (trophic level $n - 1$), the trophic-level efficiency would be 14%. Trophic-level transfer efficiency appears to average around 10%, though there is much variation. In some marine food chains, for example, it can exceed 30%.

Trophic-level transfer efficiency is low for two reasons. First, many organisms cannot digest all their prey. They take only the easily digestible plant leaves or animal tissue such as muscles and guts, leaving the hard wood or bones behind. Second, much of the energy assimilated by animals is used in maintenance, so most energy is lost from the system as heat. The 10% average transfer rate of energy from one trophic level to another also necessitates short food webs of no more than four or five levels. Relatively little energy is available for the higher levels.

The Pyramid of Numbers Trophic-level transfer efficiencies can be expressed in a graphical form called an Eltonian pyramid, named after British ecologist Charles Elton. The best-known pyramid, and the one described by Elton in 1927, is the **pyramid of numbers**, in which the number of individuals decreases at each trophic level, with a huge number of individuals at the base and fewer individuals at the top. Elton's example was that of a small pond where the numbers of protozoa may run into the millions and those of *Daphnia*, their predators, number in the hundreds of thousands. Hundreds of beetle larvae may feed on *Daphnia*, and tens of fish feed on the beetles. Many other examples of this type of pyramid are known. For example, in a grassland there may be hundreds of individual plants per square metre, dozens of insects that feed on the plants, and a few spiders feeding on the insects, and birds that feed on the spiders (**Figure 56.8a**).

However, one can also think of several exceptions to this pyramid. An oak tree, one

Figure 56.8 Ecological pyramids in food webs. (a) In this pyramid of numbers, the abundance of species in an American grassland decreases with increasing trophic level. (b) An inverted pyramid of numbers based on organisms living in a British temperate forest. (c) When the amount of biological material is used instead of numbers of individuals, the pyramid is termed a *pyramid of biomass*. Note the presence of decomposers that decompose material at all trophic levels. (d) An inverted pyramid of biomass in the English Channel. (e) A pyramid of energy for Silver Springs, Florida. Note the large energy production of decomposers, despite their small biomass.

(a) Pyramid of numbers

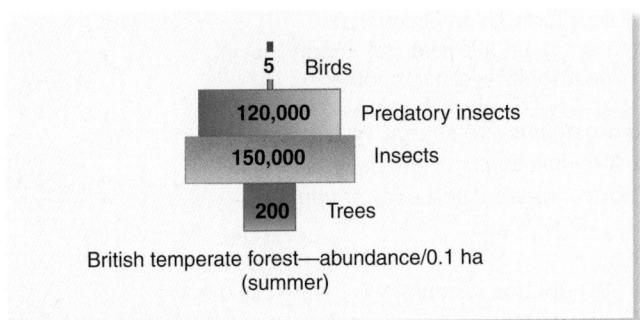

(b) Inverted pyramid of numbers

(c) Pyramid of biomass

(d) Inverted pyramid of biomass

(e) Pyramid of energy

single producer, supports hundreds of herbivorous beetles, caterpillars, and other primary consumers, which in turn may support thousands of predators and parasites. This is called an inverted pyramid of numbers (**Figure 56.8b**). The best way to reconcile this apparent exception is to weigh the organisms in each trophic level, creating a **pyramid of biomass**. At the bottom of the pyramid is the standing crop, the total autotroph biomass in an ecosystem present at any one point in time. Looking at the biomass at each trophic level rather than at numbers of organisms shows an upright pyramid. In 1957 Howard Odum measured the pyramid of biomass for a freshwater ecosystem in Silver Springs, Florida (**Figure 56.8c**). Beds of eelgrass (genus *Sagittaria*) and attached algae make up most of the producers. Insects, snails, herbivorous fishes, and turtles eat the producers. Other fishes form the secondary and tertiary consumers. Odum also noted the presence of fungi and bacteria, which were involved in decomposition on all trophic levels.

Even when biomass is used as the measure, inverted pyramids can still occur, albeit rarely. In some marine and lake systems, the biomass of phytoplankton supports a higher biomass of zooplankton (**Figure 56.8d**). This is possible because the rate of production of phytoplankton biomass is much higher than that of zooplankton, and the small phytoplankton **standing crop** processes large amounts of energy.

However, by expressing the pyramid in terms of production rate, it is no longer inverted. The **pyramid of energy**, which shows the rate of energy production rather than standing crop, is never inverted (**Figure 56.8e**). The laws of thermodynamics ensure that the highest amounts of free energy are found at the lowest trophic levels. The energy pyramid for Silver Springs also shows that large amounts of energy pass through decomposers, despite their relatively small biomass.

Biomagnification Can Occur in Higher Trophic Levels

Thus far, we have considered how available biomass and energy flow can influence the properties of food chains and webs. An issue that faces organisms is the tendency of certain chemical elements to accumulate or build up within food chains. This increase in the concentration of a substance in living organisms is called **biomagnification**, and the passage of DDT in food chains provides a startling example.

Dichlorodiphenyltrichloroethane (DDT) was first synthesized by chemists in 1874. In 1939 its insecticidal properties were recognized by Paul Müller, a Swiss scientist who won a Nobel Prize in 1948 for his discovery and subsequent research on the uses of the chemical. The first important application of DDT was in human health programs during and after World War II, particularly to control mosquito-borne malaria, and at that time its use in agriculture also began. The global production of DDT peaked in 1970, when 175 million kilograms of the insecticide were manufactured.

DDT has several chemical and physical properties that profoundly influence the nature of its ecological impact. First, DDT is persistent in the environment; it is not easily degraded to other, less toxic chemicals by microorganisms or by physical

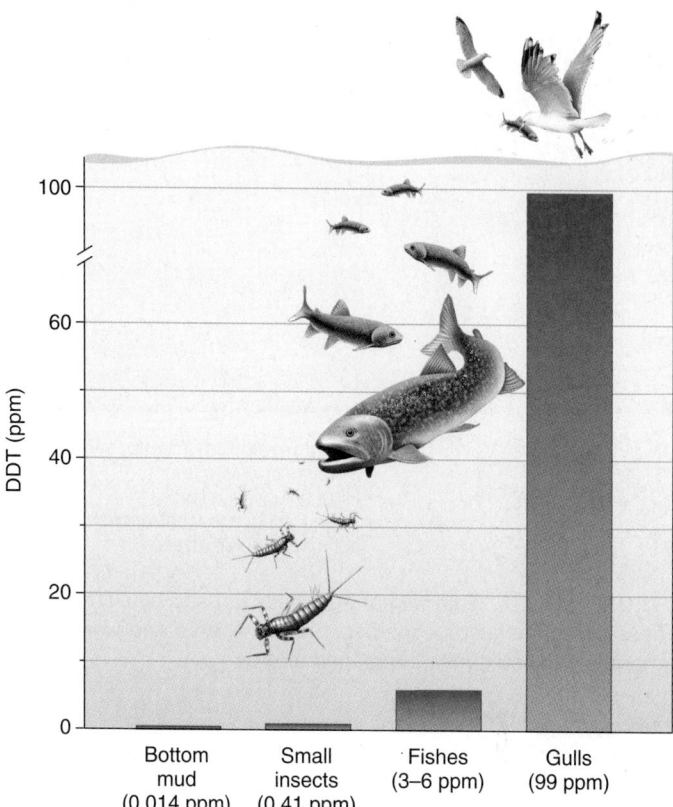

Figure 56.9 Biomagnification in a Lake Ontario food chain. The DDT tissue concentration in gulls, a tertiary consumer, was about 240 times that in the small insects sharing the same environment. The biomagnification of DDT in lipids causes its concentration to increase at each successive link in the food chain.

agents such as light and heat. The typical persistence in soil of DDT is about 10 years, which is two to three times longer than the persistence of most other insecticides. Another important characteristic of DDT is its low solubility in water and its high solubility in fats or lipids. In the environment, most lipids are present in living tissue. Therefore, because of its high lipid solubility, DDT tends to concentrate in biological tissues.

Because biomagnification occurs at each step of the food chain, organisms at higher trophic levels can amass especially large concentrations of DDT in their lipids. A typical pattern of biomagnification is illustrated in **Figure 56.9**, which shows the relative amounts of DDT found in a Lake Ontario food chain. The largest concentration of the insecticide was found in gulls, tertiary consumers that feed on fish that, in turn, eat small insects. An unanticipated effect of DDT on bird species was its interference with the metabolic process of eggshell formation. The result was thin-shelled eggs that often broke under the weight of incubating birds (**Figure 56.10**). DDT was responsible for a dramatic decrease in the populations of many birds due to failed reproduction. Relatively high levels of the chemical were also found to be present in some game fish, which became unfit for human consumption.

Because of growing awareness of the adverse effects of DDT, most industrialized countries, including Canada, had

DDT (dichlorodiphenyltrichloroethane)
- Persists in environment
- High solubility in lipids
- Found in high concentrations
  at higher trophic levels

Figure 56.10 Thinning of eggshells caused by DDT.
These peregrine falcon eggs became thin shelled and were
probably crushed by the incubating adult.

banned the use of the chemical by the early 1970s. The good
news is that following the outlawing of DDT, populations of
the most severely affected bird species have recovered. Had
scientists initially possessed a more thorough knowledge of
how DDT accumulated in food chains, however, some of the
damage to the bird populations might have been prevented.
DDT is still used in some developing countries to kill mosquitoes that vector malaria, although there has been significant movement toward the use of alternative pest control
technologies.

Other environmental contaminants, such as mercury, have
also been studied. In 2009 Alexander Bond and Anthony Diamond from the University of New Brunswick published a paper
on the biomagnification of mercury in a variety of tissue samples from seven seabird species on Machias Seal Island in the
Lower Bay of Fundy. Their study employed stable isotope ratios
of carbon ($\delta^{13}C$) and nitrogen ($\delta^{15}N$) to evaluate the relationship
between carbon source, trophic position, and mercury (Hg) lev-
els. They concluded that Leach's Storm-petrels (*Oceanodroma
l-eucorhoa*) and razorbills (*Alca torda*) had the highest Hg levels
due to their feeding behaviours, preying either on mesopelagic
fish that accumulate Hg or on larger, older fish that have accumulated heavy metals over their lifetimes.

56.2 / ENERGY PRODUCTION IN ECOSYSTEMS

Learning Outcomes:

1. Explain how energy production is calculated.
2. Discuss the different ways in which primary production
   is influenced in terrestrial and aquatic ecosystems.
3. Describe what limits secondary production in ecosystems.

In this section, we will take a closer look at energy production. Because the bulk of the Earth's biosphere, 99.9% by mass,
consists of primary producers, when we measure ecosystem
energy production we are primarily interested in plants, algae,
or cyanobacteria. Since plants represent the first, or primary,
trophic level, we measure plant production as **gross primary
production (GPP)**. Gross primary production is equivalent
to the carbon fixed during photosynthesis. **Net primary production (NPP)** is gross primary production minus the energy
released in plant cellular respiration (R).

$$NPP = GPP - R$$

Net primary production is thus the amount of energy that is
available to primary consumers. From now on, the term *primary
production* refers to net primary production.

To measure primary production, calories can be used as
a common currency, and organisms can be viewed as caloric
equivalents. For example, 100 grams of rye grass seeds (*Secale
cereale*) has a calorific equivalent of about 380 calories, whereas
100 grams of lead tree leaves (*Leucaena leucocephala*) has a
calorific content of only 68 calories. Energy content is generally
measured using dry biomass. Dry weight is used because the
bulk of living matter in most species is water, and water content
fluctuates widely, often according to wet or dry seasons. Of the
dry weight, 95% is made up of carbon compounds, so that measuring energy flow in ecosystems is in many ways equivalent
to examining the carbon cycle (see section 56.3), and ecologists
often measure NPP in terms of carbon fixed per square metre
or per hectare.

Understanding what factors limit primary production is of vital
importance if we are to examine ecosystems as energy transformers. Furthermore, by determining these factors we can understand
how primary production varies globally. We can also examine the
effects of primary production on **secondary production**, the gain
in the biomass of heterotrophs and decomposers.

Primary Production Is Influenced in Terrestrial Ecosystems by Water, Temperature, and Nutrient Availability

In terrestrial systems, water is a major determinant of primary
production, and primary production shows an almost linear
increase with annual precipitation, at least in arid regions. Likewise, temperature, which affects production primarily by slowing
or accelerating plant metabolic rates, is also important. In North
America, the evapotranspiration rate can predict the aboveground primary production with good accuracy (**Figure 56.11**).
Recall from Chapter 55 that the evapotranspiration rate is a measure of the amount of water entering the atmosphere from the
ground through the process of evaporation from the soil and transpiration of plants, so it is a measure of both temperature and
available water. For example, a desert will have a low evapotranspiration rate because water availability is low despite high
temperature. Rates of evapotranspiration are maximized when
both temperature and moisture are at high levels, as in tropical
rain forests.

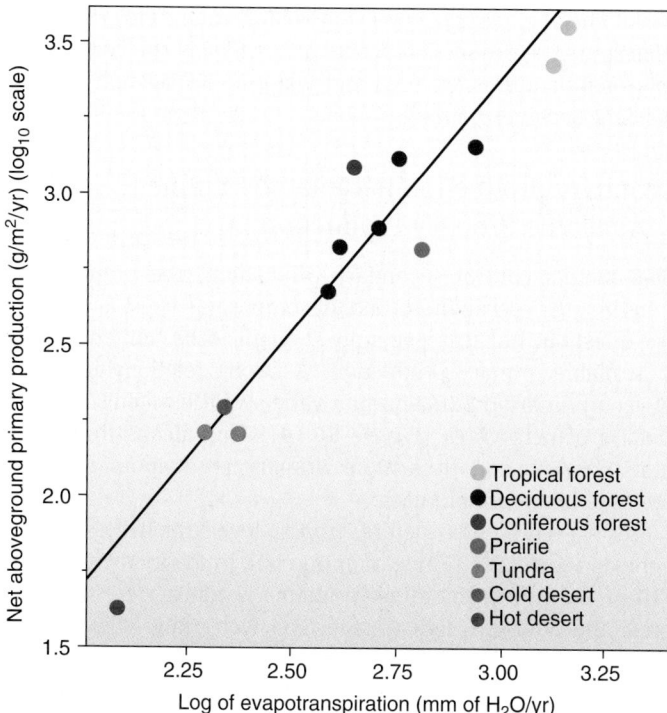

Figure 56.11 Primary production is positively correlated with the evapotranspiration rate. Warm, humid environments are ideal for plant growth. Dots represent different ecosystems.

Figure 56.12 **Primary production is constrained by the most limiting factor.** Net aboveground primary production of a salt marsh sedge (*Carex subspathacea*) in response to nutrient addition. Nitrogen is more limiting than phosphorus alone, but once nitrogen becomes available, phosphorus becomes the limiting factor.

A lack of a particular **nutrient**, or key elements in useable form, particularly nitrogen and phosphorus, can also limit primary production in terrestrial ecosystems, as agricultural practitioners know only too well. Fertilizers are commonly used to boost the production of annual crops. In 1984 Stewart Cargill and Bob Jefferies of the University of Toronto showed how a lack of both nitrogen and phosphorus was limiting to salt marsh sedges and grasses in subarctic conditions in Hudson Bay (**Figure 56.12**). Of the two nutrients, nitrogen was the most limiting; without it, the addition of phosphorus did not increase production. However, once nitrogen was added, phosphorus became the **limiting factor**; that is, the one in shortest supply for growth. Once nitrogen was added and was no longer limiting, the addition of phosphorus increased production. The addition of nitrogen and phosphorus together increased production the most. This result supports a principle known as **Liebig's law of the minimum**, which states that species biomass or abundance is limited by the scarcest factor.

Primary Production in Aquatic Ecosystems Is Limited Mainly by Nutrient Availability

The most important nutrients affecting primary production in aquatic systems are nitrogen and phosphorus, because they occur in very low concentrations. While soil contains about 0.5% nitrogen, seawater contains only 0.00005% nitrogen. Enrichment of the aquatic environment by the addition of nitrogen and phosphorus can result in large, unchecked growths of

algae called algal blooms. Such enrichment occurs naturally in areas of upwellings, where cold, deep, nutrient-rich water containing sediment from the ocean floor is brought to the surface by strong currents, resulting in very productive ecosystems and plentiful fish. Some of the largest areas of upwelling occur in the Antarctic and along the coasts of Peru and California. New nutrients wash into aquatic systems from land. Thus, aquatic ecosystems closest to shore tend to be the most productive.

Another factor that limits primary production in aquatic ecosystems is available light; light is particularly likely to be in short supply because water readily absorbs light. At 1-metre depth, more than half the solar radiation has been absorbed. By 20 metres, only 5%–10% of the radiation is left. The decrease in light availability with increasing depth limits the vertical distribution of primary production at any particular location on Earth. It should be noted that, unlike almost everything else in global ecology, ocean productivity is not influenced by latitude.

Primary Production Is Greatest in Areas of Abundant Warmth and Moisture

Knowing which factors limit primary production helps ecologists understand why mean net primary production varies across the different ecosystems on Earth (**Table 56.1**). In general, primary production is highest in tropical rain forests and decreases progressively toward the poles (**Figure 56.13**). As we saw in Chapter 55, many ecologists suggest this is the primary cause for the polar-equatorial gradient of species richness. This primary productivity gradient occurs because temperatures decrease toward the poles, and, as we have just learned, temperatures affect primary production greatly. Wetlands also tend

Table 56.1	Net Primary Production for Earth's Ecosystems

Ecosystem type	Mean net primary production (g/m²/yr)
Terrestrial	
Tropical rain forest	2,500
Tropical deciduous forest	1,600
Temperate deciduous forest	1,550
Savannah	1,080
Prairie	750
Cultivated land	610
Taiga	380
Tundra	140
Hot desert	90
Aquatic	
Algal beds and coral reefs	2,500
Wetlands	2,000
Estuaries	1,500
Upwelling zones	500
Continental shelf	360
Lake and stream	250
Open ocean	125

coastal shelves, particularly in upwelling zones. However, the greatest marine production occurs on algal beds and coral reefs, where temperatures are high and water levels are not so deep that light becomes limiting.

Secondary Production Is Generally Limited by Available Primary Production

What factors control secondary production, the productivity of herbivores, carnivores, and decomposers? This is a complex question, but it is generally thought to be limited largely by available primary production. A strong relationship exists between primary production in a variety of ecosystems and the biomass of herbivores (**Figure 56.14**). This means that more plant biomass, and thus more primary production, leads to increased herbivore biomass.

As we have noted before, trophic-level transfer efficiency averages about 10%. Thus, after one link in the food web, only 1/10 of the energy captured by plants is transferred to herbivores, and after two links in the food web, only 1/100 of the energy fixed by plants goes to carnivores. Thus, secondary production is much smaller than that of primary production. We can see this in the work of John Teal, whose 1962 work examined energy flow in a Georgia salt marsh (**Figure 56.15**). Salt marshes are among the most productive habitats on Earth in terms of amount of vegetation they produce. In salt marshes, most of the energy from the sun (incident sunlight) goes to two types of organisms: *Spartina* plants and marine algae. The *Spartina* plants are rooted in the ground, whereas the algae float on the water surface or live on the mud or on *Spartina* leaves at low tide. These photosynthetic organisms absorb about 6% of the incident sunlight. Most of the plant energy, 77.6%, is used in plant and algal cellular respiration. Of the energy that is accumulated in plant biomass, most dies in place and rots

to be extremely productive, primarily because water is not limiting and nutrient levels are high. Productivity of the open ocean is very low, falling somewhere between the productivity of deserts and that of the Arctic tundra. Marine production is high on

>01 .02 .03 .1 .2 .3 .5 1   2 3 5   10 15 20 30 50
Ocean: Chlorophyll a Concentration (mg/m³)

Maximum   Minimum
Land: Normalized Difference Land Vegetation Index

Figure 56.13   **Annual net primary productivity on Earth.**   Primary productivity generally increases from the poles to the equator.

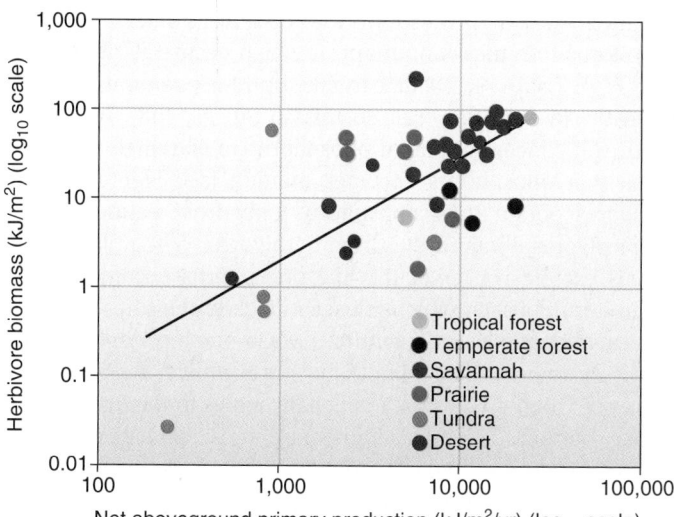

Figure 56.14 Herbivore biomass is positively correlated with net aboveground primary production. These data are taken from a variety of case studies from different biomes. Herbivore biomass can be considered a surrogate for secondary production.

on the muddy ground, to be consumed by bacteria. Bacteria are the major decomposers in this system, followed distantly by nematodes and crabs, which feed on tiny food particles as they sift through the mud. Some of this dead material is also removed from the system (exported) by the tide. The herbivores take very little of the plant production, eating only a small

proportion of the *Spartina* and none of the algae. Overall, if we view the species in ecosystems as transformers of energy, then plants and algae are by far the most important organisms on the planet, bacteria are next, and animals are a distant third.

56.3 BIOGEOCHEMICAL CYCLES

Learning Outcomes:

1. Describe the phosphorus cycle and the causes of eutrophication.
2. Outline the steps of the carbon cycle and the environmental effects of elevated atmospheric CO_2.
3. List the five main steps of the nitrogen cycle and how humans affect the nitrogen cycle.
4. Describe the processes of the water cycle and how humans affect the water cycle.

A unit of energy passes through a food web only once. In contrast, elements such as nitrogen or carbon are recycled, moving from the physical environment to organisms and back to the environment, where the cycle begins again. While energy dissipates as heat, chemical elements are available in limited amounts and are continually recycled. Because these cycles involve biological, geological, and chemical transport mechanisms, they are termed **biogeochemical cycles**. Biological mechanisms involve the absorption of chemicals by living organisms and their subsequent release back into the environment. Geological

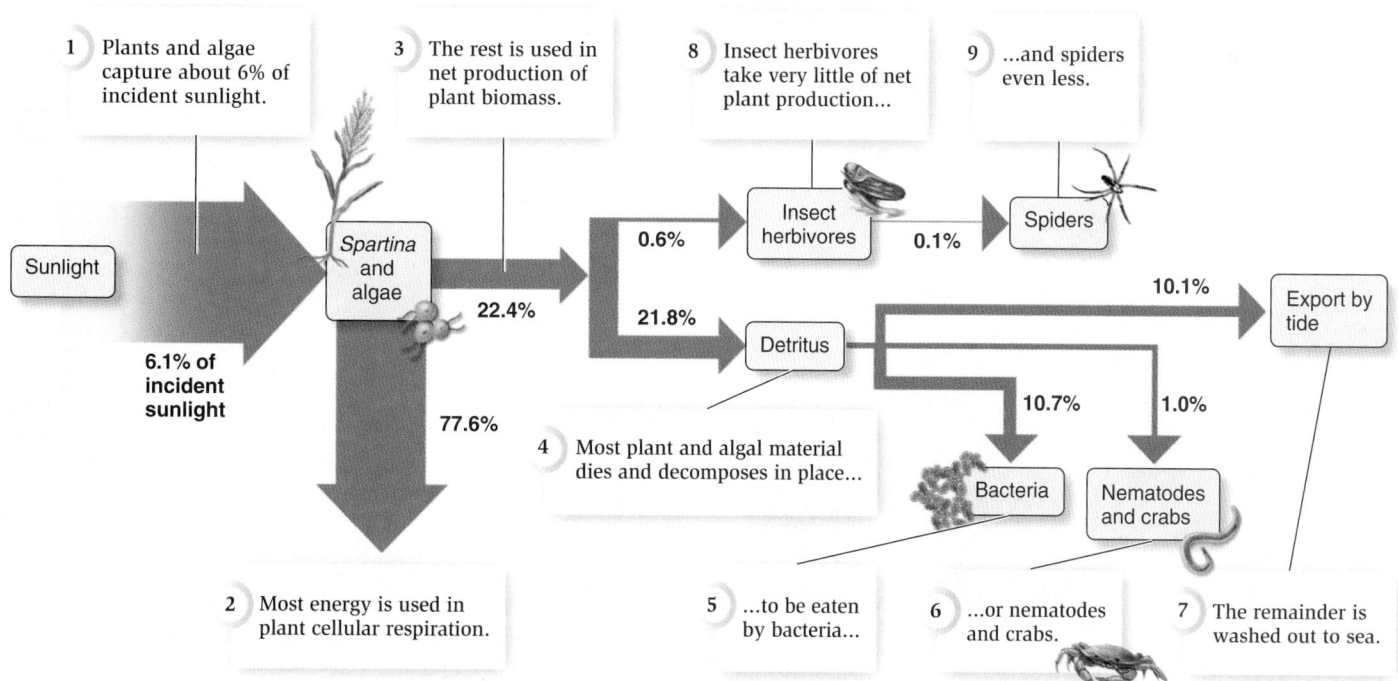

Figure 56.15 Energy-flow diagram for a Georgia salt marsh. Numbers reflect percentages of gross primary production that flows into different trophic levels or is used in plant respiration.

mechanisms include weathering and erosion of rocks, and elements transported by surface and subsurface drainage. Chemical transport mechanisms include dissolved matter in rain and snow, atmospheric gases, and dust blown by the wind.

In addition to the basic building blocks of hydrogen, oxygen, and carbon, which we discussed in Chapter 2, the elements required in the greatest amounts by living organisms are nitrogen, phosphorus, and sulphur. In this section, we take a detailed look at the cycles of these nutrients. These cycles can be divided into two broad types: local cycles, such as the phosphorus cycle, which involve elements with no mechanism for long-distance transfer; and global cycles, which involve an interchange between the atmosphere and the ecosystem. Global nutrient cycles, such as the carbon, nitrogen, and sulphur cycles, unite the Earth and its living organisms into one giant interconnected ecosystem called the **biosphere**. In our discussion we will take a particular interest in the alteration of these cycles through human activities that increase nutrient inputs, such as the burning of fossil fuels.

Phosphorus Cycles Locally Between Geological and Biological Components of Ecosystems

All living organisms require phosphorus, which becomes incorporated into ATP, the compound that provides energy for most metabolic processes. Phosphorus is a key component of other biological molecules such as DNA and RNA, and it is also an essential mineral that in many animals helps maintain a strong, healthy skeleton.

The phosphorus cycle is a relatively simple cycle (**Figure 56.16**). Phosphorus has no gaseous phase and thus no atmospheric component; that is, it is not moved around by the wind or rain. As a result, phosphorus tends to cycle only locally. The Earth's crust is the main storehouse for this element. Weathering and erosion of rocks release phosphorus into the soil. Plants

have the metabolic means to absorb dissolved ionized forms of phosphorus, the most important of which occurs as phosphate (HPO_4^{2-} or $H_2PO_4^-$). Plants can take up phosphate rapidly and efficiently. In fact, they can do this so quickly that they often reduce soil concentrations of phosphorus to extremely low levels, so that phosphorus becomes limiting (see Figure 56.12). Herbivores obtain their phosphorus only from eating plants, and carnivores obtain it by eating herbivores. When plants and animals excrete wastes or die, the phosphorus becomes available to decomposers, which release it back to the soil.

Leaching and runoff eventually wash much phosphate into aquatic systems, where plants and algae utilize it. Phosphate that is not taken up into the food chain settles to the ocean floor or lake bottom, forming sedimentary rock. Phosphorus can remain locked in sedimentary rock for millions of years, becoming available again through the geological process of uplift.

As noted previously, phosphorus is a limiting element in most aquatic systems. The more phosphorus that is added, the more that aquatic productivity increases (**Figure 56.17a**). In a

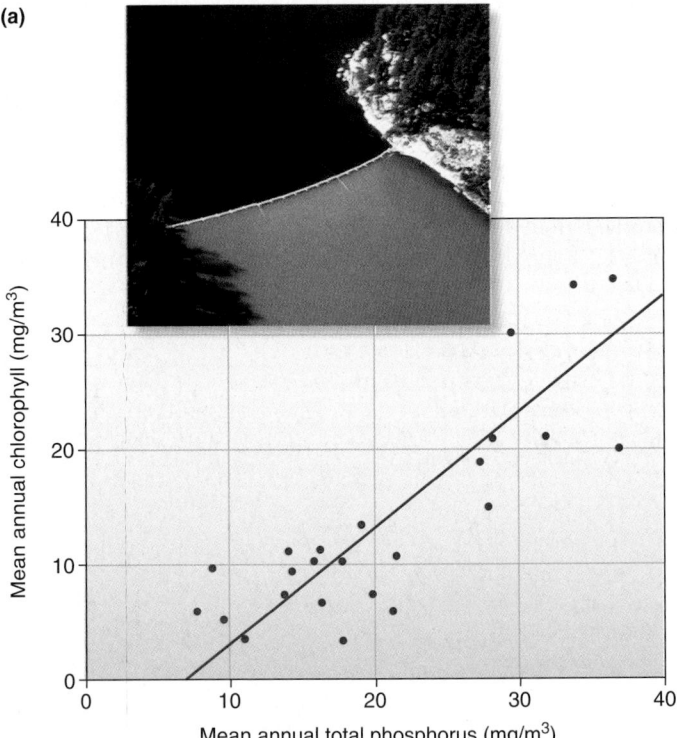
(a)

(b)

Figure 56.17 **Primary production increases with an increase in total phosphorus concentration.** (a) This aerial photograph shows the contrast in water quality of two basins, separated by a plastic curtain, of a lake in the Experimental Lakes Area near Kenora, Ontario. The lower basin received additions of carbon, nitrogen, and phosphorus, while the upper basin received only carbon and nitrogen. The bright green colour is from a surface film of algae that resulted from the added phosphorus. (b) The increase in primary production is measured as an increase in chlorophyll concentration. A higher chlorophyll concentration in the water means more algae are present.

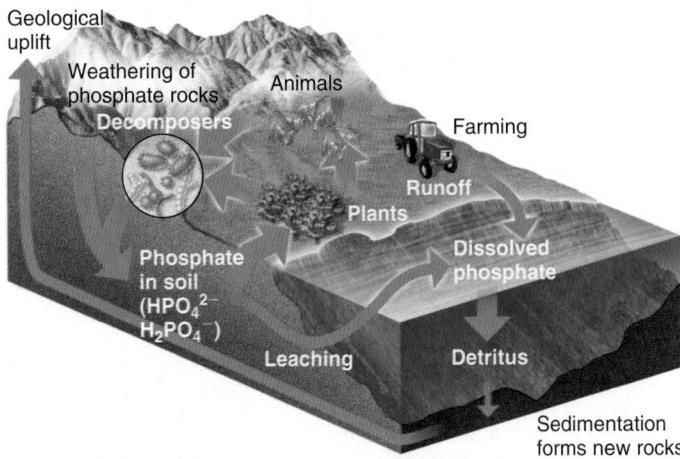

Figure 56.16 **The phosphorus cycle.** Unlike other major biogeochemical cycles, the phosphorus cycle does not have an atmospheric component and thus cycles only locally. The widths of the lines indicate the relative importance of each process.

pivotal 1974 study, while working for the federal government, biologist David Schindler (now at the University of Alberta) showed that an overabundance of phosphorus caused the rapid growth of algae and plants in an experimental lake near Kenora, Ontario (**Figure 56.17b**). The process by which elevated nutrient levels lead to an overgrowth of algae and the subsequent depletion of water oxygen levels is known as **eutrophication**. Cultural eutrophication refers to the enrichment of water with nutrients derived from human activities such as fertilizer use and sewage dumping.

Lake Erie became eutrophic in the 1960s due to both the fertilizer runoff from farms rich in phosphorus and to the industrial and domestic pollutants released from the many cities along its shores. Fish species such as blue pike, white fish, and lake trout became severely depleted. The United States and Canada teamed together to reduce the levels of discharge by 80%, primarily through eliminating phosphorus in laundry detergents and maintaining strict controls on the phosphorus content of wastewater from sewage treatment plants. Fortunately, lake systems have great potential for recovery after phosphorous inputs are reduced, and Lake Erie has experienced a reduction in the occurrence of algal blooms, an improvement in water clarity, and an increase in fish stocks.

Carbon Cycles Among Biological, Geological, and Atmospheric Pools

The movement of carbon from the atmosphere into organisms and back again is known as the carbon cycle (**Figure 56.18**). Carbon dioxide is present in the atmosphere at a level of about 380 parts per million (ppm), or about 0.04%. Autotrophs, primarily plants and algae, acquire carbon dioxide from the atmosphere and incorporate it into the organic matter of their own biomass via photosynthesis. In the process, each year plants and algae remove approximately one-seventh of the CO_2 from the atmosphere. At the same time, the decomposition of plants recycles a similar amount of carbon back into the atmosphere as CO_2. Herbivores can also return some carbon dioxide to the atmosphere, eating plants and breathing out CO_2, but the amount flowing through this part of the cycle is minimal.

Over time, much carbon is also incorporated into the shells of marine organisms, which eventually form huge limestone deposits on the ocean floor. Natural sources of CO_2 such as volcanoes, hot springs, and fires also release large amounts of CO_2. In addition, human activities, primarily the burning of **fossil fuels**—coal, petroleum, and natural gas—are increasingly causing large amounts of CO_2 to enter the atmosphere together with large volumes of particulate matter. Recently, such particulate matter has been shown to increase heritable mutations (see Genomes and Proteomes).

Direct measurements over the past five decades show a steady rise in atmospheric CO_2 (**Figure 56.19**), a pattern that shows no sign of slowing. Because of its increasing concentration in the atmosphere, CO_2 is the most troubling of the greenhouse gases, which are a primary source of global warming (see Chapter 51). Oceans absorb approximately one-third of the

Figure 56.18   The carbon cycle.   Each year, plants and algae remove about one-seventh of the CO_2 in the atmosphere. Animal respiration is so small it is not represented. The width of the arrows indicates the relative importance of each process.

Concept check: *Where are the greatest stores of global carbon?*

BioConnections: *Refer back to Table 2.2. Carbon is one of just four elements that account for the vast majority of atoms in living organisms. What are the other three and, therefore, what biogeochemical cycles might be the most important to us?*

excess atmospheric CO_2 and have therefore played a large role in mitigating climate change thus far. However, the absorbed CO_2 forms carbonic acid, which is rapidly acidifying ocean ecosystems. Organisms must expend more energy to maintain their pH balance, affecting reproductive capacity and provisioning for juvenile stages of development. In particular, changes to pH are expected to have a profound impact on organisms living within the deep sea. Elevated atmospheric CO_2 has other dramatic environmental effects, boosting plant growth but lowering the densities of herbivores that feed on them (see Featured Investigation).

The amount of carbon dioxide in the atmosphere varies with the seasons in temperate environments. Concentrations of atmospheric carbon dioxide are lowest during the northern hemisphere's summer and highest during the winter, when photosynthesis is minimal. This is because there is more land in the northern hemisphere than in the southern hemisphere and therefore more vegetation. The vegetation has a maximum photosynthetic activity during the summer, reducing the global

Figure 56.19   The burning of fossil fuels has greatly increased atmospheric CO_2 levels and temperatures.   From 1958 to 2004, atmospheric CO_2 shows an increase of nearly 20%. In addition, the graph shows a seasonal variation in CO_2. Temperatures are annual deviations from the 1961–1990 average. Measurements were recorded at Mauna Loa Observatory in Hawaii.

Concept check: *Why does the amount of CO_2 fluctuate seasonally in the graph?*

BioConnections: *Refer back to Figure 28.18. The Earth's atmospheric CO^2 level has fluctuated dramatically over time. At what point, and in which period, was it highest?*

The tundra of the Canadian Arctic has traditionally been viewed as a sink for carbon dioxide, with its small plants having steadily taken carbon dioxide out of the atmosphere via photosynthesis during the short growing season and then adding it to the frozen soils. However, as many regions in the Arctic become warmer and permafrost melts, there is an accelerated rate of soil decomposition, making the Arctic more of a carbon dioxide source and less of a sink. It is also predicted that with ever-increasing temperatures the vegetation of the tundra will shift toward larger shrubs and, eventually, trees. This in turn will affect net primary production and nutrient cycling and will have an impact on organisms at all trophic levels.

amount of carbon dioxide. During the winter, photosynthesis is low and decomposition is relatively high, causing a global increase in the gas.

GENOMES AND PROTEOMES

Pollution Can Cause Heritable Mutations

Carbon dioxide is one of many pollutants emitted from the burning of fossil fuels; others include sulphur dioxide and nitrous oxides. In addition to these atmospheric gases, the combustion of fossil fuel also results in the release of particulate matter, tiny solid and liquid particles, into the air. Larger particles are visible as smoke or soot. The small particles, when inhaled, can penetrate deeply into the lungs and become distributed throughout the body. Such exposure, whether from transportation sources, factories, power plants, or tobacco smoke, can lead to the formation of lung tumours and induce mutations in somatic cells.

A study by McMaster University's James Quinn and colleagues in 2004 showed that polluted air can also induce genetic changes in mouse sperm. In the study, the researchers put two groups of mice into separate sheds that were downwind of steel mills in Hamilton, Ontario (**Figure 56.20a**). One shed was fitted with high-efficiency particulate air (HEPA) filters, which removed particulate matter from the air, while the other was not. The researchers discovered changes in the size

Figure 56.20   Mutations caused by air pollution.   **(a)** In a study by Quinn and colleagues, mice were kept in sheds with and without HEPA air filters in Hamilton, Ontario. **(b)** The study concluded that mice kept in the filterless sheds inhaled airborne particles into their lungs, and compounds from the particles induced genetic mutations that were transmitted through the sperm cells into the next generation.

of noncoding DNA sequences in the offspring of the mice in the filterless shed. They concluded that the increased rate of mutations was paternally derived. Offspring of mice from the unfiltered shed inherited twice as many mutations as offspring of mice in the filtered shed. The study concluded that the pollutant particles, or some chemical compound associated with them, were responsible for the observed, heritable DNA changes.

What is the mechanism behind these genetic changes? Quinn and colleagues hypothesized that the inhaled pollutants are transported to the liver and metabolized to DNA-reactive compounds, and then transported to the testes and finally to the sperm stem cells where the mutations occurred (**Figure 56.20b**). The damaged DNA would then be transmitted to first-generation offspring.

FEATURE INVESTIGATION

Stiling and Drake's Experiments with Elevated CO_2 Showed an Increase in Plant Growth but a Decrease in Herbivory

How will forests of the future respond to elevated CO_2? To begin to answer such a question, ecologists ideally would enclose large areas of forests with chambers, increase the CO_2 content within the chambers, and measure the responses. This has proven to be difficult for two reasons. First, it is hard to enclose large trees in chambers, and second, it is expensive to increase CO_2 levels over such a large area. However, in a discovery-based investigation, ecologists

Peter Stiling and Bert Drake were able to increase CO_2 levels around small patches of forest at the Kennedy Space Center in Cape Canaveral, Florida. In much of Florida forest, trees are small, only 3 to 5 metres when mature, because frequent lightning-initiated fires prevent the growth of larger trees. Stiling and Drake teamed up with NASA engineers to create 16 circular, open-topped chambers (**Figure 56.21**), and in 8 of these they increased atmospheric CO_2 to double their ambient levels, from 360 to 720 ppm, the latter of which is the atmospheric level predicted for the end of the twenty-first century. The experiments were initiated in 1996 and lasted until 2004. Plants produced more biomass in elevated CO_2,

GOAL To determine the effects of elevated CO_2 on a forest ecosystem; effects on herbivory are highlighted here.

STUDY LOCATION Patches of forest at the Kennedy Space Center in Cape Canaveral, Florida.

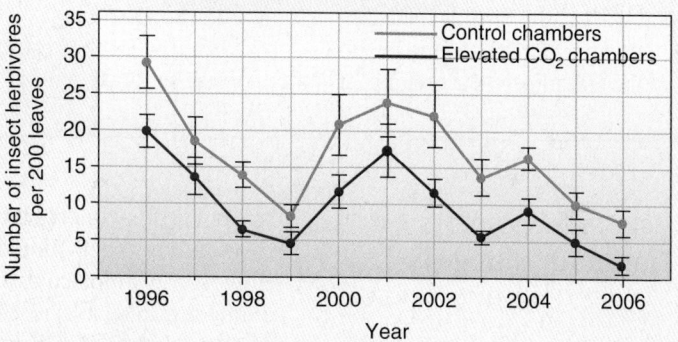

	Experimental level	Conceptual level
1 Erect 16 open-top chambers around native vegetation. Increase CO_2 levels from 360 ppm to 720 ppm in half of them.		Expected atmospheric CO_2 level is 720 ppm by end of the 21st century. Open-top chambers allow movement of herbivores in and out of chambers.
2 Conduct a yearly count of numbers of insect herbivores per 200 leaves in each chamber.		

Figure 56.21   The effects of elevated atmospheric CO_2 on insect herbivores.

Figure 56.21 *(Continued)*

3 Count number of herbivores that died due to nutritional inadequacy. Monitor attack rates on insect herbivores by natural enemies such as predators and parasitoids.

Elevated CO_2 reduces foliar nitrogen, inhibits normal insect development, and prolongs the feeding time of herbivores, allowing natural enemies greater opportunities to attack them.

4 **THE DATA**

Source of mortality*	Elevated CO_2 (% mortality)	Control (% mortality)
Nutritional inadequacy	10.2	5.0
Predators	2.4	2.0
Parasitoids	10.0	3.2

* Data refer only to mortality of larvae within leaves and do not sum to 100%. Mortality of eggs on leaves, pupae in the soil, and flying adults is unknown.

5 **CONCLUSION** Elevated CO_2 decreases insect herbivory in a Florida forest.

6 **SOURCE** Stiling, P., and Cornelissen, T. 2007. How does elevated carbon dioxide (CO_2) affect plant-herbivore interactions? A field experiment and meta-analysis of CO_2-mediated changes on plant chemistry and herbivore performance. *Global Change Biology* 13:1823–1842.

because carbon dioxide is limiting to plant growth, but the data revealed much more.

Because the chambers were open topped, insect herbivores could come and go. Insect herbivores cause the largest amount of herbivory in North American forests, because vertebrate herbivores cannot access the high foliage. Censuses were conducted of all insect herbivores but focused on leaf miners, the most common type of herbivore at this site, which are small moths whose larvae are small enough to live between the surfaces of plant leaves and create blister-like "mines" on leaves.

Densities of all insects, including leaf miners, was lower in elevated CO_2 in every year studied. Part of the reason for the decline was that even though plants increased in mass, the existing soil nitrogen was diluted over a greater volume of plant material, so that the nitrogen level in leaves decreased. This increased insect mortality by two means. First, poorer leaf quality directly increased insect death because leaf nitrogen levels may have been too low to support the normal development of the leaf miners. Second, lower

leaf quality increased the length of time insects had to feed to gain sufficient nitrogen. Increased feeding times in turn led to increased exposure to natural enemies such as parasitoids and predators such as spiders and ants, and top-down mortality also increased (see the data of Figure 56.21). Thus, in a world of elevated CO_2, plant growth may increase but herbivore densities could decrease. If some herbivores, such as butterflies, are already rare in a habitat, then an elevation in CO_2 could threaten them with extinction.

Experimental Questions

1. What was the hypothesis of the Stiling and Drake experiment?
2. What was the purpose of increasing the carbon dioxide levels in only half the chambers in the experiment and not all the chambers?
3. What were the results of the experiment? Were any of the results unexpected?

The Nitrogen Cycle Is Strongly Influenced by Biological Processes That Transform Nitrogen into Usable Forms

Nitrogen is a limiting nutrient because it is an essential component of proteins, nucleic acids, and chlorophyll. Because 78% of the Earth's atmosphere consists of nitrogen gas (N_2), it may seem that nitrogen should not be in short supply for organisms. However, N_2 molecules must be broken apart before nitrogen atoms are available to combine with other elements. Because of its triple bond, nitrogen gas is very stable and only certain bacteria can break it apart into usable forms. This process, called nitrogen fixation, is a critical component of the five-part nitrogen cycle, which also includes nitrification, assimilation, ammonification, and denitrification (**Figure 56.22**):

1. Only a few species of bacteria can accomplish **nitrogen fixation**; that is, convert atmospheric nitrogen to forms usable by other organisms. The bacteria that fix nitrogen are fulfilling their own metabolic needs, but in the process they release excess ammonia (NH_3) or ammonium (NH_4^+), which can be used by some plants. The most important of these bacteria in the soil are called *Rhizobium*, which live in nodules on the roots of legumes, including peas, beans, lentils, and peanuts, and some woody plants.

2. In the process of **nitrification**, soil bacteria convert NH_3 or NH_4^+ to nitrate (NO_3^-), a form of nitrogen commonly used by plants. The bacteria *Nitrosomonas* and *Nitrococcus* first oxidize the forms of ammonia to nitrite (NO_2^-), after which the bacteria *Nitrobacter* convert NO_2^- to NO_3^-.

3. **Assimilation** is the process by which plants and animals incorporate the NH_3, NH_4^+, and NO_3^- formed through nitrogen fixation and nitrification. Plants take up these forms of nitrogen through their roots, and animals assimilate nitrogen by eating plant tissue.

4. Ammonia can also be formed in the soil through the decomposition of plants and animals and the release of animal waste. **Ammonification** is the conversion of organic nitrogen to NH_3 and NH_4^+. This process is carried out by bacteria and fungi. Most soils are slightly acidic and, because of an excess of H^+, the NH_3 rapidly gains an additional H^+ to form NH_4^+. Because many soils lack nitrifying bacteria, ammonification is the most common pathway for nitrogen to enter the soil.

5. **Denitrification** is the reduction of nitrate (NO_3^-) to gaseous nitrogen (N_2). Denitrifying bacteria, which are anaerobic and use NO_3^- in their metabolism instead of oxygen, perform the reverse of their nitrogen-fixing counterparts by delivering nitrogen to the atmosphere. This process delivers only a relatively small amount of nitrogen to the atmosphere.

In terms of the global nitrogen budget, industrial fixation of nitrogen for the production of fertilizer makes a significant contribution to the pool of nitrogen-containing material in the soils and waters of agricultural regions. Human alterations of the nitrogen cycle have approximately doubled the rate of nitrogen input to the cycle. One problem is that fertilizer runoff can cause eutrophication of rivers and lakes, and, as the resultant algae die, decomposition by bacteria depletes the oxygen level of the water, resulting in fish die-offs. Excess nitrates in surface or groundwater systems used for drinking water are also a health hazard, particularly for infants. In the body, nitrate is converted to nitrite, which then combines with hemoglobin to form methemoglobin, a type of hemoglobin that does not carry oxygen. In infants, the production of large amounts of nitrites can cause methemoglobinemia, a dangerous condition in which the level of oxygen carried through the body decreases.

Finally, burning fossil fuels releases not only carbon but also nitrogen in the form of nitrogen oxides, which contribute to air pollution. Nitrogen oxides in turn can react with rain water to form nitric acid (HNO_3), which contributes to acid rain, decreasing the pH of lakes and streams and increasing fish mortality (see Chapter 51). While much of the acid rain problem can be traced to the sulphur cycle, nitrogen oxides are also partially to blame.

The dramatic effects of human activities on nutrient cycles in general and the nitrogen cycle in particular were illustrated by a famous long-term study by ecosystem ecologists Gene Likens, Herbert Bormann, and their colleagues at Hubbard Brook Experimental Forest in New Hampshire in the 1960s. Hubbard Brook is a 3,160-hectare reserve that consists of six catchments along a mountain ridge. A catchment is an area of land where all water eventually drains to a single outlet. In Hubbard Brook, each outlet is fitted with a permanent concrete dam that enables researchers to monitor the outflow of water and nutrients (**Figure 56.23a**). In this large-scale experiment, researchers felled all of the trees in one of the Hubbard Brook catchments (**Figure 56.23b**). The catchment was then sprayed with herbicides for three years to prevent regrowth of vegetation. An untreated catchment was used as a control.

Researchers monitored the concentrations of key nutrients in the streams exiting the two catchments for over three years. Their results revealed that the overall export of dissolved nutrients from the disturbed catchment rose to many times the normal rate (**Figure 56.23c**). The researchers determined that two

Figure 56.22 **The nitrogen cycle. The five main parts of the nitrogen cycle are** (1) nitrogen fixation, (2) nitrification, (3) assimilation, (4) ammonification, and (5) denitrification. The recycling of nitrogen from dead plants and animals into the soil and then back into plants is of paramount importance. The width of the arrows indicates the relative importance of each process.

(a) Hubbard Brook dam and weir

(b) Hubbard Brook Experimental Forest, New Hampshire

(c) Nutrient concentrations in deforested and control catchments

Figure 56.23 **The effects of deforestation on nutrient concentrations.** **(a)** Concrete dam and weir used to monitor nutrient flow from a Hubbard Brook catchment. **(b)** Deforested catchment at Hubbard Brook. **(c)** Nutrient concentrations in stream water from the experimentally deforested catchment and a control catchment at Hubbard Brook. The timing of deforestation is indicated by arrows.

phenomena were responsible. First, the enormous reduction in plants reduced water uptake by vegetation and led to 40% more precipitation passing through the groundwater to be discharged to the streams. This increased outflow caused greater rates of chemical leaching and rock and soil weathering. Second, and more significantly, in the absence of nutrient uptake in spring, when the deciduous trees would have started production, the inorganic nutrients released by decomposer activity were simply leached in the drainage water. Similar processes operate in the majority of terrestrial ecosystems where deforestation is significant.

The Sulphur Cycle Is Heavily Influenced by Human Activities

Most naturally produced sulphur in the atmosphere comes from the gas hydrogen sulphide (H_2S), which is released from volcanic eruptions and during decomposition, especially in wetland environments, where sulphur is very common (**Figure 56.24**). The H_2S quickly oxidizes into sulphur dioxide (SO_2). Because SO_2 is soluble in water, it returns to Earth as weak sulphuric acid (H_2SO_4), or natural acid rain, making the pH of natural rainwater slightly acidic, about 5.6 (see also Chapter 51). The sulphate ions, SO_4^{2-}, thus enter the soil, where sulphate-reducing bacteria may release sulphur as H_2S, or the sulphate may be incorporated by plants into their tissue.

In the presence of iron, sulphur can precipitate as ferrous sulphide, FeS_2, and be incorporated in pyritic rocks. The weathering of rocks and the decomposition of organic matter therefore

releases sulphur to solution, which runs through rivers to the sea. Because such rocks commonly overlay coal deposits, mining exposes them to the air and water, resulting in a discharge of sulphuric acid and other sulphur-containing compounds into aquatic ecosystems.

Interestingly, certain marine algae and a few salt marsh plants produce relatively large amounts of the sulphurous gas dimethyl sulphide (CH_3SCH_3). Small particles of dimethyl sulphide that diffuse to the atmosphere often form the nuclei around which water vapour can condense and form the water droplets making up clouds. Because of the sheer global extent of the oceans, changes in algal abundance and thus global dimethyl sulphide levels have the potential to alter cloud cover and thus climate. Because of its ability to cool the climate, some researchers are investigating how dimethyl sulphide production might offset global warming.

Human activity involving the combustion of fossil fuels has altered the sulphur cycle more than any of the other nutrient cycles. The burning of coal and oil to provide energy for heating or to fuel electric power stations produces huge amounts of sulphur dioxide (SO_2). This reacts with rain or snow to make human-produced acid rain (see Chapter 51). One of the main differences between human-produced acid rain and natural acid rain is its relative pH. In North America, for example, natural acid rain has a pH of about 5.6, while measurements of rain falling in southern Ontario in the 1980s showed pH values in the range of 4.1–4.5. Huge areas of the industrial northeast United States and Europe were affected by acid rain in the 1950s through the 1980s, but

Figure 56.24 **The sulphur cycle.** This cycle can be dramatically affected by human outputs through the burning of fossil fuels. The width of the arrows indicates the relative importance of each process.

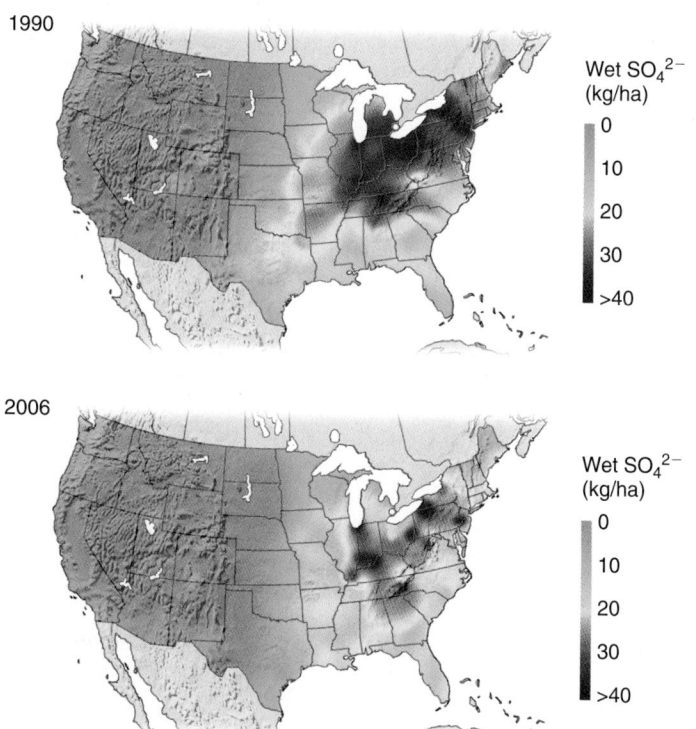

Figure 56.25 **The extent of acid rain in the United States has decreased.** Data show wet sulphate deposition due to acid rain in kilograms per hectare.

a reduction in the use of high-sulphur coal and the use of scrubbers to prevent sulphur dioxide from passing through smokestacks has reduced the problem in more recent times (**Figure 56.25**).

The Water Cycle Is Largely a Physical Process of Evaporation and Precipitation

The water cycle, or hydrological cycle, differs from the cycles of other nutrients in that very little of the water that cycles through ecosystems is chemically changed by any of the cycle's components (**Figure 56.26**). It is a physical process, fuelled by the sun's energy, rather than a chemical one, because it consists of essentially two phenomena: evaporation and precipitation. Even so, the water cycle has important biological components. Over land, 90% of the water that reaches the atmosphere is moisture that has passed through plants and exited from the leaves via evapotranspiration. However, only about 2% of the total volume of Earth's water is found in the bodies of organisms or is held frozen or in the soil. The rest cycles among bodies of water, the atmosphere, and the land.

As we noted in Chapter 51, water is limiting to the abundance of many organisms, including humans. It takes 228 litres

Figure 56.26 **The water cycle.** This cycle is primarily a physical process, not a chemical one. Solar energy drives the water cycle, causing evaporation of water from the ocean and evapotranspiration from the land. This is followed by condensation of water vapour into clouds and precipitation. The width of the arrows indicates the relative importance of each step.

of water to produce a pound of dry wheat, and 9,500 litres of water to support the necessary vegetation to produce a pound of meat. Industry is also a heavy user of water, with goods such as oil, iron, and steel requiring up to 20,000 litres of water per metric ton of product. Humans have therefore interrupted the hydrological cycle in many ways to increase the amount available. Prominent among these activities is the use of dams to create reservoirs. Such dams can greatly interfere with the migration of fish and affect their ability to reproduce and survive, as seen in fish populations from British Columbia, Quebec, and Nova Scotia. Other activities, such as tapping into underground water supplies, or **aquifers**, for drinking water removes more water than is put back by rainfall and can cause shallow ponds and lakes to dry up and sinkholes to develop.

Deforestation can also significantly alter the water cycle. When forests are cut down, less moisture is transpired into the atmosphere. This reduces cloud cover and diminishes precipitation, subjecting the area to drought. Re-establishing the forests, which calls for increased water, then becomes nearly impossible.

Such a problem has occurred on the island of Madagascar, located off the east coast of Africa. In this country, clearing of the forests for cash crops such as cotton, coffee, and tobacco has been so rapid and extensive that semiarid deserts have resulted (**Figure 56.27**). In Madagascar, as in so many other areas on Earth, deforestation and other environmental degradations are having an impact on much of the natural habitat. Appropriately,

in the following chapter, we finish our study of ecology in particular, and biology in general, with a discussion of how best to conserve the diversity of ecosystems in the future.

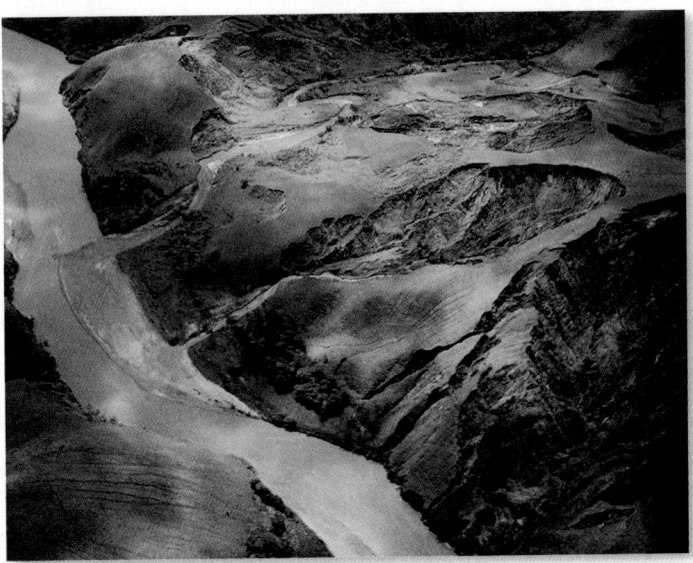

Figure 56.27   Severe erosion following deforestation in Madagascar.   After clearing and a few years of farming, the shallow soil can no longer support crops and is susceptible to erosion by rainfall.

Summary of Key Concepts

56.1 Food Webs and Energy Flow

- Ecosystem ecology concerns the movement of energy and materials through organisms and their communities. (Figure 56.1)
- Simple feeding relationships between organisms can be characterized by an unbranched food chain, and each feeding level in the chain is called a trophic level. (Figure 56.2)
- Organisms that obtain energy from light or chemicals are called autotrophs and are the primary producers. Organisms that feed on other organisms are called heterotrophs. Those organisms that feed on primary producers are called primary consumers or herbivores. Organisms that feed on primary consumers are called secondary consumers or carnivores. Consumers that get their energy from the remains and waste products of organisms are called detritivores. (Figures 56.3, 56.4)
- Food webs are a more complex model of interconnected food chains in which there are multiple links among species. (Figure 56.5)
- Food chains tend to have five or fewer levels. Energy conversions are not 100% efficient, and energy is lost within each trophic level and from one trophic level to the next. (Figure 56.6)
- Production efficiency measures the percentage of energy assimilated that becomes incorporated into new biomass. (Figure 56.7)
- Trophic-level transfer efficiency measures the energy available at one trophic level that is acquired by the level above. These efficiencies can be expressed in the form of ecological pyramids, the best known of which is the pyramid of numbers. (Figure 56.8)
- The increase in the concentration of a substance in living organisms, called biomagnification, can occur at each step of the food chain. (Figures 56.9, 56.10)

56.2 Energy Production in Ecosystems

- Plant production can be measured as gross primary production. Net primary production is gross primary production minus the energy lost in plant respiration.
- Primary production in terrestrial ecosystems is limited primarily by temperature and the availability of water and nutrients, while primary production in aquatic ecosystems is limited mainly by availability of nutrients. (Figures 56.11, 56.12)
- Ecosystems differ in their net primary production. (Table 56.1, Figure 56.13)
- Secondary production is limited by available primary production. (Figure 56.14, 56.15)

56.3 Biogeochemical Cycles

- Nutrients such as phosphorus, carbon, nitrogen, and sulphur recycle from the physical environment to organisms and back in what are called biogeochemical cycles.
- The phosphorus cycle lacks an atmospheric component and thus is a local cycle. An overabundance of phosphorus in aquatic systems can cause the overgrowth of algae and subsequent depletion of oxygen levels, called eutrophication. (Figures 56.16, 56.17)
- In the carbon cycle, autotrophs incorporate carbon dioxide from the atmosphere into their biomass; decomposition of plants and respiration recycles most of this CO_2 back to the atmosphere. Human activities, primarily the burning of fossil fuels, are causing increased amounts of CO_2 to enter the atmosphere. Air pollutants may cause mutations. (Figures 56.18, 56.19, 56.20)
- Experiments have shown that elevated levels of carbon dioxide result in an increase in plant growth but a decrease in herbivory. (Figure 56.21)

- The nitrogen cycle has five parts: nitrogen fixation, nitrification, assimilation, ammonification, and denitrification. In the nitrogen cycle, atmospheric nitrogen is unavailable for use by most organisms and must be converted to usable forms by bacteria. (Figure 56.22)

- The activities of humans, including fertilizer use, fossil fuel use, and deforestation, have dramatically altered the nitrogen cycle. (Figure 56.23)

- Sulphur enters the atmosphere through both natural sources (such as volcanoes and decomposition) and human sources, including the combustion of fossil fuels. Atmospheric sulphur dioxide returns to Earth as weak sulphuric acid (H_2SO_4) or natural acid rain. (Figure 56.24)

- Human-produced acid rain results primarily from the combustion of fossil fuels. (Figure 56.25)

- The water cycle is a physical rather than a chemical process, because it consists of essentially two phenomena: evaporation and precipitation. (Figure 56.26)

- Alteration of the water cycle by deforestation can result in climatic changes because a reduction in transpiration causes a decrease in cloud cover and precipitation. (Figure 56.27)

Test to Assess Your Learning

1. Ecosystem ecology is the study of
   a. the interaction of organisms and their environment.
   b. the processes that affect population growth.
   c. the organisms common to a particular environment.
   d. energy movement through a community.
   e. abiotic factors affecting movement in an environment.

2. Chemoautotrophic bacteria are
   a. primary consumers.
   b. secondary consumers.
   c. tertiary consumers.
   d. primary producers.
   e. decomposers.

3. When considering the average food chain, which of the following statements is true?
   a. Secondary consumers are the most abundant organisms in an ecosystem.
   b. The more lengths in the food chain, the more stable the ecosystem.
   c. Biomass decreases as you move up the food chain.
   d. The trophic level with the highest species abundance is usually the primary producers.
   e. All of the above are true.

4. Biomagnification is the result of
   a. an increase in the population size of the primary consumers.
   b. increased levels of pollutants that are released into the environment.
   c. the buildup of chemicals in organisms at a rate greater than the chemicals can be broken down.
   d. genetic mutations that are passed down from one generation to the next.
   e. none of the above.

5. The amount of energy that is fixed during photosynthesis is
   a. net primary production.
   b. biomagnification.
   c. trophic-level transfer efficiency.
   d. gross primary production.
   e. production efficiency.

6. The chain lengths in food webs are limited by
   a. the amount of energy such as sunlight available in an ecosystem.
   b. the efficiency of energy transfers that occur between trophic levels.
   c. the efficiency by which primary consumers assimilate energy into biomass.
   d. all of the above.
   e. (a) and (b) only.

7. The evapotranspiration rate
   a. can be used as a predictor for primary production.
   b. is increased when temperature decreases.
   c. is not affected by temperature.
   d. is highest in deserts.
   e. can be predicted by measuring only the water content of the soil.

8. Eutrophication is
   a. caused by an overabundance of nitrogen, which leads to an increase in bacteria populations.
   b. caused by an overabundance of nutrients, which leads to an increase in algal populations.
   c. the normal breakdown of algal plants following a pollution event.
   d. normally seen in dry, hot regions of the world.
   e. none of the above.

9. Primary producers acquire the carbon necessary for photosynthesis from
   a. decomposing plant material.
   b. carbon monoxide released from the burning of fossil fuels.
   c. carbon dioxide in the atmosphere.
   d. carbon sources in the soil.
   e. both (a) and (d).

10. Nitrogen fixation is the process
    a. that converts organic nitrogen to ammonia.
    b. by which plants and animals take up nitrates.
    c. by which bacteria convert nitrate to gaseous nitrogen.
    d. by which atmospheric nitrogen is converted to ammonia or ammonium ions.
    e. all of the above.

Articulate to Assess Your Learning

1. Define autotrophs and heterotrophs.
2. Explain why chain lengths are short in food webs.

Collaborate to Assess and Extend Your Learning

1. Outline the main trophic levels within a food chain.

2. Discuss several factors that influence primary productivity in terrestrial and aquatic ecosystems. How might global warming affect primary productivity?

3. What might the atmospheric concentration be in 2100? What effects might this have on the environment?

4. A principle of biology is that living organisms use energy. What is a fundamental difference between the passage of energy and the passage of nutrients through ecosystems?

Visit McGraw-Hill Ryerson Connect™ for additional study resources.

Conservation Biology and Biodiversity

Chapter Outline

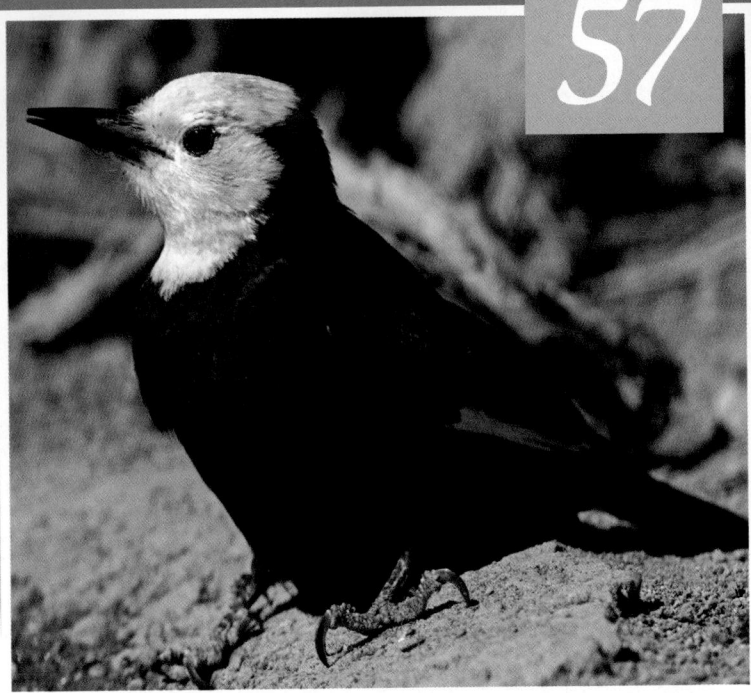

White-headed woodpecker. This woodpecker was reassessed as Endangered by COSEWIC. The main concern for this species in Canada is its small range and population (restricted to the south Okanagan valley) and habitat degradation through past logging activity, forest fire threat, and loss of mature ponderosa pines to mountain pine beetles.

Biological diversity, or **biodiversity**, can be examined at three levels: genetic diversity, species diversity, and ecosystem diversity. Each level of biodiversity provides valuable benefits to humanity. Genetic diversity consists of the amount of genetic variation that occurs within and between populations. Maintaining genetic variation in the ancient relatives of crops may be vital to the continued success of crop-breeding programs. For example, in 1977 Rafael Guzman, a Mexican biologist, discovered a previously unknown ancient relative of corn, *Zea diploperennis*, that is resistant to many of the viral diseases that infect domestic corn, *Zea mays*. Genetic engineers and crop breeders believe that this relative has valuable genes that can improve current corn crops. Because corn is the third-largest crop on Earth, the discovery of *Z. diploperennis* may well turn out to be critical to the global food supply.

The second level of biodiversity concerns species diversity, an area on which much public attention is focused. You may be familiar with legislation in Canada called the Species at Risk Act (2002), which legally protects endangered and threatened wildlife species and assists in the conservation of their biological diversity. In Canada, the Committee on the Status of Endangered Wildlife in Canada (COSEWIC) assesses and designates which wild species are in danger of disappearing. **Endangered species** are those species that are in danger of extinction throughout all or a significant portion of their range. **Threatened species** are those likely to become endangered in the future. Many species are currently threatened. According to the International Union for Conservation of Nature and Natural Resources (IUCN), more than 25% of the fish species that live on coral reefs are threatened with extinction, and 23% of all mammals, 12% of birds, and 31% of amphibians are threatened.

The third level of biodiversity is ecosystem diversity, the diversity of structure and function between ecosystems. While conservation at the level of species diversity has focused attention on species-rich ecosystems such as tropical forests, some scientists have argued that other relatively species-poor ecosystems are highly threatened and similarly need to be conserved. In Canada, many of the native prairies have been converted to agricultural use, such as southwestern Ontario and large parts of Manitoba, Saskatchewan, and Alberta. Some attempts have been made to reclaim parts of prairie ecosystems, such as Grasslands National Park in Saskatchewan. In some areas of Ontario, remnants of prairie often exist only on First Nations lands (**Figure 57.1**).

Conservation biology uses principles and knowledge from molecular biology, genetics, and ecology to protect the biological diversity of life at each of these three levels. Because it draws from nearly all chapters of this textbook, a discussion of conservation biology is an apt way to conclude our study of biology. In this chapter, we begin by examining the question of

Figure 57.1   **Ecosystem biodiversity.** This remnant of a natural prairie ecosystem is found in Alderville First Nation, Ontario. Across Canada, much of the prairie has been plowed under for agriculture.

why biodiversity should be conserved, and explore how much diversity is needed for ecosystems to function properly. We then survey the main threats to the world's biodiversity. For many species there are multiple threats, ranging from habitat loss, exploitation, and the effects of introduced species to climate change and pollution. Even if species are not exterminated, many may exist only at very small population sizes. We will see how small populations are susceptible to special problems such as inbreeding and genetic drift, emphasizing the importance of genetics in conservation biology.

Last, we consider what can be done and has been done to help conserve the world's endangered biota. This includes identifying global areas rich in species and establishing parks and refuges of the appropriate size, number, and connectivity. We also discuss conservation of particularly important types of species, and outline how ecologists have been active in restoring damaged habitats to their natural condition. We then examine how captive breeding programs have been useful in building up populations of rare species prior to their release back into the wild. Some programs have also used modern genetic techniques such as cloning to help breed and perhaps eventually increase populations of endangered species.

57.1 WHY CONSERVE BIODIVERSITY?

Learning Outcomes:

1. Discuss the benefits of biological diversity to human welfare.
2. Depict graphical representations of possible relationships between biodiversity level and ecosystem function.
3. Describe experimental evidence that shows how species diversity and ecosystem function are linked.

Biologists Paul Ehrlich and E. O. Wilson have suggested that the loss of biodiversity should be of concern to everyone for at least three reasons. First, they proposed that we have an ethical responsibility to protect what are our only known living companions in the universe. Second, humanity has obtained enormous benefits from foods, medicines, and industrial products derived from plants, animals, and microorganisms, and we have the potential to gain many more. The third reason to preserve biodiversity focuses on preserving the array of essential services provided by ecosystems, such as clean air and water. In this section, we examine some of the primary reasons that preserving biodiversity matters and explore the link between biodiversity and ecosystem functioning.

The Preservation of Biological Diversity Can Be Justified Based on the Ecological and Economic Values of Diversity as Well as on Ethical Grounds

During the latter half of the twentieth century, the reduction of the Earth's biological diversity emerged as a critical issue, one with implications for public policy. One major concern was

that loss of plant and animal resources would impair future development of important products and processes in agriculture, medicine, and industry. For example, as previously noted, *Z. diploperennis* is resistant to many corn viruses. Its genes are currently being used to develop virus-resistant types of corn. However, *Z. diploperennis* occurs naturally in only a few small areas of Mexico and could easily have been destroyed by development or cultivation of the land. If we allow such species to go extinct, we may unknowingly threaten the food supply on which much of the world depends.

The pharmaceutical industry is heavily dependent on information that is stored in plants. About 25% of the prescription drugs in Canada and the United States is derived from plants. Many medicines come from plants found only in tropical rain forests, including quinine, a drug from the bark of the Cinchona tree (*Cinchona officinalis*) that is used for malaria, and vincristine, derived from rosy periwinkle (*Catharanthus roseus*), which is a treatment for leukemia and Hodgkin's disease. There are likely many plant chemicals of therapeutic importance in the thousands of rain forest plant species that have not been fully analyzed. The continued destruction of rain forests thus could mean the loss of billions of dollars in potential plant-derived pharmaceutical products.

On a smaller scale, individual species often thought worthless can actually be valuable for research purposes. The blood of the horseshoe crab (*Limulus polyphemus*) clots when exposed to toxins produced by some bacteria. Pharmaceutical industries use the blood enzyme responsible for this clotting to ensure that their products are free of bacterial contamination. Desert pupfishes, found in isolated ponds in the southwestern United States, tolerate salinity twice that of seawater and are valuable models for research on human kidney diseases. The technology does not exist to re-create individual species, let alone biomes such as rain forests. Once a species or an ecosystem is gone, it is lost forever.

Beyond this, humans benefit not only from individual species but also from the processes of natural ecosystems (**Table 57.1**). Forests soak up carbon dioxide, maintain soil fertility, and retain water, preventing floods; estuaries provide water filtration and protect rivers and coastal shores from excessive erosion. The loss of biodiversity could disrupt an ecosystem's ability to carry out such functions. Other ecosystem functions include the maintenance of populations of natural predators to regulate pest outbreaks and reservoirs of pollinators to pollinate crops and other plants.

A 1997 paper in the journal *Nature* by economist Robert Constanza and colleagues made an attempt to calculate the monetary value of ecosystems to various economies. They came to the conclusion that, at the time, the world's ecosystems were worth more than $33 trillion a year, nearly twice the gross national product of the world's economies combined ($19 trillion; **Table 57.2**). If we were to include the value of these services in the cost of goods, most goods would cost a lot more than they currently do. While the open ocean has the greatest total global value of all ecosystems, perhaps a more meaningful statistic is the per hectare value of different ecosystems. This

Table 57.1	Examples of the World's Ecosystem Services
Service	**Example**
Atmospheric gas supply	Regulation of carbon dioxide, ozone, and oxygen levels
Climate regulation	Regulation of carbon dioxide, nitrogen dioxide, and methane levels
Water supply	Irrigation, water for industry
Pollination	Pollination of crops
Biological control	Pest population regulation
Wilderness and refuges	Habitat for wildlife
Food production	Crops, livestock
Raw materials	Fossil fuels, timber
Genetic resources	Medicines, genes for plant resistance
Recreation	Ecotourism
Cultural	Aesthetic and educational value
Disturbance regulation	Storm protection, flood control
Waste treatment	Sewage purification
Soil erosion control	Retention of topsoil, reduction of accumulation of sediments in lakes
Nutrient recycling	Nitrogen, phosphorus, carbon, and sulphur cycles

Table 57.2	Valuation of the World's Ecosystem Services		
Biome	**Total global value* ($ trillion)**	**Total value (per ha) ($)**	**Main ecosystem service**
Open ocean	8,381	252	Nutrient cycling
Coastal shelf	4,283	1,610	Nutrient cycling
Estuaries	4,100	22,832	Nutrient cycling
Tropical forest	3,813	2,007	Nutrient cycling/raw materials
Seagrass and algal beds	3,801	19,004	Nutrient cycling
Swamps and other wetlands	3,231	19,580	Water supply/disturbance regulation
Lakes and rivers	1,700	8,498	Water regulation
Tidal marsh	1,648	9,990	Waste treatment/disturbance regulation
Grasslands	906	232	Waste treatment/food production
Temperate forest	894	302	Climate regulation/waste treatment/lumber
Coral reefs	375	6,075	Recreational/disturbance regulation
Cropland	128	92	Food production
Desert	0	0	
Ice and rock	0	0	
Tundra	0	0	
Urban	0	0	
Total	33,260		

*In 1997 values.

statistic reveals that shallow aquatic ecosystems, such as estuaries and swamps, are extremely valuable because of their role in nutrient cycling, water supply, and disturbance regulation. They also serve as nurseries for aquatic life. These habitats, once thought of as useless wastelands, are among the ecosystems most endangered by pollution and development.

Arguments can be made against the loss of biodiversity on ethical grounds. As only one of many species, it has been argued that humans have no right to destroy other species and the environment around us. In 1984 E. O. Wilson popularized the concept of biophilia ("love of living systems") to explain why humans innately have deep attachments with natural habitats and species because of our close association with them for millions of years.

How Much Diversity Is Needed for Ecosystems to Function Properly?

Because biodiversity has an impact on the health of ecosystems, ecologists have explored the question of how much diversity is needed for ecosystems to function properly. Recall that in the 1950s, ecologist Charles Elton had proposed in the diversity–stability hypothesis that the more species present, the more stable the community (see Chapter 55). If we use stability as a surrogate for ecosystem function, Elton's hypothesis suggests a linear correlation between diversity and ecosystem function (**Figure 57.2a**).

In 1981 ecologists Paul and Anne Ehrlich proposed an alternative called the **rivet hypothesis** (**Figure 57.2b**). In this model, species are like the rivets on an airplane, with each species playing a small but critical role in keeping the plane (the ecosystem) airborne. The loss of a rivet weakens the plane and causes it to lose a little airworthiness. The loss of a few rivets could probably be tolerated, while the loss of more rivets would prove critical to the airplane's function.

A decade later Australian ecologist Brian Walker proposed an extension of this idea, termed the **redundancy hypothesis** (or passenger hypothesis) (**Figure 57.2c**). According to this hypothesis, most species are more like passengers on a plane—they take up space but do not add to the airworthiness. The species are said to be redundant because they could simply be eliminated or replaced by others with no loss in function. Airworthiness is primarily affected by the activity of a few crucial species, in this case the pilot or copilot, which are called keystone species (a concept we will discuss in detail later in this chapter). In this scenario, the loss of each species does not affect airworthiness unless the species is of critical importance.

In another alternative, British ecologist John Lawton included the possibility that ecosystem function changes as the

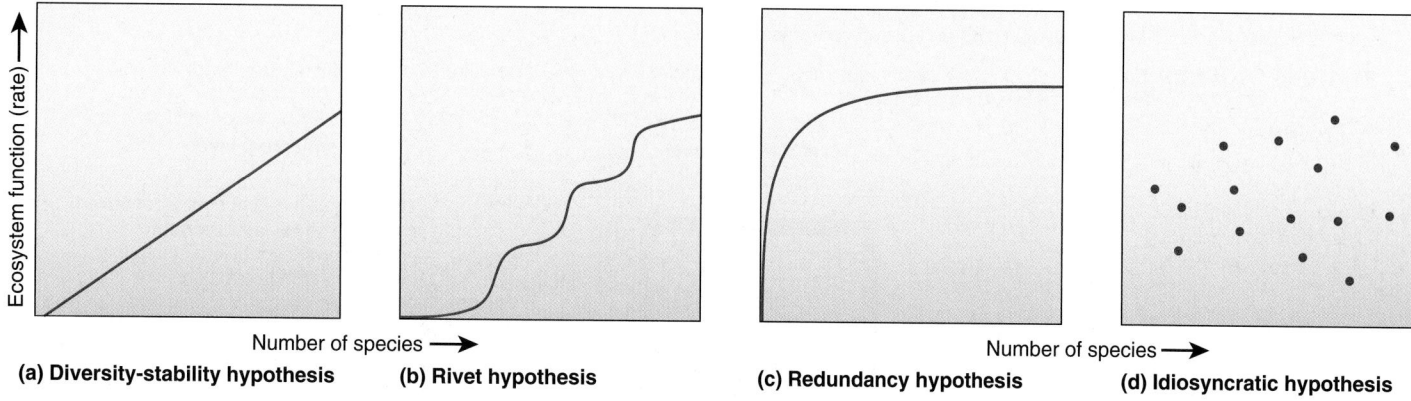

(a) Diversity-stability hypothesis   (b) Rivet hypothesis   (c) Redundancy hypothesis   (d) Idiosyncratic hypothesis

Figure 57.2 Four main models that describe the relationship between ecosystem function and biodiversity. The relationship is strongest in (a) and weakest in (d).

number of species increases or decreases, but that the direction of change is not predictable. He called this the **idiosyncratic hypothesis** (**Figure 57.2d**). Determining which model is most correct is very important, as our understanding of the effect of species loss on community function can greatly affect the way we manage our environment. As we will discuss next, experimental studies have provided data showing that reduced biodiversity does lead to reduced ecosystem functioning.

Canadian Boreal Initiative and the International Boreal Conservation Campaign (IBCC)

The Canadian Boreal Forest is a 0.56-billion hectare ecosystem that contains forests, lakes, rivers, bogs, and other wetlands. It is one of the largest intact forests left in the world (**Figure 57.3**). However, only 10% of the boreal forest has been protected; much of this is in Ontario due to 2008 provincial legislation. The rest of the boreal forest faces threats from unsustainable industrial and forestry activity, as well as oil and gas development and hydroelectric projects. Because of this development, some areas of the boreal forest are being lost at rates similar to those for tropical rain forests. The boreal forest ecosystem is a huge carbon reserve that holds 22% (186 billion metric tons) of the carbon stored on the Earth's land surface. This is equivalent to approximately 30 years' worth of carbon emissions from the burning of the world's fossil fuels. The Canadian Boreal Initiative consults with conservation

- • Cities
- ☐ Boreal region
- ▨ Boreal ecozones
- ▧ Taiga ecozones

Figure 57.3 Map showing conservation areas as part of the Canadian Boreal Initiative.

organizations, First Nations peoples, and industry to link science, policy, and conservation activities in Canada's boreal forest. The long-term goal is to permanently protect 50% of the boreal forest and ensure that the remaining lands are utilized in a balanced, sustainable approach.

FEATURE INVESTIGATION

Ecotron Experiments Showed the Relationship Between Biodiversity and Ecosystem Function

In the early 1990s Shahid Naeem and colleagues used a series of 14 environmental chambers in a facility termed the Ecotron, at Silwood Park, England, to determine how biodiversity affects ecosystem functioning. These chambers contained terrestrial communities that differed only in their

level of biodiversity (**Figure 57.4**). The number of species in each chamber was manipulated to create high-, medium-, and low-diversity ecosystems, each with four trophic levels. The trophic levels consisted of primary producers (annual plants), primary consumers (insects, snails, and slugs), secondary consumers (parasitoids that fed on the herbivores), and decomposers (earthworms and soil insects). The experiment ran for just over six months, and species were added

HYPOTHESIS Reduced biodiversity can lead to reduced ecosystem functioning.

STARTING LOCATION Ecotron, a controlled environment facility at the Natural Environment Research Council (NERC) Centre for Population Biology, in Silwood Park, England.

Experimental level · **Conceptual level**

1 Construct 14 identical experimental chambers.

Temperature- and humidity-controlled chambers are used to control environmental conditions and allow identical starting conditions in all chambers.

2 Add different combinations of species to the 14 chambers. The species added were based on three types of model communities (food webs), each with four trophic levels but with varying degrees of species richness.

Biodiversity	High	Medium	Low
Number of chambers analyzed	6	4	4

- Species present in all three systems.
- Species present in two systems.
- Species present in most diverse system only.

The three diagrams to the left each represent a single chamber. Circles represent species, and lines connecting them represent biotic interactions among the species. Note that each lower-biodiversity community is a subset of its higher-diversity counterpart and that all community types have four trophic levels.

3 Measure and analyze a range of processes, including vegetation cover and nutrient uptake.

Measurements help determine how each different type of community functions.

4 THE DATA

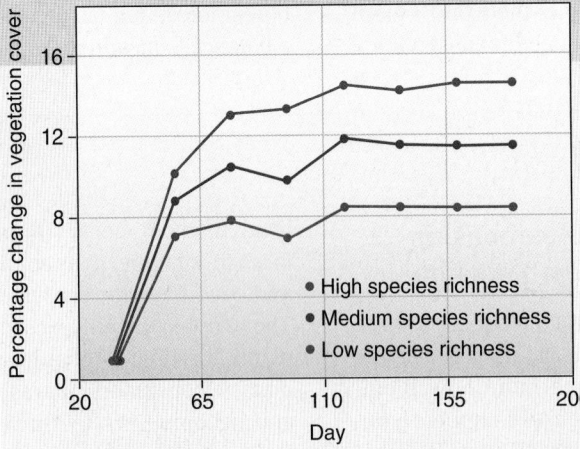

Plant productivity is linked to community diversity as measured by the percentage change in vegetation cover from initial conditions.

Data reveal that low-diversity communities have lower vegetation cover and thus are less productive than high-diversity communities.

Figure 57.4 Ecotron experiments comparing species diversity and ecosystem function.

5   CONCLUSION Increases in biodiversity lead to increases in ecosystem function. In this case, increased plant diversity results in greater vegetation cover.

6   SOURCE Naeem, S. et al. 1994. Declining biodiversity can alter the performance of ecosystems. *Nature* 368:734–737.

only after the trophic level below them was established. For example, parasitoids were not added until herbivores were abundant.

Researchers monitored and analyzed a range of measures of ecosystem function, including community respiration, decomposition, nutrient retention rates, and community productivity. The data of Figure 57.4 focuses only on community productivity. The result was that community productivity, expressed as percentage change in vegetation cover (the amount of ground covered by leaves of plants), increased as species richness increased. This occurred because of a greater variety of plant growth forms that could utilize light at different levels of the plant canopy.

A larger ground cover also meant a larger plant biomass and greater community productivity, and increased decomposition and nutrient uptake rates. For the first time, ecologists had provided an experimental demonstration that the loss of biodiversity can alter or impair the functioning of an ecosystem.

Experimental Questions

1. What was the goal of Shahid Naeem and colleagues in their experiment at Silwood Park, England?
2. What was the hypothesis tested by the researchers?
3. How did the researchers test for ecosystem functioning?

Field Experiments Also Suggest That Biodiversity Is Important for Ecosystem Function

In the mid-1990s, David Tilman and colleagues performed experiments in the field to determine how much biodiversity was necessary for proper ecosystem functioning. Previously, Tilman had suggested that species-rich grasslands were more stable; that is, they were more resistant to the ravages of drought and recovered from drought more quickly than species-poor grasslands (refer back to Figure 55.6). In these experiments, Tilman's group sowed plots, each 3 metres by 3 metres and on comparable soils, with seeds of 1, 2, 4, 6, 8, 12, or 24 species of prairie plants. Exactly which species were sown into each plot was determined randomly from a pool of 24 native species. The treatments were replicated 21 times, for a total of 147 plots. The results again showed that more diverse plots had increased productivity and used nutrients, such as nitrate, more efficiently than less diverse plots (**Figure 57.5a, b**). Furthermore, both the frequency of invasive plant species (species not originally planted in the plots) and the level of foliar fungal disease decreased with increased plant species richness (**Figure 57.5c, d**).

Although Tilman's experiments show a relationship between diversity and ecosystem function, they also suggest that a point may be reached at which function is maximized, beyond which additional species appear to have little to no impact. This supports the redundancy hypothesis. For example, uptake of nitrogen remains relatively unchanged as the number of species increases beyond six. We can also see this on a larger scale. The productivity of temperate forests in different continents is roughly the same despite different numbers of tree species present—729 in East Asia, 253 in North America, and 124 in Europe. The presence of more tree species may ensure a supply of "backups" should some of the most productive species die off from insect attack or disease. This can happen, as was seen in the demise of the American chestnut and elm trees. Diseases devastated both of these species, and their presence in American forests dramatically decreased by the mid-twentieth century (refer back to Figure 54.19). The forests filled in with other species and continued to function as before in terms of nutrient cycling and gas exchange. However, although the forests continued to function without these species, some important changes occurred. For example, the loss of chestnuts deprived bears and other animals of an important source of food and may have affected their reproductive capacity and hence the size of their populations.

57.2 THE CAUSES OF EXTINCTION AND LOSS OF BIODIVERSITY

Learning Outcomes:

1. List and describe the four main human-induced threats to species.
2. Discuss how the genetic diversity of small populations is threatened by inbreeding, genetic drift, and limited mating.

In light of research showing that the loss of species influences ecosystem function, the importance of understanding and preventing species loss takes on particular urgency. Throughout the history of life on Earth, **extinction**—the process by which species die out—has been a natural phenomenon. The average timespan of a typical animal or plant species in the fossil record is about 4 million years. To calculate the current extinction rate, we could take the total number of species estimated to be alive on Earth at present, around 10 million, and divide it by 4 million, giving an average extinction rate of 2.5 species each year. For the 5,500 species of living mammals, using the same average lifespan of around 4 million years, we would

Figure 57.5 **The functions of species richness.** The relationships between species richness and **(a)** percentage plant cover, the area of ground covered by leaves, and **(b)** uptake of nitrogen in experimental plots in Tilman's biodiversity experiments. With increasing species richness, biomass increases and nitrogen is used up, leaving less nitrogen in the soil with more species of plants. **(c)** A decrease in susceptibility to invasion of temperate grasslands by exotic species with an increase in plant species richness. **(d)** A decrease in disease severity index for plant species in temperate grasslands with an increase in plant species richness.

expect about one species to go extinct every 1,000 years; this is termed the *background extinction rate*. However, it can be argued that the fossil record is heavily biased toward successful, often geographically wide-ranging species, which undoubtedly have a longer than average persistence time. The fossil record is also biased toward vertebrates and marine molluscs, both of which fossilize well because of their hard body parts. If background extinction rates were 10 times higher than the rates perceived from the fossil record, then extinctions among the living mammals today would be expected to occur at a rate of about one every 100 years. For birds, the background extinction rate would be two species every 100 years.

It is indisputable, however, that the extinction rate for species in recent times has been far higher than this. In the past 100 years, around 20 species of mammals and over 40 species of birds went extinct (**Figure 57.6a**). The rates of species extinctions on islands in the recent past confirm the dramatic effects of human activity. The Polynesians, who colonized Hawaii in the fourth and fifth centuries, appear to have been responsible for the extinction of half of the 100 or so species of endemic land birds in the period between their arrival and that of the Europeans in the late eighteenth century. A similar impact was felt in New Zealand, which was colonized by European settlers some 500 years later than Hawaii. In New Zealand, an entire avian megafauna, consisting of huge land birds, was exterminated over the course of the century, probably through a combination of hunting and large-scale habitat destruction through burning. The term **biodiversity crisis** is often used to describe this elevated loss of species. Many scientists believe that the rate of loss is higher now than during most of geological history, and most suggest that the growth in the human population has led to the increase in the number of extinctions of other species (**Figure 57.6b**). Although the correlation of human population growth to animal extinctions does not necessarily relate to causation of animal extinction, it is human behaviour and destruction of habitat that ultimately causes animal extinction.

To understand the process of extinction in more modern times, it is essential for ecologists to examine the role of human activities and their environmental consequences. In this section, we examine why species have gone extinct in the past and look at the factors that are currently threatening species with extinction.

The Main Causes of Extinction Are Habitat Destruction, Direct Exploitation, and Introduced Species

While all causes of extinctions are not known, habitat destruction, direct exploitation, and introduced species have been major human-induced threats. Increasingly, climate change is viewed as a significant threat to species. As mentioned at the beginning of Chapter 51, human-induced climate change, or global warming, has been implicated in the dramatic decrease in the population sizes of frog species in Central and South America. Indeed, a recent study of six biodiversity-rich regions employed computer models to simulate the movement of species' ranges in response to changing climate conditions. The models predicted

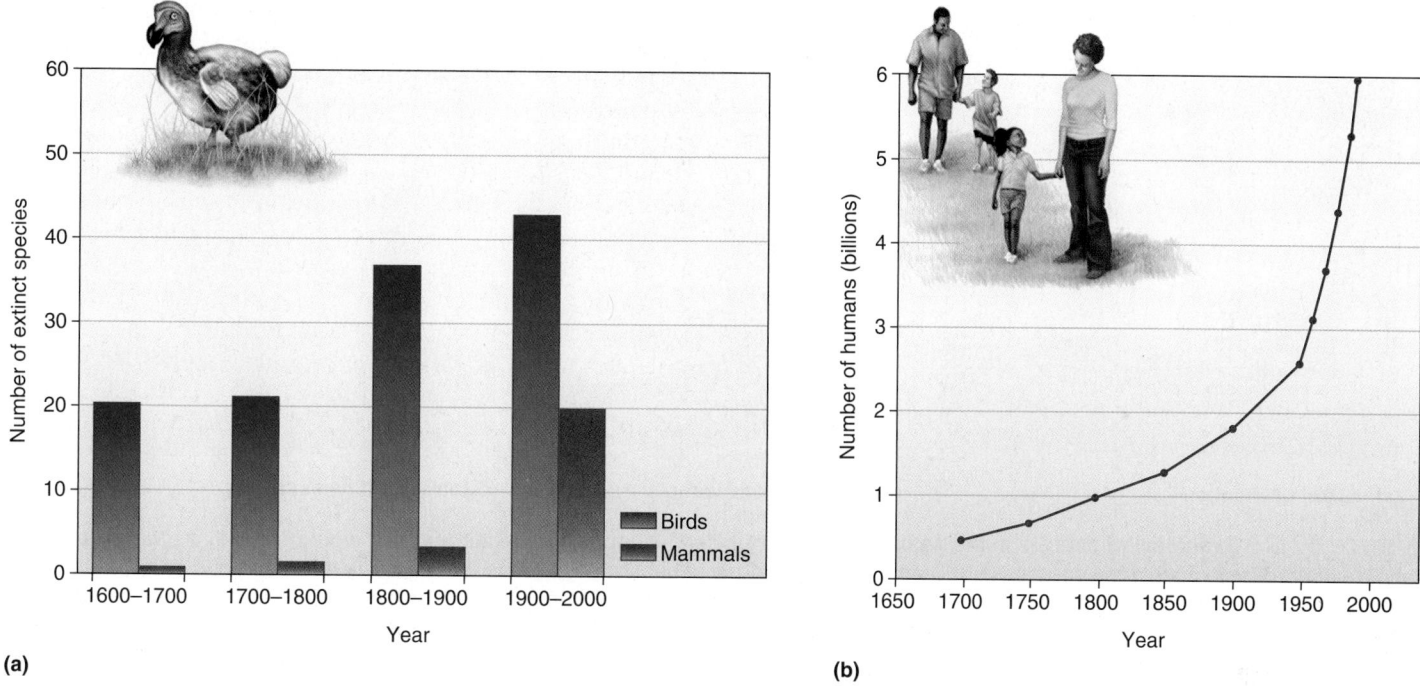

Figure 57.6 **Animal extinctions and human population growth.** (a) Increasing numbers of known extinctions in birds and mammals are concurrent with (b) exponential increases in the global human population. These figures suggest that as human numbers increase, more and more species will go extinct.

Concept check: *Why might the increasing human population result in an increase in the extinction rate of other species?*

that unless greenhouse gas emissions are cut drastically, climate change will cause 15%–37% of the species in those regions to go extinct by the year 2050.

James Grant and his students from Concordia University surveyed information on 488 species in Canada, categorized by COSEWIC as extinct, extirpated, endangered, threatened, or of special concern. By far the most prevalent threat for terrestrial and freshwater species was habitat loss resulting from agriculture and urbanization. In contrast, overexploitation was the most important threat for marine species. It appears that introduced species are a much less important threat in Canada than in the United States.

Many environmental problems stem from a common conflict between human behaviours that confer individual benefit but which in aggregate result in collective harm. This idea was presented in an article published in the journal *Science* in 1968 by Garrett Hardin titled "The Tragedy of the Commons." The argument is that when one individual can take more than their share of a resource, they receive a substantial benefit personally, whereas the negative consequence that they experience by its depletion is shared by all, and is therefore only a fraction of the size of the benefit. Such an idea is seen in cases of environmental pollution, where the polluting organization may save money at the shared expense of many.

Habitat Destruction Habitat destruction through **deforestation**, the conversion of forested areas to nonforested land, has historically been a prime cause of the extinction of species.

About one-third of the world's land surface is covered with forests, and much of this area is at risk of deforestation. While tropical forests are probably the most threatened forest type, with rates of deforestation in Africa, South America, and Asia varying between 0.6% and 0.9% per year, the destruction of forests is a global phenomenon.

Among North American terrestrial wildlife, about half of birds (272 species) and more than 10% of mammals (49 species) have an obligatory relationship with forest cover, meaning that they depend on trees for food and nesting sites. In terms of wildlife use, the oaks, whose acorns occur in the diet of at least 100 species of birds and mammals, are among the most valuable trees in North America. For many species of wildlife, the annual acorn crop is a major determinant of their abundance. Most woodpeckers nest in holes that they excavate in trees, and their food usually consists of insects collected on or in trees. The ivory-billed woodpecker (*Campephilus principalis*), the largest in North America and an inhabitant of wetlands and forests of the southeastern United States, was widely assumed to have gone extinct in the 1950s due to destruction of its habitat by heavy logging (**Figure 57.7a**). Incredibly, in 2004 the woodpecker was apparently seen in the Big Woods area of eastern Arkansas, although there has been debate over the reliability of the sighting. Many examples of plant extinctions are also found, particularly on islands such as the Hawaiian islands where many plant species have gone extinct in the last 50 years.

Deforestation is not the only form of habitat destruction. The scouring of land to plant agricultural crops can create soil

(a) Habitat destruction

(b) Direct exploitation

(c) Introduced parasites

Figure 57.7 **Extinction of species in the past.** **(a)** The ivory-billed woodpecker, the third-largest woodpecker in the world, was long thought to be extinct in the southeastern United States because of habitat destruction, but a possible sighting occurred in 2004. This nestling was photographed in Louisiana in 1938. **(b)** The great auk, once a common seabird off the Grand Banks of Newfoundland, was hunted to extinction not only for its meat, but also for its feathers for the European fashion industry. The last breeding pair was killed in Iceland in 1844. **(c)** Many Hawaiian honeycreepers were exterminated by avian malaria from introduced mosquito species. This 'i'iwi (*Vestiaria coccinea*) is one of the few remaining honeycreeper species.

erosion, increased flooding, declining soil fertility, silting of the rivers, and desertification. While the average area of land under cultivation worldwide averages about 11%, with an additional 24% given over to rangeland, this amount varies tremendously among regions. For example, Europe uses 28% of its land for crops and pasturelands, with the result that many of its native species went extinct long ago. Wetlands also have been drained for agricultural purposes. Others have been filled in for urban or industrial development. Since 1800 almost 15% of Canada's total wetland base has been drained or lost to other functions, with as much as 80% to 98% loss in urbanized regions, 70% alteration or conversion in central prairie sloughs, and 70% in our Pacific estuarine marshes. Urbanization, the development of cities on previously natural or agricultural areas, is the most human-dominated and fastest-growing type of land use worldwide and devastates the land more severely than practically any other form of habitat degradation.

Another concern to Canada is the potential destruction of habitat by oil spills. Large oil spills, which can reduce the oxygen content of water, cause significant mortality of marine animals. Within marshes, plants that become coated in oil experience substantial temperature stress, reduced photosynthesis, and stomata blockage, often resulting in immediate plant death. When the soil environment is fouled, persistent effects can endure within the ecosystem, preventing regrowth. Within the Northwest Atlantic, the cumulative effects of very small oil spills are considered just as disastrous any large-scale disaster. Chronic oil pollution off the coast of Newfoundland has resulted in the highest bird oiling rates observed anywhere in the world, with 0.77 oiled birds per kilometre observed in one study. Thick-billed murres are the most vulnerable seabird species to

oil pollution in Newfoundland and account for 56%–88% of the annual bird oil kills. There are also concerns over expansion of the Alberta tar sands where an extensive system of pipelines for delivering oil will be required. Pipeline oil spills, such as the 230,000 litres spilled in June 2012 in Alberta, may lead to habitat destruction and species loss.

Direct Exploitation Direct exploitation, particularly the hunting of animals, has been the cause of many extinctions in the past. The passenger pigeon (*Ectopistes migratorius*) was once the most common bird in North America, probably accounting for over 40% of the entire bird population. Flock sizes were estimated to be over 1 billion birds. It may seem improbable that the most common bird on the continent could be hunted to extinction for its meat, but that is just what happened. The flocking behaviour of the birds made them relatively easy targets for hunters, who used special firearms to harvest the birds in quantity. Another example is the seabird the great auk (*Pinguinus impennis*), which bore a remarkable resemblance to penguins from the southern hemisphere with its small wings, black back, white abdomen, upright posture, and flightlessness (although it was not, in fact, related to penguins). Historically the great auk ranged from the Atlantic coast in Canada to Scandinavia, Scotland, and Ireland. In Canada, it fed on fish along the continental shelf waters of the Grand Banks and bred on rocky offshore islands such as Funk Island. From the sixteenth to eighteenth centuries, large numbers of the great auk were hunted for their meat by European fishermen and whalers, despite attempts by Newfoundland's governing council in the mid-eighteenth century to petition Britain to stop the massacre of seabirds. The Funk Island birds were also slaughtered wholesale for their back feathers, which were considered to be indispensable fashion accessories in Europe. The last known breeding pair was killed in Iceland in 1844 and the last live bird was reportedly seen off the coast of Newfoundland in 1852 (**Figure 57.7b**).

Many whale species were driven to the brink of extinction prior to a moratorium on commercial whaling issued in 1988 (refer back to Figure 54.14). Steller's sea cow (*Hydrodamalis gigas*), a 9-metre-long manatee-like mammal, was hunted to extinction in the Bering Strait only 27 years after its discovery in 1740. A poignant example of human excess in hunting was the dodo (*Raphus cucullatus*), a flightless bird native only to the island of Mauritius that had no known predators. A combination of overexploitation and introduced species led to its extinction within 200 years of the arrival of humans. Sailors hunted it for its meat, and the rats, pigs, and monkeys brought to the island by humans destroyed the dodo's eggs and chicks in their ground nests.

Introduced Species

Introduced species, often called exotic species, are those species moved by humans from a native location to another location. Most often the species are introduced for agricultural purposes or as sources of timber, meat, or wool, and these species need humans for their continued survival. Others, such as plants, insects, or marine organisms, are unintentionally transported via the movement of cargo by ships or planes. Regardless of their method of introduction, some introduced species become **invasive**, spreading and outcompeting native species for space and resources.

We can categorize the interactions between introduced and native species into competition, predation, and disease. Competition may eliminate local populations and cause huge reductions in the densities of native species, but it has not yet been clearly shown to exterminate entire species. On the other hand, there have been many recorded cases of extinction from predation. Introduced predators such as rats, cats, and mongooses have accounted for at least 43% of recorded extinctions of birds on islands. Lighthouse keepers' cats have annihilated populations of ground-nesting birds on small islands around the world. The brown tree snake, which was accidentally introduced onto the island of Guam, has decimated the country's native bird populations (refer back to Figure 54.13). Parasitism and disease carried by introduced organisms have also been important in causing extinctions. Avian malaria in Hawaii, spread by introduced mosquito species, is believed to have contributed to the demise of up to 50% of native Hawaiian birds (**Figure 57.7c**).

Small Populations Are Threatened by the Loss of Genetic Diversity

Knowing why species have gone extinct helps us to recognize the threats facing living species, which in turn may make it easier to protect endangered and threatened species in the future. As we have discussed, most of the factors currently threatening species—introduced species, direct exploitation, and habitat destruction—are derived from human activities. However, even if habitats are not destroyed, many become fragmented, leading to the development of small, isolated populations that can become less viable over time. The threats to species from small population size relate to a reduction of genetic diversity that can result from three factors: inbreeding, genetic drift, and limited mating, which reduces effective population size.

Inbreeding

Inbreeding, which is mating among genetically related relatives, is more likely to take place in nature when population size becomes very small and there are a limited number of mates to choose from (see Chapter 22). In many species, survivorship of offspring declines as populations become more inbred. This phenomenon was shown experimentally as long ago as the nineteenth century. Litter size in inbred rats declined from 7.5 in 1887 to 3.2 in 1892. Furthermore, over the same time span, the level of nonproductive matings—those where no offspring were born—rose from 2% to 50%. Generally, the more inbred the population, the more severe these types of problems become.

One of the most striking examples of the effects of inbreeding in conservation biology involves the greater prairie chicken (*Tympanuchus cupido*). The male birds have a spectacular mating display that involves inflating the bright orange air sacs on their throat, stomping their feet, and spreading their tail feathers. The prairies of the midwestern United States and central Canada were once home to millions of these birds, but as the prairies were converted to farmland the range and population sizes of the bird shrank dramatically. The population of prairie chickens in Illinois decreased from 25,000 in 1933 to fewer than 50 in 1989, of which only 10 to 12 were males. Because of the decreasing numbers of males, inbreeding in the population had increased. This was reflected in the steady reduction in the hatching success of eggs (**Figure 57.8**). The prairie chicken population had entered a downward spiral toward extinction from which it could not naturally recover, a phenomenon called an **extinction vortex**. In the early 1990s conservation biologists began trapping prairie chickens in Kansas and Nebraska, where populations remained larger and more genetically diverse, and moved them to Illinois, bringing an infusion of new genetic material into the population. This translocation resulted in a rebounding of the egg-hatching success rate to 90% by 1993.

Genetic Drift

In small populations, there is a good chance that some individuals will fail to mate successfully purely by chance. This is known as the **Allee effect**, after ecologist W. C. Allee, who first described it. If an individual that fails to mate possesses a rare gene, that genetic information will not be passed on to the next generation, resulting in a loss of genetic diversity from the population. As noted in Chapter 22, **genetic drift** refers to the random change in allele frequencies attributable to chance. Because the likelihood of an allele being represented in just one or a few individuals is higher in small populations than in large populations, small, isolated populations are particularly vulnerable to this type of reduction in genetic diversity. Such isolated populations will lose a percentage of their original

Figure 57.8 **Changes in the abundance and egg-hatching success rate of prairie chickens.** As the number of males decreased inbreeding increased, resulting in a decrease in fertility as indicated by a reduced egg-hatching rate. An influx of males in the early 1990s increased the egg-hatching success rate dramatically.

Concept check: *Is the fitness of all organisms decreased by inbreeding?*

 Principle: *New properties emerge from complex interactions. The conversion of prairies to farmland reduced the available prairie chicken habitat in Illinois, and populations of the bird decreased dramatically. The consequent increase in inbreeding led to a path towards extinction that was difficult to reverse.*

diversity over time, approximately at the rate of $1/(2N)$ per generation, where N = population size. As described next, this has a greater effect in smaller versus larger populations.

If $N = 500$, then $\dfrac{1}{2N} = 1/1{,}000 =$ 0.001, or 0.1% genetic diversity lost per generation

If $N = 50$, then $\dfrac{1}{2N} = 1/100 = 0.01$, or 1% genetic diversity lost per generation

Due to genetic drift, a population of 500 will lose only 0.1% of its genetic diversity in a generation, while a population of 50 will lose 1%. Such losses become magnified over many generations. After 20 generations, the population of 500 will lose 2% of its original genetic variation, but the population of 50 will lose about 20%! For organisms that breed annually, this would mean a substantial loss in genetic variation over 20 years. Once again, this effect becomes more severe as the population size decreases.

As with inbreeding, the effects of genetic drift can be countered by immigration of individuals into a population. Even relatively low immigration rates of about one immigrant per generation (or one individual moved from one population to another) can be sufficient to counter genetic drift in a population of 100 individuals.

Limited Mating In many populations, the **effective population size**, the number of individuals that contribute genes to future populations, may be smaller than the number of individuals in the population, particularly in animals with a harem mating structure in which only a few dominant males breed.

For example, dominant elephant seal bulls control harems of females, and a few males command all the matings (refer back to Figure 52.22). If a population consists of breeding males and breeding females, the effective population size is given by:

| Number of breeding males |

| Effective population size | | Number of breeding females |

$$N_e = \frac{4N_mN_f}{N_m + N_f}$$

In a population of 500, a 50:50 sex ratio, and all individuals breeding, $N_e = (4 \times 250 \times 250)/(250 + 250) = 500$, or 100% of the actual population size. However, if 250 females breed with 10 males, $N_e = (4 \times 10 \times 250)/(10 + 250) = 38.5$, or 8% of the actual population size.

Knowledge of effective population size is vital to ensuring the success of conservation projects. In Alberta there are approximately 800 grizzly bears; BC has 10,000, Yukon has 6,500, NWT has 4,500; and Alaska has 31,000. However, in Washington, Montana, Idaho, and Wyoming, the grizzly bear (*Ursus arctos*) has declined in numbers from an estimated 100,000 in 1800 to fewer than 1,000 at present. In this area, the range of the species is now less than 1% of its historical range and is restricted to six separate populations in four states (**Figure 57.9**). Researchers have established that the effective population size of grizzly populations is generally only about 25% of the actual population size because not all bears breed. Thus, even fairly large, isolated populations, such as the 200 bears in Yellowstone National Park, are vulnerable to the harmful effects of loss of genetic variation because the effective population size may be as small as 50 individuals. It has been proposed that an exchange of grizzly bears between populations or zoo collections would help tremendously in promoting genetic variation. Even an exchange of two bears per generation between populations would greatly reduce the loss of genetic variation.

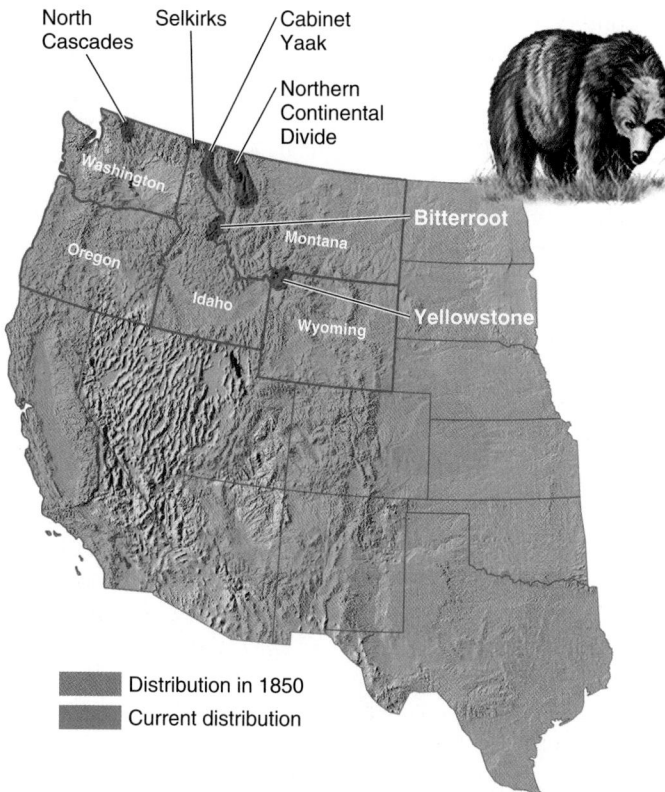

North Cascades Selkirks Cabinet Yaak

Northern Continental Divide

Washington

Oregon

Montana

Bitterroot

Idaho

Wyoming

Yellowstone

◼ Distribution in 1850
◼ Current distribution

Figure 57.9 Past and current ranges of the grizzly bear. The range of the grizzly bear is currently less than 1% of its historical range. The current range in the continental United States has contracted to just six populations in four states, as the population size has shrunk from 100,000 before the West was settled to about 1,000 today.

Concept check: *If only 500 male and 500 female grizzlies exist today, but only 25% of the males breed, what is the effective population size?*

57.3 CONSERVATION STRATEGIES

Learning Outcomes:

1. Discuss the different criteria that conservation biologists use to target areas for protection.
2. Explain how the principles of the model of island biogeography and landscape ecology are used to create nature preserves.
3. Describe different approaches conservation biologists use to protect individual species.
4. Define restoration ecology and the approaches used to restore degraded ecosystems and populations of species.

In their efforts to maintain the diversity of life on Earth, conservation biologists are currently active on many fronts and employ many strategies. We begin this section by discussing

how conservation biologists identify the global habitats richest in species. We next explore the concept of nature reserves and consider questions such as how large conservation areas should be and how far apart they should be situated. These questions are within the realm of **landscape ecology**, which studies the spatial arrangement of communities and ecosystems in a geographic area. Next we discuss how conservation efforts often focus on certain species that can have a disproportionate impact on their ecosystem. We will also examine the field of restoration ecology, focusing on how wildlife habitats can be established from degraded areas and how captive breeding programs have been used to re-establish populations of threatened species in the wild. We conclude by returning to the theme of genomes and proteomes to show how modern molecular techniques of cloning can be useful in the fight to save critically endangered species.

Habitat Conservation Focuses on Identifying Countries Rich in Species, Areas Rich in Endemics, or Representative Habitats

Conservation biologists often must make decisions regarding which species and habitats should be protected. Many conservation efforts have focused on saving habitats in so-called megadiversity countries, because they often have the greatest number of species, but more recent strategies have promoted preservation of certain key areas with the highest levels of unique species, or preservation of representative areas of all types of habitat, even relatively species-poor areas in temperate grasslands (prairies).

Megadiversity Countries One method of targeting areas for conservation is to identify those countries with the greatest numbers of species, the **megadiversity countries**. Using the number of plants, vertebrates, and selected groups of insects as criteria, biologist Russell Mittermeier and colleagues have determined that just 17 countries are home to nearly 70% of all known species. Brazil, Indonesia, and Colombia top the list, followed by Australia, Peru, Mexico, Madagascar, China, and nine other countries. The megadiversity country approach suggests that conservation efforts should be focused on the most biologically rich countries.

As we learned in Chapter 55, large areas generally have the greatest number of species, and proponents of the megadiversity country concept believe it would protect the greatest number of species. Large countries, such as Brazil, would garner most of the available international funds. Perhaps the greatest drawback of the megadiversity approach, however, is that although megadiversity areas may contain the most species, they do not necessarily contain the most unique species. The mammal species list for Peru is 344 and for Ecuador 271; of these, however, 208 species are common to both.

Areas Rich in Endemic Species Another method of setting conservation priorities, one adopted by the organization Conservation International, takes into account the number of species that are **endemic**, or found only in a particular place or region and nowhere else. This approach suggests that conservationists focus their efforts on geographic **hot spots**. To qualify as a hot spot, a region must meet two criteria: It must contain at least 1,500 species of vascular plants as endemics, and have lost at least 70% of its original habitat. Vascular plants were chosen as the primary group of organisms to determine whether an area qualifies as a hot spot mainly because most other terrestrial organisms depend on them to some extent.

Conservationists Norman Myers, Russell Mittermeier, and colleagues identified 34 hot spots that together occupy a mere 2.3% of the Earth's surface but contain 150,000 endemic plant species, or 50% of the world's total (**Figure 57.10**). Of these areas, the Tropical Andes and Sundaland (the region including Malaysia, Indonesia, and surrounding islands) have the most endemic plant species (**Table 57.3**). This approach posits that protecting geographic hot spots will prevent the extinction of a larger number of endemic species than would protecting areas

Figure 57.10 Location of major biodiversity hot spots around the world. Hot spots, shown in orange, have high numbers of endemic species.

Table 57.3	Numbers of Endemic Species Present in the Top 10 Hot Spots of the World, Ranked by the Numbers of Endemic Plants					
Rank	**Hot spot**	**Plants**	**Birds**	**Mammals**	**Reptiles**	**Amphibians**	**Freshwater fish**
1	Tropical Andes	15,000	584	75	275	664	131
2	Sundaland	15,000	146	173	244	172	350
3	Mediterranean Basin	11,700	32	25	77	27	63
4	Madagascar	11,600	183	144	367	226	97
5	Brazil's Atlantic Forest	8,000	148	71	94	286	133
6	Indo-Burma	7,000	73	73	204	139	553
7	Caribbean	6,550	167	41	468	164	65
8	Cape Floristic Province	6,210	6	4	22	16	14
9	Philippines	6,091	185	102	160	74	67
10	Brazil's Cerrado	4,400	16	14	33	26	200

of a similar size elsewhere. The main argument against using hot spots as the criterion for targeting conservation efforts is that the areas richest in endemics—tropical rain forests—would receive the majority of attention and funding, perhaps at the expense of other areas.

Representative Habitats   In a third approach to prioritizing areas for conservation, scientists have recently argued that we need to conserve representatives of all major habitats. Thus, while the Pampas region of South America—arguably the most threatened habitat on the continent because of conversion of its grasslands to agriculture—does not compare well in richness or endemics to the rain forests, it is a unique area that without preservation could disappear. By selecting habitats that are most distinct from those already preserved, many areas that are threatened but not biologically rich may be preserved in addition to the less immediately threatened, but richer, tropical forests. The best strategy of identifying areas for conservation efforts might be one that creates a "portfolio" of areas containing those with high species richness, large numbers of endemic species, and various habitat types.

The Theory and Practice of Reserve Design Incorporate Principles of Island Biogeography and Landscape Ecology

After having identified areas to preserve, conservationists must determine the size, arrangement, and management of the protected land. Among the questions conservationists ask is this: Is one large reserve preferable to an equivalent area composed of smaller reserves? Since reserves can be viewed as islands of habitat, this question theoretically can be answered with the help of the theory of island biogeography. Other questions concern whether parks should be close together or far apart, and whether they should be connected by strips of suitable habitat

to allow the movement of plants and animals between them. These large-scale questions concerning the spatial arrangement of communities and ecosystems in a geographic area fall within the field of landscape ecology. Conservationists also need to consider the fact that park design is often contingent on economic factors. Let's examine some of the many issues that conservationists address in the creation and management of protected land.

The Role of Island Biogeography   In our exploration of the equilibrium model of island biogeography (see Chapter 55), we noted that it could be applied not only to a body of land surrounded by water but also to isolated fragments of habitat. Seen this way, wildlife reserves and sanctuaries are in essence islands in a sea of human-altered land. One question for conservationists is how large a protected area should be (**Figure 57.11a**). In theory, the number of species should increase with increasing area (the species-area effect); thus, the larger the area, the greater the number of species that would be protected. In addition, larger parks have other benefits. For example, they are beneficial for organisms that require large spaces, including migrating species and species with extensive territories, such as lions and tigers.

Another question is whether it is preferable to protect one single, large reserve or several smaller ones (**Figure 57.11b**). This is called the **SLOSS debate** (for single large or several small). Proponents of the single, large reserve claim that a larger reserve is better able to preserve more and larger populations than an equal area divided into small areas. According to island biogeography, a larger block of habitat should support more species than any of the smaller blocks.

However, many empirical studies suggest that multiple small sites of equivalent area will contain more species, because a series of small sites is more likely to contain a broader variety of habitats than one large site. Looking at a variety of sites,

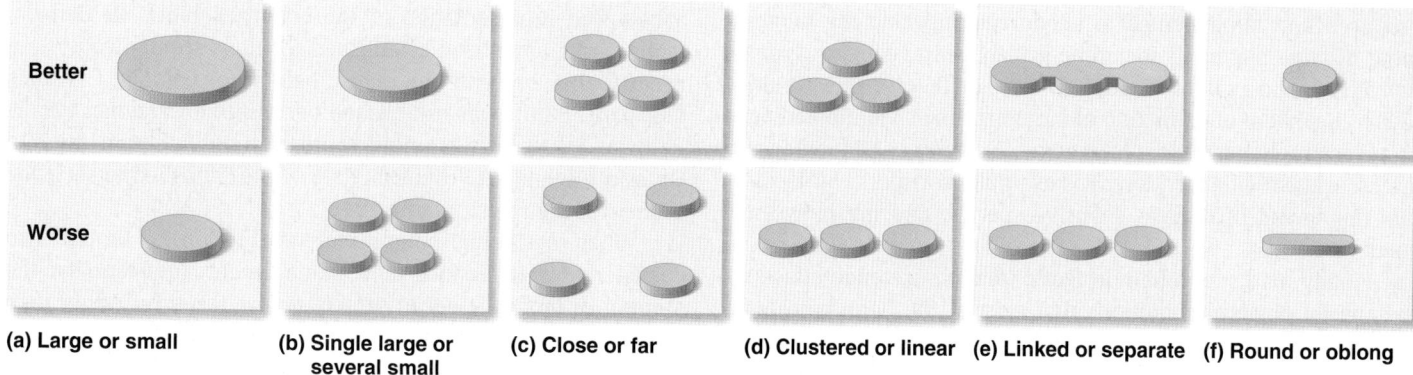

| Better / Worse | (a) Large or small | (b) Single large or several small | (c) Close or far | (d) Clustered or linear | (e) Linked or separate | (f) Round or oblong |

Figure 57.11   The theoretical design of nature reserves, based on the tenets of island biogeography.   (a) A larger reserve will hold more species and have low extinction rates. (b) Given a certain area available, it should be fragmented into as few pieces as possible. (c) If an area must be fragmented, the pieces should be as close as possible to permit dispersal. (d) To enhance dispersal, a cluster of fragments is preferable to a linear arrangement. (e) Maintaining or creating corridors between fragments may also enhance dispersal. (f) Circular-shaped areas will minimize the amount of undesirable edge habitat.

Concept check: *What are some of the potential risks in connecting areas via movement corridors?*

researchers Jim Quinn and Susan Harrison concluded that animal life was richer in collections of small parks than in fewer, larger parks. In their study, having more habitat types outweighed the effect of area on biodiversity. In addition, another benefit of a series of smaller parks is a reduction of extinction risk by a single event such as a wildfire or the spread of disease.

Landscape Ecology   **Landscape ecology** is a subdiscipline of ecology that examines the spatial arrangement of elements in communities and ecosystems. In the design of nature reserves, one question that needs to be addressed is how close reserves should be placed to one another. A related question is whether to have a linear or cluster arrangement of small reserves. Island biogeography suggests that if an area must be fragmented, the sites should be as close as possible to permit dispersal (**Figure 57.11c, d**). In practice, however, having small sites far apart may preserve more species than having them close together, since once again distant sites are likely to incorporate slightly different habitats and thus species.

Landscape ecologists have also suggested that small reserves should be linked together by biotic corridors, or **movement corridors**, which are thin strips of land that may permit the movement of species between patches (**Figure 57.11e**). Such corridors may facilitate movements of organisms that are vulnerable to predation outside their natural habitat or that have poor powers of dispersal between habitat patches. In this way, if a disaster befalls a population in one small reserve, immigrants from neighbouring populations can more easily recolonize it. This avoids the need for humans to physically move new plants or animals into an area.

Several types of habitat function as corridors, including hedgerows in Europe, which facilitate movement and dispersal of species between forest fragments. In China, corridors of habitat have been established to link small, adjacent populations of giant pandas. Riparian habitats, vegetated corridors bordering watercourses, are thought to help facilitate movement of species between lakes or rivers. In Alberta, wildlife corridors are being proposed and implemented to encourage and help the movement of large mammals including grizzly bears, cougars, lynx, wolverine, and wolves (**Figure 57.12**). In theory, this would lessen the extent of extinction of large mammals via inbreeding or a catastrophic environmental event. However, disadvantages are associated with corridors. For example, corridors can facilitate the spread of disease, invasive species, and fire between small reserves.

Finally, parks are often designed to minimize **edge effects**, the special physical conditions that exist at the boundaries or "edges" of ecosystems (see **Figure 57.11f**). Habitat edges, particularly those between natural habitats such as forests and developed land, are often different in physical characteristics from the habitat core. The interior of a forest is shaded by trees and has less wind and light than the forest edge, which is unprotected. Many forest-adapted species thus shy away from forest edges and prefer forest interiors. Circular-shaped parks are preferred over long, skinny parks because the amount of edge is minimized.

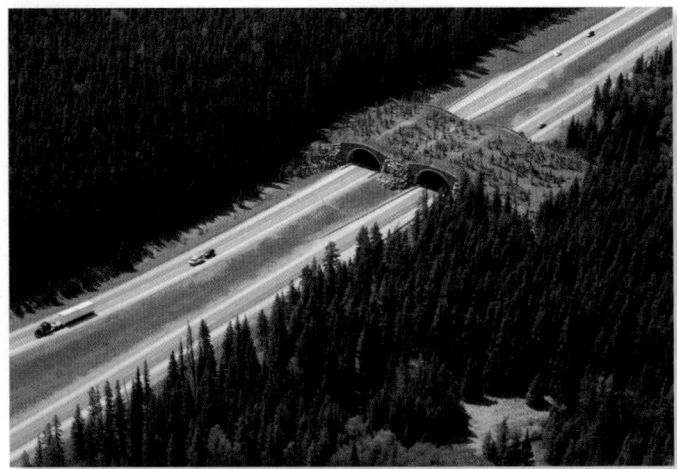

Figure 57.12   Habitat corridor found in Banff National Park.   Dr. Tony Clevenger of Montana State University researches road effects on wildlife populations. He has worked with Parks Canada to reduce wildlife loss due to car collisions and allow wildlife to migrate across highways on strategically placed corridors.

Concept check: *Why would these bridges act as habitat corridors?*

Economic Considerations in Conservation   While the principles of island biogeography theory and landscape ecology are useful in illuminating conservation issues, in reality there is often little choice as to the size, shape, and location of nature reserves. Management practicalities, costs of acquisition and management, and politics often override ecological considerations, especially in developing countries, where costs for large reserves may be relatively high. Economic considerations often enter into the choice of which areas to preserve. Typically, many countries protect areas in those regions that are the least economically valuable rather than choosing areas to ensure a balanced representation of the country's biota. In Canada, many parks have been established for their scenic beauty, not because they preserve the richest habitat for wildlife. Canada's first park, Banff, was established because the Canadian Pacific Railway wanted to promote tourism along its train line. In Ontario, Algonquin Provincial Park was established to set aside timber for the forestry industry.

When designing nature reserves, countries should also consider how to finance their management. Interestingly, the amount of money spent to protect nature reserves, rather than size, may better determine species extinction rates. According to island biogeography theory, large areas minimize the risk of extinctions because they contain sizable populations. In Africa, several parks, such as Serengeti and Selous in Tanzania, Tsavo in Kenya, and Luangwa in Zambia, are large enough to fulfill this theoretical ideal. However, in the 1980s, populations of black rhinoceros and elephants declined dramatically within these areas because of poaching, showing that a wide gap may exist between theory and reality. In reality, the rates of

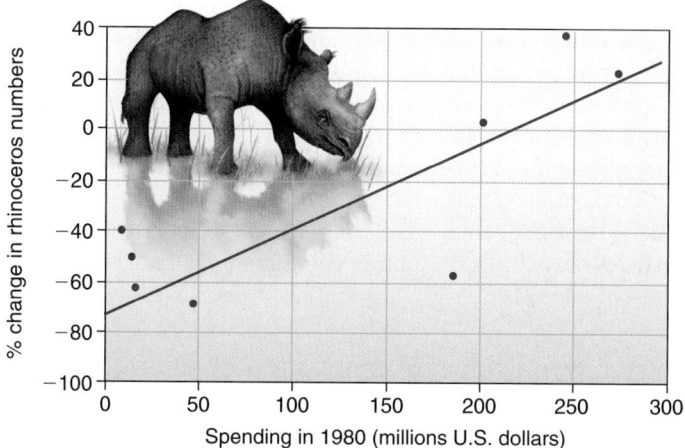

Figure 57.13 **The economics of conservation.** A positive relationship is seen between change in black rhinoceros numbers between 1980 and 1984, and conservation spending in various African countries.

decline of rhinos and elephants, largely a result of poaching, have been related directly to conservation efforts and spending (**Figure 57.13**). The remaining black rhinos, lowland gorillas, and pygmy chimpanzees in Africa and the vicuna, a llama-like animal in South America, have all shown the greatest stabilization of numbers in areas that have been heavily patrolled and where resources have been concentrated.

The Single-Species Approach Focuses Conservation Efforts on Particular Types of Species

Some plants and animals are, for reasons we will explore in this section, of more interest to conservation biologists than others. The single-species approach to conservation focuses on saving particularly important species, including indicator, umbrella, flagship, and keystone species.

Indicator Species Some conservation biologists have suggested that certain organisms can be used as **indicator species**, or species whose status provides information on the overall health of an ecosystem. Corals are good indicators of marine processes such as siltation, the accumulation of sediments transported by water. Because siltation reduces the availability of light, the abundance of many marine organisms decreases in such situations, with corals among the first to display a decline in health. A proliferation of the dark variety of the peppered moth (*Biston betularia*) has been shown to be a good indicator of polluted air. Polar bears (*Ursus maritimus*) are thought to be an indicator species for global climate change (**Figure 57.14a**). Scientists believe that global warming is causing the ice in the Arctic to melt earlier in the spring than in the past. Because polar bears rely on the ice to hunt for seals, the earlier breakup of the ice is leaving the bears less time to feed and build the fat that enables them to sustain themselves and their young. Scientists have noted a decrease in the weight of polar bears and in the survival of their cubs.

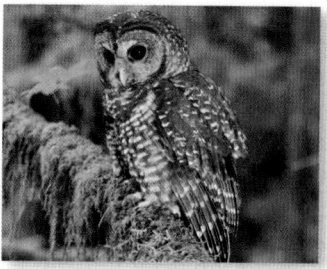

(a) Polar bear **(b) Northern spotted owl**

Figure 57.14 Indicator and umbrella species. **(a)** Polar bears have been called an indicator species of global climate change. **(b)** The Northern spotted owl is considered an umbrella species for the old-growth forest in the Pacific Northwest and British Columbia.

Umbrella Species **Umbrella species** are species whose habitat requirements are so large that protecting them would protect many other species existing in the same habitat. The Northern spotted owl (*Strix occidentalis*) of the Pacific Northwest and British Columbia is considered to be an important umbrella species (**Figure 57.14b**). A pair of birds needs at least 800 hectares of old-growth forest for survival and reproduction, so maintaining healthy owl populations is thought to help ensure survival of many other forest-dwelling species. In the southeastern United States, the red-cockaded woodpecker (*Picoides borealis*) is often seen as the equivalent of the spotted owl, since it requires large tracks of old-growth long-leaf pine (*Pinus palustris*), including old diseased trees in which it can excavate its nests. Some species, such as *Zea diploperennis*, which we discussed at the beginning of the chapter, fall into this category. For example, to protect *Z. diploperennis* in its natural environment, the state of Jalisco in Mexico bought the land where it grows and established a nature reserve and research facility there.

Flagship Species In the past, conservation resources were often allocated to a **flagship species**, a single large or instantly recognizable species. Such species were typically chosen because they were attractive and thus more readily engendered support from the public for their conservation. The concept of the flagship species, which are usually charismatic vertebrates such as the American buffalo (*Bison bison*), is often used to raise awareness for conservation in general. The giant panda (*Ailuropoda melanoleuca*) is the World Wildlife Fund's emblem for endangered species, and the woodland caribou (*Rangifer tarandus caribou*), which is the emblem on the Canadian 25 cent coin, has become a commonly cited species for conservation campaigns in Canada.

Keystone Species A different, perhaps more effective conservation strategy focuses on **keystone species**, species within a community that have a role out of proportion to their abundance.

The beaver, a relatively small animal, can completely alter a community by building a dam and flooding an entire river valley (**Figure 57.15**). The resultant lake may become a home to fish

Figure 57.15   Keystone species.   The American beaver creates large dams across streams, and the resultant lakes provide habitats for a great diversity of species.

species, wildfowl, and aquatic vegetation. A decline in the number of beavers could have serious ramifications for the remaining community members, promoting fish die-offs, waterfowl loss, and the death of vegetation adapted to waterlogged soil.

Tropical ecologist John Terborgh considers palm nuts and figs to be keystone species because they produce fruit during otherwise fruitless times of the year and are thus critical resources for tropical forest fruit-eating animals, including primates, rodents, and many birds. Together, these fruit-eaters account for as much as three-quarters of the tropical forest animal biomass. Without the fruit trees, wholesale extinction of these animals could occur. Note that a keystone species is not the same as a **dominant species**, one that has a large effect in a community because of its abundance or high biomass. For example, *Spartina* cordgrass is a dominant species in a salt marsh because of its large biomass (refer back to Figure 56.15), but it is not a keystone species.

In the southeastern United States, gopher tortoises can be regarded as keystone species because the burrows they create provide homes for an array of other animals, including mice, opossums, frogs, snakes, and insects. Many of these creatures depend on the gopher tortoise burrows and would be unable to survive without them. Gopher tortoises and some other keystone species, including beavers, are also called **ecosystem engineers**, because they create, modify, and maintain habitats. African elephants act as ecosystem engineers through their browsing activity, destroying small trees and shrubs and changing woodland habitats into grasslands.

Few studies have analyzed the community importance of keystone species, and no set criteria have been established for designating a keystone species. Nevertheless, such species do seem to affect species diversity. The conservation community is eager to identify keystone species, because by managing a keystone species they may also ensure the survival of many other species in the ecosystem. In the Rocky Mountain subalpine ecosystem, whitebark pine (*Pinus albicaulis*) is generally considered a keystone species because it grows on windswept

areas at high elevations where no other trees grow. It helps to stabilize steep slopes, influences the rate of snow melt, and provides food and shelter for many species of wildlife. For example, Clark's nutcracker (*Nucifraga columbiana*) depends on cached seeds of whitebark pine to survive the harsh winters at high elevations. Whitebark pine is found in seven of Canada's national parks: Mount Revelstoke, Glacier, Jasper, Waterton Lakes, Banff, Kootenay, and Yoho. Keystone species restoration research for whitebark pine is being done in Banff, Kootenay, and Yoho Parks.

Restoration Ecology Attempts to Rehabilitate Degraded Ecosystems

Restoration ecology is the full or partial repair or replacement of biological habitats and/or their populations that have been damaged. It can focus on restoring or rehabilitating a habitat, or it can involve attempting to return species to the wild following captive breeding. Following opencast mining for coal or phosphate, huge tracts of disturbed land must be replenished with topsoil and a large number of species such as grasses, shrubs, and trees must be replanted. Aquatic habitats may be restored by reducing human impacts. In the 1960s and 1970s, Lake Erie was highly eutrophic and the International Joint Commission sought to reverse the trend. This led to a Canada–United States agreement to reduce phosphorus in laundry detergents and to improve the treatment of sewage entering Great Lakes. This led to a sharp reduction of phosphorus entering Lake Erie and water quality improved significantly into the 1970s and 1980s. The control of eutrophication in Lake Erie is recognized worldwide as a success in restoration. (However, there are now different stressors on Lake Erie that are being addressed by the International Joint Commission, including invasive species and episodic fish die-offs caused by *Clostridium botulinum* poisoning.) Restoration can also involve **bioremediation**, the use of living organisms, usually microbes or plants, to detoxify polluted habitats such as dump sites or oil spills. Some bacteria can detoxify contaminants, while certain plants can accumulate toxins in their tissues and are then harvested, removing the poison from the system.

Habitat Restoration   The three basic approaches to habitat restoration are complete restoration, rehabilitation, and ecosystem replacement. In complete restoration, conservationists attempt to put back exactly what was there prior to the disturbance. Stéphane McLachlan at the University of Manitoba is involved in the restoration of tallgrass prairie in Manitoba, converting agricultural land back to species-rich prairies (**Figure 57.16a**). The second approach aims to return the habitat to something similar to but a little less than full restoration, a goal called rehabilitation. In Florida, phosphate mining involves removing a layer of topsoil or "overburden," mining the phosphate-rich layers, returning the overburden, and replanting the area. Exotic species such as cogongrass (*Imperata cylindrica*), an invasive Southeast Asian species, often invade these disturbed areas, and the biodiversity of the restored habitat is usually not comparable to that

(a) Complete restoration

(b) Rehabilitation

(c) Ecosystem replacement

Figure 57.16 Habitat restoration. **(a)** In Manitoba, tallgrass prairie is being restored at Beaudry Provincial Park. **(b)** In Florida, phosphate mines are so degraded that even after restoration, some exotic species such as cogongrass often invade. **(c)** These old open-pit mines in Middlesex, England, have been converted to valuable freshwater habitats, replacing the wooded area that was originally present.

of unmined areas (**Figure 57.16b**). The third approach makes no attempt to restore what was originally present but instead replaces the original ecosystem with a different one. The replacement could be an ecosystem that is simpler but more productive, as when deciduous forest is replaced after mining by simple grassland to be used for public recreation.

While any of these approaches can be employed in the habitat restoration process, a common viewpoint among environmentalists is that the endpoint of habitat restoration should be complete restoration. While in some cases full restoration is appropriate, there are also many cases where restoration is so difficult or expensive as to be impractical. Ecosystem replacement is particularly sensible for land that has been significantly damaged by past activities. It would be nearly impossible to recreate the original landscape of an area that was mined for stone or gravel. In these situations, however, wetlands or lakes may be created in the open pits (Figure 57.15c).

Captive Breeding Captive breeding, the propagation of animals and plants outside their natural habitat to produce stock for subsequent release into the wild, has proved valuable in reestablishing breeding populations following extinction or near extinction. Peter Stiling has reintroduced greenhouse-propagated populations of a rare *Opuntia* cactus in the Florida

Keys following the decimation of the original population by *Cactoblastis cactorum*, an invasive moth from the Caribbean. Zoos, aquariums, and botanical gardens often play a key role in captive breeding, propagating species that are highly threatened in the wild. They also play an important role in public education about the loss of biodiversity and the use of restoration programs.

Several classic programs illustrate the value of captive breeding and reintroduction. The peregrine falcon (*Falco peregrinus*) became extinct in nearly all of the eastern United States by the mid-1960s, a decline that was linked to the effects of DDT (refer back to Figure 56.9). In 1970 Tom Cade gathered falcons from other parts of the country to start a captive breeding program at Cornell University. Since then, the program has released thousands of birds into the wild, and in 1999 the peregrine falcon was removed from the Endangered Species List. A captive breeding program is also helping save the California condor (*Gymnogyps californicus*) from extinction. In the 1980s there were only 25 known birds, some in captivity and some in the wild. Scientists made the decision to capture the remaining wild birds in order to protect and breed them (**Figure 57.17a**). By 2006 the captive population numbered 156 individuals, and 128 birds were living in the wild, 60 in California and 68 in Arizona (**Figure 57.17b**). A milestone was reached in 2002, when a pair of captive-reared California condors bred in the wild.

(a)

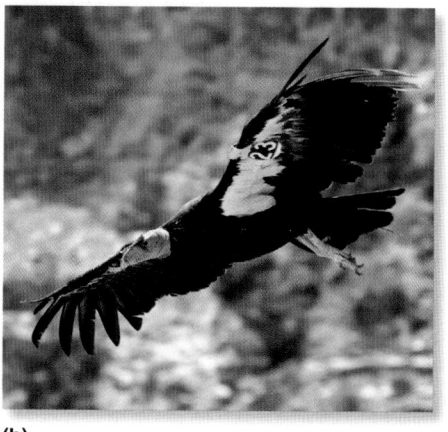

(b)

Figure 57.17 Captive breeding programs. The California condor, the largest bird in the United States with a wingspan of nearly 3 metres, has been bred in captivity in California. **(a)** A researcher at the San Diego Wild Animal Park feeds a chick with a puppet, so that the birds will not become habituated to the presence of humans. **(b)** This captive-bred condor soars over the Grand Canyon. Note the tag on the underside of its wing.

Because the number of individuals in any captive breeding program is initially small, care must be exercised to avoid inbreeding. Matings are usually carefully arranged to maximize resultant genetic variation in offspring. The use of genetic engineering to clone endangered species is a new area that may eventually help bolster populations of captive-bred species.

Conservation is clearly a matter of great importance, and a failure to value and protect our natural resources adequately could be a grave mistake. Some authors, most recently the ecologist and geographer Jared Diamond, have investigated why many great societies of the past—including Angkor Wat, Easter Island, and Norse Greenland—collapsed or vanished, leaving behind monumental ruins. Diamond has concluded that the collapse of these societies occurred partly because people inadvertently destroyed the ecological resources on which their societies depended. Modern nations such as Rwanda face similar issues. The country's population density is the highest in Africa, and it has a limited amount of land that can be used for growing crops. By the late 1980s the need to feed a growing population led to the wholesale clearing of Rwanda's

---

GENOMES AND PROTEOMES

Can Cloning Save Endangered Species?

In 1997 Ian Wilmut and colleagues at Scotland's Roslin Institute announced to the world that they had cloned a (now-famous) sheep, Dolly, from mammary cells of an adult ewe (see Chapter 18). Since then, interest has arisen among conservation biologists about whether the same technology might be used to save species on the verge of extinction. Scientists were encouraged that in January 2001, an Iowa farm cow called Bessie gave birth to a cloned Asian gaur (*Bos gaurus*), an endangered species. The gaur, an oxlike animal native to the jungles of India and Burma, was cloned from a single skin cell taken from a dead animal. To clone the gaur, scientists removed the nucleus from a cow's egg and replaced it with a nucleus from the gaur's cell. The treated egg was then placed into the cow's womb. Unfortunately, the gaur died from dysentery two days after birth, although scientists believe this was unrelated to the cloning procedure. In 2003 another type of endangered wild cattle, the Javan banteng (*Bos javanicus*), was successfully cloned (**Figure 57.18**).

Despite the promise of cloning, a number of issues remain unresolved:

1. Scientists would have to develop an intimate knowledge of different species' reproductive cycles. For sheep and cows this was routine, based on the vast experience in breeding these species, but eggs of different species, even if they could be harvested, often require different nutritive media in laboratory cultures.

2. Because it is desirable to leave natural mothers available for breeding, scientists will have to identify surrogate females of similar but more common species that can carry the fetus to term.

3. Some argue that cloning does not address the root causes of species loss, such as habitat fragmentation or poaching, and that resources would be better spent elsewhere; for example, in preserving the endangered species' remaining habitat.

4. Cloning might not be able to increase the genetic variability of the population. However, if it were possible

Figure 57.18 Cloning may help save endangered species. In 2004, this eight-month-old cloned Javan banteng made its public debut at the San Diego Zoo.

 Principle: *The genetic material provides a blueprint for sustaining life. Genetic cloning utilizes a somatic cell, which contains the complete DNA or genetic blueprint of the animal that is to be cloned.*

BioConnections: *Livestock and even pets have been cloned as well as endangered species (refer back to Figure 20.15). What are some of the arguments in favour and against genetic cloning of endangered species?*

to use cells from deceased animals, for example, from their hair or feathers, these clones could theoretically reintroduce lost genes back into the population.

Many biologists believe that while cloning may have a role in conservation, it is only part of the solution and that we should address what made the species go extinct in the first place before attempting to restore it.

forests and wetlands, with the result that little additional land was available to farm. Increased population pressure, fuelled by environmental scarcity, was likely a contributing factor in igniting the genocide of 1994.

As we've seen throughout this textbook, an understanding of biology is vital to understand and help solve many of society's problems. Within this large field, genomics and proteomics may have a huge potential for improving people's lives and society at large. These disciplines offer the opportunity to unlock new diagnoses and treatments for diseases, to improve nutrition and food production, and even to help us to restore biological diversity.

Summary of Key Concepts

57.1 Why Conserve Biodiversity?

- Biodiversity represents diversity at three levels: genetic diversity, species diversity, and ecosystem diversity. Conservation biology uses knowledge from molecular biology, genetics, and ecology to protect the biological diversity of life. (Figure 57.1)
- The preservation of biodiversity has been justified because of its economic value, because of the value of ecosystem services, and on ethical grounds. (Tables 57.1, 57.2)
- Four models exist that describe the relationship between biodiversity and ecosystem function: diversity–stability, rivet, redundancy, and idiosyncratic. (Figure 57.2)
- There are initiatives to conserve biodiversity. (Figure 57.3)
- Experiments both in the lab and in the field have shown that increased biodiversity results in increased ecosystem function. (Figures 57.4, 57.5)

57.2 The Causes of Extinction and Loss of Biodiversity

- Extinction—the process by which species die out—has been a natural phenomenon throughout the history of life on Earth. Extinction rates in recent times, however, have been much higher than in the past, a phenomenon called the biodiversity crisis. (Figure 57.6)
- The main causes of extinctions have been and continue to be habitat destruction, direct exploitation, and introduced species. (Figure 57.7)
- Reduced population size can lead to a reduction of genetic diversity through inbreeding, genetic drift, and limited mating, which reduces effective population size.
- Inbreeding, mating among genetically related relatives, can lead to a reduction in fertility. (Figure 57.8)
- Knowledge of a species' effective population size is vital to ensure the success of conservation projects. (Figure 57.9)

57.3 Conservation Strategies

- Habitat conservation strategies commonly target megadiversity countries, countries with the largest number of species; biodiversity hot spots, areas with the largest number of endemic species (i.e., those unique to the area); and representative habitats, areas that represent the major habitats. (Figure 57.10, Table 57.3)

- Conservation biologists employ many strategies in protecting biodiversity. Principles of the equilibrium model of island biogeography and landscape ecology are used in the theory and practice of park reserve design to determine, for example, whether the park should take the form of one single or several small reserves. (Figures 57.11, 57.12)
- Economic considerations also play an important role in reserve creation, and it has been shown that conservation spending is positively related to population size. (Figure 57.13)
- The single-species approach focuses conservation efforts on indicator species, umbrella species, flagship species, and keystone species. Indicator species are species whose status can provide information on the overall health of an ecosystem. Umbrella species are species whose habitat requirements are so large that preserving them would also preserve many other species. Flagship species are usually charismatic or instantly recognizable species, and keystone species have an effect out of proportion to their abundance. (Figures 57.14, 57.15)
- Restoration ecology seeks to repair or replace populations and their habitats. Three basic approaches to habitat restoration are complete restoration, rehabilitation, and ecosystem replacement. (Figure 57.16)
- Captive breeding is the propagation of animals outside their natural habitat. Several programs have illustrated the success of captive breeding and reintroduction to the wild. (Figure 57.17)
- Cloning of endangered species has been accomplished on a very small scale and despite its limitations may have a role in conservation biology. (Figure 57.18)

Test to Assess Your Learning

1. Which of the following statements best describes an endangered species?
   a. a species that is likely to become extinct in a portion of its range
   b. a species that has disappeared in a particular community but is present in other natural environments
   c. a species that is extinct
   d. a species that is in danger of becoming extinct throughout all or a significant portion of its range
   e. both (b) and (d)

2. Biological diversity is important and should be preserved because
   a. food, medicines, and industrial products are all benefits of biodiversity.
   b. ecosystems provide valuable services to us in many ways.
   c. many species can be used as valuable research tools.
   d. we have an ethical responsibility to protect our environment.
   e. all of the above are correct.

3. The impact on an ecosystem of a particular species is dependent on how critical the species is to the ecosystem. This statement defines the _____ hypothesis.
   a. rivet
   b. redundancy
   c. idiosyncratic
   d. diversity-stability
   e. community ecology

4. The research conducted by Tilman and colleagues demonstrated that
   a. as diversity increases, productivity increases.
   b. as diversity decreases, productivity increases.
   c. areas with higher diversity demonstrate less efficient use of nutrients.
   d. species richness increases lead to an increase in invasive species.
   e. increased diversity results in increased susceptibility to disease.

5. The process by which species die out is termed
   a. endangerment.
   b. death.
   c. extant.
   d. extinction.
   e. conservation biology.

6. Which of the following is not a prime cause of extinction?
   a. predation by introduced species
   b. habitat destruction
   c. direct exploitation
   d. disease brought by invasive species
   e. bioremediation

7. The negative result of inbreeding is
   a. an increase in genetic diversity that leads to new genetic diseases.
   b. a decrease in genetic diversity that limits how a species can adapt.
   c. a decrease in number of mates.
   d. mating between related individuals.
   e. all of the above.

8. The number of individuals that contribute genes to future populations is called
   a. the effective population size.
   b. the adult population size.
   c. the breeding coefficient.
   d. the gene pool.
   e. the female population size.

9. Small strips of land that connect and allow organisms to move between small patches of natural habitat are called
   a. biological conduits.
   b. edge effects.
   c. movement corridors.
   d. migration pathways.
   e. landscape breaks.

10. Bioremediation is
   a. a process that restores a disturbed habitat to its original state.
   b. a process that uses microbes or plants to detoxify contaminated habitats.
   c. the legislation requiring rehabilitation of a disturbed habitat.

   d. a process of capturing all of the living individuals of species for breeding purposes.
   e. the process of removing tissue from a dead organism in the hopes of cloning it.

Articulate to Assess Your Learning

1. What are the three levels at which biodiversity can be examined?

2. Define conservation biology.

3. Distinguish among an umbrella species, a flagship species, and a keystone species.

Collaborate to Assess and Extend Your Learning

1. More than 300 species of birds regularly breed in Canada's boreal forest. What types of resources do you think the boreal forest provides for these birds?

2. Discuss several species-specific approaches to conservation biology.

3. Look back at Figure 57.11 and design an experiment to investigate the best design for an ecological reserve. Discuss the challenges of conducting large-scale experiments.

4. A principle of biology is that the genetic material, DNA, provides a dynamic plan for sustaining life. Explain why it is crucial to maintain biodiversity.

Visit McGraw-Hill Ryerson Connect™ for additional study resources.

WHAT'S NEW?

An interview with Dr. Liette Vasseur from Brock University by Jason Causarano, a fourth-year student at Brock University.

Jason Causarano

Dr. Liette Vasseur

Dr. Vasseur is a Professor of Biological Sciences at Brock University. She is also Minjiang Scholar at the Fujian Agriculture and Forestry University in Fuzhou, China.

> ### What got you interested in ecosystems and behaviour? Have you always been interested in ecology?

I decided to go into biology, ecology, when I was about 14 or 15 years old. I was always interested by these aspects. It might be related to the fact that I grew up on a farm and both my father and grandfather were florists.

> ### How did your research career start? What is your current research focused on?

I really got hooked on research (and especially ecological research) when I was doing my BSc at the Université de Sherbrooke. I had an Undergraduate Student Research Award from the Natural Sciences and Engineering Research Council of Canada (NSERC), and this really turned me on. This is why I went straight to my MSc (at Université du Quebec) then my PhD (at Queen's University).

My current research has diversified, and balances between fundamental and applied research. I am focusing on plant ecology and the responses of plants to changes (climate extremes or invasion, etc.) but also push further at the ecosystem level to understand how these interactions can be used for the benefits of ecosystem services, such as in crop cultivation.

> ### What was your favourite ecosystem to research in?

I think agroecosystem is probably the one in which I am currently the most interested. There are many aspects still to understand and also to manage in a way to improve its sustainability.

> ### Climate change: How is current research helping us understand its impact?

These are several projects that are integrating climate change directly and indirectly. Currently I have some projects examining extreme events, which, in many regions of the world, are increasing in frequency and/or intensity. Other projects are also exploring the long-term impacts of changes in CO_2 and other environmental factors. Working with coastal communities, my interest is more related to sea-level rise and storm surges, which can damage ecosystems quite rapidly. This is especially true in regions where coastal ecosystems are already under stress (e.g., mangroves) due to human activities.

> ### Do you think the general public is more knowledgeable about global climate change now? How has this impacted ecosystem conservation efforts?

I think there are many myths and some confusion out there. We still have deniers who also make it more difficult. Because it is global and difficult to perceive on a daily basis, people tend to put this on the back burner. Working with farmers, most are looking at surviving and making a living today and hoping for a good crop. Climate change remains a longer-term issue for them. It is the same working with fishers. Global warming has impacted and will immensely impact conservation. As the chair of the Ecology and Conservation Section of the Canadian Botanical Association, I am very well aware that this is a very important subject that the section intends to work on in the near future (most likely through a position paper). The reason is that there is a misunderstanding of the need (or not) to protect our rare species because they are common, for example, in the United States. The challenge is that our populations may have different genetic makeup that will lead them to better survive than the southern populations. We do not have enough knowledge for all those species to know this. This is why it is so important to continue their protection.

> ### You have been a Minjiang Scholar at Fujian Agriculture and Forestry University (FAFU). How did your career steer you toward this, and what type of work have you been doing in China?

I started working in China in 1997 as the director of a new Canadian International Development Agency Tier 1 UPCD project entitled Community-Based Conservation Management in China and Vietnam. FAFU (and Dr. Minsheng You, my collaborator) was one of our partners. We worked together through this project, and over the years we continue to develop more projects. I became adjunct professor at FAFU in 2006 and increased our research activities through publications and by helping students. As a Minjiang Scholar, I can better support the research there and help supervise graduate students. Dr. You is very successful and has had over 40 graduate students! The projects are mainly in applied ecology, especially in agroecosystems where we use the approach of biodiversity improvement to sustainably manage pest and crop productivity.

> **Hailing from Québec, what are some of the advantages you have experienced from being a bilingual scientist?**

I think there are many. I have been involved in many different committees, associations, etc. I have been able to work in both English countries and French countries (such as Burkina Faso in West Africa). It also helped me when I was appointed to the Joint Public Advisory Committee of the North American Commission for Environmental Cooperation. (I also knew more Spanish at the time, though I am losing it now!)

> **You are also heavily involved with women's studies, belonging to several groups supporting the work of women in science. What led you to become so involved in these organizations?**

Yes, in fact, I am currently the president of AFFESTIM (Association de la francophonie à propos des femmes en sciences, technologies, ingénierie, et mathématiques); one of the VPs of CCWEST (Canadian Council of Women in Sciences, Engineering, and Technologies); and one of the VPs of INWES (International Network of Women Engineers and Scientists). So I cover French- and English-speaking associations in Canada as well as having a link with the international one. What led me to this? Knowing that women are still marginalized and often will give up. Interestingly, the situation is worsening after improving in the 1990s. The issues of sexism and dealing with family demand remain among the main challenges. Very early, girls are being told that they may not be able to get there.

> **What advice would you give to students thinking about pursuing a career in ecological research?**

Like any job: first, love what you are doing. If in any job you count your hours, it is most likely because you don't like it. You have to make sure in ecology that you also love the outdoors and learn outside the normal courses. The reason is that you need to know some of the basic knowledge. For example, if you are working on plant diversity and you cannot identify species, you'll be in deep trouble. The main challenge is that many universities are not teaching this anymore.

There are so many questions that remain unanswered. Each project that I start brings at least another dozen questions! Research life is fascinating. You never know where it will take you!

Glossary

A

A band   A wide, dark band produced by the orderly parallel arrangement of the thick filaments in the middle of each sarcomere.

abiotic   The term used to describe interactions between organisms and their nonliving environment.

aboral   Refers to the region opposite the mouth.

abortion   Procedures or circumstances that cause the death of an embryo or fetus after implantation.

abscisic acid   One of several plant hormones that help a plant to cope with environmental stress.

absorption   The process in which digested nutrients are transported from the digestive cavity into an animal's circulatory system.

absorption spectrum   A diagram that depicts the wavelengths of electromagnetic radiation that are absorbed by a pigment.

absorptive state   One of two alternating phases in the use of nutrients; occurs when ingested nutrients enter the blood from the gastrointestinal tract. The other phase is the postabsorptive state.

acclimatization   The process of fine-tuning an animal's adaptive mechanisms to a changing environment.

accommodation   The process in which contraction and relaxation of the ciliary muscles adjust the lens according to the angle at which light enters the eye.

acid hydrolases   Hydrolytic enzymes found in lysosomes that function at acidic pH and use a molecule of water to break a covalent bond.

acid precipitation   Precipitation with a pH of less than 5.6; acid rain results from the burning of fossil fuels, which releases sulphur dioxide and nitrogen oxide into the atmosphere, which in turn react with oxygen in the air to form sulphuric acid and nitric acid. These fall to the surface in rain or snow.

acidic   A solution that has a pH below 7.

acids   Molecules that release hydrogen ions in solution.

acoelomates   Animals that lack body cavities.

acquired antibiotic resistance   The common phenomenon of a previously susceptible strain becoming resistant to a specific antibiotic.

acquired immune deficiency syndrome (AIDS)   A disease caused by the human immunodeficiency virus (HIV) that leads to a defect in the immune system of infected individuals.

acquired (specific) immunity   Immunity that is not genetically inherited. It can result from the development of antibodies in response to an antigen.

acrocentric   Describes a chromosome in which the centromere is near one end.

acromegaly   A condition in which a person's GH levels remain elevated after growth has ceased, and the continued excess GH causes many bones, like those of the hands and feet, to thicken and enlarge.

acrosomal reaction   An event in fertilization in which the binding of a sperm cell to proteins located in the egg cell plasma membrane triggers a series of events producing the fast block to polyspermy and the entry of the sperm cell's nucleus into the egg cell.

acrosome   A special structure at the tip of a sperm's head that contains proteolytic enzymes that help break down the plasma membrane of the ovum at fertilization.

actin   A cytoskeletal protein.

actin microfilaments   Thin protein filaments composed of actin proteins that form part of the cytoskeleton, support the plasma membrane, and play a key role in cell strength, shape, and movement.

action potentials   The movement of electrical impulses along the plasma membrane, which occur in animal nerve axons and some plant cells.

action spectrum   The rate of photosynthesis plotted as a function of different wavelengths of light.

activation energy   An initial input of energy in a chemical reaction that allows the molecules to get close enough to cause a rearrangement of bonds.

activators   Transcription factors that bind to DNA and increase the rate of transcription.

active immunity   The acquired response to exposure to any type of antigen.

active site   The location in an enzyme where the chemical reaction takes place.

active transport   The transport of a solute across a membrane against its gradient—that is, from a region of low concentration to higher concentration. In the case of ions, active transport is against an electrochemical gradient.

adaptation   The processes and structures through which organisms adjust to short-term or long-term changes in their environment.

adaptive radiation   The process whereby a single ancestral species evolves into a wide array of descendant species that differ greatly in their habitat, form, or behaviour.

adenine (A)   A purine base found in DNA and RNA.

adenosine triphosphate (ATP)   A nucleotide that is a common energy source for all cells.

adenylyl cyclase   An enzyme in the plasma membrane that synthesizes cAMP from ATP.

adherens junctions   These junctions are one type of anchoring junction, one that has the cell adhesion molecule cadherin attached to adherens molecules attached to the actin filaments.

adiabatic cooling   The process in which increasing elevation leads to a decrease in air temperature.

adventitious root   A root that is produced on the surfaces of stems (and sometimes leaves) of vascular plants; also, roots that develop at the bases of stem cuttings.

aerenchyma   Spongy plant tissue with large air spaces.

aerobic   Refers to a process that occurs in the presence of oxygen; a form of metabolism that requires oxygen.

aerobic respiration   During this type of respiration, O_2 is consumed and CO_2 is released.

aerotolerant anaerobes   Microorganisms that do not use oxygen but are not poisoned by it either.

afferent arteriole   A blood vessel that provides a pathway for blood into a tissue or organ. For example, an afferent arteriole in the kidney supplies each glomerulus with blood.

afferent neurons   *See* sensory neurons.

aflatoxins   Fungal toxins that cause liver cancer and are a major health concern worldwide.

age-specific fertility rate   The rate of offspring production for females of a certain age; used to help calculate how a population grows.

age structure   The relative numbers of individuals of each defined age group in a population.

AIDS   *See* acquired immune deficiency syndrome.

air sacs   Part of the avian respiratory system; air sacs—not lungs—expand when a bird inhales and shrink when it exhales, and they do not participate in gas exchange.

akinete   A thick-walled cell used to survive unfavourable conditions in a dormant state.

aldosterones   Steroid hormones made by the adrenal glands.

algae   A term that applies to about 10 phyla of protists that include both photosynthetic and nonphotosynthetic species.

alimentary canal   The single elongated tube of a digestive system with an opening at either end, through which food and eventually wastes pass from one end to the other.

alkaloids   A group of structurally related secondary metabolites that all contain nitrogen and usually have a cyclic, ringlike structure.

allantois   An extraembryonic membrane in the amniotic egg that serves as a disposal sac for metabolic wastes.

allee effect   The phenomenon that some individuals will fail to mate successfully purely by chance; for example, because of the failure to find a mate.

allele frequencies   The sum of frequencies of all alleles for a gene locus equals one. Each individual allele frequency is the number of copies of an allele divided by the total number of alleles in a population.

alleles   Alternate forms of a particular gene.

allelochemical   A powerful plant chemical, often a root exudates, that kills other plant species.

allodiploid   An alloploid that has one set of chromosomes from two different species.

allometric growth   The pattern whereby different parts of the body grow at different rates with respect to each other.

allopatric speciation   A form of speciation that occurs when a population becomes geographically isolated from other populations and evolves into one or more new species.

allopatry   Species occurring in different geographic areas.

alloploid   An organism that contains at least one set of chromosomes from two or more different species.

allopolyploid   An organism that contains two or more complete sets of chromosomes from two or more different species.

allosteric site   A site where a molecule can bind noncovalently and affect the function of the active site. The binding of a molecule to an allosteric site causes a conformational change in the enzyme that inhibits its catalytic function.

allotetraploid   A type of allopolyploid that contains two complete sets of chromosomes from two species for a total of four sets.

alternation of generations   The phenomenon that occurs in plants (and some protists) in which the life cycle alternates between multicellular diploid organisms, called sporophytes, and multicellular haploid organisms, called gametophytes.

alternative splicing   The splicing of pre-mRNA in more than one way to create two or more different polypeptides.

altruism   Behaviour that appears to benefit others at a cost to the self.

alveoli   Saclike structures of the lungs where gas exchange occurs; singular is alveolus.

amensalism   One-sided competition, where the interaction is detrimental to one species but not to the other.

Ames test   A test that helps ascertain whether or not an agent is a mutagen by using a strain of a bacterium, *Salmonella typhimurium*.

amino acids   The building blocks of proteins. All amino acids have a common structure in which a carbon atom, called the *a*-carbon, is linked to an amino group (NH_2) and a carboxyl group (COOH). The *a*-carbon also is linked to a hydrogen atom and a particular side chain.

amino terminus   *See* N-terminus.

aminoacyl site (A site)   One of the three sites for tRNA binding to the ribosome; the others

are the peptidyl site (P site) and the exit site (E site). The A site is the site where incoming tRNA molecules bind to the mRNA (except for the initiator tRNA).

aminoacyl tRNA   *See* charged tRNA.

aminoacyl-tRNA synthetase   An enzyme that catalyzes the attachment of amino acids to tRNA molecules.

ammonia (NH3)   One of the most highly toxic of the nitrogenous wastes because it disrupts pH, ion electrochemical gradients, and many chemical reactions that involve oxidations and reductions; typically produced in many aquatic species.

ammonification   The conversion of organic nitrogen to NH_3 and NH_4^+.

amnion   An innermost extraembryonic membrane in the amniotic egg; it protects the developing embryo in a fluid-filled sac called the amniotic cavity.

amniotes   A group of tetrapods with amniotic eggs that includes turtles, lizards, snakes, crocodiles, birds, and mammals.

amniotic egg   The structure that contains the developing embryo and the four separate extraembryonic membranes that it produces: the amnion, the yolk sac, the allantois, and the chorion.

amoeba   A protist cell that moves by pseudopodia, which involves extending cytoplasm into filaments or lobes.

amoebocytes   Mobile cells within a sponge's mesohyl that absorb food from choanocytes, digest it, and carry the nutrients to other cells.

amphibians   Specialized tetrapods that have successfully invaded the land but must return to the water to reproduce.

amphipathic   Meaning, in molecules, that they have a hydrophobic (water-fearing) region and a hydrophilic (water-loving) region.

ampulla   A muscular sac at the base of each tube foot of an echinoderm that stores water.

amygdala   An area of the brain known to be critical for understanding and remembering emotional situations.

amylase   A digestive enzyme involved in the digestion of starch.

anabolic reactions   Metabolic reactions that promote the synthesis of larger molecules from smaller precursor molecules.

anabolism   The synthesis of cellular molecules and macromolecules, which usually requires an input of energy.

anaerobic   Refers to a process that occurs in the absence of oxygen; a form of metabolism that does not require oxygen.

anaerobic respiration   The breakdown of organic molecules in the absence of oxygen.

anagenesis   The pattern of speciation in which a single species is transformed into a different species over many generations.

analogous structures   Traits that are the result of convergent evolution; structures have arisen independently, two or more times, because species have occupied similar types of environments on Earth.

anaphase   The phase of mitosis during which the sister chromatids separate from each other and move to opposite poles; the poles themselves also move farther apart.

anatomy   The study of the morphology of living organisms, such as plants and animals.

anchoring junctions   A junction found between animal cells that attaches cells to one another and to the ECM.

androecium   The aggregate of stamens that forms a third type of whorl of flower organs.

androgens   Steroid hormones produced by the male testes that affect most aspects of male reproduction.

anemia   A condition characterized by lower than normal levels of hemoglobin, which reduces the amount of oxygen that can be stored in the blood.

aneuploidy   Describes an alteration in the number of particular chromosomes so that the total number of chromosomes is not an exact multiple of a set.

angina pectoris   Chest pain during exertion caused by the tissues being deprived of oxygen.

angiosperms   Flowering plants; the term means *enclosed seed*, which reflects the presence of seeds within fruits.

animal cap assay   A type of experiment used extensively to identify factors (proteins) secreted by embryonic cells that induce cells in the animal pole to differentiate into mesoderm.

Animalia   One of the four traditional eukaryotic kingdoms of the domain Eukarya.

animal pole   In triploblast organisms, the pole of the egg where less yolk and more cytoplasm are concentrated.

anion   An ion that has a net negative charge.

annual   A plant that dies after producing seed during its first year of life.

antagonist   A muscle or group of muscles that produces oppositely directed movements at a joint.

antenna complex   *See* light-harvesting complex.

anterior   Refers to the end of an animal where the head is found.

anteroposterior axis   One of the three axes along which the adult body pattern is organized; the others are the dorsoventral axis and the right-left axis.

anther   A cluster of microsporangia in a flower that produces pollen and then opens to release it.

antheridia   Round or elongate gametangia that produce plant sperm.

anthropoids   Members of a class of primates that includes the monkeys and the hominoids; species are larger-brained and diurnal.

antibiotics   Compounds that are usually made by microorganisms that inhibit the growth of certain microorganisms.

antibodies   Protein secreted by plasma cells that are part of the immune response; antibodies travel all over the body to reach antigens identical to those that stimulated their production, and then they combine with these antigens and guide an attack that eliminates the antigens or the cells bearing them.

anticodon   A three-nucleotide sequence in tRNA that is complementary to a codon in mRNA.

antidiuretic hormone (ADH)   A hormone secreted by the posterior pituitary gland that acts on kidney cells to decrease urine production.

antigen   Any foreign molecule that the host does not recognize as self and that triggers a specific immune response.

antigen-presenting cells (APCs)   Cells bearing fragments of antigen, called antigenic determinants or epitopes, complexed with the cell's MHC proteins.

antiparallel   An arrangement in DNA where one strand runs in the 5` to 3` direction while the other strand is oriented in the 3` to 5` direction.

antiporters   A class of transporters that bind two or more ions or molecules and transport them in opposite directions.

apical-basal polarity   An architectural feature of plants in which they display an upper, apical pole and a lower, basal pole; shoot apical meristem occurs at the apical pole, and the root apical meristem occurs at the basal pole.

apical-basal-patterning genes   A category of genes that are important in early stages of plant development, during which the apical and basal axes are formed.

apical constriction   A cellular process during gastrulation that is crucial to development; a reduction in the diameter of the actin rings connected to the adherens junctions causes the cells to elongate toward their basal end.

apical meristems   Actively dividing cells that occur at the growing tips of plants.

apical region   The region of a plant that projects upward, usually from the soil, and produces the leaves and flowers.

apomixis   A natural asexual reproductive process in which plant fruits and seeds are produced in the absence of fertilization.

apoplast   The continuum of water-soaked cell walls and intercellular spaces in a plant.

apoplastic transport   The movement of solutes through cell walls and the spaces between cells.

apoptosis   Programmed cell death.

aposematic coloration   Warning coloration that advertises an organism's unpalatable taste.

appendix   A fingerlike projection in the gastro-intestinal tract of animals having no known essential function but that may at one time have been an important part of the body's defence mechanisms.

aquaporins   Three-dimensional cell pores that allow water to diffuse through the membrane.

aqueous humour   A thin liquid in the anterior cavity behind the cornea of the vertebrate eye.

aquifers   Underground water sources.

arbuscular mycorrhizae   Symbiotic associations between glomalean fungi and the roots of vascular plants.

Archaea   One of the three domains of life; the other two are Bacteria and Eukarya. When not capitalized, it refers to a cell or species within the domain Archaea.

archegonia   Flask-shaped plant gametangia that enclose an egg cell.

archenteron   A cavity formed by the embryo during gastrulation that will become the organism's digestive tract.

area hypothesis   The proposal that larger areas contain more species than smaller areas because they can support larger populations and a greater range of habitats.

arteriole   A single-celled layer of endothelium surrounded by one or two layers of smooth muscle and connective tissue that delivers blood to the capillaries and distributes blood to regions of the body in proportion to metabolic demands.

arteries   Blood vessels that carry blood away from the heart.

artifacts   Artificial structures or alteration of natural structures caused by the way the specimen was prepared for viewing.

artificial selection   *See* selective breeding.

asci   Fungal sporangia shaped like sacs that produce and release sexual ascospores.

ascocarp   The type of fruiting body produced by ascomycete fungi.

ascomycetes   A phylum of fungi that produce sexual spores in saclike asci located at the surfaces of fruiting bodies known as ascocarps.

ascospore   The type of sexual spore produced by the ascomycete fungi.

aseptate   The condition of not being partitioned into smaller cells; usually refers to fungal cells.

asexual reproduction   A reproductive strategy that occurs when offspring are produced from a single parent, without the fusion of gametes from two parents. The offspring are therefore clones of the parent.

assimilation   In the case of nitrogen, the process by which plants and animals incorporate the ammonia and NO_3^- formed through nitrogen fixation and nitrification.

associative learning   A change in behaviour caused by an association between a stimulus and a response.

assort   The process of distributing.

asthma   A disease in which the smooth muscles around the bronchioles contract more than usual, increasing resistance to airflow.

astral microtubules   Microtubules that emanate from a microtubule organizing centre and are oriented away from the centre of the cell.

AT/GC rule   Refers to the phenomenon that an A in one DNA strand always hydrogen bonds with a T in the opposite strand, while a G in one strand bonds with a C. Thus the amount of A = T and G = C.

atherosclerosis   The condition in which large plaques may occlude (block) the lumen of an artery.

atmospheric pressure   The pressure exerted by the gases in air on the body surfaces of animals.

atom   The smallest functional unit of matter that forms all chemical substances and cannot be further broken down into other substances by ordinary chemical or physical means.

atomic nucleus   The centre of an atom.

atomic number   The number of protons in an atom.

ATP-dependent chromatin remodelling complexes   Enzyme complexes that catalyze a loosening in the compaction of chromatin; this loosening facilitates the ability of RNA polymerase to recognize and transcribe a gene.

ATP-driven pump   A common category of pump found in all living cells; this transporter has a binding site for ATP and hydrolyzes ATP to actively transport solutes against a gradient.

ATP synthase   An enzyme that uses the energy stored in an H^+ electrochemical gradient for the synthesis of ATP via chemiosmosis.

atrial natriuretic peptide (ANP)   A peptide secreted from the atria of the heart whenever blood levels of sodium increase; ANP causes a natriuresis by decreasing sodium reabsorption in the kidney tubules.

atrioventricular (AV) node   Specialized cardiac cells that sit near the junction of the atria and ventricles and conduct the electrical events from the atria to the ventricles.

atrioventricular (AV) valves   One-way valves through which blood moves from the atria into the ventricles of the vertebrate heart.

atrium   In the heart, a single filling chamber that collects blood from the tissues.

atrophy   A reduction in the size of a structure, such as a muscle.

atropine   A potent toxin derived from the deadly nightshade plant.

audition   The sense of hearing.

autoimmune disease   In humans and many other vertebrates, the situation in which the body's normal state of immune tolerance breaks down, with the result that antibody-mediated or T-cell-mediated attacks are directed against the body's own cells and tissues.

autonomic nervous system   The division of the peripheral nervous system that regulates homeostasis and organ function; also called the visceral nervous system.

autophagosome   Cellular material enclosed in a double membrane, produced by the process of autophagy.

autophagy   Meaning "the eating of one's self." A process whereby cellular material, such as a worn-out organelle, becomes enclosed in a double membrane and degraded.

autosomes   All the chromosomes found in the cell nucleus of eukaryotes, except for the sex chromosomes.

autotomy   In echinoderms, the ability to intentionally detach a body part, such as a limb, that will later regenerate.

autotroph   An organism that has metabolic pathways that directly harness energy from either inorganic molecules or light.

auxin One of several types of hormones considered to be the "master" plant hormones because they influence plant structure, development, and behaviour in many ways, often working with other hormones.

auxin efflux carriers Plasma membrane proteins belonging to the PIN family, which transport auxin out of plant cells.

auxin influx carrier A plasma membrane protein that transports auxin into plant cells.

auxin-response genes A diverse set of genes that are promoted into expression by auxin

avirulence genes (*AVR* genes) Genes that encode a virulence-enhancing elicitor, which regulates plant defence responses.

Avogadro's constant As first described by Italian physicist Amedeo Avogadro, 1 mole of any element contains the same number of particles: 6.022×10^{23}.

***Avr* genes** Abbreviation for avirulence genes.

axillary bud A bud that occurs in the axil, the upper angle where a twig or leaf joins the stem.

axon An extension of the plasma membrane that is involved in sending signals from a neuron to neighbouring cells.

axoneme The internal structure of eukaryotic cilia and flagella consisting of microtubules, the motor protein dynein, and linking proteins.

axon hillock The part of the axon closest to the cell body.

B

B cells Lymphocytes responsible for specific immunity.

bacilli Rods; one of the five major shapes of prokaryotic cells.

backbone The linear arrangement of phosphates and sugar molecules in a DNA or RNA strand.

Bacteria One of the three domains of life; the other two are Archaea and Eukarya. When not capitalized, it refers to a cell or species within the domain Bacteria.

bacterial artificial chromosome (BAC) A cloning vector in bacteria that can contain large DNA inserts.

bacterial colony A clone of genetically identical cells formed from a single cell.

bacteriophage (or phage) A virus that infects bacteria.

bacteroids Modified bacterial cells found in mature root nodules of plants infected by Rhizobia that enable the fixation of atmospheric nitrogen.

baculum A bone in the penis of a number of mammals that aids in erection.

balanced polymorphism The phenomenon in which two or more alleles are kept in balance and therefore are maintained in a population over many generations.

balancing selection A type of natural selection that maintains genetic diversity in a population.

balloon angioplasty A common treatment to restore blood flow through a blood vessel.

A thin tube with a tiny, inflatable balloon at its tip is threaded through the artery to the diseased area; inflating the balloon compresses the plaque against the arterial wall, widening the lumen.

barometric pressure Atmospheric pressure (as indicated by a barometer) caused by the weight of the column of air. At sea level, atmospheric pressure has an average value of one atmosphere and gradually decreases as altitude increases.

baroreceptor A pressure-sensitive region within the walls of certain arteries that contains the endings of nerve cells; these regions help to maintain blood pressure in the normal range for an animal.

Barr body A highly condensed X chromosome.

basal metabolic rate (BMR) The metabolic rate of an animal under resting conditions, in good health, and not under stress of any kind.

basal nuclei Clusters of neuronal cell bodies that surround the thalamus on both sides and lie beneath the cerebral cortex; involved in planning and learning movements and also function via a complex circuitry to initiate or inhibit movements.

basal region The region of a plant that produces the roots.

basal transcription A low level of transcription resulting from the core promoter.

base (1) A component of nucleotides that is a single or double ring of carbon and nitrogen atoms. (2) A molecule that when dissolved in water lowers the H^+ concentration.

base pairing The hydrogen bonding that can occur between the nitrogenous bases of antiparallel polynucleotides.

base substitution A mutation that involves the substitution of a single base in the DNA for another base.

basic local alignment search tool (BLAST) A computer program that can identify homologous genes that are found in a database.

basidia Club-shaped structures on which the sexual spores of basidiocarp are produced.

basidiocarps The fruiting bodies produced by basidiomycete fungi.

basidiomycetes A group of fungi whose sexual spores are produced on the surfaces of club-shaped structures (basidia).

basidiospores Sexual spores of the basidiomycete fungi.

basophils Cells that secrete the anticlotting factor heparin at the site of an infection, which helps the circulation flush out the infected site; basophils also secrete histamine, which attracts infection-fighting cells and proteins.

Batesian mimicry The mimicry of an unpalatable species (the model) by a palatable one (the mimic).

behaviour The observable response of organisms to external or internal stimuli.

behavioural ecology A subdiscipline of organismal ecology that focuses on how the

behaviour of an individual organism contributes to its survival and reproductive success, which in turn eventually affects the population density of the species.

benign A precancerous condition.

benthic zone Ecological region at the lowest level of a lake or ocean that includes the sediment surface.

bidirectional replication In DNA replication, the two DNA strands unwind, and DNA replication proceeds outward from the origin in opposite directions.

biennials Plants that do not reproduce during the first year of life but may reproduce the following year.

Bilateria Bilaterally symmetrical animals, which means they can be divided equally by a vertical plane at the midline.

bile A substance produced by the liver that contains bicarbonate ions, cholesterol, phospholipids, a number of organic wastes, and a group of substances collectively termed *bile salts*.

bile salts A group of substances produced in the liver that solubilize dietary fat and increase its accessibility to digestive enzymes.

binary fission The process of cell division in Bacteria and Archaea in which the cells divide into two cells.

binocular vision A type of vision in animals with both eyes located at the front of the head; the overlapping images coming into both eyes are processed together in the brain to form one perception.

binomial nomenclature The standard method for naming species. Each species has a genus name and species epithet.

biochemical pathway A pathway that consists of a series of chemical/enzymatic reactions that transform precursor molecules into one or more different compounds.

biodiversity Biological diversity, including genetic diversity, species diversity, and ecosystem diversity.

biodiversity crisis The idea that there is currently an elevated loss of species on Earth, far beyond the normal extinction rate of species.

biofilm An aggregation of microorganisms that secrete adhesive mucilage, thereby gluing themselves to surfaces.

biogeochemical cycles The continuous movement of nutrients, such as phosphorus, carbon, and nitrogen, from the physical environment to organisms and back.

biogeography The study of the geographic distribution of extinct and modern species.

bioinformatics A field of study that uses computers to study biological information.

biological control One way to control an exotic species by importing the plant's natural enemies.

biological diversity Number and variety of living organisms found in a specified geographic region. Also known as biodiversity.

biological evolution The phenomenon that populations of organisms change over generations. As a result, some organisms become more successful at survival and reproduction.

biological nitrogen fixation   The natural activity of producing nitrogen fertilizers, performed only by certain prokaryotes.

biological species concept   A species is a group of individuals whose members have the potential to interbreed with one another in nature to produce viable, fertile offspring but cannot successfully interbreed with members of other species.

bioluminescence   A phenomenon that results from chemical reactions that give off light rather than heat.

biomagnification   The increase in the concentration of a substance in living organisms with each increase in trophic level in a food web.

biomass   A quantitative estimate of the total mass of living matter in a given area, usually measured in grams or kilograms per square metre.

biome   A major type of habitat characterized by distinctive plant and animal life.

bioremediation   The use of living organisms, usually microbes or plants, to detoxify polluted habitats, such as dump sites or oil spills.

biosphere   The regions on Earth and in the atmosphere where living organisms exist.

biosynthetic reactions   Chemical reactions that make larger molecules from smaller precursors; also called anabolic reactions.

biotechnology   The use of living organisms or the products of living organisms for human benefit.

biotic   The term used to describe interactions among organisms.

biparental inheritance   A pattern in which both the male and the female gametes contribute particular genes to the offspring.

bipedal   Having the ability to walk on two feet.

bipolar cells   Cells in the eye that make synapses with the photoreceptors and relay responses to the ganglion cells.

bivalent   Homologous pairs of sister chromatids associated with each other, lying side by side.

blade   The flattened portion of a leaf.

blastocoel   A cavity created when an embryo takes up water after the formation of the outer epithelial layer; it provides a space into which cells will migrate to form the digestive tract and other structures of the embryo.

blastocyst   The mammalian counterpart of a blastula.

blastomeres   The two half-size daughter cells produced by each cell division during cleavage.

blastopore   A small opening created when a band of tissue invaginates during gastrulation. It forms the primary opening of the archenteron to the outside.

blastula   An animal embryo at the stage when it forms an outer epithelial layer and an inner cavity.

blending inheritance   An early hypothesis of inheritance that stated that the seeds that

dictate hereditary traits blend together from generation to generation, and the blended traits are then passed to the next generation.

blood   A fluid connective tissue consisting of cells and (in mammals) cell fragments suspended in a solution of water containing dissolved nutrients, proteins, gases, and other molecules. Blood has four components: plasma, leukocytes, erythrocytes, and thrombocytes or platelets.

blood doping   An example of hormone misuse in which the number of red blood cells in the circulation is boosted to increase the oxygen-carrying capacity of the blood.

body mass index (BMI)   A method of assessing body fat and health risk that involves calculating the ratio of weight compared with height; weight in kilograms is divided by the square of the height in metres.

bottleneck effect   A form of genetic drift in which a population size is dramatically reduced and then rebounds. Genetic drift is common when the population size is small.

Bowman's capsule   A sac at the beginning of the tubular component of a nephron in the mammalian kidney.

brain   The structure in the head of animals that controls sensory and motor functions of the entire body.

brain hormone   Produced by specialized nerve cells in some insects and other invertebrates, it stimulates the prothoracic glands to secrete ecdysone and cause moulting.

brassinosteroid   One of several plant hormones that help a plant to cope with environmental stress.

bronchi   Tubes branching from the trachea and leading to a lung.

bronchioles   Thin-walled, small tubes that can dilate or constrict to prevent foreign particles from reaching delicate lung tissue.

bronchodilators   Compounds that bind to the muscles around bronchioles and cause them to relax and widen.

brown fat   A specialized tissue in small mammals, such as hibernating bats, small rodents living in cold environments, and many newborn mammals, including humans, that can help to generate heat and maintain body temperature.

Brownian motion   A nondirectional vibration and movement of molecules due to the energy of heat.

brush border   The combination of villi and microvilli in the small intestine, which increase the surface area about 600-fold over that of a flat-surfaced tube having the same length and diameter.

buccal pumping   A form of breathing in which animals open their mouths to let in air and then close and raise the floor of the mouth, creating a positive pressure and pumping water or air across the gills or into the lungs; found in fish and amphibians.

budding   A form of asexual reproduction in which a portion of the parent organism pinches off to form a complete new individual.

buds   Miniature plant shoots having a dormant shoot apical meristem.

buffer   A compound that acts to minimize pH fluctuations in the fluids of living organisms. Buffer systems can raise or lower pH as needed.

bulbourethral glands   Paired accessory glands that secrete an alkaline mucus that protects sperm by neutralizing the acidity in the urethra.

bulk flow   The mass movement of liquid in a plant caused by pressure, gravity, or both.

C

C3 plants   Plants that can incorporate CO_2 into organic molecules only via RuBP to make 3PG, a three-carbon molecule.

C4 plants   Plants that uses PEP carboxylase to initially fix CO_2 into a four-carbon molecule and later uses rubisco to fix CO_2 into simple sugars.

cadherin   A cell adhesion molecule found in animal cells that promotes cell-to-cell adhesion.

callose   A carbohydrate that plays crucial roles in plant development and plugging wounds in plant phloem.

Calvin cycle   The cycle that includes carbon fixation, reduction, and carbohydrate production, and the regeneration of ribulose bisphosphate (RuBP). During this process, ATP is used as a source of energy and NADPH is used as a source of high-energy electrons so that CO_2 can be incorporated into carbohydrate.

calyx   The sepals that form the outermost whorl of a flower.

CAM plants C_4 plants that take up carbon dioxide at night.

Cambrian explosion   An event during the Cambrian period (543 mya to 490 mya) in which there was an abrupt increase (on a geological scale) in the diversity of animal species.

cancer   A disease caused by gene mutations that lead to uncontrolled cell growth.

canopy   The uppermost layer of tree foliage.

capillaries   Thin-walled vessels that are the site of gas and nutrient exchange between the blood and interstitial fluid.

capping   A 7-methylguanosine covalently attached at the 5` end of mature mRNAs of eukaryotes.

capsid   A protein coat enclosing a virus's genome.

CAP site   One of two regulatory sites near the *lac* promoter; this site is a DNA sequence recognized by the catabolite activator protein (CAP).

capsule   A very thick, gelatinous glycocalyx produced by certain strains of bacteria that invade animals' bodies. The capsule may help them avoid being destroyed by the animal's immune (defence) system.

carapace   The hard protective covering of a crustacean.

carbohydrates   Organic molecules with the general formula $C(H_2O)$.

carbon fixation In this process, inorganic CO_2 is incorporated into an organic molecule such as a carbohydrate.

carboxyl terminus *See* C-terminus.

carcinogens Agents that increase the likelihood of developing cancer, usually a mutagen.

carcinomas Cancers of epithelial cells.

cardiac cycle The events that produce a single heartbeat, which are divided into two phases: diastole and systole.

cardiac muscle A type of muscle tissue found only in hearts and in which physical and electrical connections between individual cells enable many of the cells to contract simultaneously.

cardiac output (CO) The amount of blood the heart pumps per unit time, usually expressed in units of L/min.

cardiovascular disease Diseases affecting the heart and blood vessels.

cardiovascular system A system containing three components: blood or hemolymph, blood vessels, and one or more hearts.

cargo receptors Protein receptors embedded within cell membranes that function to bind vesicles destined for the cell interior.

carnivores Animals that consume animal flesh or fluids.

carotenoids Pigment molecules found in chloroplasts that imparts a colour that ranges from yellow to orange to red.

carpels Organs within flowers that produce ovules containing female gametophytes.

carriers *See* transporters.

carrying capacity (*K*) The upper boundary for a population size.

Casparian strips Suberin ribbons on the walls of endodermal cells of plant roots; prevent apoplastic transport of ions into vascular tissues.

caspase A group of proteolytic enzymes that play roles in apoptosis.

catabolic reactions Reactions in which larger compounds are broken down into smaller molecules; often associated with the release of energy.

catabolism A metabolic pathway that results in the breakdown of larger molecules into smaller molecules. Such reactions are often exergonic.

catabolite activator protein (CAP) An activator protein also known as the cAMP receptor protein (CRP). CAP is needed for activation of the *lac* operon.

catabolite repression In bacteria, a process whereby transcriptional regulation is influenced by the presence of glucose.

catalase An enzyme within peroxisomes that breaks down hydrogen peroxide to water and oxygen gas.

catalepsies Lack of responses to external stimuli, often characterized by muscular rigidity.

catalyst An agent that speeds up the rate of a chemical reaction without being consumed during the reaction.

cataracts Accumulations of protein in the lens of the eye; cause blurring, poor night vision.

cation An ion that has a net positive charge.

cation exchange With regard to soil, the process in which hydrogen ions are able to replace mineral cations on the surfaces of humus or clay particles.

cDNA library A collection of recombinant vectors that have cDNA inserts.

cecum The first portion of the large intestine in humans and other similarly sized animals and mammals.

celiac sprue A common genetic disorder in humans that results in a loss of intestinal surface area caused by an allergic sensitivity to the wheat protein gluten.

cell adhesion The phenomenon in which cells adhere to each other. Cell adhesion provides one way to convey positional information between neighbouring cells.

cell adhesion molecules (CAMs) Membrane proteins found in animal cells that promote cell adhesion.

cell body A part of a neuron that contains the cell nucleus and other organelles. Also called a *soma*.

cell coat Also called the glycocalyx, the carbohydrate-rich zone on the surface of certain animal cells that shields the cell from mechanical and physical damage.

cell communication The process through which cells can detect and respond to signals in their extracellular environment. In multicellular organisms, cell communication is also needed to coordinate cellular activities within the whole organism.

cell cycle The series of phases eukaryotic cells progress through to divide.

cell differentiation Refers to the phenomenon in which cells become specialized into particular cell types.

cell fate The ultimate morphological features that a cell or group of cells will adopt.

cell junctions Specialized structures that adhere cells to one another and to the ECM.

cell signalling Part of a complex communication system that governs basic cellular activities and coordinates cell actions.

cell surface receptors Receptors found in the plasma membrane that enable a cell to respond to different kinds of signalling molecules.

cellular differentiation The process by which different cells within a developing organism acquire specialized forms and functions through the expression of cell-specific genes.

cellular respiration A process by which living cells obtain energy from organic molecules.

cellular response Adaptation at the cellular level that often involves a cell responding to signals in its environment.

cell wall A relatively rigid, porous structure that supports and protects the plasma membrane and cytoplasm of prokaryotic, plant, fungal, and certain protist cells.

centimorgans (cMs) *See* map units (mu).

central cell In the female gametophyte of a flowering plant, a large cell that contains two nuclei; after double fertilization it forms the first cell of the nutritive endosperm tissue.

central dogma Refers to the steps of gene expression at the molecular level. DNA is transcribed into mRNA and mRNA is translated into a polypeptide.

central nervous system (CNS) In complex animals, the brain and a nerve cord, which in vertebrates extends from the brain through the vertebral column.

central region The region of a plant apical meristem that produces stem tissue.

central zone The area of a plant apical meristem where undifferentiated stem cells are maintained.

centrioles A pair of structures within the centrosome of animal cells. Most plant cells and many protists lack centrioles.

centromere The region where the two sister chromatids are tightly associated; the centromere binds to the kinetochore.

centrosomes Structures seen in animal cells, often near the cell nucleus, that are at the nucleating site for the growth of microtubules.

cephalization The localization of sensory structures at the anterior end of the body of animals.

cephalothorax The fused head and thorax structure in species of the class Arachnida and Crustacea.

cerebellum The part of the hindbrain, along with the pons, responsible for monitoring and coordinating body movements.

cerebral cortex The surface layer of grey matter that covers the cerebrum of the brain.

cerebral ganglia In flatworms, a paired structure that receives input from photoreceptors in eyespots and sensory cells.

cerebrospinal fluid Fluid that surrounds the exterior of the brain and spinal cord and absorbs physical shocks to the brain resulting from sudden movements or blows to the head.

cerebrum A group of structures in the forebrain that are responsible for the higher functions of conscious thought, planning, and emotion in vertebrates.

character displacement The tendency for two species to diverge in morphology and thus resource use because of competition.

characters Visible characteristics of organisms, such as the appearance of seeds, pods, flowers, and stems.

charged tRNA (aminoacyl tRNA) A tRNA with its attached amino acid.

checkpoint protein A protein that senses if a cell is in the proper condition to divide and prevents a cell from progressing through the cell cycle if it is not.

checkpoints Critical regulatory points found in the cell cycle of eukaryotic cells. At these checkpoints, a variety of proteins act as sensors to determine if a cell is in the proper condition to divide.

chemical element Each specific type of atom—nitrogen, hydrogen, oxygen, and so on.

chemical energy The potential energy contained within covalent bonds in molecules.

chemical equilibrium In a chemical reaction, it occurs when the rate of formation of products equals the rate of formation of reactants.

chemical reaction A reaction that occurs when one or more substances are changed into other substances. This can happen when two or more elements or compounds combine to form a new compound, when one compound breaks down into two or more molecules, or when electrons are added to or taken away from an atom.

chemical selection A chemical within a mixture has special properties or advantages that cause it to increase compared with other chemicals in the mixture.

chemical synapse A synapse in which a chemical called a neurotransmitter is released from the nerve terminal and acts as a signal from the presynaptic to the postsynaptic cell.

chemiosmosis A process for making ATP in which energy stored in an ion electrochemical gradient is used to make ATP from ADP and P_i.

chemoautotroph An organism able to use energy obtained by chemical modifications of inorganic compounds to synthesize organic compounds.

chemoheterotrophs An organism that must obtain organic molecules for both energy and as a carbon source.

chemoreceptor A specialized cell located in the vertebrate aorta, carotid arteries, and brainstem that detects the circulating levels of hydrogen ions and the partial pressures of carbon dioxide and oxygen, and relays that information through nerves or interneurons to the respiratory centres.

chiasma The connection at a crossover site of two chromosomes.

chimeric gene A gene formed from the fusion of two gene fragments to each other.

chitin A tough, nitrogen-containing polysaccharide that forms the external skeleton of many insects and the cell walls of fungi.

chlorophyll A green pigment found in photosynthetic plants, algae, and bacteria.

chlorophyll *a* Type of chlorophyll pigment found in cyanobacteria, and photosynthetic algae and plants.

chlorophyll *b* Type of chlorophyll pigment found in green algae and plants.

chloroplast genome The chromosome found in chloroplasts.

chloroplasts Organelles surrounded by a double membrane that are responsible for capturing the energy from light in photosynthetic eukaryotes.

chlorosis The yellowing of plant leaves caused by various types of mineral deficiency.

choanocytes Specialized cells of sponges that function to trap and eat small particles.

chondrichthyans Members of the class Chondrichthyes, including sharks, skates, and rays.

chordates Organisms with a spinal cord.

chorion An extraembryonic membrane in the amniotic egg that, along with the allantois, exchanges gases between the embryo and the surrounding air.

chorionic gonadotropin (CG) An LH-like hormone made by the placenta that maintains the corpus luteum.

chromatin The biochemical composition of chromosomes, which contain DNA and many types of proteins.

chromosomes Packaged units of genetic material composed of DNA and the associated proteins. Each cell has a characteristic number of chromosomes. Eukaryotes have chromosomes in their cell nuclei, in plastids, and in mitochondria.

chromosome theory of inheritance An explanation of how the steps of meiosis account for the inheritance patterns observed by Mendel.

chylomicrons Large fat droplets coated with amphipathic proteins that perform an emulsifying function similar to that of bile salts; they are formed in intestinal epithelial cells from absorbed fats in the diet.

chyme A solution of food particles in the stomach that contains water, salts, molecular fragments of proteins, nucleic acids, polysaccharides, droplets of fat, and various other small molecules.

chymotrypsin A protease involved in the breakdown of proteins in the small intestine.

chytrids Simple, early diverging lineages of fungi; commonly found in aquatic habitats and moist soil, where they produce flagellate reproductive cells.

cilia Organelles that facilitate cell movement or movement of particles along the surface of cells; cilia are shorter and more numerous on cells than are flagella.

ciliates Protists that move by means of cilia, which are tiny hairlike extensions on the outsides of cells.

circadian rhythms Biological processes, governed by metabolic processes, that typically have a 24-hour oscillating cycle.

circulatory system A system that transports necessary materials to all cells of an animal's body, and transports waste products away from cells. The three basic types of circulatory systems are gastrovascular cavities, open systems, and closed systems.

***cis*-acting element** See *cis*-effect.

***cis*-effect** A DNA segment that must be adjacent to the gene(s) that it regulates. The *lac* operator site is an example of a *cis*-acting element.

cisternae Flattened, fluid-filled tubules within the cell.

citric acid cycle A cycle that results in the breakdown of carbohydrates to carbon dioxide; also known as the Krebs cycle.

clade See monophyletic group.

cladistic approach An approach that reconstructs a phylogenetic tree by comparing primitive and shared derived characters.

cladogenesis A pattern of speciation in which a species is divided into two or more species.

cladogram A phylogenetic tree based on a cladistic approach.

claspers Extensions of the pelvic fin of a chondrichthyan, used by the male to transfer sperm to the female.

classes Subdivisions of a phylum.

classical conditioning A type of associative learning in which an involuntary response comes to be associated positively or negatively with a stimulus that did not originally elicit the response.

cleavage A succession of rapid cell divisions with no significant growth that produces a hollow sphere of cells called a blastula.

cleavage furrow In animal cells, an area that constricts like a drawstring to separate the cells.

climate The prevailing weather pattern in a given region.

climate change Changes in long-term weather patterns caused, to a large extent, by the build-up of greenhouse gases in the atmosphere.

climax community A distinct end point of succession.

clitoris Located at the anterior part of the labia minora, erectile tissue that becomes engorged with blood during sexual arousal and is very sensitive to sexual stimulation.

clonal deletion A process that explains why individuals normally lack active lymphocytes that respond to self-components; T cells with receptors capable of binding self-proteins are destroyed by apoptosis.

clonal inactivation A process that explains why individuals normally lack active lymphocytes that respond to self-components; the process occurs outside the thymus and causes potentially self-reacting T cells to become nonresponsive.

clonal selection The process by which certain cells are selected to proliferate as clones.

closed circulatory system A circulatory system in which blood flows throughout an animal entirely within a series of vessels and is kept separate from the interstitial fluid.

closed conformation Tightly packed chromatin that cannot be transcribed into RNA.

clumped The most common pattern of dispersion within a population, in which individuals are gathered in small groups.

cnidocil On the surface of a cnidocyte, a hairlike trigger that detects stimuli.

cnidocytes Characteristic features of cnidarians; a stinging cell that functions in defence or the capture of prey.

coacervates Droplets that form spontaneously from the association of charged polymers, such as proteins, carbohydrates, or nucleic acids.

coactivator A protein that increases the rate of transcription but does not directly bind to DNA itself.

cocci Spheres; one of the five major shapes of prokaryotic cells.

cochlea A coiled structure containing the hair cells and other structures that generate the responses that travel via the auditory nerve to the brain.

coding strand The DNA strand opposite to the template (or noncoding strand).

codominance The phenomenon in which a single individual expresses both alleles.

codons Units of function for which the sequence of three specific ribonucleotides specifies a particular amino acid or a stop codon; codons function during translation.

coefficient of relatedness The probability that any two individuals will share a copy of a particular gene as a quantity, *r*.

coelomates Animals with a true coelom.

coenzymes Organic molecules that participate in the chemical reaction but are left unchanged after the reaction is completed.

coevolution The process by which two or more species of organisms influence each other's evolutionary pathways.

cofactors Inorganic ions that temporarily bind to the surface of an enzyme and promote a chemical reaction.

cognitive learning The ability to solve problems with conscious thought and without direct environmental feedback.

cohesion-tension theory The explanation for long-distance water transport as the combined effect of the cohesive forces of water and evaporative tension.

cohort A group of organisms of the same age.

coleoptile A protective sheath that encloses the first bud of an epicotyl in a mature monocot embryo.

coleorhiza A protective envelope that encloses the monocot hypocotyl.

colinearity rule The phenomenon whereby the order of homeotic genes along the chromosome correlates with their expression along the anteroposterior axis of the body.

collagen A protein secreted from animal cells that forms large fibres in the extracellular matrix.

collecting duct A tubule in the human vertebrate kidney that collects urine from nephrons.

collenchyma cells Flexible cells that make up collenchyma tissue.

collenchyma tissue A tissue that provides support to plant organs.

colligative properties The properties of water that depend on the amounts of dissolved substances. For example, the colligative properties of water cause certain solutes to function as antifreeze in certain organisms and thereby lower the freezing point.

colloid A gel-like substance in the follicles of the thyroid gland.

colon A part of the large intestine consisting of three relatively straight segments: the ascending, transverse, and descending portions. The terminal portion of the descending colon is S-shaped, forming the sigmoid colon, which empties into the rectum.

colony hybridization A method that uses a labelled probe that recognizes a specific gene to identify that gene in a DNA library.

combinatorial control The phenomenon whereby a combination of many factors determines the expression of any given gene.

commensalism An interaction that benefits one species and leaves the other unaffected.

communication The use of specially designed visual, chemical, auditory, or tactile signals to modify the behaviour of others.

community An assemblage of many populations that live in the same place at the same time.

community ecology The study of how populations of species interact and form functional communities.

competent The term used to describe bacterial strains that have the ability to take up DNA from the environment.

competition An interaction that affects two or more species negatively, as they compete for food or other resources.

competitive exclusion hypothesis The proposal that two species with the same resource requirements cannot occupy the same niche.

competitive inhibitors Molecules that bind to the active site of an enzyme and inhibit the ability of the substrate to bind.

complement The family of plasma proteins that provides a means for extracellular killing of microbes without prior phagocytosis.

complementary In DNA, you can predict the sequence in one DNA strand if you know the sequence in the opposite strand according to the AT/GC rule.

complementary DNA (cDNA) DNA molecules that are made from mRNA as a starting material.

complete flowers Flowers that possess all four types of flower organs.

complete metamorphosis A dramatic change in body form in the majority of insects, from larva to a very different looking adult.

compound A molecule comprising two or more different elements.

compound eyes Image-forming eyes in arthropods and some annelids consisting of several hundred to several thousand light detectors called ommatidia.

computational molecular biology An area of study that uses computers to characterize the molecular components of living things.

concentration The amount of a solute dissolved in a unit volume of solution.

concept mapping A graphic technique to display relationships between concepts and processes.

conduction The process in which the body surface loses or gains heat through direct contact with cooler or warmer substances.

cone pigments The several types of visual pigments in cones.

cones (1) Photoreceptors found in the vertebrate eye; they are less sensitive to low levels of light but can detect colour. Cones are used in daylight by most diurnal vertebrate species and by some insects. (2) The reproductive structures of conifer plants.

congestive heart failure The condition resulting from the failure of the heart to pump blood normally; this results in fluid buildup in the lungs (congestion).

conidia A type of asexual reproductive cell produced by many fungi.

Conifers A phylum of gymnosperm plants, Coniferophyta.

conjugation A type of genetic transfer between bacteria that involves a direct physical interaction between two bacterial cells.

connective tissues Clusters of cells that connect, anchor, and support the structures of an animal's body; derived from mesenchyme and include blood, adipose (fat-storing) tissue, bone, cartilage, loose connective tissue, and dense connective tissue.

connexon A channel that forms gap junctions consisting of six connexin proteins in one cell aligned with six connexin proteins in an adjacent cell.

conservation biology The study that uses principles and knowledge from molecular biology, genetics, and ecology to protect the biological diversity of life at all levels.

constant regions In immunology, the amino acid sequences of the Fc domains, which are identical for all immunoglobulins of a given class.

constitutive genes Genes that exhibit relatively constant levels of expression in all conditions over time.

consumers Consumers are animals that eat or consume food as opposed to producers (plants) that make their own food.

contig A series of clones that contain overlapping pieces of chromosomal DNA.

continental drift The phenomenon whereby over billions of years, the major landmasses, known as the continents, have shifted their positions, changed their shapes, and in some cases become separated from each other.

continental shelf Part of a continent that extends underwater to the deep ocean floor.

continuous traits Traits that show continuous variation over a large range of values (e.g., height).

contrast In microscopy, relative differences in the lightness, darkness, or colour between adjacent regions in a sample. Contrast improves the ability to discern adjacent objects.

control sample The sample in an experiment that is treated just like an experimental sample except that it is not subjected to one particular variable. For example, the control and experiment samples may be treated identically except that the temperature may vary for the experimental sample.

convection   The transfer of heat by the movement of air or water next to the body.

convergent evolution   The process whereby two different species from different lineages show similar characteristics because they occupy similar environments.

convergent traits   Structures or features that are the same or similar in unrelated organisms as a result of independent evolutionary events; similarities result because the organisms adapt to similar niches or environments. *See* analogous structures.

copulation   The process of sperm being deposited within the reproductive tract of the female.

core promoter   For a eukaryotic structural gene, refers to the transcriptional start site and TATA box.

Coregonus clupeaformis   A species of freshwater whitefish found throughout much of Canada, commonly referred to as Lake Whitefish.

corepressor   A small effector molecule that binds to a repressor protein to inhibit transcription.

Coriolis effect   The effect of Earth's rotation on the surface flow of wind.

cork cambium   A secondary meristem in a plant that produces cork tissue.

cornea   A thin, clear layer on the front of the vertebrate eye.

corolla   The petals of a flower, which occur in the whorl to the inside of the calyx and the outside of the stamens.

corona   The ciliated crown of members of the phylum Rotifera.

coronary arteries   Arteries that carry oxygen and nutrients to the heart muscle.

coronary artery bypass   A common treatment to restore blood flow through a blood vessel. A piece of healthy blood vessel is removed from one part of the body and surgically grafted onto the coronary circulation in such a way that blood bypasses the diseased artery.

coronary artery disease   A condition that occurs when plaques form in the coronary vessels.

corpus luteum   A structure that is responsible for secreting hormones that stimulate the development of the uterus needed for sustaining the embryo in the event of a pregnancy. If pregnancy does not occur, the corpus luteum degenerates.

cortex   The area of a plant stem or root beneath the epidermis that is largely composed of parenchyma tissue.

cortical reaction   An event in fertilization in which calcium and IP_3 produce additional barriers to more than one sperm cell binding to and uniting with an egg, a process called the slow block to polyspermy.

cotranslational sorting   The sorting process in which the synthesis of certain eukaryotic proteins begins in the cytosol and then halts temporarily until the ribosome has become bound to the ER membrane. After this occurs, translation resumes and the polypeptide is synthesized into the ER lumen or ER membrane.

cotransporters   *See* symporters.

cotyledons   Embryonic seed leaves.

countercurrent exchange mechanism   An arrangement of water and blood flow in which water enters a fish's mouth and flows between the lamellae of the gills in the opposite direction to blood flowing through the lamellar capillaries.

countercurrent heat exchange   A method of regulating heat loss to the environment; many animals conserve heat by returning it to the body's core and keeping the core much warmer than the extremities.

covalent bonds   Chemical bonds that occur when atoms share pairs of electrons.

CpG islands   Clusters of CpG sites. CpG refers to the nucleotides of C and G in DNA that are connected by a phosphodiester linkage.

cranial nerves   Nerves in the peripheral nervous system that directly connect to the brain; cranial nerves are located in the head and transmit incoming and outgoing information between the peripheral nervous system and the brain.

craniates   Chordates that have a brain encased in a skull and possesses a neural crest.

cranium   A protective bony or cartilaginous housing that encases the brain of a craniate.

cretinism   A disease caused by insufficient levels of thyroid hormone in the fetus; axons fail to become wrapped with myelin during fetal life, which leads to slow conduction speeds and abnormal connections between brain neurons. This results in profound mental defects that cannot be reversed unless treatment begins immediately after birth.

critical innovations   Fundamental changes.

crop   A storage organ that is a dilation of the lower esophagus; found in most birds and many invertebrates, including insects and some worms.

cross-bridges   Regions of myosin molecules that extend from the surface of the thick filaments toward the thin filaments in a skeletal muscle.

cross-bridge cycle   During muscle contraction, the sequence of events that occurs between the time when a cross-bridge binds to a thin filament and when it is set to repeat the process.

cross-fertilization   The fusion of gametes formed by different individuals.

crossing over   The exchange of genetic material between homologous chromosomes, which allows for increased variation in the genetic information each parent passes to the offspring.

cryptic coloration   The blending of an organism with the background colour of its habitat; also known as camouflage.

cryptochromes   Blue-light receptors found in plants and protists.

C-terminus   The location of the last amino acid in a polypeptide.

cupula   A gelatinous structure within the lateral line organ that helps an organism to detect changes in water movement.

cuticle   A coating of wax and cutin that helps to reduce water loss from plant surfaces. Also, a

nonliving covering that serves to both support and protect an animal.

cutin   A polyester polymer produced at the surfaces of plants; helps to prevent attack by pathogens.

cycads   A phylum of gymnosperm plants, Cycadophyta.

cyclic adenosine monophosphate (cyclic AMP or cAMP)   A small effector molecule that is produced from ATP via an enzyme known as adenylyl cyclase; a second messenger molecule that is involved in many signal transduction pathways.

cyclic electron flow   *See* cyclic photophosphorylation.

cyclic photophosphorylation   A pattern of electron flow in the thylakoid membrane that is cyclic and generates ATP alone.

cyclin-dependent kinases (cdks)   Proteins responsible for advancing a cell through the phases of the cell cycle. Their function is dependent on the binding of a cyclin.

cyclins   Proteins responsible for advancing a cell through the phases of the cell cycle by binding to a cyclin-dependent kinase.

cyst   A one-to-few-celled structure that often has a thick, protective wall and can remain dormant through periods of unfavourable climate or low food availability.

cytogenetics   The field of genetics that involves the microscopic examination of chromosomes.

cytokines   A family of proteins that function in both nonspecific and specific immune defences by providing a chemical communication network that synchronizes the components of the immune response.

cytokinesis   The division of the cytoplasm to produce two distinct daughter cells.

cytokinin   A type of plant hormone; promotes cell division in addition to other effects.

cytoplasm   The region of the cell that is contained within the plasma membrane.

cytoplasmic inheritance   *See* extranuclear inheritance.

cytoplasmic streaming   A phenomenon in which the cytoplasm circulates throughout the cell to distribute resources efficiently in large cells, such as algal or plant cells.

cytosine (C)   A pyrimidine base found in DNA and RNA.

cytoskeleton   In eukaryotes, a network of three different types of protein filaments called microtubules, intermediate filaments, and actin filaments.

cytosol   The region of a eukaryotic cell that is inside the plasma membrane and outside the organelles.

cytosolic leaflet   The portion of the membrane's lipid bilayer that faces the cytosol.

cytotoxic T cells   Lymphocytes that travel to the location of their target, bind to the target by combining with an antigen on it, and directly kill the target via secreted chemicals.

D

daltons (Da)   Units of mass that have one-twelfth the mass of a carbon atom, or about the mass of a proton or a hydrogen atom.

Darwinian fitness   The relative likelihood that a genotype will contribute to the gene pool of the next generation as compared with other genotypes.

database   A large number of computer data files that are collected, stored in a single location, and organized for rapid search and retrieval.

day-neutral plant   A plant that flowers regardless of the night length, as long as day length meets the minimal requirements for plant growth.

death-inducing signalling complex (DISC)   The complex in a cell between the death receptors, FADD, and procaspase.

death receptors   They stimulate a pathway that leads to apoptosis (cell death) when they become bound to an extracellular ligand.

decomposer   *See detritivores.*

defecation   The expulsion of feces that occurs through the final portion of the digestive canal, the anus; contractions of the rectum and relaxation of associated sphincter muscles expel the feces.

defensive mutualism   A mutually beneficial interaction often involving an animal defending a plant or a herbivore in return for food or shelter.

deficiency   A segment of chromosomal material that is missing.

deforestation   The conversion of forested areas by humans to nonforested land.

degenerate   In the genetic code, this means that more than one codon can specify the same amino acid.

dehydration   A reduction in the amount of water in the body.

delayed implantation   A reproductive cycle in which a fertilized egg reaches the uterus but does not implant until later, when environmental conditions are more favourable for the newly produced young.

delayed ovulation   A reproductive cycle in which the ovarian cycle in females is halted before ovulation, and sperm are stored and nourished in the female's uterus over the winter. On arousal from hibernation in the spring, the female ovulates one or more eggs, which are fertilized by the stored sperm.

deletion   A missing region of a chromosome.

demographic transition   The shift in birth and death rates accompanying human societal development.

demography   The study of birth rates, death rates, age distributions, and the sizes of populations.

dendrites   Types of extensions or projections that arise from the cell body; chemical and electrical messages from other neurons are received by the dendrites, and electrical signals move toward the cell body.

dendritic cells   Types of cells derived from bone marrow stem cells that play an important role in nonspecific immunity; these cells are scattered throughout most tissues, where they perform various macrophage functions.

denitrification   The reduction of nitrate to gaseous nitrogen.

density   In the context of populations, the numbers of organisms in a given unit area.

density-dependent factor   A mortality factor whose influence varies with the density of the population.

density gradient centrifugation   A technique used to separate macromolecules of different densities by determining where they reach equilibrium in a density gradient established by centrifugation.

density-independent factor   A mortality factor whose influence is not affected by changes in population size or density.

deoxyribonucleic acid (DNA)   One of two classes of nucleic acids; the other is ribonucleic acid (RNA). A DNA molecule consists of two strands of nucleotides coiled around each other to form a double helix and held together by hydrogen bonds, according to the AT/GC rule.

deoxyribose   A five-carbon sugar found in DNA.

depolarization   The change in the membrane potential that occurs when the cell becomes less polarized; that is, less negative relative to the surrounding fluid.

dermal tissue   The covering on various parts of a plant.

desertification   The overstocking of land with domestic animals that can greatly reduce grass coverage through overgrazing, turning the area desertlike.

desmosomes   Cell junctions that serve to rivet two cells together at a particular location, using cadherin proteins.

determinate cleavage   A characteristic of protostome development in which the fate of each embryonic cell is determined very early.

determinate growth   Growth in plants, such as occurs in a flower, that is of limited duration.

determined   The term used to describe a cell that is destined to differentiate into a particular cell type.

detritivores   Consumers that get their energy from the remains and waste products of organisms.

detritus   Unconsumed plants that die and decompose, along with the dead remains of animals and animal waste products.

deuterostomes   Animals exhibiting radial cleavage, indeterminate cleavage, and the blastopore becomes the anus; includes echinoderms and vertebrates.

development   A series of changes in the state of a cell, a tissue, an organ, or an organism; the underlying process that gives rise to the structure and function of living organisms.

developmental genetics   A field of study aimed at understanding how gene expression controls the process of development.

diaphragm   A large muscle that subdivides the thoracic cavity from the abdomen in mammals.

diastole   The first phase of the cardiac cycle, in which the ventricles fill with blood coming from the atria through the open AV valves.

diazotrophs   Bacteria that fix nitrogen.

dideoxy chain-termination method   The most common method of DNA sequencing; it uses dideoxynucleotides as a reagent.

dideoxy chain-termination method or dideoxy sequencing   A procedure used to sequence cloned DNA that employs dideoxynucleotides to terminate chain synthesis.

dideoxy sequencing   *See dideoxy chain-termination method.*

differential gene regulation   The phenomenon in which the expression of genes is altered. Differential gene expression allows cells to adapt to environmental conditions, change during development, and differentiate into particular cell types.

differentiated   The term used to describe the actual alteration of a cell's morphology and physiology.

diffusion   For dissolved substances, this occurs when a solute moves from a region of high concentration to a region of lower concentration.

digestion   The process of breaking down nutrients in food into smaller molecules that can be directly used by cells.

digestive system   In a vertebrate, this system consists of the alimentary canal plus several associated structures, not all of which are found in all vertebrates: the tongue, teeth, salivary glands, liver, gallbladder, and pancreas.

dihybrid   An offspring that is a hybrid with respect to two traits.

dikaryotic   The occurrence of two genetically distinct nuclei in the cells of fungal hyphae after mating has occurred.

dinosaur   A term meaning *terrible lizard* used to describe some of the extinct fossil reptiles.

dioecious   The term to describe plants that produce staminate and carpellate flowers on separate plants.

diploblastic   Having two distinct germ layers: ectoderm and endoderm but not mesoderm.

diploid   Containing two set of chromosomes; or $2n$.

diploid-dominant species   Species in which the diploid organism is the prevalent organism in the life cycle. Animals are an example.

dipole   A molecule that is polar, having a skewed distribution of charge across the molecule; H_2O is one example.

dipole-dipole force   The molecular attraction that occurs between oppositely charged poles of nearby polar molecules.

direct calorimetry   A method of determining basal metabolic rate that involves quantifying the amount of heat generated by the animal.

direct repair   Refers to a DNA repair system in which an enzyme finds an incorrect structure in the DNA and directly converts it back to the correct structure.

directional selection   A pattern of natural selection that favours individuals at one extreme of a phenotypic distribution that have greater reproductive success in a particular environment.

disaccharide   A carbohydrate composed of two monosaccharides.

discontinuous traits   Traits with only a few discrete alternative phenotypes (e.g., smooth or wrinkled seeds).

discovery-based science   The collection and analysis of data without the need for a preconceived hypothesis. Also called *discovery science*.

dispersion   A pattern of spacing in which individuals in a population are clustered together or spread out to varying degrees.

dispersive mutualisms   Mutually beneficial interactions often involving plants and pollinators that disperse their pollen, and plants and fruit eaters that disperse the plant's seeds.

disruptive selection   A pattern of natural selection that favours the survival of two or more different genotypes that produce different phenotypes.

dissociation constant (K_d)   An equilibrium constant between a ligand and a protein, such as a receptor or an enzyme.

diversity–stability hypothesis   The proposal that species-rich communities are more stable than those with fewer species.

DNA fingerprinting   A technology that identifies individuals by using properties of their DNA.

DNA library   A collection of vectors, each containing a particular fragment of chromosomal DNA or cDNA.

DNA ligase   An enzyme that catalyzes the formation of a covalent bond between nucleotides in adjacent DNA fragments to complete the replication process in the lagging strand.

DNA methylase   An enzyme that attaches methyl groups to bases in DNA.

DNA methylation   A process in which methyl groups are attached to bases in DNA. This usually inhibits gene transcription by preventing the binding of activator proteins or by promoting the compaction of chromatin.

DNA microarrays   A hybridization-based technique used to monitor the expression of thousands of genes simultaneously.

DNA repair systems   One of several systems to reverse DNA damage before a permanent mutation can occur.

DNA replication   The mechanism by which DNA can be copied.

DNA sequencing   A method to determine the base sequence of DNA.

DNA transposons   Mobile genetic elements that encode an enzyme (transposase) that enables them to excise from their location and insert into a new chromosomal location.

domains   (1) Defined regions of proteins with distinct structure and function. (2) The three major categories of life: Bacteria, Archaea, and Eukarya.

domestication   A process that involves artificial selection of plants or animals for traits desirable to humans.

dominant   A term that describes a trait that is seen in both true breeding parents and heterozygotes.

dominant species   A species that has a large effect in a community because of its high abundance or high biomass.

dormancy   A phase of metabolic slowdown in a plant.

dorsal   Refers to the upper side of an animal.

dorsoventral axis   One of the three axes along which the adult body pattern is organized; the others are the anteroposterior axis and the right–left axis.

dosage compensation   The phenonomen that gene dosage is compensated between males and females. In mammals, the inactivation of one X chromosome in the female reduces the number of expressed copies (doses) of X-linked genes from two to one.

double fertilization   In angiosperms, the process in which two different fertilization events occur, producing both a zygote and a nutritive endosperm tissue.

duplication   A section of a chromosome that occurs two or more times.

dynamic instability   The oscillation of a single microtubule between growing and shortening phases; important in many cellular activities, including the sorting of chromosomes during cell division.

dyspepsia   Stomach pain, heartburn, and bloating caused by stomach acid within the esophagus.

E

ecdysis   The periodic shedding and re-formation of the exoskeleton.

ecdysone   A steroid hormone synthesized and secreted by the prothoracic glands of certain invertebrates, such as arthropods; in response to this hormone, a larva moults and begins a new growth period until it must shed its skin again in response to another episode of ecdysone secretion.

Ecdysozoa   A clade of moulting animals that encompasses primarily the arthropods and nematodes.

echolocation   The phenomenon in which certain species generate high-frequency sound waves to determine the distance and location of an object.

ecological footprint   The amount of productive land needed to support each person on Earth.

ecological species concept   A species concept that considers a species within its native environment. Each species occupies its own ecological niche.

ecology   The study of interactions among organisms and between organisms and their environments.

ecosystem   The biotic community of organisms in an area and the abiotic environment affecting that community.

ecosystem ecology   The study of the flow of energy and cycling of nutrients among organisms within a community and between organisms and the environment.

ecosystem engineers   Species that create, modifiy, and maintain habitats.

ectoderm   The outermost layer of cells formed during gastrulation that covers the surface of the embryo and differentiates into the epidermis and nervous system.

ectomycorrhizal fungi   Symbiotic fungi that form a sheath around the roots of plants.

ectoparasites   Parasites that live on the outside of the host's body.

ectotherms   Animals whose body temperature changes with the environmental temperature.

edge effect   A special physical condition that exists at the boundary or "edge" of an area.

effective population size   The number of individuals that contribute genes to future populations, often smaller than the actual population size.

effector cells   Components of the immune response; these cells carry out the attack response.

effectors   Molecules that directly influence cellular responses.

efferent arterioles   Blood vessels that provide a pathway for blood out of a tissue or organ. For example, efferent arterioles move blood out of the glomerulus.

efferent neuron   *See* motor neurons.

egg   Also, egg cell. The female gamete.

ejaculation   The movement of semen through the urethra by contraction of muscles at the base of the penis.

ejaculatory duct   The structure within the male penis through which semen is released.

elasticity   The ability to stretch rather than break when subjected to force, but return to the original shape once the force is gone.

elastin   A protein that makes up elastic fibres in the extracellular matrix of animals.

electrical synapse   A synapse that directly passes electric current from the presynaptic to the postsynaptic cell via gap junctions.

electrocardiogram (ECG or EKG)   A record of the electrical impulses generated during the cardiac cycle.

electrochemical gradient   The combined effect of both an electrical and a chemical gradient; determines the direction that an ion will move.

electrogenic pump   A pump that generates an electrical gradient across a membrane.

electromagnetic receptors   Sensory receptors that detect radiation within a wide range of the electromagnetic spectrum, including visible, ultraviolet, and infrared light, as well as electrical and magnetic fields in some animals.

electromagnetic spectrum   All possible wavelengths of electromagnetic radiation, from relatively short wavelengths (gamma rays) to much longer wavelengths (radio waves).

electrons   Negatively charged particles found in orbitals around atomic nuclei. For atoms, the number of protons is equal to the number of electrons.

electron transport chain (ETC)   A group of protein complexes and small organic molecules embedded in the inner mitochondrial membrane. The components accept and donate electrons to each other in a linear manner. The movement of electrons produces an H^+ electrochemical gradient.

electronegativity   A measure of an atom's ability to attract electrons from another atom to its outer shell.

11-nm fibre   An intermediate stage of chromosome condensation, created as eukaryotic DNA is wrapped around two molecules each of histones H2a, H2b, H3, and H4 to form a structure known as the nucleosome.

elicitors   Compounds produced by bacterial and fungal pathogens that promote virulence.

elimination   The process of undigested material passing out of the body.

elongation factors   In translation, proteins that are needed for the growth of a polypeptide.

elongation stage   The second step in transcription or translation, in which RNA strands or polypeptides are made, respectively.

embryo   The early stages of development in a multicellular organism during which the organization of the organism is largely formed.

embryogenesis   The process by which embryos develop from single-celled zygotes by mitotic divisions.

embryonic development   The process by which a fertilized egg is transformed into an organism with distinct physiological systems and body parts.

embryonic germ cells (EG cells)   At the early fetal stage of development, the cells that later give rise to sperm or eggs cells. These cells are pluripotent.

embryonic stem cells (ES cells)   Cells in the early mammalian embryo that can differentiate into almost every cell type of the body.

embryophytes   A synonym for the land plants.

emerging virus   A new virus.

emulsification   A process during digestion that disrupts the large lipid droplets into many tiny droplets, thereby increasing their total surface area and exposure to lipase action.

enantiomers   A pair of stereoisomers that exist as non-superimposable mirror images of each other.

endangered species   Those species that are in danger of extinction throughout all or a significant portion of their range.

endemic   The term to describe organisms that are naturally found only in a particular location.

endergonic   Refers to a reaction that has a positive free energy change and does not proceed spontaneously.

endocrine disruptors   Chemicals found in water and soil exposed to pollution runoff that have a molecular structure that in some cases resembles estrogen sufficiently to bind to estrogen receptors.

endocrine glands   Structures that contain epithelial cells that secrete hormone molecules into the bloodstream, where they circulate throughout the body.

endocrine system   All the endocrine glands and other organs with hormone-secreting cells.

endocytosis   A process in which the plasma membrane invaginates, or folds inward, to form a vesicle that brings substances into the cell.

endoderm   The innermost layer of cells formed during gastrulation that lines the gut and gives rise to many internal organs.

endodermis   Specialized tissue in plants that stops the diffusion of water and dissolved minerals from the environment into roots and allows for selective uptake of minerals.

endomembrane system   A network of membranes that includes the nuclear envelope, which encloses the nucleus, and the endoplasmic reticulum, Golgi apparatus, lysosomes, peroxisomes, secretory vesicles, vacuoles, and plasma membrane.

endomycorrhizae   Partnerships between plants and fungi in which the fungal hyphae grow into the spaces between root cell walls and plasma membranes.

endoparasites   Parasites that live inside the host's body.

endophytes   Mutualistic fungi that live compatibly within the tissues of various types of plants.

endoplasmic reticulum (ER)   A convoluted network of membranes in the cell's cytoplasm that forms flattened, fluid-filled tubules or cisternae.

endoskeleton   An internal skeleton covered by soft tissue; composed of calcareous plates overlaid by a thin skin in echinoderms and composed of a bony skeleton overlaid by muscles in invertebrates.

endosperm   A nutritive tissue that increases the efficiency with which food is stored and used in the seeds of flowering plants.

endospores   Cells with a tough coat that are produced inside the cells of certain bacteria and then released when the enclosing cell dies and breaks down.

endosporic gametophytes   Plant gametophytes that grow within the confines of microspore and megaspore walls.

endosymbiosis   A symbiotic relationship in which the smaller species—the symbiont—lives inside the larger species.

endosymbiosis theory   A theory that mitochondria and chloroplasts originated from bacteria that took up residence within a primordial eukaryotic cell.

endosymbiotic   Describes a relationship in which one organism lives inside the other.

endothelium   A single-celled inner layer of a blood vessel, which forms a smooth lining in contact with the blood.

endothermic   A term to describe that ability of an organism to generate and retain body heat through its metabolism.

endotherms   Animals that generate their own internal heat.

energy   The ability to promote change.

energy expenditure   The amount of energy an animal uses in a given period of time to power all of its metabolic requirements.

energy flow   The movement of energy through an ecosystem.

energy intermediates   Molecules, such as ATP or NADH, that are directly used to drive endergonic reactions in cells.

energy shells   Regions of atoms, outside the atom's nucleus, in which electrons can move.

enhancement effect   The phenomenon whereby maximal activation of the pigments in photosystems I and II is achieved when organisms are exposed to two wavelengths of light.

enhancers   Response elements in eukaryotes that increase the rate of transcription.

enterocoelous   In deuterostomes, a pattern of development in which a layer of mesoderm cells forms outpockets that bud off from the developing gut to form the coelom.

enthalpy (*H*)   The total energy of a system.

entomology   The study of insects.

entropy   The degree of disorder in a system.

environmental science   The application of ecology to real-world problems.

enzyme   A protein responsible for speeding up a chemical reaction in a cell.

enzyme-linked receptors   Receptos found in all living species that typically have two important domains: an extracellular domain, which binds a signalling molecule, and an intracellular domain, which has a catalytic function.

enzyme-substrate complex   The binding between an enzyme and substrate.

eosinophils   Phagocytes found in large numbers in mucosal surfaces lining the gastrointestinal, respiratory, and urinary tracts, where they fight off parasitic invasions.

epicotyl   The portion of an embryonic plant stem with two tiny leaves in a first bud that is located above the point of attachment of the cotyledons.

epidermis   A layer of dermal tissue that helps protect a plant from damage.

epididymis   A coiled, tubular structure located on the surface of the testis; it is here that the sperm complete their differentiation by becoming motile and gaining the capacity to fertilize ova.

epigenetic inheritance   An inheritance pattern in which modification of a gene or chromosome during egg formation, sperm formation, or early stages of embryo growth alters gene expression in a way that is fixed during an individual's lifetime.

epinephrine   A hormone secreted by the adrenal glands; also known as adrenaline.

episome   A plasmid that can integrate into the bacterial chromosome.

epistasis   A gene interaction in which the alleles of one gene mask the expression of the alleles of another gene.

epithelial placodes   Regions of slightly thickened epithelial cells.

epithelial tissues   Sheets of densely packed cells that covers the body or individual organs or lines the walls of various cavities inside the body.

epitopes   Antigenic determinants; the peptide fragments of the antigen that are complexed to the MHC proteins and presented to the helper T cell.

equilibrium   (1) In a chemical reaction, occurs when the rate of the forward reaction is balanced by the rate of the reverse reaction. (2) In a population, the situation in which the population size stays the same.

equilibrium model of island biogeography   A model to explain the process of succession on new islands that states that the number of species on an island tends toward an equilibrium number that is determined by the balance between immigration rates and extinction rates.

equilibrium potential   In membrane physiology, the membrane potential at which the flow of an ion is at equilibrium—no net movement in either direction.

ER lumen   A single compartment enclosed by the ER membrane.

ER signal sequence   A sorting signal in a polypeptide usually located near the amino terminus that is recognized by signal recognition particle and directs the polypeptide to the ER membrane.

erythrocytes   *See* red blood cells.

erythrocytic cycle   Part of the life cycle of the malarial parasite that takes place in the blood cells.

erythropoietin (EPO)   A hormone made by the liver and kidneys in response to any situation in which additional blood cells are required, such as when animals lose blood following an injury; when abused, as in blood doping, the concentration of red blood cells reaches such high levels that the blood becomes much thicker than normal.

esophagus   The tubular structure that forms a pathway from the throat to the stomach.

essential amino acids   Those amino acids that are required in the diet of particular organisms. In humans, they include isoleucine, leucine, lysine, methionine, phenylalanine, threonine, tryptophan, and valine.

essential elements   Chemical elements that are divided into macronutrients (e.g., carbon), necessary for building cellular components, and micronutrients (e.g., iron) that are not needed in large quantities but act as cofactors for enzymes.

essential fatty acids   Fatty acids that are polyunsaturated, such as linoleic acid, that cannot be synthesized by animal cells and must therefore be consumed in the diet.

essential nutrients   Compounds that cannot be synthesized from any ingested or stored precursor molecule and so must be obtained from a dietary source.

estradiol   The major estrogen in many animals, including humans.

estrogens   Steroid hormones produced by the female ovaries that affect most aspects of reproduction.

ethology   Scientific studies of animal behaviour.

ethylene   A plant hormone that is particularly important in coordinating plant developmental and stress responses.

euchromatin   The less condensed regions of a chromosome; areas that are capable of gene transcription.

eudicots   One of the two largest lineages of flowering plants; the embryo possesses two seed leaves.

Eukarya   One of the three domains of life; the other two are Bacteria and Archaea.

eukaryote   Cells or organisms from the domain Eukarya. The distinguishing feature is cell compartmentalization, which includes a cell nucleus. *Eukaryote* means "true nucleus," and includes protists, fungi, plants, and animals.

eukaryotic   Refers to organisms having cells with internal compartments that serve various functions; includes all members of the domain Eukarya.

Eumetazoa   A subgroup of animals having more than one type of tissue and, for the most part, different types of organs.

euphotic zone   A fairly narrow zone close to the surface of an aquatic environment, where light is sufficient to allow photosynthesis to exceed respiration.

euphylls   Leaves with branched veins.

euphyllophytes   The clade that includes pteridophytes and seed plants.

euploid   An organism that has a chromosome number that is a multiple of a chromosome set ($1n$, $2n$, $3n$, etc.).

eusociality   The phenomenon whereby sterile castes evolve in social insects in which the vast majority of females, known as workers, rarely reproduce but instead help one reproductive female (the queen) to raise offspring.

Eustachian tube   A connection from the middle ear to the pharynx, which maintains the pressure in the middle ear at atmospheric pressure.

eustele   A ring of vascular tissue arranged around a central pith of nonvascular tissue; typical of progymnosperms, gymnosperms, and angiosperms.

eutherian   A placental mammal and member of the subclass Eutheria.

eutrophic   Waters that contain relatively high levels of nutrients, such as phosphate or nitrogen, and typically exhibit high levels of primary productivity and low levels of biodiversity.

eutrophication   The process by which elevated nutrient levels lead to an overgrowth of algae or aquatic plants and the subsequent depletion of water oxygen levels.

evaporation   The transformation of water from the liquid to the gaseous state; a method used to transfer heat by vaporizing water from the skin and membranes lining the respiratory tract.

evapotranspiration rate   The rate at which water moves into the atmosphere through the processes of evaporation from the soil and transpiration of plants.

evolutionary developmental biology (evo-devo)   A field of biology that compares the development of different organisms in an attempt to understand ancestral relationships between organisms and the developmental mechanisms that bring about evolutionary change.

evolutionary lineage concept   A sequence of species that form a direct line of descent.

excitable cells   The term used to describe neurons and muscle cells, because they have the capacity to generate electrical signals.

excitation-contraction coupling   The sequence of events by which an action potential in the plasma membrane of a muscle fibre leads to cross-bridge activity.

excitatory postsynaptic potential (EPSP)   The response from an excitatory neurotransmitter depolarizing the postsynaptic membrane; the depolarization brings the membrane potential closer to the threshold potential that would trigger an action potential.

excurrent siphon   A tunicate structure used to expel water.

exergonic   Refers to reactions that release free energy and occur spontaneously.

exit site (E site)   A site for the tRNA binding in the ribosome; the other two are the peptidyl site (P site) and the aminoacyl site (A site). This is the site where the uncharged tRNA exits.

exocytosis   A process in which material inside the cell is packaged into vesicles and excreted into the extracellular medium.

exoerythrocytic cycle   Part of the life cycle of malarial parasite that takes place in the liver cells, outside the blood cells.

exons   Portions of an RNA molecule that are found in the mature RNA molecule after splicing is finished.

exon shuffling   A form of mutation in which exons are inserted into genes and thereby create proteins with additional functional domains.

exoskeleton   An external skeleton that surrounds and protects most of the body surface of animals such as insects.

expansins   Proteins that occur in the plant cell wall and fosters cell enlargement.

experimental sample   The sample in an experiment that is subjected to some type of variation that does not occur for the control sample.

exploitation competition   Organisms compete indirectly through the consumption of a limited resource, with each obtaining as much as it can.

exponential growth   J-shaped rapid population growth that occurs when the per capita growth rate remains above zero.

extensors   Muscles that straighten a limb.

external fertilization   Fertilization that occurs in aquatic environments, when eggs and sperm are released into the water in close enough proximity for fertilization to occur.

extinction   The end of the existence of a species or group of species.

extinction vortex   A downward spiral toward extinction from which a species cannot naturally recover.

extracellular fluid   The fluid in an organism's body that is outside the cells, composed of plasma and interstitial fluid.

extracellular matrix (ECM)   A network of material that is secreted from cells and forms a complex mesh outside cells. The ECM provides strength, support, and organization.

extranuclear inheritance   In eukaryotes, the transmission of genes that are located outside the cell nucleus.

extremophiles   Organisms that occur primarily in extreme habitats.

eyecup   In planaria, a primitive eye that detects light and its direction.

F

**(5`) CAP**   A molecule of 7-methyl guanine that is added to messenger RNA, post-transcriptionally at the 5` end of the mRNA.

F factor   A segment of DNA called a fertility factor that plays a role in bacterial conjugation.

F_1 generation   The first filial generation in a genetic cross.

F_2 generation   The second filial generation in a genetic cross.

facilitated diffusion   A method of passive transport that involves the aid of a transport protein.

facilitation   A mechanism for succession in which a species facilitates or makes the environment more suitable for subsequent species.

facultative aerobe   A microorganism that can use oxygen in aerobic respiration, obtain energy via anaerobic fermentation, or use inorganic chemical reactions to obtain energy.

facultative mutualism   An interaction that is beneficial but not essential to the survival and reproduction of either species.

families   Subdivisions of an Order.

fast block to polyspermy   A depolarization of the egg that blocks other sperm from binding to the egg membrane proteins.

fast fibres   Muscle fibres containing myosin with high ATPase activity.

fast-glycolytic fibres   Skeletal muscle fibres that have high myosin activity but cannot make as much ATP as oxidative fibres, because their source of ATP is glycolysis; best suited for rapid, intense actions.

fast-oxidative fibres   Skeletal muscle fibres that have high myosin activity and can make large amounts of ATP; used for long-term activities.

fate mapping   A technique in which a small population of cells within an embryo is specifically labelled with a harmless dye, and the fate of these labelled cells is followed to a later stage of embryonic development.

feedback inhibition   A form of regulation in which the product of a metabolic pathway inhibits an enzyme that acts early in the pathway, thus preventing the overaccumulation of the product.

feedforward regulation   The process by which an animal's body begins preparing for a change in some variable before it even occurs.

female-enforced monogamy hypothesis   The suggestion that males are monogamous because females stop their male partners from being polygynous.

female gametophyte   In plants, a haploid generation that produces one or more eggs but does not produce sperm cells.

fermentation   The breakdown of organic molecules to produce energy without any net oxidation of an organic molecule.

Ferrell cell   The middle cell in the three-cell circulation of wind in each hemisphere.

fertilization   The union of two gametes, such as an egg cell with a sperm cell, to create a zygote.

fertilizers   Soil additives that enhance plant growth by providing essential elements.

fetus   The maturing embryo, after the eighth week of gestation in humans.

fibrin   A protein that forms a mesh of threadlike fibres that wrap around and between platelets and blood cells, enlarging and thickening a blood clot.

fibrous root system   The root system of monocots, which consists of multiple adventitious roots that grow from the stem base.

fidelity   Refers to the high level of accuracy in DNA replication.

filament   The elongate portion of a flower's stamen; contains vascular tissue that delivers nutrients from parental sporophytes to anthers.

filtrate   In the process of filtration, the material that passes through the filter and enters the excretory organ for either further processing or excretion.

filtration   The passive removal of water and small solutes from the blood.

first law of thermodynamics   Energy cannot be created or destroyed; it is also called the law of conservation of energy.

5¢ cap   A molecule of 7-methyl guanine that is added to messenger RNA, post-transcriptionally at the 5` end of the mRNA.

fixation   Treatment of a cell, tissue, and so on, in an attempt to preserve the natural structure.

fixed action pattern (FAP)   An animal behaviour that, once initiated, will continue until completed.

fixed nitrogen   Combined forms of soil nitrogen, such as ammonia (NH_3), ammonium ion (NH_4^+), or nitrate ion (NO_3^-), which make nitrogen available to plants.

flaccid   In plants, a cellular condition in which the concentration of solutes on both sides of the plasma membrane is equal and therefore the plasma membrane does not appress the cell wall.

flagella   Relatively long cell organelles that facilitate cellular movement or the movement of extracellular fluids.

flagellates   Protists that use one or more flagella to move in water or cause water motions useful in feeding.

flagship species   A single large or instantly recognizable species.

flame cells   Cells that exist primarily to maintain osmotic balance between an organism's body and surrounding fluids; present in flatworms.

flatus   Intestinal gas, which is a mixture of nitrogen and carbon dioxide, with small amounts of hydrogen, methane, and hydrogen sulphide.

flavonoids   Phenolic secondary metabolites that provide plants with protection from UV damage or colours organs such as flower petals.

flexors   A muscle that bends a limb at a joint.

florigen   The hypothesized flowering hormone, now identified as the mRNA, that produces FT (flowering time) protein in the shoot apex.

flowering plants   The angiosperms, which produce ovules within the protective ovaries of flowers; when ovules develop into seeds, angiosperm ovaries develop into fruits, which function in seed dispersal.

flowers   Reproductive shoots; a stem branch that produces reproductive organs instead of leaves.

flow-through systems   Forms of ventilation in fish in which water moves unidirectionally such that the gills are constantly in contact with fresh, oxygenated water.

fluid feeders   Animals that lick or suck fluid from plants or animals and do not need teeth except to puncture an animal's skin.

fluid-mosaic model   The accepted model of the plasma membrane; its basic framework is the semifluid phospholipid bilayer with a mosaic of proteins. Carbohydrates can be attached to lipids or proteins.

focal adhesions   A type of anchoring junction that anchors cells to the extracellular matrix as integrin proteins bind with actin filaments.

follicle   A structure within the ovary where each ovum undergoes growth and development before it is ovulated.

follicle-stimulating hormone (FSH)   A gonadotropin that stimulates follicle development.

food chain A linear depiction of energy flow between organisms, with each organism feeding on and deriving energy from the preceding organism.

food-induced thermogenesis A rise in metabolic rate for a few hours after eating that produces heat.

food web A complex model of interconnected food chains in which there are multiple links between species.

foot In molluscs, a muscular structure usually used for movement.

forebrain One of three major divisions of the vertebrate brain; the other two divisions are the midbrain and hindbrain.

fossil fuels Fuels, such as coal, petroleum, and natural gas, formed in Earth from protist, plant, or animal remains.

fossils Recognizable remains of past life on Earth.

founder effect A small group of individuals separates from a larger population and establishes a colony in a new location; genetic drift is common because of the small population size.

fovea A small area on the retina directly behind the lens that is responsible for the sharpness with which we and other animals see in daylight.

frameshift mutation A mutation that involves the addition or deletion of nucleotides that are not in multiples of three nucleotides.

free energy (G) In living organisms, the usable energy; that is, the amount of available energy that can be used to do work.

free radical A molecule containing an atom with a single, unpaired electron in its outer shell. A free radical is unstable and interacts with other molecules by taking electrons from their atoms.

frequency In regard to sound, the number of complete wavelengths that occur in one second, measured in number of waves per second, or Hertz (Hz).

frugivores Herbivores that are adapted primarily to feed on fruits.

fruiting bodies The visible fungal reproductive structures; composed of densely packed hyphae that typically grow out of the substrate.

fruits Structures that develop from flower organs, encloses seeds, and fosters seed dispersal in the environment.

functional genomics Genomic methods aimed at studying the expression of a genome.

functional groups Functional chemical add-ons with specific chemical features that modify the chemical properties of the molecules to which they are added. Each functional group exhibits the same properties in all molecules in which it occurs.

fundamental niche The optimal range in which a particular species best functions.

Fungi One of the four traditional eukaryotic kingdoms of the domain Eukarya.

funguslike protists Heterotrophic organisms that often resemble true fungi in having thread-like, filamentous bodies and absorbing nutrients from its environment.

G

G banding A staining procedure for chromosomes that produces an alternating pattern of G bands that is unique for each type of chromosome.

G proteins Intracellular proteins that bind guanosine triphosphate (GTP) and guanosine diphosphate (GDP) and participate in intracellular signalling pathways.

G0 A stage in which cells exit the cell cycle and postpone their division.

G1 The first gap phase of the cell cycle.

G2 The second gap phase of the cell cycle.

Gadus morhua Fish species commonly called Atlantic cod.

gallbladder A small sac underneath the liver that is a storage site for bile that allows the release of large amounts of bile to be precisely timed to the consumption of fats.

gametangia Specialized structures produced by many land plants in which developing gametes are protected by a jacket of tissue.

gametes Cells derived from products of meiosis that can differentiate into cells that can fuse with another gamete, such as sperm and egg during fertilization

gametic life cycle In this type of life cycle, all cells except the gametes are diploid, and gametes are produced by meiosis.

gametogenesis The formation of gametes.

gametophytes In plants and many multicellular protists, the haploid forms of the organism stage that produce gametes by mitosis.

ganglia Groups of neuronal cell bodies that perform basic functions of integrating inputs from sense organs and controlling motor outputs, usually in the peripheral nervous system.

gap gene A type of segmentation gene; when a mutation inactivates a gap gene, several adjacent segments are missing in the larva.

gap junctions Junctions found between animal cells that provide passageways for intercellular transport.

gas exchange The process of moving oxygen and carbon dioxide in opposite directions between cells and blood, and between blood and the environment.

gas vesicles Cytoplasmic structures used by cyanobacteria and some other bacteria that live in aquatic habitats to adjust their buoyancy.

gastrovascular cavity A body cavity with a single opening to the outside; it functions as both a digestive system and a circulatory system.

gastrula An embryo that is the result of gastrulation; it has three cellular layers called the ectoderm, endoderm, and mesoderm.

gastrulation A process in which an area in the blastula invaginates and folds inward, creating different embryonic cell layers called germ layers.

gated channels Channels that can open to allow the diffusion of solutes and close to prohibit diffusion.

gel electrophoresis A technique used to separate macromolecules by using an electric field that causes them to pass through a gel matrix.

gene addition In recombinant DNA technology, the insertion of a new gene into an organism at a random position.

gene amplification An increase in the copy number of a gene.

gene cloning The process of making multiple copies of a gene.

gene expression Gene function both at the trait level and at the molecular level.

gene family A group of homologous genes within a single species.

gene flow Occurs when individuals migrate between different populations and cause changes in the genetic composition of the resulting populations.

gene interaction A situation in which a single trait is controlled by two or more genes.

gene knockout An organism in which both copies of a functional gene have been replaced with nonfunctional copies. Experimentally, this can occur via gene replacement.

gene mutations Small changes in the DNA sequences of genes structure that can be inherited.

gene pool All the genes in a population.

gene regulation The ability of cells to control their level of gene expression.

gene replacement The phenomenon in which a cloned gene recombines with the normal gene on a chromosome and replaces it.

genera Plural of genus.

general lineage concept The idea that species are lineages and that multiple criteria may be used to identify them.

general transcription factors (GTFs) Five different proteins that play a role in initiating transcription at the core promoter of structural genes in eukaryotes.

generative cell In seed plants, the male gametophyte cell that divides to produce sperm cells.

genes Units of heredity that contribute to the characteristics or traits of organisms. At the molecular level, genes are composed of organized sequences of DNA.

genetic code A code that specifies the relationship between the sequence of nucleotides in the codons found in mRNA and the sequence of amino acids in a polypeptide.

genetic drift The random change in a population's allele frequencies from one generation to the next that is attributable to chance. It occurs more quickly in small populations.

genetic engineering The direct manipulation of genes for practical purposes.

genetic linkage map A diagram that describes the linear arrangement of genes that are linked to each other along the same chromosome.

genetic linkage mapping The process of determining the relative locations of genes or other DNA segments along a chromosome. Also called mapping.

genetic mosaic An individual with somatic regions that are genetically different from each other.

genetic transfer   The process by which genetic material is transferred from one bacterial cell to another.

genetically modified organisms (GMOs)   *See* transgenic.

genetics   The study of genes—their structure, function, and inheritance.

genome   The complete genetic composition of a cell or a species.

genomic imprinting   A phenomenon in which a segment of DNA is imprinted, or marked, in a way that affects gene expression throughout the life of the individual who inherits that DNA.

genomic library   A type of DNA library in which the inserts are derived from chromosomal DNA.

genomics   Techniques that are used in the molecular analysis of the entire genome of a species.

genotype   The genetic composition of an individual.

genotype frequencies   The number of individuals with a given genotype divided by the total number of individuals.

genus   In taxonomy, a subdivision of a family.

geological timescale   A timeline of the Earth's history from its origin about 4.55 billion years ago to the present.

geometric isomers   Steroisomers in which the two hydrogen atoms linked to the two carbons of a carbon–carbon double bond are on the same side of the carbons (creating a *cis* double bond) or are on the opposite sides (creating a *trans* double bond).

germ layers   Embryonic cell layers such as the ectoderm, mesoderm, or endoderm.

germ line   Cells that give rise to gametes, such as egg and sperm cells.

germ plasm   Cytoplasmic determinants that help define and specify the primordial germ cells in the gastrula stage.

germination   A dispersed plant seed absorbs water, becomes metabolically active, and grows out of the seed coat, producing a seedling.

giant axons   Very large axons in certain species such as squid that facilitate high-speed nerve conduction and rapid responses to stimuli.

gibberellic acid   A type of gibberellin.

gills   Specialized filamentous organs in aquatic animals that aid in obtaining oxygen and eliminating carbon dioxide.

ginkgos   A phylum of gymnosperms; Ginkgophyta.

gizzard   In the stomach of a bird, the muscular structure with a rough inner lining capable of grinding food into smaller fragments.

glaucoma   A condition in which drainage of aqueous humour in the eye becomes blocked and the pressure inside the eye increases as the fluid level rises. If untreated, damages cells in the retina and leads to irreversible loss of vision.

glia   Cells that surround the neurons; a major class of cells in nervous systems that perform various functions.

glomerular filtration rate (GFR)   The rate at which the glomerular filtrate (the fluid that leaves the glomerular capillaries and enters Bowman's space) is formed.

glomerulus   A cluster of interconnected, fenestrated capillaries in the renal corpuscle of the kidney; the site of filtration in the kidneys.

glucagon   A peptide hormone secreted by the pancreas that raises blood glucose levels.

gluconeogenesis   A mechanism for maintaining blood glucose levels; enzymes in the liver convert noncarbohydrate precursors into glucose, which are then secreted into the blood.

glucose sparing   A metabolic adjustment that reserves the glucose produced by the liver for use by the nervous system.

glycocalyx   (1) An outer viscous covering surrounding a bacterium. The glycocalyx, which is secreted by the bacterium, traps water and helps protect bacteria from drying out. (2) A carbohydrate covering that is found outside animal cells.

glycogenolysis   A mechanism for maintaining blood glucose levels; stored glycogen can be broken back down into molecules of glucose by hydrolysis.

glycolipid   A lipid that has carbohydrate attached to it.

glycolysis   A metabolic pathway that breaks down glucose to pyruvate.

glycolytic fibres   Skeletal muscle fibres that have few mitochondria but possess both a high concentration of glycolytic enzymes and large stores of glycogen.

glycoprotein   A protein that has carbohydrate attached to it.

glycosaminoglycan (GAG)   The most abundant type of polysaccharide in the extracellular matrix (ECM) of animals, consisting of repeating disaccharide units that give a gel-like character to the ECM of animals.

glycosidic bond   The type of covalent bond that forms between two sugar molecules.

glycosylation   The attachment of carbohydrate to a protein or lipid, producing a glycoprotein or glycolipid.

glyoxysomes   Specialized organelles within plant seeds that contain enzymes needed to convert fats to sugars.

gnathostomes   All vertebrate species that possess jaws.

gnetophytes   A phylum of gymnosperms; Gnetophyta.

Golgi apparatus   A stack of flattened, membrane-bounded compartments that performs three overlapping functions: secretion, processing, and protein sorting.

gonads   The testes in males and the ovaries in females, where the gametes are formed.

G-protein-coupled receptors (GPCRs)   A common type of receptor found in the cells of eukaryotic species that interacts with G proteins to initiate a cellular response.

graded potential   The depolarization or hyperpolarization of a cell that varies depending on the strength of the stimulus.

gradualism   A concept that suggests that species evolve continually over long spans of time.

grains   The characteristic single-seeded fruits of cereal grasses, such as rice, corn, barley, and wheat.

Gram stain   A method used to help detect and distinguish bacteria based on the fact that certain stains are preferentially taken up by bacterial cells.

granum (plural: grana)   A structure composed of stacked tubules within the thylakoid membrane of chloroplasts.

gravitropism   Plant growth in response to the force of gravity.

grazers   Herbivores that feed almost constantly on grasses.

greenhouse effect   The process in which shortwave solar radiation passes through the atmosphere to warm Earth but is radiated back to space as long-wave infrared radiation. Much of this radiation is absorbed by atmospheric gases and reradiated back to Earth's surface, causing its temperature to rise.

grey matter   Brain tissue that consists of neuronal cell bodies, dendrites, and some unmyelinated axons.

groove   In the DNA double helix, an indentation where the atoms of the bases make contact with the surrounding water.

gross primary production (GPP)   The measure of biomass production by photosynthetic organisms; equivalent to the carbon fixed during photosynthesis.

ground meristem   A type of primary plant tissue meristem that gives rise to ground tissue.

ground tissues   Plant tissues that provide a variety of functions, including photosynthesis, storage of carbohydrates, and support. Ground tissue can be subdivided into three types: parenchyma, collenchyma, and sclerenchyma.

group selection   The premise that natural selection produces outcomes beneficial for the whole group or species rather than for individuals.

guanine (G)   A purine base found in DNA and RNA.

guard cells   Specialized plant cells flanking epidermal pores (stomata) that allow them to close when conditions are too dry and open under moist conditions, allowing the entry of CO_2 needed for photosynthesis.

gustation   The sense of taste.

gut   The gastrointestinal (GI) tract.

guttation   The phenomena that occurs in the early morning as root pressure pushes droplets of water out at the edges of leaves.

gymnosperms   Plants that produce seeds that are exposed rather than enclosed in fruits.

gynoecium   The aggregate of carpels that forms the innermost whorl of flower organs.

H

H zone   A narrow, light region in the centre of the A band of the sarcomere that corresponds to the space between the two sets of thin filaments in each sarcomere.

H⁺ electrochemical gradient   A transmembrane gradient for H^+ composed of both a membrane potential and a concentration difference for H^+ across the membrane.

habituation   The form of nonassociative learning in which an organism learns to ignore a repeated stimulus.

Hadley cell   The most prominent of the three cells in the three-cell circulation of wind in each hemisphere.

hair cells   Mechanoreceptors that are specialized epithelial cells with deformable stereocilia.

half-life   (1) In the case of organic molecules in a cell, refers to the time it takes for 50% of the molecules to be broken down. (2) In the case of radioisotopes, the time it takes for half the molecules to decay and emit radiation.

halophytes   Plants that can tolerate higher than normal salt concentrations in the cell sap and thus can occupy coastal salt marshes or saline deserts.

Hamilton's rule   The proposal that an altruistic gene will be favoured by natural selection when $r > C/B$ where r is the coefficient of relatedness of the donor (the altruist) to the recipient, B is the benefit received by the recipients of the altruism, and C is the cost incurred by the donor.

haplodiploidy   A genetic system in which females develop from fertilized eggs and are diploid but males develop from unfertilized eggs and are haploid.

haploid   Containing one set of chromosomes, or $1n$.

haploid-dominant species   Species in which the haploid organism is the prevalent organism in the life cycle. Examples include fungi and some protists.

Hardy-Weinberg equation   An equation ($p^2 + 2pq + q^2 = 1$) that relates allele and genotype frequencies; the equation predicts an equilibrium if the population size is very large, mating is random, the populations do not migrate, no natural selection occurs, and no new mutations are formed.

heart   A muscular structure that pumps blood through blood vessels.

heart attack   *See* myocardial infarction (MI).

heat of fusion   The amount of heat energy that must be withdrawn or released from a substance to cause it to change from the liquid to the solid state.

heat of vaporization   The heat required to vaporize one mole of any substance at its boiling point under standard pressure.

heavy chains   Parts of an immunoglobulin molecule.

helper T cells   Lymphocytes that assist in the activation and function of B cells and cytotoxic T cells.

hematocrit   The volume of blood that is composed of red blood cells, usually between 40% and 65% among vertebrates.

hemidesmosomes   Structures that use integrin proteins to *connect cells to the extracellular matrix by* integrin interacting with intermediate filaments.

hemiparasites   Parasitic organisms that generally photosynthesize but lack a root system to draw water and thus depend on the host for that function.

hemizygous   The term used to describe the single copy of an X-linked gene in a male.

hemocyanin   A copper-containing pigment that gives the blood or hemolymph a bluish tint.

hemodialysis   A medical procedure used to artificially perform the kidneys' excretory filtration and cleansing functions.

hemoglobin   An oxygen-binding protein found within the cytosol of red blood cells.

hemolymph   Blood and interstitial fluid combined in one fluid compartment in many invertebrates.

hemophilia   A genetic disorder in which the body is unable to form blood clots effectively. There are also problems with coagulation.

hemorrhage   A loss of blood from a ruptured blood vessel.

herbaceous plants   Plants that produce little or no wood and are composed mostly of primary vascular tissues.

herbivores   Animals that eat only plants.

herbivory   Refers to herbivores feeding on plants.

heredity   The genetic transmission of genes/traits from one generation to the next.

hermaphrodites   Individuals that can produce both sperm and eggs.

hermaphroditism   A form of sexual reproduction in which individuals have both male and female reproductive systems.

heterochromatin   The highly compacted regions of chromosomes; in general, these regions are transcriptionally inactive because of their tight conformation.

heterocysts   Specialized cells of some cyanobacteria in which nitrogen fixation occurs.

heterogametic sex   In organisms with sex chromosomes, this is the sex that gives two types of gametes—one type producing females and one type producing males.

heterokaryons   In fungi, mycelia having nuclei of two or more genetic types.

heterospory   In plants, the formation of two different types of spores, microspores and megaspores; microspores produce male gametophytes and megaspores produce female gametophytes.

heterotherms   Animals that have a body temperature that varies with the environment.

heterotrophic   Requiring organic food from the environment.

heterotrophs   Organisms that cannot produce their own organic food and thus must obtain organic food from other organisms.

heterozygote advantage   A phenomenon in which a heterozygote has a higher Darwinian fitness compared with the corresponding homozygotes.

heterozygous   An individual with two different alleles of the same gene.

hibernation   The state of torpor in an animal over months.

high affinity   Refers to the binding of an ion or a molecule to a protein very tightly. The substance will bind at a very low concentration.

hindbrain   One of three major divisions of the vertebrate brain; the other two divisions are the midbrain and forebrain.

hippocampus   The area of the brain whose main function appears to be establishing memories for spatial locations, facts, and sequences of events; composed of several layers of cells that are connected in a circuit.

histone acetyltransferase   An enzyme that attaches acetyl groups to histone proteins.

histone code hypothesis   The pattern of histone modification recognized by particular proteins. The pattern of covalent modifications of amino terminus tails provides binding sites for proteins that subsequently affect the degree of chromatin compaction.

histone variant   Histone proteins that exhibit minor differences in their sequences; when incorporated into chromatin these variants can alter chromatin structure and influence transcription (either positively or negatively).

histones   A group of proteins involved in the formation of nucleosomes.

holoblastic cleavage   A complete type of cell cleavage in certain animals in which the entire zygote is bisected into two equal-sized blastomeres.

holoparasites   Parasitic organisms that lack chlorophyll and are totally dependent on the host plant for its water and nutrients.

homeobox   A 180-bp sequence within the coding sequence of homeotic genes.

homeodomain   A region of a protein that functions in binding to the DNA.

homeostasis   The process through which living organisms regulate their cells and bodies to maintain relatively stable internal conditions.

homeotherms   Animals that maintain their body temperature within a narrow range.

homeotic genes   Genes that control the developmental fate of particular segments or regions of an animal's body.

hominids   Gibbons, gorillas, orangutans, chimpanzees, or humans, and all their recent ancestors.

hominin   Either an extinct or a modern form of humans.

homogametic sex   In organisms with sex chromosomes, this is the sex that gives each of its gametes the same type of sex chromosome.

homologous genes   Genes that are derived from the same ancestral gene and that have accumulated random mutations that make their sequences slightly different.

homologous structures   Structures that are similar to each other because they are derived from the same ancestral structure.

homologues   Pairs of chromosomes in a diploid organism that are evolutionarily related.

homology   A fundamental similarity that occurs because of descent from a common ancestor.

homophilic like-to-like binding mechanism   A type of cell–cell adhesion that occurs when two cells each have the same type of cadherin molecules and can form a homodimer.

homozygous   An individual with two identical copies of an allele.

horizontal gene transfer   The transfer of genes between different species.

hormones   Chemical messengers that are produced in a gland or other structure and act on distant target cells in one or more parts of the body.

hornworts   A phylum of bryophytes; Anthocerophyta.

host   The prey organism in a parasitic association.

host cell   A cell that is infected by a virus, fungus, or bacterium.

host plant resistance   The ability of plants to prevent herbivory.

host range   The number of species and cell types that a virus or bacterium can infect.

hot spots   Human-impacted geographic areas with a large number of endemic species. To qualify as a hot spot, a region must contain at least 1,500 species of vascular plants as endemics and have lost at least 70% of its original habitat.

***Hox* complexes**   A cluster of adjacent homeotic genes in vertebrates that controls the formation of structures along the anteroposterior axis.

***Hox* genes**   A class of genes involved in pattern formation in early embryos.

Human Genome Project   The largest genome project in history, which was a 13-year effort coordinated by the U.S. Department of Energy and the National Institutes of Health. The goals of the project were to identify all human genes, to sequence the entire human genome, to address the legal and ethical implications resulting from the project, and to develop programs to manage the information gathered from the project.

human immunodeficiency virus (HIV)   A retrovirus that is the causative agent of acquired immune deficiency syndrome (AIDS).

humoral immunity   A type of specific immunity in which plasma cells secrete antibodies that bind to antigens.

humus   A collective term for the organic constituents of soils.

hybrid breakdown   A postzygotic mechanism of reproductive isolation in which an interspecies hybrid is viable and fertile, but subsequent generations harbour detrimental genetic abnormalities.

hybrid inviability   A postzygotic mechanism of reproductive isolation in which an egg of one species is fertilized by a sperm from another species, but the fertilized egg cannot develop past the early embryonic stages.

hybrid sterility   A postzygotic mechanism of reproductive isolation in which an interspecies hybrid is viable but sterile.

hybrid zones   Areas where two populations can interbreed.

hybridization   A situation in which two individuals with different characteristics are mated or crossed to each other; the offspring are referred to as hybrids.

hydrogen bonds   Dipole–dipole forces that occur when the hydrogen of a polar molecule interacts with a highly electronegative atom of nitrogen, oxygen, or florine (usually oxygen or nitrogen in biological systems).

hydrolysis   The process in which reactions use water to break apart other molecules.

hydrophilic   "Water-loving"—generally, ions and molecules that contain polar covalent bonds will dissolve in water and are said to be hydrophilic.

hydrophobic   "Water-fearing"—molecules that are not attracted to water molecules. Such molecules are composed predominantly of carbon and hydrogen and are relatively insoluble in water. Because carbon–carbon and carbon–hydrogen bonds are nonpolar, the atoms in such compounds are electrically neutral.

hydrostatic skeleton   A fluid-filled body cavity surrounded by muscles that gives support and shape to the body of organisms.

hypermutation   A process that primarily involves numerous C to T point mutations that is crucial to enabling lymphocytes to produce a diverse array of immunoglobulins capable of recognizing many different antigens.

hyperpolarization   The change in the membrane potential that occurs when the cell becomes more polarized.

hypersensitive response (HR)   A plant's local defensive response to pathogen attack.

hyperthyroidism   A hyperactive thyroid gland.

hypertonic   When the solute concentration inside the cell is higher relative to the outside of the cell.

hyphae   Microscopic, branched filaments of the body of a fungus.

hypocotyl   The portion of an embryonic plant stem located below the point of attachment of the cotyledons.

hypothalamus   A gland located below the thalamus at the floor of the forebrain; it controls functions of the gastrointestinal and reproductive systems, and it regulates many basic behaviours, such as eating and drinking.

hypothesis   In biology, a proposed explanation for a natural phenomenon based on previous observations or experimental studies.

hypothyroidism   An underactive thyroid gland.

hypotonic   When the solute concentration outside the cell is lower relative to the inside of the cell.

I

I band   A light band that lies between the A bands of two adjacent sarcomeres.

idiosyncratic hypothesis   A theory that includes the possibility that ecosystem function changes as the number of species increases or decreases, but that the direction of change is not predictable.

immune system   The cells and organs within an animal's body that contribute to immune defences.

immune tolerance   The process by which the body distinguishes between self- and nonself-components.

immunity   The ability of an animal to ward off internal threats, including the invasion of potentially harmful microorganisms, such as bacteria; the presence of foreign molecules, such as the products of microorganisms; and the presence of abnormal cells, such as cancer cells.

immunization   *See* vaccinations.

immunoglobulins   Y-shaped proteins with two heavy chains and two light chains that provide immunity to foreign substances; antibodies are a type of immunoglobulin.

immunological memory   The immune system's ability to produce a secondary immune response.

imperfect flower   A flower that lacks either stamens or carpels.

implantation   The first event of pregnancy, when the blastocyst embeds within the uterine endometrium.

imprinting   (1) The development of a species-specific pattern of behaviour. A form of learning, with a large innate component, within a limited time. (2) In genetics, the marking of DNA that occurs differently between males and females.

inactivation gate   A string of amino acids that juts out from a channel protein into the cytosol.

inborn error of metabolism   A genetic defect in the ability to metabolize certain compounds.

inbreeding   Mating among genetically related relatives.

inbreeding depression   The phenomenon whereby inbreeding produces homozygotes that are less fit, thereby decreasing the reproductive success of a population.

inclusive fitness   The term used to designate the total number of copies of genes passed on through an organism's relatives, as well as the organism's own reproductive output.

incomplete dominance   The phenomenon in which a heterozygote that carries two different alleles exhibits a phenotype that is intermediate between the corresponding homozygous individuals.

incomplete flowers   Flowers that lack one or more of the four flower organ types.

incomplete metamorphosis A gradual change in body form in some insects from different nymphal stages, called instars, into a similar-looking adult.

incurrent siphon A tunicate structure used to draw water through the mouth.

indeterminate cleavage A characteristic of deuterostome development in which each cell produced by early cleavage retains the ability to develop into a complete embryo.

indeterminate growth Growth in which plant shoot apical meristems continuously produce new stem tissues and leaves as long as conditions remain favourable.

indicator species A species whose status provides information on the overall health of an ecosystem.

indirect calorimetry A method of determining basal metabolic rate in which the rate at which an animal uses oxygen is measured.

individual selection The proposal that adaptive traits generally are selected because they benefit the survival and reproduction of the individual rather than the group.

individualistic model A view of the nature of a community that considers it to be an assemblage of species coexisting primarily because of similarities in their physiological requirements and tolerances.

induced fit Occurs when a substrate binds to an enzyme and the enzyme undergoes a conformational change that causes the substrate to bind more tightly to the enzyme.

induced mutations Mutations brought about by environmental agents that enter the cell and then alter the structure of DNA.

inducer In transcription, a small effector molecule that increases the rate of transcription.

inducible operon In this type of operon, the presence of a small effector molecule causes transcription to occur.

induction (1) In development, the process by which a cell or group of cells governs the developmental fate of neighbouring cells. (2) In molecular genetics, the process by which transcription has been turned on by the presence of a small effector molecule.

industrial nitrogen fixation The human activity of producing nitrogen fertilizers.

infertility The inability to produce viable offspring.

inflammation An innate local response to infection or injury characterized by local redness, swelling, heat, and pain.

inflorescence A cluster of flowers on a plant.

infundibular stalk The structure that is physically connected to a multilobed endocrine gland sitting directly below the hypothalamus, called the pituitary gland.

ingestion The act of taking food into the body, via a structure, such as a mouth.

ingroup A monophyletic group in a cladogram of interest.

inheritance of acquired characteristics Jean-Baptiste Lamarck's hypothesis that species change over many generations by adapting to new environments. He thought behavioural changes modified traits, and he hypothesized that such modified traits were inherited by offspring.

inhibition A mechanism for succession in which space is all important, and order of colonization determines subsequent community structure.

inhibitory postsynaptic potential (IPSP) The response from an inhibitory neurotransmitter hyperpolarizing the postsynaptic membrane, which reduces the likelihood of an action potential.

initiation stage In transcription or translation, the first step that initiates the process.

initiator tRNA A specific tRNA that recognizes the start codon AUG in mRNA and binds to it.

innate The term used to describe behaviours that seem to be genetically programmed.

innate (nonspecific) immunity The body's defences that are present at birth and act against foreign materials in much the same way regardless of the specific identity of the invading material; includes the body's external barriers and a set of cellular and chemical defences that oppose substances that breach those barriers.

inner bark The thin layer of phloem that conducts most of the sugar transport in a woody stem.

inner ear One of the three main compartments of the mammalian ear; composed of the bony cochlea and the vestibular system, which plays a role in balance.

inner segment The part of the cells found in the rods and cones of the eye that contains the cell nucleus and other cytoplasmic organelles.

inside-out signalling Occurs when the cytosol affects the structure of an integrin and thereby changes its ability to bind to components in the ECM.

instar A stage of growth in an insect with incomplete metamorphosis.

insulin A hormone made by the pancreas that binds to a cell surface receptor and stimulates a signalling pathway that acts in cells to facilitate the diffusion of glucose from blood into the cytosol of cells.

insulin-like growth factor-1 (IGF-1) A hormone that in mammals stimulates the elongation of bones, especially during puberty, when mammals become reproductively mature.

integral membrane proteins Proteins that cannot be released from the membrane unless they are dissolved with an organic solvent or detergent—in other words, one would have to disrupt the integrity of the membrane to remove it.

integrase An enzyme, sometimes encoded by viruses, that catalyzes the integration of the viral genome into a host-cell chromosome.

integrins Cell-surface receptor proteins found in animal cells that connect cells and the extracellular matrix.

integuments In plants, modified leaves that enclose the megasporangium to form an ovule.

interactome The whole set of molecular interactions in cells; the associations that foster biochemical processes.

intercostal muscles Muscles that surround and connect the ribs in the chest.

interference competition Competition in which individuals interact directly with one another by physical force or intimidation.

interferon A protein that generally inhibits viral replication inside host cells.

intermediate filaments Protein filaments within the cytoskeleton that help maintain cell shape and rigidity.

intermediate-disturbance hypothesis The proposal that moderately disturbed communities are more diverse than undisturbed or highly disturbed communities.

internal fertilization Fertilization that occurs in terrestrial animals, in which sperm are deposited within the reproductive tract of the female during the act called copulation.

interneuron A type of neuron that forms interconnections between other neurons.

internode The region of stem on a plant between adjacent nodes.

interphase The G_1, S, and G_2 phases of the cell cycle. It is the phase of the cell cycle during which the chromosomes are decondensed and found in the nucleus.

intersexual selection Sexual selection between members of the opposite sex.

interspecies hybrid The offspring resulting from two species mating.

interspecific The term used to describe competition between individuals of different species.

interstitial fluid Part of the extracellular fluid; the fluid-filled spaces that surround cells.

intertidal zone The area where the land meets the sea, which is alternately submerged and exposed by the daily cycle of tides.

intracellular fluid The fluid inside cells.

intranuclear spindle A spindle that forms within an intact nuclear envelope during nuclear division.

intrasexual selection Sexual selection between members of the same sex.

intraspecific The term used to describe competition between individuals of the same species.

intrinsic rate of increase The situation in which conditions are optimal for a population, and the per capita growth rate is at its maximum rate.

introduced species A species moved by humans from a native location to another location.

introns Noncoding portions of transcribed regions that are found in between the coding sequences of genes.

invasive The term used to describe introduced species that spread on their own, often outcompeting native species for space and resources.

inverse density-dependent factor A mortality factor whose influence decreases with increasing population size.

inversion A change in the direction of the genetic material along a single chromosome.

invertebrates Animals that lack vertebrae.

in vitro   Literally, *in glass*. An approach to studying a process in living cells that involves isolating and purifying cellular components outside the cell.

in vivo   Meaning *in life*. An approach to studying a process in living cells.

iodine-deficient glucag   Glucagon generally elevates the amount of glucose in the blood by promoting gluconeogenesis and glycogenolysis. Glucagon activity is hindered when iodine is lacking.

ion   At atom or molecule that gains or loses one or more electrons and acquires a net electric charge.

ion-dipole force   The attraction that occurs between an ion and a polar molecule of opposite charge.

ion electrochemical gradient   A dual gradient for an ion that is composed of both an electrical gradient and a chemical gradient for that ion.

ionic bond   The bond that occurs when a cation binds to an anion.

ionotropic receptor   A ligand-gated ion channel that opens in response to binding of a neurotransmitter molecule.

iris   The circle of pigmented smooth muscle that is responsible for eye colour.

iron regulatory element (IRE)   A response element within the ferritin mRNA to which the iron regulatory protein binds.

iron regulatory protein (IRP)   An RNA-binding protein that regulates the translation of the mRNA that encodes ferritin.

islets of Langerhans   Spherical clusters of endocrine cells that are scattered in great numbers throughout the endocrine pancreas.

isomers   Two structures with an identical molecular formula but different structures and characteristics.

isotherm   A line on a map connecting points of equal temperature.

isotonic   When the solute concentrations on both sides of the plasma membrane are equal.

isotopes   Elements that exist in multiple forms that differ in the number of neutrons they contain.

iteroparity   The pattern of repeated reproduction at intervals throughout the life cycle.

J

joint   The juncture where two or more bones of a vertebrate endoskeleton come together.

juvenile hormones   In larval development, they are secreted by a structure behind the brain and inhibit maturation of the larva into a pupa.

K

K/T event   An ancient cataclysm that involved at least one large meteorite or comet that crashed into Earth near the present-day Yucatan Peninsula in Mexico about 65 million years ago.

karyogamy   The process of nuclear fusion.

karyotype   A photographic representation of the chromosomes that reveals how many chromosomes are found within an actively dividing cell.

kcal   Abbreviation for kilocalorie, where 1,000 calories = 1 kcal. Represents the amount of energy required to raise the temperature of a litre of water by one degree at sea level.

keystone species   A species within a community that has a role out of proportion to its abundance.

kin selection   Selection for behaviour that lowers an individual's own fitness but enhances the reproductive success of a relative.

kinesis   A movement in response to a stimulus, but one that is not directed toward or away from the source of the stimulus.

kinetic energy   Energy associated with movement.

kinetic skull   A defining characteristic of the class Lepidosauria, in which the joints between various parts of the skull are extremely mobile.

kinetochore   A group of proteins necessary for sorting each chromosome that binds to the centromere.

kinetochore microtubules   Microtubules that emanate from a microtubule organizing centre are oriented away from the centre of the cell and are stabilized as they associate with the kinetochores.

Koch's postulates   A series of steps used to determine whether a particular organism causes a specific disease.

K-selected species   A type of life history strategy, where species have a low rate of per capita population growth but good competitive ability.

L

labia majora   In the female genitalia, large outer folds that surround the external opening of the reproductive tract.

labia minora   In the female genitalia, smaller, inner folds near the external opening of the reproductive tract.

labour   A three-stage process that includes (1) dilation and thinning of the cervix to allow passage of the fetus out of the uterus; (2) the movement of the fetus through the cervix and the vagina and out into the world; and (3) the contraction of blood vessels within the placenta and umbilical cord, blocking further blood flow, making the newborn independent from the mother; the placenta detaches from the uterine wall and is delivered a few minutes after the birth of the baby.

lac **operon**   An operon in the genome of *E. coli* that contains the genes for the enzymes that allow it to metabolize lactose.

lactation   In most mammals, a period after birth in which the young are nurtured by milk produced by the mother.

lacteal   A vessel in the centre of each intestinal villus; lipids are absorbed by the lacteals, which eventually empty into the circulatory system.

lamellae   Platelike structures in the internal gills of fish that branch from structures called filaments.

landscape ecology   The study of the influence of large-scale spatial patterns of land use or habitat type on ecological processes.

larva   A free-living organism that is morphologically very different from the embryo and adult.

larynx   The area beyond the throat where the vocal cords lie.

latent   The term used to describe when a prophage or provirus remains inactive for a long time.

lateral line   A system of sense organs found in fish and some other aquatic vertebrates, used to detect movement and vibration in the surrounding water.

lateral line system   A sensory system in fish and some toads that allows them to detect changes in their environment; hair cells detect changes in water currents brought about by waves, nearby moving objects, and low-frequency sounds travelling through the water.

law of independent assortment   The alleles of different genes assort independently during gamete formation.

law of segregation of alleles   The phenomenon that the two copies of a gene segregate from each other during gamete formation and transmission from parent to offspring.

leaching   The dissolution and removal of inorganic ions as water percolates through materials such as soil.

leading strand   A DNA strand made in the same direction that the replication fork is moving. The strand is synthesized as one long continuous molecule.

leaf   A flattened plant organ that emerges from stems and functions in photosynthesis or other ways.

leaf abscission   The process by which a leaf drops after the formation of an abscission zone at the point where a leaf petiole connects with the stem. The abscission zone consists of an inner protective layer of cork cells whose tough walls help to prevent pathogen attack and dehydration, and an outer layer of cells having thin walls that break easily.

leaf primordia   Small bumps that occur at the sides of a shoot apical meristem and develop into young leaves.

leaf veins   Vascular strands (xylem and/or phloem) that allow long-distance transport of metabolites in plants.

leaflet   (1) Half of a phospholipid bilayer. (2) A portion of a compound leaf.

learning   The ability of an animal to make modifications to a behaviour based on previous experience.

leaves   Plural of leaf. Leaves are specialized organs in vascular plants that are used for photosynthesis.

leghemoglobin   Legume hemoglobin, a pink protein typically produced by legume nodules that helps regulate local oxygen concentrations.

legumes   Members of the pea (bean) family. Also their distinctive fruits, dry pods that develop from one carpel and open down both sides when seeds are mature.

lens   (1) A structure of the eye that focuses light. (2) The glass components of a light microscope or electromagnetic parts of an electron microscope that allow the production of magnified images of microscopic structures.

lentic   Referring to a freshwater habitat characterized by standing water.

leptin   A molecule produced by adipose cells in proportion to fat mass; controls appetite and metabolic rate.

leukocytes   White blood cells; involved in non-specific immunity.

Liebig's law of the minimum   Species biomass or abundance is limited by the scarcest factor.

life cycle   The sequence of events that characterize the steps of development of the individuals of a given species.

life table   A table that provides data on the number of individuals alive in particular age classes.

ligand   An ion or a molecule that binds to a protein, such as an enzyme or a receptor.

ligand-gated channels   Channels controlled by the noncovalent binding of small molecules—called ligands—such as hormones or neurotransmitters.

ligand-gated ion channels   Cell surface receptors that bind a ligand and then can function as an ion channel. Ligand binding either opens or closes a channel.

light chains   Parts of an immunoglobulin molecule.

light-harvesting complex   A component of photosystem II and photosystem I composed of several dozen pigment molecules that are anchored to proteins. The role of these complexes is to absorb photons of light.

light reactions   One of two stages in the process of photosynthesis. During the light reactions, photosystem II and photosystem I absorb light energy and produce O_2, ATP, and NADPH.

lignin   A tough polymer that adds strength and decay resistance to cell walls of tracheids, vessel elements, and other cells of plants.

lignophytes   Modern and fossil seed plants, and seedless ancestors that produced wood.

limbic system   The system primarily involved in the formation and expression of emotions; also plays a role in learning, memory, and the perception of smells; includes certain areas of the telencephalon and parts of the diencephalon.

limiting factor   The factor that is most scarce in relation to need.

limnetic   Pertaining to or living in the open water of a freshwater pond or lake. The limnetic zone is the well-lit, open surface water in a lake, away from shore.

lineage   The genetic relationship between an individual or a group of individuals and its ancestors; a series of ancestors in a population that shows a progression of changes.

linkage   The phenomenon of two genes that are close together on the same chromosome tending to be transmitted as a unit.

lipase   The major digestive fat-digesting enzyme from the pancreas.

lipid anchors   Lipid molecules that are attached covalently to proteins, post-translationally. The lipid attachments allow the proteins to be stably embedded in one leaflet of the bilayer.

lipid exchange protein   A protein that extracts a lipid from one membrane, diffuses through the cell, and inserts the lipid into another membrane.

lipid raft   A region of one leaflet of a biological membrane that has a distinctive lipid composition that typically has straight chain fatty acyl tails that allow the lipids to pack more tightly and hence be more stably associated.

lipids   A category of organic molecules composed predominantly of hydrogen and carbon atoms. Lipids are nonpolar and therefore very insoluble in water. They include fats, phospholipids, and steroids.

lipolysis   Breakdown of lipids.

lipopolysaccharides   Lipids having covalently bound carbohydrates. Major components of the thin, outer envelope that encloses the cell walls of Gram-negative bacteria.

liposomes   Vesicles surrounded by a lipid bilayer.

littoral   Pertaining to the shore of a lake, sea, or ocean.

liver   An organ in vertebrates that performs diverse metabolic functions and is the site of bile production.

liverworts   A phylum of bryophytes; formally called Hepatophyta.

lobe-finned fish   Fish in which the fins are part of the body, and they are supported by skeletal extensions of the pectoral and pelvic areas that are moved by muscles residing in the fins.

lobe fins   The Actinistia (coelacanths) and Dipnoi (lungfish) and tetrapods; also called Sarcopterygii.

locomotion   The movement of an animal from place to place.

locus   The physical location of a gene on a chromosome.

logistic equation $dN / dt = rN (K - N)/K$, where dN/dt is the rate of population change, r is the per capita rate of population growth, N is the population size, and $(K - N)/K$ represents the proportion of unused resources remaining.

logistic growth   The S-shaped pattern in which the growth of a population typically slows down as it approaches carrying capacity.

long-day plants   Plants that flower in spring or early summer, when the nights are shorter (and thus the days are longer) than a defined period.

loop domains   Chromosomal segments that are compacted by interacting with specific protein molecules.

loop of Henle   A sharp, hairpinlike loop in the tubule of the nephron of the kidney consisting of a descending limb coming from the proximal tubule and an ascending limb leading to the distal convoluted tubule.

lophophore   A horseshoe-shaped crown of tentacles used for feeding.

Lophotrochozoa   A clade that encompasses the annelids, molluscs, and several other phyla; they are distinguished by two morphological features—the lophophore, a crown of tentacles used for feeding, and the trochophore larva, a distinct larval stage.

lotic   Referring to a freshwater habitat characterized by running water.

lumen   The internal space of an organelle.

lungfish   The Dipnoi; fish that have primitive lungs and that live in oxygen-poor freshwater swamps and ponds.

lungs   Structures used to bring oxygen into the circulatory system and remove carbon dioxide.

luteinizing hormone (LH)   A gonadotropin.

lycophylls   Relatively small leaves having a single unbranched vein; the type of leaves produced by lycophytes.

lycophytes   Members of a phylum of vascular land plants whose leaves are lycophylls; Lycopodiophyta.

lymphatic system   A system of vessels along with a group of organs and tissues where most leukocytes reside. The lymphatic vessels collect excess interstitial fluid and return it to the blood.

lymphocytes   A type of leukocyte that is responsible for specific immunity; the two types are B cells and T cells.

Lyon hypothesis   *See* X inactivation.

lysogenic cycle   The growth cycle of a bacteriophage consisting of integration, prophage replication, and excision.

lysosomes   Small organelles found in animal cells that contain acid hydrolases that degrade macromolecules.

lytic cycle   The growth cycle of a bacteriophage in which the production and release of new viruses lyses the host cell.

M

M line   A narrow, dark band in the centre of the H zone that corresponds to proteins that link together the central regions of adjacent thick filaments.

M phase   The sequential events of mitosis and cytokinesis.

macroevolution   Evolutionary changes that create new species and groups of species.

macromolecule   Many molecules bonded together to form a polymer. Carbohydrates, proteins, and nucleic acids (e.g., DNA and RNA) are important macromolecules found in living organisms.

macronutrients Elements required by plants in amounts of at least 1 g/kg of plant dry matter.

macroparasites Parasites that live in the host but release infective juvenile stages outside the host's body.

macrophages Phagocytes capable of engulfing viruses and bacteria; strategically located where they will encounter invaders.

macular degeneration A condition in which photoreceptor cells in and around the fovea of the retina are lost; associated with loss of sharpness and colour vision.

madreporite A sievelike plate on the surface of an echinoderm where water enters the water vascular system.

magnification The ratio between the size of an image produced by a microscope and its actual size.

major groove A groove that spirals around the DNA double helix. The major groove provides a location in which a protein can bind to a particular sequence of bases and affect the expression of a gene.

major histocompatibility complex (MHC) A gene family that encodes the plasma membrane self-proteins that must be complexed with the antigen in order for T-cell recognition to occur.

malabsorption Any interference with the secretion of bile or the action of bile salts in the intestine that decreases the absorption of fats, including fat-soluble vitamins.

male assistance hypothesis A hypothesis to explain the existence of monogamy that maintains that males remain with females to help them rear their offspring.

male gametophyte A haploid plant life cycle phase that produces sperm.

malignant A growth of cells that has progressed to the cancerous stage.

Malpighian tubules Delicate projections that protrude into the hemolymph from the digestive tract of insects and some other taxa and function as an excretory organ.

mammals Vertebrates that are members of the class Mammalia that nourish their young with milk secreted by mammary glands. Another distinguishing feature is hair.

mammary gland A gland in female members of mammal species that secretes milk.

manganese cluster A site where the oxidation of water occurs in photosystem II.

mantle A fold of skin that drapes over the visceral mass of a mollusc and secretes a shell in those species that form shells.

mantle cavity The chamber in a mollusc mantle that houses delicate gills.

many-eyes hypothesis The idea that increased group size decreases predators' success because of increased predator detection ability.

map distance The distance between genes along chromosomes, which is calculated as the number of recombinant offspring divided by the total number of offspring times 100.

mapping The process of determining the relative locations of genes or other DNA segments along a chromosome. Also called genetic linkage mapping.

map units (mu) These units are a measure of the amount of genetic exchange. One map unit is the genetic distance that generates 1% recombinant types.

mark-recapture technique The capture and tagging of animals so they can be released and recaptured, allowing an estimate of population size.

marsupials Members of a group of seven mammalian orders and about 280 species found in the subclass Metatheria.

mass extinctions When many species become extinct at the same time.

mass-specific BMR The amount of energy expended per gram of body mass.

mastax The circular muscular pharynx in the mouth of rotifers.

mast cells Cells derived from bone marrow stem cells that play an important role in nonspecific immunity; these cells are found throughout connective tissues and secrete many locally acting molecules, notably histamine.

mate-guarding hypothesis A hypothesis to explain the existence of monogamy that theorizes that males stay with a female to prevent her from being fertilized by other males.

maternal effect An inheritance pattern in which the genotype of the mother determines the phenotype of her offspring.

maternal effect genes Genes that are usually inherited only from mothers and hence follow a maternal effect inheritance pattern.

maternal inheritance A phenomenon in which offspring inherit particular genes only from the female parent (through the egg).

maturation promoting factor (MPF) The factor that causes oocytes to progress (or mature) from G_2 to M phase.

mature mRNA In eukaryotes, transcription produces a longer RNA, pre-mRNA, which undergoes certain processing events before it exits the nucleus; mature mRNA is the final functional product.

mean fitness of the population The average zreproductive success of members of a population.

mechanoreceptors Sensory receptors that transduce mechanical energy such as pressure, touch, stretch, movement, and sound.

mechanosensitive channels Channels that are sensitive to changes in membrane tension.

mediator A large protein complex that plays a role in initiating transcription at the core promoter of structural genes in eukaryotes.

medulla oblongata The part of the hindbrain that coordinates many basic reflexes and bodily functions, such as breathing, that maintain the normal homeostatic processes of the animal.

medusa A cnidarian body form that is motile; jellyfish exist predominantly in the medusa form.

megadiversity countries Those countries with the greatest numbers of species; used in targeting areas for conservation.

megaspores In seed plants and some seedless plants, the large spores that produce a female gametophyte within the spore wall.

meiosis The process by which haploid cells are produced from a cell that was originally diploid.

meiosis I The first division of meiosis when the homologues are separated into different cells.

meiosis II The second division of meiosis in which sister chromatids are separated to different cells.

Meissner's corpuscles Structures that sense touch and light pressure and that lie just beneath the skin surface.

membrane attack complex (MAC) A multiunit protein formed by the activation of complement proteins; the complex creates water channels in the microbial plasma membrane and causes the microbe to swell and burst.

membrane potential The difference between the electric charges inside and outside the cell; also called a potential difference (or voltage).

membrane transport The movement of ions or molecules across a cell membrane.

memory The retention of information over time.

memory cells A component of the immune response; these cells remain poised to recognize the antigen if it returns in the future.

Mendelian inheritance The inheritance patterns of genes that segregate and assort independently.

meninges A protective structure in the central nervous system consisting of three layers of sheathlike membranes.

meningitis A potentially life-threatening infectious disease in which the meninges become inflamed.

menopause The event during which a woman permanently stops having ovarian cycles.

menstrual cycle Also called the uterine cycle; the cyclical changes in the lining of the uterus that occur in parallel with the ovarian cycle.

menstruation A period of bleeding at the beginning of the menstrual cycle.

mer A synonym for repeat unit in chemistry. Used as a suffix, it indicates the number of subunits found in a molecule; for example, monomer (one subunit), polymer (several subunits).

meristems In plants, organized tissues that include actively dividing cells and a reservoir of stem cells.

meroblastic cleavage An incomplete type of cell cleavage, in which only the region of the egg containing cytoplasm at the animal pole undergoes cell division.

merozygote A strain of bacteria containing an F' factor.

mesoderm A layer of cells formed during gastrulation that develops between the ectoderm and endoderm; gives rise to skeleton, muscles, and much of the circulatory system.

mesoglea A gelatinous substance that connects the two germ layers in the Radiata.

mesohyl A gelatinous, protein-rich matrix in between the choanocytes and the epithelial cells of a sponge.

mesophyll The internal tissue of a plant leaf whose cells carry out photosynthesis.

messenger RNA (mRNA) RNA that contains the information to specify a polypeptide with a particular amino acid sequence; its job is to carry information from the DNA to the ribosome.

metabolic cycle A biochemical cycle in which particular molecules enter while others leave; the process is cyclical because it involves a series of organic molecules that are regenerated with each turn of the cycle.

metabolic pathways In living cells, a series of chemical reactions; each step being catalyzed by a specific enzyme.

metabolic rate The total energy expenditure of an organism per unit of time.

metabolism The sum total of all chemical reactions that occur within an organism. Also, a specific set of chemical reactions occurring at the cellular level.

metabotropic receptors G-protein-coupled receptors that are coupled to an intracellular signalling pathway that initiate changes in a postsynaptic cell.

metacentric Describes a chromosome in which the centromere is near the middle.

metagenomics A field of study that seeks to identify and analyze the collective microbial genomes contained in a community of organisms, including, for microbial genomes, those that are not easily cultured in the laboratory.

metamorphosis The process in which a pupal or juvenile organism changes into a mature adult with very different characteristics.

metanephridia Excretory organs found in a variety of invertebrates; a type of tubular nephridium.

metanephridial system The filtration system used by annelids to cleanse the blood.

metaphase The phase of mitosis during which the chromosomes are aligned along the metaphase plate.

metaphase plate A plane halfway between the poles on which the sister chromatids align during metaphase.

metastasis When cancerous tumours invade healthy tissues and spread through the bloodstream or surrounding body fluids.

Metazoa The collective term for animals.

methanogens Several groups of anaerobic archaea that convert CO_2, methyl groups, or acetate to methane and release it from their cells.

methanotrophs Aerobic bacteria that consume methane.

methyl-CpG-binding proteins Proteins that bind methylated DNA sequences.

micelles Hollow spheres formed by long amphipathic molecules when mixed with water. In animals, micelles aid in absorption during digestion of poorly soluble products; they consist of bile salts, phospholipids, fatty acids, and monoglycerides clustered together.

microclimate Local variations of the climate within a given area.

microevolution The term used to describe changes in a population's gene pool from generation to generation.

micronutrients Elements required by plants in amounts at or less than 0.1 g/kg of plant dry mass.

microparasites Parasites that multiply within their host, usually within the cells.

micropyle A small opening in the integument of a seed plant ovule through which pollen tubes grow.

microRNAs (miRNAs) Small RNA molecules, typically 22 nucleotides long, that silence the expression of specific mRNAs, either by inhibiting translation or by promoting the degradation of mRNAs.

microscope A magnification tool that enables researchers to study the structure and function of cells.

microspheres A small water-filled vesicle surrounded by a macromolecular boundary.

microspores In seed plants and some seedless plants, the small spores that produce male gametophytes within spore walls.

microtubule-organizing centre (MTOC) These are regions of eukaryotic cells form that emanate microtubules; in animal cells the MTOCs are associated with centrioles.

microtubules Cytoskeleton fibres that consist of hollow protein filaments composed of tubulin proteins that are important for cell organization, shape, and movement.

microvilli Small projections in the surface membranes of epithelial cells in the small intestine.

midbrain One of three major divisions of the vertebrate brain; the other two divisions are the hindbrain and forebrain.

middle ear One of the three main compartments of the mammalian ear; contains three small bones called ossicles that connect the eardrum with the oval window.

middle lamella A layer composed primarily of carbohydrate that cements adjacent plant cell walls together.

migration Long-range seasonal movement among animals to feed or breed.

mimicry The resemblance of an organism (the mimic) to another organism (the model).

mineralization The general process by which phosphorus, nitrogen, CO_2, and other minerals are released from organic compounds.

mineralocorticoid A steroid hormone, such as aldosterone, that regulates the balance of certain minerals in the body.

minerals Inorganic ions required by a living organism. Minerals are used to build skeletons, maintain the balance of salts and water in the body, provide a source of electric current across plasma membranes, and provide a mechanism for exocytosis and muscle contraction, among other functions.

minor groove A smaller groove that spirals around the DNA double helix.

missense mutation A base substitution that changes a single amino acid in a polypeptide sequence.

mitochondrial genome The chromosome found in mitochondria.

mitochondrion Literally, *thread granule*. An organelle found in eukaryotic cells that supplies most of the cell's ATP.

mitogen-activated protein kinases (MAP kinases) A group of protein kinases that are key transducers of signals by ligands that cause the cell to initiate division.

mitosis In eukaryotes, the process in which nuclear division results in two nuclei; each daughter cell receives the same complement of chromosomes.

mitotic cell division A process whereby a eukaryotic cell divides to produce two new cells that are genetically identical to the original cell.

mitotic spindle *See* mitotic spindle apparatus.

mitotic spindle apparatus The structure responsible for organizing and sorting the chromosomes during mitosis.

mixotrophs Organisms that are able to use autotrophy as well as phagotrophy or osmotrophy to obtain organic nutrients.

model organisms Species selected to represent a related group of organisms. They are usually selected based on an aspect of their life history or lifecycle that makes them useful in studying a particular biological phenomenon. Information gained from studies of model organisms is used to guide research on other related, and often more important, species.

moderately repetitive sequences DNA sequences found a few hundred to several thousand times in a genome.

modern synthesis of evolution Within a population of interbreeding organisms, natural variation exists that is caused by random changes in the genetic material. Such genetic changes can affect the phenotype of an individual in a positive, negative, or neutral way. If a genetic change promotes an individual's reproductive success, natural selection can increase the prevalence of that trait in future generations.

molarity The number of moles of a solute dissolved in 1 litre of water.

mole The amount of any substance that contains the same number of particles as there are atoms in exactly 12 grams of carbon: 12 grams of carbon equals 1 mole, while 1 gram of hydrogen equals 1 mole.

molecular clock A clock on which to measure evolutionary time.

molecular formula A representation of a molecule that consists of the chemical symbols for all the atoms present and subscripts that show how many of those atoms are present.

molecular homologies Similarities that indicate that living species evolved from a common ancestor or interrelated group of common ancestors.

molecular machines   Machines whose sizes are measured in nanometres and have moving parts and do useful work.

molecular pharming   An avenue of research that involves the production of medically important proteins in agricultural crops or animals.

molecular phenotypes   Phenotypes that are detected not by observing a trait in an organism but by using a few cells from the organism to detect a DNA difference through molecular techniques, such as a band on a gel or a dot signifying DNA hybridization.

molecular recognition   The process whereby surfaces on various protein subunits recognize each other in a very specific way, causing them to bind to each other and promote the assembly process.

molecular systematics   A field of study that involves the analysis of genetic data, such as DNA sequences, to identify and study genetic homology and construct phylogenetic trees.

molecules   Two or more atoms connected by chemical bonds.

monocots   One of the two largest lineages of flowering plants; the embryo produces a single seed leaf.

monocular vision   A type of vision in animals with eyes on the sides of the head; the animal sees a wide area at one time, though depth perception is reduced.

monocytes   Phagocytes that circulate in the blood for only a few days, after which they take up permanent residence as macrophages in different organs.

monoecious   The term to describe plants that produce carpellate and staminate flowers on the same plant.

monogamy   A mating system in which one male mates with one female, and most individuals have mates.

monohybrids   The F_1 offspring, also called single-trait hybrids, of true-breeding parents that differ with regard to a single trait.

monomers   In the context of macromolecules, monomers are the simple, often repeated, molecules used to make larger molecules that consist of a series of the monomer units connected by the same type of covalent bond.

monomorphic gene   A gene that exists predominantly as a single allele in a population.

monophagous   The term used to define parasites that feed on one species or two or three closely related hosts.

monophyletic group   A group of species, a taxon, consisting of the most recent common ancestor and all of its descendants.

monosaccharides   Simple sugars.

monosomic   An aneuploid organism that has one too few chromosomes.

monotremes   Comprises three species in the mammalian order Monotremata, which are found in Australia and New Guinea: the duck-billed platypus and two species of echidna.

morphogenetic field   A group of embryonic cells that ultimately produce a specific body structure.

morphogens   Molecules that impart positional information and promote developmental changes at the cellular level.

morphological species concept   A way of classifying species based on structural or anatomical traits.

morula   The mammal embryo in species having undergone holoblastic cleavage.

mosaics   Individuals in which some cells throughout the body show genetic differences. For example, in female mammals, about half of the somatic cells will express one X-linked allele, while the rest of the somatic cells will express the other allele.

mosses   A phylum of bryophytes; Bryophyta.

motor end plate   The region of the muscle fibre plasma membrane that lies directly under the axon terminal.

motor neurons   A neuron that sends signals away from the central nervous system and elicits some type of response. Also called an efferent neuron.

motor proteins   Cellular proteins that use ATP as a source of energy to promote movement; they consist of three domains called the head, hinge, and tail.

movement corridors   Thin strips of habitat that may permit the movement of individuals between larger habitat patches.

mucigel   A gooey plant substance that lubricates roots, aiding in their passage through the soil; helps in water and mineral absorption, prevents root drying, and provides an environment hospitable to beneficial microbes.

mucilage   A mixture of polysaccharides and polypeptides secreted from plants and some microorganisms.

Müllerian mimicry   A type of mimicry in which many noxious species converge to look the same, thus reinforcing the basic distasteful design.

multimeric proteins   Proteins that are composed of more than one polypeptide chain; also said to have a quarternary structure.

multiple alleles   The occurrence of a gene that exists as three or more alleles in a population.

multiple sclerosis (MS)   A disease in which a person's own body, for reasons that are unknown, attacks and destroys myelin as if it were a foreign substance. Eventually, these repeated attacks leave scarred (sclerotic) areas of tissue in the nervous system and impair the function of myelinated neurons that control movement, speech, memory, and emotion.

multipotent   A term used to describe a stem cell that can differentiate into several cell types but far fewer than pluripotent cells can.

muscle   A grouping of muscle tissue bound together by a succession of connective tissue layers.

muscle fibres   A grouping of muscles bound together into fascicles by a succession of connective tissue layers.

muscle tissues   Clusters of cells that are specialized to contract, generating the mechanical forces that produce body movement, exert pressure on a fluid-filled cavity, or decrease the diameter of a tube.

mutagens   Agents known to cause mutation.

mutant alleles   Rare alleles that have been created by mutation.

mutation   A heritable change in the genetic material.

mutualism   An interaction in which both species benefit.

mycelia   Fungal bodies composed of microscopic branched filaments known as hyphae.

mycorrhizae   Associations between the hyphae of certain fungi and the roots of most plants.

myelin sheath   In the nervous system, an insulating layer made up of specialized glial cells wrapped around the axons.

myocardial infarction (MI)   The death of cardiac muscle cells, which can occur if a region of the heart is deprived of blood for an extended time. Also called a heart attack.

myofibrils   Cylindrical bundles within muscle fibres, each of which contains thick and thin filaments.

myogenic bHLH genes   A small group of genes that initiate muscle development in animals.

myogenic heart   A heart in which the signalling mechanism that initiates contraction resides within the cardiac muscle itself.

myoglobin   An oxygen-binding protein that increases the availability of oxygen in the muscle fibre by providing an intracellular reservoir of oxygen.

myosin   A motor protein in muscle.

N

nacre   The smooth, iridescent lining of the shells of oysters, mussels, abalone, and other molluscs.

NAD + (nicotinamide adenine dinucleotide)   A dinucleotide that functions as an energy intermediate molecule. It combines with two electrons and H^+ to form NADH.

NADPH (nicotinamide adenine dinucleotide phosphate)   An electron carrier whose structure differs from NADH by the presence of an additional phosphate group.

nanometre fibre   An intermediate stage of chromosome condensation, created as eukaryotic DNA is wrapped around two molecules each of histones H2a, H2b, H3, and H4 to form a structure known as the nucleosome.

natural killer (NK) cells   A type of leukocyte that is part of the body's nonspecific defences because it recognizes general features on the surface of cancer cells or any virus-infected cells.

natural selection   The process that culls those individuals that are less likely to survive and reproduce in a particular environment while allowing other individuals with traits that confer greater reproductive success to increase in numbers.

nauplius The first larval stage in a crustacean.

navigation A mechanism of migration that involves the ability not only to follow a compass bearing but also to set or adjust it.

nectar A sugar-rich substance produced by many flowers that serves as a food reward for pollinators; in some plants, nectar is produced by other plant parts as a reward for insects that protect the plant.

negative control Transcriptional regulation by repressor proteins.

negative feedback loop A system in which a change in the variable being regulated brings about responses that move the variable in the opposite direction.

negative frequency-dependent selection A pattern of natural selection in which the fitness of a genotype decreases when its frequency becomes higher; the result is a balanced polymorphism.

negative pressure filling The mechanism by which reptiles, birds, and mammals ventilate their lungs.

nekton Free-swimming animals in the open ocean that can swim against the currents to locate food.

nematocysts Powerful capsules with an inverted coiled and barbed thread in the stinging cells of cnidarians.

nephrons Several million single-cell-thick tubules that are the functional units of the kidney.

Nernst equation The formula that gives the equilibrium potential for an ion at any given concentration gradient.

nerve cords In more complex invertebrates, structures that extend from the anterior end of the animal to the tail.

nerve impulses A way that neurons communicate, involving changes in the amount of electric charge across a cell's plasma membrane.

nerve net Interconnected neurons with no central control organ.

nerves Structures found in the peripheral nervous system that are composed of multiple neurons and make contact with structures outside the central nervous system and transmit signals that enter or leave the CNS.

nervous system Groups of cells that sense internal and environmental changes and transmit signals that enable an animal to respond in an appropriate way.

nervous tissues Clusters of cells that initiate and conduct electrical signals from one part of an animal's body to another part.

net primary production (NPP) Gross primary production minus the energy lost in plant cellular respiration.

net reproductive rate The population growth rate per generation.

neural crest A cell lineage that gives rise to all neurons and supporting cells of the peripheral nervous system in vertebrates; in addition, it gives rise to melanocytes and to cells that form facial cartilage and parts of the adrenal gland.

neural tube In chordates, a structure formed from ectoderm located dorsal to the notochord; all neurons and their supporting cells in the central nervous system originate from neural precursor cells derived from the neural tube.

neurogenesis The production of new neurons by cell division.

neurohormones Hypothalamic-releasing hormones made in and secreted by neurons whose cell bodies are in the hypothalamus.

neuromodulators Short chains of amino acids that can alter or modulate the response of the postsynaptic neuron to other neurotransmitters.

neuromuscular junction The junction between a motor neuron's axon and a muscle fibre.

neurons Another name for nerve cells. Highly specialized cells that communicate with other cells of their kind and with other types of cells by electrical or chemical signals.

neuroscience The scientific study of nervous systems.

neurotransmitter A small signalling molecule that is synthesized and stored in nerve cells.

neurulation The embryological process responsible for initiating central nervous system formation.

neutralism The phenomenon in which two species occur together but in fact do not interact in any measurable way.

neutral mutations Mutations that do not affect the function of the encoded protein.

neutral theory of evolution States that most genetic variation is due to the accumulation of neutral mutations that have attained high frequencies in a population via genetic drift.

neutral variation Variation that does not favour any particular genotype.

neutrons Electrically neutral particles found in the centre of atoms.

neutrophils Phagocytic cells and the most abundant type of leukocyte; neutrophils engulf bacteria by endocytosis.

niche The physical distribution and ecological role of an organism.

nitrification The conversion by soil bacteria of NH_3 or NH_4^+ to nitrate ($NO_3^{'''}$), a form of nitrogen commonly used by plants.

nitrogenase An enzyme used in the biological process of fixing nitrogen.

nitrogen fixation A specialized metabolic process in which certain prokaryotes use the enzyme nitrogenase to convert inert atmospheric nitrogen gas into ammonia; also, the industrial process by which humans produce ammonia fertilizer from nitrogen gas.

nitrogen-limitation hypothesis The proposal that organisms select food based on its nitrogen content.

nitrogenous base A single- or double-ring molecule with carbon and nitrogen atoms.

nitrogenous wastes Molecules that include nitrogen from amino groups; these wastes are toxic at high concentrations and must be eliminated from the body.

nociceptors Sensory receptors that respond to extreme heat, cold, and pressure, as well as to certain molecules such as acids; also known as pain receptors.

nocturnal enuresis Bed wetting.

node The region of a plant stem from which one or more leaves, branches, or buds emerge.

nodes of Ranvier Exposed areas in the axons of myelinated neurons that contain many voltage-gated Na^1 channels.

Nod factors Nodulation factors; compounds produced by nitrogen-fixing bacteria in response to flavonoids secreted from the roots of potential host plants; the Nod factors bind to receptors in plant root membranes, starting a process that allows the bacteria to invade roots.

nodules Small swellings on a plant root that contain nitrogen-fixing bacteria.

Nodulins Plant proteins that foster root nodule development.

noncompetitive inhibitors Molecules that bind to an enzyme at a location that is outside the active site and inhibit the enzyme's function.

noncyclic electron flow The combined action of photosystem II and photosystem I in which electrons flow in a linear manner to produce NADPH.

non-Darwinian evolution Also "survival of the luckiest" to contrast it with Darwin's "survival of the fittest" theory; the idea that much of the modern variation in gene sequences is explained by neutral variation rather than adaptive variation.

nondisjunction An event in which the chromosomes do not sort properly during cell division.

nonparental types *See* recombinants.

nonpolar molecule A molecule composed predominantly of nonpolar bonds.

nonrandom mating The phenomenon that individuals choose their mates based on their genotypes or phenotypes.

nonrecombinants Offspring whose allele combinations have not changed from the parental generation.

nonsense codons *See* stop codons.

nonsense mutation A mutation that changes a normal codon into a stop codon; this causes translation to be terminated earlier than expected, producing a truncated polypeptide.

nonshivering thermogenesis An increase in the metabolic rate and therefore heat production that is not due to increased muscle activity and is caused by chronic cold exposure.

nonvascular plants Plants that do not produce lignified vascular tissue, such as a modern bryophyte or extinct pretracheophyte polysporangiophytes.

norepinephrine   A neurotransmitter; also known as noradrenaline.

norm of reaction   A description of how a trait can change depending on the environmental conditions.

notochord   A single flexible rod that lies between the digestive tract and the nerve cord in a chordate.

N-terminus   The location of the first amino acid in a polypeptide.

nuclear envelope   A double-membrane structure that encloses the cell's nucleus.

nuclear genome   The chromosomes found in the nucleus of the cell.

nuclear lamina   A collection of filamentous proteins that line the inner nuclear membrane.

nuclear matrix   A filamentous network of proteins that is found inside the nucleus and lines the inner nuclear membrane. The nuclear matrix serves to organize the chromosomes.

nuclear pores   Protein-passageways for the movement of molecules and macromolecules into and out of the nucleus; formed where the inner and outer nuclear membranes make contact with each other.

nucleic acids   Organic molecules composed of nucleotides. The two types of nucleic acids are deoxyribonucleic acid (DNA) and ribonucleic acid (RNA).

nucleoid   A region of a bacterial cell in which the genetic material (DNA) is located.

nucleoli   Prominent organelles found within the nucleus of nondividing cell where ribosome assembly occurs.

nucleoplasm   The aqueous interior of the nucleus.

nucleosome   A structural unit of eukaryotic chromosomes composed of an octamer of histones (eight histone proteins) wrapped with DNA.

nucleosome-free region (NFR)   Regions of a chromosome that are devoid of packaging of DNA by histone octamers.

nucleotide   An organic molecule having three components: a phosphate group, a five-carbon sugar (either ribose or deoxyribose), and a single or double ring of carbon and nitrogen atoms known as a base.

nucleotide excision repair (NER)   A common type of DNA repair system that removes (excises) a region of the DNA where the damage occurs. This system can fix many different types of DNA damage, including UV-induced damage, chemically modified bases, missing bases, and various types of cross-links.

nuclei   (1) In cell biology, organelles found in eukaryotic cells that contain most of the cell's genetic material. The primary function involves the protection, organization, and expression of the genetic material. (2) In chemistry, the regions of atoms that contain protons and neutrons. (3) In neurobiology, a group of neuronal cell bodies in the brain that are devoted to a particular function.

nutrient   Any substance that is needed for survival, growth, development, repair, or reproduction and is taken up by a living organism.

O

obligate aerobes   Microorganisms that require oxygen.

obligate anaerobes   Microorganisms that are poisoned by oxygen.

obligatory mutualism   An interaction in which neither species can live without the other.

ocelli   Photosensitive organs.

Okazaki fragments   Short segments of DNA synthesized in the lagging strand during DNA replication.

olfaction   The sense of smell.

olfactory bulbs   The part of the limbic system of the brain that process information about smells.

oligodendrocytes   In vertebrates, specialized glial cells that wrap around the axons to form an insulating layer.

oligotrophic   The term used to describe a young lake that starts off clear and with little plant life.

ommatidia   Independent visual units in the eye of insects that function as separate photoreceptors capable of forming independent images.

omnivores   Animals that have the ability to eat and survive on both plant and animal products.

oncogenes   Mutant genes derived from a protooncogene; an oncogene is overactive, thus contributing to uncontrolled cell growth and promoting cancer.

one gene–one polypeptide theory   The concept that one structural gene codes for one polypeptide.

oogenesis   Gametogenesis, which results in the production of egg cells.

oogonia   In animals, diploid germ cells that give rise to the female gametes, the eggs.

open circulatory system   A circulatory system in which hemolymph, which is no different from the interstitial fluid, flows throughout the body and is not confined to special vessels.

open complex   Also called the transcription bubble; a small bubblelike structure between two DNA strands that occurs during transcription.

open conformation   Loosely packed chromatin that can be transcribed into RNA.

open ocean   Stretch of water that is neither close to the bottom of the ocean nor close to the shore.

operant conditioning   A form of behaviour modification; a type of associative learning in which an animal's behaviour is reinforced by a consequence, either a reward or a punishment.

operator   A DNA sequence in bacteria that is recognized by activator or repressor proteins that regulate the level of gene transcription.

operculum   A protective flap that covers the gills of a bony fish.

operon   An arrangement of two or more genes in bacteria that are under the transcriptional control of a single promoter.

opportunistic   A term used to describe animals that have a strong preference for one type of food but can adjust their diet if the need arises.

opposable thumb   A thumb that can be placed opposite the fingers of the same hand, which gives animals a precision grip that enables the manipulation of small objects.

opsin   A protein that is a component of visual pigments.

optic nerve   A structure of the eye that carries the electrical signals to the brain.

optimal foraging theory   The concept that in a given circumstance, an animal seeks to obtain the most energy possible with the least expenditure of energy.

optimality theory   The theory that predicts that an animal should behave in a way that maximizes the benefits of a behaviour minus its costs.

oral   Refers to the region of an animal where the mouth is located; refers to the top side of a radial animal.

orbitals   The regions surrounding the nucleus of an atom where the probablility is high of finding a particular electron.

orders   In taxonomy, subdivisions of a class.

organ   Two or more types of tissue combined to perform a common function. For example, the heart is composed of several types of tissues, including muscle, nervous, and connective tissue.

organelle   A subcellular structure or membrane-bounded compartment with its own unique structure and function.

organic farming   The production of crops without the use of commercial inorganic fertilizers, growth substances, and pesticides.

organic molecules   Carbon-containing molecules, so named originally because they are found in living organisms.

organismal ecology   The investigation of how adaptations and choices by individuals affect their reproduction and survival.

organismic model   A view of the nature of a community that considers it to be equivalent to a superorganism; individuals, populations, and communities have a relationship to one another that resembles the associations found among cells, tissues, and organs.

organizing centre   A group of cells that ensures the proper organization of the meristem and preserves the correct number of actively dividing stem cells.

organogenesis   The developmental stage during which cells and tissues form organs.

organ system   Different organs that work together to perform an overall function in an organism.

orientation   A mechanism of migration in which animals have the ability to follow a compass bearing and travel in a straight line.

origin of replication   A site within a chromosome that serves as a starting point for DNA replication.

Orthologs   Homologous genes in different species.

osculum   A large opening at the top of a sponge.

osmoconformers   Animals whose osmolarity conforms to that of their environment.

osmolarity   The solute concentration of a solution of water, expressed as milliOsmoles/litre (mOsm/L).

osmoregulators   Animals that maintain constant stable internal salt concentrations and osmolarities, even when living in water with very different osmolarities from their body fluids.

osmosis   The movement of water across membranes to balance solute concentrations. Water diffuses from a solution that is hypotonic (lower solute concentration) into a solution that is hypertonic (higher solute concentration).

osmotic adjustment   The process by which a plant increases the solute concentration of its cytosol.

osmotic pressure   The hydrostatic pressure required to stop the net flow of water across a membrane due to osmosis.

osmotrophs   Organisms that rely on osmotrophy (uptake of small organic molecules via osmosis) as a form of nutrition.

osteoblasts   Cells that form bone.

osteoclasts   Cells that break down bone.

osteoporosis   A condition in which bone mineral density is reduced, bone architecture deteriorates, and the bones are at increased risk of fracture.

ostia   Small openings in the heart of an arthropod, through which hemolymph re-enters the heart.

ostracoderms   An umbrella term for several classes of primitive, heavily armoured fish, now extinct, that lacked a jaw.

otoliths   Granules of calcium carbonate found in the gelatinous substance that embeds hair cells in the ear.

outer bark   Protective layers of mostly dead cork cells that cover the outside of woody stems and roots.

outer ear   One of the three main compartments of the mammalian ear; consists of the external ear, or pinna, and the auditory canal.

outer segment   The highly convoluted plasma membranes found in the rods and cones of the eye.

outgroup   A species or group of species that is most closely related to an ingroup.

outside-in signalling   Occurs when an integrin binds to a component in the ECM, which transmits a signal to the cytosol, thereby affecting activities inside the cell.

ova   Haploid reproductive cells or gametes of females. Both animals and embryophytes have ova. Plural of ovum, meaning egg.

ovarian cycle   The development of an ovarian follicle, the release of an ovum, and the formation and regression of a corpus luteum.

ovary   In plants, a tissue that produces and nourishes ovules.

oviduct   A thin tube with undulating fimbriae (fingers) that extend out to the ovary; also called the fallopian tube.

oviparity   Development of the embryo within an egg.

oviparous   Describes an organism whose embryos develop within an egg outside the mother.

ovoviparous   Describes an organism that retains eggs inside the body, where the young hatch.

ovoviviparity   Development of the embryo involving aspects of both viviparity and oviparity; eggs covered with a thin shell are produced and hatch inside the mother's body, but the offspring receive no nourishment from the mother.

ovulation   The release of the ovum from the ovary.

ovule   In a plant, a megaspore-producing megasporangium and enclosing tissues known as integuments.

oxidation   A process that involves the removal of electrons; occurs during the breakdown of small organic molecules.

oxidative fibres   Skeletal muscle fibres that contain numerous mitochondria and have a high capacity for oxidative phosphorylation.

oxidative phosphorylation   A process during which NADH and $FADH_2$ are oxidized to make more ATP via the phosphorylation of ADP.

oxygen-hemoglobin dissociation curve   A graph that shows the relationship between O_2 binding and P_{O_2}. When P_{O_2} is high, more O_2 binds to hemoglobin, while fewer O_2 molecules are bound when P_{O_2} is low.

oxytocin   A hormone secreted by the posterior pituitary gland that stimulates contractions of the smooth muscles in the uterus of a pregnant mammal, which facilitates the birth process; after birth, it is important in milk secretion.

P

P generation   The parental generation in a genetic cross.

P protein   Phloem protein; the proteinaceous material produced in sieve tube elements of plant phloem as a response to wounding.

pacemaker   *See* sinoatrial (SA) node.

Pacinian corpuscles   Structures located deep beneath the surface of the skin that respond to deep pressure or vibration.

paedomorphosis   The retention of juvenile traits in an adult organism.

pair-rule gene   A type of segmentation gene; a defect in this gene may cause alternating segments or parts of segments to be deleted.

paleontologists   Scientists who study fossils.

palisade parenchyma   Photosynthetic ground tissue in a plant that consists of closely packed, elongate cells adapted to absorb sunlight efficiently.

pancreas   An elongated gland located behind the stomach that secretes digestive enzymes and a fluid rich in bicarbonate ions.

pangenesis   An idea proposed by the ancient Greek physician Hippocrates that suggested that "seeds" produced by all parts of the body are collected and transmitted to offspring at the time of conception, and that these seeds cause offspring to resemble their parents.

parabronchi   A series of parallel air tubes that make up the lungs and are the regions of gas exchange in birds.

paracrine   Refers to a type of cellular communication in which molecules are released into the interstitial fluid and act on nearby cells.

paralogs   Homologous genes within a single species.

paraphyletic taxon   A group that contains a common ancestor and some, but not all, of its descendants.

parapodia   Fleshy, footlike structures in the polychaetes that are pushed into the substrate to provide traction during movement.

parasite   A predatory organism that feeds off another organism but does not normally kill it outright.

parasitism   An association in which one organism feeds off another but does not normally kill it outright.

parasympathetic division   The division of the autonomic nervous system that is involved in maintaining and restoring body functions.

parathyroid hormone (PTH)   A hormone that acts on bone to stimulate the activity of cells that dissolve the mineral part of bone.

Parazoa   A subgroup of animals that are not generally thought to possess specialized tissue types or organs, although they may have several distinct types of cells; the one phylum in this group is the Porifera (sponges).

parenchyma cells   Plant cells that are thin walled and alive at maturity.

parenchyma tissue   Plant tissue that is composed of parenchyma cells.

parental types   *See* nonrecombinants.

parthenogenesis   An asexual process in which an offspring develops from an unfertilized egg.

partial pressure   The individual pressure of each gas in the air; the sum of these pressures is known as atmospheric pressure.

particulate inheritance   The idea that the determinants of hereditary traits are transmitted intact from one generation to the next.

parturition   The birth of an organism.

passive diffusion   Diffusion that occurs through a membrane without the aid of a transport protein.

passive immunity   A type of acquired immunity that confers protection against disease through the direct transfer of antibodies from one individual to another.

passive transport   The diffusion of a solute across a membrane in a process that is energetically favourable and does not require an input of energy.

patch clamping   An electrophysiological technique that aids in the study of ion channels in single cells; the pipette connected to the cell may also be used to introduce specific substances (e.g., drugs, hormones) to the cell and to examine the consequences on ion channel activity.

pathogens   Microorganisms that cause disease symptoms in their host.

pattern formation   The process that gives rise to a plant or animal with a particular body structure.

pedal glands   Glands in the foot of a rotifer that secrete a sticky substance that aids in attachment to the substrate.

pedicel   A narrow, waistlike point of attachment in a spider or insect body.

pedicellariae   The spines and jawlike pincers that cover the skeleton of an echinoderm and deter the settling of animals such as barnacles.

pedigree analysis   An examination of the inheritance of human traits in families.

pedipalps   In spiders, a pair of appendages that have various sensory, predatory, or reproductive functions.

pelagic   Any water in a sea or lake that is neither close to the bottom nor near the shore can be said to be in the pelagic zone.

pelagic zone   The open ocean, where water depth averages 4,000 metres and nutrient concentrations are typically low.

penis   A male external accessory sex organ found in many animals that is involved in copulation.

pentadactyl limbs   Limbs ending in five digits.

PEP carboxylase   An enzyme in C_4 plants that adds CO_2 to phosphoenolpyruvate (PEP) to produce the four-carbon compound oxaloacetate.

pepsin   An active enzyme in the stomach that begins the digestion of protein.

peptide bond   The covalent bond that links together amino acids in a polypeptide.

peptidoglycan   A polymer composed of protein and carbohydrate that is an important component of the cell walls of most bacteria.

peptidyl site (P site)   One of the three sites for tRNA binding to the ribosome; the others are the aminoacyl site (A site) and the exit site (E site). The polypeptide is usually in the P site.

peptidyl transfer reaction   As a peptide bond is formed, the polypeptide is removed from the tRNA in the P site and transferred to the amino acid at the A site.

per capita growth rate (r)   The per capita birth rate minus the per capita death rate; the rate that determines how populations grow over any period.

perception   An awareness of the sensations that are experienced.

perennials   Plants that live for more than two years, often producing seeds each year after they reach reproductive maturity.

perfect flowers   Flowers that have both stamens and carpels.

perianth   Refers to flower petals and sepals collectively.

pericarp   The wall of a plant's fruit.

pericycle   A cylinder of plant tissue that has cell division (meristematic) capacity and that encloses the root vascular tissue.

peripheral membrane proteins   Proteins that are noncovalently bound to regions of integral membrane proteins that project out from the membrane or are noncovalently bound to the polar head groups of phospholipids.

peripheral nervous system (PNS)   All neurons and projections of their plasma membranes that are outside of and connect with the CNS, such as projections that end on muscle and gland cells.

peripheral zone   The area of a plant that contains dividing cells that will eventually differentiate into plant structures.

periphyton   Communities of microorganisms that are attached by mucilage to underwater surfaces, such as rocks, sand, and plants.

peristalsis   Rhythmic, spontaneous waves of muscle contraction that begin near the mouth in the esophagus and move toward the stomach.

peritubular capillaries   Capillaries near the junction of the cortex and medulla in the nephron of the kidney.

permafrost   A layer of permanently frozen soil.

peroxisomes   Small organelles found in all eukaryotic cells that catalyze detoxifying reactions.

petals   Flower organs that are frequently brightly coloured and usually serve to attract insects or other animals for pollen transport.

petiole   In eudicot plants, the structure that attaches blades to the stem.

pH   A log scale used to describe the concentrations of the ions H^+ and OH^-, equal to the negative logarithm to the base 10 of the H^+ concentration.

phagocytes   Cells capable of phagocytosis; phagocytes provide nonspecific defence against pathogens that enter the body.

phagocytosis   A form of endocytosis that involves the formation of a membrane vesicle called a phagosome, or phagocytic vacuole, that engulfs a large particle, such as a bacterium.

phagotrophs   Organisms that specialize in phagotrophy (particle feeding) by means of phagocytosis as a form of nutrition.

pharyngeal slits   Filter-feeding devices in primitive chordates.

pharynx   The area at the back of the throat where inhaled air from the mouth and nose converges.

phenolic   Refers to compounds that contain a cyclic ring of carbon with three double bonds, known as a benzene ring, that is covalently linked to a single hydroxyl group.

phenotypes   The characteristics of an organism that are the result of the expression of its genes.

pheromones   Powerful chemical attractants used to manipulate the behaviour of others.

phloem   A specialized conducting tissue at the centre of a plant's stem.

phloem loading   The process of conveying sugars to sieve-tube elements for long-distance transport.

phoresy   A form of commensalism in which individuals of one species use individuals of a second species for transportation.

phosphodiester linkage   Refers to a double linkage (two phosphoester bonds) that holds together adjacent nucleotides in DNA and RNA strands.

phosphodiesterase   An enzyme that breaks down cAMP into AMP.

phospholipids   Lipids that are similar in structure to triglycerides, but the third hydroxyl group of each glycerol is linked to a phosphate group instead of a fatty acid. They are a key component of biological membranes.

photoautotrophs   Organisms that use the energy from light to make organic molecules from inorganic sources.

photoheterotrophs   Organisms that are able to use light energy to generate ATP, but which must take in organic compounds from the environment.

Photons   Massless particles travelling in a wavelike pattern and moving at the speed of light.

photoperiodism   A plant's ability to measure and respond to night length, and indirectly, day length, as a way of detecting seasonal change.

photophosphorylation   The synthesis of ATP within chloroplasts that is driven by the chemiosmotic process wherein light energy is absorbed and converted to chemical energy (ATP).

photoreceptors   Electromagnetic receptors that respond to visible light energy.

photorespiration   The metabolic process occurring in C_3 plants that results when the enzyme rubisco combines with oxygen instead of carbon dioxide and produces only one molecule of PGA instead of two PGA, thereby reducing photosynthetic efficiency.

photostasis   An energy balance in photoautotrophs whereby the captured photon energy is counterbalanced by its use in metabolic reactions and/or its dissipation by heat loss.

photosynthesis   The process whereby light energy is captured by plant, algal, or cyanobacterial cells and used to synthesize organic molecules from CO_2 and H_2O (or H_2S).

photosystem I (PSI)   One of two distinct complexes of proteins and pigment molecules in the thylakoid membrane that absorbs light.

photosystem II (PSII)   The complex of proteins and pigment molecules in the thylakoid membrane that generates oxygen from water.

phototropin   The main blue-light sensor involved in phototropism.

phototropism   The tendency of a plant to grow toward a light source.

phyla   The subdivisions of a kingdom.

phyllotaxy   The patterned arrangement of leaves on a plant stem; new stems, leaves, lateral

roots, and flowers occur at regular intervals in a specific pattern.

phylogenetic tree A diagram that describes a phylogeny; such a tree is a hypothesis of the evolutionary relationships among various species, based on the information available to and gathered by systematists.

phylogeny The evolutionary history of a species or group of species.

physiology The study of the functions of cells and body parts of living organisms.

phytochrome A red- and far-red-light receptor.

phytomer A modular unit of plant development that consists of four parts: a stem node and an internode, a leaf, and an axillary meristem or bud at the base of the leaf.

phytoplankton Microscopic algae and cyanobacteria that float or actively move through water.

phytoremediation The process of removing harmful metals from soils by growing hyperaccumulator plants on metal-contaminated soils, and then harvesting and burning the plants to ashes for disposal and/or metal recovery.

pigment A molecule that can absorb light energy.

pili Threadlike surface appendages that allow prokaryotes to attach to each other during mating or to move across surfaces.

piloting A mechanism of migration in which an animal moves from one familiar landmark to the next.

pinocytosis A form of endocytosis that involves the formation of membrane vesicles from the plasma membrane as a way for cells to internalize the extracellular fluid.

pistil A flower structure that may consist of a single carpel or multiple, fused carpels, and is differentiated into stigma, style, and ovary.

pit A small cavity in a plant cell wall where secondary wall materials, such as lignin, are absent.

pitch The tone of a sound wave.

pituitary dwarfism A condition in which a person's anterior pituitary gland fails to make adequate amounts of GH during childhood, so the concentrations of GH and IGF-1 in the blood will be lower than normal and growth is stunted.

pituitary giant A person who has a tumour of the GH-secreting cells of the anterior pituitary gland and thus produces excess GH during childhood and adulthood; the person can grow very tall.

pituitary gland A multilobed endocrine gland sitting directly below the hypothalamus.

placenta A structure through which humans and other eutherian mammals retain and nourish their young within the uterus via the transfer of nutrients and gases.

placental transfer tissues In plants, nutritive tissues that aid in the transfer of nutrients from maternal parent to embryo.

Plantae A eukaryotic kingdom of the domain Eukarya; includes multicellular organisms that have cellulose-rich cell walls and plastids, and that are adapted in many ways to terrestrial habitats (or if aquatic, derived from terrestrial ancestors).

plants Organisms that are members of the kingdom Plantae.

plant tissue culture A laboratory process to produce thousands of identical plants having the same desirable characteristics.

plaques (1) Deposits of lipids, fibrous tissue, and smooth muscle cells that may develop in blood vessels. (2) Bacterial biofilms that may form on the surfaces of teeth.

plasma The fluid part of blood; part of the extracelluar fluid.

plasma cells Cells that synthesize and secrete antibodies.

plasma membrane The biomembrane that separates the internal contents of a cell from its external environment.

plasmids Small circular DNA molecules found naturally in many strains of bacteria and also occasionally in eukaryotic cells.

plasmodesmata Membrane-lined, ER-containing channels that connect the cytoplasm of adjacent plant cells.

plasmogamy The fusion of the cytoplasm between two gametes.

plasmolysis The shrinkage of algal or plant cytoplasm that occurs when water leaves the cell by osmosis, with the result that the plasma membrane no longer presses on the cell wall.

plastids Organelles found in plant and algal cells, which are bound by two membranes and contain DNA and large amounts of chlorophyll (chloroplasts), carotenoids (chromoplasts), or starch (amyloplasts).

platelets Cell fragments in the blood of mammals that play a crucial role in the formation of blood clots.

pleiotropy The phenomenon in which a mutation in a single gene can have multiple effects on an individual's phenotype.

pluripotent Refers to the ability of embryonic stem cells to differentiate into almost every cell type of the body.

point mutation A mutation that affects only a single base pair within the DNA or that involves the addition or deletion of a single base pair to a DNA sequence.

polar cell The highest latitude cell in the three-cell circulation of wind in each hemisphere.

polarized (1) In cell biology, refers to cells that have different sides, such as the apical and basal sides of epithelial cells. (2) In neuroscience, refers to the electrical gradient across the membrane. A neuron with a large electrical gradient across its plasma membrane is said to be highly polarized.

polar microtubules Microtubules that emanate from a microtubule organizing centre, are oriented toward the centre of the cell, and ultimately become stabilized by their association with a polar microtubule from the opposite pole.

polar transport The process whereby auxin primarily flows downward in shoots and into roots.

pole cells The primordial germ cells that are the first cells to form at the posterior end of the embryo in certain species, such as *Drosophila*.

pollen Tiny male gametophytes enclosed by sporopollenin-containing microspore walls.

pollen coat A layer of material that covers the sporopollenin-rich pollen wall.

pollen grains Immature male gametophytes.

pollen tube A mature male gametophyte consisting of a germinated pollen grain with a long, thin pollen tube that carries haploid sperm cells.

pollen wall A tough, sporopollenin wall at the surface of a pollen grain.

pollination syndromes The pattern of coevolved traits between particular types of flowers and specific pollinators.

pollination The process in which pollen grains are transported to an angiosperm flower or a gymnosperm cone by means of wind or animal pollinators.

pollinators Animals that carry pollen between angiosperm flowers (or cones of gymnosperms).

polyandry A form of mating in which one female mates with several males.

poly A tail A string of adenine nucleotides at the 3` end of most mature mRNAs in eukaryotes.

polycistronic mRNA An mRNA that contains the coding sequences for two or more structural genes.

polycythemia A condition of increased hemoglobin caused by increased hematocrit.

polygenic A trait in which several or many genes contribute to the outcome of the trait.

polygyny A form of mating in which one male mates with more than one female in a single breeding season, but females mate with only one male.

polyketides A group of secondary metabolites that are produced by bacteria, fungi, plants, insects, dinoflagellates, molluscs, and sponges.

polymerase chain reaction (PCR) A technique to make many copies of a gene *in vitro*; primers are used that flank the region of DNA to be amplified.

polymers Large macromolecules formed by linking together many smaller molecules called monomers through condensation reactions.

polymorphic gene A gene that commonly exists as two or more alleles in a population.

polymorphism The phenomenon that many traits or genes display variation within a population.

polyp A cnidarian body form that is sessile; corals exhibit the polyp form.

polypeptide A linear sequence of amino acids; the term denotes structure.

polyphagous Refers to parasites that feed on many host species.

polyphyletic taxon A group that consists of members of several evolutionary lines and does not include the most recent common ancestor of the included lineages.

polyploid   An organism that has three or more sets of chromosomes.

polysaccharides   Monosaccharides linked together to form long polymers.

pons   The part of the hindbrain, along with the cerebellum, responsible for monitoring and coordinating body movements.

population   A group of individuals of the same species that can interbreed with one another.

population ecology   The study of how populations grow and what promotes and limits growth.

population genetics   The study of genes and genotypes in a population.

portal veins   Veins that not only collect blood from capillaries—like all veins—but also form another set of capillaries, as opposed to returning the blood directly to the heart like other veins.

positional information   Molecules that are provided to a cell that allow it to determine its position relative to other cells.

positive control   Transcriptional regulation by activator proteins.

positive feedback loop   The acceleration of a process, leading to what is sometimes called an explosive system.

positive pressure filling   The method by which amphibians ventilate their lungs—the animals gulp air and force it under pressure into the lungs, as if inflating a balloon.

postabsorptive state   One of two alternating phases in the use of nutrients; occurs when the gastrointestinal tract is empty of nutrients and the body's own stores must supply energy. The other phase is the absorptive state.

posterior   Refers to the rear (tailend) of an animal.

postsynaptic cell   The cell that receives the electrical or chemical signal sent from a neuron.

post-translational covalent modification   A process of changing the structure of a protein, usually by covalently attaching functional groups.

post-translational sorting   The uptake of proteins into the nucleus, mitochondria, chloroplasts, and peroxisomes that occurs after the protein is completely made (i.e., is completely translated).

postzygotic isolating mechanisms   Mechanisms that prevent interbreeding by blocking the development of a viable and fertile individual after fertilization has taken place.

potential energy   The energy that a substance possesses because of its structure or location.

power stroke   The process in which an energized myosin cross-bridge binds to actin and triggers the movement of the bound cross-bridge.

PPAR-delta   Peroxisome proliferator-activated receptors (PPARs) are a group of nuclear receptor proteins that function as transcription factors regulating the expression of genes.

prebiotic soup   The medium formed by the slow accumulation of molecules in the early oceans over a long period before the existence of life.

predation   An interaction where the action of the predator results in the death of the prey.

predators   Animals that kill live prey.

predator satiation   The synchronous production of many progeny by all individuals in a population to satiate predators and thereby allow some progeny to survive; commonly called *masting* when discussed in relation to seed herbivory in trees.

pregnancy   The time during which a developing embryo and fetus grows within the uterus of the mother. The period of pregnancy is also known as *gestation.*

preinitiation complex   The structure of the completed assembly of GTFs and RNA polymerase II at the TATA box before transcription of eukaryotic structural genes.

pressure-flow hypothesis   The explanation for phloem transport that says sieve-tube elements near source tissues have higher solute contents while sieve-tube elements near sink tissues have a lower solute concentration. Water that contains solutes moves from phloem into sink tissues. The resulting water pressure difference drives the bulk flow of phloem sap from source to sink tissues.

pressure potential   The component of water potential caused by hydrostatic pressure; an element in the water potential equation.

presynaptic cell   The cell that sends the electrical or chemical signal from a neuron to another cell.

prezygotic isolating mechanism   A mechanism that stops interbreeding by preventing the formation of a zygote.

primary active transport   A type of transport that involves pumps that directly use energy and generate a solute gradient.

primary cell wall   In plants, a cell wall that is synthesized first between the two newly made daughter cells.

primary electron acceptor   The molecule to which a high-energy electron from an excited pigment molecule, such as P680, is transferred.

primary endosymbiosis   The process by which a eukaryotic host cell acquires prokaryotic endosymbionts or plastids or mitochondria derived from a prokaryotic endosymbiont.

primary immune response   The response to an initial exposure to an antigen.

primary meristems   Meristematic tissues that increase plant length and produce new organs.

primary metabolism   The synthesis and breakdown of molecules and macromolecules that are found in all forms of life and are essential for cell structure and function.

primary nondisjunction   The failure of homologous chromosomes to move to opposite poles during the first meiotic division.

primary oocytes   In animals, the first stage of producing female gametes by meiosis.

primary plastids   A plastid that arose from a prokaryote as the result of endosymbiosis.

primary producers   Autotrophs, which typically harvest light energy from the sun; located at the base of the food chain.

primary spermatocytes   In animals, the first stage of producing sperm by meiosis.

primary structure   The linear sequence of the amino acids of a polypeptide. One of four levels of protein structure.

primary succession   Succession on newly exposed sites that were not previously occupied by soil and vegetation.

primary tissues   Plant tissues generated as the result of primary growth at apical meristems.

primary vascular tissue   Plant tissue composed of primary xylem and phloem.

primordial germ cells   A specialized group of cells in an embryo that migrates to the future site of gonad development.

principle of parsimony   The preferred hypothesis is the one that is the simplest.

principle of species individuality   A view of the nature of a community; each species is distributed according to its physiological needs and population dynamics; most communities intergrade continuously and competition does not create distinct vegetational zones.

prions   Nonliving proteinaceous infectious agents that cause a group of rare, fatal brain diseases affecting humans and other mammals.

probability   The chance that an event will have a particular outcome.

proboscis   The coiled tongue of a butterfly or moth, which can be uncoiled, enabling it to drink nectar from flowers.

procambium   A type of primary plant tissue meristem that produces vascular tissue.

producers   Organisms that synthesize the organic compounds used by other organisms for food.

productivity hypothesis   The proposal that greater production by plants results in greater overall species richness.

progesterone   A hormone secreted by the female ovaries that plays a key role in pregnancy.

progymnosperms   An extinct group of plants having wood but not seeds that evolved before the gymnosperms.

prokaryotes   Members of one of the two categories into which all forms of life can be placed, based on cell structure; the other is eukaryote. Prokaryotic cells lack a nucleus having an envelope with pores; includes bacteria and archaea.

prometaphase   A phase of mitosis during which the mitotic spindle is completely formed.

promoter   The site in the DNA where transcription begins.

proofreading   The ability of DNA polymerase to identify a mismatched nucleotide and remove it from the daughter strand.

prophage   Refers to the DNA of a phage that has become integrated into the bacterial chromosome.

proplastids   Unspecialized plastid-structures that form plastids under appropriate conditions.

prosimians   Members of a class of primates that includes the smaller species, such as bush babies, lemurs, pottos, and tarsiers.

prostate gland   A structure that secretes a thin fluid that protects sperm once they are deposited within the female reproductive tract.

prosthetic groups   Small molecules that are permanently attached to the surface of an enzyme and aid in catalysis.

protandrous   Pertaining to an organism in which the males emerge before females; can also refer to a floral system in which the anthers release their pollen before the stigma of the same flower is receptive.

proteases   Enzymes that cleave proteins into smaller polypeptides.

proteasome   A molecular machine that is the primary pathway for protein degradation in archaea and eukaryotic cells.

protein kinase cascade   The sequential activation of multiple protein kinases in a row.

protein kinases   Enzymes that transfer phosphate groups from ATP to a protein.

protein phosphatases   Enzymes responsible for removing phosphate groups from proteins.

protein subunit   The individual polypeptides that each adopt a tertiary structure and then assemble with each other to make up most functional proteins.

proteoglycans   Glycosaminoglycans in the extracellular matrix linked to a core protein.

proteome   All the types and relative amounts of proteins that are made in a particular cell at a particular time and under specific conditions. The proteome largely determines a cell's structure and function.

protist   A eukaryotic organism that is not a member of the animal, plant, or fungal kingdoms; lives in moist habitats and is typically microscopic.

protobiont   The term used to describe the first nonliving structures that evolved into living cells.

protoderm   A type of primary plant tissue meristem that generates the outermost dermal tissue.

protogynous   Pertaining to an organism in which the females are active before males; can also refer to a floral system in which the stigma is receptive before the pollen is shed from the anthers of the same flower.

protonephridia   The simplest filtration mechanism for cleansing the blood; used in flatworms.

proton-motive force   See H$^+$ electrochemical gradient.

protons   Positively charged particles found in the nucleus of the atom. The number of protons in an atom is called the atomic number and defines each type of element.

proto-oncogene   A normal gene that, if mutated, can become an oncogene.

protostomes   Animals that exhibit spiral determinate cleavage and in which the blastopore becomes the mouth; includes molluscs, annelid worms, and arthropods.

protozoa   A term commonly used to describe diverse heterotrophic protists.

proventriculus   The glandular portion of the stomach of a bird.

provirus   Refers to viral DNA that has become incorporated into a eukaryotic chromosome.

proximal convoluted tubule   The segment of the tubule of the nephron in the kidney that drains Bowman's capsule.

proximate causation   A specific genetic and physiological mechanism of behaviour.

pseudocoelom   A coelom that is not completely lined by tissue derived from mesoderm.

pseudocoelomates   Animals with a pseudocoelom.

pteridophytes   A phylum of vascular plants having euphylls but not seeds; Pteridophyta.

pulmocutaneous circulation   The routing of blood from the heart through different vessels to the gas-exchange organs (lungs and skin) of frogs and some other amphibians.

pulmonary circulation   The pumping of blood from the right side of the heart to the lungs to release carbon dioxide and pick up oxygen from the atmosphere.

pulmonary hypertension   Hypertension that occurs in the pulmonary side of the circulation, usually caused by a diseased or damaged left ventricle that fails to pump out the usual amount of blood with each beat.

pulse-chase experiment   A procedure in which researchers administer a pulse of radioactively labelled materials to cells so that they make radioactive products. This is followed by the addition of nonlabelled materials called a chase.

pump   A transporter that directly couples its conformational changes to an energy source, such as ATP hydrolysis.

punctuated equilibrium   A concept that suggests that the tempo of evolution is more sporadic than gradual. Species rapidly evolve into new species followed by long periods of equilibrium with little evolutionary change.

Punnett square   A common method for predicting the outcome of simple genetic crosses.

pupa   The organism resulting after the larval stages in insects that gives rise to an adult organism via metamorphosis.

pupil   A small opening in the eye of a vertebrate that transmits different patterns of light emitted from images in the animal's field of view.

purine   The bases adenine (A) and guanine (G), with double (fused) rings of nitrogen and carbon atoms.

pyramid of biomass   A measure of efficiency in which the organisms at each trophic level are weighed.

pyramid of numbers   An expression of trophic-level transfer efficiency, in which the number of individuals decreases at each trophic level, with a huge number of individuals at the base and fewer individuals at the top.

pyramid of production   A measure of efficiency in which rates of production are shown rather than standing crop; the laws of thermodynamics ensure that the highest amounts of free energy are found at the lowest trophic levels.

pyrimidine   The bases cytosine (C), thymine (T), and uracil (U) with a single ring.

Q

quantitative traits   See continuous traits.

quorum sensing   A mechanism by which prokaryotic cells are able to communicate when they reach a critical population size.

R

radial cleavage   A mechanism of development in which the cleavage planes are either parallel or perpendicular to the vertical axis of the egg.

radially symmetrical   A type of body plan in which the arrangement of body parts/tissues is regular about a central axis.

Radiata   Radially symmetrical animals, which means they can be divided equally by a longitudinal plane passing through the central axis; includes cnidarians and ctenophores.

radiation   The emission of electromagnetic waves from the surfaces of objects.

radicle   An embryonic root, which extends from the plant hypocotyl.

radioisotope dating   A common way to estimate the age of a fossil by analyzing the elemental isotopes within the accompanying rock.

radioisotopes   Isotopes found in nature that are inherently unstable and do not exist for long periods. Such isotopes emit energy called radiation in the form of subatomic particles.

radula   A unique, protrusible, tonguelike organ in a mollusc that has many teeth and is used to eat plants, scrape food particles off rocks, or bore into shells of other species and tear flesh.

rain shadow   An area in which precipitation is noticeably less, such as on the side of the mountain sheltered from air movement.

ram ventilation   A mechanism used by fish to ventilate their gills; fish swim or face upstream with their mouths open, allowing water to enter into their buccal cavity and from there across their gills.

random   A pattern of dispersion within a population, in which individuals do not appear to be specially positioned relative to anyone else.

random genetic drift   A change in allele frequencies caused by random sampling error.

rate-limiting step   The slowest step in a pathway.

ray-finned fish   The Actinopterygii, which includes all bony fish except the coelacanths and lungfish.

reabsorption In the production of urine, the process in which useful solutes in the filtrate are recaptured and transported back into the body fluids of an animal.

reaction mechanism In the case of the Na^1/K^1 pump, a molecular roadmap of the steps that direct the pumping of ions across the plasma membrane.

reading frame Refers to the idea that codons are read from the start codon in groups of three bases each.

receptor A cellular protein that recognizes a signalling molecule.

receptor-mediated endocytosis A common form of endocytosis in which a receptor is specific for a given cargo.

receptor potential The membrane potential in a sensory receptor cell.

receptor tyrosine kinase A class of receptors that, on activation, become kinases that initiate a signal transduction pathway

recessive A term that describes a trait that is seen in true breeding parents, but is masked in heterozygotes.

recombinant DNA technology The use of laboratory techniques to isolate and manipulate fragments of DNA.

recombinants Offspring that have a different combination of traits from the parental generation.

recombinant vector A vector containing a piece of chromosomal DNA.

recombination frequency The frequency of crossing over between two genes.

red blood cells Cells that serve the critical function of transporting oxygen throughout the body; also known as erythrocytes.

redox reaction A type of reaction in which the electron that is removed during the oxidation of an atom or a molecule must be transferred to another atom or molecule, which becomes reduced; short for a reduction–oxidation reaction.

reduction A process that involves the addition of electrons to an atom or a molecule.

reductionism An approach that involves reducing complex systems to simpler components as a way to understand how the system works. In biology, reductionists study the parts of a cell or an organism as individual units.

reflex arc A simple circuit that allows an organism to respond rapidly to inputs from sensory neurons and consists of only a few neurons.

refractory The term used to describe a cell that is unresponsive to another stimulus.

regeneration A form of asexual reproduction in which a complete organism forms from small fragments of its body.

regulatory gene A gene whose function is to regulate the expression of other genes.

regulatory sequences In the regulation of transcription, these are sequences that function as sites for binding regulatory proteins. Regulatory sequences and their proteins control whether a gene is turned on or off.

regulatory transcription factors Proteins that bind to DNA in the vicinity of a promoter and affects the rate of transcription of one or more nearby genes.

relative abundance The frequency of occurrence of species in a community.

release factor A protein that recognizes the three stop codons in the termination stage of translation and promotes the termination of translation.

renal corpuscle A filtering component in the nephron of the kidney.

repetitive sequences Short DNA sequences that are present in many copies in a genome.

replica plating A technique in which a replica of bacterial colonies is transferred to a new Petri plate.

replication (1) The performing of experiments several or many times. (2) The copying of DNA strands.

repressible operon In this type of operon, a small effector molecule inhibits transcription.

repressors Transcription factors that bind to DNA and inhibit transcription.

reproduction The process by which organisms produce offspring.

reproductive isolating mechanisms The mechanisms that prevent interbreeding between different species.

reproductive isolation Mechanisms that prevent one species from successfully interbreeding with other species.

reproductive success The production of fertile offspring by a genotype.

resistance (R) The tendency of blood vessels to slow down the flow of blood through their lumens.

resistance genes (R genes) Plant genes that have evolved as part of a defence system in response to pathogen attack.

resolution In microscopy, the ability to observe two adjacent objects as distinct from one another; a measure of the clarity of an image.

resonance energy transfer The process by which the energy (not the electron itself) can be transferred to adjacent pigment molecules.

resource partitioning The differentiation of niches, both in space and in time, that enables similar species to coexist in a community.

respiratory centres Several regions of the brainstem in vertebrates that initiate expansion of the lungs.

respiratory chain *See* electron transport chain.

respiratory distress syndrome of the newborn The situation in which a human baby is born prematurely, before sufficient surfactant is produced, and many alveoli quickly collapse.

respiratory pigments Protein/metal ion complexes that bind to oxygen.

respiratory system All components of the body that contribute to the exchange of gas between the external environment and the blood; in mammals, includes the nose, mouth, airways, lungs, and muscles and connective tissues that

encase these structures within the thoracic (chest) cavity.

response elements DNA sequences that are recognized by regulatory transcription factors that regulate the expression of genes.

resting potential The difference in charges across the plasma membrane in an unstimulated cell.

restoration ecology The full or partial repair or replacement of biological habitats and/or their populations that have been damaged.

restriction enzymes Enzymes that recognize particular DNA sequences and cleave the DNA backbone at two sites.

restriction point A point in the cell cycle in which a cell has become committed to dividing.

restriction sites The base sequences recognized by restriction enzymes.

retina A sheetlike layer of photoreceptors at the back of the eye.

retinal A derivative of vitamin A that is capable of absorbing light energy.

retroelement or retrotransposon A type of transposable element that moves via an RNA intermediate.

retroviruses RNA viruses that use reverse transcription to produce viral DNA that can be integrated into the host cell genome.

reverse transcriptase A viral enzyme that catalyzes the synthesis of viral DNA, starting with viral RNA as a template.

rhabdom A column of photosensitive microvilli in the eye that project from the cell membranes of retinula cells, which are the photoreceptor cells of the ommatidium.

rhizobia The collective term for proteobacteria involved in the nitrogen-fixation symbioses with plants that are important in nature and to agriculture.

rhizomorphs Fungal mycelia that have the shape of roots.

rhodopsin The visual pigment in rods.

ribonucleic acid (RNA) One of two classes of nucleic acids; the other is deoxyribonucleic acid (DNA). RNA consists of a single strand of nucleotides.

ribose A five-carbon sugar found in RNA.

ribosomal initiation factors In the initiation stage of translation, these proteins facilitate the interactions between mRNA, the first tRNA, and the ribosomal subunits.

ribosomal RNA (rRNA) An RNA that forms part of ribosomes, which provide the site where translation occurs.

ribosomes Organelles composed of proteins and rRNA that provide the sites where protein synthesis occurs.

ribozymes RNA molecules that exhibit enzymatic activity.

right-left axis In bilateral animals, one of the three axes along which the adult body pattern is organized; the others are the dorsoventral axis and the anteroposterior axis.

ring canal A structure in the water vascular system of echinoderms.

rivet hypothesis An alternative to the diversity–stability hypothesis. In this model, species are like the rivets on an airplane, with each species playing a small but critical role in keeping the plane (the ecosystem) airborne. The loss of a rivet weakens the plane and causes it to lose a little airworthiness. The loss of a few rivets could probably be tolerated, while the loss of more rivets would prove critical to the airplane's function.

RNA-induced silencing complex (RISC) The complex that mediates RNA interference via microRNAs.

RNA interference (RNAi) Refers to a type of mRNA silencing that interferes with the proper expression of an mRNA.

RNA polymerase The enzyme that synthesizes strands of RNA during gene transcription.

RNA processing A step in gene expression between transcription and translation; the RNA transcript, termed pre-mRNA, is modified in ways that make it a functionally active mRNA.

RNA world A hypothetical period on primitive Earth when both the information needed for life and the enzymatic activity of living cells were contained solely in RNA molecules.

rods Photoreceptors found in the vertebrate eye; they are very sensitive to low-intensity light but do not readily discriminate different colours. Rods are used mostly at night, and they send signals to the brain that generate a black-and-white visual image.

root apical meristem A niche of stem cells in plant roots that are responsible for generating all root tissues.

root cortex A region of ground parenchyma located between the epidermis and vascular tissue of mature plant roots.

root hairs Long, thin root epidermal cells that function to absorb water and minerals, usually from soil.

root pressure A process whereby plants are able to refill embolized vessels.

roots Plant organs that provide anchorage in the soil and also foster efficient uptake of water and minerals.

root system The collection of roots and root branches produced by root apical meristems.

rough endoplasmic reticulum (rough ER) The part of the ER that is studded with ribosomes; this region plays a key role in the initial synthesis and sorting of proteins that are destined for the ER, Golgi apparatus, lysosomes, vacuoles, plasma membrane, or outside the cell.

r-selected species A type of life history strategy, where species have a high rate of per capita population growth but poor competitive ability.

rubisco The enzyme that catalyzes the first step in the Calvin cycle in which CO_2 is incorporated into an organic molecule.

Ruffini corpuscles A variety of oval-shaped, encapsulated nerve endings in the subcutaneous tissue.

S

S The synthesis phase of the cell cycle.

saltatory conduction A type of conduction in which sodium ions move into the cell and the charge moves rapidly through the cytosol to the next node, where the action potential continues.

sarcoma A tumour of connective tissue, such as bone or cartilage.

sarcomere One complete unit of the repeating pattern of thick and thin filaments within a myofibril.

sarcoplasmic reticulum A cellular organelle that provides a muscle fibre's source of the cytosolic calcium involved in muscle contraction.

satiety A feeling of fullness.

satiety signals Responses to eating that remove the sensation of hunger and set the time before hunger returns again.

saturated fatty acid A fatty acid in which all the carbons are linked by single covalent bonds.

scavengers Animals that eat the remains of dead animals.

schizocoelous In protostomes, a pattern of development in which a solid mass of mesoderm cells splits to form the cavity that becomes the coelom.

Schwann cells The glial cells that form myelin on axons that travel outside the brain and spinal cord.

scientific method A methodology to test the validity of a hypothesis. The experimentation often involves a comparison between control and experimental samples.

sclera The white of the vertebrate eye; a strong outer sheet that in the front is continuous with a thin, clear layer known as the cornea.

sclereids Star- or stone-shaped plant cells having tough, lignified cell walls.

sclerenchyma tissue Rigid plant tissue composed of tough-walled fibres and sclereids.

scurvy A potentially fatal vitamin C deficiency in humans characterized by weakness, bleeding gums, and tooth loss.

seaweeds Multicellular protists that occur in marine habitats and may display a relatively large and complex body.

secondary active transport A type of transport that involves using an existing gradient to drive the active transport of another solute.

secondary cell wall A plant cell wall that is synthesized and deposited between the plasma membrane and the primary cell wall after a plant cell matures and has stopped increasing in size.

secondary consumer An organism that eats primary consumers; also called a carnivore.

secondary endosymbiosis A process that occurs when a eukaryotic host cell acquires a eukaryotic endosymbiont that has a primary plastid.

secondary growth A process in plants in which the secondary meristems increase the girth of plant stems and roots by producing secondary tissues.

secondary immune response An immediate and heightened production of additional specific antibodies against a particular antigen that elicited a primary immune response.

secondary metabolism Involves the synthesis of chemicals that are not essential for cell structure and growth and are usually not required for cell survival, but are advantageous to the organism.

secondary metabolites Molecules that are produced by secondary metabolism.

secondary nondisjunction The failure of sister chromatids to move to opposite poles during the second meiotic division.

secondary oocyte In animals, the large egg cell that is the result of meiosis I.

secondary phloem The inner bark of a woody plant.

secondary plastids Plastids that have originated by the endosymbiotic incorporation into a host eukaryote of a eukaryotic cell that has a primary plastid.

secondary production The measure of production of heterotrophs and decomposers.

secondary spermatocytes The haploid cells produced in the primary spermatocyte by meiosis I.

secondary structure The bending or twisting of proteins into a helices or b sheets. One of four levels of protein structure.

secondary succession Succession on a site that has already supported life but that has undergone a disturbance.

secondary xylem *See* wood.

second law of thermodynamics The transfer of energy or the transformation of energy from one form to another increases the entropy, or the degree of disorder of a system.

second messengers Small nonprotein signalling molecules or ions that relay the activating signal to other components of a signalling pathway and typically causes rapid and transient responses.

secretion In the production of urine, the process in which some solutes are actively transported from the interstitial fluid surrounding the epithelial cells of the tubules of an excretory organ, into the tubule lumens.

seed coat A hard and tough covering that develops from the ovule's integument and protects the plant's embryo.

seed plants The informal name for gymnosperms and angiosperms.

seeds Reproductive structures produced by flowering plants and other seed plants, usually as the result of sexual reproduction.

segmentation Describes when an animal body is divided into nearly identical subunits called segments.

segmentation genes Genes that control the segmentation pattern of an animal embryo.

segmented A developmental feature in which specific body regions are generated in a reiterative fashion.

segment-polarity gene A type of segmentation gene; a mutation in this gene causes portions of segments to be missing either an anterior or a posterior region and causes adjacent regions to become mirror images of each other.

segregate To separate, as in chromosomes during mitosis.

selectable marker A gene whose presence can allow organisms (such as bacteria) to grow under a certain set of conditions. For example, an antibiotic resistance gene is a selectable marker that allows bacteria to grow in the presence of the antibiotic.

selective breeding Programs and procedures designed to modify traits in domesticated species.

self-fertilization Fertilization that involves the union of a female gamete and male gamete from the same individual.

self-incompatibility Rejection of pollen that is genetically too similar to the pistil of a plant.

selfish DNA hypothesis The hypothesis that transposable elements exist because they have the characteristics that allow them to insert themselves into the host cell DNA but do not provide any advantage.

self-pollination The process in which pollen from the anthers of a flower is transferred to the stigma of the same flower or between flowers of the same plant.

self-splicing The phenomenon that RNA itself can catalyze the removal of its own intron(s).

semelparity A reproductive pattern in which organisms produce all their offspring in a single reproductive event.

semicircular canals Structures of the ear that can detect circular motions of the head.

semiconservative replication The type of DNA replication that occurs for cellular DNA, in which the two strands of one helix unwind and each serves as a template to produce a complementary strand.

semifluid A quality of motion within biomembranes; considered two-dimensional, which means that movement occurs within the plane of the membrane.

semilunar valves A one-way valve into the systemic and pulmonary arteries through which blood is pumped.

seminal vesicles Paired accessory glands that secrete fructose, the main nutrient for sperm, into the urethra to mix with the sperm.

seminiferous tubules Tightly packed structures in the testis, where spermatogenesis takes place.

senescent Cells that have doubled many times and have reached a point where they have lost the capacity to divide any further.

sense A system that consists of sensory cells that respond to a specific type of chemical or physical stimulus and send signals to the central nervous system, where the signals are received and interpreted.

sensory neurons Neurons that detect or sense information from the outside world, such as light, sound, touch, and heat; sensory neurons also detect internal body conditions, such as blood pressure and body temperature. Also called afferent neurons.

sensory receptor A specialized cell whose function it is to receive sensory inputs.

sensory transduction The process by which incoming stimuli are converted into neural signals.

sepals Flower organs that often function to protect the unopened flower bud.

septa Cross-walls; examples include the cross-walls that divide the hyphae of most fungi into many small cells, and the structure that separates the old and new chambers of a nautilus.

setae Chitinous bristles in the integument of many invertebrates.

sex chromosomes A distinctive pair of chromosomes that are different in males and females.

sex-influenced inheritance The phenomenon in which an allele is dominant in one sex but recessive in the other.

sex linked Refers to genes that are found on one sex chromosome but not on the other.

sex pili Hairlike structures made by bacterial F_1 cells that bind specifically to F_2 cells.

sexual reproduction A process that requires a fertilization event in which two gametes unite to create a cell called a zygote.

sexual selection A type of natural selection that is directed at certain traits of sexually reproducing species that make it more likely for individuals to find or choose a mate and engage in successful mating.

Shannon diversity index (H_S) A means of measuring the diversity of a community; $H_S = -\Sigma\, p_i \ln p_i$.

shared ancestral character Is a character displayed in a species through multiple generations. The character had to be present in the ancestors. Also known as a synapotypic trait.

shared derived character A trait that is shared by a group of organisms but not by a distant common ancestor.

shattering The process by which ears of wild grain crops break apart and disperse seeds.

shell A tough, protective covering that is impermeable to water and prevents the embryo from drying out.

shivering thermogenesis Rapid muscle contractions in an animal, without any locomotion, to raise body temperature.

shoot apical meristem A small group of stem cells at the apex of a plant that give rise to all aboveground tissues.

short-day plants Plants that flower only when the nights are longer than a defined period. Such night length occurs in late summer, fall, and winter, when days are short.

short-interfering RNAs (siRNAs) Small RNA molecules that can prohibit gene expression by causing mRNAs with a complementary sequence to be destroyed.

short tandem repeat sequences (STRs) Sequences found in multiple sites in the genome of humans and other species that vary in length among different individuals.

shotgun DNA sequencing A strategy for sequencing an entire genome by randomly sequencing many different DNA fragments.

sickle-cell anemia A disease caused by a genetic mutation in a hemoglobin gene in which sickle-shaped red blood cells are less able to move smoothly through capillaries and can block blood flow, resulting in severe pain and cell death of the surrounding tissue.

sieve plate pores Perforations in a plant's sieve plate.

sieve plates The perforated end walls of a mature sieve-tube element.

sieve-tube elements A component of the phloem tissues of flowering plants; these structures are arranged end to end to form transport pipes.

sigma factor A protein that plays a key role in bacterial promoter recognition and recruits RNA polymerase to the promoter.

signal An agent that can influence the properties of cells.

signal peptide A few consecutive amino acids of a larger peptide that serve to direct the polypeptide to a specific compartment of the cell.

signal recognition particle (SRP) A protein–RNA complex that recognizes the ER signal sequence and pauses translation; SRP then binds to a receptor in the ER membrane, which docks the ribosome over a translocation channel.

signal transduction pathway A group of proteins that convert an initial signal to a different signal inside the cell.

signal transduction The process in which a cell perceives a physical or chemical signal, thereby switching on an intercellular pathway that leads to a cellular response.

sign stimulus A factor that initiates a fixed-action pattern of behaviour.

silencers DNA response elements that prevent transcription of a given gene when its expression is not needed.

silent mutation A gene mutation that does not alter the amino acid sequence of the polypeptide, even though the nucleotide sequence has changed.

simple Mendelian inheritance The inheritance pattern of traits affected by a single gene that is found in two variants, one of which is completely dominant over the other.

simple translocation A single piece of chromosome that is attached to another chromosome.

single factor cross A cross in which an experimenter follows the variants of a single trait.

single-strand binding proteins   Proteins that bind the single strands of parental DNA during DNA replication and prevent the strands from re-forming a double helix.

sinoatrial (SA) node   A collection of modified cardiac cells that spontaneously and rhythmically generates action potentials that spread across the entire atria; also known as the pacemaker of the heart.

sister chromatids   The two duplicated chromatids that are still joined to each other after DNA replication.

skeletal muscles   Types of muscle tissue that are attached to bones in vertebrates and to the exoskeleton of invertebrates.

skeleton   A structure or structures that serve one or more functions related to support, protection, and locomotion.

sliding filament mechanism   The way in which a muscle fibre shortens during muscle contraction.

SLOSS debate   In conservation biology, the debate over whether it is preferable to protect one single, large reserve or several smaller ones (SLOSS stands for single large or several small).

slow block to polyspermy   Events that produce barriers to more sperm penetrating an already fertilized egg.

slow fibres   Skeletal muscle fibres with a low rate of myosin ATP hydrolysis.

slow-oxidative fibres   Skeletal muscle fibres that have a low rate of myosin ATP hydrolysis but have the ability to make large amounts of ATP; used for prolonged, regular activity.

small effector molecules   With regard to transcription, refers to molecules that exert their effects by binding to a regulatory transcription factor and causing a conformational change in the protein.

small intestine   A tube that leads from the stomach to the large intestine where nearly all digestion of food and absorption of food nutrients and water occur.

smooth endoplasmic reticulum (smooth ER)   The part of the ER that is not studded with ribosomes. This region is continuous with the rough ER and functions in diverse metabolic processes, such as detoxification, carbohydrate metabolism, accumulation of calcium ions, and synthesis and modification of lipids.

smooth muscles   Muscle tissues that surround hollow tubes and cavities inside the body's organs, such that their contraction can propel the contents of those organs.

soil horizons   Layers of soil, ranging from topsoil to bedrock.

solute potential   The osmotic potential; an element in the water potential equation.

solutes   Substance dissolved in a liquid.

solution   A liquid that contains one or more dissolved solutes.

solvent   The liquid in which a solute is dissolved.

soma   *See* cell body.

somatic cells   The type of cell that constitutes all cells of the body excluding the germ-line cells. Examples include skin cells and muscle cells.

somatic embryogenesis   The production of plant embryos from body (somatic) cells.

somatic nervous system   The division of the peripheral nervous system that senses the external environmental conditions and controls skeletal muscles.

somites   Blocklike structures of mesoderm that are formed during neurulation.

soredia   Small clumps of hyphae surrounding a few algal cells that can disperse in wind currents; an asexual reproductive structure produced by lichens.

sorting signals   Short amino acid sequences in a protein's structure that direct the protein to its correct location.

source pool   The pool of species on the mainland that is available to colonize an island.

Southern blotting   A method in which a labelled probe, which is a strand of DNA from a specific gene, is used to identify that gene in a mixture of many chromosomal DNA fragments.

speciation   The formation of new species.

species   A group of related organisms that share a distinctive form in nature.

species–area effect   The relationship between the amount of available area and the number of species present.

species concepts   Different approaches for distinguishing species, including the phylogenetic, biological, evolutionary, and ecological species concepts.

species interactions   A part of the study of population ecology that focuses on interactions, such as predation, competition, parasitism, mutualism, and commensalism.

species richness   The numbers of species in a community.

specific heat   The amount of heat required per unit of mass to raise the temperature of that mass by one degree Celsius.

Spemann's organizer   An extremely important morphogenetic field in the early gastrula; the organizer secretes morphogens responsible for inducing the formation of a new embryonic axis.

sperm   Refers to a "male" gamete that is generally smaller than the "female" gamete (egg); the "male" gamete is often motile or, in many species of plants, is transported to the egg via a pollen tube.

spermatids   In animals, the haploid cells produced by the secondary spermatocytes by meiosis II; these cells eventually differentiate into sperm cells.

spermatogenesis   The formation of sperm.

spermatogonia   In animals, diploid germ cells that give rise to the male gametes, the spermatozoa.

spermatophytes   All the living and fossil seed plant phyla.

sperm storage   A method of synchronizing the production of offspring with favourable environmental conditions; female animals store and nourish sperm in their reproductive tract for long periods of time.

spicules   Needlelike silica structures that form elaborate latticelike skeletons in some types of sponges.

spinal cord   In vertebrates and simpler chordates, the structure that connects the brain to all areas of the body and constitutes the central nervous system.

spinal nerves   Nerves that connect the peripheral nervous system and the spinal cord.

spinnerets   The abdominal silk glands of a spider; also found in the mouths of caterpillars.

spiracles   Pores to the trachea that are found in the bodies of insects.

spiral cleavage   A mechanism of development in which the planes of cell cleavage are oblique to the axis of the embryo.

spirilli   Rigid, spiral-shaped prokaryotic cells; one of the five major shapes of prokaryotic cells.

spirochaetes   Flexible, spiral-shaped prokaryotic cells; one of the five major shapes of prokaryotic cells.

spliceosomes   Complex assemblages of several subunits known as snRNPs that remove introns from eukaryotic pre-mRNA.

splicing   The process whereby introns are removed from RNA and the remaining exons are connected to each other.

spongin   A tough protein that lends skeletal support to a sponge.

spongocoel   A central cavity in the body of a sponge.

spontaneous mutations   Mutations resulting from abnormalities in biological processes, often due to nonspecific effects of reactive chemical intermediates.

spontaneous reaction   A chemical reaction that proceeds without an input of energy resulting from the rearrangement of atoms/bonds to yield a product that is more stable than its precursor.

sporangia   Structures that produce and disperse the spores of plants, fungi, or protists.

spores   Single-celled reproductive structures that are dispersed into the environment and are able to grow into new fungal hyphae, plant gametophytes, or protists if suitable conditions exist.

sporic life cycle   *See* alternation of generations.

sporophytes   The diploid generation of plants or multicellular protists that have a sporic life cycle; this generation produces haploid spores by the process of meiosis.

sporopollenin   The tough material that composes much of the walls of plant spores and helps to prevent cellular damage during transport in air.

stabilizing selection   A pattern of natural selection that favours the survival of individuals with intermediate phenotypes.

stamens   Flower structures that produce the male gametophyte, pollen.

standard metabolic rate (SMR)   A method for measuring the BMR of ectotherms at a standard temperature for each species—one that approximates the average temperature that a species normally encounters.

standing crop   The total biomass in an ecosystem at any one point in time.

start codon   A three-base sequence—usually AUG—that specifies the first amino acid in a polypeptide.

statocysts   Organs of equilibrium found in many animal species.

statoliths   (1) Tiny granules of sand or other dense objects that aid in equilibrium in many vertebrates. (2) In plants, a starch-heavy plastid that allows both roots and shoots to detect gravity.

stem cells   Cells that divide and may differentiate in numerous ways to produce all cells of the bodies of animals and plants.

stems   Plant organs that produce buds, leaves, branches, and reproductive structures.

stereocilia   Deformable projections that resemble hairs on a mechanoreceptor.

stereoisomers   Isomers with identical bonding relationships, but the spatial positioning of the atoms differs in the two isomers.

sternum   The breastbone.

steroids   Lipid molecules containing four interconnected rings of carbon atoms; they function as hormones in animals and plants.

sticky ends   Single-stranded ends of DNA fragments that will hydrogen-bond to each other because of their complementary sequences.

stigma   (1) A topmost portion of the pistil, which receives and recognizes pollen of the appropriate species or genotype. (2) In many protists, a red cellular structure.

stomach   A saclike organ that most likely evolved as a means of storing food; it partially digests some of the macromolecules in food and regulates the rate at which the contents empty into the small intestine.

stomata   Surface pores on plant surfaces that can be closed to retain water or opened to allow the entry of CO_2 needed for photosynthesis and the exit of oxygen and water vapour.

stop codons   Specialized codons that specify chain termination in protein synthesis.

strain   Within a given species, a lineage that has genetic differences compared with another lineage.

streptophyte algae   Green algae of a very large group of organisms, of the division Streptophytina.

streptophytes   Any of a very large group of organisms, of the division Streptophytina, which includes the green algae and most other plants.

stretch receptors   Mechanoreceptors found widely in organs and muscle tissues that can be distended.

striated muscle   Skeletal and cardiac muscle with a series of light and dark bands perpendicular to the muscle's long axis.

stroke   The condition that occurs when blood flow to part of the brain is disrupted.

stroke volume (SV)   The amount of blood ejected with each beat, or stroke, of the heart.

stroma   The fluid-filled region of the chloroplast between the thylakoid membrane and the inner membrane.

stromatolite   A layered calcium carbonate structure produced by cyanobacteria in an aquatic environment.

structural gene   Refers to most genes, which produce an mRNA molecule that contains the information to specify a polypeptide with a particular amino acid sequence.

structural isomers   Isomers that contain the same atoms but in different bonding relationships.

style   The elongate pistil structure through which the pollen tube of a flower grows.

stylets   Sharp, piercing organs in the mouth of nematodes and some insects.

submetacentric   Describes a chromosome in which the centromere is off centre.

subsidence zones   Areas of high pressure that are the sites of the world's tropical deserts, because the subsiding air is relatively dry, having released all of its moisture over the equator.

substrate-level phosphorylation   A method of synthesizing ATP that occurs when an enzyme directly transfers a phosphate from one molecule to a different molecule.

substrates   The reactant molecules and ions that bind to an enzyme at the active site and participate in a chemical reaction.

succession   The gradual and continuous change in species composition and community structure over time.

sugar sink   The plant tissues or organs in which more sugar is consumed than is produced by photosynthesis.

sugar source   The plant tissues or organs that produce more sugar than they consume in respiration.

sum rule   The probability that one of two or more mutually exclusive outcomes will occur is the sum of the probabilities of the possible outcomes.

supercoiling   A method of compacting chromosomes; the phenomenon of forming additional coils around the long, thin DNA molecule.

supergroups   Groups of phyla used to organize eukaryotes into monophyletic groups.

surface area/volume (SA/V) ratio   The ratio between a structure's surface area and the volume in which the structure is contained.

surfactant   A mixture of proteins and amphipathic lipids produced in certain alveolar cells that acts to reduce surface tension in lungs.

survivorship curve   A graphical plot of the numbers of surviving individuals at each age.

suspension feeders   Aquatic animals that sift water, filtering out the organic matter and expelling the rest.

suspensor   A short chain of cells at the base of an early angiosperm embryo that provides anchorage and nutrients.

swim bladder   A gas-filled, balloonlike structure that helps a fish to remain buoyant in the water even when it is completely stationary.

swimmerets   The abdominal appendages in a crustacean that provide movement.

symbiosis   An intimate association between two or more organisms.

symbiotic   Describes a relationship in which two or more different species live in direct contact with each other.

sympathetic division   The division of the autonomic system that is responsible for rapidly activating systems that provide immediate energy to the body in response to danger or stress.

sympatric speciation   A form of speciation that occurs when members of a species that initially occupy the same habitat within the same range diverge into two or more different species.

sympatry   Species occurring in the same geographic area.

symplast   A plant's protoplasts (the cell contents without the cell walls) and its plasmodesmata.

symplastic transport   The movement of a substance from the cytosol of one cell to the cytosol of an adjacent cell via membrane-lined channels called plasmodesmata.

symport   A transport process in which two molecules move in the same direction across the plasma membrane.

symporters   Transporters that bind two or more ions or molecules and transport them in the same direction across membranes.

synapse   A junction where a nerve terminal meets a target neuron, muscle cell, or gland and can communicate with other cells.

synapsis   The process of forming a bivalent.

synaptic cleft   The extracellular space between two neurons.

synaptic integration   The summation of EPSPs generated at one time, which can bring the membrane potential to the threshold potential at the axon hillock for action potential firing.

synaptic plasticity   A change in synapses that occurs as a result of learning.

synaptic signalling   A specialized form of paracrine signalling that occurs in the nervous system of animals.

synergids   In the female gametophyte of a flowering plant, the two cells adjacent to the egg cell that help to import nutrients from maternal sporophyte tissues.

synthetic genomics   The creation of genes, gene modules, and ultimately, life, by employing DNA synthesis and recombinant DNA techniques.

systematics   The study of biological diversity and evolutionary relationships among organisms, both extinct and modern.

systemic acquired resistance (SAR) A whole-plant defensive response to pathogenic microorganisms.

systemic circulation The pumping of blood from the left side of the heart to the body to drop off oxygen and nutrients and pick up carbon dioxide and wastes. The blood then returns to the right side of the heart.

systemic hypertension An arterial blood pressure above normal, which in humans ranges from systolic/diastolic pressures of about 90/60 to 120/80 mmHg; often called hypertension or high blood pressure.

systems biology A field of study in which researchers study living organisms in terms of their underlying network structure—groups of structural and functional connections—rather than their individual molecular components.

T

T cells Lymphocytes that directly kill infected, mutated, or transplanted cells.

tagmata The fusion of body segments into functional units.

tapetum lucidum A reflective layer of tissue located beneath the photoreceptors at the back of the eye of certain animals.

taproot system The root system of eudicots, which has one main root with many branch roots.

taste buds A group of chemosensory cells that detect particular molecules in food.

TATA box One of three features found in most promoters; the others are the transcriptional start site and response elements.

taxis A directed type of response either toward or away from a stimulus.

taxon A group of species that are evolutionarily related to each other. In taxonomy, each species is placed into several taxons that form a hierarchy from large (domain) to small (genus).

taxonomy The field of biology that is concerned with the theory, practice, and rules of classifying living and extinct organisms and viruses.

telocentric Desribes a chromosome in which the centromere is at the end.

telomerase An enzyme that catalyzes the replication of the telomere.

telomeres Regions at the ends of eukaryotic chromosomes with special DNA sequences that allow the ends to be replicated.

telophase The phase of mitosis during which the chromosomes decondense and the nuclear membrane re-forms.

temperate phages Bacteriophages that may spend some of their time in the lysogenic cycle.

template The DNA strand that is used as a template for RNA synthesis or DNA replication.

termination codons *See* stop codons.

termination stage The final stage of transcription or translation in which the process ends.

terminator A sequence that specifies the end of transcription.

terpenoids Synthesized from five-carbon isoprene units, they are the largest major class of secondary metabolites; also called isoprenoids.

territory A fixed area in which an individual or a group excludes other members of its own species, and sometimes other species, by aggressive behaviour or territory marking.

tertiary consumers Organisms that feed on secondary consumers.

tertiary endosymbiosis The acquisition by eukaryotic protist host cells of plastids from cells that possess secondary plastids.

tertiary plastids Plastids acquired by the incorporation into a host cell of an endosymbiont having a secondary plastid.

tertiary structure The three-dimensional shape of a single polypeptide. One of four levels of protein structure.

testcross In a testcross one parent (called the tester) can donate only the recessive allele. Test crosses are usually done to allow the genotype of the nontester parent to be determined.

testes The male gonads of certain animals, where sperm are produced.

testosterone The primary androgen in vertebrates.

tetraploid An organism or a cell that has four sets of chromosomes.

tetrapods Vertebrate animals having four legs or leglike appendages.

thalamus In vertebrates, a gland that plays a major role in relaying sensory information to appropriate parts of the cerebrum and, in turn, sending outputs from the cerebrum to other parts of the brain. It receives input from all sensory systems and is involved in the perception of pain and the degree of mental arousal in the cortex.

theory In biology, a broad explanation of some aspect of the natural world that is substantiated by a large body of evidence. Biological theories incorporate observations, hypothesis testing, and the laws of other disciplines, such as chemistry and physics. A theory makes valid predictions.

thermodynamics The study of energy interconversions.

thermoreceptors Sensory receptors that respond to cold and heat.

theropods A group of bipedal saurischian dinosaurs.

thick filaments Skeletal muscle structures composed almost entirely of the motor protein myosin.

thigmotropism Touch responses in plants.

thin filaments Skeletal muscle structures that contain the cytoskeletal protein actin, as well as two other proteins—troponin and tropomyosin—that play important roles in regulating contraction.

thoracic breathing Breathing in which coordinated contractions of muscles expand the rib cage, creating a negative pressure to suck air in and then forcing it out later; found in amniotes.

threatened species Those species that are likely to become endangered in the future.

threshold concentration The concentration above which a morphogen will exert its effects but below which it is ineffective.

threshold potential The membrane potential that is sufficient to open voltage-gated Na^1 channels and to trigger an action potential, typically around −50 mV.

thrombocytes Intact cells in the blood of vertebrates other than mammals that play a crucial role in the formation of blood clots.

thylakoid lumen The fluid-filled compartment within the thylakoid.

thylakoid membrane A membrane within the chloroplast that forms many flattened, fluid-filled tubules that enclose a single, convoluted compartment. It is the site where the light-dependent reactions of photosynthesis occurs.

thylakoids Flattened, platelike membranous regions found in cyanobacterial cells and the chloroplasts of photosynthetic protists and plants; the location of the light reactions of photosynthesis.

thymine (T) A pyrimidine base found in DNA.

thymine dimer One type of pyrimidine dimer; a site at which two adjacent thymine bases become covalently cross-linked to each other.

thyroglobulin A protein found in the colloid of the thyroid gland.

thyroxine A thyroid hormone that contains iodine and helps regulate metabolic rate.

tidal ventilation A type of breathing in which the lungs are inflated with air and then the chest muscles and diaphragm relax and recoil back to their original positions as an animal exhales. During exhalation, air leaves via the same route that it entered during inhalation, and no new oxygen is delivered to the airways at that time.

tidal volume The volume of air that is normally breathed in and out at rest.

tight junctions Junctions that form tight seals between adjacent epithelial cells and thereby prevent molecules from leaking between cells; also called occluding junctions.

Ti plasmid Tumour-inducing plasmid found in *Agrobacterium tumefaciens;* it is used as a cloning vector to transfer genes into plant cells.

tissues The association of many cells of the same type, such as muscle tissue.

tolerance A mechanism for succession in which any species can start the succession, but the eventual climax community is reached in a somewhat orderly fashion; early species neither facilitate nor inhibit subsequent colonists.

topsoil The uppermost layer of soil that is rich in organic matter and microorganisms.

torpor The strategy in the smallest endotherms of lowering internal body temperature to just a few degrees above that of the environment to conserve energy.

torus The nonporous, flexible central region of a conifer pit that functions like a valve.

total fertility rates (TFRs) The average number of live births females have during their lifetime.

total peripheral resistance (TPR) The sum of all the resistance in all the arterioles.

totipotent The ability of a fertilized egg to produce all the cell types in the adult organism; also the ability of unspecialized plant cells to regenerate an adult plant.

trachea (1) A sturdy tube arising from the spiracles of an insect's body involved in respiration. (2) The name of the tube leading to the lungs of air-breathing vertebrates.

tracheal system In insects, a series of finely branched air tubes called tracheae that lead into the body from pores called spiracles.

tracheary elements The tracheids and vessel elements in a plant.

tracheids Dead, lignified plant cells that conduct water, along with dissolved minerals and certain organic compounds.

tracheophytes A term used to describe the vascular plants.

tract A parallel bundle of myelinated axons.

traffic signals *See* sorting signals.

traits *See* characters.

transcription The use of a gene sequence to make a copy of RNA: transcription occurs in three stages called initiation, elongation, and termination.

transcription factors Proteins that interact with RNA polymerases and influence their ability to transcribe genes.

transcriptional start site The site in a promoter where transcription begins.

transduction A type of genetic transfer between bacteria in which a virus infects a bacterial cell and then transfers some of that cell's DNA to another bacterium.

trans-effect In both prokaryotes and eukaryotes, a form of genetic regulation that can occur even though two DNA segments are not physically adjacent. The action of the lac repressor on the *lac* operon is a *trans*-effect.

transepithelial transport The transport of substances from the lumen to the blood.

transfection Gene cloning in which a viral vector is the recombinant vector carrying the desired gene.

transfer RNA (tRNA) An RNA that carries amino acids and is used to translate mRNA into polypeptides.

transformation A type of genetic transfer between bacteria in which a segment of DNA from the environment is taken up by a competent cell and incorporated into the bacterial chromosome.

transgenic The term used to describe an organism that carries genes that were introduced by using molecular techniques, such as gene cloning.

transition state In a chemical reaction, a state in which the original bonds have stretched to their limit; once this state is reached, the reaction can proceed to the formation of products.

transitional form An organism that provides a link between earlier and later forms in evolution.

translation The process of synthesizing a specific polypeptide on a ribosome; a nucleotide sequence in mRNA is used to make an amino acid sequence of a polypeptide. The process of translation occurs in three stages: initiation, elongation, and termination.

translocation A phenomenon that occurs when one segment of a chromosome becomes attached to a different chromosome.

transmembrane gradient The phenomenon that the concentration of a solute is higher on one side of a membrane than on the other.

transmembrane proteins Proteins that have one or more regions that are physically embedded in the hydrophobic region of the cell's phospholipid bilayer.

transmembrane transport The export of a material from one cell into the intercellular space, followed by import of the same substance by an adjacent cell.

transpiration The evaporative loss of water from plant surfaces into sun-heated air.

transporters Membrane proteins that bind a solute and undergo a conformational change to allow the movement of the solute across a membrane.

transposable elements (TEs) Segments of DNA that can move from one chromosomal location to another.

transposase An enzyme that facilitates transposition.

transposition The process in which a short segment of DNA moves within a cell from its original site to a new site in the genome.

transverse tubules (T-tubules) Invaginations of the plasma membrane that open to the extracellular fluid and conduct action potentials from the outer surface of a muscle fibre to the myofibrils.

trichomes Projections from the epidermal tissue of a plant that offers protection from excessive light, ultraviolet radiation, extreme air temperature, or attack by herbivores.

trichromatic colour vision The ability to distinguish blue, green, and red colours.

triglycerides A category of biomolecule that each consists of a glycerol molecule to which three fatty acids have been attached.

triiodothyronine A thyroid hormone that contains iodine and helps regulate metabolic rate.

triplet A group of three bases that functions as a codon.

triploblastic Having three distinct germ layers: endoderm, ectoderm, and mesoderm.

triploid An organism or a cell that has three sets of chromosomes.

trisomic An aneuploid organism that has one too many chromosomes.

trochophore larva A distinct larval stage of many invertebrate phyla.

trophic level Each feeding level in a food chain.

trophic-level transfer efficiency The amount of energy at one trophic level that is acquired by the trophic level above and incorporated into biomass.

tropism The movement of an organism or part in response to an external stimulus (e.g., movement of leaves to track the sun).

tropomyosin A protein that plays an important role in regulating muscle contraction. It blocks the interaction of actin and myosin, except in the presence of troponin.

troponin A protein that plays an important role in regulating muscle contraction. When combined with Ca^{2+}, it influences tropomyosin to initiate contraction.

trp operon An operon of *E. coli* that encodes enzymes required to make the amino acid tryptophan, a building block of cellular proteins.

true-breeding line A strain that continues to exhibit the same trait after several generations of self-fertilization or inbreeding.

tryglicerides Also known as triacylglycerols, they are fats formed by bonding glycerol to three fatty acids.

trypsin A protease involved in the breakdown of proteins in the small intestine.

t-snares Proteins in a target membrane that recognize and bind v-snares in a membrane vesicle.

tube cell Plant cells that store proteins and lipids that may be used during later stages of male gametophyte development, after pollen has germinated. This cell forms the pollen tube that after pollination grows to reach the female gametophyte.

tube feet Echinoderm structures that function in movement, gas exchange, and feeding.

tumour An overgrowth of cells that serves no useful purpose.

tumour-suppressor gene A gene that when normal (i.e., not mutant) encodes a protein that prevents cancer; however, when a mutation eliminates its function, cancer can occur.

tunic A nonliving structure that encloses a tunicate, made of a protein and a cellulose-like material called tunicin.

turgid The term used to describe a plant cell whose cytosol is so full of water that the plasma membrane presses right up against the cell wall; as a result, turgid cells are firm or swollen.

turgor pressure *See* osmotic pressure.

type 1 diabetes mellitus (T1DM) A disease in which the pancreas does not produce sufficient insulin; as a result, extracellular glucose cannot cross plasma membranes, and so glucose accumulates to very high concentrations in the blood.

type 2 diabetes mellitus (T2DM) A disease in which the pancreas functions normally, but the cells of the body lose much of their ability to respond to insulin.

U

ubiquitin A small protein in eukaryotic cells that directs unwanted proteins to a proteasome by its covalent attachment.

ultimate causation The reason a particular behaviour evolved, in terms of its effect on reproductive success.

umbrella species A species whose habitat requirements are so large that protecting them would protect many other species existing in the same habitat.

uniform A pattern of dispersion within a population, in which individuals maintain a certain minimum distance between themselves to produce an evenly spaced distribution.

Uniporters Transporters that bind single molecules or ions and transport them across the membrane.

unipotent A term used to describe a stem cell found in the adult that can produce only daughter cells that differentiate into one cell type.

unsaturated fatty acid A fatty acid that contains one or more carbon–carbon double bonds.

upwellings In the ocean, phenomena that carry mineral nutrients from the bottom waters to the surface.

uracil (U) A pyrimidine base found in RNA.

urea A nitrogenous waste commonly produced in many terrestrial species.

uremia A condition characterized by the presence of nitrogenous wastes, such as urea, in the blood; typically results from kidney disease.

ureter A structure in the kidney through which urine flows from the kidney into the urinary bladder.

urethra The structure through which urine is eliminated from the body.

uric acid A nitrogenous waste commonly produced in many terrestrial species.

urinary bladder The structure that collects urine before it is eliminated.

urinary system The structures that collectively act to filter blood or hemolymph and excrete wastes while recapturing useful compounds. In humans, it includes the two kidneys, two ureters, the urinary bladder, and the urethra.

urine The liquid waste excreted by the body. It contains mostly water, salt, urea, and uric acid.

uterine cycle The cyclical changes that occur in the uterus in parallel with the ovarian cycle in a female mammal.

uterus A large, conical-shaped structure that consists of an inner lining of glandular and secretory cells called the endometrium, and a thick muscular layer called the myometrium; the uterus is specialized for carrying the developing fetus.

V

vaccinations Injections into the body of small quantities of living or dead microbes, small quantities of toxins, or harmless antigenic molecules derived from a microorganism or its toxin, resulting in primary immune responses including the production of memory cells. Subsequent natural exposure to the immunizing antigen results in a response that can prevent or reduce the severity of disease.

vacuoles Membrane-bound vesicles found in eukaryotic cells that function in storage, regulation of cell volume, and degradation.

vagina A tubular, smooth muscle structure in the female into which sperm are deposited.

valence electron An electron in the outer shell that is available to combine with other atoms. Such electrons allow atoms to form chemical bonds with each other.

van der Waal forces A general term for a collection of stabilizing forces that are not covalent or ionic bonds. It refers to electrostatic interactions either between different molecules or between different regions of the same larger molecule.

variable region A domain within an immunoglobulin that serves as the antigen-binding site.

vasa recta capillaries Capillaries in the medulla in the nephron of the kidney.

vascular bundles Primary plant vascular tissues that occur in a group.

vascular cambium A meristematic tissue of plants that produces both wood and inner bark.

vascular plants Plants that can transport water, sugar, and salts throughout the plant body via xylem and phloem tissues.

vascular tissues Plant tissues that make up the vascular system, which conducts materials within the plant body and also provides support.

vas deferens A muscular tube through which sperm leave the epididymis.

vasoconstriction A decrease in blood vessel radius; an important mechanism for directing blood flow away from specific regions of the body.

vasodilation An increase in blood vessel radius; an important mechanism for directing blood flow to specific regions of the body.

vector A type of DNA that acts as a carrier of a DNA segment that is to be cloned.

vegetal pole In triploblast organisms, the pole of the egg where the yolk is most concentrated.

vegetative growth The production of new tissues by the shoot apical meristem and root apical meristem during seedling development and growth of mature plants.

veliger A free-swimming larva that has a rudimentary foot, shell, and mantle.

ventilation The process of bringing oxygenated water or air into contact with a gas-exchange surface.

ventral Refers to the lower side of an animal.

ventricle In the heart, a chamber to pump blood out of the heart.

venules In animals, the small, thin-walled extensions of capillaries that empty into larger vessels called veins that return blood to the heart for another trip around the circulation.

vertebrae A bony or cartilaginous column of interlocking structures that provides support and also protects the nerve cord, which lies within its tubelike structure.

vertebrates Organisms with a backbone.

vertical evolution A process that involves genetic changes in a series of ancestors, which form a lineage.

vesicles Small membrane-enclosed sacs within a cell.

vessel element A type of plant cell that conducts water, along with dissolved minerals and certain organic compounds.

vessels In a plant, a pipelinelike file of dead, water-conducting vessel elements.

vestibular system The organ of balance in vertebrates, located in the inner ear next to the cochlea.

vestigial structures Anatomical features that have no apparent function but resemble structure of a presumed ancestor.

vibrios Comma-shaped prokaryotic cells; one of the five major shapes of prokaryotic cells.

villi Fingerlike projections extending from the luminal surface into the lumen of the small intestine; these are specializations that aid in digestion and absorption.

viral envelope A structure enclosing the capsid that consists of a membrane derived from the plasma membrane of the host cell and embedded with virally encoded spike glycoproteins.

viral genome The genetic material in a virus.

viral reproductive cycle The series of steps that results in the production of new viruses after a virus infects a cell.

viral vector A type of vector that is derived from a virus and used in cloning experiments.

viroid An RNA particle that infects plant cells.

virulence The infection of tissue.

virulent phages Bacteriophages that follow only the lytic cycle.

virus A small infectious particle that consists of nucleic acid enclosed in a protein coat.

visceral mass In molluscs, a structure that rests atop the foot and contains the internal organs.

vitalism An outdated belief that organic molecules were created by, and therefore imparted with, a vital life force contained within a plant or an animal's body.

vitamin D A molecule that regulates calcium levels in the blood through an action on intestinal transport of calcium ions.

vitamins Important organic nutrients that serve as a coenzyme for metabolic and biosynthetic reactions.

vitreous humour A thick liquid in the large posterior cavity of the vertebrate eye, which helps maintain the shape of the eye.

viviparity The process in which the embryo develops within the mother.

viviparous The term used to describe an organism whose eggs develop within the uterus, receiving nourishment from the mother via a placenta.

voltage-gated channels Channels that open and close in response to changes in the amount of electric charge across the membrane.

volts Units of measurement of the difference in charge (the electrical force), such as between the interior and exterior of the cell.

v-snares Proteins incorporated into the vesicle membrane during vesicle formation that are recognized by t-snares in a target membrane.

W

wall potential *See* pressure potential.

water potential The potential energy of water.

water vascular system A network of canals powered by hydraulic power; that is, by water pressure generated by the contraction of muscles that enables the extension and contraction of the tube feet, allowing echinoderms to move slowly.

wavelength The distance from the peak of one sound or light wave to the next.

waxy cuticle A protective waterproof layer of wax and polyester present on most surfaces of vascular plant sporophytes.

weathering The physical and chemical break-down of rock.

white blood cells Cells that develop from the inner parts (the marrow) of certain bones in vertebrates; all white blood cells (known as leukocytes) perform vital functions that defend the body against infection and disease.

white matter Brain tissue that consists of myelinated axons that are bundled together in large numbers to form tracts.

whorls In a flower, four concentric rings of sepals, petals, stamens, and carpels.

wild-type allele One or more prevalent alleles in a population.

wood A secondary plant tissue composed of numerous pipelike arrays of dead, empty, water-conducting cells whose walls are strengthened by an exceptionally tough sec-ondary metabolite known as lignin.

woody plants Plants that produce both primary and secondary vascular tissues.

X

X inactivation The phenomenon in which one X chromosome in the somatic cells of female mammals is inactivated, meaning that its genes are not expressed.

xenoestrogens Synthetic compounds that exert estrogen-like actions or, in some cases, inhibit the actions of the body's own estrogen; the consequences are dramatic on fertility and development of embryos and fetuses.

X-inactivation centre (Xic) A short region on the X chromosome known to play a critical role in X inactivation.

X-linked genes Genes found on the X chromo-some but not on the Y.

X-linked inheritance The pattern displayed by pairs of dominant and recessive alleles located on X chromosomes.

xylem A plant vascular tissue that conducts water, minerals, and organic compounds.

xylem loading The process by which root xylem parenchyma cells transport ions and water across their membranes into the xylem apoplast, which includes the vessel elements and tracheids.

Y

yeasts Fungi that can occur as single cells and that reproduce by budding.

yolk sac An extraembryonic membrane in the amniotic egg that encloses a stockpile of nutrients, in the form of yolk, for the developing embryo.

Z

Z line A network of proteins that anchor thin filaments in a sarcomere.

Z scheme According to this scheme, an electron absorbs light energy twice, and it loses some of that energy as it flows along the electron transport chain in the thylakoid membrane. The energy diagram of this process occurs in a zigzag pattern.

zero population growth The situation in which no changes in population size occur.

zoecium A nonliving case that houses a bryozoan.

zone of elongation The area above the root apical meristem of a plant where cells extend by water uptake, thereby dramatically increas-ing root length.

zone of maturation The area above the zone of elongation in a plant where root cell differen-tiation and tissue specialization occur.

zooplankton Aquatic organisms including minute animals consisting of some worms, copepods, tiny jellyfish, and the small larvae of invertebrates and fish that graze on the phytoplankton.

zwitterion A molecule that is neutral (no net charge) but has one side of the molecule with a positive charge and another side with a nega-tive charge.

zygomycetes Fungi that produce distinc-tive, large zygospores as the result of sexual reproduction.

zygospore A dark-pigmented, thick-walled spore that matures within the zygosporangium of zygomycete fungi.

zygote A diploid cell, formed by the fusion of two gametes, that divides, develops into an embryo, and eventually becomes an adult organism.

zygotic life cycle In this type of life cycle, hap-loid cells transform into gametes.

Photo Credits

© Peter E. Smith, Natural Sciences Image Library; **F43.13e**: Doug Perrine/naturepl.com; **F43.15**: All: Lynne Glazer Imagery; **F43.16a**: © Dr. LR/Photo Researchers, Inc.; **F43.16b**: © Tim Arnett, University College London

Chapter 44: **P44.1**: © SPL/Photo Researchers, Inc.; **F44.1a**: © Ron Koss, Biological Sciences, University of Alberta, www.biology.ualberta.ca/courses.hp/zool250/z250.htm; **F44.6b**: © Dr. David Phillips/Visuals Unlimited; **F44.8a**: © Dennis Kunkel/Microscopy, Inc.; **F44.11**: © BSIP LAURENT; **F44.13**: (right): © Carolina Biological Supply/Visuals Unlimited; **F44.15**: © Ed Reschke/Getty Images; **F44.21**: © BIO-PHOTO ASSOCIATES/SPL/Photo Researchers, Inc.; **F44A.1**: © Sovereign/TSM/Phototake

Chapter 45: **P45.1**: © brianlatino/Alamy RF; **F45.3 (top)**: © Ken Lucas/Visuals Unlimited; **F45.3 (bottom)**: © Todd Pierson; **F45.4a**: © Hal Beral/V + W/The Image Works; **F45.4b**: © Jane Burton/Bruce Coleman/Photoshot; **F45.5a**: © Jane Burton/naturepl.com; **F45.5c**: © Electron Microscopy Unit, Royal Holloway University of London; **F45.7**: (top right): © Ed Reschke/Getty Images; **F45.10b**: © Pr. M. Brauner/Photo Researchers, Inc.; **F45.17**: Dr. Stanley Flegler/Visuals Unlimited/Getty Images; **F45.18a**: © Astrid & Hanns-Frieder Michler/Science Photo Library; **F45.18b**: © Dr. John D. Cunningham/Visuals Unlimited

Chapter 46: **P46.1**: © Joshua Nemeth; **F46.4 (inset)**: © Frans Lanting/Minden Pictures; **F46.12**: © STEVE GSCHMEISSNER/SPL/Photo Researchers, Inc.

Chapter 47: **P47.1**: © Sovereign/ISM/Phototake; **F47.6a (left inset)**: © S. Goodwin & Dr. Max Hincke, Division of Clinical and Functional Anatomy, University of Ottawa; **F47.6a (left inset)**: © S. Goodwin & Dr. Max Hincke, Division of Clinical and Functional Anatomy, University of Ottawa; **F47.6b**: © Bob Daemmrich/The Image Works; **F47.7**: (bottom right): © Carolina Biological Supply/Visuals Unlimited; **F47.13a**: (left): Copyright © 2007 Massachusetts Medical Society. All Rights reserved. New England Journal of Med. Vol 340, p. 524, 1999.; **F47.13b**: (middle): © Bart's Medical Library/Phototake; **F47.13c**: (right): Copyright © 2007 Massachusetts Medical Society. All Rights reserved. New England Journal of Med. Vol 340, p. 524, 1999

Chapter 48: **P48.1**: David Liebman © Pink Guppy; **F48.1a**: © Clouds Hill Imaging Ltd./CORBIS; **F48.1b**: © WaterFrame/Alamy; **F48.3b**: F51.3a (right) © Dr. Stanley Flegler/Visuals Unlimited; **F48.3d**: F48.3b (right): © P.M. Motta & G. Familiari/Univ. La Sapienza/Photo Researchers, Inc. ; **F48.4a**: © David Cole/Alamy; **F48.4b**: © Philippe LEBEAUX http://www.animailes.com; **F48.5a**: © Joe McDonald/Visuals Unlimited; **F48.5b**: © Christopher Arnesen/Getty Images; **F48.13a**: © Claude Edelmann/Photo Researchers, Inc.; **F48.13b**: © Photo Lennart Nilsson/Albert Bonniers Forlag AB, A Child Is Born, Dell Publishing Company; **F48.13c**: © Photo Lennart Nilsson/Albert

Bonniers Forlag AB, A Child Is Born, Dell Publishing Company

Chapter 49: **P49.1a**: Matsui et al., "Effects of Ethanol on Photoreceptors and Visual Function in Developing Zebrafish," Investigative Ophthalmology & Visual Science, October 2006, Vol. 47, No. 10, pp. 4589–4597, Fig. 1. Copyright © Association for Research in Vision and Ophthalmology. Image Courtesy of Jonathan Matsui; **P49.1b**: Matsui et al., "Effects of Ethanol on Photoreceptors and Visual Function in Developing Zebrafish," Investigative Ophthalmology & Visual Science, October 2006, Vol. 47, No. 10, pp. 4589–4597, Fig. 1. Copyright © Association for Research in Vision and Ophthalmology. Image Courtesy of Jonathan Matsui; **F49.4a**: © Dr. Richard Kessel & Dr. Gene Shih/Visuals Unlimited; **F49.4b**: © Dr. Richard Kessel & Dr. Gene Shih/Visuals Unlimited; **F49.4c**: © Tom Fleming; **F49.6**: Courtesy Hiroki Nishida, Biological Sciences, Osaka University; **F49.10a**: Courtesy Dr. Laurence D. Etkin, University of Texas M.D. Anderson Cancer Center. With Permission of Malgorzata Kloc. This article was published in Mechanisms of Development, Vol. 75, Issues 1–2, Malgorzata Kloc, Carolyn Larabell, Agnes Pui-Yee Chan and Laurence D. Etkin, "Contribution of METRO pathway localized molecules to the organization of the germ cell lineage," Pages 81–93. Elsevier Science Ireland Ltd. July 1998; **F49.10b**: © F.R. Turner/Indiana University; **F49.11**: (left): Courtesy Kathryn Tosney; **F49.12a**: Courtesy Kathryn Tosney; **F49.12b**: Courtesy Kathryn Tosney; **F49.16 (5)**: © Richard Harland, U.C. Berkeley

Chapter 50: **P50.1**: © Dr. David M. Phillips/Visuals Unlimited; **F50.13**: © Dr. Fred Hossler/Visuals Unlimited; **B50.1**: Neha Janmohamed; B50.1a Photo courtesy of Aileen Huston; B50.1b Photo courtesy of Dr. Tatersall

Chapter 51: **P51.1**: U8P51.1a © Dr. John Stewart, Vancouver ; U8P51.1b Peter Stiling; U8P51.1c © David Tilley; U8P51.1d © Paul Springett/Alamy; U8P51.1e © Tom Bean; U8P51.1f © Frans Lanting/Corbis; U8P51.1g © Rick Beaver ; © Brian de Alwis; **F51.1**: David M. Dennis/Animals Animals; **F51.2a**: Eyewave/Dreamstime.com/GetStock.com; **F51.2b**: © Roger Wilmshurst; Frank Lane Picture Agency/CORBIS; **F51.2c**: © FAO/Giampiero Diana; **F51.2d**: ©Juan Medina/Reuters/CORBIS; **F51.7b**: ©Michael McCoy/Photo Researchers, Inc.; **F51.9**: © Jonathan Bird/Getty Images; **F51.10**: © Bruce Forster/Getty Images; **F51.13a**: © FLPA/D P Wilson/age fotostock; **F51.13b**: © Biophoto Associates/Photo Researchers, Inc.; **F51.15a**: © Jeffrey L. Rotman/CORBIS; **F51.15b**: Image courtesy of FGBNMS/UNCWNURC; **F51.16**: Virginia P. Weinland/Photo Researchers, Inc.; **F51.17a**: Peter Wakely/English Nature; **F51.17b**: G.A. Matthews/SPL/Photo Researchers, Inc.; **F51.26a**: Jean-Paul Ferrero/ardea.com; **F51.26b**: ©Theo Allofs/theoallofs.com; **F51.26c**: © Phillip Colla; **F51.26d**: © Reimar Gaertner/worldofstock.com; **F51.26e**: Tom and Pat Leeson; **F51.26f**: ©Joe McDonald/Visuals Unlimited; **F51.26g**: ©D. Robert & Lorri Franz/CORBIS; **F51.26h**: © Joe McDonald/Visuals Unlimited; **F51.26i**: Art Wolfe/Getty

Images; **F51.26j**: MICHIO HOSHINO/Minden Pictures; **F51.26k**: © Dr. John Stewart, Vancouver; **F51.27a**: photo by Garry Fletcher. Marine Education Consulting, Victoria, B.C. http://racerocks.ca/metchosinmarine/marineecosystems.htm; **F51.27b**: ©Stephen Frink/CORBIS; **F51.27c**: ©Jeffrey L. Rotman/CORBIS; **F51.27d**: © Visuals Unlimited/Corbis; **F51.27e**: © Thomas Kitchin & Victoria Hurst/Getty Images; **F51.27f**: © Kip Ladage

Chapter 52: **F52.1**: Photo taken by Ken Jones. © MCB Andrade 2002.; **F52.3a**: © L.P. Brower, Sweet Briar College; **F52.3b**: © L.P. Brower, Sweet Briar College; **F52.4a**: ©Lilo Hess/Time Life Pictures/Getty Images; **F52.4b**: ©Lilo Hess/Time Life Pictures/Getty Images; **F52.4c**: ©Lilo Hess/Time Life Pictures/Getty Images; **F52.5**: ©Joe McDonald/CORBIS; **F52.7b**: (inset) © Frans Lanting/Corbis; **F52.8**: © Bianca Lavies; **F52.11a**: ©Tony Camacho/Photo Researchers, Inc.; **F52.11b**: Gregory G. Dimijian/Photo Researchers, Inc.; **F52.11c**: ©Wolfgang Kaehler/CORBIS; **F52.12a**: ©Phil Degginger/Alamy; **F52.12b**: Ferfregory/Dreamstime.com/GetStock.com; **F52.12c**: J.E. Lloyd, UF Entomology; **F52.13a**: ©MARK MOFFETT/MINDEN PICTURES; **F52.15**: © Cyril Ruoso/Biosphoto; **F52.17**: Peter Stiling; **F52.18**: Richard H. Hansen/Photo Researchers, Inc.; **F52.19**: ©Raymond Mendez/Animals Animals; **F52.20**: Stephen A. Marshall; **F52.22b**: © Minden Pictures/Masterfile; **F52.23a**: Masahiro Iijima/ardea.com; **F52.23b**: © WILDLIFE GmbH/Alamy; **F52.23c**: © Dr. K. Martha M. Jones, Cape Breton University; **F52.24a**: © Wayne Lynch/All Canada Photos; **F52.24b**: Copyright ©GERLACH NATURE PHOTOGRAPHY/Animals Animals–Earth Scenes—All rights reserved.

Chapter 53: **P53.1**: © David Tilley; **F53.1**: ©W. Wayne Lockwood, M.D. /CORBIS; **F53.2a**: ©Phil Banko/CORBIS; **F53.2b**: ©Fritz Polking; Frank Lane Picture Agency/CORBIS; **F53.2c**: ©Bob Krist/CORBIS; **F53.3a**: © Doug Sherman/Geofile; **F53.3b**: © George Grall/National Geographic/Getty Images; **F53.3c**: ©M.Watson/ardea.com; **F53.9**: Graph of Whooping Crane recovery created by McGraw-Hill Ryerson using data from www.pnr-rpn.ec.gc.ca/nature/endspecies/whooping/db01s02.en.html for population data for the Wood Buffalo & Texas population up to 2007/2008. Used with permission of Environment Canada.; **F53.16**: © Royalty-Free/Corbis

Chapter 54: **P54.1**: © Ian McAllister/Getty Images; **F54.11a**: ©Dr. Thomas Eisner/Visuals Unlimited; **F54.11b**: ©Hans D. Dossenbach/Ardea London Ltd; **F54.11c**: ©Thomas Aichinger/V&W/The Image Works; **F54.11d**: Suzanne L. & Joseph T. Collins/Photo Researchers, Inc.; **F54.11d (2)**: Michael Fogden/OSF/Animals Animals; **F54.11e**: ©Paul Springett/Alamy; **F54.11f**: © Michael Woodhouse; **F54.11g**: © De Agostini/Getty Images; **F54.12c**: (inset) Tom & Pat Leeson/Photo Researchers, Inc.; **F54.15a**: © Glen Allison/Getty Images; **F54.15b**: Toyofumi Mori/The Image Bank/Getty Images; **F54.15c**: Gilbert S. Grant/Photo Researchers, Inc.; **F54.15d**: © John Dudak/Phototake; **F54.17**: © A & J Visage/Alamy; **F54.20a**: ©Dynamic Graphics Group/Creatas/Alamy; **F54.20b**: ©Michael & Patricia Fogden/

Index

A

A band, 1010
abalone, 726
ABC model for flower development, 438, 438*f*
abdomen, 736
Abelson leukemia virus, 322*t*
Abilify, 969*t*
abiotic, 1183
abiotic environments, 1260–1262
abiotic factors, 1248*f*
abl gene, 321–322
ABO blood type, 379–380, 380*f*
abomasum, 918
aboral, 706
abscisic acid, 806*t*, 813, 854*f*, 855, 856–859, 878
absolute zero, 34
absorption, 186, 186*f*, 907, 908*f*, 913–914
  active absorption, 913–914
  amino acids, 932
  carbohydrates, 920–921, 921*f*
  fats, 923
  malabsorption, 923–924
  mechanisms of, in vertebrates, 920–934
  minerals, 923–924
  passive absorption, 913–914
  proteins, 922–923
  small intestine, 918–919
  triglycerides, 932
  vitamins, 923–924
  water, 923–924
absorption spectrum, 187
absorptive state, 931, 932*f*, 933–936
acacia trees (*Acacia collinsii*), 1274*f*
Acanthodii, 753
Acanthoplegma spp., 624*f*
Acanthostega, 757, 757*f*
acceptor stem, 267
acclimatization, 947
accommodation, 994
Acetabularia (genus), 617
acetaldehyde, 176
acetaminophen, 137
acetyl, 179
acetyl-CoA, 166
acetyl group, 163, 166, 166*f*
acetyl groups, 294
acetylation, 336, 478
acetylcholine, 220, 964, 964*f*, 965–966
acetylsalicylic acid, 3, 4*f*
achondroplasia, 378
acid hydrolases, 85
acid precipitation, 1196–1197
acid rain, 1316, 1317*f*
acidic waters, 1196
acids
  in blood, 1062
  defined, 40

pH, 40–41
  relative acidities of common substances, 40*f*
  strong acid, 40
  weak acid, 40
acne, 605
acoelomates, 707, 709*f*, 714
acquired antibiotic resistance, 417
acquired characteristics, 513
acquired immune deficiency syndrome (AIDS), 207, 398, 643*f*, 646, 733, 1177
  see also human immunodeficiency virus (HIV)
acquired (specific) immunity, 1159, 1163–1174
  antibodies, 1166–1167
  antigen, attack against, 1166
  antigen, recognition of, 1165
  B cells, 1163, 1166–1167, 1170–1171, 1173
  cell-mediated immunity, 1171–1173
  cytotoxic T cells, 1171–1173
  humoral immune responses, 1170–1171, 1171*f*
  immune response, stages of, 1165–1166, 1165*f*
  immunological memory, 1173–1174
  lymphatic system, 1164–1165, 1165*f*
  lymphocytes, 1163–1165, 1166
  T-cell receptors, 1169–1170, 1169*f*
  T cells, 1170–1171, 1173
acrocentric, 348
acromegaly, 1113
acrosomal reaction, 1142, 1144*f*
acrosome, 1124
actin, 92, 598, 1010, 1011
actin filaments, 88, 89*f*, 92–93, 123, 172
actin microfilaments, 104
Actinistia, 751, 752*t*, 754, 756
Actinobacteria, 596*t*, 601
actinobacteria, 837
actinomorphic flowers, 872
Actinopterygii, 751, 752*t*, 754, 755
action potentials, 958–961, 959*f*, 960*f*, 982–984
action spectrum, 187, 187*f*
activated phytochrome, 816, 817
activation energy, 156, 157*f*
activator protein, 287
activators, 280–281, 289, 290–291, 291*f*
active immunity, 1174
active site, 157
active transport, 141, 141*f*, 147, 148*f*, 843–844
adaptation, 6, 205, 515, 516*f*, 519
adaptive radiation, 555, 555*f*, 1264*f*
adaptor proteins, 213, 223*f*

adaxial leaf surface, 787
adenine (A), 64, 234, 237, 811
adenosine diphosphate (ADP), 157*f*
  ATP, hydrolyzed, 89, 148
  breakdown from ATP, 155
  phosphorylation, 191
adenosine monophosphate (AMP), 219
adenosine triphosphate (ATP), 49, 155
  α-proteobacteria, 505
  aminoacyl-tRNA synthetases, 267
  ATP-binding sites, 161
  ATP-driven ion pumps, 148–149
  ATP-driven pumps, 147
  ATP synthase, 100–101, 170–174, 172*f*
  binding, 89
  breakdown to ADP, 155
  Calvin cycle, 194
  catabolic reactions, 158–160
  cell movement, 92–94
  and cellular respiration, 162
  chemiosmosis, 170
  cross-bridge cycle, 1011–1013
  cyclic AMP, 214*f*
  endergonic reactions, 155–156
  endotherms, 943
  energy, release of, 155
  energy, transfer of, 936
  glycolysis, 165–166, 175–176
  hydrolysis, 89, 92, 100, 104, 134, 147, 148, 155, 155*f*, 160, 843–844
  light reactions, 184
  muscle fibres, 1017
  oxidative phosphorylation, 163–165, 167–170, 169*f*, 505
  phosphorylation of ADP, 191
  as protein energy source, 160–161
  resynthesis, 160
  synthesis, 158, 931
    assembly of, 101
    chemiosmosis, 159
    conformational changes, 171, 172*f*
    cyclic electron flow, 189–191
    endosymbiosis and, 117
    mitochondria, 618
    mitochondrion, 78*f*, 94–95
    oxygen, 78*f*, 1048, 1048*f*
    photosynthesis, 193
    photosystems II and I, 188–189, 188*f*
    substrate-level phosphorylation, 159
   transition state, 156
adenoviruses, 398, 399*t*, 401*f*
adenylate cyclase, 217
adenylates, 834–836
adenylyl cyclase, 214
adherens junctions, 123
adhesive proteins, 118–119

adiabatic cooling, 1198–1199
adipocytes, 434
adipose cells, 939
adipose tissue, 892*f*, 1110
ADP. *See* adenosine diphosphate (ADP)
adrenal cortex, 221, 1097, 1116
adrenal gland hormones, 1105–1107
adrenal glands, 1106, 1116–1117
adrenal medulla, 1116
adrenaline, 214, 1043
adrenocorticotropic hormone (ACTH), 221, 1102, 1102*t*
adventitious roots, 788
aerenchyma, 818
aerobes, 605
aerobic respiration, 162
aerobic species, 503
aerotolerant anaerobes, 606–607
afferent arteriole, 1084
afferent neurons, 952
aflatoxins, 645
Africa, 569, 1334, 1335, 1338
African clawed frog (*Xenopus laevis*), 421
African cycad (*Encephalartos laurentianus*), 684
African cyclids, 541–543, 541*f*
African forest elephant (*Loxodonta cyclotis*), 569, 569*f*, 572
African long-tailed widowbird (*Euplectes progne*), 1231
African savannah, 1302, 1302*f*
African savannah elephant (*Loxodonta africana*), 569
agar, 620–621, 808
agave plants, 1240*f*
age, 541
age classes, 1239–1241
Age of Amphibians, 757
Age of Dinosaurs, 509, 671, 684, 685
Age of Fishes, 508
Age of Mammals, 510
age-specific fertility rate, 1244–1245
age structure, 1252–1253, 1253*f*
agility, 1267
agiotensin-converting enzyme (ACE) inhibitors, 4*f*
Aglaophyton major, 670
agnathans, 751
Agre, Peter, 144, 146, 1089–1090
Agriculture and Agri-Food Canada, 19
Agrobacterium tumefaciens, 456–458, 457*f*, 466, 595, 608, 609*f*
Agropyron cristatum, 1186
Agropyron spicata, 1185
Aguinaldo, Anna Marie, 711–713
AIDS. *See* acquired immune deficiency syndrome (AIDS)
aintegumenta gene, 438*t*
air sacs, 766, 1058–1059, 1058*f*
akinetes, 604–605, 604*f*
alanine, 57*f*

W